Climate Change Reconsidered II

Biological Impacts

Lead Authors/Editors

Craig D. Idso (USA), Sherwood B. Idso (USA), Robert M. Carter (Australia), S. Fred Singer (USA)

Contributing Authors and Reviewers

David J. Barnes (Australia), Daniel B. Botkin (USA), Raymond A. Cloyd (USA), Susan Crockford (Canada), Weihong Cui (China), Kees DeGroot (The Netherlands), Robert G. Dillon (USA), John Dale Dunn (USA), Ole Henrik Ellestad (Norway), Fred Goldberg (Sweden), Barry Goldman (Australia), H. Dickson Hoese (USA), Morten Jødal (Norway), Madhav Khandekar (Canada), Miroslav Kutilek (Czech Republic), Steven W. Leavitt (USA), Howard Maccabee (USA), Jennifer Marohasy (Australia), Cliff Ollier (Australia), Jim Petch (United Kingdom), Robert J. Reginato (USA), Paul Reiter (France), Tom Segalstad (Norway), Gary Sharp (USA), Walter Starck (Australia), David Stockwell (Australia), Mitchell Taylor (Canada), Gerd Weber (Germany), Bastow Wilson (New Zealand), Raphael Wust (Australia)

Several additional reviewers wish to remain anonymous.

Editors

Diane Carol Bast (USA), S.T. Karnick (USA)

NIPCC

NONGOVERNMENTAL INTERNATIONAL PANEL
ON CLIMATE CHANGE

Reviews of *Climate Change Reconsidered II: Physical Science*

"I fully support the efforts of the Nongovernmental International Panel on Climate Change (NIPCC) and publication of its latest report, *Climate Change Reconsidered II: Physical Science,* to help the general public to understand the reality of global climate change."

Kumar Raina, Former Deputy Director General
Geological Survey of India

"*Climate Change Reconsidered II* fulfills an important role in countering the IPCC part by part, highlighting crucial things they ignore such as the Little Ice Age and the recovery (warming) which began in 1800–1850. In contrast to the IPCC, which often ignores evidence of past changes, the authors of the NIPCC report recognize that climatology requires studying past changes to infer future changes."

Syun-Ichi Akasofu, Founding Director & Professor of Physics Emeritus
International Arctic Research Center, University of Alaska Fairbanks

"The work of the NIPCC to present the evidence for natural climate warming and climate change is an essential counter-balance to the biased reporting of the IPCC. They have brought to focus a range of peer-reviewed publications showing that natural forces have in the past and continue today to dominate the climate signal."

Ian Clark, Department of Earth Sciences
University of Ottawa, Canada

"The CCR-II report correctly explains that most of the reports on global warming and its impacts on sea-level rise, ice melts, glacial retreats, impact on crop production, extreme weather events, rainfall changes, etc. have not properly considered factors such as physical impacts of human activities, natural variability in climate, lopsided models used in the prediction of production estimates, etc. There is a need to look into these phenomena at local and regional scales before sensationalization of global warming-related studies."

S. Jeevananda Reddy, Former Chief Technical Advisor
United Nations World Meteorological Organization

"Library shelves are cluttered with books on global warming. The problem is identifying which ones are worth reading. The NIPCC's CCR-II report is one of these. Its coverage of the topic is comprehensive without being superficial. It sorts through conflicting claims made by scientists and highlights mounting evidence that climate sensitivity to carbon dioxide increase is lower than climate models have until now assumed."

Chris de Freitas, School of Environment
The University of Auckland, New Zealand

"Rather than coming from a pre-determined politicized position that is typical of the IPCC, the NIPCC constrains itself to the scientific process so as to provide objective information. If we (scientists) are honest, we understand that the study of atmospheric processes/dynamics is in its infancy. Consequently, the work of the NIPCC and its most recent report is very important."

Bruce Borders, Professor of Forest Biometrics
Warnell School of Forestry and Natural Resources, University of Georgia

"I support [the work of the NIPCC] because I am convinced that the whole field of climate and climate change urgently needs an open debate between several 'schools of thought,' in science as well as other disciplines, many of which jumped on the IPCC bandwagon far too readily. Climate, and even more so impacts and responses, are far too complex and important to be left to an official body like the IPCC."

Sonja A. Boehmer-Christiansen
Reader Emeritus, Department of Geography, Hull University
Editor, *Energy & Environment*

Climate Change Reconsidered II

Biological Impacts

Published by THE HEARTLAND INSTITUTE
One South Wacker Drive #2740
Chicago, Illinois 60606 U.S.A.
phone +1 (312) 377-4000
fax +1 (312) 377-5000
www.heartland.org

1-10 copies	$154 per copy
11-50 copies	$123 per copy
51-100 copies	$98 per copy
101 or more	$79 per copy

Please use the following citation for this report:

Idso, C.D, Idso, S.B., Carter, R.M., and Singer, S.F. (Eds.) 2014. *Climate Change Reconsidered II: Biological Impacts*. Chicago, IL: The Heartland Institute.

This print version is black and white. A color version is available for free online at www.climatechangereconsidered.org.

ISBN-13 – 978-1-934791-43-1
ISBN-10 – 1-934791-43-1

2014

1 2 3 4 5 6

Foreword

For the past five years, The Heartland Institute has been proud to partner with the Center for the Study of Carbon Dioxide and Global Change and the Science and Environmental Policy Project (SEPP) to produce authoritative and independent assessments of the latest science concerning climate change. The present volume in the Climate Change Reconsidered series focuses on the biological impacts of rising temperatures and atmospheric carbon dioxide (CO_2) levels.

The United Nations' Intergovernmental Panel on Climate Change (IPCC) insists that rising temperatures and CO_2 levels have harmful effects on Earth's plant and animal life. But as this report demonstrates, IPCC's claims are at odds with literally thousands of real-world observations, model-based projections, and laboratory and in-the-field experiments. The reality is that the world is getting greener over time as plants, animals, and humans benefit from higher temperatures and CO_2-enriched air.

NIPCC: A Brief History

The Nongovernmental International Panel on Climate Change, or NIPCC, is an international panel of scientists and scholars who came together to understand the causes and consequences of climate change. NIPCC has no formal attachment to or sponsorship from any government or government agency.

NIPCC seeks to objectively analyze and interpret data and facts without conforming to any specific agenda. This organizational structure and purpose stand in contrast to those of IPCC, which *is* government-sponsored, politically motivated, and predisposed to believing that climate change is a problem in need of a U.N. solution.

NIPCC traces its beginnings to an informal meeting held in Milan, Italy in 2003 organized by Dr. S. Fred Singer and the Science and Environmental Policy Project (SEPP). The purpose was to produce an independent evaluation of the available scientific evidence on the subject of carbon dioxide-induced global warming in anticipation of the release of IPCC's *Fourth Assessment Report* (AR4). NIPCC scientists concluded IPCC was biased with respect to making future projections of climate change, discerning a significant human-induced influence on current and past climatic trends, and evaluating the impacts of potential carbon dioxide-induced environmental changes on Earth's biosphere.

To highlight such deficiencies in IPCC's AR4, in 2008 SEPP partnered with The Heartland Institute to produce *Nature, Not Human Activity, Rules the Climate.* In 2009, the Center for the Study of Carbon Dioxide and Global Change joined the original two sponsors to produce *Climate Change Reconsidered: The 2009 Report of the Nongovernmental International Panel on Climate Change (NIPCC)*, the first comprehensive alternative to the alarmist reports of IPCC.

In 2010, a Web site (www.nipccreport.org) was created to highlight scientific studies NIPCC scientists believed likely would be downplayed or ignored by IPCC during preparation of its next assessment report. In 2011, the three sponsoring organizations produced *Climate Change Reconsidered: The 2011 Interim Report of the Nongovernmental International Panel on Climate Change (NIPCC)*.

In 2013, a division of the Chinese Academy of Sciences translated and published an abridged edition of the 2009 and 2011 NIPCC reports in a single volume. Also in 2013, NIPCC released *Climate Change Reconsidered II: Physical Science,* the first of three volumes bringing the original 2009 report up-to-date with research from the 2011 *Interim Report* plus research as current as the third quarter of 2013. A new Web site was created (www.ClimateChange Reconsidered.org) to feature the new report and future volumes, including the current one, and news about their release.

The current volume is the second volume in the Climate Change Reconsidered II series, subtitled *Biological Impacts*. A third and final volume, subtitled *Human Welfare, Energy, and Policies,* is also being released in 2014.

CCR II: Biological Impacts

In this new report, Lead Authors/Editors Craig D. Idso, Robert M. Carter, and S. Fred Singer have been joined by a fourth author, Sherwood B. Idso, one of the world's most distinguished soil scientists and authorities on the impact of CO_2 on plants. Together, they worked with a team of more than 30 scientists from 13 countries to produce a report that is comprehensive, objective, and faithful to the scientific method. The sheer size of this volume—more than 1,000 pages and containing references to thousands of peer-reviewed articles and books—suggests what an extraordinary research, writing, and editing endeavor this turned out to be.

As they did for previous volumes in the Climate Change Reconsidered series, NIPCC authors paid special attention to peer-reviewed articles that were either overlooked by IPCC or that contain data, discussion, or implications arguing against IPCC's claim that "human interference" in the global climate has "dangerous" consequences for the natural world and human populations. They found a large body of evidence produced by thousands of scientists over the course of many years that directly challenges IPCC's narrative. Study after study reveals that warming produces more benefits than harms for a wide range of plants and animals and, not insignificantly, humans as well. So plentiful is the research and so clear are the conclusions that one can only wonder how IPCC's authors overlooked them.

The Lead Authors/Editors briefly discuss their perspective and findings in the Preface, followed by an Executive Summary beginning on page 1 summarizing the volume's principal findings. Most notably, its authors say IPCC has exaggerated the negative impacts of global warming and rising atmospheric CO_2 levels: "We find no net harm to the global environment or to human health, and often find the opposite: net benefits to plants, including important food crops, and to animals and human health."

Acknowledgements

As we did in the forewords of previous volumes in the Climate Change Reconsidered series, we extend our sincere thanks and appreciation to the scientists and other experts who helped write this report and its precursors, to those who conducted the original research that is summarized and cited, and to those who participated in the peer-review process. Editors could not hope to work for a team of wiser, more distinguished, or more patient writers.

Funding for this effort once again came from three family foundations, none of them having any commercial interest in the topic. We thank them for their generosity. No government or corporate funds were solicited or received to support this project.

Diane Carol Bast
Executive Editor
The Heartland Institute

S.T. Karnick
Research Director
The Heartland Institute

Preface

Climate Change Reconsidered II: Biological Impacts (CCR-IIb) is produced by the Nongovernmental International Panel on Climate Change (NIPCC), a collaboration of three organizations—the Center for the Study of Carbon Dioxide and Global Change, Science and Environmental Policy Project (SEPP), and The Heartland Institute. The four Lead Authors/ Editors—Craig D. Idso, Sherwood B. Idso, Robert M. Carter, and S. Fred Singer—assembled and worked closely with more than 30 contributors and reviewers from 13 countries. This report was subjected to the common standards of peer review. Reviewers who agreed to be identified are listed on the title page.

CCR-IIb is the second of three volumes in the Climate Change Reconsidered II series. The first volume, *Climate Change Reconsidered II: Physical Science* (CCR-IIa) was published in September 2013. It examined the theory, models, and evidence regarding the science of climate change and concluded the human impact on global climate is small and any warming that may occur as a result of human carbon dioxide (CO_2) and other greenhouse gas emissions is likely to have little effect on global temperatures, the cryosphere (ice-covered areas), hydrosphere (oceans, lakes, and rivers), or weather. (See Figure 1.) The current volume focuses on scientific research on the impacts of rising temperatures and atmospheric CO_2 levels on the biological world. It finds no net harm to the global environment or to human health and often finds the opposite: net benefits to plants, including important food crops, and to animals and human health.

CCR-IIb broadly tracks and critiques the work of IPCC's Working Group II, which is expected to release its report on the impacts of climate change around the same time as this report is presented. It appears IPCC is continuing its pattern of selectively reporting data to present an alarmist view of the impacts of climate change. A draft of Working Group II's forthcoming *Summary for Policymakers* identifies eight "key risks":

i. Risk of death, injury, and disrupted livelihoods in low-lying coastal zones and small island developing states, due to sea-level rise, coastal flooding, and storm surges.

ii. Risk of food insecurity linked to warming, drought, and precipitation variability, particularly for poorer populations.

iii. Risk of severe harm for large urban populations due to inland flooding.

iv. Risk of loss of rural livelihoods and income due to insufficient access to drinking and irrigation water and reduced agricultural productivity, particularly for farmers and pastoralists with minimal capital in semi-arid regions.

v. Systemic risks due to extreme events leading to breakdown of infrastructure networks and critical services.

vi. Risk of loss of marine ecosystems and the services they provide for coastal livelihoods, especially for fishing communities in the tropics and the Arctic.

vii. Risk of loss of terrestrial ecosystems and the services they provide for terrestrial livelihoods.

viii. Risk of mortality, morbidity, and other harms during periods of extreme heat, particularly for vulnerable urban populations.

Figure 1.
Physical Science Summary

- Global climate models are unable to make accurate projections of climate even 10 years ahead, let alone the 100-year period that has been adopted by policy planners. The output of such models should therefore not be used to guide public policy formulation.

- Neither the rate nor the magnitude of the reported late twentieth century surface warming (1979–2000) lay outside the range of normal natural variability, nor were they in any way unusual compared to earlier episodes in Earth's climatic history.

- Solar forcing of temperature change is likely more important than is currently recognized.

- No unambiguous evidence exists of dangerous interference in the global climate caused by human-related CO_2 emissions. In particular, the cryosphere is not melting at an enhanced rate; sea-level rise is not accelerating; and no systematic changes have been documented in evaporation or rainfall or in the magnitude or intensity of extreme meteorological events.

- Any human global climate signal is so small as to be nearly indiscernible against the background variability of the natural climate system. Climate change is always occurring.

- A phase of temperature stasis or cooling has succeeded the mild warming of the twentieth century. Similar periods of warming and cooling due to natural variability are certain to occur in the future irrespective of human emissions of greenhouse gases.

- *Source:* Idso, C.D., Carter, R.M., and Singer, S.F. (Eds.) 2013. *Climate Change Reconsidered II: Physical Science.* Chicago, IL: The Heartland Institute.

The research summarized in CCR-IIb effectively refutes five of these apocalyptic forecasts. The remaining three "key risks"—the harm coastal and inland flooding will do to people and to infrastructure—are addressed in the first and third volumes of the Climate Change Reconsidered II series.

A careful reading of the chapters below reveals thousands of peer-reviewed scientific journal articles do not support and often contradict IPCC's alarmist narrative. NIPCC scientists have worked hard to remain true to the facts in their representations of the studies cited in this work. The research is usually quoted directly and at some length, along with a description of the methodology used and qualifications that accompanied the stated conclusions. Editorial commentary is generally limited to introductions and sometimes brief conclusions at the end of sections.

Whether the subject is the likely effects of warming on crops, trees, weeds, birds, butterflies, or polar bears, it seems IPCC invariably picks the studies and models that paint global warming in the darkest possible hues. IPCC sees "death, injury, and disrupted livelihoods"—to borrow a phrase from Working Group II—everywhere it looks.

Oftentimes, IPCC's pessimistic forecasts fly in the face of scientific observations. The global ecosystem is not suffering from the rising temperatures and atmospheric CO_2 levels IPCC has called "unprecedented," despite all the models and hypotheses IPCC's authors marshal to make that case. Real-world data show conclusively that most plants flourish when exposed to higher temperatures and higher levels of CO_2 and that the planet's terrestrial biosphere is undergoing a great post-Industrial Revolution greening that is causing deserts to retreat and forests to expand, enlarging habitat for wildlife. Essentially the same story can be told of global warming's impact on terrestrial animals, aquatic life, and human health.

Why are these research findings and this perspective missing from IPCC's reports? NIPCC has been publishing volumes containing this research for five years—long enough, one would think, for the authors of IPCC's reports to have taken notice, if only to disagree. But the draft of the Working Group II contribution to IPCC's *Fifth Assessment Report* suggests otherwise. Either IPCC's authors purposely ignore this research because it runs counter to their thesis that any human impact on climate must be bad and therefore stopped at any cost, or they are inept and have failed to conduct a proper and full scientific investigation of the pertinent literature. Either way,

IPCC is misleading the scientific community, policymakers, and the general public. Because the stakes are high, this is a grave disservice.

We are not alone in questioning the accuracy or reliability of IPCC reports. In 2010, the InterAcademy Council, an international organization representing the world's leading national academies of science, produced an audit of IPCC procedures. In its report, *Climate Change Assessments: Review of the Processes & Procedures of the IPCC*, the IAC decried the lack of independent review, reliance on unpublished and non-peer-reviewed sources, refusal by some of the lead authors to share their data with critics, and political interference in the selection of authors and contributors.

How CO_2 enrichment has affected global food production and biospheric productivity is a matter of fact, not opinion. The evidence is overwhelming that it has and will continue to help plants thrive, leading to greater biodiversity, shrinking deserts, expanded habitat for wildlife, and more food for a growing human population. In sharp contrast to IPCC's pessimistic forecast of declining food production, NIPCC's authors say a future warming of the climate coupled with rising atmospheric CO_2 levels will boost global agricultural production and help meet the food needs of the planet's growing population. They find the positive direct effects of CO_2 on crop yields tend to overcome any negative effects associated with changed weather conditions. Journalists, policymakers, and the interested public should demand to know why IPCC either hides or is silent about these truths.

We acknowledge, as we did in the prefaces to previous volumes in this series, that not every scientist whose work we cite disagrees with IPCC positions even though their research points in different directions. We recognize there may be some among the thousands of scientists we quote who are dismayed to see their work cited in a book written by "skeptics." We ask them to read this book with an open mind and ask themselves how much of what they think they know to be true is based on trust, perhaps misplaced, in claims propagated by IPCC. Even scientists need to be reminded sometimes that skepticism, not conformity, is the higher value in the pursuit of knowledge.

We thank all those who participated in the writing, reviewing, editing, and proofreading of this volume. This was a huge undertaking that involved thousands of hours and scores of people over the course of several years. The result exceeded our hopes, and we trust it meets your expectations.

Craig D. Idso, Ph.D.
Chairman
Center for the Study of Carbon Dioxide and Global Change

Sherwood B. Idso, Ph.D.
President
Center for the Study of Carbon Dioxide and Global Change

Robert M. Carter, Ph.D.
Emeritus Fellow
Institute of Public Affairs (Australia)

S. Fred Singer, Ph.D.
President
Science and Environmental Policy Project

Table of Contents

Table of Contents

Executive Summary

This report is produced by the Nongovernmental International Panel on Climate Change (NIPCC), a joint project of three organizations: Center for the Study of Carbon Dioxide and Global Change, Science and Environmental Policy Project (SEPP), and The Heartland Institute. Four Lead Authors/Editors—Craig D. Idso, Sherwood B. Idso, Robert M. Carter, and S. Fred Singer—assembled and worked closely with more than 30 authors, contributors, and reviewers. This volume was subjected to the common standards of peer review.

This work provides the scientific balance that is missing from the overly alarmist reports of the United Nations' Intergovernmental Panel on Climate Change (IPCC), which are highly selective in their review of climate science and controversial with regard to their projections of future climate change. Although IPCC claims to be unbiased and to have based its assessment on the best available science, we have found this not to be the case. In many instances conclusions have been seriously exaggerated, relevant facts have been distorted, and key scientific studies have been ignored.

1. Impact on Plants and Soil

Carbon dioxide (CO_2) is the basis of nearly all life on Earth. It is the primary raw material utilized by most plants to produce the organic matter from which they construct their tissues. Not surprisingly, thousands of laboratory and field experiments conducted over the past 200 years demonstrate that plant productivity and growth both rise as the CO_2 concentration of the air increases.

As early as 1804, de Saussure showed that peas exposed to high CO_2 concentrations grew better than control plants in ambient air, and work conducted in the early 1900s significantly increased the number of species in which a growth-enhancing effect of atmospheric CO_2 enrichment was observed to occur (Demoussy, 1902–1904; Cummings and Jones, 1918). By the time a group of scientists convened at Duke University in 1977 for a workshop on Anticipated Plant Responses to Global Carbon Dioxide Enrichment, an annotated bibliography of 590 scientific studies dealing with CO_2 effects on vegetation had been prepared (Strain, 1978). This body of research demonstrated increased levels of atmospheric CO_2 generally produce increases in plant photosynthesis, decreases in plant water loss by transpiration, increases in leaf area, and increases in plant branch and fruit numbers, to name but a few of the most commonly reported benefits. (See Figure 1.)

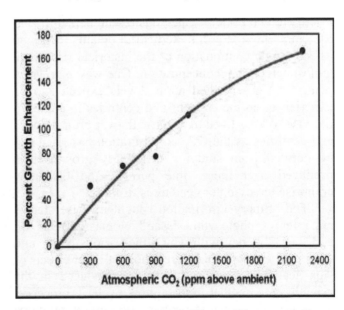

Figure 1. Positive Impact of CO_2 on Plants and Trees. Adapted from Idso, K.E. (1992).

1

Five years later, at the International Conference on Rising Atmospheric Carbon Dioxide and Plant Productivity, it was concluded a doubling of the air's CO_2 concentration likely would lead to a 50% increase in photosynthesis in C_3 plants, a doubling of water use efficiency in both C_3 and C_4 plants, significant increases in biological nitrogen fixation in almost all biological systems, and an increase in the ability of plants to adapt to a variety of environmental stresses (Lemon, 1983). In the years since, many other studies have been conducted on hundreds of different plant species, repeatedly confirming the growth-enhancing, water-saving, and stress-alleviating advantages that elevated atmospheric CO_2 concentrations bestow upon Earth's plants and soils (Idso and Singer, 2009; Idso and Idso, 2011).

Chapter 1 focuses on basic plant productivity responses to elevated CO_2 and includes in two appendices tabular presentations of more than 5,500 individual plant photosynthetic and biomass responses to CO_2-enriched air, finding nearly all plants experience increases in these two parameters at higher levels of CO_2. Chapter 1 also examines the effect of elevated CO_2 on ecosystems including forests, grasslands, peatlands, wetlands, and soils. This review of the literature reveals elevated CO_2 improves the productivity of ecosystems both in plant tissues aboveground and in the soils beneath them.

2. Impact on Plant Characteristics

There are two principal methods researchers utilize to ascertain how Earth's terrestrial plants will be affected by a continuation of the historical rise in the atmosphere's CO_2 concentration. One way is to grow plants in CO_2-enriched air to levels expected to be experienced in the decades and centuries to come. In the case of long-lived trees, growth over prior decades and centuries as the CO_2 concentration has risen can be derived from studying the yearly growth rings produced over those time periods and that now comprise the living or dead trees' trunks.

The primary information sought in these studies are rates of photosynthesis and biomass production and the efficiency with which the various plants and trees utilize water. There are a host of other effects of significance, including substances produced in the growth process that impact how well it proceeds, substances deposited in the parts of agricultural crops that are harvested for human and animal consump-

tion, and substances that determine whether insect pests find the foliage or fruit of a certain crop or tree to be to their liking. Finally, there is the question of whether forest soils will have sufficient nitrogen to sustain the long-term CO_2-enhanced growth rates of long-lived trees.

Chapter 2 examines these and other effects of atmospheric CO_2 enrichment on plant characteristics. Extensive research finds those effects are overwhelmingly positive. For example, rising CO_2 levels promote plant growth by increasing the concentrations of plant hormones that stimulate cell division, cell elongation, and protein synthesis; by enabling plants to produce more and larger flowers; by increasing the production of glomalin, an important protein created by fungi living in symbiotic association with the roots of most vascular plants; and by affecting leaf characteristics of agricultural plants that lead to higher rates and efficiencies of photosynthesis and growth as well as increased resistance to herbivory and pathogen attack.

3. Impact on Plants Under Stress

According to IPCC, a warmer future will introduce new sources of stress on the biological world, including increases in forest fires, droughts, and extreme heat events. IPCC fails to ask whether the higher levels of atmospheric CO_2 its models also predict will aid or hinder the ability of plants to cope with these challenges. Had it looked, IPCC would have discovered an extensive body of research showing how atmospheric CO_2 enrichment ameliorates the negative effects of a number of environmental plant stresses. The relative percentage growth enhancement produced by an increase in the air's CO_2 concentration is generally greater under stressful and resource-limited conditions than when growing conditions are ideal.

Chapter 3 reports research on the effects of rising CO_2 levels on the ability of plants to cope with pathogenic invaders, drought, rising temperatures, the deleterious effects of heavy metals in soil, herbivory by insects and animals, and shortages of essential nutrients in soil such as nitrogen. Rising CO_2 typically reduces and can completely override the negative effects of ozone pollution on the photosynthesis, growth, and yield of nearly all agricultural crops and trees that have been experimentally evaluated. Rising CO_2 also can help plants overcome stresses imposed by the buildup of soil salinity from repeated irrigation.

4. Likely Future Impacts on Plants

Chapter 4 analyzes how atmospheric CO_2 enrichment has boosted global food production and biospheric productivity since the beginning of the Industrial Revolution. It also reports how rising CO_2 helps plants avoid temperature-induced extinctions, which many models predict could occur if global temperatures rise significantly in the future. Whereas IPCC forecasts severe food shortages, the preponderance of evidence suggests the many yield-enhancing benefits of rising atmospheric CO_2 will help ensure more food is grown to meet the needs of the planet's growing population.

Chapter 4 also reports on the current health of the terrestrial biosphere, analyzing the productivity of the globe as a whole followed by regional analyses on continental and sub-continental scales. According to IPCC, the productivity of the terrestrial biosphere should be declining because of rising temperatures and other perceived negative climatic changes. In contrast, empirical data show it to be increasing, in large measure due to the aerial fertilization effect of rising atmospheric CO_2.

Chapter 4 concludes with an examination of topics pertaining to biodiversity, plant extinctions, and plant evolution, which represent three important topics in assessing the future of Earth's terrestrial biosphere.

5. Impact on Terrestrial Animals

IPCC's *Fourth Assessment Report* claimed "new evidence suggests that climate-driven extinctions and range retractions are already widespread" and the "projected impacts on biodiversity are significant and of key relevance, since global losses in biodiversity are irreversible (*very high confidence*)" (IPCC, 2007). However, as shown in the first volume of the Climate Change Reconsidered II series, *Physical Science,* there is a growing divide between IPCC's climate model simulations and real-world observations of global warmth. The species-modeling research IPCC almost exclusively relies on to make these predictions depends on climate models known to exaggerate future global warming and extreme weather events.

Even assuming IPCC climate models were unbiased and reasonably accurate at regional scales, the "climate envelope" models used by IPCC are deeply flawed due to assumptions about the immobility of species that are routinely contradicted by real-world observations. IPCC also improperly characterizes the adaptive responses (e.g., range shifts, phenotypic or genetic adaptations) of many species as supporting their model-based extinction claims, when in reality such adaptive responses provide documentary evidence of species resilience.

Chapter 5 begins with a review and analysis of IPCC-based species extinction claims, highlighting many of the problems inherent in the models on which such claims are based. The model projections are then evaluated against real-world observations of various animal species and their response to what IPCC has called the unprecedented rise in temperature and atmospheric CO_2 levels of the twentieth and twenty-first centuries. Results of that evaluation reveal that although there likely will be some changes in species population dynamics, few if any species likely will be driven even close to extinction. In a number of instances, real-world data indicate warmer temperatures and higher atmospheric CO_2 concentrations will be highly beneficial, favoring a proliferation of species. IPCC continues to ignore such positive externalities of rising temperature and atmospheric CO_2.

6. Impact on Aquatic Life

IPCC postulates that human interference in the climate will significantly harm aquatic life by causing temperatures of the world's water bodies to rise and through the absorption of CO_2 from the atmosphere into water, thereby lowering the pH of freshwater and ocean water (a process referred to as "acidification"). In both scenarios, IPCC projects marine and freshwater species will be negatively impacted and will experience future declines, which in some instances may be so severe as to cause species extinctions.

In contrast, the material presented in Chapter 6, representing the findings of hundreds of peer-reviewed research analyses, suggests a much better future is in store for Earth's aquatic life. Many laboratory and field studies demonstrate growth and developmental improvements in response to higher temperatures and reduced water pH levels. Other research illustrates the capability of coral and other marine and freshwater species to tolerate and adapt to the rising temperature (see Figure 2) and pH decline of the planet's water bodies. When these observations are considered, the pessimistic projections of IPCC give way to considerable optimism with respect to the future of the planet's marine life.

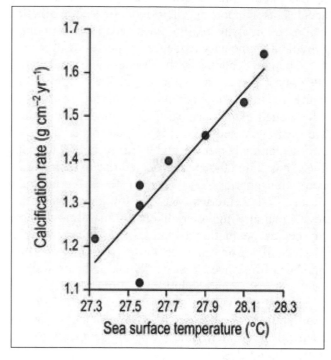

Figure 2. Coral calcification rates rise with seawater temperature. Adapted from Carricart-Ganivet and Gonzalez-Diaz (2009).

7. Impact on Human Health

Carbon dioxide is invisible, odorless, nontoxic, and does not seriously affect human health until the CO_2 content of the air reaches approximately 15,000 ppm, more than 37 times greater than the current concentration of atmospheric CO_2 (Luft *et al.*, 1974). There is no reason to be concerned about any direct adverse human health consequences of the ongoing rise in the air's CO_2 content now or in the future, as even extreme model projections do not indicate anthropogenic activities will raise the air's CO_2 concentration above 1,000 to 2,000 ppm. Nevertheless, IPCC contends rising CO_2 concentrations are causing several indirect threats to human health, which they project will worsen as the air's CO_2 concentration rises in the future.

In a draft Technical Summary of its upcoming report, Working Group II claims, "The health of human populations is sensitive to shifts in weather patterns and other aspects of climate change [*very high confidence*] and "There is emerging evidence of non-linearities in response (such as greater-than-expected mortality due to heat waves) as climates become more extreme" (IPCC, 2013, p. 16; italics in original, bold removed).

Research reviewed in CCR-IIb, however, shows IPCC's view of the impacts of rising temperatures and atmospheric CO_2 on human health is simply wrong. Numerous peer-reviewed studies demonstrate a warmer planet is beneficial to humanity, as warmer temperatures in all parts of the world lead to decreases in temperature-related mortality. The medical literature shows warmer temperatures and a smaller difference between daily high and low temperatures, as occurred during the twentieth and early twenty-first centuries, reduce mortality rates due to cardiovascular and respiratory disease and stroke occurrence.

Similarly, the research is quite clear that climate has exerted only a minimal influence on recent trends in vector-borne diseases such as malaria, dengue fever, and tick-borne diseases. Other factors, many of them related to economic and technological setbacks or progress and not to weather, are far more important in determining the transmission and prevalence of such diseases.

Finally, and perhaps surprisingly, IPCC entirely overlooks the positive effects of rising levels of atmospheric CO_2 on human health. Carbon dioxide fertilization has been shown to enhance certain health-promoting substances in plants, such as antioxidants, vitamin C, and fatty acids, and promote the growth of plants such as St. John's wort used for the treatment of a variety of illnesses. In this way, global warming portends great health benefits for humans. IPCC makes no mention of these benefits.

The remainder of this executive summary consists of key findings organized by chapter.

Key Findings by Chapter

Chapter 1. CO₂, Plants, and Soils

- Results obtained under 3,586 separate sets of experimental conditions conducted on 549 plant species reveal nearly all plants experience increases in dry weight or biomass in response to atmospheric CO_2 enrichment (henceforth referred to as "rising CO_2"). Additional results obtained under 2,094 separate experimental conditions conducted on 472 plant species reveal nearly all plants experience increases in their rates of photosynthesis in response to rising CO_2.

- Long-term CO_2 enrichment studies confirm the findings of shorter-term experiments, demonstrating that the growth-enhancing, water-conserving, and stress-alleviating effects of rising CO_2 likely persist throughout plant lifetimes.

- Forest productivity and growth rates around the world have increased gradually since the Industrial Revolution in concert with, and in response to, the historical increase in the air's CO_2 concentration. Therefore, as CO_2 continues to rise, forests likely will respond by exhibiting significant increases in biomass production and they likely will grow more robustly and significantly expand their ranges.

- Modest increases in air temperature tend to increase carbon storage in forests and their soils. Thus, old-growth forests can be significant carbon sinks and their capacity to sequester carbon in the future will be enhanced as CO_2 continues to rise.

- As CO_2 continues to rise, the productivity of grassland species will increase even under unfavorable growing conditions characterized by less-than-adequate soil moisture, inadequate soil nutrition, elevated air temperature, and physical stress imposed by herbivory.

- The thawing of permafrost caused by increases in air temperature likely will not transform peatlands from carbon sinks to carbon sources. Instead, rapid terrestrialization likely will act to intensify carbon-sink conditions.

- Rising CO_2 likely will enhance the productivity and carbon sequestering ability of Earth's wetlands. In addition, rising CO_2 may help some coastal wetlands counterbalance the negative impacts of rising seas.

- Rising CO_2 likely will allow greater numbers of beneficial bacteria (that help sequester carbon and nitrogen) to exist within soils and anaerobic water environments, thereby benefitting both terrestrial and aquatic ecosystems.

- The aerial fertilization effect of rising CO_2 likely will result in greater soil carbon stores due to increased carbon input to soils, even in nutrient-poor soils and in spite of predicted increases in temperature. The carbon-sequestering capability of Earth's vegetation likely will act as a significant brake on the rate-of-rise of the air's CO_2 content and thereby help to mute the magnitude of any CO_2-induced global warming.

- Rising CO_2 has significantly reduced the erosion of valuable topsoil over the past several decades; the continuing increase in atmospheric CO_2 can maintain this trend and perhaps even accelerate it for the foreseeable future.

Chapter 2. Plant Characteristics

- Rising CO_2 enhances plant growth, development, and ultimate yield (in the case of agricultural crops) by increasing the concentrations of plant hormones that stimulate cell division, cell elongation, and protein synthesis.

- Rising CO_2 enables plants to produce more and larger flowers, as well as other flower-related changes having significant implications for plant productivity and survival, almost all of which are positive.

- Rising CO_2 increases the production of glomalin, a protein created by fungi living in symbiotic association with the roots of 80 percent of the planet's vascular plants, where it is having a huge positive impact on the biosphere.

- Rising CO_2 likely will affect many leaf characteristics of agricultural plants, with the majority of the changes leading to higher rates and efficiencies of photosynthesis and growth as well as increased resistance to herbivory and pathogen attack.

- Rising CO_2 stimulates photosynthesis in nearly all plants, enabling them to produce more nonstructural carbohydrates that can be used to create important carbon-based secondary compounds, one of which is lignin.

- Rising CO_2 leads to enhanced plant fitness, flower pollination, and nectar production, leading to increases in fruit, grain, and vegetable yields of agricultural crops as well as productivity increases in natural vegetation.

- As rising CO_2 causes many plants to increase biomass, the larger plants likely will develop more extensive root systems enabling them to extract greater amounts of mineral nutrients from the soil.

- Rising CO_2 causes plants to sequentially reduce the openness of their stomata, thus restricting unnecessary water loss via excessive transpiration, while some plants also reduce the density (number per area) of stomates on their leaves.

- Rising CO_2 significantly enhances the condensed tannin concentrations of the vast majority of trees and grasses, providing them with stronger defenses against various herbivores both above and below ground. This in turn reduces the amount of methane, a potent greenhouse gas, released to the atmosphere by ruminants browsing on tree leaves and grass.

- As the air's CO_2 content rises, many plant species may not experience photosynthetic acclimation even under conditions of low soil nitrogen. In the event that a plant cannot balance its carbohydrate sources and sinks, CO_2-induced acclimation provides a way of achieving that balance by shifting resources away from the site of photosynthesis to enhance sink development or other important plant processes.

Chapter 3. Plants Under Stress

- Rising CO_2 exerts a greater positive influence on diseased as opposed to healthy plants because it significantly ameliorates the negative effects of stresses imposed on plants by pathogenic invaders.

- Rising CO_2 helps many plants use water more efficiently, helping them overcome stressful conditions imposed by drought or other less-than-optimum soil moisture conditions.

- Enhanced rates of plant photosynthesis and biomass production from rising CO_2 will not be diminished by any global warming that might accompany it in the future. In fact, if ambient air temperatures rise concurrently, the growth-promoting effects of atmospheric CO_2 enrichment will likely rise even more.

- Although rising CO_2 increases the growth of many weeds, the fraction helped is not as large as that experienced by non-weeds. Thus, CO_2 enrichment of the air may provide non-weeds with greater protection against weed-induced decreases in productivity.

- Rising CO_2 improves plants' abilities to withstand the deleterious effects of heavy metals where they are present in soils at toxic levels.

- Rising CO_2 reduces the frequency and severity of herbivory against crops and trees by increasing production of natural substances that repel insects, leading to the production of more symmetrical leaves that are less susceptible to attacks by herbivores, and making trees more capable of surviving severe defoliation.

- Rising CO_2 increases net photosynthesis and biomass production by many agricultural crops, grasses, and grassland species even when soil nitrogen concentrations tend to limit their growth. Additional CO_2-induced carbon input to the soil stimulates microbial decomposition and thus leads to more available soil nitrogen, thereby conclusively disproving the progressive nitrogen limitation hypothesis.

- Rising CO_2 typically reduces and can completely override the negative effects of ozone pollution on the photosynthesis, growth, and yield of nearly all agricultural crops and trees that have been experimentally evaluated.

- Rising CO_2 can help plants overcome stresses imposed by the buildup of soil salinity from repeated irrigation.

- Rising CO_2 is a powerful antidote for the deleterious biological impacts that might be caused by an increase in the flux of UV-B radiation at the surface of Earth due to depletion of the planet's stratospheric ozone layer.

Chapter 4. Earth's Vegetative Future

- The vigor of Earth's terrestrial biosphere has been increasing with time, revealing a great post-Industrial Revolution greening of the Earth that extends across the entire globe. Over the past 50 years global carbon uptake has doubled from 2.4 ± 0.8 billion tons in 1960 to 5.0 ± 0.9 billion tons in 2010.

- The atmosphere's rising CO_2 content, which IPCC considers to be the chief culprit behind all of its "reasons for concern" about the future of the biosphere, is most likely the primary cause of the observed greening trend.

- The observed greening of the Earth has occurred in spite of all the many real and imagined assaults on Earth's vegetation, including fires, disease, pest outbreaks, air pollution, deforestation, and climatic change. Rising CO_2 is making the biosphere more resilient to stress even as it becomes more lush and productive.

- Agricultural productivity in the United States and across the globe dramatically increased over the last three decades of the twentieth century, a phenomenon partly due to new cultivation techniques but also due partly to warmer temperatures and higher CO_2 levels.

- A future warming of the climate coupled with rising CO_2 will further boost global agricultural production and help meet the food needs of the planet's growing population.

- The positive direct effects of higher levels of atmospheric CO_2 on future crop yields are likely to dominate any hypothetical negative effects associated with changing weather conditions, just as they have during the twentieth and early twenty-first centuries.

- Plants can adjust their physiology to accommodate a warming of both the magnitude and rate-of-rise typically predicted by climate models, should such a warming actually occur.

- Evidence continues to accumulate for substantial heritable variation of ecologically important plant traits, including root allocation, drought tolerance, and nutrient plasticity, which suggests rapid evolution is likely to occur based on epigenetic variation alone. Rising CO_2 will exert significant selection pressure on plants, which can be expected to improve their performance in the face of various environmental stressors via the process of micro-evolution.

- As good as things currently are for world agriculture, natural selection and bioengineering could bring about additional beneficial effects. For example, highly CO_2-responsive genotypes of a wide variety of plants could be selected to take advantage of their genetic ability to optimize their growth in response to rising CO_2.

Chapter 5. Terrestrial Animals

- IPCC's forecast of future species extinction relies on a narrow view of the literature that is highly selective and based almost entirely on model projections as opposed to real-world observations; the latter often contradict the former.

- Numerous shortcomings are inherent in the models utilized in predicting the impact of climate on the health and distributions of animal species. Assumptions and limitations make them unreliable.

- Research suggests amphibian populations will suffer little, if any, harm from projected CO_2-induced global warming, and they may even benefit from it.

- Although some changes in bird populations and their habitat areas have been documented in the literature, linking such changes to CO_2-induced global warming remains elusive. Also, when there have been changes, they often are positive, as many species have adapted and are thriving in response to rising temperatures of the modern era.

- Polar bears have survived historic changes in climate that have exceeded those of the twentieth century or are forecast by computer models to occur in the future. In addition, some populations of polar bears appear to be stable despite rising temperatures and summer sea ice declines. The biggest threat they face is not from global warming but hunting by humans, which historically has taken a huge toll on polar bear populations.

- The net effect of climate change on the spread of parasitic and vector-borne diseases is complex and at this time appears difficult to predict. Rising temperatures increase the mortality rates as well as the development rates of many parasites of veterinary importance, and temperature is only one of many variables that influence the range of viruses and other sources of diseases.

- Existing published research indicates rising temperatures likely will not increase, and may decrease, plant damage from leaf-eating herbivores, as rising atmospheric CO_2 boosts the production of certain defensive compounds in plants that are detrimental to animal pests.

- Empirical data on many animal species, including butterflies, other insects, reptiles, and mammals, indicate global warming and its myriad ecological effects tend to foster the expansion and proliferation of animal habitats, ranges, and populations, or otherwise have no observable impacts one way or the other.

- Multiple lines of evidence indicate animal species are adapting, and in some cases evolving, to cope with climate change of the modern era, as expected by Darwinian evolution and well-established ecological concepts.

Chapter 6. Aquatic Life

- Multiple studies from multiple ocean regions confirm ocean productivity tends to increase with temperature. Subjects of this research include phytoplankton and macroalgae, corals, crustaceans, and fish.

- Aquatic life has survived decadal, centennial, and millennial-scale climate oscillations that have persisted for millions of years. Evidence indicates they are well-equipped to adapt to forecasted increases in temperature, if necessary.

- Many aquatic species demonstrate the capability to adjust their individual critical thermal maximum (the upper temperature at which the onset of behavioral incapacitation occurs) upwards in response to temperature increases forecast by IPCC.

- The decline in ocean pH levels in the year 2100 (as compared to preindustrial times) may only be half the 0.4 value IPCC has calculated.

- The natural variability in ocean pH levels often is much greater than the change in pH levels forecast by IPCC.

- Natural fluctuations in pH may have a large impact on the development of resilience in marine populations, as heterogeneity in the environment with regard to pH and pCO_2 exposure may result in populations that are acclimatized to variable pH or extremes in pH.

- Caution should be applied when interpreting results from laboratory-based studies of lower seawater pH levels. Such studies often are incapable, or fall far short, of mimicking conditions in the real world, and thus they frequently yield results quite different than what is observed in nature.

- Rising temperatures and atmospheric CO_2 levels do not pose a significant threat to aquatic life. Many aquatic species have shown considerable tolerance to temperatures and CO_2 values predicted for the next few centuries, and many have demonstrated a likelihood of positive responses in empirical studies.

- Rising seawater temperature is conducive to enhanced coral calcification, leading some experts to forecast coral calcification will increase by about 35% beyond pre-industrial levels by 2100, and no extinction of coral reefs will occur in the future.

- For those species showing negative responses, there are adequate reasons to conclude such responses will be largely mitigated through phenotypic adaptation or evolution during the many decades to centuries the pH concentration is projected to fall. A similar assessment can be made with respect to the impact of rising temperatures or a combination of rising temperature and marine/freshwater "acidification."

Chapter 7. Human Health

- Warmer temperatures lead to a decrease in temperature-related mortality, including deaths associated with cardiovascular disease, respiratory disease, and strokes. The evidence of this benefit comes from research conducted in every major country of the world.

- In the United States the average person who died because of cold temperature exposure lost in excess of 10 years of potential life, whereas the average person who died because of hot temperature exposure likely lost no more than a few days or weeks of life.

- In the United States, some 4,600 deaths are delayed each year as people move from cold northeastern states to warm southwestern states. Between 3 and 7% of the gain in longevity experienced over the past three decades was due simply to people moving to warmer states.

- Cold-related deaths are far more numerous than heat-related deaths in the United States, Europe, and almost all countries outside the tropics. Coronary and cerebral thrombosis account for about half of all cold-related mortality.

- Global warming is reducing the incidence of cardiovascular diseases related to low temperatures and wintry weather by a much greater degree than it increases the incidence of cardiovascular diseases associated with high temperatures and summer heat waves.

- Extensive scientific examination and research contradict the claim that malaria will expand across the globe and intensify as a result of CO_2-induced warming.

- Concerns over large increases in vector-borne diseases such as dengue as a result of rising temperatures are unfounded and unsupported by the scientific literature, as climatic indices are poor predictors for dengue disease.

- Although temperature and climate largely determine the geographical distribution of ticks, they are not among the significant factors determining the incidence of tick-borne diseases.

- Rising CO_2 is not only raising the productivity of Earth's common food plants but also significantly increasing the quantity and potency of the many health-promoting substances found in their tissues, which are the ultimate sources of sustenance for essentially all animals and humans.

- Rising CO_2 positively impacts the production of numerous health-promoting substances found in medicinal or "health food" plants, and this phenomenon may have contributed to the increase in human life span that has occurred over the past century or so.

- There is little reason to expect any significant CO_2-induced increases in human-health-harming substances produced by plants as atmospheric CO_2 levels continue to rise.

References

Carricart-Ganivet, J.P. and Gonzalez-Diaz, P. 2009. Growth characteristics of skeletons of *Montastraea annularis* (Cnidaria: Scleractinia) from the northwest coast of Cuba. *Ciencias Marinas* **35**: 237–243.

Idso, C.D. and Idso, S.B. 2011. *The Many Benefits of Atmospheric CO₂ Enrichment*. Vales Lake Publishing, LLC, Pueblo West, Colorado, USA.

Idso, C.D. and Singer, S.F. 2009. *Climate Change Reconsidered: 2009 Report of the Nongovernmental*

International Panel on Climate Change (NIPCC). The Heartland Institute, Chicago, Illinois, USA.

Idso, K.E. 1992. Plant responses to rising levels of atmospheric carbon dioxide. *Climatological Publications Scientific Paper* No. 23, Office of Climatology, Arizona State University, Tempe, Arizona.

IPCC. 2007. *Climate Change 2007: Impacts, Adaptation and Vulnerability.* Contribution of Working Group II to the Fourth Assessment Report of the Intergovernmental Panel on Climate Change. Parry, M.L., Canziani, O.F., Palutikof, J.P., van der Linden, P.J., and Hanson, C.D. (Eds.) Cambridge University Press, Cambridge, UK.

IPCC. 2013. Technical Summary. In: *Climate Change 2014: Impacts, Adaptation, and Vulnerability.* Contribution of Working Group II to the Fifth Assessment Report of the Intergovernmental Panel on Climate Change, draft dated October 28, 2013.

Lemon, E.R. (Ed.) 1983. *CO_2 and Plants: The Response of Plants to Rising Levels of Atmospheric Carbon Dioxide.* Westview Press, Boulder, CO.

Luft, U.C., Finkelstein, S., and Elliot, J.C. 1974. Respiratory gas exchange, acid-base balance, and electrolytes during and after maximal work breathing 15 mm Hg $PICO_2$. In: Nahas, G. and Schaefer, K.E. (Eds.) *Carbon Dioxide and Metabolic Regulations.* Springer-Verlag, New York, NY, pp. 273–281.

Strain, B.R. 1978. *Report of the Workshop on Anticipated Plant Responses to Global Carbon Dioxide Enrichment.* Department of Botany, Duke University, Durham, NC.

1

CO$_2$, Plants, and Soils

Key Findings

Introduction

Key Findings

The key findings of the present chapter are listed below.

- Results from 3,586 separate experimental conditions conducted on 549 plant species reveal nearly all plants will experience increases in dry weight or biomass in response to atmospheric CO$_2$ enrichment. Results from an additional 2,094 separate experimental conditions conducted on 472 plant species reveal nearly all plants will experience increases in photosynthesis in response to atmospheric CO$_2$ enrichment.

- Long-term CO$_2$ enrichment studies confirm the findings of shorter-term experiments, demonstrating the effects of elevated atmospheric CO$_2$ likely persist across plant lifetimes.

- Several studies indicate plants are not harmed by super-elevated atmospheric CO$_2$ concentrations an

order of magnitude or more greater than the globe's current mean. Instead, positive growth responses are reported, some of which are particularly large. Most plants will display enhanced rates of photosynthesis and biomass production as the atmosphere's CO$_2$ concentration rises.

- Forest growth rates throughout the world have increased over the years in concert with, and in response to, the historical increase in the air's CO$_2$ concentration. As the atmosphere's CO$_2$ concentration continues to rise, forests likely will respond by exhibiting significant increases in biomass production, and thus they likely will grow more robustly and significantly expand their ranges, as is already being documented in many parts of the world.

- Where tropical forests have not been decimated by the targeted and direct destructive actions of people, such as the felling and burning of trees, forest productivity has been growing with the passing of time, rising with the increasing CO_2 content of the air. It has been doing so despite changes in atmospheric, soil, and water chemistry, including twentieth century global warming, which IPCC claims to have been unprecedented over the past one to two millennia.

- In contrast to frequently stated assumptions, old-growth forests can be significant carbon sinks, and their capacity to sequester carbon in the future will be enhanced as the atmospheric CO_2 content rises.

- Future increases in air temperature likely will have a positive effect on carbon storage in forests and their associated soils.

- As the air's CO_2 concentration increases, the productivity of grassland species will increase, even under unfavorable growing conditions characterized by less-than-adequate soil moisture, inadequate soil nutrition, elevated air temperature, and physical stress imposed by herbivory.

- In contrast to IPCC projections, the thawing of permafrost caused by increases in air temperature and CO_2 will not likely transform peatlands from carbon-sink to carbon-source ecosystems. Instead, as permafrost thaws, plants and trees can begin to grow again on these lands and in so doing, they sequester carbon.

- Rising atmospheric CO_2 likely will enhance the productivity and carbon sequestering ability of wetlands. In addition, elevated CO_2 may assist some coastal wetlands in counterbalancing the negative impacts of rising seas.

- Rising atmospheric CO_2 concentrations likely will allow greater numbers of beneficial bacteria, which help sequester carbon and nitrogen, to exist within soils and anaerobic water environments, a two-pronged phenomenon benefiting both terrestrial and aquatic ecosystems.

- The aerial fertilization effect of atmospheric CO_2 enrichment likely will result in greater soil carbon stores due to increased carbon-input into soils, even in nutrient-poor soils and in spite of predicted increases in temperature. In addition, the soil-carbon-sequestering capability of Earth's vegetation likely will act as a significant brake on the rate-of-rise of the air's CO_2 content and thereby help to mute the magnitude of any CO_2-induced global warming.

- The historical increase in the atmosphere's CO_2 concentration has significantly reduced erosion of valuable topsoil over the past several decades, and the continuing increase in atmospheric CO_2 can maintain this trend, and perhaps even accelerate it, throughout the foreseeable future.

Introduction

The United Nations' Intergovernmental International Panel on Climate Change (IPCC) insists that rising CO_2 levels, accompanied by even modest warming, will have harmful effects on plant life. In a draft of its Summary for Policymakers (SPM) to accompany its 2014 report, Working Group II says, "Without adaptation, local temperature increases of 1°C or more above preindustrial levels are projected to negatively impact yields for the major crops (wheat, rice, maize) in tropical and temperate regions, although individual locations may benefit (*medium confidence*). With or without adaptation, climate change will reduce median yields by 0 to 2% per decade for the rest of the century, as compared to a baseline without climate change" (IPCC 2014, p. 10).

These claims are at odds with the preponderance of research in this area dating as far back as the early 1900s (Demoussy, 1902–1904; Cummings and Jones, 1918) and as recent as 2013 (Isbell et al., 2013; Zhou *et al.*, 2013). Two previous volumes in the *Climate Change Reconsidered* series (Idso and Singer, 2009; Idso, Carter, and Singer, 2011) contained extensive literature reviews that also contradict IPCC's conclusions, suggesting once again IPCC is ignoring research appearing in peer-reviewed journals that contradicts its preferred narrative.

The current chapter begins with an analysis, in Section 1.1, of basic plant productivity responses to elevated CO_2. It references a tabular presentation of more than 5,000 individual plant photosynthetic and biomass responses appearing in Appendices 3 and 4. Section 1.2 surveys the literature on the effects of CO_2 on various eco-systems including forests, grasslands, peatlands, wetlands, and soils, finding in each case the beneficial effects of rising atmospheric concentrations of CO_2 more than offset any negative effects.

References

Cummings, M.B. and Jones, C.H. 1918. *The Aerial Fertilization of Plants with Carbon Dioxide.* Vermont Agricultural Station Bulletin No. 211.

Demoussy, E. 1902–1904. Sur la vegetation dans des atmospheres riches en acide carbonique. *Comptes Rendus Academy of Science Paris* **136**: 325–328; **138**: 291–293; **139**: 883–885.

Idso, C.D. and Singer, S.F. 2009. *Climate Change Reconsidered: 2009 Report of the Nongovernmental International Panel on Climate Change (NIPCC).* The Heartland Institute, Chicago, Illinois, USA.

Idso, C.D., Carter, R.M., and Singer, S.F. 2011. *Climate Change Reconsidered: 2011 Interim Report of the Nongovernmental International Panel on Climate Change (NIPCC).* The Heartland Institute, Chicago, Illinois, USA.

IPCC. 2014. Summary for Policymakers. In *Climate Change 2014: Impacts, Adaptation, and Vulnerability. Contribution of Working Group II to the Fifth Assessment Report of the Intergovernmental Panel on Climate Change* Draft dated October 28, 2013.

Isbell, F., Reich, P.B., Tilman, D., Hobbie, S.E., Polasky, S., and Binder, S. 2013. Nutrient enrichment, biodiversity loss, and consequent declines in ecosystem productivity. *Proceedings of the National Academy of Sciences USA* **110**: 11,911–11,916.

Zhou, X., Chen, C., Wang, Y, Smaill, S., and Clinton, P. 2013. Warming rather than increased precipitation increases soil recalcitrant organic carbon in a semiarid grassland after 6 years of treatments. *PLOS ONE* **8**: e53761.

1.1 Plant Responses to Atmospheric CO₂ Enrichment

1.1.1 Dry Weight (Biomass)

- Results from 3,586 separate experimental conditions conducted on 549 plant species reveal nearly all plants will experience increases in dry weight or biomass in response to atmospheric CO_2 enrichment.

Perhaps the best-known consequence of an increase in the air's CO_2 content is its stimulation of plant productivity (dry matter content or biomass). This growth enhancement occurs because carbon dioxide is the primary raw material utilized by plants to produce the organic matter out of which they construct their tissues. Consequently, the more CO_2 there is in the air, the bigger and better plants grow.

Table 1.1.1 in Appendix 3 reports the results of hundreds of peer-reviewed scientific studies indicating the biomass growth response of plants to a standardized 300 ppm increase in atmospheric CO_2 concentration. Plants are listed by common and/or scientific names, followed by the number of experimental studies conducted on each plant, the mean biomass response to a 300 ppm increase in the air's CO_2 content, and the standard error of that mean. Whenever the CO_2 increase for a given study was not exactly 300 ppm, a linear adjustment was computed. For example, if the CO_2 increase was 350 ppm and the growth response was a 60% enhancement, the adjusted 300 ppm CO_2 growth response was calculated as (300/350) x 60% = 51%.

The data in the table are printed by permission of the Center for the Study of Carbon Dioxide and Global Change and were taken from its Plant Growth database on 1 January 2014. The table summarizes CO_2 enrichment results from 3,586 separate experimental conditions conducted on 549 plant species. The responses are overwhelmingly positive. New data are added to the database at approximately weekly intervals and can be accessed free of charge at the center's website at http://www.co2science.org/data/plant_growth/dry/dry_subject.php. This online database also archives information pertaining to the experimental conditions under which each plant growth experiment was conducted, as well as the complete reference to the journal article from which the experimental results were obtained. The center's online database also lists percent increases in plant biomass for 600 and/or 900 ppm increases in the air's CO_2 concentration.

1.1.2 Plant Photosynthesis (Net CO₂ Exchange Rate)

- Results from 2,094 separate experimental conditions conducted on 472 plant species reveal nearly all plants will experience increases in photosynthesis in response to atmospheric CO_2 enrichment.

Table 1.1.2 in Appendix 4 reports the results of peer-reviewed scientific studies measuring the photosynthetic growth response of plants to a 300 ppm increase in atmospheric CO_2 concentration. Plants are listed by common and/or scientific names, followed by the number of experimental studies conducted on each plant, the mean photosynthetic response to a 300 ppm increase in the air's CO_2 content, and the standard error of that mean. Whenever the CO_2 increase for a given study was not exactly 300 ppm, a linear adjustment was computed. For example, if the CO_2 increase was 350 ppm and the growth response was a 60% enhancement, the adjusted 300 ppm CO_2 growth response was calculated as $(300/350) \times 60\% = 51\%$.

The data in the table appear by permission of the Center for the Study of Carbon Dioxide and Global Change and were taken from its Plant Growth database on 1 January 2014. In all, the table summarizes CO_2 enrichment results from 2,094 separate experimental conditions conducted on 472 plant species. The responses are overwhelmingly positive.

New data are added to the database at approximately weekly intervals and can be accessed free of charge at the center's website at http://www.co2science.org/data/plant_growth/dry/dry _subject.php. This online database also archives information pertaining to the experimental conditions under which each plant growth experiment was conducted, as well as the complete reference to the journal article from which the experimental results were obtained. The center's online database also lists percent increases in plant photosynthetic rate for 600 and/or 900 ppm increases in the air's CO_2 concentration.

1.1.3 Long-Term Studies

One of the more commonly voiced concerns about atmospheric CO_2 enrichment is whether the plant growth enhancements observed in short-term laboratory and field studies will persist over the lifespan of plants. The subsections below investigate this topic with respect to both woody and non-woody plants, leaving no doubt as to the sustained response of plants to elevated atmospheric CO_2.

1.1.3.1 Non-Woody Plants

- Several long-term studies of various non-woody plants reveal sustained beneficial responses to elevated concentrations of atmospheric CO_2 over periods of many years.

In Switzerland, Niklaus et al. (2001) exposed a species-rich but nutrient-poor and water-limited, calcareous grassland dominated by *Bromus erectus* (which accounted for approximately half of the ecosystem's aboveground vegetative biomass) to atmospheric CO_2 concentrations of approximately 360 and 600 ppm for six years, using screen-aided CO_2 control (SACC) technology. CO_2-induced increases in biomass production in years one through six of the experiment were, respectively, 5%, 20%, 22%, 27%, 31%, and 18%, for an average of 23.6% over the last five years of the study (Niklaus and Körner, 2004). This biomass increase ultimately increased carbon stocks in plant shoots and roots by 17 and 24%, respectively, and enhanced carbon stocks in vegetative litter by 34%. The net effect of these increases was an initial air-to-soil carbon flux of 210 g C m^{-2} year^{-1}. After six years of treatment, however, the CO_2-enriched soils held only about 44% of the carbon expected from this influx rate, due to the low soil residence time of the newly input carbon. Nevertheless, the study showed atmospheric CO_2 enrichment can in fact enhance plant growth and carbon sequestration in low-nutrient and water-limited soils.

In Italy, Bettarini et al. (1998) measured the stomatal densities and conductances of the leaves of 17 species of plants growing in the vicinity of a natural CO_2-emitting spring that has produced twice-ambient atmospheric CO_2 concentrations for at least two centuries, while making similar measurements on plants of the same species located further from the spring, where normal CO_2 concentrations prevail. The elevated CO_2 decreased leaf stomatal conductances in all but one of the species by 19 to 73%. These reductions, however, were not accompanied by decreases in stomatal density, which remained unaffected by long-term atmospheric CO_2 enrichment in all but three species. Consequently, life-long exposure to elevated CO_2 reduced plant water use primarily by controlling leaf stomatal function, not by changing leaf anatomical features (i.e., the number of stomata per unit leaf area).

These findings are encouraging, but it has been suggested they cannot persist indefinitely in all situations. The productivity of Earth's temperate grasslands, for example, is often limited by the availability of soil nitrogen (Vitousek and Howarth, 1991), and both empirical and modeling studies have suggested the magnitude and duration of grassland growth responses to rising levels of atmospheric CO_2 may be constrained by inadequate supplies of soil nitrogen (Rastetter et al., 1997; Luo and Reynolds, 1999; Thornley and Cannell, 2000).

In light of this mix of real-world observations and theoretical calculations, it would seem only natural to hypothesize, as Richter et al. (2003) do, "that increased below-ground translocation of photoassimilates at elevated pCO_2 would lead to an increase in immobilization of N due to an excess supply of energy to the roots and rhizosphere," and that this phenomenon would lead ultimately to a reduction in the size of the growth-promoting effect of elevated atmospheric CO_2 that is manifest in short-term CO_2 enrichment experiments and at the start of long-term studies.

To test this hypothesis, Richter et al. (2003) measured gross rates of N mineralization, NH_4^+ consumption, and N immobilization in soils on which monocultures of Lolium perenne and Trifolium repens had been exposed to ambient (360 ppm) and elevated (600 ppm) concentrations of atmospheric CO_2 at high and low rates of soil nitrogen addition for seven years in the Swiss free-air CO_2 enrichment (FACE) study conducted near Zurich. After seven years of treatment, they report, "gross mineralization, NH_4^+ consumption and N immobilization in both the L. perenne and the T. repens swards did not show significant differences." In addition, the size of the microbial N pool and immobilization of applied mineral ^{15}N were not significantly affected by the elevated CO_2.

Richter et al. note the results of their study "did not support the initial hypothesis and indicate that below-ground turnover of N, as well as N availability, measured in short-term experiments are not strongly affected by long-term exposure to elevated CO_2." They conclude "differences in plant N demand and not changes in soil N mineralization/immobilization are the driving factors for N dynamics in these meadow grassland systems."

Thus, as also found in the woody plant studies of Finzi and Schlesinger (2003) and Schafer et al. (2003) conducted in the Duke Forest FACE experiment, Richter et al.'s work provides no evidence the growth responses of Earth's grasslands to atmospheric CO_2 enrichment will ever be significantly reduced from what is suggested by moderate-term studies of a few to several years' duration.

In a study of the same L. perenne and T. repens ecosystems that helps to explain some of these observations, Gamper et al. (2004) analyzed the effects of elevated CO_2 and N fertilization (14 vs. 56 g N m^{-2}) on arbuscular mycorrhizal fungi. They report, "at elevated CO_2 and under both N treatments, AMF root colonization of both host plant species was increased" and "colonization levels of all three measured intraradical AMF structures (hyphae, arbuscules and vesicles) tended to be higher." In addition, they found an increase in non-AMF root colonization under elevated CO_2. As a result, they

"hypothesize that AMF provide non-P-nutritional benefits under the phosphorus-rich soil conditions of our field experiment" and these benefits "may include improved N nutrition and increased protection against pathogens and/or herbivores."

In another long-term study conducted in Switzerland, Ainsworth et al. (2003b) analyzed data from what has become the longest-running FACE experiment ever conducted anywhere in the world. The impetus for their analysis was the speculation that, in their words, "elevated CO_2 may partition resources away from leaves and, through increased production, sequester nutrients into organic matter causing deficiencies which indirectly cause decreased photosynthetic capacity." In this regard, they cite the theoretical study of these considerations conducted by Luo and Reynolds (1999), who "predicted that the initial stimulation of photosynthetic production in grasslands would be lost within nine years of a step increase in CO_2, as imposed in FACE experiments."

With real-world data obtained over nearly a decade of experimentation with white clover (Trifolium repens) grown in monoculture in the Swiss FACE array, Ainsworth et al. (2003b) characterized the photosynthetic responses of the plants to the extra 240 ppm of CO_2 delivered to them in the spring and autumn of the eighth year of the experiment. They determined there was no acclimation or down-regulation of photosynthetic capacity in the spring of the year. In the autumn, however, there was a down-regulation of approximately 20%, but it occurred "late in the growing season, when the 24-hour mean temperature had dropped below 10°C, and nightly frosts were occurring," under which conditions "shoot growth is limited and the sink for carbohydrate is small, and acclimation of photosynthesis to elevated CO_2 would be expected."

In spite of that acclimation and the stress of those cold conditions, the average photosynthetic rate of the CO_2-enriched plants at that time of year was still 37% greater than the ambient-treatment plants. Therefore, the five scientists conclude their results "do not support the prediction that the response of grassland species to elevated CO_2 will be short-lived as the demand for nutrients increases." This conclusion clearly contradicts the claim of Luo and Reynolds and others' similar claims, for as Ainsworth et al. reiterate in the concluding sentence of their paper, "contrary to the belief that the response of grassland species to elevated CO_2 will be short-lived, stimulation of photosynthesis in T. repens remained after eight years of exposure to elevated CO_2."

In another report on this longest FACE study ever

conducted on a grassland species, Ainsworth *et al.* (2003a) note "photosynthesis is commonly stimulated in grasslands with experimental increases in atmospheric CO_2 concentration, a physiological response that could significantly alter the future carbon cycle if it persists in the long term." However, they also note "an acclimation of photosynthetic capacity suggested by theoretical models and short-term experiments could completely remove this effect of CO_2." This suggests, in their words, "perennial systems will respond to elevated CO_2 in the short term, but the response for grasslands will be short-lived (Roumet *et al.*, 2000)," and they cite Luo and Reynolds (1999) as suggesting an effective CO_2-induced stimulatory period of less than 10 years for both high- and low-productivity grasslands.

The only way to resolve the issue is to conduct a long-term experiment—such as the sour orange tree study of Idso and Kimball (2001)—which is exactly what the eight-member Ainsworth *et al.* (2003a) team of American, British, Italian, and Swiss scientists did in its ten-year study of perennial ryegrass (*Lolium perenne*).

The study was conducted in Switzerland within three replicate blocks of two 18-m-diameter FACE rings maintained at either 360 or 600 ppm CO_2 throughout each growing season of the entire 10-year period. The experimental plots, established in 1993 on a field of perennial ryegrass planted in August 1992, were further subdivided into low and high nitrogen fertilization treatments, and the plants grown within them were periodically harvested several times a year. In addition, the authors write, "more than 3,000 measurements characterized the response of leaf photosynthesis and stomatal conductance to elevated CO_2 across each growing season for the duration of the experiment."

Ainsworth *et al.* (2003a) report, "over the 10 years as a whole, growth at elevated CO_2 resulted in a 43% higher rate of light-saturated leaf photosynthesis and a 36% increase in daily integral of leaf CO_2 uptake." The 36% increase in daily CO_2 uptake was, in their words, "almost identical to the 38% increase seen on the first day of measurements in August 1993 and the 39% stimulation on the last day of measurements in May 2002."

The researchers also reported a seasonal trend in the CO_2-induced increase in the daily integral of CO_2 fixation, which ranged from 25% in the spring to 41% in the summer and 48% in the fall. The scientists say this finding "is consistent with theoretical expec-tation, where because of the differing sensitivities of Rubisco oxygenase and carboxylase activity, the proportionate stimulation of photosynthesis by a given increase in CO_2 will rise with temperature (Long, 1991)." This phenomenon has also been observed in a number of other plants.

Ainsworth *et al.* (2003a) additionally note "the percentage increase in photosynthetic carbon uptake in the first 20 days following a harvest (45%) was nearly double the percentage increase later in the regrowth cycle (23%)." This finding indicates CO_2-induced growth stimulation is greatest when the plant source:sink ratio is small; i.e., when there are few photosynthesizing leaves and many photosynthate-storing roots, so the CO_2-induced enhancement of photosynthesis need not immediately decline for lack of a sufficient repository to deposit the fruits of its labors, so to speak.

Summing up, the international team of scientists says the CO_2-induced photosynthetic stimulation "was maximal following harvest, at the warmest times of year and with a high supply of nitrogen." They concluded, "this open-air field experiment provides no support for the prediction that stimulation of photosynthesis under elevated CO_2 is a transient phenomenon," or as they phrase it in the abstract of their paper, "in contrast with theoretical expectations and the results of shorter duration experiments, the present results provide no [evidence of] significant change in photosynthetic stimulation across a 10-year period, nor greater acclimation ... in the latter years in either nitrogen treatment."

The ultimate plant response is biomass production, which was studied in the same experiment by Schneider *et al.* (2004), who state, "in 1993, the CO_2 response of harvested biomass was 7.2%, increasing to 32% in 2002." At low N, they report the CO_2 response "varied annually." Nevertheless, it too exhibited a slowly increasing (though non-significant) trend, suggesting, given enough time, it might have gained statistical significance as well.

In addition, Schneider *et al.* report, "at high N supply, more N was mobilized from the soil after long-term exposure to elevated CO_2 than after ambient CO_2," in contrast to the suggestion of Hungate *et al.* (2003) that just the opposite likely would occur. At low N, the Swiss team writes, "the reduced availability of N constantly limited the harvestable biomass to elevated CO_2 throughout the experiment," more in harmony with Hungate *et al.*'s suggestion. This limitation may have been slightly reduced over the course of the 10-year study, and a still longer experiment may be needed to resolve the issue in the case of low-N soils.

Rasse *et al.* (2005) evaluated the long-term effects of atmospheric CO$_2$ enrichment on the net CO$_2$ exchange, shoot density, and shoot biomass of the wetland sedge, *Scirpus olneyi*, in a long-term *in situ* elevated CO$_2$ experiment at the Smithsonian Environmental Research Center on the USA's Chesapeake Bay. They found, in every one of the 17 years of the experiment's duration to the time of their analysis, the net CO$_2$ exchange rate and shoot biomass and density of the plants growing in the CO$_2$-enriched (ambient +340 ppm) air were all greater than among the plants growing in ambient air. The extra CO$_2$ boosted the net CO$_2$ exchange rate by 80% in the first year of the study, but the enhancement declined to about 35% by the end of the third year and remained relatively constant at that value over the following 15 years.

Shoot biomass and density also increased, but whereas the CO$_2$-induced stimulation of the net CO$_2$ exchange rate remained essentially constant over the past 15 years, the CO$_2$-induced stimulations of shoot biomass and density increased over time. After five years of a nearly constant stimulation of 16%, for example, shoot density increased in near-linear fashion to a value 128% above the ambient-air value at the end of year 17. The response of shoot biomass to CO$_2$ enrichment was also nearly linear, reaching a value approximately 70% above ambient at year 17. The trends in shoot density and biomass do not appear to be leveling off.

Net CO$_2$ exchange, shoot density, and shoot biomass were closely correlated with bay water salinity in this study: the higher the salinity, the more detrimental were its effects on these variables. Nevertheless, even at the highest levels of salinity reported, atmospheric CO$_2$ enrichment was able to produce a positive, albeit reduced, stimulatory effect on net CO$_2$ exchange. For shoot biomass and density, the responses were better still: Not only did atmospheric CO$_2$ enrichment essentially eradicate the detrimental effects of salinity, there was, Rasse *et al.* note, "circumstantial evidence suggesting that salinity stress increased the stimulation of shoot density by elevated atmospheric CO$_2$ concentration."

This experiment demonstrated several important findings. First, as the researchers state, their results "leave no doubt as to the sustained response of the salt marsh sedge to elevated atmospheric CO$_2$ concentration." Second, since the initial responses of the three growth variables declined or remained low during the first few years of the study, but leveled out or increased thereafter, much more long-term research needs to be carried out in order to ascertain the full

and correct impacts of atmospheric CO$_2$ enrichment on plants. In the case of the wetland sedge of this study, for example, it took ten years before an increasing trend in the shoot density could be recognized clearly. Finally, there is the authors' "most important finding": "that a species response to elevated atmospheric CO$_2$ concentration can continually increase when [it] is under stress and declining in its natural environment."

Gifford (2004) describes the findings of an international FACE workshop on *Short- and Long-Term Effects of Elevated Atmospheric CO$_2$ on Managed Ecosystems*, concentrating on a few key aspects of the aerial fertilization effect of atmospheric CO$_2$ enrichment and how it likely will be expressed in the real world as the air's CO$_2$ content rises.

He begins by noting Kimball *et al.* (2002) compared what was learned about elevated CO$_2$ effects on 11 different crops from recent FACE experiments with what had been learned from prior chamber studies, including open-top chambers. He reports Kimball *et al.* determined the FACE experiments confirmed, under longer-term field conditions and with but a couple exceptions, "all the prior quantitative chamber findings on crops grown and measured in elevated CO$_2$ concentration compared with ambient CO$_2$ concentration."

Next, Gifford notes the subsequent study of Long *et al.* (2004) confirms, "with greater statistical rigor and for a much wider range of species including crops, pasture species and trees, most of the conclusions of the evaluation by Kimball *et al.* (2002)." He reports Long presented an elegant exposition of how plants optimize "the deployment of N from photosynthetic machinery to growth organs such that a balance between C-source and C-sinks is maintained in the plant under elevated CO$_2$ concentration—a response that generally increases nitrogen use efficiency (Wolfe *et al.*, 1998)." In addition, he reports, several FACE studies demonstrate an increased abundance of legumes in CO$_2$-enriched plots, and this observation "is supportive of the notion that, in the long run, elevated CO$_2$ concentration may cause N-fixation to entrain more atmospheric N$_2$ into the ecosystem, leading ultimately to fuller expression of the increased growth and standing biomass potential that the elevated CO$_2$ provides (Gifford, 1992)."

Next, in an update of the analysis of Hendry *et al.* (1997), which focused on the effects of the rapidly fluctuating atmospheric CO$_2$ concentrations characteristic of FACE experiments, the technique's primary developer (George Hendry) concluded, according to

Gifford, plant photosynthesis rates "can be decreased by 17% or more for the mean concentration reported when that mean is of large CO_2 fluctuations on the order of half the mean, and the deviations from the mean occur over a minute or longer." In light of this finding, Gifford writes, "FACE technology might be systematically understating the effect of globally elevated CO_2 on ecosystem productivity."

Gifford sums up the consensus of the participants at the FACE workshop with respect to "the CO_2 fertilizing effect," stating, "the evidence for its existence in the real world continues to consolidate."

References

Ainsworth, E.A., Davey, P.A., Hymus, G.J., Osborne, C.P., Rogers, A., Blum, H., Nosberger, J., and Long, S.P. 2003a. Is stimulation of leaf photosynthesis by elevated carbon dioxide concentration maintained in the long term? A test with *Lolium perenne* grown for 10 years at two nitrogen fertilization levels under Free Air CO_2 Enrichment (FACE). *Plant, Cell and Environment* **26**: 705–714.

Ainsworth, E.A., Rogers, A., Blum, H., Nosberger, J., and Long, S.P. 2003b. Variation in acclimation of photosynthesis in *Trifolium repens* after eight years of exposure to Free Air CO_2 Enrichment (FACE). *Journal of Experimental Botany* **54**: 2769–2774.

Bettarini, I., Vaccari, F.P., and Miglietta, F. 1998. Elevated CO_2 concentrations and stomatal density: observations from 17 plant species growing in a CO_2 spring in central Italy. *Global Change Biology* **4**: 17–22.

Finzi, A.C. and Schlesinger, W.H. 2003. Soil-nitrogen cycling in a pine forest exposed to 5 years of elevated carbon dioxide. *Ecosystems* **6**: 444–456.

Gamper, H., Peter, M., Jansa, J., Luscher, A., Hartwig, U.A., and Leuann, A. 2004. Arbuscular mycorrhizal fungi benefit from 7 years of free air CO_2 enrichment in well-fertilized grass and legume monocultures. *Global Change Biology* **10**: 189–199.

Gifford, R.M. 1992. Interaction of carbon dioxide with growth-limiting environmental factors in vegetation productivity: Implications for the global carbon cycle. *Advances in Bioclimatology* **1**: 25–58.

Gifford, R.M. 2004. The CO_2 fertilising effect—does it occur in the real world? *New Phytologist* **163**: 221–225.

Hendrey, G.R., Long, S.P., McKee, I.F., and Baker, N.R. 1997. Can photosynthesis respond to short term fluctuations in atmospheric carbon dioxide? *Photosynthesis Research* **51**: 170–184.

Hungate, B.A., Dukes, J.S., Shaw, M.R., Luo, Y., and

Field, C.B. 2003. Nitrogen and climate change. *Science* **302**: 1512–1513.

Idso, S.B. and Kimball, B.A. 2001. CO_2 enrichment of sour orange trees: 13 years and counting. *Environmental and Experimental Botany* **46**: 147–153.

Kimball, B.A., Kobayashi, K., and Bindi, M. 2002. Responses of agricultural crops to free-air CO_2 enrichment. *Advances in Agronomy* **77**: 293–368.

Long, S.P. 1991. Modification of the response of photosynthetic productivity to rising temperature by atmospheric CO_2 concentrations: has its importance been underestimated? *Plant, Cell and Environment* **14**: 729–739.

Long, S.P., Ainsworth, E.A., Rogers, A., and Ort, D.R. 2004. Rising atmospheric carbon dioxide: Plants FACE the future. *Annual Review of Plant Biology* **55**: 591–628.

Luo, Y. and Reynolds, J.F. 1999. Validity of extrapolating field CO_2 experiments to predict carbon sequestration in natural ecosystems. *Ecology* **80**: 1568–1583.

Niklaus, P.A. and Körner, C. 2004. Synthesis of a six-year study of calcareous grassland responses to *in situ* CO_2 enrichment. *Ecological Monographs* **74**: 491–511.

Niklaus, P.A., Wohlfender, M., Siegwolf, R., and Körner, C. 2001. Effects of six years atmospheric CO_2 enrichment on plant, soil, and soil microbial C of a calcareous grassland. *Plant and Soil* **233**: 189–202.

Rasse, D.P., Peresta, G., and Drake, B.G. 2005. Seventeen years of elevated CO_2 exposure in a Chesapeake Bay Wetland: sustained but contrasting responses of plant growth and CO_2 uptake. *Global Change Biology* **11**: 369–377.

Rastetter, E.B., Agren, G.I., and Shaver, G.R. 1997. Responses of N-limited ecosystems to increased CO_2: a balanced-nutrition, coupled-element-cycles model. *Ecological Applications* **7**: 444–460.

Richter, M., Hartwig, U.A., Frossard, E., Nosberger, J., and Cadisch, G. 2003. Gross fluxes of nitrogen in grassland soil exposed to elevated atmospheric pCO_2 for seven years. *Soil Biology & Biochemistry* **35**: 1325–1335.

Roumet, C., Garnier, E., Suzor, H., Salager, J.-L., and Roy, J. 2000. Short and long-term responses of whole-plant gas exchange to elevated CO_2 in four herbaceous species. *Environmental and Experimental Botany* **43**: 155–169.

Schafer, K.V.R., Oren, R., Ellsworth, D.S., Lai, C.-T., Herrick, J.D., Finzi, A.C., Richter, D.D., and Katul, G.G. 2003. Exposure to an enriched CO_2 atmosphere alters carbon assimilation and allocation in a pine forest ecosystem. *Global Change Biology* **9**: 1378–1400.

Schneider, M.K., Luscher, A., Richter, M., Aeschlimann, U., Hartwig, U.A., Blum, H., Frossard, E., and Nosberger,

J. 2004. Ten years of free-air CO$_2$ enrichment altered the mobilization of N from soil in *Lolium perenne* L. swards. *Global Change Biology* **10**: 1377–1388.

Thornley, J. and Cannell, M. 2000. Dynamics of mineral N availability in grassland ecosystems under increased [CO$_2$]: hypotheses evaluated using the Hurley Pasture Model. *Plant and Soil* **224**: 153–170.

Vitousek, P.M. and Howarth, R.W. 1991. Nitrogen limitation on land and in the sea: how can it occur? *Biogeochemistry* **13**: 87–115.

Wolfe, D.W., Gifford, R.M., Hilbert, D., and Luo, Y. 1998. Integration of photosynthetic acclimation to CO$_2$ at the whole plant level. *Global Change Biology* **4**: 879–893.

1.1.3.2 Woody Plants

The aerial fertilization effect of atmospheric CO$_2$ enrichment will continue to benefit woody plants significantly.

1.1.3.2.1 Oak

- Multiple-year studies point to the likelihood oak trees of all species will grow ever more productively as the air's CO$_2$ content climbs higher, and they will be better able to withstand droughty conditions and more effectively sequester carbon in the years and decades ahead.

After burning to the ground a natural scrub-oak ecosystem comprised of *Quercus myrtifolia*, *Q. chapmanii*, and *Q. geminata*, located on an island just off the coast of central Florida, USA, Ainsworth *et al.* (2002) erected 16 open-top chambers on the site and fumigated them with air of either 380 or 700 ppm CO$_2$. In the third and fourth years of the experiment, they report, the extra CO$_2$ increased photosynthetic rates in regenerating *Q. myrtifolia* and *Q. chapmanii* trees by as much as 150% without inducing any degree of photosynthetic acclimation or down-regulation. *Q. geminata* did exhibit signs of acclimation, but after three years of exposure to elevated CO$_2$, the three species still exhibited an average increase of 53% in their combined mean rate of photosynthesis.

In a subsequent analysis of other data from the same experiment, Dijkstra *et al.* (2002) evaluated the effects of elevated CO$_2$ on the growth of the three oak species by means of allometric relationships between stem diameter and aboveground biomass (AGB), which they derived from destructive measurements made on trees growing on an adjacent site. They found, in their words, "increased AGB in elevated CO$_2$ was apparent after eight months (44%), and the relative stimulation increased over time, from 55% at the end of 1997, 66% at the end of 1998, to 75% at the end of 1999." They also report at the time of the last measurement, the AGB of the dominant *Q. myrtifolia* had increased by 73%, the AGB of the subdominant *Q. geminata* had increased by only 23%, and the AGB of the subdominant *Q. chapmanni* had risen by more than 150%. With respect to individual years, they note even though the mean increase in AGB during the drought year of 1998 was 51% lower than it was during 1997 and 54% lower than in 1999, "elevated CO$_2$ significantly increased annual increment in AGB by 122% during the drought year 1998, compared to a 65% increase in 1997 and a 116% increase in 1999."

In another study of the Florida scrub-oak ecosystem, Hymus *et al.* (2003) report the extra CO$_2$ supplied to the CO$_2$-enriched chambers in their experiment increased maximum net ecosystem exchange of CO$_2$ (NEE) and the apparent quantum yield of NEE during the photoperiod. They also state the magnitude of the stimulation of maximum NEE, expressed per unit ground area, "was seasonal, rising from 50% in the winter to 180% in the summer," in accord with what is known about the interactive effects of atmospheric CO$_2$ enrichment and daily, seasonal, and multiyear warming. Hymus *et al.* additionally note their study was the largest to show "the effects of elevated CO$_2$ on NEE measured *in situ*, and is the first to be carried out in a woody ecosystem," where the beneficial effects of atmospheric CO$_2$ enrichment are "still evident after 6 years regeneration in the elevated CO$_2$."

Another way of studying the long-term effects of atmospheric CO$_2$ enrichment on trees and shrubs was pioneered by researchers in Italy, where many natural springs emit copious quantities of CO$_2$ into the air, raising atmospheric CO$_2$ concentrations over modest tracts of land by various amounts. By measuring the air's CO$_2$ content at different places around these "CO$_2$ springs" over the course of long-term experiments conducted there, mean canopy-level atmospheric CO$_2$ concentrations can be determined, and woody plants growing at those locations are typically assumed to have lived their entire lives at the measured CO$_2$ concentrations.

In a study of *Quercus ilex* trees, some growing close to, and others distant from, certain of these CO$_2$ springs, Paoletti *et al.* (1998) found, in moving from an atmospheric CO$_2$ concentration of 350 ppm to 750 ppm, leaf stomatal frequency dropped by a factor of nearly 1.5, but there were no further reductions in this parameter as the air's CO_2 concentration rose as high as 2,600 ppm. They also note the amount of wax comprising the leaf cuticle increased nearly threefold between 750 and 2,600 ppm CO_2, but between 350 and 750 ppm CO_2 there was no difference in this leaf property. The net effect of these several responses was thus a continuous decline in water loss from the trees as the air's CO_2 content continuously rose, which led to a concomitant continuous increase in their water use efficiencies.

In another study conducted in Italy in the vicinity of natural CO_2 springs, Stylinski et al. (2000) worked with Quercus pubescens trees grown in ambient air and at an atmospheric CO_2 concentration of approximately 700 ppm throughout the entire 40 to 50 years of their existence. The CO_2-enriched trees exhibited photosynthetic rates 36–77% greater than those of the trees growing in ambient air; and the researchers did not detect signs of any photosynthetic down-regulation in the CO_2-enriched trees. In fact, they found no differences between the CO_2-enriched and ambient-treatment trees in terms of rubisco activity and content, total nitrogen content, chlorophyll content, and carotenoid content. As a result, they conclude "enhanced leaf photosynthetic rates at the CO_2 springs could increase carbon sequestrating and productivity of whole tree canopies" and "higher carbon acquisition by Q. pubescens and other species could slow the rise in atmospheric CO_2."

Blaschke et al. (2001) also studied gas exchange in mature Q. pubescens and Q. ilex trees exposed to atmospheric CO_2 concentrations of approximately 370 and 700 ppm for their entire lives. The average net photosynthetic rates of the CO_2-enriched trees were, respectively, 69% and 26% greater than those of the trees growing in ambient air. In addition, the stomatal conductances of the CO_2-enriched Q. pubescens trees were approximately 23% lower than those of trees of the same species growing in ambient air, and the CO_2-enriched Q. ilex trees displayed no stomatal response to elevated CO_2. Nevertheless, both species exhibited significant CO_2-induced increases in water use efficiency.

One less-than-ideal aspect of the Italian CO_2 springs is that they emit higher-than-normal concentrations of the phytotoxic air pollutants H_2S and SO_2 (Schulte et al., 1999). This fact, however, makes the springs perfect settings in which to study the relative strengths of two competing phenomena: the growth-promoting effect of elevated CO_2 and the growth-retarding effect of elevated H_2S and SO_2.

Grill et al. (2004) analyzed various properties of leaves and acorns produced on Q. ilex and Q. pubescens trees growing at double-to-triple normal atmospheric CO_2 concentrations near the CO_2 springs, as well as the same characteristics of leaves and acorns growing on similar trees located some distance away in ambient-CO_2 air. In addition, they analyzed several characteristics of seedlings they sprouted from acorns produced by the CO_2-enriched and ambient-treatment trees, and they used chromosome stress tests "to investigate whether alterations in sulphur-regime have negative consequences for seedlings."

In reporting their findings, Grill et al. say "acorns from CO_2 springs contained significantly higher sulphur concentrations than controls (0.67 vs. 0.47 mg g^{-1} dry weight in Q. ilex cotyledons and 1.10 vs. 0.80 in Q. pubescens)," indicating the trees were indeed affected by the H_2S and SO_2 contained in the air in the vicinity of the CO_2 springs. They also report Q. ilex seedlings grown from CO_2-spring acorns showed elevated rates of chromosomal aberrations in their root tips, suggesting the presence of a permanent pollution-induced stress. Nevertheless, as demonstrated by the results of several other studies conducted near the springs, the CO_2-enriched air— even in the presence of phytotoxic H_2S and SO_2— significantly enhanced the trees' photosynthetic prowess: by 26–69% in the study of Blaschke et al. (2001), by 36–77% in the study of Stylinski et al. (2000), and by 175–510% in the study of Tognetti et al. (1998).

In a study in Italy that did not make use of natural CO_2 springs, Marek et al. (2001) constructed open-top chambers around 30-year-old Q. ilex trees growing in perennial evergreen stands and continuously exposed them to atmospheric CO_2 concentrations of 350 and 700 ppm for five more years. Throughout this period, the extra CO_2 increased rates of net photosynthesis in Sun and shade leaves by 68% and 59%, respectively, and photosynthetic acclimation was not apparent in any of the CO_2-enriched trees' leaves. In addition, the light compensation point—the light intensity at which photosynthetic carbon uptake is equivalent to respiratory carbon loss—was 24% and 30% lower in the Sun and shade leaves of the CO_2-enriched trees than in the corresponding leaves of trees growing in ambient air. These findings suggest Q. ilex trees growing in CO_2-enriched air should exhibit net carbon gains earlier in the morning and maintain them later into the evening than trees exposed to ambient air. Together with the stimulatory effect of higher CO_2 concentrations on photosynthesis, this observation further suggests carbon sequestration by this tree species will likely be much greater in a higher-CO$_2$ world of the future.

Although all of the reports described above imply the ongoing rise in the air's CO$_2$ content will do only good to the long-term growth and health of oak trees, Gartner *et al.* (2003) were concerned the wood of the trees might be more vulnerable to embolism in a CO$_2$-enriched atmosphere. They investigated this question with *Quercus ilex* seedlings grown for more than a year in climate-controlled greenhouses in either ambient air or air enriched to twice the ambient concentration of CO$_2$. Contrary to their hypothesis, they found the "plants grown in elevated CO$_2$ did not differ significantly in vulnerability to embolism or kS [specific conductivity] from plants grown in ambient CO$_2$." In addition, they report "Tognetti *et al.* (1999) found no significant effect of elevated CO$_2$ on vulnerability to embolism or kS of branch samples from *Q. ilex* trees growing near CO$_2$ vents compared with trees growing at normal ambient CO$_2$."

In one final study conducted under entirely natural, real-world conditions, Waterhouse *et al.* (2004) determined the intrinsic water use efficiency (IWUE) responses of three tree species growing across northern Europe—one of which was pedunculate oak (*Quercus robur*) growing at three sites in England and two sites in Finland—to the increase in atmospheric CO$_2$ concentration experienced between 1895 and 1994, using parameters derived from measurements of stable carbon isotope ratios of tree-ring cellulose. They report "all species at all the sites show a long-term increase in their values of IWUE during the past century," noting "the main cause of this common behavior is likely to be the increase in atmospheric CO$_2$ concentration."

Linearly extrapolating these responses (which occurred over a period of time when the air's CO$_2$ concentration rose by approximately 65 ppm) to what would be expected for the more common 300 ppm increase employed in the majority of atmospheric CO$_2$ enrichment experiments, the IWUE increase Waterhouse *et al.* observed for *Q. robur* amounted to 158 ± 14%, as best as can be determined from the graphs of their results. A response of this magnitude is probably not due to rising CO$_2$ alone, but instead to the positive synergism that occurs when atmospheric CO$_2$ and temperature rise together (see Section 3.13, Temperature Stress, in Chapter 3), as these parameters have done over the past century or so, clearly demonstrating high temperatures and high CO$_2$ concentrations benefit plants.

The findings of the several papers reviewed above point to the likelihood oak trees of all species will grow more productively as the air's CO$_2$ content climbs higher, will likely be better able to withstand droughty conditions, and will more effectively sequester carbon in the years and decades ahead.

References

Ainsworth, E.A., Davey, P.A., Hymus, G.J., Drake, B.G., and Long, S.P. 2002. Long-term response of photosynthesis to elevated carbon dioxide in a Florida scrub-oak ecosystem. *Ecological Applications* **12**: 1267–1275.

Blaschke, L., Schulte, M., Raschi, A., Slee, N., Rennenberg, H., and Polle, A. 2001. Photosynthesis, soluble and structural carbon compounds in two Mediterranean oak species (*Quercus pubescens* and *Q. ilex*) after lifetime growth at naturally elevated CO$_2$ concentrations. *Plant Biology* **3**: 288–297.

Dijkstra, P., Hymus, G., Colavito, D., Vieglais, D.A., Cundari, C.M., Johnson, D.P., Hungate, B.A., Hinkle, C.R., and Drake, B.G. 2002. Elevated atmospheric CO$_2$ stimulates aboveground biomass in a fire-regenerated scrub-oak ecosystem. *Global Change Biology* **8**: 90–103.

Gartner, B.L., Roy, J., and Huc, R. 2003. Effects of tension wood on specific conductivity and vulnerability to embolism of *Quercus ilex* seedlings grown at two atmospheric CO$_2$ concentrations. *Tree Physiology* **23**: 387–395.

Grill, D., Muller, M., Tausz, M. Strnad, B., Wonisch, A., and Raschi, A. 2004. Effects of sulphurous gases in two CO$_2$ springs on total sulphur and thiols in acorns and oak seedlings. *Atmospheric Environment* **38**: 3775–3780.

Hymus, G.J., Johnson, D.P., Dore, S., Anderson, H.P., Hinkle, C.R., and Drake, B.G. 2003. Effects of elevated atmospheric CO$_2$ on net ecosystem CO$_2$ exchange of a scrub-oak ecosystem. *Global Change Biology* **9**: 1802–1812.

Marek, M.V., Sprtova, M., De Angelis, P., and Scarascia-Mugnozza, G. 2001. Spatial distribution of photosynthetic response to long-term influence of elevated CO$_2$ in a Mediterranean *macchia* mini-ecosystem. *Plant Science* **160**: 1125–1136.

Paoletti, E., Nourrisson, G., Garrec, J.P., and Raschi, A. 1998. Modifications of the leaf surface structures of *Quercus ilex* L. in open, naturally CO$_2$-enriched environments. *Plant, Cell and Environment* **21**: 1071–1075.

Schulte, M., Raiesi, F.G., Papke, H., Butterbach-Bahl, K., van Breemen, N., and Rennenberg, H. 1999. CO$_2$

concentration and atmospheric trace gas mixing ratio around natural CO_2 vents in different Mediterranean forests in central Italy. In: Raschi, A., Vaccori, F.P., and Miglietta, F. (Eds.). *Ecosystem Response to CO_2: The Maple Project Results*. European Communities, Brussels, Belgium, pp. 168–188.

Stylinski, C.D., Oechel, W.C., Gamon, J.A., Tissue, D.T., Miglietta, F., and Raschi, A. 2000. Effects of lifelong [CO_2] enrichment on carboxylation and light utilization of *Quercus pubescens* Willd. examined with gas exchange, biochemistry and optical techniques. *Plant, Cell and Environment* **23**: 1353–1362.

Tognetti, R., Johnson, J.D., Michelozzi, M., and Raschi, A. 1998. Response of foliar metabolism in mature trees of *Quercus pubescens* and *Quercus ilex* to long-term elevated CO_2. *Environmental and Experimental Botany* **39**: 233–245.

Tognetti, R., Longobucco, A., and Raschi, A. 1999. Seasonal embolism and xylem vulnerability in deciduous evergreen Mediterranean trees influenced by proximity to a carbon dioxide spring. *Tree Physiology* **19**: 271–277.

Waterhouse, J.S., Switsur, V.R., Barker, A.C., Carter, A.H.C., Hemming, D.L., Loader, N.J., and Robertson, I. 2004. Northern European trees show a progressively diminishing response to increasing atmospheric carbon dioxide concentrations. *Quaternary Science Reviews* **23**: 803–810.

1.1.3.2.2 Pine

It is important to know how Earth's trees will respond to the ongoing rise in the air's CO_2 content over the long-term; the only way to obtain such knowledge is to enrich the air in which they grow in long-term experiments. The following subsections review what has been learned in this regard with respect to various pine tree species.

1.1.3.2.2.1 Loblolly

- The "aerial fertilization effect" of atmospheric CO_2 enrichment will continue to significantly benefit Earth's loblolly pine forests as the atmosphere's CO_2 concentration rises.

In what was originally considered a long-term study, Tissue *et al.* (1997) grew loblolly pine seedlings for four years in open-top chambers maintained at atmospheric CO_2 concentrations of 350 and 650 ppm. Throughout the summers of this experiment, the seedlings in the CO_2-enriched chambers displayed photosynthetic rates 60 to 130% greater than those of the seedlings growing in ambient air, and during the colder winter months, they exhibited photosynthetic rates 14 to 44% greater. These persistent increases in the rate of net carbon uptake increased biomass accumulation rates in the CO_2-enriched seedlings by fully 90%, prompting the scientists conducting the study to declare loblolly pines growing in a CO_2-enriched world of the future "could be a large sink for fossil fuel carbon emitted to the atmosphere."

In another study of the same trees, Telewski *et al.* (1999) report elevated CO_2 did not significantly affect anatomical features of xylem cells, including their cell wall to cell interior ratio, resin canal area, and resin canal density, but it did significantly increase annual growth-ring widths by 93, 29, 15, and 37% during the four consecutive years of the study. Also, although not significantly so, the extra CO_2 increased average ring density in the same four years by 60, 4, 3, and 5%, leading the researchers to state, "projected increases in the atmospheric content of CO_2 may result in increased wood production without a loss in structural strength." The tendency for wood density to increase in CO_2-enriched air portends the possibility of increased structural strength in the years ahead.

By far the longest study of loblolly pines was the free-air CO_2 enrichment (FACE) experiment conducted at Duke Forest in the Piedmont region of North Carolina, USA, where in August 1996 three 30m-diameter CO_2 delivery rings began to enrich the air around the 13-year-old trees they encircled to 200 ppm above the atmosphere's ambient CO_2 concentration, and three other FACE rings served as ambient-air control plots, as described by Hendrey *et al.* (1999).

In this study, LaDeau and Clark (2001) report, by the fall 1999 the CO_2-enriched trees "were twice as likely to be reproductively mature and produced three times more cones per tree." Similarly, the trees growing in the CO_2-enriched air produced 2.4 times more cones in fall 2000. From August 1999 through July 2000, the two scientists also collected three times as many seeds in the CO_2-enriched FACE rings as they did in the ambient-air control rings.

LaDeau and Clark note naturally regenerated loblolly pine stands of the southeastern United States "are profoundly seed-limited for at least 25 years." Thus, as the air's CO_2 content rises, the researchers state, "this period of seed limitation may be reduced," which is more good news about this highly prized tree, in addition to the fact, according to William Schlesinger, codirector of the Duke project (Tangley, 2001), "trees in the high-CO_2 plots grew 25% faster than controls did during the first three growing seasons of the experiment."

One year later, Finzi *et al.* (2002) report over the first four years of differential CO_2 exposure in this study, the trees in the CO_2-enriched plots maintained average yearly rates of dry matter production 32% greater than the trees growing in ambient air. The average uptake of nitrogen from the soil was enhanced by 28% in the CO_2-enriched plots, and the CO_2-enriched trees displayed a 10% increase in nitrogen-use efficiency.

Several other papers dealing with various aspects of the experiment were published about the same time. As recounted by Luo *et al.* (2003), these analyses reveal the existence of a CO_2-induced "sustained photosynthetic stimulation at leaf and canopy levels [Myers *et al.*, 1999; Ellsworth, 2000; Luo *et al.*, 2001; Lai *et al.*, 2002], which resulted in sustained stimulation of wood biomass increment [Hamilton *et al.*, 2002] and a larger carbon accumulation in the forest floor at elevated CO_2 than at ambient CO_2 [Schlesinger and Lichter, 2001]." Based upon these findings and what they imply about rates of carbon removal from the atmosphere and its different residence times in plant, litter, and soil carbon pools, Luo *et al.* (2003) developed a model for studying the sustainability of carbon sequestration in forests. Applying this model to a situation where the atmospheric CO_2 concentration gradually rises from a value of 378 ppm in 2000 to a value of 710 ppm in 2100, they calculated the carbon sequestration rate of the Duke Forest would rise from an initial value of 69 g m^{-2} yr^{-1} to a final value of 201 g m^{-2} yr^{-1}.

Schafer *et al.* (2003) linked a leaf-level CO_2 assimilation model (Katul *et al.*, 2000) with a light attenuation model (Campbell and Norman, 1998; Stenberg, 1998) and measurements of sap-flux-based canopy conductance (Kostner *et al.*, 1992; Ewers and Oren, 2000) to create what they call a canopy conductance-constrained CO_2 assimilation model, which they tested with measurements of net ecosystem exchange and net ecosystem production in the ambient and CO_2-enriched plots of the Duke Forest FACE study. They then used it to assess the effects of elevated CO_2 on carbon uptake and allocation to different components of the forest's carbon budget under ambient and CO_2-enriched conditions. They report during the third and fourth years of the study, the extra 200 ppm of CO_2 supplied to the CO_2-enriched FACE plots increased the uptake of CO_2 by 39% in the dominant *Pinus taeda* L. trees.

These results were most impressive. However, many scientists at that time questioned whether the productivity gains associated with CO_2 enrichment would persist in the long term. Even Schafer *et al.* suggested "if nutrient limitation imposes a constraint on future productivity," as was widely believed would be the case, "it is likely that carbon allocation to the production of wood will decrease in favor of the allocation to fine root production, rhizodeposition, and mycorrhizal symbionts," citing Norby *et al.* (1992, 2001). They further suggested this decrease could "result in a rapid return of fixed carbon to the atmosphere (Merbach *et al.*, 1999)," and thus, "high rates of carbon fixation under elevated CO_2 will result in an acceleration of the carbon cycle through the forest ecosystem with little of the carbon remaining in long-term storage pools."

Indeed, it was well-accepted that the productivity of Earth's temperate forests was limited by the availability of soil nitrogen (Vitousek and Howarth, 1991). This was especially believed to be the case in the southeastern United States, where pine-hardwood forests often remove so much nitrogen from the soils in which they grow that they induce what Finzi and Schlesinger (2003) describe as "a state of acute nutrient deficiency that can only be reversed with fertilization." It would seem only natural, therefore, to presume (as they hypothesized in the early stages of the Duke Forest FACE study) "the increase in carbon fluxes to the microbial community under elevated CO_2 would increase the rate of nitrogen immobilization over mineralization," which would ultimately lead to a decline in—and perhaps the total negation of—the significant CO_2-induced stimulation of forest net primary production that developed over the first two years of the experiment (DeLucia *et al.*, 1999; Hamilton *et al.*, 2002).

To test this hypothesis, Finzi and Schlesinger (2003) measured and analyzed the pool sizes and fluxes of inorganic and organic nitrogen in the forest floor and top 30 cm of mineral soil during the first five years of differential atmospheric CO_2 treatment in the Duke Forest FACE study, where half the plots were fumigated to maintain a mean CO_2 concentration 200 ppm above ambient. They report the extra CO_2 "significantly increased the input of carbon and nitrogen to the forest floor and the mineral soil." Nevertheless, the researchers state "there was no statistically significant change in the cycling rate of nitrogen derived from soil organic matter under elevated CO_2." Indeed, "neither the rate of net nitrogen mineralization nor gross $^{15}NH_4^+$ dynamics were significantly altered by elevated CO_2." In addition, they acknowledge "there was no statistically significant difference in the concentration or net flux of organic and inorganic nitrogen in the forest floor and top 30-cm of mineral soil after five years of CO_2 fumigation," concluding "microbial biomass was not a larger sink for nitrogen."

On the basis of these results from the first five years of the Duke Forest FACE study, Finzi and Schlesinger rejected their original hypothesis that elevated levels of atmospheric CO_2 would significantly increase the rate of nitrogen immobilization by the microbial community, although they contend "elevated CO_2 will only increase the productivity of this forest during the initial stages of stand development, with nitrogen limitation constraining additional carbon sequestration under elevated CO_2 well before this stand reaches its equilibrium biomass."

Crous and Ellsworth (2004) measured the photosynthetic rates of different-age needles at different crown positions on the loblolly pine trees at the Duke Forest FACE facility in the sixth year of the study, and then compared their results with the results of similar measurements made over the prior five years. Although they report there was "some evidence of moderate photosynthetic down-regulation ... in 1-year-old needles across the fifth to sixth year of CO_2 exposure," the two researchers state "strong photosynthetic enhancement in response to elevated CO_2 (e.g., +60% across age classes and canopy locations) was observed across the years."

Also at the conclusion of the sixth year of the study, Lichter et al. (2005) reviewed what had been learned about the effects of the extra CO_2 on the soil carbon dynamics of Duke Forest. Their work revealed, since the beginning of the study, organic carbon accumulated in the forest floor of the elevated CO_2 plots at a rate 52 ± 16 g C m^{-2} yr^{-1} greater than expected during reforestation under ambient CO_2 conditions, as represented by the rate of carbon accumulation in the forest floor of the ambient CO_2 plots. This additional carbon sink, in the words of the researchers, "resulted from increased carbon inputs of 50 ± 30 g C m^{-2} yr^{-1} to the forest floor in response to CO_2 enhancement of primary production." And since there was "no evidence that the overall rate of decomposition of the forest floor decreased under the elevated CO_2 treatment," they conclude "the additional carbon sink in the forest floor of the elevated CO_2 treatment ... is wholly dependent on the net primary production enhancement and increased carbon inputs," which after a total of six years had increased the forest floor's organic carbon content by approximately 27%, as best as can be determined from their plotted data. In addition, the data gave no indication this trend was on the verge of declining

anytime soon.

With respect to the underlying mineral soil, Lichter et al. said they could detect no statistically significant treatment effects on the carbon content of the bulk mineral soil or the intra-aggregate particulate organic matter and mineral-associated organic matter fractions after six years of CO_2 enrichment. Nevertheless, there was a nearly statistically significant (P = 0.11) increase of 18.5% in the free light fraction of the organic matter in the top 15 cm of the soil profile, as well as a 3.9% increase in the total intra-aggregate particulate organic matter there. The sum of the organic carbon in these two different categories plus the mineral-associated organic carbon was 11.5% greater in the CO_2-enriched plots than in the ambient treatment plots.

Although the scientists remained pessimistic and continued to assert "forest soils are unlikely to sequester significant additional quantities of atmospheric carbon associated with CO_2 fertilization because of the low rates of carbon input to refractory and protected soil organic matter pools," the CO_2-enriched trees of their study continued to demonstrate a large and unabated growth advantage over the ambient-CO_2 trees. In addition, both the forest floor and the surface soil horizon beneath the CO_2-enriched trees continued to accumulate more organic carbon than the forest floor and surface soil horizon beneath the ambient-CO_2 trees.

LaDeau and Clark (2006) determined the reproductive responses (cone and seed production) of the loblolly pine trees at the Duke Forest FACE site to atmospheric CO_2 enrichment. They state, "carbon dioxide enrichment affected mean cone production both through early maturation and increased fecundity," such that "trees in the elevated CO_2 plots produced twice as many cones between 1998 and 2004 as trees in the ambient plots." They also report trees grown in elevated CO_2 "made the transition to reproductive maturation at smaller [trunk] diameters," and they "not only reached reproductive maturation at smaller diameters, but also at younger ages." By 2004, for example, "roughly 50% of ambient trees and 75% of fumigated trees [had] produced cones." In addition, they observe, "22% of the trees in high CO_2 produced between 40 and 100 cones during the study, compared with only 9% of ambient trees."

The two scientists say their findings indicate their previously documented "short-term responses indeed persist," contradicting the opinions of those who downplay the biological benefits of atmospheric CO_2 enrichment. Furthermore, noting "P. taeda trees that produce large seed crops early in their life span tend to continue to be prolific producers (Schultz, 1997)," they conclude "individual responses seen in this young forest may be sustained over their life span."

At the eight-year point of the long-term FACE experiment, Moore *et al.* (2006) conducted a study that represented a turning point in most scientists' thinking about what had come to be known as the Progressive Nitrogen Limitation hypothesis. They analyzed measurements of the basal areas of the trees' trunks at approximately 1.4 m above ground level made at monthly intervals since the inception of the experiment. This work revealed, in response to the 50% increase in atmospheric CO$_2$ concentration employed in the Duke Forest FACE study, there was "a sustained increase in basal area increment over the first 8 years of the experiment" that varied between 13 and 27% with variations in weather and the timing of growth. In addition, the six scientists found "there was no evidence of a decline in the relative enhancement of tree growth by elevated CO$_2$ as might be expected if soil nutrients were becoming progressively more limiting," which amazed many researchers (including several who were working on the experiment themselves), considering the low-fertility state of the soil in which the experiment was being conducted. Nevertheless, and despite many researchers' presumptions the CO$_2$-induced growth stimulation of long-lived woody plants would gradually (and drastically) decline over time, there was no evidence that was occurring in the Duke Forest FACE study. The trees kept growing at a significantly elevated rate, even when nutrient limitations would have been expected to have kept them from doing so.

Two years later, Pritchard *et al.* (2008a) used minirhizotrons to characterize the fine root development of the trees from autumn 1998 through autumn 2004. Averaged over all six years of the study, they found the extra 200 ppm of CO$_2$ increased average fine-root standing crop by 23%, in good agreement with the stimulation of the forest's net primary productivity of 18–24% observed over the period 1996–2002.

The nine researchers write, "the positive effects of CO$_2$ enrichment on fine root growth persisted 6 years following minirhizotron tube installation (8 years following initiation of the CO$_2$ fumigation)," providing once again no hint of progressive nitrogen limitation of the stimulatory effect of atmospheric CO$_2$ enrichment in a situation where one might have expected to have encountered it. In partial explanation of this finding, Pritchard *et al.* note the distal tips of fine roots are "the primary site for initiation of

mycorrhizal partnerships which are critical for resource acquisition and could also influence whether or not forests can sustain higher productivity in a CO$_2$-enriched world." Nearly all evidence obtained to date suggests trees can indeed sustain a significant CO$_2$-induced increase in net primary productivity over the long term, and the reason they can do so may reside in the CO$_2$-induced stimulation of the growth of their important fine-root tips, as suggested by Pritchard *et al.*

In a related contemporaneous paper, Pritchard *et al.* (2008b) state data from long-term FACE experiments "have yet to provide convincing evidence in support of the progressive nitrogen limitation hypothesis." They report exposure to elevated concentrations of atmospheric CO$_2$ had increased net primary productivity by 59%, 24%, 23%, and 30% at the Rhinelander, Wisconsin (USA), Oak Ridge National Laboratory (USA), Tuscania (Italy), and Duke, North Carolina (USA) FACE sites, respectively, "with little evidence to indicate a diminished response through time," citing Finzi *et al.* (2007).

The leading hypothesis to explain these sustained high growth responses had been that atmospheric CO$_2$ enrichment leads to greater fine-root production and increased allocation of carbon to ectomycorrhizal fungi living in symbiotic association with plant roots, a dual phenomenon that leads to (1) the exploration of a greater volume of soil by plants in search of much-needed nitrogen, and (2) a more thorough search of each unit volume of soil. Consequently, Pritchard *et al.* (2008b) focused their attention on the role played by ectomycorrhizal fungi for five years in the Duke Forest FACE study.

Summed across all years of the study, the five researchers found the extra 200 ppm of CO$_2$ enjoyed by the trees in the high-CO$_2$ treatment did not influence mycorrhizal production in the top 15 cm of the forest soil, but it increased mycorrhizal root-tip production by 194% throughout the 15–30 cm depth interval. In addition, the production of soil rhizomorph length was 27% greater in CO$_2$-enriched plots than in the ambient-air plots.

In discussing their findings, Pritchard *et al.* note the CO$_2$-induced "stimulation of carbon flow into soil has increased the intensity of root and fungal foraging for nutrients" and "the shift in distribution of mycorrhizal fungi to deeper soils may enable perennial plant systems to acquire additional soil nitrogen to balance the increased availability of ecosystem carbohydrates in CO$_2$-enriched atmospheres." This additional acquisition of nitrogen in the

CO_2-enriched plots of the Duke Forest study amounts to approximately 12 g N per m^2 per year and is well above estimated rates of N acquisition by the combined phenomena of N deposition, heterotrophic N fixation, and net N mineralization, which range from 3.4 to 6.0 g N per m^2 per year, as per Finzi *et al.* (2006, 2007), Hofmockel and Schlesinger (2007), and Hofmockel *et al.* (2007). Consequently, in concluding their commentary on the results of their work, Pritchard *et al.* write, "the notion that CO_2 enrichment expands the volume of soil effectively explored by roots and fungi, and that foraging in a given volume of soil also seems to intensify, provides compelling evidence to indicate that CO_2 enrichment has the potential to stimulate productivity (and carbon sequestration) in nitrogen-limited ecosystems more than previously expected."

Jackson *et al.* (2009) describe belowground data they obtained at the Duke Forest FACE site, then present a synthesis of these and other results obtained for the years 1996 through 2008, to determine "which, if any, variables show evidence for a decrease in their response to atmospheric CO_2 during that time frame." Their analyses indicate, among many other things, "on average, in elevated CO_2, fine-root biomass in the top 15 cm of soil increased by 24%," and in recent years the fine-root biomass increase "grew stronger, averaging ~30% at high CO_2." In terms of coarse roots having diameters greater than 2 mm and extending to a soil depth of 32 cm, they report biomass sampled in 2008 was "twice as great in elevated CO_2." From the graphical representation of their results, it can be calculated the coarse-root biomass was fully 130% greater, which is astounding, particularly since the extra 200 ppm of CO_2 supplied to the air surrounding the CO_2-enriched trees represented an enhancement of only about 55% above ambient conditions. In the concluding sentence of their paper's abstract, Jackson *et al.* state, "overall, the effect of elevated CO_2 belowground shows no sign of diminishing."

In discussing their findings, the four researchers write, "if progressive nitrogen limitation were occurring in this system, we would expect differences in productivity to diminish for trees in the elevated vs. ambient CO_2 plots," but "in fact there is little evidence from estimates of aboveground or total net primary productivity in the replicated Duke experiment that progressive nitrogen limitation is occurring there or at other forest FACE experiments," even "after more than a decade of manipulation" of the air's CO_2 content, citing—with respect to the latter portion of their statement—Finzi *et al.* (2007).

These most recent findings, plus all that preceded them, indicate there are many extremely well-documented observational—as opposed to theoretical—reasons to conclude the "aerial fertilization effect" of atmospheric CO_2 enrichment will significantly benefit Earth's forests as the atmosphere's CO_2 concentration rises.

References

Campbell, G.S. and Norman, J.M. 1998. *An Introduction to Environmental Biophysics.* Second Edition. Springer Verlag, New York, NY.

Crous, K.Y. and Ellsworth, D.S. 2004. Canopy position affects photosynthetic adjustments to long-term elevated CO_2 concentration (FACE) in aging needles in a mature *Pinus taeda* forest. *Tree Physiology* **24**: 961–970.

DeLucia, E.H., Hamilton, J.G., Naidu, S.L., Thomas, R.B., Andrews, J.A., Finzi, A., Lavine, M., Matamala, R., Mohan, J.E., Hendrey, G.R., and Schlesinger, W.H. 1999. Net primary production of a forest ecosystem with experimental CO_2 enrichment. *Science* **284**: 1177–1179.

Ellsworth, D.S. 2000. Seasonal CO_2 assimilation and stomatal limitations in a *Pinus taeda* canopy with varying climate. *Tree Physiology* **20**: 435–444.

Ewers, B.E. and Oren, R. 2000. Analysis of assumptions and errors in the calculation of stomatal conductance from sap flux measurements. *Tree Physiology* **20**: 579–589.

Finzi, A.C., DeLucia, E.H., Hamilton, J.G., Richter, D.D., and Schlesinger, W.H. 2002. The nitrogen budget of a pine forest under free air CO_2 enrichment. *Oecologia* **132**: 567–578.

Finzi, A.C., Moore, D.J.P., DeLucia, E.H., Lichter, J., Hofmockel, K.S., Jackson, R.B., Kim, H.-S., Matamala, R., McCarthy, H.R., Oren, R., Pippen, J.S., and Schlesinger, W.H. 2006. Progressive nitrogen limitation of ecosystem processes under elevated CO_2 in a warm-temperate forest. *Ecology* **87**: 15–25.

Finzi, A.C., Norby, R.J., Calfapietra, C., Gallet-Budynek, A., Gielen, B., Holmes, W.E., Hoosbeek, M.R., Iversen, C.M., Jackson, R.B., Kubiske, M.E., Ledford, J., Liberloo, M., Oren, R., Polle, A., Pritchard, S., Zak, D.R., Schlesinger, W.H., and Ceulemans, R. 2007. Increases in nitrogen uptake rather than nitrogen-use efficiency support higher rates of temperate forest productivity under elevated CO_2. *Proceedings of the National Academy of Sciences, USA* **104**: 14,014–14,019.

Finzi, A.C. and Schlesinger, W.H. 2003. Soil-nitrogen cycling in a pine forest exposed to 5 years of elevated carbon dioxide. *Ecosystems* **6**: 444–456.

Hamilton, J.G., DeLucia, E.H., George, K., Naidu, S.L.,

Finzi, A.C., and Schlesinger, W.H. 2002. Forest carbon balance under elevated CO$_2$. *Oecologia* 10.1007/s00442-002-0884-x.

Hendrey, G.R., Ellsworth, D.S., Lewin, K.F., and Nagy, J. 1999. A free-air enrichment system for exposing tall forest vegetation to elevated atmospheric CO$_2$. *Global Change Biology* **5**: 293–310.

Hofmockel, K.S. and Schlesinger, W.H. 2007. Carbon dioxide effects on heterotrophic dinitrogen fixation in a temperate pine forest. *Soil Science Society of America Journal* **71**: 140–144.

Hofmockel, K.S., Schlesinger, W.H., and Jackson, R.B. 2007. Effects of elevated atmospheric CO$_2$ on amino acid and NH$_4^+$-N cycling in a temperate pine ecosystem. *Global Change Biology* **13**: 1950–1959.

Jackson, R.B., Cook, C.W., Pippen, J.S., and Palmer, S.M. 2009. Increased belowground biomass and soil CO$_2$ fluxes after a decade of carbon dioxide enrichment in a warm-temperate forest. *Ecology* **90**: 3352–3366.

Katul, G.G., Ellsworth, D.S., and Lai, C.-T. 2000. Modeling assimilation and intercellular CO$_2$ from measured conductance: a synthesis of approaches. *Plant, Cell and Environment* **23**: 347–353.

Kostner, B.M.M., Schulze, E.-D., Kelliher, F.M., *et al.* 1992. Transpiration and canopy conductance in a pristine broad leafed forest of *Nothofagus*: an analysis of xylem sap flow and eddy correlation measurements. *Oecologia* **91**: 350–359.

LaDeau, S.L. and Clark, J.S. 2001. Rising CO$_2$ levels and the fecundity of forest trees. *Science* **292**: 95–98.

LaDeau, S.L. and Clark, J.S. 2006. Elevated CO$_2$ and tree fecundity: the role of tree size, interannual variability, and population heterogeneity. *Global Change Biology* **12**: 822–833.

Lai, C.T., Katul, G., Butnor, J., Ellsworth, D., and Oren, R. 2002. Modeling nighttime ecosystem respiration by a constrained source optimization method. *Global Change Biology* **8**: 124–141.

Lichter, J., Barron, S.H., Bevacqua, C.E., Finzi, A.C., Irving, K.F., Stemmler, E.A., and Schlesinger, W.H. 2005. Soil carbon sequestration and turnover in a pine forest after six years of atmospheric CO$_2$ enrichment. *Ecology* **86**: 1835–1847.

Luo, Y., Medlyn, B., Hui, D., Ellsworth, D., Reynolds, J., and Katul, G. 2001. Gross primary productivity in the Duke Forest: Modeling synthesis of the free-air CO$_2$ enrichment experiment and eddy-covariance measurements. *Ecological Applications* **11**: 239–252.

Luo, Y., White, L.W., Canadell, J.G., DeLucia, E.H., Ellsworth, D.S., Finzi, A., Lichter, J., and Schlesinger, W.H. 2003. Sustainability of terrestrial carbon sequestration: A case study in Duke Forest with inversion approach. *Global Biogeochemical Cycles* **17**: 10.1029/2002GB001923.

Merbach, W., Mirus, E., Knof, G., Remus, R., Ruppel, S., Russow, R., Gransee, A., and Schuize, J. 1999. Release of carbon and nitrogen compounds by plant roots and their possible ecological importance. *Zeitschrift fur Pflanzenerna'hrung und Bodenkunde* **162**: 373–383.

Moore, D.J.P., Aref, S., Ho, R.M., Pippen, J.S., Hamilton, J.G., and De Lucia, E.H. 2006. Annual basal area increment and growth duration of *Pinus taeda* in response to eight years of free-air carbon dioxide enrichment. *Global Change Biology* **12**: 1367–1377.

Myers, D.A., Thomas, R.B., and DeLucia, E.H. 1999. Photosynthetic capacity of loblolly pine (*Pinus taeda* L.) trees during the first year of carbon dioxide enrichment in a forest ecosystem. *Plant, Cell and Environment* **22**: 473–481.

Norby R.J., Gunderson, C.A., Wullschleger, S.D., O'Neill, E.G., and McCracken, M.K. 1992. Productivity and compensatory response of yellow poplar trees in elevated CO$_2$. *Nature* **357**: 322–324.

Norby R.J., Todd, D.E., Fults, J., and Johnson, D.W. 2001. Allometric determination of tree growth in CO$_2$ enriched sweetgum stand. *New Phytologist* **150**: 477–487.

Pritchard, S.G., Strand, A.E., McCormack, M.L., Davis, M.A., Finzi, A.C., Jackson, R.B., Matamala, R., Rogers, H.H., and Oren, R. 2008a. Fine root dynamics in a loblolly pine forest are influenced by free-air-CO$_2$-enrichment: a six-year-minirhizotron study. *Global Change Biology* **14**: 588–602.

Pritchard, S.G., Strand, A.E., McCormack, M.L., Davis, M.A., and Oren, R. 2008b. Mycorrhizal and rhizomorph dynamics in a loblolly pine forest during 5 years of free-air-CO$_2$-enrichment. *Global Change Biology* **14**: 1–13.

Schafer, K.V.R., Oren, R., Ellsworth, D.S., Lai, C.-T., Herrick, J.D., Finzi, A.C., Richter, D.D., and Katul, G.G. 2003. Exposure to an enriched CO$_2$ atmosphere alters carbon assimilation and allocation in a pine forest ecosystem. *Global Change Biology* **9**: 1378–1400.

Schultz, R.P. 1997. *Loblolly Pine—The Ecology and Culture of Loblolly Pine (Pinus taeda L.)*. USDA Forest Service Agricultural Handbook 713. USDA Forest Service, Washington, DC, USA.

Schlesinger, W.H. and Lichter, J. 2001. Limited carbon storage in soil and litter of experimental forest plots under increased atmospheric CO$_2$. *Nature* **411**: 466–469.

Stenberg, P. 1998. Implications of shoot structure on the rate of photosynthesis at different levels in a coniferous canopy using a model incorporating grouping and penumbra. *Functional Ecology* **12**: 82–91.

Tangley, L. 2001. High CO_2 levels may give fast-growing trees an edge. *Science* **292**: 36–37.

Telewski, F.W., Swanson, R.T., Strain, B.R., and Burns, J.M. 1999. Wood properties and ring width responses to long-term atmospheric CO_2 enrichment in field-grown loblolly pine (*Pinus taeda* L.). *Plant, Cell and Environment* **22**: 213–219.

Tissue, D.T., Thomas, R.B., and Strain, B.R. 1997. Atmospheric CO_2 enrichment increases growth and photosynthesis of *Pinus taeda*: a 4-year experiment in the field. *Plant, Cell and Environment* **20**: 1123–1134.

Vitousek, P.M. and Howarth, R.W. 1991. Nitrogen limitation on land and in the sea: how can it occur? *Biogeochemistry* **13**: 87–115.

1.1.3.2.2.2 Scots

- Evidence gleaned from multiyear studies suggests the historical rise in the atmosphere's CO_2 concentration has significantly enhanced the growth and well-being of Scots pine trees over the past century or more and will likely do the same for them in decades yet to come.

Researchers planted three-year-old pot-grown Scots pine (*Pinus sylvestris* L.) seedlings in the ground in four open-top chambers at the University of Antwerp in Belgium on 21 March 1996, and they continuously maintained them at atmospheric CO_2 concentrations of either 350 or 750 ppm, to determine the long-term effects of elevated CO_2 on various aspects of the growth and development of this important timber species, as described by Jach and Ceulemans (1999). To make the experimental results as representative as possible of the natural world, no nutrients or irrigation waters were applied to the soils during the entire period of the investigation.

During the second year of the study, Jach and Ceulemans (2000a) discovered the photosynthetic rates of current and one-year-old CO_2-enriched needles were 62 and 65% greater, respectively, than the photosynthetic rates of comparable needles on seedlings growing in ambient air. Simultaneously, Jach and Ceulemans (2000b) found dark respiration rates expressed on a needle-mass basis were 27 and 33% lower in current-year and one-year-old needles, respectively, on the CO_2-enriched trees than on the ambient-treatment trees. After three years of differential CO_2 exposure, Jach *et al.* (2000)

determined the extra CO_2 of the study had increased total seedling biomass production by 55%, even though the experimental soils were relatively nutrient-poor.

Possibly to compensate for this deficiency of nutrients, Jach *et al.* found the elevated CO_2 had increased root biomass by more than 150%, which would likely have enhanced the ability of the CO_2-enriched seedlings to explore a greater volume of soil for the nutrients they required to sustain their augmented growth and development. The three researchers conclude, "it is likely that on nutrient-poor forest sites valuable gains to the timber industry may be achieved under future climatic conditions, since increased root production may enhance both nutrient availability, and hence timber production, as well as increase wind stability."

At the three-year point of the study, Gielen *et al.* (2000) determined elevated CO_2 did not significantly impact the photochemical quantum efficiency of photosystem II, nor did it affect any parameters associated with chlorophyll fluorescence, suggesting atmospheric CO_2 enrichment did not modify the light-dependent reactions of photosynthesis. They did find, however, elevated CO_2 reduced needle nitrogen and chlorophyll contents by 33 and 26%, respectively, although these reductions were statistically insignificant. Nonetheless, these latter observations suggest the light-independent reactions of photo-synthesis were being modified by long-term exposure to elevated CO_2 in a manner indicating photosynthetic acclimation that allows for the redistribution of limiting resources, such as nitrogen, to other areas of the tree where they may be more needed.

At the four-year point of the study, Lin *et al.* (2001) found elevated CO_2 reduced needle stomatal density by an average of 7.4% while increasing needle thickness, mesophyll tissue area, and total cross-sectional area by 6.4, 5.7, and 10.4%, respectively. In addition, atmospheric CO_2 enrichment increased the average relative area occupied by phloem cells by 4.4%. The first of these observations suggests Scots pine trees will be better able to conserve water and cope with periods of drought in a future high-CO_2 world. In addition, the increase in mesophyll tissue portends an increase in photosynthetic rates, and the increase in phloem cell area suggests a greater capacity for transport of photosynthetic sugars from needles to actively growing sink tissues.

Finally, Waterhouse *et al.* (2004) determined the intrinsic water use efficiency response of Scots pines growing in South Bedfordshire in England to the increase in the air's CO_2 content between 1895 and 1994, using parameters derived from measurements of stable carbon isotope ratios of tree-ring cellulose. The found there was a long-term increase in intrinsic water use efficiency during the prior century, and the main cause of this behavior was likely "the increase in atmospheric CO_2 concentration."

Linearly extrapolating the response (which occurred over a period of time when the air's CO_2 concentration rose by approximately 65 ppm) to what would be expected for a 300 ppm increase, the intrinsic water use efficiency increase they derived amounts to 195%, as best as can be determined from the graphs of their results. This substantial response is probably not due to the rising CO_2 alone but to the positive synergism that occurs when atmospheric CO_2 and temperature rise together.

The evidence gained from the last of these multiyear studies suggests the historical rise in the atmosphere's CO_2 concentration has significantly enhanced the growth and well-being of Earth's Scots pine trees over the past century or more, and the evidence of the other studies suggests the ongoing rise in atmospheric CO_2 (and possibly temperature as well) will likely do the same for decades yet to come.

References

Gielen, B., Jach, M.E., and Ceulemans, R. 2000. Effects of season, needle age and elevated atmospheric CO_2 on chlorophyll fluorescence parameters and needle nitrogen concentration in (Pinus sylvestris L.). Photosynthetica 38: 13–21.

Jach, M.E. and Ceulemans, R. 1999. Effects of elevated atmospheric CO_2 on phenology, growth and crown structure of Scots pine (Pinus sylvestris L.) seedlings after two years of exposure in the field. Tree Physiology 19:289–300.

Jach, M.E. and Ceulemans, R. 2000a. Effects of season, needle age and elevated atmospheric CO_2 on photosynthesis in Scots pine (Pinus sylvestris L.). Tree Physiology 20: 145–157.

Jach, M.E. and Ceulemans, R. 2000b. Short- versus long-term effects of elevated CO_2 on night-time respiration of needles of Scots pine (Pinus sylvestris L.). Photosynthetica 38: 57–67.

Jach, M.E., Laureysens, I., and Ceulemans, R. 2000. Above- and below-ground production of young Scots pine (Pinus sylvestris L.) trees after three years of growth in the field under elevated CO_2. Annals of Botany 85: 789–798.

Lin, J., Jach, M.E., and Ceulemans, R. 2001. Stomatal density and needle anatomy of Scots pine (Pinus sylvestris) are affected by elevated CO_2. New Phytologist 150: 665–674.

Waterhouse, J.S., Switsur, V.R., Barker, A.C., Carter, A.H.C., Hemming, D.L., Loader, N.J., and Robertson, I. 2004. Northern European trees show a progressively diminishing response to increasing atmospheric carbon dioxide concentrations. Quaternary Science Reviews 23: 803–810.

1.1.3.2.2.3 Other Pine Trees

- Aleppo and Shortleaf pines will likely experience greatly enhanced growth and development as the atmospheric CO_2 content continues its upward trajectory.

Clues to how Earth's trees will respond to future increases in atmospheric CO_2 concentration may be obtained from studies of how they have responded to historical increases in the air's CO_2 content. This section reviews what has been learned for two less-analyzed species of pine tree: Aleppo pine (Pinus halepensis Mill.) and Shortleaf pine (Pinus echinata Mill.).

Rathgeber et al. (2003) used tree-ring width and density chronologies (in both earlywood and latewood) from 21 stands of Aleppo pines in the Provence region of southeast France to calibrate the BIOME3 biogeochemistry model of forest productivity in terms of growth responses to known historical changes in atmospheric temperature, precipitation, and CO_2 concentration. They then used the calibrated model to calculate changes in the mean productivity of the same forest stands that could be expected to result from changes in these parameters driven by a doubling of the air's CO_2 content, as calculated by Meteo-France's ARPEGE atmospheric general circulation model when downscaled to that specific part of the country.

In response to the predicted changes in climate, forest productivity increased moderately for all stands (17% to 24%), and in response to the aerial fertilization effect of the doubling of the air's CO_2 content, it rose considerably more (72% to 86%). Even more impressively, when the climatic changes and atmospheric CO_2 increase were considered together, forest productivity increased still more (107% to 141%).

This latter response range is even greater than what is implied by the sum of the individual responses, due to the amplifying synergy of the atmospheric compositional and climatic factors on basic plant physiological processes. Therefore, the researchers conclude, "although the detected effects of global change during the 20th century were slight, acceleration of these changes is likely to lead to great changes in the future productivity of *P. halepensis* forests." Their study suggests a doubling of the air's CO_2 content could more than double the growth of Aleppo pine forests in southeast France.

Working with Shortleaf pine in the Ozark Mountains of Missouri, USA, Voelker *et al.* (2006) cross-dated a large number of increment cores and aligned the ring-width data by pith date for accurate age-constant assessments of growth over the past 150 years, thereby circumventing "changes in growth trend associated with differences in physiological functioning during development, as well as the need for statistical detrending that removes an unknown degree of long-term environmental signal, the so-called segment length curse that applies to standard dendrochronological investigations." In addition, they similarly analyzed previously acquired data for Shortleaf pine stretching back to nearly AD 1600. Since 1850, the stem growth of the trees rose "coincidently with increases in atmospheric CO_2," such that the overall trend in ring-width in recent years is "nearly two times that" experienced prior to 1850. In addition, "long-term increases in radial growth appear unrelated to historical disturbance levels for the region, to long-term changes in relevant climatic variables, or to productivity of sites sampled." Consequently, the four Department of Forestry researchers from the University of Missouri (USA) conclude the rising atmospheric CO_2 concentration—aided by continued nitrogen deposition—will likely "stimulate further increases in the rates of stand development and carbon storage."

References

Rathgeber, C., Nicault, A., Kaplan, J.O., and Guiot, J. 2003. Using a biogeochemistry model in simulating forests productivity responses to climatic change and [CO_2] increase: example of *Pinus halepensis* in Provence (southeast France). *Ecological Modelling* **166**: 239–255.

Voelker, S.L., Muzika, R.-M., Guyette, R.P., and Stambaugh, M.C. 2006. Historical CO_2 growth enhancement declines with age in *Quercus* and *Pinus*. *Ecological Monographs* **76**: 549–564.

1.1.3.2.3 Sour Orange

- The long-term equilibrium response of sour orange trees to a 75% increase in the air's CO_2 concentration after 17 years of study was a CO_2-enriched/ambient-treatment biomass ratio of 1.69 for all above-ground parts of the trees (other than fruit), 1.85 for the cumulative amount of biomass due to fruit production, and 1.07 for the vitamin C content of the fruit (though this latter ratio was based on samples from the fourth through the 12th years of the experiment only).

In July 1987, as described by U.S. Department of Agriculture researchers Idso and Kimball (2001), eight 30-cm-tall sour orange tree (*Citrus aurantium* L.) seedlings were planted directly into the ground at the Agricultural Research Service's U.S. Water Conservation Laboratory in Phoenix, Arizona, where they were enclosed in pairs within four clear-plastic-wall open-top chambers. In November of that year, the two scientists began to continuously pump ambient air through two of the chambers via perforated plastic tubes that lay upon the ground beneath the trees, and through the other two chambers they pumped air enriched with carbon dioxide to a concentration 300 ppm greater than the surrounding ambient air, which had an average CO_2 concentration of 400 ppm. Thus began one of the longest atmospheric CO_2 experiments ever conducted anywhere in the world.

Throughout the experiment, the Phoenix global-change research team irrigated and fertilized the trees according to standard agronomic practices in the area, to keep them as free as possible from water and nutrient stresses. They measured the circumferences of the trees' trunks at a height of 45 cm above the surface of the ground at the midpoint of every month. At the end of the second and third years of the study, they also determined the total trunk and branch volume of each tree from trunk and branch length and diameter measurements. From these data they developed a relationship between trunk cross-sectional area and trunk plus branch volume that applied equally well to the CO_2-enriched and ambient-treatment trees. Then they made numerous wood density measurements that allowed them to calculate the total aboveground woody biomass of each tree at the midpoint of every month. In addition, all the oranges produced by the trees were picked, counted, and weighed each year, and a large number of the fruit were dried in ovens to determine the amount of dry matter they contained. The two researchers thus developed a yearly record of total fruit biomass production to accompany their monthly record of wood biomass production.

As the experiment progressed, the CO₂-enriched/ambient-treatment ratio of cumulative aboveground wood biomass rose rapidly from an initial value of unity to a value slightly greater than 3.0 at the two-year point of the study, as shown in Figure 1.1.3.2.3.1, which depicts the changing ratio of the aboveground wood biomass of the CO₂-enriched trees to the ambient-treatment trees over the first two years of the study.

From the data of Figure 1.1.3.2.3.1, it could reasonably be assumed the CO₂-enriched/ambient-treatment wood biomass ratio might rise a little higher but would have to level off sometime soon. Hence, the researchers decided to continue collecting data to determine the long-term asymptotic growth response of the trees. After seven additional months, they obtained the results depicted in Figure 1.1.3.2.3.2.

To the researchers' surprise, the wood biomass ratio not only did not rise any higher, or even level out, it began a steep decline. Projecting forward in time, it appeared a continuation of the new trend could result in all the biomass advantage acquired by the CO₂-enriched trees possibly disappearing altogether over the next couple of years. To continue the experiment, they obtained the additional data depicted in Figure 1.1.3.2.3.3.

The results portrayed in Figure 1.1.3.2.3.3 were enlightening. They suggest, after an initial "overshoot" of the long-term response of the trees to atmospheric CO₂ enrichment, things finally settled down and a final answer was obtained: The ultimate equilibrium response of the trees was a 150% increase in wood biomass production in response to the 75% increase in the air's CO₂ concentration. The research team continued collecting data, only to be surprised once again as depicted in Figure 1.1.3.2.3.4.

The results portrayed in Figure 1.1.3.2.3.3 were enlightening. They suggest, after an initial "overshoot" of the long-term response of the trees to atmospheric CO₂ enrichment, things finally settled down and a final answer was obtained: The ultimate equilibrium response of the trees was a 150% increase in wood biomass production in response to the 75% increase in the air's CO₂ concentration. The research team continued collecting data, only to be surprised once again as depicted in Figure 1.1.3.2.3.4.

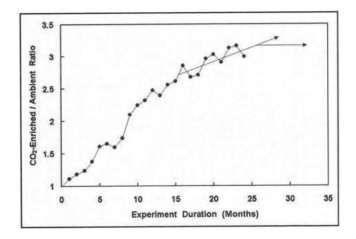

Figure 1.1.3.2.3.1. The CO₂-enriched/ambient-treatment ratio of total aboveground sour orange tree wood biomass plotted as a function of time since the start of the experiment, along with arrows that depict two logical projections of what might happen to this ratio if the experiment were continued beyond the last point shown. Adapted from Idso and Kimball (2001).

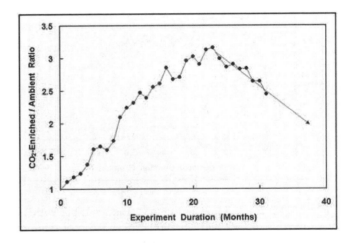

Figure 1.1.3.2.3.2. Same as Figure 1.1.3.2.3.1, but with seven additional months of data and a new forward projection of the CO₂-enriched/ambient-treatment wood biomass ratio. Adapted from Idso and Kimball (2001).

After having maintained a near-constant value for more than a year and a half, the wood biomass ratio began to decline again, as shown in Figure 1.1.3.2.3.4 not as rapidly as it had the first time, but at a still substantial rate. As it dropped ever-lower, the researchers decided to continue collecting data, which yielded the results depicted in Figure 1.1.3.2.3.5.

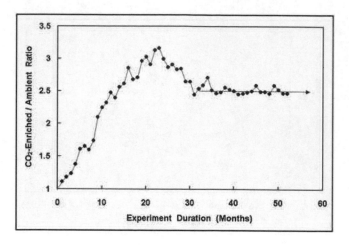

Figure 1.1.3.2.3.3. Same as Figure 1.1.3.2.3.2, but with 21 additional months of data and a new forward projection of the wood biomass ratio. Adapted from Idso and Kimball (2001).

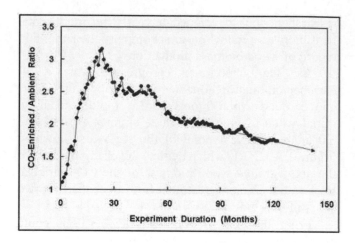

Figure 1.1.3.2.3.5. Same as Figure 1.1.3.2.3.4, but with 58 months of additional data and one more projection of the CO_2-enriched/ambient-treatment wood biomass ratio. Adapted from Idso and Kimball (2001).

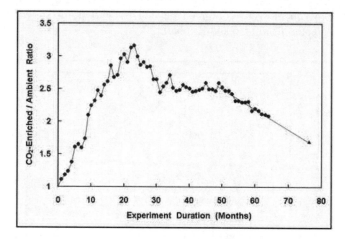

Figure 1.1.3.2.3.4. Same as Figure 1.1.3.2.3.3, but with 12 more months of data and yet another forward projection of the CO_2-enriched/ambient-treatment wood biomass ratio. Adapted from Idso and Kimball (2001).

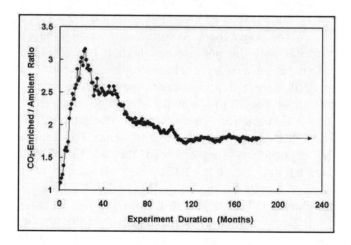

Figure 1.1.3.2.3.6. Same as Figure 1.1.3.2.3.5, but with 60-plus months of additional data and one last forward projection of the wood biomass ratio. Adapted from Idso and Kimball (2001).

This time, the change was to a reduced rate of decline in the wood biomass ratio, and it persisted for nearly five years. At this point, the experiment had passed the decade point, and it appeared the wood biomass ratio was going to continue to decline slowly and probably approach some asymptotic limit that might not be much greater than unity. As that possibility would be of extreme significance, Idso and Kimball continued collecting data, obtaining the results portrayed in Figure 1.1.3.2.3.6.

Finally, at the nine-year point of the study, the CO_2-enriched/ambient-treatment wood biomass ratio leveled out at 1.80, which the researchers concluded was the true long-term growth response of the trees to the 75% increase in atmospheric CO_2 concentration.

Providing additional support for this conclusion, fruit production began in the third year of the study, when the CO_2-enriched trees produced an average of 25 fruit per tree and the ambient-treatment trees produced an average of only one fruit per tree. Thereafter, the cumulative CO_2-enriched/ ambient-treatment fruit biomass ratio also dropped substantially, ultimately leveling out just a little above the 1.80 CO_2-enriched/ ambient-treatment wood biomass ratio. These findings, Idso and Kimball (2001) write, "are indicative of the likelihood that the CO_2-enriched trees may have reached an equilibrium condition with respect to the CO_2-induced enhancement of wood biomass and fruit production, and that they will not substantially depart from these steady-state responses over the remainder of their lifespan."

Giving added confidence to these conclusions was the ancillary study of Leavitt *et al.* (2003). They evaluated the intrinsic water use efficiencies of the trees via analyses of the stable carbon isotopes of leaves collected from each of them every two months throughout 1992, as well as on three occasions in 1994–95, plus wood samples extracted five years later from two cores that passed through the center of each tree's trunk at a height of 45 cm above the ground. The ultimate finding of this endeavor was an 80% increase in intrinsic water use efficiency in response to the 75% increase in atmospheric CO_2 concentration employed in the study. Since the earlier work of Idso *et al.* (1993) had demonstrated there was very little difference in leaf stomatal conductance between the two CO_2 treatments, nearly all this water use efficiency increase had to have resulted from the CO_2-induced increase in net primary productivity that led to the 80% increases in wood and fruit production.

This result may be typical of trees in general. In a massive review of the pertinent scientific literature, Saxe *et al.* (1998) observed "increasing numbers of experiments show a lack of stomatal sensitivity to CO_2," especially when the data come "from long-term experiments on larger trees rooted directly in the ground," as also may be deduced from Eamus (1996). And Feng (1999) reports, for 23 sets of trees in locations across western North America, the average stable-carbon-isotope-derived increase in intrinsic water use efficiency (iWUE) that occurred in response to the historical increase in the air's CO_2 concentration experienced over the period 1800–1985 yielded essentially the same value of iWUE/ CO_2 as derived from the sour orange tree study of Leavitt *et al.* In addition, even greater natural CO_2-induced increases in iWUE have been documented in various trees in Europe: by Bert *et al.* (1997) in the case of white fir, and by Hemming (1998) in the cases of beech, oak, and pine.

Perhaps the most convincing evidence for the validity of the long-term equilibrium response of the sour orange trees in the CO_2-enriched chambers came from the harvesting of the trees after 17 years of study at the conclusion of the experiment, in January 2005, as described by Kimball *et al.* (2007). The scientists found the final CO_2-enriched/ambient-treatment biomass ratio of all of the above-ground parts of the trees (other than fruit) was 1.69, and "the cumulative amount of biomass due to fruit production over the duration of the experiment was increased 85% due to elevated CO_2." In addition, they report, "the vitamin C content of the fruit was increased 7% based on samples taken from the fourth through the 12th years of the experiment," citing Idso *et al.* (2002). Many more oranges were produced by the trees in the CO_2-enriched chambers, and those oranges were of a higher quality as well.

In addition, Idso *et al.* (2001) discovered three soluble proteins in the leaves of the sour orange trees whose synthesis and transference from second- to first-year leaves in the early springtime of each year were influenced by the atmosphere's CO_2 concentration in ways likely to facilitate the trees' large positive photosynthetic and biomass responses to atmospheric CO_2 enrichment. The proteins appeared to function as vacuolar storage proteins, which may supply each year's first flush of new foliage with the large amounts of nitrogen needed to sustain the ultra-enhanced spring branch growth of the CO_2-enriched trees, which was four to six times more rapid than the trees growing in ambient air in their experiment (Idso *et al.*, 2000), and which likely provided the yearly initial impetus for the 70 to 80% long-term growth enhancement of the trees maintained throughout the remainder of each year of the last half of their long-term study.

References

Bert, D., Leavitt, S.W., and Dupouey, J.-L. 1997. Variations in wood $\delta^{13}C$ and water use efficiency of *Abies alba* during the last century. *Ecology* **78**: 1588–1595.

Eamus, D. 1996. Responses of field grown trees to CO_2 enrichment. *Commonwealth Forestry Review* **75**: 39–47.

Feng, X. 1999. Trends in intrinsic water use efficiency of natural trees for the past 100–200 years: A response to atmospheric CO_2 concentration. *Geochimica et Cosmochimica Acta* **63**: 1891–1903.

Hemming, D.L. 1998. *Stable Isotopes in Tree Rings: Biosensors of Climate and Atmospheric Carbon-Dioxide Variations*. Ph.D. Dissertation. University of Cambridge, Cambridge, UK.

Idso, C.D., Idso, S.B., Kimball, B.A., Park, H.-S., Hoober, J.K., and Balling Jr., R.C. 2000. Ultra-enhanced spring branch growth in CO_2-enriched trees: Can it alter the phase of the atmosphere's seasonal CO_2 cycle? *Environmental and Experimental Botany* **43**: 91–100.

Idso, K.E., Hoober, J.K., Idso, S.B., Wall, G.W., and Kimball, B.A. 2001. Atmospheric CO_2 enrichment influences the synthesis and mobilization of putative vacuolar storage proteins in sour orange tree leaves. *Environmental and Experimental Botany* **48**: 199–211.

Idso, S.B. and Kimball, B.A. 2001. CO_2 enrichment of sour orange trees: 13 years and counting. *Environmental and Experimental Botany* **46**: 147–153.

Idso, S.B., Kimball, B.A., Akin, D.E., and Kridler, J. 1993. A general relationship between CO_2-induced reductions in stomatal conductance and concomitant increases in foliage temperature. *Environmental and Experimental Botany* **33**: 443–446.

Idso, S.B., Kimball, B.A., Shaw, P.E., Widmer, W., Vanderslice, J.T., Higgs, D.J., Montanari, A., and Clark, W.D. 2002. The effect of elevated atmospheric CO_2 on the vitamin C concentration of (sour) orange juice. *Agriculture, Ecosystems and Environment* **90**: 1–7.

Kimball, B.A., Idso, S.B., Johnson, S., and Rillig, M.C. 2007. Seventeen years of carbon dioxide enrichment of sour orange trees: final results. *Global Change Biology* **13**: 2171–2183.

Leavitt, S.W., Idso, S.B., Kimball, B.A., Burns, J.M., Sinha, A., and Stott, L. 2003. The effect of long-term atmospheric CO_2 enrichment on the intrinsic water use efficiency of sour orange trees. *Chemosphere* **50**: 217–222.

Saxe, H., Ellsworth, D.S., and Heath, J. 1998. Tree and forest functioning in an enriched CO_2 atmosphere. *New Phytologist* **139**: 395–436.

1.1.3.2.4 Spruce

- Spruce trees have a good chance of indefinitely maintaining the long-term positive growth responses to the ongoing rise in the air's CO_2 content, even when growing on nutrient-deficient soils.

Spunda *et al.* (1998) grew 15-year-old Norway spruce (*Picea abies*) trees in open-top chambers maintained at atmospheric CO_2 concentrations of 350 and 700 ppm for four years. At the end of this period they found current-year shoots of the trees growing in the CO_2-enriched chambers displayed rates of net photosynthesis 78% greater than those exhibited by the current-year shoots of the trees growing in ambient air.

Spinnler *et al.* (2003) grew Norway spruce seedlings originating from eight different provenances for four full years on a nutrient-poor acidic soil and a nutrient-rich calcareous soil placed in lysimeters located within open-top chambers maintained at CO_2 concentrations of either 370 or 570 ppm. When growing in the nutrient-poor soil, total spruce biomass increased by 9 to 38% across the eight different provenances, and in the nutrient-rich soil it increased by 10 to 74%.

In an experiment that ran for five years and focused on Sitka spruce (*Picea sitchensis*), Liu *et al.* (2002) grew seedlings in open-top chambers maintained for five years at CO_2 concentrations of either 350 or 700 ppm. For the first three years, the seedlings were grown in well-watered and -fertilized pots placed within the chambers. They were then planted directly in native nutrient-deficient forest soil and maintained for two more years in larger open-top chambers, either with or without an extra supply of nitrogen (N).

After the first three years of growth in pots, the CO_2-enriched trees were found to possess 11.6% more total biomass than the ambient-treatment trees. At the end of the next two years of the study, the trees supplied with extra N possessed 15.6% more total biomass than their similarly treated ambient-air counterparts, and those receiving no extra N had 20.5% more total biomass than their ambient-air counterparts.

Liu *et al.* make a point of noting these CO_2-induced increases in growth occurred in spite of a down-regulation of photosynthesis and a reduction of foliar rubisco activity. In addition, they report "visual foliar N-deficiency symptoms (needle yellowing and chlorosis) were obvious on some of the saplings with no added N supply during the final year of the experiment." However, they further note "such N deficiency is common in many boreal forest sites, and therefore a growth response to rising atmospheric CO_2 can be expected to occur in such forests," in support of which they state, "growth responses to elevated CO_2 despite nutrient stress have been reported previously in Scots pine (Kellomaki and Wang, 1997), grass (Cannell and Thornley, 1998) and Sitka spruce (Centritto *et al.*, 1999; Murray *et al.*, 2000)."

These findings, plus those cited by Liu *et al.*, indicate spruce trees (and other species) have a good chance of indefinitely maintaining long-term positive growth responses to the ongoing rise in the air's CO_2 content, even on nutrient-deficient soils.

References

Cannell, M.G.R. and Thornley, H.M. 1998. N-poor ecosystems may respond more to elevated [CO_2] than N-rich ones in the long term, a model analysis of grassland. *Global Change Biology* **4**: 101–112.

Centritto, M., Lee, H.S.J., and Jarvis, P.G. 1999. Long-term effects of elevated carbon dioxide concentration and provenance on four clones of Sitka spruce (*Picea sitchensis*). I. Plant growth, allocation and ontogeny. *Tree Physiology* **19**: 799–806.

Kellomaki, S. and Wang, K.Y. 1997. Photosynthetic response of Scots pine to elevated CO_2 and nitrogen supply: results of a branch-in-bag experiment. *Tree Physiology* **17**: 231–240.

Liu, S.R., Barton, C., Lee, H., Jarvis, P.G., and Durrant, D. 2002. Long-term response of Sitka spruce (*Picea sitchensis* (Bong.) Carr.) to CO_2 enrichment and nitrogen supply. I. Growth, biomass allocation and physiology. *Plant Biosystems* **136**: 189–198.

Murray, M.B., Smith, R.I., Friend, A., and Jarvis, P.G. 2000. Effect of elevated [CO_2] and varying nutrient application rates on physiology and biomass accumulation of Sitka spruce (*Picea sitchensis*). *Tree Physiology* **20**: 421–434.

Spinnler, D., Egli, P., and Körner, C. 2003. Provenance effects and allometry in beech and spruce under elevated CO_2 and nitrogen on two different forest soils. *Basic and Applied Ecology* **4**: 467–478.

Spunda, V., Kalina, J., Cajanek, M., Pavlickova, H., and Marek, M.V. 1998. Long-term exposure of Norway spruce to elevated CO_2 concentration induces changes in photosystem II mimicking an adaptation to increased irradiance. *Journal of Plant Physiology* **152**: 413–419.

1.1.3.2.5 Sweetgum

- Long-term FACE studies of mature sweetgum trees demonstrate significant increases in net primary production and give no evidence of decline.

In spring 1988, a single-species sweetgum (*Liquidambar styraciflua* L.) plantation was established in nutrient-rich soil at the Oak Ridge National Environmental Research Park in Roane County, Tennessee, USA, where a group of scientists constructed five circular FACE plots of 25 meters' diameter several years later. They began initial atmospheric CO_2 enrichment to a daytime average concentration of 533 ppm (as opposed to the ambient concentration of 394 ppm) in two of the plots in April 1998, well after the 1996 date at which the young forest's canopy had achieved closure and the trees had entered the stable linear growth phase in which annual growth increments are approximately the same each year (as opposed to the exponential growth that precedes this more mature state).

In April 1997 (a full year before the start of differential CO_2 treatments), the scientists began monthly bole circumference measurements at a height of 1.3 meters above the ground on every tree within 10 meters of the centers of the ambient and CO_2-enriched plots. Several of these trees were subsequently sacrificed to determine their aboveground biomass, and a relationship was developed between this parameter and the tree basal area derived from the bole circumference measurements. Based on these data, Norby *et al.* (2001) state, "there was no pretreatment bias to confound subsequent effects of CO_2 on growth."

Over the next two years of differential CO_2 exposure, they determined the increase in atmospheric CO_2 concentration employed in their study increased the biomass production of the trees by an average of 24% over the first two years of the experiment. That result indicated, they write, "large trees have the capacity to respond to elevated CO_2 just as much as younger trees that are in exponential growth," which had been highly conjectural until that time.

After three years of exposure to different CO_2 concentrations (reported at this subsequent time to be 360 and 550 ppm in the ambient and CO_2-enriched plots, respectively), Gunderson *et al.* (2002) found the 53% increase in the air's CO_2 concentration imposed on the trees was boosting rates of net photosynthesis by 46% in both upper- and mid-canopy foliage. In addition, they report there was no decline in photosynthetic enhancement over the preceding three years of their study.

Norby *et al.* (2002) state the elevated CO_2 increased ecosystem net primary productivity of the trees by 21% in all of the three preceding years, stating once again, "this experiment has provided the first evidence that CO_2 enrichment can increase productivity in a closed-canopy deciduous forest." After an additional year of measurements, Norby *et al.* (2003) determined net primary productivity was enhanced by an average of 22% over years 2–5 of the study, reaffirming their conclusions of the year before.

A second long-term FACE study of sweetgum trees was conducted at the Duke Forest in the Piedmont region of North Carolina, USA, where the soils are low in available nitrogen and phosphorus. In August 1996, three 30m-diameter CO_2 delivery rings began to enrich the air around the then-13-year-old trees they encircled—including loblolly pine (1733 stems per ha), sweetgum (620 stems per ha), and yellow poplar (68 stems per ha)—to 190 ppm above the ambient CO_2 concentration, and three other FACE rings were used as ambient-air control plots.

In the initial stages of this study, Herrick and Thomas (1999) found elevated CO_2 significantly increased photosynthetic rates in both Sun and shade leaves, with the greatest CO_2-induced photosynthetic stimulation occurring in August, when the mean maximum air temperature was 4°C higher and monthly rainfall was 66% lower than in June. In June, the extra CO_2 increased photosynthetic rates of Sun and shade leaves by 92 and 54%, respectively, whereas in August corresponding increases were 166 and 68%.

Two years later, Herrick and Thomas (2001) observed mean photosynthetic enhancements of 63 and 48% in Sun and shade leaves during the middle portion of the study's third full growing season, indicating little to no down-regulation of photosynthesis over the first three years of the experiment. After two more years, Herrick and Thomas (2003) found there were still large increases in the net photosynthetic rates of the leaves of the CO_2-enriched trees: 51 to 96% in Sun leaves and 23 to 51% in shade leaves.

These two long-term FACE studies of mature sweetgum trees demonstrate significant increases in net primary production and give no evidence of decline.

References

Gunderson, C.A., Sholtis, J.D., Wullschleger, S.D., Tissue, D.T., Hanson, P.J., and Norby, R.J. 2002. Environmental and stomatal control of photosynthetic enhancement in the canopy of a sweetgum (*Liquidambar styraciflua* L.) plantation during 3 years of CO_2 enrichment. *Plant, Cell and Environment* **25**: 379–393.

Herrick, J.D. and Thomas, R.B. 1999. Effects of CO_2 enrichment on the photosynthetic light response of Sun and shade leaves of canopy sweetgum trees (*Liquidambar styraciflua*) in a forest ecosystem. *Tree Physiology* **19**: 779–786.

Herrick, J.D. and Thomas, R.B. 2001. No photosynthetic down regulation in sweetgum trees (*Liquidambar styraciflua* L.) after three years of CO_2 enrichment at the Duke Forest FACE experiment. *Plant, Cell and Environment* **24**: 53–64.

Herrick, J.D. and Thomas, R.B. 2003. Leaf senescence and late-season net photosynthesis of Sun and shade leaves of overstory sweetgum (*Liquidambar styraciflua*) grown in elevated and ambient carbon dioxide concentrations. *Tree Physiology* **23**: 109–118.

Norby, R.J., Hanson, P.J., O'Neill, E.G., Tschaplinski, T.J.,

Weltzin, J.F., Hansen, R.A., Cheng, W., Wullschleger, S.D., Gunderson, C.A., Edwards, N.T., and Johnson, D.W. 2002. Net primary productivity of a CO_2-enriched deciduous forest and the implications for carbon storage. *Ecological Applications* **12**: 1261–1266.

Norby, R.J., Sholtis, J.D., Gunderson, C.A., and Jawdy, S.S. 2003. Leaf dynamics of a deciduous forest canopy: no response to elevated CO_2. *Oecologia* 10.1007/s00442-003-1296-2.

Norby, R.J., Todd, D.E., Fults, J., and Johnson, D.W. 2001. Allometric determination of tree growth in a CO_2-enriched sweetgum stand. *New Phytologist* **150**: 477–487.

1.1.4 Lifetime Exposure to Elevated CO_2

- Trees and shrubs growing for multiple generations in CO_2-enriched air near CO_2-emitting springs and vents provide a unique opportunity for evaluating the effects of permanently elevated atmospheric CO_2 concentrations on their physiology and growth. Such effects indicate a doubling, tripling, or even greater enhancement of the atmosphere's CO_2 concentration will only further improve the productivity and water use efficiency of woody plants.

A number of woody plants, including shrubs and trees, have been growing for multiple generations in CO_2-enriched air near CO_2-emitting springs and vents at various locations around the world. These circumstances provide unique settings for evaluating the effects of permanently elevated atmospheric CO_2 concentrations on their physiology and productivity.

Taking advantage of one of these natural situations—CO_2-emitting springs near Pisa, Italy—Tognetti *et al.* (2000a) studied the water relations of three woody shrubs (*Erica arborea, Myrtus communis,* and *Juniperus communis*) growing at small distances from the springs, where atmospheric CO_2 concentrations of approximately 700 ppm prevailed, as well as at greater distances from the springs, where normal concentrations of 360 ppm prevailed at the time of their study. Two common responses were evident in all the shrubs: The CO_2-enriched air reduced leaf stomatal conductances and increased leaf water potentials (making them less negative and, therefore, less stressful). The group of five scientists conclude the CO_2-induced adjustments in the shrubs' internal water relations would likely allow them "to endure severe periodic drought."

In an analysis of other aspects of the same study, Tognetti *et al.* (2000b) report the plants growing in the CO₂-enriched air closer to the springs experienced increased leaf turgor pressure, particularly during the warmer summer months, which is also indicative of better plant water relations. And in another study at that location, Tognetti *et al.* (2002) found elevated CO₂ altered the elastic cell-wall properties of all three shrubs in such a way as to endow the shrubs with greater capacities for water uptake from the soil than by control plants growing in ambient air. In addition, the CO₂-enriched shrubs displayed greater relative water content than did ambiently grown plants as leaf water potentials declined with available soil moisture.

Bartak *et al.* (1999) studied various physiological processes of mature *Arbutus unedo* trees growing in the general vicinity of CO₂-emitting vents located in central Italy. At different distances from the vents, physiological measurements were made on trees exposed to average atmospheric CO₂ concentrations of approximately 355 ppm (ambient) and 465 ppm (CO₂-enriched) over 30 years. Bartak *et al.* determined this modest 30% increase in atmospheric CO₂ concentration boosted net photosynthetic rates in the perennial evergreen species by 110 to 140%, depending on light intensity. They also found the CO₂-enriched trees experienced no photosynthetic acclimation to the extra vent-derived CO₂ to which they were continuously exposed.

At the high end of the CO₂ concentration spectrum, Fernandez *et al.* (1998) studied a number of the effects of very high CO₂ levels produced by natural CO₂ springs on an indigenous tree during the rainy and dry seasons in Venezuela. They found the ultra-high CO₂ concentrations—some as much as 100 times the current global mean—were in no way detrimental to the trees. Instead, photosynthesis was stimulated by the high CO₂ in all seasons and in spite of the likely presence of toxic hydrocarbons and sulfur gases typically released to the air along with CO₂ in such situations. During the dry season, in fact, trees growing away from the springs at ambient CO₂ levels displayed net losses of carbon from their leaves, whereas trees growing near the springs at elevated CO₂ concentrations exhibited net carbon gains. In addition, the high CO₂ concentrations reduced leaf stomatal densities by about 70%, causing the water use efficiency of the trees to rise twofold and 19-fold, respectively, during the rainy and dry seasons, when measured at a CO₂ concentration of 1,000 ppm compared to an ambient concentration of 350 ppm, which represents less than a tripling of the air's CO₂ content.

Consequently, and because of the trees' long-term exposure to these high CO₂ concentrations under totally natural conditions, Fernandez *et al.* conclude their work provides "a positive answer to the question of whether increases in carbon assimilation will be sustained throughout the growing season and over multiple seasons" in a high-CO₂ world of the future.

Schwanz *et al.* (1998) measured various parameters in leaves of mature holm and white oak trees growing near natural CO₂ springs in central Italy for 30 to 50 years in order to determine the effects of elevated CO₂ on their antioxidative systems. They report elevated CO₂ decreased the activities of superoxide dismutase, which detoxifies highly reactive oxygen species, by approximately 30 and 47% in leaves of holm and white oak trees, respectively, when compared with activities measured in leaves of trees growing some distance away from the CO₂-emitting springs. Trees of both species growing near the springs also exhibited lower activities of catalase and other enzymes involved in the degradation of hydrogen peroxide (H_2O_2), which is produced during photorespiration. Thus, atmospheric CO₂ enrichment generally decreased the activities of protective enzymes that reduce oxidative stress brought about by unfavorable environmental factors such as drought, high light intensity, high air temperature, and aerial pollutants.

To determine whether the CO₂-induced decreases in the antioxidative machinery of the CO₂-enriched trees increased their susceptibility to oxidative damage, the authors evaluated the degree of lipid peroxidation within the leaves. They report trees growing near the CO₂-emitting springs did not display increased levels of lipid peroxidation in their leaves, and in some cases they exhibited significant reductions in their amounts of lipid peroxidation. Thus, as the CO₂ content of the air increases, most plants will likely experience an amelioration of unfavorable environmental growing conditions that often lead to oxidative stresses within leaves.

This study was the first to identify changes in leaf physiology that have persisted for decades in response to elevated CO₂. Specifically, it shows reductions in antioxidative enzymes, which have been observed in seedlings, can persist indefinitely as trees mature. Furthermore, because these enzymes remove reactive compounds that can cause cellular damage, their reduced activities at high CO₂ implies plants experience less intrinsic oxidative stress and produce fewer harmful oxidants as the amount of CO₂ in the air increases. Thus this beneficial consequence of atmospheric CO₂ enrichment should allow plants to increase their productivity, growth, and yield as the air's CO₂ content climbs.

Rapparini *et al.* (2004) measured isoprenoid emissions over two consecutive years from two species of mature oak trees—the deciduous downy oak (*Quercus pubescens* Willd.) and the evergreen holm oak (*Quercus ilex* L.)—growing close to a natural CO_2 spring in central Italy, where atmospheric CO_2 concentrations averaged about 1,000 ppm, and at a nearby control site where the air's CO_2 content was unaffected by the spring. Rapparini *et al.* report long-term exposure to high levels of atmospheric CO_2 did not significantly affect actual isoprenoid emissions from the trees—emissions experienced under prevailing environmental conditions at the time of measurement. However, they report, "when leaves of plants grown in the control site were exposed for a short period to an elevated CO_2 level by rapidly switching the CO_2 concentration in the gas-exchange cuvette, both isoprene and monoterpene basal emissions were clearly inhibited," where basal emissions are defined as those that occur at standard measuring conditions of 30°C air temperature and 1,000 μmol m^{-2} s^{-1} light intensity.

In commenting on these findings, the authors say "these results generally confirm the inhibitory effect of elevated CO_2 on isoprenoid emission." In addition, they note the absence of a CO_2 effect on actual emissions might indicate "an interaction with multiple stresses," such as the "recurrent droughts" that are typical of the Mediterranean climate in which the experiment was conducted, and these stresses are known to enhance isoprenoid emissions. Thus, evidence continues to mount for the beneficial phenomenon of CO_2-induced decreases in isoprene emissions.

Paoletti *et al.* (2007) measured rates of net photosynthesis during a two-week period in June 2002 "at the end of the spring rains," when midday air temperatures rose above 40°C, in upper, sunlit leaves of mature holm oak (*Quercus ilex* L.) trees growing close to (5 m) and further away from (130 m) a natural CO_2-emitting spring near Laiatico (Pisa, Italy), where the trees had experienced lifetime exposure to atmospheric CO_2 concentrations of approximately 1,500 and 400 ppm, respectively.

At the midpoint of the 14-day measurement period, the net photosynthetic rates of the leaves on the trees growing closest to the CO_2 spring were approximately 250% greater than those of the leaves on the trees growing 125 meters further away, where the air's CO_2 concentration was 1,100 ppm less. The four Italian researchers say "the considerable photosynthetic stimulation at the very high CO_2 site suggests no photosynthetic down-regulation over long-term CO_2 enrichment."

Polle *et al.* (2001) collected acorns from mature holm oak (*Quercus ilex* L.) trees growing naturally for their entire lifetimes at ambient and twice-ambient atmospheric CO_2 concentrations due to their different distances from a CO_2-emitting spring in central Italy. After germinating the acorns, the resulting seedlings were grown for eight months at both atmospheric CO_2 concentrations to determine whether atmospheric CO_2 enrichment of parent trees had any effect on seedling response to atmospheric CO_2 enrichment.

The results reveal elevated CO_2 increased whole-plant biomass by 158% and 246% in seedlings derived from acorns produced in ambient and twice-ambient atmospheric CO_2 concentrations, respectively, so the final biomass of the CO_2-enriched seedlings derived from acorns produced in the CO_2-enriched air was 25% greater than the CO_2-enriched seedlings derived from acorns produced in ambient air. In addition, gas exchange measurements indicate CO_2-enriched seedlings derived from acorns produced on CO_2-enriched trees exhibited less-pronounced photosynthetic acclimation to elevated CO_2 concentrations than CO_2-enriched seedlings derived from acorns produced on trees exposed to ambient air.

Onoda *et al.* (2009) state the ongoing rise in the air's CO_2 content "is likely to act as a selective agent" among Earth's plants, citing Woodward *et al.* (1991), Thomas and Jasienski (1996), Ward *et al.* (2000), Kohut (2003), Ward and Kelly (2004), and Lau *et al.* (2007). They report, "evolutionary responses have been found in selection experiments with short-lived organisms, such as *Arabidopsis thaliana* (e.g. development rate and biomass production; Ward *et al.*, 2000) and *Chlamydomonas reinhardtii* (e.g. photosynthesis and cell size; Collins and Bell, 2004)." They hasten to add, however, "the evolutionary response of wild plants (especially long-lived plants) is, in general, difficult to evaluate using growth experiments," because of the long time spans needed to evaluate the phenomenon properly.

They avoid this problem in their study by utilizing plants growing around natural CO_2 springs where they "have been exposed to a CO_2-enriched atmosphere over many generations," which provides what they call "a unique opportunity to explore the micro-evolutionary response of wild plants to elevated CO_2."

The three researchers write, "the adaptation of leaf photosynthesis to elevated CO_2 was tested by a common garden experiment with herbaceous species originating from three different natural CO_2 springs in Japan: Nibu, Ryuzin-numa and Yuno-kawa," where "several genotypes were collected from each high-CO$_2$ area (spring population) and nearby control areas (control population), and each genotype was propagated or divided into two ramets, and grown in pots at 370 and 700 ppm CO$_2$." The researchers assessed the plants' photosynthetic nitrogen use efficiency (PNUE), water use efficiency (WUE), and degree of carbohydrate accumulation in the plants' leaves, which if too large can lead to the down-regulation of photosynthesis.

Onoda *et al.* report "high CO$_2$ concentration directly and greatly increased PNUE and WUE, suggesting that plants will show higher growth rates at a given resource availability." They also found "a significant reduction in stomatal conductance, which contributed to higher WUE, and a trend of reduced down-regulation of photosynthesis with a lower starch accumulation," and they note these results suggest "there is substantial room for plant evolution in high-CO$_2$ environments." Further to this point, they say a still-to-be-published molecular study "also found relatively large genetic differentiation across the CO$_2$ gradient in these plants." Consequently, as a result of their own work and "the increasing number of studies on CO$_2$ springs (e.g. Fordham *et al.*, 1997; Polle *et al.*, 2001; Schulte *et al.* 2002) and selection experiments (Ward *et al.*, 2000; Collins and Bell, 2004)," Onoda *et al.* conclude, "high CO$_2$ will act as a selection agent" as the air's CO$_2$ content rises. This phenomenon should enable plants to fare even better in the CO$_2$-enriched air of the future than they do currently.

The several observations above suggest a doubling, tripling, or even greater enhancement of the atmosphere's CO$_2$ concentration will only further improve the productivity and water use efficiencies of woody plants.

References

Bartak, M., Raschi, A., and Tognetti, R. 1999. Photosynthetic characteristics of Sun and shade leaves in the canopy of *Arbutus unedo* L. trees exposed to *in situ* long-term elevated CO$_2$. *Photosynthetica* **37**: 1–16.

Collins, S. and Bell, G. 2004. Phenotypic consequences of 1000 generations of selection at elevated CO$_2$ in a green alga. *Nature* **431**: 566–569.

Fernandez, M.D., Pieters, A., Donoso, C., Tezara, W., Azuke, M., Herrera, C., Rengifo, E., and Herrera, A. 1998. Effects of a natural source of very high CO$_2$ concentration on the leaf gas exchange, xylem water potential and stomatal characteristics of plants of *Spatiphylum*

cannifolium* and *Bauhinia multinervia*. *New Phytologist* **138**: 689–697.

Fordham, M., Barnes, J.D., Bettarini, I., Polle, A., Slee, N., Raines, C., Miglietta, F., and Raschi, A. 1997. The impact of elevated CO$_2$ on growth and photosynthesis in *Agrostis canina* L ssp. *monteluccii* adapted to contrasting atmospheric CO$_2$ concentrations. *Oecologia* **110**: 169–178.

Kohut, R. 2003. The long-term effects of carbon dioxide on natural systems: issues and research needs. *Environment International* **29**: 171–180.

Lau, J.A., Shaw, R.G., Reich, P.B., Shaw, F.H., and Tiffin, P. 2007. Strong ecological but weak evolutionary effects of elevated CO$_2$ on a recombinant inbred population of *Arabidopsis thaliana*. *New Phytologist* **175**: 351–362.

Onoda, Y., Hirose, T., and Hikosaka, K. 2009. Does leaf photosynthesis adapt to CO$_2$-enriched environments? An experiment on plants originating from three natural CO$_2$ springs. *New Phytologist* **182**: 698–709.

Paoletti, E., Seufert, G., Della Rocca, G., and Thomsen, H. 2007. Photosynthetic responses to elevated CO$_2$ and O$_3$ in *Quercus ilex* leaves at a natural CO$_2$ spring. *Environmental Pollution* **147**: 516–524.

Polle, A., McKee, I., and Blaschke, L. 2001. Altered physiological and growth responses to elevated [CO$_2$] in offspring from holm oak (*Quercus ilex* L.) mother trees with lifetime exposure to naturally elevated [CO$_2$]. *Plant, Cell & Environment* **24**: 1075–1083.

Rapparini, F., Baraldi, R., Miglietta, F., and Loreto, F. 2004. Isoprenoid emission in trees of *Quercus pubescens* and *Quercus ilex* with lifetime exposure to naturally high CO$_2$ environment. *Plant, Cell and Environment* **27**: 381–391.

Schulte, M., Von Ballmoos, P., Rennenberg, H., and Herschbach, C. 2002. Life-long growth of *Quercus ilex* L. at natural CO$_2$ springs acclimates sulphur, nitrogen and carbohydrate metabolism of the progeny to elevated pCO$_2$. *Plant, Cell & Environment* **25**: 1715–1727.

Schwanz, P. and Polle, A. 1998. Antioxidative systems, pigment and protein contents in leaves of adult mediterranean oak species (*Quercus pubescens* and *Q. ilex*) with lifetime exposure to elevated CO$_2$. *New Phytologist* **140**: 411–423.

Thomas, S.C. and Jasienski, M. 1996. Genetic variability and the nature of microevolutionary response to elevated CO$_2$. In: Körner, C. and Bazzaz, F.A. (Eds.) *Carbon Dioxide, Populations and Communities*. Academic Press, Inc., San Diego, California, USA, pp. 51–81.

Tognetti, R., Minnocci, A., Penuelas, J., Rashi, A., and Jones, M.B. 2000a. Comparative field water relations of three Mediterranean shrub species co-occurring at a natural CO$_2$ vent. *Journal of Experimental Botany* **51**: 1135–1146.

Tognetti, R., Rashi, A., and Jones, M.B. 2000b. Seasonal patterns of tissue water relations in three Mediterranean shrubs co-occurring at a natural CO_2 spring. *Plant, Cell and Environment* **23**: 1341–1351.

Tognetti, R., Raschi, A., and Jones M.B. 2002. Seasonal changes in tissue elasticity and water transport efficiency in three co-occurring Mediterranean shrubs under natural long-term CO_2 enrichment. *Functional Plant Biology* **29**: 1097–1106.

Ward, J.K., Antonovics, J., Thomas, R.B., and Strain, B.R. 2000. Is atmospheric CO_2 a selective agent on model C_3 annuals? *Oecologia* **123**: 330–341.

Ward, J.K. and Kelly, J.K. 2004. Scaling up evolutionary responses to elevated CO_2: lessons from *Arabidopsis*. *Ecology Letters* **7**: 427–440.

Woodward, F.I., Thompson, G.B., and McKee, I.F. 1991. The effects of elevated concentrations of carbon dioxide on individual plants, populations, communities and eco-systems. *Annals of Botany* **67**: 23–38.

1.1.5 Growth Response to Very High CO_2 Concentrations

- Several studies indicate plants are not harmed by super-elevated atmospheric CO_2 concentrations an order of magnitude or more greater than the globe's current mean. Positive growth responses are reported in all instances. Thus it is likely most plants will display enhanced rates of photosynthesis and biomass production as the atmosphere's CO_2 concentration rises.

Terrestrial plants grown in elevated atmospheric CO_2 typically exhibit increased rates of photosynthesis and biomass production. Most of the studies establishing this fact have historically utilized CO_2 concentration increases on the order of 300 to 400 ppm, which represents an approximate doubling of the atmosphere's current CO_2 concentration. This section examines the growth response of plants when the air's CO_2 content is *super*-enriched, to a concentration an order of magnitude or more larger.

Louche-Tessandier *et al.* (1999) grew potato plantlets inoculated with an arbuscular mycorrhizal fungus at ambient and super-elevated (10,000 ppm) CO_2 for one month at a number of different light intensities. They report the high CO_2 treatment stimulated root colonization by the fungus, but biomass production in the CO_2-enriched inoculated plantlets increased significantly only when they were grown at high light intensity.

Also studying potatoes, Teixeira da Silva *et al.* (2005) grew single-node explants of sweet potato (*Ipomoea batatas* cv. Naruto Kintok) for five weeks *in vitro* within special culture vessels supplied with a 3% sugar-containing agar, during which time the vessels were maintained at atmospheric CO_2 concentrations of either 400 ppm (ambient) or 1,000, 2,000, or 3,000 ppm The plants were then transplanted into soil and grown *ex vitro* for three additional weeks. Relative to the plants exposed to ambient air, those exposed to air of 1,000, 2,000, and 3,000 ppm CO_2 produced 20%, 20%, and 65% more total biomass, respectively, after having been grown for five weeks *in vitro*, and they produced 20%, 32%, and 82% more biomass, respectively, after having been grown for three additional weeks *ex vitro*. Thus, for sweet potato plants, a several-fold increase in the atmosphere's CO_2 concentration appears to pose no problem to the plants' growth and development.

Dempster *et al.* (2009) grew a mixture of cowpeas, pinto beans, and wheat for three months, measuring the net fixation rate of carbon by the entire three-crop system during the greater portion of this "growing season." Relative to a CO_2 concentration of 385 ppm, net photosynthesis at 1,000 ppm, 2,000 ppm, and 2,800 ppm were 150%, 275%, and 355% greater, respectively. The authors note the "high productivity from these crops and the increase of fixation rates with elevated CO_2 concentration supports the concept that enhanced CO_2 can be a useful strategy for remote life support systems," presumably on long manned space flights or outposts on other planets or moons.

Schubert and Jahren (2011) grew radishes (*Raphanus sativus*) from seed to maturity (four months) in standard potting soil within eight growth chambers maintained at optimum temperature, humidity, and soil water and fertility conditions in air of eight different CO_2 concentrations (348, 388, 413, 426, 760, 1,090, 1,425, and 1,791 ppm). They then harvested the plants and determined their above- and below-ground biomass, both of which they found to be well described by a two-parameter rectangular hyperbola, "employing the method used by Hunt *et al.* (1991, 1993) for assessing the trajectory of the biomass response for 36 herbaceous species grown under CO_2 levels ranging from 365 to 812 ppm."

Going from the lowest to the highest CO_2 concentration employed in their study, the two U.S. researchers state above-ground biomass rose by a modest 58%, but below-ground biomass rose by a phenomenal 279%, the trajectory of which "greatly exceeded a trajectory based on extrapolation of previous experiments for plants grown at CO_2 < 800 ppm." Commenting on these findings, Schubert and Jahren state, "if the below-ground biomass enhancement that we have quantified for *R. sativus* represents a generalized root-crop response that can be extrapolated to agricultural systems, below-ground fertilization under very high CO_2 levels could dramatically augment crop production in some of the poorest nations of the world." They continue, "needless to say, a doubling or tripling of below-ground crop tissue due to CO_2 fertilization would be welcome on both a nutritional and economic basis."

Gouk *et al.* (1999) grew orchid plantlets at ambient and super-elevated (10,000 ppm) CO_2 for three months. In their study, the extra CO_2 more than doubled plant dry weight, stimulated the induction of new roots, increased the total chlorophyll contents of both roots and leaves, and boosted tissue starch contents nearly 20-fold, all without any disruption of or damage to chloroplasts.

Also working with orchids were Norikane *et al.* (2010), who grew *Cymbidium* (Music Hour 'Maria') shoots in air augmented with either 0, 3,000, or 10,000 ppm CO_2 under photosynthetic photon flux densities of either 45 or 75 µmol m^{-1} s^{-1} provided by cold cathode fluorescent lamps for 90 days. The plants then were transferred to *ex vitro* culture for an additional 30 days. Relative to plants grown *in vitro* in ambient air, the percentage increases in shoot and root dry weight due to enriching the air in which the plants grew by 3,000 ppm CO_2 were, respectively, 216% and 1,956% under the low light regime and 249% and 1,591% under the high light regime. Corresponding increases for the plants grown in air enriched with an extra 10,000 ppm CO_2 were 244% and 2,578% under the low light regime and 310% and 1,879% under the high light regime.

In the *ex vitro* experiment, percentage increases in shoot and root dry weight due to enriching the air in which the plants grew by 3,000 ppm CO_2 were, respectively, 223% and 436% under the low light regime and 279% and 469% under the high light regime. Corresponding increases for the plants grown in air enriched with an extra 10,000 ppm CO_2 were 271% and 537% under the low light regime and 332% and 631% under the high light regime. The four Japanese researchers conclude "super-elevated CO_2 enrichment of in vitro-cultured *Cymbidium* could positively affect the efficiency and quality of commercial production of clonal orchid plantlets."

Hew *et al.* (1995) grew orchids at ambient and 10,000 ppm CO_2 and found the elevated CO_2 boosted dry weights by 28 to 37%. Likewise, Tisserat *et al.*

(2002) fumigated mint and thyme with air containing 10,000 ppm CO_2 and determined the super-CO_2-enrichment increased the fresh weights of the two species by 3.1- and 5.8-fold, respectively.

In a study of an epiphytic fern, Ong *et al.* (1998) grew the seedless vascular species *Pyrrosia piloselloides* (which is less adapted to terrestrial habitats than its seed-producing relatives) from spores in small containers maintained at atmospheric CO_2 concentrations of 350, 515, and 3,360 ppm to study the effects of elevated CO_2 on the fern's photosynthesis and growth. Forty days after germination, light-saturated rates of net photosynthesis were 22% and 114% greater at 515 and 3,360 ppm, respectively, than they were at 350 ppm. Over time, the elevated CO_2 induced photosynthetic acclimation in the plants, but in a concentration-dependent manner. After 100 days of exposure to elevated CO_2, for example, the photosynthetic stimulation of plants grown at 515 ppm CO_2 had dropped to 10%, representing a 50% decline from their original stimulation, but the photosynthetic adjustment was much less at the super-enriched CO_2 concentration of 3,360 ppm—plants in this treatment reduced their original photosynthetic enhancement by only 10%.

As part of their acclimation response to elevated CO_2, gametophytes exposed to 515 and 3,360 ppm CO_2 reallocated limiting resources away from their photosynthetic apparatus, as indicated by respective 11 and 28% reductions in their tissue chlorophyll contents. Despite these reductions, resulting from an optimization of resources at elevated CO_2 concentrations, total gametophytic dry mass at 515 and 3,360 ppm was still 43 and 214% greater, respectively, than at ambient CO_2, at physiological maturity (100 and 80 days for plants grown at 515 and 3,360 ppm CO_2, respectively).

These findings suggest Earth's rising atmospheric CO_2 content likely will promote the photosynthesis and growth of ferns, which are considered more primitive forms of terrestrial plant life than the planet's more-numerous seed-bearing plants. Thus, ferns should continue to maintain their presence in many ecosystems across the globe. Ong *et al.* conclude, the "sum responses of *Pyrrosia piloselloides* gametophytes to elevated CO_2 concentration suggest greater success against competitors in the future environment, enabling this fern to continue to establish itself in a future world with high atmospheric CO_2."

Teixeira Da Silva *et al.* (2006) grew ornamental *Spathiphyllum* cv. Merry plantlets for five weeks in novel culture vessels on a sugar-free liquid medium at low light intensity in controlled-environment chambers maintained at atmospheric CO_2 concentrations of 375, 1,000, 2,000, or 3,000 ppm. Relative to the growth experienced by the plantlets exposed to ambient air of 375 ppm CO_2, the plantlets exposed to 1,000, 2,000, and 3,000 ppm CO_2 produced 39%, 81%, and 129% more shoot dry weight, respectively, plus 316%, 639%, and 813% more root dry weight, respectively, for corresponding total CO_2-induced biomass enhancements of 61%, 127%, and 185%.

Ali *et al.* (2005) worked with the ginseng plant (*Panax ginseng*), which is widely cultivated in China, South Korea, and Japan, the roots of which have been used for medicinal purposes since Greek and Roman times and are well known for their anti-inflammatory, diuretic, and sedative properties and are also acknowledged to be effective healing agents (Gillis, 1997; Ali *et al.*, 2005). Ginseng roots normally require four to six years to accumulate the amounts of the various phenolic compounds needed to produce their health-promoting effects. In an important step toward developing an efficient culture system for the commercial production of ginseng roots, Ali *et al.* investigated the effects of growing them in suspension culture in bioreactors maintained in equilibrium with air enriched to CO_2 concentrations of 10,000 ppm, 25,000 ppm, and 50,000 ppm for periods of up to 45 days.

Of most immediate concern in such an experiment would be the effects of the ultra-high CO_2 concentrations on root growth. Would they be toxic and lead to biomass reductions or even root death? The answer was a resounding no. After 45 days of growth at 10,000 ppm CO_2, for example, root dry weight was increased by 37% relative to the dry weight of roots produced in bioreactors in equilibrium with normal ambient air. Root dry mass was increased by 27% after 45 days at 25,000 ppm CO_2, and by 9% after 45 days at 50,000 ppm CO_2. Thus, although the optimum CO_2 concentration for ginseng root growth likely resided at some value lower than 10,000 ppm in this study, the concentration at which root growth rate was reduced below that characteristic of ambient air was somewhere significantly above 50,000 ppm, for even at that extremely high CO_2 concentration, ginseng root growth was greater than in ambient air.

Almost everything else measured by Ali *et al.* was even more dramatically enhanced by the ultra-high CO_2 concentrations employed in their experiment. After 45 days of treatment, total root phenolic concentrations were 58% higher at 10,000 ppm CO_2 than at ambient CO_2, 153% higher at 25,000 ppm CO_2, and 105% higher at 50,000 ppm CO_2, as best as can be determined from the bar graphs of their results. Likewise, total root flavonoid concentrations were enhanced by 228%, 383%, and 232%, respectively, at the same ultra-high CO_2 concentrations. Total protein contents rose by 14%, 22%, and 30%; non-protein thiol contents by 12%, 43%, and 62%; and cysteine contents by 27%, 65%, and 100% under the identical respective set of conditions. There were equally large CO_2-induced increases in the activities of a large number of phenol biosynthetic enzymes.

Discussing the implications of their results, Ali *et al.* write, "the consumption of foodstuffs containing antioxidant phytonutrients such as flavonoids, polyphenolics, ascorbate, cysteine and non-protein thiol is advantageous for human health," citing Cervato *et al.* (2000) and Noctor and Foyer (1998). They thus conclude their technique for the culture of ginseng roots in CO_2-enriched bioreactors could be used for the large-scale production of an important health-promoting product that could be provided to the public in much greater quantities than is currently possible.

Levine *et al.* (2008) grew well-watered and well-fertilized wheat plants (*Triticum aestivum*, cv Yocoro roho) from seed in custom-designed root modules—"consisting of a porous tube embedded in Turface (1–2 mm particle size) substrate containing 5 g Osmocote time release fertilizer per liter"— housed in Plexiglas chambers maintained at atmospheric CO_2 concentrations of 400, 1,500, or 10,000 ppm for periods of 14, 21, and 28 days. They measured a number of plant metabolic properties, among which were the leaf concentrations of several flavonoids capable of scavenging reactive oxygen species (ROS).

They found "elevated CO_2 promoted the accumulation of secondary metabolites (flavonoids) progressively to a greater extent as plants became mature." As best as can be determined from the bar graphs of their results, for example, the percentage increase in total wheat leaf flavonoid concentration in going from an atmospheric CO_2 concentration of 400 to 1,500 ppm was 22%, 38%, and 27% (the one exception to this general rule) at 14, 21, and 28 days after planting, respectively. In going from a CO_2 concentration of 400 to 10,000 ppm, the percentage increase in total flavonoid concentration was 38%, 56%, and 86%, respectively, at 14, 21, and 28 days after planting. In addition, they report "both elevated CO_2 levels resulted in an overall 25% increase in biomass over the control plants."

With respect to the cultivation of trees, Tisserat (2005) notes "vitrified shoots are characterized as being small, succulent (i.e., 'glassy' or 'wet' in appearance) and immature, but [are] capable of readily proliferating additional axillary shoots." However, he also notes vitrified shoots of the type that are cultured *in vitro* "do not transfer readily into soil well." Consequently, because there is a need for literally millions of sweetgum seedlings to be planted annually (Lin *et al.*, 1995), it would be advantageous if a technique could be developed to increase the success of transferring tissue-culture-produced vitrified shoots to *ex vitro* growth in soil.

In searching for a technique to accomplish this feat, Tisserat first produced sweetgum shoots in an automated plant culture system in which ten times more shoots developed than in prior plant culture systems, and where vitrification was observed in fully 80% of the shoots. He then studied the effects of ultra-high atmospheric CO$_2$ concentrations on the vitrified shoots when they were transferred to soil and grown in air enriched with CO$_2$ to concentrations as high as 30,000 ppm. After four weeks of growth at atmospheric CO$_2$ concentrations of 350, 1,500, 3,000, 10,000, and 30,000 ppm, survival percentages of 1cm-long explants were found to be 48.6, 56.5, 65.7, 93.1, and 67.1%, respectively, and corresponding survival percentages of 2cm-long explants were 61.2, 64.1, 69.2, 93.9, and 64.3%. For these same CO$_2$ concentrations, the numbers of leaves produced per shoot were 4.17, 5.38, 5.85, 6.14, and 4.83, and the numbers of roots produced per shoot were 5.35, 8.58, 9.19, 9.66, and 9.82. Also, leaf and shoot lengths were similarly enhanced by the suite of increased CO$_2$ concentrations.

Tisserat concludes the procedures he developed should "minimize the time and labor involved in sweetgum micropropagation" and "can be readily adapted to the micropropagation of other woody and non-woody plants." Tisserat's results suggest anthropogenic emissions will never raise the air's CO$_2$ concentration so high as to retard the growth and development of sweetgum trees and, by implication, many (if not most) other plants. Even in those cases where plant growth responses did decline between 10,000 and 30,000 ppm in Tisserat's study, for example, the responses at 30,000 ppm CO$_2$ were still greater than those observed at 350 ppm.

Tisserat and Vaughn (2003) grew four-week-old loblolly pine seedlings for 30 days at the same suite of atmospheric CO$_2$ concentrations within 17.6-liter transparent containers, where the seedlings were watered three times per week but not fertilized. Three repetitions of this procedure revealed seedling fresh weight, needle number, root number, and shoot length increased 341%, 200%, 74%, and 75%, respectively, after 30 days of growth at 10,000 ppm CO$_2$. There were no further increases—or decreases—when going to an atmospheric CO$_2$ concentration of 30,000 ppm. Also, associated with increased growth and morphogenesis, the researchers found a corresponding increase in secondary metabolites (more than 99% of which were a- and ß-pinene) in the ultra-high CO$_2$ environments, and they note "high a- and ß-pinene levels may confer an additional positive survival advantage" on the seedlings, because these substances "have fungicidal and insecticidal activity (Harbone, 1982; Klepzig *et al.*, 1995)."

In a field study, Fernandez *et al.* (1998) investigated the effects of even higher CO$_2$ concentrations (some as great as 35,000 ppm) on an herb and a tree growing in the vicinity of natural CO$_2$ springs in Venezuela. These high CO$_2$ concentrations stimulated the photosynthetic rates of both plants in all seasons of the year. In the dry season, this effect was particularly important: Plants exposed to elevated CO$_2$ continued to maintain positive net photosynthetic rates, whereas those exposed to ambient air a few tens of meters away exhibited negative rates, which if prolonged, would be expected to lead to their eventual demise. The researchers thus note their work provides "a positive answer to the question of whether increases in carbon assimilation will be sustained throughout the growing season and over multiple seasons." It also demonstrates very high atmospheric CO$_2$ concentrations—some as much as two orders of magnitude greater than the current global mean—are not detrimental to but in fact helped the plants they investigated.

Garcia *et al.* (1994) grew two Eldarica pine (*Pinus eldarica* L.) seedlings out-of-doors in a field of Avondale loam at Phoenix, Arizona (USA) within transparent open-top enclosures. They maintained one for 15 months at a mean atmospheric CO$_2$ concentration of 402 ppm and one at 788 ppm. They then measured short-term whole-tree net photosynthetic rates (one-hour averages) at a number of different CO$_2$ concentrations (changed at 1.5-hour intervals) ranging from ambient (360 ppm) to 3,000 ppm.

Garcia *et al.* report "the two trees responded identically to short-term atmospheric CO$_2$ enrichment to about a tripling of the ambient CO$_2$ concentration." As the CO$_2$ content of the air was increased further, they write, "the net CO$_2$ assimilation responses of the two trees diverged: the photosynthetic response curve of the low-CO$_2$-grown tree exhibited the classical form of a rate-limiting rectangular hyperbola, while that of the high-CO$_2$-grown tree maintained its linearity to the highest CO$_2$ concentration investigated." At this latter CO$_2$ concentration (3,000 ppm), the photosynthetic rate of the low-CO$_2$-grown tree had long since plateaued at a value approximately five times its value at 360 ppm, whereas the photosynthetic rate of the high-CO$_2$-grown tree was still rising linearly at a value approximately ten times greater than what it had exhibited at 360 ppm. The three researchers conclude, "atmospheric CO$_2$ enrichment produces a type of up-regulation of carbon assimilation in Eldarica pine trees, as long-term exposure to elevated CO$_2$ enabled the high-CO$_2$-grown tree to continue to respond to further increases in the CO$_2$ content of the air while the photosynthetic rate of the tree grown in ambient air reached an asymptotic limit." This observation suggests plants may continuously adapt to—and thereby continuously profit from—the ongoing increase of the air's CO$_2$ content.

Tisserat *et al.* (2008) grew three types of well-watered two-week-old *Cuphea viscosissima* x *C. lanceolata* L. (McCoy GT #1, Morton GT #1, and Morris heavy) seedlings within 162-L transparent containers maintained for 30 days at atmospheric CO$_2$ concentrations of either 350, 1,500, 3,000, 10,000, or 30,000 ppm CO$_2$, after which they were harvested and assessed for a number of measures of growth. The authors report the "fresh weight of seedlings, leaves per seedling, roots per seedling, and seedling length in cuphea Morris heavy seedlings increased 607%, 184%, 784%, and 175%, respectively, after 30-day exposure to 10,000 ppm CO$_2$ over those obtained from seedlings grown on ambient [350 ppm] CO$_2$ levels," with a leveling off of growth stimulation between 10,000 and 30,000 ppm CO$_2$. They further note the other two cuphea varieties "showed similar response trends."

The three USDA Agricultural Research Service scientists say their data suggest "ultrahigh CO$_2$ treatments may be effective for enhancing cuphea growth and benefit breeding treatments." In addition, their data indicate large increases in the air's CO$_2$ concentration can lead to huge increases in plant growth and development.

The results of the several studies reviewed above indicate plants are not harmed by super-elevated atmospheric CO$_2$ concentrations an order of magnitude or more greater than the globe's current mean. The studies all report positive growth responses, with some being particularly large, even huge. Most plants should display enhanced rates of photosynthesis and biomass production as the atmosphere's CO$_2$ concentration rises.

References

Ali, M.B., Hahn, E.J., and Paek, K.-Y. 2005. CO$_2$-induced total phenolics in suspension cultures of *Panax ginseng* C.A. Mayer roots: role of antioxidants and enzymes. *Plant Physiology and Biochemistry* **43**: 449–457.

Cervato, G., Carabelli, M., Gervasio, S., Cittera, A., Cazzola, R., and Cestaro, B. 2000. Antioxidant properties of oregano (*Origanum vulgare*) leaf extracts. *Journal of Food Biochemistry* **24**: 453–465.

Dempster, W.F., Nelson, M., Silverstone, S., and Allen, J.P. 2009. Carbon dioxide dynamics of combined crops of wheat, cowpea, pinto beans in the Laboratory Biosphere closed ecological system. *Advances in Space Research* **43**: 1229–1235.

Fernandez, M.D., Pieters, A., Donoso, C., Tezara, W., Azuke, M., Herrera, C., Rengifo, E., and Herrera, A. 1998. Effects of a natural source of very high CO$_2$ concentration on the leaf gas exchange, xylem water potential and stomatal characteristics of plants of *Spatiphylum cannifolium* and *Bauhinia multinervia*. *New Phytologist* **138**: 689–697.

Garcia, R.L., Idso, S.B., and Kimball, B.A. 1994. Net photosynthesis as a function of carbon dioxide concentration in pine trees grown at ambient and elevated CO$_2$. *Environmental and Experimental Botany* **34**: 337–341.

Gillis, C.N. 1997. *Panax ginseng* pharmacology: a nitric oxide link? *Biochemical Pharmacology* **54**: 1–8.

Gouk, S.S., He, J., and Hew, C.S. 1999. Changes in photosynthetic capability and carbohydrate production in an epiphytic CAM orchid plantlet exposed to super-elevated CO$_2$. *Environmental and Experimental Botany* **41**: 219–230.

Harbone, J.B. 1982. *Introduction to Ecological Biochemistry*. Academic Press, New York, NY, USA.

Hew, C.S., Hin, S.E., Yong, J.W.H., Gouk, S.S., and Tanaka, M. 1995. *In vitro* CO$_2$ enrichment of CAM orchid plantlets. *Journal of Horticultural Science* **70**: 721–736.

Hunt, R., Hand, D.W., Hannah, M.A., and Neal, A.M. 1991. Response to CO$_2$ enrichment in 27 herbaceous species. *Functional Ecology* **5**: 410–421.

Hunt, R., Hand, D.W., Hannah, M.A., and Neal, A.M. 1993. Further responses to CO$_2$ enrichment in British herbaceous species. *Functional Ecology* **7**: 661–668.

Klepzig, K.D., Kruger, E.L., Smalley, E.B., and Raffa, K.F. 1995. Effects of biotic and abiotic stress on induced accumulation of terpenes and phenolics in red pines inoculated with bark beetle-vectored fungus. *Journal of Chemical Ecology* **21**: 601–625.

Kubler, J.E., Johnston, A.M., and Raven, J.A. 1999. The effects of reduced and elevated CO$_2$ and O$_2$ on the seaweed *Lomentaria articulata. Plant, Cell and Environment* **22**: 1303–1310.

Levine, L.H., Kasahara, H., Kopka, J., Erban, A., Fehrl, I., Kaplan, F., Zhao, W., Littell, R.C., Guy, C., Wheeler, R., Sager, J., Mills, A., and Levine, H.G. 2008. Physiologic and metabolic responses of wheat seedlings to elevated and super-elevated carbon dioxide. *Advances in Space Research* **42**: 1917–1928.

Lin, X., Bergmann, B.A., and Stomp, A.-M. 1995. Effect of medium physical support, shoot length and genotype on *in vitro* rooting and plantlet morphology of sweetgum. *Journal of Environmental Horticulture* **13**: 117–121.

Louche-Tessandier, D., Samson, G., Hernandez-Sebastia, C., Chagvardieff, P., and Desjardins, Y. 1999. Importance of light and CO$_2$ on the effects of endomycorrhizal colonization on growth and photosynthesis of potato plantlets (*Solanum tuberosum*) in an *in vitro* tripartite system. *New Phytologist* **142**: 539–550.

Noctor, G. and Foyer, C.H. 1998. Ascorbate and glutathione: keeping active oxygen under control. *Annual Review of Plant Physiology and Plant Molecular Biology* **49**: 249–279.

Norikane, A., Takamura, T., Morokuma, M., and Tanaka, M. 2010. In vitro growth and single-leaf photosynthetic response of *Cymbidium* plantlets to super-elevated CO$_2$ under cold cathode fluorescent lamps. *Plant Cell Reports* **29**: 273–282.

Ong, B.-L., Koh, C.K-K., and Wee, Y.-C. 1998. Effects of CO$_2$ on growth and photosynthesis of *Pyrrosia piloselloides* (L.) Price gametophytes. *Photosynthetica* **35**: 21–27.

Schubert, B.A. and Jahren, A.H. 2011. Fertilization trajectory of the root crop *Raphanus sativus* across atmospheric pCO$_2$ estimates of the next 300 years. *Agriculture, Ecosystems and Environment* **140**: 174–181.

Teixeira da Silva, J.A., Giang, D.T.T., and Tanaka, M. 2005. Micropropagation of sweet potato (*Ipomoea batatas*) in a novel CO$_2$-enriched vessel. *Journal of Plant Biotechnology* **7**: 67–74.

Teixeira Da Silva, J.A., Giang, D.T.T., and Tanaka, M. 2006. Photoautotrophic micropropagation of *Spathiphyllum. Photosynthetica* **44**: 53–61.

Tisserat, B. 2005. Establishing tissue-cultured sweetgum plants in soil. *HortTechnology* **15**: 308–312.

Tisserat, B. and Vaughn, S.F. 2003. Ultra-high CO$_2$ levels enhance loblolly pine seedling growth, morphogenesis, and secondary metabolism. *HortScience* **38**: 1083–1085.

Tisserat, B., Vaughn, S.F., and Berhow, M.A. 2008. Ultrahigh CO$_2$ levels enhance cuphea growth and morphogenesis. *Industrial Crops and Products* **27**: 133–135.

Tisserat, B., Vaughn, S.F., and Silman, R. 2002. Influence of modified oxygen and carbon dioxide atmospheres on mint and thyme plant growth, morphogenesis and secondary metabolism *in vitro. Plant Cell Reports* **20**: 912–916.

1.2 Ecosystem Responses to CO$_2$ Enrichment

1.2.1 Forests

Forests contain perennial trees that remove CO$_2$ from the atmosphere during the process of photosynthesis and store its carbon within their woody tissues for decades to periods of sometimes more than a thousand years. It is important to understand how increases in the air's CO$_2$ content affect forest productivity and carbon sequestration, which has a great impact on the rate of rise of the air's CO$_2$ concentration. The subsections below review scientific publications pertaining to these subjects.

1.2.1.1 Tropical

- Where tropical forests have not been decimated by the targeted and direct destructive actions of human society, such as the felling and burning of trees, forest productivity has been growing ever-greater with the passing of time, rising with the increasing CO$_2$ content of the air. This has occurred despite all concomitant changes in atmospheric, soil, and water chemistry, including twentieth century global warming, which IPCC claims to have been unprecedented over the past one to two millennia.

Perhaps the most striking evidence for the significant growth enhancement of Earth's forests being driven by the historical increase in the air's CO$_2$ concentration was provided by Phillips and Gentry (1994). Noting turnover rates of mature tropical forests correlate well with measures of net productivity (Weaver and Murphy, 1990), the two scientists assessed the turnover rates of 40 tropical forests around the world in order to test the hypothesis that global forest productivity was increasing, *in situ*. They found the turnover rates of these highly productive forests had indeed been rising since at least 1960, with an apparent pan-tropical acceleration since 1980. In discussing what might have been causing this phenomenon, they state, "the accelerating increase in turnover coincides with an accelerating buildup of CO_2." As Pimm and Sugden (1994) state in a companion article, it was "the consistency and simultaneity of the changes on several continents that [led] Phillips and Gentry to their conclusion that enhanced productivity induced by increased CO_2 is the most plausible candidate for the cause of the increased turnover."

Four years later, Phillips *et al.* (1998) reported another impressive finding. Working with data on tree basal area (a surrogate for tropical forest biomass) for the period 1958–1996, which they obtained from several hundred plots of mature tropical trees around the world, they found the average forest biomass for the tropics as a whole had increased substantially. They calculate the increase amounted to approximately 40% of the missing terrestrial carbon sink of the entire globe. Hence, they suggest, "intact forests may be helping to buffer the rate of increase in atmospheric CO_2, thereby reducing the impacts of global climate change," as Idso (1991a,b) had earlier suggested. Phillips *et al.* also identified the aerial fertilization effect of the increasing CO_2 concentration of the atmosphere as one of the primary factors responsible for this phenomenon. Other contemporary studies (Grace *et al.*, 1995; Malhi *et al.*, 1998) support their findings, verifying the fact neotropical forests were indeed accumulating ever-more carbon at ever-increasing rates. Phillips *et al.* (2002) subsequently suggested this phenomenon was occurring "possibly in response to the increasing atmospheric concentrations of carbon dioxide (Prentice *et al.*, 2001; Malhi and Grace, 2000)."

Lin *et al.* (1998) measured the ecosystem carbon exchange rate of a 1,700-m^3 synthetic rainforest mesocosm alternately maintained at atmospheric CO_2 concentrations of either 430 or 740 ppm. This enormous study site, managed by Columbia University, was located in the 1.25 ha naturally lit Biosphere 2 research "dome," which contained several large synthetic ecosystems enclosed by stainless steel sheets and glass. After the dome's air was stabilized at a treatment CO_2 level for about a week, the rainforest mesocosm was isolated from the rest of the dome for one to three days so its carbon exchange rate could be measured. This work revealed

the 72% increase in atmospheric CO_2 concentration increased the daytime net ecosystem carbon exchange rate of the synthetic rainforest by 79%, without affecting the amount of carbon respired from the soil, indicating the increased carbon uptake in the CO_2-enhanced ecosystem was primarily caused by increased canopy net photosynthesis, as the elevated CO_2 had no significant effect on soil respiration.

Wurth *et al.* (1998) enclosed upper-canopy leaves of four species of trees located in a semi-deciduous tropical forest near Panama City, Republic of Panama, in small transparent cups enriched with CO_2 to about twice the current ambient concentration, to determine the effects of elevated CO_2 on sugar and starch production in the trees' leaves. "Against expectation," they write, they determined the elevated CO_2 caused 30 and 100% increases in leaf sugar and starch concentrations, respectively, for all four of the tropical tree species, regardless of whether they were sampled in the morning or evening or under high or low light intensities. This finding demonstrates atmospheric CO_2 enrichment can significantly stimulate individual-leaf total nonstructural carbohydrate contents in tropical tree species, even when there is a very large "sink" (the rest of the tree) to which the carbohydrates readily could be exported.

Working concurrently in Panama, Lovelock *et al.* (1998) grew ten tropical tree species in open-top chambers on the edge of a tropical forest for six months at both ambient and twice-ambient atmospheric CO_2 concentrations, to determine the effects of elevated CO_2 on them. They found the leaf starch concentrations of the trees approximately doubled in the doubled-CO_2 environment.

Lovelock *et al.* (1999b) enclosed branchlets of 30m-tall *Luehea seemannii* trees in small open-top chambers suspended within their upper canopies, and exposed them to atmospheric CO_2 concentrations of 360 or 750 ppm for nearly 40 weeks, to study the effects of elevated CO_2 on photosynthesis, growth, and reproduction in this deciduous tropical tree. They found the leaves of branchlets grown in elevated CO_2 had net photosynthetic rates approximately 30% greater than those in leaves of ambiently grown branchlets. However, the extra carbohydrates produced by this phenomenon were not used by CO_2-enriched branchlets to increase leaf growth or reproductive efforts. Instead, they were stored away in terminal woody tissues, which led the four researchers to speculate the enhanced carbohydrate storage in terminal branchlets may facilitate greater first-flush leaf growth the following year.

Breaking from experimental work to conduct a

mini-review of the scientific literature dealing with subtropical and tropical fruit tree responses to atmospheric CO_2 enrichment to that point in time, Schaffer *et al.* (1999) found exposure to elevated CO_2 concentrations significantly enhanced photosynthesis in leaves of avocado, banana, citrus, mango, and mangosteen trees. After being exposed to an atmospheric CO_2 concentration of 800 ppm for one year, for example, the leaves of mangosteen trees displayed photosynthetic rates 40 to 60% greater than rates observed in ambiently grown leaves.

In addition, atmospheric CO_2 enrichment increased biomass accumulation in each of these species, and in macadamia trees as well. In most cases, elevated CO_2 also increased total yield and fruit weight. However, when it did not immediately increase yield in avocado, mango, and macadamia, plants showed a preferential allocation of carbon belowground to their roots, suggesting "increasing water and nutrient uptake resulting from increased root mass would eventually increase assimilate partitioning to the aboveground organs," ultimately enhancing yield.

Sheu and Lin (1999) grew 50-day-old seedlings of the subtropical tree *Schima superba* for six additional months in pots placed within glass chambers maintained at atmospheric CO_2 concentrations of 360 and 720 ppm. In addition, at each CO_2 concentration half of the seedlings were grown at an optimal day/night temperature regime of 25/20°C, and the other half were subjected to a higher temperature treatment of 30/25°C. The CO_2-enriched seedlings exhibited photosynthetic rates 20% greater than those displayed by ambiently grown trees at the original "optimal" day/night temperatures, and their photosynthetic rates were fully 40% greater than those displayed by the ambiently grown trees in the elevated temperature regime, demonstrating the optimal growth temperature for this species had to have increased with the increasing CO_2 concentration. As a result, the CO_2-enriched seedlings displayed total dry weights 14 and 49% greater than control seedlings at the lower and higher set of growth temperatures, respectively.

Lovelock *et al.* (1999a) grew seedlings of the tropical tree *Copaifera aromatica* for 50 days in pots placed in open-top chambers maintained at atmospheric CO_2 concentrations of 390 and 860 ppm. After 14 days of differential CO_2 exposure, half the seedlings in each treatment were subjected to mechanical defoliation, which removed about 40% of their leaf area and enabled the three researchers to study the influence of simulated herbivory on the CO_2 growth response of this species.

During the experiment, the seedlings grown in the elevated CO_2 treatment displayed rates of net photosynthesis between 50 and 100% greater than those of plants grown in ambient CO_2, regardless of defoliation, which had little to no impact on photosynthesis in either CO_2 treatment. Mechanical defoliation did, however, temporarily reduce seedling leaf area and leaf relative growth rates in both CO_2 environments. But by the end of the experiment, leaf relative growth rates had recovered, and there were no differences between defoliated and undefoliated seedlings in either CO_2 treatment. In contrast, the leaf area of defoliated seedlings never recovered to match undefoliated controls in either CO_2 treatment. But defoliated seedlings grown at ambient CO_2 ultimately attained leaf areas 77% of their un-defoliated controls, and those exposed to elevated CO_2 attained leaf areas 67% of their respective controls.

Despite that difference, the defoliated seedlings grown in elevated CO_2 still possessed about 20% more leaf area than the defoliated plants grown in ambient CO_2. In addition, final plant dry weight, which better represents the total impact of any stress upon a plant and indicates how well a plant is able to deal with a stress, was 15% greater in defoliated seedlings exposed to elevated CO_2 than in defoliated seedlings growing in ambient CO_2. Therefore, even with leaf destruction resulting from herbivory, *Copaifera aromatica* seedlings likely will exhibit increased photosynthetic rates and greater biomass accumulation as the air's CO_2 content rises.

Hoffmann *et al.* (2000) germinated and grew specimens of a tree common to the Brazilian savannah (*Keilmeyera coriacea*) in controlled-environment chambers maintained at combinations of ambient (350 ppm) and elevated (700 ppm) atmospheric CO_2 concentration and low- and high-strength soil nutrient solutions. At 10 weeks post-germination, they clipped to the ground half of the seedlings in each treatment, to simulate burning and allow the five researchers to study the interactive effects of elevated CO_2 and soil nutrients on seedling growth and regrowth with and without the presence of a simulated burning event.

Among the uncut seedlings, the doubled atmospheric CO_2 treatment increased total dry weight by about 50%, and the high nutrient solution increased it by 22%, with no significant interactions between the two factors. In seedlings subjected to the simulated burning, elevated CO_2 had a significant impact on regrowth, but only in the presence of high soil nutrient availability, when it stimulated regrowth by nearly 300%. This observation, coupled with the knowledge that large pulses of nutrients typically become available in soils following burning events, led Hoffmann *et al.* to conclude, "under elevated CO_2, enhanced growth following fire will reduce the time required for individuals to regain the pre-burn size, minimizing the negative effect of fire on population growth." As a result, they write, "greater growth rates and higher capacities of regeneration under elevated CO_2 are expected to increase the ability of woody plants to withstand the high fire frequencies currently prevalent in moist savannahs throughout the tropics."

Aidar *et al.* (2002) note the leguminous *Hymenaea courbaril* L. tree—which is commonly known as jatoba and grows to a height of 20 to 30 meters with a trunk diameter of 200 cm—is "a late secondary/climax species that is one of the most important trees in mature tropical forests of the Americas." It occurs "in more than 30% of 43 inventories made in the extra-Amazonian riparian forests (Rodrigues and Nave, 2000)," they write, and it shows "wide distribution in [the] neotropics, from the Caribbean isles, Mexico and Peru to Southeastern Brazil (Allen and Allen, 1981)."

The six scientists sprouted and grew jatoba seedlings in pots placed in small open-top chambers maintained at atmospheric CO_2 concentrations of 360 and 720 ppm in a shaded glasshouse (to simulate the low light regime at the forest floor where the seeds typically germinate) for 70 days. During that time they measured rates of net photosynthesis in seedlings with and without cotyledons, which they removed from half of the plants.

These efforts revealed a persistent doubling of photosynthesis both with and without cotyledons, when the seedlings were exposed to elevated CO_2. In addition, the scientists observed a 35% increase in the water use efficiency of the seedlings. As a result, Aidar *et al.* state, "under the climatic conditions forecasted on the basis of the present carbon dioxide emissions, *Hymenaea courbaril* should establish faster in its natural environment and might also serve as an efficient mechanism of carbon sequestration within the forest." They also opine the CO_2-induced increase in water use efficiency may enable jatoba "to tolerate dryer and more open environments, which should allow them to better cope with drought stress or a more seasonal climate." Finally, they state the jatoba tree likely would exhibit similar positive responses to even greater emissions of CO_2 because light-saturated photosynthesis in jatoba seedlings continued to rise in response to increasing atmospheric CO_2 concentrations well above 1,000 ppm. In addition, they report they "have measured the saturation level of some other tropical trees from the rain forest (*Caesalpinia echinata*, *Piptadenia gonoacantha*, *Tibouchina granulose*, *T. pulchra*) and all of them [also] saturate at relatively high CO_2 concentrations." It is thus quite likely neotropical forests in general are suited to much higher-than-present atmospheric CO_2 concentrations and would fare far better than they do today in a CO_2-enriched world of the future.

Laurance *et al.* (2004a) reported accelerated growth in the 1990s relative to the 1980s for the large majority (87%) of tree genera in 18 one-hectare plots spanning an area of about 300 km^2 in central Amazonia, and Laurance *et al.* (2004b) observed similarly accelerated tree community dynamics in the 1990s relative to the 1980s. And in Laurance *et al.* (2005), the scientists once again suggest these "pervasive changes in central Amazonian tree communities were most likely caused by global- or regional-scale drivers, such as increasing atmospheric CO_2 concentrations (Laurance *et al.*, 2004a,b)."

Expanding upon this theme, Laurance *et al.* (2005) interpret the observed changes as "being consistent with an ecological 'signature' expected from increasing forest productivity (cf., Phillips and Gentry, 1994; Lewis *et al.* 2004a,b; Phillips *et al.*, 2004)." However, they note Nelson (2005) had challenged this conclusion, so Laurance *et al.* went on to consider his arguments in some detail, methodically dismantling them one by one.

Others questioned the findings of Phillips *et al.* (Sheil, 1995; Sheil and May, 1996; Condit, 1997; Clark, 2002; Clark *et al.*, 2003), and in response to these challenges, Phillips and 17 other researchers (Lewis *et al.*, 2005), including one scientist who had earlier criticized the group's conclusions, published a new analysis vindicating their earlier results.

One of the primary criticisms of Phillips *et al.*'s findings was their meta-analyses included sites with a wide range of tree census intervals (2–38 years), which critics contended could be confounding. In their detailed study of this potential problem, however, Lewis *et al.* (2005) found a re-analysis of Phillips *et al.*'s published results shows the pan-tropical increase in turnover rates over the late twentieth century "cannot be attributed to combining data with differing census intervals." Or as they state in another place, "the conclusion that turnover rates have increased in tropical forests over the late 20th century is robust to the charge that this is an artifact due to the combination of data that vary in census interval (cf. Sheil, 1995)."

Lewis *et al.* additionally note "Sheil's (1995) original critique of the evidence for increasing turnover over the late 20th century also suggests that the apparent increase could be explained by a single event, the 1982–83 El Niño Southern Oscillation (ENSO), as many of the recent data spanned this event." However, Lewis *et al.* report "recent analyses from Amazonia have shown that growth, recruitment and mortality rates have simultaneously increased within the same plots over the 1980s and 1990s, as has net above-ground biomass, both in areas largely unaffected, and in those strongly affected, by ENSO events (Baker *et al.*, 2004a; Lewis *et al.*, 2004a; Phillips *et al.*, 2004)." These developments further support the view there has been an increase in forest growth rates throughout the world that has gradually accelerated over the years in concert with the historical increase in the air's CO$_2$ concentration.

In another analysis of the subject, Lewis (2006) reports, over the prior two decades, intact tropical forests had exhibited "concerted changes in their ecology, becoming, on average, faster growing—more productive—and more dynamic, and showing a net increase in above-ground biomass," and the rates of increase of all these factors were greater than the previously documented increases. In addition, Lewis notes "preliminary analyses also suggest the African and Australian forests are showing structural changes similar to South American forests."

As for what had been causing this suite of concerted changes, Lewis writes, "the results appear to show a coherent fingerprint of increasing net primary productivity across tropical South America, caused by a long-term increase in resource availability (Lewis *et al.*, 2004a,b)."

As to what "resources" might have been involved, Lewis postulates four possibilities: increases in solar radiation, air temperature, nutrient deposition, and atmospheric CO$_2$ concentration. After analyzing each of them in detail, he concludes, "the most parsimonious explanation is the increase in atmospheric CO$_2$, because of the undisputed long-term historical increase in CO$_2$ concentrations, the key role of CO$_2$ in photosynthesis, and the demonstrated positive effects of CO$_2$ fertilization on plant growth rates including experiments on whole temperate-forest stands (Ainsworth and Long, 2005)." As he states in another place in his review, the explanation resides in "the anthropogenic increase in atmospheric carbon dioxide concentrations, increasing forest net primary productivity leading to accelerated forest growth and dynamics."

In light of the voluminous and undeniable real-world observations Lewis reported, it is clear that where tropical forests have not been damaged by the felling and burning of trees, forest productivity has been growing ever-greater with the passing of time, rising with the increasing CO$_2$ content of the air. Research published since 2004 suggests this view is widely shared in the scientific community.

Working in a primary rain forest in Ariuana, Brazil, Hietz *et al.* (2005) collected samples of wood from 37 tropical cedar (*Cedrela odorata* L.) trees between 11 and 151 years old in 2001 and from 16 big-leaf mahogany (*Swietenia macrophylla* King) trees between 48 and 126 years old at that time. They then measured wood cellulose δ^{13}C in 10-year growth increments. They found cellulose δ^{13}C decreased by 1.3 per mil in *Cedrela* and by 1.1 per mill in *Swietenia* over the past century, with the largest changes occurring during the past 50 years. Based on these data and known trends in atmospheric CO$_2$ and δ^{13}CO$_2$, they calculated the intrinsic water use efficiency of the trees increased by 34% in *Cedrela* and by 52% in *Swietenia* over this period, which they say is about the same as what was deduced from similar measurements of the wood of temperate trees (Freyer, 1979; Bert *et al.*, 1997; Feng, 1999). And because "water is probably not a strong limiting factor in tropical rain forest trees," they conclude "the gain in water use efficiency translates mostly to increased carbon assimilation, which may explain the observed increase in tree growth and turnover (Phillips, 1996; Laurance *et al.*, 2004),"

Three years later, Phillips *et al.* (2008) synthesized recent observational results from the network of Amazon-forest researchers known as RAINFOR (*Red Amazonica de Inventarios Forestales*), which represents the combined long-term ecological monitoring efforts of 35 institutions from around the world, with plots spanning Amazonia "from the driest southeast to the wettest northwest and the least fertile east to the most fertile west." The team of five researchers report finding evidence for "concerted changes in the structure, dynamics and composition of old-growth Amazonian forests in the late twentieth century," noting "in the 1980s and 1990s, mature forests gained biomass and underwent accelerated growth and dynamics, all consistent with a widespread, long-acting stimulation of growth" that was "normally distributed" and "occurred across regions and environmental gradients and through time," indicating "continued biomass sink strength through to the end of the century."

In numerical terms, they state, "in the late twentieth century, biomass of trees of more than

10cm diameter increased by 0.62 t C ha^{-1} yr^{-1} averaged across the basin," which implies "a carbon sink in Neotropical old-growth forest of at least 0.49 Pg C yr^{-1}." They add, "if other biomass and necromass components are increased proportionally, then the old-growth forest sink here has been 0.79 Pg C yr^{-1}, even before allowing for any gains in soil carbon stocks." This finding, they write, is "consistent with the evidence from recent global inversions of atmospheric CO_2 measurements and local aircraft measurements of atmospheric CO_2 profiles, showing that the tropics are either carbon-neutral or sink regions, despite widespread deforestation."

As to what has been driving these changes, the five researchers state "the simplest explanation for the ensemble result—more biomass, more stems, faster recruitment, faster mortality, faster growth and more lianas—is that improved resource availability has increased net primary productivity, in turn increasing growth rates." They conclude "the only change for which there is unambiguous evidence that the driver has widely changed and that such a change should accelerate forest growth is the increase in atmospheric CO_2," because of "the undisputed long-term increase in concentrations, the key role of CO_2 in photosynthesis, and the demonstrated effects of CO_2 fertilization on plant growth rates."

Lloyd and Farquhar (2008)—as part of an international workshop held at Oriel College, Oxford, UK, in March 2007—reviewed the effects of rising temperatures and atmospheric CO_2 concentrations on the productivity of tropical forest trees. Based on their examination of the pertinent scientific literature, and using a mixture of observations and climate model outputs together with a simple parameterization of leaf-level photosynthesis incorporating known temperature sensitivities, they could find "no evidence for tropical forests currently existing 'dangerously close' to their optimum temperature range." Quite to the contrary, they state increases in photosynthetic rates associated with increases in ambient CO_2 over forthcoming decades should "more than offset" any decline in photosynthetic productivity due to higher leaf temperatures, leaf-to-air vapor pressure deficits, or autotrophic respiration rates. And they affirm "the magnitude and pattern of increases in forest dynamics across Amazonia observed over the last few decades are consistent with a CO_2-induced stimulation of tree growth." Thus not only have past increases in the atmosphere's CO_2 content and temperature apparently been a boon to the productivity of Amazonia's tropical forests—as well as the world's other tropical forests—the materials

reviewed by these two highly regarded scientists, as well as their own original research, indicate the productivity of Earth's tropical forests will likely rise even higher in response to predicted future increases in the atmosphere's temperature and CO_2 concentration.

A subsequent report by Oliver L. Phillips of the UK's University of Leeds and 65 coauthors (Phillips et al., 2009) suggests a similar conclusion. The scientists note, over the prior quarter-century of intensive region-wide measurements, the productivity of the Amazon rainforest—even in its extreme old age—has been "increasing with time," in support of which they cite the comprehensive observational studies of Phillips et al. (1998), Nemani et al. (2003), Baker et al. (2004a), Lewis et al. (2004), and Ichii et al. (2005). In their own new study, they find, although extremely severe drought conditions can indeed bring a halt to biomass accumulation in old growth tropical forests—and sometimes even lead to minor reductions in biomass due to selective tree mortality—the vast majority of the aged trees are able to regain their photosynthetic capability and add to their prior store of biomass once the moisture stress subsides, thanks in large measure to the enhanced growth and water use efficiency experienced by nearly all woody plants as the air's CO_2 content rises.

Lewis et al. (2009) documented changes in aboveground carbon storage in 79 permanent sample plots spanning 40 years (1968–2007), located in closed-canopy moist forest, spanning West, Central, and Eastern Africa, based on data regarding more than 70,000 individual trees spread across ten countries. They found "aboveground carbon storage in live trees increased by 0.63 Mg C ha^{-1} year^{-1} between 1968 and 2007," and "extrapolation to unmeasured forest components (live roots, small trees, necromass) and scaling to the continent implies a total increase in carbon storage in African tropical forest trees of 0.34 Pg C year^{-1}."

The 33 researchers say the observed changes in carbon storage "are similar to those reported for Amazonian forests per unit area, providing evidence that increasing carbon storage in old-growth forests is a pan-tropical phenomenon," and "combining all standardized inventory data from this study and from tropical America and Asia together yields a comparable figure of 0.49 Mg C ha^{-1} year^{-1}," which equates to "a carbon sink of 1.3 Pg C year^{-1} across all tropical forests during recent decades" and could account for roughly half of the so-called missing carbon sink.

As for the identity of the driving force that

seemed to have breathed new life into old trees, Lewis *et al.* write, in the concluding sentence of the abstract of their paper, "taxon-specific analyses of African inventory and other data suggest that widespread changes in resource availability, such as increasing atmospheric carbon dioxide concentrations, may be the cause of the increase in carbon stocks, as some theory (Lloyd and Farquhar, 1996) and models (Friedlingstein *et al.*, 2006; Stephens *et al.*, 2007; Ciais *et al.*, 2008) predict."

Laurance *et al.* (2009) report what they learned while working within 20 one-hectare plots in approximately 300 km^2 of intact rainforests in the Amazon, where they evaluated forest dynamics over the period 1981–2003, based on data for 21,667 individual trees. Their "large-scale, long-term study appears to illustrate two contrasting patterns: (1) long-term trends in which tree mortality, recruitment, turnover, and basal area are progressively increasing over time in most (80–100%) of our study plots; and (2) shorter-term fluctuations in which strong pulses of tree mortality and poor growth have more transitory impacts on forest dynamics."

With respect to the first of these findings, Laurance *et al.* note "the increasing forest dynamics, growth and basal area observed are broadly consistent with the CO$_2$ fertilization hypothesis." With respect to the second finding, they state "tree mortality peaked, and tree recruitment and growth declined during atypically wet periods," and "tree growth was fastest during dry periods, when reduced cloudiness might have increased available solar radiation." These findings indicate the historical increase in the atmosphere's CO$_2$ concentration, driven by the burning of fossil fuels, has been good for the Amazon's trees and very likely for the rest of the region's plants and animals, even in the face of a local warming of 0.26°C per decade reported for the region since the mid-1970s.

In assessing this latter suggestion, Lapola *et al.* (2009) used a potential vegetation model (CPTEC-PVM2) "to analyze biome distribution in tropical South America under a range of climate projections," while taking into consideration the aerial fertilization and transpiration-reducing effects of atmospheric CO$_2$ enrichment. The Brazilian and German researchers say their modeling work revealed, "if the CO$_2$ 'fertilization effect' indeed takes place and is maintained in the long term in tropical forests, then it will avoid biome shifts in Amazonia in most of the climate scenarios, even if the effect of CO$_2$ fertilization is halved." They state the CO$_2$ fertilization effect, "when fully or half considered,

overwhelms the impacts arising from temperature (in agreement with Lloyd and Farquhar, 2008) and even some of the precipitation changes projected by most of the global climate models, resulting in higher net primary production by the end of the century."

Gloor *et al.* (2009) write, "analysis of earlier tropical plot data has suggested that large-scale changes in forest dynamics are currently occurring in Amazonia (Phillips and Gentry, 1994; Phillips *et al.*, 2004), and that an increase in aboveground biomass has occurred, with increases in mortality tending to lag increases in growth (Phillips *et al.*, 1998; Baker *et al.*, 2004a,b; Lewis *et al.*, 2004)." However, they state this conclusion has been challenged recently by what they call an overzealous application of the "Slow in, Rapid out" dictum. This concept is based on the fact forest growth is a slow process, whereas mortality can be dramatic and singular in time, such that sampling over relatively short observation periods may miss these more severe events, leading to positively biased estimates of aboveground biomass trends, when either no trend or negative trends actually exist.

In evaluating this claim, Gloor *et al.* statistically characterize "the disturbance process in Amazon old-growth forests as recorded in 135 forest plots of the RAINFOR network up to 2006," as well as other independent research programs; and they "explored the consequences of sampling artifacts using a data-based stochastic simulator." The researchers say this work revealed, "over the observed range of annual aboveground biomass losses, standard statistical tests show that the distribution of biomass losses through mortality follow an exponential or near-identical Weibull probability distribution and not a power law as assumed by others." In addition, they write, "the simulator was parameterized using both an exponential disturbance probability distribution as well as a mixed exponential-power law distribution to account for potential large-scale blow-down events," and "in both cases, sampling biases turn out to be too small to explain the gains detected by the extended RAINFOR plot network." In light of these findings, Gloor *et al.* conclude their results lend "further support to the notion that currently observed biomass gains for intact forests across the Amazon are actually occurring over large scales at the current time, presumably as a response to climate change," which many of their earlier papers explicitly state as including the aerial fertilization effect of the historical increase in the air's CO$_2$ content.

Lewis *et al.* (2009) set out to evaluate tropical forest inventory data, plant physiology experiments, ecosystem flux observations, Earth observations, atmospheric measurements, and dynamic global vegetation models, which, "taken together," they write, "provide new opportunities to cross-validate results." The five researchers confirm both theory and experiments suggest, over the past several decades, "plant photosynthesis should have increased in response to increasing CO_2 concentrations, causing increased plant growth and forest biomass." Also in this regard, they report, "long-term plot data collectively indicate an increase in carbon storage, as well as significant increases in tree growth, mortality, recruitment, and forest dynamism." In addition, they confirm satellite measurements "indicate increases in productivity and forest dynamism," and "five Dynamic Global Vegetation Models, incorporating plant physiology, competition, and dynamics, all predict increasing gross primary productivity, net primary productivity, and carbon storage when forced using late-twentieth century climate and atmospheric CO_2 concentration data." In addition, they state "the predicted increases in carbon storage via the differing methods are all of similar magnitude (0.2% to 0.5% per year)."

"Collectively," therefore, Lewis *et al.* conclude, "these results point toward a widespread shift in the ecology of tropical forests, characterized by increased tree growth and accelerating forest dynamism, with forests, on average, getting bigger (increasing biomass and carbon storage)"—results just the opposite of what IPCC predicted.

Friend (2010) worked with the Hybrid6.5 model of terrestrial primary production, which simulates the carbon, nitrogen, phosphorus, water and energy fluxes, and structural changes in terrestrial ecosystems at hourly to decadal timescales and at spatial scales ranging from individual plants to the whole Earth, while employing the climate change anomalies predicted by the GISS-AOM GCM under the A1B emissions scenario for the 2090s relative to observed modern climate. With atmospheric CO_2 increased from 375.7 ppm to 720 ppm—a 92% increase—Friend calculated the percentage changes in terrestrial plant production that would occur throughout the world in response to (1) the projected climate changes alone and (2) the projected concurrent changes in climate and atmospheric CO_2 concentration.

In response to the projected climate changes alone between 2001–2010 and 2091–2100, the net primary production (NPP) of the entire planet was reduced by 2.5%, with the largest negative impacts occurring over southern Africa, central Australia, northern Mexico, and the Mediterranean region,

where reductions of more than 20% were common. At the other extreme, climatic impacts were modestly positive throughout most of the world's boreal forests, as might have been expected when these colder regions received an influx of welcome heat.

But when both climate and atmospheric CO_2 concentrations were changed concurrently, the story was vastly different, with a mean increase in global NPP of 37.3%, driven by mean increases of 43.9–52.9% among C_3 plants and 5.9% among C_4 species. In this case of concurrent increases in the globe's air temperature and CO_2 concentration, the largest increases occurred in tropical rainforests and C_3 grass and croplands.

Jaramillo *et al.* (2010) looked back in time—way back in time—to the days of the Paleocene-Eocene Thermal Maximum (PETM) of some 56 million years ago, which they note "was one of the most abrupt global warming events of the past 65 million years (Kennett and Stott, 1991; Zachos *et al.*, 2003; Westerhold *et al.*, 2009)." It was driven, as they describe it, by "a massive release of ^{13}C-depleted carbon (Pagani *et al.*, 2006; Zeebe *et al.*, 2009)" that led to "an approximate 5°C increase in mean global temperature in about 10,000 to 20,000 years (Zachos *et al.*, 2003)." During this period of warming, according to many scientists, Earth's tropical ecosystems "suffered extensively because mean temperatures are surmised to have exceeded the ecosystems' heat tolerance (Huber, 2008)."

In an attempt to discover whether that warming did major damage to rainforests, the 29 researchers from eight countries analyzed pollen and spore contents and the stable carbon isotopic composition of organic materials obtained from three tropical terrestrial PETM sites in eastern Colombia and western Venezuela. Their work reveals—contrary to the prevailing wisdom of the recent past—the onset of the PETM was "concomitant with an increase in diversity produced by the addition of many taxa (with some representing new families) to the stock of preexisting Paleocene taxa." And they report this increase in biodiversity "was permanent and not transient."

In discussing their findings, Jaramillo *et al.* write, "today, most tropical rainforests are found at mean annual temperatures below 27.5°C," and they note several scientists have argued "higher temperatures could be deleterious to the health of tropical ecosystems," citing Huber (2008, 2009) and Tewksbury *et al.* (2008) in this regard. They report tropical warming during the PETM was postulated to have produced intolerable conditions for tropical ecosystems. Nevertheless, they reiterate, at the sites they studied, "tropical forests were maintained during the warmth of the PETM (~31° to 34°C)," concluding "it is possible that higher Paleocene CO$_2$ levels (Royer, 2010) contributed to their success."

Rasineni *et al.* (2011a) introduce their study by explaining "excess light limits photosynthesis by photoinhibition, resulting in reduced carbon gain and also causing photo-damage (Oquist and Huner, 1993; Pastenes *et al.*, 2003; Allakhverdiev and Murata, 2004; Nishiyama *et al.*, 2006)," and "plants grown in tropical climates usually experience significantly high irradiance leading to the strong midday depression of photosynthesis (Hymus *et al.*, 2001)."

To investigate how this problem might be overcome, the authors conducted an experiment utilizing two open-top chambers in the Botanical Gardens of the University of Hyderabad, India. Each chamber contained four six-month-old specimens of the fast-growing tropical *Gmelina arborea* tree, which they maintained at optimum moisture and nutrient levels. During the course of their experiment the three scientists measured several plant physiological properties and processes related to leaf photosynthesis and photosystem II (PSII) photochemistry and photo-inhibition at both ambient and elevated CO$_2$ concentrations (360 and 460 ppm, respectively), working with "well-expanded and light-exposed leaves randomly chosen from the upper half of the plant canopy."

Their work revealed no significant differences in CO$_2$ assimilation rates between the ambient- and elevated CO$_2$-grown plants during early morning hours; but thereafter, they report, "photosynthesis typically maximized between 0900 hours and 1000 hours in both ambient and elevated CO$_2$-grown plants," which experienced net photosynthetic rates of 20 and 32.5 µmol/m^2/s, respectively, for a CO$_2$-induced enhancement of 62%. For the more standard CO$_2$ enrichment of 300 ppm, that would be roughly equivalent to an enhancement of 180%. Subsequently, during the following midday period of 1100–1300 hours, the rate of net photosynthesis was still significantly enhanced by about 37% (roughly equivalent to a 300-ppm-induced increase of more than 100%) in the elevated CO$_2$ treatment, after which the difference between the net photosynthetic rates of the two CO$_2$ treatments once again became insignificant. Noting the "elevated CO$_2$ treatment mitigated PSII-photoinhibition through enhanced electron transport rates and through efficient biochemical reactions in leaves of *G. arborea*," Rasineni *et al.* conclude their data "demonstrate that

future increases in atmospheric CO$_2$ may have positive effects on photochemical efficiency in fast growing tropical tree species," allowing them to take great advantage of the high-light midday period of potential maximum growth in Earth's tropical regions.

Bonal *et al.* (2011) introduce their work by writing, "an increase in tree radial growth increment over recent decades in Amazonian tropical rainforests has been observed, leading to increased above-ground biomass at most study sites," citing Phillips *et al.* (1998, 2009) and Malhi *et al.* (2004), noting "the stimulating impact on photosynthesis of increased CO$_2$ concentrations in the air (C$_a$) could explain these growth patterns (Lloyd and Farquhar, 2008)." Further investigating this phenomenon, the 11 researchers assessed the impacts of historical environmental changes on several leaf morphological and physiological traits of two tropical rainforest species (*Dicorynia guiunensis*; *Humiria balsamifera*) abundant in the Guiana shield (Northern Amazonia), working with leaf samples from different international herbariums that covered a 200-year time period (AD 1790–2004).

Bonal *et al.* state their results revealed "a clear response of leaf physiological characteristics to increasing C$_a$ for both species," consistent with previous studies "from different ecosystems (Penuelas and Azcon-Bieto, 1992; Beerling *et al.*, 1993; Van de Water *et al.*, 1994; Pedicino *et al.*, 2002; Penuelas *et al.*, 2008), and with data from tree rings in Europe (Bert *et al.*, 1997; Duquesnay *et al.*, 1998; Saurer *et al.*, 2004), Africa (Gebrekirstos *et al.*, 2009) and in tropical rainforests (Hietz *et al.*, 2005; Silva *et al.*, 2009; Nock *et al.*, 2011)." More specifically, they say their results point to "an increase in water use efficiency over recent decades of about 23.1 and 26.6% for *Humiria* and *Dicorynia*, respectively," driven mostly by increases in leaf photosynthesis. And they state "the range of change in water use efficiency for these two species was consistent with many results observed not only in tropical forests (Hietz *et al.*, 2005; Nock *et al.*, 2011), but in boreal (Saurer *et al.*, 2004) and temperate forests (Francey and Farquhar, 1982; Penuelas and Azcon-Bieto, 1992; Bert *et al.*, 1997; Duquesnay *et al.*, 1998)." Bonal *et al.* conclude the responses of the two tree species they studied to increasing C$_a$ appear to be "simply related to the availability of CO$_2$ in the air (fertilization effect)," and "this trend seems to be consistent with recent tree growth patterns in the Amazonian region."

Rasineni *et al.* (2011b) describe growing well-watered and -fertilized five-week-old fast-growing

Gmelina arborea trees out-of-doors at the University of Hyderabad, India, in open-top chambers maintained at ambient and ambient+100 ppm atmospheric CO_2 concentrations throughout the 120 days of that region's spring and summer seasons, while they periodically made numerous measurements of the trees' physical properties and physiological prowess. The trees in the modestly elevated CO_2 chambers exhibited net photosynthetic rates 38% greater than the trees growing in ambient air. Also, aided by a significant CO_2-induced reduction in leaf transpiration rates, the mean instantaneous water use efficiency of the leaves of the CO_2-enriched trees was 87% greater than the ambient-treatment trees. As a result of these CO_2-induced plant physiological benefits, the above-ground biomass of the CO_2-enriched trees at the end of the growing season was 45% greater than the trees growing in ambient air, and their total biomass (above and below ground) was 53% higher.

In discussing their findings, Rasineni *et al.* note elevated atmospheric CO_2 "persistently enhanced all the growth characteristics in *Gmelina*, including plant height, number of branches, internodes, internodal distance, aerial biomass and total plant biomass." They suggest "high sink demand and better growth dynamics" are what led to the huge sustained increase in carbon sequestration in the tropical deciduous tree. They conclude their findings indicate "there are management options for creating short-rotation deciduous tree plantations to achieve increased sequestration of carbon in a future elevated CO_2 environment."

Dick *et al.* (2012) introduce the final study we review here by noting, "tropical rain forest has been a persistent feature in South America for at least 55 million years" and "at times in the past, Amazon surface air temperatures have been higher than those today," citing Feely and Silman (2010), Hoorn *et al.* (2010), Jaramilo *et al.* (2010), and Haywood *et al.* (2011). They also report "experiments show that tropical plants can photosynthesize and maintain a positive carbon balance under higher temperatures than those occurring today (Krause *et al.*, 2010; Way and Oren, 2010)." So the question naturally arises: How high can Amazon temperatures rise and its trees still survive?

Dick *et al.* hypothesize "the older the age of a species prior to the Pleistocene, the warmer the climate it has previously survived," noting Pliocene and late-Miocene air temperatures of 2.6 to 5 million years ago (Ma) and late-Miocene air temperatures of 8 to 10 Ma across Amazonia were "similar to AD 2100 temperature projections under low and high carbon emission scenarios, respectively." They note "some 56.3 Ma during the Paleocene-Eocene Thermal Maximum (PETM), global mean temperature increased by 5–6°C over a period of <= 20 ka," citing Haywood *et al.* (2011). And they affirm "fossil pollen from the PETM showed an increase in tree diversity in three South American rainforest sites with abundant rainfall (Jaramillo *et al.*, 2010)." Thus they used comparative phylogeographic analyses to determine the age of the tropical tree *species* currently found in Amazonia. The four researchers report, "9 of 12 widespread Amazon tree species have Pliocene or earlier lineages (>2.6 Ma), with seven dating from the Miocene (>5.6 Ma) and three >8 Ma."

Based on these findings, Dick *et al.* conclude "the remarkably old age of these species suggests that Amazon forests passed through warmth similar to AD 2100 levels [predicted by climate models] and that in the absence of other major environmental changes, near-term high temperature-induced mass species extinction is unlikely."

These and the many other positive findings of the studies reviewed above indicate rising atmospheric CO_2 concentrations probably will enhance the rates of photosynthesis and biomass production of tropical and sub-tropical trees, even under conditions of herbivory, water stress, and elevated air temperature. That, in turn, likely will allow greater sequestration of carbon in Earth's tropical and sub-tropical forests.

References

Aidar, M.P.M., Martinez, C.A., Costa, A.C., Costa, P.M.F., Dietrich, S.M.C., and Buckeridge, M.S. 2002. Effect of atmospheric CO_2 enrichment on the establishment of seedlings of jatoba, *Hymenaea courbaril* L. (Leguminosae, Caesalpinioideae). *Biota Neotropica* **2**: BN01602012002.

Allakhverdiev, S.I. and Murata, N. 2004. Environmental stress inhibits the synthesis de novo of proteins involved in the photodamage-repair cycle of photosystem II in Synechocystis sp. PCC 6803. *Biochimica et Biophysica Acta* **1657**: 23–32.

Allen, O.N. and Allen, E.K. 1981. *The Leguminosae*. The University of Wisconsin Press, Madison, Wisconsin, USA, pp. 337–338.

Baker, T.R., Phillips, O.L., Malhi, Y., Almeida, S., Arroyo, L., Di Fiore, A., Erwin, T., Higuchi, N., Killeen, T.J., Laurance, S.G., Laurance, W.F., Lewis, S.L., Monteagudo, A., Neill, D.A., Núñez Vargas, P., Pitman, N.C.A., Silva, J.N.M., and Vásquez Martínez, R. 2004a. Increasing biomass in Amazonian forest plots. *Philosophical Transactions of the Royal Society of London Series B—Biological Sciences* **359**: 353–365.

Baker, T.R., Phillips, O.L., Malhi, Y., Almeida, S., Arroyo, L., Di Fiore, A., Erwin, T., Killeen, T.J., Laurance, S.G., Laurance, W.F., Lewis, S.L., Lloyd, J., Monteagudo, A., Neil, D.A., Patiño, S., Pitman, N.C.A., Silva, J.M.N., and Vásquez Martínez, R. 2004b. Variation in wood density determines spatial patterns in Amazonian forest biomass. *Global Change Biology* **10**: 545–562.

Beerling, D.J., Mattey, D.P., and Chaloner, W.G. 1993. Shifts in the $\delta^{13}C$ composition of *Salix herbacea* L. leaves in response to spatial and temporal gradients of atmospheric CO$_2$ concentration. *Proceedings of the Royal Society of London* **253**: 53–60.

Bert, D., Leavitt, S.W., and Dupouey, J.L. 1997. Variations of wood $\delta^{13}C$ and water use efficiency of *Abies alba* during the last century. *Ecology* **78**: 1588–1596.

Bonal, D., Ponton, S., Le Thiec, D., Richard, B., Ningre, N., Herault, B., Ogee, J., Gonzalez, S., Pignal, M., Sabatier, D., and Guehl, J.-M. 2011. Leaf functional response to increasing atmospheric CO$_2$ concentrations over the last century in two northern Amazonian tree species: a historical $\delta^{13}C$ and $\delta^{18}O$ approach using herbarium samples. *Plant, Cell and Environment* **34**: 1332–1344.

Ciais, P., Piao, S.-L., Cadule, P., Friedlingstein, P., and Chedin, A. 2008. Variability and recent trends in the African carbon balance. *Biogeosciences* **5**: 3497–3532.

Clark, D.A. 2002. Are tropical forests an important carbon sink? Reanalysis of the long-term plot data. *Ecological Applications* **12**: 3–7.

Clark, D.A., Piper, S.C., Keeling, C.D., and Clark, D.B. 2003. Tropical rain forest tree growth and atmospheric carbon dynamics linked to interannual temperature variation during 1984–2000. *Proceedings of the National Academy of Sciences, USA* **100**: 10.1073/pnas.0935903100.

Condit, R. 1997. Forest turnover, density, and CO$_2$. *Trends in Ecology and Evolution* **12**: 249–250.

Dick, C.W., Lewis, S.L., Maslin, M., and Bermingham, E. 2012. Neogene origins and implied warmth tolerance of Amazon tree species. *Ecology and Evolution* **3**: 162–169.

Duquesnay, A., Breda, N., Stievenard, M., and Dupouey, J.L. 1998. Changes of tree-ring $\delta^{13}C$ and water use efficiency of beech (*Fagus sylvatica* L.) in north-eastern France during the past century. *Plant, Cell and Environment* **21**: 565–572.

Feeley, K.J. and Silman, M.R. 2010. Biotic attrition from tropical forests correcting for truncated temperature niches. *Global Change Biology* **16**: 1830–1836.

Feng, X. 1999. Trends in intrinsic water use efficiency of natural trees for the past 100–200 years: a response to atmospheric CO$_2$ concentration. *Geochimica et Cosmochimica Acta* **63**: 1891–1903.

Francey, R.J. and Farquhar, G.D. 1982. An explanation of $^{13}C/^{12}C$ variations in tree rings. *Nature* **297**: 28–31.

Freyer, H.D. 1979. On the ^{13}C record in tree rings. Part I. ^{13}C variations in northern hemispheric trees during the last 150 years. *Tellus* **31**: 124–137.

Friedlingstein, P., Cox, P., Betts, R., Bopp, L., von Bloh, W., Brovkin, V., Cadule, P., Doney, S., Eby, M., Fung, I., Bala, G., John, J., Jones, C., Joos, F., Kato, T., Kawamiya, M., Knorr, W., Lindsay, K., Matthews, H.D., Raddatz, T., Rayner, P., Reick, C., Roeckner, E., Schnitzler, K.-G., Schnur, R., Strassmann, K., Weaver, A.J., Yoshikawa, C., and Zeng, N. 2006. Climate-carbon cycle feedback analysis: Results from the (CMIP)-M-4 model intercomparison. *Journal of Climate* **19**: 3337–3353.

Friend, A.D. 2010. Terrestrial plant production and climate change. *Journal of Experimental Botany* **61**: 1293–1309.

Gebrekirstos, A., Worbes, M., Teketay, D., Fetene, M., and Mitlohner, R. 2009. Stable carbon isotope ratios in tree rings of co-occurring species from semi-arid tropics in Africa: patterns and climatic signals. *Global and Planetary Change* **66**: 253–260.

Gloor, M., Phillips, O.L., Lloyd, J.J., Lewis, S.L., Malhi, Y., Baker, T.R., Lopez-Gonzalez, G., Peacock, J., Almeida, S., Alves de Oliveira, A.C., Alvarez, E., Amaral, I., Arroyo, L, Aymard, G., Banki, O., Blanc, L., Bonal, D., Brando, P., Chao, K.-J., Chave, J., Davila, N., Erwin, T., Silva, J., DiFiore, A., Feldpausch, T.R., Freitzs, A., Herrera, R., Higuchi, N., Honorio, E., Jimenez, E., Killeen, T., Laurance, W., Mendoza, C., Monteagudo, A., Andrade, A. Neill, D., Nepstad, D., Nunez Vargas, P., Penuela, M.C., Pena Cruz, A., Prieto, A., Pitman, N., Quesada, C., Salomao, R., Silveira, M., Schwarz, M., Stropp, J., Ramirez, F., Ramirez, H., Rudas, A., ter Steege, H., Silva, N., Torres, A., Terborgh, J., Vasquez, R., and van der Heijden, G. 2009. Does the disturbance hypothesis explain the biomass increase in basin-wide Amazon forest plot data? *Global Change Biology* **15**: 2418–2430.

Grace, J., Lloyd, J., McIntyre, J., Miranda, A.C., Meir, P., Miranda, H.S., Nobre, C., Moncrieff, J., Massheder, J., Malhi, Y., Wright, I., and Gash, J. 1995. Carbon dioxide uptake by an undisturbed tropical rain-forest in Southwest Amazonia, 1992–1993. *Science* **270**: 778–780.

Haywood, A.M., Ridgwell, A., Lunt, D.J., Hill, D.J., Pound, M.J., Dowsett, H.J., Dolan, A.M., Francis, J.E., and Williams, M. 2011. Are there pre-Quaternary geological analogues for a future greenhouse warming? *Philosophical Transactions of the Royal Society A: Mathematical, Physical and Engineering Sciences* **369**: 933–956.

Hietz, P., Wanek, W., and Dunisch, O. 2005. Long-term

trends in cellulose $\delta^{13}C$ and water use efficiency of tropical *Cedrela* and *Swietenia* from Brazil. *Tree Physiology* **25**: 745–752.

Hoffmann, W.A., Bazzaz, F.A., Chatterton, N.J., Harrison, P.A., and Jackson, R.B. 2000. Elevated CO_2 enhances resprouting of a tropical savanna tree. *Oecologia* **123**: 312–317.

Hoorn, C., Wesselingh, F.P., ter Steege, H., Bermudez, M.A., Mora, A., Sevink, J., Sanmartin, I., Sanchez-Meseguer, A., Anderson, C.L., Figueiredo, J.P., Jaramillo, C., Riff, D., Negri, F.R., Hooghiemstra, H., Lundberg, J., Stadler, T., Sarkinen, T., and Antonelli, A. 2010. Amazonia through time: Andean uplift, climate change, landscape evolution, and biodiversity. *Science* **330**: 927–931.

Huber, M. 2008. A hotter greenhouse? *Science* **321**: 353–354.

Huber, M. 2009. Snakes tell a torrid tale. *Nature* **457**: 669–670.

Hymus, G.J., Baker, N.R., and Long, S.P. 2001. Growth in elevated CO_2 can both increase and decrease photochemistry and photoinhibition of photosynthesis in a predictable manner. *Dactylis glomerata* growth in two levels of nitrogen nutrition. *Plant Physiology* **127**: 1204–1211.

Ichii, K., Hashimoto, H., Nemani, R., and White, M. 2005. Modeling the interannual variability and trends in gross and net primary productivity of tropical forests from 1982 to 1999. *Global and Planetary Change* **48**: 274–286.

Idso, S.B. 1991a. The aerial fertilization effect of CO_2 and its implications for global carbon cycling and maximum greenhouse warming. *Bulletin of the American Meteorological Society* **72**: 962–965.

Idso, S.B. 1991b. Reply to comments of L.D. Danny Harvey, Bert Bolin, and P. Lehmann. *Bulletin of the American Meteorological Society* **72**: 1910–1914.

Jaramillo, C., Ochoa, D., Conteras, L., Pagani, M., Carvajal-Ortiz, H., Pratt, L.M., Krishnan, S., Cardona, A., Romero, M., Quiroz, L., Rodriguez, G., Rueda, M.J., de la Parra, F., Moron, S., Green, W., Bayona, G., Montes, C., Quintero, O., Ramirez, R., Mora, G., Schouten, S., Bermudez, H., Navarrete, R., Parra, F., Alvaran, M., Osorno, J., Crowley, J.L., Valencia, V., and Vervoort, J. 2010. Effects of rapid global warming at the Paleocene-Eocene boundary on neotropical vegetation. *Science* **330**: 957–961.

Kennett, J.P. and Stott, L.D. 1991. Abrupt deep-sea warming, palaeoceanographic changes and benthic extinctions at the end of the Palaeocene. *Nature* **353**: 225–229.

Krause, G.H., Winter, K., Krause, B., Jahns, P., Garcia, M., Aranda, J., and Virgo, A. 2010. High-temperature tolerance

of a tropical tree, *Ficus insipida*: methodological reassessment and climate change considerations. *Functional Plant Biology* **37**: 890–900.

Lapola, D.M., Oyama, M.D., and Nobre, C.A. 2009. Exploring the range of climate biome projections for tropical South America: The role of CO_2 fertilization and seasonality. *Global Biogeochemical Cycles* **23**: 10.1029/2008GB003357.

Laurance, W.F., Nascimento, H.E.M., Laurance, S.G., Condit, R., D'Angelo, S., and Andrade, A. 2004b. Inferred longevity of Amazonian rainforest trees based on a long-term demographic study. *Forest Ecology and Management* **190**: 131–143.

Laurance, W.F., Oliveira, A.A., Laurance, S.G., Condit, R., Dick, C.W., Andrade, A., Nascimento, H.E.M., Lovejoy, T.E., and Ribeiro, J.E.L.S. 2005. Altered tree communities in undisturbed Amazonian forests: A consequence of global change? *Biotropica* **37**: 160–162.

Laurance, W.F., Oliveira, A.A., Laurance, S.G., Condit, R., Nascimento, H.E.M., Sanchez-Thorin, A.C., Lovejoy, T.E., Andrade, A., D'Angelo, S., and Dick, C. 2004a. Pervasive alteration of tree communities in undisturbed Amazonian forests. *Nature* **428**: 171–175.

Lewis, S.L. 2006. Tropical forests and the changing Earth system. *Philosophical Transactions of the Royal Society B* **361**: 195–210.

Lewis, S.L., Lloyd, J., Sitch, S., Mitchard, E.T.A., and Laurance, W.F. 2009. Changing ecology of tropical forests: Evidence and drivers. *Annual Review of Ecology, Evolution, and Systematics* **40**: 529–549.

Lewis, S.L., Lopez-Gonzalez, G., Sonke, B., Affum-Baffoe, K., Baker, T.R., Ojo, L.O., Phillips, O.L., Reitsma, J.M., White, L., Comiskey, J.A., Djuikouo K., M.-N., Ewango, C.E.N., Feldpausch, T.R., Hamilton, A.C., Gloor, M., Hart, T., Hladik, A., Lloyd, J., Lovett, J.C., Makana, J.-R., Malhi, Y., Mbago, F.M., Ndangalasi, H.J., Peacock, J., Peh, K. S.-H., Sheil, D., Sunderland, T., Swaine, M.D., Taplin, J., Taylor, D., Thomas, S.C., Votere, R., and Woll, H. 2009. Increasing carbon storage in intact African tropical forests. *Nature* **457**: 1003–1006.

Lewis, S.L., Malhi, Y., and Phillips, O.L. 2004b. Fingerprinting the impacts of global change on tropical forests. *Philosophical Transactions of the Royal Society of London Series B—Biological Sciences* **359**: 437–462.

Lewis, S.L., Phillips, O.L., Baker, T.R., Lloyd, J., Malhi, Y., Almeida, S., Higuchi, N., Laurance, W.F., Neill, D.A., Silva, J.N.M., Terborgh, J., Lezama, A.T., Vásquez Martinez, R., Brown, S., Chave, J., Kuebler, C., Núñez Vargas, P., and Vinceti, B. 2004a. Concerted changes in tropical forest structure and dynamics: evidence from 50 South American long-term plots. *Philosophical*

Transactions of the Royal Society of London Series B— Biological Sciences **359**: 421–436.

Lewis, S.L., Phillips, O.L., Sheil, D., Vinceti, B., Baker, T.R., Brown, S., Graham, A.W., Higuchi, N., Hilbert, D.W., Laurance, W.F., Lejoly, J., Malhi, Y., Monteagudo, A., Vargas, P.N., Sonke, B., Nur Supardi, M.N., Terborgh, J.W., and Vasquez, M.R. 2005. Tropical forest tree mortality, recruitment and turnover rates: calculation, interpretation and comparison when census intervals vary. *Journal of Ecology* **92**: 929–944.

Lin, G., Marino, B.D.V., Wei, Y., Adams, J., Tubiello, F., and Berry, J.A. 1998. An experimental and modeling study of responses in ecosystems carbon exchanges to increasing CO$_2$ concentrations using a tropical rainforest mesocosm. *Australian Journal of Plant Physiology* **25**: 547–556.

Lloyd, J. and Farquhar, G.D. 2008. Effects of rising temperatures and [CO$_2$] on the physiology of tropical forest trees. *Philosophical Transactions of the Royal Society B* **363**: 1811–1817.

Lovelock, C.E., Posada, J., and Winter, K. 1999a. Effects of elevated CO$_2$ and defoliation on compensatory growth and photosynthesis of seedlings in a tropical tree, *Copaifera aromatica*. *Biotropica* **31**: 279–287.

Lovelock, C.E., Virgo, A., Popp, M., and Winter, K. 1999b. Effects of elevated CO$_2$ concentrations on photosynthesis, growth and reproduction of branches of the tropical canopy trees species, *Luehea seemannii* Tr. & Planch. *Plant, Cell and Environment* **22**: 49–59.

Lovelock, C.E., Winter, K., Mersits, R., and Popp, M. 1998. Responses of communities of tropical tree species to elevated CO$_2$ in a forest clearing. *Oecologia* **116**: 207–218.

Malhi, Y., Baker, T.R., Phillips, O.L., Almeida, S., Alvarez, E., Arroyo, L., Chave, J., Czimczik, C.I., Di Fiore, A., Higuchi, N., Killeen, T.J., Laurance, S.G., Laurance, W.F., Lewis, S.L., Montoya, L.M.M., Agudo, A., Neill, D.A., Vargas, P.N., Patino, S., Pitman, N.C.A., Quesadah, C.A., Salomao, R., Silva, J.N.M., Lezama, A.T., Martinez, R.V., Terborgh, J., Vinceti, B., and Lloyd, J. 2004. The above-ground coarse wood productivity of 104 Neotropical forest plots. *Global Change Biology* **10**: 563–591.

Malhi Y. and Grace, J. 2000. Tropical forests and atmospheric carbon dioxide. *Trends in Ecology and Evolution* **15**: 332–337.

Malhi, Y., Nobre, A.D., Grace, J., Kruijt, B., Pereira, M.G.P., Culf, A., and Scott, S. 1998. Carbon dioxide transfer over a Central Amazonian rain forest. *Journal of Geophysical Research* **103**: 31,593–31,612.

Nelson, B.W. 2005. Pervasive alteration of tree communities in undisturbed Amazonian forests. *Biotropica* **37**: 158–159.

Nemani, R.R., Keeling, C.D., Hashimoto, H., Jolly, W.M., Piper, S.C., Tucker, C.J., Myneni, R.B., and Running, S.W. 2003. Climate-driven increases in global terrestrial net primary production from 1982 to 1999. *Science* **300**: 1560–1563.

Nishiyama, Y., Allakhverdiev, S.I., and Murata, N. 2006. A new paradigm for the action of reactive oxygen species in the photoinhibition of photosystem II. *Biochimica et Biophysica Acta* **1757**: 742–749.

Nock, C.A., Baker, P.J., Wanek, W., Albrecht, L., Grabner, M., Bunyavejchewin, S., and Hietz, P. 2011. Long-term increases in intrinsic water use efficiency do not lead to increased stem growth in a tropical monsoon forest in western Thailand. *Global Change Biology* **17**: 1049–1063.

Oquist, G. and Huner, N.P.A. 1993. Cold-hardening-induced resistance to photoinhibition of photosynthesis in winter rye is dependent upon an increased capacity for photosynthesis. *Planta* **189**: 150–156.

Pagani, M., Caldeira, K, Archer, D., and Zachos, J.C. 2006. An ancient carbon mystery. *Science* **314**: 1556–1557.

Pastenes, C., Santa-Maria, E., Infante, R., and Franck, N. 2003. Domestication of the Chilean guava (*Ugni molinae* Turcz.), a forest understory shrub, must consider light intensity. *Scientia Horticulturae* **98**: 71–84.

Pedicino, L., Leavitt, S.W., Betancourt, J.L., and Van De Water, P.K. 2002. Historical variations in δ^{13}C leaf of herbarium specimens on the Southwestern U.S. *Western North American Naturalist* **62**: 348–359.

Penulas, J. and Azcon-Bieto, J. 1992. Changes in leaf δ^{13}C of herbarium plant species during the last 3 centuries of CO$_2$ increase. *Plant, Cell and Environment* **15**: 485–489.

Penuelas, J., Hunt, J.M., Ogaya, R., and Jump, A.S. 2008. Twentieth century changes of tree-ring δ^{13}C at the southern range-edge of *Fagus sylvatica*: increasing water use efficiency does not avoid the growth decline induced by warming at low altitudes. *Global Change Biology* **14**: 1076–1088.

Phillips, O.L. 1996. Long-term environmental change in tropical forests: increasing tree turnover. *Environmental Conservation* **23**: 235–248.

Phillips, O.L., Aragao, L.E.O.C., Lewis, S.L., Fisher, J.B., Lloyd, J., Lopez-Gonzalez, G., Malhi, Y., Monteagudo, A., Peacock, J., Quesada, C.A., van der Heijden G., Almeida, S., Amaral, I., Arroyo, L., Aymard, G., Baker, T.R., Banki, O., Blanc, L., Bonal, D., Brando, P., Chave, J., de Oliveira, A.C.A., Cardozo, N.D., Czimczik, C.I., Feldpausch, T.R., Freitas, M.A., Gloor, E., Higuchi, N., Jimenez, E., Lloyd, G., Meir, P., Mendoza, C., Morel, A., Neill, D.A., Nepstad, D., Patino, S., Penuela, M.C., Prieto, A., Ramirez, F., Schwarz, M., Silva, J., Silveira, M., Thomas, A.S., ter Steege, H., Stropp, J., Vasquez, R., Zelazowski, P., Davila,

E.A., Andelman, S., Andrade, A., Chao, K.-J., Erwin, T., Di Fiore, A., Honorio C., E., Keeling, H., Killeen, T.J., Laurance, W.F., Cruz, A.P., Pitman, N.C.A., Vargas, P.N., Ramirez-Angulo, H., Rudas, A., Salamao, R., Silva, N., Terborgh, J., and Torres-Lezama, A. 2009. Drought sensitivity of the Amazon rainforest. *Science* **323**: 1344–1347.

Phillips, O.L., Baker, T.R., Arroyo, L., Higuchi, N., Killeen, T.J., Laurance, W.F., Lewis, S.L., Lloyd, J., Malhi, Y., Monteagudo, A., Neill, D.A., Núñez Vargas, P., Silva, J.N.M., Terborgh, J., Vásquez Martínez, R., Alexiades, M., Almeida, S., Brown, S., Chave, J., Comiskey, J.A., Czimczik, C.I., Di Fiore, A., Erwin, T., Kuebler, C., Laurance, S.G., Nascimento, H.E.M., Olivier, J., Palacios, W., Patiño, S., Pitman, N.C.A., Quesada, C.A., Saldias, M., Torres Lezama, A., and Vinceti, B. 2004. Pattern and process in Amazon tree turnover: 1976–2001. *Philosophical Transactions of the Royal Society of London Series B—Biological Sciences* **359**: 381–407.

Phillips, O.L. and Gentry, A.H. 1994. Increasing turnover through time in tropical forests. *Science* **263**: 954–958.

Phillips, O.L., Lewis, S.L., Baker, T.R., Chao, K.-J., and Higuchi, N. 2008. The changing Amazon forest. *Philosophical Transactions of the Royal Society B* **363**: 1819–1827.

Phillips, O.L., Malhi, Y., Higuchi, N., Laurance, W.F., Nunez, P.V., Vasquez, R.M., Laurance, S.G., Ferreira, L.V., Stern, M., Brown, S., and Grace, J. 1998. Changes in the carbon balance of tropical forests: Evidence from long-term plots. *Science* **282**: 439–442.

Phillips, O.L., Malhi, Y., Vinceti, B., Baker, T., Lewis, S.L., Higuchi, N., Laurance, W.F., Vargas, P.N., Martinez, R.V., Laurance, S., Ferreira, L.V., Stern, M., Brown, S., and Grace, J. 2002. Changes in growth of tropical forests: Evaluating potential biases. *Ecological Applications* **12**: 576–587.

Pimm, S.L. and Sugden, A.M. 1994. Tropical diversity and global change. *Science* **263**: 933–934.

Prentice, I.C., Farquhar, G.D., Fasham, M.J.R., Goulden, M.L., Heimann, M., Jaramillo, V.J., Kheshgi, H.S., Le Quere, C., Scholes, R.J., Wallace, D.W.R., Archer, D., Ashmore, M.R., Aumont, O., Baker, D., Battle, M., Bender, M., Bopp, L.P., Bousquet, P., Caldeira, K., Ciais, P., Cox, P.M., Cramer, W., Dentener, F., Enting, I.G., Field, C.B., Friedlingstein, P., Holland, E.A., Houghton, R.A., House, J.I., Ishida, A., Jain, A.K., Janssens, I.A., Joos, F., Kaminski, T., Keeling, C.D., Keeling, R.F., Kicklighter, D.W., Hohfeld, K.E., Knorr, W., Law, R., Lenton, T., Lindsay, K., Maier-Reimer, E., Manning, A.C., Matear, R.J., McGuire, A.D., Melillo, J.M., Meyer, R., Mund, M., Orr, J.C., Piper, S., Plattner, K., Rayner, P.J., Sitch, S., Slater, R., Taguchi, S., Tans, P.P., Tian, H.Q., Weirig, M.F., Whorf, T., and Yool, A. 2001. The carbon cycle and atmospheric carbon dioxide. Chapter 3 of the Third Assessment Report of the Intergovernmental Panel on Climate Change. *Climate Change 2001: The Scientific Basis*. Cambridge University Press, Cambridge, UK, pp. 183–238.

Rasineni, G.K., Guha, A., and Reddy, A.R. 2011a. Elevated atmospheric CO_2 mitigated photoinhibition in a tropical tree species, *Gmelina arborea*. *Journal of Photochemistry and Photobiology B: Biology* **103**: 159–165.

Rasineni, G.K., Guha, A., and Reddy, A.R. 2011b. Responses of *Gmelina arborea*, a tropical deciduous tree species, to elevated atmospheric CO_2: Growth, biomass productivity and carbon sequestration efficacy. *Plant Science* **181**: 428–438.

Royer, D.L. 2010. Fossil soils constrain ancient climate sensitivity. *Proceedings of the National Academy of Sciences, USA* **107**: 517–518.

Saurer, M., Siegwolf, R.T.W., and Schweingruber, F.H. 2004. Carbon isotope discrimination indicates improving water use efficiency of trees in northern Eurasia over the last 100 years. *Global Change Biology* **10**: 2109–2120.

Schaffer, B., Whiley, A.W., and Searle, C. 1999. Atmospheric CO_2 enrichment, root restriction, photosynthesis, and dry-matter partitioning in subtropical and tropical fruit crops. *HortScience* **34**: 1033–1037.

Sheil, D. 1995. Evaluating turnover in tropical forests. *Science* **268**: 894.

Sheil, D. and May, R.M. 1996. Mortality and recruitment rate evaluations in heterogeneous tropical forests. *Journal of Ecology* **84**: 91–100.

Sheu, B.-H. and Lin, C.-K. 1999. Photosynthetic response of seedlings of the sub-tropical tree *Schima superba* with exposure to elevated carbon dioxide and temperature. *Environmental and Experimental Botany* **41**: 57–65.

Silva, L.C.R., Anand, M., Oliveira, J.M., and Pillar, V.D. 2009. Past century changes in *Araucaria angustifolia* (Bertol.) Kuntze water use efficiency and growth in forest and grassland ecosystems of southern Brazil: implications for forest expansion. *Global Change Biology* **15**: 2109–2120.

Stephens, B.B., Gurney, K.R., Tans, P.P., Sweeney, C., Peters, W., Bruhwiler, L., Ciais, P., Ramonet, M., Bousquet, P., Nakazawa, T., Aoki, S., Machida, T., Inoue, G., Vinnichenko, N., Lloyd, J., Jordan, A., Heimann, M., Shibistova, O., Langenfelds, R.L., Steele, L.P., Francey, R.J., and Denning, A.S. 2007. Weak northern and strong tropical land carbon uptake from vertical profiles of atmospheric CO_2. *Science* **316**: 1732–1735.

Tewksbury, J.J., Huey, R.B., and Deutsch, C.A. 2008.

Putting the heat on tropical animals. *Science* **320**: 1296–1297.

Van de Water, P.K., Leavitt, S.W., and Betancourt, J.L. 1994. Trends in stomatal density and $^{13}C/^{12}C$ ratios of *Pinus flexilis* needles during last glacial-interglacial cycle. *Science* **264**: 239–243.

Way, D.A. and Oren, R. 2010. Differential responses to changes in growth temperature between trees from different functional groups and biomes: a review and synthesis of data. *Tree Physiology* **30**: 669–688.

Weaver, P.L. and Murphy, P.G. 1990. Forest structure and productivity in Puerto Rico's Luquillo Mountains. *Biotropica* **22**: 69–82.

Westerhold, T., Rohl, U., McCarren, H.K., and Zachos, J.C. 2009. Latest on the absolute age of the Paleocene-Eocene Thermal Maximum (PETM): New insights from exact stratigraphic position of key ash layers + 19 and - 17. *Earth and Planetary Science Letters* **287**: 412–419.

Wurth, M.K.R., Winter, K., and Körner, C. 1998. Leaf carbohydrate responses to CO_2 enrichment at the top of a tropical forest. *Oecologia* **116**: 18–25.

Zachos, J.C., Wara, M.W., Bohaty, S., Delaney, M.L., Petrizzo, M.R., Brill, A., Bralower, T.J., and Premoli-Silva, I. 2003. A transient rise in tropical sea surface temperature during the Paleocene-Eocene Thermal Maximum. *Science* **302**: 1551–1554.

Zeebe, R.E., Zachos, J.C., and Dickens, G.R. 2009. Carbon dioxide forcing alone insufficient to explain Palaeocene-Eocene Thermal Maximum warming. *Nature Geoscience* **2**: 576–580.

1.2.1.2 Other Forest Observations

- Forest growth rates throughout the world have gradually accelerated over the years in concert with, and in response to, the historical increase in the air's CO_2 concentration. As the atmosphere's CO_2 concentration rises, forests likely will respond by exhibiting significant increases in biomass production, and thus likely will grow much more robustly and significantly expand their ranges, as is already being documented in many parts of the world.

In a small booklet published by the University of Minnesota (USA) nearly two decades ago, Idso (1995) laid out the evidence for a worldwide increase in the growth rates of Earth's forests coeval with the progression of the Industrial Revolution and the rising CO_2 content of the atmosphere. The development of this concept began with LaMarche *et al.* (1984), who analyzed annual growth rings of two species of pine tree growing near the timberline in California, Colorado, Nevada, and New Mexico, and in doing so discovered large increases in growth rate between 1859 and 1983, which exceeded what might have been expected from climatic trends but were consistent with the global trend of atmospheric CO_2.

The next stage of the research was inspired by a study of ring-width measurements of Douglas fir trees in British Columbia, Canada, which also revealed a marked increase in the growth rates of the trees in later decades (Parker *et al.*, 1987). This finding led the principal investigator of the project to state "environmental influences other than increased CO_2 have not been found that would explain this [phenomenon]." West (1988) reports much the same thing with respect to long-leaf pines in Georgia—their annual growth increments had begun to rise at an unusual rate about 1920, increasing by approximately 30% by the mid-1980s. He states, "the increased growth cannot be explained by trends in precipitation, temperature, or Palmer Drought Severity Index," leaving the rising CO_2 content of the atmosphere as the likely cause of the observed increase in productivity.

Contemporaneously, stands of Scots pines in northern Finland were found to have experienced growth increases ranging from 15 to 43% between 1950 and 1983 (Hari *et al.*, 1984; Hari and Arovaara, 1988). As for the cause of this phenomenon, the researchers involved in the work state "CO_2 seems to be the only environmental factor that has been changing systematically during this century in the remote area under study," and it was thus to this factor that they looked for an explanation of their observations.

A few years later, Graybill and Idso (1993) reported very long ring-width chronologies (some stretching back nearly 1,800 years) of high-altitude, long-lived bristlecone, foxtail, and limber pine trees in Arizona, California, Colorado, and Nevada all showed an unprecedented upward growth trend beginning in the 1850s that continued as far toward the present as the records extended. Comparisons of the chronologies with temperature and precipitation records ruled out the possibility either of these variables played a significant role in enhancing the trees' growth rates, strongly implicating the historical rise in the air's CO_2 concentration as the factor responsible for their ever-increasing productivity over the prior century and a half.

Duquesnay *et al.* (1998) analyzed the relative

amounts of ^{12}C and ^{13}C present in yearly growth rings of beech trees raised in silviculture regimes in northeastern France. They discovered the trees' intrinsic water-use efficiencies rose by approximately 33% during the prior century, as the atmosphere's CO_2 concentration rose from approximately 280 to 360 ppm. Rathgeber *et al.* (2000) used tree-ring density data to create a historical productivity baseline for forest stands of *Pinus halepensis* in southeastern France, from which they determined the net productivity of such forests likely would increase by 8 to 55% with a doubling of the air's CO_2 content.

Running a forest growth model based on empirical observations reported in the literature, Lloyd (1999) determined the rise in the atmospheric CO_2 concentration since the onset of the Industrial Revolution likely increased the net primary productivity of mature temperate deciduous forests by about 7%. In addition, he determined a proportional increase in anthropogenic nitrogen deposition likely increased forest net primary productivity by 25%. When he combined the two effects, the net primary productivity stimulation rose to 40%, which, as a result of synergetic interactions, was actually more than the sum of the growth enhancements resulting from the individual increases in CO_2 and nitrogen acting by themselves.

Medlyn *et al.* (1999) conducted a meta-analysis of data from 15 atmospheric CO_2 enrichment studies of European forest species growing in field environments to determine their overall photo-synthetic response to elevated (approximately doubled) atmospheric CO_2 concentrations. The resulting meta-analysis by the 21 researchers revealed the twice-ambient CO_2 concentrations stimulated the trees' net photosynthetic rates by an average of 51%.

In 1996, circular Free-Air CO_2 Enrichment (FACE) plots (30m diameter) maintained at atmospheric CO_2 concentrations of 360 and 560 ppm were established in a 15-year-old loblolly pine (*Pinus taeda*) plantation in North Carolina, USA, to study the effects of elevated CO_2 on the growth and productivity of this particular forest community, which also had several hardwood species present in its understory. Based on some of the first sets of data to come out of this endeavor, Hymus *et al.* (1999) report net photosynthetic rates of the CO_2-enriched loblolly pines trees were 65% greater than rates observed in control trees exposed to ambient air. These greater rates of carbon fixation contributed to the 24% greater growth rates observed in the CO_2-enriched pine trees in the first year of this long-term study, according to Naidu and DeLucia (1999). In

addition, DeLucia and Thomas (2000) report the elevated CO_2 increased rates of net photosynthesis by 50 to 160% in four subdominant hardwood species present in the forest understory. Moreover, for one species—sweetgum (*Liquidambar styraciflua*)—the extra CO_2 enhanced the rates of net photosynthesis in Sun and shade leaves by 166 and 68%, respectively, even when the trees were naturally subjected to summer seasonal stresses imposed by high temperature and low soil water availability, as Herrick and Thomas (1999) report. After two years of atmospheric CO_2 enrichment, total ecosystem net primary productivity in the CO_2-enriched plots was found to be 25% greater than what was measured in control plots fumigated with ambient air.

In a similar large-scale study, circular (25m diameter) FACE plots maintained at atmospheric CO_2 concentrations of 400 and 530 ppm were constructed within a ten-year-old sweetgum plantation in Tennessee, USA, to study the effects of elevated CO_2 on the growth and productivity of this forest community. After two years of treatment, Norby *et al.* (2001) report the modest 35% increase in the air's CO_2 content boosted tree biomass production by an average of 24%. In addition, Wullschleger and Norby (2001) note the CO_2-enriched trees displayed rates of transpirational water loss approximately 10% lower than those exhibited by control trees growing in ambient air. As a result, elevated CO_2 enhanced seasonal water-use efficiencies of the mature sweetgum trees by 28 to 35%.

On a smaller scale, Pritchard *et al.* (2001) constructed idealized ecosystems containing five different species representative of regenerating long-leaf pine (*Pinus palustris* Mill.) communities of the southeastern United States, fumigating them for 18 months with air containing 365 and 720 ppm CO_2, to study the effects of elevated CO_2 on this forest community. They report elevated CO_2 increased the above- and below-ground biomass of the dominant longleaf pine individuals by 20 and 62%, respectively. At the ecosystem level, elevated CO_2 stimulated total aboveground biomass production by an average of 35%. Berntson and Bazzaz (1998) report similar results for regenerating temperate forest communities, documenting a 31% increase in Transition Hardwood-White Pine-Hemlock forest mesocosm biomass in response to two years of fumigation with twice-ambient concentrations of atmospheric CO_2.

Near the turn of the century, therefore, it was becoming quite clear that as the atmosphere's CO_2 concentration continued to rise, forests likely would respond by exhibiting significant increases in biomass production, with the result that they likely would grow much more robustly and significantly expand their ranges, as was already being documented in many parts of the world, including Kansas, USA (Knight *et al.*, 1994) and the Budal and Sjodal valleys of Norway (Olsson *et al.*, 2000).

In the first of these cases, aerial photographs taken over a 46-year period were used to analyze the dynamics and spatial extent of gallery forest on the Konza Prairie Research Natural Area (KPRNA) in Kansas, USA, between 1939 and 1985. Over the 46-year period of study, total gallery forest area increased from 157 hectares to 241 hectares. Looking further back in time and studying additional historical information obtained from the Original Land Office Surveys of KPRNA, the scientists found total forest area in the region increased fully 97% between 1859 and 1939, leading Knight *et al.* to conclude there was "no question that the absolute amount of forested areas has increased."

Taking an even longer view of the subject, the explorer Coronado in 1541 stated, in reference to the Great Plains of America, "there is not any kind of wood in all these plains, away from the gullies and rivers, which are very few." Clearly, therefore, a dramatic increase in forest growth has occurred in this region since that time, and especially over the last century and a half. One of the reasons for this increase is certainly the historical increase in Earth's atmospheric CO_2 concentration. Rising from a value of 265 ppm at the time of Coronado, to a value of 370 ppm in 1994, the increased CO_2 likely had a pronounced positive impact on the photosynthesis and growth of woody species on every continent of the globe where trees are found, as has been further elucidated by Idso (1995).

In Norway, domestic livestock have been raised on mountains for the past 4,000 years, but especially since the sixteenth century, which saw the development of the summer farming system there. Olsson *et al.* (2000) thus speculated this activity originally reduced forested areas, and changes in farming practices more recently allowed the forests to return. Investigating this hypothesis, they studied two valleys—Budal and Sjodal—in mid-Norway, which they say were representative of core areas of the Norwegian summer farming ecosystems "shaped by human activities rooted in pre-history." Specifically, they analyzed changes in land use and landscape patterns in the two areas over the period 1960–1993. This work revealed grasslands and heathlands that had long dominated the mountain slopes of the two

study areas were, in their words, "today decreasing due to forest invasion," which they say is characterized by "the spread of subalpine woodlands, and a raised treeline."

Olsson *et al.* conclude the expansion of the subalpine Norwegian woodlands was "primarily related to changes in the human use of those areas," which in their estimation were "much more influential than possible effects of climate change." However, it is also possible the concurrent rise in the atmosphere's CO_2 concentration may have played a role in the forests' comeback. In any event, the ongoing increase in the presence of forests in the mountain valleys of Norway is but one more manifestation of the spreading of woody species over the face of the planet, which is helping to slow the rate of rise of the atmosphere's CO_2 concentration.

Walker *et al.* (2000) grew ponderosa pine (*Pinus ponderosa* Dougl.) seedlings for five years in open-top chambers having atmospheric CO_2 concentrations of 350, 525, and 700 ppm on soils of low, medium, and high nitrogen content, to determine the interactive effects of these two variables on the long-term growth response of this particular tree species. They found the moderate level of atmospheric CO_2 enrichment (525 ppm) had the greatest effect on tree height and trunk diameter in the first three years of the experiment. By years four and five, trees grown at 700 ppm CO_2 exhibited the greatest growth responses to elevated CO_2. At final harvest, the trees exposed to twice-ambient levels of atmospheric CO_2 had heights 43, 64, and 25% greater than those of trees exposed to ambient air and conditions of high, medium, and low levels of soil nitrogen, respectively. Similarly, trunk diameters of trees fumigated with 700 ppm CO_2 for five years were 24, 73, and 20% greater than trunk diameters of ambiently grown trees exposed to high, medium, and low levels of soil nitrogen.

Naumburg and Ellsworth (2000) measured photosynthetic rates in leaves of four hardwood saplings growing beneath the canopy of a *Pinus taeda* forest, several portions of which were exposed to either ambient or enriched (ambient + 200 ppm) atmospheric CO_2 concentrations in a FACE study spanning two years. The measurements were made under conditions of both low and high light intensity, which commonly exist beneath maturing forest canopies because of shading and intermittent illumination by sunflecks, respectively. Thus the two researchers studied the effects of elevated CO_2 on sapling performance under the variable light conditions prevailing beneath the canopies of real-world forests.

The data indicate elevated CO_2 increased the mean photosynthetic rates of four hardwood understory saplings by 60 and 40% under high and low light conditions, respectively. Also, in going from shaded to lighted conditions, elevated CO_2 had no effect on photosynthetic induction, with ambient and CO_2-enriched species both reaching 90% of their maximal transient photosynthetic rates at approximately the same time. However, in going from lighted to shaded conditions, elevated CO_2 extended the time during which maximal rates of photosynthesis were maintained. Thus, elevated CO_2 slowed the rate of photosynthetic decline caused by the onset of shading, and as a result, the shaded leaves of CO_2-enriched saplings maintained greater rates of photosynthesis for longer periods of time than did shaded leaves of saplings growing in ambient air, which allowed the CO_2-enriched leaves to sequester greater amounts of carbon than was expected from photosynthetic measurements made under steady-state conditions.

As the air's CO_2 content rises, therefore, saplings growing beneath the canopies of larger trees will likely increase their rates of photosynthesis under both high and low light conditions characteristic of intermittent shading and illumination by sunflecks. Moreover, because elevated CO_2 concentrations allow saplings to maintain higher rates of photosynthesis for longer periods of time when going from lighted to shaded conditions, such trees should be able to sequester greater quantities of carbon than they do now. So powerful is this phenomenon, in fact, the two researchers state current estimates of the enhancement of long-term carbon gains by forests under conditions of elevated atmospheric CO_2 "could be underestimated by steady-state photosynthetic measures."

Hamilton et al. (2001) investigated the short- and long-term respiratory responses of loblolly pine (*Pinus taeda*) and sweetgum (*Liquidambar styraciflua*) trees to the ambient and elevated atmospheric CO_2 concentrations (360 and 560 ppm) of the 30-meter-diameter FACE plots of the long-running loblolly pine plantation experiment in North Carolina, USA, where the deciduous trees had naturally established themselves beneath the primarily coniferous canopy. They report the modest 200 ppm increase in atmospheric CO_2 concentration resulted in no significant short-term suppression of dark respiration rates in needles of loblolly pine. It did, however, reduce rates of dark respiration in sweetgum leaves by an average of 10%. The long-term exposure to elevated CO_2 also did not appear to alter maintenance respiration, which is the amount of CO_2 needed to maintain existing tissue, in either of the tested species. But growth respiration, the amount of CO_2 respired when constructing new tissues, was reduced by 21% in loblolly pine and 39% in sweetgum leaves that reached the top of the canopy. Thus, as the air's CO_2 content rises, it is likely these two forest species will exhibit increased rates of photosynthesis that will provide them with more of the raw materials required for constructing new and greater amounts of biomass, and the costs of respiration during the synthesis of new tissues likely will be reduced, thus allowing greater amounts of carbon to be retained in the trees and thereby helping to reduce the rate of rise of the atmosphere's CO_2 concentration.

Working at the same location, Hussain et al. (2001) collected seeds from trees exposed to both atmospheric CO_2 concentrations to study the effects of elevated CO_2 on seed characteristics, germination success, and early seedling growth. Seeds collected from CO_2-enriched trees were 91% heavier than seeds collected from trees growing in ambient air. In addition, the CO_2-enriched seeds had a lipid content 265% greater than that observed in seeds produced on the ambient-treatment trees, and the germination success for seeds developed under atmospheric CO_2 enrichment was more than three times greater than control seeds developed at ambient CO_2, regardless of germination CO_2 concentration. Also, the seeds from the CO_2-enriched trees germinated approximately five days earlier than their ambiently produced counterparts, again regardless of germination CO_2 concentration. And seedlings developing from seeds collected from CO_2-enriched trees displayed significantly greater root lengths and needle numbers than those developing from trees exposed to ambient air, also regardless of current growth CO_2 concentration. Thus, as the CO_2 content of the air increases, loblolly pine trees likely will display significant increases in their photosynthetic rates, and the enhanced carbohydrate supplies resulting from this phenomenon likely will be used to increase seed weight and lipid content. These seeds consequently should exhibit significant increases in germination success, and their enhanced lipid content likely will lead to greater root lengths and needle numbers in developing seedlings. Thus, when these seedlings become photosynthetically active, they likely will photosynthesize and produce biomass at greater rates than those currently exhibited by seedlings growing under ambient CO_2 concentrations, in a positive cycle that keeps repeating.

Kellomaki and Wang (2001) grew birch seedlings (*Betula pendula* Roth.) for approximately five months in enclosed environmental chambers maintained at atmospheric CO$_2$ concentrations of 350 and 700 ppm. The seedlings were simultaneously exposed to ambient or elevated (ambient plus 3°C) air temperatures to study the interactive effects of elevated CO$_2$ and temperature on the growth of this common boreal forest species. During the most rapid phase of growth observed in the study, elevated CO$_2$ increased rates of net photosynthesis by 21 and 28% at the ambient and elevated air temperatures, respectively. These increases in carbon uptake led to corresponding biomass increases of 17 and 18%, which suggest boreal forests likely will increase their carbon-sequestering abilities, locking up increasing amounts of carbon within their woody tissues as the air's CO$_2$ content increases.

Hamilton *et al.* (2002) report what they learned from the Duke Forest FACE Experiment over four years. This ecosystem—a predominantly loblolly pine (*Pinus taeda* L.) forest with sweetgum (*Liquidambar styraciflua* L.) and yellow poplar (*Liriodendron tulipifera* L.) trees as sub-dominants, together with numerous other trees, shrubs, and vines—was established in 1983 following the clear-cutting of a regenerating forest in 1979. The experiment was begun in August 1996, when three 30-meter-diameter FACE plots were enriched with CO$_2$ to atmospheric concentrations 200 ppm above ambient, and three similar plots were maintained at ambient conditions as controls. Based on the standing pool of ecosystem biomass in 1998 and more recent measurements of various carbon fluxes, Hamilton *et al.* calculated a complete carbon budget for the forest for that particular year. They found the extra CO$_2$ supplied to the FACE plots stimulated net ecosystem productivity (NEP) by 41%, and for a 300 ppm increase in atmospheric CO$_2$ concentration—the most common increment of CO$_2$ enrichment employed in CO$_2$ enrichment experiments over the years—this result translates into a CO$_2$-induced NEP increase on the order of 60%. That improvement represents a significant stimulation of biological carbon sequestration, especially for trees growing on a soil the researchers described as being of "low nitrogen and phosphorus availability."

Norby *et al.* (2002) describe a FACE study established in a ten-year-old stand of sweetgum (*Liquidambar styraciflua* L.) trees growing in a forest plantation on nutrient-rich soils in Tennessee, USA, where the trees were exposed to atmospheric CO$_2$ concentrations of 360 and 550 ppm. In response to

that CO$_2$ increase, ecosystem net primary productivity rose by 21% in all three years of their study; aboveground woody biomass rose by 33% in the first year, 15% in the second year, and 7% in the third year; and net primary productivity remained unchanged. The biomass drop occurred because an increasing amount of newly fixed carbon in the CO$_2$-enriched trees was being utilized to increase fine-root and leaf production in each progressive year. Over the three-year period of their study, however, 77% of the additional fixed carbon was nevertheless allocated to aboveground woody biomass, leading the 11 researchers to conclude, "this experiment has provided the first evidence that CO$_2$ enrichment can increase productivity in a closed-canopy deciduous forest."

Rathgeber *et al.* (2003) used tree-ring width and density chronologies (both earlywood and latewood) from 21 stands of Aleppo pine (*Pinus halepensis* Mill.) in the Provence region of southeast France to calibrate the BIOME3 biogeochemistry model of forest productivity in terms of growth responses to known historical changes in atmospheric temperature, precipitation, and CO$_2$ concentration. They then used the BIOME3 model to calculate changes in the mean productivity of the same forest stands expected to result from changes in these parameters driven by a doubling of the air's CO$_2$ content, as calculated by Meteo-France's ARPEGE atmospheric general circulation model when downscaled to that specific part of the country. In response to the predicted changes in climate, forest productivity increased moderately for all stands (17% to 24%); in response to the aerial fertilization effect of the doubling of the atmosphere's CO$_2$ concentration, it increased considerably more (72% to 86%). Even more impressively, when the climatic changes and atmospheric CO$_2$ increase were considered together, forest productivity increased still more (107% to 141%). That response was greater than that provided by the sum of their individual contributions, as a result of the amplifying synergy among these factors with respect to their combined impact on basic plant physiological processes.

Bergh *et al.* (2003) used a boreal version of a process-based simulation model (BIOMASS) to quantify the individual and combined effects of elevated air temperature (2 and 4°C above ambient) and CO$_2$ concentration (350 ppm above ambient) on the net primary production (NPP) of both coniferous (*Pinus sylvestris*, *Picea abies*) and deciduous broad-leaf (*Fagus sylvatica*, *Populus trichocarpa*) forests growing in Denmark, Finland, Iceland, Norway, and

Sweden. For three of the four species (*P. sylvestris*, *P. abies*, *P. trichocarpa*), air temperature increases of 2 and 4°C led to mean NPP increases of 11 and 20%, respectively. For the other species (*F. sylvatica*), there were corresponding 21 and 48% decreases in NPP. When the atmosphere's CO_2 concentration was simultaneously increased from 350 to 700 ppm, the corresponding mean NPP increases of the three-species group rose to 41 and 55%, and the NPP of *F. sylvatica* jumped from -21 and -48% to +37 and +10%. Finally, when the atmosphere's CO_2 content was doubled at the prevailing ambient air temperature, the mean NPP value of the three-species group rose by 27%, and *F. sylvatica* rose by 58%. Consequently, as the air's CO_2 content climbs higher, the major tree species of Denmark, Finland, Iceland, Norway, and Sweden should become significantly more productive, and if air temperature also rises, most of them will grow even better.

In a study conducted at the Poplar Free Air CO_2 Enrichment (PopFACE) facility described by Miglietta *et al.* (2001), located near Viterbo in Central Italy, Bernacchi *et al.* (2003) worked with three hybrid poplars they describe as "so fast growing that they provide a rare opportunity to grow a plantation forest from planting to canopy closure of tall trees (greater than 9 m) in just 3 years." This was done in a field previously used for wheat cultivation planted with the hybrid *Populus* x *euramericana* Dode (Guinier)—(*P. deltoides* Bart. ex Marsh. x *P. nigra* L., I–214)—with the exception of six 30m x 30m square plots that each contained a 22m-diameter FACE ring. Three of the rings were maintained at 370 ppm CO_2, and the other three were maintained at 550 ppm CO_2. Within each of them were grown equal-area sections of *P. alba* L. (genotype 2AS1), *P. nigra* L. (genotype Jean Pourtet), and *P. x euramericana* (genotype I–214), which were maintained free of drought by a drip irrigation system. Periodic measurements of net photosynthesis and stomatal conductance were made over the three-year period of growth from the seedling to closed-canopy forest stage.

Bernacchi *et al.* found no response of leaf stomatal conductance to atmospheric CO_2 enrichment. In the case of net photosynthesis, however, the team of seven scientists observed a 38% increase in light-saturated net photosynthesis at 25°C, which they describe as being "close to the maximum theoretically possible," in response to the 49% increase in atmospheric CO_2 concentration employed in their study. Daily integrated rates of *in situ* photosynthesis were even higher, rising by 40% to almost 90%

(approximately equivalent to 150% in response to a 300 ppm increase in the air's CO_2 concentration). The cause of this increase, Bernacchi *et al.* write, was "daytime leaf temperatures were typically over 30°C resulting in a larger stimulation of leaf photosynthesis by elevated CO_2 than would be evident at 25°C (Long, 1991)." This stimulation of daily net photosynthesis illustrates the enormous potential for Earth's trees, even in closed-canopy forests, to respond positively to the ongoing rise in the air's CO_2 content.

Su and Sang (2004) used an ecosystem process model, BIOME-BGC, to explore the sensitivity of the net primary productivity (NPP) of an oak (*Quercus liaotungensis* Koidz) forest ecosystem in the Beijing area of China to global climate changes projected to be caused by rising atmospheric CO_2 concentrations. Under a doubling of the air's CO_2 concentration from 355 to 710 ppm, the Beijing oak forest's NPP was calculated to rise by 14.0%, and with a concomitant temperature increase of 2°C, its NPP was calculated to rise by 15.7%. With an additional 20% increase in precipitation, it rose by 25.7%. Finally, with a 20% increase in precipitation and a 4°C increase in temperature, it rose by 25.7%.

In contrast to typical model-based claims of future climate, researchers find many projections of ecosystem responses to potential environmental change are not catastrophically negative, even when the increases in air temperature they employ are unrealistically large, such as the 4°C rise employed by Su and Sang. In fact, as in this particular case, many of the responses are actually positive, and strongly so.

One of the reasons for this discrepancy is the tendency of modelers to downplay or disregard altogether the many mitigating effects of atmospheric CO_2 enrichment, including increased plant growth, significantly reduced plant water loss by transpiration and thereby greatly enhanced plant water use efficiency, and physiological changes to plants to where they prefer warmer temperatures, a phenomenon expressed by an increase in the temperature at which plants photosynthesize most efficiently. Any projections of ecosystem responses to potential climate change, and especially those that assume the rising CO_2 content of the atmosphere is their cause, must include these very real phenomena. And when they are included, the results are often positive, as in the work of Su and Sang.

Hanson *et al.* (2005) used models that performed well in a multiyear simulation of the current carbon and water budgets of an upland-oak forest (Hanson *et al.*, 2004) to evaluate the influence of single and multifactor environmental change scenarios projected for 2100, with and without modifications to account for physiological and growth responses learned from long-term field experimental studies (Winnett, 1998). The environmental changes they evaluated were a 385 ppm increase in CO$_2$, a 20 ppb increase in O$_3$, a 4°C increase in temperature, and a 20% increase in winter precipitation, and the responses to those changes "were derived primarily from field experimental studies on deciduous trees and forest systems."

Initial simplistic model projections of annual net ecosystem carbon exchange (NEEa) for the single-factor change scenarios yielded NEEa responses of +191% for CO$_2$, -206% for temperature, 0% for precipitation, and -35% for O$_3$; the combined influence of the four environmental changes yielded a 29% reduction in mean NEEa. However, as Hanson *et al.* report, "when experimentally observed physiological adjustments were included in the simulations (e.g. acclimation of leaf respiration to warming), the combined influence of the year 2100 scenario resulted in a 20% increase in NEEa, not a decrease." In addition, "consistent with the annual model's predictions, simulations with a forest succession model run for gradually changing conditions from 2000 to 2100 indicated an 11% increase in stand wood biomass in the future compared with current conditions." Thus, even with the unrealistically extreme temperature change investigated in their study, which came from IPCC's Third Assessment Report (Houghton *et al.*, 2001) and the US National Assessment Synthesis Team's report on climate-change impacts (NAST, 2000), the knowledge gained from real-world experiments demonstrates desirable plant responses to atmospheric CO$_2$ enrichment are sufficient to override the negative influence of inflated warming and produce a significant enhancement in NEEa.

In a study published in the *Proceedings of the National Academy of Sciences*, a team of 19 researchers (Norby *et al.*, 2005) note "experiments have unequivocally shown that plants can grow faster and larger in a CO$_2$-enriched atmosphere, and the mechanisms of response are well understood." Furthermore, they state computer simulations of climatic responses to atmospheric CO$_2$ "will be incorrect if the magnitude of the CO$_2$ fertilization effect is not represented accurately." To help overcome this deficiency (but one of many inherent in even the most advanced of today's climate models (Lupo and Kininmonth, 2013)), they provide an analysis of the net primary productivity (NPP)

response of closed-canopy forests to increases in the air's CO$_2$ concentration in the only Free-Air CO$_2$ Enrichment (FACE) studies conducted on assemblages of trees large enough and spatially concentrated enough to meet this important criterion of realism.

The four multiyear experiments Norby *et al.* analyzed were: (1) the Duke-FACE study near Durham, North Carolina, USA, which was initiated in an established monoculture plantation of evergreen loblolly pine (*Pinus taeda*) trees, (2) the ORNL-FACE study near Oak Ridge, Tennessee, USA, which was initiated in an established monoculture of deciduous sweetgum (*Liquidambar styraciflua*) trees, (3) the Aspen-FACE study near Rhinelander, Wisconsin, USA, which was initiated on bare ground but ultimately comprised multi-tree assemblages dominated by *Populus* species, and (4) the POP-EUROFACE study near Tuscania (Viterbo), Italy, which also was initiated on bare ground and ultimately comprised of multi-tree assemblages dominated by *Populus* species.

To be compatible with the first two experiments in terms of the trees' state of development, no data were used from the latter two experiments until the trees had grown to the point where their canopies were completely closed. Under these conditions, and across all appropriate years of all experiments (six years in the Duke-FACE study, five years in the ORNL-FACE study, one and three years in different portions of the Aspen-FACE study, and two years in the POP-EUROFACE study), the average atmospheric CO$_2$ concentration in the ambient-air control plots was 376 ppm, and the average concentration in the CO$_2$-enriched plots was 550 ppm, yielding an average CO$_2$ concentration differential of 174 ppm between the two CO$_2$ treatments.

In what the four groups of researchers describe as a "surprising consistency of response across diverse sites," they found forest NPP was enhanced by 23 ± 2% at the median NPP of their combined data set in response to the 174 ppm increase in the air's CO$_2$ concentration. This NPP stimulation is substantial, considering most of the CO$_2$ stimulation figures seen in the scientific literature are for a 300 ppm increase in atmospheric CO$_2$ concentration. Linearly extrapolating Norby *et al.*'s median result to correspond to this greater CO$_2$ concentration differential yields a NPP stimulation of approximately 40% or just slightly less, because as the air's CO$_2$ content rises, the NPP stimulation provided by extra CO$_2$ rises slightly more slowly.

Norby *et al.* note the data in their analyses came

from "fast-growing, early successional stands, and there had been no evidence to date for a negative feedback on NPP through nitrogen availability in these stands," as some had suggested would occur. Norby et al. confidently conclude, "the effect of CO_2 fertilization on forest NPP is now firmly established, at least for young stands in the temperate zone."

Nevertheless, nitrogen availability does play a role in this phenomenon. In the Duke-FACE study, for example, where Norby et al. say "a wide range of response to CO_2 enrichment across replicate plots correlated with differences in soil nitrogen availability," the scientists observed "under low nitrogen availability, CO_2 enrichment increased NPP by 19%, whereas under intermediate and high nitrogen availability the percent CO_2 stimulation was 27%," or 42% greater (27%/19% = 1.42). This observation is very important, for it is "almost certain," as Shaw et al. (2002) write, significant nitrogen deposition originating from anthropogenic activities will continue to accompany the ongoing rise in the atmosphere's CO_2 concentration throughout the foreseeable future; and this phenomenon should further boost forest NPP.

Lloyd (1999) calculated that from AD 1730 to the early 1980s the increase in temperate deciduous forest NPP due solely to the historical increase in the atmosphere's CO_2 concentration was approximately 7%, and the increase in NPP due to a modest proportional increase in nitrogen deposition over the same time period would have been about 25%. However, when CO_2 and nitrogen increased together in the model Lloyd employed, the NPP stimulation was 40%, even more than the sum of the individual contributions of the extra CO_2 and nitrogen. Although this exercise does not allow for a precise prediction of the percentage stimulation of forest NPP in response to future concomitant increases in atmospheric CO_2 content and nitrogen deposition, it does suggest the increase will likely be significantly larger than what is suggested by Norby et al., who deal solely with the effects of increasing CO_2.

In spite of the many positive responses discussed above, some researchers have suggested the biological response of forests to rising CO_2 may saturate sometime in the future, and the predicted climatic effects of anthropogenic CO_2 emissions might ultimately overpower this positive effect and cause a significant downturn in forest productivity. Davi et al. (2006) studied this possibility.

Noting "predictions for the second half of the 21st century diverge, with some models predicting that the terrestrial carbon sink will tend to level off, while others predict a decrease," Davi et al. say they were "hoping to shed more light on this important subject." To do so, they used a meteorological model and a moderate CO_2 emission scenario (B2 of IPCC) to calculate a 1960–2100 average temperature increase of 3.1°C and a mean summer rainfall decrease of 27%, which the nine scientists used as input to a physiologically based multi-layer process-based ecosystem productivity model (which contained a carbon allocation sub-model coupled with a soil model) to evaluate the net productivity changes of six French forest ecosystems representative of oceanic, continental, and Mediterranean climates dominated, respectively, by deciduous species (Fagus sylvatica, Quercus robur), coniferous species (Pinus pinaster, Pinus sylvestris), and sclerophyllous evergreen species (Quercus ilex). These ecosystems, they write, "are representative of a significant proportion of forests in western Europe."

"By comparing runs with and without CO_2 effects," Davi et al. write, they found "CO_2 fertilization is responsible from 1960 to 2100 for an NEP [net ecosystem productivity] enhancement of about 427 g(C) on average for all sites (= 3.05 g(C) m^{-2} $year^{-1}$)." They also report the CO_2 fertilization effect turns a warming-and-drying-induced "decrease of NEP into an increase." In addition, they write, "no saturation of this effect on NEP is found because the differences between the simulations with and without CO_2 fertilization continuously increase with time." Therefore, even in the face of what was projected to be a truly "unprecedented" global warming and drying scenario, the real-world physiological effects of atmospheric CO_2 enrichment included in the ecosystem productivity model employed by Davi et al. more than compensated for the deleterious effects of the dramatic climate-change scenario on the productivity of major European forests.

Sefcik et al. (2007) studied the interactive effects of elevated atmospheric CO_2 concentration (658 ppm vs. the ambient concentration of 383 ppm), nitrogen (N) deposition (ambient and ambient + 30 kg N ha^{-1} $year^{-1}$), and light availability (limited and saturated) for two full growing seasons on leaf photosynthesis, growth, and survival of understory seedlings of six different hardwood tree species—paper birch (Betula papyrifera), quaking aspen (Populus tremuloides), sugar maple (Acer saccharum), American beech (Fagus grandifolia), eastern white pine (Pinus strobus), and black cherry (Prunus serotina)—which were enclosed by open-top chambers within a 90-year-old N-limited northern hardwood forest in northern Lower Michigan, USA.

Over the course of this two-year study, the 72% increase in the air's CO_2 concentration increased light-limited photosynthesis in the six tree species by an average of 47%, and it increased light-saturated photosynthesis by fully 60%. With respect to survival, at low N-availability seedling survival rates were similar in the ambient and elevated CO_2 treatments at 57% ± 5% and 55% ± 4%, respectively. In addition, as the researchers describe it, "for plants grown with high N availability, those grown in ambient CO_2 demonstrated 78 ± 4% survival, while those grown in elevated CO_2 exhibited the greatest survival rate of all of the treatment combinations with an 85 ± 2% survival rate." Sefcik et al. conclude, "N deposition may alleviate some photosynthetic acclimation [i.e., down-regulation] to long-term CO_2 enrichment in N-limited understory seedlings." They therefore further conclude, "increasing CO_2 and nitrogen deposition from fossil fuel combustion can directly impact seedling physiology and survivorship," quite obviously for the better.

Su et al. (2007) used a process-based model (BIOME-BGC) to investigate the likely response of Picea schrenkiana forest to future climate changes and atmospheric carbon dioxide concentration increases in the Tianshan Mountains of northwestern China, which they validated by comparing simulated net primary productivity (NPP) under current climatic conditions with independent, field-measured data. The specific climate change scenario employed in this endeavor was a double-CO_2-induced temperature increase of 2.6°C and a precipitation increase of 25%. When the precipitation increase predicted by the model was considered by itself, the NPP of the P. schrenkiana forest increased by 14.5%. The predicted temperature increase by itself increased forest NPP by 6.4%, and the CO_2 increase by itself boosted NPP by 2.7%. When the predicted increases in precipitation and temperature occurred together, forest NPP increased by a larger 18.6%, just slightly less than the sum of the two individual effects. When the CO_2 concentration increase was added to the mix and all three factors increased together, the Chinese researchers found forest NPP "increased dramatically, with an average increase of about 30.4%." Su et al. thus conclude, "the effects of precipitation and temperature change were simply additive," but the synergy between the effects of climate change and doubled CO_2 made the whole response much larger than the sum of its separate responses because "feedback loops associated with the water and nitrogen cycles [which may be influenced significantly by atmospheric CO_2 enrichment]

ultimately influence the carbon assimilation response."

Koutavas (2008), in prefacing his work, notes "tree rings are the primary archive used in annually resolved climate reconstructions spanning recent centuries to millennia, and as such their response to non-climatic factors requires careful evaluation." Stating an important consideration in this regard "is whether radial growth in trees over the 20th century has been influenced by anthropogenic effects, particularly the rising concentration of CO_2 in the global atmosphere," he further notes "LaMarche et al. (1984) were the first to attribute late 20th century growth enhancement in high-elevation bristlecone and limber pines from the western US to CO_2 fertilization." He adds, "Graybill and Idso (1993) further argued that a CO_2 growth effect can be detected in tree-ring chronologies from the southwest US in species exhibiting a strip-bark morphology."

In further exploring this subject, Koutavas analyzed ring-width variations obtained from cores of eight Greek fir (Abies cephalonica) trees growing at elevations between 1,300 and 1,600 meters on the southern slopes of Mt. Ainos on the island of Cephalonia in the Ionian Sea west of mainland Greece, while employing climate data from the University of East Anglia to determine whether any growth changes noted over the period of the ring-width record (AD 1840–2005) could be ascribed to any regional climate changes to which the trees might have been exposed.

The results of Koutavas's work are depicted in Figure 1.2.1.2.1. As can be seen from these data, and as Koutavas states, there was a "strong acceleration of growth over the second half of the 20th century" and "the sustained increase in growth since 1990 in particular was unprecedented over the full length of the data set." He also states these positive growth trends "bear no relationship to regional temperature or precipitation variations and therefore are unlikely to be climatically induced." And he affirms "disturbance effects from human activities are also unlikely, as the study site lies in a remote forest area with difficult access." Thus, about the only rational explanation for the late twentieth-century growth acceleration seen in the ring-width data is Koutavas's suggestion: "the enhanced growth reflects a fertilization effect due to rising CO_2 in the global atmosphere."

Martinez-Vilalta et al. (2008) used tree-ring data from the Catalan Ecological and Forest Inventory "to study the temporal variability of Scots pine stem radial growth (period 1901–1997) across a relatively large region (Catalonia, NE Spain) situated close to

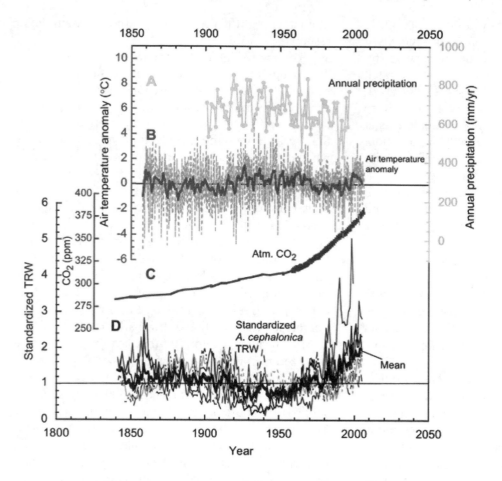

Figure 1.2.1.2.1. Annual precipitation totals, annual air temperature anomalies, atmospheric CO_2 concentrations (from Mauna Loa and Antarctica's Law Dome ice core), and the mean standardized tree-ring series (TRW) of the Greek fir trees. Adapted from Koutavas (2008).

the southern limit of the distribution of the species." The inventory included 10,664 plots randomly distributed throughout the forested area of Catalonia, where Scots pine was present in 30.2% of the plots and was the dominant tree species in 18.4% of them. The five researchers state their results "showed an overall increase of 84% in Scots pine BAI [basal area increment] during the 20th century, consistent with most previous studies for temperate forests." They note, "this trend was associated with increased atmospheric CO_2 concentra-tion," which they interpret to be "a fertilization effect." There was also, however, "a marked increase in temperature across the study region (0.19°C per decade on average)," but they report "this warming had a negative impact on radial growth, particularly at the drier sites," although "its magnitude was not enough to counteract the fertilization effect."

Peng *et al.* (2009) validated the process-based TRIPLEX model of forest growth and carbon and

nitrogen cycling against observed data. They then used the calibrated model to investigate the potential impacts of projected increases in the atmosphere's CO_2 concentration on the climate of northeast China and its interactions with the aerial fertilization effect of the increase in atmospheric CO_2 in computing changes likely to occur in the net primary productivity (NPP) and carbon budget of the region's forests. The model validation results show "the simulated tree total volume, NPP, total biomass and soil carbon are consistent with observed data across the Northeast of China, demonstrating that the improved TRIPLEX model is able to simulate forest growth and carbon dynamics of the boreal and temperate forest ecosystems at regional scale." Second, the seven scientists note the application of the appropriately calibrated model indicates climate change would increase forest NPP and biomass carbon but decrease overall soil carbon under all three of the climate change scenarios they studied. However, they report, "the combined effects of climate change and CO_2 fertilization on the increase of NPP were estimated to be 10–12% for [the] 2030s and 28–37% in [the] 2090s," because "the simulated effects of CO_2 fertilization significantly offset the soil carbon loss due to climate change alone."

Peng *et al.* thus conclude "overall, future climate change and increasing atmospheric CO_2 will have a significant impact on the forest ecosystems of Northeastern China," also noting their findings clearly indicate the impact would be beneficial. In addition, they write, "the results of the effects of CO_2 fertilization on NPP simulated by TRIPLEX1.0 are consistent with the recent FACE experiments in temperate forests in North America and Europe (Norby *et al.*, 2005), global analyses of Melillo *et al.* (1993) and Mathews (2007), and site-specific investigations in Canadian boreal forest ecosystems (Peng and Apps, 1998, 1999)." This consistency leads them to the further conclusion, "the effect of CO$_2$ fertilization on forest NPP is now firmly established."

Cole *et al.* (2010) note quaking aspen (*Populus tremuloides* Michx.) is "a dominant forest type in north-temperate, montane, and boreal regions of North America" and is, in fact, "the most widely distributed tree species on the continent." They also note aspen and related poplars are "quintessential foundation species (Ellison *et al.*, 2005), shaping the structure and function of the communities and ecosystems in which they occur (Whitham *et al.*, 2006; Schweitzer *et al.*, 2008; Madritch *et al.*, 2009)." This being the case, they attempted to determine how this keystone species may have responded to the increase in atmospheric CO$_2$ concentration that occurred over the past several decades, especially within the context of the climatic changes that occurred concurrently.

To do so, the four researchers collected branches from 919 trees after their leaves had dropped in the fall, obtaining samples that represented 189 genets or clones (five trees per clone) at 11 sites distributed throughout three regions of Wisconsin (USA). The sampled trees ranged from five to 76 years of age and came from second-growth unmanaged forests south of the areas defoliated by forest tent caterpillars in 1980–1982, 1989–1990, and 2001–2002. In addition, they recorded trunk diameter at breast height for each sampled tree, which, in their words, "is very highly correlated with total biomass in aspen," citing Bond-Lamberty *et al.* (2002).

Results of the analysis, they report, reveal "age-specific ring width increased over time" and "the greatest increase occurred for relatively young trees, so that young trees grew faster in recent years than did young trees several decades ago." During the past half-century, for example, the growth of trees 11–20 years old rose by 60%. In addition, they observe "rising CO$_2$ causes ring width to increase at all moisture levels, apparently resulting from improved water use efficiency," so "the overall increase results from historical increases in both CO$_2$ and water availability." And when they separate out the impacts of the two factors, they find "the effect of rising CO$_2$ had been to increase ring width by about 53%," as a result of "a 19.2% increase in ambient CO$_2$ levels during the growing season, from 315.8 ppm in 1958 (when CO$_2$ records began) to 376.4 ppm in 2003."

This is a truly remarkable finding; and Cole *et al.* comment, "the magnitude of the growth increase uncovered by this analysis raises the question of how much other major forest species may have responded to the joint effects of long-term changes in CO$_2$ and precipitation." It seems likely other tree species may have experienced similar growth stimulations, particularly in light of Tans (2009), who demonstrated Earth's land surfaces were a net source of CO$_2$ to the atmosphere until about 1940—primarily due to the felling of forests and the plowing of grasslands to make way for expanded agricultural activities—but who reports, from 1940 onward, as shown in Figure 1.2.1.2.2, the terrestrial biosphere has become, in the mean, an increasingly greater sink for CO$_2$, and that it has done so even in the face of massive global deforestation, for which it has apparently more than compensated. The combined findings of the two studies of Tans and Cole *et al.* clearly attest to the ability of the ongoing rise in the air's CO$_2$ content to transform the face of Earth.

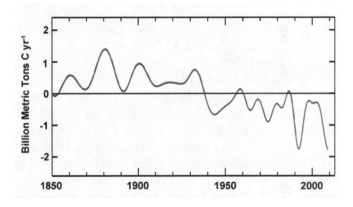

Figure 1.2.1.2.2. Five-year smoothed rates of carbon transfer from land to air (+) or from air to land (-) vs. time. Adapted from Tans (2009).

According to Knapp and Soule (2011), "atmospheric CO$_2$ concentrations have increased by over 27% since the early 20th century, resulting in enhanced radial tree growth in natural environments for numerous tree species in a variety of climatic regions (e.g., LaMarche *et al.*, 1984; Knapp *et al.*, 2001; Soule and Knapp, 2006; Voelker *et al.*, 2006; Wang *et al.*, 2006; Koutavas, 2008)." In addition, they note, "the principal benefit of elevated CO$_2$ for radial growth has been linked to increased intrinsic water use efficiency (iWUE), which is the ratio of net CO$_2$ assimilation through leaf stomata to leaf stomatal conductance." And they report "increases in iWUE based on carbon isotope chronologies have been identified for trees growing in both controlled (e.g., Leavitt *et al.*, 2003) and natural environments (e.g., Bert *et al.*, 1997; Feng, 1999; Tang *et al.*, 1999;

Arneth *et al.*, 2002; Saurer *et al.*, 2004; Waterhouse *et al.*, 2004; Liu *et al.*, 2007)."

The two researchers "examined radial growth responses of ponderosa pine (*Pinus ponderosa* var. *ponderosa*) between 1905–1954 and 1955–2004 to determine if the effects of increased intrinsic water use efficiencies caused by elevated atmospheric CO_2 concentrations were age-specific," working with 209 cores collected from mature trees (ranging in age from at least 100 to more than 450 years) from five sites in the USA's northern Rocky Mountains. They also calculated iWUE using carbon isotope data from 1850 to 2004.

The authors found, "(1) responses to elevated atmospheric CO_2 in old-growth ponderosa forests are age-specific; (2) radial growth increases in older trees coincided with increased iWUE; (3) ponderosa had increased growth rates in their third, fourth, and fifth centuries of life; and (4) age-specific growth responses during 1955–2004 are unique since at least the mid-16th century." They also report "increases in iWUE during 1955–2004 were 11% greater than during 1905–1954."

Knapp and Soule say their findings "demonstrate that old-growth ponderosa pine forests of the northern Rockies have likely benefited from the effects of increased atmospheric CO_2 since the mid-20th century and that the benefits increase with tree age." And since the CO_2-induced radial growth increases in the older trees "were significantly associated with rising iWUE," they opine the "accelerated growth rates are likely caused by more efficient water use in the semiarid environment where the trees were sampled."

In concluding, the two scientists state "old-growth trees can be highly responsive to environmental changes," especially the ongoing rise in the air's CO_2 content, as their work clearly demonstrates. They note even what many might call ancient trees are still "capable of increased growth rates several hundred years after establishment," citing McDowell *et al.* (2003) and Martinez-Vilalta *et al.* (2007).

Using data from the website of the International Tree-Ring Data Bank as well as from cores collected previously and stored in their laboratory at The Pennsylvania State University (USA), Johnson and Abrams (2009) explored growth rate (basal area increment, BAI) relationships across age classes (from young to old) for eight tree species commonly found throughout the eastern United States: bigtooth aspen (*Populus grandidentata* Michx.), blackgum (*Nyssa sylvatica* Marsh.), black oak (*Quercus velutina*

Lam.), chestnut oak (*Quercus Montana* L.), hemlock (*Tsuga canadensis* L. Carr.), pitch pine (*Pinus rigida* Mill.), red oak (*Quercus rubra*), and white oak (*Quercus alba* L.). The two researchers report "a remarkable finding of this study was that even the oldest trees of several species had slow but increasing BAI values, which continued throughout the life of most trees." They characterize this finding as "remarkable," they explain, because it "contradicts the sigmoidal growth model that predicts growth rate should plateau and then decline, as middle age trees approach old age," citing Ryan and Yoder (1997) and Weiner and Thomas (2001). They also report, "over the last 50–100 years, younger trees within a species grew faster than did the older trees when they were of the same respective age," which is what Knapp and Soule (2011) found for ponderosa pine trees in the USA's northern Rocky Mountains.

Further discussing their findings, the two researchers from Pennsylvania State University's School of Forest Resources write, "it seems reasonable to assume" the greater growth rates of older trees of the current era compared to older trees of older times "may be due to a stimulatory effect of anthropogenic global change defined in the broadest sense," including "increased CO_2 levels, warming temperatures, increased precipitation, and changes in precipitation chemistry," noting "yearly average temperatures, atmospheric CO_2 and nitrogen levels have increased in the eastern US (as well as much of the rest of the world) over the last 50–100 years."

In another study from Soule and Knapp (2011), the two researchers "examined changes in and relationships between radial growth and intrinsic water use efficiency (iWUE) of ponderosa pine (*Pinus ponderosa*) trees, climate, and atmospheric CO_2 in the western United States since the mid-nineteenth century." They developed "tree-ring chronologies for eight sites in three climate regions and using carbon isotope data to calculate pentadal values of iWUE," and then "examined relationships among radial growth, climate, iWUE, and CO_2 via correlation and regression analyses." They found "trends toward higher rates of iWUE for ponderosa pine are panregional, occurring at eight sites within three distinct climatic regimes and for two subspecies," and these results "are similar to those reported by Feng (1999) for several coniferous tree species found throughout western North America." They also note "increasing iWUE has been reported for conifers at other northern hemisphere locations (e.g., Bert *et al.*, 1997; Saurer *et al.*, 2004)." They conclude "future increases in iWUE are likely for ponderosa pine within our study regions as CO$_2$ levels increase," and they state they found "significant improvements in radial growth rates during drought years after 1950." These findings suggest "increased iWUE associated with rising CO$_2$ can positively impact tree growth rates in the western United States and is thus an evolving component of forest ecosystem processes." Soule and Knapp also state, "if potential climate changes lead to increasing aridity in the western United States, additional increases in iWUE associated with future increases in CO$_2$ might ameliorate growth declines associated with drought conditions."

Working within lichen woodlands of the forest zone of Eastern Canada between longitudes 70 and 72°W, Girard *et al.* (2011) acquired data enabling them to calculate radial, height, and volume growth rates at every 15 minutes of latitude from 47°30'N to 52°41'N for black spruce (*Picea mariana*) trees ranging in age from 34 to 188 years. Dividing the trees into a young group and an old group, with ages ranging between 34 and 93 years for the young group and between 109 and 188 years for the old group, the three Canadian researchers report same-age "radial, height and volume growth rates of trees in stands younger than 100 years were 46%, 51%, and 38%, respectively, greater than those of trees in stands older than 100 years." And for the two youngest stands, with mean ages of 34 and 43 years, they state "black spruce showed radial, height and volume growth rates of 66%, 74%, and 71%, respectively, greater than those in woodlands older than 100 years." Further discussing their findings, Girard *et al.* cite several other studies demonstrating "tree productivity in northern forests of eastern North America has increased significantly since the middle of the 19th century," namely Payette *et al.* (1985), D'Arrigo *et al.* (1987), D'Arrigo *et al.* (1992), and Lavoie and Payette (1994). They also note "similar trends have been observed in the American West," citing Graumlich *et al.* (1989) and Peterson *et al.* (1990).

Introducing his study, Parn (2012) writes "the potential productivity of a forest site has been regarded as natural and stable in a long-term perspective (Elfving *et al.*, 1996)," but "environmental changes such as increase of CO$_2$ in the atmosphere, deposition of pollutants and climate changes since the 1950s have had various effects on forest ecosystems," and "the increasing human impact on the environment makes the stability of the site conditions questionable." Thus the author set out to learn whether these environmental changes may have affected the growth of Scots pine trees. Specifically,

Parn studied the growth history of trees of identical cambial age but two different calendar ages at two different sites: Koiguste on Saaremaa island, the largest of the Estonian islands in the Baltic Sea, and Pirita in North Estonia near the Estonian capital. The age of the old stand at the Koiguste site was 160 years and that of the young stand 55 years, and the ages of the old and young stands at the Pirita site were 155 and 55 years, respectively. At both of these locations, Parn writes, "the differences in the radial growth of successive stand generations were assessed using the average tree-ring widths of the same cambial age of stands at age of 30, 40 and 50 years."

Parn found "the radial growth of young generations exceeded that of old stands at the same cambial age," and "approximately similar results were obtained when latewood widths were used instead of the tree-ring widths in the analysis." In addition, he reports "a fairly strong positive effect of the mean temperatures of the spring months on the latewood width can be observed." He notes a similar "strong link between the latewood width and spring temperatures was described by Miina (2000) for Scots pines in eastern Finland, by Savva *et al.* (2003) for pines from different provenances in Russia, and by Drobyshev *et al.* (2004) for pines in the Komi Republic." As for what was responsible for these findings, Parn suggests "it may be assumed that long-term climate change may have caused, at least partly, the increasing growth of young generations of pine" and "the increased nitrogen deposition and elevated CO$_2$ level during the second half of the 20th century may have had some positive influence."

References

Ainsworth, E.A. and Long, S.P. 2005. What have we learned from 15 years of free-air CO$_2$ enrichment (FACE)? A meta-analytic review of the responses of photosynthesis, canopy properties and plant production to rising CO$_2$. *New Phytologist* **165**: 351–372.

Arneth, A., Lloyd, J., Santruckova, H., Bird, M., Grigoryev, S., Kalaschnikov, Y.N., Sukachev, V.N., Gleixner, G., and Schulze, E.-D. 2002. Response of central Siberian Scots pine to soil water deficit and long-term trends in atmospheric CO$_2$ concentration. *Global Biogeochemical Cycles* **16**: 10.1029/2000GB001374.

Bergh, J., Freeman, M., Sigurdsson, B., Kellomaki, S., Laitinen, K., Niinisto, S., Peltola, H., and Linder, S. 2003. Modelling the short-term effects of climate change on the productivity of selected tree species in Nordic countries. *Forest Ecology and Management* **183**: 327–340.

Bernacchi, C.J., Calfapietra, C., Davey, P.A., Wittig, V.E., Scarascia-Mugnozza, G.E., Raines, C.A., and Long, S.P. 2003. Photosynthesis and stomatal conductance responses of poplars to free-air CO_2 enrichment (PopFACE) during the first growth cycle and immediately following coppice. *New Phytologist* **159**: 609–621.

Berntson, G.M. and Bazzaz, F.A. 1998. Regenerating temperate forest mesocosms in elevated CO_2: belowground growth and nitrogen cycling. *Oecologia* **113**: 115–125.

Bert, D., Leavitt, S.W., and Dupouey, J.-L. 1997. Variations of wood $\delta^{13}C$ and water use efficiency of *Abies alba* during the last century. *Ecology* **78**: 1588–1596.

Bond-Lamberty, B., Wang, C., and Gower, S.T. 2002. Aboveground and belowground biomass and sapwood area allometric equations for six boreal tree species of northern Manitoba. *Canadian Journal of Forest Research* **32**: 1441–1450.

Cole, C.T., Anderson, J.E., Lindroth, R.L., and Waller, D.M. 2010. Rising concentrations of atmospheric CO_2 have increased growth in natural stands of quaking aspen (*Populus tremuloides*). *Global Change Biology* **16**: 2186–2197.

D'Arrigo, R., Jacoby, G., and Free, R. 1992. Tree-ring width and maximum latewood density at the North-American tree line: Parameters of climatic change. *Canadian Journal of Forest Research* **22**: 1290–1296.

D'Arrigo, R., Jacoby, G., and Fung, I. 1987. Boreal forests and atmosphere biosphere exchange of carbon dioxide. *Nature* **329**: 321–323.

Davi, H., Dufrene, E., Francois, C., Le Maire, G., Loustau, D., Bosc, A., Rambal, S., Granier, A., and Moors, E. 2006. Sensitivity of water and carbon fluxes to climate changes from 1960–2100 in European forest ecosystems. *Agricultural and Forest Meteorology* **141**: 35–56.

DeLucia, E.H., Hamilton, J.G., Naidu, S.L., Thomas, R.B., Andrews, J.A., Finzi, A., Lavine, M., Matamala, R., Mohan, J.E., Hendrey, G.R., and Schlesinger, W.H. 1999. Net primary production of a forest ecosystem with experimental CO_2 enrichment. *Science* **284**: 1177–1179.

DeLucia, E.H. and Thomas, R.B. 2000. Photosynthetic responses to CO_2 enrichment of four hardwood species in a forest understory. *Oecologia* **122**: 11–19.

Drobyshev, I., Niklasson, M., and Angelstam, P. 2004. Contrasting tree-ring data with fire record in a pine-dominated landscape in the Komi Republik (Eastern European Russia): recovering a common climate signal. *Silva Fennica* **38**: 43–53.

Duquesnay, A., Breda, N., Stievenard, M., and Dupouey, J.L. 1998. Changes of tree-ring $\delta^{13}C$ and water use efficiency of beech (*Fagus sylvatica* L.) in north-eastern France during the past century. *Plant, Cell and Environment* **21**: 565–572.

Elfving, B., Tegnhammar, L., and Tveite, B. 1996. Studies on growth trends of forests in Sweden and Norway. In: Spiecker, H., Mielikainen, K., Kohl, M., and Skovsgaard, J.P. (Eds.) *Growth Trends in European Forests*. EFI Research Report No. 5. Springer-Verlag, Berlin, Germany, pp. 61–70.

Ellison, A.M., Bank, M.S., Clinton, B.D., Colburn, E.A., Elliott, K., Ford, C.R., Foster, D.R., Kloeppel, B.D., Knoepp, J.D., Lovett, G.M., Mohan, J., Orwig, D.A., Rodenhouse, N.L., Sobczak, W.V., Stinson, K.A., Stone, J.K., Swan, C.M., Thompson, J., Holle, B.V., and Webster, J.R. 2005. Loss of foundation species: consequences for the structure and dynamics of forested ecosystems. *Frontiers in Ecology and the Environment* **3**: 479–486.

Feng, X. 1999. Trends in intrinsic water use efficiency of natural trees for the past 100–200 years: a response to atmospheric concentration. *Geochimica et Cosmochimica Acta* **63**: 1891–1903.

Girard, F., Payette, S., and Gagnon, R. 2011. Dendroecological analysis of black spruce in lichen-spruce woodlands of the closed-crown forest zone in eastern Canada. *Ecoscience* **18**: 279–294.

Graumlich, L.J., Brubaker, L.B., and Grier, C.C. 1989. Long-term trends in forest net primary productivity: Cascade Mountains, Washington. *Ecology* **70**: 405–410.

Graybill, D.A. and Idso, S.B. 1993. Detecting the aerial fertilization effect of atmospheric CO_2 enrichment in tree-ring chronologies. *Global Biogeochemical Cycles* **7**: 81–95.

Hamilton, J.G., DeLucia, E.H., George, K., Naidu, S.L., Finzi, A.C., and Schlesinger, W.H. 2002. Forest carbon balance under elevated CO_2. *Oecologia* DOI 10.1007/s00442-002-0884-x.

Hamilton, J.G., Thomas, R.B., and DeLucia, E.H. 2001. Direct and indirect effects of elevated CO_2 on leaf respiration in a forest ecosystem. *Plant, Cell and Environment* **24**: 975–982.

Hanson, P.J., Samuelson, L.J., Wullschleger, S.D., Tabberer, T.A., and Edwards, G.S. 1994. Seasonal patterns of light-saturated photosynthesis and leaf conductance for mature and seedling *Quercus rubra* L. foliage: differential sensitivity to ozone. *Tree Physiology* **14**: 1351–1366.

Hanson, P.J., Wullschleger, S.D., Norby, R.J., Tschaplinski, T.J., and Gunderson, C.A. 2005. Importance of changing CO_2, temperature, precipitation, and ozone on carbon and water cycles of an upland-oak forest: incorporating experimental results into model simulations. *Global Change Biology* **11**: 1402–1423.

Hari, P. and Arovaara, H. 1988. Detecting CO_2 induced enhancement in the radial increment of trees. Evidence from the northern timberline. *Scandinavian Journal of Forest Research* **3**: 67–74.

Hari, P., Arovaara, H., Raunemaa, T., and Hautojarvi, A. 1984. Forest growth and the effects of energy production: A method for detecting trends in the growth potential of trees. *Canadian Journal of Forest Research* **14**: 437–440.

Herrick, J.D. and Thomas, R.B. 1999. Effects of CO_2 enrichment on the photosynthetic light response of Sun and shade leaves of canopy sweetgum trees (*Liquidambar styraciflua*) in a forest ecosystem. *Tree Physiology* **19**: 779–786.

Houghton, J.T., Ding, Y., Griggs, D.J., Noguer, M., van der Linden, P.J., Dai, X., Maskell, K., and Johnson, C.A. 2001. Climate Change 2001. In: Maskell, K. and Johnson, C.A. (Eds.) *The Scientific Basis: Contribution of Working Group I to the Third Assessment Report of the Intergovernmental Panel on Climate Change (IPCC)*. Cambridge University Press, Cambridge, United Kingdom.

Hussain, M., Kubiske, M.E., and Connor, K.F. 2001. Germination of CO_2-enriched *Pinus taeda* L. seeds and subsequent seedling growth responses to CO_2 enrichment. *Functional Ecology* **15**: 344–350.

Hymus, G.J., Ellsworth, D.S., Baker, N.R., and Long, S.P. 1999. Does free-air carbon dioxide enrichment affect photochemical energy use by evergreen trees in different seasons? A chlorophyll fluorescence study of mature loblolly pine. *Plant Physiology* **120**: 1183–1191.

Idso, S.B. 1995. *CO₂ and the Biosphere: The Incredible Legacy of the Industrial Revolution*. Department of Soil, Water and Climate, University of Minnesota, St. Paul, Minnesota, USA.

Johnson, S.E. and Abrams, M.D. 2009. Age class, longevity and growth rate relationships: protracted growth increases in old trees in the eastern United States. *Tree Physiology* **29**: 1317–1328.

Kellomaki, S. and Wang, K.-Y. 2001. Growth and resource use of birch seedlings under elevated carbon dioxide and temperature. *Annals of Botany* **87**: 669–682.

Knapp, P.A. and Soule, P.T. 2011. Increasing water use efficiency and age-specific growth responses of old-growth ponderosa pine trees in the Northern Rockies. *Global Change Biology* **17**: 631–641.

Knapp, P.A., Soule, P.T., and Grissino-Mayer, H.D. 2001. Detecting the potential regional effects of increased atmospheric CO_2 on growth rates of western juniper. *Global Change Biology* **7**: 903–917.

Knight, C.L., Briggs, J.M., and Nellis, M.D. 1994.

Expansion of gallery forest on Konza Prairie Research Natural Area, Kansas, USA. *Landscape Ecology* **9**: 117–125.

Koutavas, A. 2008. Late 20th century growth acceleration in Greek firs (*Aibes cephalonica*) from Cephalonia Island, Greece: A CO_2 fertilization effect? *Dendrochronologia* **26**: 13–19.

LaMarche Jr., V.C., Graybill, D.A., Fritts, H.C., and Rose, M.R. 1984. Increasing atmospheric carbon dioxide: Tree ring evidence for growth enhancement in natural vegetation. *Science* **223**: 1019–1021.

Lavoie, C. and Payette, S. 1994. Recent fluctuations of the lichen spruce forest limit in subarctic Quebec. *Journal of Ecology* **82**: 725–734.

Leavitt, S.W., Idso, S.B., Kimball, B.A., Burns, J.M., Sinha, A., and Stott, L. 2003. The effect of long-term atmospheric CO_2 enrichment on the intrinsic water use efficiency of sour orange trees. *Chemosphere* **50**: 217–222.

Liu, X., Shao, X., Liang, E., Zhao, L., Chen, T., Qin, D., and Ren, J. 2007. Species dependent responses of juniper and spruce to increasing CO_2 concentration and to climate in semi-arid and arid areas of northwestern China. *Plant Ecology* **193**: 195–209.

Lloyd, J. 1999. The CO_2 dependence of photosynthesis, plant growth responses to elevated CO_2 concentrations and their interaction with soil nutrient status, II. Temperate and boreal forest productivity and the combined effects of increasing CO_2 concentrations and increased nitrogen deposition at a global scale. *Functional Ecology* **13**: 439–459.

Long, S.P. 1991. Modification of the response of photosynthetic productivity to rising temperature by atmospheric CO_2 concentrations: Has its importance been underestimated? *Plant, Cell and Environment* **14**: 729–739.

Lupo, A. and Kininmonth, W. 2013. Global climate models and their limitations. In Idso, C.D., Carter, R.M., and Singer, S.F. (Eds.) *Climate Change Reconsidered II: Physical Science*. Chicago, IL: The Heartland Institute.

Madritch, M.D., Greene, S.G., and Lindroth, R.L. 2009. Genetic mosaics of ecosystem functioning across aspen-dominated landscapes. *Oecologia* **160**: 119–127.

Martinez-Vilalta, J., Lopez, B.C., Adell, N., Badiella, L., and Ninyerola, M. 2008. Twentieth century increase of Scots pine radial growth in NE Spain shows strong climate interactions. *Global Change Biology* **14**: 2868–2881.

Martinez-Vilalta, J., Vanderklein, D., and Mencuccini, M. 2007. Tree height and age-related decline in growth in Scots pine (*Pinus sylvestris* L.). *Oecologia* **150**: 529–544.

Matthews, H.D. 2007. Implications of CO₂ fertilization for future climate change in a coupled climate-carbon model. *Global Change Biology* **13**: 1–11.

McDowell, N., Brooks, J.R., Fitzgerald, S.A., and Bond, B.J. 2003. Carbon isotope discrimination and growth response of old *Pinus ponderosa* trees to stand density reductions. *Plant, Cell and Environment* **26**: 631–644.

Medlyn, B.E., Badeck. F.-W., De Pury, D.G.G., Barton, C.V.M., Broadmeadow, M., Ceulemans, R., De Angelis, P., Forstreuter, M., Jach, M.E., Kellomaki, S., Laitat, E., Marek, M., Philippot, S., Rey, A., Strassemeyer, J., Laitinen, K., Liozon, R., Portier, B., Roberntz, P., Wang, K., and Jarvis, P.G. 1999. Effects of elevated [CO_2] on photosynthesis in European forest species: a meta-analysis of model parameters. *Plant, Cell and Environment* **22**: 1475–1495.

Melillo, J.M., McGuire, A.D., Kicklighter, D.W., Moore, B., Vorosmarty, C.J., and Schloss, A.L. 1993. Global climate change and terrestrial net primary production. *Nature* **363**: 234–240.

Miglietta, F., Peressotti, A., Vaccari, F.P., Zaldei, A., deAngelis, P., and Scarascia-Mugnozza, G. 2001. Free-air CO_2 enrichment (FACE) of a poplar plantation: The POPFACE fumigation system. *New Phytologist* **150**: 465–476.

Miina, J. 2000. Dependence of tree-ring, earlywood and latewood indices of Scots pine and Norway spruce on climatic factors in eastern Finland. *Ecological Modeling* **132**: 259–273.

Naidu, S.L. and DeLucia, E.H. 1999. First-year growth response of trees in an intact forest exposed to elevated CO_2. *Global Change Biology* **5**: 609–613.

National Assessment Synthesis Team (NAST). 2000. *Climate Change Impacts on the United States: The Potential Consequences of Climate Variability and Change.* US Global Change Research Program, Washington, DC.

Naumburg, E. and Ellsworth, D.S. 2000. Photosynthetic sunfleck utilization potential of understory saplings growing under elevated CO_2 in FACE. *Oecologia* **122**: 163–174.

Norby, R.J., DeLucia, E.H., Gielen, B., Calfapietra, C., Giardina, C.P., King, S.J., Ledford, J., McCarthy, H.R., Moore, D.J.P., Ceulemans, R., De Angelis, P., Finzi, A.C., Karnosky, D.F., Kubiske, M.E., Lukac, M., Pregitzer, K.S., Scarasci-Mugnozza, G.E., Schlesinger, W.H., and Oren, R. 2005. Forest response to elevated CO_2 is conserved across a broad range of productivity. *Proceedings of the National Academy of Sciences USA* **102**: 18,052–18,056.

Norby, R.J., Hanson, P.J., O'Neill, E.G., Tschaplinski, T.J., Weltzin, J.F., Hansen, R.A., Cheng, W., Wullschleger, S.D., Gunderson, C.A., Edwards, N.T., and Johnson, D.W. 2002. Net primary productivity of a CO_2-enriched deciduous forest and the implications for carbon storage. *Ecological Applications* **12**: 1261–1266.

Norby, R.J., Todd, D.E., Fults, J., and Johnson, D.W. 2001. Allometric determination of tree growth in a CO_2-enriched sweetgum stand. *New Phytologist* **150**: 477–487.

Olsson, E.G.A., Austrheim, G., and Grenne, S.N. 2000. Landscape change patterns in mountains, land use and environmental diversity, Mid-Norway 1960–1993. *Landscape Ecology* **15**: 155–170.

Parker, M.L. 1987. Recent abnormal increase in tree-ring widths: A possible effect of elevated atmospheric carbon dioxide. In: Jacoby Jr., G.C. and Hornbeck, J.W. (Eds.) *Proceedings of the International Symposium on Ecological Aspects of Tree-Ring Analysis.* U.S. Department of Energy, Washington, DC, pp. 511–521.

Parn, H. 2012. Changes in the radial growth of two consecutive generations of Scots pine (*Pinys sylvestris* L.) stands. *Baltic Forestry* **18**: 12–24.

Peng, C.H. and Apps, M.J. 1998. Simulating carbon dynamics along the Boreal Forest Transect Case Study (BFTCS) in the Central of Canada: II. Sensitivity to climate change. *Global Biogeochemical Cycles* **12**: 393–402.

Peng, C.H. and Apps, M.J. 1999. Modeling response of net primary productivity (NPP) of boreal forest ecosystems to changes in climate and fire disturbance regimes. *Ecological Modeling* **122**: 175–193.

Peng, C., Zhou, X., Zhao, S., Wang, X., Zhu, B., Piao, S., and Fang, J. 2009. Quantifying the response of forest carbon balance to future climate change in Northeastern China: Model validation and prediction. *Global and Planetary Change* **66**: 179–194.

Peterson, D.L., Arbaugh, M.J., Robinson, L.J., and Derderian, B.R. 1990. Growth trends of whitebark pine and lodgepole pine in a sub-alpine Sierra-Nevada forest, California, USA. *Arctic and Alpine Research* **22**: 233–243.

Pritchard, S.G., Davis, M.A., Mitchell, R.J., Prior, A.S., Boykin, D.L., Rogers, H.H., and Runion, G.B. 2001. Root dynamics in an artificially constructed regenerating longleaf pine ecosystem are affected by atmospheric CO_2 enrichment. *Environmental and Experimental Botany* **46**: 35–69.

Rathgeber, C., Nicault, A., Guiot, J., Keller, T., Guibal, F., and Roche, P. 2000. Simulated responses of *Pinus halepensis* forest productivity to climatic change and CO_2 increase using a statistical model. *Global and Planetary Change* **26**: 405–421.

Rathgeber, C., Nicault, A., Kaplan, J.O., and Guiot, J. 2003. Using a biogeochemistry model in simulating forests productivity responses to climatic change and [CO_2] increase: example of *Pinus halepensis* in Provence (southeast France). *Ecological Modelling* **166**: 239–255.

Rodrigues, R.R. and Nave, A.G. 2000. Heterogeneidade floristica das matas ciliares. In: Rodrigues, R.R. and Leitao Filho, H.F. (Eds.) *Matas Ciliares: Conservacao e Recuperacao.* Editora da USP/FAPESP, 2000. Sao Paulo, Brazil, pp. 45–71.

Ryan, M.G. and Yoder, B.J. 1997. Hydraulic limits to tree height and tree growth. *Bioscience* **47**: 235–242.

Saurer, M.S., Siegwolf, R.T.W., and Schweingruber, F. 2004. Carbon isotope discrimination indicates improving water use efficiency of trees in northern Eurasia over the last 100 years. *Global Change Biology* **10**: 2109–2120.

Savva, Y.V., Schweingruber, F.H., Vaganov, E.A., and Milyutin, L.I. 2003. Influence of climate changes on tree-ring characteristics of Scots pine provenances in southern Siberia (forest-steppe). *IAWA Journal* **24**: 371–383.

Schweitzer, J.A., Madritch, M.D., Bailey, J.K., LeRoy, C.J., Fischer, D.G., Rehill, B.J., Lindroth, R.L., Hagerman, A.E., Wooley, S.C., Hart, S.C., and Whitham, T.G. 2008. The genetic basis of condensed tannins and their role in nutrient regulation in a *Populus* model system. *Ecosystems* **11**: 1005–1020.

Sefcik, L.T., Zak, D.R., and Ellsworth, D.S. 2007. Seedling survival in a northern temperate forest understory is increased by elevated atmospheric carbon dioxide and atmospheric nitrogen deposition. *Global Change Biology* **13**: 132–146.

Shaw, M.R., Zavaleta, E.S., Chiariello, N.R., Cleland, E.E., Mooney, H.A., and Field, C.B. 2002. Grassland responses to global environmental changes suppressed by elevated CO$_2$. *Science* **298**: 1987–1990.

Soule, P.T. and Knapp, P.A. 2006. Radial growth rate increases in naturally-occurring ponderosa pine trees: a late 20th century CO$_2$ fertilization effect? *New Phytologist* **171**: 379–390.

Soule, P.T. and Knapp, P.A. 2011. Radial growth and increased water use efficiency for ponderosa pine trees in three regions in the western United States. *The Professional Geographer* **63**: 379–391.

Su, H.-X. and Sang, W.-G. 2004. Simulations and analysis of net primary productivity in *Quercus liaotungensis* forest of Donglingshan Mountain Range in response to different climate change scenarios. *Acta Botanica Sinica* **46**: 1281–1291.

Su, H.-X., Sang, W., Wang, Y., and Ma, K. 2007. Simulating *Picea schrenkiana* forest productivity under climatic changes and atmospheric CO$_2$ increase in Tianshan Mountains, Xinjiang Autonomous Region, China. *Forest Ecology and Management* **246**: 273–284.

Tang, K., Feng, X., and Funkhouser, G. 1999. The δ^{13}C of trees in full-bark and strip-bark bristlecone pines in the White Mountains of California. *Global Change Biology* **5**: 33–40.

Tans, P. 2009. An accounting of the observed increase in oceanic and atmospheric CO$_2$ and an outlook for the future. *Oceanography* **22**: 26–35.

Voelker, S.L., Muzika, R., Guyette, R.P., and Stambaugh, M.C. 2006. Evidence for historic CO$_2$ enhancement of tree-ring growth shows a decline through age in *Quercus velutina*, *Quercus coccinea* and *Pinus echinata*. *Ecological Monographs* **76**: 549–564.

Walker, R.F., Johnson, D.W., Geisinger, D.R., and Ball, J.T. 2000. Growth, nutrition, and water relations of ponderosa pine in a field soil as influenced by long-term exposure to elevated atmospheric CO$_2$. *Forest Ecology and Management* **137**: 1–11.

Wang, G.G., Chhin, S., and Baurle, W.L. 2006. Effect of natural atmospheric CO$_2$ fertilization suggested by open-grown white spruce in a dry environment. *Global Change Biology* **12**: 601–610.

Waterhouse, J.S., Switsur, V.R., Barker, A.C., Carter, A.H.C., Hemming, D.L., Loader, N.J., and Robertson, I. 2004. Northern European trees show a progressively diminishing response to increasing atmospheric carbon dioxide concentrations. *Quaternary Science Reviews* **23**: 803–810.

Weiner, J. and Thomas, S.C. 2001. The nature of tree growth and the age-related decline in forest productivity. *Oikos* **94**: 374–376.

West, D.C. 1988. Detection of forest response to increased atmospheric carbon dioxide. In: Koomanoff, F.A. (Ed.) *Carbon Dioxide and Climate: Summaries of Research in FY 1988*. U.S. Department of Energy, Washington, DC, p. 57.

Whitham, T.G., Bailey, J.K., and Schweitzer, J.A. 2006. A framework for community and ecosystem genetics from genes to ecosystems. *Nature Reviews Genetics* **7**: 510–523.

Winnett, S.M. 1998. Potential effects of climate change on US forests: a review. *Climate Research* **11**: 39–49.

Wullschleger, S.D. and Norby, R.J. 2001. Sap velocity and canopy transpiration in a sweetgum stand exposed to free-air CO$_2$ enrichment (FACE). *New Phytologist* **150**: 489–498.

1.2.1.3 Growth Rates of Old vs. Young Trees

- In contrast to frequently stated assumptions, old-growth forests can be significant carbon sinks, and their capacity to sequester carbon in the future will be enhanced as the air's CO$_2$ content rises.

The planting and preservation of forests has long been acknowledged to be an effective and environmentally friendly means of slowing climate-model-predicted CO_2-induced global warming. This prescription for moderating potential climate change is based on two well-established and very straightforward facts: (1) the carbon that trees use to construct their tissues comes from the air, and (2) its extraction from the atmosphere slows the rate of rise of the air's CO_2 content.

Although simple in concept, this potential partial solution to the putative global warming problem has been under attack for several years by those who want to address the issue solely through forced reductions in anthropogenic CO_2 emissions (see Pearce, 1999). The tack they take in this campaign is to claim carbon sequestration by forests is viable only when forests are young and growing vigorously; as forests age, they assert, they gradually lose their carbon sequestering prowess, so forests more than one hundred years old become essentially useless for removing CO_2 from the air. They further claim such old stands yearly lose as much CO_2 via respiration as they acquire via photosynthesis. Here we examine the validity of such assertions based on actual measurements made on older trees.

In Panama (Condit *et al.*, 1995), Brazil (Chambers *et al.*, 1998; Laurance *et al.*, 2004; Chambers *et al.*, 2001), and many parts of the southwestern United States (Graybill and Idso, 1993), individual trees of a number of different species have been shown to live for nearly one-and-a-half millennia. At a hundred or so years of age, these super-consumers of CO_2 are mere youngsters. In their *really* old age, their appetite for the vital gas, though diminished, is not lost. Chambers *et al.* (1998) note the long-lived trees of Brazil continue to experience protracted slow growth even at 1,400 years of age. The protracted slow growth (evident in yearly increasing trunk diameters) of very old and large trees can absorb a tremendous amount of CO_2 out of the air each year, especially when—as noted by Chambers *et al.* (1998) with respect to the Brazilian forests in the central Amazon—about 50% of forests' aboveground biomass is contained in less than the largest 10% of their trees. Consequently, since the lifespan of these massive, long-lived trees is considerably greater than the projected lifespan of the entire "Age of Fossil Fuels," their cultivation and preservation represents an essentially *permanent* partial solution to the perceived problem of global warming that is ascribed to anthropogenic CO_2 emissions.

As important as are these facts about trees,

however, an even more important fact comes into play in the case of forests and their ability to sequester carbon over long periods of time. This little-acknowledged piece of information is the fact that the forest itself—conceptualized as a huge super-organism—is the unit of primary importance in determining the ultimate amount of carbon that can be sequestered on a unit area of land.

That this difference in perspective can have enormous consequences is demonstrated by Cary *et al.* (2001), who note most models of forest carbon sequestration wrongly assume "age-related growth trends of individual trees and even-aged, monospecific stands can be extended to natural forests." When they compared the predictions of such models against real-world data gathered from northern Rocky Mountain subalpine forests that ranged in age from 67 to 458 years, they found aboveground net primary productivity in 200-year-old natural stands is almost twice as great as in modeled stands, and the difference between the two increases linearly throughout the entire sample age range.

What explains the huge discrepancy? Cary *et al.* suggest long-term recruitment and the periodic appearance of additional late-successional species (increasing biodiversity) may have significant effects on stand productivity, infusing the primary unit of concern (the ever-evolving forest super-organism) with greater vitality than would have been projected on the basis of characteristics possessed by the unit earlier in its life. They also note the failure to include effects of size- or age-dependent decreases in stem and branch respiration per unit of sapwood volume in models of forest growth can cause overestimates of respiration in older stands by a factor of two to five.

How serious are these model shortcomings? For the real-world forests studied by Cary *et al.*, they produce predictions of carbon sequestration only a little over half as large as what is observed in nature for 200-year-old forests, and for 400-year-old forests they produce results only about a third as large as what is characteristic of the real world. As the forests grew older still, the difference between reality and model projections grew right along with them.

Paw U *et al.* (2004) note old-growth forests generally have been considered to "represent carbon sources or are neutral (Odum, 1963, 1965)," stating "it is generally assumed that forests reach maximum productivity at an intermediate age and productivity declines in mature and old-growth stands (Franklin, 1988), presumably as dead woody debris and other respiratory demands increase." Particularly, they report a number of articles have suggested "old-growth conifer forests are at equilibrium with respect to net ecosystem productivity or net ecosystem exchange (DeBell and Franklin, 1987; Franklin and DeBell, 1988; Schulze *et al.*, 1999), as an age-class end point of ecosystem development."

To see whether these claims had any merit, Paw U *et al.* used an eddy covariance technique to estimate the CO_2 exchange rate of the oldest forest ecosystem (500 years old) in the AmeriFlux network of carbon-flux measurement stations—the Wind River old-growth forest in southwestern Washington, USA, which is composed mainly of Douglas-fir and western Hemlock—for 16 months, from May 1998 to August 1999. Throughout this period, the 14 scientists report, "there were no monthly averages with net release of CO_2," and the cumulative net ecosystem exchange showed "remarkable sequestration of carbon, comparable to many younger forests." They conclude, "in contrast to frequently stated opinions, old-growth forests can be significant carbon sinks," noting "the old-growth forests of the Pacific Northwest can contribute to optimizing carbon sequestration strategies while continuing to provide ecosystem services essential to supporting biodiversity."

Binkley *et al.* (2004) also addressed whether old forests gain or lose carbon. They revisited an aging aspen forest in the Tesuque watershed of northern New Mexico, USA—which between 1971 and 1976 (when it was between 90 and 96 years old) was thought to have had a negative net ecosystem production rate of -2.0 Mg ha^{-1} yr^{-1}—and measured the basal diameters of all trees in the central 0.01 ha of each of 27 plots arrayed across the watershed. They then used the same regression equations employed in the earlier study to calculate live tree biomass as of 2003.

"Contrary to expectation," Binkley *et al.* write, "live tree mass in 2003 [186 Mg ha^{-1}] was significantly greater than in 1976 [149 Mg ha^{-1}] (P = 0.02), refuting the hypothesis that live tree mass declined." They report the annual net increment of live tree mass was about 1.37 Mg ha^{-1} yr^{-1} from age 96 to age 123 years, only 12% less than the mean annual increment of live tree mass experienced over the forest's initial 96 years of existence (149 Mg ha^{-1} / 96 yr = 1.55 Mg ha^{-1} yr^{-1}). Consequently, in response to the question they posed when embarking on their study—"Do old forests gain or lose carbon?"—Binkley *et al.* conclude, "old aspen forests continue to accrue live stem mass well into their second century, despite declining current annual increments."

Hollinger *et al.* (1994) obtained similar results for a 300-year-old *Nothofagus* site in New Zealand, as did Law *et al.* (2001) for a 250-year-old ponderosa pine site in the northwestern United States, Falk *et al.* (2002) for a 450-year-old Douglas fir/western hemlock site in the same general area, and Knohl *et al.* (2003) for a 250-year-old deciduous forest in Germany. In commenting on these findings, the latter investigators say they found "unexpectedly high carbon uptake rates during two years for an unmanaged 'advanced' beech forest, which is in contrast to the widely spread hypothesis that 'advanced' forests are insignificant as carbon sinks." Thus, for the forest they studied, "assimilation is clearly not balanced by respiration, although this site shows typical characteristics of an 'advanced' forest at a comparatively late stage of development."

What has put the planet's trees on this healthier trajectory of being able to sequester significant amounts of carbon in their old age, when past theory (based on past observations) decreed they should be in a state of no-net-growth or even negative growth? The answer is rather simple. For any tree of age 250 years or more, the greater portion of its life (at least two-thirds of it) was spent in an atmosphere of much-reduced CO_2 content. Up until 1920, for example, the air's CO_2 concentration had never been above 300 ppm throughout the entire lives of such trees, whereas it is currently 400 ppm, or 33% higher. And older trees spent even greater portions of their lives in air of even lower CO_2 concentration. Thus the phenomenon that has given new life to old trees and allows them to "live long and prosper" is most likely the aerial fertilization effect produced by the flooding of the air with the CO_2 that resulted from the Industrial Revolution and is currently being maintained by its aftermath (Idso, 1995).

Greenep *et al.* (2003) found "the capacity for enhanced photosynthesis in trees growing in elevated CO_2 is unlikely to be lost in subsequent generations." That finding and the others previously cited suggest Earth's forests will remain strong sinks for atmospheric carbon far beyond the date at which IPCC's models indicate they would have given back to the atmosphere most of the carbon they had removed from it over their existence to that point in time. Subsequent reports have validated this assessment.

Zhou *et al.* (2006), for example, also note "old-growth forests have traditionally been considered negligible as carbon sinks because carbon uptake has been thought to be balanced by respiration." Thus they report "the soil carbon balance of old-growth forests has received little attention." In an attempt to rectify this situation, they "conducted a study to measure the long-term (1979 to 2003) dynamics of soil organic carbon stock in old-growth forests (age > 400 years) at the Dinghushan Biosphere Reserve in Guangdong Province, China." The eight scientists report "soil organic carbon concentration in the top 20-cm soil layer increased between 1979 and 2003 from about 1.4% to 2.35% at an average rate of 0.035% each year," and "measurements on a total of 230 composite soil samples collected between 1979 and 2003 suggested that soil organic carbon stock in the top 20-cm soil layer increased significantly during that time ($P < 0.0001$), with an average rate of 0.61 Mg C ha^{-1} year^{-1}." In discussing their findings, Zhou et al. state although "the driving forces for this observed high rate of soil organic carbon increase in the old-growth forests are not clear at present," their study "suggests that the carbon cycle processes in the belowground system of these forests are changing in response to the changing environment."

Luyssaert et al. (2008) conducted a literature survey to test the hypothesis that forests continue to acquire and sequester carbon from the atmosphere for hundreds of years. They compiled data from 519 plot studies conducted throughout the world's boreal and temperate forests (30% and 70% of the studies, respectively), skipping the tropics because of the low number of tropical sites that possessed the net ecosystem production (NEP) and forest age estimates needed for their analysis. They report, "in forests between 15 and 800 years old, the NEP is usually positive; that is, the forests are CO_2 sinks." In fact, they write, "young forests rather than old-growth forests are very often conspicuous sources of CO_2 because the creation of new forests (whether naturally or by humans) frequently follows disturbance to soil and the previous vegetation, resulting in a decomposition rate of coarse woody debris, litter and soil organic matter that exceeds the net primary production of the regrowth." Discussing the implications of their findings, the team of American, Belgian, British, French, German, and Swiss researchers writes, "because old-growth forests steadily accumulate carbon for centuries, they contain vast quantities of it," and "they will lose much of this carbon to the atmosphere if they are disturbed, so carbon-accounting rules for forests should give credit for leaving old-growth forests intact" to let them sequester even more carbon.

Phillips et al. (2008) note there was "a long held view," as they describe it, that "old trees exhibit little potential for growth." They therefore state "it may seem reasonable to conclude that old trees are not responsive to increased CO_2." They go on to demonstrate that view was far from correct.

The three researchers begin their analysis of the subject by stating, "hydraulic constraints in tall trees," such as those of great age, "constitute a fundamental form of water limitation; indeed, one that is indistinguishable from soil water limitations," citing Koch et al. (2004) and Woodruff et al. (2004). They also report "recent research indicates that tree size and its hydraulic correlates, rather than age per se, controls carbon gain in old trees," as indicated by Mencuccini et al. (2005). These findings imply, in their words, "factors that alleviate internal or external resource constraints on old trees could improve physiological function and ultimately growth," which is something elevated CO_2 does quite well by increasing plant water use efficiency. They list several phenomena that suggest "a fundamental potential for old growth trees to show greater photosynthesis and growth under industrial age increases in CO_2 than they would under constant, pre-industrial CO_2 levels."

Drawing from their own work, Phillips et al. report "500- and 20-year-old Douglas-fir trees both show high sensitivity of photosynthesis to atmospheric CO_2," presenting data that clearly demonstrate "under optimal conditions there exists the potential for an approximately 30% increase in photosynthetic rate with an increase in CO_2 from pre-industrial to current levels [i.e., from 280 to 385 ppm] in old trees." They note "the phenomenon of twentieth-century ring-width increase," which could thus be expected to accompany the twentieth century increase in the air's CO_2 concentration, has in fact been detected in several other studies, including LaMarche et al., (1984), Jacoby (1986), Graybill (1987), Kienast and Luxmoore (1988), Graumlich (1991), Knapp et al. (2001), Bunn et al. (2005), and Soule and Knapp (2006), to which could be added Graybill and Idso (1993).

A year later, Phillips et al. (2009) noted, over the past quarter-century of intensive region-wide measurements, the productivity of the Amazon rainforest—even in its extreme old age—has been "increasing with time," citing the comprehensive observational studies of Phillips et al. (1998), Nemani et al. (2003), Baker et al. (2004), Lewis et al. (2004), and Ichii et al. (2005). Phillips et al. sought to determine what negative effect a severe drought might have on South America's surprisingly productive tropical mega-forest. What the international team of scientists wanted to know, essentially, was whether such a decline in the availability of water might wipe out the super ecosystem's biomass gains of prior decades, thereby fulfilling one of the models' worst-case catastrophic scenarios.

Focusing their attention on the Amazonian drought of 2005, which they describe as "one of the most intense droughts of the past 100 years" and "a possible analog of future events," the 66 researchers, who had monitored a host of forest plots across the Amazon basin over the prior quarter-century, utilized tree diameter, wood density, and allometric models to compute the basin's woody biomass at each time of measurement, both before and after the drought, deriving the results plotted in Figure 1.2.1.3.1.

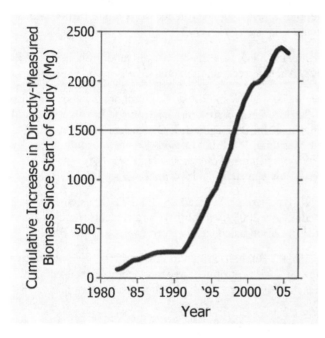

Figure 1.2.1.3.1. The post-1980 cumulative biomass increase of Amazon trees ≥ 10 cm in diameter as a function of the mid-date of each forest-plot census interval, portrayed as a 50-interval moving mean. Adapted from Phillips *et al.* (2009).

As may readily be seen from these real-world measurement-based results, the great Amazonian drought of 2005 resulted in only a slight hiatus in the strong upward trend of tree biomass accumulation exhibited over the prior two decades, which occurred, as Phillips *et al.* note, through a multidecadal period spanning both wet and dry conditions, the latter of which are not even detectable in their wood biomass data. Hence, although extremely severe drought conditions can indeed bring a temporary halt to biomass accumulation in old growth tropical forests—and sometimes even lead to minor

reductions in biomass due to selective tree mortality—the vast majority of the trees are able to regain their photosynthetic capacity and add to their prior store of biomass once the moisture stress subsides, thanks in large measure to the enhanced growth (Lin *et al.*, 1998) and water use efficiency (Hietz *et al.*, 2005) experienced by nearly all woody plants as the air's CO_2 content rises.

Lloyd and Farquhar (2008) provide additional support for this attribution, concluding "the magnitude and pattern of increases in forest dynamics across Amazonia observed over the last few decades are consistent with a CO_2-induced stimulation of tree growth." Phillips *et al.* (2008) provided still more support for the premise, concluding the simplest explanation for the phenomenon is "improved resource availability has increased net primary productivity, in turn increasing growth rates." They also note "the only change for which there is unambiguous evidence that the driver has widely changed and that such a change should accelerate forest growth is the increase in atmospheric CO_2," because of "the undisputed long-term increase in [its] concentration, the key role of CO_2 in photosynthesis, and the demonstrated effects of CO_2 fertilization on plant growth rates."

Lewis *et al.* (2009) found further support for this view in records of old-growth forests of tropical Africa, where they had invested a great amount of time and effort in documenting changes in aboveground carbon storage in 79 permanent plots spanning 40 years (1968–2007), located in closed-canopy moist forest, spanning West, Central, and Eastern Africa, based on data from more than 70,000 individual trees across ten countries. They found "aboveground carbon storage in live trees increased by 0.63 Mg C ha⁻¹ year⁻¹ between 1968 and 2007" and "extrapolation to unmeasured forest components (live roots, small trees, necromass) and scaling to the continent implies a total increase in carbon storage in African tropical forest trees of 0.34 Pg C year⁻¹."

In discussing these results, the 33 researchers write the observed changes in carbon storage were "similar to those reported for Amazonian forests per unit area, providing evidence that increasing carbon storage in old-growth forests is a pan-tropical phenomenon." They also note "combining all standardized inventory data from this study and from tropical America and Asia together yields a comparable figure of 0.49 Mg C ha⁻¹ year⁻¹," which equates to "a carbon sink of 1.3 Pg C year⁻¹ across all tropical forests during recent decades," accounting for roughly half of the global missing carbon sink. Lewis *et al.* conclude, "taxon-specific analyses of African inventory and other data suggest that widespread changes in resource availability, such as increasing atmospheric carbon dioxide concentrations, may be the cause of the increase in carbon stocks, as some theory (Lloyd and Farquhar, 1996) and models (Friedlingstein *et al.*, 2006; Stephens *et al.*, 2007; Ciais *et al.*, 2008) predict."

Tan *et al.* (2011) report stands of trees with ages greater than 200 years have been demonstrated by several research groups to act as carbon sinks in both coniferous and mixed forests, citing Hollinger *et al.* (1994), Law *et al.* (2001), Roser *et al.* (2002), Knohl *et al.* (2003), Paw U *et al.* (2004), Desai *et al.* (2005), and Guan *et al.* (2006). They buttress this claim with the results of their own study of the subject, in which they employed an eddy covariance technique to examine the carbon balance of a more-than-300-year-old subtropical evergreen broadleaved forest located in the center of the largest subtropical land area of the world in the Ailao Mountain Nature Reserve (24°32'N, 101°01'E) of Yunnan Province in Southwest China.

There, in addition to their micrometeorologically based eddy flux carbon budget estimation, the six scientists conducted a tree inventory of one hectare of forest located within the footprint of the eddy flux tower they employed in November 2003 and again in November 2007. They then compared measurements of tree diameter at breast height (DBH) between the two times and employed site-specific allometric equations to derive mean yearly biomass production. Finally, they assessed aboveground litter production via the amount captured each year in 25 litter traps randomly distributed within the one-hectare plot.

Tan *et al.* thus determined the mean annual net ecosystem production of the forest was approximately 9 tC/ha/year, which suggests, in their words, "this forest acts as a large carbon sink." In addition, their inventory data indicate about 6 tC/ha/year was contributed by biomass and necromass. And they report approximately 60% of the biomass increment was contributed by the growth of large trees with breast height diameters greater than 60 cm.

The research cited above clearly shows the notion of old trees contributing next to nothing to global carbon sequestration is manifestly invalid.

References

Baker, T.R., Phillips, O.L., Malhi, Y., Almeida, S., Arroyo, L., Di Fiore, A., Erwin, T., Higuchi, N., Killeen, T.J.,

Laurance, S.G., Laurance, W.F., Lewis, S.L., Monteagudo, A., Neill, D.A., Núñez Vargas, P., Pitman, N.C.A., Silva, J.N.M., and Vásquez Martínez, R. 2004. Increasing biomass in Amazonian forest plots. *Philosophical Transactions of the Royal Society of London Series B—Biological Sciences* **359**: 353–365.

Binkley, D., White, C.S., and Gosz, J.R. 2004. Tree biomass and net increment in an old aspen forest in New Mexico. *Forest Ecology and Management* **203**: 407–410.

Bunn, A.G., Graumlich, L.J., and Urban, D.L. 2005. Trends in twentieth-century tree growth at high elevations in the Sierra Nevada and White Mountains, USA. *The Holocene* **15**: 481–488.

Carey, E.V., Sala, A., Keane, R., and Callaway, R.M. 2001. Are old forests underestimated as global carbon sinks? *Global Change Biology* **7**: 339–344.

Chambers, J.Q., Higuchi, N., and Schimel, J.P. 1998. Ancient trees in Amazonia. *Nature* **391**: 135–136.

Chambers, J.Q., Van Eldik, T., Southon, J., and Higuchi, N. 2001. Tree age structure in tropical forests of central Amazonia. In: Bierregaard, R.O., Gascon, C., Lovejoy, T., and Mesquita, R. (Eds.) *Lessons from Amazonia: Ecology and Conservation of a Fragmented Forest*. Yale University Press, New Haven, CT, USA, pp. 68–78.

Ciais, P., Piao, S.-L., Cadule, P., Friedlingstein, P., and Chedin, A. 2008. Variability and recent trends in the African carbon balance. *Biogeosciences* **5**: 3497–3532.

Condit, R., Hubbell, S.P., and Foster, R.B. 1995. Mortality-rates of 205 neotropical tree and shrub species and the impact of a severe drought. *Ecological Monographs* **65**: 419–439.

DeBell, D.S. and Franklin, J.S. 1987. Old-growth Douglas-fir and western hemlock: a 36-year record of growth and mortality. *Western Journal of Applied Forestry* **2**: 111–114.

Desai, A.R., Paw, U.K.T., Cook, B.D., Davis, K.J., and Carey, E.V. 2005. Comparing net ecosystem exchange of carbon dioxide between an old-growth and mature forest in the upper Midwest, USA. *Agricultural and Forest Meteorology* **128**: 33–55.

Falk, M., Paw, U.K.T., and Schroeder, M. 2002. Interannual variability of carbon and energy fluxes for an old-growth rainforest. In: *Proceedings of the 25th Conference on Agricultural and Forest Meteorology*. American Meteorological Society, Boston, Massachusetts, USA.

Franklin, J.F. 1988. Pacific Northwest Forests. In: Barbour, M.G. and Billings, W.D. (Eds.) *North American Terrestrial Vegetation*. Cambridge University Press, New York, New York, USA, pp. 104–131.

Franklin, J.F. and DeBell, D.S. 1988. Thirty-six years of

tree population change in an old-growth Pseudotsuga-Tsuga forest. *Canadian Journal of Forest Research* **18**: 633–639.

Friedlingstein, P., Cox, P., Betts, R., Bopp, L., von Bloh, W., Brovkin, V., Cadule, P., Doney, S., Eby, M., Fung, I., Bala, G., John, J., Jones, C., Joos, F., Kato, T., Kawamiya, M., Knorr, W., Lindsay, K., Matthews, H.D., Raddatz, T., Rayner, P., Reick, C., Roeckner, E., Schnitzler, K.-G., Schnur, R., Strassmann, K., Weaver, A.J., Yoshikawa, C., and Zeng, N. 2006. Climate-carbon cycle feedback analysis: Results from the (CMIP)-M-4 model intercomparison. *Journal of Climate* **19**: 3337–3353.

Graumlich, L.J. 1991. Subalpine tree growth, climate, and increasing CO$_2$: an assessment of recent growth trends. *Ecology* **72**: 1–11.

Graybill, D.A. 1987. A network of high elevation conifers in the western US for detection of tree-ring growth response to increasing atmospheric carbon dioxide. In: Jacoby, G.C. and Hornbeck, J.W. (Eds.) *Proceedings of the International Symposium on Ecological Aspects of Tree-Ring Analysis*. U.S. Department of Energy Conference Report DOE/CONF8608144, pp. 463–474.

Graybill, D.A. and Idso, S.B. 1993. Detecting the aerial fertilization effect of atmospheric CO$_2$ enrichment in tree-ring chronologies. *Global Biogeochemical Cycles* **7**: 81–95.

Greenep, H., Turnbull, M.H., and Whitehead, D. 2003. Response of photosynthesis in second-generation *Pinus radiata* trees to long-term exposure to elevated carbon dioxide partial pressure. *Tree Physiology* **23**: 569–576.

Guan, D., Wu, J.B., Zhao, X.S., Han, S.J., Yu, G.R., Sun, X.M., and Jin, C.J. 2006. CO$_2$ fluxes over an old temperate mixed forest in northeastern China. *Agricultural and Forest Meteorology* **137**: 138–149.

Hietz, P., Wanek, W., and Dunisch, O. 2005. Long-term trends in cellulose δ^{13}C and water use efficiency of tropical *Cedrela* and *Swietenia* from Brazil. *Tree Physiology* **25**: 745–752.

Hollinger, D.Y., Kelliher, F.M., Byers, J.N., Hunt, J.E., McSeveny, T.M., and Weir, P.L. 1994. Carbon dioxide exchange between an undisturbed old-growth temperate forest and the atmosphere. *Ecology* **75**: 143–150.

Ichii, K., Hashimoto, H., Nemani, R., and White, M. 2005. Modeling the interannual variability and trends in gross and net primary productivity of tropical forests from 1982 to 1999. *Global and Planetary Change* **48**: 274–286.

Idso, S.B. 1995. *CO$_2$ and the Biosphere: The Incredible Legacy of the Industrial Revolution*. Department of Soil, Water and Climate, University of Minnesota, St. Paul, Minnesota, USA.

Jacoby G.C. 1986. Long-term temperature trends and a positive departure from the climate-growth response since the 1950s in high elevation lodgepole pine from California. In: Rosenzweig, C. and Dickinson, R. (Eds.) *Proceedings of the NASA Conference on Climate-Vegetation Interactions*. Office for Interdisciplinary Earth Studies (OIES), University Corporation for Atmospheric Research (UCAR), Boulder, Colorado, USA, pp. 81–83.

Kienast, F. and Luxmoore, R.J. 1998. Tree-ring analysis and conifer growth responses to increased atmospheric CO$_2$ levels. *Oecologia* **76**: 487–495.

Knapp, P.A., Soule, P.T., and Grissino-Mayer, H.D. 2001. Detecting potential regional effects of increased atmospheric CO$_2$ on growth rates of western juniper. *Global Change Biology* **7**: 903–917.

Knohl, A., Schulze, E.-D., Kolle, O., and Buchmann, N. 2003. Large carbon uptake by an unmanaged 250-year-old deciduous forest in Central Germany. *Agricultural and Forest Meteorology* **118**: 151–167.

Koch, G.W., Sillett, S.C., Jennings, G.M., and Davis, S.D. 2004. The limits to tree height. *Nature* **428**: 851–854.

LaMarche Jr., V.C., Graybill, D.A., Fritts, H.C., and Rose, M.R. 1984. Increasing atmospheric carbon dioxide: tree ring evidence for growth enhancement in natural vegetation. *Science* **225**: 1019–1021.

Laurance, S.G.W., Laurance, W.F., Nascimento, H.E.M., Andrade, A., Fearnside, P.M., Rebello, E.R.G., and Condit, R. 2009. Long-term variation in Amazon forest dynamics. *Journal of Vegetation Science* **20**: 323–333.

Laurance, W.F., Nascimento, H.E.M., Laurance, S.G., Condit, R., D'Angelo, S., and Andrade, A. 2004. Inferred longevity of Amazonian rainforest trees based on a long-term demographic study. *Forest Ecology and Management* **190**: 131–143.

Law, B.E., Goldstein, A.H., Anthoni, P.M., Unsworth, M.H., Panek, J.A., Bauer, M.R., Fracheboud, J.M., and Hultman, N. 2001. Carbon dioxide and water vapor exchange by young and old ponderosa pine ecosystems during a dry summer. *Tree Physiology* **21**: 299–308.

Lewis, S.L., Lopez-Gonzalez, G., Sonke, B., Affum-Baffoe, K., Baker, T.R., Ojo, L.O., Phillips, O.L., Reitsma, J.M., White, L., Comiskey, J.A., Djuikouo K, M.-N., Ewango, C.E.N., Feldpausch, T.R., Hamilton, A.C., Gloor, M., Hart, T., Hladik, A., Lloyd, J., Lovett, J.C., Makana, J.-R., Malhi, Y., Mbago, F.M., Ndangalasi, H.J., Peacock, J., Peh, K. S.-H., Sheil, D., Sunderland, T., Swaine, M.D., Taplin, J., Taylor, D., Thomas, S.C., Votere, R., and Woll, H. 2009. Increasing carbon storage in intact African tropical forests. *Nature* **457**: 1003–1006.

Lewis, S.L., Phillips, O.L., Baker, T.R., Lloyd, J., Malhi, Y., Almeida, S., Higuchi, N., Laurance, W.F., Neill, D.A.,

Silva, J.N.M., Terborgh, J., Lezama, A.T., Vásquez Martinez, R., Brown, S., Chave, J., Kuebler, C., Núñez Vargas, P., and Vinceti, B. 2004. Concerted changes in tropical forest structure and dynamics: evidence from 50 South American long-term plots. *Philosophical Transactions of the Royal Society of London Series B—Biological Sciences* **359**: 421–436.

Lin, G., Marino, B.D.V., Wei, Y., Adams, J., Tubiello, F., and Berry, J.A. 1998. An experimental and modeling study of responses in ecosystems carbon exchanges to increasing CO_2 concentrations using a tropical rainforest mesocosm. *Australian Journal of Plant Physiology* **25**: 547–556.

Lloyd, J. and Farquhar, G.D. 1996. The CO_2 dependence of photosynthesis, plant growth responses to elevated atmospheric CO_2 concentrations and their interaction with soil nutrient status. 1. General principles and forest ecosystems. *Functional Ecology* **10**: 4–32.

Lloyd, J. and Farquhar, G.D. 2008. Effects of rising temperatures and [CO_2] on the physiology of tropical forest trees. *Philosophical Transactions of the Royal Society B* **363**: 1811–1817.

Luyssaert, S., Schulze, E.-D., Borner, A., Knohl, A., Hessenmoller, D., Law, B.E., Ciais, P., and Grace, J. 2008. Old-growth forests as global carbon sinks. *Nature* **455**: 213–215.

Mencuccini, M., Martinez-Vilalta, J., Vanderklein, D., Hamid, H.A., Korakaki, E., and Lee, S. 2005. Size-mediated ageing reduces vigor in trees. *Ecology Letters* **8**: 1183–1190.

Nemani, R.R., Keeling, C.D., Hashimoto, H., Jolly, W.M., Piper, S.C., Tucker, C.J., Myneni, R.B., and Running. S.W. 2003. Climate-driven increases in global terrestrial net primary production from 1982 to 1999. *Science* **300**: 1560–1563.

Odum, E.P. 1963. *Ecology*. Holt, Rinehart and Winston, New York, New York, USA.

Odum E.P. 1965. *Fundamentals of Ecology*. Saunders, Philadelphia, Pennsylvania, USA.

Paw U, K.T., Falk, M., Suchanek, T.H., Ustin, S.L., Chen, J., Park, Y.-S., Winner, W.E., Thomas, S.C., Hsiao, T.C., Shaw, R.H., King, T.S., Pyles, R.D., Schroeder, M., and Matista, A.A. 2004. Carbon dioxide exchange between an old-growth forest and the atmosphere. *Ecosystems* **7**: 513–524.

Phillips, O.L., Aragao, L.E.O.C., Lewis, S.L., Fisher, J.B., Lloyd, J., Lopez-Gonzalez, G., Malhi, Y., Monteagudo, A., Peacock, J., Quesada, C.A., van der Heijden G., Almeida, S., Amaral, I., Arroyo, L., Aymard, G., Baker, T.R., Banki, O., Blanc, L., Bonal, D., Brando, P., Chave, J., de Oliveira, A.C.A., Cardozo, N.D., Czimczik, C.I., Feldpausch, T.R., Freitas, M.A., Gloor, E., Higuchi, N., Jimenez, E., Lloyd, G., Meir, P., Mendoza, C., Morel, A., Neill, D.A., Nepstad, D., Patino, S., Penuela, M.C., Prieto, A., Ramirez, F., Schwarz, M., Silva, J., Silveira, M., Thomas, A.S., ter Steege, H., Stropp, J., Vasquez, R., Zelazowski, P., Davila, E.A., Andelman, S., Andrade, A., Chao, K.-J., Erwin, T., Di Fiore, A., Euradice Honorio C., Keeling, H., Killeen, T.J., Laurance, W.F., Cruz, A.P., Pitman, N.C.A., Vargas, P.N., Ramirez-Angulo, H., Rudas, A., Salamao, R., Silva, N., Terborgh, J., and Torres-Lezama, A. 2009. Drought sensitivity of the Amazon rainforest. *Science* **323**: 1344–1347.

Phillips, N.G., Buckley, T.N., and Tissue, D.T. 2008. Capacity of old trees to respond to environmental change. *Journal of Integrative Plant Biology* **50**: 1355–1364.

Phillips, O.L., Malhi, Y., Higuchi, N., Laurance, W.F., Nunez, P.V., Vasquez, R.M., Laurance, S.G., Ferreira, L.V., Stern, M., Brown, S., and Grace, J. 1998. Changes in the carbon balance of tropical forests: Evidence from long-term plots. *Science* **282**: 439–442.

Roser, C., Montagnani, L., Schulze, E.D., Mollicone, D., Kolle, O., Meroni, M., Papale, D., Marchesini, L.B., Federici, S., and Valetini, R. 2002. Net CO_2 exchange rates in three different successional stages of the "Dark Taiga" of central Siberia. *Tellus* **54**: 642–654.

Schulze, E.-D., Lloyd, J., Kelliher, F.M., Wirth, C., Rebmann, C., Luhker, B., Mund, M., Knohl, A., Milyuokova, I.M., and Schulze, W. 1999. Productivity of forests in the Eurosiberian boreal region and their potential to act as a carbon sink: a synthesis. *Global Change Biology* **5**: 703–722.

Soule, P.T. and Knapp, P.A. 2006. Radial growth rate increases in naturally occurring ponderosa pine trees: a late-20th century CO_2 fertilization effect? *New Phytologist* **171**: 379–390.

Stephens, B.B., Gurney, K.R., Tans, P.P., Sweeney, C., Peters, W., Bruhwiler, L., Ciais, P., Ramonet, M., Bousquet, P., Nakazawa, T., Aoki, S., Machida, T., Inoue, G., Vinnichenko, N., Lloyd, J., Jordan, A., Heimann, M., Shibistova, O., Langenfelds, R.L., Steele, L.P., Francey, R.J., and Denning, A.S. 2007. Weak northern and strong tropical land carbon uptake from vertical profiles of atmospheric CO_2. *Science* **316**: 1732–1735.

Tan, Z.-H., Zhang, Y.-P., Schaefer, D., Yu, G.-R., Liang, N., and Song, Q.-H. 2011. An old-growth subtropical Asian evergreen forest as a large carbon sink. *Atmospheric Environment* **45**: 1548–1554.

Woodruff, D.R., Bond, J.B., and Meinzer, F.C. 2004. Does turgor limit growth in tall trees? *Plant, Cell and Environment* **27**: 229–236.

1.2.1.4 Carbon Sequestration

As the CO_2 content of the air increases, nearly all plants, including those of various forest ecosystems, respond by increasing their photosynthetic rates and producing more biomass. These phenomena allow long-lived perennial species characteristic of forest ecosystems to sequester large amounts of carbon within their trunks and branches aboveground and their roots belowground for extended periods of time. These processes, in turn, significantly counterbalance CO_2 emissions produced by mankind's use of fossil fuels. The subsections below review information about forest-species sequestration of the carbon they remove from the atmosphere in response to rising atmospheric CO_2 and rising temperature.

1.2.1.4.1 The Influence of CO₂

- Elevated CO_2 enhances photosynthetic rates and biomass production in forest trees, and both of these phenomena lead to greater amounts of carbon sequestration. Elevated CO_2 also enhances carbon sequestration by reducing carbon losses arising from plant respiration and in some cases from decomposition. Thus, as the air's CO_2 content rises, the ability of forests to sequester carbon rises along with it, appropriately tempering the rate of rise of the air's CO_2 content.

In reviewing studies of individual trees, it is clear elevated levels of atmospheric CO_2 increase photosynthesis and growth in both broad-leaved and coniferous species (see Section 1.1.3.1). When broad-leaved trembling aspen (*Populus tremuloides*) were exposed to twice-ambient levels of atmospheric CO_2 for 2.5 years, for example, Pregitzer *et al.* (2000) reported 17 and 65% increases in fine root biomass at low and high levels of soil nitrogen, respectively, and Zak *et al.* (2000) observed 16 and 38% CO_2-induced increases in total tree biomass when subjected to the same respective levels of soil nitrogen.

Also focusing on a broad-leaved species, Marek *et al.* (2001) constructed open-top chambers around 30-year-old mature oak (*Quercus ilex*) trees growing naturally in perennial evergreen stands in central Italy, where they were continually exposed to atmospheric CO_2 concentrations of either 350 or 700 ppm for five years, to determine the long-term effects of elevated CO_2 on photosynthesis in this important tree species. The researchers found the elevated CO_2 increased rates of net photosynthesis in Sun-exposed

and shaded leaves by 68 and 59%, respectively, in comparison with control rates measured on similar leaves of trees exposed to ambient air. In addition, after measuring short-term photosynthetic rates at various atmospheric CO_2 concentrations, the four researchers found photosynthetic acclimation was not apparent in leaves of these mature trees exposed to long-term atmospheric CO_2 enrichment. They also report the CO_2 light compensation point—the light level at which photosynthetic carbon uptake is equivalent to respiratory carbon loss—was 24 and 30% lower in the Sun-exposed and shaded leaves, respectively, of the CO_2-enriched trees than what was measured in corresponding leaves of the ambient-air trees.

As the air's CO_2 content increases, therefore, it is likely the stimulatory effect of elevated CO_2 on photosynthesis in oak seedlings will persist in the long term within mature trees, without showing any signs of photosynthetic acclimation. And because elevated CO_2 significantly lowers the light compensation point in mature oak trees, which allows them to exhibit net carbon gains earlier in the mornings and maintain them later into the evenings, the stimulatory effect of elevated CO_2 on daily carbon uptake should be further enhanced. Together, these two observations suggest carbon sequestration by this and perhaps other tree species may be more substantial in future CO_2-enriched atmospheres than what had long been thought to be the case.

In a FACE study conducted at the Oak Ridge National Environmental Research Park in Roane County, Tennessee, USA, Norby *et al.* (2004) planted one-year-old bare-rooted sweetgum (*Liquidambar styraciflua* L.) seedlings in the ground in 1988 to create an experimental forest. Eight years later, five 25m-diameter FACE rings were constructed to enclose about 90 trees each. A year after that, when pretreatment measurements were made, the trees were about 2 m tall with an average diameter of 11 cm. At this point, the trees were in a linear growth phase and the canopy was no longer expanding. A year later, in April 1998, exposure to elevated CO_2 was begun in two of the plots and was continued each year thereafter throughout each subsequent growing season (April to November).

Over the last four years of the study (years 3–6), the atmospheric CO_2 concentrations of the ambient and CO_2-enriched plots averaged 391 ppm and 544 ppm (39% more than ambient), respectively. During this period, the net primary production of the CO_2-enriched plots averaged 22% more than the ambient plots, but there was no discernible "bulking up" of the trees. So where had the extra biomass attributable to the extra CO_2 been going?

In July 1997, the Oak Ridge scientists installed five mini-rhizotron tubes in each FACE plot. These transparent tubes extended to a depth of 60 cm below the soil surface and were inclined at a 60-degree angle from the vertical. Each was equipped with a video recorder collecting images biweekly throughout the growing season, and the data were digitized and used to calculate a number of different root parameters on the same biweekly basis. In analyzing the images, Norby et al. report "the CO_2 effect on annual [root] production was highly significant, with production 2.2-fold higher in CO_2-enriched plots from 2000–2003." They also state "CO_2 enrichment significantly increased peak-standing root crop by altering allocation such that the potential for root occupancy of the soil volume was increased," noting "this response was manifested especially in the deeper distribution of roots in the soil profile." In particular, they say the peak-standing root crop exhibited "3-fold more length at 30–45 cm and 4-fold more at 45–60 cm," impressive considering the enhancement of the air's CO_2 concentration employed in this study was only 39%.

The Oak Ridge investigators also determined the mass of fine roots produced in a given year accounted for 11–34% of forest net primary production. They remark this "preferential allocation to fine roots should significantly reduce the potential for additional carbon (C) sequestration in trees in elevated CO_2," which was proven true in their study. However, as they continue, "sequestration of some of that C in the forest remains a possibility" because "as fine roots die, their C enters the soil system where there is the potential for movement into long-lived organic matter pools." They note "soil analysis indicates that there is increased accumulation of new C in CO_2-enriched plots, particularly in micro-aggregate fractions that facilitate movement of C into pools with long residence times." And they state "it may become especially important that the greatest increases in root production in elevated CO_2 occur in deeper soil, where sequestration into longer-lived pools may be more likely."

Norby et al. further note "the CO_2-induced increase in fine-root standing crop in summer could also be an important mechanism for conferring increased resistance to late-season droughts," and "the stimulation of root growth in deeper soil could be particularly important in buffering trees against seasonal droughts." This being the case, the huge allocation of net primary production the CO_2-enriched

trees send belowground and distribute to greater depths may enable them to sequester more biomass in their aboveground woody tissues, if it helps them remain able to produce biomass during droughty periods that might otherwise bring to a halt the net productivity of trees growing in ambient air.

Karberg et al. (2005) describe how "free air CO_2 and O_3 enrichment technology was used at the Aspen FACE project in Rhinelander, Wisconsin [USA] to understand how elevated atmospheric CO_2 and O_3 interact to alter pCO_2 and DIC [dissolved inorganic carbon] concentrations in the soil." The experimental setting consisted of three blocks of four treatments—control, elevated CO_2, elevated O_3, and elevated CO_2 + O_3—where ambient CO_2 was 360 ppm, elevated CO_2 was 542 ppm, ambient O_3 was 33 ppb, and elevated O_3 was 49 ppb. Half of each FACE ring was planted with trembling aspen, a quarter with a 1:1 mix of trembling aspen and paper birch, and a quarter with a mix of trembling aspen and sugar maple. In this setting, the researchers applied the CO_2 and O_3 treatments over the 2002 growing season, which ran from 28 May to 11 October, and retrieved biweekly samples of the soil air and solution from depths of 15, 30, and 125 cm for various chemical analyses in the laboratory.

The authors found "measured concentrations of soil CO_2 and calculated concentrations of DIC increased over the growing season by 14 and 22%, respectively, under elevated atmospheric CO_2 and were unaffected by elevated tropospheric O_3." In addition, Karberg et al. write, "the increased concentration of DIC altered inorganic carbonate chemistry by increasing system total alkalinity by 210%, likely due to enhanced chemical weathering [of primary minerals]," and they note a mixing model they employed "showed that new atmospheric CO_2 accounted for approximately 90% of the C leaving the system as DIC."

In discussing their findings, the Michigan scientists state the CO_2-induced increase in soil solution DIC, which ultimately makes its way to rivers that reach oceans, "represents a potential long-lived sequestration reservoir in deep ocean sediments," noting further it suggests "aggrading forest ecosystems may be used to capture and sequester atmospheric CO_2 through inorganic processes," which can transfer it to the bottoms of faraway seas, as also has been demonstrated and discussed by Raymond and Cole (2003) and Wang and Cai (2004). And, of course, increases in the air's CO_2 concentration can significantly increase this phenomenon.

Rasineni *et al.* (2011) write, "carbon sequestration as a climate change mitigation policy has received significant attention over the past several years," and planting young fast-growing trees to absorb excess atmospheric CO_2 "has recently gained potentiality, leading to identification of tree species with high CO_2 sequestration capacity." As their contribution, they grew well-watered and well-fertilized five-week-old fast-growing *Gmelina arborea* trees out-of-doors at the University of Hyderabad, India, in open-top chambers maintained at ambient and ambient plus 100 ppm atmospheric CO_2 concentrations throughout the 120 days of that region's spring and summer seasons, while they periodically made numerous measurements of the trees' physical properties and physiological performance.

At the conclusion of the spring and summer growing seasons, the three researchers found the trees in the modestly elevated CO_2 chambers exhibited net photosynthetic rates 38% greater than trees growing in ambient air. Aided by a significant CO_2-induced reduction in leaf transpiration rates, the mean instantaneous water use efficiency of the leaves of the CO_2-enriched trees was 87% greater than the ambient-treatment trees. These CO_2-induced plant physiological benefits raised the aboveground biomass of the CO_2-enriched trees at the end of the growing season to be 45% greater than trees growing in ambient air, and their total biomass (above and below ground) was 53% higher.

Discussing their findings, Rasineni *et al.* note elevated atmospheric CO_2 "persistently enhanced all the growth characteristics in *Gmelina*, including plant height, number of branches, internodes, internodal distance, aerial biomass and total plant biomass." They suggest "high sink demand and better growth dynamics" led to the huge sustained increase in carbon sequestration in the tropical deciduous tree. Thus, they conclude their findings point to the likelihood "there are management options for creating short-rotation deciduous tree plantations to achieve increased sequestration of carbon in a future elevated CO_2 environment."

Barton and Jarvis (1999) report fumigating branches of Sitka spruce (*Picea sitchensis*) with air of 700 ppm CO_2 for four years raised rates of net photosynthesis in current and second-year needles to be 100 and 43% higher, respectively, than photosynthetic rates of needles exposed to ambient air. In addition, ponderosa pine (*Pinus ponderosa*) grown at 700 ppm CO_2 for close to 2.5 years exhibited rates of net photosynthesis in current-year needles 49% greater than those of needles exposed to air containing 350 ppm CO_2 (Houpis *et al.*, 1999). As to biomass production, Saxe *et al.* (1998) reviewed the then-existent literature on the topic, finding "close to a doubling" of the air's CO_2 concentration led to an approximate 50% increase in the biomass production of angiosperm trees and a 130% increase in the biomass production of coniferous species.

Pritchard *et al.* (2001) reconstructed ecosystems representative of regenerating longleaf pine communities of the southeastern USA in large soil bins placed in open-top chambers maintained at CO_2 concentrations of 365 and 720 ppm for 18 months, while they studied the effects of elevated CO_2 on root dynamics and growth in this important forest community. The five species included in the regenerating forest stands were longleaf pine (*Pinus palustris* Mill.), sand post oak (*Quercus margaretta*), a C_4 bunch grass called wiregrass (*Aristida stricta* Michx.), a C_4 perennial legume called rattlebox (*Crotalaria rotundifolia* Walt. Ex Genmel), and a herbaceous C_3 perennial called butterfly weed (*Asclepias tuberosa* L.).

They report the elevated CO_2 increased the total aboveground biomass of the longleaf pine and sand post oak by approximately 20 and 50%, respectively. It had no effect on the aboveground biomass produced by the three non-woody herbaceous species. Thus, at the ecosystem level, elevated CO_2 increased total aboveground biomass by an average of 35%, and belowground it increased the root biomass of longleaf pine by 62%. In contrast, sand post oak, which was very responsive to elevated CO_2 aboveground, exhibited no significant CO_2-induced changes belowground, and the three herbaceous species displayed an average CO_2-induced reduction in root biomass of 28%. At the whole-community level, therefore, the CO_2-enriched plots displayed 37% greater root length production per day and 47% greater root length mortality per day at soil depths between 10 and 30 cm than was observed in control plots exposed to ambient CO_2 concentrations.

Consequently, as the air's CO_2 content increases, the ability of longleaf pine trees to compete for soil moisture and nutrients in regenerating stands of longleaf pine savannahs will likely be enhanced by the large preferential CO_2-induced increases in the trees' root systems. This phenomenon likely will give longleaf pine a significant edge over its primary competitors—sand post oak and wiregrass. Pritchard *et al.* remark these competitive shifts suggest "longleaf pine savannahs may flourish in a future CO_2-enriched world." If that happens, the trees and the soil beneath them likely will become a major repository of sequestered carbon. Sand post oak also should do well as the air's CO_2 content increases, significantly enhancing the carbon-sequestering power of the total community, which should undergo a shift from savannah to forest, with a consequent greater storage of both above- and below-ground carbon.

Another study of the suitability of forests as long-term carbon sinks was conducted by Lou *et al.* (2003). They analyzed data from the Duke Forest FACE experiment, in which three 30-meter-diamerer plots within a 13-year-old forest (composed primarily of loblolly pines with sweetgum and yellow poplar trees as sub-dominants, together with numerous other trees, shrubs, and vines that occupied still-smaller niches) began to be enriched with an extra 200 ppm of CO_2 in August 1996, while three similar plots were maintained at the ambient atmospheric CO_2 concentration. A number of papers describing different facets of this long-term study have been published, and as recounted by Lou *et al.* they have revealed the existence of a CO_2-induced "sustained photosynthetic stimulation at leaf and canopy levels [Myers *et al.*, 1999; Ellsworth, 2000; Luo *et al.*, 2001; Lai *et al.*, 2002], which has resulted in sustained stimulation of wood biomass increment [Hamilton *et al.*, 2002] and a larger carbon accumulation in the forest floor at elevated CO_2 than at ambient CO_2 [Schlesinger and Lichter, 2001]."

Based on these findings and what they imply about rates of carbon removal from the atmosphere and its different residence times in plant, litter, and soil carbon pools, Luo *et al.* developed a model for studying the sustainability of forest carbon sequestration. Applying this model to a situation where the atmospheric CO_2 concentration gradually rises from a value of 378 ppm in 2000 to a value of 710 ppm in 2100, they calculated the carbon sequestration rate of the Duke Forest would rise from an initial value of 69 g m^{-2} yr^{-1} to a final value of 201 g m^{-2} yr^{-1}. That is a far cry from the model-based IPCC projections, which have long suggested forests will have released much of the carbon they had previously absorbed as early as the year 2050 (Pearce, 1999).

The preceding findings fit well with the work of Fan *et al.* (1998), who used atmospheric measurements to calculate the broad-leaf forested region of North America between 15° and 51°N latitude possesses a current carbon sink that can annually remove all the CO_2 emitted into the air from fossil fuel combustion in both Canada and the United States. Looking to the future, White *et al.* (2000) calculated coniferous and mixed forests north of 50°N latitude likely will expand their northern and southern boundaries by about 50% as a result of the combined effects of increasing atmospheric CO_2, rising temperature, and nitrogen deposition.

Nitrogen deposition is an important variable. White *et al.* (2000) note it can play an interactive role with increasing atmospheric CO_2 to increase plant growth and carbon sequestration. Some researchers, however, have questioned the magnitude of that role. Nadelhoffer *et al.* (1999), for example, conclude nitrogen deposition from human activities is "unlikely to be a major contributor" to the large CO_2 sink that exists in northern temperate forests. Houghton *et al.* (1998), however, suggest nitrogen deposition holds equal weight with CO_2 fertilization in the production of terrestrial carbon sinks; and Lloyd (1999) demonstrates simultaneous CO_2 and nitrogen increases lead to greater modeled forest productivity than what is predicted by the sum of the individual contributions of these two variables.

Thomas *et al.* (2010) used "spatially extensive forest inventory data to discern [1] the effect of nitrogen deposition on the growth and survival of the 24 most common tree species of the northeastern and north-central United States, as well as [2] the effect of nitrogen deposition on carbon sequestration in trees across the breadth of the northeastern US." The four researchers found "nitrogen deposition (which ranged from 3 to 11 kg ha^{-1} yr^{-1}) enhanced the growth of eleven species and decreased the growth of three species," and "enhanced [the] growth of all tree species with arbuscular mycorrhizal fungi associations." That led to "a 40% enhancement over pre-industrial conditions," which "includes the direct effects of nitrogen deposition on tree growth through soil fertilization, foliar nitrogen uptake and other potential interactions between nitrogen deposition and other environmental changes, including CO_2 fertilization." To give some feeling for the significance of the size of this response, they note it "exceeds the 23% enhancement of net primary production anticipated for the year 2050 from a doubling of atmospheric CO_2 over preindustrial levels, as estimated using free-air CO_2 enrichment studies," citing Norby *et al.* (2005).

Thomas *et al.* thus conclude "nitrogen deposition is an important mechanism contributing to carbon sequestration within these temperate forests," but they maintain this phenomenon is still "unlikely to explain all of the observed terrestrial carbon sink." Nevertheless, it goes a long way toward doing so, while demonstrating the major benefits of the concomitant increases in the air's CO$_2$ content and the temperature with which it has interacted over the course of the Industrial Revolution and after, the latter increases of which IPCC characterizes as negatively affecting the biosphere. Clearly, these CO$_2$ increases are not doing harm, and neither is the concomitant increase in anthropogenic nitrogen deposition. These phenomena have interacted with each other in such a way as to greatly increase the productivity of Earth's forests, both in temperate latitudes, as demonstrated by Thomas *et al.*, and in tropical regions, as revealed by many of the other studies reviewed in this section and chapter.

On a related note, woody plant encroachment upon arid and semiarid grasslands and savannas has been a ubiquitous natural phenomenon experienced throughout the world over the past century or more (Idso, 1995), driven—at least partially, many believe—by the contemporaneous rise in the air's CO$_2$ concentration (Knapp and Soule, 1998; Soule and Knapp, 1999). This phenomenon may be responsible for sequestering much of the planet's so-called missing carbon, an unidentified but growing repository of organic matter needed to explain the less-than-predicted rate-of-rise of the air's CO$_2$ content calculated on the basis of known sources and sinks of this important greenhouse gas, as demonstrated by Hibbard *et al.* (2001).

Working in the La Copita Research Area southwest of Alice, Texas, Hibbard *et al.* analyzed several chemical and physical properties of the top ten centimeters of soils in remnant herbaceous areas and patches of woody vegetation in various stages of invasive development. Compared to soils beneath herbaceous vegetation, the soils beneath the tree/shrub areas were found to have much greater concentrations of both carbon (C) and nitrogen (N). A companion study of soil C and N across woody patches ranging in age from 10 to 110 years revealed these variables had experienced a linear increase through time.

The source of these C and N increases was woody plant roots. The authors write they "were surprised by the magnitude of root biomass in surficial soils of woody patches, which greatly exceeded that of herbaceous patches and which greatly exceeded that of foliar litter inputs." Citing a number of studies of rates of root turnover in herbaceous and woody-plant ecosystems, they conclude "the role of belowground inputs in fueling changes in surficial soil C and N stocks ... accompanying shifts from grass to woody plant domination may therefore be more substantial

than previously appreciated."

As to how much more substantial such changes might be, the researchers note "the contrasts between woody and herbaceous patches reported here are conservative in that they do not include an assessment of whole plant C and N stocks," i.e., root biomass below ten centimeters depth and woody biomass aboveground. With respect to the first of these factors, they cite several studies that have detected greater soil C concentrations beneath woody vs. herbaceous vegetation to depths of 100 to 400 centimeters. With respect to the second factor, they likewise cite evidence suggesting "plant C mass has increased tenfold with the conversion of grassland to savanna woodland over the past 100 years."

As to what their findings imply about the world as a whole, Hibbard *et al.* note since "woody plant expansion into drylands has been geographically widespread over the past century," and "40% of the terrestrial biosphere consists of arid and semiarid savanna, shrubland, and grassland ecosystems, this type of vegetation change may be of significance to the global C and N cycle." However, they say, a full understanding of the significance of this phenomenon will require better information on "the historic or modern rate, areal extent, and pattern of woody plant expansion in the world's drylands."

McCarron *et al.* (2003) measured the effects of shrub encroachment in a mesic grassland on soil CO$_2$ flux, extractable inorganic N, and N mineralization beneath isolated C$_3$ shrub communities (islands) of *Cornus drummondii* and surrounding undisturbed native tallgrass prairie at the Konza Prairie Biological Station in northeast Kansas, USA, during the 1999 and 2000 growing seasons. They determined—as had Norris (2000) and Smith (2001) before them—the invasion of mesic grasslands by woody plants leaves soil carbon stores essentially unaltered while greatly boosting aboveground inventories of sequestered carbon. Those observations provide more evidence the invasion of mesic grasslands by shrubs and trees enhances the biological sequestration of carbon in these widespread and globally dispersed ecosystems that cover vast areas of the Earth's surface.

Hyvonen *et al.* (2007) led an international team of forest researchers—22 scientists from nine countries (Belgium, Denmark, France, Finland, Iceland, Italy, Sweden, the United Kingdom, and the United States)—investigating "whether the mature forests that are C sinks today will continue to be sinks as the climate changes." One way of addressing this question is to look at what has happened to forests that matured several decades ago and have experienced the concurrent increases in air temperature and atmospheric CO_2 concentration of the past half-century or more, a period over which IPCC claims both of these factors rose at unprecedented rates and to unprecedented levels.

Good candidates for this assessment are old-growth forests, such as those of Amazonia, which for most of the past century were believed to be close to dynamic equilibrium. In one of the first studies to dispel this long-held notion, Phillips and Gentry (1994) analyzed the turnover rates—which are close correlates of net productivity (Weaver and Murphy, 1990)—of 40 tropical forests around the world. They found the growth rates of these forests had been increasing steadily since at least 1960 and had undergone an apparent acceleration in growth rate some time after 1980. A few years later, Phillips *et al.* (1998) analyzed forest growth rate data for the period 1958 to 1996 for several hundred plots of mature tropical trees around the world. They found tropical forest biomass, as a whole, increased substantially over the period of record. The increase in the Neotropics was equivalent to approximately 40% of the missing terrestrial carbon sink of the entire globe. Laurance *et al.* (2004a) reported accelerated growth in the 1990s relative to the 1980s for the large majority (87%) of tree genera in 18 one-hectare plots spanning an area of about 300 km^2 in central Amazonia, and Laurance *et al.* (2004b) observed similarly accelerated tree community dynamics in the 1990s relative to the 1980s.

This wealth of pertinent positive findings provides strong reason to reject the model-based view of forest carbon sinks turning into forest carbon sources in the decades ahead. If anything, real-world observations suggest today's forest carbon sinks may become even stronger carbon sinks as air temperatures and atmospheric CO_2 concentrations continue to rise.

Agren *et al.* (2007) used official forestry statistics on standing tree volumes and harvests to estimate the standing stock of tree components for each year between 1926 and 2000 throughout all of Sweden for the country's two most dominant tree species—Norway spruce (*Picea abies*) and Scots pine (*Pinus sylvestris*)—which together constituted 80.6% of the country's standing tree stock. For each of these tree components they estimated annual litter production, the decomposition of different litter fractions in the soil, and ultimate turnover rates, with soil carbon stocks for all sites evaluated to a depth of one meter or to bedrock, if bedrock was encountered at less than a meter depth.

Agren *et al.* report "there was a steady increase in carbon stocks in Swedish forests in the period 1926–2000," such that forest ecosystems in 2000 contained 35% more carbon than they did in 1926, with tree biomass being responsible for nearly three-quarters of the total increase in carbon stocks. For comparative purposes, they note the total amount of carbon sequestered amounted to just under half that emitted to the air by the burning of fossil fuels in Sweden.

With respect to the soil component of the carbon sequestered, the Swedish scientists arrived at a value of 1.7 Tg/year, or just under a quarter of the total sequestered carbon (7.1 Tg/year). In addition, they write, "the current soil carbon stock is not in equilibrium with the current rate of litter production," as "the increase in soil carbon stocks since 1926 is only 33% of what would be required to be in equilibrium with current tree biomass." This state of affairs, however, was only to be expected, as Agren and Bosatta (1998) calculate, for forest litter typical of coniferous needles and Swedish climatic conditions, "50% of the steady state value is reached after ca. 200 years but 15,000 years are required to reach 80%."

Clearly, carbon stocks in Swedish forests have been growing significantly faster than expected, especially considering that from 1951 to 2000, the forested area of the country actually declined by 1%. Modern global warming, atmospheric CO_2 enrichment, nitrogen deposition, and management factors all probably contributed to the increase, which as noted above has compensated for just under half the country's carbon emissions from the burning of fossil fuels. In addition, forest extraction of carbon from the air likely will continue well into the future in Sweden, as Agren *et al.* opine "the time since the last glaciation has probably not been long enough to reach a steady state," and since the factors that determine steady state appear to be changing in ways that continue to increase the magnitude of the equilibrium condition.

Smittenberg *et al.* (2006) begin their paper by noting "refractory organic matter makes up approximately half of the SOC [soil organic carbon] pool because of its resistance to degradation, and it is this pool that is ultimately responsible for long-term terrestrial carbon storage." However, they suggest current ideas about the long-term buildup of SOC are questionable because our understanding of the phenomenon is largely derived from studies of present-day soils, due to a paucity of long-term records of SOC dynamics.

To provide more information about this

phenomenon, the scientists worked with high-temporal-resolution sediments of Saanich Inlet, Canada, obtained from seven well-dated cores that contained layers ranging in age from recent to 5,500 years before present, as well as layers just below the well-dated section and a late Pleistocene layer. Smittenberg *et al.* analyzed the distribution, stable carbon isotopic composition, and radiocarbon composition of long-chain *n*-alkanes derived predominantly from C_3 vascular plant material produced upon boreal-forest-covered watersheds that drain into rivers that empty into the inlet. These *n*-alkanes may thus serve as proxies for recalcitrant terrigenous organic matter produced upon the watersheds.

The scientists found the average *n*-alkane ages have been increasing in a near-linear fashion toward the present, strongly suggesting any loss due to mineralization or erosion is still largely outpaced by the accumulation. They interpret this finding to imply "the accumulation of refractory organic carbon in soils that developed after the deglaciation of the American Pacific Northwest is ongoing and may still be far from equilibrium with mineralization and erosion rates." This further suggests, in their words, "the turnover time of this carbon pool is 10,000 to 100,000 years or more and not 1,000 to 10,000 years as is often used in soil carbon models."

Smittenberg *et al.* therefore conclude their findings "challenge the notion that the current production of refractory organic matter is balanced by decomposition and erosion after a few thousand years, as inferred via chrono-sequences or soil respiration measurements." They also state their findings place the terrestrial biosphere "in a more prominent position as a slow but progressively important atmospheric carbon sink on geologic time scales," and it "may even influence current predictions about carbon cycling and soil carbon storage in response to elevated atmospheric CO_2 levels," hinting the potential for refractory organic carbon sequestration in a world with a CO_2-accreting atmosphere may be greater than what previously has been believed, but with the effect having its main impact on time scales of more than a thousand years.

Ciais *et al.* (2008a) analyzed national forest inventory data and timber harvest statistics of the EU-15 countries excluding Luxembourg, plus Norway and Switzerland, for the period AD 1950–2000. They found over this half-century interval, the net primary productivity (NPP) of Europe's forests rose by about 67%, while their biomass carbon stocks rose by approximately 75%. This build-up of forest carbon stocks, in the words of the 13 researchers, "appears to result from woody NPP exceeding losses by timber harvest and natural disturbances such as fire and wind throw," and they note their analyses suggests 70–80% of the observed increase in NPP has likely been due to "changes in climate and to the fertilizing effect of CO_2."

Buttressing their conclusions in this regard, Ciais *et al.* note "another independent model-based analysis that accounted for changing age-classes, management and land use (Zaehle *et al.*, 2006) further indicates that forest NPP increases were mainly driven by climate change and CO_2." In addition, they note "real increases of biomass increment have occurred and are still occurring," as "corroborated by tree-ring studies and by measurements of long-term permanent sample plots (Becker *et al.*, 1995; Nicolussi *et al.*, 1995; Spiecker, 1996; Rolland *et al.*, 1998; Motta and Nola, 2001)."

The international group of scientists (from Belgium, China, Finland, France, Germany, Italy, the Netherlands, Romania, and the United States) write, "European forests still have the potential to realize a build-up of their carbon stocks by a factor of two, within the next century." However, they state this "potential CO_2 sink is threatened by the proposal of the European Commission to increase the share of renewable energy to 20% of the total energy consumption by 2020," and "this will almost double the wood demand for biomass energy (Ragwitz *et al.*, 2005) in the EU-15 from 55% of harvested wood in 2001 to 100% in 2020 at current harvest levels." Summing up this latter situation, Ciais *et al.* conclude "a return to using wood as biofuel ... could cancel out the benefits of carbon storage over the past five decades."

Lewis *et al.* (2009) invested a great amount of time and effort in documenting changes in aboveground carbon storage in "79 permanent sample plots spanning 40 years (1968–2007), located in closed-canopy moist forest, spanning West, Central and Eastern Africa," based on data from more than 70,000 individual trees across ten countries. They found "aboveground carbon storage in live trees increased by 0.63 Mg C ha^{-1} year^{-1} between 1968 and 2007," and "extrapolation to unmeasured forest components (live roots, small trees, necromass) and scaling to the continent implies a total increase in carbon storage in African tropical forest trees of 0.34 Pg C year^{-1}."

The 33 researchers say the observed changes in carbon storage "are similar to those reported for Amazonian forests per unit area, providing evidence that increasing carbon storage in old-growth forests is a pan-tropical phenomenon," and "combining all standardized inventory data from this study and from tropical America and Asia together yields a comparable figure of 0.49 Mg C ha^{-1} year^{-1}." This equates to "a carbon sink of 1.3 Pg C year^{-1} across all tropical forests during recent decades," which can account for roughly half of the so-called missing carbon sink.

In identifying the driving force that breathed new life into old trees, Lewis *et al.* write in the concluding sentence of the abstract of their paper, "taxon-specific analyses of African inventory and other data suggest that widespread changes in resource availability, such as increasing atmospheric carbon dioxide concentrations, may be the cause of the increase in carbon stocks, as some theory (Lloyd and Farquhar, 1996) and models (Friedlingstein *et al.*, 2006; Stephens *et al.*, 2007; Ciais *et al.*, 2008b) predict."

All these findings indicate elevated CO_2 enhances photosynthetic rates and biomass production in forest trees, both of which lead to greater amounts of carbon sequestration. Elevated CO_2 also enhances carbon sequestration by reducing carbon losses arising from plant respiration. Karnosky *et al.* (1999), for example, report aspen seedlings grown for one year at 560 ppm CO_2 displayed dark respiration rates 24% lower than rates exhibited by trembling aspen grown at 360 ppm CO_2. Also, elevated CO_2 has been shown to decrease maintenance respiration, which it did by 60% in western hemlock seedlings exposed to an atmospheric CO_2 concentration of nearly 1,600 ppm (McDowell *et al.*, 1999).

In a thorough review of these topics, Drake *et al.* (1999) conclude, on average, a doubling of the atmospheric CO_2 concentration reduces plant respiration rates by approximately 17%. This finding contrasts strikingly with the much smaller effects reported by Amthor (2000), who found an average reduction in dark respiration of only 1.5% for nine deciduous tree species exposed to 800 ppm CO_2. The period of CO_2 exposure in his much-shorter experiments, however, was but a mere 15 minutes. Thus, if the air's CO_2 content doubles, plants will likely sequester something on the order of 17% more carbon than ambiently grown plants, solely as a consequence of CO_2-induced reductions in respiration. This stored carbon is in addition to that sequestered as a result of CO_2-induced increases in plant photosynthetic rates.

Still, some researchers have expressed concern about the fate of the extra carbon stored in plant tissues as a consequence of atmospheric CO_2 enrichment, fearing it may rapidly return to the atmosphere following tissue senescence and decomposition, as opposed to being locked away for long periods of time.

In addressing such concerns, it is important to note atmospheric CO_2 enrichment typically reduces, or has no effect upon, decomposition rates of senesced plant material. De Angelis *et al.* (2000), for example, note when leaf litter from Mediterranean forest species exposed to 710 ppm CO_2 for 3.5 years was collected and allowed to decompose at 710 ppm CO_2 for approximately one year, it decomposed at a rate 4% less than leaf litter produced and incubated at ambient CO_2 for one year. Similarly, leaf litter collected from yellow-poplar (*Liriodendron tulipifera*) seedlings exposed to 700 ppm CO_2 for four years contained 12% more biomass than leaf litter collected from seedlings grown at ambient CO_2, following two years of decomposition at their respective CO_2 growth concentrations (Scherzel *et al.*, 1998). Hirschel *et al.* (1997) found no significant CO_2-induced effects on decomposition rates in tropical rainforest species, as Scherzel *et al.* (1998) also found for eastern white pine (*Pinus strobes*). Others have reported similar findings.

Cotrufo *et al.* (1998) grew two-year-old ash and sycamore seedlings for one growing season in closed-top chambers maintained at atmospheric CO_2 concentrations of 350 and 600 ppm. The high-CO_2 air increased lignin contents in the litter produced from both tree species, which likely contributed to the decreased litter decomposition rates observed in the CO_2-enriched chambers. After one year of incubation, for example, litter bags from the CO_2-enriched trees of both species had about 30 percent more dry mass remaining in them than litter bags from the ambient trees. In addition, woodlouse arthropods consumed 16 percent less biomass when fed litter generated from seedlings grown at 600 ppm CO_2 than when fed litter generated from seedlings grown in ambient air.

Cotrufo and Ineson (2000) grew beech seedlings for five years in open-top chambers fumigated with air containing either 350 or 700 ppm CO_2. Subsequently, woody twigs from each CO_2 treatment were collected and incubated in native forest soils for 42 months. They determined there was no significant effect of the differential CO_2 exposure during growth on subsequent woody twig decomposition, although the mean decomposition rate of the CO_2-enriched twigs was 5 percent less than the ambient-treatment twigs.

Conway *et al.* (2000) grew two-year-old ash tree seedlings in solar domes maintained at atmospheric

CO$_2$ concentrations of 350 and 600 ppm, after which naturally senesced leaves were collected, inoculated with various fungal species, and incubated for 42 days. They found the elevated CO$_2$ significantly reduced the amount of nitrogen in the senesced leaves, thus giving the CO$_2$-enriched leaf litter a higher carbon-to-nitrogen ratio than the litter collected from the seedlings growing in ambient air. This change likely contributed to the observed reductions in the amount of fungal colonization present on the senesced leaves from the CO$_2$-enriched treatment, which would be expected to result in reduced rates of leaf decomposition.

King *et al.* (2001) grew aspen seedlings for five months in open-top chambers receiving atmospheric CO$_2$ concentrations of 350 and 700 ppm. At the end of this period, they collected naturally senesced leaf litter, analyzed it, and allowed it to decompose under ambient conditions for 111 days. Although the elevated CO$_2$ slightly lowered leaf litter nitrogen content, it had no effect on litter sugar, starch, or tannin concentrations. With little to no CO$_2$-induced effects on leaf litter quality, there was no CO$_2$-induced effect on litter decomposition.

Dilustro *et al.* (2001) erected open-top chambers around portions of a regenerating oak-palmetto scrub ecosystem in Florida, USA and maintained them at CO$_2$ concentrations of either 350 or 700 ppm. They then incubated ambient- and elevated-CO$_2$-produced fine roots for 2.2 years in the chamber soils, which were nutrient-poor and often water-stressed. They found the elevated CO$_2$ did not significantly affect the decomposition rates of the fine roots originating from either the ambient or CO$_2$-enriched environments.

Thus it would appear the ongoing rise in the air's CO$_2$ content will not materially alter the rate of decomposition of the world's soil organic matter. This means the rate at which carbon is sequestered in forest soils should continue to increase as the productivity of Earth's plants is increased by the aerial fertilization effect of the rising atmospheric CO$_2$ concentration.

Another concern, which for a time was thought to limit the sequestering power of forests under rising atmospheric CO$_2$ but which has been thoroughly debunked, is what has come to be known as the progressive nitrogen limitation hypothesis. Some researchers suggested the striking CO$_2$-induced growth enhancements initially experienced by woody plants in scientific studies would disappear gradually over time, as the plants slowly deplete the soils in which they are growing of their initial store of nitrogen.

Long-term atmospheric CO$_2$-enrichment experiments show this progressive nitrogen limitation hypothesis is not supported by real-world data, as even soils low in nitrogen at the start of many long-term atmospheric CO$_2$ enrichment experiments have continued to supply sufficient nitrogen to maintain the initial high level of the CO$_2$-induced stimulation of plant growth.

In the introduction to a paper on the subject that summarizes nine years of work at the Duke Forest FACE experiment in North Carolina (USA), where portions of an aggrading loblolly pine (*Pinus taeda*) plantation had been continuously exposed to an extra 200 ppm of CO$_2$ since 1996, Lichter *et al.* (2008) note progressive nitrogen limitation (PNL) may "accompany C sequestration in plants and soils stimulated by CO$_2$ fertilization, gradually attenuating the CO$_2$ response." They then describe what they learned about this PNL hypothesis over the nine years of the Duke Forest experiment.

First, the nine researchers report their data pertaining to forest-floor carbon pools indicate the existence of "a long-term steady-state sink" of about 30 g C per m^2 per year, which represents "a substantial increase in forest-floor C storage under elevated CO$_2$ (i.e. 29%)," and which they attribute to "increased litterfall and root turnover during the first 9 years of the study." Second, below the forest floor, they say, of the mineral soil C formed during the past nine years, "approximately 20% has been allocated to stable pools that will likely remain protected from microbial activity and associated release as CO$_2$."

The research team also found "a significant widening of the C:N ratio of soil organic matter in the upper mineral soil under both elevated and ambient CO$_2$," which suggests, as they describe it, "enhanced rates of soil organic matter decomposition are increasing mineralization and uptake to provide the extra N required to support the observed increase in primary productivity under elevated CO$_2$." Pritchard *et al.* (2008) report this CO$_2$-induced increase in productivity amounts to approximately 30% annually, and they add there is "little evidence to indicate a diminished response through time," citing Finzi *et al.* (2007), who found the same to be true at the long-term forest FACE studies being conducted at Rhinelander, Wisconsin (USA), Oak Ridge National Laboratory (USA), and Tuscania (Italy).

Thus, contrary to the PNL hypothesis, in the case of North Carolina's Duke Forest, "even after nine years of experimental CO$_2$ fertilization," as Lichter *et al.* describe it, "attenuation of the CO$_2$-induced productivity enhancement has not been observed."

This finding at this location is extremely significant, because the growth of pine-hardwood forests in the southeastern United States often removes so much nitrogen from the soils in which they grow that they induce what Finzi and Schlesinger (2003) describe as "a state of acute nutrient deficiency that can only be reversed with fertilization." No fertilization was done during the Duke Forest FACE study.

Langley *et al.* (2009) note "it has been suggested that stimulation of productivity with elevated CO_2 ties up nitrogen in plant litter, which, if not offset by increases in N-use efficiency or N supply, will limit the ecosystem CO_2 response," citing Reich *et al.* (2006). The six scientists "employed an acid-hydrolysis-incubation method and a net nitrogen-mineralization assay to assess stability of soil carbon pools and short-term nitrogen dynamics in a Florida scrub-oak ecosystem after six years of exposure to elevated CO_2," at a multiple open-top-chamber facility on a barrier island located at NASA's Kennedy Space Center on the east coast of central Florida, USA. Langley *et al.* report elevated atmospheric CO_2 (to 350 ppm above ambient concentrations) tended to increase net N mineralization in the top 10 cm of the soil, but it also decreased total soil organic carbon content there by 21%. That loss of carbon mass was equivalent to only "roughly one-third of the increase in plant biomass that occurred in the same experiment." In addition, the strongest increases in net N mineralization were observed in the 10–30 cm depth increment, and "release of N from this depth may have allowed the sustained CO_2 effect on productivity in this scrub-oak forest," which over the four years leading up to their study "increased litterfall by 19–59%," according to Hungate *et al.* (2006).

Much more information rebutting the PNL hypothesis is presented in Chapter 3, Section 3.11, where is it demonstrated atmospheric CO_2 enrichment generally enables plants to find the extra nitrogen they need to take full advantage of the aerial fertilization effect of elevated atmospheric CO_2 concentrations, which increases total ecosystem carbon content, resulting in a negative feedback to anthropogenic CO_2 emissions. As the air's CO_2 content rises, the ability of forests to sequester carbon rises along with it, while tempering the rate of rise of the air's CO_2 content.

References

Agren, G.I. and Bosatta, E. 1998. *Theoretical Ecosystem Ecology—Understanding Element Cycles.* Cambridge University Press, Cambridge, UK.

Agren, G.I., Hyvonen, R., and Nilsson, T. 2007. Are Swedish forest soils sinks or sources for CO_2—model analyses based on forest inventory data. *Biogeochemistry* **82**: 217–227.

Amthor, J.S. 2000. Direct effect of elevated CO_2 on nocturnal in situ leaf respiration in nine temperate deciduous tree species is small. *Tree Physiology* **20**: 139–144.

Barton, C.V.M. and Jarvis, P.G. 1999. Growth response of branches of *Picea sitchensis* to four years exposure to elevated atmospheric carbon dioxide concentration. *New Phytologist* **144**: 233–243.

Becker, M., *et al.* 1995. In: Landmann, G. and Bonneau, M. (Eds.) *Forest Decline and Atmospheric Deposition Effects in the French Mountains.* Springer-Verlag, Berlin, Germany, pp. 120–142.

Chambers, J.Q., Higuchi, N., and Schimel, J.P. 1998. Ancient trees in Amazonia. *Nature* **391**: 135–136.

Ciais, P., Piao, S.-L., Cadule, P., Friedlingstein, P.. and Chedin, A. 2008b. Variability and recent trends in the African carbon balance. *Biogeosciences* **5**: 3497–3532.

Ciais, P., Schelhaas, M.J., Zaehle, S., Piao, S.L., Cescatti, A., Liski, J., Luyssaert, S., Le-Maire, G., Schulze, E.-D., Bouriaud, O., Freibauer, A., Valentini, R., and Nabuurs, G.J. 2008a. Carbon accumulation in European forests. *Nature Geoscience* **1**: 425–429.

Conway, D.R., Frankland, J.C., Saunders, V.A., and Wilson, D.R. 2000. Effects of elevated atmospheric CO_2 on fungal competition and decomposition of *Fraxinus excelsior* litter in laboratory microcosms. *Mycology Research* **104**: 187–197.

Cotrufo, M.F. and Ineson, P. 2000. Does elevated atmospheric CO_2 concentration affect wood decomposition? *Plant and Soil* **224**: 51–57.

Cotrufo, M.F., Briones, M.J.I., and Ineson, P. 1998. Elevated CO_2 affects field decomposition rate and palatability of tree leaf litter: importance of changes in substrate quality. *Soil Biology and Biochemistry* **30**: 1565–1571.

De Angelis, P., Chigwerewe, K.S., and Mugnozza, G.E.S. 2000. Litter quality and decomposition in a CO_2-enriched Mediterranean forest ecosystem. *Plant and Soil* **224**: 31–41.

Dilustro, J.J., Day, F.P., and Drake, B.G. 2001. Effects of

elevated atmospheric CO$_2$ on root decomposition in a scrub oak ecosystem. *Global Change Biology* **7**: 581–589.

Drake, B.G., Azcon-Bieto, J., Berry, J., Bunce, J., Dijkstra, P., Farrar, J., Gifford, R.M., Gonzalez-Meler, M.A., Koch, G., Lambers, H., Siedow, J., and Wullschleger, S. 1999. Does elevated atmospheric CO$_2$ inhibit mitochondrial respiration in green plants? *Plant, Cell and Environment* **22**: 649–657.

Ellsworth, D.S. 2000. Seasonal CO$_2$ assimilation and stomatal limitations in a *Pinus taeda* canopy with varying climate. *Tree Physiology* **20**: 435–444.

Fan, S., Gloor, M., Mahlman, J., Pacala, S., Sarmiento, J., Takahashi, T., and Tans, P. 1998. A large terrestrial carbon sink in North America implied by atmospheric and oceanic carbon dioxide data and models. *Science* **282**: 442–446.

Finzi, A.C., Norby, R.J., Calfapietra, C., Gallet-Budynek, A., Gielen, B., Holmes, W.E., Hoosbeek, M.R., Iversen, C.M., Jackson, R.B., Kubiske, M.E., Ledford, J., Liberloo, M., Oren, R., Polle, A., Pritchard, S., Zak, D.R., Schlesinger, W.H., and Ceulemans, R. 2007. Increases in nitrogen uptake rather than nitrogen-use efficiency support higher rates of temperate forest productivity under elevated CO$_2$. *Proceedings of the National Academy of Sciences, USA* **104**: 14,014–14,019.

Finzi, A.C. and Schlesinger, W.H. 2003. Soil-nitrogen cycling in a pine forest exposed to 5 years of elevated carbon dioxide. *Ecosystems* **6**: 444–456.

Friedlingstein, P., Cox, P., Betts, R., Bopp, L., von Bloh, W., Brovkin, V., Cadule, P., Doney, S., Eby, M., Fung, I., Bala, G., John, J., Jones, C., Joos, F., Kato, T., Kawamiya, M., Knorr, W., Lindsay, K., Matthews, H.D., Raddatz, T., Rayner, P., Reick, C., Roeckner, E., Schnitzler, K.-G., Schnur, R., Strassmann, K., Weaver, A.J., Yoshikawa, C., and Zeng, N. 2006. Climate-carbon cycle feedback analysis: Results from the (CMIP)-M-4 model intercomparison. *Journal of Climate* **19**: 3337–3353.

Hamilton, J.G., DeLucia, E.H., George, K., Naidu, S.L., Finzi, A.C., and Schlesinger, W.H. 2002. Forest carbon balance under elevated CO$_2$. *Oecologia* DOI 10.1007/s00442-002-0884-x.

Hibbard, K.A., Archer, S., Schimel, D.S., and Valentine, D.W. 2001. Biogeochemical changes accompanying woody plant encroachment in a subtropical savanna. *Ecology* **82**: 1999–2011.

Hirschel, G., Körner, C., and Arnone III, J.A. 1997. Will rising atmospheric CO$_2$ affect leaf litter quality and in situ decomposition rates in native plant communities? *Oecologia* **110**: 387–392.

Houghton, R.A., Davidson, E.A., and Woodwell, G.M. 1998. Missing sinks, feedbacks, and understanding the role of terrestrial ecosystems in the global carbon balance. *Global Biogeochemical Cycles* **12**: 25–34.

Houpis, J.L.J., Anderson, P.D., Pushnik, J.C., and Anschel, D.J. 1999. Among-provenance variability of gas exchange and growth in response to long-term elevated CO$_2$ exposure. *Water, Air, and Soil Pollution* **116**: 403–412.

Hungate, B.A., Johnson, D.W., Dijkstra, P., Hymus, G., Stiling, P., Megonigal, J.P., Pagel, A.L., Moan, J.L., Day, F., Li, J., Hinkle, C.R., and Drake, B.G. 2006. Nitrogen cycling during seven years of atmospheric CO$_2$ enrichment in a scrub oak woodland. *Ecology* **87**: 26–40.

Hyvonen, R., Agren, G.I., Linder, S., Persson, T., Cotrufo, M.F., Ekblad, A., Freeman, M., Grelle, A., Janssens, I.A., Jarvis, P.G., Kellomaki, S., Lindroth, A., Loustau, D., Lundmark, T., Norby, R.J., Oren, R., Pilegaard, K., Ryan, M.G., Sigurdsson, B.D., Stromgren, M., van Oijen, M., and Wallin, G. 2007. The likely impact of elevated [CO$_2$], nitrogen deposition, increased temperature and management on carbon sequestration in temperate and boreal forest ecosystems: a literature review. *New Phytologist* **173**: 463–480.

Idso, S.B. 1995. *CO$_2$ and the Biosphere: The Incredible Legacy of the Industrial Revolution.* Special Publication, Kuehnast Lecture Series. Department of Soil, Water & Climate, University of Minnesota, St. Paul, Minnesota, USA.

Karberg, N.J., Pregitzer, K.S., King, J.S., Friend, A.L., and Wood, J.R. 2005. Soil carbon dioxide partial pressure and dissolved inorganic carbonate chemistry under elevated carbon dioxide and ozone. *Oecologia* **142**: 296–306.

Karnosky, D.F., Mankovska, B., Percy, K., Dickson, R.E., Podila, G.K., Sober, J., Noormets, A., Hendrey, G., Coleman, M.D., Kubiske, M., Pregitzer, K.S., and Isebrands, J.G. 1999. Effects of tropospheric O$_3$ on trembling aspen and interaction with CO$_2$: results from an O$_3$-gradient and a FACE experiment. *Water, Air, and Soil Pollution* **116**: 311–322.

King, J.S., Pregitzer, K.S., Zak, D.R., Kubiske, M.E., Ashby, J.A., and Holmes, W.E. 2001. Chemistry and decomposition of litter from *Populus tremuloides* Michaux grown at elevated atmospheric CO$_2$ and varying N availability. *Global Change Biology* **7**: 65–74.

Knapp, P.A. and Soule, P.T. 1998. Recent *Juniperus occidentalis* (Western Juniper) expansion on a protected site in central Oregon. *Global Change Biology* **4**: 347–357.

Lai, C.T., Katul, G., Butnor, J., Ellsworth, D., and Oren, R. 2002. Modeling nighttime ecosystem respiration by a constrained source optimization method. *Global Change Biology* **8**: 124–141.

Langley, J.A., McKinley, D.C., Wolf, A.A., Hungate, B.A., Drake, B.G., and Megonigal, J.P. 2009. Priming depletes soil carbon and releases nitrogen in a scrub-oak ecosystem exposed to elevated CO$_2$. *Soil Biology & Biochemistry* **41**: 54–60.

Laurance, W.F., Nascimento, H.E.M., Laurance, S.G., Condit, R., D'Angelo, S., and Andrade, A. 2004b. Inferred longevity of Amazonian rainforest trees based on a long-term demographic study. *Forest Ecology and Management* **190**: 131–143.

Laurance, W.F., Oliveira, A.A., Laurance, S.G., Condit, R., Nascimento, H.E.M., Sanchez-Thorin, A.C., Lovejoy, T.E., Andrade, A., D'Angelo, S., and Dick, C. 2004a. Pervasive alteration of tree communities in undisturbed Amazonian forests. *Nature* **428**: 171–175.

Lewis, S.L., Lopez-Gonzalez, G., Sonke, B., Affum-Baffoe, K., Baker, T.R., Ojo, L.O., Phillips, O.L., Reitsma, J.M., White, L., Comiskey, J.A., Djuikouo K., M.-N., Ewango, C.E.N., Feldpausch, T.R., Hamilton, A.C., Gloor, M., Hart, T., Hladik, A., Lloyd, J., Lovett, J.C., Makana, J.-R., Malhi, Y., Mbago, F.M., Ndangalasi, H.J., Peacock, J., Peh, K. S.-H., Sheil, D., Sunderland, T., Swaine, M.D., Taplin, J., Taylor, D., Thomas, S.C., Votere, R., and Woll, H. 2009. Increasing carbon storage in intact African tropical forests. *Nature* **457**: 1003–1006.

Lichter, J., Billings, S.A., Ziegler, S.E., Gaindh, D., Ryals, R., Finzi, A.C., Jackson, R.B., Stemmler, E.A., and Schlesinger, W.H. 2008. Soil carbon sequestration in a pine forest after 9 years of atmospheric CO_2 enrichment. *Global Change Biology* **14**: 2910–2922.

Lloyd, J. 1999. The CO_2 dependence of photosynthesis, plant growth responses to elevated CO_2 concentrations and their interaction with soil nutrient status, II. Temperate and boreal forest productivity and the combined effects of increasing CO_2 concentrations and increased nitrogen deposition at a global scale. *Functional Ecology* **13**: 439–459.

Lloyd, J. and Farquhar, G.D. 1996. The CO_2 dependence of photosynthesis, plant growth responses to elevated atmospheric CO_2 concentrations and their interaction with soil nutrient status. 1. General principles and forest ecosystems. *Functional Ecology* **10**: 4–32.

Luo, Y., Medlyn, B., Hui, D., Ellsworth, D., Reynolds, J., and Katul, G. 2001. Gross primary productivity in the Duke Forest: Modeling synthesis of the free-air CO_2 enrichment experiment and eddy-covariance measurements. *Ecological Applications* **11**: 239–252.

Luo, Y., White, L.W., Canadell, J.G., DeLucia, E.H., Ellsworth, D.S., Finzi, A., Lichter, J., and Schlesinger, W.H. 2003. Sustainability of terrestrial carbon sequestration: A case study in Duke Forest with inversion approach. *Global Biogeochemical Cycles* **17**: 10.1029/2002GB001923.

Marek, M.V., Sprtova, M., De Angelis, P., and Scarascia-Mugnozza, G. 2001. Spatial distribution of photosynthetic response to long-term influence of elevated CO_2 in a Mediterranean *macchia* mini-ecosystem. *Plant Science* **160**: 1125–1136.

McCarron, J.K., Knapp, A.K., and Blair, J.M. 2003. Soil C and N responses to woody plant expansion in a mesic grassland. *Plant and Soil* **257**: 183–192.

McDowell, N.G., Marshall, J.D., Qi, J., and Mattson, K. 1999. Direct inhibition of maintenance respiration in western hemlock roots exposed to ambient soil carbon dioxide concentrations. *Tree Physiology* **19**: 599–605.

Motta, R. and Nola, P. 2001. Growth trends and dynamics in sub-alpine forest stands in the Varaita Valley (Piedmont, Italy) and their relationships with human activities and global change. *Journal of Vegetation Science* **12**: 219–230.

Myers, D.A., Thomas, R.B., and DeLucia, E.H. 1999. Photosynthetic capacity of loblolly pine (*Pinus taeda* L.) trees during the first year of carbon dioxide enrichment in a forest ecosystem. *Plant, Cell and Environment* **22**: 473–481.

Nadelhoffer, K.J., Emmett, B.A., Gundersen, P., Kjonaas, O.J., Koopmans, C.J., Schleppi, P., Tietema, A., and Wright, R.F. 1999. Nitrogen deposition makes a minor contribution to carbon sequestration in temperate forests. *Nature* **398**: 145–148.

Nicolussi, K., Bortenschlager, S., and Körner, C. 1995. Increase in tree-ring width in subalpine *Pinus cembra* from the central Alps that may be CO_2-related. *Trees* **9**: 181–189.

Norris, M. 2000. *Biogeochemical Consequences of Land Cover Change in Eastern Kansas*. In: Division of Biology, Kansas State University, Manhattan, Kansas, USA.

Norby, R.J., DeLucia, E.H., Gielen, B., Calfapietra, C., Giardina, C.P., King, S.J., Ledford, J., McCarthy, H.R., Moore, D.J.P., Ceulemans, R., De Angelis, P., Finzi, A.C., Karnosky, D.F., Kubiske, M.E., Lukac, M., Pregitzer, K.S., Scarasci-Mugnozza, G.E., Schlesinger, W.H., and Oren, R. 2005. Forest response to elevated CO_2 is conserved across a broad range of productivity. *Proceedings of the National Academy of Sciences* **102**: 18,052–18,056.

Norby, R.J., Ledford, J., Reilly, C.D., Miller, N.E., and O'Neill, E.G. 2004. Fine-root production dominates response of a deciduous forest to atmospheric CO_2 enrichment. *Proceedings of the National Academy of Sciences USA* **101**: 9689–9693.

Pearce, F. 1999. That sinking feeling. *New Scientist* **164** (2209): 20–21.

Phillips, O.L. and Gentry, A.H. 1994. Increasing turnover through time in tropical forests. *Science* **263**: 954–958.

Phillips, O.L., Malhi, Y., Higuchi, N., Laurance, W.F., Nunez, P.V., Vasquez, R.M., Laurance, S.G., Ferreira, L.V., Stern, M., Brown, S., and Grace, J. 1998. Changes in the carbon balance of tropical forests: Evidence from long-term plots. *Science* **282**: 439–442.

Pregitzer, K.S., Zak, D.R., Maziasz, J., DeForest, J., Curtis, P.S., and Lussenhop, J. 2000. Interactive effects of atmospheric CO$_2$ and soil-N availability on fine roots of *Populus tremuloides*. *Ecological Applications* **10**: 18–33.

Pritchard, S.G., Davis, M.A., Mitchell, R.J., Prior, A.S., Boykin, D.L., Rogers, H.H., and Runion, G.B. 2001. Root dynamics in an artificially constructed regenerating longleaf pine ecosystem are affected by atmospheric CO$_2$ enrichment. *Environmental and Experimental Botany* **46**: 35–69.

Pritchard, S.G., Strand, A.E., McCormack, M.L., Davis, M.A., and Oren, R. 2008. Mycorrhizal and rhizomorph dynamics in a loblolly pine forest during 5 years of free-air-CO$_2$-enrichment. *Global Change Biology* **14**: 1–13.

Ragwitz et al. 2005. FORRES Analysis of the Renewable Energy Sources' Evolution up to 2020. Final Report. (Karlsruhe, 2005).

Rasineni, G.K., Guha, A., and Reddy, A.R. 2011. Responses of *Gmelina arborea*, a tropical deciduous tree species, to elevated atmospheric CO$_2$: Growth, biomass productivity and carbon sequestration efficacy. *Plant Science* **181**: 428–438.

Raymond, P.A. and Cole, J.J. 2003. Increase in the export of alkalinity from North America's largest river. *Science* **301**: 88–91.

Reich, P.B., Hungate, B.A., and Luo, Y. 2006. Carbon-nitrogen interactions in terrestrial ecosystems in response to rising atmospheric carbon dioxide. *Annual Review of Ecology, Evolution and Systematics* **37**: 611–636.

Rolland, C., Petitcolas, V., and Michalet, R. 1998. Changes in radial tree growth for *Picea abies*, *Larix deciduas*, *Pinus cembra* and *Pinus uncinata* near the alpine timberline since 1750. *Trees* **13**: 40–50.

Saxe, H., Ellsworth, D.S., and Heath, J. 1998. Tree and forest functioning in an enriched CO$_2$ atmosphere. *New Phytologist* **139**: 395–436.

Scherzel, A.J., Rebbeck, J., and Boerner, R.E.J. 1998. Foliar nitrogen dynamics and decomposition of yellow-poplar and eastern white pine during four seasons of exposure to elevated ozone and carbon dioxide. *Forest Ecology and Management* **109**: 355–366.

Schlesinger, W.H. and Lichter, J. 2001. Limited carbon storage in soil and litter of experimental forest plots under increased atmospheric CO$_2$. *Nature* **411**: 466–469.

Smith, D. 2001. Changes in Carbon Cycling as Forests Expand into Tallgrass Prairie: Mechanisms Driving Low Soil Respiration Rates in Juniper Forests. In: Division of Biology, Kansas State University, Manhattan, Kansas, USA.

Smittenberg, R.H., Eglinton, T.I., Schouten, S., and Damste, J.S.S. 2006. Ongoing buildup of refractory organic carbon in boreal soils during the Holocene. *Science* **314**: 1283–1286.

Soule, P.T. and Knapp, P.A. 1999. Western juniper expansion on adjacent disturbed and near-relict sites. *Journal of Range Management* **52**: 525–533.

Spiecker, H. 1996. *Growth Trends in European Forests*. European Forest Institute Research Report 5. Springer-Verlag, Berlin, Germany.

Stephens, B.B., Gurney, K.R., Tans, P.P., Sweeney, C., Peters, W., Bruhwiler, L., Ciais, P., Ramonet, M., Bousquet, P., Nakazawa, T., Aoki, S., Machida, T., Inoue, G., Vinnichenko, N., Lloyd, J., Jordan, A., Heimann, M., Shibistova, O., Langenfelds, R.L., Steele, L.P., Francey, R.J., and Denning, A.S. 2007. Weak northern and strong tropical land carbon uptake from vertical profiles of atmospheric CO$_2$. *Science* **316**: 1732–1735.

Thomas, R.Q., Canham, C.D., Weathers, K.C., and Goodale, C.L. 2010. Increased tree carbon storage in response to nitrogen deposition in the US. *Nature Geoscience* **3**: 13–17.

Wang, Z.A. and Cai, W.-J. 2004. Carbon dioxide degassing and inorganic carbon export from a marsh-dominated estuary (the Duplin River): A marsh CO$_2$ pump. *Limnology and Oceanography* **49**: 341–354.

Weaver, P.L. and Murphy, P.G. 1990. Forest structure and productivity in Puerto Rico's Luquillo Mountains. *Biotropica* **22**: 69–82.

White, A., Cannell, M.G.R., and Friend, A.D. 2000. The high-latitude terrestrial carbon sink: a model analysis. *Global Change Biology* **6**: 227–245.

Zaehle, S., Sitch, S., Prentice, I.C., Liski, J., Cramer, W., Erhard, M., Hickler, T., and Smith, B. 2006. The importance of age-related decline in forest NPP for modeling regional carbon balances. *Ecological Applications* **16**: 1555–1574.

Zak, D.R., Pregitzer, K.S., Curtis, P.S., Vogel, C.S., Holmes, W.E., and Lussenhop, J. 2000. Atmospheric CO$_2$, soil-N availability, and allocation of biomass and nitrogen by *Populus tremuloides*. *Ecological Applications* **10**: 34–46.

1.2.1.4.2 The Influence of Temperature

- If air temperatures rise in the future they likely will have a positive effect on carbon storage in forests and their associated soils.

The planting of forests with the objective of removing CO$_2$ from the atmosphere and sequestering its carbon in soil organic matter—which tends to slow the rate of rise of the air's CO_2 content—has come under fire as being only a stopgap measure in the quest to moderate global warming. Pearce (1999) even referred to the concept as a dangerous delusion, saying "planned new forests, called 'carbon sinks,' will swiftly become saturated with carbon and begin returning most of their carbon to the atmosphere."

The rationale for this contention was that rising temperatures will increase rates of soil respiration, thereby causing forest ecosystems to return CO_2 to the air at a faster rate than they remove it from the atmosphere via photosynthesis. Proponents of the theory argue future rates of photosynthesis will "flatten out," according to Pearce, and respiration rates will "soar." Much like the theory of CO_2-induced global warming, however, a number of studies have shown quite conclusively this theory is not supported by real-world observations, which in fact directly contradict the theory.

A data-driven analysis by Fan *et al.* (1998) revealed the carbon-sequestering abilities of North America's forests between 15 and 51°N latitude are so robust they can yearly remove from the atmosphere all of the CO_2 annually released to it by fossil fuel consumption in both the United States and Canada—and this calculation was done during a time said to have the warmest temperatures on record. Similarly, Phillips *et al.* (1998) demonstrate carbon sequestration in tropical forests has increased substantially over the past 42 years in spite of any temperature increases during that time.

Liski *et al.* (1999) studied soil carbon storage across a temperature gradient in a modern-day Finnish boreal forest, reporting carbon sequestration in the soil of this forest increased with temperature. Contemporaneously, King *et al.* (1999) showed aspen seedlings increased their photosynthetic rates and biomass production as temperatures rose from 10 to 29°C, putting to rest the idea that high-temperature-induced increases in respiration rates would cause net losses in carbon fixation.

Giardina and Ryan (2000) analyzed organic carbon decomposition data derived from forest soils of 82 sites on five continents. Based on this worldwide assemblage of real-world data, they state carbon decomposition rates "are not controlled by temperature limitations to microbial activity, and that increased temperature alone will not stimulate the decomposition of forest-derived carbon in mineral soil." They report, "despite a 20°C gradient in mean annual temperature," soil carbon mass loss was "insensitive to temperature."

A group of 30 scientists (Valentini *et al.*, 2000) collected data on net ecosystem carbon exchange in 15 European forests, and they report their results "confirm that many European forest ecosystems act as carbon sinks." Their data also demonstrate the warmer forests of southern Europe annually sequester far more carbon than the cooler forests of northern Europe, again in direct contradiction of claims warmer temperatures must inevitably lead to forest carbon loss.

Grace and Rayment (2000) present still more evidence refuting the claim forests "will swiftly become saturated with carbon and begin returning most of their carbon to the atmosphere." Specifically, they cite a number of additional studies that "show quite clearly," as they put it, "that old undisturbed forests, as well as middle-aged forests, are net absorbers of CO_2." They also note these real-world observations mean "forests are serving as a carbon sink, providing a global environmental service by removing CO_2 from the atmosphere and thus reducing the rate of CO_2-induced warming." Further commenting on the work of Giardina and Ryan (2000) and Valentini *et al.* (2000), Grace and Rayment unequivocally state, "the results from these two papers should send a powerful message to those working with models of global vegetation change," namely, "that the doomsday view of runaway global warming now seems unlikely."

One of the simpler ways Earth's deciduous forests increase their storage of carbon is to leaf out progressively earlier each spring and remain photosynthetically active increasingly later every fall. This gradual lengthening of the growing season allows trees to remove more carbon dioxide from the atmosphere each succeeding year. This phenomenon, in turn, reduces the annual rate of rise of the air's CO_2 content, completing a negative feedback loop that slows the CO_2-induced portion of the warming that originally set the whole process in motion.

White *et al.* (1999) investigated in detail several aspects of this multistage phenomenon in a study of 88 years of data spanning the period 1900 to 1987, obtained from 12 locations in the eastern U.S. deciduous forest from Charleston, SC (32.8°N latitude) to Burlington, VT (44.5°N latitude). They determined a 1°C increase in mean annual air temperature increased the length of the forest's growing season by approximately five days. In addition, they demonstrated this relationship was linear over the entire mean annual air temperature range investigated, which stretched from 7 to 19°C and included growing seasons ranging in length from

150 to 210 days.

The second step of White *et al.*'s analysis was a bit more complicated, as they had to determine how much extra CO_2 was removed from the air for each day's temperature-induced extension of the growing season. They began by using an ecosystem process model that had previously been validated in other studies to predict carbon fluxes for the 12 forest sites. Using daily meteorological data, the model first calculated annual dates of the appearance and disappearance of "greenness"—the length of the photosynthetically active growing season—for each of the 88 years of records at each site. Then it calculated the net ecosystem production (NEP = gross primary production minus the sum of autotrophic and heterotrophic respiration) for each day of the 88 growing seasons at each site and summed each year's results to obtain 88 annual NEP totals for each site.

Plotting these yearly totals of net CO_2 removal from the atmosphere as functions of yearly growing season length for each site, White *et al.* report a one-day extension in growing season increased the mean forest NEP of the 12 sites by 1.6%, with greater increases in the colder northern sites (1.9% for Burlington, VT) and smaller increases in the warmer southern sites (1.4% for Charleston, SC).

As for how significant these numbers are, if Earth were to undergo a mean global warming of 1°C, according to the first of the two relationships derived by White *et al.*, this temperature increase would result in the eastern U.S. deciduous forest increasing the length of its growing season by approximately five days. Their second relationship suggests this growing season expansion would lead to an 8% increase in total carbon sequestration (5 days x 1.6% per day = 8%).

Moreover, this temperature-driven phenomenon may be much stronger than is implied by this simple exercise. In a study of 30 years of phenological data derived from observations of identical clones of trees and shrubs maintained by the European network of the International Phenological Gardens—located in the area bounded by latitudes 42 and 69° N and by longitudes 10° W and 27° E—Menzel and Fabian (1999) report the mean date of spring bud-break had increased by fully six days "since the early 1960s," and leaf senescence in the fall was delayed by an average of 4.8 days over the same period. Using the northernmost NEP enhancement factor derived by White *et al.*—which in all likelihood is a conservative choice, as White *et al.*'s northernmost forest site is at about the same latitude as the southernmost part of the latitudinal gradient spanned by Menzel and

Fabian's study area—the 10.8 extra warming-induced growing-season days produce a 20.5% increase in annual carbon sequestration (10.8 days x 1.9% per day = 20.5%).

Melillo *et al.* (2002) studied an even-aged mixed hardwood stand of the Harvard Forest in central Massachusetts, USA, where they installed buried heating cables at 10cm depths, spaced 20cm apart, in 6m by 6m plots, half of which were not operated to produce any heat (serving as "disturbance control" plots) and half of which maintained the average soil temperature approximately 5°C above ambient. At monthly intervals from April through November of each year of their 10-year study, the researchers measured CO_2 evolution rates from the soils of both sets of plots.

Over the first six years of the study, Melillo *et al.* observed an approximate 28% increase in CO_2 emissions from the heated plots relative to the non-heated plots. However, "over the last four years of the study, the 'stimulatory' effect of warming on soil respiration markedly decreased"; so much so, in fact, that from 1998 through 2000 there was "only about a 5% increase in soil respiration in the warmed versus disturbance control plots," and by the tenth year of the study "soil respiration showed no significant response to warming."

This exemplary study showed just how important it is to do experiments … and to do *long-term* experiments. Most prior theoretical studies, for example, had tended to predict what the scientists observed over the first six years of their measurement program—a large warming-induced increase in respiratory carbon loss from the forest soil—which likely would have been accepted as the long-term truth if they had terminated their work at any time during that period. Continuing their measurements for four more years, however, the scientists discovered what is likely the true long-term response—no significant change in soil respiratory carbon loss. That was but the beginning of what they learned.

Concurrent with their soil CO_2 evolution measurements, Melillo *et al.* measured rates of net nitrogen mineralization, finding "over the entire 10-year study period, warming resulted in a cumulative increase in net nitrogen mineralization." Also, partially overlapping Melillo *et al.*'s long-term warming experiment was a long-term nitrogen fertilization study of a similar hardwood stand in the Harvard Forest described by Magill *et al.* (2000), where after nine years, they report, "12.7% of the total amount of nitrogen fertilizer added ended up in the woody tissue of the stand's trees."

Assuming an identical portion of the increased nitrogen made available by the warming of their experiment ended up in the woody tissues of the trees they studied, Melillo *et al.* calculate this phenomenon "would result in an additional 1560 g m^{-2} of carbon storage in the vegetation over the decade of warming." Hence, having previously determined the soil carbon loss stimulated by their applied warming for the entire 10-year period was 944 g m^{-2}, the net result of the two competing phenomena for the complete forest ecosystem was a net carbon gain on the order of 600 g m^{-2}.

In discussing the significance of this unexpected but positive finding, Melillo *et al.* note there is other independent "direct field evidence that soil warming enhances carbon storage in trees." Citing Bergh *et al.* (1999) and Jarvis and Linder (2000), they say in a similar long-term study these investigators also found "there was a significant (more than 50%) increase in stem-wood growth of the trees on the heated plots relative to the controls."

These independent experimental observations suggest claims to the contrary have no backing in empirical science. Both the aerial fertilization effect of atmospheric CO_2 enrichment and the soil fertilization effect of the increase in nitrogen mineralization induced by global warming increase carbon sequestration in forest ecosystems, providing a strong, double-barreled, negative-feedback brake on the impetus for warming created by the enhanced greenhouse effect of the ongoing rise in the air's CO_2 content.

Perfors *et al.* (2003) utilized overhead infrared radiative heaters to continuously warm five plots of ungrazed montane meadow at the Rocky Mountain Biological Laboratory in Gunnison County, Colorado, USA. Five similar but unheated plots served as controls. In the heated plots, the extra downward flux of infrared radiation warmed the top 15 cm of soil by about 1.5°C and dried it by about 15% on a gravimetric basis during the growing season, prolonging the snow-free season at each end by a total of approximately 20 days. The scientists also developed and applied a method for extracting the age-detrended growth rate of common sagebrush—*Artemisia tridentata* (Nutt.), ssp. *vaseyana*, a perennial shrub that is abundant throughout much of the semiarid western United States—to determine the effect of a modest warming on the distribution of this common woody plant.

The scientists found annual sagebrush growth rates in the heated plots were approximately 50% greater than those in the control plots, due primarily to the warming-induced increase in the length of the snow-free season. The three researchers report their observations and analysis "suggest that global climate change, which is expected to result in a contracted period of snow accumulation in the montane west, will result in increased growth and range expansion of sagebrush near high-elevation range boundaries in the western US." And although Saleska *et al.* (2002) had demonstrated the experimental warming treatment decreased soil organic carbon content, Perfors *et al.* suggest, over the long term, "because sagebrush litter is more recalcitrant to decomposition than is the litter from the forb species that are in decline in the heated plots of our climate manipulation experiment, enhanced sagebrush growth could also contribute to a negative feedback [to CO_2-induced warming] by increasing the turnover time of soil carbon."

Monson *et al.* (2006) studied the effect of changes in snow cover on soil carbon cycling during natural climatic variations over a six-year period at the Niwot Ridge AmeriFlux site in the U.S. Rocky Mountains (40°1'58"N, 105°32'47"W). They used eddy covariance measurements to assess the net CO_2 exchange of a subalpine montane forest ecosystem, special chambers for measuring soil respiration beneath snow, various instruments to characterize a number of snow properties, and standard techniques for identifying soil microbial populations and assessing their growth kinetics and substrate-use. They report "microbes collected from under the snowpack could grow exponentially at 0°C," and "their growth rates increased rapidly with increasing temperature," so anything that decreased the temperature of their environment decreased forest soil respiration in winter, as they typically observed to be the case. They also note "a shallower snowpack has less insulation potential, causing colder soil temperatures," and "long-term monitoring of mountain snow packs in the western USA and Europe have shown trends towards decreasing depth, with several mountain ranges experiencing 50–75% decreases, and these have been attributed to positive temperature anomalies (Laternser and Schneebeli, 2003; Scherrer *et al.*, 2004; Mote *et al.*, 2005)."

Because rising air temperatures cause decreases in snow depth, decreases in snow depth in turn lead to colder soil temperatures, and colder soil temperatures lead to reduced microbial respiration, global warming may actually lead to greater quantities of carbon being trapped in the soils of montane forest ecosystems. As Monson *et al.* describe it, "decreases in the winter snow pack will generally cause decreases in the loss of respired CO_2 from the soils of forest ecosystems, thus enhancing the potential for soil carbon sequestration." Thus their work reveals yet another negative feedback mechanism whereby Earth's biosphere acts to resist changes in temperature caused by thermal pressures exerted by independent climate forcing factors.

Chen *et al.* (2006) note "CO$_2$ fluxes measured on micrometeorological towers in many flux networks worldwide (Baldocchi *et al.*, 2001) ... can only sample a very small fraction of the land surface as each can only represent a footprint area of about 1 km^2." Hence they sought "ways to retrieve carbon cycle information from atmospheric CO$_2$ concentration measurements, which have much larger footprints (10^3–10^4 km^2) (Lin *et al.*, 2003) than flux towers." They analyzed a 13-year (1990–1996, 1999–2004) hourly averaged atmospheric CO$_2$ concentration database obtained from a 40 m tower at Fraserdale, Ontario, Canada (together with temperature, humidity, and wind speed measured at 20 and 40 meters and precipitation at ground level). They compared their results with a marine boundary layer CO$_2$ dataset representing the free troposphere above the tower.

The eight researchers report in warmer years the planetary boundary layer over their measurement site was more depleted of CO$_2$, which suggests the 10^3–10^4 km^2 land area of the boreal ecosystem upwind of the tower sequestered more carbon in such years. They say this finding "suggests that gross primary productivity increased considerably faster with temperature than did ecosystem respiration," a relationship they found to be true for both annual temperatures (from year to year) and 10-day mean temperatures (throughout the growing season). These findings led them to conclude "the fact that the temperature sensitivity of gross primary productivity is larger than that of ecosystem respiration suggests that global warming could lead to increased carbon sequestration in boreal ecosystems."

Burton *et al.* (2008) note "increases in terrestrial ecosystem respiration as temperatures warm could create a positive feedback that causes atmospheric CO$_2$ concentration, and subsequently global temperature, to increase more rapidly," but they also note "if plant tissue respiration acclimates to temperature over time, this feedback loop will be weakened, reducing the potential temperature increase." In an attempt to determine which of these scenarios is more likely to occur, the three researchers employed published values of annual root respiration rates to assess "the cross-ecosystem rate of increase with temperature." They then examined "the potential for trade-offs between root metabolic capacity and biomass in regulating ecosystem root respiration, using published values for mid-growing season root specific respiration rates and root biomass." Finally, they determined whether "relationships that occur across ecosystems adapted to different climates might also exist within an ecosystem that is subjected to warming," by analyzing data obtained "from soil warming studies, including recent measurements of fine root respiration made at three warming experiments at Harvard Forest."

Burton *et al.* report their analyses of the pertinent scientific literature show "a clear trend for decreasing root metabolic capacity (respiration rate at a standard temperature) with increasing mean annual temperature"; "no instances of high growing season respiration rates and high root biomass occurring together"; and in the soil warming experiments at Harvard Forest, "decreases in metabolic capacity for roots from the heated plots." Thus Burton *et al.* conclude "these findings clearly suggest that modeling efforts that allow root respiration to increase exponentially with temperature, with Q$_{10}$ values of 2 or more, may over-predict root contributions to ecosystem CO$_2$ efflux for future climates and underestimate the amount of carbon available for other uses, including net primary productivity," rebuffing long-espoused claims to the contrary.

The studies cited above indicate rising air temperatures likely would have a positive effect on carbon storage in forests and their associated soils, instead of exerting a negative influence on forest carbon sequestration.

References

Baldocchi, D., Falge, E., Gu, L.H., Olson, R., Hollinger, D., Running, S., Anthoni, P., Bernhofer, C., Davis, K., Evans, R., Fuentes, J., Goldstein, A., Katul, G., Law B., Lee, X.H., Malhi, Y., Meyers, T., Munger, W., Oechel, W., Paw U, K.T., Pilegaard, K., Schmid, H.P., Valentini, R., Verma, S., Vesala, T., Wilson, K., and Wofsy, S. 2001. FLUXNET: A new tool to study the temporal and spatial variability of ecosystem-scale carbon dioxide, water vapor, and energy flux densities. *Bulletin of the American Meteorological Society* **82**: 2415–2434.

Bergh, J., Linder, S., Lundmark, T., and Elfving, B. 1999. The effect of water and nutrient availability on the productivity of Norway spruce in northern and southern Sweden. *Forest Ecology and Management* **119**: 51–62.

Burton, A.J., Melillo, J.M., and Frey, S.D. 2008.

Adjustment of forest ecosystem root respiration as temperature warms. *Journal of Integrative Plant Biology* **50**: 1467–1483.

Chen, J.M., Chen, B., Higuchi, K., Liu, J., Chan, D., Worthy, D., Tans, P., and Black, A. 2006. Boreal ecosystems sequestered more carbon in warmer years. *Geophysical Research Letters* **33**: 10.1029/2006GL025919.

Fan, S., Gloor, M., Mahlman, J., Pacala, S., Sarmiento, J., Takahashi, T., and Tans, P. 1998. A large terrestrial carbon sink in North America implied by atmospheric and oceanic carbon dioxide data and models. *Science* **282**: 442–446.

Giardina, C.P. and Ryan, M.G. 2000. Evidence that decomposition rates of organic carbon in mineral soil do not vary with temperature. *Nature* **404**: 858–861.

Grace, J. and Rayment, M. 2000. Respiration in the balance. *Nature* **404**: 819–820.

Jarvis, P. and Linder, S. 2000. Constraints to growth of boreal forests. *Nature* **405**: 904–905.

King, J.S., Pregitzer, K.S., and Zak, D.R. 1999. Clonal variation in above- and below-ground responses of *Populus tremuloides* Michaux: Influence of soil warming and nutrient availability. *Plant and Soil* **217**: 119–130.

Laternser, M. and Schneebeli, M. 2003. Long-term snow climate trends of the Swiss Alps (1931–99). *International Journal of Climatology* **23**: 733–750.

Lin, C., Gerbig, C., Wofsy, S.C., Andrews, A.E., Daube, B.C., Davis, K.T., and Grainger, C.A. 2003. A near-field tool for simulating the upstream influence of atmospheric observations: The Stochastic Time-Inverted Lagrangian Transport (STILT) model. *Journal of Geophysical Research* **108**: 10.1029/2002JD003161.

Liski, J., Ilvesniemi, H., Makela, A., and Westman, C.J. 1999. CO_2 emissions from soil in response to climatic warming are overestimated—The decomposition of old soil organic matter is tolerant of temperature. *Ambio* **28**: 171–174.

Magill, A.H., Aber, J.D., Berntson, G.M., McDowell, W.H., Nadelhoffer, K.J., Melillo, J.M., and Steudler, P. 2000. Long-term nitrogen additions and nitrogen saturation in two temperate forests. *Ecosystems* **3**: 238–253.

Melillo, J.M., Steudler, P.A., Aber, J.D., Newkirk, K., Lux, H., Bowles, F.P., Catricala, C., Magill, A., Ahrens, T., and Morrisseau, S. 2002. Soil warming and carbon-cycle feedbacks to the climate system. *Science* **298**: 2173–2176.

Menzel, A. and Fabian, P. 1999. Growing season extended in Europe. *Nature* **397**: 659.

Monson, R.K., Lipson, D.L., Burns, S.P., Turnipseed, A.A., Delany, A.C., Williams, M.W., and Schmidt, S.K.

2006. Winter forest soil respiration controlled by climate and microbial community composition. *Nature* **439**: 711–714.

Mote, P.W., Hamlet, A.F., Clark, M.P., and Lettenmaier, D.T. 2005. Declining mountain snow pack in Western North America. *Bulletin of the American Meteorological Society* **86**: 39–49.

Pearce, F. 1999. That sinking feeling. *New Scientist* **164** (2209): 20–21.

Perfors, T., Harte, J., and Alter, S.E. 2003. Enhanced growth of sagebrush (*Artemisia tridentata*) in response to manipulated ecosystem warming. *Global Change Biology* **9**: 736–742.

Phillips, O.L., Malhi, Y., Higuchi, N., Laurance, W.F., Nunez, P.V., Vasquez, R.M., Laurance, S.G., Ferreira, L.V., Stern, M., Brown, S., and Grace, J. 1998. Changes in the carbon balance of tropical forests: Evidence from long-term plots. *Science* **282**: 439–442.

Saleska, S.R., Shaw, M.R., Fischer, M.L., Dunne, J.A., Still, C.J., Holman, M.L., and Harte, J. 2002. Plant community composition mediates both large transient decline and predicted long-term recovery of soil carbon under climate warming. *Global Biogeochemical Cycles* **16**: 10.1029/2001GB001573.

Scherrer, S.C., Appenzeller, C., and Laternser, M. 2004. Trends in Swiss alpine snow days—The role of local and large-scale climate variability. *Geophysical Research Letters* **31**: 10.1029/2004GL020255.

Valentini, R., Matteucci, G., Dolman, A.J., Schulze, E.-D., Rebmann, C., Moors, E.J., Granier, A., Gross, P., Jensen, N.O., Pilegaard, K., Lindroth, A., Grelle, A., Bernhofer, C., Grunwald, T., Aubinet, M., Ceulemans, R., Kowalski, A.S., Vesala, T., Rannik, U., Berbigier, P., Loustau, D., Gudmundsson, J., Thorgeirsson, H., Ibrom, A., Morgenstern, K., Clement, R., Moncrieff, J., Montagnani, L., Minerbi, S., and Jarvis, P.G. 2000. Respiration as the main determinant of carbon balance in European forests. *Nature* **404**: 861–865.

White, M.A., Running, S.W., and Thornton, P.E. 1999. The impact of growing-season length variability on carbon assimilation and evapotranspiration over 88 years in the eastern US deciduous forest. *International Journal of Biometeorology* **42**: 139–145.

1.2.2 Grasslands

Most of Earth's terrestrial plant life evolved around 500 to 400 million years ago, when the atmospheric CO_2 concentration was possibly 10 to 20 times higher than it is today. As a consequence, the biochemical pathways and enzymes involved in carbon fixation should be better adapted to significantly higher-than-present atmospheric CO$_2$ levels, which has in fact been demonstrated to be the case. As the atmosphere's CO$_2$ content has dropped from that early point in time, it has caused most of Earth's vegetation to become less efficient at extracting carbon dioxide from the air. However, the recent ongoing rise in atmospheric CO$_2$ concentration is gradually increasing photosynthetic rates and stimulating vegetative productivity and the terrestrial sequestration of carbon around the globe. The subsections below review some of the recent evidence for these phenomena in various grassland species.

1.2.2.1 General Responses to Elevated CO$_2$

- As the air's CO$_2$ concentration increases, the productivity of Earth's grassland species also should increase, even under unfavorable growing conditions characterized by less-than-adequate soil moisture, inadequate soil nutrition, elevated air temperature, and physical stress imposed by herbivory.

Wand *et al.* (1999) provided an overview of the effects of elevated atmospheric CO$_2$ concentrations on photosynthesis in grasses by analyzing the pertinent peer-reviewed literature published between 1980 and 1997. These authors report a doubling of the air's CO$_2$ content increases photosynthetic rates of C$_3$ and C$_4$ grasses by 33 and 25%, respectively. Importantly, their results also demonstrate, contrary to some circulating opinions, C$_4$ plants can—and do—respond positively to increases in the air's CO$_2$ content.

Another good summary of grassland community responses to atmospheric CO$_2$ enrichment followed a year later in the comprehensive review of Campbell *et al.* (2000), who compiled and analyzed more than 165 peer-reviewed scientific journal articles dealing with pastures and rangelands. Although their review includes many responses of individual species, it provides a conservative estimate of community responses as well: an average 17% increase for a doubling of the air's CO$_2$ content. Therefore, as the atmospheric CO$_2$ concentration increases, it is likely grassland communities will exhibit increases in photosynthesis and biomass production, which will invariably lead to enhanced carbon sequestration in the soils beneath them. This conclusion is borne out in many additional studies.

Szente *et al.* (1998) grew two grass and two broad-leaved species common to loess grasslands of Budapest in open-top chambers for 231 days at atmospheric CO$_2$ concentrations of 350 and 700 ppm. The elevated CO$_2$ caused photosynthetic enhancements of 136 and 486% in the grass and broad-leaved species, respectively. After growing microcosms of the C$_3$ grass *Danthonia richardsonii* for four years in glasshouses receiving atmospheric CO$_2$ concentrations of 360 and 720 ppm, Lutze and Gifford (1998) report the elevated CO$_2$ increased total microcosm biomass by an average of 24%. Similarly, in the four-year study of Leadley *et al.* (1999), species-rich Swiss grasslands exposed to atmospheric CO$_2$ concentrations of 600 ppm in open-top and open-bottom chambers produced 29% more community biomass than control grasslands exposed to air of 350 ppm CO$_2$. And tallgrass prairie ecosystems in Kansas, USA, exposed to twice-ambient levels of atmospheric CO$_2$ displayed significant CO$_2$-induced enhancements of biomass, but only during relatively dry years (Owensby *et al.*, 1999).

Cotrufo and Gorissen (1997) grew three grasses (*Lolium perenne*, *Agrostis capillaries*, and *Festuca ovina*) at atmospheric CO$_2$ concentrations of 350 and 700 ppm for approximately two months before harvesting. On average, atmospheric CO$_2$ enrichment increased plant biomass by approximately 20%, with greater carbon partitioning to roots, as opposed to shoots. Also, in a much shorter two-week study performed on tall fescue (*Festuca ovina*), Newman *et al.* (1999) report twice-ambient levels of atmospheric CO$_2$ increased plant biomass by 37% relative to plants grown in ambient air.

In two additional studies, researchers grew perennial ryegrass (*Lolium perenne*) in controlled environmental chambers receiving atmospheric CO$_2$ concentrations of 350 and 700 ppm for approximately 14 weeks. After assessing plant growth, the authors reported CO$_2$-induced increases in shoot (van Ginkel and Gorissen, 1998) and root (van Ginkel *et al.*, 2000) biomass of 28 and 41%, respectively. Hodge *et al.* (1998) also report, for the same species, plants grown at an atmospheric CO$_2$ concentration of 720 ppm for a mere 21 days exhibited total biomass values 175% greater than those observed for control plants exposed to air of 450 ppm CO$_2$.

Lüscher *et al.* (1998) collected nine to 14 genotypes for each of 12 native grassland species from two permanent meadows near Zurich, Switzerland, and transplanted them into artificial gaps created in well-fertilized swards of *Lolium perenne* growing in FACE arrays maintained at 350 and 700 ppm CO$_2$, to determine inter- and intraspecific species growth responses to elevated CO_2 by harvesting aboveground biomass several times over a three-year period. CO_2-induced biomass increases varied with plant type, being greatest for legumes followed by non-legume dicotyledonous species and, last, monocotyledonous grasses. There were no significant differences in CO_2 responsiveness within genotypes for any of the 12 species.

Suter *et al.* (2002) grew perennial ryegrass (*Lolium perenne* L.) in field plots, as part of a FACE experiment, and in controlled-environment chambers, to compare growth and carbon allocation responses of this important forage crop to elevated atmospheric CO_2 concentrations under different experimental protocols. In both regimes, the control and elevated CO_2 concentrations were maintained for approximately two months at 350 and 600 ppm, respectively. The overall growth response of perennial ryegrass to elevated CO_2 was consistently greater for plants grown in the FACE experiment than for plants grown in the controlled-environment chambers. Elevated CO_2, for example, increased total dry matter production by 65 and 54% in the FACE and controlled-environment chambers, respectively. In addition, it enhanced root dry weights by 109 and 47% for plants gown in the FACE and controlled-environment chambers, respectively.

Bhatt *et al.* (2007) transplanted 30-day-old seedlings of *Cenchrus ciliaris* to open-top chambers—maintained at either the ambient atmospheric CO_2 concentration (360 ppm) or at an elevated CO_2 concentration (600 ppm)—in which the plants were grown for an additional 120 days, "using recommended agronomical practices" and with irrigation "given as and when required." During this time of outdoor field growth, the researchers measured numerous plant properties and physiological processes. At the end of the experiment, the plants were harvested and other pertinent measurements made. Among other things, Bhatt *et al.* report the extra 240 ppm of CO_2 employed in their experiment increased several plant parameters by the following percentages: plant height (44%), number of tillers (33%), leaf length (23%), leaf width (51%), leaf area index (234%), net photosynthetic rate per unit leaf area (25%), net photosynthetic rate per unit ground area (316%), total fresh weight (134%), total dry weight (193%), and whole-crop photosynthetic water use efficiency (34%). The three Indian researchers conclude "*C. ciliaris* grown in elevated CO_2 throughout the crop season may produce more fodder in terms of green biomass."

Several researchers have examined the effects of CO_2 enrichment on grasslands under varying soil nitrogen and fertility regimes. In a model-based study, Cannell and Thornley (1998) used the Hurley Pasture Model to simulate growth responses of perennial ryegrass (*Lolium perenne* L.) to a step increase in atmospheric CO_2 concentration (350 to 700 ppm) under conditions of low and high soil nitrogen. At high soil nitrogen conditions, elevated CO_2 stimulated net primary productivity and plant biomass by approximately 30% within a few years. Under low soil nitrogen conditions, elevated CO_2 caused a much greater stimulation of approximately 114%, although it took longer (five to ten years) to attain this greater degree of growth enhancement.

Navas *et al.* (1999) grew mixed communities of two grasses and two legumes across a range of soil nitrogen contents at ambient (357ppm) and enriched (712 ppm) atmospheric CO_2 concentrations for two months. Although soil nitrogen content had a much greater influence on community productivity than did atmospheric CO_2 concentration, communities fumigated with CO_2-enriched air tended to produce greater amounts of biomass than those exposed to ambient air. Likewise, Jongen and Jones (1998) report an eight-month exposure to twice-ambient levels of atmospheric CO_2 increased the community biomass of semi-natural grasslands characteristic of the Irish lowlands by 26%.

Reich *et al.* (2001) grew 16 perennial grassland species as monocultures in FACE plots maintained at atmospheric CO_2 concentrations of 360 and 560 ppm and low and high levels of soil nitrogen for two years. Interestingly, they found no interactions between atmospheric CO_2 concentration and soil nitrogen for any measured plant parameter. Nonetheless, elevated CO_2 increased total plant biomass for forbs, legumes, and C_3 grasses by 31, 18, and 9%, respectively, and it decreased the growth of C_4 grasses by 4%.

In a two-year study, Stocklin *et al.* (1999) grew simulated low-fertility Swiss grasslands in glasshouses receiving atmospheric CO_2 concentrations of 360 and 600 ppm. The authors report elevated CO_2 concentrations stimulated total biomass production by an average of 23% in these nutrient-poor grassland communities. And in another two-year experiment, Niklaus *et al.* (1998) note swards of calcareous grasslands exposed to atmospheric CO_2 concentrations of 600 ppm displayed total biomass values 25% greater than those exhibited by control swards grown in ambient air of 350 ppm CO_2.

Zaller and Arnone (1999) established open-top chambers in a species-rich grassland located near Basel, Switzerland and fumigated them continuously with atmospheric CO$_2$ concentrations of 350 and 600 ppm, except during winter months, for nearly one-and-a-half years, to see whether graminoids, non-legume forbs, and legumes growing near earthworm surface casts were more responsive to atmospheric CO$_2$ enrichment than those growing further away from these nutrient-rich microsites. Generally, plants growing in close proximity to earthworm casts produced more biomass than similar plants growing further away, regardless of CO$_2$ concentration. When assessing the influence of earthworm casts on plant responsiveness to atmospheric CO$_2$ enrichment, no statistically significant results were detected. Nonetheless, the average growth response of graminoids to elevated CO$_2$ was greater for those plants growing closer to earthworm casts than for those growing further away from them. This finding suggests plant growth responses to atmospheric CO$_2$ enrichment may be increased if local plant niches are closely associated with earthworm casts, which provide limiting nutrients to facilitate greater plant growth.

Also working in Switzerland, Niklaus *et al.* (2003) enriched the air above plots of a nutrient-poor, species-rich calcareous grassland in the northwestern portion of the country with an extra 240 ppm of CO$_2$ via a set of novel windscreens that "operated around the clock" except during midwinter (December-February). Among several other findings, the authors report during the six years of their experiment, aboveground plant biomass accumulation increased in response to CO$_2$ by an average of 21%. Simultaneously, there was an increase in soil moisture due to CO$_2$-induced reductions in plant transpiration. They also report microbial nitrogen (N) pools did not change, "indicating that elevated CO$_2$ did not stimulate net microbial immobilization of N which could have imposed a negative feedback on plant growth [but didn't]."

Contemporaneously, in a paper produced from the same experimental site, Ebersberger *et al.* (2003) assessed the impact of the extra CO$_2$ after six growing seasons on N-mineralization in the grassland soil and the activities of the soil microbial enzymes invertase, xylanase, urease, protease, arylsulfatase, and alkaline phosphatase in both the spring and summer. Results indicate the extra CO$_2$ increased N-mineralization significantly ($P = 0.02$, *a priori* linear contrast) by 30% in the spring and insignificantly ($P = 0.6$) by 3% in the summer. In addition, at both sampling times all measured enzyme activities were higher in the CO$_2$-enriched treatment, with the single exception of xylanase in summer. The strongest responder in the spring was alkaline phosphatase (up 32%, $P = 0.02$),

followed by urease (up 21%, $P = 0.13$). In the summer, the best responder was urease (up 21%, $P = 0.2$), followed by protease (up 17%, $P = 0.09$) and invertase (up 14%, $P = 0.07$). The authors attribute the increased N-mineralization and enzyme activity of the soil biota to the higher moisture content of the soil in the CO$_2$-enriched plots (due to a CO$_2$-induced decrease in stand transpiration) and/or the CO$_2$-induced increase in root biomass (up 24%, $P = 0.02$, in June 1999).

The observations of Ebersberger *et al.* are significant because soil microorganisms hold a key position in terrestrial ecosystems, as they mineralize organic matter and make its nitrogen available for use by plants. Hence, it is encouraging to note, in the words of the authors, "that elevated CO$_2$ will enhance below-ground C- and N-cycling in grasslands," even nutrient-poor grasslands such as the one they studied.

Morgan *et al.* (2001) grew the C$_3$ grass *Pascopyrum smithii*, the C$_4$ grass *Bouteloua gracilis*, and the C$_3$ legume *Medicago sativa* for 20 days post-defoliation in growth chambers receiving atmospheric CO$_2$ concentrations of 355 and 700 ppm and low or high levels of soil nitrogen, to determine how these factors affect the regrowth of these forage species. After 20 days post-defoliation, *Medicago sativa* plants grown in elevated CO$_2$ had attained total dry weights about 62% greater than those reached by ambiently grown plants, regardless of soil nitrogen, the scientists report. *Pascopyrum smithii* plants were more sensitive to soil nitrogen; whole plant regrowth was stimulated by 150 and 68% under conditions of high and low soil nitrogen, respectively. Elevated CO$_2$ had no positive effect on the regrowth of the C$_4$ grass, which fared better under high vs. low soil nitrogen conditions.

As the CO$_2$ concentration of the air increases, C$_3$ forage species subjected to natural or mechanical defoliation likely will respond by increasing their regrowth biomass in a plant-dependent and soil-nitrogen-dependent manner. Leguminous nitrogen-fixing C$_3$ species, for example, likely will exhibit enhanced regrowth irrespective of soil nitrogen content, and non-nitrogen-fixing C$_3$ species likely will exhibit greater regrowth on soils containing more, rather than less, nitrogen. Moreover, the regrowth of C$_4$ species may be less responsive to atmospheric CO$_2$ enrichment than C$_3$ species. Thus, future increases in the air's CO$_2$ content should promote, or at the very least not impair, prairie regrowth following defoliation by either animals or machinery.

Edwards *et al.* (2005) grew well-watered mixtures of two plants—the legume white clover

(*Trifolium repens* L.) and C_4 buffalo grass (*Stenotaphrum secundatum* (Walt.) Kuntze)—which were initially equal in plantlet size, number, and spatial distribution—for 15 months in sand placed in large plastic containers located in greenhouses maintained at different atmospheric CO_2 concentrations (360 and 700 ppm) under three sand nutrient conditions (zero-N/low-P, zero-N/high-P, plus-N/high-P). Ten harvests were made of all plant biomass over a height of 5 cm above the sand surface, after which the scientists determined the total carbon contents of the whole plants and their respective soils. The slightly less than a doubling of the air's CO_2 concentration employed in this study led to increases of 27%, 55%, and 23% in final-harvest whole plant biomass in the zero-N/low-P, zero-N/high-P, and plus-N/high-P soil treatments, respectively.

Hartwig *et al.* (2002) grew perennial ryegrass (*Lolium perenne* L.) in environmental chambers receiving atmospheric CO_2 concentrations of 350 and 600 ppm for 60 days. In addition, they subjected plants to low and high levels of soil nitrogen and inoculated some with arbuscular mycorrhizal fungi. Thus the authors studied the interactive effects of elevated CO_2, soil nitrogen, and arbuscular mycorrhizal fungi on growth in this important grassland species. They found elevated CO_2 increased plant biomass by 10 and 17% at low and high levels of soil nitrogen, respectively. When plants were inoculated with the arbuscular mycorrhizal fungi, elevated CO_2 enhanced plant biomass only by 3% at low soil nitrogen, but it increased it by 41% at high soil nitrogen. Thus, at high soil nitrogen, the presence of this symbiotic fungi more than doubled the plant growth response to atmospheric CO_2 enrichment. In addition, the amount of root colonization by the arbuscular mycorrhizal fungi increased by 56% in the high CO_2 treatment.

Arbuscular mycorrhizal fungi are important because nearly all grassland species form symbiotic relationships with mycorrhizal fungi. Arbuscular mycorrhizal fungi commonly colonize roots of grasses and form symbiotic structures known as arbuscules, short-lived organs that facilitate carbon and nutrient exchange between the fungi and their host plants. The presence of these symbiotic relationships often increases grassland vitality and productivity, and several other researchers have set out to understand how rising atmospheric CO_2 concentrations may affect these relationships.

In an earlier study, Wilson and Hartnett (1998) grew 36 grass species common to tallgrass prairie ecosystems with and without the presence (induced by inoculation) of arbuscular mycorrhizae. They report fungal inoculation increased the average dry mass of perennial C_4 species by 85%. Fungal inoculation had no significant effects on dry mass production in perennial C_3 species or in any annual grasses, regardless of their photosynthetic physiology. Thus, a large number of plant-fungal interactions exist at ambient CO_2 concentrations that may be modified by exposure to elevated CO_2.

In a similar study, Rillig *et al.* (1998a) grew monocultures of three grasses and two herbs that co-occur in Mediterranean annual grasslands, in pots placed in open-top chambers receiving ambient and twice-ambient concentrations of atmospheric CO_2 for four months. They report elevated CO_2 significantly increased the percent root colonization by arbuscular mycorrhizal fungal hyphae in all five species, which ultimately could lead to greater biomass production in these annual grassland plants.

In another four-month study using the same experimental enclosures, Rillig *et al.* (1998b) grew the annual grass *Bromus hordeaceus* at ambient and elevated atmospheric CO_2 concentrations. In this study, elevated CO_2 did not increase the percent root colonized by fungal hyphae, but it did significantly increase the percent root colonized by arbuscules, indicating elevated CO_2 can enhance fungal-plant interactions by modifying fungal structures other than hyphae.

In two related long-term studies, Rillig *et al.* (1999a,b) constructed open-top chambers on two adjacent serpentine and sandstone grassland communities in California, USA, fumigating them with air containing 350 and 700 ppm of CO_2 for six years. In corroboration of their earlier short-term results, they report elevated CO_2 did not increase the percent root colonized by fungal hyphae (Rillig *et al.*, 1999a) but it enhanced the percent root colonized by arbuscules in serpentine and sandstone grasslands by three- and ten-fold, respectively (Rillig *et al.*,1999b). Such observations suggest increases in the air's CO_2 concentration will positively impact plant-fungal interactions on grasslands by increasing percent root colonization by either mycorrhizal fungal hyphae or arbuscules, both of which aid in carbon and nutrient exchanges between the two interacting symbionts. Earth's grasslands thus should exhibit increased productivity—even above and beyond that normally caused by atmospheric CO_2 enrichment—due to these enhanced relationships that can make soil nutrients more available for plant uptake and use.

Johnson *et al.* (2003) grew communities of 14 common prairie plants in 12 greenhouse chambers at

Flagstaff, Arizona, USA. Six of the chambers were maintained at an atmospheric CO_2 concentration of 450 ppm, and six were maintained at 688 ppm (equivalent to 368 and 560 ppm at sea level, respectively) during daylight hours. Each of the CO_2 treatments also was subdivided into treatments possessing living or dead arbuscular mycorrhizal (AM) fungal inoculum and low or enriched soil nitrogen (N) content. After one growing season under these conditions, Johnson *et al.* write, "plant species richness was highest in mesocosms with elevated CO_2, +AM fungi, and low soil N." They conclude, "in some plant species elevated CO_2 can increase the net benefits of mycorrhizae by reducing their relative carbon cost." Thus, not only did the extra CO_2 directly help the various plant species involved in the study, it also helped them indirectly—by promoting the growth of AM fungi that provided additional benefits to the plants. This study also suggests increases in the air's CO_2 content should have a tendency to maintain, and possibly even increase, the species richness of prairie ecosystems, especially those where soil nitrogen content is less than optimal.

Also focusing on species richness, or biodiversity, Edwards *et al.* (2001) conducted a FACE experiment utilizing atmospheric CO_2 concentrations of 360 and 475 ppm on a sheep-grazed dry-land pasture located in Manawatu, New Zealand. In each of the two years of their study, elevated CO_2 increased seed production and dispersal in seven of the eight most abundant pasture species: the grasses *Anthoxanthum odoratum*, *Lolium perenne*, and *Poa pratensis*; the legumes *Trifolium repens* and *Trifolium subterranean*; and the herbs *Hypochaeris radicata* and *Leontodon saxatilis*. In some of these species, the elevated CO_2 increased the number of seeds produced per reproductive structure, and in all of the species it increased the number of reproductive structures per unit ground area.

These CO_2-induced increases in seed production contributed to the increase in the numbers of species observed in the CO_2-enriched experimental plots. In addition, atmospheric CO_2 enrichment helped maintain biodiversity by increasing the number of *H. radicata*, *L. saxatilis*, *T. repens*, and *T. subterranean* seedlings that survived for at least seven months in both study years, and it additionally lengthened the survival time of *A. odoratum* and *L. perenne* in the initial year of experimentation. As the atmospheric CO_2 concentration increases further, therefore, it should help to maintain, and maybe even increase, the biodiversity of these dry-land pasture communities by increasing the numbers of both common and uncommon species they contain.

Teyssonneyre *et al.* (2002) grew three C_3 grasses (*Lolium perenne*, *Festuca arundinacea*, and *Holcus lanatus*) as monocultures and two-species mixtures for five months in plastic tunnels maintained at atmospheric CO_2 concentrations of 350 and 700 ppm, cutting the grasses either frequently or infrequently to stimulate competition for light. In monoculture, the high-CO_2 treatment increased total aboveground biomass by 22%, 22%, and 4% in *Festuca*, *Holcus*, and *Lolium*, respectively. In two-species mixtures, elevated CO_2 caused a 22% reduction in the amount of *Lolium* in the *Lolium x Festuca* mixture under the infrequent cutting regime, and it caused 30% and 67% reductions in the amount of *Lolium* in the *Lolium x Holcus* mixture under the frequent and infrequent cutting regimes, respectively.

De Deyn *et al.* (2003) begin their study by noting aboveground vertebrate herbivores "can indirectly benefit subdominant plant species through selective feeding on dominants (Crawley, 1997; Olff and Ritchie, 1998)." They then note root symbionts below the soil surface "can enhance plant species diversity by improving the nutrient uptake and growth of subdominants (van der Heijden *et al.*, 1998)," further noting root pathogens "can do so by suppressing dominant host plant species (Bever, 1994)." They then expanded the scope of these types of interactions by exploring the impact of invertebrate soil fauna on plant biodiversity.

De Deyn *et al.* established 32 microcosms of plant species mixtures characteristic of recently abandoned grassland (early succession), grassland under restoration for 20 years (mid-succession), and species-rich natural grassland (the ultimate target state). These microcosms were inoculated with soil fauna from one of the three grassland successional stages. The density and composition of the soil fauna added to the microcosms were the same as those of the three grassland successional stages and included microfauna (nematodes), mesofauna (micro-arthropods), and macrofauna (beetle larvae). After four and six months of these treatments, the researchers clipped the microcosm plants at 4 cm above the soil surface and determined the harvested dry weights of all individual plant species. After 12 months they clipped the plants at the soil surface and determined their root dry weights again.

De Deyn *et al.* report "the soil fauna decreased the shoot biomass of the early succession plant species after 6 months, as well as plant species from the mid-succession stage, whereas the shoot biomass of the target plant species was increased." Hence, they note, "addition of the soil fauna also enhanced plant species diversity." Results obtained at the end of the experiment further suggest "the invertebrate root herbivores were selectively feeding on roots of dominant plants," which "provided an indirect advantage for the subdominant plant species, which were only marginally suppressed in the presence of soil fauna." The researchers also report the positive contributions of soil fauna and mycorrhizal fungi seemed to be additive. Such findings suggest the ongoing rise in the air's CO_2 content may enhance ecosystem species richness, as a consequence of the tendency for atmospheric CO_2 enrichment to increase both mycorrhizal fungi and soil fauna populations.

Working in central Texas (USA) with elongated field chambers designed to expose tallgrass prairie vegetation comprised of a mix of seven different species—four C_4 grasses (*Bouteloua curtipendula*, *Schizachyrium scoparium*, *Sorghastrum nutans,* and *Tridens albescens*) and three forbs (*Salvia azurea*, *Solidago canadensis*, and *Desmanthus illinoensis*)— to a continuous atmospheric CO_2 gradient spanning the preindustrial to elevated CO_2 concentration range of 250 to 500 ppm, Polley *et al.* (2011) measured the concentrations of ten elements found in the above-ground tissues of three of the C_4 grasses (*B. curtipendula*, *S. scoparium,* and *S. nutans*) that are common competitive dominants in assemblages of tallgrass prairie vegetation, which they grew on three soil types over three growing seasons. Polley *et al.* report "the CO_2 effect on relative abundances of *Bouteloua* and *Sorghastrum* had far greater impact on element concentrations in grass stands than did change in element levels of individual species," and "elements that were most limiting relative to the nutritional requirements of cattle generally occurred at lowest concentrations in *Bouteloua*, the species most strongly disadvantaged at elevated CO_2." Also, "CO_2 enrichment favored a grass, *Sorghastrum*, with relatively high concentrations of these elements, thereby increasing mean concentrations of several elements in grass assemblages."

The four researchers say their results "highlight the importance of accounting for change in species abundances and composition when predicting CO_2 effects on ecosystem functioning and services," as is also indicated by Polley *et al.* (2010), who conclude, "by favoring one grass species over another, CO_2 enrichment from pre-industrial to elevated levels increased concentrations of several nutritionally important elements in prairie grasses," further noting this "improvement in the nutritional quality of plants for herbivores" represents an "underappreciated

impact that CO_2 enrichment may have on ecosystem functioning by changing plant composition."

Isbell *et al.* (2013) write, "anthropogenic drivers of environmental change often have multiple effects, including changes in biodiversity, species composition, and ecosystem functioning," but "it remains unknown whether such shifts in biodiversity and species composition may, themselves, be major contributors to the total, long-term impacts of anthropogenic drivers on ecosystem functioning." To discover how this phenomenon may operate, Isbell *et al.* set out to analyze temporal trends in the effects of nitrogen enrichment on the productivity, plant diversity, and species compositions of naturally assembled grasslands in a long-term nitrogen-addition experiment conducted at the Cedar Creek Ecosystem Science Reserve in central Minnesota (USA), where they measured aboveground peak biomass and the number and abundances of plant species in each plot from 1982 to 2008. They then similarly analyzed data from the BioCON (Biodiversity, CO_2 and N) experiment located at the same reserve, "to quantify the extent to which N enrichment and elevated CO_2 influence productivity by non-randomly changing grassland plant diversity," which they did in the latter instance from 1998 to 2011.

The six scientists report "although chronic nitrogen enrichment initially increased productivity, it also led to loss of plant species, including initially dominant species, which then caused substantial diminishing returns from nitrogen fertilization." In contrast, they report, "elevated CO_2 did not decrease grassland plant diversity" but "consistently promoted productivity over time," both by its direct aerial fertilization effect and by its non-significant yet real tendency to enhance species diversity.

Greer *et al.* (2000) studied the effects of elevated air temperature and CO_2 concentration on photosynthesis in five pasture species grown for approximately one month in controlled environment chambers. They found the CO_2-induced photosynthetic enhancement rose with increasing air temperature. At twice-ambient levels of atmospheric CO_2, average photosynthetic rates were 36 and 70% greater than for control plants grown under ambient CO_2 concentrations at air temperatures of 18 and 28°C, respectively.

Kudernatsch *et al.* (2008) conducted a warming-only (no change in CO_2) experiment on species-rich *Carex sempervirens* (CS) and species-poor *Carex firma* (CF) calcareous grasslands in the Berchtesgaden National Park of Southeast Germany. They installed several open-top chambers on the plants in each of three successive years just after snowmelt was complete in the spring and removed them just before snowfall commenced in the autumn. This led to snow-free-season increases in mean daily air temperature of 0.7°C in the CS grasslands and 1.4°C in the CF grasslands, along with corresponding mean daily soil temperature increases of 0.2 and 0.8°C. The authors report "growth and/or reproduction of 12 of the 14 studied species were significantly stimulated by warming," "only two species showed no response," and "none of the species experienced decreases in growth or reproduction." They also found "a significant effect of warming on nutrient availability could not be detected," leading them to conclude "the observed response of vegetation is therefore mainly caused by direct and not by indirect temperature effects."

In 1982–1984, Madsen *et al.* (2011) "studied the ecology of non-breeding moulting geese in Jameson Land, low Arctic East Greenland," finding the geese "consumed most of the graminoid production in available moss fens," leading them to conclude "the geese had filled up the available habitat." Nevertheless, they came back in 2008 to see what had happened over the intervening period of significant global—and local—warming.

Madsen *et al.* replicated what they had done in their earlier study in terms of both methodology and analysis. In addition, they determined the above-ground biomass of the graminoid marsh vegetation, to compare it with what it had been determined to be in 1983 and 1984 by Madsen and Mortensen (1987). The researchers report the data they obtained in late July 2008 yielded a standing crop biomass of 98.2 g/m^2, which was 2.34 times greater than what had been measured in the same location in late July 1984. After listing three lines of evidence for concluding from their original field studies in 1982–1984 the "habitat capacity of Jameson Land for moulting geese was close to being reached," they now report, between that earlier time and 2008, "the number of moulting geese in Jameson Land tripled."

In further support of their observations, they note, "on Bylot Island, northeast Canada, graminoid above-ground production in wetlands has increased by 84% between 1990 and 2007, most likely as a consequence of climate warming," citing Cadieux *et al.* (2008). Also, they write, "on Svalbard, it is known that early snow melt has a dramatic positive effect on the density of nesting geese and their fecundity," citing Madsen *et al.* (2007) and noting "the climate in East Greenland has been warming during the last 30 years."

Other researchers have investigated the impact of elevated CO_2 and water stress on grasslands.

Szente *et al.* (1998) studied two grasses and two broad-leaved species common to loess grasslands in the vicinity of Budapest in open-top chambers maintained at atmospheric CO_2 concentrations of 350 and 700 ppm. After 231 days, the grasses and broad-leaved species exhibited CO_2-induced increases in seasonal plant water use efficiencies of 72 and 366%, respectively, the scientists report. Clark *et al.* (1999) likewise note mixed grassland species from a New Zealand pasture exposed to an atmospheric CO_2 concentration of 700 ppm consistently displayed greater water use efficiencies than species growing in ambient air, due mostly to CO_2-induced increases in photosynthesis. In a two-year CO_2-enrichment study of a tallgrass prairie ecosystem located in Kansas, USA, Adams *et al.* (2000) found plants in open-top chambers fumigated with twice-ambient levels of atmospheric CO_2 exhibited significantly reduced rates of stomatal conductance and transpirational water loss, which also enhanced plant daily average water use efficiency throughout the entire study, but via reduced water loss as opposed to the enhanced photosynthesis observed by Clark *et al.*

In an eight-year CO_2-enrichment study of a tallgrass prairie ecosystem located in Kansas, USA, Owensby *et al.* (1999) report prairie communities in open-top chambers fumigated with twice-ambient levels of atmospheric CO_2 maintained greater amounts of soil moisture than communities exposed to ambient air in every year of the study. Likewise, in an experiment lasting four years, Lutze *et al.* (1998) grew swards of *Danthonia richardsonii* at various soil nitrogen contents in glasshouses receiving atmospheric CO_2 concentrations of 360 and 720 ppm. Averaged across all nitrogen regimes, CO_2-enriched swards used about 25% less water than swards grown at 360 ppm CO_2, which consequently allowed the CO_2-enriched microcosms to maintain greater soil water contents throughout the study.

In a two-year experiment, Arnone and Bohlen (1998) grew intact monoliths of calcareous grasslands in controlled environments fumigated with air containing 350 and 600 ppm CO_2. They found CO_2-induced reductions in transpirational water loss were likely responsible for the higher soil moisture contents observed in the CO_2-enriched monoliths, which were 10 to 20% greater than those observed in monoliths exposed to ambient air. And Zaller *et al.* (1997) established open-top and open-bottom chambers in a species-rich grassland located near Basel, Switzerland, subjecting them to atmospheric

CO_2 concentrations of 350 and 600 ppm. They report mean annual soil moisture contents in the CO_2-enriched chambers were 10% greater than those observed in control chambers treated with air containing 350 ppm CO_2.

Grunzweig and Körner (2001) constructed model grasslands representative of the Negev of Israel and placed them in growth chambers with atmospheric CO_2 concentrations of 280, 440, and 600 ppm for five months, to determine the effects of elevated CO_2 on these semi-arid plant communities. They found elevated CO_2 reduced rates of evapotranspiration and increased soil moisture contents in model grassland communities exposed to atmospheric CO_2 concentrations of 440 and 600 ppm. Between two periods of imposed drought, soil moisture was 22 and 27% higher in communities exposed to 440 and 600 ppm CO_2, respectively, than in control communities exposed to pre-industrial levels of atmospheric CO_2. Such increases in soil moisture content may have contributed to peak ecosystem CO_2 uptake rates 21 and 31% greater at 400 and 600 ppm CO_2 than at 280 ppm CO_2. In addition, atmospheric CO_2 enrichment had no effect on nighttime respiratory carbon losses from the ecosystems. Thus, these semi-arid grasslands were acting as carbon sinks under CO_2-enriched conditions. Elevated CO_2 (440 and 600 ppm) increased total community biomass by 14% over that produced by communities exposed to the subambient CO_2 concentration. Also, when the total biomass produced was related to the total amount of water loss via evapotranspiration, communities grown at atmospheric CO_2 concentrations of 440 and 600 ppm exhibited CO_2-induced increases in water use efficiency 17 and 28% higher than those displayed by control communities exposed to air of 280 ppm CO_2.

As atmospheric CO_2 concentrations increase, semi-arid grasslands common to the Negev of Israel likely will exhibit increases in photosynthesis and biomass production, as the study shows. Moreover, such increases in biomass likely will occur while using less water. Model ecosystems exposed to elevated atmospheric CO_2 concentrations lost less water through evapotranspiration and consequently had greater soil moisture contents than ecosystems that were not CO_2-enriched. Thus it would appear the water-use efficiencies of these grasslands likely will increase in future years as the air's CO_2 content increases further. Most importantly, the gas exchange measurements—including the null effect of elevated CO_2 on dark respiration—and the biomass data obtained for the ecosystems demonstrate these grasslands likely will become increasingly effective carbon sinks, removing ever-greater amounts of carbon from the air.

Derner *et al.* (2001) grew two C_4 grasses (*Schizachyrium scoparium* Nash and *Andropogon gerardii* Vitman.) common to tallgrass prairies in pots placed in a 38-meter-long controlled environment chamber located in a ventilated glasshouse. This chamber was composed of five 7.6m lengths of a 0.76m-deep and 0.45m-wide soil container topped with a transparent and tunnel-shaped polyethylene cover attached to its upper edges. Various other plants placed in this tunnel served as photosynthetic "sinks" for CO_2 as a commercial blower moved air through the chamber sections. Thus a CO_2 gradient was created through the "long and winding tunnel," from near 350 ppm at its entrance to approximately 200 ppm at its end. In addition, these two C_4 grasses were subjected to relative soil water contents 90 or 50% of their total soil water holding capacities. Thus the authors were able to study how the historical rise in the air's CO_2 content has influenced growth in these grasses under different soil moisture conditions.

Data from the two C_4 grasses were pooled, as there were no significant differences between species. With respect to aboveground growth, shoot biomass was 57% greater at the ambient (350 ppm), rather than the subambient (200 ppm), atmospheric CO_2 concentration, and the increase in relative water content enhanced shoot biomass by 82%. Root growth (root length, mass, surface area, and volume) was 15–27% greater at the ambient, as opposed to the subambient, atmospheric CO_2 concentration, and 40–51% greater at high, versus low, soil water content.

Since the 150 ppm increase in atmospheric CO_2 concentration employed in this study is actually less than the rise in this parameter that has occurred since the end of the last great ice age, Derner *et al.* state "C_4 grasses may have already experienced an augmentation in root growth which is comparable to that experienced with a doubling of current CO_2 concentrations." There is every reason to conclude such grasses will continue to respond positively to future increases in the air's CO_2 content. In addition, as the atmospheric CO_2 concentration rises, it likely will decrease water use in these prairie grasses, due to CO_2-induced reductions in stomatal conductance, causing the indirect effects of greater soil moisture to enhance their growth further.

Working with open-top chambers maintained at ambient and twice-ambient atmospheric CO_2 concentrations, Ferretti *et al.* (2003) investigated "the dynamics of soil water isotopes and water cycling in a mixed C$_3$/C$_4$ grassland in the western Great Plains region of the USA," which is predominantly carpeted by the C$_4$ grass *Bouteloua gracilis* (H.B.K.) Lag. (blue grama) and the C$_3$ grasses *Stipa comata* Trin and Rupr. (needle-and-thread grass) and *Pascopyrum smithii* (Rydb.) A. Love (western wheatgrass). In addition to documenting a mean plant biomass increase of 50% in the elevated CO$_2$ treatment over the two years of their study, the authors observed significantly wetter soils in the elevated CO$_2$ treatment, which they say were "most likely a result of improved soil-water conservation as a result of reduced stomatal conductance under elevated CO$_2$."

Noting "elevated CO$_2$ had the effect of increasing soil-water conservation as has been previously found (e.g., Morgan *et al.*, 2001; Volk *et al.*, 2000)," and "reduced evaporation was mainly responsible for greater soil water content under elevated CO$_2$," Ferretti *et al.* remark "the most significant effect of elevated CO$_2$ on the hydrologic budget in water limited ecosystems is likely to be an increase in soil water storage (Jackson *et al.*, 1998)," as was found in their study. It is likely this phenomenon contributed significantly to the growth enhancement observed in the CO$_2$-enriched treatment, which was more than what might have been expected from the aerial fertilization effect of elevated CO$_2$ operating alone.

Also focusing on water stress, Niklaus and Körner (2004) used screen-aided CO$_2$ control (SACC) technology to enrich the air above a water-limited and phosphorus-poor temperate calcareous grassland in Switzerland with an extra 235 ppm of CO$_2$ for a total of six years, over which period they measured several individual and community plant parameters. They report peak percentage increases in biomass production in years 1 through 6 of the experiment were, respectively, 5%, 20%, 22%, 27%, 31%, and 18%, for an average of 23.6% over the last five years of the study. Year-to-year variability in this factor was best predicted by precipitation and resulting soil moisture differences, with the "obvious mechanism," the authors write, being "soil moisture savings due to reduced stomatal conductance under elevated CO$_2$," which would tend to "alleviate effects of water limitation more in dry years." In addition, although Niklaus and Körner note "low available phosphorous ultimately limited community productivity and responses to CO$_2$," this deficiency—coupled with a deficiency of water—was not sufficient to counter the growth-promoting effect of atmospheric CO$_2$ enrichment, which in this case was equivalent to a 30% increase in growth in response to a standard 300 ppm increase in the air's CO$_2$ concentration.

Because many grasslands are subject to grazing pressure from herbivores, it is also important to see how this stress phenomenon affects photosynthetic responses to atmospheric CO$_2$ enrichment. Rogers *et al.* (1998) grew swards of perennial ryegrass in a FACE experiment utilizing atmospheric CO$_2$ concentrations of 360 and 600 ppm. In addition, they supplied swards with low and high levels of soil nitrogen and subjected them to cutting treatments to simulate herbivory. Under these conditions, elevated CO$_2$ stimulated photosynthetic rates by approximately 35%, regardless of soil nitrogen supply or cutting treatment. In a similar FACE experiment, two forbs and one grass species common to chalk grassland swards of Europe were grown for 14 months at 355 and 600 ppm CO$_2$ to study the influence of simulated grazing on their photosynthetic responses to atmospheric CO$_2$ enrichment (Bryant *et al.*, 1998). Prior to simulated grazing, the CO$_2$-induced photosynthetic response of the grass and one forb species were both around 28%, and the other forb was non-responsive to elevated CO$_2$. After grazing, however, both forbs exhibited a much larger 40% increase in photosynthesis, and the grass slightly increased its positive response to 30%. The data from these two studies suggest grazing pressure from herbivores will not reduce CO$_2$-induced increases in photosynthesis, and may in fact cause them to rise.

The studies reviewed above suggest increases in the air's CO$_2$ concentration lead to rising productivity of Earth's grassland species, even under unfavorable growing conditions characterized by less-than-adequate soil moisture, inadequate soil nutrition, elevated air temperature, and physical stress imposed by herbivory.

References

Adams, N.R., Owensby, C.E., and Ham, J.M. 2000. The effect of CO$_2$ enrichment on leaf photosynthetic rates and instantaneous water use efficiency of *Andropogon gerardii* in the tallgrass prairie. *Photosynthesis Research* **65**: 121–129.

Arnone III, J.A. and Bohlen, P.J. 1998. Stimulated N$_2$O flux from intact grassland monoliths after two growing seasons under elevated atmospheric CO$_2$. *Oecologia* **116**: 331–335.

Bever, J.D. 1994. Feedback between plants and their soil communities in an old field community. *Ecology* **75**: 1965–1977.

Bhatt, R.K., Baig, M.J., and Tiwari, H.S. 2007. Growth, biomass production, and assimilatory characters in

Cenchrus ciliaris L. under elevated CO_2 condition. *Photosynthetica* **45**: 296–298.

Bryant, J., Taylor, G., and Frehner, M. 1998. Photosynthetic acclimation to elevated CO_2 is modified by source:sink balance in three component species of chalk grassland swards grown in a free air carbon dioxide enrichment (FACE) experiment. *Plant, Cell and Environment* **21**: 159–168.

Cadieux, M.C., Gauthier, G., Gagnon, C.A., Bety, J., and Berteaux, D. 2008. Monitoring the Environmental and Ecological Impacts of Climate Change on Bylot Island, Sirmilik National Park. Universite Laval, Quebec, Canada.

Campbell, B.D., Stafford Smith, D.M., Ash, A.J., Fuhrer, J., Gifford, R.M., Hiernaux, P., Howden, S.M., Jones, M.B., Ludwig, J.A., Manderscheid, R., Morgan, J.A., Newton, P.C.D., Nosberger, J., Owensby, C.E., Soussana, J.F., Tuba, Z., and ZuoZhong, C. 2000. A synthesis of recent global change research on pasture and rangeland production: reduced uncertainties and their management implications. *Agriculture, Ecosystems and Environment* **82**: 39–55.

Cannell, M.G.R. and Thornley, J.H.M. 1998. N-poor ecosystems may respond more to elevated [CO_2] than N-rich ones in the long term. A model analysis of grassland. *Global Change Biology* **4**: 431–442.

Clark, H., Newton, P.C.D., and Barker, D.J. 1999. Physiological and morphological responses to elevated CO_2 and a soil moisture deficit of temperate pasture species growing in an established plant community. *Journal of Experimental Botany* **50**: 233–242.

Cotrufo, M.F. and Gorissen, A. 1997. Elevated CO_2 enhances below-ground C allocation in three perennial grass species at different levels of N availability. *New Phytologist* **137**: 421–431.

Crawley, M.J. 1997. *Plant Ecology*. Blackwell Science, Oxford, UK.

De Deyn, G.B., Raaljmakers, C.E., Zoomer, H.R., Berg, M.P., de Rulter, P.C., Verhoef, H.A., Bezemer, T.M., and van der Putten, W.H. 2003. Soil invertebrate fauna enhances grassland succession and diversity. *Nature* **422**: 711–713.

Derner, J.D., Polley, H.W., Johnson, H.B., and Tischler, C.R. 2001. Root system response of C_4 grass seedlings to CO_2 and soil water. *Plant and Soil* **231**: 97–104.

Ebersberger, D., Niklaus, P.A., and Kandeler, E. 2003. Long term CO_2 enrichment stimulates N-mineralisation and enzyme activities in calcareous grassland. *Soil Biology & Biochemistry* **35**: 965–972.

Edwards, E.J., McCaffery, S., and Evans, J.R. 2005. Phosphorus status determines biomass response to elevated

CO_2 in a legume: C_4 grass community. *Global Change Biology* **11**: 1968–1981.

Edwards, G.R., Clark, H., and Newton, P.C.D. 2001. The effects of elevated CO_2 on seed production and seedling recruitment in a sheep-grazed pasture. *Oecologia* **127**: 383–394.

Ferretti, D.F., Pendall, E., Morgan, J.A., Nelson, J.A., LeCain, D., and Mosier, A.R. 2003. Partitioning evapotranspiration fluxes from a Colorado grassland using stable isotopes: Seasonal variations and ecosystem implications of elevated atmospheric CO_2. *Plant and Soil* **254**: 291–303.

Greer, D.H., Laing, W.A., Campbell, B.D., and Halligan, E.A. 2000. The effect of perturbations in temperature and photon flux density on the growth and photosynthetic responses of five pasture species. *Australian Journal of Plant Physiology* **27**: 301–310.

Grunzweig, J.M. and Körner, C. 2001. Growth, water and nitrogen relations in grassland model ecosystems of the semi-arid Negev of Israel exposed to elevated CO_2. *Oecologia* **128**: 251–262.

Hartwig, U.A., Wittmann, P., Braun, R., Hartwig-Raz, B., Jansa, J., Mozafar, A., Luscher, A., Leuann, A., Frossard, E., and Nosberger, J. 2002. Arbuscular mycorrhiza infection enhances the growth response of *Lolium perenne* to elevated atmospheric pCO_2. *Journal of Experimental Botany* **53**: 1207–1213.

Hodge, A., Paterson, E., Grayston, S.J., Campbell, C.D., Ord, B.G., and Killham, K. 1998. Characterization and microbial utilisation of exudate material from the rhizosphere of *Lolium perenne* grown under CO_2 enrichment. *Soil Biology and Biochemistry* **30**: 1033–1043.

Isbell, F., Reich, P.B., Tilman, D., Hobbie, S.E., Polasky, S., and Binder, S. 2013. Nutrient enrichment, biodiversity loss, and consequent declines in ecosystem productivity. *Proceedings of the National Academy of Sciences USA* **110**: 11,911–11,916.

Jackson, R.B., Sala, O.E., Paruelo, J.M., and Mooney, H.A. 1998. Ecosystem water fluxes for two grasslands in elevated CO_2: A modeling analysis. *Oecologia* **113**: 537–546.

Johnson, N.C., Wolf, J., and Koch, G.W. 2003. Interactions among mycorrhizae, atmospheric CO_2 and soil N impact plant community composition. *Ecology Letters* **6**: 532–540.

Jongen, M. and Jones, M.B. 1998. Effects of elevated carbon dioxide on plant biomass production and competition in a simulated neutral grassland community. *Annals of Botany* **82**: 111–123.

Kudernatsch, T., Fischer, A., Bernhardt-Romermann, M., and Abs, C. 2008. Short-term effects of temperature enhancement on growth and reproduction of alpine grassland species. *Basic and Applied Ecology* **9**: 263–274.

Leadley, P.W., Niklaus, P.A., Stocker, R., and Körner, C. 1999. A field study of the effects of elevated CO₂ on plant biomass and community structure in a calcareous grassland. *Oecologia* **118**: 39–49.

Lüscher, A., Hendrey, G.R., and Nosberger, J. 1998. Long-term responsiveness to free air CO₂ enrichment of functional types, species and genotypes of plants from fertile permanent grassland. *Oecologia* **113**: 37–45.

Lutze, J.L. and Gifford, R.M. 1998. Carbon accumulation, distribution and water use of *Danthonia richardsonii* swards in response to CO₂ and nitrogen supply over four years of growth. *Global Change Biology* **4**: 851–861.

Madsen, J., Jaspers, C., Tamstorf, M., Mortensen, C.E., and Riget, F. 2011. Long-term effects of grazing and global warming on the composition and carrying capacity of graminoid marshes for moulting geese in East Greenland. *Ambio* **40**: 638–649.

Madsen, J. and Mortensen, C.E. 1987. Habitat exploitation and interspecific competition of moulting geese in East-Greenland. *Ibis* **129**: 25–44.

Madsen, J., Tamstorf, M., Klaassen, M., Eide, N., Glahder, C., Riget, F., Nyegaard, H., and Cottaar, F. 2007. Effects of snow cover on the timing and success of reproduction in high-Arctic pink-footed geese *Anser brachyrhynchus*. *Polar Biology* **30**: 1363–1372.

Morgan, J., LeCain, D., Mosier, A., and Milchunas, D. 2001. Elevated CO₂ enhances water relations and productivity and affects gas exchange in C₃ and C₄ grasses of the Colorado shortgrass steppe. *Global Change Biology* **7**: 451–466.

Morgan, J.A., Skinner, R.H., and Hanson, J.D. 2001. Nitrogen and CO₂ affect regrowth and biomass partitioning differently in forages of three functional groups. *Crop Science* **41**: 78–86.

Navas, M.-L., Garnier, E., Austin, M.P., and Gifford, R.M. 1999. Effect of competition on the responses of grasses and legumes to elevated atmospheric CO₂ along a nitrogen gradient: differences between isolated plants, monocultures and multi-species mixtures. *New Phytologist* **143**: 323–331.

Newman, J.A., Gibson, D.J., Hickam, E., Lorenz, M., Adams, E., Bybee, L., and Thompson, R. 1999. Elevated carbon dioxide results in smaller populations of the bird cherry-oat aphid *Rhopalosiphum padi*. *Ecological Entomology* **24**: 486–489.

Niklaus, P.A., Alphei, J., Ebersberger, D., Kampichlers, C., Kandeler, E., and Tscherko, D. 2003. Six years of in situ CO₂ enrichment evoke changes in soil structure and soil biota of nutrient-poor grassland. *Global Change Biology* **9**: 585–600.

Niklaus, P.A. and Körner, C. 2004. Synthesis of a six-year study of calcareous grassland responses to *in situ* CO₂ enrichment. *Ecological Monographs* **74**: 491–511.

Niklaus, P.A., Leadley, P.W., Stocklin, J., and Körner, C. 1998. Nutrient relations in calcareous grassland under elevated CO₂. *Oecologia* **116**: 67–75.

Olff, H. and Ritchie, M.E. 1998. Effects of herbivores on grassland plant diversity. *Trends in Ecology and Evolution* **13**: 261–265.

Owensby, C.E., Ham, J.M., Knapp, A.K., and Auen, L.M. 1999. Biomass production and species composition change in a tallgrass prairie ecosystem after long-term exposure to elevated atmospheric CO₂. *Global Change Biology* **5**: 497–506.

Polley, H.W., Fay, P.A., Jin, V.L., and Combs Jr., G.F. 2011. CO₂ enrichment increases element concentrations in grass mixtures by changing species abundances. *Plant Ecology* **212**: 945–957.

Polley, H.W., Morgan, J.A., and Fay, P.A. 2010. Application of a conceptual framework to interpret variability in rangeland responses to atmospheric CO₂ enrichment. *Journal of Agricultural Science* **149**: 1–14.

Reich, P.B., Tilman, D., Craine, J., Ellsworth, D., Tjoelker, M.G., Knops, J., Wedin, D., Naeem, S., Bahauddin, D., Goth, J., Bengtson, W., and Lee, T.A. 2001. Do species and functional groups differ in acquisition and use of C, N and water under varying atmospheric CO₂ and N availability regimes? A field test with 16 grassland species. *New Phytologist* **150**: 435–448.

Rillig, M.C., Allen, M.F., Klironomos, J.N., Chiariello, N.R., and Field, C.B. 1998a. Plant species-specific changes in root-inhabiting fungi in a California annual grassland: responses to elevated CO₂ and nutrients. *Oecologia* **113**: 252–259.

Rillig, M.C., Allen, M.F., Klironomos, J.N., and Field, C.B. 1998b. Arbuscular mycorrhizal percent root infection and infection intensity of *Bromus hordeaceus* grown in elevated atmospheric CO₂. *Mycologia* **90**: 199–205.

Rillig, M.C., Field, C.B., and Allen, M.F. 1999a. Fungal root colonization responses in natural grasslands after long-term exposure to elevated atmospheric CO₂. *Global Change Biology* **5**: 577–585.

Rillig, M.C., Field, C.B., and Allen, M.F. 1999b. Soil biota responses to long-term atmospheric CO₂ enrichment in two California annual grasslands. *Oecologia* **119**: 572–577.

Rogers, A., Fischer, B.U., Bryant, J., Frehner, M., Blum, H., Raines, C.A., and Long, S.P. 1998. Acclimation of photosynthesis to elevated CO₂ under low-nitrogen nutrition is affected by the capacity for assimilate utilization. Perennial ryegrass under free-air CO₂ enrichment. *Plant Physiology* **118**: 683–689.

Stocklin, J. and Körner, Ch. 1999. Interactive effects of elevated CO_2, P availability and legume presence on calcareous grassland: results of a glasshouse experiment. *Functional Ecology* **13**: 200–209.

Suter, D., Frehner, M., Fischer, B.U., Nosberger, J., and Lüscher, A. 2002. Elevated CO_2 increases carbon allocation to the roots of *Lolium perenne* under free-air CO_2 enrichment but not in a controlled environment. *New Phytologist* **154**: 65–75.

Szente, K., Nagy, Z., and Tuba, Z. 1998. Enhanced water use efficiency in dry loess grassland species grown at elevated air CO_2 concentration. *Photosynthetica* **35**: 637–640.

Teyssonneyre, F., Picon-Cochard, C., and Soussana, J.F. 2002. How can we predict the effects of elevated CO_2 on the balance between perennial C_3 grass species competing for light? *New Phytologist* **154**: 53–64.

van der Heijden, M.G.A., Klironomos, J.N., Ursic, M., Moutoglis, P., Streitwolf-Engel, R., Boller, T., Wiemken, A., and Sanders, I.R. 1998. Mycorrhizal fungal diversity determines plant biodiversity, ecosystem variability and productivity. *Nature* **396**: 69–72.

van Ginkel, J.H., Gorissen, A., and Polci, D. 2000. Elevated atmospheric carbon dioxide concentration: effects of increased carbon input in a *Lolium perenne* soil on microorganisms and decomposition. *Soil Biology & Biochemistry* **32**: 449–456.

van Ginkel, J.H. and Gorissen, A. 1998. In situ decomposition of grass roots as affected by elevated atmospheric carbon dioxide. *Soil Science Society of America Journal* **62**: 951–958.

Volk, M., Niklaus, P.A., and Körner, C. 2000. Soil moisture effects determine CO_2 responses of grassland species. *Oecologia* **125**: 380–388.

Wand, S.J.E., Midgley, G.F., Jones, M.H., and Curtis, P.S. 1999. Responses of wild C_4 and C_3 grass (Poaceae) species to elevated atmospheric CO_2 concentration: a meta-analytic test of current theories and perceptions. *Global Change Biology* **5**: 723–741.

Wilson, G.W.T. and Hartnett, D.C. 1998. Interspecific variation in plant responses to mycorrhizal colonization in tallgrass prairie. *American Journal of Botany* **85**: 1732–1738.

Zaller, J.G. and Arnone III, J.A. 1999. Interactions between plant species and earthworm casts in a calcareous grassland under elevated CO_2. *Ecology* **80**: 873–881.

Zaller, J.G. and Arnone III, J.A. 1997. Activity of surface-casting earthworms in a calcareous grassland under elevated atmospheric CO_2. *Oecologia* **111**: 249–254.

1.2.2.2 Carbon Sequestration

- Research indicates soils beneath grasslands will significantly increase their carbon-storing capability as atmospheric CO_2 concentrations rise.

Carbon sequestration by grasslands is a less-investigated topic than carbon sequestration by forests. Nevertheless, several researchers have examined how grassland ecosystems might respond in this regard as the air's CO_2 concentration rises.

Fitter *et al.* (1997) transferred monoliths of two contrasting grasslands, a species-rich turf growing over limestone and a species-poor turf growing over a peaty soil, from Moor House National Nature Reserve in the United Kingdom to four "solardomes" at Lancaster University, where they maintained them for two years under natural daylight and air temperatures close to ambient. One set of two solardomes was exposed to ambient air and another set to air enriched with an extra 250 ppm CO_2. At various times throughout the experiment, the researchers made a number of measurements of above- and below-ground growth.

Shoot biomass was unaltered by the elevated level of atmospheric CO_2, but root biomass was enhanced by 40 to 50%. Furthermore, especially in the peat soil, root turnover was highly accelerated in the CO_2-enriched treatment—so much so, in fact, the authors conclude the increase in root biomass observed at the end of the experiment "was almost certainly a large underestimate of the amount of carbon transferred to the soil." The authors further note the increased productivity the two grassland ecosystems exhibited under elevated atmospheric CO_2 concentrations, along with the consequent increases in soil organic matter, are "likely to persist."

Cotrufo and Gorissen (1997) grew three grass species (*Lolium perenne* L. cv. Barlet, *Agrostis capillaris* L. cv. Bardot, and *Festuca ovina* L. cv. Barok) in 0.65-liter pots under two different levels of soil nitrogen in growth chambers maintained at 350 and 700 ppm CO_2 in continuously ^{14}C-labeled atmospheres. They harvested half the plants after 32 days and the other half after 55 days. They analyzed the shoots, roots, and soils for total carbon (C) and ^{14}C content.

They found elevated CO_2 increased the whole-plant dry weights of all three species by an average of 20% and, in general, increased root growth more than shoot growth. It also increased soil microbial biomass by slightly more than 15%. Of the ^{14}C that was fixed, 90% remained in the plant and 10% was transferred to the soil. There, 7% was found in the bulk soil and 3% was found in the rhizosphere soil close to the plant roots, split about equally between soil microbial biomass and soil residue.

The authors state what they observed "is consistent with the general finding that the soil microbial biomass is C-limited, and supports the hypothesis that a greater C input below-ground, as a result of increased size of the root system, at high CO$_2$ elicits an increase in soil microbial biomass." They also state "elevated CO$_2$ will induce an increase in relative C allocation to below-ground sinks independent of nitrogen level." Finally, they conclude their findings for all three grasses confirm "elevated CO$_2$ could result in greater soil C stores due to increased C-input into soils," as well as "a higher residence time for C in soils, thus counteracting increased decomposition under higher temperatures." Thus, they write, "we may well expect that this increased C input below-ground will be sustained in the longer term." This phenomenon clearly would be expected to reduce the level to which atmospheric CO$_2$ concentrations would rise in its absence.

Casella and Soussana (1997) grew perennial ryegrass (*Lolium perenne* L. cv. Preference) swards in large containers at two different levels of soil nitrogen supply for two years at ambient and elevated (700 ppm) CO$_2$ concentrations, as well as at ambient and elevated (+3°C) temperature. The soils were maintained at field capacity via irrigation, but the water supply was reduced in summer to simulate characteristic summer water deficits. Throughout the experiment, they made a number of measurements on the plants and soils, including canopy gas exchanges, plant water soluble carbohydrates, and biomass production. The authors report "a relatively large part of the additional photosynthetic carbon is stored below-ground during the two first growing seasons after exposure to elevated CO$_2$, thereby increasing significantly the below-ground carbon pool." At low and high soil nitrogen supply, for example, the elevated CO$_2$ increased soil carbon storage by 32 and 96%, respectively, "with no significant increased temperature effect." The elevated temperature actually helped to increase soil carbon storage, because the enhanced soil desiccation at +3°C helped restrict below-ground respiration. Casella and Soussana conclude "this stimulation of the below-ground carbon sequestration in temperate grassland soils could exert a negative feed-back on the current rise of the atmospheric CO$_2$ concentration."

Lutze and Gifford (1998) grew microcosms of the C$_3$ grass *Danthonia richardsonii* for four years in glasshouses with atmospheric CO$_2$ concentrations of 360 or 720 ppm and three levels of soil nitrogen to determine the effects of elevated CO$_2$ and soil nutrition on microcosm carbon gain and water use. They conducted destructive harvests of plant material at six-month intervals throughout the project. Results indicated carbon accumulation in the microcosms was strongly correlated with soil nitrogen: Nitrogen was limiting productivity, even in the highest fertilization treatment. Nevertheless, when averaged across all harvests and nitrogen regimes, elevated CO$_2$ significantly increased total microcosm carbon gains by 15–34%, in spite of a 9% reduction in leaf area index. In addition, elevated CO$_2$ increased senesced leaf material per unit ground area at all harvests and nitrogen treatments by an average of 31%. Consequently, these phenomena led to final soil carbon contents in CO$_2$-enriched microcosms 4, 9, and 17% greater than in ambient microcosms at low, medium, and high soil nitrogen treatments, respectively. Elevated CO$_2$ also reduced microcosm water use by 25% across all nitrogen treatments, thereby allowing greater soil volumetric water contents to exist in CO$_2$-enriched microcosms.

Nitschelm *et al.* (1997) report white clover exposed to an atmospheric CO$_2$ concentration of 600 ppm for one growing season channeled 50% more newly fixed carbon compounds into the soil than similar plants exposed to ambient air. In addition, the clover's roots decomposed at a rate 24% slower than roots of control plants, as also has been reported for white clover by David *et al.* (2001). These observations suggest rising CO$_2$ content will greatly enhance soil carbon sequestration under white clover ecosystems.

Van Ginkel *et al.* (1996) exposed mini-ecosystems comprised entirely of perennial ryegrass species to an atmospheric CO$_2$ concentration of 700 ppm for two months, finding a 92% increase in root growth and 19% and 14% decreases in root decomposition rates one and two years, respectively, after incubating ground roots in soils. Van Ginkel and Gorissen (1998) followed up this work, showing a 13% reduction in the decomposition rates of CO$_2$-enriched perennial ryegrass roots in both disturbed and undisturbed root profiles. This and other work led the authors to calculate CO$_2$-induced reductions in the decomposition of perennial ryegrass litter, which enhances soil carbon sequestration, could be large enough to remove over half of the anthropogenic CO$_2$ emissions that may be released in the next century (Van Ginkel *et al.*, 1999).

Van Ginkel *et al.* (2000) found elevated CO$_2$

decreased root decomposition rates of perennial ryegrass grown at 700 ppm CO_2 by 14% after 230 days of incubation in elevated CO_2. In addition, the scientists determined raising the incubation temperature by 2 °C had little effect on the CO_2-induced reductions in decomposition rate, for they were still 12% lower than those measured at 350 ppm CO_2. In a shorter-term experiment the researchers found even a 6 °C increase in air temperature could not counterbalance the CO_2-induced reductions in decomposition rate.

These results suggest future increases in the air's CO_2 content likely will cause slight reductions in rates of plant litter decomposition, thus allowing more carbon to remain sequestered from the atmosphere for longer periods of time, and this will be the case even if Earth's air temperature rises.

In some cases, however, atmospheric CO_2 enrichment has been reported to have little or no significant effect on litter quality and subsequent rates of litter decomposition. Hirschel et al. (1997) took fallen leaves from species common to alpine and calcareous grasslands and incubated them in mesh nylon bags placed on the soil surfaces of their respective mesocosms, subjecting them to ambient and twice-ambient concentrations of atmospheric CO_2. After one year of incubation, the decomposition rates of the litter produced under the ambient and elevated CO_2 conditions did not differ significantly from each other, except in the case of one alpine sedge, which exhibited reduced rates of decomposition under atmospheric CO_2 enrichment. Dukes and Field (2000) reported similar results after incubating litter derived from various combinations of grassland species common to California, USA, for an eight-month period at atmospheric CO_2 concentrations of 350 and 700 ppm and finding minimal effects of elevated CO_2 on decomposition rates.

In a five-year study of a grassland growing on a moderately fertile soil at Stanford University's Jasper Ridge Biological Preserve in central California—which utilized 20 open-top chambers (ten each at 360 and 720 ppm CO_2)—Hu et al. (2001) found a doubling of the air's CO_2 content increased both soil microbial biomass and plant nitrogen uptake. With less nitrogen left in the soil to be used by a larger number of microbes, microbial respiration per unit of soil microbe biomass significantly declined in the elevated CO_2 environments; with this decrease in microbial decomposition, there was an increase in carbon accumulation in the soil.

Hu et al. conclude this CO_2-induced chain of events could readily cause terrestrial grassland ecosystems to become significantly stronger net carbon (C) sinks than they are currently, especially if their plants become more efficient at acquiring nitrogen (N) from soils of low C:N organic matter ratio. They also suggest such CO_2-enhanced grassland N acquisition might be prompted by increased root colonization by symbiotic mycorrhizal fungi, which has been found to be a rather common consequence of atmospheric CO_2 enrichment (Rillig et al., 1998, 2000). Hence, the scientists conclude, as have many others, the carbon sequestered by these means "could partially offset the effects of anthropogenic CO_2 emissions on atmospheric CO_2 [concentration]."

How much extra carbon can be sequestered in the planet's grassland soils as a result of a doubling of the air's CO_2 content? A good first approximation at an answer is provided by Williams et al. (2000), who studied this phenomenon for eight years in a Kansas (USA) tallgrass prairie, utilizing open-top chambers enclosing mixtures of C_3 and C_4 grasses continually fumigated with air of either ambient or twice-ambient atmospheric CO_2 concentration. Williams et al. found the average soil water content in the first 15 cm of the soil profile was approximately 15% greater beneath the chambers receiving the extra supply of CO_2, due, presumably, to CO_2-induced reductions in plant stomatal conductance that blunted transpirational water loss. The saved moisture, in turn, enabled plants to be more productive during the growing season, and with a significant portion of that extra productivity directed belowground into roots, there was a nearly equivalent increase in soil microbial activity across the final five years of the study. The authors report there was an 8% increase in total soil carbon content over the course of the study.

Extrapolating this value to all of Earth's temperate grasslands, which make up about 10% of the land area of the globe, Williams et al. calculate the CO_2-induced increase in soil carbon sequestration could amount to an additional 1.3 Pg of carbon being sequestered in just the top 15 cm of the world's grassland soils over the next century.

Riedo et al. (2000) used a mechanistic pasture simulation model (PaSim) to predict changes in net primary productivity and carbon stocks in differently managed grasslands in response to increased atmospheric CO_2 concentration and climate change. Results indicated elevated CO_2 alone, or in combination with increased air temperature, enhanced net primary productivity at all simulated sites by 30 to 40%. In addition, the effects of elevated CO_2 and elevated air temperature were generally positive with respect to grassland carbon stocks. Such simulations suggest the increasing CO_2 content of the air likely will stimulate primary productivity in managed grasslands, thus leading to greater biomass production and enhanced carbon storage in their associated soils. Grasslands cover nearly 20% of the land surface of the globe and store at least 10% of the soil organic matter of the planet.

Cardon *et al.* (2001) erected open-top chambers on two Mediterranean grassland communities in California, USA. They fumigated them for two years with air containing either ambient or twice-ambient atmospheric CO_2 concentrations. In addition, plants were grown with either low or high soil nutrient availability. The main thrust of this research was to use isotopic labeling to study the effects of elevated atmospheric CO_2 and soil nutrient availability on the decomposition of old and new organic carbon in the two grassland soils. Results indicated when soil nutrient availability was high, elevated CO_2 reduced the decomposition of older soil organic carbon by approximately 30% throughout the study. Thus, the turnover time and stabilization of this soil carbon pool was increased by elevated CO_2 exposure. However, the movement of newly fixed carbon into the older stabilized pools was decreased with atmospheric CO_2 enrichment, due to its preferential utilization by soil microbes. Thus, soil microbes switched from using older to newer soil organic carbon under CO_2-enriched conditions.

Thus, as the atmosphere's CO_2 content rises, carbon sequestration in the soils of Mediterranean grasslands likely will increase for two reasons. First, it should rise as a consequence of the greater retention times conferred upon the carbon in older soil organic carbon pools, which represent the largest reservoir of terrestrial carbon on Earth. Second, even though soil microbes exhibit a preference for newer carbon under CO_2-enriched conditions, it should rise because of the great increase in the amount of carbon going into newer soil carbon pools due to CO_2-enhanced root exudation, root turnover, and other types of litter production.

Higgins *et al.* (2002) constructed open-top chambers in portions of an annual grassland located in a Mediterranean-type climate in California, USA. They fumigated them with air of either 360 or 720 ppm CO_2 to study the effects of elevated CO_2 on root production and turnover. By the end of the growing season, the plants in the elevated-CO_2 chambers had increased their production of new root length by nearly 60%, but their root turnover rates were no different from those of the plants in the

ambient-treatment chambers. There was also an 18% increase in soil moisture content in the CO_2-enriched chambers. Thus, as the CO_2 content of the air increases, belowground biomass production should increase in this particular type of annual grassland, either directly from CO_2-induced increases in photosynthesis or indirectly from CO_2-induced reductions in water use, which tend to increase soil moisture content.

Hartwig *et al.* (2002) grew swards of perennial ryegrass (*Lolium perenne* L.) and the N_2-fixing white clover (*Trifolium repens* L.) in boxes placed in FACE plots receiving atmospheric CO_2 concentrations of 350 and 600 ppm in combination with low and high soil nitrogen fertilization for four years, to study the interactive effects of these variables on biomass production and nitrogen retention in these two contrasting ecosystems. They found elevated CO_2 increased average aboveground biomass in the white clover ecosystem by 80% but had no effect on aboveground biomass production in the perennial ryegrass ecosystem. Below the surface of the soil, however, just the opposite occurred: the extra CO_2 increased root biomass in the perennial ryegrass ecosystem by 94% while having no effect on the root biomass of white clover.

The total amount of nitrogen taken into the white clover ecosystem was significantly greater than that taken into the perennial ryegrass ecosystem. Elevated CO_2 exposure could explain much of this increase, as it roughly doubled the amount of nitrogen input through symbiotic N_2-fixation in the white clover. Nonetheless, all combinations of variables led to ecosystem nitrogen gains after four years of growth, with greater gains under higher, rather than lower, nitrogen fertilization. In addition, elevated CO_2 increased ecosystem nitrogen gains in all cases except in perennial ryegrass under low nitrogen fertilization.

These findings suggest as the air's CO_2 concentration increases, swards of perennial ryegrass and white clover likely will display increased rates of photosynthesis and greater biomass production. CO_2-induced increases in biomass most likely will be manifested aboveground in white clover and belowground in perennial ryegrass. In addition, both ecosystems should exhibit increased gains in nitrogen (except, perhaps, in the case of perennial ryegrass growing on low-nitrogen soils), with greater nitrogen gains occurring in white clover, as a result of CO_2-induced increases in symbiotic N_2-fixation.

Pendall *et al.* (2004) explain rhizodeposition is "the addition of C [carbon] from roots to soil C pools," and they note "because up to 80% of the biomass and at least 50% of net primary production can occur below-ground in grasslands, changes in rhizodeposition will have a large impact on C cycling in these ecosystems (Milchunas and Lauenroth, 2001)," which may significantly impact the amount of carbon sequestered in grassland soils. Against this backdrop, Pendall *et al.* used open-top chambers to study various responses of a native C_3-C_4 grassland ecosystem in the shortgrass steppe region of northeastern Colorado, USA, to a doubling of the air's CO_2 concentration (from 360 to 720 ppm) in an experiment that lasted five years. Total aboveground biomass was increased by an average of 33% over the course of the study in the CO_2-enriched chambers, and belowground biomass increased by an average of 23%. In addition, over the last four years of the experiment, rhizodeposition increased by 137% in the chambers exposed to elevated CO_2. However, Pendall *et al.* report "decomposition increased nearly as much as rhizodeposition," leading to little net increase in soil C storage in the CO_2-enriched chambers relative to that found in the ambient-air chambers.

Although there was little increase in soil carbon sequestration in the CO_2-enriched chambers of this particular study, more biomass was produced in them each year, both above- and below-ground, than in the ambient-air chambers; and much more biomass made its way into the soil of the CO_2-enriched chambers. Hence it is likely that over the course of several decades the small yearly differences in soil C storage would eventually end up producing a substantially larger stash of carbon in the soil of the CO_2-enriched chambers.

Over the course of an eight-year open-top-chamber CO_2-enrichment (to twice ambient concentrations) study of a pristine (annually burned) tallgrass prairie north of Manhattan, Kansas, USA, composed of a mixture of C_3 and C_4 species, Williams *et al.* (2004) measured changes in the active, slow, and passive pools of carbon (C) and nitrogen (N), to determine how they were affected by the doubled atmospheric CO_2 concentration of their reasonably long-term experiment. They report, "on average, elevated CO_2 induced a 60% increase in root growth," citing Owensby *et al.* (1999). They also found potentially mineralizable C was enhanced by 19% and 24%, respectively, in the 0–5 cm and 5–15 cm soil horizons, which they suggest implies "increases in plant inputs have outpaced increases in decomposition rates" in those layers. Likewise, they report potentially mineralizable N was enhanced by 14% in the 0–5 cm layer, and CO_2 enrichment resulted in greater recalcitrant N in the 5–15 cm soil layer. Regarding these latter findings, they hypothesize "greater N translocated to aboveground biomass from deeper soil depths could ultimately be stored in roots and rhizomes near the soil surface, and would eventually turnover and become a part of the surface soil N pool."

Williams *et al.* conclude "the 60% increase in root growth during the 8-year study was the likely catalyst for the greater potentially mineralizable soil C pools in the enriched CO_2 treatment," and this finding "confirms that C can accrue in soils under elevated CO_2." Specifically, they determined the total amount of extra new carbon sequestered in the soil due to their doubling of the air's CO_2 concentration was 4 Mg C ha^{-1} over the eight-year period, for an annual rate of extra (CO_2-induced) carbon sequestration of 0.5 Mg ha^{-1} year^{-1}.

Working with a temperate grassland on the North Island of New Zealand under permanent grazing by sheep, cattle, and goats since at least 1940, Allard *et al.* (2005) measured above- and below-ground plant growth and litter production, along with root turnover and soil particulate organic matter quantity and quality, after almost four years of exposure to an extra ~105 ppm of atmospheric CO_2 (a target concentration of 475 ppm) in a moderate-term FACE experiment. The researchers report the elevated CO_2 did not alter aboveground herbage biomass and leaf litter production, but root growth rate and turnover "were strongly stimulated by CO_2 particularly at low soil moisture contents during summer." As a result of the root responses, they also found "significantly more plant material was returned to the soil under elevated CO_2 leading to an accumulation of coarse (>1 mm) particulate organic matter (POM)," with a similar but not-yet-significant trend in fine POM. In addition, they state there was a CO_2-induced lowering of POM carbon/nitrogen ratio, which they "attributed to the higher proportion of legumes in the pasture under elevated CO_2."

The six New Zealand and French researchers say their results "show that in grazed pastures with high plant species diversity we might expect extra carbon sequestration in soil organic matter mainly through an increase in carbon input rather than a decreasing quality of accumulating organic matter." That they could detect the changes they did over so short a time interval, and with so small an increase in the atmosphere's CO_2 concentration, is impressive, but it is just one among many similar findings of Jastrow *et al.* (2005) and the many studies the latter scientists reviewed in their meta-analysis of the subject. In addition, Allard *et al.* found indications of increased soil nitrogen in their CO_2-enriched treatment, just as Jastrow *et al.* did, reinforcing the latter group's conclusions about this subject as well.

Edwards *et al.* (2005) grew well-watered mixtures of two plants—the legume white clover (*Trifolium repens* L.) and C_4 buffalo grass (*Stenotaphrum secundatum* (Walt.) Kuntze)—which were initially equal in plantlet size, number, and spatial distribution, for 15 months in sand placed in large plastic containers in greenhouses maintained at different atmospheric CO_2 concentrations (360 and 700 ppm) under three sand nutrient conditions (zero-N/low-P, zero-N/high-P, plus-N/high-P). They made ten harvests of all plant biomass over a height of 5 cm above the sand surface, after which the total carbon contents of the whole plants and their respective soils were determined. The slightly less than a doubling of the air's CO_2 concentration employed in this study led to increases of 22%, 41%, and 374% in the amounts of new carbon found in the soils in the zero-N/low-P, zero-N/high-P, and plus-N/high-P soil treatments, respectively. In addition, corresponding increases of 22%, 53%, and 53% in total new mesocosm carbon contents (comprised of soil plus plant carbon) were reported in each respective treatment. Thus, soil P deficiency in this study severely limited the ability of elevated CO_2 to stimulate total mesocosm carbon capture, and lack of N was most harmful to soil carbon capture. Consequently, in grasslands managed for animal production, Edwards *et al.* say "it may be possible to increase their potential to sequester C as atmospheric CO_2 increases by altering land management," especially in ways that relieve these nutrient deficiencies, as also has been suggested by Jones and Donnelly (2004).

Pendall and King (2007) conducted a series of long-term (170–330 days) laboratory incubation experiments to examine changes in soil organic matter pool sizes and turnover rates in soil collected from an open-top chamber (OTC) atmospheric CO_2 enrichment study in the shortgrass steppe of northeastern Colorado, USA, where the air in the ambient CO_2 chambers (ACs) and elevated CO_2 chambers (ECs) had atmospheric CO_2 concentrations of 360 and 720 ppm, respectively. This degree of CO_2 enrichment enhanced both above- and below-ground plant growth by 15–35%. The authors found the "active pool carbon increased in EC relative to AC treatments systematically over the first 3 years of exposure to elevated CO_2 in topsoils and to a lesser degree in subsoils," noting "these results are consistent with independent results from the same OTC study showing that rhizodeposition rates

doubled (Pendall *et al.*, 2004) and root production increased under elevated CO_2 (Milchunas *et al.*, 2005)." In addition, they report "new carbon turnover was not enhanced by elevated CO_2," indicating "new carbon inputs under elevated CO_2 are not simply lost to mineralization" and "pool sizes may continue to increase under elevated CO_2." Such findings, in the words of the two researchers, "suggest that soil carbon storage may increase in semi-arid grasslands under elevated CO_2."

Adair *et al.* (2009) employed mass balance calculations to quantify the effects of biodiversity, atmospheric CO_2 concentration, and soil nitrogen (N) content on the total amount of C allocated belowground by plants (total belowground C allocation or TBCA), as well as ecosystem C storage, in an eight-year experiment that was part of the BioCON study of a periodically burned Minnesota grassland. The authors report annual TBCA increased in response to all three treatment variables—"elevated CO_2, enriched N, and increasing diversity"—and it was also "positively related to standing root biomass." Upon removing the influence of root biomass, however, they state the effects of N and diversity became neutral or even negative (depending on the year), but "the effect of elevated CO_2 remained positive." In years with fire, "greater litter production in high diversity, elevated CO_2, and enhanced N treatments increased annual ecosystem C loss." Thus, under normal non-fire conditions, elevated CO_2, N, and biodiversity generally tend to increase ecosystem carbon gain, but if grasslands are frequently burned, they could remain neutral in this regard.

Belay-Tedla *et al.* (2009) note "the stability of carbon (C) and nitrogen (N) in soil organic matter (SOM) to perturbations such as global warming is critically important," because "on a global scale, the soil contains 1500 Pg (1 Pg = 10^{15} g) of organic carbon and 300 Pg of total nitrogen" in its uppermost meter, so "relatively small changes in the amounts of soil C and N may therefore bring about substantial effects on atmospheric concentrations," which in the case of the carbon contained in CO_2 may feed back either positively or negatively to enhance or reduce the original global warming.

In a study designed to explore these interactions in a specific biome, Belay-Tedla *et al.* "used sulfuric acid hydrolysis to quantify changes in labile and recalcitrant C and N fractions of soil in a tallgrass prairie ecosystem that had been continuously warmed with or without clipping for about 2.5 years," conducting their work in "an old-field tallgrass prairie abandoned from agriculture 30 years ago and without grazing during the past 20 years" in the Great Plains Apiaries of McClain County, Oklahoma, USA. Infrared heaters suspended 1.5 m above the ground warmed half the plots 24 hours a day, 365 days a year, for the 2.5-year period, increasing the daily mean air temperature at 25 cm above the ground by 1.1°C and soil temperature at 2.5 cm depth by 2.0°C.

The five researchers found "significant increases in both labile C and N (including microbial biomass) pools in response to experimental warming," which "largely resulted from increased above- and below-ground biomass." They also observed "a possible shift to a fungi-dominated microbial community," noting "such a shift could favor soil C storage" as well. In addition, they report evidence suggesting "warming increased the percentage of total N for microbial biomass N," and this enhanced N use efficiency "may be conducive for a continued supply of organic inputs." Belay-Tedla et al. conclude their combined findings favor "long-term N retention and C accumulation in soils, leading to negative feedbacks of terrestrial ecosystems to climate warming."

Ayres et al. (2008) investigated various responses of atmospheric CO_2 enrichment to approximately 350 ppm above ambient in experiments conducted on three grassland ecosystems in Colorado and California (USA) and Montpellier, France. The authors state "soil moisture increased in response to elevated CO_2 in the California, Colorado, and French stud[ies] (Hungate et al., 1997; Nijs et al., 2000; Morgan et al., 2004)." As to the plants, the authors state "elevated CO_2 increased root biomass by approximately 3–32% in the first 5 years of the Coloradoan study (Pendall et al., 2004), by 23% after 6 years in the Californian study (Rillig et al., 1999), and by 31% after 6 months in the French study (Dhillion et al., 1996)." Regarding nematodes, the researchers write, "CO_2 enrichment did not significantly affect the family richness, diversity, or PPI [plant parasitic nematode index] of herbivorous nematodes in the Colorado, California, or French study," noting "in each experiment, neutral effects were the most frequent response to CO_2 enrichment." Commenting on these findings, the seven researchers state "one consequence of increased root production, without changes in belowground herbivore populations, might be greater plant inputs to soil," which "may lead to greater soil organic matter pools in grassland ecosystems, potentially enhancing soil carbon sequestration."

The research findings discussed above suggest grasslands will become increasingly productive and provide an ever-increasing brake on the upward trend in the air's CO_2 concentration.

References

Adair, E.C., Reich, P.B., Hobbie, S.E., and Knops, J.M.H. 2009. Interactive effects of time, CO_2, N, and diversity on total belowground carbon allocation and ecosystem carbon storage in a grassland community. *Ecosystems* **12**: 1037–1052.

Allard, V., Newton, P.C.D., Lieffering, M., Soussana, J.-F., Carran, R.A., and Matthew, C. 2005. Increased quantity and quality of coarse soil organic matter fraction at elevated CO_2 in a grazed grassland are a consequence of enhanced root growth rate and turnover. *Plant and Soil* **276**: 49–60.

Ayres, E., Wall, D.H., Simmons, B.L., Field, C.B., Milchunas, D.G., Morgan, J.A., and Roy, J. 2008. Belowground nematode herbivores are resistant to elevated atmospheric CO_2 concentrations in grassland ecosystems. *Soil Biology & Biochemistry* **40**: 978–985.

Belay-Tedla, A., Zhou, X., Su, B., Wan, S., and Luo, Y. 2009. Labile, recalcitrant, and microbial carbon and nitrogen pools of a tallgrass prairie soil in the US Great Plains subjected to experimental warming and clipping. *Soil Biology & Biochemistry* **41**: 110–116.

Cardon, Z.G., Hungate, B.A., Cambardella, C.A., Chapin, F.S., Field, C.B., Holland, E.A., and Mooney, H.A. 2001. *Soil Biology & Biochemistry* **33**: 365–373.

Casella, E. and Soussana, J-F. 1997. Long-term effects of CO_2 enrichment and temperature increase on the carbon balance of a temperate grass sward. *Journal of Experimental Botany* **48**: 1309–1321.

Cotrufo, M.F. and Gorissen, A. 1997. Elevated CO_2 enhances below-ground C allocation in three perennial grass species at different levels of N availability. *New Phytologist* **137**: 421–431.

David, J.-F., Malet, N., Couteaux, M.-M., and Roy, J. 2001. Feeding rates of the woodlouse *Armadillidium vulgare* on herb litters produced at two levels of atmospheric CO_2. *Oecologia* **127**: 343–349.

Dhillion, S.D., Roy, J., and Abrams, M. 1996. Assessing the impact of elevated CO_2 on soil microbial activity in a Mediterranean model ecosystem. *Plant & Soil* **187**: 333–342.

Dukes, J.S. and Field, C.B. 2000. Diverse mechanisms for CO_2 effects on grassland litter decomposition. *Global Change Biology* **6**: 145–154.

Edwards, E.J., McCaffery, S., and Evans, J.R. 2005. Phosphorus status determines biomass response to elevated

CO$_2$ in a legume:C$_4$ grass community. *Global Change Biology* **11**: 1968–1981.

Fitter, A.H., Graves, J.D., Wolfenden, J., Self, G.K., Brown, T.K., Bogie, D., and Mansfield, T.A. 1997. Root production and turnover and carbon budgets of two contrasting grasslands under ambient and elevated atmospheric carbon dioxide concentrations. *New Phytologist* **137**: 247–255.

Hartwig, U.A., Luscher, A., Nosberger, J., and van Kessel, C. 2002. Nitrogen-15 budget in model ecosystems of white clover and perennial ryegrass exposed for four years at elevated atmospheric pCO$_2$. *Global Change Biology* **8**: 194–202.

Higgins, P.A.T., Jackson, R.B., Des Rosiers, J.M., and Field, C.B. 2002. Root production and demography in a California annual grassland under elevated atmospheric carbon dioxide. *Global Change Biology* **8**: 841–850.

Hirschel, G., Körner, C., and Arnone III, J.A. 1997. Will rising atmospheric CO$_2$ affect leaf litter quality and in situ decomposition rates in native plant communities? *Oecologia* **110**: 387–392.

Hu, S., Chapin III, F.S., Firestone, M.K., Field, C.B., and Chiariello, N.R. 2001. Nitrogen limitation of microbial decomposition in a grassland under elevated CO$_2$. *Nature* **409**: 188–191.

Hungate, B.A., Holland, E.A., Jackson, R.B., Chapin, F.S., Mooney, H.A., and Field, C.B. 1997. The fate of carbon in grasslands under carbon dioxide enrichment. *Nature* **388**: 576–579.

Jastrow, J.D., Miller, R.M., Matamala, R., Norby, R.J., Boutton, T.W., Rice, C.W., and Owensby, C.E. 2005. Elevated atmospheric carbon dioxide increases soil carbon. *Global Change Biology* **11**: 2057–2064.

Jones, M.B. and Donnelly, A. 2004. Carbon sequestration in temperate grassland ecosystems and the influence of management, climate and elevated CO$_2$. *New Phytologist* **164**: 423–439.

Lutze, J.L. and Gifford, R.M. 1998. Carbon accumulation, distribution and water use of *Danthonia richardsonii* swards in response to CO$_2$ and nitrogen supply over four years of growth. *Global Change Biology* **4**: 851–861.

Milchunas, D. and Lauenroth, W. 2001. Belowground primary production by carbon isotope decay and long-term root biomass dynamics. *Ecosystems* **4**: 139–150.

Milchunas, D.G., Mosier, A.R., Morgan, J.A., LeCain, D.R., King, J.Y., and Nelson, J.A. 2005. Root production and tissue quality in a shortgrass steppe exposed to elevated CO$_2$: using a new ingrowth method. *Plant and Soil* **268**: 111–122.

Morgan, J.A., Mosier, A.R., Milchunas, D.G., LeCain,

D.R., Nelson, J.A., and Parton, W.J. 2004. CO$_2$ enhances productivity, alters species composition, and reduces digestibility of shortgrass steppe vegetation. *Ecological Applications* **14**: 208–219.

Nijs, I., Roy, J., Salager, J.-L., and Fabreguettes, J. 2000. Elevated CO$_2$ alters carbon fluxes in early successional Mediterranean ecosystems. *Global Change Biology* **6**: 981–994.

Nitschelm, J.J., Lüscher, A., Hartwig, U.A., and van Kessel, C. 1997. Using stable isotopes to determine soil carbon input differences under ambient and elevated atmospheric CO$_2$ conditions. *Global Change Biology* **3**: 411–416.

Owensby, C.E., Ham, J.M., Knapp, A.K., and Auen, L.M. 1999. Biomass production and species composition change in a tallgrass prairie ecosystem after long-term exposure to elevated atmospheric CO$_2$. *Global Change Biology* **5**: 497–506.

Pendall, E. and King, J.Y. 2007. Soil organic matter dynamics in grassland soils under elevated CO$_2$: Insights from long-term incubations and stable isotopes. *Soil Biology & Biochemistry* **39**: 2628–2639.

Pendall, E., Mosier, A.R., and Morgan, J.A. 2004. Rhizodeposition stimulated by elevated CO$_2$ in a semiarid grassland. *New Phytologist* **162**: 447–458.

Riedo, M., Gyalistras, D., and Fuhrer, J. 2000. Net primary production and carbon stocks in differently managed grasslands: simulation of site-specific sensitivity to an increase in atmospheric CO$_2$ and to climate change. *Ecological Modelling* **134**: 207–227.

Rillig, M.C., Allen, M.F., Klironomos, J.N., and Field, C.B. 1998. Arbuscular mycorrhizal percent root infection and infection intensity of *Bromus hordeaceus* grown in elevated atmospheric CO$_2$. *Mycologia* **90**: 199–205.

Rillig, M.C., Field, C.B., and Allen, M.F. 1999. Soil biota responses to long-term atmospheric CO$_2$ enrichment in two California annual grasslands. *Oecologia* **119**: 572–577.

Rillig, M.C., Hernandez, G.Y., and Newton, P.C.D. 2000. Arbuscular mycorrhizae respond to elevated atmospheric CO$_2$ after long-term exposure: evidence from a CO$_2$ spring in New Zealand supports the resource balance model. *Ecology Letters* **3**: 475–478.

Van Ginkel, J.H. and Gorissen, A. 1998. In situ decomposition of grass roots as affected by elevated atmospheric carbon dioxide. *Soil Science Society of America Journal* **62**: 951–958.

Van Ginkel, J.H., Gorissen, A., and Polci, D. 2000. Elevated atmospheric carbon dioxide concentration: effects of increased carbon input in a *Lolium perenne* soil on microorganisms and decomposition. *Soil Biology & Biochemistry* **32**: 449–456.

Van Ginkel, J.H., Gorissen, A., and van Veen, J.A. 1996. Long-term decomposition of grass roots as affected by elevated atmospheric carbon dioxide. *Journal of Environmental Quality* **25**: 1122–1128.

Van Ginkel, J.H., Whitmore, A.P., and Gorissen, A. 1999. *Lolium perenne* grasslands may function as a sink for atmospheric carbon dioxide. *Journal of Environmental Quality* **28**: 1580–1584.

Williams, M.A., Rice, C.W., Omay, A., and Owensby, C. 2004. Carbon and nitrogen pools in a tallgrass prairie soil under elevated carbon dioxide. *Soil Science Society of America Journal* **68**: 148–153.

Williams, M.A., Rice, C.W., and Owensby, C.E. 2000. Carbon dynamics and microbial activity in tall grass prairie exposed to elevated CO_2 for 8 years. *Plant and Soil* **227**: 127–137.

1.2.3 Peatlands

- In contrast to IPCC projections, the thawing of permafrost caused by increases in air temperature and CO_2 will not likely transform peatlands from carbon-sink to carbon-source ecosystems. Instead, as permafrost thaws, plants and trees can begin to grow again on these lands and in so doing, they sequester carbon.

Peatlands contain a vast amount of sequestered carbon—about as much, in fact, as is contained in the entire atmosphere. As a result, they are vital elements of the planet's carbon cycle and can significantly impact its climate. This section reviews the findings of several papers that bear upon this topic.

IPCC predicts global warming will release long-sequestered carbon in Earth's peatlands to the atmosphere, possibly freeing enough of it at a sufficiently rapid rate to rival CO_2 emissions from anthropogenic sources. The end result of this scenario would be a strong positive feedback to the ongoing rise in the air's CO_2 content, which IPCC contends will lead to further warming of the planet. However, multiple studies have shown this scenario to be highly unlikely or altogether false.

One of the first cracks in this positive-feedback hypothesis was revealed by Oechel *et al.* (2000). They showed long-term measurements of net ecosystem CO_2 exchange rates in wet-sedge and moist-tussock tundra communities of the Alaskan Arctic indicated these ecosystems were changing gradually from carbon sources to carbon sinks. The transition occurred between 1992 and 1996, at the apex of a regional warming trend that culminated with the highest summer temperature and surface water deficit of the previous four decades.

The scientists who documented this dramatic and unexpected biological transformation describe it as "a previously undemonstrated capacity for ecosystems to metabolically adjust to long-term changes in climate." This ecological acclimation process is only one of several recognized phenomena that have caused scientists to radically revise their thinking about global change in Arctic regions.

Camill *et al.* (2001) investigated changes in peat accumulation across a regional gradient of mean annual temperature in Manitoba, Canada; net above-ground primary production and decomposition for major functional plant groups of the region; and soil cores from several frozen and thawed bog sites used to determine long-term changes in organic matter accumulation following the thawing of boreal peatlands. In direct contradiction of earlier thinking on the subject, but in confirmation of the more recent findings of Camill (1999a,b), the researchers report aboveground biomass and decomposition "were more strongly controlled by local succession than regional climate." In other words, over a period of several years, natural changes in plant community composition generally "have stronger effects on carbon sequestration than do simple increases in temperature and aridity." Their core-derived assessments of peat accumulation over the past two centuries demonstrated rates of biological carbon sequestration can almost double following the thawing of permafrost, in harmony with the findings of Robinson and Moore (2000) and Turetsky *et al.* (2000), who found rates of organic matter accumulation in other recently thawed peatlands to have risen by 60–72 percent.

Griffis and Rouse (2001) drew on the findings of experiments conducted over the past quarter-century at a subarctic sedge fen near Churchill, Manitoba, Canada, to develop an empirical model of net ecosystem CO_2 exchange there. The fundamental finding of this endeavor was "carbon acquisition is greatest during wet and warm conditions," as is generally predicted for the world as a whole by today's most advanced climate models. However, regional climate change predictions are not very dependable, so the two scientists investigated the consequences of a 4°C increase in temperature accompanied by both a 30 percent increase and decrease in precipitation. "In all cases," they observe, "the equilibrium response showed substantial increases in carbon acquisition." One of the reasons for this finding, Griffis and Rouse explain, is "arctic ecosystems photosynthesize below their temperature optimum over the majority of the growing season," so increasing temperatures enhance plant growth rates considerably more than they increase plant decay rates.

In summing up their findings, Griffis and Rouse state "warm surface temperatures combined with wet soil conditions in the early growing season increase above-ground biomass and carbon acquisition throughout the summer season." They note, "wet spring conditions can lead to greater CO$_2$ acquisition through much of the growing period even when drier conditions persist." They thus conclude if climate change plays out as described by current climate models—if the world becomes warmer and wetter—"northern wetlands should therefore become larger sinks for atmospheric CO$_2$."

Mauquoy et al. (2002) analyzed three cores obtained from a raised peat bog in the UK (Walton Moss) and a single core obtained from a similar bog in Denmark (Lille Vildmose) for macro- and micro-fossils (pollen), bulk density, loss on ignition, carbon/nitrogen ratios, and humification, which they ^{14}C dated by accelerator mass spectrometry. Among a variety of findings, they determined "the lowest carbon accumulation values for the Walton Moss monoliths between ca. cal AD 1300 and 1800 and between ca. cal AD 1490 and 1580 for Lille Vildmose occurred during the course of Little Ice Age deteriorations." They describe this finding as being much the same as the observation "made by Oldfield et al. (1997) for a Swedish 'aapa' mire between ca. cal AD 1400 and 1800." They also report carbon accumulation before this, in the Medieval Warm Period, was higher, as was also the case after the Little Ice Age, as Earth transitioned to the Modern Warm Period. Consequently, whereas IPCC predicts warming will hasten the release of carbon from ancient peat bogs, real-world data demonstrate just the opposite is more likely.

In a similar study, but one that concentrated more on the role of nitrogen than of temperature, Turunen et al. (2004) derived recent (0–150 years) and long-term (2,000–10,000 years) apparent carbon accumulation rates for several ombrotrophic peatlands in eastern Canada with the help of ^{210}Pb- and ^{14}C-dating of soil-core materials. This work revealed the average long-term apparent rate of C accumulation at 15 sites was 19 ± 8 g C m^{-2} yr^{-1}, comparable to long-term rates observed in Finnish bogs by Tolonen and Turunen (1996) and Turunen et al. (2002). Recent C accumulation rates at 23 sites, however, were much

higher, averaging 73 ± 17 g C m^{-2} yr^{-1} These results, the scientists write, are "similar to results from Finland (Tolonen and Turunen, 1996; Pitkanen et al., 1999) and for boreal Sphagnum dominated peat deposits in North America (Tolonen et al., 1988; Wieder et al., 1994; Turetsky et al., 2000)." Noting recent rates of C accumulation are "strikingly higher" than long-term rates, Turunen et al. suggest increased N deposition "leads to larger rates of C and N accumulation in the bogs, as has been found in European forests (Kauppi et al., 1992; Berg and Matzner, 1997), and could account for some of the missing C sink in the global C budget."

Payette et al. (2004) quantified the main patterns of change in a subarctic peatland on the eastern coast of Canada's Hudson Bay, which were caused by permafrost decay between 1957 and 2003, based on detailed surveys conducted in 1973, 1983, 1993, and 2003. They found there was continuous permafrost thawing throughout the period of observation, so "about 18 percent of the initial frozen peatland surface was melted in 1957," and thereafter "accelerated thawing occurred with only 38 percent, 28 percent and 13 percent of the original frozen surface still remaining in 1983, 1993 and 2003, respectively." This process, in their words, was one of "terrestrialization" via the establishment of fen/bog vegetation, which nearly always results in either no net loss of carbon or actual carbon sequestration. Thus Payette et al. conclude, "contrary to current expectations, the melting of permafrost caused by recent climate change does not transform the peatland to a carbon-source ecosystem." Instead, they write, "rapid terrestrialization exacerbates carbon-sink conditions and tends to balance the local carbon budget."

In a study of experimental warming of Icelandic plant communities designed to see whether the warming of high-latitude tundra ecosystems would result in significant losses of species and reduced biodiversity, Jonsdottir et al. (2005) conducted a field experiment to learn how vegetation might respond to moderate warming at the low end of what is predicted by most climate models for a doubling of the air's CO$_2$ content. They studied the effects of three to five years of modest surface warming (1°–2°C) on two widespread but contrasting tundra plant communities; one was a nutrient-deficient and species-poor moss heath, the other a species-rich dwarf shrub heath. At the end of the study, no changes in community structure were detected in the moss heath. In the dwarf shrub heath, the number of deciduous and evergreen dwarf shrubs increased more than 50%, bryophytes decreased by 18%, and canopy height increased by 100%, but the researchers report they "detected no changes in species richness or other diversity measures in either community and the abundance of lichens did not change." Although Jonsdottir et al.'s study was a relatively short-term experiment as far as ecosystem studies go, its results indicate a rise in temperature need not diminish the species diversity of high-latitude tundra ecosystems and may have a positive influence on plant growth.

In a study with an entirely new element of complexity, Cole et al. (2002) constructed 48 small microcosms from soil and litter they collected near the summit of Great Dun Fell, Cumbria, England. Subsequent to "defaunating" this material by reducing its temperature to –80°C for 24 hours, they thawed and inoculated it with native soil microbes. Half of the microcosms were incubated in the dark at 12°C and half at 18°C for two weeks, to establish near-identical communities of the soils' natural complement of microflora in each microcosm. The first temperature was chosen to represent mean August soil temperature at a depth of 10 cm at the site of soil collection, and the latter was picked to be "close to model predictions for soil warming that might result from a doubling of CO_2 in blanket peat environments."

Next, ten seedlings of *Festuca ovina*, an indigenous grass of blanket peat, were planted in each of the microcosms, and 100 enchytraeid worms were added to each of half of the mini-ecosystems, producing four experimental treatments: ambient temperature, ambient temperature plus enchytraeid worms, elevated temperature, and elevated temperature plus enchytraeid worms. Then, the 48 microcosms—sufficient to destructively harvest three replicates of each treatment four times throughout the course of the 64-day experiment—were arranged in a fully randomized design and maintained at either 12° or 18°C with alternating 12-hour light and dark periods, given distilled water every two days to maintain their original weights.

The researchers report finding elevated temperature reduced the ability of the enchytraeid worms to enhance the loss of carbon from the microcosms. At the normal ambient temperature, the presence of the worms enhanced dissolved organic carbon (DOC) loss by 16 percent, while at the elevated temperature expected for a doubling of the air's CO_2 content they had no effect on DOC. In addition, Cole et al. note, "warming may cause drying at the soil surface, forcing enchytraeids to burrow to deeper subsurface horizons," and since the worms are

known to have little influence on soil carbon dynamics below a depth of about 4 cm (Cole et al., 2000), the researchers conclude this additional consequence of warming will further reduce the ability of enchytraeids to enhance carbon loss from blanket peatlands. In summing up their findings, Cole et al. conclude "the soil biotic response to warming in this study was negative," because it resulted in a reduced loss of carbon to the atmosphere.

As to the effects of elevated CO_2 itself on the loss of DOC from soils, Freeman et al. (2004) note riverine transport of DOC has increased markedly in many places throughout the world over the past few decades (Schindler et al., 1997; Freeman et al., 2001; Worrall et al., 2003), and they suggest this phenomenon may be related to the historical increase in the air's CO_2 content.

The researchers' first piece of evidence for this conclusion came from a three-year study of monoliths (11cm diameter x 20cm deep cores) taken from three Welsh peatlands—a bog that received nutrients solely from rainfall, a fen that gained more nutrients from surrounding soils and groundwater, and a riparian peatland that gained even more nutrients from nutrient-laden water transported from other terrestrial ecosystems via drainage streams—which they exposed to either ambient air or air enriched with an extra 235 ppm of CO_2 in a solardome facility. This study revealed the DOC released by monoliths from the three peatlands was significantly enhanced—by 14% in the bog, 49% in the fen, and 61% in the riparian peatland—by the additional CO_2 to which they were exposed. That is the order of response expected from what is known about the stimulation of net primary productivity due to atmospheric CO_2 enrichment—it is low in the face of low soil nutrients, intermediate when soil nutrient concentrations are intermediate, and high when soil nutrients are present in abundance. Consequently, Freeman et al. conclude the DOC increases they observed "were induced by increased primary production and DOC exudation from plants."

To further test their hypothesis, they followed the translocation of labeled ^{13}C through the plant-soil systems of the different peat monoliths for about two weeks after exposing them to ~99 percent-pure [13]CO_2 for five hours. This exercise revealed the plants in the ambient-air and CO_2-enriched treatments assimilated 22.9 and 35.8 mg of ^{13}C from the air, respectively; the amount of DOC recovered from the leachate of the CO_2-enriched monoliths was 0.6% of that assimilated, or 0.215 mg (35.8 mg x 0.006 = 0.215 mg); and the proportion of DOC in the soil solution of the CO_2-

enriched monoliths derived from recently assimilated CO_2 (the ^{13}C labeled CO_2) was 10 times higher than the control.

This latter observation suggests the amount of DOC recovered from the leachate of the ambient-air monoliths was only about a tenth as much as that recovered from the leachate of the CO_2-enriched monoliths, which puts the former amount at about 0.022 mg. Hence, what really counts—the net sequestration of ^{13}C experienced by the peat monoliths over the two-week period (which equals the amount that went into them minus the amount that went out), comes to 22.9 mg minus 0.022 mg = 22.878 mg for the ambient-air monoliths and 35.8 mg minus 0.215 mg = 35.585 mg for the CO_2-enriched monoliths. In the end, therefore, even though the CO_2-enriched monoliths lost 10 times more ^{13}C via root exudation than did the ambient-air monoliths, they still sequestered about 55% more ^{13}C overall, primarily in living-plant tissues.

Cai and Yu (2011) employed multiproxy data derived from a sediment core they extracted from Tannersville Bog near the edge of the Pocono Mountains in Monroe County, Pennsylvania (USA) to document the bog's historical peat accumulation pattern and rate, as well as climate variations experienced by this "temperate tree-covered poor fen" located at "the extreme warm end of climate space for northern peatlands."

The two authors report, "carbon accumulation rates increased from 13.4 to 101.2 g C/m^2/year during the last 8,000 years," with a long-term average value of 27.3 g C/m^2/year. This mean rate significantly exceeds the 18.6 g C/m^2/year obtained for boreal, subarctic, and arctic peatlands based on measurements made at 33 sites in the Northern Hemisphere (Yu *et al.*, 2009). This fact led the authors to conclude their relatively high accumulation rate "was likely caused by high primary production associated with a warmer and wetter temperate climate." Cai and Yu say their study implies "northern peatlands can continue to serve as carbon sinks under a warmer and wetter climate, providing a negative feedback to climate warming."

Beilman *et al.* (2009) undertook further illumination of the relationship between climate and carbon accumulation in peatlands. They used "a network of cores from 77 peatland sites to determine controls on peat carbon content and peat carbon accumulation over the last 2000 years across Russia's West Siberian Lowland," the world's largest wetland region. They found carbon accumulation over the past two millennia varied significantly with mean annual air temperature, growing ever-greater as air temperature rose from -9 to 0°C, with maximum carbon accumulation occurring between -1 and 0°C, which is "where air-soil temperature differences optimize net primary production relative to soil respiration, e.g., near 0°C (Swanson *et al.*, 2000)." On average, the researchers report "cores from non-permafrost sites have accumulated four times more peat by depth and twice as much carbon than cores from permafrost sites."

In light of these findings, Beilman *et al.* write, the "relationship between temperature and peat carbon sequestration, and the current spatial distribution of peatland ecosystems, should be an important consideration in future attempts to anticipate the impact of climate warming on the carbon sink potential of the West Siberian Lowland region." With respect to that impact, they opine, "permafrost thaw may promote a boost in peat carbon sequestration in affected sites," and, therefore, "future warming could result in a shift northward in long-term West Siberian Lowland carbon sequestration."

Bao *et al.* (2010) also counter the claim peatland ecosystems will release great quantities of previously sequestered carbon to the atmosphere in the form of CO_2 and methane as temperatures warm. Working in the Changbai mountain region that runs along the boundary between China and North Korea, this group of researchers extracted eight peat cores, which they analyzed for numerous parameters, including those required to calculate the recent rate of carbon accumulation (RERCA) in the peatlands of that region over the past two centuries.

The four researchers report "obvious increasing trends in RERCA were observed in all peat cores," as "organic carbon content declined from the top to the substrate." In addition, they state the temporal increase in RERCA in the upper regions of the cores—which likely corresponded to the warmest segment of their two-century study period—"changed to a much greater extent in recent decades than in the earlier period of peat formation."

Flanagan and Syed (2011) write, "northern peatland ecosystems are consistent net carbon (C) sinks that account for between one-quarter to one-third of the global soil carbon pool (Gorham, 1991; Turunen *et al.*, 2002)," noting their sequestration of carbon "results from moderate rates of ecosystem photosynthesis that exceed decomposition and autotrophic plant respiration (Gorham, 1991)." The scientists set out to conduct a long-term experiment to explore IPCC's contention that "exposure to warmer temperatures and drier conditions associated with climate change will shift the balance between ecosystem photosynthesis and respiration providing a positive feedback to atmospheric CO_2 concentration." They used the eddy covariance technique "to determine the sensitivity of ecosystem photosynthesis, respiration and net CO_2 exchange to variations in temperature and water table depth associated with inter-annual shifts in weather over a six-year period."

Their work was conducted in "a moderately rich treed fen"—which they described as "the most abundant peatland type in western Canada"—at a peatland flux station northeast of Athabasca, Alberta, which was established in 2003 as part of the Fluxnet-Canada Research Network (Margolis *et al.*, 2006), and which during 2007–2009 was part of the follow-on Canadian Carbon Program. The researchers report, "contrary to previous predictions, both ecosystem photosynthesis and respiration showed similar increases in response to warmer and drier conditions," such that "the ecosystem remained a strong net sink for CO_2 with an average net ecosystem production of 189 ± 47 gC/m^2/year." These "current net CO_2 uptake rates were much higher than carbon accumulation in peat determined from analyses of the relationship between peat age and cumulative carbon stock." Flanagan and Syed conclude, "in the absence of fire or other major disturbance, significant net carbon sequestration could continue for decades at this site and help to reduce the positive feedback of climate change on increasing atmospheric CO_2 concentration."

Also working in Canada, Turetsky *et al.* (2007) explored "the influence of differing permafrost regimes (bogs with no surface permafrost, localized permafrost features with surface permafrost, and internal lawns representing areas of permafrost degradation) on rates of peat accumulation at the southernmost limit of permafrost in continental Canada." The five American researchers say the work revealed "surface permafrost inhibits peat accumulation and that degradation of surface permafrost stimulates net carbon storage in peatlands." In fact, they report, "unfrozen bogs and internal lawns had net organic matter accumulation rates two-times faster than rates of accumulation in localized permafrost features over the most recent 25-year horizon."

Turetsky *et al.* say their data suggest "permafrost degradation within peatland environments, likely triggered by climate change, could serve as a negative feedback to net radiative forcing via enhanced carbon accumulation as peat." They note, however, "increased methane emissions to the atmosphere will partially or even completely offset this enhanced peatland carbon sink for at least 70 years following permafrost degradation." Nevertheless, they write, because "internal lawns succeed relatively quickly (within 70 years) to more bog-like conditions and [since] bogs in continental Canada are associated with low methane emissions, the degradation of localized permafrost in peatlands is likely over the long-term to serve as a negative feedback to radiative forcing."

Daimaru *et al.* (2002) dug 27 soil pits at various locations in and around the central location of a snowpatch grassland on the southeastern slope of Japan's Mt. Zarumori (~39.8°N, 140.8°E), examining the peat content of the soil and determining its age based on ^{14}C dating and tephrochronology. They report "peaty topsoils were recognized at seven soil pits in the dense grassland" where the snow melts earlier in the season and the period for plant growth is the longest. In contrast, soils located in areas where the snowmelt occurs later in the season "lacked peaty topsoil." Beneath these carbon-poor topsoils, Daimaru *et al.* found a carbon-rich layer they were able to date back to the Medieval Warm Period, suggesting the buried peat layers in the poor vegetation area accumulated in consequence of the warmer temperatures of that period. Consequently, as has been found in each of the other peatland studies referenced above, real-world observations show IPCC-based predictions—in terms of the influence of Earth's peatlands on the planet's temperature—do not match observational data. In stark contrast, these land types provide a negative feedback to global warming: When peatlands warm, they extract more, not less, CO_2 from the atmosphere, effectively applying a brake on rising temperatures, as opposed to pushing the planet past a tipping point toward a state of catastrophic runaway global warming.

At least one model-based study has reached the same conclusion. Noting "throughout the Holocene, northern peatlands have both accumulated carbon and emitted methane," so "their impact on climate radiative forcing has been the net of cooling (persistent CO_2 uptake) and warming (persistent CH_4 emission)," Frolking and Roulet (2007) developed Holocene peatland carbon flux trajectories based on estimates of contemporary CH_4 flux, total accumulated peat C, and peatland initiation dates, which they used as inputs to a simple atmospheric perturbation model to calculate the net radiative impetus for surface air temperature change. The two researchers determined the impact on the current atmosphere of northern peatland development and carbon cycling through the Holocene is a net deficit of 40–80 Pg CO_2-C (~20–40 ppm of atmospheric CO_2) and a net excess of ~200–400 Tg CH_4 (~75–150 ppb of atmospheric CH_4).

Frolking and Roulet note early in the Holocene the capture of CO_2 and emission of CH_4 by Earth's northern peatlands is likely to have produced a net warming impetus of up to +0.1 W m⁻². Over the following 8,000 to 11,000 years, however, they say Earth's peatlands have been doing just the opposite, and the current radiative forcing due to these atmospheric CO_2 and CH_4 perturbations represents a net cooling force on the order of -0.22 to -0.56 W m⁻², further establishing that the impetus for global cooling due to carbon sequestration by Earth's peatlands historically has been—and currently is—significantly greater than the global warming potential produced by their emissions of methane.

Finally, in an experimental as opposed to historical study, Fenner *et al.* (2007) collected intact peat monoliths—comprised predominantly of *Sphagnum* (*S. subnitens* Russ. and Warnst.) and *Festuca ovina* L., with small amounts of *Juncus effusus* L. and *Polytrichum commune* Hedw.—in perfusion systems that allowed for fine control of the water table and lateral water movements, which they maintained for approximately three years in solardomes with atmospheric CO_2 concentrations of ambient or ambient plus 235 ppm, while daily supplying the mini-ecosystems with synthetic rainwater comparable in volume and nutrient content to that received at the site from which the monoliths were extracted.

At the end of their three-year experiment, the seven UK researchers write, "species composition showed a shift from a *Sphagnum*-dominated community to one in which vascular monocotyledonous species dominated," as *S. subnitens* cover declined by 39% under elevated CO_2, whereas *J. effusus* cover increased from less than 1% in the control perfusion systems to 40% in the systems exposed to elevated CO_2. Also, "aboveground plant biomass showed a substantial increase under elevated CO_2 (115%, $P < 0.01$) as did belowground biomass (96%, $P < 0.01$)." In addition, they report "*J. effusus* roots were observed to be particularly thick, deep, and extensive under elevated CO_2."

The research summarized above suggests as the air's CO_2 content rises, the carbon content of the planet's peatlands most likely also will continue to rise, and dramatically so, notwithstanding model-based projections to the contrary.

References

Bao, K., Yu, X., Jia, L., and Wang, G. 2010. Recent carbon accumulation in Changbai Mountain peatlands, northeast China. *Mountain Research and Development* **30**: 33–41.

Beilman, D.W., MacDonald, G.M., Smith, L.C., and Reimer, P.J. 2009. Carbon accumulation in peatlands of West Siberia over the last 2000 years. *Global Biogeochemical Cycles* **23**: 10.1029/2007GB003112.

Berg, B. and Matzner, E. 1997. Effect of N deposition on decomposition of plant litter and soil organic matter in forest systems. *Environmental Reviews* **5**: 1–25.

Cai, S. and Yu, Z. 2011. Response of a warm temperate peatland to Holocene climate change in northeastern Pennsylvania. *Quaternary Research* **75**: 531–540.

Camill, P. 1999a. Patterns of boreal permafrost peatland vegetation across environmental gradients sensitive to climate warming. *Canadian Journal of Botany* **77**: 721–733.

Camill, P. 1999b. Peat accumulation and succession following permafrost thaw in the boreal peatlands of Manitoba, Canada. *Ecoscience* **6**: 592–602.

Camill, P., Lynch, J.A., Clark, J.S., Adams, J.B., and Jordan, B. 2001. Changes in biomass, aboveground net primary production, and peat accumulation following permafrost thaw in the boreal peatlands of Manitoba, Canada. *Ecosystems* **4**: 461–478.

Cole, L., Bardgett, R.D., and Ineson, P. 2000. Enchytraeid worms (Oligochaeta) enhance mineralization of carbon in organic upland soils. *European Journal of Soil Science* **51**: 185–192.

Cole, L., Bardgett, R.D., Ineson, P., and Hobbs, P.J. 2002. Enchytraeid worm (Oligochaeta) influences on microbial community structure, nutrient dynamics and plant growth in blanket peat subjected to warming. *Soil Biology & Biochemistry* **34**: 83–92.

Daimaru, H., Ohtani, Y., Ikeda, S., Okamoto, T., and Kajimoto, T. 2002. Paleoclimatic implication of buried peat layers in a subalpine snowpatch grassland on Mt. Zarumori, northern Japan. *Catena* **48**: 53–65.

Fenner, N., Ostle, N.J., McNamara, N., Sparks, T., Harmens, H., Reynolds, B., and Freeman, C. 2007. Elevated CO_2 effects on peatland plant community carbon dynamics and DOC production. *Ecosystems* **10**: 635–647.

Flanagan, L.B. and Syed, K.H. 2011. Stimulation of both photosynthesis and respiration in response to warmer and drier conditions in a boreal peatland ecosystem. *Global Change Biology* **17**: 2271–2287.

Freeman, C., Evans, C.D., Monteith, D.T., Reynolds, B., and Fenner, N. 2002. Export of organic carbon from peat soils. *Nature* **412**: 785.

Freeman, C., Fenner, N., Ostle, N.J., Kang, H., Dowrick, D.J., Reynolds, B., Lock, M.A., Sleep, D., Hughes, S., and Hudson, J. 2004. Export of dissolved organic carbon from peatlands under elevated carbon dioxide levels. *Nature* **430**: 195–198.

Frolking, S. and Roulet, N.T. 2007. Holocene radiative forcing impact of northern peatland carbon accumulation and methane emissions. *Global Change Biology* **13**: 1079–1088.

Gorham, E. 1991. Northern peatlands: role in the carbon cycle and probable responses to climatic warming. *Ecological Applications* **1**: 185–192.

Griffis, T.J. and Rouse, W.R. 2001. Modelling the interannual variability of net ecosystem CO_2 exchange at a subarctic sedge fen. *Global Change Biology* **7**: 511–530.

Jonsdottir, I.S., Magnusson, B., Gudmundsson, J., Elmarsdottir, A., and Hjartarson, H. 2005. Variable sensitivity of plant communities in Iceland to experimental warming. *Global Change Biology* **11**: 553–563.

Kauppi, P.E., Mielikainen, K., and Kuusela, K. 1992. Biomass and carbon budget of European forests. *Science* **256**: 70–74.

Margolis, H.A., Flanagan, L.B., and Amiro, B.D. 2006. The Fluxnet-Canada research network: influence of climate and disturbance on carbon cycling in forests and peatlands. *Agricultural and Forest Meteorology* **140**: 1–5.

Mauquoy, D., Engelkes, T., Groot, M.H.M., Markesteijn, F., Oudejans, M.G., van der Plicht, J., and van Geel, B. 2002. High-resolution records of late-Holocene climate change and carbon accumulation in two north-west European ombrotrophic peat bogs. *Palaeogeography, Palaeoclimatology, Palaeoecology* **186**: 275–310.

Oechel, W.C., Vourlitis, G.L., Hastings, S.J., Zulueta, R.C., Hinzman, L., and Kane, D. 2000. Acclimation of ecosystem CO_2 exchange in the Alaskan Arctic in response to decadal climate warming. *Nature* **406**: 978–981.

Payette, S., Delwaide, A., Caccianiga, M., and Beauchemin, M. 2004. Accelerated thawing of subarctic peatland permafrost over the last 50 years. *Geophysical Research Letters* **31**: 10.1029/2004GL020358.

Pitkanen, A., Turunen, J., and Tolonen, K. 1999. The role of fire in the carbon dynamics of a mire, Eastern Finland. *The Holocene* **9**: 453–462.

Robinson, S.D. and Moore, T.R. 2000. The influence of permafrost and fire upon carbon accumulation in high boreal peatlands, Northwest Territories, Canada. *Arctic, Antarctic and Alpine Research* **32**: 155–166.

Schindler, D.W., Curtis, P.J., Bayley, S.E., Parker, B.R., Beaty, K.G., and Stainton, M.P. 1997. Climate-induced changes in the dissolved organic carbon budgets of boreal lakes. *Biogeochemistry* **36**: 9–28.

Swanson, D.K., Lacelle, B., and Tarnocai, C. 2000. Temperature and the boreal-subarctic maximum in soil organic carbon. *Geog. Phys. Quat.* **54**: 157–167.

Tolonen, K., Davis, R.B., and Widoff, L. 1988. Peat accumulation rates in selected Maine peat deposits. *Maine Geological Survey, Department of Conservation Bulletin* **33**: 1–99.

Tolonen, K. and Turunen, J. 1996. Accumulation rates of carbon in mires in Finland and implications for climate change. *The Holocene* **6**: 171–178.

Turetsky, M.R., Wieder, R.K., Vitt, D.H., Evans, R.J., and Scott, K.D. 2007. The disappearance of relict permafrost in boreal North America: Effects on peatland carbon storage and fluxes. *Global Change Biology* **13**: 1922–1934.

Turetsky, M.R., Wieder, R.K., Williams, C.J., and Vitt, D.H. 2000. Organic matter accumulation, peat chemistry, and permafrost melting in peatlands of boreal Alberta. *Ecoscience* **7**: 379–392.

Turunen, J., Roulet, N.T., Moore, T.R., and Richard, P.J.H. 2004. Nitrogen deposition and increased carbon accumulation in ombrotrophic peatlands in eastern Canada. *Global Biogeochemical Cycles* **18**: 10.1029/2003 GB002154.

Turunen, J., Tomppo, E., Tolonen, K., and Reinikainen, A. 2002. Estimating carbon accumulation rates of undrained mires in Finland: Application to boreal and subarctic regions. *The Holocene* **12**: 69–80.

Wieder, R.K., Novak, M., Schell, W.R., and Rhodes, T. 1994. Rates of peat accumulation over the past 200 years in five Sphagnum-dominated peatlands in the United States. *Journal of Paleolimnology* **12**: 35–47.

Worrall, F., Burt, T., and Shedden, R. 2003. Long term records of riverine dissolved organic matter. *Biogeochemistry* **64**: 165–178.

Yu, Z.C., Beilman, D.W., and Jones, M.C. 2009. Sensitivity of northern peatland carbon dynamics to Holocene climate change. In: Baird, A.J., Belyea, L.R., Comax, X., Reeve, A., and Slater, I. (Eds.) *Carbon Cycling in Northern Peatlands.* American Geophysical Union, Washington, DC, USA, pp. 55–69.

1.2.4 Wetlands

- Rising atmospheric CO_2 likely will enhance the productivity and carbon sequestering ability of wetlands. In addition, elevated CO_2 may assist some coastal wetlands in counterbalancing the negative impacts of rising seas.

The early works of Jacob *et al.* (1995) and Drake *et*

al. (1996a) were among the first to demonstrate atmospheric CO$_2$ enrichment enhances vegetative productivity in wetland ecosystems. Drake *et al.* (1996b) also showed elevated levels of atmospheric CO$_2$ reduce insect and fungal damage to wetland plants (Drake *et al.*, 1996b). Since that time, many other studies have reinforced these initial findings and revealed still other positive wetland impacts of the ongoing rise in the air's CO$_2$ content.

Rasse *et al.* (2003) developed a model for calculating net ecosystem exchange (NEE) of CO$_2$ between C$_3$ wetland sedge (*Scirpus olneyi* Gray) communities and the atmosphere, based on published ecophysiological data and measurements of various photosynthetic parameters made at the Chesapeake Bay CO$_2$-enrichment study described by Curtis *et al.* (1989a,b). This model indicated the *S. olneyi* community responded favorably to a near-doubled atmospheric CO$_2$ concentration by increasing its NEE by 35–40%, which Rasse *et al.* compare to the mean net photosynthetic increase of 60% reported by Norby *et al.* (1999) in an extensive review that included several tree species and ecosystems. Rasse *et al.* write, "because *Scirpus*-dominated ecosystems are extremely productive (Drake and Leadley, 1991), a 35–40% productivity increase might represent a larger additional amount of carbon fixed as compared to a 60% increase in less productive forest ecosystems." In addition, because there are about six million square kilometers of wetlands worldwide, with approximately 15% of that area located in temperate regions (Mitsch *et al.*, 1994), Rasse *et al.* conclude "temperate C$_3$ wetlands have a huge potential for increased plant productivity [and, therefore, carbon sequestration] during the 21st century."

Dakora and Drake (2000) exposed plant communities of *Scirpus olneyi* and the C$_4$ grass *Spartina patens* to atmospheric CO$_2$ concentrations of 360 and 660 ppm in open-top chambers to study the effects of elevated CO$_2$ on nitrogenase activity and nitrogen fixation in these plants and in the non-symbiotic nitrogen-fixing microbes that inhabit the sediments in which the plants grow. They report the extra CO$_2$ increased nitrogenase activity by 35 and 13% in *S. olneyi* and *S. patens*, respectively, and these stimulations led to increases in nitrogen incorporation of 73 and 23%, respectively, in the same plants. These responses, they add, are "in rough proportion to the relative effect of elevated CO$_2$ on canopy photosynthesis measured throughout the day." They also report the elevated CO$_2$ significantly stimulated nitrogenase activity in the non-symbiotic nitrogen-

fixing microbes living in the soil sediments, suggesting increases in the air's CO$_2$ content produce "an increase in the N$_2$-fixing activity of free-living [microbes] in the marsh ecosystem."

Hussein *et al.* (2004) measured carbon sequestration along two transects across submerging coastal landscapes (Hell Hook and Cedar Creek) of the Chesapeake Bay in Dorchester County, Maryland, USA, and used this data to develop a model of carbon sequestration by coastal marshes. They found "coastal marsh soils are accreting vertically and migrating laterally over the [adjacent] low-lying forest soils to keep pace with sea-level rise," and during the past 150 years, the rate of carbon sequestration by the marsh soils averaged 83.5 ± 23 g m^{-2} yr^{-1}, whereas prior to that period it had averaged 29.2 ± 5.35 g m^{-2} yr^{-1}.

These sequestration rates are much greater than those of either local forest or agricultural soils. In addition, the three scientists report, "carbon sequestration in mineral soils of agro- and upland-forest ecosystems is generally of limited capacity and tends to reach steady-state condition within relatively short time," but "in coastal marsh soils, carbon sequestration will continue to occur with time by accumulation in the organic horizons, and with increasing storage capacity." Based on a model they developed from their data, for example, Hussein *et al.* project sea-level rise will cause carbon sequestration by coastal marsh ecosystems over the next 100 years to average 400 ± 162 g m^{-2} yr^{-1}. Thus they conclude, "coastal marsh ecosystems tend to sequester carbon continuously with increasing storage capacity as marsh age progresses," and "carbon sequestration in coastal marsh ecosystems under positive accretionary balance acts as a negative feedback mechanism to global warming."

Returning to the Chesapeake Bay wetland study at the 17-year point of its progression, Rasse *et al.* (2005) evaluated the long-term effects of atmospheric CO$_2$ enrichment on the net CO2 exchange, shoot density, and shoot biomass of the wetland sedge, *Scirpus olneyi*, as well as how these effects have been influenced by salinity, one of the main environmental stressors of the wetland. In every year of the past 17 years, they found the net CO$_2$ exchange rate and shoot biomass and density of the plants growing in the CO$_2$-enriched (ambient +340 ppm) air were greater than those of the plants growing in ambient air. The extra CO$_2$ also boosted the net CO$_2$ exchange rate by 80% in the first year of the study, but the enhancement declined to about 35% by the end of the third year and remained relatively constant at that value over the following 15 years. Shoot biomass and density also increased, but whereas the CO_2-induced stimulation of the net CO_2 exchange rate remained essentially constant over the last 15 years, the CO_2-induced stimulations of shoot biomass and density increased over time. After five years of a nearly constant stimulation of 16%, for example, shoot density increased in near linear fashion to a value 128% above the ambient-air value at the end of year 17. The response of shoot biomass to CO_2 enrichment was also nearly linear, reaching a value approximately 70% above ambient at year 17. In addition, the trends in shoot density and biomass do not appear to be leveling off, leading one to wonder just how high the CO_2-induced stimulations ultimately will rise.

Salinity was closely correlated with net CO_2 exchange, shoot density, and shoot biomass, such that the higher the salinity, the more detrimental were its effects on these variables. Nevertheless, even at the highest levels of salinity reported, atmospheric CO_2 enrichment was able to produce a positive, albeit reduced, stimulatory effect on net CO_2 exchange. For shoot biomass and density, the responses were better still. Not only did atmospheric CO_2 enrichment essentially eradicate the detrimental effects of salinity, there was, in the words of Rasse *et al.*, "circumstantial evidence suggesting that salinity stress increased the stimulation of shoot density by elevated atmospheric CO_2 concentration."

This experiment demonstrates several important things. First, as the researchers state, their results "leave no doubt as to the sustained response of the salt marsh sedge to elevated atmospheric CO_2 concentration." Second, given that the initial responses of the three growth variables declined or remained low during the first few years of the study, but leveled out or increased thereafter, it is clear much more long-term research needs to be carried out if we are to ascertain the full and correct impacts of atmospheric CO_2 enrichment on plants. In the case of the wetland sedge of this study, for example, it took about ten growing seasons before an increasing trend in the shoot density could be recognized. Finally, there is the researchers' "most important finding"—"that a species response to elevated atmospheric CO_2 concentration can continually increase when [it] is under stress and declining in its natural environment."

Erickson *et al.* (2007) present data "on 18 years of measurement of above and belowground biomass, tissue N concentration and total standing crop of N for a *Scirpus olneyi*-dominated (C_3 sedge) community, a *Spartina patens*-dominated (C_4 grass) community and a C_3-C_4-mixed species community exposed to ambient and elevated (ambient + 340 ppm) atmospheric CO_2 concentration [via open-top chamber technology] in natural salinity and sea level conditions of a Chesapeake Bay wetland." This report shows "elevated atmospheric CO_2 enhancement of C_3 biomass was sustained through time in the *S. olneyi*-dominated community, averaging about 40% for shoots and 26% for roots, whereas elevated CO_2 had no significant overall effect on biomass production in the C_4 grass community." In addition, the authors state, "the greatest amount of carbon was added to the *S. olneyi*-dominated community during years when shoot N concentration was reduced the most, suggesting that the availability of N was not the most or even the main limitation to elevated CO_2 stimulation of carbon accumulation in this ecosystem." These findings, the four researchers conclude, "demonstrate that elevated CO_2 effects on biomass production can be sustained through time," even when N availability is at the lowest of levels typically encountered in the wetland. They note similar CO_2-induced "sustained enhancement of growth has been found in a scrub oak ecosystem (Dijkstra *et al.*, 2002; Hymus *et al.*, 2002), a tallgrass prairie (Owensby *et al.*, 1999) and several forested ecosystems (Norby *et al.*, 2005), indicating that increased productivity of many ecosystems will follow global increases in atmospheric CO_2 concentration."

Working with *Phragmites australis*—a wetland plant found in every U.S. state and numerous other places around the world—in a study with very different implications, Scholefield *et al.* (2004) measured isoprene emissions from plants growing at different distances from a natural CO_2 spring located in central Italy, where atmospheric CO_2 concentrations of approximately 350, 400, 550, and 800 ppm likely had prevailed for the entire lifetimes of the plants. They found as long-term atmospheric CO_2 concentrations rose, plant isoprene emissions dropped: Over the first 50 ppm increase in the air's CO_2 concentration, they were reduced to approximately 65% of what they were at ambient CO_2, and for CO_2 increases of 200 and 450 ppm, they were respectively reduced to only about 30% and 7% of what they were in ambient-CO_2 air, as best we can determine from the bar graph of the authors' data.

These CO_2-induced reductions in plant isoprene emissions are significant because isoprene, a highly reactive non-methane hydrocarbon (NMHC) emitted by vegetation in copious quantities at current atmospheric CO_2 concentrations, is responsible for the production of vast amounts of plant- and animal-harming ozone (Chameides *et al.*, 1988; Harley *et al.*,

1999). Poisson *et al.* (2000), for example, calculated current concentrations of NMHC emissions (the vast majority of which are isoprene) increase surface ozone concentrations by 50–60% over land and by as much as 40% over the world's oceans. In addition, biogenic NMHCs (with isoprene being the most important) play a major role in the global tropospheric chemistry of methane, one of the atmosphere's most powerful greenhouse gases, boosting methane's atmospheric lifetime by approximately 14% above what it would be without isoprene (Poisson *et al.*, 2000). This being the case, if other plants behave similarly—and much evidence suggests they do (Monson and Fall, 1989; Loreto and Sharkey, 1990; Sharkey *et al.*, 1991; Loreto *et al.*, 2001; Rosenstiel *et al.*, 2003)—the ongoing rise in the air's CO$_2$ content can be expected to enhance plant productivity, mitigate the deleterious consequences of one of Earth's worst air pollutants (ozone), and reduce the atmospheric lifetime of one of the planet's most powerful greenhouse gases (methane).

As background for their work, Langley *et al.* (2009) note "tidal wetlands experiencing increased rates of sea-level rise (SLR) must increase rates of soil elevation gain to avoid permanent conversion to open water." As for how that might happen, they note "root zone expansion by accumulation of plant material is essential to maintaining a constant surface elevation relative to rising sea level." Against this backdrop, in Kirkpatrick Marsh—a microtidal sub-estuary of Chesapeake Bay, where each of several 200-m^2 plots was outfitted with a surface elevation table (SET) to measure soil elevation change—Langley *et al.* exposed half of the plots to an extra 340 ppm of CO$_2$ for two years. Data "from a greenhouse mesocosm experiment (Cherry *et al.*, 2009) were used to examine how elevated CO$_2$ might affect elevation response under simulated SLR scenarios."

The five researchers report the extra CO$_2$ of their marsh experiment increased fine root productivity by an average of 36% over the two-year study, and aboveground biomass production was increased by as much as 30%, "consistent with a 20-year record of elevated CO$_2$ treatment in a previous CO$_2$ study on the same marsh (Erickson *et al.*, 2007)." In addition, they say the elevated CO$_2$ caused an increase in root zone thickness of 4.9 mm/year compared with only 0.7 mm/year in the ambient CO$_2$ treatment, so there was "a slight loss of elevation in ambient CO$_2$ (-0.9 mm/year) compared with an elevation gain (3.0 mm/year) in the elevated CO$_2$ treatment." Furthermore, they report the greenhouse mesocosm

experiment of Cherry *et al.* (2009) "revealed that the CO$_2$ effect was enhanced under salinity and flooding conditions likely to accompany future SLR."

Langley *et al.* conclude, "by stimulating biogenic contributions to marsh elevation, increases in the greenhouse gas, CO$_2$, may paradoxically aid some coastal wetlands in counterbalancing rising seas." They say their findings "bear particular importance given the threat of accelerating SLR to coastal wetlands worldwide," citing the recent EPA report of Reed *et al.* (2008) which suggests "a 2-mm increase in the rate of SLR will threaten or eliminate a large portion of mid-Atlantic marshes." Once again, however, the proven and positive growth-promoting effect of atmospheric CO$_2$ enrichment more than compensates for its hypothetical and negative global-warming effect.

Kirwan *et al.* (2009) write, "when subjected to future [projected] rates of sea level rise, numerical models and statistical projections predict that marshland worldwide will decline on the order of 10–50% during the next 50–100 years," and "such a decline could represent a catastrophic loss of ecosystem services by one of Earth's most valuable coastal environments." To explore this subject further, Kirwan *et al.* "compiled 56 measurements of aboveground annual productivity for *Spartina alterniflora*, the dominant macrophyte in North American coastal wetlands," along the Gulf Coast and Eastern Seaboard of the United States, as well as the east coast of Canada.

The researchers report, "despite local and temporal variability, a significant (r = 0.83; $P < 0.000001$) latitudinal gradient of 25 g m^{-2}/year per degree of latitude exists across the entire geographic range of the compilation." In addition, "the latitudinal gradient in productivity appears to be driven by temperature," noting "annual productivity most significantly correlates with mean annual temperature and the annual number of growing degree days." Consequently, Kirwan *et al.* estimate the response of *S. alterniflora* productivity to future increases in global temperature, noting their results suggest "an increase in global temperature of 2–4°C by 2100 (IPCC, 2007) would cause productivity to increase by about 50–100 g m^{-2}/year." For mid-Atlantic and northern marshes with current productivities ranging from 450 to 250 g m^{-2}/year, they say the result they obtained "represents approximately a 10–40% increase in annual productivity," which they describe as being of "a magnitude similar to that of marsh lost due to sea level change (10–50%)," as calculated by numerical models for the same time period. They therefore conclude, "increased growth under a warming climate may compensate for the amount of productivity lost by eroding marshland."

The increase in atmospheric CO_2 concentration expected for the current century likely will boost marsh productivity even more, further strengthening this conclusion. In addition, it is widely recognized, as Kirwan *et al.* state, "increased vegetation growth will tend to promote higher marsh accretion rates, stabilize channel expansion, and decrease the ability for waves to erode the marsh platform." As a result, they conclude, "the combined impacts of future global change (e.g. sea level, temperature, CO_2) could actually increase the total productivity of marshland."

Mateos-Naranjo *et al.* (2010) obtained 15 cm-diameter clumps of *S. maritima* from a low-marsh site along the southwest coast of Spain in April 2007, which they transplanted into individual plastic pots filled with pearlite that rested on shallow trays filled with Hoagland's solution of three different salinities (0, 170, or 510 mM NaCl). The research team maintained the plants in controlled environment chambers having atmospheric CO_2 concentrations of either 380 ppm or 700 ppm (an increase of 84%) for periods of 30 days, during which time they measured a number of plant properties and processes. The four researchers report the 84% increase in the atmosphere's CO_2 concentration stimulated the growth of *S. maritima* by about 65% in all three salinity treatments; the graphical representation of the halophyte's water use efficiency indicates this important property of the plant was enhanced by approximately 10%, 100%, and 160% in the 0, 170, and 510 mM salinity treatments, respectively, because "increasing CO_2 concentration has a positive effect on the photochemical apparatus, helping to counteract salt stress experienced by plants at current CO_2 concentrations." The UK and Spanish scientists say their results suggest the productivity of *S. maritima* "might increase in a future scenario of rising atmospheric CO_2 concentration in environments with salinities as high as that of seawater," good news for what they describe as "an important pioneer and ecosystem engineer in salt marshes."

Kathilankal *et al.* (2011) made a series of physiological measurements on smooth cordgrass, which is believed to possess C_4 physiology, at two locations in the Virginia Coast Reserve's Long Term Ecological Research area—Fowling Point Marsh (a lagoon salt marsh) and Oyster Marsh (a mainland fringing marsh)—to investigate how light, temperature, and intercellular CO_2 concentration affected the marsh plant's rate of photosynthesis. They used the functional relationships between these environmental variables and *S. alterniflora's* physiological responses to improve C_4-leaf photosynthesis models ultimately employed to determine the net impact of potential increases in air temperature and atmospheric CO_2 concentration on the productivity of smooth cordgrass in a CO_2-enriched and warmer world.

Instead of acting like a C_4 plant, the modeling studies and field measurements indicate "*S. alterniflora* exhibited physiological traits similar to C_3-C_4 intermediate plants," so one could expect "atmospheric warming in conjunction with an increase in atmospheric CO_2 would enhance photosynthesis in *S. alterniflora*," the six scientists discovered. In further support of this conclusion, they note "McKee and Rooth (2008) reported a significant stimulation in *S. alterniflora* biomass in plants grown under elevated CO_2," and "warming experiments in New England (Charles and Dukes, 2009) demonstrated that *S. alterniflora* increased productivity with increasing temperature," while the plant's optimum temperature for photosynthesis also will "likely increase in response to enriched CO_2 conditions," citing Simon *et al.* (1984).

In the concluding paragraph of their report, Kathilankal *et al.* declare "in a scenario of atmospheric warming and increased atmospheric CO_2 levels, *S. alterniflora* will likely respond positively to both changes," and they suggest these responses "will result in increased *S. alterniflora* productivity," which should be beneficial for western Atlantic intertidal marshes and the many beneficial services that smooth cordgrass provides to those ecosystems.

References

Chameides, W.L., Lindsay, R.W., Richardson, J., and Kiang, C.S. 1988. The role of biogenic hydrocarbons in urban photochemical smog: Atlanta as a case study. *Science* **241**: 1473–1475.

Charles, H. and Dukes, J.S. 2009. Effects of warming and altered precipitation on plant and nutrient dynamics of a New England salt marsh. *Ecological Applications* **19**: 1758–1773.

Cherry, J.A., McKee, K., and Grace, J.B. 2009. Elevated CO_2 enhances biological contributions to elevation change in coastal wetlands by offsetting stressors associated with sea-level rise. *Journal of Ecology* **97**: 67–77.

Curtis, P.S., Drake, B.G., Leadly, P.W., Arp, W.J., and Whigham, D.F. 1989a. Growth and senescence in plant communities exposed to elevated CO_2 concentrations on an estuarine marsh. *Oecologia* **78**: 20–26.

Curtis, P.S., Drake, B.G., and Whigham, D.F. 1989b. Nitrogen and carbon dynamics in C$_3$ and C$_4$ estuarine marsh plants grown under elevated CO$_2$ *in situ*. *Oecologia* **78**: 297–301.

Dakora, F.D. and Drake, B.G. 2000. Elevated CO$_2$ stimulates associative N$_2$ fixation in a C$_3$ plant of the Chesapeake Bay wetland. *Plant, Cell and Environment* **23**: 943–953.

Dijkstra, P., Hymus, G.J., and Colavito, D., *et al.* 2002. Elevated atmospheric CO$_2$ stimulates shoot growth in a Florida scrub oak ecosystem. *Global Change Biology* **8**: 90–103.

Drake, B.G. and Leadley, P.W. 1991. Canopy photosynthesis of crops and native plant communities exposed to long-term elevated CO$_2$. *Plant, Cell and Environment* **14**: 853–860.

Drake, B.G., Muehe, M.S., Peresta, G., Gonzalez-Meler, M.A., and Matamala, R. 1996a. Acclimation of photosynthesis, respiration and ecosystem carbon flux of a wetland on Chesapeake Bay, Maryland to elevated atmospheric CO$_2$ concentration. *Plant and Soil* **187**: 111–118.

Drake, B.G., Peresta, G., Beugeling, E., and Matamala, R. 1996b. Long-term elevated CO$_2$ exposure in a Chesapeake Bay wetland: Ecosystem gas exchange, primary production, and tissue nitrogen. In: Koch, G.W. and Mooney, H.A. (Eds.) *Carbon Dioxide and Terrestrial Ecosystems*. Academic Press, San Diego, CA, pp. 197–213.

Erickson, J.E., Megonigal, J.P., Peresta, G., and Drake, B.G. 2007. Salinity and sea level mediate elevated CO$_2$ effects on C$_3$-C$_4$ plant interactions and tissue nitrogen in a Chesapeake Bay tidal wetland. *Global Change Biology* **13**: 202–215.

Harley, P.C., Monson, R.K., and Lerdau, M.T. 1999. Ecological and evolutionary aspects of isoprene emission from plants. *Oecologia* **118**: 109–123.

Hussein, A.H., Rabenhorst, M.C., and Tucker, M.L. 2004. Modeling of carbon sequestration in coastal marsh soils. *Soil Science Society of America Journal* **68**: 1786–1795.

Hymus, G.J., Pontailler, J.Y., and Li, J., *et al.* 2002. Seasonal variability in the effect of elevated CO$_2$ on ecosystem leaf area index in a scrub-oak ecosystem. *Global Change Biology* **8**: 931–940.

Jacob, J., Greitner, C., and Drake, B.G. 1995. Acclimation of photosynthesis in relation to Rubisco and nonstructural carbohydrate content and *in situ* carboxylase activity in *Scirpus olneyi* grown at elevated CO$_2$ in the field. *Plant, Cell and Environment* **18**: 875–884.

Kathilankal, J.C., Mozdzer, T.J., Fuentes, J.D., McGlathery, K.J., D'Odorico, P., and Zieman, J.C. 2011. Physiological responses of *Spartina alterniflora* to varying environmental conditions in Virginia marshes. *Hydrobiologia* **669**: 167–181.

Kirwan, M.L., Guntenspergen, G.R., and Morris, J.T. 2009. Latitudinal trends in *Spartina alterniflora* productivity and the response of coastal marshes to global change. *Global Change Biology* **15**: 1982–1989.

Langley, J.A., McKee, K.L., Cahoon, D.R., Cherry, J.A., and Megonigal, J.P. 2009. Elevated CO$_2$ stimulates marsh elevation gain, counterbalancing sea-level rise. *Proceedings of the National Academy of Sciences, USA* **106**: 6182–6186.

Loreto, F., Fischbach, R.J., Schnitzler, J.-P., Ciccioli, P., Brancaleoni, E., Calfapietra, C., and Seufert, G. 2001. Monoterpene emission and monoterpene synthase activities in the Mediterranean evergreen oak *Quercus ilex* L. grown at elevated CO$_2$ concentrations. *Global Change Biology* **7**: 709–717.

Loreto F. and Sharkey, T.D. 1990. A gas exchange study of photosynthesis and isoprene emission in red oak (*Quercus rubra* L.). *Planta* **182**: 523–531.

Mateos-Naranjo, E., Redondo-Gomez, S. Andrades-Moreno, L., and Davy, A.J. 2010. Growth and photosynthetic responses of the cordgrass *Spartina maritima* to CO$_2$ enrichment and salinity. *Chemosphere* **81**: 725–731.

McKee, K.L. and Rooth, J.E. 2008. Where temperate meets tropical: Multi-factorial effects of elevated CO$_2$, nitrogen enrichment, and competition on a mangrove-salt marsh community. *Global Change Biology* **14**: 971–984.

Monson, R.K. and Fall, R. 1989. Isoprene emission from aspen leaves. *Plant Physiology* **90**: 267–274.

Mitsch, W.J., Mitsch, R.H., and Turner, R.E. 1994. Wetlands of the Old and New Worlds: ecology and management. In: Mitsch, W.J. (Ed.) *Global Wetlands Old World and New*. Elsevier, Amsterdam, The Netherlands.

Norby, R.J., DeLucia, E.H., and Gielen, B., *et al.* 2005. Forest response to elevated CO$_2$ is conserved across a broad range of productivity. *Proceedings of the National Academy of Science* **102**: 18,052–18,056.

Norby, R.J., Wullschleger, S.D., Gunderson, C.A., Johnson, D.W., and Ceulemans, R. 1999. Tree responses to rising CO$_2$ in field experiments: implications for the future forest. *Plant, Cell and Environment* **22**: 683–714.

Owensby, C.E., Ham, J.M., and Knapp, A.K., *et al.* 1999. Biomass production and species composition change in a tallgrass prairie ecosystem after long-term exposure to elevated atmospheric CO$_2$. *Global Change Biology* **5**: 497–506.

Poisson, N., Kanakidou, M., and Crutzen, P.J. 2000.

Impact of non-methane hydrocarbons on tropospheric chemistry and the oxidizing power of the global troposphere: 3-dimensional modeling results. *Journal of Atmospheric Chemistry et al.*: 157–230.

Rasse, D.P., Li, J.-H., and Drake, B.G. 2003. Carbon dioxide assimilation by a wetland sedge canopy exposed to ambient and elevated CO_2: measurements and model analysis. *Functional Ecology* 17: 222–230.

Rasse, D.P., Peresta, G., and Drake, B.G. 2005. Seventeen years of elevated CO_2 exposure in a Chesapeake Bay Wetland: sustained but contrasting responses of plant growth and CO_2 uptake. *Global Change Biology* 11: 369–377.

Reed, D.J., *et al.* 2008. Site-Specific Scenarios for Wetlands Accretion as Sea Level Rises in the Mid-Atlantic Region. Section 2.1. Background Documents Supporting Climate Change Science Program Synthesis and Assessment Product. Titus, J.G. and Strange, E.M. (Eds.). EPA 430R07004, U.S. Environmental Protection Agency, Washington, DC.

Rosentiel, T.N., Potosnak, M.J., Griffin, K.L., Fall, R., and Monson, R.K. 2003. Increased CO_2 uncouples growth from isoprene emission in an agriforest ecosystem. *Nature* 421: 256–259.

Scholefield, P.A., Doick, K.J., Herbert, B.M.J., Hewitt, C.N.S., Schnitzler, J.-P., Pinelli, P., and Loreto, F. 2004. Impact of rising CO_2 on emissions of volatile organic compounds: isoprene emission from *Phragmites australis* growing at elevated CO_2 in a natural carbon dioxide spring. *Plant, Cell and Environment* 27: 393–401.

Sharkey, T.D., Loreto, F., and Delwiche, C.F. 1991. High carbon dioxide and Sun/shade effect on isoprene emissions from oak and aspen tree leaves. *Plant, Cell and Environment* 14: 333–338.

1.2.5 Soils

1.2.5.1 Bacteria

- Rising atmospheric CO_2 concentrations likely will allow greater numbers of beneficial bacteria (those that help sequester carbon and nitrogen) to exist in soils and anaerobic water environments. This two-pronged phenomenon would be a great boon to terrestrial and aquatic ecosystems.

Nearly all of Earth's plant life responds favorably to increases in the air's CO_2 content by exhibiting enhanced rates of photosynthesis and biomass production. Consequently, these phenomena tend to increase soil carbon contents by increasing root exudation of organic compounds and the amount of plant litter returned to the soil. Thus, it can be expected that CO_2-mediated increases in soil carbon content will affect soil bacterial communities. This section explores the findings of several scientists who have studied the effects of elevated CO_2 on bacteria.

Regarding beneficial terrestrial bacteria, Ronn *et al.* (2003) grew wheat (*Triticum aestivum* L. cv. Minaret) in open-top chambers fumigated with either ambient air or air enriched with an extra 320 ppm of CO_2; on two occasions during the growing season they assessed various plant and soil characteristics, total protozoan numbers, and numbers of culturable bacteria. They found "higher numbers of bacterivorous protozoa in soil under plants grown at elevated CO_2 and larger amounts of root-derived substrates in the soil at plant maturity." Ronn *et al.* note "protozoan grazing generally enhances carbon and nitrogen mineralization in soil," which typically results in more nitrogen being made available to plants. This phenomenon, in turn, enables plants to increase their biomass (as was observed in the CO_2-enriched plants in this experiment) without suffering reductions in tissue nitrogen concentration (as also was observed in the CO_2-enriched plants in this experiment). The end result of these linked phenomena was thus more high-quality wheat production in response to atmospheric CO_2 enrichment.

Montealegre *et al.* (2002) obtained similar results by growing white clover (*Trifolium repens* L.) and perennial ryegrass (*Lolium perenne* L.) in free-air CO_2 enrichment (FACE) plots maintained at atmospheric CO_2 concentrations of 350 and 600 ppm for three years and then sampling the soil to determine the effects of elevated CO_2 on its bacterial populations. Although elevated CO_2 increased the total number of bacteria and respiring bacteria in the bulk soil beneath white clover by 40 and 70%, respectively, it had no significant impact on bulk-soil bacterial numbers beneath perennial ryegrass. When the total bacterial numbers in the *rhizosphere* soil—which lies within about 1.5 mm of plant roots and is characterized by heightened biological activity and chemical weathering of minerals—were expressed on a per unit land area basis, the scientists found elevated CO_2 increased the total number of bacteria and respiring bacteria beneath white clover by about 100 and 250%, respectively, and it increased the total number of bacteria and respiring bacteria beneath perennial ryegrass by approximately 85 and 125%, respectively.

In a related study from the same FACE clover

and ryegrass plots, Marilley *et al.* (1999) report atmospheric CO$_2$ enrichment also altered the profile of bacterial communities in a plant species-dependent manner. In ryegrass, for example, elevated CO$_2$ increased the dominance of *Pseudomonas* species, which enhance plant growth by many different mechanisms. In white clover, it increased the dominance of *Rhizobium* species, which enhance plant growth by making atmospheric nitrogen available for utilization. After three years of differential CO$_2$ treatment in the same FACE experiment, Montealegre *et al.* (2000) determined the genetic structure of 120 isolates of the symbiotic bacterium *Rhizobium leguminosarum* associated with roots of white clover, finding atmospheric CO$_2$ enrichment favored some of the isolates over others. When these isolates were mixed with isolates favored in ambient air and the resulting combination was exposed to CO$_2$-enriched air, the isolates favored by elevated CO$_2$ produced 17% more nodules on roots than the isolates favored in ambient air.

Zak *et al.* (2000) grew six genotypically different aspen (*Populus tremuloides*) cuttings in open-top chambers for 2.5 growing seasons in Michigan, USA, at atmospheric CO$_2$ concentrations of 350 and 700 ppm under adequate and inadequate supplies of soil nitrogen, reporting the effects of elevated CO$_2$ and soil nitrogen on soil microbial composition, biomass, and functioning. Although atmospheric CO$_2$ enrichment had no effect on soil microbial biomass, even after 2.5 years of treatment, high soil nitrogen supply increased it fivefold over that observed in low soil nitrogen plots. Similarly, elevated CO$_2$ did not significantly impact microbial community composition, whereas high soil nitrogen supply did. Atmospheric CO$_2$ did not influence microbial rates of nitrogen mineralization, nor did it alter the microbial demand for inorganic nitrogen.

The several observations of Zak *et al.* suggest the increased fine root biomass and turnover, which led to greater carbon inputs to the soils of the CO$_2$-enriched plots, were not significant enough to elicit any responses in microbial community composition, biomass, and functioning, likely due to the enormous amount of background organic carbon present in the experimental soils, which was approximately 1,000-fold greater than that contributed by the aspen roots. Notwithstanding this observation, the authors conducted an eloquent review of the scientific literature pertaining to this topic, and they conclude when root-associated soil carbon inputs are sufficiently large, relative to native soil organic carbon contents, they can influence microbial community composition, biomass, and functioning.

Therefore, as atmospheric CO$_2$ concentrations rise, it is likely aspen trees will exhibit significant increases in growth, regardless of soil nitrogen availability. These growth increases will occur both above- and below-ground, stimulating greater carbon inputs to soils. Because most forest soils are already relatively rich in organic carbon, however, it is likely the extra carbon inputs resulting from the increasing CO$_2$ content of the air will have little impact on soil microbial composition, biomass, and functioning.

Fu *et al.* (2008) employed semi-continuous culturing methods that used filtered, microwave-sterilized surface Sargasso seawater enriched with phosphate and trace nutrients to examine the physiological responses of steady-state iron (Fe)-replete and Fe-limited cultures of the biogeochemically critical marine unicellular diazotrophic cyanobacterium *Crocosphaera watsonii* at 380 ppm and 750 ppm CO$_2$ levels. When the seawater was replete with iron, they found daily primary production at 750 ppm CO$_2$ was 21% greater than it was at 380 ppm, but when the seawater was iron-limited, daily primary production at 750 ppm CO$_2$ was 150% greater than it was at 380 ppm. With respect to N$_2$ fixation, rates varied little between the two CO$_2$ treatments when the seawater was iron-limited, but when the seawater was replete with iron, N$_2$ fixation at 750 ppm CO$_2$ was 60% greater than it was at 380 ppm.

In discussing their findings, Fu *et al.* write "several studies examining the marine diazotrophic cyanobacterium *Trichodesmium* have shown significant increases in N$_2$ fixation and photosynthesis in response to elevated CO$_2$ concentration (Hutchins *et al.*, 2007; Levitan *et al.*, 2007; Ramos *et al.*, 2007)," and they say their data "extend these findings to encompass the marine unicellular N$_2$-fixing cyanobacterium *Crocosphaera*." This group, they add, "is now recognized as being perhaps equally as important as *Trichodesmium* to the ocean nitrogen cycle (Montoya *et al.*, 2004)." Consequently, they conclude, "anthropogenic CO$_2$ enrichment could substantially increase global oceanic N$_2$ and CO$_2$ fixation," which would be a boon to the marine biosphere.

Feng *et al.* (2009) measured a number of characteristics of purple phototrophic bacteria (PPB) within the rhizosphere and bulk soils of a rice/wheat rotation system at the Nianyu Experimental Station in Jiangsu Province, China, under two CO$_2$ treatments. Rice fields, in their words, "represent the most important agricultural ecosystems in Asia, since rice and wheat are the main source for food supply, and more than 90% of rice fields around the world are located in Asia," and "purple phototrophic bacteria (PPB) are thought to be crucial in the nutrient cycling of rice fields." The Chinese researchers say PPB "thrive in the anaerobic portions of all kinds of aquatic environments, and have long been recognized as one of the key players in global carbon and nitrogen cycles." The researchers grew rice plants (*Oryza sativa* L.) under standard paddy culture at two levels of soil nitrogen (N) fertility (low and high) and two levels of atmospheric CO_2 concentrations (ambient and ambient +200 ppm).

Throughout this period they measured a number of PPB characteristics. Feng *et al.* report, "based on denaturant gradient gel electrophoresis (DGGE) analysis of *pufM* gene encoding the M subunit of anoxygenic PPB light reaction center, elevated CO_2 appeared to enhance the biodiversity of PPB in flooded paddy soils." They continue, "this was further supported by canonical correspondence analysis (CCA) of DGGE fingerprinting pattern of *pufM* genes in paddy soils as well as Shannon diversity indices." They also note "real-time quantitative PCR analysis of *pufM* gene further indicated that PPB abundance was stimulated by elevated CO_2 in bulk soil," and "N fertilization enhanced the biodiversity of PPB under elevated atmospheric CO_2." Feng *et al.* state the significance of these findings by noting "PPB inoculation into the flood water [in rice paddy culture] could lead to grain yield increase by 29% (Elbadry *et al.*, 1999; Harada *et al.*, 2005)," and "PPB are thought to be capable of fixing nitrogen." Feng *et al.* (2011) expressed similar sentiments in discussing the results of the same experiment, acknowledging the importance of elevated CO_2 concentrations on PPB to "enhance the microbial food chain and promote the growth and yield of crops."

The above observations suggest rising atmospheric CO_2 levels likely will allow similar or greater numbers of bacteria to exist in terrestrial environments, enhancing carbon and nitrogen sequestration, which in turn will stimulate the growth and productivity of the surrounding environments.

References

Elbadry, M., Gamal-Eldin, H., and Elbanna, K. 1999. Effects of *Rhodobacter capsulatus* inoculation in combination with graded levels of nitrogen fertilizer on growth and yield of rice in pots and lysimeter experiments. *World Journal of Microbiology and Biotechnology* **15**: 393–395.

Feng, Y., Lin, X., Wang, Y., Zhang, J., Mao, T., Yin, R., and Zhu, J. 2009. Free-air CO_2 enrichment (FACE) enhances the biodiversity of purple phototrophic bacteria in flooded paddy soil. *Plant and Soil* **324**: 317–328.

Feng, Y., Lin, X., Zhang, J., Mao, T., and Zhu, J. 2011. Soil purple phototrophic bacterial diversity under double cropping (rice-wheat) with free-air CO_2 enrichment (FACE). *European Journal of Soil Science* **62**: 533–540.

Fu, F.-X., Mulholland, M.R., Garcia, N.S., Beck, A., Bernhardt, P.W., Warner, M.E., Sanudo-Wilhelmy, S.A., and Hutchins, D.A. 2008. Interactions between changing pCO$_2$, N$_2$ fixation, and Fe limitation in the marine unicellular cyanobacterium *Crocosphaera*. *Limnology and Oceanography* **53**: 2472–2484.

Harada, N., Nishiyama, M., Otsuka, S., and Matsumoto, S. 2005. Effects of inoculation of phototrophic bacteria on grain yield of rice and nitrogenase activity of paddy soil in a pot experiment. *Soil Science and Plant Nutrition* **51**: 361–367.

Hutchins, D.A., Fu, F.-X., Zhang, Y., Warner, M.E., Feng, Y., Portune, K., Bernhardt, P.W., and Mulholland, M.R. 2007. CO_2 control of *Trichodesmium* N$_2$ fixation, photosynthesis, growth rates, and elemental ratios: Implications for past, present, and future ocean biogeochemistry. *Limnology and Oceanography* **52**: 1293–1304.

Levitan, O., Rosenberg, G., Setlik, I., Setlikova, E., Grigel, J., Klepetar, J., Prasil, O., and Berman-Frank, I. 2007. Elevated CO_2 enhances nitrogen fixation and growth in the marine cyanobacterium *Trichodesmium*. *Global Change Biology* **13**: 531–538.

Marilley, L., Hartwig, U.A., and Aragno, M. 1999. Influence of an elevated atmospheric CO_2 content on soil and rhizosphere bacterial communities beneath *Lolium perenne* and *Trifolium repens* under field conditions. *Microbial Ecology* **38**: 39–49.

Montealegre, C.M., van Kessel, C., Blumenthal, J.M., Hur, H.G., Hartwig, U.A., and Sadowsky, M.J. 2000. Elevated atmospheric CO_2 alters microbial population structure in a pasture ecosystem. *Global Change Biology* **6**: 475–482.

Montealegre, C.M., van Kessel, C., Russelle, M.P., and Sadowsky, M.J. 2002. Changes in microbial activity and composition in a pasture ecosystem exposed to elevated atmospheric carbon dioxide. *Plant and Soil* **243**: 197–207.

Montoya, J.P., Holl, C.M., Zehr, J.P., Hansen, A., Villareal, T.A., and Capone, D.G. 2004. High rates of N$_2$ fixation by unicellular diazotrophs in the oligotrophic Pacific Ocean. *Nature* **430**: 1027–1031.

Ramos, J.B.E., Biswas, H., Schulz, K.G., Laroche, J., and Riebesell, U. 2007. Effect of rising atmospheric carbon dioxide on the marine nitrogen fixer *Trichodesmium*.

Global Biogeochemical Cycles **21**: 10.1029/ 2006GB002898.

Ronn, R., Ekelund, F., and Christensen, S. 2003. Effects of elevated atmospheric CO$_2$ on protozoan abundance in soil planted with wheat and on decomposition of wheat roots. *Plant and Soil* **251**: 13–21.

Zak, D.R., Pregitzer, K.S., Curtis, P.S., and Holmes, W.E. 2000. Atmospheric CO$_2$ and the composition and function of soil microbial communities. *Ecological Applications* **10**: 47–59.

1.2.5.2 Carbon Sequestration

- The aerial fertilization effect of atmospheric CO$_2$ enrichment likely will result in greater soil carbon stores due to increased carbon-input into soils, even in nutrient-poor soils and in spite of predicted increases in temperature. In addition, the soil-carbon-sequestering capability of Earth's vegetation likely will act as a significant brake on the rate of rise of the air's CO$_2$ content and thereby help to mute any CO$_2$-induced impetus for global warming.

As the CO$_2$ content of the air increases, nearly all plants respond favorably by increasing their photosynthetic rates and producing greater amounts of biomass. Invariably, this phenomenon leads to greater inputs of carbon to the soil in the form of roots, root exudates, and senesced plant material. Much research has been conducted to determine whether these biological inputs will increase the carbon sequestering abilities of soils, particularly if air temperatures rise, which some scientists have predicted will enhance plant litter decomposition rates to the point they will exacerbate global warming. This section summarizes research that has addressed this subject.

Atmospheric CO$_2$ enrichment typically has but a small effect on the decomposition rates of senesced plant materials. Nonetheless, CO$_2$ enrichment often leads to significantly greater soil carbon sequestration, as demonstrated by De Angelis *et al.* (2000), who report a 4% reduction in the decomposition rate of leaf litter beneath stands of 30-year-old Mediterranean forest species enriched with air of 710 ppm CO$_2$, concluding, "if this effect is coupled to an increase in primary production [which nearly always occurs in response to elevated CO$_2$] there will be a net rise of C-storage in the soils of forest ecosystems." Similarly, in a study of soybean

and sorghum plant residues grown at 705 ppm CO$_2$, where decomposition rates were not affected by elevated CO$_2$, Henning *et al.* (1996) concluded "the possibility exists for increased soil C storage under field crops in an elevated CO$_2$ world," due to the greater residue production resulting from CO$_2$-enhanced plant growth.

In a study that revealed how these phenomena once manifested themselves in a field of clover (*Trifolium repens* L.) at the Swiss Federal Institute of Technology near Zurich, a 71% increase in atmospheric CO$_2$ concentration increased above-ground growth by 146%, and it increased the pumping of newly fixed carbon into the soil of the CO$_2$-enriched plots by approximately 50% (Nitschelm *et al.* 1997). In addition, root decomposition in the CO$_2$-enriched plots was found to be 24% less than in the ambient-treatment plots. The researchers conclude, "the occurrence at elevated CO$_2$ of both greater plant material input, through higher yields, and reduced residue decomposition rates would be expected to impact soil carbon storage significantly." In a similar study of the effects of a doubling of the air's CO$_2$ concentration on three grass species, Cotrufo and Gorissen (1997) conclude "elevated CO$_2$ could result in greater soil carbon stores due to increased carbon-input into soils."

One year later, Verburg *et al.* (1998) grew one-year-old heather plants (*Calluna vulgaris* L.) for two months in greenhouses maintained at atmospheric CO$_2$ concentrations of 380 and 580 ppm in combination with low and high levels of soil nitrogen before exposing them to ^{14}CO$_2$ for one day, to study the fate of recently fixed carbon in their experimental plant-soil system. They found the extra CO$_2$ increased net ^{14}C uptake in heather by approximately 43%, irrespective of soil nitrogen content. In addition, soil ^{14}C increased in elevated CO$_2$ plots by 17% and 25% at low and high soil nitrogen levels, respectively. Also, although total soil respiration initially was higher in the CO$_2$-enriched plots (for two days post ^{14}CO$_2$ labeling), it declined and became significantly lower than the soil respiration rate displayed by plots exposed to ambient air within two weeks. That trend persisted throughout the remaining four weeks of the study. Thus it would appear soil carbon sequestration beneath heather communities likely will increase in the future with further increases in the air's CO$_2$ concentration.

Similar results have been reported for other shrubs and trees that possess the ability to store more carbon in their associated soils than do grasses, as noted by Gill and Burke (1999). Pregitzer *et al.*

(2000), for example, grew aspen seedlings for 2.5 years at 700 ppm CO_2 and observed fine root biomass was 65 and 17% greater than that produced by seedlings growing at ambient CO_2 concentration on nitrogen-rich and nitrogen-poor soils, respectively. The researchers state such increases in soil carbon inputs "can be substantial," even under low soil nitrogen conditions. Rouhier and Reed (1999) also note soil carbon was significantly greater beneath seedlings of birch grown at 700 ppm CO_2 than it was beneath seedlings grown at 350 ppm CO_2. Leavitt *et al.* (1994) found 10% of the organic carbon present in soils beneath CO_2-enriched cotton plants grown for only three years at 550 ppm CO_2 came from the extra CO_2, which was stable-isotope labeled to trace its path through this woody agricultural species and into the soil.

In a study that included air temperature as a variable, Casella and Soussana (1997) grew perennial ryegrass (*Lolium perenne* L.) in ambient and elevated (700 ppm) CO_2 at two different levels of soil nitrogen and at ambient and elevated (+3°C) temperature for two years. They found "a relatively large part of the additional photosynthetic carbon is stored below-ground during the two first growing seasons after exposure to elevated CO_2, thereby increasing significantly the below-ground carbon pool." At the low and high levels of soil nitrogen supply, for example, the elevated CO_2 increased soil carbon storage by 32 and 96%, respectively, "with no significant increased temperature effect," which led the two scientists to conclude, in spite of predicted increases in temperature, "this stimulation of the below-ground carbon sequestration in temperate grassland soils could exert a negative feed-back on the current rise of the atmospheric CO_2 concentration." Along these same lines, van Ginkel and Gorissen (1998) and van Ginkel *et al.* (1999)—who performed similar experiments using *Lolium perenne*—conclude the effects of atmospheric CO_2 enrichment on increasing plant growth and decreasing decomposition rates of plant litter are "more than sufficient to counteract the positive feedback [on decomposition rates] caused by [an] increase in air temperature."

Fitter *et al.* (1999) heated upland grass ecosystem soils by nearly 3°C and found root production and root death were increased by equivalent amounts. Hence, they conclude elevated temperatures "will have no direct effect on the soil carbon store [in upland grass communities]." Similarly, Johnson *et al.* (2000) warmed Arctic tundra ecosystems by nearly 6°C for eight years, reporting warming had no

significant effect on ecosystem respiration. In addition, Liski *et al.* (1999) showed carbon storage in soils of both high- and low-productivity boreal forests increased with temperature along a temperature gradient in Finland. Thus it is clear any warming likely will have little or no impact on soil carbon sequestration rates, and if there is an impact, it may be positive.

Increased soil carbon storage occurring from the ongoing rise in the air's CO_2 content should have wide-ranging positive influences on agriculture. In considering soil carbon storage in the context of global climate change, Rosenzweig and Hillel (2000) state "our management of the soil should be aimed at enhancing soil organic matter for the multiple complementary purposes of improving soil fertility and soil structure, reducing erosion, and helping to mitigate the greenhouse effect." In an experiment where soybeans were grown at an atmospheric CO_2 concentration of 500 ppm, Islam *et al.* (1999) report soil particulate organic carbon content was significantly increased, as were the amounts of dissolved carbon, humic, and fulvic acids. These findings led them to conclude "one of the main benefits arising from the greater supply of organic residues to soils under CO_2 enrichment is an improvement of soil structure." In a similar study, Insam *et al.* (1999) note fumigation of artificial tropical ecosystems with 610 ppm CO_2 for about 1.5 years increased humic substances in their soils by nearly 30%.

Ross *et al.* (2000) collected soil samples from around a natural CO_2 vent in New Zealand to determine the effects of elevated CO_2 (510–900 ppm vs. 440–460 ppm) on soil carbon and nitrogen contents. The soil at the site was considered to be a gley, and the overlying vegetation was typical of native grasslands in the area, consisting of both C_3 and C_4 species. They found several decades of exposure to elevated atmospheric CO_2 significantly increased the soil's organic carbon and total nitrogen contents by 24%, and it increased microbial carbon and nitrogen contents by 116%. These results led Ross *et al.* to conclude storage of C and N in gley soils "can increase under prolonged exposure to elevated CO_2" and "increased storage of soil organic matter at such springs can occur, even when soil C concentrations are already high." Thus, as the air's CO_2 content rises, vegetated gley soils will sequester increasingly greater amounts of both carbon and nitrogen, and they will exhibit enhanced biological activity both above- and below-ground.

Hu *et al.* (2001) studied carbon and nitrogen

relations in the plants and moderately fertile soil of a sandstone grassland at Stanford University's Jasper Ridge Biological Preserve in central California near the conclusion of a five-year study conducted between 1992 and 1997, where two CO$_2$ treatments (360 and 720 ppm) were maintained in 20 open-top chambers (ten replicates per treatment). This effort revealed the rise in atmospheric CO$_2$ increased both soil microbial biomass and plant nitrogen uptake, the net effect being less nitrogen was left in the soil for microbes to use, which resulted in decreased microbial respiration per unit biomass and, hence, decreased microbial decomposition and increased ecosystem carbon accumulation.

King *et al.* (2001) grew O$_3$-sensitive and O$_3$-tolerant aspen (*Populus tremuloides* Michx.) clones alone and in mixed stands of paper birch (*Betula papyrifera* Marsh.) for two years in 30m-diameter free-air CO$_2$ enrichment (FACE) plots in Rhinelander, Wisconsin, which they maintained at CO$_2$ concentrations of 360 and 560 ppm with and without exposure to elevated O$_3$ (1.5 times ambient concentrations), to study the interactive effects of these parameters on fine-root production and belowground carbon cycling in the soils associated with these stands. They found the elevated CO$_2$ significantly enhanced the production of fine root biomass by 133 and 83% for aspen and aspen-birch mixed stands, respectively. In contrast, elevated O$_3$ had no effect on fine-root biomass, but simultaneous exposure to elevated O$_3$ and CO$_2$ increased fine-root biomass by approximately 66% for both types of stands. And when averaged across both stands, elevated CO$_2$ also increased dead root biomass by 140%, but another example of elevated CO$_2$ increasing carbon inputs to soils.

In August 1996, Andrews and Schlesinger (2001) and a number of other researchers established circular FACE plots (30 meters in diameter) that they exposed to air of either 360 or 560 ppm CO$_2$. This modest increase in the air's CO$_2$ content increased the weathering rate of parent rock material, as indicated by a 271% increase in soil mineral cation concentration and a 162% increase in soil alkalinity after the second year of CO$_2$ enrichment. In addition, the elevated CO$_2$ increased the flux of dissolved inorganic carbon compounds to the groundwater by 33%. Extrapolating this phenomenon to the global land area covered by forests, the two researchers remark the observed increase in the efflux of dissolved inorganic carbon compounds to groundwater "may act to buffer the rate of CO$_2$ increase in the atmosphere over geologic time periods."

Working in the same plots at the same time, Pritchard *et al.* (2001) studied the effects of elevated CO$_2$ on belowground root dynamics as assessed by mini-rhizotrons inserted into the low-nutrient (nitrogen and phosphorus) soils of the experimental plots. After one year of treatment, they report total standing root length and root numbers per minirhizotron were 16 and 34% greater, respectively, in the CO$_2$-enriched plots than in the ambient-air plots. In addition, the elevated CO$_2$ increased the diameter of living and dead roots by 8 and 6%, respectively, and annual root production and root mortality were 26 and 46% greater in the CO$_2$-enriched plots than in the control plots. All of these phenomena would be expected to result in enhanced carbon sequestration in the soils in which the trees were rooted.

In another contemporaneous paper, Cardon *et al.* (2001) write, "soil organic carbon (SOC) is the largest reservoir of organic carbon in the terrestrial biosphere." They affirm this in introducing their experimental study of the potential effects of the ongoing rise in the air's CO$_2$ content on this vast store of material, which was once the "C" in the CO$_2$ of much of Earth's atmosphere, where it was freely wafted about prior to being assimilated by plants and sequestered in the soil.

Occupying such a pivotal position as it does in the planetary carbon cycle, SOC is of great interest to scientists who worry about its stability. Among other things, Cardon *et al.* wanted to know whether allowing more CO$_2$ to be emitted to the atmosphere would lead to even more carbon being sequestered in the soil (a logical hypothesis), or if it would somehow cause a reduction in what was already there (a less logical hypothesis but one that cannot be ignored).

Cardon *et al.* studied soil carbon income and outgo in a number of small microcosms of two annual C$_3$ grassland communities (sandstone and serpentine) of contrived high and low soil-nutrient availability maintained out-of-doors in open-top chambers at the Jasper Ridge Biological Preserve in Stanford, California, from October 1994 through August 1996. Key to their study was the utilization of isotopic tracer techniques to determine the sizes of the various SOC pools through time. They grew the C$_3$ plants in a soil obtained from a C$_4$ grassland in Colorado, which ensured that the original organic carbon of their experimental soil would have a different isotopic signature from the organic carbon that would be injected into it by the C$_3$ plants that grew upon it. In addition, the carbon of the fossil fuel-derived CO$_2$ supplied to the CO$_2$-enriched chambers had yet a third unique isotopic signature.

They found the extra CO_2 supplied to half of the mini-ecosystems increased the total root biomass in the serpentine grassland microcosms by a factor of three in both high and low soil-nutrient availability treatments, and it increased total root biomass in the sandstone grassland microcosms by a factor of four in both the high and low soil-nutrient availability treatments. Thus there was a tremendous CO_2-induced increase in the amount of organic material that eventually would become available for incorporation into the soils of both grassland microcosms.

With so much new organic matter being added to the soils of the CO_2-enriched microcosms, Cardon et al. hypothesized previously carbon-limited microbes in these soils would alter their survival strategy and turn from breaking down older, more recalcitrant soil organic matter to attack the more abundant and labile rhizodeposits being laid down in the newly carbon-rich soils of the CO_2-enriched microcosms. This rhizodeposition, as they christened it, consists of "all deposition of organic carbon from living root systems to soils, including compounds lost through root exudation, sloughing of dead cells during root growth, and fine root turnover," which, as noted above, was dramatically enhanced by atmospheric CO_2 enrichment.

The upshot of this scenario—which seems thoroughly vindicated in light of the observations about to be described—is that the experimentally imposed increase in atmospheric CO_2 concentration actually retarded the decomposition of the older SOC of the imported soil. Also, this phenomenon effectively increased the turnover time of the original SOC, significantly increasing its stability.

"If this reduction in breakdown of older SOC is sustained," write Cardon et al., "an increased retention of carbon in older SOC pools might be expected under elevated relative to ambient CO_2." Therefore, not only does atmospheric CO_2 enrichment lead to higher rates of carbon input to soils, it likely also leads to slower rates of carbon withdrawal from them. That allows ever-more carbon to be locked away in Earth's soil bank as the air's CO_2 content rises. And that phenomenon appears to keep the air's rate of CO_2 rise from accelerating too greatly, even in the face of yearly increases in anthropogenic CO_2 emissions.

Since biological activity generally increases with rising temperatures—especially when the initial temperature is below the freezing point of water—it might be reasoned global warming would enhance rates of soil microbial respiration, leading to increases in the soil-to-air flux of CO_2. However, as Neilsen et al. (2001) noted, "over-winter processes account for a significant portion (20–70%) of annual ecosystem carbon and nitrogen cycling and soil-atmosphere trace gas fluxes." Therefore, it was not immediately apparent what the ultimate consequences of warming-induced reductions in the frequency and severity of freezing would be.

To find the answer, Neilsen et al. collected samples of soil from a northern hardwood-dominated forest in New Hampshire, USA. These samples, from nearly pure stands of sugar maple (*Acer saccharum* Marshall) and yellow birch (*Betula alleghaniensis* Britton), were placed in small vessels and either maintained at the normal laboratory temperature of 20–25°C or subjected to mild and severe freezes of -3 and -13°C, respectively, for ten days, after which all samples were kept at the normal laboratory temperature for 23 additional days. Neilsen et al. measured the evolution of CO_2 from the soils at the beginning and end of the full 33-day period, as well as at three other times during the course of the experiment.

They found freezing had a significant effect on CO_2 evolution from the soils. Cumulative 33-day totals of respiration (in units of mg carbon per kg of soil) for the soil samples taken from the maple stand were 1,497, 2,120, and 3,882 for the control and -3 and -13°C temperature treatments, respectively, which represent carbon loss enhancements (relative to the control) of 42 and 159% for the -3 and -13°C treatments, respectively, an increased carbon loss of $13 \pm 1\%$ for each degree C below freezing. For the soil samples taken from the birch stand, the corresponding respiration numbers were 1,734, 2,866, and 5,063, representing carbon loss enhancements of 65 and 192% for the -3 and -13°C treatments, respectively, or an increased carbon loss of $18 \pm 3\%$ for each degree C below freezing.

It can be readily appreciated how these research results relate to the subject of global warming effects on soil carbon sequestration. As temperatures gradually warm over the course of many years and climate zones move poleward in latitude and upward in elevation, regions that experienced many hard freezes in the past will experience fewer of them in the future, and other regions will undergo a shift from hard freezes to mild freezes. Still other regions that experienced mild freezes in the past will experience fewer—or none—in the future. And in all of these situations, together with every permutation that falls somewhere between them, there will be a tendency for less carbon to be released to the atmosphere, which means more will remain sequestered in the soil.

The great deserts of Africa and Asia have a huge potential for sequestering carbon, because they are currently so barren their soil carbon contents have essentially nowhere to go but up. The problem with this scenario, however, is that their soils blow away with every wisp of wind that disturbs their surfaces. The ongoing rise in the air's CO_2 content could do much to reverse this trend. At higher atmospheric CO_2 concentrations, nearly all plants are more efficient at utilizing water (Morison, 1985). Hence, as the air's CO_2 content rises, the vegetation that rings Earth's deserts should be able to encroach upon them and more effectively protect their surfaces from the ravages of wind, thereby reducing soil and carbon losses due to erosion. Also, rising atmospheric CO_2 concentrations should increase the stability of surface soil crusts held together by lichens and/or algae (Tuba et al., 1998; Brostoff et al., 2002), which also should help to reduce the deleterious effects of wind erosion (Evans and Johansen, 1999). In addition, many of the algal components of desert soil crusts are nitrogen-fixers (Evans and Belnap, 1999), and their CO_2-enhanced presence should lead to more nitrogen being made available to other plants, which should accelerate the development of soil-protecting ecosystems even more.

The end result of all these phenomena working together is greater carbon storage, both above- and below-ground, in what was previously little more than a source of dust for the rest of the world. And therein lies one of the great unanticipated benefits of the CO_2-induced greening of the globe's deserts: less airborne dust to spread havoc across Earth.

To better understand this phenomenon, it is helpful to refer to an article in the *American Scientist* magazine titled "The Global Transport of Dust." Griffin et al. (2002) began their essay with a description of the magnitude of soil materials wafted about by the wind. "By some estimates," they write, "as much as two billion metric tons of dust are lifted into the Earth's atmosphere every year." Riding along on those particles are "pollutants such as herbicides and pesticides and a significant number of micro-organisms—bacteria, viruses and fungi." The four scientists calculate there are easily enough bacteria thus moved about the planet each year "to form a microbial bridge between Earth and Jupiter."

And although it does not traverse interplanetary space, dust from Africa and Asia does cross both the Atlantic and Pacific Oceans. Griffin et al. report, for example, dust storms originating in North Africa "routinely affect the air quality in Europe and the Middle East" and millions of tons of African sediment "fall on the North Amazon Basin of South America every year." Likewise, Prospero (2001) notes everyone in the United States living east of the Mississippi River is affected by dust of African origin. And in April 2001, Griffin et al. report, a large dust cloud originating over the Gobi Desert of China "moved eastward across the globe, crossing Korea, Japan, the Pacific (in five days), North America (causing sporadic reports of poor air quality in the United States), the Atlantic Ocean and then Europe."

Many of the biological entities associated with the dust particles that are thus dispersed about the planet have serious consequences for plants, animals, and humans. Airborne fungi from Africa that frequently make their way to the Americas, for example, cause sugar cane rust, coffee rust, and banana leaf spot. Griffin et al. also describe how the scourge of Caribbean sea fans—*Aspergillus sydowii*—"is also found in the Caribbean atmosphere during African dust events," noting the region's "sea fans and other coral reef organisms have experienced a steady decline since the late 1970s," when worsening drought in Africa predisposed increasing amounts of soil there to wind erosion (Prospero, 2001). They also state they expect "future research will show that many other coral diseases are spread by dust from both Africa and Asia."

As to human health effects, Griffin et al. note "African dust is reported to be a vector for the meningococcal meningitis pathogen *Neisseria meningitis* in sub-Saharan Africa," and outbreaks of the disease often followed localized or regional dust events that resulted in many fatalities. They also report a 17-fold increase in the incidence of asthma on the island of Barbados since 1973, "which corresponds to the period when the quantities of African dust in the region started to increase."

Because the dust clouds that reach the Americas from Africa and Asia have traveled such long distances, most of the larger particles they originally contained generally fall out along the way. The particles that remain, therefore, are typically very small—so small, in fact, that Griffin et al. report, "once they are inhaled into the lungs they cannot be exhaled." What makes this situation especially serious is the tiny dust particles typically are heavily coated with iron, and a substantial fraction of that iron is released to the lung tissue when the particles are deposited there. And iron, as Prospero notes, is "particularly efficient in producing an inflammatory response in the lungs."

In light of these observations, it is clear the slow but steady acceleration of carbon sequestration in the deserts of Africa and Asia, which is being provided by the ongoing rise in the air's CO_2 content, is producing more than just local benefits. Plants and animals far and wide, on land and in the sea, together with people everywhere, will ultimately benefit, if they are not already doing so, from the reduced airborne-dispersal of pathogens responsible for many debilitating diseases, as source-region soils become better protected against the erosive power of the wind. And if natural carbon sequestration tendencies can bring about these ancillary benefits, so too can those of man. Consequently, citizens involved in local carbon sequestration projects can take satisfaction their efforts are having a positive impact on the global environment in more ways than one. Even if rising concentrations of atmospheric CO_2 have no substantial impact on the world's climate, there are many other reasons to be involved in projects designed to enhance the productivity of the planet's managed and natural ecosystems, not the least of which is the reduction of airborne dust caused by wind-induced soil erosion.

Moving from desert to tropical isle, Dilustro et al. (2002) note soils store approximately three times more carbon than plants do, but almost all of that carbon is transferred to the soil through plants. They also note plant root responses to elevated CO_2 have been largely overlooked in this regard, and they thus conclude some of the carbon missing from current global carbon cycle models may be sequestered belowground. Intrigued by the possibility that enhanced carbon transfer to soils via plants responding to the aerial fertilization effect of atmospheric CO_2 enrichment may account for much of the carbon that exits the atmosphere each year, the four researchers designed an experiment to provide some potential answers to this important question.

On a small barrier island in the northern part of the Kennedy Space Center, Florida, USA, the group of scientists erected 16 open-top chambers around clumps of evergreen scrub oaks and associated saw palmetto shrubs that comprised a fire-adapted ecosystem that historically had been maintained by natural fire cycles of 10- to 15-year intervals, which had last been burned in February 1996, just prior to the start of their experiment. They maintained half of the chambers at the CO_2 concentration of the ambient air, and the other half—starting on 15 May 1996—at CO_2 concentrations approximately 350 ppm above ambient. In addition, in the soils of each of the 16 chambers, the scientists inserted two mini-rhizotron

tubes to a depth of 101 cm, through which they viewed the growth and development of the ecosystem's fine-roots at three-month intervals, from March 1996 to December 1997, via tiny video camera systems.

Dilustro et al. write "our hypothesis that elevated atmospheric CO_2 would increase fine-root density, productivity, mortality and turnover was demonstrated." By the end of the 21-month study period, the fine-root length density of the re-sprouting trees and shrubs in the ambient-air chambers had attained a mean of 7.53 mm cm^{-2} in the top 101 cm of soil, and the re-sprouting plants in the CO_2-enriched chambers had attained a mean of 21.36 mm cm^{-2}, indicating a CO_2-induced increase of 184% in this important root property. Concomitantly, there was also a 55% increase in ecosystem aboveground biomass, and all this happened, the scientists note, "despite water and nutrient limited conditions."

Dilustro et al. state "the increased rates of fine root growth coupled with no change in decomposition rate suggest a potential increased rate of carbon input into the soil." Furthermore, their detailed fine-root data for June 1997 indicate a mean CO_2-induced increase in fine-root length density of approximately 75% in the top three-fourths of the soil profile, and an increase on the order of 125% in the bottom quarter. Hence, there are strong indications the bottom layer of soil was being supplied with a greater proportion of extra carbon than were the upper soil layers.

Ritchie and McCarty (2003) write, "recent studies indicate that soil erosion and redeposition may establish an ecosystem disequilibrium that will promote carbon sequestration in the biosphere (Stallard, 1998; Harden et al., 1999)." In this scenario, they continue, "soil erosion on the uplands moves soil carbon to deposition sites on the landscape and promotes soil carbon replacement at the eroded sites from the production of vegetative biomass." Often, these deposition sites are riparian systems with high net primary productivity, which also leads to increased onsite storage of carbon. As to the validity of these concepts, Ritchie and McCarty note "the capacity of riparian and flood plain systems to capture sediments has been documented (Ritchie et al., 1975; Walling et al., 1999) as well as the ability of these systems to store carbon has been documented (Lal et al., 1998)."

The two researchers collected and analyzed for carbon content profiles of soils obtained from an upland area and adjacent riparian system into which the upland area drained. Results indicated the riparian system acted as a filter, removing eroded soil materials from the overland flow before they reached the stream that drained the area, so that soil carbon content was significantly greater in the riparian soils than in the upland soils. Ritchie and McCarty report carbon storage in the riparian soils was 3.8 times greater than in the upland soils in the upper 20 cm of the soil profile and 4.7 times greater in the upper 30 cm, and they report the earlier work of Ritchie and McCarty (2001) suggests "there may be as much as 10–15 times more carbon in the total profile (0–200 cm) of the riparian soils." These results put a bright new face on what was long believed to be a phenomenon of no virtue whatsoever—precipitation-driven soil erosion. In addition, they provide a new reason for protecting Earth's wetlands: preserving an important sink for atmospheric CO$_2$.

Working concurrently, Jongmans *et al.* (2003) carried out a micro-morphological study of structural development and organic matter distribution in two calcareous marine loam soils on which pear trees had been grown for the prior 45 years. The soil of one of these Dutch orchards exhibited little or no earthworm activity, and the soil of the other orchard exhibited high earthworm activity, a difference resulting from different levels of heavy metal contamination of the soils of the two orchards due to the prior use of different amounts of fungicides.

The absence of earthworms in the first orchard led to topsoil compaction, restricted litter incorporation into the mineral portion of the soil, less fragmentation of particulate organic matter, and restricted mixing of organic matter with the mineral soil's clay fraction. Furthermore, without earthworms there were no earthworm casts, and the five researchers point out "the rate of organic matter decomposition can be decreased in worm casts compared to bulk soil aggregates," citing Martin (1991) and Haynes and Fraser (1998).

Thus, based on their own findings and others, Jongmans *et al.* conclude "earthworms play an important role in the intimate mixing of organic residues and fine mineral soil particles and the formation of organic matter-rich micro-aggregates and can, therefore, contribute to physical protection of organic matter, thereby slowing down organic matter turnover and increasing the soil's potential for carbon sequestration." These points take on added significance when we consider elevated levels of atmospheric CO$_2$ tend to increase earthworm populations and activities, as has been demonstrated by Zaller and Arnone (1997, 1999). Thus, the ongoing rise in the air's CO$_2$ content likely will help more of the extra organic matter that is produced under CO$_2$-enriched conditions to remain in the soil even longer than it otherwise would remain due to the organic-matter-conserving nature of the increased activities of the increased earthworm populations shown to occur as a consequence of increases in the atmosphere's CO$_2$ concentration.

Prior *et al.* (2004) speculate "enhanced aboveground crop growth under elevated CO$_2$, leading to more soil surface residue and greater percent ground cover (Prior *et al.*, 1997) coupled with positive shifts in crop root systems (Prior *et al.*, 2003), may have the potential to alter soil structural characteristics." To see whether this inference was correct, and if it was, to see whether elevated atmospheric CO$_2$ concentrations tend to enhance or degrade soil physical properties, Prior *et al.* grew soybean (*Glycine max* (L.) Merr. cv. Stonewall) and sorghum (*Sorghum bicolor* (L.) Moench cv. Savanna 5) plants from seed to maturity for five consecutive growing seasons in open-top chambers maintained at atmospheric CO$_2$ concentrations of either 360 or 720 ppm. The soil in which the plants grew had been fallow for more than 25 years prior to the start of the study and was located in a huge outdoor bin, where at the end of each growing season aboveground non-yield residues (stalks, soybean pod hulls, and sorghum chaff), including 10% (by weight) of the grain yield, were allowed to remain on the surfaces of the plots to simulate no-tillage farming, after which measurements of soil properties made at the beginning of the experiment were compared with similar measurements made at its conclusion.

The elevated CO$_2$ had no effect on soil bulk density in the sorghum plot, but lowered it in the soybean plot by approximately 5%. The elevated CO$_2$ also had no effect on soil saturated hydraulic conductivity in the sorghum plot, but increased it in the soybean plot by about 42%. Soil aggregate stability was increased in both plots, but by a greater amount in the soybean plot, and total soil carbon content was increased by 16% in the sorghum plot and 29% in the soybean plot. Consequently, the soils of both plots experienced some improvements in response to the experimental doubling of the air's CO$_2$ content, although there were more and greater improvements in the soybean plot than in the sorghum plot. Prior *et al.* conclude their findings indicate a significant "potential for improvements in soil carbon storage, water infiltration and soil water retention, and reduced erosion," valuable positive consequences they describe as "CO$_2$-induced benefits."

Krull *et al.* (2005) report "colonization of grasslands or savannas by trees over the last 50–100 years, often described as 'thickening,' has received attention due to the large potential for carbon sequestration in woody biomass." It was a hot topic because many studies have attributed thickening to "the increase in atmospheric CO_2, causing CO_2 fertilization and resulting in increased water use efficiency in C_3 plants," as discussed by Berry and Roderick (2002) and Grunzweig *et al.* (2003). In addition, they write, "much of the change in atmospheric CO_2 occurred over the last 50 years [1953–2003 = 64 ppm] with the most significant changes being in the last 20 years [1983–2003 = 33 ppm]."

Working at a site some 40 km northwest of Longreach, Queensland, Australia, Krull *et al.* measured vertical profiles of $\delta^{13}C$ and ^{14}C of bulk and size-separated soil organic matter to infer the time course of changes in these parameters along a transect spanning the dynamic transition zone between C_4-dominated grassland and C_3-dominated woodland, an ecotone that comprised different-age specimens of leguminous gidyea trees (*Acacia cambagei*) interspersed with occasional whitewood trees (*Atalaya hemiglauca*). Then, since the longtime landholder reported thickening by the Acacia trees occurred "at least since the 1950s," they tested whether the observed changes in soil carbon stocks could be reproduced by the Roth-Carbon turnover model over a 50-year time period.

The eight researchers conclude "much of the vegetation change at this site occurred over the last 50 years." In addition, they found approximately twice as much total organic carbon in the soil beneath the fully established woodland as in the soil beneath the pristine grassland. They conclude their findings "stress the importance of viewing soils as dynamic systems and indicating the potential for soil organic carbon sequestration in grazed semi-arid woodlands." Such land use represents a form of agroforestry, the virtues of which were touted by Mutuo *et al.* (2005).

Also, the findings of Krull *et al.* suggest the operation of an important negative feedback that can slow the rate-of-rise of the air's CO_2 content. The ongoing enrichment of the air with CO_2 from the burning of fossil fuels enables woody species to colonize less-productive grasslands more readily and thereby extract greater amounts of CO_2 from the atmosphere, meanwhile providing many benefits to the soil in which the trees are rooted.

Parenthetically, it is important to note papers published in journals such as *Science* and *Nature* typically attract much attention, especially when they deal with high-profile subjects such as global warming, which some have described as a threat worse than nuclear warfare or global terrorism. When a study describes a phenomenon that could exacerbate that threat, it behooves its authors and the editors of the journal in which it is published to be especially careful in the way they describe what was found and what its implications may be.

A case in point is the report of Heath *et al.* (2005), who studied soil sequestration of root-derived carbon from seedlings of six European tree species and found it to decline in response to atmospheric CO_2 enrichment. This finding led them to write, "should similar processes operate in forest ecosystems, the size of the annual terrestrial carbon sink may be substantially reduced, resulting in a positive feedback on the rate of increase in atmospheric carbon dioxide concentration." This outcome was parroted by the journal's editors, who state the new findings "raise the possibility that the future rise in atmospheric CO_2 concentrations could be higher than expected."

How reasonable are these speculations? To answer this question, it is important to know how closely—or not—the experimental setting of Heath *et al.*'s study reproduced real-world forests or orchards. Was their study a FACE experiment, such as that conducted in the Duke University Forest, where multiple 30m-diameter plots of initially 13-year-old loblolly pine trees had been exposed continuously to ambient and elevated concentrations of atmospheric CO_2 each growing season since August 1996? Or was it an out-of-doors open-top chamber study, such as the Phoenix, Arizona sour orange tree experiment, where trees were grown from the sapling stage to mature adults for 17 years of continuous CO_2 enrichment? It was in fact neither of these.

The Heath *et al.* experiment was only a 15-month study conducted in small greenhouses, where seedlings were grown in vertical sections of 16cm-diameter polyethylene tubes supplied with only 10 liters of soil, and their results are not consistent with more comprehensive experiments such as the Duke University FACE experiment. To their credit, Heath *et al.* readily acknowledge the many deficiencies of their study. They state, for example, "young trees, grown in mesocosms in a semi-controlled environment and protected from major herbivores, may respond differently from mature trees growing in a natural forest." They also note their experiment "ran for only two growing seasons" and "the input of leaf litter to the soil was excluded." With respect to these latter two points, they also state "the possibility that longer term increased inputs of leaf litter under elevated CO_2 could counteract the effect on the sequestration of root-derived carbon cannot be ruled out." And they admit, "although soil microbial respiration increased under elevated CO_2, the effect of this on the decomposition of native soil carbon is not known."

That these deficiencies likely precluded the discovery of the truth sought by Heath *et al.* in their experiment is revealed by their acknowledgment, "in contrast to our experiment, CO_2 enrichment caused an increase in soil carbon sequestration beneath *Betula* seedlings over the course of one growing season (Ineson *et al.*, 1996)," and "free-air CO_2 enrichment (FACE) also caused an increase in the sequestration of new carbon in C_4 soil cores transplanted into former agricultural ground beneath 2- to 3-year-old *Populus* saplings (Hoosbeek *et al.*, 2004)." Consequently, and after reviewing the results of still other pertinent experiments, they ultimately conclude "there is insufficient evidence to predict with certainty whether plant responses to elevated CO_2 will result in increased or decreased sequestration of new carbon in the soils of forest ecosystems."

In light of these observations, which were made in Heath *et al.*'s own paper and which suggest there is no compelling reason to conclude their results bear any resemblance to what will actually occur in the real world as the air's CO_2 content climbs, one wonders why their paper was accepted for publication in so prestigious a journal as *Science*. It seems all too likely it was not for scientific reasons at all but more likely for the support the paper could be seen as providing for the political views of the journal's editor, who strongly supported Kyoto-type regulations of anthropogenic CO_2 emissions.

In a contemporary study suffering from some of the same problems as Heath *et al.*, Bellamy *et al.* (2005) measured soil carbon contents at 2,179 locations across England and Wales between 1994 and 2003, adjacent to points where similar measurements had been made between 1978 and 1983, after which rates of change of soil carbon content were calculated for the quarter-century period 1978–2003. They report "carbon was lost from soils across England and Wales over the survey period at a mean rate of 0.6% yr^{-1}," which they attribute to "climate change," noting over the period of study "the mean temperature across England and Wales increased by about 0.5°C."

Bellamy *et al.* thus conclude, "losses of soil carbon in the UK, and by inference in other temperate regions, are likely to have been offsetting absorption by terrestrial sinks." Associated Press writer Michael McDonough begins his review of the study (7 September 2005) by stating, "rising temperatures resulting from climate change are likely causing soil in England and Wales to lose large amounts of carbon, possibly further contributing to the greenhouse gas effect." These conclusions are not as well supported as they were portrayed to be.

Bellamy *et al.* resampled only 38.5% of the original sites sampled between 1978 and 1983, so the vast majority of England and Wales, much less "other temperate regions" of the globe, was not assessed for changes in soil organic carbon (SOC) content. In addition, the five researchers claim "the relationship between rate of carbon loss and carbon content is irrespective of land use," which was key to their being able to claim "a link to climate change." However, in an accompanying article that raised several other concerns, Schulze and Freibauer (2005) write, in "re-inspecting the results, we think that the land-use factor has played a role—for example, only alteration in land use and gradual changes in land management can explain why croplands lost more carbon than other areas." They also note studies conducted in China, Finland, and Flanders "attribute most of the SOC loss to changes in land use and management." Even Bellamy *et al.* admit "various changes in land use will have contributed to carbon losses from soils across England and Wales over the survey period, both under agricultural uses (drainage schemes, post-war grassland conversion, increased stocking rates) and non-agricultural uses (afforestation on wet soils, increased erosion, increased burning of upland vegetation)." However, they state they did "not have sufficient data at the scale of the National Soil Inventory to explore these effects," so they really did *not* know the role played by land use, which meant they really did not know the role played by climate change.

Schulze and Friebauer also note the SOC losses observed by Bellamy *et al.* "occurred independently of soil properties, challenging our knowledge about SOC stability," as this observation was at odds with what had been learned about the subject over the years. They also point out the carbon losses were proportional to SOC concentration, which implies "a first-order decay of a homogeneous pool" which "contradicts the view that SOC in carbon-rich soils contains a higher fraction of stable carbon than does that in carbon-poor soils."

Finally, Schulze and Friebauer note SOC contents

may have changed in deeper soil layers than the top 15 cm layer measured by Bellamy *et al.*, possibly in compensating ways, and they are firm in their opinion "increased temperature alone seems to be too weak a driver" to have caused the observed changes in SOC. Thus, Bellamy *et al.* merely scratched the surface of the controversial topic in a way that failed to reveal the truth.

Callesen *et al.* (2003) measured SOC contents of forest floors and mineral soils to a depth of 100 cm in 234 well-drained Danish, Finnish, Norwegian, and Swedish forests between latitudes 55° and 68°N and longitudes 6° and 28°E. They then performed a number of analyses with the data, the first of which they say revealed "soil organic carbon in forest floors and mineral soil + forest floors was positively correlated with temperature and precipitation in the study region." They also report "a similar increase in SOC with temperature and precipitation was found in nine pine stands on sandy soils in the same latitude range but between 22° and 29°E (Vucetich *et al.*, 2000) representing the same temperature gradient but a lower precipitation range." And they affirm the positive correlation with temperature was greatest for coarse-textured soils, less for medium-textured soils, and negligible for fine-textured soils.

The Nordic scientists write, "the increase in SOC with temperature and precipitation is interpreted as an indirect effect of higher net primary production," further noting in Europe "increasing site productivity has been reported in both nemoral forests and in boreal forests at higher latitudes (Eriksson and Karlsson, 1996; Skovsgaard and Henriksen, 1996; Cannell *et al.*, 1998)," and this increase "could be attributed to increased atmospheric CO_2 concentrations along with the fertilizer effect of nitrogen deposition, and management regimes optimizing forest production." These broad-based findings suggest just the opposite of what Bellamy *et al.* had claimed to be occurring in the top 15 cm of soils in England and Wales had actually been happening in the top 100 cm of soils throughout much of Europe, producing a negative feedback to both rising air temperatures and atmospheric CO_2 concentrations.

Lichter *et al.* (2005) reviewed what had been learned to that point in time about the effects of an atmospheric CO_2 enrichment of 200 ppm on the soil carbon dynamics of the Duke Forest (an aggrading loblolly pine stand near Chapel Hill, North Carolina, USA) during the first six years of the long-term FACE experiment being conducted there. Over this period, they report, organic C accumulated in the forest floor of the elevated CO_2 plots at a rate 52 ± 16 g C m^{-2} yr^{-1} greater than what would have been expected during reforestation under ambient CO_2 conditions, as represented by the rate of C accumulation in the forest floor of the ambient CO_2 plots.

This additional C sink, in their words, "resulted from increased C inputs of 50 ± 30 g C m^{-2} yr^{-1} to the forest floor in response to CO_2 enhancement of primary production." And since there was "no evidence that the overall rate of decomposition of the forest floor decreased under the elevated CO_2 treatment," they conclude "the additional C sink in the forest floor of the elevated CO_2 treatment ... is wholly dependent on the net primary production enhancement and increased C inputs," which after six years had increased the forest floor's organic C content by approximately 27%, as best as could be determined from their plotted data. The data gave no indication this trend will decline anytime soon.

With respect to the underlying mineral soil, Lichter *et al.* report they detected no statistically significant treatment effects on the C content of the bulk mineral soil or the intra-aggregate particulate organic matter and mineral-associated organic matter fractions after six years of CO_2 enrichment. Nevertheless, there was a nearly statistically significant ($P = 0.11$) increase of 18.5% in the free light fraction of the organic matter in the top 15 cm of the soil profile, and a 3.9% increase in the total intra-aggregate particulate organic matter there. The sum of the organic C in these two categories plus the mineral-associated organic C was 11.5% greater in the CO_2-enriched plots than in the ambient treatment plots.

Although Lichter *et al.* expressed pessimism and a belief "forest soils are unlikely to sequester significant additional quantities of atmospheric C associated with CO_2 fertilization because of the low rates of C input to refractory and protected soil organic matter pools," the CO_2-enriched trees of their study continued to demonstrate a large and unabated growth advantage over the ambient-CO_2 trees, and both the forest floor and the surface soil horizon beneath the CO_2-enriched trees continued to accumulate more organic C than the forest floor and surface soil horizon beneath the ambient-CO_2 trees. And, therefore, the un-stimulated refractory and protected soil organic matter pools of which Lichter *et al.* write could yet begin to show increased carbon accumulation.

In addition to the naturally occurring phenomena that tend to mute the rate of rise of the anthropogenic-driven increase in the atmosphere's CO_2 concentration, there are others that owe their existence to human ingenuity. Prior *et al.* (2005) describe a multifaceted field management system developed to help farmers conserve resources and increase crop yields while simultaneously stimulating carbon sequestration in their fields.

Unlike a conventional cropping system, this conservation system employed little to no tillage and used special crop rotations. In the southern United States, where Prior *et al.* had been testing the two approaches for the prior five years, the conventional cropping system consisted of a rotation cycle where grain sorghum and soybean were rotated each year with spring tillage after winter fallow that produced only a light growth of weeds. In the conservation cropping system, grain sorghum and soybean were also rotated, but in the place of weeds were three cover crops: crimson clover, sunn hemp, and wheat, which were similarly rotated but without tillage.

To see how the two management systems compared in terms of crop production and soil carbon sequestration, and how well they might fare in the high-CO$_2$ world expected to prevail a half-century or so from now, the five U.S. Department of Agriculture scientists employed the systems for four years (two complete cropping cycles) in 7-meter-wide x 76-meter-long x 2-meter-deep bins filled with a silt loam soil, upon which they constructed a number of clear-plastic-wall open-top chambers they maintained at atmospheric CO$_2$ concentrations that averaged either 375 ppm (ambient) or 683 ppm (enriched) over the four years of their study.

In terms of the cumulative residue produced over the two cropping cycles, the scientists found little interaction between management practices and atmospheric CO$_2$ concentration, with conservation practices increasing this parameter by about 90% in both CO$_2$ treatments, elevated CO$_2$ increasing it by approximately 30% in both of the management treatments, and conservation practices and elevated CO$_2$ together increasing it by 150%. In terms of the carbon retained and incorporated into the first 5 cm of the soil at the end of the two cropping cycles, however, there were significant interactions. The elevated CO$_2$ increased this important soil property by about 10% in the conventional system, but by 45% in the conservation system, and the application of conservation practices increased 0–5 cm soil carbon storage by close to 45% in ambient-CO$_2$ air but by nearly 90% in elevated-CO$_2$ air. Together, the two treatments increased surface soil carbon storage by close to 110%.

Clearly, increasing atmospheric CO$_2$ concentra-

tions and best-management conservation practices work hand-in-hand to boost crop yields and residue production while increasing soil carbon storage, with each factor bringing out the best in the other. In addition, as Prior *et al.* note, "in an elevated CO$_2$ environment there will be larger amounts of crop residue and consequently more ground cover," so "accumulation of additional surface litter may improve water infiltration (and storage) and help ameliorate water quality problems by reducing runoff and soil erosion."

Jastrow *et al.* (2005) write many field-scale CO$_2$-enrichment studies "have failed to detect significant changes in soil C against the relatively large, spatially heterogeneous pool of existing soil organic matter, leading to the general conclusion that the potential for increased soil C is limited (Hungate *et al.*, 1997; Gill *et al.*, 2002; Hagedorn *et al.*, 2003; Lichter *et al.*, 2005)." And an additional long-held opinion, as they relate it, is, "if CO$_2$-stimulated increases in soil organic C do occur, they will be allocated to rapidly cycling, labile pools with little, if any, long-term stabilization," citing Hungate *et al.* (1997) and Lichter *et al.* (2005). By the time of Jastrow *et al.*'s writing, however, after many long and arduous experiments had been conducted and their data properly analyzed, the truth was beginning to be seen to be quite different.

The long-awaited confirmation of the more optimistic view of the subject was firmly established by Jastrow *et al.* (2005). They describe and further analyze the findings of the first five years of the deciduous forest FACE study being conducted at Oak Ridge, Tennessee (Norby *et al.*, 2001); the entire eight years of the prairie grassland open-top chamber study at Manhattan, Kansas (Owensby *et al.*, 1993); and 35 other similar studies.

They found atmospheric CO$_2$ enrichment to approximately 200 ppm above ambient "increased C stocks in the forest soil at an average rate of 44 ± 9 g C m^{-2} yr^{-1}," and "in the prairie, the incremental increase in C stocks corresponded to an average accrual rate of 59 ± 19 g C m^{-2} yr^{-1}." This happened because "both systems responded to CO$_2$ enrichment with large increases in root production," and "even though native C stocks were relatively large, over half of the accrued C at both sites was incorporated into micro-aggregates, which protect C and increase its longevity." Likewise, their meta-analysis of the 35 independent experimental observations indicated CO$_2$ enrichment ranging from 200 to 350 ppm over periods ranging from two to nine years increased soil C over soil depths ranging from 5 to 20 cm by 5.6%

(95% CI = 2.8–8.4%), "supporting the generality of the accrual measured in the forest and prairie experiments."

The seven scientists say their findings "clearly demonstrate that mineral soil C, including micro-aggregate protected pools, can increase measurably in response to a step-function increase in atmospheric CO_2 concentrations," and "the C storage capacities of mineral soils—even those with large organic matter stocks—are not necessarily saturated at present and may be capable of serving as C sinks if inputs increase as a result of passive CO_2 fertilization." In addition, they write "the meta-analysis, which included some multifactor studies and data collected over a wide range of climatic conditions, suggests that soil C accrual ... is likely to be a general response to CO_2 enrichment."

This response, Jastrow et al. state, "is not insignificant." They note, "if mineral soil C in the surface 20 cm of the world's temperate forests, temperate grasslands, shrublands, and croplands (234 Pg C ... according to Jobbagy and Jackson, 2000) were to increase by 5.6% or at a rate of 19 g C m^{-2} yr^{-1}, then 8–13 Pg of C might be accumulated within a 10-year period." That suggests the amount of carbon found in the soils of these biomes could be doubled over a period of 180 years (234 Pg C divided by 1.3 Pg C per year = 180 years).

These several observations demonstrate the soil-carbon-sequestering capability of Earth's vegetation can indeed act as a significant brake on the rate of rise of the air's CO_2 content and thereby help mute any CO_2-induced impetus for global warming.

At the Sky Oaks CO_2 enrichment site of San Diego State University in California, located in chaparral vegetation dominated by chemise (Adenostoma fasciulatum) shrubs, researchers constructed 12 2-m by 2-m by 2-m closed chambers so as to contain a central individual Adenostoma shrub and its surrounding herbaceous plants. Beginning in December 1995, they maintained the chambers continuously at six atmospheric CO_2 concentrations ranging from 250 to 750 ppm in 100-ppm increments. At various times throughout 1999, they took measurements of net ecosystem exchange of CO_2 and collected soil samples for analyses of arbuscular mycorrhizal (AM) fungi and sequestered carbon found in both bulk soil and water-stable aggregates.

Treseder et al. (2003) report "plants and soils within the chambers took up more carbon under CO_2 enrichment." Specifically, the chambers exposed to 250 to 550 ppm CO_2 released an average of 703 g C m^{-2} year^{-1}, and the chambers in the 650–750-ppm treatments absorbed an average of 160 g C m^{-2} year^{-1}. Likely driven by these dramatic CO_2-induced differences in net ecosystem exchange of CO_2, it was not surprising, as they describe it, "pools of total carbon in bulk soil and in water-stable aggregates increased 1.5- and three-fold, respectively, between the 250- and 650-ppm treatments." In addition, they found "the abundance of live AM hyphae and spores rose markedly over the same range of CO_2." Thus Treseder et al. conclude the augmentation of the carbon pools found in their study, "if common in other ecosystems, appears substantial enough to influence sequestration of CO_2 originating from fossil fuel burning and deforestation."

In another study from the same location utilizing the identical experimental chambers, Allen et al. (2005) assessed the various ways carbon entered the soil and was sequestered there. They found the "total allocation of carbon to soil increased significantly through the study period with elevated CO_2," as did "new carbon inputs into macro-aggregates." This latter observation is very important, as these aggregates, in their words, "have increasing concentrations of glomalin, a glycoprotein produced by arbuscular mycorrhizal fungi (Rillig et al., 1999)," a substance that acts to create and stabilize soil aggregates and protect the carbon they contain. In addition, the scientists report CO_2 effects on soil bacteria "were not detectable." They report microbial mass was "negatively affected by increasing CO_2," noting, "under extended nitrogen limitation the plants ultimately garner the nitrogen," and the plants "ultimately outcompete microbes for these scarce soil resources," citing Hu et al. (2001).

In concluding the discussion of their findings, Allen et al. remark, "undisturbed arid shrublands may not fix comparatively large amounts of carbon, but they may sequester a large fraction of that carbon." Noting "carbon allocated to arbuscular mycorrhizal fungi forms a large part of the macro-aggregate structure in the form of glomalin (Rillig et al., 2002)," and those aggregates "may be protected from decomposition," they conclude the enhanced formation of such aggregates in CO_2-enriched air forms "an important [carbon] sequestration pathway" in chaparral ecosystems.

Working in the Mojave Desert at the FACE facility located near Mercury, Nevada, USA, where various shrubs and perennial grasses grow, Billings and Schaeffer (2004) examined the effects of atmospheric CO_2 enrichment (to 550 ppm throughout each growing season since April 1997) on soil nitrogen (N) dynamics via measurements of foliage C and N contents and isotope composition, and by measuring resin-available N and rates of soil respiration in the field in conjunction with assessments of potential C evolution and net N mineralization derived from long-term soil incubations. Their findings showed the "effects of elevated CO_2 on soil C and N dynamics are variable and complex, with many competing processes," and "changes in soil microbial activity with elevated CO_2 ... could affect both mineralizing and immobilizing microbial processes." Nevertheless, the bulk of their observations suggest "elevated CO_2 may increase root and/or soil microbial activity," which more often than not "can result in periodic increases in resin-available N, particularly when soil moisture is available." They say these several interrelated phenomena "may translate into more plant available N at these times." The two researchers thus conclude "if increases in plant-available N are maintained, particularly when soil moisture is available, arid ecosystems may be able to sustain any increases in productivity induced by elevated CO_2."

In studying the potential for the long-term storage of carbon in Earth's soils, Lagomarsino et al. (2006) note an increase of labile carbon below ground, such as is typically provided by atmospheric CO_2 enrichment, "could induce two mechanisms acting in opposite ways: (1) an enhanced soil organic matter decomposition due to the stimulation of microbial activity through the so-called *priming effect* (Kuzyakov et al., 2000); and (2) a retarded mineralization of native soil organic carbon due to the preference of microbes for easily decomposable substrates (Cardon et al., 2001)."

In a study designed to determine which mechanism is likely the stronger of the two, Lagomarsino et al. conducted physical and chemical analyses of soils they sampled in June and October 2004 at the POPFACE experimental plantation in central Italy, where clones of *Populus alba*, *Populus nigra,* and *Populus x euramericana* had been grown since 1999 with nitrogen fertilization throughout the 2002–2004 growing seasons. Hoosbeek et al. (2004) observed a priming effect of the newly incorporated litter in the first rotation cycle of trees exposed to air containing an approximate 50% increase in atmospheric CO_2 concentration, but in the second rotation cycle Hoosbeek et al. (2006) observed an accumulation of carbon in the soil of that treatment. In harmony with this latter observation, Lagomarsino et al.'s 2004 data reveal no increase in carbon mineralization activity under elevated CO_2, but rather

a decrease of microbial basal respiration in the non-rhizospheric soil of the CO_2-enriched treatment. And noting "microbial carbon immobilization was the dominant process under elevated CO_2, limiting the carbon losses from soil," Lagomarsino et al. conclude their results suggest "a possible positive trend for carbon storage on the long term, independent of soil nitrogen availability."

Cheng et al. (2007) conducted a two-year FACE study of sorghum (*Sorghum bicolor* (L.) Moench) near Phoenix, Arizona (USA), where they studied the dynamics of soil organic carbon (SOC) pools comprised of labile and recalcitrant SOC of short and long mean residence time (MRT), respectively, under control conditions (360 ppm CO_2) and FACE conditions (560 ppm CO_2), together with water-adequate (wet) and water-deficient (dry) treatments. They note it is difficult to measure changes in total SOC content over periods of only a few years because soils typically contain large amounts of carbon compared to what they sequester annually. Their study proved no exception to this rule, as no significant differences in total SOC could be detected between the control and FACE treatments over the two years of the sorghum experiment.

Nevertheless, they learned much by other means, such as stable-carbon isotopic ($\delta^{13}C$) tracing, which revealed 53% of the final SOC in the FACE plot was in the recalcitrant or long MRT carbon pool and 47% in the labile or short MRT pool, whereas in the control plot 46% and 54% of the final SOC was in the recalcitrant and labile pools, respectively. This indicates "elevated CO_2 transferred more SOC into the slow-decay carbon pool," the ten researchers write. In addition, they report "isotopic mixing models revealed that increased new sorghum residue input to the recalcitrant pool mainly accounts for this change, especially for the upper soil horizon (0–30 cm) where new carbon in recalcitrant soil pools of FACE wet and dry treatments was 1.7 and 2.8 times as large as that in respective Control recalcitrant pools." In addition, Cheng et al. state "old C in the recalcitrant pool under elevated CO_2 was higher than that under ambient CO_2, indicating that elevated CO_2 reduces the decay of the old C in [the] recalcitrant pool."

Therefore, because "higher recalcitrant C content and lower labile C content in the soils were detected under elevated CO_2 relative to ambient CO_2 treatments, suggesting that SOC under elevated CO_2 becomes more stable against chemical and biological degradation," the ten scientists say their results imply terrestrial agro-ecosystems may play a critical role in sequestering CO_2 under future atmospheric conditions.

Bockheim (2007) explains "cryoturbation is a dominant process in permafrost regions and refers collectively to all soil movements due to frost action," and reports several prior studies suggested cryoturbation "was particularly active during mid-Holocene warming periods in the arctic." Bockheim thus studied the effect sustained warming will have on redistribution of soil organic carbon, and whether this redistribution will exacerbate or mitigate the release of CO_2 to the atmosphere. The study focused on the amount of soil organic carbon (SOC) incorporated via cryoturbation into the active layer and near-surface permafrost of 21 sites in northern Alaska, 10 of which were located in the Arctic Coastal Plain and 11 of which were in the Arctic Foothills. Based on data acquired from the 21 sites, the University of Wisconsin researcher determined "55% of the SOC density of the active layer and near-surface permafrost could be attributed to redistribution from cryoturbation," listing "five lines of evidence suggesting that increased cryoturbation from arctic warming will result in increased storage of SOC."

First, Bockheim states "once cryoturbation has moved SOC to the cold, deeper soil layers, little or no biological decomposition will take place." Second, "major organic horizons that are cryoturbated ... are 10 to 50% more dense than the equivalent uncryoturbated horizons," and "low-density SOC may be more susceptible to decomposition than high-density SOC." Third, "low-molecular-weight neutrally charged organic compounds are more biodegradable than high-molecular fractions." Fourth, "Kaiser *et al.* (2007) reported lower decomposition rates of redistributed SOC in Siberian subsoils than in equivalent material collected from the surface." And fifth, "mechanistic models (Waelbroeck *et al.*, 1997) predict that sustained arctic warming will result in permafrost thawing and a delayed long-lasting increase in SOC storage."

Bockheim concludes, "these results suggest that continued warming of the arctic may accelerate cryoturbation," and "this, in turn, will increase the incorporation of dense, high-molecular-weight SOC at depth, thereby enabling the soil to store more SOC than at present and reducing the loss of CO_2 to the atmosphere from soil respiration"—essentially just the opposite of what IPCC contends.

Pendall and King (2007) conducted a series of long-term (170–330 days) laboratory incubation experiments to examine changes in soil organic matter pool sizes and turnover rates in soil collected from an open-top chamber (OTC) atmospheric CO_2 enrichment study in the shortgrass steppe of northeastern Colorado, USA, where the air in the ambient CO_2 chambers (ACs) and elevated CO_2 chambers (ECs) had atmospheric CO_2 concentrations of 360 and 720 ppm, respectively, and where this degree of CO_2 enrichment enhanced both above- and below-ground plant growth by 15–35%. They also discovered "active pool carbon increased in EC relative to AC treatments systematically over the first 3 years of exposure to elevated CO_2 in topsoils and to a lesser degree in subsoils," and they remark, "these results are consistent with independent results from the same OTC study showing that rhizo-deposition rates doubled and root production increased under elevated CO_2." In addition, they report "new carbon turnover was not enhanced by elevated CO_2," confirming "new carbon inputs under elevated CO_2 are not simply lost to mineralization" and "pool sizes may continue to increase under elevated CO_2." The two researchers conclude, "these results suggest that soil carbon storage may increase in semi-arid grasslands under elevated CO_2," and they opine this phenomenon, in turn, would tend to mitigate the global warming thought by many to accompany increases in the air's CO_2 content.

Marhan *et al.* (2008) studied undisturbed soil cores with and without visible wheat residues extracted at the conclusion of the third year of a mini-FACE experiment conducted in a field near Hohenheim, Germany planted annually to spring wheat (*Triticum aestivum* L.). The researchers examined the effect of elevated atmospheric CO_2 concentration (an extra 160 ppm) on the decomposition of the wheat residues present in the soil by measuring CO_2 evolution from the cores, as well as the leaching of inorganic and organic carbon from them, during 191 days of core incubations in the laboratory. They found cumulative residue decomposition was not affected by elevated CO_2 when no wheat residues were visible in the cores. When such residues were visible, however, decomposition was "significantly lower" (by 19%) in the elevated compared to the ambient CO_2 treatment, which for the more common 300 ppm degree of atmospheric CO_2 enrichment roughly translates to a decomposition reduction of 36%. In addition, they report more dissolved inorganic carbon (DIC) was leached from the elevated CO_2 treatment cores, both with and without visible plant residues, than from similar cores from the ambient CO_2 treatment (47.2% and 29.5%, respectively, for their degree of CO_2 enrichment, which equates to about 88% and 55%, respectively, for a 300 ppm increase in atmospheric CO_2 concentration). These extra amounts of DIC represent "an additional possible mechanism for carbon sequestration in soils of arable cropping systems under future elevated CO_2 concentrations," they note. They also report stubble and root biomass was higher by 12.0 and 9.44%, respectively, in soil cores taken from the elevated CO_2 plots at the end of the study, which equates to approximate stubble and root biomass enhancements of 22% and 18%, respectively, for a 300 ppm increase in atmospheric CO_2 concentration. With respect to the potential for enhanced carbon sequestration in wheat (and other cereal-crop) fields in a CO_2-enriched world of the future, therefore, the six scientists conclude, "increased input of plant residues and reduced decomposition of plant-derived carbon" are "possible mechanisms for enhanced carbon sequestration under elevated atmospheric CO_2 concentration."

Hopkins et al. (2009) write there were "two sets of long-term experimental plots which have been under constant and known management for over a century and for which historical data exist that allow comparison over recent decades to determine what, if any, changes in SOC have occurred." These unique plots were the Palace Leas Meadow Hay Plots in northeast England, established in 1897, and the plots of the Park Grass Continuous Hay Experiment established in 1856 at Rothamsted in southeast England. In studying them, Hopkins et al. say they determined "there were no significant differences between 1982 and 2006 for the Palace Leas plots or between 1959 and 2002 for the Park Grass plots," leading them to conclude, "there has been no consistent decrease in SOC stocks in surface soils under old, permanent grassland in England in recent decades, even though meteorological records for both sites indicate significant warming of the soil and air between 1980 and 2000." They theorize "the lack of a consistent decline in SOC content linked to increased soil temperature since 1980 may be due to a compensatory increase in primary production," citing Jenkinson et al. (1991).

Martens et al. (2009) write, "the generally higher above and belowground productivity of C_3 plants under elevated CO_2 leads to the conclusion that more rhizo-depositions (roots and exudates) are transferred into soils, potentially increasing soil carbon content," but they note most FACE and outdoor chamber studies have failed to detect significant changes in soil organic carbon (SOC) due to the typically large amount and spatially heterogeneous nature of preexisting SOC. In an attempt to overcome these difficulties, Martens et al. cultivated well-watered and well-fertilized spring wheat (cv. Minaret) in stainless steel cylinders forced into the soil of control and free-air CO_2-enriched (to 180 ppm above ambient) plots at the experimental farm of the Federal Research Institute in Braunschweig, Germany, where between stem elongation and beginning of ripening the plants were repeatedly pulse-labeled with $^{14}CO_2$ and thereafter monitored daily for soil-borne total CO_2 and $^{14}CO_2$ until harvest, after which the distribution of ^{14}C was analyzed in all plant parts, soil, soil mineral fractions, and soil microbial biomass.

The four researchers found "in comparison to ambient conditions, 28% more $^{14}CO_2$ and 12% more total CO_2 was evolved from soil under elevated CO_2," and "in the root-free soil 27% more residual ^{14}C was found in the free-air CO_2-enriched soil than in the soil from the ambient treatment." In addition, they say, in soil samples from both treatments about 80% of residual ^{14}C was "integrated into the stable, clay bound soil organic matter pool," which suggests, "under FACE conditions a considerable contribution was made to the long-term storage of soil carbon in this soil." Thus Martens et al. were able to "show for the first time," as they describe it, "that a crop plant grown under FACE conditions deposited significantly more carbon to soil than those grown under ambient CO_2 in the field," and "the additional carbon input under elevated CO_2 did not induce an accelerated degradation of pre-existing soil organic matter (no positive priming effect)." Those findings demonstrate "wheat plants grown under elevated CO_2 can contribute to an additional net carbon gain in soils," which is especially beneficial to the biosphere.

Springsteen et al. (2010) write "woody plant expansion within grassland ecosystems is a worldwide phenomenon, and dramatic vegetation shifts from grassland to savanna/woodlands have occurred over the past 50–100 years in North America," noting one of the chief factors contributing to this phenomenon is believed to be the concomitant historical increase in the air's carbon dioxide concentration, as suggested by Archer et al. (1995), Polley (1997), Bond and Midgley (2000), and Bond et al. (2003). They also state once shrublands are established, they tend to persist for a number of possible reasons, one of which is a type of feedback phenomenon referred to as islands of fertility, which "occurs when resources accumulate in soils beneath woody plants due to litterfall, interception of wet and dry deposition, nitrogen fixation, and animal droppings," as described by Schlesinger et al. (1990),

Archer *et al.* (1995), Reynolds *et al.* (1999), and Lopez-Pintor *et al.* (2006). They report, "changes in soil attributes under woody vegetation have been documented in the arid grasslands of the southern Great Plains, including increases in soil carbon and nitrogen," citing Reynolds *et al.* (1999), Hibbard *et al.* (2001, 2003), McCulley *et al.* (2004), Schade and Hobbie (2005), and Liao *et al.* (2006).

In their work at the USDA-ARS Northern Great Plains Research Laboratory near Mandan, North Dakota (USA), Springsteen *et al.* examined near-surface (upper 15 cm) soil biogeochemistry along a 42-year (1963–2005) chrono-sequence, which encompassed grassland, woodland, and grassland-woodland transition zones in a northern Great Plains grassland, to determine the influence of woody plant expansion on soil carbon and nitrogen contents. The four researchers report total soil carbon content rose by 26% across the chrono-sequence from grassland to woodland within the 0–15 cm soil depth, and total soil nitrogen content rose by 31%. In addition, they report, the rate of woody shrub expansion from 1963 to 1988 (25 years) was ~1,800 m^2 per year at their study site, and from 1988 to 2005 (17 years) it was ~3,800 m^2 per year, or just a little more than doubled.

Yang *et al.* (2010) write, "soil stores more than twice as much carbon than does vegetation or the atmosphere," citing Schlesinger (1997), and they note many people believe "climate warming is likely to accelerate the decomposition of soil organic carbon which could lead to increased carbon release from soils, providing a positive feedback to climate change (Davidson and Janssens, 2006)." To test that belief, Yang *et al.* "conducted five consecutive regional soil surveys in China's grasslands during 2001–2005 and sampled 981 soil profiles from 327 sites across the northern part of the country," comparing their results "with data of 275 soil profiles derived from China's National Soil Inventory during the 1980s." The seven scientists report the organic carbon stock in the upper 30 cm of soil in northern China's grasslands "did not show significant association with mean annual temperature," and "grassland soil organic carbon stock did not change significantly over the past two decades."

Yang *et al.* conclude, "it has been often asserted that soil will act as a carbon source because of its sensitivity to global environmental change (e.g., Melillo *et al.*, 2002; Bellamy *et al.*, 2005; Schipper *et al.*, 2007)," but "in contrast to these previous reports, our results indicate that soil organic carbon stock in northern China's grasslands has not experienced significant changes during the past two decades,

despite measureable climate change."

Iversen *et al.* (2012) explored the fate of carbon (C) and nitrogen (N) in the soil of a sweetgum tree (*Liquidambar styraciflua* L.) plantation in Oak Ridge, Tennessee (USA) at the conclusion of a nearly 12-year FACE study. The four researchers report net primary productivity increased in response to atmospheric CO_2 enrichment "even though production in the sweetgum stand was limited by soil N availability." In addition, they write, "the majority of the additional C fixed under elevated CO_2 was allocated belowground to the production of fine roots," with the largest increases in root biomass production and mortality being "at relatively deep soil depths (i.e., below 30 cm)," with the end result "soil C and N contents were greater throughout the soil profile under elevated CO_2 at the conclusion of the experiment." With respect to carbon, for example, "soil C content was ~19% greater throughout the soil profile after more than 11 years of CO_2 enrichment."

Iversen *et al.* conclude, "the greater residence time of C in deeper soil indicates that inputs from deep roots under elevated CO_2 may increase the potential for long-term storage of C and N in forested ecosystems." They add, "this finding suggests greater C accrual in elevated CO_2 compared with ambient CO_2 during the experiment, consistent with the conclusion of a meta-analysis that indicated increased ecosystem C storage under elevated CO_2 (Luo *et al.*, 2006)." These observations presage "the potential of future forests to store C and mitigate some portion of rising atmospheric CO_2," as they state in the concluding sentence of their report.

Zhou *et al.* (2013) took advantage of a long-term field experiment with increased temperature and precipitation, established in late April 2005 in a semiarid temperate steppe in Duolun County, Inner Mongolia, China, "to investigate the effects of warming, increased precipitation and their interactions on SOC [soil organic carbon] fraction" by quantifying "labile SOC, recalcitrant SOC and stable SOC at 0–10 and 10–20 cm depths." They found "neither warming nor increased precipitation affected total SOC and stable SOC at either depth," but "increased precipitation significantly increased labile SOC at the 0–10 cm depth" and "warming decreased labile SOC and marginally but significantly increased recalcitrant SOC at the 10–20 cm depth." They also found "significant interactive effects of warming and increased precipitation on labile SOC and recalcitrant SOC at the 0–10 cm depths."

Zhou *et al.* conclude, "given that the absolute increase of SOC in the recalcitrant SOC pool was much greater than the decrease in labile SOC, and that the mean residence time of recalcitrant SOC is much greater, our results suggest that soil C storage at 10–20 cm depth may increase with increasing temperature in this semiarid grassland," which represents a net negative feedback on predicted global warming and a tremendous benefit for the terrestrial biosphere.

References

Allen, M.F., Klironomos, J.N., Treseder, K.K., and Oechel, W.C. 2005. Responses of soil biota to elevated CO₂ in a chaparral ecosystem. *Ecological Applications* **15**: 1701–1711.

Andrews, J.A. and Schlesinger, W.H. 2001. Soil CO₂ dynamics, acidification, and chemical weathering in a temperate forest with experimental CO₂ enrichment. *Global Biogeochemical Cycles* **15**: 149–162.

Archer, S., Schimel, D.S., and Holland, E.A. 1995. Mechanisms of shrubland expansion: land use, climate or CO₂? *Climatic Change* **29**: 91–99.

Bellamy, P.H., Loveland, P.J., Bradley, R.I., Lark, R.M., and Kirk, G.J.D. 2005. Carbon losses from all soils across England and Wales 1978–2003. *Nature* **437**: 245–248.

Billings, S.A. and Schaeffer, S.M. 2004. Soil microbial activity and N availability with elevated CO₂ in Mojave Desert soils. *Global Biogeochemical Cycles* **18**: 10.1029/2003GB002137.

Bockheim, J.G. 2007. Importance of cryoturbation in redistributing organic carbon in permafrost-affected soils. *Soil Science Society of America Journal* **71**: 1335–1342.

Bond, W.J. and Midgley, G.F. 2000. A proposed CO₂-controlled mechanism of woody plant invasion in grasslands and savannas. *Global Change Biology* **6**: 865–869.

Bond, W.J., Midgley, G.F., and Woodward, F.I. 2003. The importance of low atmospheric CO₂ and fire in promoting the spread of grasslands and savannas. *Global Change Biology* **9**: 973–982.

Brostoff, W.N., Sharifi, M.R., and Rundel, P.W. 2002. Photosynthesis of cryptobiotic crusts in a seasonally inundated system of pans and dunes at Edwards Air Force Base, western Mojave Desert, California: laboratory studies. *Flora* **197**: 143–151.

Callesen, I., Liski, J., Raulund-Rasmussen, K., Olsson, M.T., Tau-Strand, L., Vesterdal, L., and Westman, C.J. 2003. Soil carbon stores in Nordic well-drained forest soils—relationships with climate and texture class. *Global Change Biology* **9**: 358–370.

Cannell, M.G.R., Thornley, J.H.M., Mobbs, D.C., and Friend, A.D. 1998. UK conifer forests may be growing faster in response to increased N deposition, atmospheric CO₂ and temperature. *Forestry* **71**: 277–296.

Cardon, Z.G., Hungate, B.A., Cambardella, C.A., Chapin III, F.S., Field, C.B., Holland, E.A., and Mooney, H.A. 2001. Contrasting effects of elevated CO₂ on old and new soil carbon pools. *Soil Biology & Biochemistry* **33**: 365–373.

Casella, E. and Soussana, J.-F. 1997. Long-term effects of CO₂ enrichment and temperature increase on the carbon balance of a temperate grass sward. *Journal of Experimental Botany* **48**: 1309–1321.

Cheng, L., Leavitt, S.W., Kimball, B.A., Pinter Jr., P.J., Ottman, M.J., Matthias, A., Wall, G.W., Brooks, T., Williams, D.G., and Thompson, T.L. 2007. Dynamics of labile and recalcitrant soil carbon pools in a sorghum free-air CO₂ enrichment (FACE) agroecosystem. *Soil Biology & Biochemistry* **39**: 2250–2263.

Cotrufo, M.F. and Gorissen, A. 1997. Elevated CO₂ enhances below-ground C allocation in three perennial grass species at different levels of N availability. *New Phytologist* **137**: 421–431.

Davidson, E.A. and Janssens, I.A. 2006. Temperature sensitivity of soil carbon decomposition and feedbacks to climate change. *Nature* **440**: 165–173.

De Angelis, P., Chigwerewe, K.S., and Mugnozza, G.E.S. 2000. Litter quality and decomposition in a CO₂-enriched Mediterranean forest ecosystem. *Plant and Soil* **224**: 31–41.

Dilustro, J.J., Day, F.P., Drake, B.G., and Hinkle, C.R. 2002. Abundance, production and mortality of fine roots under elevated atmospheric CO₂ in an oak-scrub ecosystem. *Environmental and Experimental Botany* **48**: 149–159.

Eriksson, H. and Karlsson, K. 1996. Long-term changes in site index in growth and yield experiments with Norway Spruce (*Picea abies* L.) (Karst) and Scots Pine (*Pinus sylvestris*) in Sweden. *European Forest Institute Research Report* **5**: 79–87.

Evans, R.D. and Belnap, J. 1999. Long-term consequences of disturbance on nitrogen dynamics in an arid ecosystem. *Ecology* **80**: 150–160.

Evans, R.D. and Johansen, J.R. 1999. Microbiotic crusts and ecosystem processes. *Critical Reviews in Plant Sciences* **18**: 183–225.

Fitter, A.H., Self, G.K., Brown, T.K., Bogie, D.S., Graves, J.D., Benham, D., and Ineson, P. 1999. Root production and turnover in an upland grassland subjected to artificial soil warming respond to radiation flux and nutrients, not temperature. *Oecologia* **120**: 575–581.

Gill, R.A. and Burke, I.C. 1999. Ecosystem consequences of plant life form changes at three sites in the semiarid United States. *Oecologia* **121**: 551–563.

Gill, R.A., Polley, H.W., Johnson, H.B., Anderson, L.J., Maherali, H., and Jackson, R.B. 2002. Nonlinear grassland responses to past and future atmospheric CO_2. *Nature* **417**: 279–282.

Griffin, D.W., Kellogg, C.A., Garrison, V.H., and Shinn, E.A. 2002. The global transport of dust. *American Scientist* **90**: 228–235.

Hagedorn, F., Spinnler, D., Bundt, M., Blaser, P., and Siegwolf, R. The input and fate of new C in two forest soils under elevated CO_2. *Global Change Biology* **9**: 862–872.

Harden, J.W., Sharpe, J.M., Parton, W.P., Ojima, D.S., Fries, T.L., Huntington, T.G., and Dabney, S.M. 1999. Dynamic replacement and loss of soil carbon on eroding cropland. *Global Biogeochemical Cycles* **14**: 855–901.

Haynes, R.J. and Fraser, P.M. 1998. A comparison of aggregate stability and biological activity in earthworm casts and uningested soil as affected by amendment with wheat and lucerne straw. *European Journal of Soil Science* **49**: 629–636.

Heath, J., Ayres, E., Possell, M., Bardgett, R.D., Black, H.I.J., Grant, H., Ineson, P., and Kerstiens, G. 2005. Rising atmospheric CO_2 reduces sequestration of root-derived soil carbon. *Science* **309**: 1711–1713.

Henning, F.P., Wood, C.W., Rogers, H.H., Runion, G.B., and Prior, S.A. 1996. Composition and decomposition of soybean and sorghum tissues grown under elevated atmospheric carbon dioxide. *Journal of Environmental Quality* **25**: 822–827.

Hibbard, K.A., Archer, S., Schimel, D.S., and Valentine, D.W. 2001. Biogeochemical changes accompanying woody plant encroachment in a subtropical savanna. *Ecology* **82**: 1999–2011.

Hibbard, K.A., Schimel, D.S., Archer, S., Ojima, D.S., and Parton, W. 2003. Grassland to woodland transitions: integrating changes in landscape structure and biogeochemistry. *Ecological Applications* **13**: 911–926.

Hoosbeek, M.R., Li, Y., and Scarascia-Mugnozza, G. 2006. Free atmospheric CO_2 enrichment (FACE) increased labile and total carbon in the mineral soil of a short rotation Poplar plantation. *Plant and Soil* **281**: 247–254.

Hoosbeek, M.R., Lukac, M., van Dam, D., Godbold, D.L., Velthorst, E.J., Biondi, F.A., Peressotti, A., Cotrufo, M.F., de Angelis, P., and Scarascia-Mugnozza, G. 2004. More new carbon in the mineral soil of a poplar plantation under Free Air Carbon Enrichment (POPFACE): Cause of increased priming effect? *Global Biogeochemical Cycles* **18**: GB1040.

Hopkins, D.W., Waite, I.S., McNicol, J.W., Poulton, P.R., Macdonald, A.J., and O'Donnell, A.G. 2009. Soil organic carbon contents in long-term experimental grassland plots in the UK (Palace Leas and Park Grass) have *not* changed consistently in recent decades. *Global Change Biology* **15**: 1739–1754.

Hu, S., Chapin III, F.S., Firestone, M.K., Field, C.B., and Chiariello, N.R. 2001. Nitrogen limitation of microbial decomposition in a grassland under elevated CO_2. *Nature* **409**: 188–191.

Hungate, B.A., Holland E.A., Jackson, R.B., Chapin III, F.S., Mooney, H.A., and Field, C.B. 1997. The fate of carbon in grasslands under carbon dioxide enrichment. *Nature* **388**: 576–579.

Ineson, P., Cotrufo, M.F., Bol, R., Harkness, D.D., and Blum, H. 1996. Quantification of soil carbon inputs under elevated CO_2: C_3 plants in a C_4 soil. *Plant and Soil* **187**: 345.

Insam, H., Baath, E., Berreck, M., Frostegard, A., Gerzabek, M.H., Kraft, A., Schinner, F., Schweiger, P., and Tschuggnall, G. 1999. Responses of the soil microbiota to elevated CO_2 in an artificial tropical ecosystem. *Journal of Microbiological Methods* **36**: 45–54.

Islam, K.R., Mulchi, C.L. and Ali, A.A. 1999. Tropospheric carbon dioxide or ozone enrichments and moisture effects on soil organic carbon quality. *Journal of Environmental Quality* **28**: 1629–1636.

Jastrow, J.D., Miller, R.M., Matamala, R., Norby, R.J., Boutton, T.W., Rice, C.W., and Owensby, C.E. 2005. Elevated atmospheric carbon dioxide increases soil carbon. *Global Change Biology* **11**: 2057–2064.

Jenkinson, D.S., Adams, D.E., and Wild, A. 1991. Model estimates of CO_2 emissions from soil in response to global warming. *Nature* **351**: 304–306.

Jobbagy, E.G. and Jackson, R.B. 2000. The vertical distribution of soil organic carbon and its relation to climate and vegetation. *Ecological Applications* **10**: 423–436.

Johnson, L.C., Shaver, G.R., Cades, D.H., Rastetter, E., Nadelhoffer, K., Giblin, A., Laundre, J., and Stanley, A. 2000. Plant carbon-nutrient interactions control CO_2 exchange in Alaskan wet sedge tundra ecosystems. *Ecology* **81**: 453–469.

Jongmans, A.G., Pulleman, M.M., Balabane, M., van Oort, F., and Marinissen, J.C.Y. 2003. Soil structure and characteristics of organic matter in two orchards differing in earthworm activity. *Applied Soil Ecology* **24**: 219–232.

Kaiser, C., Meyer, H., Biasi, C., Rusalimova, O., Barsukov, P., and Richter, A. 2007. Conservation of soil organic matter through cryoturbation of arctic soils in Siberia.

Journal of Geophysical Research **112**: 10.1029/2006JG000258.

King, J.S., Pregitzer, K.S., Zak, D.R., Sober, J., Isebrands, J.G., Dickson, R.E., Hendrey, G.R., and Karnosky, D.F. 2001. Fine-root biomass and fluxes of soil carbon in young stands of paper birch and trembling aspen as affected by elevated atmospheric CO$_2$ and tropospheric O$_3$. *Oecologia* **128**: 237–250.

Krull, E.S., Skjemstad, J.O., Burrows, W.H., Bray, S.G., Wynn, J.G., Bol, R., Spouncer, L., and Harms, B. 2005. Recent vegetation changes in central Queensland, Australia: Evidence from δ^{13}C and ^{14}C analyses of soil organic matter. *Geoderma* **126**: 241–259.

Kuzyakov, Y., Friedel, J.K., and Stahr, K. 2000. Review of mechanisms and quantification of priming effects. *Soil Biology and Biochemistry* **32**: 1485–1498.

Lagomarsino, A., Moscatelli, M.C., De Angelis, P., and Grego, S. 2006. Labile substrates quality as the main driving force of microbial mineralization activity in a poplar plantation soil under elevated CO$_2$ and nitrogen fertilization. *Science of the Total Environment* **372**: 256–265.

Lal, R., Kimble, J.M., Follett, R.F., and Cole, C.V. 1998. *The Potential of US Cropland to Sequester Carbon and Mitigate the Greenhouse Effect.* Ann Arbor Press, Chelsea, Michigan, USA.

Leavitt, S.W., Paul, E.A., Kimball, B.A., Hendrey, G.R., Mauney, J.R., Rauschkolb, R., Rogers, H., Lewin, K.F., Nagy, J., Pinter Jr., P.J., and Johnson, H.B. 1994. Carbon isotope dynamics of free-air CO$_2$-enriched cotton and soils. *Agricultural and Forest Meteorology* **70**: 87–101.

Liao, J.D., Boutton, T.W., and Jastrow, J.D. 2006. Storage and dynamics of carbon and nitrogen in soil physical fractions following woody plant invasion of grassland. *Soil Biology and Biochemistry* **38**: 3184–3196.

Lichter, J., Barron, S.H., Bevacqua, C.E., Finzi, A.C., Irving, K.F., Stemmler, E.A., and Schlesinger, W.H. 2005. Soil carbon sequestration and turnover in a pine forest after six years of atmospheric CO$_2$ enrichment. *Ecology* **86**: 1835–1847.

Liski, J., Ilvesniemi, H., Makela, A., and Westman, C.J. 1999. CO$_2$ emissions from soil in response to climatic warming are overestimated—The decomposition of old soil organic matter is tolerant of temperature. *Ambio* **28**: 171–174.

Lopez-Pintor, A., Sal, A.G., and Benayas, J.M. R. 2006. Shrubs as a source of spatial heterogeneity—the case of *Retama sphaerocarpa* in Mediterranean pastures of central Spain. *Acta Oecologia* **29**: 247–255.

Marhan, S., Demin, D., Erbs, M., Kuzyakov, Y.,

Fangmeier, A., and Kandeler, E. 2008. Soil organic matter mineralization and residue decomposition of spring wheat grown under elevated CO$_2$ atmosphere. *Agriculture, Ecosystems and Environment* **123**: 63–68.

Martens, R., Heiduk, K., Pacholski, A., and Weigel, H.-J. 2009. Repeated ^{14}CO$_2$ pulse-labeling reveals an additional net gain of soil carbon during growth of spring wheat under free air carbon dioxide enrichment (FACE). *Soil Biology & Biochemistry* **41**: 2422–2429.

Martin, A. 1991. Short- and long-term effects of the endogenic earthworm *Millsonia anomala* (Omodeo) (Megascolecidae, Oligochaeta) of tropical savannas on soil organic matter. *Biology and Fertility of Soils* **11**: 234–238.

McCulley, R.L., Archer, S.R., Boutton, T.W., Hons, F.M., and Zuberer, D.A. 2004. Soil respiration and nutrient cycling in wooded communities developing in grassland. *Ecology* **85**: 2804–2817.

Melillo, J.M., Steudler, P.A., Aber, J.D., Newkirk, K., Lux, H., Bowles, F.P., Catricala, C., Magill, A., Ahrens, T., and Morrisseau, S. 2002. Soil warming and carbon-cycle feedbacks to the climate system. *Science* **298**: 2173–2176.

Morison, J.I.L. 1985. Sensitivity of stomata and water use efficiency to high CO$_2$. *Plant, Cell and Environment* **8**: 467–474.

Mutuo, P.K., Cadisch, G., Albrecht, A., Palm, C.A., and Verchot, L. 2005. Potential of agroforestry for carbon sequestration and mitigation of greenhouse gas emissions from soils in the tropics. *Nutrient Cycling in Agroecosystems* **71**: 45–54.

Neilsen, C.B., Groffman, P.M., Hamburg, S.P., Driscoll, C.T., Fahey, T.J., and Hardy, J.P. 2001. Freezing effects on carbon and nitrogen cycling in northern hardwood forest soils. *Soil Science Society of America Journal* **65**: 1723–1730.

Nitschelm, J.J., Lüscher, A., Hartwig, U.A., and van Kessel, C. 1997. Using stable isotopes to determine soil carbon input differences under ambient and elevated atmospheric CO$_2$ conditions. *Global Change Biology* **3**: 411–416.

Norby, R.J., Todd, D.E., Fults, J., and Johnson, D.W. 2001. Allometric determination of tree growth in a CO$_2$-enriched sweetgum stand. *New Phytologist* **150**: 477–487.

Owensby, C.E., Coyne, P.I., Ham, J.M., Auen, L.M., and Knapp, A.K. 1993. Biomass production in a tallgrass prairie ecosystem exposed to ambient and elevated CO$_2$. *Ecological Applications* **3**: 644–653.

Pendall, E. and King, J.Y. 2007. Soil organic matter dynamics in grassland soils under elevated CO$_2$: Insights from long-term incubations and stable isotopes. *Soil Biology & Biochemistry* **39**: 2628–2639.

Polley, H.W. 1997. Implications of rising atmospheric carbon dioxide concentration for rangelands. *Journal of Range Management* **50**: 561–577.

Pregitzer, K.S., Zak, D.R., Maziaasz, J., DeForest, J., Curtis, P.S., and Lussenhop, J. 2000. Interactive effects of atmospheric CO_2 and soil-N availability on fine roots of *Populus tremuloides*. *Ecological Applications* **10**: 18–33.

Prior, S.A., Rogers, H.H., Runion, G.B., Torbert, H.A., and Reicosky, D.C. 1997. Carbon dioxide-enriched agro-ecosystems: Influence of tillage on short-term soil carbon dioxide efflux. *Journal of Environmental Quality* **26**: 244–252.

Prior, S.A., Runion, G.B., Rogers, H.H., Torbert, H.A., and Reeves, D.W. 2005. Elevated atmospheric CO_2 effects on biomass production and soil carbon in conventional and conservation cropping systems. *Global Change Biology* **11**: 657–665.

Prior, S.A., Runion, G.B., Torbert, H.A., and Rogers, H.H. 2004. Elevated atmospheric CO_2 in agroecosystems: Soil physical properties. *Soil Science* **169**: 434–439.

Prior, S.A., Torbert, H.A., Runion, G.B., and Rogers, H.H. 2003. Implications of elevated CO_2-induced changes in agroecosystem productivity. *Journal of Crop Production* **8**: 217–244.

Pritchard, S.G., Rogers, H.H., Davis, M.A., Van Santen, E., Prior, S.A., and Schlesinger, W.H. 2001. The influence of elevated atmospheric CO_2 on fine root dynamics in an intact temperate forest. *Global Change Biology* **7**: 829–837.

Prospero, J.M. 2001. African dust in America. *Geotimes* **46** (11): 24–27.

Reynolds, J.F., Virginia, R.A., Kemp, P.R., de Soyza, A.G., and Tremmel, D.C. 1999. Impact of drought on desert shrubs: effects of seasonality and degree of resource island development. *Ecological Monographs* **69**: 69–106.

Rillig, M.C., Treseder, K.K., and Allen, M.F. 2002. Global change and mycorrhizal fungi. In: van der Heijden, M.G.A. and Sanders, I.R. (Eds.) *Mycorrhizal Ecology*. Springer-Verlag, New York, NY, USA, pp. 135–160.

Rillig, M.C., Wright, S.F., Allen, M.F., and Field, C.B. 1999. Rise in carbon dioxide changes soil structure. *Nature* **400**: 628.

Ritchie, J.C., Hawks, P.H., and McHenry, J.R. 1975. Deposition rates in valleys determined using fallout Cs–137. *Geological Society of America Bulletin* **86**: 1128–1130.

Ritchie, J.C. and McCarty, G.W. 2001. Sediment deposition rates and carbon content in the soils of an agricultural riparian ecosystem. *Proceedings of the Seventh Federal Interagency Sedimentation Conference* **2**: IX41-IX46.

Ritchie, J.C. and McCarty, G.W. 2003. [137]Cesium and soil carbon in a small agricultural watershed. *Soil & Tillage Research* **69**: 45–51.

Rosenzweig, C. and Hillel, D. 2000. Soils and global climate change: Challenges and opportunities. *Soil Science* **165**: 47–56.

Ross, D.J., Tate, K.R., Newton, P.C.D., Wilde, R.H., and Clark, H. 2000. Carbon and nitrogen pools and mineralization in a grassland gley soil under elevated carbon dioxide at a natural CO_2 spring. *Global Change Biology* **6**: 779–790.

Rouhier, H. and Read, D. 1999. Plant and fungal responses to elevated atmospheric CO_2 in mycorrhizal seedlings of *Betula pendula*. *Environmental and Experimental Botany* **42**: 231–241.

Schade, J.D. and Hobbie, S.E. 2005. Spatial and temporal variation in islands of fertility in the Sonoran Desert. *Biogeochemistry* **73**: 541–553.

Schipper, L.A., Baisden, T., Parfitt, R.L., Ross, C., and Claydon, J.J. 2007. Large losses of soil C and N from soil profiles under pasture in New Zealand during the past 20 years. *Global Change Biology* **13**: 1138–1144.

Schlesinger, W.H. (Ed.) 1997. *Biogeochemistry: An Analysis of Global Change*. Academic Press, San Diego, California, USA.

Schlesinger, W.H., Reynolds, J.F., Cunningham, G.L., Huenneke, L.F., Jarrell, W.M., Ross, V.A., and Whitford, W.G. 1990. Biological feedbacks in global desertification. *Science* **247**: 1043–1048.

Schulze, E.D. and Freibauer, A. 2005. Carbon unlocked from soils. *Nature* **437**: 205–206.

Skovsgaard, J.P. and Henriksen, H.A. 1996. Increasing site productivity during consecutive generations of naturally regenerated and planted beech (*Fagus sylvatica* L.) in Denmark. *European Forest Institute Research Report* **5**: 91–97.

Springsteen, A., Loya, W., Liebig, M., and Hendrickson, J. 2010. Soil carbon and nitrogen across a chronosequence of woody plant expansion in North Dakota. *Plant and Soil* **328**: 369–379.

Stallard, R.F. 1998. Terrestrial sedimentation and the carbon cycle: coupling weathering and erosion to carbon burial. *Global Biogeochemical Cycles* **12**: 231–257.

Treseder, K.K., Egerton-Warburton, L.M., Allen, M.F., Cheng, Y., and Oechel, W.C. 2003. Alteration of soil carbon pools and communities of mycorrhizal fungi in chaparral exposed to elevated carbon dioxide. *Ecosystems* **6**: 786–796.

Tuba, Z., Csintalan, Z., Szente, K., Nagy, Z., and Grace,

J. 1998. Carbon gains by desiccation-tolerant plants at elevated CO₂. *Functional Ecology* **12**: 39–44.

van Ginkel, J.H. and Gorissen, A. 1998. In situ decomposition of grass roots as affected by elevated atmospheric carbon dioxide. *Soil Science Society of America Journal* **62** : 951–958.

van Ginkel, J.H., Whitmore, A.P., and Gorissen, A. 1999. *Lolium perenne* grasslands may function as a sink for atmospheric carbon dioxide. *Journal of Environmental Quality* **28**: 1580–1584.

Verburg, P.S.J., Gorissen, A., and Arp, W.J. 1998. Carbon allocation and decomposition of root-derived organic matter in a plant-soil system of *Calluna vulgaris* as affected by elevated CO₂. *Soil Biology and Biochemistry* **30**: 1251–1258.

Vucetich, J.A., Reed, D.D., Breymeyer, A., Degorski, M., Mroz, G.D., Solon, J., Roo-Zielinska, E., and Noble, R. 2000. Carbon pools and ecosystem properties along a latitudinal gradient in northern Scots pine (*Pinus sylvestris*) forest. *Forest Ecology and Management* **136**: 135–145.

Waelbroeck, C.P., Monfray, W.C., Oechel, W.C., Hastings, S., and Vourlius, G. 1997. The impact of permafrost thawing on the carbon dynamics of tundra. *Geophysical Research Letters* **24**: 229–232.

Walling, D.E., Owens, P.N., and Leeks, G.J.L. 1999. Rates of contemporary overbank sedimentation and sediment storage on the floodplains of the main channel systems of the Yorkshire Ouse and River Tweed, UK. *Hydrological Processes* **13**: 993–1009.

Yang, Y., Fang, J., Ma, W., Smith, P., Mohammat, A., Wang, S., and Wang, W. 2010. Soil carbon stock and its changes in northern China's grasslands from 1980s to 2000s. *Global Change Biology* **16**: 3036–3047.

Zaller, J.G. and Arnone III, J.A. 1997. Activity of surface-casting earthworms in a calcareous grassland under elevated atmospheric CO₂. *Oecologia* **111**: 249–254.

Zaller, J.G. and Arnone III, J.A. 1999. Interactions between plant species and earthworm casts in a calcareous grassland under elevated CO₂. *Ecology* **80**: 873–881.

Zhou, X., Chen, C., Wang, Y, Smaill, S., and Clinton, P. 2013. Warming rather than increased precipitation increases soil recalcitrant organic carbon in a semiarid grassland after 6 years of treatments. *PLOS ONE* **8**: e53761.

1.2.5.3 Erosion

- The historical increase in the atmosphere's CO₂ concentration has significantly reduced the erosion of Earth's valuable topsoil over the past several decades, and the continuing increase in atmospheric CO₂ can maintain this trend, and perhaps even accelerate it, throughout the foreseeable future.

More than two decades ago, Idso (1989) predicted, "as a result of the direct effects of atmospheric CO₂ enrichment upon the primary plant processes of photosynthesis and transpiration ... many plants will greatly expand their ranges with augmented water use efficiencies, stabilizing the soil and protecting it from erosion." Prior to that time (and continuing well past it), study after study had concluded (and continued to conclude) soil erosion by both wind and water was running at a high sustained rate. In an article published in *Science*, Trimble and Crosson (2000) wrote, "some sources have suggested that recent erosion is as great as or greater than that of the 1930s."

Remarkably, this long-held belief in continued high or even increasing soil erosion "was based mostly on models," write Trimble and Crosson. Enlarging on this thesis, the two researchers report little physical field-based evidence other than anecdotal statements has been offered to verify the high soil erosion estimates. They note, "it is questionable whether there has ever been another perceived public problem for which so much time, effort, and money were spent in light of so little scientific evidence." The good news, according to Trimble and Crosson, is "available field evidence suggests declines of soil erosion, some very precipitous, during the past six decades."

The problem was largely a failure to realize most of the soil particles removed from one part of the land, by either wind or water, were later deposited in nearby areas, so the net loss of soil was only a very small portion of the total that was moved about by the forces of nature.

Over the course of the data-driven shift in the public's perception of U.S. soil erosion, it has become evident perceptions of several ancillary phenomena also need adjusting. Trimble and Crosson note, for example, certain studies once warned "increasingly eroded soil profiles will allow less rainfall to be infiltrated and stored," leading to "increased overland flow, erosion, and flooding." However, they note, detailed hydrologic studies indicate just the opposite was occurring: "runoff is decreasing, flood peaks are smaller, and in some places, the base flow is greater." In addition, they write, "these field studies show that more water is infiltrating into the soil and, in some cases ... significantly more water is being transpired by plants."

These real-world observations follow what would be expected on the basis of Idso's 1989 prediction. With gradually increasing atmospheric CO_2 concentrations gradually enhancing plant water use efficiencies, more plants should have gradually been spreading over the surface of the land, reducing rates of surface runoff and allowing more water to infiltrate the soil, thereby providing more water to be extracted from the soil by more plants for subsequent transpiration. These hydrologic improvements, in turn, should have improved the status of still other aspects of the planet's natural resource base, for example by increasing the stability of streams.

A pair of photographs in the Trimble and Crosson article provided a visual testament to the reality of this phenomenon. Both photos showed the same view of a portion of Bohemian Creek in La Crosse County, Wisconsin, USA. The first of the pictures, taken in 1940, showed an "eroded, shallow channel composed of gravel and cobbles, with coarse sediment deposited by overflows on the floodplain." The second, taken 34 years later in 1974, indicates the stream channel was "narrower, smaller, and more stable." In addition, Trimble and Crosson note, "the coarse sediment has been covered with fine material, and the flood plain is vegetated to the edge of the stream." And conditions improved even more over the following quarter-century, they observe.

In addition to this broad introduction to the issue of soil erosion, a number of scientific studies have focused on other specific effects of rising temperatures and atmospheric CO_2 concentrations on soil erosion.

Allen et al. (1999) analyzed sediment cores extracted from a lake in southern Italy and from the Mediterranean Sea, deriving a high-resolution climate and vegetation dataset for this region that covered the last 102,000 years. Rapid changes in vegetation were found to be correlated with rapid changes in climate, such that complete shifts in natural ecosystems sometimes occurred over periods of less than 200 years. Throughout the warmest portion of this record—the current interglacial or Holocene—the total organic carbon content of the vegetation reached its highest level, more than doubling values experienced over the rest of the record. Other proxy indicators revealed the increased vegetative cover typically was associated with less soil erosion during the more productive woody plant period of the Holocene.

Rillig et al. (2000) examined several charac-

teristics of beneficial arbuscular mycorrhizal fungi (AMF) associated with the roots of plants growing for at least 20 years along a natural CO_2 gradient near a CO_2-emitting spring in New Zealand. Enriching the air's CO_2 concentration from 370 to 670 ppm increased percent root colonization by AMF in a linear fashion—and by nearly fourfold. Similarly, fungal hyphal length experienced a more-than-threefold linear increase along the same CO_2 gradient, and total soil glomalin (a protein secreted by fungal hyphae that increases soil aggregation and stability) experienced a linear increase of approximately fivefold. Consequently, as the air's CO_2 concentration rises, the positive responses of AMF identified in this study likely will become increasingly pronounced, significantly reducing soil losses via wind and water erosion by way of CO_2-induced glomalin-mediated increases in soil aggregate stability, which should benefit terrestrial ecosystems throughout the world.

In a closely allied free-air CO_2-enrichment (FACE) study of adequately fertilized sorghum, where daylight atmospheric CO_2 concentration was increased by approximately 50%, Rillig et al. (2001) studied plants grown under both well-watered and water-stressed irrigation treatments, focusing on the effects of elevated CO_2 on the hyphal growth of AMF, two fractions of glomalin, and the production of water-stable soil aggregates. They found the 50% increase in the air's CO_2 concentration dramatically increased fungal hyphae lengths—by about 120% in the wet irrigation treatment and 240% in the dry treatment. The biological effects of the extra CO_2 in the air also increased the mass of water-stable soil aggregates—by 40% in the wet treatment and 20% in the dry treatment. In addition, the researchers write, the "two fractions of glomalin and AMF hyphal lengths were all positively correlated with soil aggregate water stability." Hence they say their study "demonstrated for the first time that elevated CO_2 can affect soil aggregation in an agricultural system," where "a soil stabilizing effect of CO_2 would be clearly advantageous."

Knox (2001) determined how the conversion of the United States' Upper Mississippi River Valley from prairie and forest to crop and pasture land by settlers in the early 1800s influenced subsequent watershed runoff and soil erosion rates. They found conversion of the region's natural landscape to agricultural uses boosted surface erosion rates to values three to eight times greater than those characteristic of pre-settlement times. In addition, the land-use conversion increased peak discharges from high-frequency floods by 200 to 400%. Since the late

1930s, however, surface runoff has been decreasing; but this decrease was "not associated with climatic causes," Knox writes, as "an analysis of temporal variation in storm magnitudes for the same period showed no statistically significant trend."

It is important to note the decreases in soil erosion rates and extreme streamflow conditions that began in the late 1930s in the Upper Mississippi River Valley were the exact opposite of predictions, which suggest these phenomena should have been increasing as a result of unprecedented CO$_2$-induced global warming. However, they likely were not related to climate factors, Knox argues, instead attributing them to the introduction of soil conservation measures such as contour plowing, strip-cropping, terracing, and minimum tillage, to which list could be added the concomitant rise in atmospheric CO$_2$ concentration and its impacts on the various beneficial phenomena discussed in this subsection.

Olafsdottir and Gudmundsson (2002) studied spatial and temporal patterns of land degradation in northeastern Iceland over the past 7,500 years based on data from excavations of 67 soil profiles, comparing their results with climatic variations known to have occurred over the same period. These activities revealed, in their words, "the deterioration in vegetation and soil cover noted coincides with the recorded deterioration in climate." During every major cold period of their record, land degradation was classified as "severe." During every major warm period, however, this condition was reversed, and soils were built up as vegetation cover expanded.

The primary implication of these findings, according to the two researchers, is "climate has a significant role in altering land cover *per se* and may trigger land degradation without the additional influence of men." Thus they conclude, "in Iceland severe land degradation could commence without anthropogenic influence—simply as a result of the cold periods."

In a FACE study conducted on the North Island of New Zealand, Newton *et al.* (2003) measured the water repellency of a grassland soil—which contained about 20 species of legumes, C$_3$ grasses, C$_4$ grasses, and forbs, and was grazed periodically by adult sheep—after five years of exposure to an extra 100 ppm of CO$_2$. They found a significant reduction in the water repellency of the soil in the elevated CO$_2$ treatment. The researchers note, "at field moisture content the repellence of the ambient soil was severe and significantly greater than that of the elevated [CO$_2$] soil."

Newton *et al.* say water repellency "is a soil property that prevents free water from entering the pores of dry soil (Tillman *et al.*, 1989)," and they report it "has become recognized as a widespread problem, occurring under a range of vegetation and soil types (agricultural, forestry and amenity; sand, loam, clay, peat and volcanic) (Bachmann *et al.*, 2001) and over a large geographical range (Europe, USA, Asia, Oceania) (Bauters *et al.*, 1998)." Specifically, they note water-repellency-induced problems for land managers include "increased losses of pesticides and fertilizers, reduced effectiveness of irrigation, increased rates of erosion, and increased runoff," and there are water-repellency-induced problems "in the establishment and growth of crops (Bond, 1972; Crabtree and Gilkes, 1999) and implications for the dynamics of natural ecosystems, particularly those subject to fire (DeBano, 2000)." The CO$_2$-induced reduction of soil water repellency discovered in this study portends a wide range of very important benefits for both agro- and natural ecosystems as the air's CO$_2$ content rises in the future.

Prior *et al.* (2004) note "enhanced aboveground crop growth under elevated CO$_2$, leading to more soil surface residue and greater percent ground cover (Prior *et al.*, 1997), coupled with positive shifts in crop root systems (Prior *et al.*, 2003), may have the potential to alter soil structural characteristics." They decided to see whether this inference was indeed true, and if true, whether elevated atmospheric CO$_2$ concentrations tend to enhance or degrade soil physical properties.

The researchers grew plots of soybean and sorghum plants from seed to maturity for five consecutive growing seasons in open-top chambers maintained at atmospheric CO$_2$ concentrations of either 360 or 720 ppm. The soil in which the plants grew had been fallow for more than 25 years prior to the start of the study and was located in a huge outdoor bin. There, at the end of each growing season, the researchers allowed aboveground non-yield residues (stalks, soybean pod hulls, and sorghum chaff), including 10% of the grain yield, to remain on the surfaces of the plots to simulate no-tillage farming. Measurements of various soil properties made at the beginning of the experiment were compared with similar measurements conducted at its conclusion.

They found elevated CO$_2$ had no effect on soil bulk density in the sorghum plot, but lowered it in the soybean plot by approximately 5% Elevated CO$_2$ also had no effect on soil saturated hydraulic conductivity in the sorghum plot, but increased it in the soybean plot by about 42%. Soil aggregate stability was increased in both plots, but by a greater amount in the soybean plot, and total soil carbon content was increased by 16% in the sorghum plot and 29% in the soybean plot. Consequently, the soils of both plots experienced some improvements in response to the experimental doubling of the atmosphere's CO_2 concentration, although there were more and greater improvements in the soybean plot than in the sorghum plot. Prior *et al.* conclude their results "indicate potential for improvements in soil carbon storage, water infiltration and soil water retention, and reduced erosion," which are positive consequences they described as "CO_2-induced benefits."

Zhang and Liu (2005) report using the general circulation model of the UK Meteorological Office's Hadley Centre to calculate expected changes in temperature and precipitation throughout the Chinese Loess Plateau over the next century. They found 2.3–4.3°C increases in daily maximum temperature, 3.6–5.3°C increases in daily minimum temperature, and 23–37% increases in annual precipitation. They used a stochastic weather generator to downscale these monthly projections to daily values, after which they ran the Water Erosion Prediction Project model of Flanagan and Nearing (1995), as modified to account for CO_2 effects on evapotranspiration and biomass production by Favis-Mortlock and Savabi (1996), for a wheat-wheat-corn rotation utilizing either conventional or conservation tillage.

Zhang and Liu determined the climate-change scenarios they investigated led to 29–79% more water runoff and 2–81% greater soil loss under conventional tillage practices, but "adoption of conservation tillage could reduce runoff by 18–38% and decrease soil loss by 56–68% as compared to the conventional tillage under the present climate." They conclude "the use of the conservation tillage would be sufficient to maintain low runoff and erosion levels and thus protect agro-ecosystems under projected climate changes." As for crop productivity, they determined the warmer, wetter, CO_2-enriched environment projected to prevail on the Chinese Loess Plateau a hundred years from now would boost yields by significant amounts: 15–44% for wheat and 40–58% for corn. Zhang and Liu express great optimism about the future, noting "the significant increases in predicted wheat and maize yields [that] were results of increased precipitation and CO_2 concentration ... outweighed the negative effect of temperature rise on crop growth."

Shifting from the physiological effects of atmospheric CO_2 enrichment on groundcover plants to the immediate impacts of certain climatic phenomena on soil erosivity, D'Asaro *et al.* (2007) begin the report of their study by stating "warmer atmospheric temperatures associated with greenhouse warming are expected to lead to a more variable hydrological cycle, including more extreme rainfall events (IPCC, 1995)," adding "this change is expected to influence the erosive power, or erosivity, of rainfall and, hence, soil erosion rates (Nearing, 2001)." As a test of this "expectation," D'Asaro *et al.* set out "to assess changes in annual and seasonal rainfall erosivity that occurred in Sicily during the twentieth century," the hundred-year period typically described by IPCC and others as having experienced an increase in global temperature unprecedented over the past two millennia (Mann and Jones, 2003; Mann *et al.*, 2003) or more (Hansen *et al.* 2006). The scientists generated long-term series (from 1916 to 1999 in most cases) of a storm erosion index based on storm rainfall amounts and intensities and then applied that index at 17 Sicilian locations (representative of different climatic zones) where the latter two parameters were routinely measured. The three Italian researchers found "the annual erosivity did not increase during the twentieth century." In fact, they write, it "decreased at a few locations."

Diodato *et al.* (2008) conducted a detailed analysis of Calore River Basin (South Italy) erosive rainfall using data from 425-year-long series of both observations (1922–2004) and proxy-based reconstructions (1580–1921). The more recent of these two series was based on a scheme that employed the Revised Universal Soil Loss Equation; documentary descriptions provided the basis for the earlier series. They write the results of this work revealed pronounced interdecadal variations, with "multi-decadal erosivity reflecting the mixed population of thermo-convective and cyclonic rainstorms with large anomalies." In addition, they report, "the so-called Little Ice Age (16th to mid-19th centuries) was identified as the stormiest period, with mixed rainstorm types and high frequency of floods and erosive rainfall."

In the concluding section of their paper, the three researchers note, "in recent years, climate change (generally assumed as synonymous with global warming) has become a global concern and is widely reported in the media." One of the chief of these concerns is that extreme weather phenomena, such as droughts and floods, will become both more frequent and more severe as the planet warms, which would lead to more soil erosion. However, Diodato *et al.* say their study indicates "climate in the Calore River Basin has been largely characterized by naturally occurring weather anomalies in past centuries (long before industrial CO_2 emissions), not only in recent years," and there has been a "relevant smoothing" of such events during the modern era.

Stankoviansky (2003) employed topographical maps and aerial photographs, field geomorphic investigation, and the study of historical documents, including those from local municipal and church sources, to determine the spatial distribution of gully landforms and the temporal history of their creation in the Myjava Hill Land of Slovakia, situated in the western part of the country near its border with the Czech Republic. This work revealed "the central part of the area, settled between the second half of the 16th and the beginning of the 19th centuries, was affected by gully formation in two periods, the first between the end of the 16th century and the 1730s and the second roughly between the 1780s and 1840s." Stankoviansky notes the gullies were formed "during periods of extensive forest clearance and expansion of farmland," and "the triggering mechanism of gullying was extreme rainfalls during the Little Ice Age." More specifically, he writes, "the gullies were formed relatively quickly by repeated incision of ephemeral flows concentrated during extreme rainfall events, which were clustered in periods that correspond with known climatic fluctuations during the Little Ice Age."

From the mid-nineteenth century to the present, Stankoviansky affirms, "there has been a decrease in gully growth because of the afforestation of gullies and especially climatic improvements since the termination of the Little Ice Age." These observations suggest extreme and destructive rainfall events were much more common in the Myjava Hill Land of Slovakia during the Little Ice Age than they have been subsequently. This view, in his words (and in many of the references he cites), "is often regarded as generally valid for Central Europe." This evidence-derived view runs counter to that of most climate alarmists, who tend to blame global warming for such destructive precipitation events and the erosive flooding they cause.

In the course of a long-term field experiment at the Kessler Farm Field Laboratory in McClain County, Oklahoma, USA, Xue et al. (2011) explored how annual clipping for biofuel feedstock production and warming caused soil erosion and accompanying carbon and nitrogen losses in tallgrass prairie. The researchers provided warming by infrared heaters suspended 1.5 m above the ground, as described by Kimball (2005), raising air temperatures by an average of 1.47°C and soil temperatures in the

clipping plots by 1.98°C. The results of this experiment revealed the average relative depth of erosion caused by clipping was 1.65 and 0.54 mm/year, respectively, in the warmed and control plots from November 21, 1999 to April 21, 2009; the soil erosion rate was 2148 g/m²/year in the warmed plots and 693 g/m²/year in the control plots; soil organic carbon was lost at a rate of 69.6 g/m²/year in the warmed plots and 22.5 g/m²/year in the control plots; and total nitrogen was lost at a rate of 4.6 g/m²/year in the warmed plots and 1.4 g/m²/year in the control plots. Xue et al. note, "the amount of carbon and nitrogen loss caused by clipping is equivalent to, or even larger than, changes caused by global change factors."

The five researchers state their results indicate "clipping for biofuel harvest results in significant soil erosion and accompanying losses of soil carbon and nitrogen, which is aggravated by warming." Also, "soil erosion is one of the most pressing global environmental challenges facing the world today, causing declining soil productivity and crop yields, which may create difficulties in meeting the rising demand for food and energy (Brink et al., 1977; Brown, 1981; Lal, 2004; MEA, 2005)." Consequently, the biofuel "cure" for the global warming "disease" might be worse than the malady itself.

Tape et al. (2011) state "recent changes in the climate of Arctic Alaska, including warmer temperatures and a lengthened growing season (Chapin et al., 2005; Serreze and Francis, 2006; Shulski and Wendler, 2007), are linked with ... increased vegetation productivity, as measured using time series of satellite vegetation indices such as Normalized Difference Vegetation Index (NDVI)," as documented by Myneni et al. (1997), Jia et al. (2003), Goetz et al. (2005), and Bhatt et al., 2010). This phenomenon, they note, "has been partly attributed to the expansion of shrubs, which has been documented using time series of aerial photography (Sturm et al., 2001; Tape et al., 2006), plot studies (Joly et al., 2007), and shrub growth ring chronologies (Forbes et al., 2010; Hallinger et al., 2010)." In light of these observations they ask, "Is the current warming and concurrent shrub expansion on older Arctic landscapes associated with increased or decreased erosion?"

Working with time series imagery from Landsat thematic mapper data covering the period 1986–2009, Tape et al. (2011) examined the landscape pattern of tall shrub distribution and expansion in the Arctic foothills, located on the north side of the Brooks Range, Alaska, and they studied sediments obtained from cores of four lakes near the Chandler River on the central North Slope of Alaska (where shrub expansion is occurring), to compare relationships among shrub cover, erosion, and runoff over the past quarter-century. Their results reveal "a background decline in erosion since 1980, superimposed by episodic erosional events," and "the background decline in erosion is associated with trends of increasing shrubs and declining peak runoff events."

The results of the many studies discussed in this review suggest the historical increase in the atmosphere's CO_2 concentration has reduced significantly the erosion of valuable topsoil worldwide over the past several decades, and the continuing increase in atmospheric CO_2 can maintain this trend, and perhaps even accelerate it, throughout the foreseeable future.

References

Allen, J.R.M., Brandt, U., Brauer, A., Hubberten, H.-W., Huntley, B., Keller, J., Kraml, M., Mackensen, A., Mingram, J., Negendank, J.F.W., Nowaczyk, N.R., Oberhansli, H., Watts, W.A., Wulf, S., and Zolitschka, B. 1999. Rapid environmental changes in southern Europe during the last glacial period. *Nature* **400**: 740–743.

Bachmann, J., Horton, R., and van der Ploeg, R.R. 2001. Isothermal and non-isothermal evaporation from four sandy soils of different water repellency. *Soil Science Society of America Journal* **65**: 1599–1607.

Bauters, T.W.J., DiCarlo, D.A., Steenhuis, T.S., and Parlange, J.-Y. 1998. Preferential flow in water-repellent soils. *Soil Science Society of America Journal* **62**: 1185–1190.

Bhatt, U.S., Walker, D., Raynolds, M., Comiso, J., Epstein, H., Jia, G., Gens, R., Pinzon, J., Tucker, C., Tweedie, C., and Webber, P. 2010. Circumpolar Arctic tundra vegetation change is linked to sea ice decline. *Earth Interactions* **14**: 120.

Bond, R.D. 1972. Germination and yield of barley when grown in a water-repellent sand. *Agronomy Journal* **64**: 402–403.

Brink, R.A., Densmore, J.W., and Hill, G.A. 1977. Soil deterioration and the growing world demand for food. *Science* **197**: 625–630.

Brown, L.R. 1981. World population growth, soil erosion, and food security. *Science* **214**: 995–1002.

Chapin III, F.S., Sturm, M., Serreze, M.C., McFadden, J.P., Key, J.R., Lloyd, A.H., McGuire, A.D., Rupp, T.S., Lynch, A.H., Schimel, J.P., Beringer, J., Chapman, W.L., Epstein, H.E., Euskirchen, E.S., Hinzman, L.D., Jia, G., Ping, C.-L.,

Tape, K.D., Thompson, C.D.C., Walker, D.A., and Welker, J.M. 2005. Role of land-surface changes in Arctic summer warming. *Science* **310**: 657–660.

Crabtree, W.L. and Gilkes, R.J. 1999. Improved pasture establishment and production on water-repellent soils. *Agronomy Journal* **91**: 467–470.

D'Asaro, F., D'Agostino, L., and Bagarello, V. 2007. Assessing changes in rainfall erosivity in Sicily during the twentieth century. *Hydrological Processes* **21**: 2862–2871.

DeBano, L.F. 2000. The role of fire and soil heating on water repellency in wildland environments: a review. *Journal of Hydrology* **231–232**: 195–206.

Diodato, N., Ceccarelli, M., and Bellocchi, G. 2008. Decadal and century-long changes in the reconstruction of erosive rainfall anomalies in a Mediterranean fluvial basin. *Earth Surface Processes and Landforms* **33**: 2078–2093.

Favis-Mortlock, D.T. and Savabi, M.R. 1996. Shifts in rates and spatial distribution of soil erosion and deposition under climate change. In: Anderson, M.G. and Brooks, S.M. (Eds.) *Advances in Hillslope Processes*. John Wiley, New York, New York, USA, pp. 529–560.

Flanagan, D.C. and Nearing, M.A. (Eds.) 1995. *USDA-Water Erosion Prediction Project: Hillslope Profile and Watershed Model Documentation*. National Soil Erosion Research Laboratory Report No. 10. NSERL, West Lafayette, Indiana, USA.

Forbes, B.C., Fauria, M.M., and Zetterberg, P. 2010. Russian Arctic warming and 'greening' are closely tracked by tundra shrub willows. *Global Change Biology* **16**: 1542–1554.

Goetz, S.J., Bunn, A.G., Fiske, G.J., and Houghton, R.A. 2005. Satellite-observed photosynthetic trends across boreal North America associated with climate and fire disturbance. *Proceedings of the National Academy of Sciences USA* **102**: 13,521–13,525.

Hallinger, M., Manthey, M., and Wilmking, M. 2010. Establishing a missing link: Warm summers and winter snow cover promote shrub expansion into alpine tundra in Scandinavia. *New Phytologist* **186**: 890–899.

Hansen, J., Sato, M., Ruedy, R., Lo, K., Lea, D.W., and Medina-Elizade, M. 2006. Global temperature change. *Proceedings of the National Academy of Sciences USA* **103**: 14,288–14,293.

Idso, S.B. 1989. *Carbon Dioxide and Global Change: Earth in Transition*. IBR Press, Tempe, AZ.

Intergovernmental Panel on Climate Change (IPCC). 1995. *Second Assessment Synthesis of Scientific-Technical Information Relevant to Interpreting Article 2 of the U.N. Framework Convention on Climate Change*. Geneva, Switzerland.

Jia, G., Epstein, H.E., and Walker, D.A. 2003. Greening of arctic Alaska, 1981–2001. *Geophysical Research Letters* **30**: 10.1029/2003GL018268.

Joly, K., Jandt, R.R., Meyers, C.R., and Cole, M.J. 2005. Changes in vegetative cover on Western Arctic Herd winter range from 1981 to 2005: Potential effects of grazing and climate change. *Rangifer* **27**: 199–206.

Kimball, B.A. 2005. Theory and performance of an infrared heater for ecosystem warming. *Global Change Biology* **11**: 2041–2056

Knox, J.C. 2001. Agricultural influence on landscape sensitivity in the Upper Mississippi River Valley. *Catena* **42**: 193–224.

Lal, R. 2004. Soil carbon sequestration impacts on global climate change and food security. *Science* **304**: 1623–1627.

Mann, M., Amman, C., Bradley, R., Briffa, K., Jones, P., Osborn, T., Crowley, T., Hughes, M., Oppenheimer, M., Overpeck, J., Rutherford, S., Trenberth, K., and Wigley, T. 2003. On past temperatures and anomalous late-20th century warmth. *EOS, Transactions, American Geophysical Union* **84**: 256–257.

Mann, M.E. and Jones, P.D. 2003. Global surface temperatures over the past two millennia. *Geophysical Research Letters* **30**: 10.1029/2003GL017814.

MEA. 2005. *Millennium Ecosystem Assessment— Ecosystems and Human Well-being: Desertification Synthesis*. World Resources Institute, Washington, DC, USA.

Myneni, R.B., Keeling, C.D., Tucker, C.J., Asrar, G., and Nemani, R.R. 1997. Increased plant growth in the northern high latitudes from 1981 to 1991. *Nature* **386**: 698–702.

Nearing, M.A. 2001. Potential changes in rainfall erosivity in the U.S. with climate change during the 21st century. *Journal of Soil and Water Conservation* **56**: 229–232.

Newton, P.C.D., Carran, R.A., and Lawrence, E.J. 2003. Reduced water repellency of a grassland soil under elevated atmospheric CO₂. *Global Change Biology* **10**: 1–4.

Olafsdottir, R. and Gudmundsson, H.J. 2002. Holocene land degradation and climatic change in northeastern Iceland. *The Holocene* **12**: 159–167.

Prior, S.A., Rogers, H.H., Runion, G.B., Torbert, H.A., and Reicosky, D.C. 1997. Carbon dioxide-enriched agro-ecosystems: Influence of tillage on short-term soil carbon dioxide efflux. *Journal of Environmental Quality* **26**: 244–252.

Prior, S.A., Runion, G.B., Torbert, H.A., and Rogers, H.H. 2004. Elevated atmospheric CO₂ in agroecosystems: Soil physical properties. *Soil Science* **169**: 434–439.

Prior, S.A., Torbert, H.A., Runion, G.B., and Rogers, H.H. 2003. Implications of elevated CO₂-induced changes in agroecosystem productivity. *Journal of Crop Production* **8**: 217–244.

Rillig, M.C., Hernandez, G.Y., and Newton, P.C.D. 2000. Arbuscular mycorrhizae respond to elevated atmospheric CO₂ after long-term exposure: evidence from a CO₂ spring in New Zealand supports the resource balance model. *Ecology Letters* **3**: 475–478.

Rillig, M.C., Wright, S.F., Kimball, B.A., Pinter, P.J., Wall, G.W., Ottman, M.J., and Leavitt, S.W. 2001. Elevated carbon dioxide and irrigation effects on water stable aggregates in a *Sorghum* field: a possible role for arbuscular mycorrhizal fungi. *Global Change Biology* **7**: 333–337.

Serreze, M.C. and Francis, J. 2006 The Arctic amplification debate. *Climatic Change* **76**: 241–264.

Shulski, M. and Wendler, G. 2007. *The Climate of Alaska*. University of Alaska Press, Fairbanks, Alaska, USA.

Sturm, M., Racine, C., and Tape, K. 2001. Increasing shrub abundance in Arctic. *Nature* **411**: 546–547.

Stankoviansky, M. 2003. Historical evolution of permanent gullies in the Myjava Hill Land, Slovakia. *Catena* **51**: 223–239.

Tape, K.D., Sturm, M., and Racine, C. 2006. The evidence for shrub expansion in Northern Alaska and the Pan-Arctic. *Global Change Biology* **12**: 686–702.

Tape, K.D., Verbyla, D., and Welker, J.M. 2011. Twentieth century erosion in Arctic Alaska foothills: The influence of shrubs, runoff, and permafrost. *Journal of Geophysical Research* **116**: 10.1029/2011JG001795.

Tilman, R.W., Scotter, D.R., and Wallis, M.G., *et al.* 1989. Water-repellency and its measurement by using intrinsic sorptivity. *Australian Journal of Soil Research* **27**: 637–644.

Trimble, S.W. and Crosson, P. 2000. U.S. soil erosion rates—myth and reality. *Science* **289**: 248–250.

Xue, X., Luo, Y., Zhou, X., Sherry, R., and Jia, X. 2011. Climate warming increases soil erosion, carbon and nitrogen loss with biofuel feedstock harvest in tallgrass prairie. *GCB Bioenergy* **3**: 198–207.

Zhang, X.-C. and Liu, W.-Z. 2005. Simulating potential response of hydrology, soil erosion, and crop productivity to climate change in Changwu tableland region on the Loess Plateau of China. *Agricultural and Forest Meteorology* **131**: 127–142.

2

Plant Characteristics

Key Findings

The key findings of this chapter are presented in the bullet points below.

- As the CO_2 content of the air rises, plant species may not experience photosynthetic acclimation—lower long-term rates of photosynthesis than occur when CO_2 concentrations are first increased—even under conditions of low soil nitrogen. In the event a plant cannot balance its carbohydrate sources and sinks, CO_2-induced acclimation can shift limiting resources away from the site of photosynthesis to strengthen sink development or enhance other important plant processes.

- Atmospheric CO_2 enrichment may increase, decrease, or have no effect on leaf chlorophyll concentration. Even when leaf chlorophyll concentration is decreased, the reallocation of its nitrogen generally occurs without any adverse consequences, as most plants displaying this response typically continue to exhibit significant increases in photosynthesis and biomass production.

- Studies of several different tree species suggest enhanced carbohydrates stored in terminal branchlets or nitrogen stored in second-year leaves may be remobilized to facilitate greater first-flush needle or leaf growth the following year as a result of atmospheric CO_2 enrichment.

- At higher atmospheric CO_2 concentrations, plants tend to produce more and larger flowers, as well as other flower-related changes having significant implications for plant productivity and survival, almost all of which are positive.

- Higher concentrations of atmospheric CO_2 tend to reduce fluctuating asymmetry in plant leaves, leading to more symmetrical leaves that appear to be less susceptible to attack by herbivores.

- Atmospheric CO_2 enrichment enhances plant growth, development, and ultimate yield (in the case of agricultural crops) by increasing the concentrations of plant hormones that stimulate cell division, cell elongation, and protein synthesis.

- Atmospheric CO_2 enrichment increases the production of glomalin, a protein created by fungi living in symbiotic association with the roots of 80% of the planet's vascular plants, which is being released to almost every soil in the world in ever-greater quantities with the passage of time, where it is having a positive impact on the biosphere.

- Increasing atmospheric CO_2 concentrations likely will affect many leaf characteristics of agricultural plants, with the majority of the changes leading to higher rates and efficiencies of photosynthesis and growth, as well as numerous other changes in leaf characteristics that help promote increased resistances to herbivory and pathogen attack.

- Atmospheric CO_2 enrichment stimulates photosynthesis in nearly all plants, enabling them to produce more nonstructural carbohydrates that can be used to create important carbon-based secondary compounds, one of which is lignin.

- The highly positive impacts of atmospheric CO_2 enrichment on lipid concentrations and characteristics in various terrestrial and aquatic plants portend nothing but good for the managed and unmanaged components of Earth's biosphere as the air's CO_2 content continues to climb.

- The stresses of low temperature have been shown to be both alleviated and enhanced in plants growing under elevated CO_2 concentrations. It appears far more plants are benefiting from such stress alleviation than experience stress augmentation.

- The diverse results of several experimental studies do not paint a clear picture of what should be expected in the way of plant monoterpene emissions in a CO_2-enriched and possibly warmer world of the future. Until a better understanding is obtained, it would be unwise to conclude much more about the situation.

- As the air's CO_2 content continues to rise, plant fitness, flower pollination, and nectar production should be enhanced, leading to increases in fruit, grain, and vegetable yields of agricultural crops, as well as similar increases in the productivity of the world's natural vegetation.

- Increases in the air's CO_2 content likely will stimulate nitrogen fixation in most herbaceous species that form symbiotic relationships with nitrogen-fixing soil bacteria—i.e., legumes—and this phenomenon likely will lead to increased nitrogen availability in soils and large increases in agricultural and natural ecosystem productivity. Likewise, increases in the air's CO_2 content will enhance the growth of Earth's leguminous trees, stimulating their fixation of nitrogen and their exudation of the resultant nitrogenous substances to the soils in which they grow, where they become available to neighboring non-leguminous vegetation, all of which promotes biospheric productivity.

- As the air's CO_2 content continues to rise, Earth's plants likely will reduce the amount of nitrogen invested in rubisco and other photosynthetic proteins while maintaining enhanced rates of photosynthesis and thereby increasing their photosynthetic nitrogen-use efficiencies.

- As the CO_2 content of the air increases, much of Earth's vegetation likely will display increases in biomass, and the larger plants likely will develop more extensive root systems and extract greater amounts of mineral nutrients from the soils in which they are rooted, enabling them to sustain their enhanced growth.

- Herbaceous plants often experience increases in foliar and fruit phenolic concentrations in response to atmospheric CO_2 enrichment, and these responses appear to have numerous positive implications for man and the biosphere. Similarly, future increases in the air's CO_2 concentration likely will enhance foliar phenolic concentrations in many trees and shrubs. This phenomenon should enhance woody-plant defense mechanisms that help deter herbivory, thereby improving forest health, robustness, and longevity.

- The wide range of results obtained by many past and current methods of detecting each year's start of spring has led to premature claims of spring's increasingly earlier annual occurrence over the course of the twentieth century. While these claims are used to support the associated claim of twentieth century CO_2-induced global warming, real-world data fail to support the bulk of these contentions.

- With respect to managed agricultural crops and the wild plants of Earth's natural ecosystems, it

appears the ongoing rise of the air's CO_2 concentration will have few negative impacts of any consequence on the nutritive value of their grains and foliage in terms of protein concentration. In tree crops such as citrus, CO_2-induced changes in the activities of certain foliar proteins could lead to vast increases in yield potential.

- The growth and biomass production of herbaceous crops are generally enhanced by CO_2-induced decreases in respiration during the dark (nighttime) period. However, scientists lack fundamental information on how respiration and the processes supported by it are physiologically controlled, thereby preventing sound interpretations of what seem to be species-specific responses of respiration to elevated CO_2. Thus the precise role of plant respiration in augmenting the sink capacity of herbaceous plants remains uncertain.

- Both above and below the soil surface, coniferous trees appear to exhibit significant reductions in respiration in CO_2-enriched air. However, deciduous trees exhibit increases and decreases, as well as cases of no change in respiration. Other studies of multiple tree species also suggest atmospheric CO_2 enrichment may either increase or decrease woody-plant respiration, but not to any great degree. The net result for Earth's trees generally likely would be of little significance.

- Elevated CO_2 nearly always increases root biomass, often even more than shoot biomass, by increasing the size of taproots and the number and size of lateral roots, along with fine-root biomass and a number of other important root properties.

- There is a reduced need for nitrogen investment in leaf rubisco in most plants growing in CO_2-enriched air, because under such conditions plants typically reallocate some of their "surplus" nitrogen to other processes essential for optimal growth and development without compromising enhanced carbon gains via photosynthesis.

- Atmospheric CO_2 enrichment has been shown to increase the amount, size, weight, carbohydrate content, lipid content, protein content, earlier production, earlier germination, and greater percent germination of various plant seeds. All of these improvements bode well for the future of Earth's biosphere.

- As the air's CO_2 content rises, most of Earth's vegetation responds by exhibiting enhanced rates of photosynthesis and greater production of carbohydrates. Many of these carbohydrates are exported from leaves and needles to provide energy or carbon skeletons to facilitate increased biomass production, after which remaining carbohydrates generally are converted into starch and stored within leaves or roots for future use.

- In addition to sequentially reducing the openness of their stomata to restrict unnecessary water loss via excessive transpiration as the air's CO_2 content rises, some plants also reduce the density (number per area) of stomates on their leaves, but only to a certain degree, beyond which this latter phenomenon would be counterproductive.

- Atmospheric CO_2 enrichment typically increases plants' ability to produce greater amounts of various forms of sugar.

- Atmospheric CO_2 enrichment significantly enhances the condensed tannin concentrations of the vast majority of Earth's trees and grasses, providing them with stronger defenses against various herbivores both above and below ground. By reducing the amount of methane released to the atmosphere via ruminants browsing on tree leaves and grass, this phenomenon should reduce the rate of rise of the air's methane concentration and thereby decrease the impetus for methane-induced global warming.

- Thylakoid membranes of chloroplasts perform a host of important functions that influence the process of carbon fixation in plants, and in CO_2-enriched air, they generally perform these functions more efficiently, enabling plants to overcome some of the deleterious effects of a host of plant stresses, including insufficient soil moisture, abnormally cold temperatures, abnormally hot temperatures, and ozone pollution.

- As the atmosphere's CO_2 concentration rises, most plants tend to exhibit increased rates of net photosynthesis and biomass production; on a per-unit-leaf-area basis, plants exposed to elevated CO_2 concentrations are likely to lose less water via transpiration because they tend to exhibit lower stomatal conductances. Therefore, the amount of carbon gained per unit of water lost per unit leaf area—water use efficiency—should increase significantly as the air's CO_2 content rises.

- Atmospheric CO_2 enrichment appears to enhance the between-cuttings savings of vegetative storage proteins (VSPs) in the roots of alfalfa crops, as well as the between-years storage of VSPs in the leaves of sour orange trees (and possibly other citrus species), so that when the next crop's or tree's growing season begins, the first flush of foliage gets a head start.

- Atmospheric CO_2 enrichment tends to increase wood density in both seedlings and mature trees, thereby also increasing a number of strength properties of their branches and trunks. However, different species of trees may respond somewhat differently to atmospheric CO_2 enrichment, and they can respond with still greater variety under different environmental conditions.

Introduction

According to a draft of IPCC Working Group II's Summary for Policymakers (SPM) to accompany its 2014 report, "without adaptation, local temperature increases of 1°C or more above preindustrial levels are projected to negatively impact yields for the major crops (wheat, rice, maize) in tropical and temperate regions, although individual locations may benefit (*medium confidence*). With or without adaptation, climate change will reduce median yields by 0 to 2% per decade for the rest of the century, as compared to a baseline without climate change" (IPCC 2014, p. 10).

The research and analysis summarized in Chapter 1 of the current report challenged IPCC's predictions by showing how rising levels of atmospheric CO_2 help plants overcome abnormally hot temperatures and other plant stresses that might accompany a warming planet. It referenced tabular presentations in Appendices 3 and 4 reporting more than 5,000 individual plant biomass and photosynthetic responses reported in the peer-reviewed literature. That chapter went on to show how elevated atmospheric CO_2 and warmer temperatures benefit various important ecosystems including forests, grasslands, peatlands, wetlands, and soils.

The current chapter continues the analysis, presenting research on the effects of elevated CO_2 on a long list of plant characteristics ranging (in alphabetical order) from antioxidants and chlorophyll to water use efficiency and wood density. The sections and subsections that follow report the results of hundreds of experiments involving plants grown in air enriched with carbon dioxide to levels expected to be experienced in the future as well as examination of yearly growth rings of long-lived trees revealing how they grew over prior years, decades, and even centuries as atmospheric CO_2 concentrations have risen. In the case of agricultural crops, grassland vegetation, and chaparral and desert species, the first of these techniques is typically employed, as it also is in the study of young tree seedlings. Growth-ring studies are reserved for more mature trees, some of which may have lived for several centuries.

The primary information being sought in these studies is rates of photosynthesis and biomass production and the efficiency with which the plants and trees utilize water. These studies also can provide information about substances produced in the growth process that affect how well it proceeds; substances deposited in the parts of agricultural crops that are harvested for human and animal consumption; and substances that determine whether the foliage or fruit of a certain crop or tree will be attractive to insect pests. Finally, these studies also can help determine whether forest soils will have sufficient nitrogen to sustain the long-term CO_2-enhanced growth rates of long-lived trees.

This chapter powerfully rebuts claims that plant species typically experience photosynthetic acclimation—a decline in rates of photosynthesis over time to less than what would have been expected based on measurements made during short-term exposure to CO_2-enriched air—even under conditions of low soil nitrogen. In the event a plant cannot balance its carbohydrate sources and sinks, CO_2-induced acclimation represents a way of achieving that balance by shifting limiting resources away from the site of photosynthesis to strengthen sink development or enhance other important plant processes. This is especially important because many estimates of the costs and benefits of future global warming assume acclimation will limit the benefits of carbon dioxide fertilization or even turn carbon sinks into net emitters. The research that follows shows convincingly that this is not the case.

Similarly, this chapter addresses head-on the claim that water shortages in a warmer world will eventually stop the higher CO_2-induced increase in plant growth and foreshadow declining plant productivity, with corresponding negative effects on food supply and human welfare. It seems Mother Nature anticipated the greater need for moisture that faster-growing plants would exhibit by minimizing their loss of water via transpiration by lowering stomatal conductances. The amount of carbon gained per unit of water lost per unit of leaf area—water use efficiency—should increase significantly as the air's CO_2 concentration rises.

This chapter also looks closely at the impact of higher CO_2 levels on plants that are significant sources of nutrition for humans directly or indirectly as feed for cattle, sheep, and other domesticated animals. The evidence is overwhelmingly positive: Higher levels of atmospheric CO_2 already are enhancing crop yields of alfalfa, citrus, rice, soybeans, and wheat. Carbon dioxide fertilization promotes the production of more and larger flowers, more symmetrical leaves (which appears to reduce herbivory), more nonstructural carbohydrates, and positive impacts on lipid concentrations and characteristics, plant fitness, flower pollination, nectar production, and more. Rising levels of CO_2 in the air will have few negative impacts of any consequence on the nutritive value of grains and foliage in terms of protein concentration, and in some tree crops such as citrus, CO_2-induced changes in the activities of certain foliar proteins could lead to vast increases in yield potential.

In short, IPCC's conclusions about the impact of future global warming on agriculture are far too pessimistic. Trends in the twentieth century and experimental research all point to a continued flourishing of crops important to human welfare was well as virtually all plants.

Reference

IPCC. 2014. Summary for Policymakers. In *Climate Change 2014: Impacts, Adaptation, and Vulnerability.* Contribution of Working Group II to the Fifth Assessment Report of the Intergovernmental Panel on Climate Change. Draft dated October 28, 2013.

2.1 Acclimation

Plants grown in elevated CO_2 environments often exhibit photosynthetic acclimation or down-regulation, typically characterized by somewhat lower long-term rates of photosynthesis than would have been expected based on measurements made during short-term exposure to CO_2-enriched air. These downward adjustments result from modest long-term decreases in the activities and/or amounts of the primary plant carboxylating enzyme rubisco.

Acclimation is said to have occurred when the photosynthetic rates of long-term CO_2-enriched plants are found to be lower than those of long-term non-CO_2-enriched plants when the normally CO_2-enriched plants are measured during brief exposures to ambient CO_2 concentrations. The subsections below review research published on acclimation in agricultural, desert, grassland, and woody tree species.

2.1.1 Agricultural Species

• As the CO_2 content of the air rises, agricultural species may not experience photosynthetic acclimation, even under conditions of low soil nitrogen, but in the event a plant cannot balance its carbohydrate sources and sinks, CO_2-induced acclimation represents a beneficial means of achieving that balance by shifting limiting resources away from the site of photosynthesis to strengthen sink development or enhance other important plant processes.

Several studies have examined the effects of elevated CO_2 on acclimation in agricultural crops. Ziska (1998), for example, reports soybeans grown at an atmospheric CO_2 concentration of 720 ppm initially exhibited photosynthetic rates 50% greater than those observed in control plants grown at 360 ppm. After the onset of photosynthetic acclimation, the CO_2-enriched plants displayed subsequent photo-synthetic rates only 30% greater than their ambiently grown counterparts. Theobald et al. (1998) grew spring wheat at twice-ambient atmospheric CO_2 concentrations and determined elevated CO_2 reduced the amount of rubisco required to sustain enhanced rates of photosynthesis, which led to a significant increase in plant photosynthetic nitrogen-use efficiency. CO_2-induced increases in photosynthetic nitrogen-use efficiency also have been reported in spring wheat by Osborne et al. (1998).

In a study incorporating both hydroponically and pot-grown wheat plants, Farage et al. (1998) demonstrated low nitrogen fertilization does not lead to photosynthetic acclimation in elevated CO_2 environments, as long as the nitrogen supply keeps pace with the relative growth rate of the plants. When spring wheat was grown at an atmospheric CO_2 concentration of 550 ppm in a free-air CO_2 enrichment (FACE) experiment with optimal soil nutrition and unlimited rooting volume, Garcia et al. (1998) found no evidence of photosynthetic acclimation.

CO_2-induced photosynthetic acclimation often results from insufficient plant sink strength, which can lead to carbohydrate accumulation in source leaves and the triggering of photosynthetic end-product feedback inhibition, which reduces net photosynthetic rates. Gesch et al. (1998) report rice plants, which have relatively limited potential for developing additional carbon sinks, grown at an atmospheric CO_2 concentration of 700 ppm exhibited increased leaf carbohydrate contents, which likely reduced rbcS mRNA levels and rubisco protein content. Similarly, Sims et al. (1998) report photosynthetic acclimation was induced in CO_2-enriched soybean plants from the significant accumulation of nonstructural carbohydrates in their leaves. However, in growing several different Brassica species at 1,000 ppm CO_2, Reekie et al. (1998) demonstrated CO_2-induced acclimation was avoided in species having well-developed carbon sinks (broccoli and cauliflower) and appeared only in species lacking significant sink strength (rape and mustard).

Thus, photosynthetic acclimation does not appear to be a direct consequence of atmospheric CO_2 enrichment but rather an indirect effect of low sink strength, which results in leaf carbohydrate accumulation that can trigger acclimation.

In some cases, plants can effectively increase their sink strength, and thus reduce the magnitude of CO_2-induced acclimation, by forming symbiotic relationships with certain species of soil fungi. Under such conditions, photosynthetic down-regulation is not triggered as rapidly, or as frequently, by end-product feedback inhibition, as excess carbohydrates are mobilized out of source leaves and sent belowground to symbiotic fungi. Louche-Tessandier et al. (1999) found photosynthetic acclimation in CO_2-enriched potatoes was less apparent when plants were simultaneously colonized by a mycorrhizal fungus. Thus, CO_2-induced acclimation appears to be closely related to the source:sink balance that exists within plants, being triggered when sink strength falls below, and source strength rises above, critical thresholds in a species-dependent manner.

Acclimation is generally regarded as a process that reduces the amount of rubisco and/or other photosynthetic proteins, which effectively increases the amount of nitrogen available for enhancing sink development or stimulating other nutrient-limited processes. Watling et al. (2000), for example, report a 50% CO_2-induced reduction in the concentration of PEP-carboxylase, the primary carboxylating enzyme in C_4 plants, within sorghum leaves. Maroco *et al.* (1999) documented CO_2-induced decreases in both PEP-carboxylase and rubisco in leaves of the C_4 crop maize.

In some cases, acclimation to elevated CO_2 is manifested by an "up-regulation" of certain enzymes. When Gesch *et al.* (2002) took rice plants from ambient air and placed them in air enriched to 700 ppm CO_2, for example, they noticed a significant increase in the activity of sucrose-phosphate synthase (SPS), a key enzyme involved in the production of sucrose. Similarly, Hussain *et al.* (1999) report rice plants grown at an atmospheric CO_2 concentration of 660 ppm displayed 20% more SPS activity during the growing season than did ambiently grown rice plants. Such increases in the activity of this enzyme could allow CO_2-enriched plants to avoid the onset of photosynthetic acclimation by synthesizing and subsequently exporting sucrose from source leaves into sink tissues before they accumulate and trigger end product feedback inhibition.

Gesch *et al.* (2000) took ambiently growing rice plants and placed them in an atmospheric CO_2 concentration of 175 ppm, which reduced photo-synthetic rates by 45%. After five days' exposure to this sub-ambient CO_2 concentration, the plants manifested an up-regulation of rubisco, which stimulated photosynthetic rates by 35%. Thus, plant acclimation responses can involve both an increase or decrease in specific enzymes, depending on the atmospheric CO_2 concentration.

Many peer-reviewed studies suggest that as the CO_2 content of the air slowly but steadily rises, agricultural species may not exhibit photosynthetic acclimation, even under conditions of low soil nitrogen. If a plant can maintain a balance between its sources and sinks for carbohydrates at the whole-plant level, for example, acclimation should not be necessary; for if Earth's atmospheric CO_2 content is rising by an average of only 1.5 ppm per year, most plants should be able to adjust their relative growth rates by the small amount that would be needed to prevent low nitrogen-induced acclimation from ever occurring, or expand their root systems by the small amount that would be needed to supply the extra nitrogen required to take full advantage of the CO_2-induced increase in leaf carbohydrate production. And if a plant cannot initially balance its sources and sinks for carbohydrates at the whole-plant level, CO_2-induced acclimation represents a beneficial secondary mechanism for achieving that balance through redistributing limiting resources away from the plant's photosynthetic machinery to strengthen sink

development or enhance other important plant processes.

References

Farage, P.K., McKee, I.F., and Long, S.P. 1998. Does a low nitrogen supply necessarily lead to acclimation of photosynthesis to elevated CO_2? *Plant Physiology* **118**: 573–580.

Garcia, R.L., Long, S.P., Wall, G.W., Osborne, C.P., Kimball, B.A., Nie, G.Y., Pinter Jr., P.J., LaMorte, R.L., and Wechsung, F. 1998. Photosynthesis and conductance of spring-wheat leaves: field response to continuous free-air atmospheric CO_2 enrichment. *Plant, Cell and Environment* **21**: 659–669.

Gesch, R.W., Boote, K.J., Vu, J.C.V., Allen Jr., L.H., and Bowes, G. 1998. Changes in growth CO_2 result in rapid adjustments of ribulose-1,5-bisphosphate carboxylase/oxygenase small subunit gene expression in expanding and mature leaves of rice. *Plant Physiology* **118**: 521–529.

Gesch, R.W., Vu, J.C.V., Boote, K.J., Allen Jr., L.H., and Bowes, G. 2000. Subambient growth CO_2 leads to increased Rubisco small subunit gene expression in developing rice leaves. *Journal of Plant Physiology* **157**: 235–238.

Gesch, R.W., Vu, J.C.V., Boote, K.J., Allen Jr., L.H., and Bowes, G. 2002. Sucrose-phosphate synthase activity in mature rice leaves following changes in growth CO_2 is unrelated to sucrose pool size. *New Phytologist* **154**: 77–84.

Hussain, M.W., Allen Jr., L.H., and Bowes, G. 1999. Up-regulation of sucrose phosphate synthase in rice grown under elevated CO_2 and temperature. *Photosynthesis Research* **60**: 199–208.

Louche-Tessandier, D., Samson, G., Hernandez-Sebastia, C., Chagvardieff, P., and Desjardins, Y. 1999. Importance of light and CO_2 on the effects of endomycorrhizal colonization on growth and photosynthesis of potato plantlets (*Solanum tuberosum*) in an *in vitro* tripartite system. *New Phytologist* **142**: 539–550.

Maroco, J.P., Edwards, G.E., and Ku, M.S.B. 1999. Photosynthetic acclimation of maize to growth under elevated levels of carbon dioxide. *Planta* **210**: 115–125.

Osborne, C.P., LaRoche, J., Garcia, R.L., Kimball, B.A., Wall, G.W., Pinter Jr., P.J., LaMorte, R.L., Hendrey, G.R., and Long, S.P. 1998. Does leaf position within a canopy affect acclimation of photosynthesis to elevated CO_2? *Plant Physiology* **117**: 1037–1045.

Reekie, E.G., MacDougall, G., Wong, I., and Hicklenton, P.R. 1998. Effect of sink size on growth response to elevated atmospheric CO_2 within the genus *Brassica*. *Canadian Journal of Botany* **76**: 829–835.

Sims, D.A., Luo, Y., and Seeman, J.R. 1998. Comparison of photosynthetic acclimation to elevated CO_2 and limited nitrogen supply in soybean. *Plant, Cell and Environment* **21**: 945–952.

Theobald, J.C., Mitchell, R.A.C., Parry, M.A.J., and Lawlor, D.W. 1998. Estimating the excess investment in ribulose-1,5-bisphosphate carboxylase/oxygenase in leaves of spring wheat grown under elevated CO_2. *Plant Physiology* **118**: 945–955.

Watling, J.R., Press, M.C., and Quick, W.P. 2000. Elevated CO_2 induces biochemical and ultrastructural changes in leaves of the C4 cereal sorghum. *Plant Physiology* **123**: 1143–1152.

Ziska, L.H. 1998. The influence of root zone temperature on photosynthetic acclimation to elevated carbon dioxide concentrations. *Annals of Botany* **81**: 717–721.

2.1.2 Chaparral and Desert Species

- The few studies of acclimation that have been conducted on chaparral and desert plants indicate that although acclimation can sometimes be quite severe, other physiological changes, such as the reductions in stomatal conductance that typically produce large increases in water use efficiency, often more than compensate for the increases in photosynthesis caused by acclimation.

Roberts *et al.* (1998) conducted a FACE experiment in southern California, USA, exposing *Adenostoma fassciculatum* shrubs to atmospheric CO_2 concentrations of 360 and 550 ppm while they studied the nature of gas-exchange in this chaparral species. After six months of CO_2 fumigation, photosynthetic acclimation occurred. However, because of reductions in stomatal conductance and transpirational water loss, the CO_2-enriched shrubs exhibited leaf water potentials less negative (and hence less stressful) than those of control plants. This CO_2-induced water conservation phenomenon should enable this woody perennial to better withstand the periods of drought that commonly occur in this southern California region, and the photosynthetic down-regulation it exhibits should allow it to more equitably distribute the limiting resources it possesses among different essential plant physiological processes.

Huxman and Smith (2001) measured seasonal gas exchange during an unusually wet El Niño year in an annual grass (*Bromus madritensis* ssp. *rubens*) and a perennial forb (*Eriogonum inflatum*) growing within FACE plots established in the Mojave Desert, USA, which they maintained at atmospheric CO_2 concentrations of 350 and 550 ppm. The elevated CO_2 consistently increased net photosynthetic rates in the annual grass without inducing photosynthetic acclimation. Even as seasonal photosynthetic rates declined post-flowering, the reduction was much less in the CO_2-enriched plants. Elevated CO_2 had no consistent effect on stomatal conductance in this species. In contrast, *Eriogonum* plants growing at 550 ppm CO_2 exhibited significant photosynthetic acclimation, especially late in the season, which led to similar rates of net photosynthesis in these plants in both CO_2 treatments. But in this species, elevated CO_2 reduced stomatal conductance over most of the growing season. And, therefore, although the two desert plants exhibited different stomatal and photosynthetic responses to elevated CO_2, both experienced significant CO_2-induced increases in water use efficiency and biomass production, highlighting the existence of different, but equally effective, species-specific mechanisms for responding positively to atmospheric CO_2 enrichment in a desert environment.

In another study conducted at the Mojave Desert FACE site, Hamerlynck *et al.* (2002) determined plants of the deciduous shrub *Lycium andersonii* grown in elevated CO_2 displayed photosynthetic acclimation, as maximum rubisco activity in the plants growing in the CO_2-enriched air was 19% lower than in the plants growing in ambient air. The elevated CO_2 did not significantly impact rates of photosynthesis. Leaf stomatal conductance, by contrast, was consistently about 27% lower in the plants grown in the CO_2-enriched air. During the last month of the spring growing season, the plants in the elevated CO_2 plots displayed leaf water potentials less negative than those exhibited by the control plants growing in ambient air. Hence, as the CO_2 content of the air increases, *Lycium andersonii* likely will respond by exhibiting significantly enhanced water use efficiency, which should greatly increase its ability to cope with the highly variable precipitation and temperature regimes of the Mojave Desert. The acclimation observed within the shrub's photosynthetic apparatus should allow it to reallocate more resources to sustaining greater amounts of biomass. Thus it is likely future increases in the air's CO_2 content will favor a "greening" of the American Mojave Desert.

References

Hamerlynck, E.P., Huxman, T.E., Charlet, T.N., and Smith,

S.D. 2002. Effects of elevated CO_2 (FACE) on the functional ecology of the drought-deciduous Mojave Desert shrub, *Lycium andersonii*. *Environmental and Experimental Botany* **48**: 93–106.

Huxman, T.E. and Smith, S.D. 2001. Photosynthesis in an invasive grass and native forb at elevated CO_2 during an El Niño year in the Mojave Desert. *Oecologia* **128**: 193—01.

Roberts, S.W., Oechel, W.C., Bryant, P.J., Hastings, S.J., Major, J., and Nosov, V. 1998. A field fumigation system for elevated carbon dioxide exposure in chaparral shrubs. *Functional Ecology* **12**: 708–719.

2.1.3 Grassland Species

- As the air's CO_2 content rises, grassland species may not exhibit photosynthetic acclimation if they can maintain a balance between their carbohydrate sources and sinks. But if this balancing act is not possible, acclimation represents a beneficial way of achieving that balance by redistributing limiting resources away from a plant's photosynthetic machinery to strengthen its sink development and/or its nutrient-gathering activities.

In nearly every reported case of photosynthetic acclimation in CO_2-enriched grassland species, rates of photosynthesis displayed by plants grown and measured at elevated concentrations of CO_2 are typically greater than those exhibited by control plants grown and measured at ambient CO_2 concentrations (Davey *et al.*, 1999; Bryant *et al.*, 1998). But as mentioned in prior sections, CO_2-induced photosynthetic acclimation often results from insufficient plant sink strength that can lead to carbohydrate accumulation in source leaves and the triggering of photosynthetic end-product feedback inhibition, which reduces rubisco activity and rates of net photosynthesis (Roumet *et al.*, 2000).

As one example of this phenomenon, Rogers *et al.* (1998) report perennial ryegrass grown at an atmospheric CO_2 concentration of 600 ppm and low soil nitrogen content exhibited leaf carbohydrate contents and rubisco activities 100% greater and 25% less, respectively, than those observed in control plants grown at 360 ppm CO_2 prior to a cutting event. But following the cutting, which effectively reduced the source:sink ratio of the plants, leaf carbohydrate contents in CO_2-enriched plants decreased and rubisco activities increased, completely ameliorating the photosynthetic acclimation in this species.

However, at high soil nitrogen, photo-synthetic acclimation to elevated CO_2 did not occur. Thus, photosynthetic acclimation appears to result from the inability of plants to develop adequate sinks at low soil nitrogen, and is not necessarily induced directly by atmospheric CO_2 enrichment.

In some cases, plants can effectively increase their sink strength and thus reduce the magnitude of CO_2-induced acclimation by forming symbiotic relationships with certain species of soil fungi. Under such conditions, photosynthetic down-regulation is not triggered as rapidly, or as frequently, by end-product feedback inhibition, as excess carbohydrates are mobilized out of source leaves and sent below-ground to the symbiotic fungi. Staddon *et al.* (1999), for example, report photosynthetic acclimation was not induced in CO_2-enriched *Plantago lanceolata* plants inoculated with a mycorrhizal fungus, but it was induced in control plants that were not inoculated with the fungus. Thus, CO_2-induced acclimation appears to be closely related to the source:sink balance that exists within plants, and which is triggered when sink strength falls below, and source strength rises above, certain critical thresholds in a species-dependent manner.

As the air's CO_2 content slowly but steadily rises, therefore, these peer-reviewed studies suggest grassland species may not exhibit photosynthetic acclimation if they can maintain a balance between their sources and sinks for carbohydrates at the whole-plant level. But in the event this balancing act is not possible, acclimation represents a beneficial secondary means of achieving that balance by redistributing limiting resources away from a plant's photosynthetic machinery to strengthen its sink development and/or its nutrient-gathering activities.

References

Bryant, J., Taylor, G., and Frehner, M. 1998. Photosynthetic acclimation to elevated CO_2 is modified by source:sink balance in three component species of chalk grassland swards grown in a free air carbon dioxide enrichment (FACE) experiment. *Plant, Cell and Environment* **21**: 159–168.

Davey, P.A., Parsons, A.J., Atkinson, L., Wadge, K., and Long, S.P. 1999. Does photosynthetic acclimation to elevated CO_2 increase photosynthetic nitrogen-use efficiency? A study of three native UK grassland species in open-top chambers. *Functional Ecology* **13**: 21–28.

Rogers, A., Fischer, B.U., Bryant, J., Frehner, M., Blum, H., Raines, C.A., and Long, S.P. 1998. Acclimation of photosynthesis to elevated CO_2 under low-nitrogen nutrition is affected by the capacity for assimilate utilization. Perennial ryegrass under free-air CO_2 enrichment. *Plant Physiology* **118**: 683–689.

Roumet, C., Garnier, E., Suzor, H., Salager, J.-L., and Roy, J. 2000. Short and long-term responses of whole-plant gas exchange to elevated CO_2 in four herbaceous species. *Environmental and Experimental Botany* **43**: 155–169.

Staddon, P.L., Fitter, A.H., and Robinson, D. 1999. Effects of mycorrhizal colonization and elevated atmospheric carbon dioxide on carbon fixation and below-ground carbon partitioning in *Plantago lanceolata*. *Journal of Experimental Botany* **50**: 853–860.

2.1.4 Tree Species

Aspen/poplar trees, growing out-of-doors and rooted in the ground, generally show little long-term photosynthetic acclimation (gradual reduction in initial experimental CO_2-induced growth stimulation), and sometimes none at all. Although there can be a steep multiyear decline in the initial huge CO_2-induced growth stimulation of citrus trees, the subsequent long-term equilibrium growth enhancement can be quite substantial. And in oak trees, both long-term and total-lifetime CO_2 enhancement of the air surrounding various species have provided evidence for a total lack of photosynthetic acclimation, indicating the many positive and enduring benefits of atmospheric CO_2 enrichment. Also, even though there may be a partial acclimation of the photosynthetic process in pine trees in some CO_2-enrichment experiments, the down-regulation is typically neither complete nor wholly detrimental, for it transfers nitrogen from the sites of photosynthesis to the sinks for photosynthates, where it is most needed when soil infertility is limiting primary productivity. Finally, studies of spruce trees reveal atmospheric CO_2 enrichment increases their photo-synthetic rates, even in the case of partial photo-synthetic acclimation, which enables them to trans-port greater amounts of soluble carbohydrates, including glucose, to active sink tissues to support their enhanced growth and development even on nutrient-poor soils.

2.1.4.1 Aspen/Poplar

- Aspen/poplar trees, growing out-of-doors and rooted in the ground, generally show little long-term acclimation (reduction in CO_2-induced growth stimulation), and sometimes none at all.

Trees grown for long periods of time in elevated CO_2 environments sometimes exhibit some degree of photosynthetic acclimation or down-regulation, typically characterized by modestly reduced rates of photosynthesis compared to what might be expected on the basis of short-term exposure to CO_2-enriched air. These reductions result from a long-term decrease in the activity and/or amount of the primary plant carboxylating enzyme *rubisco*. This section explores this phenomenon as it applies to various species of aspen/poplar trees.

Takeuchi *et al.* (2001) grew quaking aspen (*Populus tremuloides*) trees for two years in 30-meter-diameter free-air CO_2 enrichment (FACE) plots near Rhinelander, Wisconsin (USA), maintained at atmospheric CO_2 concentrations of either 360 or 560 ppm. They found elevated CO_2 stimulated the growth and closure of the trees' canopies, as indicated by light intensities measured near the seedlings' lowermost branches only 17% and 9% of values observed near their uppermost branches in the ambient and CO_2-enriched environments, respectively, which led to the light availability for photosynthesis decreasing with canopy depth, but more so for the CO_2-enriched seedlings. Nevertheless, seasonal photosynthetic rates were always greater in the CO_2-enriched seedlings, although the growth stimulation was much greater in the upper canopy than in the lower (26 and 3%, respectively). Photosynthetic acclimation also occurred in the CO_2-enriched seedlings in a depth-dependent manner, with less acclimation occurring in the upper as opposed to the lower canopy, as indicated by decreases in foliar rubisco content of 28 and 50%, respectively, in those two locations. Yet in spite of this significant acclimation, the elevated CO_2 still led to a greater total net carbon uptake, and the CO_2-enriched seedlings grew 18% taller than the seedlings exposed to ambient air.

At the EuroFACE facility near Viterbo in Central Italy, Wittig *et al.* (2005) grew stands of closely spaced (1 m x 1 m) individuals of three *Populus* species—white poplar (*P. alba*), black poplar (*P. nigra*), and robusta poplar (*P. x euramericana*)—from the time of planting through canopy closure to coppice (aboveground tree harvest) at atmospheric CO_2 concentrations of 370 and 550 ppm for three full years. Based on measurements of leaf area index and various photosynthetic parameters made at regular intervals, photosynthetic rates of different leaf classes were determined for monthly intervals and summed to obtain annual canopy photosynthesis or gross primary production (GPP) in each of the three years of the study.

The 10 researchers note, "significant stimulation of GPP driven by elevated CO_2 occurred in all 3 years, and was greatest in the first year (223-251%), but markedly lower in the second (19-24%) and third years (5-19%)." The decline in CO_2-induced growth stimulation was *not* due to photosynthetic acclimation; it was simply a consequence of canopy closure and the increased shading of leaves that accompanied it.

Averaged across all species and plots, the CO_2-induced stimulation of annual GPP was 234%, 22%, and 11% in 1999, 2000, and 2001, respectively. Averaged over the full three-year period, the GPP enhancements for *P. alba*, *P. nigra*, and *P. x euramericana* were, respectively, 17%, 17%, and 25%. The scientists note these results "were consistent with independent measurements of net primary production, determined independently from biomass increments and turnover." Thus, Wittig *et al.* say their results suggest, "with selection, nutrient and moisture supply, coppice managed plantation poplars have the potential for large and sustained increases in GPP" in response to atmospheric CO_2 enrichment.

Over the following year, as the trees sent up new sprouts and renewed their growth after coppicing, Davey *et al.* (2006) measured total daily photosynthetic carbon assimilation together with several other related physiological parameters and processes. They found "diurnal photosynthesis in poplar trees grown in elevated CO_2 over four growing seasons showed a sustained increase in photosynthesis of between 35 and 60% prior to coppicing," and "this increase in daily photosynthesis is maintained during the re-growth following coppicing in *P. x euramericana*."

These observations and their other data indicate, as the seven scientists describe it, "no long-term photosynthetic acclimation to CO_2 occurred in these plants," and "poplar trees are able to 'escape' from long-term, acclamatory down-regulation of photosynthesis through a high capacity for starch synthesis and carbon export." They also note, "Wittig *et al.* (2005) showed that the canopy photosynthetic carbon gain in these species is proportional to wood increment, implying that the increased photosynthesis will result in more carbon in wood." Therefore, the seven scientists say their findings "show that the acclamatory loss of the initial increase in photosynthetic rate under elevated CO_2 is not inevitable," and "poplar species, selected for rapid growth, may be well suited to a future elevated CO_2 environment and particularly suited to afforestation

projects aimed to increase carbon uptake into wood in the near term."

Throughout the same year and over one additional year, Liberloo *et al.* (2005) studied the regrowth of the trees under unfertilized and fertilized conditions. During those first and second growing seasons after coppicing, they found the elevated CO_2 treatment significantly increased the trees' leaf area index, with relative differences between the CO_2-enriched and control trees ranging from +1.7 to +38.7%, +4.7 to +38.5%, and +3.9 to +45% for *P. alba*, *P. nigra*, and *P. x euramericana*, respectively, for unfertilized and fertilized conditions, respectively. In addition, they report the increased leaf area index "supported increased aboveground biomass production," but only in the fertilized treatment. In light of these findings, they remark that if the CO_2-induced growth enhancement after canopy closure continues to hold true in subsequent years, it "will have important implications for the carbon balance of terrestrial ecosystems, because forests could behave as a larger carbon sink under future atmospheric conditions."

Liberloo *et al.* (2006) report results for the second three-year growth rotation of the trees. They found fertilization did not affect the growth of the second-rotation trees, "likely because of the high rates of fertilization during the previous agricultural land use." In contrast, they write, "elevated CO_2 enhanced biomass production by up to 29%, and this stimulation did not differ between above- and below-ground parts." They also report the net rate of carbon assimilation was "on average for all species stimulated up to 30% during the third year of the second rotation," and "after six years of fumigation, measurements of photosynthetic parameters along the canopy profile could not detect any clear sign of acclimation to elevated CO_2" for any of the three species. Thus, they conclude, "poplar trees are able to optimally profit from future high CO_2 concentrations, provided that they are intensively managed, planted in regions with high incident radiation and supplied with sufficient nutrients and water." Such "high-density poplar coppice cultures," in their opinion, "offer possibilities to mitigate the rise of atmospheric CO_2 by producing renewable bio-energy in an economically feasible way, whereby the elevated CO_2 stimulation might sustain over several rotation cycles."

Working at the same site but studying only robusta poplar that had been growing there for five years, Calfapietra *et al.* (2005) measured the trees' photosynthetic responses to an approximate 200-ppm increase in the air's CO_2 concentration in mid-July of the study's fifth year, comparing their results with what was observed at the beginning of the experiment, both with and without supplemental nitrogen fertilization. As they describe their findings, "even after such a long period of exposure, leaves of *Populus x euramericana* have not shown clear signs of photosynthetic acclimation." They also report CO_2 enrichment "significantly decreased stomatal conductance both on upper and lower canopy leaves," which together with the CO_2-induced stimulation of photosynthesis implies a significant sustained increase in leaf water use efficiency throughout the trees' canopies. They say their results "suggest that the photosynthetic acclimation of poplar plantations is unlikely to occur in an atmosphere enriched in CO_2 and thereby will not influence the response of poplar plantations to increasing atmospheric CO_2 concentrations either over the long term or under conditions of nitrogen deposition."

At the Aspen FACE site near Rhinelander, Wisconsin (USA), Kets *et al.* (2010) measured diurnal changes in light-saturated net photosynthesis (Pn) rate under both ambient and elevated atmospheric CO_2 and/or ozone (O_3) concentrations over wide ranges of stomatal conductance, water potential, intercellular CO_2, leaf temperature, and vapor pressure difference between leaf and air in two clones (271 and 42E) of quaking aspen (*Populus tremuloides* Michx.) trees that differed in their sensitivity to ozone and had been growing under the aforementioned experimental conditions for seven to eight years. This work revealed Pn was typically enhanced by 33 to 46% in the CO_2-enriched treatment over the course of the study, and there was a small increase in leaf chlorophyll concentration as well.

Noting "previous Aspen FACE studies have reported 25–36% increases in Pn (Noormets *et al.*, 2001; Takeuchi *et al.*, 2001; Sharma *et al.*, 2003; Ellsworth *et al.*, 2004)," the six scientists emphasize the aerial fertilization effect of atmospheric CO_2 enrichment on Pn observed in their study "has rather been increasing in time than decreasing," stating this phenomenon may be caused by the "slight but significant increase in leaf chlorophyll content per leaf area, which is rather positive acclimation in photosynthetic apparatus than negative acclimation." They cite the studies of Centritto and Jarvis (1999) and Eichelmann *et al.* (2004) in support of this conclusion.

Darbah *et al.* (2010) analyzed photosynthesis data they and others had collected at the Aspen FACE site over a period of 11 years for the same two quaking aspen clones, which were exposed to all combinations of ambient and elevated (560 ppm) CO_2 and ambient and elevated (1.5 times ambient) ozone (O_3). In addition, they studied leaf stomatal conductance under the same conditions. This work revealed, as they describe it, "no long-term photosynthetic and stomatal acclimation to elevated CO_2, O_3 or $CO_2 + O_3$ in aspen trees exposed to elevated CO_2 and/or O_3 gases for 11 years," and the aspen trees "have sustained their maximum instantaneous photosynthesis stimulation for over a decade." In discussing their findings, Darbah *et al.* say they support the observations of Liberloo *et al.* (2007), who measured a 49% increase in net photosynthetic rate in poplar trees after six years of exposure to elevated CO_2; Sholtis *et al.* (2004), who reported a 44% stimulation of net photosynthesis in sweetgum trees after three years of exposure to elevated CO_2; Crous and Ellsworth (2004), who found a photosynthetic enhancement of 51 to 69% in *Pinus taeda* trees after six years of exposure to elevated CO_2; and Davey *et al.* (2006) and Paoletti *et al.* (2007), of whose work Darbah *et al.* state, "there was no photosynthetic acclimation (down-regulation) occurring in *Quercus ilex* under long-term CO_2 enrichment." In addition, they remark, even in white clover (*Trifolium repens*), Ainsworth *et al.* (2003) found photosynthetic stimulation "remained after nine years of exposure to elevated CO_2."

Thus, as more long-term experiments are conducted on long-lived woody plants growing out-of-doors and rooted in the ground, where their roots are not artificially confined to a limited volume of soil, it is becoming abundantly clear they generally do not experience a complete cessation of the initial photosynthetic stimulation provided them by the extra CO_2 to which they are exposed in CO_2 enrichment studies. They often show very little long-term reduction in CO_2-induced growth stimulation, and sometimes no reduction at all, as is evidenced in these several studies of aspen/poplar trees.

References

Ainsworth, A.E., Rogers, A., Blum, H., Nosberger, J., and Long, S.P. 2003. Variation in acclimation of photosynthesis in *Trifolium repens* after eight years of exposure to free air CO_2 enrichment (FACE). *Journal of Experimental Botany* 54: 2769–2774.

Calfapietra, C., Tulva, I., Eensalu, E., Perez, M., De Angelis, P., Scarascia-Mugnozza, G., and Kull, O. 2005. Canopy profiles of photosynthetic parameters under elevated CO_2 and N fertilization in a poplar plantation. *Environmental Pollution* **137**: 525–535.

Centritto, M. and Jarvis, P.G. 1999. Long-term effects of elevated carbon dioxide concentration and provenance on four clones of Sitka spruce (*Picea sitchensis*). II. Photosynthetic capacity and nitrogen use efficiency. *Tree Physiology* **19**: 807–814.

Crous, K.Y. and Ellsworth, D.S. 2004. Canopy position affects photosynthetic adjustments to long-term elevated CO_2 concentration (FACE) in aging needles in a mature *Pinus taeda* forest. *Tree Physiology* **24**: 961–970.

Darbah, J.N.T., Kubiske, M.F., Nelson, N., Kets, K., Riikonen, J., Sober, A., Rouse, L., and Karnosky, D.F. 2010. Will photosynthetic capacity of aspen trees acclimate after long-term exposure to elevated CO_2 and O_3? *Environmental Pollution* **158**: 983–991.

Davey, P.A., Olcer, H., Zakhleniuk, O., Bernacchi, C.J., Calfapietra, C., Long, S.P., and Raines, C.A. 2006. Can fast-growing plantation trees escape biochemical down-regulation of photosynthesis when grown throughout their complete production cycle in the open air under elevated carbon dioxide? *Plant, Cell and Environment* **29**: 1235–1244.

Eichelmann, H., Oja, V., Rasulov, B., Padu, E., Bichele, I., Pettai, H., Mols, T., Kasparova, I., Vapaavuori, E., and Laisk, A. 2004. Photosynthetic parameters of birch (*Betula pendula* Roth) leaves growing in normal and in CO_2- and O_3-enriched atmospheres. *Plant, Cell and Environment* **27**: 479–495.

Ellsworth, D.S., Reich, P.B., Naumburg, E.S., Koch, G.W., Kubiske, M.E., and Smith, S.D. 2004. Photosynthesis, carboxylation and leaf nitrogen responses of 16 species to elevated pCO_2 across four free-air CO_2 enrichment experiments in forest, grassland and desert. *Global Change Biology* **10**: 2121–2138.

Kets, K., Darbah, J.N.T., Sober, A., Riikonen, J., Sober, J., and Karnosky, D.F. 2010. Diurnal changes in photosynthetic parameters of *Populus tremuloides*, modulated by elevated concentrations of CO_2 and/or O_3 and daily climatic variation. *Environmental Pollution* **158**: 1000–1007.

Liberloo, M., Calfapietra, C., Lukac, M., Godbold, D., Luo, Z.-B., Polle, A., Hoosbeek, M.R., Kull, O., Marek, M., Raines, C., Rubino, M., Taylor, G., Scarascia-Mugnozza, G., and Ceulemans, R. 2006. Woody biomass production during the second rotation of a bio-energy *Populus* plantation increases in a future high CO_2 world. *Global Change Biology* **12**: 1094–1106.

Liberloo, M., Dillen, S.Y., Calfapietra, C., Marinari, S., Luo, Z.B., De Angelis, P., and Ceulemans, R. 2005. Elevated CO_2 concentration, fertilization and their interaction: growth stimulation in a short-rotation poplar coppice (EUROFACE). *Tree Physiology* **25**: 179–189.

Liberloo, M., Tulva, I., Raim, O., Kull, O., and Ceulemans, R. 2007. Photosynthetic stimulation under long-term CO_2 enrichment and fertilization is sustained across a closed *Populus* canopy profile (EUROFACE). *New Phytologist* **173**: 537–549.

Noormets, A., Sober, A., Pell, E.J., Dickson, R.E., Podila, G.K., Sober, J., Isebrands, J.G., and Karnosky, D.F. 2001. Stomatal and non-stomatal limitation to photosynthesis in two trembling aspen (*Populus tremuloides* Michx.) clones exposed to elevated CO_2 and O_3. *Plant, Cell and Environment* **24**: 327–336.

Paoletti, E., Seufert, G., Della Rocca, G., and Thomsen, H. 2007. Photosynthetic response to elevated CO_2 and O_3 in *Quercus ilex* leaves at a natural CO_2 spring. *Environmental Pollution* **147**: 516–524.

Sharma, P., Sober, A., Sober, J., Podila, G.K., Kubiske, M.E., Mattson, W.J., Isebrands, J.G., and Karnosky, D.F. 2003. Moderation of CO_2-induced gas exchange responses by elevated tropospheric O_3 in trembling aspen and sugar maple. *Ekologia* **22** (S1): 304–317.

Sholtis, J.D., Gunderson, C.A., Norby, R.J., and Tissue, D.T. 2004. Persistent stimulation of photosynthesis by elevated CO_2 in a sweetgum (*Liquidambar styraciflua*) forest stand. *New Phytologist* **162**: 243–254.

Takeuchi, Y., Kubiske, M.E., Isebrands, J.G., Pregitzer, K.S., Hendrey, G., and Karnosky, D.F. 2001. Photosynthesis, light and nitrogen relationships in a young deciduous forest canopy under open-air CO_2 enrichment. *Plant, Cell and Environment* **24**: 1257–1268.

Wittig, V.E., Bernacchi, C.J., Zhu, X.-G., Calfapietra, C., Ceulemans, R., DeAngelis, P., Gielens, B., Miglietta, F., Morgan, P.B., and Long, S.P. 2005. Gross primary production is stimulated for three *Populus* species grown under free-air CO_2 enrichment from planting through canopy closure. *Global Change Biology* **33**: 644–656.

2.1.4.2 Citrus

- Although there can be a steep multiyear decline in the initial CO_2-induced growth stimulation of citrus trees, the subsequent long-term equilibrium growth enhancement can be substantial.

Trees grown for long periods of time in air enriched with CO_2 sometimes exhibit photosynthetic acclimation or down-regulation. This phenomenon is characterized by modestly reduced rates of photosynthesis (compared to what is observed during short-term exposure to CO_2-enriched air), which result from a slow decline in the activity and/or amount of the primary plant carboxylating enzyme *rubisco*. This section reports what has been learned about this phenomenon in the few experiments that have studied it in citrus trees.

Jifon *et al.* (2002) grew seedlings of sour orange (*Citrus aurantium* L.) and sweet orange (*Citrus sinensis* L.) for nearly three months in glasshouses maintained at atmospheric CO_2 concentrations of either 360 or 700 ppm, where they were either inoculated with arbuscular mycorrhizal fungi or left non-inoculated as control plants. Thus they studied the effects of both elevated CO_2 and fungal presence on photosynthesis and growth in these two citrus species of contrasting fungal acceptance: sour orange, which displays strong associations with mycorrhizal symbionts, and sweet orange, which exhibits relatively weaker relationships with such fungi.

This protocol revealed elevated CO_2 increased photosynthetic rates in non-mycorrhizal and mycorrhizal sour orange tree seedlings by 18% and 118%, respectively. Elevated CO_2 enhanced photosynthetic rates in non-mycorrhizal and mycorrhizal sweet orange seedlings by 50% and 67%, respectively.

In terms of biomass production, the mycorrhizal sour orange seedlings exposed to ambient CO_2 displayed 18% less growth than the non-mycorrhizal control seedlings, but at elevated CO_2, the mycorrhizal seedlings displayed 15% more growth than the non-mycorrhizal seedlings. Thus atmospheric CO_2 enrichment more than compensated for the carbon costs associated with maintaining the mycorrhizal fungal symbiosis in the sour orange seedlings, and sweet orange seedlings exposed to elevated CO_2 exhibited the same increase in biomass with or without fungal inoculation, indicating this species is less dependent upon fungal symbiosis in eliciting CO_2-induced growth responses.

As the air's CO_2 content continues to rise, therefore, both of these citrus species likely will respond by exhibiting enhanced rates of photosynthesis and biomass production. In sour orange trees, photosynthetic and growth responses to elevated CO_2 will likely be greater when seedlings are involved in symbiotic relationships with soil fungi. Jifon *et al.* found the degree of CO_2-induced photosynthetic acclimation or down-regulation in sour orange tree seedlings was significantly reduced when mycorrhizal fungi were present, as they served as a carbon sink for excess carbohydrates produced by photosynthesis, thereby alleviating the notorious end-product inhibition of photosynthesis. Thus, it is likely increasing atmospheric CO_2 concentrations may increase growth in nearly all tree species throughout

their normal life spans, for most are involved in symbiotic relationships with one or more types of mycorrhizal fungi.

Adam *et al.* (2004) measured numerous plant physiological processes and properties throughout the fourteenth year of a long-term study of the effects of a 75% increase (from 400 ppm to 700 ppm) in the air's CO_2 concentration on the growth and development of sour orange trees that had been grown from the seedling stage to maturity under well-watered and fertilized conditions out-of-doors at Phoenix, Arizona (USA) in clear-plastic-wall open-top enclosures. They then compared their results with those of similar measurements made in earlier years of the study.

In the second year of the experiment, net photosynthesis rates were 2.84 times greater in the CO_2-enriched enclosures than in the ambient-air enclosures. By the sixth year of the study, however, this enhancement ratio had declined to 1.75, and in the fourteenth year it had dropped to 1.45. Plotting similarly declining above-ground woody biomass ratios against these net photosynthesis ratios, Adam *et al.* derived a linear relationship with an r^2 value of 0.997 that yielded a CO_2-induced woody biomass enhancement ratio of 1.78 at the 14-year point of the study. This value for the woody biomass ratio previously had been found by Idso and Kimball (2001) to have been essentially constant from year 10 to year 14, leading Adam *et al.* to conclude the CO_2-induced net photosynthesis ratio they derived (1.45) likely also had been essentially constant over this period, indicating the final equilibrium level at which it had apparently stabilized.

Other evidence for the down-regulation of photosynthesis in the CO_2-enriched sour orange tree leaves was provided by the observation that in year 14 of the study, the pooled mean of the concentration of the large subunit of rubisco in the CO_2-enriched leaves was only 78% of that observed in the ambient-air leaves, and the concentration of the small subunit of rubisco was reduced by 34% in the CO_2-enriched leaves compared to the ambient-air leaves. In addition, the full and initial activities of rubisco under CO_2 enrichment were reduced, as were leaf chlorophyll *a* and total nitrogen concentrations.

Adam *et al.* conclude, "long-term CO_2 enrichment can result in photosynthetic down-regulation in leaves of trees, even under non-limiting nitrogen conditions." At the final equilibrium level of acclimation experienced in the sour orange trees of this long-term study, the 75% enhancement of the air's CO_2 concentration still produced an equivalent percentage increase (or possibly slightly more) in both wood and fruit production (78 and 80%, respectively).

Three years later, Kimball *et al.* (2007) described the final state of the Phoenix sour orange trees at the termination of that 17-year-long CO_2 enrichment experiment. In terms of total biomass production, which was the primary focus of their summary report, they state the CO_2-enriched to ambient-treatment ratio of annual wood plus fruit production peaked in years 2–4 of the experiment at a value of approximately 2.4, and following that peak "there was a decline through year 8." Thereafter, however, they found the annually produced-biomass ratios were, as they describe it, "more or less at a plateau that corresponded with the value of the ratio at final harvest of 1.69."

In terms of harvestable yield, the four researchers write, "the cumulative amount of biomass due to fruit production over the duration of the experiment was increased 85% due to elevated CO_2," and this increase "was entirely from an increase in fruit number." In addition, they report, "the vitamin C content of the fruit was increased 7% based on samples taken from the fourth through the 12th years of the experiment," citing the study of Idso *et al.* (2002). Not only were many more oranges produced by the trees in the CO_2-enriched chambers, but many more better-quality oranges were produced.

In the concluding discussion of one of the major implications of the study, Kimball *et al.* write, "rather than a continual acclimation"—i.e., rather than a gradual long-term decline in the aerial fertilization effect of the extra 300 ppm of CO_2 supplied to the CO_2-enriched trees—"there was a sustained enhancement of about 70% in annual fruit and incremental wood production over the last several years of the experiment." This observation led them to conclude, "the effects of elevated CO_2 on trees can be large and sustained for many years," as they demonstrated to be the case with the sour orange trees they studied: Over the entire last decade of the experiment, there was a 70% sustained increase in total biomass production and an 85% increase in fruit production in response to the 75% increase in the air's CO_2 content employed throughout the study.

References

Adam, N.R., Wall, G.W., Kimball, B.A., Idso, S.B., and Webber, A.N. 2004. Photosynthetic down-regulation over long-term CO_2 enrichment in leaves of sour orange (*Citrus aurantium*) trees. *New Phytologist* **163**: 341–347.

Idso, S.B. and Kimball, B.A. 2001. CO_2 enrichment of sour orange trees: 13 years and counting. *Environmental and Experimental Botany* **46**: 147–153.

Idso, S.B., Kimball, B.A., Shaw, P.E., Widmer, W., Vanderslice, J.T., Higgs, D.J., Montanari, A., and Clark, W.D. 2002. The effect of elevated atmospheric CO_2 on the vitamin C concentration of (sour) orange juice. *Agriculture, Ecosystems and Environment* **90**: 1–7.

Jifon, J.L., Graham, J.H., Drouillard, D.L., and Syvertsen, J.P. 2002. Growth depression of mycorrhizal Citrus seedlings grown at high phosphorus supply is mitigated by elevated CO_2. *New Phytologist* **153**: 133–142.

Kimball, B.A., Idso, S.B., Johnson, S., and Rillig, M.C. 2007. Seventeen years of carbon dioxide enrichment of sour orange trees: final results. *Global Change Biology* **13**: 2171–2183.

2.1.4.3 Oak

- Both long-term and total-lifetime CO_2 enhancement of the air surrounding various species of oak trees have provided evidence for a lack of photosynthetic acclimation, indicative of the many positive and enduring benefits of atmospheric CO_2 enrichment.

Working in Italy with mature downy oak (*Quercus pubescens*) trees located at two distances from natural CO_2-emitting springs, Stylinski *et al.* (2000) measured various physiological and biochemical properties of trees that had been exposed to atmospheric CO_2 concentrations of approximately 370 and 700 ppm for their entire 40- to 50-year life spans. The oak trees exposed to the elevated CO_2 concentration exhibited net photosynthetic rates 36 to 77% greater than those exhibited by the trees growing at the ambient CO_2 concentration. The CO_2-enriched trees showed no signs of photosynthetic down-regulation. There were no significant differences between the CO_2-enriched and ambient trees with respect to their leaves' rubisco activity, rubisco content, total nitrogen content, chlorophyll content, and carotenoid content.

Polle *et al.* (2001) collected acorns from mature holly oak (*Quercus ilex*) trees that had been growing under the same set of conditions in Italy, exposed to ambient and twice-ambient atmospheric CO_2 concentrations for their entire lifetimes. After germinating those acorns, the seedlings they produced were grown for eight months at both atmospheric CO_2 concentrations to see if atmospheric CO_2 enrichment of the parent trees had any effect on their offspring's response to atmospheric CO_2 enrichment.

The researchers found elevated CO_2 increased whole-plant biomass by 158 and 246% in seedlings derived from acorns produced in ambient and twice-ambient atmospheric CO_2 concentrations, respectively, and the final biomass of the CO_2-enriched seedlings derived from the acorns produced in the CO_2-enriched air was 25% greater than that of the CO_2-enriched seedlings derived from the acorns produced in ambient air. In addition, their gas exchange measurements indicated the CO_2-enriched seedlings derived from the acorns produced on the CO_2-enriched trees exhibited less-pronounced photosynthetic acclimation to elevated CO_2 than did the CO_2-enriched seedlings derived from the acorns produced on the trees exposed to ambient air.

Blaschke *et al.* (2001) studied the effects of long-term atmospheric CO_2 enrichment on gas exchange in both species of mature oak trees—*Quercus ilex* (a strongly drought-tolerant evergreen species) and *Quercus pubescens* (a less drought-tolerant deciduous species)—both of which were growing near CO_2-emitting springs in Italy. They made physiological and biochemical measurements on trees that had been exposed to atmospheric CO_2 concentrations of approximately 370 and 700 ppm for their 30- to 50-year lifetimes. The CO_2-enriched *Q. pubescens* and *Q. ilex* trees exhibited net photosynthetic rates 69% and 26% greater, respectively, than those displayed by trees exposed to ambient CO_2, in spite of CO_2-induced decreases of 30% and 15% in their respective foliar rubisco concentrations. In addition, stomatal conductances of CO_2-enriched *Q. pubescens* trees were approximately 23% lower than those of ambient trees, and stomatal conductances of *Q. ilex* trees displayed no CO_2-sensitivity. Both species exhibited increased water use efficiencies in the elevated CO_2 environment closest to the CO_2-emitting springs. Blaschke *et al.*'s results clearly demonstrate fully mature trees continue to exhibit enhanced rates of photosynthesis and increases in water use efficiency even after decades of exposure to elevated atmospheric CO_2 concentrations.

Marek *et al.* (2001) employed open-top chambers to boost the air's CO_2 content approximately twofold for five years around 30-year-old *Quercus ilex* trees growing in perennial evergreen stands. They found the extra CO_2 increased rates of net photosynthesis in sun-exposed and shaded leaves by 68% and 59%, respectively. After measuring short-term photosynthetic rates at various atmospheric CO_2 concentrations, they found no evidence of photosynthetic acclimation in the leaves of the mature trees. In addition, they determined the trees' light compensation point—the light level at which photosynthetic carbon uptake is matched by respiratory carbon loss—was 24% and 30% lower in sun-exposed and shaded leaves, respectively, of CO_2-enriched trees than it was in corresponding leaves of the trees growing in ambient air.

As the atmosphere's CO_2 concentration continues to increase, therefore, the work of Marek *et al.* suggests its stimulatory effect on oak tree photosynthesis will persist over the long term. In addition, because elevated CO_2 significantly lowered the light compensation point in mature oak trees, which would allow them to exhibit net carbon gains earlier in the morning and maintain them later into the evening, the stimulatory effect of elevated CO_2 on daily carbon uptake will be further enhanced. Together, these observations suggest carbon sequestration by oak trees, and perhaps other tree species, may be more substantial in future CO_2-enriched air than has been projected.

After burning a Florida (USA) scrub-oak ecosystem (dominated by *Quercus myrtifolia*, *Q. chapmanii*, and *Q. geminata*) to the ground, Ainsworth *et al.* (2002) erected open-top chambers on the site and fumigated them with ambient (380 ppm) and CO_2-enriched (700 ppm) air to study the effects of elevated CO_2 on community regeneration. During the third and fourth years of the study, they found elevated CO_2 consistently increased photosynthetic rates in *Q. myrtifolia* and *Q. chapmanii* by as much as 150% without inducing any degree of photosynthetic acclimation, although acclimation was observed in *Q. geminata*. After three years of exposure to elevated CO_2, the three oak species taken together exhibited an average increase in their rates of photosynthesis of 53%. Thus, at higher CO_2 concentrations, regenerating scrub-oak communities likely will exhibit enhanced rates of photosynthesis that will persist throughout canopy closure and maturity. These increases in photosynthesis likely will enhance community biomass production. The five researchers conclude the sustained increases in photosynthesis exhibited by *Q. myrtifolia* and *Q. chapmanii* have "translated to increased growth in these species, and there is no suggestion that this trend is changing." Carbon sequestration in regenerating and maturing scrub-oak ecosystems is likely to continue to increase with future increases in the air's CO_2 concentration.

Paoletti *et al.* (2007) measured rates of net photosynthesis in upper sunlit leaves of mature *Quercus ilex* trees growing close to (5 m) and further away from (130 m) a CO_2-emitting spring, where the trees had experienced lifetime exposure to atmospheric CO_2 concentrations of approximately 1,500 and 400 ppm, respectively. This was done during a two-week period in June 2002 at the end of the spring rains, when midday air temperatures rose above 40°C. The net photosynthetic rates of the leaves on the trees growing closest to the CO_2 spring were approximately 250% greater than those of the leaves on the trees growing 125 meters further away, where the air's CO_2 concentration was 1,100 ppm less than it was in the vicinity of the trees nearest the spring. The four Italian researchers conclude, "the considerable photosynthetic stimulation at the very high CO_2 site suggests no photosynthetic down-regulation over long-term CO_2 enrichment."

References

Ainsworth, E.A., Davey, P.A., Hymus, G.J., Drake, B.G., and Long, S.P. 2002. Long-term response of photosynthesis to elevated carbon dioxide in a Florida scrub-oak ecosystem. *Ecological Applications* **12**: 1267–1275.

Blaschke, L., Schulte, M., Raschi, A., Slee, N., Rennenberg, H., and Polle, A. 2001. Photosynthesis, soluble and structural carbon compounds in two Mediterranean oak species (*Quercus pubescens* and *Q. ilex*) after lifetime growth at naturally elevated CO_2 concentrations. *Plant Biology* **3**: 288–297.

Marek, M.V., Sprtova, M., De Angelis, P., and Scarascia-Mugnozza, G. 2001. Spatial distribution of photosynthetic response to long-term influence of elevated CO_2 in a Mediterranean *macchia* mini-ecosystem. *Plant Science* **160**: 1125–1136.

Paoletti, E., Seufert, G., Della Rocca, G., and Thomsen, H. 2007. Photosynthetic responses to elevated CO_2 and O_3 in *Quercus ilex* leaves at a natural CO_2 spring. *Environmental Pollution* **147**: 516–524.

Polle, A., McKee, I., and Blaschke, L. 2001. Altered physiological and growth responses to elevated [CO_2] in offspring from holm oak (*Quercus ilex* L.) mother trees with lifetime exposure to naturally elevated [CO_2]. *Plant, Cell and Environment* **24**: 1075–1083.

Stylinski, C.D., Oechel, W.C., Gamon, J.A., Tissue, D.T., Miglietta, F., and Raschi, A. 2000. Effects of lifelong [CO_2] enrichment on carboxylation and light utilization of *Quercus pubescens* Willd. examined with gas exchange, biochemistry and optical techniques. *Plant, Cell and Environment* **23**: 1353–1362.

2.1.4.4 Pine

- Even though there may be a partial acclimation of the photosynthetic process in pine trees in some CO_2-enrichment experiments, the down-regulation is typically neither complete nor wholly detrimental, for it transfers nitrogen from the sites of photosynthesis to the sinks for photosynthates, where it is most needed when soil infertility is limiting primary productivity.

Studies of the effects of atmospheric CO_2 enrichment on the growth and development of pine trees over the past several years have focused chiefly on three species: *Pinus radiata* (Monterey pine), *Pinus sylvestris* (Scots pine), and *Pinus taeda* (Loblolly pine).

Turnbull *et al.* (1998) grew seedlings of *P. radiata* in open-top chambers near Bromley, Christchurch (New Zealand) for four years at atmospheric CO_2 concentrations of 360 and 650 ppm. Near the conclusion of this period they measured photosynthetic parameters in current-year and one-year-old needles at each of the CO_2 concentrations to determine the effects of elevated CO_2 and leaf age on photosynthesis. This work revealed CO_2-induced increases in needle photosynthetic rate of 63% and 31% in current and one-year-old needles, respectively, suggesting needle age might be an important determinant of photosynthetic acclimation in this species. As further evidence for this hypothesis, they found atmospheric CO_2 enrichment did not induce changes in rubisco content or activity in current-year needles, but it did reduce rubisco content and activity by about 40% in one-year-old needles. After four years of CO_2 enrichment, the CO_2-induced photosynthetic enhancement persisted in each year's new flush of needles, while it experienced a partial down-regulation in older needles.

Reporting further on the same experiment, Griffin *et al.* (2000) noted a decline in older-needle rubisco content in the elevated CO_2 treatment, as well as a 40% reduction in needle stomatal conductance. The first of these changes implies that with the redistribution of nitrogen away from rubisco (which allows it to perform other vital functions), it is likely *P. radiata* will maintain high rates of net carbon uptake while using less nitrogen and other resources in doing so. Coupling these observations with the reduction in water loss due to CO_2-induced decreases in stomatal conductance, *P. radiata* seedlings probably will grow more efficiently with less water inputs in future atmospheres containing greater concentrations of CO_2.

At the conclusion of the four-year study of *P. radiata* in Christchurch, New Zealand, Greenep *et al.* (2003) took cuttings from the four-year-old Monterey pines that had experienced lifetime exposure to either ambient or elevated atmospheric CO_2 concentrations and grew them for one year in their respective CO_2 treatments in open-top chambers, where they were irrigated daily and fertilized every three months. They found the "photosynthetic rate in young needles during summer, autumn and spring was 34, 43 and 38% higher, respectively, in trees grown at elevated CO_2 than in trees grown at ambient CO_2," and "in older needles, the corresponding photosynthetic rate increases were 26, 47 and 49%." In addition, water use efficiency was 49% higher in the foliage of the elevated CO_2 treatment, although there was no change in needle stomatal conductance.

These responses were comparable to those observed in the parent trees when they were approximately the same size and age as the second-generation trees. However, there were signs of photosynthetic acclimation in the older needles of the parent trees when they were larger (in their third and fourth years) but physiologically younger than the second-generation trees, which by the time of this study (having been derived from four-year-old trees and grown for an additional year) were in their fifth year of life. Thus, the researchers suggested the down-regulation of photosynthesis observed in the parent trees in their third and fourth years "was a result of a shift in the proportion of young to old needles as the trees increased in size."

In concluding, they hypothesize, "in small trees, close proximity of active sinks, such as developing buds, to a proportionally small reservoir of source tissue (mature foliage) would increase the overall sink strength and reduce the extent of photosynthetic acclimation (down-regulation) at elevated CO_2." They note, for example, "within an immature *P. radiata* canopy, young needles may represent as much as 4 to 10 times the biomass of older needles," but "as the canopy matures this ratio approaches equality (Turnbull *et al.*, 1998)." Hence, they conclude, "down-regulation of photosynthesis at elevated CO_2 is related to tree size rather than tree age or duration of exposure," and "the capacity for enhanced photosynthesis in trees growing in elevated CO_2 is unlikely to be lost in subsequent generations."

Jach and Ceulemans (2000) studied three-year-old *Pinus sylvestris*, Scots pine, seedlings rooted in the ground and grown in open-top chambers maintained at atmospheric CO_2 concentrations of 350 and 750 ppm for two additional years to determine the long-term effects of elevated CO_2 on photosynthesis in this important European timber species. To make the experimental results more representative of the natural world, no nutrients or irrigation water were applied to the soils during their investigation.

During the second year of atmospheric CO_2 enrichment, the photosynthetic rates of the current-year and one-year-old CO_2-enriched needles were 62% and 65% greater, respectively, than the rates displayed by the needles on the seedlings growing in ambient air. When photosynthesis was measured at atmospheric CO_2 concentrations reciprocal to growth CO_2 concentrations, the researchers detected photosynthetic acclimation in the CO_2-enriched seedlings, as evidenced by a 21% reduction in their photosynthetic rates. However, Jach and Ceulemans note, "the stimulatory effect of elevated CO_2 on photosynthesis substantially exceeded the magnitude of down-regulation." Even with photosynthetic acclimation, the rate of net photosynthesis in the CO_2-enriched seedlings was more than 40% greater than the rate measured in the control seedlings exposed to ambient air.

In a parallel study of Scots pine, Gielen *et al.* (2000) worked with six-year-old seedlings rooted in the ground within open-top chambers maintained at atmospheric CO_2 concentrations of 350 and 750 ppm for three years to determine the long-term effects of elevated CO_2 on chlorophyll fluorescence and needle characteristics. No nutrients or irrigation water were applied to the soil. At the end of the period, a detailed seasonal analysis indicated elevated CO_2 did not significantly impact the photochemical quantum efficiency of photosystem II, nor did it affect any parameters associated with chlorophyll fluorescence. This indicates atmospheric CO_2 enrichment did not modify the light-dependent reactions of photosynthesis in this species.

With respect to needle characteristics, on the other hand, elevated CO_2 reduced needle nitrogen and chlorophyll contents by 33% and 26%, respectively. These observations suggest the light-independent reactions of photosynthesis were being modified by long-term exposure to elevated CO_2 in a manner indicating photosynthetic acclimation. But this acclimation of the photosynthetic process allows for the redistribution of limiting resources—such as nitrogen—away from what thus becomes a more efficient photosynthetic apparatus, so this important nutrient can be utilized in other areas of the tree where it is needed more. Thus, this CO_2-induced phenomenon can have a positive effect on growth because it allows trees to produce more biomass under conditions of low soil fertility than would otherwise be possible under ambient CO_2 concentrations, due to the mobilization of nitrogen out of photosynthetically active leaves and into actively expanding sink tissues.

Maier *et al.* (2002) constructed open-top chambers around 13-year-old *Pinus taeda*, loblolly pines, growing on infertile sandy soil and fumigated them for two more years with air containing either 350 ppm or 550 ppm of CO_2, while half of the trees at each CO_2 concentration received supplemental soil fertilization. They found the elevated CO_2 increased branch needle area by 13%, and soil fertilization increased it by 38%. Applied together, the two treatments enhanced branch needle area by 56%. In addition, the extra CO_2 enhanced the trees' net photosynthesis rates by 82%, with the trees showing no signs of photosynthetic acclimation over the two-year duration of the study.

Crous and Ellsworth (2004) studied the photosynthetic rates of different-age needles measured at different crown positions on the 19-year-old (in 2002) loblolly pine trees at the Duke Forest FACE facility in the sixth year of that long-term study, comparing them with the results of similar measurements made over the prior five years. Although there was some evidence of photosynthetic down-regulation in one-year-old needles across the fifth to sixth year of CO_2 exposure, the two researchers report "strong photosynthetic enhancement in response to elevated CO_2 (e.g., +60% across age classes and canopy locations) was observed across the years."

Looking at the concept of acclimation from a somewhat different perspective, Lichter *et al.* (2008) noted progressive nitrogen limitation (PNL) may "accompany carbon sequestration in plants and soils stimulated by CO_2 fertilization, gradually attenuating the CO_2 response," after which they described what they learned about the PNL hypothesis from a nine–year CO_2 enrichment study.

The nine researchers report their data pertaining to forest-floor carbon pools indicate the existence of "a long-term steady-state sink" of about 30 g C per m^2 per year, which represents, they write, "a substantial increase in forest-floor C storage under elevated CO_2 (i.e. 29%)," and which they attribute to "increased litterfall and root turnover during the first 9 years of the study." Of the mineral soil C formed over this period, they note "approximately 20% has been allocated to stable pools that will likely remain protected from microbial activity and associated release as CO_2."

The research team also found "a significant widening of the C:N ratio of soil organic matter in the upper mineral soil under both elevated and ambient CO_2." This suggests, as they describe it, "enhanced rates of soil organic matter decomposition are increasing mineralization and uptake to provide the extra N required to support the observed increase in primary productivity under elevated CO_2." At the Duke Forest FACE site, for example, Pritchard *et al.* (2008) say this CO_2-induced increase in productivity amounts to approximately 30% annually, and they add there is "little evidence to indicate a diminished response through time," citing Finzi *et al.* (2007), who found the same to be true at the long-term forest FACE studies being conducted at Rhinelander, Wisconsin (USA), Oak Ridge National Laboratory (USA), and Tuscania (Italy).

It thus appears several of Earth's forests thought to have access to less-than-adequate soil nitrogen supplies may be able to acquire the extra nitrogen they need to maintain the sizable increases in their growth rates that are driven by elevated concentrations of atmospheric CO_2. In the case of North Carolina's Duke Forest, for example, "even after nine years of experimental CO_2 fertilization," as Lichter *et al.* describe it, "attenuation of the CO_2-induced productivity enhancement has not been observed," as also has been noted by Finzi *et al.* (2006). This finding at this location is extremely significant, because the growth of pine-hardwood forests in the southeastern United States often removes so much nitrogen from the soils in which they grow that they induce what Finzi and Schlesinger (2003) have described as "a state of acute nutrient deficiency that can only be reversed with fertilization," which was not employed in the Duke Forest FACE study.

Even though there may sometimes be a partial acclimation of the photosynthetic process in pine trees in some CO_2-enrichment experiments, the research described above suggests the down-regulation seems never to be complete. The phenomenon may even play a positive role in shifting much-needed nitrogen from the sites of photosynthesis to the sinks for photosynthates in situations where soil fertility is a limiting factor to primary productivity.

References

Crous, K.Y. and Ellsworth, D.S. 2004. Canopy position affects photosynthetic adjustments to long-term elevated CO_2 concentration (FACE) in aging needles in a mature *Pinus taeda* forest. *Tree Physiology* **24**: 961–970.

Finzi, A.C., Moore, D.J.P., DeLucia, E.H., Lichter, J., Hofmockel, K.S., Jackson, R.B., Kim, H.-S., Matamala, R., McCarthy, H.R., Oren, R., Pippen, J.S., and Schlesinger, W.H. 2006. Progressive nitrogen limitation of ecosystem processes under elevated CO_2 in a warm-temperate forest. *Ecology* **87**: 15–25.

Finzi, A.C., Norby, R.J., Calfapietra, C., Gallet-Budynek, A., Gielen, B., Holmes, W.E., Hoosbeek, M.R., Iversen, C.M., Jackson, R.B., Kubiske, M.E., Ledford, J., Liberloo, M., Oren, R., Polle, A., Pritchard, S., Zak, D.R., Schlesinger, W.H., and Ceulemans, R. 2007. Increases in nitrogen uptake rather than nitrogen-use efficiency support higher rates of temperate forest productivity under elevated CO_2. *Proceedings of the National Academy of Sciences, USA* **104**: 14,014–14,019.

Finzi, A.C. and Schlesinger, W.H. 2003. Soil-nitrogen cycling in a pine forest exposed to 5 years of elevated carbon dioxide. *Ecosystems* **6**: 444–456.

Gielen, B., Jach, M.E., and Ceulemans, R. 2000. Effects of season, needle age and elevated atmospheric CO_2 on chlorophyll fluorescence parameters and needle nitrogen concentration in (*Pinus sylvestris* L.). *Photosynthetica* **38**: 1321.

Greenep, H., Turnbull, M.H., and Whitehead, D. 2003. Response of photosynthesis in second-generation *Pinus radiata* trees to long-term exposure to elevated carbon dioxide partial pressure. *Tree Physiology* **23**: 569–576.

Griffin, K.L., Tissue, D.T., Turnbull, M.H., and Whitehead, D. 2000. The onset of photosynthetic acclimation to elevated CO_2 partial pressure in field-grown *Pinus radiata* D. Don. after 4 years. *Plant, Cell and Environment* **23**: 1089–1098.

Jach, M.E. and Ceulemans, R. 2000. Effects of season, needle age and elevated atmospheric CO_2 on photosynthesis in Scots pine (*Pinus sylvestris* L.). *Tree Physiology* **20**: 145–157.

Lichter, J., Billings, S.A., Ziegler, S.E., Gaindh, D., Ryals, R., Finzi, A.C., Jackson, R.B., Stemmler, E.A., and Schlesinger, W.H. 2008. Soil carbon sequestration in a pine forest after 9 years of atmospheric CO_2 enrichment. *Global Change Biology* **14**: 2910–2922.

Maier, C.A., Johnsen, K.H., Butnor, J., Kress, L.W., and Anderson, P.H. 2002. Branch growth and gas exchange in 13-year-old loblolly pine (*Pinus taeda*) trees in response to elevated carbon dioxide concentration and fertilization. *Tree Physiology* **22**: 1093–1106.

Pritchard, S.G., Strand, A.E., McCormack, M.L., Davis, M.A., and Oren, R. 2008. Mycorrhizal and rhizomorph dynamics in a loblolly pine forest during 5 years of free-air-CO_2-enrichment. *Global Change Biology* **14**: 1–13.

Turnbull, M.H., Tissue, D.T., Griffin, K.L., Rogers,

G.N.D., and Whitehead, D. 1998. Photosynthetic acclimation to long-term exposure to elevated CO_2 concentration in *Pinus radiata* D. Don. is related to age of needles. *Plant, Cell and Environment* **21**: 1019–1028.

2.1.4.5 Spruce

- Studies of spruce trees reveal atmospheric CO_2 enrichment increases their photosynthetic rates, even in the case of partial photosynthetic acclimation, which enables them to transport greater amounts of soluble carbohydrates, including glucose, to active sink tissues to support their enhanced growth and development even on nutrient-poor soils.

The large increases in net photosynthesis exhibited by trees growing in CO_2-enriched air have been claimed to disappear gradually over extended periods of time, in a process known as acclimation or down-regulation. The following section reviews the findings of several studies of spruce trees that bear on this question.

Spunda *et al.* (1998) monitored 15-year-old Norway spruce trees in open-top chambers maintained at atmospheric CO_2 concentrations of 350 and 700 ppm for four additional years, to study the long-term effects of elevated CO_2 on photosynthetic acclimation. When they measured the trees' photosynthetic rates at reciprocal growth CO_2 concentrations, they found the CO_2-enriched shoots displayed a reduction of 18% compared to shoots grown in ambient air, indicating the presence of CO_2-induced photosynthetic acclimation. Likewise, when analyzing photosynthetic pigments, they found the total amounts of chlorophylls and carotenoids in needles produced in CO_2-enriched air to be 17% and 14% less, respectively, than the amounts found in needles produced in ambient air. Nevertheless, when measured at growth CO_2 concentrations, current-year CO_2-enriched shoots still displayed rates of net photosynthesis 78% greater than those exhibited by shoots of trees grown in ambient air.

Egli *et al.* (1998) rooted several saplings of different Norway spruce genotypes directly into calcareous or acidic soils in open-top chambers and exposed them to atmospheric CO_2 concentrations of 370 or 570 ppm and low or high soil nitrogen contents, in order to determine the effects of elevated CO_2 and soil quality on the saplings' photosynthesis and growth rates. They found the elevated CO_2 stimulated light-saturated rates of net photosynthesis under all conditions, with all genotypes exhibiting stimulations as great as 35%. Elevated CO_2 also led to a down-regulation of photosynthesis. Rates of leaf photosynthesis still remained higher for the trees grown in the CO_2-enriched air, despite the occurrence of this phenomenon. This increase in photosynthesis ultimately contributed to greater instantaneous water-use efficiencies of the trees grown in elevated CO_2, which were also promoted by CO_2-induced decreases in needle stomatal conductance. All these processes operating together consistently led to increased aboveground biomass production, regardless of genotype, soil type, and nitrogen content.

Wiemken and Ineichen (2000) grew Norway spruce seedlings for three years in growth chambers maintained at atmospheric CO_2 concentrations of 280, 420, and 560 ppm. In addition, the seedlings received either low, medium, or high levels of nitrogen fertilization. This work revealed nitrogen fertilization did not affect the concentrations of any sugars within mature needles of the seedlings, but atmospheric CO_2 enrichment significantly enhanced needle glucose contents in a season-dependent manner.

In the highly productive growing phases characteristic of spring and early summer, for example, glucose contents in mature needles of the CO_2-enriched trees were not significantly different from those observed in needles of the trees exposed to atmospheric CO_2 concentrations of 280 and 420 ppm. In late summer, fall, and winter, however, glucose concentrations in needles on the CO_2-enriched trees were 40% to 50% higher than those of needles on trees subjected to ambient and sub-ambient CO_2 concentrations (420 and 280 ppm, respectively). These seasonal fluctuations in needle glucose concentrations suggested to the two researchers glucose levels may be mediating a seasonal photosynthetic down-regulation in spruce needles, as had been noted previously by others.

It would appear that as the air's CO_2 content continues to rise, Norway spruce trees likely will increase their photosynthetic rates, which should result in greater needle concentrations of soluble carbohydrates, including glucose. During favorable growing conditions associated with spring and early summer, the additional glucose produced by trees growing in CO_2-enriched air likely will be mobilized and sent to active sinks to support their growth and development. As growing conditions become less favorable in late summer, glucose may not be mobilized from needles as rapidly as it was during the spring and early summer, which may lead to a seasonal photosynthetic down-regulation in this species.

In spite of this intimation of a temporary seasonal down-regulation of photosynthesis in Norway spruce seedlings, it seems logical to expect they will still exhibit greater biomass production at higher atmospheric CO_2 concentrations, as demonstrated by the findings of Spanda et al. (1998) and Egli et al. (1998) and the work of Tjoelker et al. (1998). The latter scientists studied Picea mariana (black spruce) together with quaking aspen, paper birch, tamarack, and jack pine in controlled-environment chambers for three months at atmospheric CO_2 concentrations of 370 ppm or 580 ppm and day/night temperatures ranging from 18/12°C to 30/24°C. They found the 57% increase in the CO_2 content of the air significantly stimulated net photosynthesis in all of the studied species by an average of 28%, regardless of temperature, over the three-month study period. Elevated CO_2 decreased leaf nitrogen levels in all species, causing differing degrees of photosynthetic down-regulation. However, the mobilization of nitrogen from the trees' leaves or needles, coupled with the sustained enhancement of photosynthetic rates, led to increased photosynthetic nitrogen-use efficiencies in all plants grown in elevated CO_2. In addition, the elevated CO_2 decreased stomatal conductance by 10% to 25% in all species, leading to 40% to 80% increases in their instantaneous water-use efficiencies. As in essentially all such studies conducted to date, these benefits of atmospheric CO_2 enrichment more than compensated for the incomplete acclimation that sometimes occurs.

References

Egli, P., Maurer, S., Gunthardt-Goerg, M.S., and Korner, C. 1998. Effects of elevated CO_2 and soil quality on leaf gas exchange and aboveground growth in beech-spruce model ecosystems. New Phytologist 140: 185–196.

Spunda, V., Kalina, J., Cajanek, M., Pavlickova, H., and Marek, M.V. 1998. Long-term exposure of Norway spruce to elevated CO_2 concentration induces changes in photosystem II mimicking an adaptation to increased irradiance. Journal of Plant Physiology 152: 413–419.

Tjoelker, M.G., Oleksyn, J., and Reich, P.B. 1998. Seedlings of five boreal tree species differ in acclimation of net photosynthesis to elevated CO_2 and temperature. Tree Physiology 18: 715–726.

Wiemken, V. and Ineichen, K. 2000. Seasonal fluctuations of the levels of soluble carbohydrates in spruce needles exposed to elevated CO_2 and nitrogen fertilization and glucose as a potential mediator of acclimation to elevated CO_2. Journal of Plant Physiology 156: 746–750.

2.1.5 Source/Sink Relations

- Plants with large sink capacity typically respond strongly to atmospheric CO_2 enrichment by increasing their photosynthetic rates; but when sink capacity is low, they reduce their rates of photosynthesis via photosynthetic acclimation, yielding up more of the nitrogen and other nutrients they possess to help build sink structures such as roots, tubers, or aboveground fruit.

Plants grown in elevated CO_2 for extended durations often, but not always, exhibit some degree of photosynthetic acclimation or down-regulation, typically characterized by reduced rates of photosynthesis resulting from decreased activity and/or amount of the primary plant carboxylating enzyme rubisco. When this phenomenon occurs, leaf nitrogen content often decreases, as nitrogen previously invested in rubisco is transferred to other parts of the plant. Photosynthetic acclimation to elevated CO_2 can be induced by insufficient plant sink strength, which often leads to carbohydrate accumulation in source leaves and reductions in net rates of photosynthesis. Acclimation also can result from the physical constraints of growing plants in pots or by limiting their access to important nutrients such as nitrogen. This section reviews the results of various studies of source:sink relationships on plant growth responses to atmospheric CO_2 enrichment.

In a simple experiment designed to determine how sink size naturally influences plant growth response to elevated CO_2, Reekie *et al.* (1998) grew various *Brassica* species of differing sink capacity in growth chambers receiving atmospheric CO_2 concentrations of 350 and 1,000 ppm. After four weeks, elevated CO_2 had increased the total dry weights of all *Brassica* species. However, at final harvests made after six or 12 weeks of CO_2 fumigation, significant CO_2-induced increases in total dry weight persisted only in species possessing well-developed carbon sinks. Thus, the authors' data suggest species with inherently low sink strength are more likely to experience CO_2-induced acclimation than are species with inherently large sink strength that can naturally utilize the additional carbohydrates produced under CO_2-enriched conditions to progressively increase their biomass.

In a non-invasive manipulation of plant source:sink ratios, Gesch *et al.* (1998) grew rice plants for one month in growth chambers having atmospheric CO_2 concentrations of 350 and 700 ppm before switching half of the plants in each chamber to the other CO_2 growth concentration. Within 24 hours of switching, plants moved into the elevated CO_2 environment displayed a mean 15% increase in photosynthetic rate and a mean 19% reduction in *rbcS* mRNA, whereas previously CO_2-enriched plants switched to ambient CO_2 exhibited photosynthetic rates 10% lower than those of plants grown continuously at ambient CO_2 and an analogous 19% increase in the amount of *rbcS* transcript. These observations suggest rice plants grown continuously in elevated CO_2 experienced sink limitations to growth.

In the FACE experiment of Rogers *et al.* (1998), perennial ryegrass growing at atmospheric CO_2 concentrations of 360 and 600 ppm was frequently cut to determine how physical changes in source:sink relationships influence transient growth responses to elevated CO_2. Regardless of cutting events, plants grown in elevated CO_2 with high soil nitrogen availability exhibited no signs of CO_2-induced photosynthetic acclimation. In contrast, when measured one day prior to cutting, plants grown in elevated CO_2 with low soil nitrogen availability exhibited 25% reductions in leaf rubisco content. One day after cutting, this acclimation response was completely eliminated, probably in response to rapid carbohydrate utilization to repair cut leaves. Similarly, Bryant *et al.* (1998) report simulated grazing events reversed CO_2-induced decreases in rubisco activity in leaves of chalk grassland species growing on nutrient-poor soils. The results of these studies suggest photosynthetic acclimation likely results from an indirect effect of low soil nitrogen on sink development, rather than from a direct effect of elevated CO_2 on leaf photosynthetic capacity.

Farage *et al.* (1998) investigated the role of nitrogen supply in inducing photosynthetic acclimation in CO_2-enriched wheat. In one experiment, plants were grown in pots placed within growth chambers receiving 350 ppm or 650 ppm CO_2 and were irrigated with fixed amounts of low- or high-nitrogen solutions on a regular basis, which is standard protocol for experiments utilizing potted plants. In the other experiment, plants were grown hydroponically at 350 ppm or 650 ppm CO_2 to eliminate any root restriction effects on growth. The plants were placed in nutrient solutions containing low or high concentrations of nitrogen, which were continually increased to match the rising demand of the growing plants. All plants were grown for approximately five weeks and then harvested.

Wheat plants grown in pots exhibited photosynthetic acclimation when supplied with low fixed amounts of nitrogen, and elevated CO_2 exacerbated this effect. In contrast, hydroponically grown wheat that received gradually increasing nutrient supplies, which became ever-larger with increasing plant size, exhibited no signs of photosynthetic acclimation when grown at elevated CO_2 even at low nitrogen availability. These observations led the authors to conclude low nitrogen fertilization may not lead to photosynthetic acclimation in elevated CO_2, as long as the nitrogen supply keeps pace with the relative growth rate of the plants. Consequently, it is important for researchers who use potted plants to increase plant nutrient supply in proportion to plant growth as their experiments progress, in order to avoid inducing photosynthetic acclimation via the dilution of tissue nitrogen contents that typically results from enhanced carbohydrate and biomass production in elevated CO_2.

It appears plants with inherently large sink capacity have the ability to respond strongly and persistently to atmospheric CO_2 enrichment. In other plants, a short-term reduction in source strength often overcomes sink-induced limitations on growth responses to atmospheric CO_2 enrichment. Foliar reductions resulting from clipping events—or non-invasive reductions in source strength—nearly always eliminated CO_2-induced photosynthetic acclimation. Moreover, acclimation to elevated CO_2 may actually be an indirect effect induced by insufficient amounts of soil nitrogen; if soil nitrogen content is too low, additional sink strength cannot be developed in some plants, which consequently allows carbohydrate accumulation in source leaves that can induce photosynthetic acclimation by feedback inhibition processes. As the CO_2 content of the air rises and increases plant photosynthetic rates, many plants will respond by reducing rubisco contents, which frees up large quantities of nitrogen that may be used to enhance sink strength to keep plants from exhibiting photosynthetic acclimation.

References

Bryant, J., Taylor, G., and Frehner, M. 1998. Photosynthetic acclimation to elevated CO_2 is modified by source:sink balance in three component species of chalk grassland swards grown in a free air carbon dioxide enrichment (FACE) experiment. *Plant, Cell and Environment* **21**: 159–168.

Farage, P.K., McKee, I.F., and Long, S.P. 1998. Does a low nitrogen supply necessarily lead to acclimation of photosynthesis to elevated CO_2? *Plant Physiology* **118**: 573–580.

Gesch, R.W., Boote, K.J., Vu, J.C.V., Allen Jr., L.H., and Bowes, G. 1998. Changes in growth CO_2 result in rapid adjustments of ribulose-1,5-bisphosphate carboxylase/oxygenase small subunit gene expression in expanding and mature leaves of rice. *Plant Physiology* **118**: 521–529.

Reekie, E.G., MacDougall, G., Wong, I., and Hicklenton, P.R. 1998. Effect of sink size on growth response to elevated atmospheric CO_2 within the genus *Brassica*. *Canadian Journal of Botany* **76**: 829–835.

Rogers, A., Fischer, B.U., Bryant, J., Frehner, M., Blum, H., Raines, C.A., and Long, S.P. 1998. Acclimation of photosynthesis to elevated CO_2 under low-nitrogen nutrition is affected by the capacity for assimilate utilization. Perennial ryegrass under free-air CO_2 enrichment. *Plant Physiology* **118**: 683–689.

2.2 Antioxidants

Oxidation is a chemical process that occurs naturally in plants, animals, and humans. Although the process is vital for life, it can produce free radicals, including reactive oxygen species (ROS), in a series of chain reactions that lead to cell damage and cell death. In humans, oxidative stress has been linked to cardiovascular disease, cancer, neurodegenerative disorders, and other chronic diseases. Nature's way of responding to the threats posed by such radicals is to neutralize and inhibit their reactions via complex systems of multiple types of antioxidants.

Plants, animals, and humans each harbor defense systems comprised of various types of antioxidants, including vitamin A, vitamin C, and vitamin E, and enzymes such as catalase, superoxide dismutase, and various peroxidases. Inadequate levels of antioxidants, or inhibition of antioxidant enzymes, can lead to oxidative stress.

The impact of rising atmospheric CO_2 on antioxidant compounds and enzymes found in plants is examined in Section 7.3.1.1 of Chapter 7, *Human Health*, this volume, where it is noted higher levels of atmospheric CO_2 tend to reduce oxidative stress, resulting in a reduction in antioxidant enzyme activity because fewer such enzymes are needed to counter the stress. As a result, plants are able to direct more of their limited resources into the production of other plant tissues or processes essential to their continued growth and development. In some cases, such resources are invested into the production and enhancement of antioxidative compounds, which are known to provide health benefits to animals and humans that ingest them.

2.3 Chlorophyll

- Atmospheric CO_2 enrichment may either increase, decrease, or have no effect on leaf chlorophyll concentration. Even when it is decreased, the reallocation of its nitrogen generally occurs without any adverse consequences, as most plants displaying this response typically continue to exhibit significant increases in photosynthesis and biomass production.

Plants of all types that are grown in elevated CO_2 environments often exhibit some degree of physiological adaptation. The most common of these is photosynthetic acclimation or down-regulation, which is characterized by reductions in the activity and/or amount of the primary plant carboxylating enzyme rubisco (see Section 2.1 Acclimation). In addition, plant acclimation to elevated atmospheric CO_2 may lead to reductions in leaf nitrogen and chlorophyll concentrations, the latter of which is discussed below.

Photosynthetic acclimation to elevated CO_2 is not a detrimental phenomenon, but rather a positive phenomenon that facilitates the redistribution of nitrogen and other important resources away from a plant's photosynthetic apparatus toward other sites where growth-limiting processes also need these resources. In an open-top chamber experiment on spruce saplings that lasted three years, for example, CO_2-enriched trees exhibited photosynthetic rates 62% greater than those of their ambiently grown counterparts, in spite of their lower leaf chlorophyll contents (Centritto and Jarvis, 1999). Similar studies on herbaceous (Ong *et al.*, 1998; Pritchard *et al.*, 2000) and woody (Grams *et al.*, 1999; Ormrod *et al.*, 1999) species have yielded analogous results, indicating leaf chlorophyll concentrations in these species are often much greater than what are actually needed for adequate photosynthesis in CO_2-enriched atmospheres.

Nevertheless, atmospheric CO_2 enrichment does not always result in decreased leaf chlorophyll concentrations. In an open-top chamber experiment with alfalfa, for example, plants grown at an atmospheric CO_2 concentration of 600 ppm had greater leaf chlorophyll concentrations than those observed in plants grown at 340 ppm (Sgherri *et al.*, 1998). And exposure of an orchid to a super-elevated CO_2 concentration of 10,000 ppm led to a 64% increase in leaf chlorophyll concentration relative to that measured in leaves of plants grown at ambient CO_2 (Gouk *et al.*, 1999).

In between these two responses, increases in the air's CO_2 content sometimes have been demonstrated to have no significant effect on leaf chlorophyll concentration. Sicher and Bunce (1999), for example, reported twice-ambient CO_2 concentrations elicited no change in leaf chlorophyll contents of potato plants during a three-year study. Even with higher CO_2 enrichment levels (870 ppm above ambient concentrations), Monje and Bugbee (1998) did not detect any CO_2-induced changes in leaf chlorophyll content of wheat. Similar results have been reported in woody plants, where a doubling of the atmospheric CO_2 concentration had no significant impact on leaf chlorophyll concentrations within sugar maple (Li *et al.*, 2000) and oak species (Carter *et al.*, 2000; Stylinski *et al.*, 2000).

These studies demonstrate atmospheric CO_2 enrichment may either increase, decrease, or have no effect on leaf chlorophyll concentrations, and even when leaf chlorophyll concentrations are decreased the reallocation of the nitrogen that is essential for producing chlorophyll and other photosynthetic components typically occurs without any adverse consequences. Most plants displaying this response almost always continue to exhibit significant increases in photosynthesis and biomass production.

References

Carter, G.A., Bahadur, R., and Norby, R.J. 2000. Effects of elevated atmospheric CO_2 and temperature on leaf optical properties in *Acer saccharum*. *Environmental and Experimental Botany* **43**: 267–273.

Centritto, M. and Jarvis, P.G. 1999. Long-term effects of elevated carbon dioxide concentration and provenance on four clones of Sitka spruce (*Picea sitchensis*). II. Photosynthetic capacity and nitrogen use efficiency. *Tree Physiology* **19**: 807–814.

Gouk, S.S., He, J., and Hew, C.S. 1999. Changes in photosynthetic capability and carbohydrate production in an epiphytic CAM orchid plantlet exposed to super-elevated CO_2. *Environmental and Experimental Botany* **41**: 219–230.

Grams, T.E.E, Anegg, S., Haberle, K.-H., Langebartels, C., and Matyssek, R. 1999. Interactions of chronic exposure to elevated CO_2 and O_3 levels in the photosynthetic light and dark reactions of European beech (*Fagus sylvatica*). *New Phytologist* **144**: 95–107.

Li, J.-H., Dijkstra, P., Hymus, G.J., Wheeler, R.M., Piastuchi, W.C., Hinkle, C.R., and Drake, B.G. 2000. Leaf senescence of *Quercus myrtifolia* as affected by long-term CO_2 enrichment in its native environment. *Global Change Biology* **6**: 727–733.

Monje, O. and Bugbee, B. 1998. Adaptation to high CO_2 concentration in an optimal environment: radiation capture, canopy quantum yield and carbon use efficiency. *Plant, Cell and Environment* **21**: 315–324.

Ong, B.-L., Koh, C.K-K., and Wee, Y.-C. 1998. Effects of CO_2 on growth and photosynthesis of *Pyrrosia piloselloides* (L.) Price gametophytes. *Photosynthetica* **35**: 21–27.

Ormrod, D.P., Lesser, V.M., Olszyk, D.M., and Tingey, D.T. 1999. Elevated temperature and carbon dioxide affect chlorophylls and carotenoids in Douglas-fir seedlings. *International Journal of Plant Science* **160**: 529–534.

Pritchard, S.G., Ju, Z., van Santen, E., Qiu, J., Weaver, D.B., Prior, S.A., and Rogers, H.H. 2000. The influence of elevated CO_2 on the activities of antioxidative enzymes in two soybean genotypes. *Australian Journal of Plant Physiology* **27**: 1061–1068.

Sgherri, C.L.M., Quartacci, M.F., Menconi, M., Raschi, A., and Navari-Izzo, F. 1998. Interactions between drought and elevated CO_2 on alfalfa plants. *Journal of Plant Physiology* **152**: 118–124.

Sicher, R.C. and Bunce, J.A. 1999. Photosynthetic enhancement and conductance to water vapor of field-grown *Solanum tuberosum* (L.) in response to CO_2 enrichment. *Photosynthesis Research* **62**: 155–163.

Stylinski, C.D., Oechel, W.C., Gamon, J.A., Tissue, D.T., Miglietta, F., and Raschi, A. 2000. Effects of lifelong [CO_2] enrichment on carboxylation and light utilization of *Quercus pubescens* Willd. examined with gas exchange, biochemistry and optical techniques. *Plant, Cell and Environment* **23**: 1353–1362.

2.4 Early Spring Growth

- Studies conducted on several tree species suggest either enhanced carbohydrates stored in terminal branchlets or nitrogen stored in second-year leaves may be remobilized to facilitate greater first-flush needle or leaf growth the following year as a result of atmospheric CO_2 enrichment.

Each year in the spring, when vegetation awakens from its winter dormancy and begins to grow, producing new flushes of leaves and needles, the vegetative demand for carbon is so great that plant photosynthesis actually draws down the atmosphere's CO_2 concentration in the Northern Hemisphere by several ppm (in the Southern Hemisphere too, but to a much lesser extent due to the larger surface area of oceans). In the fall, when much of the new biomass produced over the spring and summer begins to senesce and decay, large amounts of carbon are returned to the atmosphere, causing the air's CO_2 concentration to rise by several ppm. Hence, an annual oscillation is imposed on the ever-increasing CO_2 content of the atmosphere in each hemisphere, in which the CO_2 concentration first decreases with spring and summer growth and then increases with fall senescence.

In analyzing this annual atmospheric CO_2 oscillation, several scientists have noted the spring drawdown of the air's CO_2 content is beginning a few days earlier than it did several decades ago. Some have attributed this phenomenon to CO_2-induced global warming, but others have suggested the increasingly earlier occurrence of what may be called biological spring may result from an amplification of early spring branch growth that is provided by the ever-increasing aerial fertilization effect of the ongoing rise in the air's CO_2 content.

One of the first papers to anticipate this phenomenon was that of Lovelock *et al.* (1999), who enclosed branchlets of 30-m tall *Luehea seemannii* trees in open-top chambers suspended within the trees' upper canopies and fumigated them with air of either 360 or 750 ppm CO_2 for nearly 40 weeks in a study of the effects of elevated CO_2 on photosynthesis, growth, and reproduction in this deciduous tropical tree species. By these means they determined leaves of branchlets grown in CO_2-enriched air displayed net photosynthetic rates approximately 30% greater than those of leaves of branchlets grown in ambient air. The additional carbohydrates produced by this phenomenon were not used by CO_2-enriched branchlets to increase leaf growth or reproductive efforts. Instead, they were stored in terminal woody tissues. This observation led the authors to suggest enhanced carbohydrate storage in terminal branchlets may facilitate greater first-flush leaf growth the following year.

Documentation of this phenomenon was first provided by Idso *et al.* (2000), who periodically measured the lengths, dry weights, and leaf chlorophyll concentrations of new branches that each spring emerged from sour orange trees that had been growing out-of-doors in clear-plastic-wall open-top chambers for more than 10 years in air of either 400 or 700 ppm CO_2. Although new spring branch growth always began on exactly the same day in both the ambient and CO_2-enriched chambers, the initial rate of new-branch biomass production was vastly greater in the CO_2-enriched trees. Three weeks after branch growth began, for example, new branches on the CO_2-enriched trees were typically more than four times more massive than their counterparts on the ambient-treatment trees, while on a per-tree basis, there was more than six times more new-branch biomass on the trees growing in the CO_2-enriched chambers than in the ambient-air chambers. Just as rapidly as this ultra-enhancement of new branch growth began, however, it also declined, and 10 weeks into the growing season the CO_2-enriched/ambient-treatment new-branch biomass ratio had leveled out at a value commensurate with seasonal standing biomass and fruit production ratios—just under a doubling.

Based on their experimentally observed results, Idso *et al.* calculated the length of time by which the new-branch dry weight of the CO_2-enriched trees led that of the ambient-treatment trees over the first two months of the growing season, determining the 300-ppm increase in the air's CO_2 concentration caused the trees to begin the significant portion of their spring drawdown of atmospheric CO_2 fully two weeks earlier than what otherwise would have been normal. They calculated that for the 43-ppm increase in the air's CO_2 concentration experienced between 1960 and 1994, biological spring for sour orange trees should have occurred two days earlier in 1994 than it did in 1960.

By way of comparison, there was an approximate seven-day advancement in the time of occurrence of the declining phase of the atmosphere's seasonal CO_2 cycle over this time period, and surface reflectance measurements made by satellites revealed a similar advancement in the springtime "greening of the Earth" in high northern latitudes. Idso *et al.*'s data thus suggest a significant portion of this advancement may have been due to the dramatic stimulation of initial new-branch growth provided by the increase in the air's CO_2 concentration experienced over that time interval. But where did the CO_2-enriched sour orange trees get the extra nitrogen needed to support the enhanced production of new branch and leaf tissue that occurred at the beginning of the growing season?

In an experiment bearing on this question, Idso *et al.* (2001) measured the concentrations of three soluble leaf proteins having molecular masses of 33, 31, and 21 kDa at weekly intervals for one full year in the foliage of the CO_2-enriched and ambient-treatment trees. During the central portion of the year, the abundances of the three proteins were generally lower in the leaves of the CO_2-enriched trees than they were in the leaves of the ambient-treatment trees; but in the latter part of the year and continuing for a short while into the next year, this relationship was reversed, as the leaf concentrations of the three

proteins in the CO_2-enriched trees surpassed those of the proteins in the trees growing in ambient air. Then in the spring, when new growth began to appear, the concentrations of the three proteins in the foliage of the CO_2-enriched trees plummeted, possibly as a result of giving up the nitrogen they had stored over winter to supply the needs of the newly developing branches and leaves.

According to Idso *et al.*, the N-terminal amino acid sequence of the 21-kDa protein has homology with sporamin B, an implicated vegetative storage protein (VSP) that can comprise 60 to 80% of the total soluble protein found in sweet potato tubers. They also determined it shares low sequence homology with trifoliatin, a soluble leaf protein from trifoliate orange that shares 62% amino acid similarity with sporamin B and can comprise up to 65% of total leaf protein. In addition, they say "immunoelectron microscopy demonstrated the presence of the proteins within amorphous material in the vacuoles of mesophyll cells, where VSPs are commonly located."

Perhaps most telling, starting at about day-of-the-year 225, the CO_2-enriched trees experienced a period of leaf senescence and abscission that was not observed in the ambient-treatment trees. "This phenomenon," Idso *et al.* report, "peaked at about day 300, when the CO_2-enriched trees shed leaves at a rate 2.5–2.7 times greater than the normal background rate of the ambient-treatment trees, whereupon the enriched-tree leaf-fall rate diminished, returning to normal by the end of the year."

According to the hypothesis formulated by Idso *et al.*, nitrogen reabsorbed from these second-year leaves during the process of senescence became available for storage in first-year leaves of the CO_2-enriched trees, going into the 21-kDa protein starting at about day 225, into the 31-kDa protein starting at about day 265, and into the 33-kDa protein starting at about day 335, according to the trends defined by their weekly measurements of leaf protein concentrations. Then, when new branches and leaves began appearing in the spring, the stored nitrogen was remobilized from the prior first-year leaves (which now became second-year leaves) to supply the needs of the developing branch and leaf tissues, whereupon the concentrations of the three putative storage proteins in the now-second-year CO_2-enriched leaves rapidly dropped to levels once again less than those observed in similar-age ambient-treatment leaves, and they remained at that reduced level until the second-year leaves gave up even more nitrogen prior to their senescence in the fall.

Other experimental evidence for a CO_2-induced

stimulation of new spring branch growth has been provided by Olszyk *et al.* (2001), who grew Ponderosa pine seedlings out-of-doors for two years in controlled-environment chambers maintained at atmospheric CO_2 concentrations of 390 and 670 ppm in combination with low (40 ppb) and high (60 ppb) ozone concentrations. They found the elevated CO_2 enhanced mean annual rates of net photosynthesis by 39% and increased bud lengths at the end of the second growing season in the low ozone treatment by 17%, which led to a transitory stimulation (+38%) of elongation and growth of terminal buds the following spring.

That super-stimulation of initial perennial plant growth in the early spring may be a ubiquitous phenomenon is suggested by the research of Bushway and Pritts (2002). They grew over-wintering strawberry plants in controlled environment chambers maintained at ambient (375 ppm) and elevated (700 to 1,000 ppm) atmospheric CO_2 concentrations until new blooms began to form on plants. They then moved the plants to a common greenhouse maintained at the ambient CO_2 concentration. The extra CO_2 stimulated rates of photosynthesis in the leaves of the over-wintering strawberry plants by more than 50%, which led to greater amounts of starch being found in key plant organs when new spring growth began. Plants grown in elevated CO_2 had two-, three-, and four-times the amount of starch in their crowns, leaves, and roots, respectively, than their ambiently grown counterparts. In addition, plants grown in elevated CO_2 flowered and fruited an average of four and seven days earlier than plants grown in ambient air, respectively.

Lim *et al.* (2004) correlated the monthly rate of relative change in normalized difference vegetation index (NDVI), which they derived from advanced very-high-resolution radiometer data, with the rate of change in atmospheric CO_2 concentration (δCO_2) during the natural growing season within three eco-region zones of North America (the Arctic and Sub-Arctic Zone, the Humid Temperate Zone, and the Dry and Desert Zone, which they further subdivided into 17 regions) over the period 1982–1992. They explored the temporal progression of annual minimum NDVI over the period 1982–2001 throughout the eastern humid temperate zone of North America. In all 17 regions but one, "δCO_2 was positively correlated with the rate of change in vegetation greenness in the following month, and most correlations were high," which they state is consistent with a CO_2 fertilization effect of the type observed in experimental manipulations of the air's CO_2 content

that report a stimulation of photosynthesis and above-ground production at high CO_2. In addition, and most importantly, they determined the yearly "minimum vegetation greenness increased over the period 1982–2001 for all the regions of the eastern humid temperate zone in North America."

Lim *et al.* opine rising CO_2 could "increase minimum greenness by stimulating photosynthesis at the beginning of the growing season," citing Idso *et al.* (2000). Hence, by looking for a manifestation of the CO_2 fertilization effect at the time of year it is apt to be most strongly expressed, Lim *et al.* may have found it. Between 1982 and 2001, for example, the air's CO_2 concentration rose by approximately 30 ppm. From Idso *et al.*'s findings of more than a 300% initial increase in the biomass of new sour orange tree branches for a 300-ppm increase in the air's CO_2 concentration and more than a 500% initial increase in per-tree new-branch biomass, it can be calculated that yearly minimum greenness should have increased by a value between just over 30% and just over 50%, if other woody plants respond to atmospheric CO_2 enrichment as sour orange trees do. When the mean 19-year increase in NDVI for the seven regions for which Lim *et al.* present data is calculated, an increase of just over 40% is seen, indicating Lim *et al.*'s data are not only qualitatively consistent with the hypothesis of CO_2-induced ultra-stimulation of early spring branch growth, but quantitatively as well.

References

Bushway, L.J. and Pritts, M.P. 2002. Enhancing early spring microclimate to increase carbon resources and productivity in June-bearing strawberry. *Journal of the American Society for Horticultural Science* **127**: 415–422.

Idso, C.D., Idso, S.B., Kimball, B.A., Park, H.-S., Hoober, J.K., and Balling Jr., R.C. 2000. Ultra-enhanced spring branch growth in CO_2-enriched trees: Can it alter the phase of the atmosphere's seasonal CO_2 cycle? *Environmental and Experimental Botany* **43**: 91–100.

Idso, K.E., Hoober, J.K., Idso, S.B., Wall, G.W., and Kimball, B.A. 2001. Atmospheric CO_2 enrichment influences the synthesis and mobilization of putative vacuolar storage proteins in sour orange tree leaves. *Environmental and Experimental Botany* **48**: 199–211.

Lim, C., Kafatos, M., and Megonigal, P. 2004. Correlation between atmospheric CO_2 concentration and vegetation greenness in North America: CO_2 fertilization effect. *Climate Research* **28**: 11–22.

Lovelock, C.E., Virgo, A., Popp, M., and Winter, K. 1999. Effects of elevated CO_2 concentrations on photosynthesis, growth and reproduction of branches of the tropical canopy trees species, *Luehea seemannii* Tr. & Planch. *Plant, Cell and Environment* **22**: 49–59.

Olszyk, D.M., Johnson, M.G., Phillips, D.L., Seidler, R.J., Tingey, D.T., and Watrud, L.S. 2001. Interactive effects of CO_2 and O_3 on a ponderosa pine plant/litter/soil mesocosm. *Environmental Pollution* **115**: 447–462.

2.5 Flowers

- At higher atmospheric CO_2 concentrations, plants often produce more and larger flowers, as well as a number of other flower-related changes having significant implications for plant productivity and survival, almost all of which are positive.

In one of the earliest papers to address the subject of atmospheric CO_2 enrichment effects on flowers, Idso *et al.* (1990) grew water lilies in sunken metal stock tanks located out-of-doors and enclosed within clear-plastic-wall open-top chambers through which air of either 350 or 650 ppm CO_2 was continuously circulated. Over the course of two growing seasons, he and his colleagues measured plant responses to these two environmental treatments. They found the water lilies in the CO_2-enriched enclosures grew better than the water lilies in the ambient CO_2 enclosures: the leaves in the CO_2-enriched tanks were larger and more substantial, and 75% more of them were produced over the course of the initial five-month growing season.

Each of the plants in the CO_2-enriched tanks also produced twice as many flowers as the plants growing in normal air, and the flowers that blossomed in the CO_2-enriched air were more substantial than those that bloomed in the air of normal CO_2 concentration: they had more petals, the petals were longer, they had a greater percentage of dry matter content, and each flower weighed about 50% more. In addition, the stems that supported the flowers were slightly longer in the CO_2-enriched tanks, and the percentage of dry matter contents of both the flower and leaf stems were greater, so the total dry matter in the flower and leaf stems in the CO_2-enriched tanks exceeded that of the flower and leaf stems in the ambient-air tanks by approximately 60%.

Deng and Woodward (1998) studied the direct and interactive effects of elevated CO_2 and nitrogen supply on strawberries by growing them in controlled-environment glasshouses maintained at atmospheric CO_2 concentrations of either 390 or 560 ppm at three levels of nitrogen for nearly three months. They found strawberries growing at the elevated CO_2 concentration contained additional sugar and physical mass that enabled them to support significantly greater numbers of flowers and fruits than strawberry plants growing at 390 ppm CO_2. This effect ultimately led to total fresh fruit weights 42 and 17% greater in CO_2-enriched plants maintained at the highest and lowest nitrogen levels, respectively.

Lake and Hughes (1999) found a 380-ppm increase in the air's CO_2 content elicited a 35% increase in the total plant biomass of nasturtiums (*Tropaeolum majus*). Although it did not affect flower size in this species, the total flower nectar volume produced by the CO_2-enriched nasturtiums was 2.4-fold greater than that produced by ambient-grown control plants. Likewise, Dag and Eisikowitch (2000) reported atmospheric CO_2 enrichment up to 1,000 ppm doubled both the average nectar volume and sugar production per flower in greenhouse-grown melons (*Cucumis melo*).

Johnson and Lincoln (2000) report an annual plant native to the southeastern USA (*Heterotheca subaxillaris*) increased its total biomass by 20% in response to a 300-ppm increase in the air's CO_2 content. In addition, the elevated CO_2 increased reproductive flower biomass and induced flowering much earlier in the CO_2-enriched plants than in the ambient-air-grown plants. And in another experiment, Niu *et al.* (2000) found yellow and primrose pansies (*Viola* x *wittrockiana*) increased their total dry weights by 10 to 30% in response to a 600-ppm increase in the CO_2 content of the air, and atmospheric CO_2 enrichment increased flower size by 4 to 10%.

Carvalho and Heuvelink (2001) report atmospheric CO_2 enrichment positively influences several external quality characteristics of chrysanthemums, including increasing the plant's stem length, number of lateral branches, number of flowers, and size of flowers. Aloni *et al.* (2001) found a 450-ppm increase in the air's CO_2 content completely ameliorated a 75% high-temperature-induced reduction in bell pepper (*Capsicum annuum* L.) pollen production observed under ambient CO_2 concentrations. In addition, although high temperature reduced the number of seeds produced per fruit in ambient-grown plants by 68%, it reduced this parameter only by 9% in CO_2-enriched plants.

Deckmyn *et al.* (2001) grew white clover plants (*Trifolium repens* L., cv. Mervi) in four small greenhouses, two of which allowed 88% of the incoming UV-B radiation to pass through their roofs and walls, and two of which allowed 82% to pass through. One of the two greenhouses in each of the UV-B treatments was maintained at ambient CO_2 (371 ppm), and the other was maintained at elevated CO_2 (521 ppm). Midway through the four-month summer growing season, flower numbers were counted, revealing the 40% increase in atmospheric CO_2 concentration stimulated the production of flowers in the low UV-B treatment by 22% and in the slightly higher UV-B treatment by 43%.

By 2002, so many scientists had weighed in on the subject that Jablonski *et al.* (2002) conducted a meta-analysis of 159 peer-reviewed scientific journal articles published between 1983 and 2000 dealing with the effects of atmospheric CO_2 enrichment on the reproductive growth characteristics of several domesticated and wild plants. In calculating the mean responses reported in those papers, Jablonski *et al.* found for increases in the air's CO_2 concentration ranging from approximately 150 to 450 ppm (rough average of 300 ppm), across all species studied, the extra CO_2 supplied to the plants resulted in 19% more flowers, 18% more fruits, 16% more seeds, 4% greater individual seed mass, 25% greater total seed mass (equivalent to yield), and 31% greater total mass.

More studies demonstrating similar positive effects of atmospheric CO_2 enrichment on flowering characteristics followed. Silberbush *et al.* (2003), for example, grew small and large bulbs of *Hippeastrum* (which produces amaryllis flowers) in greenhouses receiving atmospheric CO_2 concentrations of 350 and 1000 ppm for about four hours of each day for 233 days with different combinations of nitrogen and potassium fertilization, in order to study the interactive effects of these parameters on bulb size. They found elevated CO_2 consistently increased bulb size across all nitrogen and potassium concentrations, with initially larger bulbs yielding the greatest size of final bulbs. On a percentage basis, smaller bulbs were slightly more responsive to atmospheric CO_2 enrichment than were larger bulbs. Under optimal nitrogen and potassium fertilization, the 650-ppm increase in the air's CO_2 concentration increased the size of smaller and larger bulbs by about 18 and 14%, respectively, suggesting as the CO_2 content of the air increases, *Hippeastrum* bulbs will increase their size, thus leading to enhanced bulb quality and flower (amaryllis) production.

Palacios and Zimmerman (2007) piped flue gas generated by the Duke Energy-North America Power Plant at Moss Landing, California (USA) approximately 1 km to a site where it was bubbled through outdoor flow-through seawater aquaria at rates that produced four different aqueous CO_2 treatments characteristic of "(1) the present day atmosphere, with approximately 16 μM CO_2(aq), (2) CO_2 projected for 2100 that increases the CO_2(aq) concentration of seawater to approximately 36 μM CO_2(aq), (3) CO_2 projected for 2200 that increases the CO_2(aq) concentration of seawater to 85 μM CO_2(aq), and (4) a dissolved aqueous CO_2 concentration of 1123 μM CO_2(aq)," which in the earlier study of Zimmerman *et al.* (1997) had tripled the light-saturated photosynthesis rate of the eelgrass they had studied.

In their newer study, the researchers report the elevated CO_2 "led to significantly higher reproductive output, below-ground biomass and vegetative proliferation of new shoots in light-replete treatments," i.e., those receiving light at 33% of the surface irradiance level. More specifically, they found "shoots growing at 36 μM CO_2(aq) were 25% larger than those in the unenriched treatment [16 μM CO_2(aq)]," and "at 85 μM CO_2(aq) shoots were 50% larger than those in the unenriched treatment and at 1123 μM CO_2(aq) shoots were almost twice as large as those in the unenriched treatment." In addition, they found, at 1123 μM CO_2(aq) "22% of the shoots differentiated into flowers, more than twice the flowering output of the other treatments at this light level."

These findings have far-reaching implications. Noting "increased CO_2(aq) is capable of increasing eelgrass reproductive output via flowering, and area-specific productivity via vegetative shoot proliferation under naturally replete light regimes," Palacios and Zimmerman state, "the resulting increases in eelgrass meadow density may initiate a positive feedback loop that facilitates the trapping of sediments and prevents their resuspension, thereby reducing turbidity and increasing light penetration in coastal habitats," such that the resulting increased light penetration "may allow seagrass colonization depths to increase even further."

The two researchers also suggest the CO_2-induced increase in the productivity of eelgrass may "enhance fish and invertebrate stocks as well." They go so far as to suggest the "deliberate injection of CO_2 to seawater may facilitate restoration efforts by improving the survival rates of recently transplanted eelgrass shoots," noting "it can buffer the negative effects of transplant shock by increasing rhizome reserve capacity and promoting shoot proliferation in light-replete environments." In addition, they say it "may also facilitate eelgrass survival in environments where conditions are periodically limiting, such as long dark winters or unusually warm summers that produce unfavorable productivity to respiration ratios," and they write, "CO_2 injection may also promote flowering and seed production necessary for expansion and maintenance of healthy eelgrass meadows." Finally, they suggest, "rising concentrations of $CO_2(aq)$ may increase vegetative propagation and seed production of other seagrass populations besides eelgrass."

In another review paper, Springer and Ward (2007) summarize "the results of 60 studies reporting flowering-time responses (defined as the time to first visible flower) of both crop and wild species at elevated CO_2." They found "all possible responses have been observed both among species as well as within species, including accelerated, delayed and no change in flowering time in response to elevated CO_2." However, they write, "flowering-time responses of wild species grown at elevated CO_2 are much more evenly distributed, in that a similar number of studies report accelerated, delayed, or no change in flowering time, whereas crops primarily showed accelerated flowering (approx. 80% exhibited accelerated flowering)." They also note, "plants utilizing both the C_3 and C_4 photosynthetic pathways show altered flowering time with elevated CO_2," but "two crop species that account for a substantial portion of the world's agricultural production, soybean [a C_3 crop] and maize [a C_4 crop], do not show consistent patterns in the response of flowering time at elevated CO_2."

Springer and Ward additionally determined "studies performed within a genus also show a lack of consistent flowering-time response to elevated CO_2," and among only 10 genotypes of a single well-studied species (*Arabidopsis thaliana*), "all possible flowering-time responses to elevated CO_2, including delayed, accelerated and unaltered flowering times, were observed." Finally, they report, "a majority of multifactor studies that measured flowering time report no interaction between elevated CO_2 and other environmental factors, such as temperature, ... nutrient availability, ... light, ... and ozone," although "a limited number of elevated CO_2 studies do show significant interactive effects with other environmental factors."

Springer and Ward thus conclude the studies they reviewed "clearly show that future increases in atmospheric CO_2 will have major effects on the flowering time of both wild and crop species," but "at this time it is not possible to account for the wide variation in flowering-time responses because knowledge of the underlying physiological and molecular mechanisms is incomplete."

Darbah *et al.* (2008) studied the effects of long-term exposure of birch (*Betula papyrifera*) trees to elevated CO_2 (an extra 200 ppm) on flower and pollen production at the Aspen FACE site in Rhinelander, Wisconsin (USA) in the eighth and ninth years (2006 and 2007) of that experiment. They found "an increase of 140% and 70% for 2006 and 2007, respectively, in the total number of trees that produced male flowers under elevated CO_2 and an increase of 260% in 2006 and 100% in 2007, respectively, in the quantity of male flowers produced under elevated CO_2."

According to the six scientists, "the increases in the number of trees and in the quantity of male flowers produced under elevated CO_2 implies that more birch pollen will be produced." They note, "these results support the findings of Curtis *et al.* (1994, 1996), Johnson and Lincoln (2000), Edwards *et al.* (2001), Jablonski *et al.* (2002), Bunce (2005) and Ladeau and Clark (2006a,b), which were that elevated CO_2 increases reproductive potential through increased pollination, and hence, fertilization and viable seed formation," in harmony with the hypothesis of Herms and Mattson (1992), and "birch trees under adequate carbohydrate status [such as provided by atmospheric CO_2 enrichment] tend to favor male flower production." They conclude by noting, "since sexual reproductive development is an important stage in the life cycle of plants, any change in the processes involved might have significant implications for the productivity of the plants and their survival." The implications in the case of birch trees and atmospheric CO_2 enrichment clearly would be positive.

Johnston and Reekie (2008) write, "there have been marked changes in plant phenology over the past century" and these changes "have been interpreted as a consequence of the increase in temperature that has been observed over this time." In addition, they speculate, "the concentration of atmospheric CO_2 may also directly affect time of flowering, even in the absence of temperature change." They examined the effects of elevated atmospheric CO_2 concentration by itself (ambient and ambient + 330 ppm) and the combined effect of elevated CO_2 and elevated air temperature (ambient + 1.5°C) on the flowering phenology of 22 species of plants in the family Asteraceae, which were grown under natural seasonally varying temperature and day length in separate compartments of a glasshouse in Wolfville,

Nova Scotia, Canada.

They found, "on average, elevated CO_2 by itself advanced flowering by four days" and "increasing temperature as well as CO_2 advanced flowering by an additional three days." They also found "CO_2 was more likely to hasten phenology in long- than in short-day species" and "early- and late-flowering species did not differ in response to elevated CO_2, but the combined effect of elevated CO_2 and temperature hastened flowering more in early- than late-flowering species." Johnston and Reekie conclude, "the direct effect of CO_2 on phenology may be as important as its indirect effect through climate change."

References

Aloni, B., Peet, M., Pharr, M., and Karni, L. 2001. The effect of high temperature and high atmospheric CO_2 on carbohydrate changes in bell pepper (*Capsicum annuum*) pollen in relation to its germination. *Physiologia Plantarum* **112**: 505–512.

Bunce, J.A. 2005. Seed yield of soybeans with daytime or continuous elevation of carbon dioxide under field conditions. *Photosynthetica* **43**: 435–438.

Carvalho, S.M.P. and Heuvelink, E. 2001. Influence of greenhouse climate and plant density on external quality of chrysanthemum (*Dendranthema grandiflorum* (Ramat.) Kitamura): first steps toward a quality model. *Journal of Horticultural Science & Biotechnology* **76**: 249–258.

Curtis, P.S., Klus, D.J., Kalisz, S., and Tonsor, S.J. 1996. Intraspecific variation in CO_2 responses in *Raphanus raphinistum* and *Plantago lanceolata*: assessing the potential for evolutionary change with rising atmospheric change. In: Korner, C. and Bazzaz, F.A. (Eds.) *Carbon Dioxide, Populations and Communities*. Academic Press, New York, NY, USA, pp. 13–22.

Curtis, P.S., Snow, A.A., and Miller, A.S. 1994. Genotype-specific effects of elevated CO_2 on fecundity in wild radish (*Raphanus raphanistum*). *Oecologia* **97**: 100–105.

Dag, A. and Eisikowitch, D. 2000. The effect of carbon dioxide enrichment on nectar production in melons under greenhouse conditions. *Journal of Apicultural Research* **39**: 88–89.

Darbah, J.N.T., Kubiske, M.E., Nelson, N., Oksanen, E., Vaapavuori, E., and Karnosky, D.F. 2008. Effects of decadal exposure to interacting elevated CO_2 and/or O_3 on paper birch (*Betula papyrifera*) reproduction. *Environmental Pollution* **155**: 446–452.

Deckmyn, G., Caeyenberghs, E., and Ceulemans, R. 2001. Reduced UV-B in greenhouses decreases white clover response to enhanced CO_2. *Environmental and Experimental Botany* **46**: 109–117.

Deng, X. and Woodward, F.I. 1998. The growth and yield responses of *Fragaria ananassa* to elevated CO_2 and N supply. *Annals of Botany* **81**: 67–71.

Edwards, G.R., Clark, H., and Newton, P.C.D. 2001. The effects of elevated CO_2 on seed production and seedling recruitment in a sheep grazed pasture. *Oecologia* **127**: 383–394.

Herms, D.A. and Mattson, W.J. 1992. The dilemma of plants: to grow or defend. *Quarterly Review of Biology* **67**: 283–335.

Idso, S.B., Allen, S.G., and Kimball, B.A. 1990. Growth response of water lily to atmospheric CO_2 enrichment. *Aquatic Botany* **37**: 87–92.

Jablonski, L.M., Wang, X., and Curtis, P.S. 2002. Plant reproduction under elevated CO_2 conditions: a meta-analysis of reports on 79 crop and wild species. *New Phytologist* **156**: 9–26.

Johnson, S.L. and Lincoln, D.E. 2000. Allocation responses to CO_2 enrichment and defoliation by a native annual plant *Heterotheca subaxillaris*. *Global Change Biology* **6**: 767–778.

Johnston, A. and Reekie, E. 2008. Regardless of whether rising atmospheric carbon dioxide levels increase air temperature, flowering phenology will be affected. *International Journal of Plant Science* **169**: 1210–1218.

LaDeau, S.L. and Clark, J.S. 2006a. Elevated CO_2 and tree fecundity: the role of tree size, interannual variability, and population heterogeneity. *Global Change Biology* **12**: 822–833.

LaDeau, S.L. and Clark, J.S. 2006b. Pollen production by *Pinus taeda* growing in elevated atmospheric CO_2. *Functional Ecology* **20**: 541–547.

Lake, J.C. and Hughes, L. 1999. Nectar production and floral characteristics of *Tropaeolum majus* L. grown in ambient and elevated carbon dioxide. *Annals of Botany* **84**: 535–541.

Niu, G., Heins, R.D., Cameron, A.C., and Carlson, W.H. 2000. Day and night temperatures, daily light integral, and CO_2 enrichment affect growth and flower development of pansy (*Viola* x *wittrockiana*). *Journal of the American Society of Horticultural Science* **125**: 436–441.

Palacios, S.L. and Zimmerman, R.C. 2007. Response of eelgrass *Zostera marina* to CO_2 enrichment: possible impacts of climate change and potential for remediation of coastal habitats. *Marine Ecology Progress Series* **344**: 1–13.

Silberbush, M., Ephrath, J.E., Alekperov, Ch., and Ben-Asher, J. 2003. Nitrogen and potassium fertilization interactions with carbon dioxide enrichment in *Hippeastrum* bulb growth. *Scientia Horticulturae* **98**: 85–90.

Springer, C.J. and Ward, J.K. 2007. Flowering time and elevated atmospheric CO$_2$. *New Phytologist* **176**: 243–255.

Zimmerman, R.C., Kohrs, D.G., Steller, D.L., and Alberte, R.S. 1997. Impacts of CO$_2$-enrichment on productivity and light requirements of eelgrass. *Plant Physiology* **115**: 599–607.

2.6 Fluctuating Asymmetry

- Higher concentrations of atmospheric CO$_2$ tend to reduce fluctuating asymmetry in plant leaves, leading to more symmetrical leaves that appear to be less susceptible to attack by herbivores.

Fluctuating asymmetry (FA) is the terminology used to describe small variations from perfect symmetry in otherwise bilaterally symmetrical characters in an organism (Moller and Swaddle, 1997). It is believed to arise in consequence of developmental instability experienced during ontogeny that is caused by various stresses, including both genetic and environmental factors (Martel *et al.*, 1999; Cornelissen and Stiling, 2005); it has been studied extensively in animals but less so in plants (Moller and Shykoff, 1999).

In the first study to address the effects of atmospheric CO$_2$ enrichment on leaf asymmetry and how herbivores respond to these effects, Cornelissen *et al.* (2004) opened up a new window through which to view the potential effects of the ongoing rise in the air's CO$_2$ content on the plant and animal components of the biosphere. They conducted their study on a native scrub-oak community at the Kennedy Space Center, Titusville, Florida (USA), which is dominated by myrtle oak (*Quercus myrtifolia*) and sand live oak (*Quercus geminata*), under atmospheric CO$_2$ concentrations of approximately 370 and 700 ppm. Based on measurements of distances from the leaf midrib to the left and right edges of the leaf at its widest point and leaf areas on the left and right sides of the leaf midrib, Cornelissen *et al.* determined "asymmetric leaves were less frequent in elevated CO$_2$, and, when encountered, they were less asymmetric than leaves growing under ambient CO$_2$." In addition, they found "*Q. myrtifolia* leaves under elevated CO$_2$ were 15.0% larger than in ambient CO$_2$ and *Q. geminata* leaves were 38.0% larger in elevated CO$_2$ conditions." They also determined "elevated CO$_2$ significantly increased tannin concentration for both *Q. myrtifolia* and *Q. geminata* leaves" and "asymmetric leaves contained significantly lower concentrations of tannins than symmetric leaves for both *Q. geminata* and *Q. myrtifolia*."

Commenting on their primary findings of reduced percentages of leaves experiencing asymmetry in the presence of elevated levels of atmospheric CO$_2$ and the lesser degree of asymmetry exhibited by affected leaves in the elevated CO$_2$ treatment, Cornelissen *et al.* state, "a possible explanation for this pattern is the fact that, in contrast to other environmental stresses, which can cause negative effects on plant growth, the predominant effect of elevated CO$_2$ on plants is to promote growth with consequent reallocation of resources (Docherty *et al.*, 1996)." Another possibility they discuss is "the fact that CO$_2$ acts as a plant fertilizer" and, as a result, "elevated CO$_2$ ameliorates plant stress compared with ambient levels of CO$_2$," which is one of the well-documented biological benefits of atmospheric CO$_2$ enrichment (Idso and Idso, 1994).

With respect to the ancillary finding of CO$_2$-induced increases in tannin concentrations in the leaves of both oaks (a mean increase of approximately 35% for *Q. myrtifolia* and 43% for *Q. geminata*), it should be noted this phenomenon may provide protection against herbivores, and part of that protection may be associated with the observed CO$_2$-induced reductions in the amount and degree of asymmetry in the leaves of the CO$_2$-enriched trees. Consistent with this hypothesis, for example, Stiling *et al.* (1999, 2003) found higher abundances of leaf miners in the leaves of the trees in the ambient CO$_2$ chambers, where asymmetric leaves were more abundant, while in the more recent study it was determined leaf miners attacked asymmetric leaves more frequently than would be expected by chance alone in both CO$_2$ treatments.

In further support of this CO$_2$-induced benefit, Cornelissen and Stiling (2005) evaluated patterns of asymmetry in 40 leaves from each of 30 trees of each of two species of oak—sand live oak (*Quercus geminata*) and turkey oak (*Q. laevis*)—at the University of South Florida Botanical Garden in Tampa, Florida (USA), well before any herbivores had begun to attack the trees that growing season. Thereafter, patterns of leaf asymmetry, leaf quality, and herbivory were examined for 30 individual trees of each of the two oak species from March to October of the same year.

These "before and after" measurements clearly indicated differential herbivory patterns neither caused nor affected patterns of leaf FA. However, the two scientists suggest "herbivores may use asymmetry as a cue to plant quality and suitable oviposition sites," as plants with a higher percentage of asymmetric leaves were attacked more frequently by various leaf miners, as were leaves on the same plant that were more asymmetric. Cornelissen and Stiling report, "asymmetric leaves of both plant species exhibited better nutritional quality for herbivores than symmetric leaves," with asymmetric leaves possessing "significantly lower concentrations of tannins [-22% for *Q. geminata* and -36% for *Q. laevis*] and higher nitrogen content [+8% for both species]."

Kaligaric *et al.* (2008) measured the degree of FA in "undamaged (not grazed, not visibly attacked by herbivores or pathogens) fully developed leaves" of the Mediterranean shrub *Myrtus communis* L. growing along an atmospheric CO_2 gradient (570, 530, 490, 450, 410, and 370 ppm) moving away from a natural CO_2 spring "I Borboi" near Lajatico (Pisa, Tuscany, Italy) at distances of 2, 18, 34, 50, 66, and 82 m, respectively, from the CO_2 source. They found "a significant and negative correlation between CO_2 concentration and leaf FA," such that "with increased CO_2 concentration the leaf FA decreased." This result, they write, "confirms what was obtained by Cornelissen *et al.* (2004) on *Quercus myrtifolia* and *Quercus geminata* (in a short-term experiment)." In addition, they note, "*Myrtus communis*, grown under elevated CO_2 concentration at 'I Borboi,' showed a reduction in xylem embolism and an increase in hydraulic efficiency (Tognetti *et al.*, 2001)," stating "improved water relations could represent a good explanation for the observed reduction in leaf FA [as the air's CO_2 content increased]."

Kaligaric *et al.* suggest "adaptation and selection could explain the tendency towards decreased leaf FA in plants from the CO_2 spring relative to ambient conditions," since "the more symmetrical leaves under long-term elevated CO_2 concentration were more developmentally stable in these conditions."

Consequently, and in light of the results discussed above, a reduction in leaf FA can be added to the ever-growing number of benefits plants likely will experience as the atmosphere's CO_2 concentration continues to rise.

References

Cornelissen, T. and Stiling, P. 2005. Perfect is best: low leaf fluctuating asymmetry reduces herbivory by leaf miners. *Oecologia* 142: 46–56.

Cornelissen, T., Stiling, P., and Drake, B. 2004. Elevated CO_2 decreases leaf fluctuating asymmetry and herbivory by leaf miners on two oak species. *Global Change Biology* 10: 27–36.

Docherty, M., Hurst, D.K., Holopainem, J.K., Whittaker, J.B., Lea, P.J., and Watt, A.D. 1996. Carbon dioxide-induced changes in beech foliage cause female beech weevil larvae to feed in a compensatory manner. *Global Change Biology* 2: 335–341.

Idso, K.E. and Idso, S.B. 1994. Plant responses to atmospheric CO_2 enrichment in the face of environmental constraints: a review of the past 10 years' research. *Agricultural and Forest Meteorology* 69: 153–203.

Kaligaric, M., Tognetti, R., Janzekovic, F., and Raschi, A. 2008. Leaf fluctuating asymmetry of Myrtus communis L., affected by increases in atmospheric CO_2 concentration: Evidence from a natural CO_2 spring. *Polish Journal of Environmental Studies* 17: 503–508.

Martel, J., Lempa, K., and Haukioja, E. 1999. Effects of stress and rapid growth on fluctuating asymmetry and insect damage in birch leaves. *Oikos* 86: 208–216.

Moller, A.P. and Shykoff, P. 1999. Morphological developmental stability in plants: patterns and causes. *International Journal of Plant Sciences* 160: S135–S146.

Moller, A.P. and Swaddle, J.P. 1997. *Asymmetry, Developmental Stability and Evolution.* Oxford University Press, Oxford, UK.

Stiling, P., Moon, D.C., Hunter, M.D., Colson, J., Rossi, A.M., Hymus, G.J., and Drake, B.G. 2003. Elevated CO_2 lowers relative and absolute herbivore density across all species of a scrub-oak forest. *Oecologia* 134: 82-87.

Stiling, P., Rossi, A.M., Hungate, B., Dijkstra, P., Hinkle, C.R., Knot III, W.M., and Drake, B. 1999. Decreased leaf-miner abundance in elevated CO_2: Reduced leaf quality and increased parasitoid attack. *Ecological Applications* 9: 240–244.

Tognetti, R., Longobucco, A., Raschi, A., and Jones, M.B. 2001. Stem hydraulic properties and xylem vulnerability to embolism in three co-occurring Mediterranean shrubs at a natural CO_2 spring. *Australian Journal of Plant Physiology* 28: 257–268.

2.7 Hormones

- Atmospheric CO_2 enrichment enhances plant growth, development, and ultimate yield (in the case of agricultural crops) by increasing the concentrations of plant hormones that stimulate cell division, cell elongation, and protein synthesis.

Investigating the effects of atmospheric CO_2 enrichment on plant hormones, Teng *et al.* (2006) grew well-watered and -fertilized thale cress (*Arabidopsis thaliana* (L.) Heynh.) plants from seed to commencement of bolting in pots within controlled-environment chambers maintained at atmospheric CO_2 concentrations of either 370 or 700 ppm, measuring several plant properties and processes. The elevated CO_2 increased the biomass production of the plants by 29% and leaf total nonstructural carbohydrates by 76%. With respect to plant hormones, it "significantly increased the IAA [indole-3-acetic acid, by 13.7%], GA3 [gibberellic acid, by 55.4%], ZR [zeatin riboside, by 15.6%], DHZR [dihydrozeatin ribosidem, by 55.9%] and iPA [isopentenyladenosine, by 74.6%] contents of leaves, but … significantly reduced the ABA [abscisic acid, by 15.2%] content."

The six Chinese researchers conclude by noting plant hormones "can enhance plant growth and development by stimulating cell division, cell elongation and protein synthesis (Yong *et al.*, 2000), whereas ABA is considered an inhibitor of leaf growth (Zhang and Davies, 1990)." In addition, they note, "plant hormone metabolism is dependent on the supply of carbohydrates (Taiz and Zeiger, 1998)." They conclude, "higher carbohydrate production," such as that induced by atmospheric CO_2 enrichment, "may result in higher hormone concentrations, which in turn may enhance plant growth." That phenomenon also was observed by Jitla *et al.* (1997) and Li *et al.* (2002), with the latter reporting elevated CO_2 increased the concentrations of several plant hormones in leaf and aerial root tips of an epiphytic CAM orchid by as much as 21-fold.

In another experiment, Li *et al.* (2009) grew six-year-old *Ginkgo biloba* tree saplings in pots containing fertile soil out-of-doors in open-top chambers maintained at either 350 or 700 ppm CO_2 at the Shenyang Arboretum of the Chinese Academy of Science in Shenyang, Liaoning Province (China) from 1 June to 30 September. In addition to measuring the growth of the trees' terminal shoots over this period, they also measured leaf concentrations of the endogenous plant-growth regulator indole-3-acetic acid (IAA). After 40 days' exposure to elevated CO_2, the IAA concentration in the plants' leaves was increased significantly relative to that of plants in the control treatment, and maximum IAA enhancement was observed 100 days after exposure, when leaf concentrations of IAA were fully 90% greater in the elevated CO_2 treatment. The growth increment of ginkgo terminal shoots in the high CO_2 chambers was increased by 44% from 20 days to 90 days of exposure to the elevated CO_2 conditions.

Jiang *et al.* (2012) write, "brassinosteroids (BRs) are a family of over 40 naturally occurring plant steroid hormones that are ubiquitously distributed in the plant kingdom," citing Clouse and Sasse (1998), Bishop and Koncz (2002), Krishna (2003), and Montoya *et al.* (2005). They report, "BRs play prominent roles in various physiological processes including the induction of a broad spectrum of cellular responses, such as stem elongation, pollen tube growth, xylem differentiation, leaf epinasty, root inhibition, induction of ethylene biosynthesis, proton pump activation, regulation of gene expression and photosynthesis, and adaptive responses to environmental stress," citing Clouse and Sasse (1998), Dhaubhadel *et al.* (1999), Khripach *et al.* (2000), Krishna (2003), and Yu *et al.* (2004). They also note, "as potent plant growth regulators, BRs are now widely used to enhance plant growth and yield of important agricultural crops," citing Khripach *et al.* (2000) and Divi and Krishna (2009).

The six scientists conducted an experiment to determine the effects of increased atmospheric CO_2 on such of these plant steroid hormones as are found in young cucumber plants, growing them at atmospheric CO_2 concentrations of either 380 (ambient) or 760 (enriched) ppm, and with or without being sprayed with a solution of brassinosteroids (0.1 µM 24-epibrassinolide).

Jiang *et al.* determined their doubling of the atmosphere's CO_2 concentration resulted in a 44.1% increase in CO_2 assimilation rate. They state the BR treatment "also significantly increased CO_2 assimilation under ambient atmospheric CO_2 conditions" and "the increase was close to that by CO_2 enrichment." Most interesting, they found the combined treatment of "plants with BR application under CO_2-enriched conditions showed the highest CO_2 assimilation rate, which was increased by 77.2% relative to the control." Likewise, they found "an elevation in the atmospheric CO_2 level from 380 to 760 ppm resulted in 20.5% and 16.0% increases in leaf area and shoot biomass accumulation, respectively," and the plants that received the BR application "exhibited 22.6% and 20.6% increases in leaf area and shoot biomass accumulation, respectively." The combined treatment of "CO_2 enrichment and BR application further improved the plant growth, resulting in 49.0% and 40.2% increases in leaf area and shoot biomass, relative to that of the control, respectively."

References

Bishop, G.J. and Koncz, C. 2002. Brassinosteroids and

plant steroid hormone signaling. *The Plant Cell* **14**: S97–S110.

Clouse, S.D. and Sasse, J.M. 1998. Brassinosteroids: essential regulators of plant growth and development. *Annual Review of Plant Physiology and Plant Molecular Biology* **49**: 427–451.

Dhaubhadel, S., Chaudhary, S., Dobinson, K.F., and Krishna, P. 1999. Treatment with 24-epibrassinolide, a brassinosteroid, increases the basic thermotolerance of *Brassica napus* and tomato seedlings. *Plant Molecular Biology* **40**: 333–342.

Divi, U.K. and Krishna, P. 2009. Brassinosteroid: a biotechnological target for enhancing corn yield and stress tolerance. *New Biotechnology* **26**: 131–136.

Jiang, Y.-P., Cheng, F., Zhou, Y.-H., Xia, X.-J., Shi, K., and Yu, J.-Q. 2012. Interactive effects of CO_2 enrichment and brassinosteroid on CO_2 assimilation and photosynthetic electron transport in *Cucumis sativus*. *Environmental and Experimental Botany* **75**: 98–106.

Jitla, D.S., Rogers, G.S., Seneweera, S.P., Basra, A.S., Oldfield, R.J., and Conroy, J.P. 1997. Accelerated early growth of rice at elevated CO_2: is it related to developmental changes in the shoot apex? *Plant Physiology* **115**: 15–22.

Khripach, V., Zhabinskii, V., and De Groot, A. 2000. Twenty years of Brassinosteroids: steroidal plant hormones warrant better crops for the XXI century. *Annals of Botany* **86**: 441–447.

Krishna, P. 2003. Brassinosteroid-mediated stress responses. *Journal of Plant Growth Regulators* **22**: 289–297.

Li, C.R., Gan, I.J., Xia, K., Zhou, X., and Hew, C.S. 2002. Responses of carboxylating enzymes, sucrose metabolizing enzymes and plant hormones in a tropical epiphytic CAM orchid to CO_2 enrichment. *Plant, Cell and Environment* **25**: 369–377.

Li, X.-M., He, X.-Y., Zhang, L.-H., Chen, W., and Chen, Q. 2009. Influence of elevated CO_2 and O_3 on IAA, IAA oxidase and peroxidase in the leaves of ginkgo trees. *Biologia Plantarum* **53**: 339–342.

Montoya, T., Normura, T., Yokota, T., Farrar, K., Harrison, K., Jones, J.G.D., Kaneta, T., Kamiya, W., Szekeres, M., and Bishop, G.R. 2005. Patterns of dwarf expression and brassinosteroid accumulation in tomato reveal the importance of brassinosteroid synthesis during fruit development. *Plant Journal* **42**: 262–269.

Taiz, L. and Zeiger, E. 1998. *Plant Physiology*. Sinauer Associates, Inc., Sunderland, Massachusetts, USA.

Teng, N., Wang, J., Chen, T., Wu, X., Wang, Y., and Lin, J. 2006. Elevated CO_2 induces physiological, biochemical and structural changes in leaves of *Arabidopsis thaliana*. *New Phytologist* **172**: 92–103

Yong, J.W.H., Wong, S.C., Letham, D.S., Hocart, C.H., and Farquhar, G.D. 2000. Effects of elevated CO_2 and nitrogen nutrition on cytokinins in the xylem sap and leaves of cotton. *Plant Physiology* **124**: 769–779.

Yu, J.Q., Huang, L.F., Hu, W.H., Zhou, Y.H., Mao, W.H., Ye, S.F., and Nogués, S. 2004. A role for brassinosteroids in the regulation of photosynthesis in *Cucumis sativus*. *Journal of Experimental Botany* **55**: 1135–1143.

Zhang, J. and Davies, W.J. 1990. Changes in the concentration of ABA in xylem sap as a function of changing soil-water status can account for changes in leaf conductance and growth. *Plant, Cell and Environment* **13**: 277–285.

2.8 Glomalin

- Atmospheric CO_2 enrichment increases the production of glomalin, a protein created by fungi living in symbiotic association with the roots of 80% of the planet's vascular plants, which is being released to almost every soil in the world in ever-greater quantities with the passage of time, where it is having a positive impact on the biosphere.

In a multifaceted research program carried out at experimental sites in northern and southern California, USA, Rillig *et al.* (1999) studied belowground ecosystem responses to elevated atmospheric CO_2 concentrations over a period of several years, focusing their attention on arbuscular mycorrhizal fungi (AMF) that form symbiotic associations with plant roots. In addition, they measured soil concentrations of an AMF-produced glycoprotein called glomalin and evaluated its response to elevated CO_2. They then studied the impact of glomalin on the formation of small soil aggregates and their subsequent stability.

The degree of soil aggregation and the stability of soil aggregates across many different soil types is closely related to the amount of glomalin in the soil. Rillig *et al.* wanted to see if the aboveground benefits of atmospheric CO_2 enrichment would trickle down, so to speak, from plant leaves to plant roots to symbiotic soil fungi to glomalin production to soil aggregate formation and, ultimately, to an enhanced stability of soil aggregates in the presence of water.

The researchers found the amount of fungal-produced glomalin in the soils of the CO_2-enriched treatments in all three of the ecosystems they studied was greater than that observed in the soils of corresponding ambient CO_2 treatments. They also observed increases in the mass of small soil aggregates in the treatments exposed to elevated CO_2, and the stability of the small soil aggregates in the CO_2-enriched treatments was greater than the stability of the aggregates in the ambient CO_2 treatments. And in one of their studies, where six CO_2 concentrations ranging from 250 to 750 ppm were imposed as treatments, they found "the proportion of soil mass in aggregates of 0.25–1 mm showed a linear increase along the CO_2 gradient," and "glomalin concentrations followed a pattern similar to that of the small aggregate size class," indicating increasing soil structure benefits with increasing concentrations of atmospheric CO_2.

In a subsequent study conducted in New Zealand, Rillig *et al.* (2000) examined several characteristics of AMF associated with the roots of plants that had been growing for at least 20 years along a natural CO_2 gradient near a CO_2-emmitting spring. They found the elevated CO_2 significantly increased percent of root colonization by AMF in a linear fashion—and nearly fourfold—in going from 370 to 670 ppm. In addition, fungal hyphal length experienced a linear increase of more than threefold along the same CO_2 gradient, and total soil glomalin experienced a linear increase of approximately fivefold.

Just as more and longer roots help plants hold soil together and prevent its erosion, so too do more and longer fungal hyphae protect soil from disruption and dispersion. In addition, fungal-produced glomalin acts like a biological glue, helping to bind tiny particles of soil into small aggregates that are much more difficult to break down and blow or wash away. To have soil glomalin concentrations increase fivefold as a consequence of less than a doubling of the air's CO_2 content is an astounding benefit.

Ross *et al.* (2000) measured soil carbon (C) and nitrogen (N) contents in areas exposed to atmospheric CO_2 concentrations on the order of 440 to 460 ppm and other areas exposed to concentrations on the order of 510 to 900 ppm, near a natural CO_2 vent in New Zealand. Their work bears on the question whether CO_2-induced increases in soil-stabilizing fungal activities might lead to increases in soil carbon sequestration.

They found several decades of differential atmospheric CO_2 exposure had increased soil organic C and total N contents by approximately 24% each, and it had increased microbial C and N contents by more than 100% each. Hence, the scientists write, "storage of C and N can increase under prolonged exposure to elevated CO_2." In addition, they conclude increased storage of soil organic matter can occur "even when soil C concentrations are already high," as they were in the situation they investigated. Consequently, not only will the capacity of soils to store carbon increase because of the increasing aerial fertilization effect of atmospheric CO_2 enrichment—which enhances plant growth and results in more carbon being transferred to the soil—increasingly active soil fungi will help to keep ever-greater portions of that carbon better preserved in increasingly more stable soils.

Augmented soil carbon sequestration is but the beginning of benefits that can be expected from CO_2-enhanced AMF growth and glomalin production. Rillig *et al.* (2001) report the results of a FACE study of sorghum they conducted near Phoenix, Arizona (USA), where they found an approximate 50% increase in the air's CO_2 content increased fungal hyphae lengths by 120% and 240% in wet and dry irrigation treatments, respectively, with the mass of water-stable soil aggregates increasing by 40% and 20% in the same respective treatments. They note, "soil structure and water-stable aggregation are crucial for facilitating water infiltration, soil-borne aspects of biogeochemical cycling processes, success of sustainable agriculture, and for providing resistance against erosional loss of soil (Oades, 1984; Elliott and Coleman, 1988; Van Veen and Kuikman, 1990; Bethlenfalvay and Lindermann, 1992; Daily, 1995; Arshad *et al.*, 1996; Coleman, 1996; Jastrow and Miller, 1997; Young *et al.*, 1998)."

In addition, Gonzalez-Chavez *et al.* (2004) found "glomalin participates in the sequestration of different PTEs [potentially toxic elements]," "the glomalin pool in the soil may have a potential to sequestrate PTEs, not only by the colonized roots, but also by the hyphae and through deposition of glomalin in soil," and "this glycoprotein may be stabilizing PTEs, reducing PTE availability and decreasing the toxicity risk to other soil microorganisms and plants." The authors note "glomalin is ... copiously produced by all AMF tested to date (Wright *et al.*, 1996, 1998; Nichols, 2003)," "AMF colonize 80% of vascular plant species (Trappe, 1987)," and AMF "are found worldwide in almost every soil."

In light of these observations, it should be evident the ongoing rise in the air's CO_2 content must be having a tremendous positive impact on the biosphere via a suite of mechanisms linked to a fungal-produced protein that only a couple decades ago was largely unknown—even to most plant and soil scientists—and similarly unappreciated.

References

Arshad, M.A., Lowery, B., and Grossman, B. 1996. Physical tests for monitoring soil quality. In: *Methods for Assessing Soil Quality*, SSSA Special Publication 49. Soil Science Society of America, Madison, Wisconsin, USA, pp. 123–141.

Bethlenfalvay, G.J. and Linderman, R.G. 1992. *Mycorrhizae in Sustainable Agriculture. ASA Special Publication 54.* American Society of Agronomy, Madison, Wisconsin, USA.

Coleman, D.C. 1996. *Fundamentals of Soil Ecology.* Academic Press, San Diego, California, USA.

Daily, G.C. 1995. Restoring value to the world's degraded lands. *Science* **269**: 350–354.

Elliott, E.T. and Coleman, D.C. 1988. Let the soil work for us. *Ecological Bulletin* **39**: 23–32.

Gonzalez-Chavez, M.C., Carrillo-Gonzalez, R., Wright, S.F., and Nichols, K.A. 2004. The role of glomalin, a protein produced by arbuscular mycorrhizal fungi, in sequestering potentially toxic elements. *Environmental Pollution* **130**: 317–323.

Jastrow, J.D. and Miller, R.M. 1997. Soil aggregate stabilization and carbon sequestration: feedbacks through organomineral associations. In: Lal, R. *et al*, (Eds.) *Soil Processes and the Carbon Cycle.* CRC Press, Boca Raton, Florida, USA, pp. 207–223.

Nichols, K. 2003. *Characterization of Glomalin—A Glycoprotein Produced by Arbuscular Mycorrhizal Fungi.* PhD Dissertation, University of Maryland, College Park, Maryland, USA.

Oades, J.M. 1984. Soil organic matter and structural stability: mechanisms and implications for management. *Plant and Soil* **76**: 319–337.

Rillig, M.C., Hernandez, G.Y., and Newton, P.C.D. 2000. Arbuscular mycorrhizae respond to elevated atmospheric CO$_2$ after long-term exposure: evidence from a CO2 spring in New Zealand supports the resource balance model. *Ecology Letters* **3**: 475–478.

Rillig, M.C., Wright, S.F., Allen, M.F., and Field, C.B. 1999. Rise in carbon dioxide changes soil structure. *Nature* **400**: 628.

Rillig, M.C., Wright, S.F., Kimball, B.A., Pinter, P.J., Wall, G.W., Ottman, M.J., and Leavitt, S.W. 2001. Elevated carbon dioxide and irrigation effects on water stable aggregates in a *Sorghum* field: a possible role for arbuscular mycorrhizal fungi. *Global Change Biology* **7**: 333–337.

Ross, D.J., Tate, K.R., Newton, P.C.D., Wilde, R.H., and Clark, H. 2000. Carbon and nitrogen pools and mineralization in a grassland gley soil under elevated carbon dioxide at a natural CO$_2$ spring. *Global Change Biology* **6**: 779–790.

Trappe, J.M. 1987. Phylogenetic and ecological aspects of mycotrophy in the angiosperms from an evolutionary standpoint. In: Safir, G.R. (Ed.). *Ecophysiology of VA Mycorrhizal Plants.* CRC Press, Boca Raton, Florida, USA, pp. 5–25.

Van Veen, J.A. and Kuikman, P.J. 1990. Soil structural aspects of decomposition of organic matter by micro-organisms. *Biogeochemistry* **11**: 213–233.

Wright, S.F., Franke-Snyder, M., Morton, J.B., and Upadhyaya, A. 1996. Time-course study and partial characterization of a protein on hyphae of arbuscular mycorrhizal fungi during active colonization of roots. *Plant and Soil* **181**: 193–203.

Wright, S.F., Upadhyaya, A., and Buyer, J.S. 1998. Comparison of N-linked oligosaccharides of glomalin from arbuscular mycorrhizal fungi and soils by capillary electrophoresis. *Soil Biology and Biochemistry* **30**: 1853–1857.

Young, I.M., Blanchart, E., and Chenu, C., *et al.* 1998. The interaction of soil biota and soil structure under global change. *Global Change Biology* **4**: 703–712.

2.9 Isoprene

A number of experimental findings indicate the ongoing rise in the air's CO$_2$ content likely will lead to significant reductions in the air's concentration of isoprene, which is responsible for the production of vast amounts of tropospheric ozone, thereby helping to reduce the atmospheric presence of the latter noxious trace gas. Other research suggests a CO$_2$-induced reduction in plant isoprene emissions will result in greater concentrations of cloud condensation nuclei, which act as a negative feedback to atmospheric warming.

The influence of atmospheric CO$_2$ on plant isoprene emissions is discussed in Section 2.5.2.2.1 of the Forcings and Feedbacks chapter of *Climate Change Reconsidered II: Physical Science* (Idso *et al.*, 2013).

Reference

Idso, C.D., Carter, R.M., and Singer, S.F. 2013. (Eds.) *Climate Change Reconsidered II: Physical Science.* Chicago, IL: The Heartland Institute.

2.10 Leaves

Nearly all crops respond to increases in the air's CO_2 content by displaying enhanced rates of photosynthesis and biomass production. The subsections below examine some of the other changes they often experience when exposed to elevated levels of atmospheric CO_2—namely, various changes in leaf characteristics.

2.10.1 Agricultural Species

- Increasing atmospheric CO_2 concentrations likely will affect many leaf characteristics of agricultural plants, with the majority of the changes leading to higher rates and efficiencies of photosynthesis and growth, with the ultimate result that agricultural yields likely will rise as the air's CO_2 content continues to rise.

As the air's CO_2 concentration rises, plants commonly reduce the concentration of the nitrogen-rich photosynthetic enzyme rubisco, which is normally present in their leaves in excess amounts at ambient atmospheric CO_2 concentrations. Consequently, elevated CO_2 exposure frequently results in reduced foliar nitrogen concentrations, which allows excess nitrogen in leaves to be mobilized away from the photosynthetic apparatus and devoted to processes more limiting to growth. In the study of Monje and Bugbee (1998), for example, a near-900-ppm increase in the air's CO_2 concentration reduced leaf nitrogen contents in wheat by 28%. Similar results were obtained for soybeans grown at twice-ambient CO_2 concentrations (Sims *et al.*, 1998); it is thus quite likely many agricultural species will exhibit reductions in foliar nitrogen content in response to atmospheric CO_2 enrichment.

In addition to nitrogen, elevated CO_2 also can mobilize other limiting resources away from a plant's photosynthetic machinery and direct them into various plant parts important to growth and development. Watling *et al.* (2000), for example, found a doubling of the air's CO_2 content reduced the thickness of specialized bundle sheath cells in sorghum by approximately 50%, which freed up important resources that were sent to other parts of the plant for utilization, as indicated by a 36% enhancement in total plant biomass.

Elevated CO_2 also may impact leaf concentrations of chlorophylls, important light-absorbing pigments involved in the photosynthetic process. In the study of Sgherri *et al.* (1998), for example, water-stressed alfalfa displayed a 30% reduction in leaf chlorophyll content, but water-stressed plants exposed to 600 ppm CO_2 exhibited only a 6% reduction. In potato, on the other hand, Sicher and Bunce (1999) found no change in leaf chlorophyll content when exposing plants to twice-ambient levels of atmospheric CO_2, nor did Monje and Bugbee (1998) in their previously mentioned study on wheat.

Excess carbohydrates resulting from enhanced photosynthetic rates often are used to increase leaf growth and development. As an example, Reddy *et al.* (1998) reported cotton plants grown at 700 ppm CO_2 displayed individual leaf areas 20% greater than those of the leaves of ambiently grown control plants. Similarly, Masle (2000) noted a 600-ppm increase in atmospheric CO_2 concentration increased individual leaf size in wheat plants by increasing the number of photosynthetic mesophyll cell layers, as well as overall leaf thickness. In a related study on sunflower, however, Sims *et al.* (1999) did not report an increase in leaf size or thickness, but they documented a CO_2-induced shift in the distribution of leaf area that concentrated 30 to 40% more of it in the upper layer of the plant canopy, where the CO_2-induced photosynthetic stimulation was greatest.

Sometimes, excess carbohydrates are used to enhance the biosynthesis of secondary carbon compounds in leaves. Estiarte *et al.* (1999), for example, found leaves of spring wheat grown at 550 ppm CO_2 displayed 14% higher total flavonoid concentrations than leaves of plants grown at 370 ppm CO_2. This observation is important because flavonoids are generally characterized as having anti-herbivory properties. Thus, less pest-induced yield losses in this important grain crop may occur in future climates characterized by elevated atmospheric CO_2 concentrations.

Increasing atmospheric CO_2 concentrations likely will affect many leaf characteristics of agricultural plants. The majority of these changes likely will lead to greater rates and higher efficiencies of photosynthesis and growth. As a result, agricultural yields likely will rise in the future, resulting in part from changes in foliar properties mediated by the ongoing rise in the air's CO_2 content.

References

Estiarte, M., Peñuelas, J., Kimball, B.A., Hendrix, D.L., Pinter Jr., P.J., Wall, G.W., LaMorte, R.L., and Hunsaker, D.J. 1999. Free-air CO_2 enrichment of wheat: leaf flavonoid concentration throughout the growth cycle. *Physiologia Plantarum* **105**: 423–433.

Masle, J. 2000. The effects of elevated CO_2 concentrations on cell division rates, growth patterns, and blade anatomy in young wheat plants are modulated by factors related to leaf position, vernalization, and genotype. *Plant Physiology* **122**: 1399–1415.

Monje, O. and Bugbee, B. 1998. Adaptation to high CO_2 concentration in an optimal environment: radiation capture, canopy quantum yield and carbon use efficiency. *Plant, Cell and Environment* **21**: 315–324.

Reddy, K.R., Robana, R.R., Hodges, H.F., Liu, X.J., and McKinion, J.M. 1998. Interactions of CO_2 enrichment and temperature on cotton growth and leaf characteristics. *Environmental and Experimental Botany* **39**: 117–129.

Sgherri, C.L.M., Quartacci, M.F., Menconi, M., Raschi, A., and Navari-Izzo, F. 1998. Interactions between drought and elevated CO_2 on alfalfa plants. *Journal of Plant Physiology* **152**: 118–124.

Sicher, R.C. and Bunce, J.A. 1999. Photosynthetic enhancement and conductance to water vapor of field-grown *Solanum tuberosum* (L.) in response to CO_2 enrichment. *Photosynthesis Research* **62**: 155–163.

Sims, D.A., Cheng, W., Luo, Y., and Seeman, J.R. 1999. Photosynthetic acclimation to elevated CO_2 in a sunflower canopy. *Journal of Experimental Botany* **50**: 645–653.

Sims, D.A., Luo, Y., and Seeman, J.R. 1998. Comparison of photosynthetic acclimation to elevated CO_2 and limited nitrogen supply in soybean. *Plant, Cell and Environment* **21**: 945–952.

Watling, J.R., Press, M.C., and Quick, W.P. 2000. Elevated CO_2 induces biochemical and ultrastructural changes in leaves of the C_4 cereal sorghum. *Plant Physiology* **123**: 1143–1152.

2.10.2 Trees

- The leaves of nearly all woody species exposed to increases in the air's CO_2 content display enhanced rates of photosynthesis, as well as a number of other changes in leaf characteristics that help promote increased resistance to attacks by herbivores and pathogens.

Norby *et al.* (2000) found a 300-ppm increase in the air's CO_2 concentration reduced the nitrogen content in the leaves of red and sugar maple trees by 19 and 25%, respectively, and Rey and Jarvis (1998) found young silver birch trees exposed to twice-ambient levels of atmospheric CO_2 displayed leaf nitrogen contents 13% below those observed in leaves of ambiently growing trees. This phenomenon also has been noticed in the needles of conifers. Gielen *et al.* (2000), for example, documented a 33% reduction in the needle nitrogen content of young Scots pines growing at 750 ppm CO_2 compared to that of control trees growing at 350 ppm CO_2.

The nitrogen thus given up by the photosynthetic machinery of both broad-leaved and coniferous trees typically is used to further enhance the overall biomass production of the trees, including roots, trunks, branches, and still more leaves.

Elevated CO_2 also can mobilize other limiting resources away from the photosynthetic process for input into still other processes important to tree growth and development. Ormrod *et al.* (1999), for example, found a 180-ppm increase in the air's CO_2 content caused 19 and 25% reductions in the chlorophyll *a* and *b* concentrations of Douglas fir needles, respectively. Similar results were reported in young Scots pines, which exhibited a 26% reduction in total needle chlorophyll concentration in response to a 350-ppm increase in the CO_2 content of the air (Gielen *et al.*, 2000). However, Carter *et al.* (2000) noted elevated CO_2 (+300 ppm) had no effect on leaf chlorophyll concentrations in sugar maple.

Excess carbohydrates resulting from CO_2-enhanced photosynthesis often are used close to their site of production to increase leaf growth. In reviewing the results of several peer-reviewed papers related to this topic, Taylor *et al.* (2001) conclude elevated CO_2 consistently enhanced leaf extension rates in poplar species, which positively correlates with increased wood production. Similarly, Ferris *et al.* (2001) report a 200-ppm increase in the air's CO_2 concentration boosted leaf area in three poplar species by approximately 40%. In addition, a doubling of the atmospheric CO_2 concentration enhanced leaf size in a native British tree species (*Alnus glutinosa*) by 17% (Poole *et al.*, 2000). In all of these cases, it is likely CO_2-induced increases in leaf turgor pressure (Tognetti *et al.*, 2000) contributed to the CO_2-induced enhancements in leaf growth, as mediated through enhanced cell division and elongation.

Sometimes, excess carbohydrates are used to enhance the biosynthesis of secondary carbon compounds within leaves, which often results in greater specific leaf areas (Cornelissen *et al.*, 1999) and defensive resistance to pathogens and herbivores. Hattenschwiler *et al.* (1999) found a 280-ppm increase in the air's CO_2 concentration significantly increased needle concentrations of tannins and phenolics in spruce trees. Similarly, a 350-ppm increase in the CO_2 content of the air enhanced total phenolics in needles of loblolly pine by 21%

(Gebauer *et al.*, 1998). Leaves of various Mediterranean forest species grown at 710 ppm CO_2 displayed 18% greater lignin concentrations than leaves from species grown at 350 ppm CO_2 (De Angelis *et al.*, 2000). However, Heyworth *et al.* (1998) did not observe any significant effects of elevated CO_2 on tannin concentrations in needles of Scots pine exposed to 700 ppm CO_2, nor did King *et al.* (2001) for aspen leaves exposed to the same atmospheric CO_2 concentration. And Schaffer *et al.* (1997) found twice-ambient levels of atmospheric CO_2 stimulated the production of foliar carbon compounds in mango trees so dramatically that the concentrations of several leaf minerals fell due to this "dilution effect."

Under certain conditions, excess carbohydrates also are used to enhance various leaf anatomical features. Paoletti *et al.* (1998), for example, report white oak trees fumigated with air containing 750 ppm CO_2 displayed leaf cuticles three times thicker than those of leaves on trees grown in air containing 350 ppm CO_2. Lin *et al.* (2001) report this same elevated CO_2 concentration enhanced needle thickness in young Scots pines by increasing the area occupied by photosynthetic mesophyll tissue. Such increases in leaf and cuticle thickness can increase resistance to herbivory and pathogenic attack, much as increased concentrations of secondary carbon compounds do.

It would appear the current upward trend in atmospheric CO_2 concentration will affect numerous leaf characteristics of woody plants. The available data suggest the resulting changes likely will lead to greater and more efficient photosynthesis and growth rates, together with increased leaf resistance to herbivory and pathogen attack. Thus, tree productivity likely will continue to increase in the future due to changes in foliar properties driven by the ongoing rise in the air's CO_2 content.

References

Carter, G.A., Bahadur, R., and Norby, R.J. 2000. Effects of elevated atmospheric CO_2 and temperature on leaf optical properties in *Acer saccharum*. *Environmental and Experimental Botany* **43**: 267–273.

Cornelissen, J.H.C., Carnelli, A.L., and Callaghan, T.V. 1999. Generalities in the growth, allocation and leaf quality responses to elevated CO_2 in eight woody species. *New Phytologist* **141**: 401–409.

De Angelis, P., Chigwerewe, K.S., and Mugnozza, G.E.S. 2000. Litter quality and decomposition in a CO_2-enriched Mediterranean forest ecosystem. *Plant and Soil* **224**: 31–41.

Ferris, R., Sabatti, M., Miglietta, F., Mills, R.F., and Taylor, G. 2001. Leaf area is stimulated in *Populus* by free air CO_2 enrichment (POPFACE), through increased cell expansion and production. *Plant, Cell and Environment* **24**: 305–315.

Gebauer, R.L.E., Strain, B.R., and Reynolds, J.F. 1998. The effect of elevated CO_2 and N availability on tissue concentrations and whole plant pools of carbon-based secondary compounds in loblolly pine (*Pinus taeda*). *Oecologia* **113**: 29–36.

Gielen, B., Jach, M.E., and Ceulemans, R. 2000. Effects of season, needle age and elevated atmospheric CO_2 on chlorophyll fluorescence parameters and needle nitrogen concentration in (*Pinus sylvestris* L.). *Photosynthetica* **38**: 13–21.

Hattenschwiler, S. and Schafellner, C. 1999. Opposing effects of elevated CO_2 and N deposition on *Lymantria monacha* larvae feeding on spruce trees. *Oecologia* **118**: 210–217.

Heyworth, C.J., Iason, G.R., Temperton, V., Jarvis, P.G., and Duncan, A.J. 1998. The effect of elevated CO_2 concentration and nutrient supply on carbon-based plant secondary metabolites in *Pinus sylvestris* L. *Oecologia* **115**: 344–350.

King, J.S., Pregitzer, K.S., Zak, D.R., Kubiske, M.E., Ashby, J.A., and Holmes, W.E. 2001. Chemistry and decomposition of litter from *Populus tremuloides* Michaux grown at elevated atmospheric CO_2 and varying N availability. *Global Change Biology* **7**: 65–74.

Lin, J., Jach, M.E., and Ceulemans, R. 2001. Stomatal density and needle anatomy of Scots pine (*Pinus sylvestris*) are affected by elevated CO_2. *New Phytologist* **150**: 665–674.

Norby, R.J., Long, T.M., Hartz-Rubin, J.S., and O'Neill, E.G. 2000. Nitrogen resorption in senescing tree leaves in a warmer, CO_2-enriched atmosphere. *Plant and Soil* **224**: 15–29.

Ormrod, D.P., Lesser, V.M., Olszyk, D.M., and Tingey, D.T. 1999. Elevated temperature and carbon dioxide affect chlorophylls and carotenoids in Douglas-fir seedlings. *International Journal of Plant Science* **160**: 529–534.

Paoletti, E., Nourrisson, G., Garrec, J.P., and Raschi, A. 1998. Modifications of the leaf surface structures of *Quercus ilex* L. in open, naturally CO_2-enriched environments. *Plant, Cell and Environment* **21**: 1071–1075.

Poole, I., Lawson, T., Weyers, J.D.B., and Raven, J.A. 2000. Effect of elevated CO_2 on the stomatal distribution and leaf physiology of *Alnus glutinosa*. *New Phytologist* **145**: 511–521.

Rey, A. and Jarvis, P.G. 1998. Long-term photosynthetic acclimation to increased atmospheric CO_2 concentration in young birch (*Betula pendula*) trees. *Tree Physiology* **18**: 441–450.

Schaffer, B., Whiley, A.W., Searle, C., and Nissen, R.J. 1997. Leaf gas exchange, dry matter partitioning, and mineral element concentrations in mango as influenced by elevated atmospheric carbon dioxide and root restriction. *Journal of the American Society of Horticultural Science* **122**: 849–855.

Taylor, G., Ceulemans, R., Ferris, R., Gardner, S.D.L., and Shao, B.Y. 2001. Increased leaf area expansion of hybrid poplar in elevated CO_2. From controlled environments to open-top chambers and to FACE. *Environmental Pollution* **115**: 463–472.

Tognetti, R., Rashi, A., and Jones, M.B. 2000. Seasonal patterns of tissue water relations in three Mediterranean shrubs co-occurring at a natural CO_2 spring. *Plant, Cell and Environment* **23**: 1341–1351.

2.10.3 Other

- The ongoing rise in the air's CO_2 content will alter many physical and physiological leaf characteristics of Earth's plants; some of these changes will lead to more efficient plant growth, including the production of important secondary carbon compounds possessing high potential for combating a number of human maladies.

Nearly all plants respond to increases in the air's CO_2 content by displaying enhanced rates of photosynthesis and biomass production. Simultaneously, plants often exhibit changes in leaf characteristics. This review summarizes some of the CO_2-induced leaf responses observed in non-agricultural and non-woody species.

When the air's CO_2 concentration is experimentally increased, plants commonly reduce their foliar concentrations of the nitrogen-rich photosynthetic enzyme rubisco. Consequently, exposure to elevated CO_2 concentrations frequently results in lowered foliar nitrogen concentrations. This adjustment allows excess nitrogen to be mobilized away from the photosynthetic process and into processes more limiting to growth.

Schappi and Korner (1997), for example, note two species common to the Swiss Alps displayed reduced foliar nitrogen concentrations in response to atmospheric CO_2 enrichment. However, Goverde *et al.* (1999) found no change in the leaf nitrogen contents of *Lotus corniculatus* plants exposed to twice-ambient atmospheric CO_2 concentrations, nor did David *et al.* (2001) in leaves of *Medicago* and *Trifolium* species. In the latter study, the authors report a CO_2-induced *increase* in leaf nitrogen content for a certain *Galactites* species. Nevertheless, in a review of 67 published experimental observations made on several dozen species, Norby *et al.* (2001) conclude a doubling of the air's CO_2 concentration reduced leaf nitrogen content by, on average, approximately 7%.

At the other end of the spectrum of leaf responses to atmospheric CO_2 enrichment, excess carbohydrates resulting from CO_2-induced increases in photosynthetic rates often are used to enhance the biosynthesis of secondary carbon compounds. Norby *et al.* (2001), for example, analyzed 46 published experimental observations and determined a doubling of the atmospheric CO_2 content increased leaf lignin concentrations in a number of species by an average of 6.5%. Leaf chlorophyll contents also have been reported to increase in young orchid plantlets exposed to elevated CO_2 concentrations (Gouk *et al.*, 1999). Also, Goverde *et al.* (1999) observed elevated CO_2 concentrations increased leaf tannin concentrations in *Lotus corniculatas*, although Kerslake *et al.* (1998) could not discern any CO_2 effect on foliar phenolic concentrations in *Calluna vulgaris*.

Idso and Idso (2001) note a near-tripling of the air's CO_2 content enhanced the concentration of the heart-helping compound digoxin in the woolly foxglove by about 12%, and a 75% increase in the air's CO_2 content produced 6 to 28% increases in the concen-trations of five substances produced by spider lilies that have proven effective in treating a number of human cancers and viral diseases.

The ongoing rise in the air's CO_2 concentration will alter many physical and physiological leaf characteristics of Earth's plants. The data suggest the resulting changes will lead to more efficient plant growth and increase the production of secondary carbon compounds, some of which have high potential for combating human diseases. Thus, the increasing CO_2 content of the air may indirectly—but significantly—improve the quality of human life.

References

David, J.-F., Malet, N., Couteaux, M.-M., and Roy, J. 2001. Feeding rates of the woodlouse *Armadillidium vulgare* on herb litters produced at two levels of atmospheric CO_2. *Oecologia* **127**: 343–349.

Gouk, S.S., He, J., and Hew, C.S. 1999. Changes in photosynthetic capability and carbohydrate production in an epiphytic CAM orchid plantlet exposed to super-elevated CO_2. *Environmental and Experimental Botany* **41**: 219–230.

Goverde, M., Bazin, A., Shykoff, J.A., and Erhardt, A. 1999. Influence of leaf chemistry of *Lotus corniculatus* (Fabaceae) on larval development of *Polyommatus icarus* (Lepidoptera, Lycaenidae): effects of elevated CO_2 and plant genotype. *Functional Ecology* **13**: 801–810.

Idso, S.B. and Idso, K.E. 2001. Effects of atmospheric CO_2 enrichment on plant constituents related to animal and human health. *Environmental and Experimental Botany* **45**: 179–199.

Kerslake, J.E., Woodin, S.J., and Hartley, S.E. 1998. Effects of carbon dioxide and nitrogen enrichment on a plant-insect interaction: the quality of *Calluna vulgaris* as a host for *Operophtera brumata*. *New Phytologist* **140**: 43–53.

Norby, R.J., Cotrufo, M.F., Ineson, P., O'Neill, E.G., and Canadell, J.G. 2001. Elevated CO_2, litter chemistry, and decomposition: a synthesis. *Oecologia* **127**: 153–165.

Schappi, B. and Korner, C. 1997. *In situ* effects of elevated CO_2 on the carbon and nitrogen status of alpine plants. *Functional Ecology* **11**: 290–299.

2.11 Lignin

- Atmospheric CO_2 enrichment stimulates photosynthesis in nearly all plants, enabling them to produce more nonstructural carbohydrates that can be used to create important carbon-based secondary compounds, one of which is lignin.

Lignin is important because it tends to inhibit the biodegradation of organic materials. Some studies suggest plant lignin concentrations tend to decline in response to increases in the air's CO_2 concentration. In one such study—a five-year open-top chamber experiment—Cotrufo and Ineson (2000) found a doubling of the air's CO_2 concentration decreased lignin concentrations in twigs of beech seedlings by approximately 12%. Nevertheless, after 42 months of incubation in native forest soils, the decomposition rate of the CO_2-enriched twigs was still 5% less than that of the twigs grown in ambient air. Likewise, in an open-top chamber study of an agricultural crop (tall fescue), Newman *et al.* (2003) found doubling the air's CO_2 content reduced forage lignin concentration by 14%.

At the other end of the spectrum, a larger number of experiments has revealed CO_2-induced increases in plant lignin concentrations. With the CO_2-induced production of more lignin in plant tissues, the ongoing rise in the air's CO_2 content could lead to enhanced carbon sequestration in the world's soils, because plant-produced organic matter supplied to soils would be more resistant to decomposition; the end result of this phenomenon would be a slowing of the rate-of-rise of the atmosphere's CO_2 concentration, which could reduce the magnitude of CO_2-induced global warming.

In a two-year study of ash and sycamore seedlings grown in closed-top chambers (solardomes) at CO_2 concentrations of either 350 ppm (ambient) or 600 ppm (enriched), Cotrufo *et al.* (1998) observed greater concentrations of lignin in the litter produced by both species, and after one year of incubating the litter from the two CO_2 treatments in bags placed within a forest soil, the bags containing the litter produced by the CO_2-enriched trees of both species had about 30% more dry mass remaining in them than did the bags containing the litter produced by the ambient-treatment trees. In addition, woodlouse arthropods consumed 16% less litter in the CO_2-enriched chambers than in the ambient-treatment chambers.

Higher plant lignin concentrations also were observed in oak seedlings growing in doubled-CO_2 air (700 ppm as opposed to 350 ppm) in the controlled-environment greenhouse study of Staudt *et al.* (2001), as well as in trembling aspen seedlings growing in doubled-CO_2 air in the open-top chamber study of Tuchman *et al.* (2003). And in an open-top chamber study of a 30-year-old mixed-stand of various Mediterranean forest species growing near the coast of central Italy, De Angelis *et al.* (2000) determined doubled-CO_2 air increased leaf-litter lignin concentrations by 18%, which was accompanied by an 8% reduction in the initial loss of mass from the decomposing CO_2-enriched litter and a 4% reduction one year later.

Booker *et al.* (2000) observed higher lignin concentrations in the roots of CO_2-enriched cotton, a perennial woody plant, as did Booker *et al.* (2005) in CO_2-enriched soybean, an annual herbaceous plant. They conclude, "one result of increased residue production and higher levels of recalcitrant material such as lignin being added to the soil is that soil carbon sequestration should increase, a response anticipated to occur with increasing concentrations of atmospheric CO_2."

More often than not, however, experiments of this type have found no significant changes in the tissue lignin concentrations of plants grown in CO_2-enriched air. Studies in this category include the work of Hirschel *et al.* (1997) dealing with plants growing in an alpine grassland, a lowland calcareous grassland, and a lowland, wet, tropical rainforest; Booker and Maier (2001) and Finzi and Schlesinger (2002) dealing with loblolly pine trees; Peñuelas *et al.* (2002) investigating three species of shrub in Pisa, Italy; and Billings *et al.* (2003) dealing with four species of shrub in the Mojave Desert, Nevada, USA.

Norby *et al.* (2001) conducted a meta-analytic review that considered this issue from a number of different perspectives. Based on 46 experimental observations, they determined elevated atmospheric CO_2 concentrations increased leaf-litter lignin concentrations by an average of 6.5%. These increases in lignin content occurred only in woody species. Leaf-litter lignin concentrations were not affected by elevated CO_2 when plants were grown in open-top chambers, FACE plots, or in the proximity of CO_2-emitting springs. In analyzing 101 observations, Norby *et al.* found elevated CO_2 had no consistent effect on leaf litter decomposition rate in any experimental setting.

Almost all of the studies conducted to date on woody species, where there is some evidence of an increase in leaf-litter lignin concentration (and there thus remains a possibility of CO_2-enhanced carbon sequestration), have been of short duration compared to the lifespans of various forest components. The long-term consequences of modest CO_2-induced increases in woody-plant lignin concentrations for soil carbon sequestration will not be known until several experiments of much longer duration than any conducted so far have been conducted. Nevertheless, as Booker *et al.* (2005) remind us, because there is also considerably more litter produced by almost all plants in CO_2-enriched air, soil carbon sequestration should continue to increase as the air's CO_2 content continues to rise.

References

Billings, S.A., Zitzer, S.F., Weatherly, H., Schaeffer, S.M., Charlet, T., Arnone III, J.A., and Evans, R.D. 2003. Effects of elevated carbon dioxide on green leaf tissue and leaf litter quality in an intact Mojave Desert ecosystem. *Global Change Biology* 9: 729–735.

Booker, F.L. and Maier, C.A. 2001. Atmospheric carbon dioxide, irrigation, and fertilization effects on phenolic and nitrogen concentrations in loblolly pine (*Pinus taeda*) needles. *Tree Physiology* 21: 609–616.

Booker, F.L., Prior, S.A., Torbert, H.A., Fiscus, E.L., Pursley, W.A., and Hu, S. 2005. Decomposition of soybean grown under elevated concentrations of CO_2 and O_3. *Global Change Biology* 11: 685–698.

Booker, F.L., Shafer, S.R., Wei, C.-M., and Horton, S.J. 2000. Carbon dioxide enrichment and nitrogen fertilization effects on cotton (*Gossypium hirsutum* L.) plant residue chemistry and decomposition. *Plant and Soil* 220: 89–98.

Cotrufo, M.F., Briones, M.J.I., and Ineson, P. 1998. Elevated CO_2 affects field decomposition rate and palatability of tree leaf litter: importance of changes in substrate quality. *Soil Biology and Biochemistry* 30: 1565–1571.

Cotrufo, M.F. and Ineson, P. 2000. Does elevated atmospheric CO_2 concentration affect wood decomposition? *Plant and Soil* 224: 51–57.

De Angelis, P., Chigwerewe, K.S., and Mugnozza, G.E.S. 2000. Litter quality and decomposition in a CO_2-enriched Mediterranean forest ecosystem. *Plant and Soil* 224: 31–41.

Finzi, A.C. and Schlesinger, W.H. 2002. Species control variation in litter decomposition in a pine forest exposed to elevated CO_2. *Global Change Biology* 8: 1217–1229.

Hirschel, G., Korner, C., and Arnone III, J.A. 1997. Will rising atmospheric CO_2 affect leaf litter quality and in situ decomposition rates in native plant communities? *Oecologia* 110: 387–392.

Newman, J.A., Abner, M.L., Dado, R.G., Gibson, D.J., Brookings, A., and Parsons, A.J. 2003. Effects of elevated CO_2, nitrogen and fungal endophyte-infection on tall fescue: growth, photosynthesis, chemical composition and digestibility. *Global Change Biology* 9: 425–437.

Norby, R.J., Cotrufo, M.F., Ineson, P., O'Neill, E.G., and Canadell, J.G. 2001. Elevated CO_2, litter chemistry, and decomposition: a synthesis. *Oecologia* 127: 153–165.

Peñuelas, J., Castells, E., Joffre, R., and Tognetti, R. 2002. Carbon-based secondary and structural compounds in Mediterranean shrubs growing near a natural CO_2 spring. *Global Change Biology* 8: 281–288.

Staudt, M., Joffre, R., Rambal, S., and Kesselmeier, J. 2001. Effect of elevated CO_2 on monoterpene emission of young *Quercus ilex* trees and its relation to structural and ecophysiological parameters. *Tree Physiology* 21: 437–445.

Tuchman, N.C., Wahtera, K.A., Wetzel, R.G., and Teeri, J.A. 2003. Elevated atmospheric CO_2 alters leaf litter quality for stream ecosystems: an *in situ* leaf decomposition study. *Hydrobiologia* 495: 203–211.

2.12 Lipids

- The highly positive effects of atmospheric CO_2 enrichment on lipid concentrations and characteristics in various terrestrial and aquatic plants portend benefits for both the managed and unmanaged components of Earth's biosphere as the air's CO_2 content continues to climb.

Lipids are hydrophobic molecules consisting mainly of fats, oils, and waxes that possess long non-polar hydrocarbon groups arranged in chains commonly called fatty acid chains, one type of which (phospholipids) is a major component of plant and animal membranes. They are extremely important to the well-being of nearly all living organisms.

Seeking to discover how lipids are affected by elevated concentrations of atmospheric CO_2, Sgherri et al. (1998) grew alfalfa in open-top chambers at ambient (340 ppm) and enriched (600 ppm) CO_2 concentrations for 25 days. They then withheld water from the plants for five additional days. They found the plants grown at the elevated CO_2 concentration maintained greater leaf lipid to protein ratios, especially under conditions of water stress. In addition, leaf lipid contents of the plants grown in the CO_2-enriched air were 22 and 83% greater than those of the plants grown in ambient air for periods of ample and insufficient soil moisture, respectively. Also, the degrees of unsaturation of two of the most important lipids of the thylakoid membranes (which are found within chloroplasts and contain chlorophyll, other pigments that absorb sunlight, and specialized protein complexes that convert sunlight into usable cellular energy during photosynthesis) were approximately 20 and 37% greater in the high- compared to the low-CO_2 treatments during times of adequate and inadequate soil moisture, respectively.

Sgherri et al. suggest the greater lipid contents observed in CO_2-enriched air and their increased degree of unsaturation may allow thylakoid membranes to maintain a more fluid and stable environment, critical during periods of water stress in enabling plants to continue photosynthetic carbon uptake. Some researchers have suggested adaptive plant responses such as these may allow plants to better cope with any altered environmental condition that produces stress.

With greater amounts of CO_2 in the atmosphere, the resulting greater lipid contents of thylakoid membranes plus their greater degree of unsaturation may provide greater membrane stability and integrity, thereby allowing proper functioning in times of drought or other adverse environmental conditions. In some cases, these CO_2-induced adaptations may mean the difference between a plant's living or dying.

Consider, for example, the stress of exposure to overly cold temperatures that often leads to chilling injury in plants and the role played by membrane lipid unsaturation in alleviating those injuries.

Hugly and Somerville (1992) worked with wild-type Arabidopsis thaliana and two mutants of the species that were deficient in thylakoid lipid unsaturation. They found "chloroplast membrane lipid polyunsaturation contributes to the low-temperature fitness of the organism," and that it is required for some aspect of chloroplast biogenesis. When lipid polyunsaturation was low, for example, they observed what they called "dramatic reductions in chloroplast size, membrane content, and organization in developing leaves." They found a positive correlation "between the severity of chlorosis in the two mutants at low temperatures and the degree of reduction in polyunsaturated chloroplast lipid composition."

Kodama et al. (1994) demonstrate the low-temperature-induced suppression of leaf growth and concomitant induction of chlorosis observed in wild-type plants is much less evident in transgenic plants containing a gene that allows for greater expression of unsaturation in the fatty acids of leaf lipids. They conclude substantially unsaturated fatty acids "are undoubtedly an important factor contributing to cold tolerance."

Moon et al. (1995) found heightened unsaturation of the membrane lipids of chloroplasts stabilized the photosynthetic machinery of transgenic tobacco plants against low-temperature photo-inhibition "by accelerating the recovery of the photosystem II protein complex." Kodama et al. (1995), also working with transgenic tobacco plants, showed increased fatty acid desaturation is one of the prerequisites for normal leaf development at low, nonfreezing temperatures. Ishizaki-Nishizawa et al. (1996) found transgenic tobacco plants with a reduced level of saturated fatty acids in most membrane lipids "exhibited a significant increase in chilling resistance."

These observations are laden with significance for Earth's agro-ecosystems, since many economically important crops, such as rice, maize, and soybeans, are classified as chilling-sensitive: they experience injury or death at temperatures between 0 and 15°C (Lyons, 1973). If atmospheric CO_2 enrichment enhances their production of thylakoid lipids and their degree of unsaturation, as it does in alfalfa, a continuation of the ongoing rise in the air's CO_2

content could increase the abilities of these agricultural species to withstand periodic exposure to debilitating low temperatures; this phenomenon could provide the extra boost to food production that will be needed to sustain the planet's increasing numbers in the future (Tilman *et al.*, 2001).

Hussain *et al.* (2001) collected and analyzed seeds from loblolly pine trees exposed to atmospheric CO_2 concentrations of either 350 or 560 ppm since 1996 in the Duke Forest FACE study. The seeds collected from the CO_2-enriched trees were 90% heavier than seeds collected from the trees growing in ambient air, and their mean lipid content was 265% greater. The germination success of seeds developed under CO_2-enriched conditions was more than three times greater than that of the seeds from the ambient-air treatment, regardless of germination CO_2 concentration. In addition, seeds from the CO_2-enriched trees germinated approximately five days earlier, regardless of germination CO_2 concentration, and the seedlings derived from the seeds collected from the CO_2-enriched trees displayed significantly greater root lengths and needle numbers than those derived from seeds collected from the ambient-treatment trees.

Schwanz and Polle (1998) evaluated the degree of lipid peroxidation in leaves of mature holm and white oak trees that had been growing in the vicinity of natural CO_2 springs in central Italy for close to half a century. They found the trees growing in close proximity to the CO_2-emitting springs often exhibited lipid peroxidation reductions, which indicate less intrinsic oxidative stress and the presence of fewer internal harmful oxidants.

Yu *et al.* (2004) grew the marine microalgae *Platymonas subcordiformis* in the laboratory at ambient levels of atmospheric CO_2 concentration and UV-B radiation flux density, as well as at elevated levels of 5,000 ppm CO_2 and the UV-B radiation flux anticipated to result from a 25% stratospheric ozone depletion under clear sky conditions in summer. They report the elevated UV-B treatment by itself significantly increased the production of the toxic superoxide anion and hydrogen peroxide, as well as malonyldialdehyde, an end product of lipid peroxidation. Elevated CO_2 by itself did just the opposite. In the treatment consisting of elevated UV-B and elevated CO_2, the concentrations of these three substances were all lower than those observed in the elevated UV-B and ambient CO_2 treatment. Yu *et al.* conclude, "CO_2 enrichment could reduce oxidative stress of reactive oxygen species to *P. subcordiformis*, and reduce the lipid peroxidation damage of UV-B to *P. subcordiformis*."

An interesting aspect of these findings is what they imply about coral bleaching. In the introduction to their review of this important subject, Smith *et al.* (2005) report, "photoinhibition of photosynthesis and photodamage to photosystem II of the zooxanthellae, with the consequent increase in the production of damaging reactive oxygen species (ROS), have been implicated as the cause of thermal bleaching (Brown, 1997; Fitt *et al.*, 2001; Lesser, 2004; Tchernov *et al.*, 2004)." At the end of their review, they report the "thermal bleaching of many corals is ultimately the result of the destruction of photosynthetic pigments by ROS," and the production by the zooxanthellae of one particular ROS, hydrogen peroxide, "may be a signal that triggers a response in the host cell to eject the zooxanthellae or shed the host cell from the coral." Combining these observations with the finding of Yu *et al.* that CO_2 enrichment counters the production of hydrogen peroxide, it follows that some degree of atmospheric CO_2 enrichment should likewise cause host cells to not eject their zooxanthellae.

Goverde *et al.*, 2002) examined the impact of atmospheric CO_2 enrichment on lipid concentrations in the body of an animal, specifically, the satyrid butterfly (*Coenonympha pamphilus*), larvae of which were raised in semi-natural, undisturbed calcareous grassland plots exposed to atmospheric CO_2 concentrations of 370 and 600 ppm for five growing seasons. Among other things, this work revealed the elevated atmospheric CO_2 concentration increased lipid concentrations in the bodies of adult male butterflies by nearly 14%. Since these compounds are used as energy resources in these and other butterflies, this animal species—and perhaps others— likely will exhibit positive responses to future increases in the air's CO_2 concentration.

References

Brown, B.E. 1997. Coral bleaching: causes and consequences. *Coral Reefs* **16**: S129–S138.

Fitt, W.K., Brown, B.E., and Warner, M.E., *et al.* 2001. Coral bleaching: interpretation of thermal tolerance limits and thermal thresholds in tropical corals. *Coral Reefs* **20**: 51–65.

Goverde, M., Erhardt, A., and Niklaus, P.A. 2002. *In situ* development of a satyrid butterfly on calcareous grassland exposed to elevated carbon dioxide. *Ecology* **83**: 1399–1411.

Hugly, S. and Somerville, C. 1992. A role for membrane lipid polyunsaturation in chloroplast biogenesis at low temperature. *Plant Physiology* **99**: 197–202.

Hussain, M., Kubiske, M.E., and Connor, K.F. 2001. Germination of CO_2-enriched *Pinus taeda* L. seeds and subsequent seedling growth responses to CO_2 enrichment. *Functional Ecology* **15**: 344–350.

Ishizaki-Nishizawa, O., Fujii, T., Azuma, M., Sekiguchi, K., Murata, N., Ohtani, T., and Toguri T. 1996. Low-temperature resistance of higher plants is significantly enhanced by a nonspecific cyanobacterial desaturase. *Nature Biotechnology* **14**: 1003–1006.

Kodama, H., Hamada, T., Horiguchi, G., Nishimura, M., and Iba, K. 1994. Genetic enhancement of cold tolerance by expression of a gene for chloroplast w-3 fatty acid desaturase in transgenic tobacco. *Plant Physiology* **105**: 601–605.

Kodama, H., Horiguchi, G., Nishiuchi, T., Nishimura, M., and Iba, K. 1995. Fatty acid desaturation during chilling acclimation is one of the factors involved in conferring low-temperature tolerance to young tobacco leaves. *Plant Physiology* **107**: 1177–1185.

Lesser, M.P. 2004. Experimental biology of coral reef systems. *Journal of Experimental Marine Biology and Ecology* **300**: 217–252.

Lyons, J.M. 1973. Chilling injury in plants. *Annual Review of Plant Physiology* **24**: 445–466.

Moon, B.Y., Higashi, S.-I., Gombos, Z., and Murata, N. 1995. Unsaturation of the membrane lipids of chloroplasts stabilizes the photosynthetic machinery against low-temperature photoinhibition in transgenic tobacco plants. *Proceedings of the National Academy of Sciences, USA* **92**: 6219–6223.

Schwanz, P. and Polle, A. 1998. Antioxidative systems, pigment and protein contents in leaves of adult mediterranean oak species (*Quercus pubescens* and *Q. ilex*) with lifetime exposure to elevated CO_2. *New Phytologist* **140**: 411–423.

Sgherri, C.L.M., Quartacci, M.F., Menconi, M., Raschi, A., and Navari-Izzo, F. 1998. Interactions between drought and elevated CO_2 on alfalfa plants. *Journal of Plant Physiology* **152**: 118–124.

Smith, D.J., Suggett, D.J., and Baker, N.R. 2005. Is photoinhibition of zooxanthellae photosynthesis the primary cause of thermal bleaching in corals? *Global Change Biology* **11**: 1–11.

Tchernov, D., Gorbunov, M.Y., de Vargas, C., Yadav, S.N., Milligan, A.J., Haggblom, M., and Falkowski, P.G. 2004. Membrane lipids of symbiotic algae are diagnostic of sensitivity to thermal bleaching in corals. *Proceedings of the National Academy of Sciences USA* **101**: 13,531–13,535.

Tilman, D., Fargione, J., Wolff, B., D'Antonio, C., Dobson, A., Howarth, R., Schindler, D., Schlesinger, W.H., Simberloff, D., and Swackhamer, D. 2001. Forecasting agriculturally driven global environmental change. *Science* **292**: 281–284.

Yu, J., Tang, X-X., Zhang, P-Y., Tian, J-Y., and Cai, H-J. 2004. Effects of CO_2 enrichment on photosynthesis, lipid peroxidation and activities of antioxidative enzymes of *Platymonas subcordiformis* subjected to UV-B radiation stress. *Acta Botanica Sinica* **46**: 682–690.

2.13 Low Temperature

- The stresses of low temperature have been shown to be both alleviated and enhanced in plants growing under elevated CO_2 concentrations. It appears far more plants are benefiting from such stress alleviation than are experiencing stress augmentation.

Loik *et al.* (2000) grew three *Yucca* species (*brevifolia, schidigera,* and *whipplei*) in pots placed in glasshouses maintained at atmospheric CO_2 concentrations of 360 and 700 ppm and day/night air temperatures of 40/24°C for seven months, after which some of the plants were subjected to a two-week day/night air temperature treatment of 20/5°C. In addition, leaves from each *Yucca* species were removed and placed in a freezer cooled at a rate of 3°C per hour until a minimum temperature of -15°C was reached. These manipulations indicated elevated CO_2 lowered the air temperature at which 50% low-temperature-induced cell mortality occurred by 1.6, 1.4, and 0.8°C in *brevifolia, schidigera,* and *whipplei*, respectively. On the basis of the result obtained for *Y. brevifolia*, Dole *et al.* (2003) estimate "the increase in freezing tolerance caused by doubled CO_2 would increase the potential habitat of this species by 14%."

Obrist *et al.* (2001) observed just the opposite response. In an open-top chamber study of a temperate grass ecosystem growing on a nutrient-poor calcareous soil in northwest Switzerland, portions of which had been exposed to atmospheric CO_2 concentrations of 360 and 600 ppm for six years, they found the average temperature at which 50% low-temperature-induced leaf mortality occurred in five prominent species rose by an average of 0.7°C in response to the extra 240 ppm of CO_2 employed in their experiment.

Most relevant investigations, however, have

produced evidence of positive CO_2 effects on plants' low-temperature tolerance. Sigurdsson (2001), for example, grew black cottonwood seedlings near Gunnarsholt, Iceland within closed-top chambers maintained at ambient and twice-ambient atmospheric CO_2 concentrations for three years, finding elevated CO_2 tended to hasten the end of the growing season. This effect was interpreted as enabling the seedlings to better avoid the severe cold-induced dieback of newly produced tissues that often occurs with the approach of winter in this region. Likewise, Wayne *et al.* (1998) found yellow birch seedlings grown at an atmospheric CO_2 concentration of 800 ppm exhibited greater dormant bud survivorship at low air temperatures than did seedlings grown at 400 ppm CO_2.

Schwanz and Polle (2001) investigated the effects of elevated CO_2 on chilling stress in micropropagated hybrid poplar clones that were subsequently potted and transferred to growth chambers maintained at either ambient (360 ppm) or elevated (700 ppm) CO_2 for three months. They found "photosynthesis was less diminished and electrolyte leakage was lower in stressed leaves from poplar trees grown under elevated CO_2 as compared with those from ambient CO_2." Although severe chilling caused pigment and protein degradation in all stressed leaves, the damage was expressed to a lower extent in leaves from the elevated CO_2 treatment. This CO_2-induced chilling protection was accompanied by a rapid induction of superoxide dismutase activity and by slightly higher stabilities of other antioxidative enzymes.

Sgherri *et al.* (1998) report raising the air's CO_2 concentration from 340 to 600 ppm increased lipid concentrations in alfalfa thylakoid membranes while inducing a higher degree of unsaturation in the most prominent of those lipids. Under well-watered conditions, for example, the 76% increase in atmospheric CO_2 enhanced overall thylakoid lipid concentration by about 25%, while it increased the degree of unsaturation of the two main lipids by approximately 17% and 24%. Under conditions of water stress, these responses were even greater, as thylakoid lipid concentration rose by approximately 92%, and the degree of unsaturation of the two main lipids rose by about 22% and 53%.

What these observations have to do with a plant's susceptibility to chilling injury is evident from a number of studies conducted over the past decade. For example, Hugly and Somerville (1992) studied wild-type *Arabidopsis thaliana* and two mutants deficient in thylakoid lipid unsaturation, finding "chloroplast membrane lipid polyunsaturation

contributes to the low-temperature fitness of the organism" and it "is required for some aspect of chloroplast biogenesis." When lipid polyunsaturation was low, they observed "dramatic reductions in chloroplast size, membrane content, and organization in developing leaves." They found a positive correlation "between the severity of chlorosis in the two mutants at low temperatures and the degree of reduction in polyunsaturated chloroplast lipid composition."

Kodama *et al.* (1994) demonstrate the low-temperature-induced suppression of leaf growth and concomitant induction of chlorosis observed in wild-type tobacco plants is much less evident in transgenic plants containing a gene that allows for greater expression of unsaturation in the fatty acids of leaf lipids. They conclude substantially unsaturated fatty acids "are undoubtedly an important factor contributing to cold tolerance."

Moon *et al.* (1995) found heightened unsaturation of the membrane lipids of chloroplasts stabilized the photosynthetic machinery of transgenic tobacco plants against low-temperature photoinhibition "by accelerating the recovery of the photosystem II protein complex." Likewise, Kodama *et al.* (1995), also working with transgenic tobacco plants, showed increased fatty acid desaturation is one of the prerequisites for normal leaf development at low, nonfreezing temperatures. Ishizaki-Nishizawa *et al.* (1996) demonstrate transgenic tobacco plants with a reduced level of saturated fatty acids in most membrane lipids "exhibited a significant increase in chilling resistance."

Many economically important crops, such as rice, maize, and soybeans, are classified as chilling-sensitive—they experience injury or death at temperatures between 0 and 15°C (Lyons, 1973). If atmospheric CO_2 enrichment enhances their production and degree-of-unsaturation of thylakoid lipids, as it does in alfalfa, a continuation of the ongoing rise in the air's CO_2 content could increase the abilities of these critically important agricultural species to withstand periodic exposure to debilitating low temperatures, and this could provide the extra boost in food production that will be needed to sustain the planet's increasing numbers in the years and decades ahead.

Earth's natural ecosystems also would benefit from a CO_2-induced increase in thylakoid lipids containing more-highly-unsaturated fatty acids. Many plants of tropical origin, for example, suffer cold damage when temperatures fall below 20°C (Graham and Patterson, 1982). With improved lipid characteristics provided by the ongoing rise in the air's CO_2 content, such plants would be able to expand their ranges both poleward and upward in a higher-CO_2 world.

Baczek-Kwinta and Koscielniak (2003) grew two hybrid maize (*Zea mays* L.) genotypes—KOC 9431 (chill-resistant) and K103xK85 (chill-sensitive)—from seed in air of either ambient (350 ppm) or elevated (700 ppm) CO_2 concentration (AC or EC, respectively), after which the plants were exposed to air of 7°C for 11 days and then recovered in ambient air of 20°C for one day. Throughout this period, physiological and biochemical parameters were measured on the plants' third fully expanded leaves.

Under such conditions, Baczek-Kwinta and Koscielniak report, "EC inhibited chill-induced depression of net photosynthetic rate (PN), especially in leaves of chill-resistant genotype KOC 9431." This phenomenon "was distinct not only during chilling, but also during the recovery of plants at 20°C." They note, "seedlings subjected to EC showed 4-fold higher PN when compared to AC plants." They also determined "EC diminished the rate of superoxide radical formation in leaves in comparison to the AC control." In addition, "electrolyte leakage from the [leaf membrane] tissue, a parameter reflecting membrane injury, was significantly lower in samples of plants subjected to EC than AC." Finally, they report enrichment of air with CO_2 successfully inhibited the decrease in the maximal quantum efficiency of photosystem 2, both after chilling and during the one-day recovery period. Taking all these positive effects of elevated CO_2 together, the authors conclude, "the increase in atmospheric CO_2 concentration seems to be one of the protective factors for maize grown in cold temperate regions."

Melkonian *et al.* (2004) grew well-watered and fertilized mature bean plants (*Phaseolus vulgaris* L., cv. Bush Blue Lake 274) in CO_2-controlled growth chambers maintained at concentrations of either 350 or 700 ppm at 25/18°C day/night temperatures. The plants then received 24 hours of chilling at 6.5°C (8 hours light, 10 hours dark, 6 hours light), after which there was a 24-hour recovery period under pre-chill growing conditions, followed by a second 24 hours of chilling and a 48-hour recovery period consisting of pre-chill conditions. Throughout this time, net photosynthesis measurements were made two to three hours before and after each shift in temperature.

According to the authors, prior to chilling, net photosynthesis was approximately 20% higher at elevated compared to ambient CO_2. During chilling, plants of both treatments exhibited near-identical

much-reduced values. Subsequently, however, and "consistent with previous research [Boese *et al.*, 1997] on this cultivar," in the words of Melkonian *et al.*, "post-chilling recovery was more rapid at elevated compared to ambient CO_2."

Alam *et al.* (2005) grew eight-month-old saplings of two clones (PB 235 and RRII 105) of *Hevea brasiliensis*, a tree species indigenous to humid tropical climates, in 0.75-m^3 polybags filled with garden soil during the two coldest months of the year in warm and cool regions of peninsular India having mean minimum temperatures of 22.0 and 10.0°C, respectively, while they measured a number of photosynthetic properties of the trees' leaves. The authors report, "irrespective of the differences in growth environment, higher CO_2 in the ambient air during measurements improved the photochemical efficiency of the plants as reflected in higher net photosynthetic rate, effective photosystem 2 quantum efficiency, and photochemical quenching." The Indian scientists conclude their results imply "inhibition in photochemical efficiency due to sub-optimal temperatures could be improved considerably with higher CO_2 concentration by making more CO_2 available to photosynthesis."

Kostiainen *et al.* (2006) studied the effects of elevated carbon dioxide (CO_2) and ozone (O_3) on various wood properties of two initially seven-year-old fast-growing silver birch (*Betula pendula* Roth) clones grown out-of-doors at Suonenjoki, Finland for three additional years in open-top chambers maintained at ambient and 1.9x ambient CO_2 concentrations in combination with ambient and 1.5x ambient O_3 concentrations. The Finnish researchers note "the concentration of nonstructural carbo-hydrates (starch and soluble sugars) in tree tissues is considered a measure of carbon shortage or surplus for growth (Korner, 2003)." Hence, they say "starch accumulation observed under elevated CO_2 in this study indicates a surplus of carbohydrates produced by enhanced photosynthesis of the same trees (Riikonen *et al.*, 2004)." In addition, they report, "during winter, starch reserves in the stem are gradually transformed to soluble carbohydrates involved in freezing tolerance (Bertrand *et al.*, 1999; Piispanen and Saranpaa, 2001), so the increase in starch concentration may improve acclimation in winter."

Bigras and Bertrand (2006) grew well-watered and fertilized black spruce (*Picea mariana* Mill. BSP) plants from seed in containers filled with a 3:1 mixture of peat:vermiculite in mini-greenhouses located within a larger greenhouse where they were exposed—at ambient and elevated (370 and 710 ppm) concentrations of atmospheric CO_2)—to environmental conditions that simulated "a growth period (Summer, April 17–September 15) followed by hardening (Fall, September 16–November 5; Winter, November 6–February 5) and dehardening (Spring, February 6–February 28)." During these periods numerous plant properties and physiological processes were measured.

In October, during the process of hardening, Bigras and Bertrand found "bud set began earlier in elevated CO_2 than in ambient CO_2" and "an increase in seedling cold tolerance in early fall was related to early bud set in elevated CO_2." In addition, their results "showed reductions in dark respiration and light compensation point during cold acclimation and de-acclimation can contribute to increased productivity in elevated CO_2." They "observed an increase in light-saturated photosynthetic rate in response to elevated CO_2 during the growth, hardening and de-hardening periods" which "varied seasonally between 12 and 50%." The net result of these and other CO_2-induced plant benefits was a 38% increase in total plant mass at the end of the growing season that slowly declined to a value of 18% at the end of the winter.

Bertrand et al. (2007) grew well-watered and fertilized alfalfa (Medicago sativa L.) plants which they inoculated with one of two strains (either A2 or NRG34) of the nitrogen-fixing symbiont Sinorhizobium meliloti from seed in 12.5-cm-diameter pots filled with non-sterile topsoil within controlled-environment chambers maintained at atmospheric CO_2 concentrations of either 400 or 800 ppm for two months under optimal light (600 $\mu mol/m^2/s$ for 16 hours per day) and day/night temperatures of 22/17°C and for two final weeks at a reduced light level of 200 $\mu mol/m^2/s$ for 8 hours per day and a cold day/night temperature regime of 5/2°C. Over this time they periodically measured plant physiological functions and characteristics.

At the end of the experiment, the researchers determined the total biomass of the plants in the elevated CO_2 treatment was approximately 33% greater than that of the plants in the control treatment when infected with the A2 strain of S. meliloti, but about 36% greater when infected with the NRG34 strain. Plants in the 800 ppm CO_2 treatment were found to be less freezing-tolerant than those in the 400 ppm treatment, and the plants inoculated with the NRG34 strain were determined to be less freezing-tolerant than those inoculated with the A2 strain.

Providing some comparative background for their

freezing tolerance results, Bertrand et al. write, "CO_2 enrichment led to more severe frost damage in leaves of Eucalyptus pauciflora (Barker et al., 2005) and Ginko biloba (Terry et al., 2000), and in a native temperate grassland (Obrist et al., 2001), whereas it increased frost resistance of Betula allaghanensis (Wayne et al., 1998) and Picea mariana (Bigras and Bertrand, 2006) but had no effect on freezing tolerance of Picea abies (Dalen et al., 2001)." This suggests there may not be a single freezing tolerance response to atmospheric CO_2 enrichment that is typical of plants in general. However, because their results suggest "it is possible to select or identify rhizobial strains to improve alfalfa performance under high CO_2," Bertrand et al. conclude the "freezing tolerance as well as the expression of key over-wintering genes of alfalfa can be altered by the strain of rhizobium." This should enable farmers to obtain the best of both worlds, as it were, by benefiting from the significant growth stimulation produced by the ongoing rise in the air's CO_2 content while selecting a strain of rhizobium capable of compensating for a possible CO_2-induced reduction in freezing tolerance.

Hanninen et al. (2007) note "according to the hypothesis presented by Cannell (1985), climatic warming may paradoxically increase the risk of frost damage in boreal and temperate regions, because the trees will deharden and even start to grow during intermittent mild periods in winter and get damaged during subsequent periods of frost." Likewise, they write, "Kellomaki et al. (1995) predicted that frost damage caused by a premature dehardening would severely restrict growth of Scots pine under a climatic warming scenario in central Finland."

Hanninen et al. investigated this subject using whole-tree chambers (WTCs) surrounding groups of 40-year-old Norway spruce (Picea abies (L.) Karst.) trees growing under natural conditions in northern Sweden, studying the effects of atmospheric CO_2 enrichment (to 700 ppm above the ambient value of 365 ppm) and global warming (ranging from 2.8°C above ambient in summer to 5.6°C above ambient in winter) on the timing of spring bud burst in the trees.

The researchers report the timing of bud burst was unaffected by elevated CO_2, but "the trees growing at an elevated temperature hardened later and dehardened earlier than the control trees." However, they note, the difference was "much smaller" than that implied by Cannell (1985) and predicted by Kellomaki et al. (1995). Hanninen et al. conclude, "regardless of the warming taking place during winter, boreal coniferous trees are able to retain their dormancy and frost hardiness until around the spring equinox," explaining, "high temperatures during bud dormancy induction increase the chilling requirement of rest completion, or in some other way delay bud burst during spring," citing Heide (2003) and Junttila *et al.* (2003). These observations thus suggest, they write, "boreal trees may be able to prevent premature dehardening and growth onset under climatic warming," thereby thwarting scenarios of deleterious frost damage in the face of global warming.

In a study focusing only on temperature, Loik *et al.* (2004) note a warming of the climate may cause plants to come out of winter dormancy earlier in the spring, and "because physiologically active plants are more vulnerable than dormant plants to a transient low-temperature event (Larcher, 1995), earlier acclimation to warmer temperatures and onset of photosynthetic activity ... may make plants more susceptible to damage [caused by temporary but extreme cold weather] that reduces overall functional leaf surface area and productivity." They tested this hypothesis for specimens of the evergreen shrub *Artemisia tridentata* and the sub-alpine herbaceous *Erythronium grandiflorum* that had been growing at 3,050 meters in the Rocky Mountains of Colorado (USA), "where overhead infrared heaters have continually simulated atmospheric forcing of the future (Harte *et al.*, 1995)," enhancing the downward infrared radiation flux by 22 Wm^{-2}.

Specifically, they compared the photosynthetic responses of the plants before, during, and after an imposed *in situ* freezing event, where air and leaf temperatures of selected plants were "continually decreased, as would occur during a natural episodic freezing event." This environmental manipulation started at an ambient temperature of about 10°C and adjusted to -30°C over a period of 10 hours, mimicking what occurs naturally at this site about once every 10 years.

The authors report "the infrared warming treatment did not reduce the ability of the subalpine herbaceous geophyte *Erythronium grandiflorum* to tolerate *in situ* freezing, in contrast to our hypothesis." The warming treatment in fact "led to a significant increase in photosynthetic tolerance of an experimentally imposed *in situ* freezing event for the Great Basin Desert evergreen shrub *Artemisia tridentata* ... in contrast to our hypothesis." Loik *et al.* suggest "enhanced tolerance of episodic freezing is a result of enhanced physiological activity, in particular, higher plant water potentials and photosynthetic gas exchange caused by the infrared treatment effects on soil water content and soil temperature," leading to "an increased level of

photosynthates available for allocation to cryo-protection or other acclimation mechanisms (Iba, 2002)." Loik *et al.* thus conclude that, contrary to prior expectations, some species of plants will not be negatively affected by episodic freezing events in a warmer world, and others "may exhibit enhanced tolerance of subzero air temperatures under a future warmer climate."

References

Alam, B., Nair, D.B., and Jacob, J. 2005. Low temperature stress modifies the photochemical efficiency of a tropical tree species Hevea brasiliensis: effects of varying concentration of CO_2 and photon flux density. *Photosynthetica* **43**: 247–252.

Baczek-Kwinta, R. and Koscielniak, J. 2003. Antioxidative effect of elevated CO_2 concentration in the air on maize hybrids subjected to severe chill. *Photosynthetica* **41**: 161–165.

Barker, D.H., Loveys, B.R., Egerton, J.J.G., Gorton, H., Williams, W.E., and Ball, M.C. 2005. CO_2 enrichment predisposes foliage of a eucalypt to freezing injury and reduces spring growth. *Plant, Cell and Environment* **28**: 1506–1515.

Bertrand, A., Prevost, D., Bigras, F.J., and Castonguay, Y. 2007. Elevated atmospheric CO_2 and strain of rhizobium alter freezing tolerance and cold-induced molecular changes in alfalfa (*Medicago sativa*). *Annals of Botany* **99**: 275–284.

Bertrand, A., Robitaille, G., Nadeau, P., and Castonguay, Y. 1999. Influence of ozone on cold acclimation in sugar maple seedlings. *Tree Physiology* **19**: 527–534.

Bigras, F.J. and Bertrand, A. 2006. Responses of *Picea mariana* to elevated CO_2 concentration during growth, cold hardening and dehardening: phenology, cold tolerance, photosynthesis and growth. *Tree Physiology* **26**: 875–888.

Boese, S.R., Wolfe, D.W., and Melkonian, J. 1997. Elevated CO_2 mitigates chilling-induced water stress and photosynthetic reduction during chilling. *Plant, Cell and Environment* **20**: 624–632.

Cannell, M.G.R. 1985. Analysis of risks of frost damage to forest trees in Britain. In: Tigerstedt, P.M.A., Puttonen, P., and Koski, V. (Eds.) *Crop Physiology of Forest Trees*, Helsinki University Press, Helsinki, Finland, pp. 153–165.

Dalen, L.S., Johnsen, O., and Ogner, G. 2001. CO_2 enrichment and development of freezing tolerance in Norway spruce. *Physiologia Plantarum* **113**: 533–540.

Dole, K.P., Loik, M.E., and Sloan, L.C. 2003. The relative importance of climate change and the physiological effects of CO_2 on freezing tolerance for the future distribution of *Yucca brevifolia*. *Global and Planetary Change* **36**: 137–146.

Graham, D. and Patterson, B.D. 1982. Responses of plants to low, non-freezing temperatures: proteins, metabolism, and acclimation. *Annual Review of Plant Physiology* **33**: 347–372.

Hanninen, H., Slaney, M., and Linder, S. 2007. Dormancy release of Norway spruce under climatic warming: testing ecophysiological models of bud burst with a whole-tree chamber experiment. *Tree Physiology* **27**: 291–300.

Harte, J., Torn, M.S., Chang, F., Feifarek, B., Kinzig, A.P., Shaw, R., and Shen, K. 1995. Global warming and soil microclimate: results from a meadow-warming experiment. *Ecological Applications* **5**: 132–150.

Heide, O.M. 2003. High autumn temperature delays spring bud burst in boreal trees, counterbalancing the effect of climatic warming. *Tree Physiology* **23**: 931–936.

Hugly, S. and Somerville, C. 1992. A role for membrane lipid polyunsaturation in chloroplast biogenesis at low temperature. *Plant Physiology* **99**: 197–202.

Iba, K. 2002. Acclimative response to temperature stress in higher plants: Approaches of gene engineering for temperature tolerance. *Annual Review of Plant Biology* **53**: 225–245.

Ishizaki-Nishizawa, O., Fujii, T., Azuma, M., Sekiguchi, K., Murata, N., Ohtani, T., and Toguri T. 1996. Low-temperature resistance of higher plants is significantly enhanced by a nonspecific cyanobacterial desaturase. *Nature Biotechnology* **14**: 1003–1006.

Junttila, O., Nilsen, J., and Igeland, B. 2003. Effect of temperature on the induction of bud dormancy in ecotypes of *Betula pubescens* and *Betula pendula*. *Scandinavian Journal of Forest Research* **18**: 208–217.

Kellomaki, S., Hanninen, H., and Kolstrom, M. 1995. Computations on frost damage to Scots pine under climatic warming in boreal conditions. *Ecological Applications* **5**: 42–52.

Kodama, H., Hamada, T., Horiguchi, G., Nishimura, M., and Iba, K. 1994. Genetic enhancement of cold tolerance by expression of a gene for chloroplast w-3 fatty acid desaturase in transgenic tobacco. *Plant Physiology* **105**: 601–605.

Kodama, H., Horiguchi, G., Nishiuchi, T., Nishimura, M., and Iba, K. 1995. Fatty acid desaturation during chilling acclimation is one of the factors involved in conferring low-temperature tolerance to young tobacco leaves. *Plant Physiology* **107**: 1177–1185.

Korner, C. 2003. Carbon limitation in trees. *Journal of Ecology* **91**: 4–17.

Kostiainen, K., Jalkanen, H., Kaakinen, S., Saranpaa, P., and Vapaavuori, E. 2006. Wood properties of two silver birch clones exposed to elevated CO_2 and O_3. *Global Change Biology* **12**: 1230–1240.

Larcher, W. 1995. *Physiological Plant Ecology*. Springer-Verlag, New York, New York, USA.

Loik, M.E., Huxman, T.E., Hamerlynck, E.P., and Smith, S.D. 2000. Low temperature tolerance and cold acclimation for seedlings of three Mojave Desert *Yucca* species exposed to elevated CO_2. *Journal of Arid Environments* **46**: 43–56.

Loik, M.E., Still, C.J., Huxman, T.E., and Harte, J. 2004. *In situ* photosynthetic freezing tolerance for plants exposed to a global warming manipulation in the Rocky Mountains, Colorado, USA. *New Phytologist* **162**: 331–341.

Lyons, J.M. 1973. Chilling injury in plants. *Annual Review of Plant Physiology* **24**: 445–466.

Melkonian, J., Owens, T.G., and Wolfe, D.W. 2004. Gas exchange and co-regulation of photochemical and nonphotochemical quenching in bean during chilling at ambient and elevated carbon dioxide. *Photosynthesis Research* **79**: 71–82.

Moon, B.Y., Higashi, S.-I., Gombos, Z., and Murata, N. 1995. Unsaturation of the membrane lipids of chloroplasts stabilizes the photosynthetic machinery against low-temperature photoinhibition in transgenic tobacco plants. *Proceedings of the National Academy of Sciences, USA* **92**: 6219–6223.

Obrist, D., Arnone III, J.A., and Korner, C. 2001. *In situ* effects of elevated atmospheric CO_2 on leaf freezing resistance and carbohydrates in a native temperate grassland. *Annals of Botany* **87**: 839–844.

Piispanen, R. and Saranpaa, P. 2001. Variation of non-structural carbohydrates in silver birch (*Betula pendula* Roth) wood. *Trees* **15**: 444–451.

Riikonen, J., Lindsberg, M.-M., Holopainen, T., Oksanen, E., Lappi, J., Peltonen, P., and Vapaavuori, E. 2004. Silver birch and climate change: variable growth and carbon allocation responses to elevated concentrations of carbon dioxide and ozone. *Tree Physiology* **24**: 1227–1237.

Schwanz, P. and Polle, A. 2001. Growth under elevated CO_2 ameliorates defenses against photo-oxidative stress in poplar (*Populus alba x tremula*). *Environmental and Experimental Botany* **45**: 43–53.

Sgherri, C.L.M., Quartacci, M.F., Menconi, M., Raschi, A., and Navari-Izzo, F. 1998. Interactions between drought and elevated CO_2 on alfalfa plants. *Journal of Plant Physiology* **152**: 118–124.

Sigurdsson, B.D. 2001. Elevated [CO_2] and nutrient status modified leaf phenology and growth rhythm of young

Populus trichocarpa trees in a 3-year field study. *Trees* **15**: 403–413.

Terry, A.C., Quick, W.P., and Beerling, D.J. 2000. Long-term growth of *Ginkgo* with CO_2 enrichment increases leaf ice nucleation temperatures and limits recovery of the photosynthetic system from freezing. *Plant Physiology* **124**: 183–190.

Wayne, P.M., Reekie, E.G., and Bazzaz, F.A. 1998. Elevated CO_2 ameliorates birch response to high temperature and frost stress: implications for modeling climate-induced geographic range shifts. *Oecologia* **114**: 335–342.

2.14 Monoterpenes

- The diverse results of several experimental studies do not paint a clear picture of what should be expected in the way of plant monoterpene emissions in a CO_2-enriched and possibly warmer world of the future.

Monoterpenes constitute a major fraction of the biogenic volatile organic compounds or BVOCs given off by plants; they help protect Earth's terrestrial vegetation by acting as scavengers of reactive oxygen species produced within plants experiencing significant heat stress (Peñuelas and Llusia, 2003). They also function as deterrents of pathogens and herbivores and are known to aid wound-healing after herbivore damage (Pichersky and Gershenzon, 2002). In addition, monoterpenes may attract pollinators and herbivore predators (Peñuelas *et al.*, 1995; Shulaeve *et al.*, 1997), and they have the ability to generate large quantities of organic aerosols that may alter the planet's climate by producing cloud condensation nuclei that can lead to a cooling of Earth's surface (during the day) via an enhanced reflection of incoming solar radiation.

In light of these observations, it is natural to want to know how plant monoterpene production might be affected by the ongoing rise in the atmosphere's CO_2 concentration, as well as by any warming that might yet occur as Earth continues to recover from the global chill of the Little Ice Age. What follows is a review of the findings of studies that have investigated various aspects of this subject.

Vuorinen *et al.* (2004) grew well-watered and fertilized white cabbage plants from seed for 25 days in growth chambers maintained at atmospheric CO_2 concentrations of either 360 or 720 ppm. One group of plants in each CO_2 treatment experienced no larval insect feeding, another experienced 48 hours of feeding by larvae of a crucifer specialist (*Plutella xylostella*), and yet another group experienced 48 hours of feeding by larvae of a generalist herbivore (*Spodoptera littoralis*), after which several BVOCs released by each group of plants were collected from the air surrounding them and analyzed. The researchers conclude, "total monoterpene emission per shoot dry weight was approximately 27% reduced from plants grown at elevated CO_2," and they report there was no difference in larval-induced damage to the plants between the ambient-air and CO_2-enriched treatments.

An earlier study of holly oak trees by Loreto *et al.* (2001) also found decreases in monoterpene emissions in response to atmospheric CO_2 enrichment, and Constable *et al.* (1999) found no effect of elevated CO_2 on monoterpene emissions from Ponderosa pine and Douglas fir trees. This may mean the effects of atmospheric CO_2 enrichment on plant monoterpene emissions are nil or even negative.

Baraldi *et al.* (2004) exposed sections of a southern California chaparral ecosystem to atmospheric CO_2 concentrations ranging from 250 to 750 ppm in 100-ppm increments for four years within naturally lit glass chambers, measuring net ecosystem CO_2 exchange (NEE) and emission rates of BVOCs, which were mainly monoterpenes. The seven scientists found NEE exhibited a marked linear increase in response to increasing atmospheric CO_2 concentration, more than tripling its rate in going from 400 to 700 ppm at 0400, 1200, and 1600 hours in June, and rising from moderately negative to weak positive values in December. They found "total trace gas emissions expressed on a ground area basis were low and did not respond to increasing CO_2 concentrations" in the winter; in summer, when "BVOC emissions were of an order of magnitude greater than during winter," they found the different levels of CO_2 still "did not affect the emission rates" of monoterpenes.

Rapparini *et al.* (2004) measured BVOC emissions from mature downy and holly oak trees growing close to a natural CO_2 spring in central Italy, where atmospheric CO_2 concentrations averaged about 1,000 ppm, and at a nearby control site where the air's CO_2 content was unaffected by the spring. They too found long-term exposure to high levels of atmospheric CO_2 did not significantly affect BVOC emissions from the trees. However, when leaves of plants grown in the control site were exposed for a short period to an elevated CO_2 level by rapidly switching the CO_2 concentration in the gas-exchange cuvette, monoterpene basal emissions "were clearly inhibited," where basal emissions are those that occur at standard measuring conditions of 30°C air temperature and 1000 μmol m^{-2} s^{-1} light intensity.

The studies thus appear to suggest atmospheric CO_2 enrichment has little or no effect on plant monoterpene emissions, and that if there is any effect at all, it is negative. But the situation is not nearly that straightforward, as demonstrated by Staudt et al. (2001). These four researchers also grew holly oak, albeit holly oak seedlings, within two compartments of a controlled-environment greenhouse—one of which was maintained at an atmospheric CO_2 concentration of 350 ppm and one of which was maintained at 700 ppm—where air temperature and vapor pressure deficit were set to track outside ambient conditions and the plants were exposed to natural sunlight and watered every other week. Various growth parameters and physiological responses of the seedlings were measured over a four-month period that began when the trees had been exposed to the two CO_2 treatments for a total of 10 months. They report the elevated CO_2 treatment increased the leaf area of the young oaks by 40%, their leaf biomass by 50%, and their trunk and branch biomass by 90%. The plants in the elevated CO_2 treatment "released 2.8-fold more monoterpenes per plant than plants grown in ambient CO_2," on top of which Peñuelas and Llusia (2003) state, warming "increases the emission rates of most BVOCs exponentially."

Raisanen et al. (2008) studied to what extent a doubling of the air's CO_2 content and 2–6°C increases in air temperature (+2°C in summer, +4°C in spring and autumn, +6°C in winter), applied singly or together, might impact emissions of monoterpenes from 20-year-old Scots pine seedlings. They constructed closed-top chambers over parts of a naturally seeded stand of the trees in eastern Finland, which they exposed to these treatments for five years. Over the five-month growing season of May–September, the three researchers found total monoterpene emissions in the elevated-CO_2-only treatment were 5% greater than those in the ambient-CO_2-ambient-temperature treatment, and emissions in the elevated-temperature-only treatment were 9% less than those in ambient air. In the presence of both elevated CO_2 and elevated temperature, there was an increase of fully 126% in the total amount of monoterpenes emitted over the growing season.

The diverse results of these studies do not paint a clear picture of what should be expected in the way of plant monoterpene emissions in a CO_2-enriched and possibly warmer world of the future.

References

Baraldi, R., Rapparini, F., Oechel, W.C., Hastings, S.J., Bryant, P., Cheng, Y., and Miglietta, F. 2004. Monoterpene emission responses to elevated CO_2 in a Mediterranean-type ecosystem. New Phytologist 161: 17–21.

Constable, J.V.H., Litvak, M.E., Greenberg, J.P., and Monson, R.K. 1999. Monoterpene emission from coniferous trees in response to elevated CO_2 concentration and climate warming. Global Change Biology 5: 255–267.

Loreto, F., Fischbach, R.J., Schnitzler, J.P., Ciccioli, P., Brancaleoni, E., Calfapietra, C., and Seufert, G. 2001. Monoterpene emission and monoterpene synthase activities in the Mediterranean evergreen oak Quercus ilex L. grown at elevated CO_2 concentrations. Global Change Biology 7: 709–717.

Peñuelas, J. and Llusia, J. 2003. BVOCs: plant defense against climate warming? Trends in Plant Science 8: 105–109.

Peñuelas, J., Llusia, J., and Estiarte, M. 1995. Terpenoids: a plant language. Trends in Ecology and Evolution 10: 289.

Pichersky, E. and Gershenzon, J. 2002. The formation and function of plant volatiles: perfumes for pollinator attraction and defense. Current Opinion in Plant Biology 5: 237–243.

Raisanen, T., Ryyppo, A., and Kellomaki, S. 2008. Effects of elevated CO_2 and temperature on monoterpene emission of Scots pine (Pinus sylvestris L.). Atmospheric Environment 42: 4160–4171.

Rapparini, F., Baraldi, R., Miglietta, F., and Loreto, F. 2004. Isoprenoid emission in trees of Quercus pubescens and Quercus ilex with lifetime exposure to naturally high CO_2 environment. Plant, Cell and Environment 27: 381–391.

Shulaev, V., Silverman, P., and Raskin, I. 1997. Airborne signaling by methyl salicylate in plant pathogen resistance. Nature 385: 718–721.

Staudt, M., Joffre, R., Rambal, S., and Kesselmeier, J. 2001. Effect of elevated CO_2 on monoterpene emission of young Quercus ilex trees and its relation to structural and ecophysiological parameters. Tree Physiology 21: 437–445.

Vuorinen, T., Reddy, G.V.P., Nerg, A.-M., and Holopainen, J.K. 2004. Monoterpene and herbivore-induced emissions from cabbage plants grown at elevated atmospheric CO_2 concentration. Atmospheric Environment 38: 675–682.

2.15 Nectar

- As the air's CO_2 content continues to rise, plant

fitness, flower pollination, and nectar production should be enhanced, leading to increases in fruit, grain, and vegetable yields of agricultural crops, as well as similar increases in the productivity of the world's natural vegetation.

Lake and Hughes (1999) grew nasturtiums (*Tropaeolum majus*) from seed through flowering and senescence (77 days) in growth chambers maintained at atmospheric CO_2 concentrations of either 380 or 760 ppm to determine the effects of elevated CO_2 on the vegetative and reproductive growth of the flowers, as well as several of the flowers' characteristics, including nectar quantity and quality. They found the doubled CO_2 concentration increased total plant biomass by 35% and root biomass by 78%, and it increased nectar volume in the CO_2-enriched flowers by 2.4-fold. It did so without lowering the sugar and amino acid characteristics of the nectar.

Dag and Eisikowitch (2000) divided a 0.5-acre greenhouse located in the center of the Arava Valley in the southern part of Israel into two parts, one of which was exposed to ambient air and one of which was exposed to air that had a CO_2 concentration of 1,000 ppm throughout the morning, 400 ppm between 1300 and 1500 hours, and 600 ppm until the next morning. Under these conditions they grew melons (*Cucumis melo*). In the melons' early flowering stage, the scientists collected and measured the volume of nectar produced per flower between 0900 and 1530 hours along with the sugar concentration of the nectar. They found average nectar volumes per flower were significantly higher in the CO_2-enriched sector of the greenhouse than in the control sector, sometimes by as much as 100%; since the sugar concentration of the nectar was found to be the same in both treatments, sugar production per flower was stimulated by an identical amount (as much as 100%) in the CO_2-enriched air. As a result, and noting the only pollinator used in greenhouse production of melons in Israel is the honey bee, the two researchers conclude, "improvement in nectar reward can increase the attractiveness of the flowers to the bees, increase pollination activity and consequently increase the fruit set and the yield."

Erhardt *et al.* (2005) grew well-watered *Epilobium angustifolium* L. plants (perennial temperate clonal herbs that colonize nutrient-rich open habitats) from the seeds of five genotypes in pots containing 12 liters of loamy soil maintained at high and low levels of nutrients by weekly supplying them with 25 ml of either 1.0 N (high level) or 0.5 N (low level) Hoagland's solution. The experiment lasted from April 1995 to July 1996 (two full growing seasons) and was conducted in naturally lit controlled environment chambers housed within a greenhouse. Half of the chambers were supplied with ambient air having a CO_2 concentration of about 350 ppm and half were supplied with CO_2-enriched air having a concentration of about 650 ppm. Under these conditions, and in the second year of the study when most of the plants were flowering, nectar was extracted from the flowers, and its volume and sugar concentration were determined, along with its amino acid concentration and the total amino acid content per flower. The researchers found "elevated CO_2 significantly increased nectar production per day (+51%, p < 0.01), total sugar per flower (+41%, p < 0.05), amino acid concentration (+65%, p < 0.05) and total amino acids per flower (+192%, p < 0.001)." These responses occurred with all genotypes.

Erhardt *et al.* note Galen and Plowright (1985) found "increased nectar rewards led to longer bumblebee tenure on flowers and greater pollen receipt in *E. angustifolium*, and that bees visited more flowers per plant on plants with more nectar." In addition, they report, "in other plant species higher nectar rewards also usually led to increases in components of plant fitness," citing Thomson (1986), Mitchell and Waser (1992), Mitchell (1993), Hodges (1995), and Irwin and Brody (1999).

References

Dag, A. and Eisikowitch, D. 2000. The effect of carbon dioxide enrichment on nectar production in melons under greenhouse conditions. *Journal of Apicultural Research* **39**: 88–89.

Erhardt, A., Rusterholz, H.-P., and Stocklin, J. 2005. Elevated carbon dioxide increases nectar production in *Epilobium angustifolium* L. *Oecologia* **146**: 311–317.

Galen, C. and Plowright, R.C. 1985. The effects of nectar level and flower development on pollen carry-over in inflorescences of fireweed (*Epilobium augustifolium*) (Onagraceae). *Canadian Journal of Botany* **63**: 488–491.

Hodges, S.A. 1995. The influence of nectar production on hawkmoth behavior, self pollination, and seed production in *Mirabilis multiflora* (Nyctaginaceae). *American Journal of Botany* **82**: 197–204.

Irwin, R.E. and Brody, A.K. 1999. Nectar-robbing bumble bees reduce the fitness of *Ipomopsis aggregata* (Polemoniaceae). *Ecology* **80**: 1703–1712.

Lake, J.C. and Hughes, L. 1999. Nectar production and floral characteristics of *Tropaeolum majus* L. grown in ambient and elevated carbon dioxide. *Annals of Botany* **84**: 535–541.

Mitchell, R.J. 1993. Adaptive significance of *Ipomopsis aggregata* nectar production: observation and experiment in the field. *Evolution* **47**: 25–35.

Mitchell, R.J. and Waser, N.M. 1992. Adaptive significance of *Ipomopsis aggregata* nectar production: pollination success of single flowers. *Ecology* **73**: 633–638.

Thomson, J.D. 1986. Pollen transport and deposition by bumble bees in Erythronium: influences of floral nectar and bee grooming. *Journal of Ecology* **74**: 329–341.

2.16 Nitrogen Fixation

Increases in the air's CO_2 content likely will stimulate nitrogen fixation in most herbaceous species that form symbiotic relationships with nitrogen-fixing soil bacteria. This phenomenon likely will lead to increased nitrogen availability in soils and large increases in both agricultural and natural ecosystem productivity. Increases in the air's CO_2 content also will greatly enhance the growth of Earth's leguminous trees, stimulating their fixation of nitrogen and their exudation of the resultant nitrogenous substances to the soils in which they grow, where they become available to neighboring non-leguminous vegetation.

2.16.1 Herbaceous Plants

- Increases in the air's CO_2 content likely will stimulate nitrogen fixation in most legumes, herbaceous species that form symbiotic relationships with nitrogen-fixing soil bacteria. This phenomenon likely will lead to increased nitrogen availability in soils, ultimately leading to large CO_2-induced increases in agricultural and natural ecosystem productivity.

Nearly all of Earth's plants respond to increases in the air's CO_2 content by exhibiting increased rates of photosynthesis and biomass production. Additionally, most leguminous species—i.e., those that form symbiotic relationships with nitrogen-fixing bacteria—also find their ability to acquire nitrogen to be enhanced when exposed to CO_2-enriched air. This phenomenon could increase their positive growth responses to elevated CO_2 even more and ultimately make more soil nitrogen available to co-occurring species. This section reviews several scientific studies of these phenomena that have been conducted on herbaceous plants.

Luscher *et al.* (1998) exposed several different grassland species to elevated levels of atmospheric CO_2 and observed nitrogen-fixing species tend to produce more biomass than non-nitrogen-fixing species, possibly in response to CO_2-induced increases in the nitrogenase activity of symbiotic nitrogen-fixing bacteria associated with their roots. Dakora and Drake (2000) found a 300-ppm increase in the air's CO_2 concentration increased nitrogenase activity in a C_3 and a C_4 wetland species by 35 and 13%, respectively. Marilley *et al.* (1999) found enriching the air with CO_2 increased the dominance of nitrogen-fixing *Rhizobium* bacterial species associated with the roots of white clover. Arnone (1999), however, reported atmospheric CO_2 enrichment had no effect on symbiotic nitrogen fixation in *Trifolium alpinum*, a grassland species common to the Swiss Alps.

In a FACE study conducted on lucerne, plants fumigated with air containing 600 ppm CO_2 significantly increased their total tissue nitrogen content derived from symbiotic nitrogen-fixation (Luscher *et al.*, 2000). Plants grown on soil containing high nitrogen nearly doubled their symbiotically derived tissue nitrogen content, which rose from 21 to 41%, and plants grown on soils containing low nitrogen increased their symbiotically derived nitrogen content from 82 to 88%. In a related study performed on the same species, a doubling of the air's CO_2 content increased root nodule biomass by 40 and 100% in well-watered and water-stressed plants, respectively, as the CO_2-enriched plants obtained 31 and 97% more total nitrogen than control plants under the same conditions (De Luis *et al.* 1999).

Lee *et al.* (2003b) investigated the effects of atmospheric CO_2 concentration (365 and 700 ppm) and nitrogen fertilization (low-N field soil + 0, 4, 8, 12, 16 and 20 g N m^{-2} $year^{-1}$) on leaf net photosynthesis, whole plant growth, and carbon and nitrogen acquisition in the N_2-fixing wild lupine (*Lupinus perennis*) in controlled-environment chambers, where plants were grown from seed in pots for one full growing season. The mean rate of leaf net photosynthesis in the CO_2-enriched chambers was 39% greater than in the ambient-air chambers, irrespective of N treatment, and total plant biomass at final harvest was 80% greater in the CO_2-enriched chambers, again irrespective of N treatment. Elevated CO_2 increased plant total N by 57%, with the extra N coming from enhanced symbiotic N_2 fixation related to an increased number and overall mass of nodules. Although partial photosynthetic acclimation to CO_2

enrichment occurred, the four researchers report the plants maintained significantly higher rates of photosynthesis and more efficient carbon capture per unit leaf N (average + 60%) in elevated CO_2 compared to ambient CO_2, indicating a substantial CO_2-induced increase in nitrogen use efficiency.

In mixed species experiments, Niklaus et al. (1998) found artificially constructed calcareous grassland swards were considerably more responsive to CO_2-enriched air when legumes were present than when they were absent. In addition, they found elevated CO_2 stimulated nitrogen fixation, particularly when soil phosphorus was not limiting to growth. Thus, under conditions of adequate soil phosphorus, symbiotically derived nitrogen likely would become available for the use of non-nitrogen-fixing species.

Lee et al. (2003a) grew the N_2-fixing *Lupinus perennis* in monoculture and in nine-species plots exposed to ambient air and air enriched to 560 ppm CO_2. The proportion of *Lupinus* N derived from symbiotic N_2 fixation in monoculture increased from 44% in ambient air to 57% in CO_2-enriched air, and in the nine-species plots it increased from 43% in ambient air to 54% in CO_2-enriched air. Combined with the CO_2-induced increases in plant biomass production, this resulted in a doubling of N fixed per plot under elevated compared to ambient CO_2. Hartwig et al. (2002) obtained a similar result, observing a 70% increase in the air's CO_2 concentration to roughly double the amount of nitrogen input through symbiotic N_2-fixation by white clover in a clover-ryegrass mixed ecosystem.

These findings indicate increases in the air's CO_2 content likely will stimulate nitrogen fixation in most legumes, and this phenomenon likely will lead to increased nitrogen availability in soils, ultimately leading to increases in agro- and natural ecosystem productivity.

References

Arnone, J.A., III. 1999. Symbiotic N_2 fixation in a high Alpine grassland: effects of four growing seasons of elevated CO_2. *Functional Ecology* 13: 383–387.

Dakora, F.D. and Drake, B.G. 2000. Elevated CO_2 stimulates associative N_2 fixation in a C_3 plant of the Chesapeake Bay wetland. *Plant, Cell and Environment* 23: 943–953.

De Luis, J., Irigoyen, J.J., and Sanchez-Diaz, M. 1999. Elevated CO_2 enhances plant growth in droughted N_2-fixing alfalfa without improving water stress. *Physiologia Plantarum* 107: 84–89.

Hartwig, U.A., Luscher, A., Nosberger, J., and van Kessel, C. 2002. Nitrogen-15 budget in model ecosystems of white clover and perennial ryegrass exposed for four years at elevated atmospheric pCO_2. *Global Change Biology* 8: 194–202.

Lee, T.D., Reich, P.B., and Tjoelker, M.G. 2003a. Legume presence increases photosynthesis and N concentrations of co-occurring non-fixers but does not modulate their responsiveness to carbon dioxide enrichment. *Oecologia* 10.1007/s00442-003-1309-1.

Lee, T.D., Tjoelker, M.G., Reich, P.B., and Russelle, M.P. 2003b. Contrasting growth response of an N_2-fixing and non-fixing forb to elevated CO_2: dependence on soil N supply. *Plant and Soil* 255: 475–486.

Luscher, A., Hartwig, U.A., Suter, D., and Nosberger, J. 2000. Direct evidence that symbiotic N_2 fixation in fertile grassland is an important trait for a strong response of plants to elevated atmospheric CO_2. *Global Change Biology* 6: 655–662.

Luscher, A., Hendrey, G.R., and Nosberger, J. 1998. Long-term responsiveness to free air CO_2 enrichment of functional types, species and genotypes of plants from fertile permanent grassland. *Oecologia* 113: 37–45.

Marilley, L., Hartwig, U.A., and Aragno, M. 1999. Influence of an elevated atmospheric CO_2 content on soil and rhizosphere bacterial communities beneath *Lolium perenne* and *Trifolium repens* under field conditions. *Microbial Ecology* 38: 39–49.

Niklaus, P.A., Leadley, P.W., Stocklin, J., and Korner, C. 1998. Nutrient relations in calcareous grassland under elevated CO_2. *Oecologia* 116: 67–75.

2.16.2 Woody Plants

- Continued increases in the air's CO_2 content will greatly enhance the growth of Earth's leguminous trees, stimulate their fixation of nitrogen, and increase their root exudations of nitrogenous substances to the soils in which they grow, where they become available for uptake by neighboring non-leguminous vegetation.

Nearly all of Earth's plants respond to increases in the air's CO_2 content by exhibiting enhanced rates of photosynthesis and biomass production. In addition, leguminous species possess the special ability to form symbiotic relationships with nitrogen-fixing bacteria, which can indirectly increase plant responses to elevated CO_2 by making more nitrogen available for plant uptake and utilization. This review summarizes the results of some of the studies that report the effects of atmospheric CO_2 enrichment on these phenomena in woody plants.

Olesniewicz and Thomas (1999) grew black locust (*Robinia pseudoacacia*) seedlings for approximately two months in controlled environment chambers maintained at atmospheric CO_2 concentrations of 350 and 710 ppm, determining the elevated CO_2 increased total plant biomass by 180%. In addition, the extra CO_2 increased nitrogen-fixation by 69%, nodule mass by 92%, and the amount of seedling nitrogen derived from nitrogen-fixation by 212%. Working with the same species under much the same conditions, Uselman *et al.* (1999) determined between 1 and 2% of the total symbiotically fixed nitrogen is exuded from the tree's roots to become available for uptake by neighboring vegetation.

Schortemeyer *et al.* (1999) grew seedlings of *Acacia melanoxylon*, a leguminous nitrogen-fixing tree native to south-eastern Australia, for six weeks in growth cabinets maintained at atmospheric CO_2 concentrations of 350 and 700 ppm in hydroponic solutions with nitrogen concentrations ranging from 3 to 6,400 mmol m^{-3}. Although atmospheric CO_2 enrichment did not stimulate symbiotic nitrogen fixation, averaged across all nitrogen treatments the seedlings grown in elevated CO_2 displayed net photosynthetic rates 22% higher than those of control seedlings, and they did not exhibit any signs of photosynthetic acclimation. These positive responses likely contributed to the doubled final biomass observed in the CO_2-enriched seedlings in all but the two lowest nitrogen concentrations, where final biomass was unaffected by elevated CO_2.

In a subsequent study of seven *Acacia* species native to Australia, Schortemeyer *et al.* (2002) once again grew seedlings in environmental chambers maintained at atmospheric CO_2 concentrations of 350 and 700 ppm, but this time for nearly five months. They found the elevated CO_2 enhanced rates of net photosynthesis by 19 to 56% among all species and led to an average total plant dry weight increase of 86%. In addition, the elevated CO_2 increased the total amount of nitrogen fixed per plant by an average of 65%.

Temperton *et al.* (2003) measured total biomass and a number of physiological processes of N_2-fixing *Alnus glutinosa* or common alder trees, which were grown for three years (1994–1996) in open-top chambers maintained at either ambient or elevated (ambient + 350 ppm) concentrations of atmospheric CO_2 and two soil nitrogen regimes (full nutrient solution or no fertilizer). The six scientists measured

nitrogen fixation by *Frankia* spp. in the root nodules of the trees, finding nitrogenase activity was consistently higher in the elevated CO_2 treatment in both 1995 and 1996. In addition, they report, "in October 1996, elevated CO_2 had a significant effect on total nodule dry mass, and there was a trend toward heavier nodules in the elevated CO_2 treatment than in the ambient CO_2 treatment." They conclude, "most single-species studies on the effect of elevated CO_2 on N_2-fixing species have reported stimulation of growth, nodule mass and nitrogenase activity (Norby, 1987; Arnone and Gordon, 1990; Hibbs *et al.*, 1995; Vogel and Curtis, 1995; Tissue *et al.*, 1997; Vogel *et al.*, 1997; Thomas *et al.*, 2000)," which is similar to what they observed.

These findings indicate continued increases in the air's CO_2 content will enhance the growth of Earth's leguminous trees, stimulate their fixation of nitrogen, and increase their root exudations of nitrogenous substances.

References

Arnone, J.A. and Gordon, J.C. 1990. Effect of nodulation, nitrogen fixation and CO_2 enrichment on the physiology, growth and dry mass allocation of seedlings of *Alnus rubra* Bong. *New Phytologist* **116**: 55–66.

Hibbs, D.E., Chan, S.S., Castellano, M., and Niu, C.-H. 1995. Response of red alder seedlings to CO_2 enrichment and water stress. *New Phytologist* **129**: 569–577.

Norby, R.J. 1987. Nodulation and nitrogenase activity in nitrogen fixing woody plants stimulated by CO_2 enrichment of the atmosphere. *Physiologia Plantarum* **71**: 77–82.

Olesniewicz, K.S. and Thomas, R.B. 1999. Effects of mycorrhizal colonization on biomass production and nitrogen fixation of black locust (*Robinia pseudoacacia*) seedlings grown under elevated atmospheric carbon dioxide. *New Phytologist* **142**: 133–140.

Schortemeyer, M., Atkin, O.K., McFarlane, N., and Evans, J.R. 1999. The impact of elevated atmospheric CO_2 and nitrate supply on growth, biomass allocation, nitrogen partitioning and N_2 fixation of *Acacia melanoxylon*. *Australian Journal of Plant Physiology* **26**: 737–774.

Schortemeyer, M., Atkin, O.K., McFarlane, N., and Evans, J.R. 2002. N_2 fixation by *Acacia* species increases under elevated atmospheric CO_2. *Plant, Cell and Environment* **25**: 567–579.

Temperton, V.M., Grayston, S.J., Jackson, G., Barton, C.V.M., Millard, P., and Jarvis, P.G. 2003. Effects of elevated carbon dioxide concentration on growth and nitrogen fixation in *Alnus glutinosa* in a long-term field experiment. *Tree Physiology* **23**: 1051–1059.

Thomas, R.B., Bashkin, M.A., and Richter, D.D. 2000. Nitrogen inhibition of nodulation and N_2 fixation of a tropical N_2-fixing tree (*Gliricida sepium*) grown in elevated atmospheric CO_2. *New Phytologist* **145**: 233–243.

Tissue, D.T., Thomas, R.B., and Strain, B.R. 1997. Atmospheric CO_2 enrichment increases growth and photosynthesis of *Pinus taeda*: a 4-year experiment in the field. *Plant, Cell and Environment* **20**: 1123–1134.

Uselman, S.M., Qualls, R.G., and Thomas, R.B. 1999. A test of a potential short cut in the nitrogen cycle: The role of exudation of symbiotically fixed nitrogen from the roots of a N-fixing tree and the effects of increased atmospheric CO_2 and temperature. *Plant and Soil* **210**: 21–32.

Vogel, C.S. and Curtis, P.S. 1995. Leaf gas exchange and nitrogen dynamics of N_2-fixing field-grown *Alnus glutinosa* under elevated atmospheric CO_2. *Global Change Biology* **1**: 55–61.

Vogel, C.S., Curtis, P.S., and Thomas, R.B. 1997. Growth and nitrogen accretion of dinitrogen-fixing *Alnus glutinosa* (L.) Gaertn. under elevated carbon dioxide. *Plant Ecology* **130**: 63–70.

2.17 Nitrogen Use Efficiency

- As the air's CO_2 content continues to rise, Earth's plants likely will reduce the amount of nitrogen invested in rubisco and other photosynthetic proteins while maintaining enhanced rates of photosynthesis and thereby increasing their photosynthetic nitrogen-use efficiencies.

Long-term exposure to elevated atmospheric CO_2 concentrations often, but not always, elicits photosynthetic acclimation or down-regulation in plants, which is typically accompanied by reduced amounts of rubisco and/or other photosynthetic proteins typically present in excess amounts in plants grown in ambient air. As a consequence, foliar nitrogen concentrations often decrease with atmospheric CO_2 enrichment, as nitrogen is mobilized out of leaves and into other areas of the plant to increase its availability for enhancing sink development or stimulating other nutrient-limited processes.

In reviewing the scientific literature on this subject, one quickly notices that even though photosynthetic acclimation has occurred, CO_2-enriched plants still nearly always display rates of photosynthesis greater than those of control plants exposed to ambient air. Consequently, photosynthetic nitrogen-use efficiency—the amount of carbon converted into sugars during the photosynthetic process per unit of leaf nitrogen—often increases in CO_2-enriched plants.

Davey *et al.* (1999), for example, found CO_2-induced reductions in foliar nitrogen contents and concomitant increases in photosynthetic rates led to photosynthetic nitrogen-use efficiencies in the CO_2-enriched (to 700 ppm CO_2) grass *Agrostis capillaris* 27 and 62% greater than those observed in control plants grown at 360 ppm CO_2 under moderate and low soil nutrient conditions, respectively. Similarly, they found elevated CO_2 enhanced photosynthetic nitrogen-use efficiencies in *Trifolium repens* by 66 and 190% under moderate and low soil nutrient conditions, respectively, and in *Lolium perenne* by 50%, regardless of soil nutrient status. Other researchers report similar CO_2-induced enhancements of photosynthetic nitrogen-use efficiency in wheat (Osborne *et al.*, 1998) and in *Leucadendron* species (Midgley *et al.*, 1999).

In some cases, researchers report nitrogen-use efficiency in terms of the amount of biomass produced per unit of plant nitrogen. Niklaus *et al.* (1998), for example, report intact swards of CO_2-enriched calcareous grasslands grown at 600 ppm CO_2 attained total biomass values 25% greater than those of control swards exposed to ambient air while extracting the same amount of nitrogen from the soil as ambiently grown swards. Deng and Woodward (1998) reported similar results for strawberry, noting the growth-based nitrogen-use efficiencies of plants grown at 560 ppm CO_2 were 23 and 17% greater than those of ambiently grown plants simultaneously subjected to high and low soil nitrogen availability, respectively.

The scientific literature suggests as the air's CO_2 content continues to rise, Earth's plants likely will respond by reducing the amount of nitrogen invested in rubisco and other photosynthetic proteins while maintaining enhanced rates of photosynthesis, which should increase their photosynthetic nitrogen-use efficiencies. As overall plant nitrogen-use efficiency increases, plants likely will grow ever better on soils containing less-than-optimal levels of nitrogen.

References

Davey, P.A., Parsons, A.J., Atkinson, L., Wadge, K., and Long, S.P. 1999. Does photosynthetic acclimation to elevated CO_2 increase photosynthetic nitrogen-use efficiency? A study of three native UK grassland species in open-top chambers. *Functional Ecology* **13**: 21–28.

Deng, X. and Woodward, F.I. 1998. The growth and yield responses of *Fragaria ananassa* to elevated CO_2 and N supply. *Annals of Botany* **81**: 67–71.

Midgley, G.F., Wand, S.J.E,. and Pammenter, N.W. 1999. Nutrient and genotypic effects on CO_2-responsiveness: photosynthetic regulation in *Leucadendron* species of a nutrient-poor environment. *Journal of Experimental Botany* **50**: 533–542.

Niklaus, P.A., Leadley, P.W., Stocklin, J., and Korner, C. 1998. Nutrient relations in calcareous grassland under elevated CO_2. *Oecologia* **116**: 67–75.

Osborne, C.P., LaRoche, J., Garcia, R.L., Kimball, B.A., Wall, G.W., Pinter Jr., P.J., LaMorte, R.L., Hendrey, G.R., and Long, S.P. 1998. Does leaf position within a canopy affect acclimation of photosynthesis to elevated CO_2? *Plant Physiology* **117**: 1037–1045.

2.18 Nutrient Acquisition

- As the CO_2 content of the air increases, much of Earth's vegetation likely will display increases in biomass. The larger plants likely will develop more extensive root systems and extract greater amounts of mineral nutrients from the soils in which they are rooted, enabling them to sustain their enhanced growth.

With respect to acquiring nitrogen, Zak *et al.* (2000) found aspen seedlings grown for 2.5 years at twice-ambient CO_2 concentrations displayed an average total seedling nitrogen content 13% greater than that displayed by control seedlings grown in ambient air, in spite of an average reduction in tissue nitrogen concentration of 18%. Elevated CO_2 enhanced total nitrogen uptake from the soil, even though tissue nitrogen concentrations in the CO_2-enriched plants were diluted by the enhanced biomass of the much larger CO_2-enriched seedlings.

On a per-unit-biomass basis, Smart *et al.* (1998) note there were no differences in the total amounts of nitrogen within CO_2-enriched and ambiently grown wheat seedlings after three weeks of exposure to atmospheric CO_2 concentrations of 360 and 1,000 ppm. Nevertheless, the CO_2-enriched seedlings exhibited greater rates of soil nitrate extraction than the ambient-grown plants did.

Similarly, BassiriRad *et al.* (1998) report a doubling of the atmospheric CO_2 concentration doubled the uptake rate of nitrate in the C_4 grass *Bouteloua eriopoda*. However, they also report elevated CO_2 had no effect on the rate of nitrate uptake in *Prosopis*, and it actually decreased the rate of nitrate uptake by 55% in *Larrea*. Nonetheless,

atmospheric CO_2 enrichment increased total biomass in these two species by 55 and 69%, respectively. Thus, although the uptake rate of this nutrient was depressed under elevated CO_2 conditions in the latter species, the much larger CO_2-enriched plants likely still extracted more total nitrate from the soil than did the ambient-grown plants of the experiment.

Nasholm *et al.* (1998) determined trees, grasses, and shrubs can absorb significant amounts of organic nitrogen from soils. Thus, plants do not have to wait for the mineralization of organic nitrogen before they extract the nitrogen they need from soils to support their growth and development. As a result, the forms of nitrogen removed from soils by plants (nitrate vs. ammonium) and their abilities to remove different forms may not be as important as was once thought.

Finzi *et al.* (2002) found, on average, loblolly pine exposed to an extra 200 ppm of CO_2 maintained rates of net primary productivity 25% greater, and produced 32% more biomass, than trees growing in ambient air. The elevated CO_2 also increased the total amount of nitrogen present in the trees' biomass. The average annual requirement for nitrogen rose by 16% for the trees growing in the air enriched with CO_2. To compensate for this increased nitrogen demand, the average uptake of nitrogen from the soil was enhanced by 28% in the CO_2-enriched plot—which says a lot, considering the soils in the study region are characteristically low in available nitrogen. In addition, average nitrogen-use efficiency rose by approximately 10% with atmospheric CO_2 enrichment.

With respect to the uptake of phosphate, Staddon *et al.* (1999) report *Plantago lanceolata* and *Trifolium repens* plants grown at 650 ppm CO_2 for 2.5 months exhibited total plant phosphorus contents much greater than those displayed by plants grown at 400 ppm CO_2, because atmospheric CO_2 enrichment significantly enhanced plant biomass. Similarly, Rouhier and Read (1998) report enriching the air around *Plantago lanceolata* plants with an extra 190 ppm of CO_2 for three months led to increased uptake of phosphorus and greater tissue phosphorus concentrations than were observed in plants growing in ambient air.

Greater uptake of phosphorus also can occur due to CO_2-induced increases in root absorptive surface area or enhancements in specific enzyme activities. In addressing the first of these phenomena, BassiriRad *et al.* (1998) report a doubling of the air's CO_2 concentration significantly increased the belowground biomass of *Bouteloua eriopoda* and doubled its uptake rate of phosphate. However, elevated CO_2 had no effect on uptake rates of phosphate in *Larrea* and *Prosopis*. Because the CO_2-enriched plants grew so much bigger, however, they still removed more phosphate from the soil on a per-plant basis. With respect to the second phenomenon, activity of phosphatase—the primary enzyme responsible for the conversion of organic phosphate into usable inorganic forms—increased by 30 to 40% in wheat seedlings growing at twice-ambient CO_2 concentrations (Barrett *et al.*, 1998).

With respect to another nutrient, iron, Jin *et al.* (2009) grew 20-day-old plants for an additional seven days within controlled-environment chambers maintained at atmospheric CO_2 concentrations of either 350 or 800 ppm in an iron (Fe)-sufficient medium with a soluble Fe source or under Fe-limited conditions in a medium containing the sparingly soluble hydrous Fe(III)-oxide. Their results indicate plant growth was increased by the elevated CO_2 in both the Fe-sufficient and Fe-limited media, with shoot fresh weight increasing by 22% and 44%, respectively, and root fresh weight increasing by 43% and 97%, respectively. In addition, Jin *et al.* report, "the elevated CO_2 under Fe-limited conditions enhance[d] root growth, root hair development, proton release, root FCR [ferric chelate reductase] activity, and expressions of *LeFRO1* and *LeIRT1* genes [which respectively encode FCR and the Fe(II) transporter in tomato], all of which enable plants to access and accumulate more Fe." They add, "the associated increase in Fe concentrations in the shoots and roots alleviated Fe-deficiency-induced chlorosis."

Jin *et al.* note the bioavailability of iron to terrestrial plants "is often limited (Guerinot and Yi, 1994), particularly in calcareous soils, which represent 30% of the Earth's surface (Imsande, 1998)," and thus conclude, "Fe nutrition in plants is likely to be affected by the continued elevation of atmospheric CO_2, which, in turn, will affect crop production." As their work strongly suggests, those important effects should be highly beneficial. Even wider biospheric benefits are suggested by the work of Sasaki *et al.* (1998), who demonstrated both the ferric reductase activity and Fe uptake capacity of the marine alga *Chlorococcum littorale* cultured in Fe-limited media have been significantly enhanced by elevated CO_2 concentrations.

Haase *et al.* (2008) grew barley (*Hordeum vulgare* L. cv. Europa) plants from seed for four weeks—both hydroponically in nutrient solution having adequate or less-than-adequate iron (Fe) concentrations (+Fe and -Fe, respectively), as well as in rhizobox microcosms filled with soil under the same two conditions of iron availability—in controlled-environment chambers maintained at atmospheric CO_2 concentrations of either 400 or 800 ppm. The elevated atmospheric CO_2 treatments stimulated biomass production in both Fe-sufficient and Fe-deficient barley plants, in both hydroponics and soil culture. In addition, they found three CO_2-induced modifications in plant activity: "(i) increased internal Fe use efficiency, (ii) stimulation of root growth, and (iii) increased root exudation of Fe-mobilizing phytosiderophores in the sub-apical root zones." Since phytosiderophores act as metal chelators that mobilize sparingly soluble inorganic forms of iron and zinc and make them more readily available to plants, the researchers suggest atmospheric CO_2 enrichment increases the competitiveness of plants such as barley with rhizosphere microorganisms in their quest for these often difficult-to-obtain trace elements. This phenomenon helps to explain the strong growth response of barley to atmospheric CO_2 enrichment even when iron availability is low.

In a study dealing with multiple nutrients, Schaffer *et al.* (1997) grew two mango ecotypes, one evolving from a warm, humid tropical climate and the other from a cool, dry subtropical region, for 12 months in glasshouses with atmospheres of either 350 or 700 ppm CO_2 to determine the effects of atmospheric CO_2 enrichment on plant growth and leaf mineral nutrient concentrations. According to the researchers, although atmospheric CO_2 enrichment led to partial photosynthetic acclimation in both ecotypes, greater net carbon gains were achieved with elevated CO_2, as indicated by greater plant dry mass values for trees grown at 700 ppm CO_2. Elevated CO_2 also tended to decrease foliar concentrations of mineral nutrients (N, P, K, Ca, Mg, S, Cl, Fe, Zn, Mn, Cu, and B) in both mango cultivars, most likely due to a dilution effect, since atmospheric CO_2 enrichment increased leaf dry mass. Although the instantaneous doubling of the atmospheric CO_2 concentration in this experiment reduced the concentrations of leaf mineral elements, Schaffer *et al.* state, "given the slow rate at which global atmospheric CO_2 concentration is increasing, it is possible that plants will adapt to elevated ambient CO_2 concentrations over time with respect to mineral nutrition," as did sour orange trees after 85 months of exposure to elevated CO_2 (Peñuelas *et al.*, 1997).

Lieffering *et al.* (2004) analyzed the elemental concentrations of archived grain samples from temperate rice (*Oryza sativa* L. cv. Akitakomachi) crops grown previously under FACE conditions out-of-doors in a fertile agricultural field (Okada *et al.*, 2001), where an approximate 200-ppm increase in the air's CO_2 concentration increased rice grain yields by about 14% (Kim *et al.*, 2003a,b).

Of the five macro-nutrients they measured (N, P, K, Mg, S), Lieffering *et al.* found "only N showed a decrease in concentration with elevated CO_2 in both years," and all six of the micro-nutrients studied (Zn, Mn, Fe, Cu, B, Mo) exhibited concentration increases. For Zn and Mn, in particular, they state, "there was a strong tendency [for concentrations] to increase," and the same could have been said of Fe, which in the second year of the study exhibited a CO_2-induced concentration increase on the order of 68%, as best as can be determined from Lieffering *et al.*'s bar graphs.

Lieffering *et al.* note their study of the effects of elevated CO_2 on grain elemental concentrations under real-world field conditions is "the first such report for a staple food crop: all other previously reported data were obtained from plants growing in pots and in some kind of enclosure." In contrast to the results obtained in most of these latter root-confining experiments, they note that, other than for N, "no dilution of [the] elements in the grain was observed, contrary to the general conclusions of Loladze (2002)." Therefore, they conclude, "as long as there is a readily available supply of nutrients and the nutrient uptake capacity response to elevated CO_2 is equal [to] or greater than the whole plant biomass response [which was the case in their experiment, except for N], then no dilution should be observed."

Natali *et al.* (2009) noted "increased production of fine roots with CO_2 enrichment (Norby *et al.*, 2004; Pritchard *et al.*, 2008) may allow plants to match increased carbon assimilation with increased uptake of soil-derived elements." They "examined CO_2 effects of a suite of metal micronutrients and contaminants in forest trees and soils at two free-air CO_2 enrichment sites—a loblolly pine forest in North Carolina (Duke) and a sweetgum plantation in Tennessee [Oak Ridge National Laboratory (ORNL)]—as well as at an open-top chamber experiment in a scrub-oak community in Florida [Smithsonian Environmental Research Center (SERC)]." They "did not find an overall decline in foliar metal concentrations with CO_2 enrichment," but they *did* find dilution effects for metal micronutrients were generally "less than for non-essential trace metals," and "some essential plant metals were greater under elevated CO_2 (for example, a 28% increase in Mn across species and sites)." Natali *et al.* conclude their results "should alleviate some concerns

that rising CO_2 concentrations will result in broad-scale decreases in the concentrations of all elements essential for plant function and animal nutrition," as proposed by Loladze (2002). They also state their generally opposite results for nonessential trace elements (some of which can be toxic) "may be applicable to contaminated systems," stating, "elevated CO_2 may, through dilution effects, alleviate aluminum toxicity."

In a somewhat different type of study, Urabe and Waki (2009) grew three algal species—*Scenedesmus obliquus* (green algae), *Cyclotella* sp. (diatoms), and *Synechococcus* sp. (cyanobacteria)—in mono- and mixed-cultures at ambient (360 ppm) and high (2,000 ppm) CO_2 levels and allowed a planktonic herbivore (*Daphnia*) to feed on the different algal populations thereby produced either individually or in various mixtures, to see if there was any CO_2-induced effect on herbivore growth. The two researchers found "both in the mono- and mixed cultures, algal steady state abundance increased but algal P:C and N:C ratios decreased when they were grown at high CO_2." They also found "*Daphnia* fed monospecific algae cultured at high CO_2 had decreased growth rates despite increased algal abundance." But "when fed mixed algae cultured at high CO_2, especially consisting of diatoms and cyanobacteria or the three algal species," they found "*Daphnia* maintained high growth rates despite lowered P and N contents relative to C in the algal diets." The findings indicate, they write, "algal diets composed of multiple species can mitigate the adverse effects of elevated CO_2 on herbivore performance," and "in environments with high CO_2, herbivores may find a new diet producer or a combination of producer species to best meet their nutritional demands."

The experimental data accumulated to date suggest much of Earth's vegetation likely will display increases in biomass as the air's CO_2 content rises, and considerable evidence suggests the larger plants thereby produced will develop more extensive root systems and extract greater amounts of mineral nutrients from the soils in which they are rooted, enabling them to sustain their enhanced growth.

References

Barrett, D.J., Richardson, A.E., and Gifford, R.M. 1998. Elevated atmospheric CO_2 concentrations increase wheat root phosphatase activity when growth is limited by phosphorus. *Australian Journal of Plant Physiology* **25**: 87–93.

BassiriRad, H., Reynolds, J.F., Virginia, R.A., and Brunelle, M.H. 1998. Growth and root NO_3^- and PO_4^{3-} uptake capacity of three desert species in response to atmospheric CO_2 enrichment. *Australian Journal of Plant Physiology* 24: 353–358.

Finzi, A.C., DeLucia, E.H., Hamilton, J.G., Richter, D.D., and Schlesinger, W.H. 2002. The nitrogen budget of a pine forest under free air CO_2 enrichment. *Oecologia* 132: 567–578.

Guerinot, M.L. and Yi, Y. 1994. Iron: nutritious, noxious, and not readily available. *Plant Physiology* 104: 815–820.

Haase, S., Rothe, A., Kania, A., Wasaki, J., Romheld, V., Engels, C., Kandeler, E., and Neumann, G. 2008. Responses to iron limitation in *Hordeum vulgare* L. as affected by the atmospheric CO_2 concentration. *Journal of Environmental Quality* 37: 1254–1262.

Imsande, J. 1998. Iron, sulfur, and chlorophyll deficiencies: a need for an integrative approach in plant physiology. *Physiologia Plantarum* 103: 139–144.

Jin, C.W., Du, S.T., Chen, W.W., Li, G.X., Zhang, Y.S., and Zheng, S.J. 2009. Elevated carbon dioxide improves plant iron nutrition through enhancing the iron-deficiency-induced responses under iron-limited conditions in tomato. *Plant Physiology* 150: 272–280.

Kim, H.-Y., Lieffering, M., Kobayashi, K., Okada, M., Mitchell, M.W., and Gumpertz, M. 2003b. Effects of free-air CO_2 enrichment and nitrogen supply on the yield of temperate paddy rice crops. *Field Crops Research* 83: 261–270.

Kim, H.-Y., Lieffering, M., Kobayashi, K., Okada, M., and Miura, S. 2003a. Seasonal changes in the effects of elevated CO_2 on rice at three levels of nitrogen supply: a free-air CO_2 enrichment (FACE) experiment. *Global Change Biology* 9: 826–837.

Lieffering, M., Kim, H.-Y., Kobayashi, K., and Okada, M. 2004. The impact of elevated CO_2 on the elemental concentrations of field-grown rice grains. *Field Crops Research* 88: 279–286.

Loladze, I. 2002. Rising atmospheric CO_2 and human nutrition: towards globally imbalanced plant stoichiometry. *Trends in Ecology and Evolution* 17: 457–461.

Nasholm, T., Ekblad, A., Nordin, A., Giesler, R., Hogberg, M., and Hogberg, P. 1998. Boreal forest plants take up organic nitrogen. *Nature* 392: 914–916.

Natali, S.M., Sañudo-Wilhelmy, S.A., and Lerdau, M.T. 2009. Plant and soil mediation of elevated CO_2 impacts on trace metals. *Ecosystems* 12: 715–727.

Norby, R.J., Ledford, J., Reilly, C.D., Miller, N.E., and O'Neill, E.G. 2004. Fine-root production dominates response of a deciduous forest to atmospheric CO_2 enrichment. *Proceedings of the National Academy of Sciences, USA* 101: 9689–9693.

Okada, M., Lieffering, M., Nakamura, H., Yoshimoto, M., Kim. H.-Y., and Kobayashi, K. 2001. Free-air CO_2 enrichment (FACE) using pure CO_2 injection: system description. *New Phytologist* 150: 251–260.

Peñuelas, J., Idso, S.B., Ribas, A., and Kimball, B.A. 1997. Effects of long-term atmospheric CO_2 enrichment on the mineral concentration of *Citrus aurantium* leaves. *New Phytologist* 135: 439–444.

Pritchard, S.G., Strand, A.E., McCormack, M.L., Davis, M.A., Finzi, A., Jackson, R.B., Matamala, R., Rogers, H.H., and Oren, R. 2008. Fine root dynamics in a loblolly pine forest are influenced by free-air-CO_2-enrichment: a six-year-minirhizotron study. *Global Change Biology* 14: 588–602.

Rouhier, H. and Read, D.J. 1998. The role of mycorrhiza in determining the response of *Plantago lanceolata* to CO_2 enrichment. *New Phytologist* 139: 367–373.

Sasaki, T., Kurano, N., and Miyachi, S. 1998. Induction of ferric reductase activity and of iron uptake capacity in *Chlorococcum littorale* cells under extremely high-CO_2 and iron-deficient conditions. *Plant & Cell Physiology* 39: 405–410.

Schaffer, B., Whiley, A.W., Searle, C., and Nissen, R.J. 1997. Leaf gas exchange, dry matter partitioning, and mineral element concentrations in mango as influenced by elevated atmospheric carbon dioxide and root restriction. *Journal of the American Society of Horticultural Science* 122: 849–855.

Smart, D.R., Ritchie, K., Bloom, A.J., and Bugbee, B.B. 1998. Nitrogen balance for wheat canopies (*Triticum aestivum* cv. Veery 10) grown under elevated and ambient CO_2 concentrations. *Plant, Cell and Environment* 21: 753–763.

Staddon, P.L., Fitter, A.H., and Graves, J.D. 1999. Effect of elevated atmospheric CO_2 on mycorrhizal colonization, external mycorrhizal hyphal production and phosphorus inflow in *Plantago lanceolata* and *Trifolium repens* in association with the arbuscular mycorrhizal fungus *Glomus mosseae*. *Global Change Biology* 5: 347–358.

Urabe, J. and Waki, N. 2009. Mitigation of adverse effects of rising CO_2 on a planktonic herbivore by mixed algal diets. *Global Change Biology* 15: 523–531.

Zak, D.R., Pregitzer, K.S., Curtis, P.S., Vogel, C.S., Holmes, W.E., and Lussenhop, J. 2000. Atmospheric CO_2, soil-N availability, and allocation of biomass and nitrogen by *Populus tremuloides*. *Ecological Applications* 10: 34–46.

2.19 Phenolics

Herbaceous plants often experience increases in foliar and fruit phenolic concentrations in response to atmospheric CO_2 enrichment, and these responses appear to have a number of positive implications for both man and the biosphere. Future increases in the air's CO_2 concentration likely will enhance foliar phenolic concentrations in many trees and shrubs, and this should enhance woody-plant defense mechanisms that help deter herbivory, thereby improving forest health, robustness, and longevity.

2.19.1 Herbaceous Species

- Many, but not all, herbaceous plants experience increases in foliar and fruit phenolic concentrations in response to atmospheric CO_2 enrichment. These responses appear to have a number of positive implications for both man and the biosphere.

In the presence of elevated concentrations of atmospheric CO_2, many of Earth's plants display an enhanced rate of photosynthetic carbon uptake, which leads to an increased production of plant secondary carbon compounds, including phenolics. Since the resulting increases in plant foliar phenolic concentrations often enhance plant resistance to herbivore and pathogen attack, this section reviews the results of some studies that have dealt with this important subject in herbaceous plants.

Hoorens et al. (2002) grew two plants common to dune grasslands of the Netherlands (Calamagrostis epigejos and Vicia lathyroides), along with two species common to Dutch peatlands (Carex rostrata and Sphagnum recurvum), in greenhouses fumigated with air containing either 390 or 700 ppm CO_2 for five months. Then, after senescence had occurred, they collected the resulting leaf litter and analyzed it for the presence of various substances. Among other things, they found elevated CO_2 had little impact on the presence of phenolics in Calamagrostis and Sphagnum litter, but it increased phenolic concentrations in Vicia and Carex litter by 20 and 32%, respectively.

Castells et al. (2002) grew 14 genotypes of two perennial grasses common to the Mediterranean area (Dactylis glomerata and Bromus erectus) in glasshouses maintained at atmospheric CO_2 concentrations of 350 and 700 ppm in order to determine whether elevated CO_2 impacts phenolic production in a genotypic-dependent manner. Their research indicates doubling the air's CO_2 concentration increased total phenolic concentrations in Dactylis and Bromus by 15 and 87%, respectively, and there were no significant CO_2 x genotype interactions in either species. As the atmosphere's CO_2 concentration continues to rise, therefore, these two perennial grasses likely will exhibit greater resistance to herbivory without having to sacrifice their genotypic diversity.

Wetzel and Tuchman (2005) grew cattails for three years in open-bottom root boxes out-of-doors within clear-plastic-wall open-top chambers maintained at either ambient (360 ppm) or elevated (720 ppm) atmospheric CO_2 concentrations from early spring through leaf senescence. During this period, green and naturally senesced leaves were collected and analyzed for the fraction of leaf mass composed of total phenolics. The researchers found green leaf material contained 27.6% more total phenolics when the plants were grown in CO_2-enriched as opposed to ambient air, and senesced leaf material grown in CO_2-enrihced air contained 40.6% more total phenolics than similar leaves produced in ambient air.

In a study with human health implications, Wang et al. (2003) grew strawberry plants in six clear-acrylic open-top chambers, two of which were maintained at the ambient atmospheric CO_2 concentration, two of which were maintained at ambient + 300 ppm CO_2, and two of which were maintained at ambient + 600 ppm CO_2 from early spring 1998 through June 2000. During this time, the researchers harvested the strawberry fruit, they write, "at the commercially ripe stage" in both 1999 and 2000. They analyzed the fruit for the presence of a number of different health-promoting substances with "potent antioxidant properties." They found CO_2 enrichment increased fruit ascorbic acid, glutathione, phenolic acid, flavonol, and anthocyanin concentrations, and plants grown under the CO_2 enriched conditions also had higher oxygen radical absorbance activity against many types of harmful oxygen radicals in the fruit.

References

Castells, E., Roumet, C., Peñuelas, J., and Roy, J. 2002. Intraspecific variability of phenolic concentrations and their responses to elevated CO_2 in two mediterranean perennial grasses. Environmental and Experimental Botany 47: 205–216.

Hoorens, B., Aerts, R., and Stroetenga, M. 2002. Litter quality and interactive effects in litter mixtures: more negative interactions under elevated CO$_2$? *Journal of Ecology* **90**: 1009–1016.

Wang, S.Y., Bunce, J.A., and Maas, J.L. 2003. Elevated carbon dioxide increases contents of antioxidant compounds in field-grown strawberries. *Journal of Agricultural and Food Chemistry* **51**: 4315–4320.

Wetzel, R.G. and Tuchman, N.C. 2005. Effects of atmospheric CO$_2$ enrichment and sunlight on degradation of plant particulate and dissolved organic matter and microbial utilization. *Archiv fur Hydrobiologie* **162**: 287–308.

2.19.2 Woody Species

- Future increases in the air's CO$_2$ concentration likely will enhance foliar phenolic concentrations in many shrubs and trees. This, in turn, should enhance woody-plant defense mechanisms that help deter herbivory and thus improve forest health, robustness, and longevity.

As the air's CO$_2$ content continues to rise, many of Earth's plants are experiencing enhanced rates of photosynthetic carbon uptake, which commonly leads to increased production of plant secondary carbon compounds, including phenolics that often enhance plant resistance to herbivore and pathogen attack. This section examines the results of several studies dealing with this important subject.

Peñuelas *et al.* (2002) sampled leaves of three species of shrubs growing close to, and further away from, CO$_2$-emitting springs in Pisa, Italy, to determine the long-term effects of elevated atmospheric CO$_2$ on foliar concentrations of carbon-based secondary compounds. The researchers found the extra 340 ppm of CO$_2$ near the springs had very few long-term significant effects on foliar concentrations of most such substances, including phenolics, and those effects that were observed varied according to specific compound and plant species. Their findings are somewhat atypical of what is often observed, as several studies of temperate-region trees have shown leaf phenolic concentrations to rise by 20 to 60% in response to a doubling of the air's CO$_2$ content (Koricheva *et al.*, 1998; Peñuelas and Estiarte, 1998; McDonald *et al.*, 1999; Agrell *et al.*, 2000; Hartley *et al.*, 2000), as also was reported by Parsons *et al.* (2003) with respect to the total fine-root phenolic concentrations of warm-temperate conifers studied by King *et al.* (1997), Entry *et al.* (1998), and Runion *et al.* (1999).

Gebauer *et al.* (1998) grew loblolly pine seedlings in glasshouses maintained at atmospheric CO$_2$ concentrations of 350 and 700 ppm for five months while subjecting them to four levels of soil nitrogen fertilization. Across all of these nitrogen regimes, the extra CO$_2$ increased the above- and below-ground concentrations of seedling total phenolics by 21 and 35%, respectively.

Booker and Maier (2001) also worked with loblolly pines, measuring concentrations of total soluble phenolics in needles exposed for two years in branch chambers to ambient air and air enriched to as much as 350 ppm CO$_2$ above ambient. They found needle concentrations of total soluble phenolics increased about 11% in response to the elevated CO$_2$, noting this response was related to "the balance between carbohydrate sources and sinks," so "the greater the source:sink ratio, the greater the concentration of phenolic compounds (Herms and Mattson, 1992; Peñuelas and Estiarte, 1998)."

In contrast, Hamilton *et al.* (2004) studied the understory of the loblolly pine plantation in the Duke Forest FACE study, finding no evidence of significant changes in total leaf phenolics in either of two years, in agreement with the results of "another study performed at the Duke Forest FACE site that also found no effect of elevated CO$_2$ on the chemical composition of leaves of understory trees (Finzi and Schlesinger, 2002)." Nevertheless, they state, "elevated CO$_2$ led to a trend toward reduced herbivory in [the] deciduous understory in a situation that included the full complement of naturally occurring plant and insect species." In 1999, for example, they found "elevated CO$_2$ reduced overall herbivory by more than 40% with elm showing greater reduction than either red maple or sweetgum," and in 2000 they observed "the same pattern and magnitude of reduction."

In a similar FACE study of an ecosystem dominated by three species of oak tree (*Quercus myrtifolia*, *Q. chapmanii*, and *Q. geminata*) plus the nitrogen-fixing legume *Galactia elliottii* at the Kennedy Space Center in Florida (USA), Hall *et al.* (2005) detected no significant differences between the CO$_2$-enriched and ambient-treatment leaves of any single species in terms of condensed tannins, hydrolyzable tannins, total phenolics, or lignin. When all four species were considered together, however, there were always greater concentrations of all four leaf constituents in the CO$_2$-enriched leaves, with across-species mean increases of 6.8% for condensed tannins, 6.1% for hydrolyzable tannins, 5.1% for total phenolics, and 4.3% for lignin. In addition, there were large CO_2-induced decreases in all leaf damage categories associated with herbivory: chewing (-48%, $P < 0.001$), mines (-37%, $P = 0.001$), eye spot gall (-45%, $P < 0.001$), leaf tier (-52%, $P = 0.012$), leaf mite (-23%, $P = 0.477$), and leaf gall (-16%, $P = 0.480$). The five researchers conclude the changes in leaf chemical constituents and herbivore damage "suggest that damage to plants may decline as atmospheric CO_2 levels continue to rise."

Wetzel and Tuchman (2005) grew trembling aspen seedlings for three years in open-bottom root boxes out-of-doors within clear-plastic-wall open-top chambers maintained at either ambient (360 ppm) or elevated (720 ppm) atmospheric CO_2 concentrations from early spring through leaf senescence. Green and naturally senesced leaves were collected and analyzed for the fraction of leaf mass composed of total phenolics. Green leaf material contained 19.1% more total phenolics when the experimental seedlings were grown in CO_2-enriched as opposed to ambient air, and senesced leaf material grown in CO_2-enriched air contained 63.2% more total phenolics than similar leaf material grown in ambient air.

In Finland, Kuokkanen et al. (2003) grew two-year-old birch trees in the field in closed-top chambers exposed to either ambient air of 350 ppm CO_2 or air enriched to a CO_2 concentration of 700 ppm at either ambient temperatures or ambient temperatures plus 3°C for one full growing season. During the middle of summer, when carbon-based secondary compounds of birch leaves are usually fairly stable, they picked several leaves from each tree and measured the concentrations of a number of physiologically important substances. The concentration of total phenolics significantly increased in the birch leaves produced in the CO_2-enriched air, as also has been observed in the experiments of Lavola and Julkunen-Titto (1994), Williams et al. (1994), Kinney et al. (1997), Bezemer and Jones (1998), and Kuokkanen et al. (2001).

Coley et al. (2002) studied nine species of tropical trees rooted in the ground and grown in their natural environment near the Smithsonian Tropical Research Institute's experiment site in central Panama. Their six-month open-top chamber study produced impressive results, with eight of the nine species exhibiting positive leaf phenolic/tannin responses to a doubling of the air's CO_2 content, the largest of which was a concentration increase of 119%. The single negative response was a 27% decline, and the mean response of all nine species was an increase of 48%. These results are comparable to those obtained for temperate-region trees, and they provide the basis for Coley et al.'s primary conclusion: Although "both temperate and tropical trees show large interspecific variation in the extent of their response to CO_2 ... the overwhelming pattern is for an increase in phenolics by approximately 50%."

The results of these several studies suggest future increases in the air's CO_2 concentration likely will enhance foliar phenolic concentrations in many shrubs and trees. This phenomenon, in turn, should enhance woody-plant defense mechanisms that help deter herbivory, which should improve forest health, robustness, and longevity.

References

Agrell, J., McDonald, E.P., and Lindroth, R.L. 2000. Effects of CO_2 and light on tree phytochemistry and insect performance. Oikos 88: 259–272.

Bezemer, T.M. and Jones, T.H. 1998. Plant-insect herbivore interactions in elevated atmospheric CO_2, quantitative analyses and guild effects. Oikos 82: 212–222.

Booker, F.L. and Maier, C.A. 2001. Atmospheric carbon dioxide, irrigation, and fertilization effects on phenolic and nitrogen concentrations in loblolly pine (Pinus taeda) needles. Tree Physiology 21: 609–616.

Coley, P.D., Massa, M., Lovelock, C.E., and Winter, K. 2002. Effect of elevated CO_2 on foliar chemistry of saplings of nine species of tropical tree. Oecologia 133: 62–69.

Entry, J.A., Runion, G.B., Prior, S.A., Mitchell, R.J., and Rogers, H.H. 1998. Influence of CO_2 enrichment and nitrogen fertilization on tissue chemistry and carbon allocation in longleaf pine seedlings. Plant and Soil 200: 3–11.

Finzi, A.C. and Schlesinger, W.H. 2002. Species control variation in litter decomposition in a pine forest exposed to elevated CO_2. Global Change Biology 8: 1217–1229.

Gebauer, R.L.E., Strain, B.R., and Reynolds, J.F. 1998. The effect of elevated CO_2 and N availability on tissue concentrations and whole plant pools of carbon-based secondary compounds in loblolly pine (Pinus taeda). Oecologia 113: 29–36.

Hall, M.C., Stiling, P., Moon, D.C., Drake, B.G., and Hunter, M.D. 2005. Effects of elevated CO_2 on foliar quality and herbivore damage in a scrub oak ecosystem. Journal of Chemical Ecology 31: 267–285.

Hamilton, J.G., Zangerl, A.R., Berenbaum, M.R., Pippen, J., Aldea, M., and DeLucia, E.H. 2004. Insect herbivory in an intact forest understory under experimental CO_2 enrichment. *Oecologia* **138**: 10.1007/s00442-003-1463-5.

Hartley, S.E., Jones, C.G., Couper, G.C., and Jones, T.H. 2000. Biosynthesis of plant phenolic compounds in elevated atmospheric CO_2. *Global Change Biology* **6**: 497–506.

Herms, D.A. and Mattson, W.J. 1992. The dilemma of plants: to grow or defend. *Quarterly Review of Biology* **67**: 283–335.

King, J.S., Thomas, R.B., and Strain, B.R. 1997. Morphology and tissue quality of seedling root systems of *Pinus taeda* and *Pinus ponderosa* as affected by varying CO_2, temperature, and nitrogen. *Plant and Soil* **195**: 107–119.

Kinney, K.K., Lindroth, R.L., Jung, S.M., and Nordheim, E.V. 1997. Effects of CO_2 and NO_3 availability on deciduous trees, phytochemistry and insect performance. *Ecology* **78**: 215–230.

Koricheva, J., Larsson, S., Haukioja, E., and Keinanen, M. 1998. Regulation of woody plant metabolism by resource availability: hypothesis testing by means of a meta-analysis. *Oikos* **83**: 212–226.

Kuokkanen, K., Julkunen-Titto, R., Keinanen, M., Niemela, P., and Tahvanainen, J. 2001. The effect of elevated CO_2 and temperature on the secondary chemistry of *Betula pendula* seedlings. *Trees* **15**: 378–384.

Kuokkanen, K., Yan, S., and Niemela, P. 2003. Effects of elevated CO_2 and temperature on the leaf chemistry of birch *Betula pendula* (Roth) and the feeding behavior of the weevil *Phyllobius maculicornis*. *Agricultural and Forest Entomology* **5**: 209–217.

Lavola, A. and Julkunen-Titto, R. 1994. The effect of elevated carbon dioxide and fertilization on primary and secondary metabolites in birch, *Betula pendua* (Roth). *Oecologia* **99**: 315–321.

McDonald, E.P., Agrell, J., and Lindroth, R.L. 1999. CO_2 and light effects on deciduous trees: growth, foliar chemistry and insect performance. *Oecologia* **119**: 389–399.

Parsons, W.F.J., Kopper, B.J., and Lindroth, R.L. 2003. Altered growth and fine root chemistry of *Betula papyrifera* and *Acer saccharum* under elevated CO_2. *Canadian Journal of Forest Research* **33**: 842–846.

Peñuelas, J., Castells, E., Joffre, R., and Tognetti, R. 2002. Carbon-based secondary and structural compounds in Mediterranean shrubs growing near a natural CO_2 spring. *Global Change Biology* **8**: 281–288.

Peñuelas, J. and Estiarte, M. 1998. Can elevated CO_2 affect secondary metabolism and ecosystem function? *Trees* **13**: 20–24.

Runion, G.B., Entry, J.A., Prior, S.A., Mitchell, R.J., and Rogers, H.H. 1999. Tissue chemistry and carbon allocation in seedlings of *Pinus palustris* subjected to elevated atmospheric CO_2 and water stress. *Tree Physiology* **19**: 329–335.

Wetzel, R.G. and Tuchman, N.C. 2005. Effects of atmospheric CO_2 enrichment and sunlight on degradation of plant particulate and dissolved organic matter and microbial utilization. *Archiv fur Hydrobiologie* **162**: 287–308.

Williams, R.S., Lincoln, D.E., and Thomas, R.B. 1994. Loblolly pine grown under elevated CO_2 affects early instar pine sawfly performance. *Oecologia* **98**: 64–71.

2.20 Phenology

- The wide range of results obtained by many past and current methods of detecting each year's start-of-spring has led some researchers to claim spring has been arriving earlier over the course of the twentieth century. These observations are used to support the associated claim of twentieth-century CO_2-induced global warming, often said to result in the mistiming of the yearly start-up of the component links of various ecosystems' food chains. Real-world data, however, do not support the bulk of these contentions.

The progressively earlier arrival of spring with each succeeding year is widely viewed as an indicator of global warming. Scheifinger *et al.* (2002) and Schaber and Badeck (2005) claim to have detected earlier spring arrival in Europe over the course of the twentieth century. One difficulty with such studies, however, is the lack of a commonly agreed-upon metric for the arrival of spring.

White *et al.* (2009) compared 10 algorithms for processing satellite Normalized Difference Vegetation Index (NDVI) data for this purpose, based on the expectation that satellite data, with their continental coverage, should allow such trends to be more easily detected. A question that remains, however, is whether the various methods employed measure the same things or correspond to on-the-ground measurements.

White *et al.*'s study covered the period 1982–2006, using 16,000 ground-based phenological measurements from across North America as well as data on snow melt and hydrology. Using the 10 methods of extracting a start-of-spring (SOS) signal from the satellite data, they ended up with a range of fully 60 days around the 10-model mean estimate.

The 10 methods also tended to be biased toward detecting SOS earlier than ground-based phenology data indicated, and to have weak correlations with the ground data, perhaps because there were difficulties classifying pixels in some cases, particularly for desert, semi-tropical, and Mediterranean (California) zones in which the arrival of "spring" is not a well-defined phenomenon.

In the end, the 21 researchers state they "found no evidence for time trends in spring arrival from ground- or model-based data," and "using an ensemble estimate from two methods that were more closely related to ground observations than other methods, SOS trends could be detected for only 12% of North America," with 7% showing a trend to earlier spring and 5% exhibiting a trend toward later spring. That suggests the wide range of results obtained by most past and current methods of detecting the start of spring may have led to premature claims of spring's increasingly earlier annual occurrence over the latter part of the twentieth century. And that finding, in turn, raises significant concerns about the validity of near-surface air temperature measurements that suggest North America has warmed significantly over the past several decades.

In the introduction to another study of the subject, however, Johnston and Reekie (2008) state there have "been marked changes in plant phenology over the past century," and these changes "have been interpreted as a consequence of the increase in temperature that has been observed over this time." In an added twist to the subject, they speculate, "the concentration of atmospheric CO_2 may also directly affect time of flowering, even in the absence of temperature change."

The two researchers examined the effect of elevated atmospheric CO_2 concentration by itself (ambient and ambient + 330 ppm), as well as the combined effect of elevated CO_2 and elevated air temperature (ambient + 1.5°C), on the flowering phenology of 22 species of plants in the Asteraceae family, which were grown under natural, seasonally varying temperature and daylength in separate compartments of a glasshouse in Wolfville, Nova Scotia, Canada. The researchers found, "on average, elevated CO_2 by itself advanced flowering by four days" and "increasing temperature as well as CO_2 advanced flowering by an additional three days." They also found, "CO_2 was more likely to hasten phenology in long- than in short-day species," and "early- and late-flowering species did not differ in response to elevated CO_2," but "the combined effect of elevated CO_2 and temperature hastened flowering more in early- than late-flowering species." They conclude, with respect to time of flowering in Asteraceae species, "the direct effect of CO_2 on phenology may be as important as its indirect effect through climate change," further complicating the interpretation of a progressively earlier start of spring as an indication of regional or global warming.

Some scientists express concern that global warming may "throw off" the timing of lifecycle stages of certain food chain components, leading to a mismatch among the unique needs of different ecosystem trophic levels that could spell disaster for some species. Visser and Both (2005) warn of such an "insufficient adjustment" to climate change.

Bauer *et al.* (2010) studied the effect of 47 years of warming (1961–2007) on the time of leafing-out of dominant English Oak (*Quercus robur*) trees at four research sites in the Czech Republic located in full-grown, multiaged floodplain forests that had been under no forestry management. They also studied the time of appearance of the two most abundant species of caterpillars in the floodplain forests, the Winter Moth (*Operophtera brumata*) and the Tortrix Moth (*Tortrix viridana*), and the first and mean laying dates of two of the ecosystem's most common birds: Great Tits (*Parus major*) and Collared Flycatchers (*Ficedula albicollis*).

The seven scientists found "mean annual temperature showed a significant increase of 0.27–0.33°C per decade, with approximately the same magnitude of change during spring at all sites." They also found, "on average (all four sites), the bud burst date for English Oak has advanced by 7.9 days and full foliage by 8.9 days, with approximately the same shifts being recorded for the peak of the beginning and end of frass for herbivorous caterpillars," which was the observational variable they used to characterize the caterpillars' presence. Finally, they write, "the first laying date of Great Tits has advanced by between 6.2 to 8.0 days," and "the mean laying date has advanced by 6.4 to 8.0 days." They found the "Collared Flycatcher first laying date has advanced by 8.5 to 9.2 days over the past 47 years, and the mean laying date by 7.7 to 9.6 days."

Bauer *et al.* state, because "trends in the timing of reproduction processes of both bird species are coherent with the trends in development of English Oak and with peak herbivorous caterpillar activity," it is apparent in this specific food chain the common temporal shifting of the different organisms' phenological stages toward the beginning of the year "does not appear to have led to mistiming in the trophic food chain." Hence, other food chains also may not be as seriously disrupted by global warming as many have postulated they could be. More work of this nature, however, is clearly needed before any generalizations are warranted.

References

Bauer, Z., Trnka, M., Bauerova, J., Mozny, M., Stepanek, P., Bartosova, L., and Zalud, Z. 2010. Changing climate and the phenological response of great tit and collared flycatcher populations in floodplain forest ecosystems in Central Europe. *International Journal of Biometeorology* **54**: 99–111.

Johnston, A. and Reekie, E. 2008. Regardless of whether rising atmospheric carbon dioxide levels increase air temperature, flowering phenology will be affected. *International Journal of Plant Science* **169**: 1210–1218.

Schaber, J. and Badeck, F. 2005. Plant phenology in Germany over the 20th Century. *Regional Environmental Change* **5**: 37–46.

Scheifinger, H., Menzel, A., Koch, E., Peter, C., and Ahas, R. 2002. Atmospheric mechanisms governing the spatial and temporal variability of phenological phases in central Europe. *International Journal of Climatology* **22**: 1739–1755.

Visser, M.E. and Both, C. 2005. Shifts in phenology due to global climate change: the need for yardstick. *Proceedings of the Royal Society B* **272**: 2561–2569.

White, Michael A., de Beurs, K.M., Kidan, K., Inouye, D.W., Richardson, A.D., Jensen, O.P., O'Keefe, J., Zhang, G., Nemani, R.R., van Leeuwen, W.J.D., Brown, J.F., de Wit, A., Schaepman, M., Lin, X., Dettinger, M., Bailey, A.S., Kimball, J., Schwartz, M.D., Baldocchi, D.D., Lee, J.T., and Lauenroth, W.K. 2009. Intercomparison, interpretation, and assessment of spring phenology in North America estimated from remote sensing for 1982–2006. *Global Change Biology* **15**: 2335–2359.

2.21 Protein

• In both managed agricultural crops and the wild plants of Earth's natural ecosystems, the ongoing rise of the air's CO_2 concentration likely will have few negative impacts of any consequence on the nutritive value of their grains and foliage in terms of protein concentration. In tree crops such as citrus, CO_2-induced changes in the activities of certain foliar proteins could lead to vast increases in yield potential.

In a review of the scientific literature on the effects of atmospheric CO_2 enrichment on plant constituents of significance to human health, Idso and Idso (2001) cite a number of studies where elevated levels of atmospheric CO_2 either increased, decreased, or had no effect on the protein concentrations of various agricultural crops. The first two of these consequences also were observed by Kaddour and Fuller (2004) and Veisz et al. (2005) in wheat.

In the case of this particular crop—which according to Wittwer (1995) was "the most widely grown plant in the world" at that time, contributing "more calories and protein to the human diet than any other food"—Pleijel et al. (1999) analyzed the results of 16 open-top chamber experiments that had been conducted on spring wheat in Denmark, Finland, Sweden, and Switzerland between 1986 and 1996. In addition to CO_2 enrichment of the air, these experiments included increases and decreases in atmospheric ozone (O_3). Pleijel et al. found when increasing O_3 pollution reduced wheat grain yield, it simultaneously increased the protein concentration of the grain. They also found when O_3 was scrubbed from the air and grain yield was thereby increased, the protein concentration of the grain was decreased. This same relationship described the degree to which grain protein concentration dropped when atmospheric CO_2 enrichment increased grain yield. Hence, whenever the grain yield of the wheat was changed—by CO_2, O_3, or even water stress, which was also a variable in one of the experiments—grain protein concentrations moved up or down along a common linear relationship in the opposite direction to the change in grain yield.

In an earlier study of CO_2 and O_3 effects on wheat grain yield and quality, Rudorff et al. (1996) obtained essentially the same result. They observed, for example, "flour protein contents were increased by enhanced O_3 exposure and reduced by elevated CO_2," but "the combined effect of these gases was minor." Hence, they conclude, "the concomitant increase of CO_2 and O_3 in the troposphere will have no significant impact on wheat grain quality."

Evans (1993) found similar relationships for several other crops, further observing them to be greatly affected by soil nitrogen availability. It is highly likely, therefore, that the differing availability of soil nitrogen could have been responsible for some of the results observed in the many other studies reviewed by Idso and Idso (2001). That is precisely what the study of Rogers et al. (1996) suggests. Although they observed CO_2-induced reductions in the protein concentration of flour derived from wheat plants growing at low soil nitrogen concentrations, no such reductions were evident when the soil nitrogen supply was increased. Hence, Pleijel *et al.* conclude, the oft-observed negative impact of atmospheric CO_2 enrichment on grain protein concentration probably would be alleviated by higher applications of nitrogen fertilizers.

Kimball *et al.* (2001) confirmed that hypothesis. They studied the effects of a 50% increase in atmospheric CO_2 concentration on wheat grain nitrogen concentration and the baking properties of the flour derived from that grain throughout four years of free-air CO_2 enrichment experiments. In the first two years of their study, soil water content was an additional variable, and in the last two years, soil nitrogen content was a variable. The most influential factor in reducing grain nitrogen concentration was determined to be low soil nitrogen. Under this condition, atmospheric CO_2 enrichment further reduced grain nitrogen and protein concentrations, although the change was much less than that caused by low soil nitrogen. When soil nitrogen was not limiting, however, increases in the air's CO_2 concentration did not affect grain nitrogen and protein concentrations, nor did they reduce the baking properties of the flour derived from the grain. Hence, it would appear that given sufficient water and nitrogen, atmospheric CO_2 enrichment can increase wheat grain yield without sacrificing grain protein concentration in the process.

Atmospheric CO_2 enrichment has been found in some studies to increase the protein concentration of wheat. Agrawal and Deepak (2003), for example, grew two cultivars of wheat (*Triticum aestivum* L. cv. Malviya 234 and HP1209) in open-top chambers maintained at atmospheric CO_2 concentrations of 350 and 600 ppm alone and in combination with 60 ppb SO_2 to study the interactive effects of elevated CO_2 and this major air pollutant on crop growth. They found exposure to the elevated SO_2 caused a 13% decrease in foliar protein concentrations in both cultivars, but when the plants were concomitantly exposed to an atmospheric CO_2 concentration of 600 ppm, leaf protein levels decreased by only 3% in HP1209 and increased by 4% in Malviya 234.

In the case of rice—which according to Wittwer (1995) was "the basic food for more than half the world's population," supplying "more dietary energy than any other single food"—Jablonski *et al.* (2002) conducted a wide-ranging review of the scientific literature, finding rice, too, appeared to suffer no reduction in grain nitrogen (protein) concentration in response to atmospheric CO_2 enrichment. They also found no CO_2-induced decrease in seed nitrogen concentration in the studies of legumes they reviewed. This finding is significant because, as Wittwer (1995) notes, legumes "are a direct food resource providing 20% of the world's protein for human consumption" and "about two thirds of the world's protein concentrate for livestock feeding." In addition, Jablonski *et al.* found the biomass of the CO_2-enriched wheat, rice, and legumes was increased significantly above that of the same crops grown in normal air. Hence, there likely will be a vast increase in the total amount of protein that can be made available to humanity in a future CO_2-enriched world, both directly via food crops and indirectly via livestock.

Thomas *et al.* (2003) noted "oil and protein comprise ~20 and 40%, respectively, of the dry weight of soybean seed." This "unique chemical composition," they write, "has made it one of the most valuable agronomic crops worldwide." In addition, "the intrinsic value of soybean seed is in its supply of essential fatty acids and amino acids in the oil and protein, respectively." They report Heagle *et al.* (1998) "observed a positive significant effect of CO_2 enrichment on soybean seed oil and oleic acid concentration."

Legumes and their responses to atmospheric CO_2 enrichment also figure prominently in studies of mixed forage crops. In a study of nitrogen cycling in grazed pastures on the North Island of New Zealand, for example, Allard *et al.* (2003) found under elevated CO_2, leaves of the individual species exhibited lower nitrogen concentrations but higher water-soluble carbohydrate (WSC) concentrations. They also note "there was a significantly greater proportion of legume in the diet at elevated CO_2," and this "shift in the botanical composition towards a higher proportion of legumes counter-balanced the nitrogen decrease observed at the single species scale, resulting in a nitrogen concentration of the overall diet that was unaffected by elevated CO_2." They further report, "changes at the species level and at the sward level appeared to combine additively in relation to WSC." Hence, they note, "as there was a significant correlation between WSC and digestibility (as previously observed by Dent and Aldrich, 1963 and Humphreys, 1989), there was also an increase in digestibility of the high CO_2 forage." This result, they write, "matches that found in a Mini-FACE experiment under cutting (Teyssonneyre, 2002; Picon-Cochard *et al.*, 2004)," where "digestibility also increased in response to CO_2 despite reduced crude protein concentration." These data, plus the strong relationship between soluble sugars (rather than nitrogen) and digestibility, led them to suggest "the widespread response to CO_2 of increased soluble sugars might lead to an increase in forage digestibility."

Luscher et al. (2004) found much the same in their review of the subject, which was based primarily on studies conducted at the Swiss FACE facility that hosted what had by then become the world's longest continuous atmospheric CO_2 enrichment study of a naturally occurring grassland. There, in response to an approximate two-thirds increase in the atmosphere's CO_2 concentration, leaf nitrogen (N) concentrations of white clover (Trifolium repens L.) and perennial ryegrass (Lolium perenne L.) were reduced by 7% and 18%, respectively, when they were grown separately in pure stands. As Luscher et al. report, "the considerably lower concentration of N under elevated CO_2, observed for L. perenne leaves in pure stands, was found to a much lesser extent for L. perenne leaves in the bi-species mixture with T. repens (Zanetti et al., 1997; Hartwig et al., 2000)." Furthermore, "under elevated CO_2 the proportion of N-rich T. repens (40 mg N g^{-1} dry matter) increased in the mixture at the expense of the N-poor L. perenne (24 mg N g^{-1} dry matter when grown in mono-culture)," the end result being "the concentration of N in the harvested biomass of the mixture showed no significant reduction."

That this phenomenon is likely ubiquitous is suggested by the still more comprehensive review by Campbell et al. 2000), who analyzed research conducted between 1994 and 1999 by a worldwide network of 83 scientists associated with the Global Change and Terrestrial Ecosystems (GCTE) Pastures and Rangelands Core Research Project 1 (CRP1). This program had resulted in the publication of more than 165 peer-reviewed scientific journal articles. Campbell et al. determined from this massive collection of data the legume content of grass-legume swards typically was increased by approximately 10% in response to a doubling of the air's CO_2 content.

Luscher et al. (2004) state, "the nutritive value of herbage from intensively managed grassland dominated by L. perenne and T. repens ... is well above the minimum range of the concentration of crude protein necessary for efficient digestion by ruminants (Barney et al. 1981)." Hence, they conclude, "a small decrease in the concentration of crude protein in intensively managed forage production systems [which may never occur, as noted above] is not likely to have a negative effect on the nutritive value or on the intake of forage." In addition, in a CO_2-enriched world of the future there would be

much more such forage produced per unit of land and water devoted to the enterprise, clearly making the ongoing rise in the air's CO_2 content a big plus for animal husbandry.

Newman et al. (2003) investigated the effects of two levels of nitrogen fertilization and an approximate doubling of the air's CO_2 content on the growth and chemical composition of tall fescue (Festuca arundinacea Schreber cv. KY-31), both when infected and uninfected with a mutualistic fungal endophyte (Neotyphodium coenophialum Morgan-Jones and Gams). They found the elevated CO_2 reduced the crude protein content of the forage by an average of 21% in three of the four situations studied: non-endophyte-infected plants in both the low and high nitrogen treatments, and endophyte-infected plants in the high nitrogen treatment. There was no protein reduction for endophyte-infected plants in the low nitrogen treatment.

Newman et al. note, "the endophyte is present in many native and naturalized populations and the most widely sown cultivars of F. arundinacea," so the first two situations in which the CO_2-induced protein reduction occurred (those involving non-endophyte-infected plants) are not typical of the real world. In addition, since the dry-weight biomass yield of the forage was increased by fully 53% under the low nitrogen regime, and since the 10-times-greater high nitrogen regime boosted yields only by an additional 8%, there would appear to be no need to apply extra nitrogen to F. arundinacea in a CO_2-enriched environment.

Consequently, under best management practices in a doubled-CO_2 world of the future, little or no nitrogen would be added to the soil, and there would be little or no reduction in the crude protein content of F. arundinacea. But there would be more than 50% more of it produced on the same amount of land.

With respect to the final plant quality (forage digestibility) studied by Newman et al., increasing soil nitrogen lowered in vitro neutral detergent fiber digestibility in both ambient and CO_2-enriched air, and this phenomenon was most pronounced in the elevated CO_2 treatment. Under low nitrogen conditions there again was no decline in plant digestibility. Hence, there is a second good reason not to apply extra nitrogen to F. arundinacea in a high CO_2 world of the future, and little need to do so.

With respect to the unmanaged world of nature, increases in the air's CO_2 content often, but not always (Goverde et al., 1999), lead to greater decreases in the concentrations of nitrogen and protein in the foliage of C_3 as compared to C_4 grasses

(Wand *et al.*, 1999). As a result, in the words of Barbehenn *et al.* (2004a), "it has been predicted that insect herbivores will increase their feeding damage on C_3 plants to a greater extent than on C_4 plants (Lincoln *et al.*, 1984, 1986; Lambers, 1993)."

To test this hypothesis, Barbehenn *et al.* (2004a) grew *Lolium multiflorum* Lam. (Italian ryegrass, a common C_3 pasture grass) and *Bouteloua curtipendula* (Michx.) Torr. (sideoats gramma, a native C_4 rangeland grass) in chambers maintained at either the ambient atmospheric CO_2 concentration of 370 ppm or the doubled CO_2 concentration of 740 ppm for two months, after which newly molted sixth-instar larvae of *Pseudaletia unipuncta* (a grass-specialist noctuid) and *Spodoptera frugiperda* (a generalist noctuid) were allowed to feed on the grasses. As expected, foliage protein concentration decreased by 20% in the C_3 grass, but by only 1% in the C_4 grass, when grown in the CO_2-enriched air. However, and "contrary to our expectations," Barbehenn *et al.* write, "neither caterpillar species significantly increased its consumption rate to compensate for the lower concentration of protein in [the] C_3 grass," and "this result does not support the hypothesis that C_3 plants will be subject to greater rates of herbivory relative to C_4 plants in future [high-CO_2] atmospheric conditions (Lincoln *et al.*, 1984)." In addition, "despite significant changes in the nutritional quality of *L. multiflorum* under elevated CO_2," they report "no effect on the relative growth rate of either caterpillar species on either grass species resulted," and there were "no significant differences in insect performance between CO_2 levels."

In a similar study, Barbehenn *et al.* (2004b) allowed grasshopper (*Melanoplus sanguinipes*) nymphs reared to the fourth-instar stage to feed on the grasses. Once again, "contrary to the hypothesis that insect herbivores will increase their feeding rates disproportionately in C_3 plants under elevated atmospheric CO_2," they found "*M. sanguinipes* did not significantly increase its consumption rate when feeding on the C_3 grass grown under elevated CO_2." They suggest this observation implies "post-ingestive mechanisms enable these grasshoppers to compensate for variable nutritional quality in their host plants," and some of these post-ingestive responses may include "changes in gut size, food residence time, digestive enzyme levels, and nutrient metabolism (Simpson and Simpson, 1990; Bernays and Simpson, 1990; Hinks *et al.*, 1991; Zanotto *et al.*, 1993; Yang and Joern, 1994a,b)." Their data indicate *M. sanguinipes* growth rates may have increased, perhaps

by as much as 12%, when feeding upon the C_3 foliage that had been produced in the CO_2-enriched air.

With respect to both managed agricultural crops and the wild plants of Earth's natural ecosystems, it appears the ongoing rise of the air's CO_2 concentration will have few negative impacts of any consequence on the nutritive value of their grains and foliage in terms of protein concentration. In tree crops such as citrus, CO_2-induced changes in the activities of certain foliar proteins could lead to vast increases in their yield potential, as elucidated by the work of Idso *et al.* (2001).

References

Agrawal, M. and Deepak, S.S. 2003. Physiological and biochemical responses of two cultivars of wheat to elevated levels of CO_2 and SO_2, singly and in combination. *Environmental Pollution* **121**: 189–197.

Allard, V., Newton, P.C.D., Lieffering, M., Clark, H., Matthew, C., Soussana, J.-F., and Gray, Y.S. 2003. Nitrogen cycling in grazed pastures at elevated CO_2: N returns by ruminants. *Global Change Biology* **9**: 1731–1742.

Barbehenn, R.V., Karowe, D.N., and Chen, Z. 2004b. Performance of a generalist grasshopper on a C_3 and a C_4 grass: compensation for the effects of elevated CO_2 on plant nutritional quality. *Oecologia* **140**: 96–103.

Barbehenn, R.V., Karowe, D.N., and Spickard, A. 2004a. Effects of elevated atmospheric CO_2 on the nutritional ecology of C_3 and C_4 grass-feeding caterpillars. *Oecologia* **140**: 86–95.

Barney, D.J., Grieve, D.G., Macleod, G.K., and Young, L.G. 1981. Response of cows to a reduction in dietary crude protein from 17 to 13% during early lactation. *Journal of Dairy Science* **64**: 25–33.

Bernays, E.A. and Simpson, S.J. 1990. Nutrition. In: Chapman, R.F. and Joern, A. (Eds.) *Biology of Grasshoppers*. Wiley, New York, NY, pp. 105–127.

Campbell, B.D., Stafford Smith, D.M., Ash, A.J., Fuhrer, J., Gifford, R.M., Hiernaux, P., Howden, S.M., Jones, M.B., Ludwig, J.A., Manderscheid, R., Morgan, J.A., Newton, P.C.D., Nosberger, J., Owensby, C.E., Soussana, J.F., Tuba, Z., and ZuoZhong, C. 2000. A synthesis of recent global change research on pasture and rangeland production: reduced uncertainties and their management implications. *Agriculture, Ecosystems and Environment* **82**: 39–55.

Dent, J.W. and Aldrich, D.T.A. 1963. The inter-relationships between heading date, yield, chemical composition and digestibility in varieties of perennial ryegrass, timothy, cooksfoot and meadow fescue. *Journal of the National Institute of Agricultural Botany* **9**: 261–281.

Evans, L.T. 1993. *Crop Evolution, Adaptation and Yield.* Cambridge University Press, Cambridge, UK.

Goverde, M., Bazin, A., Shykoff, J.A., and Erhardt, A. 1999. Influence of leaf chemistry of *Lotus corniculatus* (Fabaceae) on larval development of *Polyommatus icarus* (Lepidoptera, Lycaenidae): effects of elevated CO_2 and plant genotype. *Functional Ecology* **13**: 801–810.

Hartwig, U.A., Luscher, A., Daepp, M., Blum, H., Soussana, J.F., and Nosberger, J. 2000. Due to symbiotic N2 fixation, five years of elevated atmospheric pCO_2 had no effect on litter N concentration in a fertile grassland ecosystem. *Plant and Soil* **224**: 43–50.

Heagle, A.S., Miller, J.E., and Pursley, W.A. 1998. Influence of ozone stress on soybean response to carbon dioxide enrichment: III. Yield and seed quality. *Crop Science* **38**: 128–134.

Hinks, C.R., Cheeseman, M.T., Erlandson, M.A., Olfert, O., and Westcott, N.D. 1991. The effects of kochia, wheat and oats on digestive proteinases and the protein economy of adult grasshoppers, *Malanoplus sanguinipes*. *Journal of Insect Physiology* **37**: 417–430.

Humphreys, M.O. 1989. Water-soluble carbohydrates in perennial ryegrass breeding. III. Relationships with herbage production, digestibility and crude protein content. *Grass and Forage Science* **44**: 423–430.

Idso, K.E., Hoober, J.K., Idso, S.B., Wall, G.W., and Kimball, B.A. 2001. Atmospheric CO_2 enrichment influences the synthesis and mobilization of putative vacuolar storage proteins in sour orange tree leaves. *Environmental and Experimental Botany* **48**: 199–211.

Idso, S.B. and Idso, K.E. 2001. Effects of atmospheric CO_2 enrichment on plant constituents related to animal and human health. *Environmental and Experimental Botany* **45**: 179–199.

Jablonski, L.M., Wang, X., and Curtis, P.S. 2002. Plant reproduction under elevated CO_2 conditions: a meta-analysis of reports on 79 crop and wild species. *New Phytologist* **156**: 9–26.

Kaddour, A.A. and Fuller, M.P. 2004. The effect of elevated CO_2 and drought on the vegetative growth and development of durum wheat (*Triticum durum* Desf.) cultivars. *Cereal Research Communications* **32**: 225–232.

Kimball, B.A., Morris, C.F., Pinter Jr., P.J., Wall, G.W., Hunsaker, D.J., Adamsen, F.J., LaMorte, R.L., Leavitt, S.W., Thompson, T.L., Matthias, A.D., and Brooks, T.J. 2001. Elevated CO_2, drought and soil nitrogen effects on wheat grain quality. *New Phytologist* **150**: 295–303.

Lambers, H. 1993. Rising CO_2, secondary plant metabolism, plant-herbivore interactions and litter decomposition. Theoretical considerations. *Vegetatio* **104/105**: 263–271.

Lincoln, D.E., Couvet, D., and Sionit, N. 1986. Responses of an insect herbivore to host plants grown in carbon dioxide enriched atmospheres. *Oecologia* **69**: 556–560.

Lincoln, D.E., Sionit, N., and Strain, B.R. 1984. Growth and feeding response of *Pseudoplusia includens* (Lepidoptera: Noctuidae) to host plants grown in controlled carbon dioxide atmospheres. *Environmental Entomology* **13**: 1527–1530.

Luscher, A., Daepp, M., Blum, H., Hartwig, U.A., and Nosberger, J. 2004. Fertile temperate grassland under elevated atmospheric CO_2—role of feed-back mechanisms and availability of growth resources. *European Journal of Agronomy* **21**: 379–398.

Newman, J.A., Abner, M.L., Dado, R.G., Gibson, D.J., Brookings, A., and Parsons, A.J. 2003. Effects of elevated CO_2, nitrogen and fungal endophyte-infection on tall fescue: growth, photosynthesis, chemical composition and digestibility. *Global Change Biology* **9**: 425–437.

Picon-Cochard, C., Teyssonneyre, F., and Besle, J.M., *et al.* 2004. Effects of elevated CO_2 and cutting frequency on the productivity and herbage quality of a semi-natural grassland. *European Journal of Agronomy* **20**: 363–377

Pleijel, H., Mortensen, L., Fuhrer, J., Ojanpera, K., and Danielsson, H. 1999. Grain protein accumulation in relation to grain yield of spring wheat (*Triticum aestivum* L.) grown in open-top chambers with different concentrations of ozone, carbon dioxide and water availability. *Agriculture, Ecosystems and Environment* **72**: 265–270.

Rogers, G.S., Milham, P.J., Gillings, M., and Conroy, J.P. 1996. Sink strength may be the key to growth and nitrogen responses in N-deficient wheat at elevated CO_2. *Australian Journal of Plant Physiology* **23**: 253–264.

Rudorff, B.F.T., Mulchi, C.L., Fenny, P., Lee, E.H., and Rowland, R. 1996. Wheat grain quality under enhanced tropospheric CO_2 and O_3 concentrations. *Journal of Environmental Quality* **25**: 1384–1388.

Simpson, S.J. and Simpson, C.L. 1990. The mechanisms of nutritional compensation by phytophagous insects. In: Bernays, E.A. (Ed.) *Insect-Plant Interactions*, Vol. 2. CRC Press, Boca Raton, FL, pp. 111–160.

Teyssonneyre, F. 2002. Effet d'une augmentation de la concentration atmospherique en CO_2 sur la prairie permanete et sur la competition entre especes prairiales associees. Ph.D. thesis, Orsay, Paris XI, France.

Thomas, J.M.G., Boote, K.J., Allen Jr., L.H., Gallo-Meagher, M., and Davis, J.M. 2003. Elevated temperature and carbon dioxide effects on soybean seed composition and transcript abundance. *Crop Science* **43**: 1548–1557.

Veisz, O., Bencze, S., and Bedo, Z. 2005. Effect of elevated CO_2 on wheat at various nutrient supply levels. *Cereal Research Communications* **33**: 333–336.

Wand, S.J.E., Midgley, G.F., Jones, M.H., and Curtis, P.S. 1999. Responses of wild C_4 and C_3 grass (Poaceae) species to elevated atmospheric CO_2 concentration: a meta-analytic test of current theories and perceptions. *Global Change Biology* **5**: 723–741.

Wittwer, S.H. 1995. *Food, Climate, and Carbon Dioxide: The Global Environment and World Food Production.* CRC Press, Boca Raton, FL.

Yang, Y. and Joern, A. 1994a. Gut size changes in relation to variable food quality and body size in grasshoppers. *Functional Ecology* **8**: 36–45.

Yang, Y. and Joern, A. 1994b. Influence of diet quality, developmental stage, and temperature on food residence time in the grasshopper *Melanoplus differentialis*. *Physiological Zoology* **67**: 598–616.

Zanetti, S., Hartwig, U.A., Van Kessel, C., Luscher, A., Bebeisen, T., Frehner, M., Fischer, B.U., Hendrey, G.R., Blum, G., and Nosberger, J. 1997. Does nitrogen nutrition restrict the CO_2 response of fertile grassland lacking legumes? *Oecologia* **112**: 17–25.

Zanotto, F.P., Simpson, S.J., and Raubenheimer, D. 1993. The regulation of growth by locusts through post-ingestive compensation for variation in the levels of dietary protein and carbohydrate. *Physiological Entomology* **18**: 425–434.

2.22 Respiration

Nearly all of Earth's plants respond favorably to increases in the air's CO_2 concentration by exhibiting enhanced rates of photosynthesis and biomass production during the light part of each day. However, the observed increases in these parameters (especially biomass production) are also due, in part, to CO_2-induced reductions in carbon losses via respiration during both the day and night (the latter called "dark respiration"). The subsections below examine what has been learned about both of these types of respiration from experiments conducted on various herbaceous and woody plants.

2.22.1 Herbaceous Plants

The growth and biomass production of herbaceous crops generally is enhanced by CO_2-induced decreases in respiration during the dark (nighttime) period. However, fundamental information is still lacking on how respiration and the processes supported by it are physiologically controlled, thereby preventing sound interpretations of what seem to be species-specific responses of respiration to elevated CO_2. The precise role of plant respiration in augmenting the sink capacity of herbaceous plants remains uncertain.

2.22.1.1 Crops

- The growth and biomass production of herbaceous crops generally is enhanced by CO_2-induced decreases in respiration during the dark (nighttime) period.

Baker *et al.* (2000) grew rice in Soil-Plant-Atmosphere Research (SPAR) units at atmospheric CO_2 concentrations of 350 and 700 ppm during daylight hours. Under these conditions, rates of dark respiration decreased in both CO_2 treatments with short-term increases in the air's CO_2 concentration at night. However, when dark respiration rates were measured at the CO_2 growth concentrations of the plants, they were not significantly different from each other.

Cousins *et al.* (2001) grew sorghum at atmospheric CO_2 concentrations of 370 and 570 ppm in a free-air CO_2 enrichment (FACE) facility near Phoenix, Arizona (USA). Within six days of planting, the photosynthetic rates of the second leaves of the CO_2-enriched plants were 37% greater than those of the second leaves of the ambiently grown plants. This CO_2-induced photosynthetic enhancement slowly declined with time, stabilizing at about 15% between 23 and 60 days after planting. In addition, when measuring photosynthetic rates at a reduced oxygen concentration of 2%, they observed 16 and 9% increases in photosynthesis for the ambient and CO_2-enriched plants, respectively, which suggests the extra 200 ppm of CO_2 was reducing photorespiratory carbon losses, although this phenomenon did not account for all of the CO_2-induced stimulation of photosynthesis.

Das *et al.* (2002) grew tropical nitrogen-fixing mungbean plants in open-top chambers maintained at atmospheric CO_2 concentrations of either 350 or 600 ppm for two growing seasons, with the extra CO_2 being provided between either days 0 and 20 or days 21 and 40 after germination. The elevated CO_2 decreased rates of respiration by 54 to 62%, with the greatest declines occurring during the first 20 days after germination.

Wang *et al.* (2004) grew well-watered and

fertilized South American tobacco plants from seed in 8.4-liter pots (one plant per pot) filled with sand and housed in controlled-environment growth chambers maintained at atmospheric CO_2 concentrations of either 365 or 730 ppm for nine weeks. Over this period they found the ratio of net photosynthesis per unit leaf area (A) to dark respiration per unit leaf area (Rd) "changed dramatically." Whereas A/Rd was the same in both treatments at the beginning of the measurement period, a month later it had doubled in the CO_2-enriched environment but had risen by only 58% in the ambient CO_2 treatment. Speaking of this finding, the three researchers state, "if the dynamic relationship between A and Rd observed in *N. sylvestris* is applicable to other species, it will have important implications for carbon cycling in terrestrial ecosystems, since plants will assimilate CO_2 more efficiently as they mature."

Bunce (2005) grew soybeans in the field in open-top chambers maintained at atmospheric CO_2 concentrations of ambient and ambient +350 ppm at the Beltsville Agricultural Research Center in Maryland (USA), where net carbon dioxide exchange rate measurements were performed on a total of 16 days between 18 July and 11 September of 2000 and 2003, during the flowering to early pod-filling stages of the growing season. Averaging his results over the course of the study, Bunce found daytime net photosynthesis per unit leaf area was 48% greater in the plants growing in the CO_2-enriched air, and nighttime respiration per unit leaf area was unaffected by elevated CO_2. However, because the extra 350 ppm of CO_2 increased leaf dry mass per unit area by an average of 23%, respiration per unit of mass was significantly lower for the leaves of the soybeans growing in the CO_2-enriched air.

Wang and Curtis (2002) conducted a meta-analysis of the results of 45 area-based dark respiration (Rda) and 44 mass-based dark respiration (Rdm) assessments of the effects of a doubling of the air's CO_2 concentration on 33 species of plants derived from 37 scientific studies. The mean leaf Rda of the suite of herbaceous plants studied was significantly higher (+29%, $P < 0.01$) at elevated CO_2 than at ambient CO_2. When the herbaceous plants were separated into groups that had experienced durations of CO_2 enrichment either shorter or longer than 60 days, the short-term studies exhibited a mean Rda increase of 51% ($P < 0.05$), and the long-term studies exhibited no effect. Hence, for conditions of continuous atmospheric CO_2 enrichment, herbaceous plants likely would experience no change in leaf Rda. In addition, the two researchers found plants exposed to elevated CO_2 for < 100 days "showed significantly less of a reduction in leaf Rdm due to CO_2 enrichment (-12%) than did plants exposed for longer periods (-35%, $P < 0.01$)." Hence, for long-term conditions of continuous atmospheric CO_2 enrichment, herbaceous crops likely would experience an approximate 35% decrease in leaf Rdm.

Bunce (2004) grew six 16-plant batches of soybeans in a single controlled-environment chamber, one to a pot filled with 1.8 liters of vermiculite that was flushed daily with a complete nutrient solution. In three experiments conducted at day/night atmospheric CO_2 concentrations of 370/390 ppm, air temperatures were either 20, 25, or 30°C, and in three other experiments conducted at an air temperature of 25°C, atmospheric CO_2 concentrations were either 40, 370, or 1,400 ppm. At the end of the normal 16 hours of light on the 17th day after planting, half of the plants were harvested and used for the measurement of a number of physical parameters, and measurements of the plant physiological processes of respiration, translocation, and nitrate reduction were made on the other half of the plants over the following eight-hour dark period.

Plotting translocation and nitrate reduction as functions of respiration, Bunce found "a given change in the rate of respiration was accompanied by the same change in the rate of translocation or nitrate reduction, regardless of whether the altered respiration was caused by a change in temperature or by a change in atmospheric CO_2 concentration." Bunce concludes, "the parallel responses of translocation and nitrate reduction for both the temperature and CO_2 treatments make it unlikely that the response of respiration to one variable [CO_2] was an artifact while the response to the other [temperature] was real." Hence, there is reason to believe the oft-observed decreases in dark respiration experienced by plants exposed to elevated levels of atmospheric CO_2, as per the review and analysis studies of Drake *et al.* (1999) and Wang and Curtis (2002), are indeed real and not the result of measurement system defects.

References

Baker, J.T., Allen Jr., L.H., Boote, K.J., and Pickering, N.B. 2000. Direct effects of atmospheric carbon dioxide concentration on whole canopy dark respiration of rice. *Global Change Biology* **6**: 275–286.

Bunce, J.A. 2004. A comparison of the effects of carbon dioxide concentration and temperature on respiration, translocation and nitrate reduction in darkened soybean leaves. *Annals of Botany* **93**: 665–669.

Bunce, J.A. 2005. Response of respiration of soybean leaves grown at ambient and elevated carbon dioxide concentrations to day-to-day variation in light and temperature under field conditions. *Annals of Botany* **95**: 1059–1066.

Cousins, A.B., Adam, N.R., Wall, G.W., Kimball, B.A., Pinter Jr., P.J., Leavitt, S.W., LaMorte, R.L., Matthias, A.D., Ottman, M.J., Thompson, T.L., and Webber, A.N. 2001. Reduced photorespiration and increased energy-use efficiency in young CO_2-enriched sorghum leaves. *New Phytologist* **150**: 275–284.

Das, M., Zaidi, P.H., Pal, M., and Sengupta, U.K. 2002. Stage sensitivity of mungbean (*Vigna radiata* L. Wilczek) to an elevated level of carbon dioxide. *Journal of Agronomy and Crop Science* **188**: 219–224.

Drake, B.G., Azcon-Bieto, J., Berry, J., Bunce, J., Dijkstra, P., Farrar, J., Gifford, R.M., Gonzalez-Meler, M.A., Koch, G., Lambers, H., Siedow, J., and Wullschleger, S. 1999. Does elevated atmospheric CO_2 inhibit mitochondrial respiration in green plants? *Plant, Cell and Environment* **22**: 649–657.

Wang, X., Anderson, O.R., and Griffin, K.L. 2004. Chloroplast numbers, mitochondrion numbers and carbon assimilation physiology of *Nicotiana sylvestris* as affected by CO_2 concentration. *Environmental and Experimental Botany* **51**: 21–31.

Wang, X. and Curtis, P. 2002. A meta-analytical test of elevated CO_2 effects on plant respiration. *Plant Ecology* **161**: 251–261.

2.22.1.2 Other Herbaceous Plants

- Fundamental information is still lacking on how respiration and the processes supported by it are physiologically controlled in herbaceous plants, thereby preventing sound interpretations of what seem to be species-specific responses of respiration to elevated CO_2. The role of plant respiration in augmenting the sink capacity of terrestrial ecosystems remains uncertain.

Rabha and Uprety (1998) grew India mustard plants for an entire season in open-top chambers with either ambient or enriched (600 ppm) atmospheric CO_2 concentrations and adequate or inadequate soil moisture levels. The elevated CO_2 concentration reduced leaf dark respiration rates by about 25% in both soil moisture treatments, which suggests a greater proportion of the increased carbohydrate pool

in the CO_2-enriched plants remained within them to facilitate increases in growth and development.

Ziska and Bunce (1999) grew four C_4 plants in controlled environment chambers maintained at either full-day (24-hour) atmospheric CO_2 concentrations of 350 and 700 ppm or a nocturnal-only CO_2 concentration of 700 ppm (with 350 ppm CO_2 during the day) for about three weeks. In this study, 24-hour CO_2 enrichment caused a significant increase in the photosynthesis (+13%) and total dry mass (+21%) of only one of the four C_4 species (*Amaranthus retroflexus*). There was no significant effect of nocturnal-only CO_2 enrichment on this species, indicating the observed increase in biomass, resulting from 24-hour atmospheric CO_2 enrichment, was not facilitated by greater carbon conservation stemming from a CO_2-induced reduction in dark respiration.

Grunzweig and Korner (2001) constructed model grasslands representative of the Negev of Israel and placed them in growth chambers maintained at atmospheric CO_2 concentrations of 280, 440, and 600 ppm for five months. They also found atmospheric CO_2 enrichment had no effect on nighttime respiratory carbon losses.

Van der Heijden *et al.* (2000) grew peat moss hydroponically within controlled environment chambers maintained at atmospheric CO_2 concentrations of 350 and 700 ppm for up to six months, subjecting the peat moss to three different levels of nitrogen deposition. In all cases, they found the elevated CO_2 reduced rates of dark respiration consistently throughout the study by 40 to 60%.

Gonzalez-Meler *et al.* (2004) reviewed the scientific literature on the effects of atmospheric CO_2 enrichment on plant respiration from the cellular level to the level of entire ecosystems. They report finding, "contrary to what was previously thought, specific respiration rates are generally not reduced when plants are grown at elevated CO_2." Nevertheless, they note, "whole ecosystem studies show that canopy respiration does not increase proportionally to increases in biomass in response to elevated CO_2." This suggests respiration per unit biomass likely is reduced somewhat by atmospheric CO_2 enrichment. However, they also found "a larger proportion of respiration takes place in the root system [when plants are grown in CO_2-enriched air]," which once again obfuscates the issue.

The three researchers remark, "fundamental information is still lacking on how respiration and the processes supported by it are physiologically controlled, thereby preventing sound interpretations of what seem to be species-specific responses of respiration to elevated CO_2," concluding "the role of plant respiration in augmenting the sink capacity of terrestrial ecosystems is still uncertain."

References

Gonzalez-Meler, M.A., Taneva, L., and Trueman, R.J. 2004. Plant respiration and elevated atmospheric CO_2 concentration: Cellular responses and global significance. *Annals of Botany* **94**: 647–656.

Grunzweig, J.M. and Korner, C. 2001. Growth, water and nitrogen relations in grassland model ecosystems of the semi-arid Negev of Israel exposed to elevated CO_2. *Oecologia* **128**: 251–262.

Rabha, B.K. and Uprety, D.C. 1998. Effects of elevated CO_2 and moisture stress on Brassica juncea. *Photosynthetica* **35**: 597–602.

Van der Heijden, E., Verbeek, S.K., and Kuiper, P.J.C. 2000. Elevated atmospheric CO_2 and increased nitrogen deposition: effects on C and N metabolism and growth of the peat moss *Sphagnum recurvum* P. Beauv. Var. *mucronatum* (Russ.) Warnst. *Global Change Biology* **6**: 201–212.

Ziska, L.H. and Bunce, J.A. 1999. Effect of elevated carbon dioxide concentration at night on the growth and gas exchange of selected C_4 species. *Australian Journal of Plant Physiology* **26**: 71–77.

2.22.2 Woody Plants

- Both above and below the soil surface, coniferous trees appear to exhibit significant reductions in respiration in CO_2-enriched air. However, deciduous trees exhibit both increases and decreases, as well as cases of no change. It again appears atmospheric CO_2 enrichment may either increase or decrease woody-plant respiration, but not to any great degree, so the net result for Earth's trees likely would be of little significance.

Plant growth rates are determined largely by the relative magnitudes of carbon gain via photosynthesis and carbon loss via respiration. Although much is known about the effects of atmospheric CO_2 enrichment on the first of these phenomena, much less is known about its effects on the second. The subsections below examine the various effects of CO_2-enriched air on respiration in various types of woody plants.

2.22.2.1 Coniferous Trees

- Both above and below the soil surface, coniferous trees may exhibit significant reductions in respiration in a high-CO_2 world of the future.

Jach and Ceulemans (2000) grew three-year old Scots pine seedlings out-of-doors and rooted in the ground in open-top chambers maintained at atmospheric CO_2 concentrations of either 350 or 750 ppm for two years. To make the experiment more representative of the natural world, they applied no nutrients or irrigation water to the soils in which the trees grew for the duration of the study. After two years of growth under these conditions, dark respiration on a needle mass basis in the CO_2-enriched seedlings was 27 and 33% lower in current-year and one-year-old needles, respectively. The researchers conclude the greater reduction in the older needles arises from the greater duration of elevated CO_2 exposure experienced by those needles.

Hamilton *et al.* (2001) studied the short- and long-term respiratory responses of loblolly pines in a free-air CO_2-enrichment (FACE) study established in 1996 on 13-year-old trees in a North Carolina (USA) plantation, where the CO_2-enriched trees were exposed to an extra 200 ppm of CO_2. This modest increase in the atmosphere's CO_2 concentration produced no significant short-term suppression of dark respiration rates in the trees' needles. Neither did long-term exposure to elevated CO_2 alter maintenance respiration, the amount of CO_2 that is respired to maintain existing plant tissues. However, growth respiration, the amount of CO_2 respired when constructing new tissues, was reduced by 21%.

McDowell *et al.* (1999) grew five-month-old seedlings of western hemlock in root boxes subjected to various root-space CO_2 concentrations (ranging from 90 to 7,000 ppm) for periods of several hours to determine the effects of soil CO_2 concentration on growth, maintenance, and total root respiration. Although elevated CO_2 had no effect on growth respiration, it significantly affected maintenance and total respiration. At a soil CO_2 concentration of 1585 ppm, for example, total and maintenance respiration rates of roots were 55 and 60% lower, respectively, than at 395 ppm. The impact of elevated CO_2 on maintenance respiration was so strong, in fact, it exhibited an exponential decline of about 37% for every doubling of soil CO_2 concentration. This observation is especially important because maintenance respiration comprised 85% of total root respiration in this study.

George *et al.* (2003) begin their work by noting, "several studies have documented a decrease in the specific rate of fine-root respiration for trees grown in elevated atmospheric CO_2," citing Callaway *et al.* (1994), BassiriRad *et al.* (1997), and Crookshanks *et al.* (1998). Then, citing Cotrufo *et al.* (1998) as a basis for the idea that "growth under elevated CO_2 causes a decrease in the nitrogen concentration of roots," which in turn suggests "a reduction in protein concentration," they hypothesize, "the energy required for protein turnover may decline in elevated CO_2 causing a reduction in maintenance respiration," and the resultant "decrease in maintenance respiration with elevated CO_2 may contribute to increases in growth respiration."

To test this hypothesis, George *et al.* measured the maintenance respiration of non-growing fine roots in the absence of nutrients, while quantifying growth respiration from calculated construction costs and the observed production rates of fine roots in two major forest FACE studies: the Duke Forest study of a loblolly pine (*Pinus taeda* L.) plantation and the Oak Ridge National Laboratory (ORNL) Forest study of a sweetgum (*Liquidambar styraciflua* L.) plantation.

Based on unpublished data of R.J. Norby and D.W. Johnson from the ORNL Forest and the data of Finzi *et al.* (2002) from the Duke Forest, George *et al.* report, contrary to their initial assumption, as well as that of Hungate *et al.* (2003), they "were unable to detect an effect of elevated CO_2 on the nitrogen concentration of fine roots for either species." They found a significant reduction of fine-root maintenance respiration in the loblolly pine plantation, but no significant difference in this parameter between the two sweetgum CO_2 treatments. Assessments of CO_2-induced increases in fine-root production in the study of Matamala and Schlesinger (2000) for the loblolly pines and in the study of Norby *et al.* (2002) for the sweetgum trees revealed fine-root biomass increases of 87% in the first case and 77% in the second case in response to an approximate 200-ppm increase in atmospheric CO_2 concentration.

George *et al.* state, "the C:N ratio of fine roots grown in elevated CO_2 was not altered and consequently did not explain the trend of reduced annual fine-root maintenance respiration and the increase in annual fine-root growth respiration for loblolly pine." Instead, they conclude, "for these forests it appears that an increase in fine-root production is the primary factor contributing to the increase in annual growth respiration under elevated CO_2." Hence, they end up rejecting their original hypothesis.

In a non-CO_2-enrichment study, Bronson and Gower (2010) state, "the boreal forest historically has been considered a carbon sink," but "autotrophic respiration is [supposedly] more sensitive than photosynthesis to increases in temperature (Ryan, 1991; Amthor, 1994)." Therefore, in response to global warming, "most models predict autotrophic respiration will increase at a greater rate than photosynthesis, which infers decreased carbon use efficiency and net primary production (Ryan, 1995; VEMAP Members, 1995; Ryan *et al.*, 1996)." This further implies "a substantial increase in temperature could turn the boreal forest into a carbon source (Goulden *et al.*, 1998)," and this positive feedback could lead to an intensification of global warming.

Bronson and Gower studied black spruce trees (*Picea mariana* (Mill.) B.S.P.) growing in large, enclosed greenhouse chambers about 20 km south of Thompson, Manitoba, Canada (55°53'N, 98°20'W). Soil-heating cables were used to warm air and soil temperatures about 5°C over ambient control temperatures. The researchers measured light-saturated net photosynthesis, foliage respiration, and stem respiration in heated and control forest plots during the 2005, 2006, and 2007 growing seasons. Throughout the study, they found "both the older foliage, which developed before the experiment, and the new foliage, developed during the experiment, had similar rates of light-saturated net photosynthesis, foliage respiration and stem respiration across all treatments," which, they write, "underscores the ability of black spruce to maintain homeostasis in a 5°C warmer environment." In addition, while noting many global change models predict a doubling of respiration for every 10°C increase in temperature, Bronson and Gower state in the concluding sentence of their paper, "the results from this and other whole-ecosystem warming experiments do not support this model assumption."

Lhotakova *et al.* (2012) measured rates of light-saturated net photosynthesis and dark respiration in current-year needles of sun-exposed (3rd whorl) and shaded (6th whorl) parts of the canopies of originally 10-year-old Norway spruce (*Picea abies*) trees that were transplanted into native soil (which was given an initial fertilizer treatment) and grown for an additional eight years in the Beskydy Mountains of the Czech Republic within semi-open glass domes having adjustable windows, where the trees were exposed to either the ambient-air CO_2 concentration (AC, which varied from 365 to 377 ppm over the course of the long-term experiment) or to an enriched-air CO_2 concentration (EC, which was maintained at a steady value of 700 ppm).

Based on the graphical representations of Lhotakova *et al.*'s findings, it can be calculated that at the end of the eight-year CO_2 enrichment experiment there was a CO_2-induced increase in light-saturated net photosynthesis of approximately 115% in the trees' Sun-exposed needles and about 55% in their shaded needles. It can likewise be calculated there was an approximate 20% decrease in the mean dark respiration rate of the trees' Sun-exposed needles and about 40% in their shaded needles.

The nine Czech scientists conclude, "the positive effect of EC on net CO_2 assimilation rates, as we observed in juvenile Norway spruce trees in the present study, was also shown in other long-term studies on conifers," citing Maier *et al.* (2008), Kosvancova *et al.* (2009), Crous *et al.* (2008), and Logan *et al.* (2009). In addition, "it appears that forest trees, including conifers, suppress respiration rates under long-term CO_2 enrichment," citing Zhou *et al.* (2007) and Gonzalez-Meler *et al.* (2009). Thus they conclude, "the observed stimulation of light-saturated net photosynthesis simultaneously with suppressed dark respiration under EC may lead to higher biomass accumulation," as Runion *et al.* (2006) had observed earlier and reported for longleaf pine trees.

The results of the experiments described in this section suggest coniferous trees may exhibit reductions in respiration both above and below the soil surface in a high-CO_2 world of the future.

References

Amthor, J.S. 1994. Scaling CO_2 photosynthesis relationships from the leaf to the canopy. *Photosynthesis Research* **39**: 321–350.

BassiriRad, H., Griffin, K.L., Reynolds, J.F., and Strain, B.R. 1997. Changes in root NH^+_4 and NO^-_3 absorption rates of loblolly and ponderosa pine in response to CO_2 enrichment. *Plant and Soil* **190**: 1–9.

Bronson, D.R. and Gower, S.T. 2010. Ecosystem warming does not affect photosynthesis or aboveground autotrophic respiration for boreal black spruce. *Tree Physiology* **30**: 441–449.

Callaway, R.M., DeLucia, E.H., Thomas, E.M., and Schlesinger, W.H. 1994. Compensatory responses of CO_2 exchange and biomass allocation and their effects on the relative growth rate of ponderosa pine in different CO_2 and temperature regimes. *Oecologia* **98**: 159–166.

Cotrufo, M.F., Ineson, P., and Scott, A. 1998. Elevated CO_2 reduces the nitrogen concentration of plant tissues. *Global Change Biology* **4**: 43–54.

Crookshanks, M., Taylor, G., and Broadmeadow, M. 1998. Elevated CO_2 and tree root growth: contrasting responses in *Fraxinus excelsior*, *Quercus petraea* and *Pinus sylvestris*. *New Phytologist* **138**: 241–250.

Crous, K.Y., Walters, M.B., and Ellsworth, D.S. 2008. Elevated CO_2 concentration affects leaf photosynthesis-nitrogen relationships in Pinus taeda over nine years in FACE. *Tree Physiology* **28**: 607–614.

Finzi, A.C., DeLucia, E.H., Hamilton, J.G., Richter, D.D., and Schlesinger, W.H. 2002. The nitrogen budget of a pine forest under free air CO_2 enrichment. *Oecologia* **132**: 567–578.

George, K., Norby, R.J., Hamilton, J.G., and DeLucia, E.H. 2003. Fine-root respiration in a loblolly pine and sweetgum forest growing in elevated CO_2. *New Phytologist* **160**: 511–522.

Gonzalez-Meler, M.A., Blanc-Betes, E., Flower, C.E., Ward, J.K., and Gomez-Casanovas, N. 2009. Plastic and adaptive responses of plant respiration to changes in atmospheric CO_2 concentration. *Physiologia Plantarum* **137**: 473–484.

Goulden, M.L., Wofsy, S.C., and Harden, J.W. 1998. Sensitivity of boreal forest carbon balance to soil thaw. *Science* **279**: 214–217.

Hamilton, J.G., Thomas, R.B., and DeLucia, E.H. 2001. Direct and indirect effects of elevated CO_2 on leaf respiration in a forest ecosystem. *Plant, Cell and Environment* **24**: 975–982.

Hungate, B.A., Dukes, J.S., Shaw, M.R., Luo, Y., and Field, C.B. 2003. Nitrogen and climate change. *Science* **302**: 1512–1513.

Jach, M.E. and Ceulemans, R. 2000. Short- versus long-term effects of elevated CO_2 on night-time respiration of needles of Scots pine (*Pinus sylvestris* L.). *Photosynthetica* **38**: 57–67.

Kosvancova, M., Urban, O., Sprtova, M., Hrstka, M., Kalina, J., Tomaskova, I., Spunda, V., and Marek, M.V. 2009. Photosynthetic induction in broadleaved *Fagus sylvatica* and coniferous *Picea abies* cultivated under ambient and elevated CO_2 concentrations. *Plant Science* **177**: 123–130.

Lhotakova, Z., Urban, O., Dubankova, M., Cvikrova, M., Tomaskova, I., Kubinova, L., Zvara, K., Marek, M.W., and Albrechtova, J. 2012. The impact of long-term CO_2 enrichment on Sun and shade needles of Norway spruce (*Picea abies*): Photosynthetic performance, needle anatomy and phenolics accumulation. *Plant Science* **188–189**: 60–70.

Logan, B.A., Combs, A., Myers, K., Kent, R., Stanley, L., and Tissue, D.T. 2009. Seasonal response of photosynthetic electron transport and energy dissipation in the eighth year of exposure to elevated atmospheric CO_2 (FACE) in *Pinus taeda* (loblolly pine). *Tree Physiology* **29**: 789–797.

Maier, C.A., Palmroth, S., and Ward, E. 2008. Short-term effects of fertilization on photosynthesis and leaf morphology of field-grown loblolly pine following long-term exposure to elevated CO_2 concentration. *Tree Physiology* **28**: 597–606.

Matamala, R. and Schlesinger, W.H. 2000. Effects of elevated atmospheric CO_2 on fine root production and activity in an intact temperate forest ecosystem. *Global Change Biology* **6**: 967–979.

McDowell, N.G., Marshall, J.D., Qi, J., and Mattson, K. 1999. Direct inhibition of maintenance respiration in western hemlock roots exposed to ambient soil carbon dioxide concentrations. *Tree Physiology* **19**: 599–605.

Norby, R.J., Hanson, P.J., O'Neill, E.G., Tschaplinski, T.J., Weltzin, J.F., Hansen, R.A., Cheng, W., Wullschleger, S.D., Gunderson, C.A., Edwards, N.T., and Johnson, D.W. 2002. Net primary productivity of a CO_2-enriched deciduous forest and the implications for carbon storage. *Ecological Applications* **12**: 1261–1266.

Runion, G.B., Davis, M.A., Pritchard, S.G., Prior, S.A., Mitchell, R.J., Torbert, H.A., Rogers, H.H., and Dute, R.R. 2006. Effects of elevated atmospheric carbon dioxide on biomass and carbon accumulation in a model regenerating longleaf pine community. *Journal of Environmental Quality* **35**: 1478–1486.

Ryan, M.G. 1991. Effects of climate change on plant respiration. *Ecological Applications* **1**: 157–167.

Ryan, M.G. 1995. Foliar maintenance respiration of sub-alpine and boreal trees and shrubs in relation to nitrogen-content. *Plant, Cell and Environment* **18**: 765–772.

Ryan, M.G., Hunt, E.R., McMurtrie, R.E., Agren, G.I., Aber, J.D., Friend, A.D., Rastetter, E.B., Pulliam, W.M., Raison, R.J., and Linder, S. 1996. Comparing models of ecosystem function for temperate conifer forests. In: Greymeyer, A.I., Hall, D.O., Agren, G.I., and Melillo, J.M. (Eds.) *Global Change: Effects on Coniferous Forests and Grasslands*. John Wiley, New York, New York, USA, pp. 313–361.

VEMAP Members. 1995. Vegetation Ecosystem Modeling and Analysis Project: Comparing biogeography and biogeochemistry models in a continental-scale of terrestrial ecosystem response to climate change and CO_2 doubling. *Global Biogeochemical Cycles* **9**: 407–437.

Zhou, Y.M., Han, S.J., Zhang, H.S., Xin, L.H., and Zheng, J.Q. 2007. Response of needle dark respiration of *Pinus koraiensis* and *Pinus sylvestriformis* to elevated CO_2 concentrations for four growing seasons' exposure. *Science in China Series D—Earth Sciences* **50**: 613–619.

2.22.2.2 Deciduous Trees

- Several experiments conducted on deciduous trees indicate there are both increases and decreases in respiration rates in response to atmospheric CO_2 enrichment, as well as cases of no change in respiration. More data are needed before any general conclusions may be drawn.

Wang and Curtis (2001) grew cuttings of two male and two female trembling aspen trees for about five months on soils containing low and high nitrogen contents in open-top chambers maintained at atmospheric CO_2 concentrations of 380 and 765 ppm. They found gender had little effect on dark respiration rates, but elevated CO_2 increased them, by 6% and 32% in the low and high soil nitrogen treatments, respectively. On the other hand, Karnosky *et al.* (1999) grew both O_3-sensitive and O_3-tolerant aspen clones for one full year in free-air CO_2-enrichment (FACE) plots maintained at atmospheric CO_2 concentrations of 360 and 560 ppm, finding the extra CO_2 decreased dark respiration rates by 24%.

Gielen *et al.* (2003) measured stem respiration rates of white, black, and robusta poplar trees in a high-density forest plantation in the third year of a FACE experiment in which the CO_2 concentration of the air surrounding the trees was increased to a value of approximately 550 ppm. They write, "stem respiration rates were not affected by the FACE treatment," and "FACE did not influence the relationships between respiration rate and both stem temperature and relative growth rate." In addition, they found "no effect of the FACE treatment on Rm [maintenance respiration, which is related to the sustaining of existing cells] and Rg [growth respiration, which is related to the synthesis of new tissues]."

Hamilton *et al.* (2001) studied respiratory responses of sweetgum trees growing in the understory of a loblolly pine plantation (but occasionally reaching the top of the canopy) to an extra 200 ppm of CO_2 in a FACE study conducted in North Carolina (USA). They determined the modest increase in the air's CO_2 concentration did not appear to alter maintenance respiration to any significant degree, but it reduced dark respiration by an average of 10% and growth respiration of leaves at the top of the canopy by nearly 40%.

References

Gielen, B., Scarascia-Mugnozza, G., and Ceulemans, R.

2003. Stem respiration of *Populus* species in the third year of free-air CO_2 enrichment. *Physiologia Plantarum* **117**: 500–507.

Hamilton, J.G., Thomas, R.B., and DeLucia, E.H. 2001. Direct and indirect effects of elevated CO_2 on leaf respiration in a forest ecosystem. *Plant, Cell and Environment* **24**: 975–982.

Karnosky, D.F., Mankovska, B., Percy, K., Dickson, R.E., Podila, G.K., Sober, J., Noormets, A., Hendrey, G., Coleman, M.D., Kubiske, M., Pregitzer, K.S., and Isebrands, J.G. 1999. Effects of tropospheric O_3 on trembling aspen and interaction with CO_2: results from an O_3-gradient and a FACE experiment. *Water, Air, and Soil Pollution* **116**: 311–322.

Wang, X. and Curtis, P.S. 2001. Gender-specific responses of *Populus tremuloides* to atmospheric CO_2 enrichment. *New Phytologist* **150**: 675–684.

2.22.2.3 Multiple Tree Studies

- Experimental results are contradictory, suggesting atmospheric CO_2 enrichment may either increase, decrease, or have little effect on woody-plant respiration.

Amthor (2000) measured dark respiration rates of intact leaves of nine tree species growing naturally in an American deciduous forest. Within a specially designed leaf chamber, the CO_2 concentration surrounding individual leaves was stabilized at 400 ppm for 15 minutes, and their respiration rates were measured for 30 minutes, after which the CO_2 concentration in the leaf chamber was raised to 800 ppm for 15 minutes and respiration data were again recorded for the same leaves. This revealed elevated CO_2 had little effect on leaf dark respiration rates. The extra 400 ppm of CO_2 within the measurement cuvette decreased the median respiration rate by only 1.5% across the nine tree species; this observation led Amthor to state the "rising atmospheric CO_2 concentration has only a small direct effect on tree leaf respiration in deciduous forests." He calculated that effect could be "more than eliminated by a 0.22°C temperature increase." He thus concludes, "future direct effects of increasing CO_2 in combination with warming could stimulate tree leaf respiration in their sum," and this consequence "would translate into only slight, if any, effects on the carbon balance of temperate deciduous forests in a future atmosphere containing as much as [800 ppm] CO_2."

Amthor's conclusion is debatable, however, because it is based on extrapolation of the short-term respiratory responses of individual leaves exposed to elevated CO_2 for only an hour or two, to that of entire trees, many of which will experience rising CO_2 levels for a century or more during their lifetimes. Trees are long-lived organisms that should not be expected to reveal the nature of their long-term responses to elevated atmospheric CO_2 concentrations on as short a time scale as 15 minutes. Their respiratory responses may change significantly with the passage of time as they acclimate and optimize their physiology and growth patterns to the gradually rising CO_2 content of Earth's atmosphere, as evidenced by the findings of two other studies.

In the first study, Wang and Curtis (2002) conducted a meta-analysis of the results of 45 area-based dark respiration (Rda) and 44 mass-based dark respiration (Rdm) assessments of the effects of an approximate doubling of the air's CO_2 concentration on 33 species of plants (both herbaceous and woody) derived from 37 scientific publications. The mean leaf Rda of the woody plants they analyzed was unaffected by elevated CO_2. There was, however, an effect on mean leaf Rdm, and it was determined to be time-dependent. The woody plants exposed to elevated CO_2 for less than 100 days, the reviewing scientists write, "showed significantly less of a reduction in leaf Rdm due to CO_2 enrichment (-12%) than did plants exposed for longer periods (-35%, P < 0.01)." Hence, for conditions of continuous long-term atmospheric CO_2 enrichment, the results of Wang and Curtis's analysis suggest woody plants may experience an approximate 35% decrease in leaf Rdm.

In the second study, Drake *et al.* (1999) also conducted a comprehensive analysis of the peer-reviewed scientific literature to determine the effects of elevated atmospheric CO_2 concentrations on plant respiration rates. They found atmospheric CO_2 enrichment typically decreased respiration rates in mature foliage, stems, and roots of CO_2-enriched plants relative to rates measured in plants grown in ambient air. When normalized on a biomass basis, they determined a doubling of the atmosphere's CO_2 concentration likely would reduce plant respiration rates by an average of 18%. To determine the potential effects of this phenomenon on annual global carbon cycling, which the 12 researchers say "will enhance the quantity of carbon stored by forests," they put a 15% CO_2-induced respiration reduction into a carbon sequestration model, finding an additional 6 to 7 Gt of carbon would remain sequestered within the terrestrial biosphere each year, substantially strengthening the terrestrial carbon sink.

Davey *et al.* (2004) reached a different conclusion, noting, "Averaged across many previous investigations, doubling the CO_2 concentration has frequently been reported to cause an instantaneous reduction of leaf dark respiration measured as CO_2 efflux." But they point out "no known mechanism accounts for this effect, and four recent studies [Amthor (2000); Amthor *et al.* (2001); Jahnke (2001); Jahnke and Krewitt (2002)] have shown that the measurement of respiratory CO_2 efflux is prone to experimental artifacts that could account for the reported response."

Davey *et al.* employed a high-resolution dual channel oxygen analyzer in an open gas exchange system to measure the respiratory O_2 uptake of nine species of plants in response to a short-term increase in atmospheric CO_2 concentration, as well as the response of seven species to long-term elevation of the air's CO_2 content in four field experiments. They found "[more than] six hundred separate measurements of respiration failed to reveal any decrease in respiratory O_2 uptake with an instantaneous increase in CO_2." Nor could they detect any response to a fivefold increase in the air's CO_2 concentration or the total removal of CO_2 from the air. They also note, "this lack of response of respiration to elevated CO_2 was independent of treatment method, developmental stage, beginning or end of night, and the CO_2 concentration at which the plants had been grown." In the long-term field studies, there was a respiratory response, but it was small (7% on a leaf mass basis), and it was positive, not negative.

The most reasonable conclusion from these contradictory results is that atmospheric CO_2 enrichment induces both increases and decreases in respiration rates, as well as cases of no change in respiration. More data are needed before any general conclusions may be drawn.

References

Amthor, J.S. 2000. Direct effect of elevated CO_2 on nocturnal in situ leaf respiration in nine temperate deciduous tree species is small. *Tree Physiology* **20**: 139–144.

Amthor, J.S., Koch, G.W., Willms, J.R., and Layzell, D.B. 2001. Leaf O_2 uptake in the dark is independent of coincident CO_2 partial pressure. *Journal of Experimental Botany* **52**: 2235–2238.

Davey, P.A., Hunt, S., Hymus, G.J., DeLucia, E.H., Drake, B.G., Karnosky, D.F., and Long, S.P. 2004. Respiratory oxygen uptake is not decreased by an instantaneous elevation of [CO_2], but is increased with long-term growth in the field at elevated [CO_2]. *Plant Physiology* **134**: 520–527.

Drake, B.G., Azcon-Bieto, J., Berry, J., Bunce, J., Dijkstra, P., Farrar, J., Gifford, R.M., Gonzalez-Meler, M.A., Koch, G., Lambers, H., Siedow, J., and Wullschleger, S. 1999. Does elevated atmospheric CO_2 inhibit mitochondrial respiration in green plants? *Plant, Cell and Environment* **22**: 649–657.

Jahnke, S. 2001. Atmospheric CO_2 concentration does not directly affect leaf respiration in bean or poplar. *Plant, Cell and Environment* **24**: 1139–1151.

Jahnke, S. and Krewitt, M. 2002. Atmospheric CO_2 concentration may directly affect leaf respiration measurement in tobacco, but not respiration itself. *Plant, Cell and Environment* **25**: 641–651.

Wang, X. and Curtis, P. 2002. A meta-analytical test of elevated CO_2 effects on plant respiration. *Plant Ecology* **161**: 251–261.

2.23 Roots

As indicated in the subsections below, elevated CO_2 nearly always increases root biomass—often even more than shoot biomass—by increasing the size of taproots and the number and size of lateral roots, along with fine-root biomass and a number of other important root properties.

2.23.1 Crops

- As the air's CO_2 content continues to rise, most crops will develop larger and more extensive root systems that should help them to better cope with periods of reduced soil moisture. This chain of events should make the soil environment more favorable for plant growth and development in a high-CO_2 world of the future.

Hodge and Millard (1998) grew narrowleaf plantain (*Plantago lanceolata*) seedlings for six weeks in controlled environment growth rooms maintained at atmospheric CO_2 concentrations of either 400 or 800 ppm. By the end of this period, the plants in the 800-ppm air exhibited increases in shoot and root dry matter production 159 and 180% greater, respectively, than the corresponding dry matter increases experienced by the plants growing in 400-ppm air, and the amount of plant carbon recovered from the potting medium (sand) was 3.2 times greater in the elevated-CO_2 treatment. Thus, the belowground growth stimulation provided by atmospheric CO_2 enrichment was greater than that experienced aboveground.

Wechsung et al. (1999) grew spring wheat (Triticum aestivum) in rows in a FACE study employing atmospheric CO_2 concentrations of 370 and 550 ppm and irrigation treatments that periodically replaced either 50 or 100% of prior potential evapotranspiration, in an effort to determine the effects of elevated CO_2 and water stress on root growth. They found elevated CO_2 increased in-row root dry weight by an average of 22% during the growing season under both the wet and dry irrigation regimes. In addition, during the vegetative growth phase, atmospheric CO_2 enrichment increased inter-row root dry weight by 70%, indicating plants grown in elevated CO_2 developed greater lateral root systems than plants grown at ambient CO_2. During the reproductive growth phase, elevated CO_2 stimulated the branching of lateral roots into inter-row areas, but only when water was limiting to growth. In addition, the CO_2-enriched plants tended to display greater root dry weights at a given depth than did ambiently grown plants.

In a comprehensive review of all prior FACE experiments conducted on agricultural crops, Kimball et al. (2002) determined for a 300-ppm increase in atmospheric CO_2 concentration, the root biomass of wheat, ryegrass, and rice experienced an average increase of 70% at ample water and nitrogen, 58% at low nitrogen, and 34% at low water. Clover experienced a 38% increase at ample water and nitrogen and a 32% increase at low nitrogen. Cotton exhibited a 96% increase in root biomass at ample water and nitrogen.

Zhao et al. (2000) germinated pea (Pisum sativum) seeds and exposed the young plants to various atmospheric CO_2 concentrations in controlled environment chambers to determine whether elevated CO_2 affects root border cells, which are major contributors of root exudates in this and most other agronomic plants. They found elevated CO_2 increased the production of root border cells in pea seedlings. In going from ambient air to air enriched to 3,000 and 6,000 ppm CO_2, border-cell numbers increased by more than 50 and 100%, respectively. Hence, as the CO_2 content of the air continues to rise, peas (and possibly many other crop plants) likely will produce greater numbers of root border cells, which should increase the amounts of root exudations occurring in their rhizospheres, which further suggests associated soil microbial and fungal activities will be stimulated

as a result of the increases in plant-derived carbon inputs these organisms require to meet their energy needs.

Van Ginkel et al. (1996) grew perennial ryegrass (Lolium perenne) plants from seed in two growth chambers for 71 days under continuous $^{14}CO_2$-labeling of the atmosphere at CO_2 concentrations of 350 and 700 ppm at two soil nitrogen levels. At the conclusion of this part of the experiment, the plants were harvested and their roots dried, pulverized, and mixed with soil in one-liter pots placed in two wind tunnels in an open field, one of which had ambient air of 361 ppm CO_2 flowing through it, and one of which had air of 706 ppm CO_2 flowing through it. Several of the containers were then seeded with more Lolium perenne, others were similarly seeded the following year, and still others were kept bare for two years. At the ends of the first and second years, the different degrees of decomposition of the original plant roots were assessed.

The scientists determined shoot and root growth were enhanced by 13 and 92%, respectively, by the extra CO_2 in the initial 71-day portion of the experiment, again demonstrating the significant benefits often conferred on plant roots by atmospheric CO_2 enrichment. They also found the decomposition of the high-CO_2-grown roots in the high-CO_2 wind tunnel was 19% lower than that of the low-CO_2-grown roots in the low-CO_2 wind tunnel at the end of the first year. Decomposition was 14% lower at the end of the second year in the low-nitrogen-grown plants but equivalent in the high-nitrogen-grown plants. It was also determined the presence of living roots reduced the decomposition rate of dead roots below the dead-root-only decomposition rate observed in the bare soil treatment. Van Ginkel et al. conclude, "the combination of higher root yields at elevated CO_2 combined with a decrease in root decomposition will lead to a longer residence time of C in the soil and probably to a higher C storage."

References

Hodge, A. and Millard, P. 1998. Effect of elevated CO_2 on carbon partitioning and exudate release from Plantago lanceolata seedlings. Physiologia Plantarum **103**: 280–286.

Kimball, B.A., Kobayashi, K., and Bindi, M. 2002. Responses of agricultural crops to free-air CO_2 enrichment. Advances in Agronomy **77**: 293–368.

Van Ginkel, J.H., Gorissen, A., and van Veen, J.A. 1996. Long-term decomposition of grass roots as affected by elevated atmospheric carbon dioxide. *Journal of Environmental Quality* **25**: 1122–1128.

Wechsung, G., Wechsung, F., Wall, G.W., Adamsen, F.J., Kimball, B.A., Pinter Jr., P.J., LaMorte, R.L., Garcia, R.L., and Kartschall, T. 1999. The effects of free-air CO_2 enrichment and soil water availability on spatial and seasonal patterns of wheat root growth. *Global Change Biology* **5**: 519–529.

Zhao, X., Misaghi, I.J., and Hawes, M.C. 2000. Stimulation of border cell production in response to increased carbon dioxide levels. *Plant Physiology* **122**: 181–188.

2.23.2 Grasses

- Root biomass in grasslands may have increased markedly as the air's CO_2 content rose following the termination of the last glacial period, but even more substantial increases are expected if the air's CO_2 content continues to rise as projected, implying ever-greater grassland root biomass.

Many and varied experiments have addressed how the roots of grasses respond to increases in the air's CO_2 concentration and/or soil temperature. Regarding warming, Fitter *et al.* (1999) studied a site on the Great Dun Fell in the United Kingdom, where they determined root birth and death rates from biweekly minirhizotron video images obtained over one experiment of six months' duration and another of 18 months' duration in an upland grassland, where the soils of half of the treatment replications were artificially maintained 2.8°C above ambient at a depth of 2 cm. This warming increased both root production and root death by approximately equivalent amounts. Therefore, they conclude, "the effect of a warmer climate will be a similar acceleration in both [root] birth and death processes and these will have no direct effect on the soil carbon store."

Regarding atmospheric CO_2 enrichment, Crookshanks *et al.* (1998) sprouted seeds of the small and fast-growing *Arabidopsis thaliana* plant on agar medium in Petri dishes and grew the resulting immature plants in controlled-environment chambers maintained at atmospheric CO_2 concentrations of either 355 or 700 ppm. Visual assessments of root growth were made after emergence of the roots from the seeds, and microscopic investigations of root cell properties were conducted. The scientists found the CO_2-enriched plants directed a greater proportion of their newly produced biomass into root- as opposed to shoot-growth, and the young plants produced longer primary roots and more and longer lateral roots. These effects were found to be related to the CO_2-induced stimulation of mitotic activity, accelerated cortical cell expansion, and increased cell wall plasticity.

Milchunas *et al.* (2005) conducted a five-year open-top chamber study (ambient CO_2 = 360 ppm, enriched CO_2 = 720 ppm) in semiarid shortgrass steppe grassland at the USDA-ARS Central Plains Experimental Range in north central Colorado (USA), where 88% of the ecosystem's biomass was provided by three codominant species—*Bouteloua gracilis* (H.B.K.) Lag., *Stipa comata* (Trin and Rupr.), and *Pascopyrum smithii* (Rybd.)—and where a subfrutescent shrub (*Artemesia frigida* Willd.) was also abundant. They obtained video-image data on root growth and decay in each treatment-replicate from 18 minirhizotron tubes that acquired video images to a depth of 40 cm four to five times a year. Root biomass data were obtained from two 20-cm-diameter cylinders driven into the ground within each chamber and collected yearly in the autumn.

They found root-length growth was 52% greater in the CO_2-enriched chambers than in the ambient-air chambers, and root-length losses were 37% greater in the elevated-CO_2 air. The difference between the CO_2-induced growth and decay stimulations was largely attributable to the 41% longer lifespan of the CO_2-enriched roots, which resulted in a CO_2-induced root-length pool size increase of 41%. In the upper part of the soil profile, root diameters typically were observed to be larger in the CO_2-enriched chambers, leading to an ultimate CO_2-induced root biomass increase of 59%. The four researchers conclude the "slower turnover of new soil carbon, and increased life span of roots suggest an increased storage of carbon under elevated CO_2."

Ayres *et al.* (2008) report the responses of belowground nematode herbivores to atmospheric CO_2 enrichment to approximately 350 ppm above ambient in experiments conducted on three grassland ecosystems in Colorado and California (USA) and Montpellier, France. They found soil moisture increased in response to elevated CO_2 in all three experiments, citing Hungate *et al.* (1997), Nijs *et al.* (2000), and Morgan *et al.* (2004), and "elevated CO_2 increased root biomass by approximately 3–32% in the first five years of the Coloradoan study (Pendall *et al.*, 2004), by 23% after six years in the Californian study (Rillig *et al.*, 1999), and by 31% after six months in the French study (Dhillion *et al.*, 1996)." With respect to the nematodes, they state, "CO_2 enrichment did not significantly affect the family richness, diversity, or plant parasitic nematode index of herbivorous nematodes in the Colorado, California, or French study," noting "in each experiment, neutral effects were the most frequent response to CO_2 enrichment." The seven researchers conclude, "one consequence of increased root production, without changes in belowground herbivore populations, might be greater plant inputs to soil," which "may lead to greater soil organic matter pools in grassland ecosystems, potentially enhancing soil carbon sequestration."

Adair et al. (2009) employed mass balance calculations to quantify the effects of biodiversity, atmospheric CO_2 concentration, and soil nitrogen (N) content on the total amount of carbon (C) allocated belowground by plants (total belowground C allocation or TBCA), and ecosystem C storage, in an eight-year experiment that was part of the BioCON study of a periodically burned Minnesota grassland. They found annual TBCA increased in response to all three treatment variables—elevated CO_2, enriched N, and increasing diversity—and it was also "positively related to standing root biomass." Upon removing the influence of root biomass, however, the effects of N and diversity became neutral or even negative (depending on the year), but "the effect of elevated CO_2 remained positive." In years with fire, they found "greater litter production in high diversity, elevated CO_2, and enhanced N treatments increased annual ecosystem C loss." Therefore, under non-fire conditions, elevated CO_2, N, and biodiversity generally would tend to increase ecosystem carbon gain, but if grasslands are frequently burned, they could remain neutral in this regard.

Anderson et al. (2010) studied various root responses of a C_3-C_4 grassland community at Temple, Texas (USA) over a CO_2 concentration gradient stretching from 230 to 550 ppm, which they created in two CO_2-gradient above-ground "tunnels" of clear polyethylene film. One of the 60-m-long and 1.5-m-wide chambers had ambient air pumped into one end of it; by the time that air exited the chamber through its other end, its CO_2 concentration was reduced by the photosynthetic activity of the plants within the chamber to a value of approximately 230 ppm. The other chamber had air enriched to a CO_2 concentration of 550 ppm pumped into one end of it; as this air exited out the other end of that chamber, its CO_2 concentration was reduced to a value approximately equivalent to that of the ambient air (~380 ppm). The researchers assessed community ingrowth root biomass along the lengths of the tunnels every two to four months from May 1997 through

November 1999, using two ingrowth cores in each five-meter chamber section, and they calculated root biomass response as the ratio of each measurement date's result to that prevailing at the start of the experiment in May 1997.

Based on the linear relationship they derived from the 20 ingrowth biomass assessments they conducted, Anderson et al. found "a 40% increase in the ingrowth root biomass ratio from 380 to 480 ppm as compared with a 36% increase from 280 to 380 ppm." When excluding one extremely variable data point and using a power function they fit to the data, "the contrast is even greater: a 50% increase from 380 to 480 ppm vs. a 41% increase from 280 to 380 ppm." In going from the linear relationship to the power function, the r^2 value of the relationship jumped from 0.10 to 0.50, and P dropped from 0.095 to less than 0.001.

The six scientists conclude, "root biomass in grasslands may have changed markedly as atmospheric CO_2 increased since the last glacial period, but ... more substantial changes are ahead if the air's CO_2 content doubles by the end of this century as predicted." Those anticipated "changes" should all be positive, implying greater grassland root biomass—and all the good things that phenomenon implies—as the air's CO_2 content continues to climb.

References

Adair, E.C., Reich, P.B., Hobbie, S.E., and Knops, J.M.H. 2009. Interactive effects of time, CO_2, N, and diversity on total belowground carbon allocation and ecosystem carbon storage in a grassland community. Ecosystems 12: 1037–1052.

Anderson, L.J., Derner, J.D., Polley, H.W., Gordon, W.S., Eissenstat, D.M., and Jackson, R.B. 2010. Root responses along a subambient to elevated CO_2 gradient in a C_3-C_4 grassland. Global Change Biology 16: 454–468.

Ayres, E., Wall, D.H., Simmons, B.L., Field, C.B., Milchunas, D.G., Morgan, J.A., and Roy, J. 2008. Belowground nematode herbivores are resistant to elevated atmospheric CO_2 concentrations in grassland ecosystems. Soil Biology & Biochemistry 40: 978–985.

Crookshanks, M., Taylor, G., and Dolan, L. 1998. A model system to study the effects of elevated CO_2 on the developmental physiology of roots: the use of Arabidopsis thaliana. Journal of Experimental Botany 49: 593–597.

Dhillion, S.D., Roy, J., and Abrams, M. 1996. Assessing the impact of elevated CO_2 on soil microbial activity in a Mediterranean model ecosystem. Plant & Soil 187: 333–342.

Fitter, A.H., Self, G.K., Brown, T.K., Bogie, D.S., Graves, J.D., Benham, D., and Ineson, P. 1999. Root production and turnover in an upland grassland subjected to artificial soil warming respond to radiation flux and nutrients, not temperature. *Oecologia* **120**: 575–581.

Hungate, B.A., Holland, E.A., Jackson, R.B., Chapin, F.S., Mooney, H.A., and Field, C.B. 1997. The fate of carbon in grasslands under carbon dioxide enrichment. *Nature* **388**: 576–579.

Milchunas, D.G., Morgan, J.A., Mosier, A.R., and LeCain, D.R. 2005. Root dynamics and demography in shortgrass steppe under elevated CO_2, and comments on minirhizotron methodology. *Global Change Biology* **11**: 1837–1855.

Morgan, J.A., Mosier, A.R., Milchunas, D.G., LeCain, D.R., Nelson, J.A., and Parton, W.J. 2004. CO_2 enhances productivity, alters species composition, and reduces digestibility of shortgrass steppe vegetation. *Ecological Applications* **14**: 208–219.

Nijs, I., Roy, J., Salager, J.-L., and Fabreguettes, J. 2000. Elevated CO_2 alters carbon fluxes in early successional Mediterranean ecosystems. *Global Change Biology* **6**: 981–994.

Pendall, E., Mosier, A.R., and Morgan, J.A. 2004. Rhizodeposition stimulated by elevated CO_2 in a semiarid grassland. *New Phytologist* **162**: 447–458.

Rillig, M.C., Field, C.B., and Allen, M.F. 1999. Soil biota responses to long-term atmospheric CO_2 enrichment in two California annual grasslands. *Oecologia* **119**: 572–577.

2.23.3 Trees

The ongoing rise in the air's CO_2 content enables Earth's conifers and deciduous trees to increase the volume of soil from which they access water and nutrients, thus allowing them to more thoroughly explore that enlarged volume of soil and acquire greater amounts of these essential resources needed for growth. Numerous experimental findings indicate possible concurrent increases in air temperature and nitrogen deposition will enable them to become even more robust and productive.

2.23.3.1 Conifers

- The ongoing rise in the air's CO_2 content enables Earth's conifers to increase the volume of soil from which they access water and nutrients, allowing them to more thoroughly explore that enlarged volume of soil and acquire more of these essential resources for growth, the aerial fertilization effect of atmospheric CO_2 enrichment.

Janssens *et al.* (1998) grew three-year-old Scots pine seedlings for six months in open-top chambers maintained at ambient and 700 ppm atmospheric CO_2 concentrations. They found the extra CO_2 increased total root length by 122% and total root dry mass by 135%. In a study that employed close to the same degree of enhancement of the atmosphere's CO_2 content, Pritchard *et al.* (2001a) grew ecosystems representative of regenerating longleaf pine forests of the southeastern USA for 18 months in large soil bins located within open-top chambers. They found the aboveground parts of the seedlings experienced a growth enhancement of only 20%, but the root biomass of the trees was increased by more than three times as much (62%).

Working with FACE technology, Pritchard *et al.* (2001b) studied 14-year-old loblolly pine trees after a year of exposure to an extra 200 ppm of CO_2. They found total root length and root numbers were 16 and 34% greater, respectively, in the CO_2-enriched plots than in the ambient-air plots. In addition, the elevated CO_2 increased the diameter of living and dead roots by 8 and 6%, respectively, and annual root production was 26% greater in the CO_2-enriched plots. For the degree of CO_2 enrichment used in the prior two studies, this latter increase corresponded to a root biomass increase of about 45%.

In an open-top chamber study of a model ecosystem composed of a mixture of spruce and beech seedlings, Wiemken *et al.* (2001) investigated the effects of a 200-ppm increase in the air's CO_2 concentration that prevailed for four years. On nutrient-poor soils, the extra CO_2 led to a 30% increase in fine-root biomass, and on nutrient-rich soils it led to a 75% increase. As before, these numbers corresponded to increases of about 52% and 130%, respectively, for atmospheric CO_2 enhancements on the order of those employed by Janssens *et al.* (1998) and Pritchard *et al.* (2001a).

Wiemken *et al.* also found the extra CO_2 increased the amount of symbiotic fungal biomass associated with the trees' fine roots by 31% on nutrient-poor soils and 100% on nutrient-rich soils, which for the degree of atmospheric CO_2 enrichment used in the studies of Janssens *et al.* (1998) and Pritchard *et al.* (2001a) translate into increases of about 52% and 175%, respectively.

Tingey *et al.* (2005) used minirhizotron tubes to study the effects of atmospheric CO_2 enrichment (to approximately 350 ppm above ambient) on the fine-root architecture of seedlings of Ponderosa pine (*Pinus ponderosa*) growing in open-top chambers at the U.S. Forest Service's Institute of Forest Genetics near Placerville, California (USA), over a period of four years. They found elevated CO_2 increased both fine root extensity (the degree of soil exploration) and intensity (the extent that roots use explored areas) but had no effect on mycorrhizae. They presume the latter observation to be due to the fact that soil nitrogen was not limiting to growth in their study. More specifically, they report, "extensity increased 1.5- to 2-fold in elevated CO_2 while intensity increased only 20% or less," noting similar extensity results were obtained over shorter periods of four months to two years by Arnon (1997), Berntson and Bazzaz (1998), DeLucia et al. (1997), and Runion et al. (1997), and similar intensity results had been obtained by Berntson (1994).

Phillips et al. (2006) grew well-watered (via drip irrigation) 1.5-year-old ponderosa pine seedlings for four additional years in open-top chambers maintained at the ambient atmospheric CO_2 concentration and at ambient + 175 ppm and ambient + 300 ppm CO_2, while imposing three levels of soil nitrogen (N) fertilization (0, 10 and 20 g N m^{-2} year^{-1}) upon the plants. Every two months throughout this period, they collected video images of the roots that were visible on the surfaces of three minirhizotron tubes installed in each chamber. They learned yearly values of fine-root standing crop, production, and mortality were consistently higher in the elevated CO_2 treatments throughout the study. They also report, "in this same study, Johnson et al. (2000) found elevated CO_2 increased fine-root life span," and because the elevated CO_2 increased fine-root length, the amount of root length that died each year was greater in the CO_2 enriched treatments. Therefore, they write, "the higher rates of mortality in absolute terms for elevated CO_2 are driven by increased standing crop and not reduced life spans."

The work of Phillips et al. came to bear upon the progressive nitrogen limitation (PNL) hypothesis, which posits the benefits of atmospheric CO_2 enrichment must ultimately dwindle away because the productivity of Earth's temperate forests often is limited by insufficient soil nitrogen, as is typically the case in the southeastern United States, where the growth of pine and hardwood forests can remove so much nitrogen from the soils on which the forests grow that it induces what Finzi and Schlesinger (2003) have described as "a state of acute nutrient deficiency that can only be reversed with fertilization." Phillips et al. found, however, the increased fine-root length they observed "explains how additional N was provided to support the increased whole plant growth observed in [their]

elevated CO_2 treatments, and corresponds with the increased extent and intensity of the root system architecture discussed by Tingey et al. (2005)." This "mining of soil N," as they describe it, "can in some cases go on for substantial lengths of time," and there was "no evidence that PNL occurred during the course of [their] study," citing Johnson et al. (2006).

Pritchard et al. (2008) described what they learned from minirhizotrons they employed in work conducted at the Duke Forest FACE facility to characterize the influence of free-air-CO_2-enrichment (ambient + 200 ppm) on fine roots for six years (Autumn 1998 through Autumn 2004) in an 18-year-old loblolly pine (Pinus taeda) plantation near Durham, North Carolina (USA). Over six years they observed the extra 200 ppm of CO_2 increased average fine-root standing crop by 23%, in line with the overall stimulation of forest net primary productivity of 18–24% they observed for 1996–2002. They found "the positive effects of CO_2 enrichment on fine root growth persisted six years following minirhizotron tube installation (eight years following initiation of the CO_2 fumigation)," and no hint of any progressive nitrogen limitation of the stimulatory effect of atmospheric CO_2 enrichment in a situation where one might have been expected it. In partial explanation of this important finding, Pritchard et al. conclude the distal tips of fine roots are "the primary site for initiation of mycorrhizal partnerships which are critical for resource acquisition and could also influence whether or not forests can sustain higher productivity in a CO_2-enriched world."

Phllips et al. (2009) write, "O_3 stress often decreases carbon allocation to roots, leading to reductions in root biomass and growth," citing Andersen (2003) and Grantz et al. (2006). They add, "reduced carbohydrate stores in roots can lead to increased susceptibility to other stresses even after O_3 exposure ends," citing Andersen et al. (1997), but stating, on the other hand, CO_2 tends to promote just the opposite behavior by promoting fine-root production and the benefits this phenomenon provides, citing Norby et al. (2004, 2005). In an experiment designed to determine which of the two trace gases (CO_2 or O_3) has the greater impact on the growth and development of the fine roots of ponderosa pine trees, they grew Pinus ponderosa seedlings for three years in one-meter-deep containers filled with reconstructed pine-forest soil within sunlit controlled-environment chambers maintained at mean atmospheric CO_2 concentrations of either 420 or 690 ppm, and at mean O_3 conditions described by daily SUM06 index values of either 0 or 15.7 ppm h (representing the sum of hourly O_3 concentrations $>=$ 0.06 ppm). Images of fine roots growing along the upper surfaces of four minirhizotron tubes installed within each soil bin were collected every 28 days by a color video camera.

The researchers found "elevated CO_2 increased both the number of fine roots produced and their life span," and "increased O_3 did not reduce the effect of elevated CO_2." Fine root biomass at the end of the study in the CO_2-enriched treatment was consistently higher in each soil horizon and 16% higher in total. In addition, the greater fine-root survivorship in the elevated CO_2 treatment was associated with increasing root depth and increasing fine-root diameter, as also has been observed by Eissenstat et al. (2000), Guo et al. (2008), and Joslin et al. (2006). Averaged over the course of the experiment, they found a slight (3.3%) decrease in soil respiration in the elevated CO_2 treatment, as observed by Tingey et al. (2006). Consequently, in the words of the four U.S. Environmental Protection Agency scientists who conducted the work, "elevated O_3 did not result in significant negative impacts on ponderosa pine seedling fine-root survival ... or in countering the increased survivorship caused by elevated CO_2."

Johansson et al. (2009) write, "ectomycorrhizal (ECM) fungi, forming the dominant type of symbiotic association with trees in boreal forests, receive as much as 25% of the total carbon assimilated by plants," and in return, "the extraradical fungal mycelium is directly involved in mobilization and uptake of nutrients which are, in part, passed on to the host plant." This important function is performed by the fungal exudation of a variety of low molecular weight organic compounds, polymer degrading enzymes, siderophores, polymeric carbohydrates, and fatty acids, the dominant components of which "play important roles in enhancing mineral weathering, nutrient mobilization and uptake by plants." They investigated certain aspects of this complex suite of phenomena in seedlings of Scots pine (*Pinus sylvestris*) trees grown in the laboratory in liquid culture for six weeks with either no ECM fungi or one of eight such species associated with their roots, during which period they were exposed to air of either 350 or 700 ppm CO_2, and after which a number of analyses were performed to identify and quantify the variety of exudates produced by the fungi.

Johansson et al. observed "a clear impact of elevated CO_2 on exudation of soluble low molecular weight organic compounds," and these exudates "increased by 120–270%" due to "the increased carbon availability to the plant-fungus system." This process was driven by the elevated atmospheric CO_2 concentration that increased net CO_2 assimilation rates by approximately 40% for both ECM and non-mycorrhizal seedlings. It led to a mean increase of 27% in the total biomass production of the seedlings infected with the eight species of ECM fungi, but it led to only a 14% increase in the biomass of the non-infected seedlings. Therefore, the four researchers conclude the phenomena they observed "may contribute to nutritional feedback mechanisms to sustain tree growth when nutrients become limiting," such as some have hypothesized might occur over time in trees growing on low-fertility soils in CO_2-enriched air. (For much more on this subject, see the Progressive Limitation Hypothesis, Section 3.11, this volume.) The findings of this study, however, as well as those of the study of de Graaff et al. (2009)— which was published in the same issue of *Soil Biology & Biochemistry*—clearly indicate Earth's plants should be well-equipped to deal with this hypothetical and now largely discredited roadblock to higher plant productivity in a CO_2-enriched world of the future.

The results described above add to the growing body of evidence suggesting the ongoing rise in the atmosphere's CO_2 concentration will enable conifers to continue to increase the volume of soil from which they can access water and nutrients, enabling them to more thoroughly explore that enlarged volume of soil. Both of these responses should allow them to acquire more of these essential resources and thereby realize the enhanced potential for growth that is provided them by the aerial fertilization effect of atmospheric CO_2 enrichment. The ongoing rise in the air's CO_2 content thus bodes well for the growth of the planet's coniferous forests and for all the creatures that depend upon them for food and shelter, as well as for the ability of the trees to provide lumber for mankind and to sequester carbon while doing so. These consequences have great virtue in and of themselves, and the latter one provides a powerful negative feedback or brake on CO_2-induced global warming.

References

Andersen, C.P. 2003. Source-sink balance and carbon allocation below ground in plants exposed to ozone. *New Phytologist* **157**: 213–228.

Andersen, C.P., Wilson, R., Plocher, M., and Hogsett, W.E. 1997. Carry-over effects of O_3 on root growth and carbohydrate concentration of ponderosa pine seedlings. *Tree Physiology* **17**: 805–811.

Arnone, J.A. 1997. Temporal responses of community fine

root populations to long-term elevated atmospheric CO_2 and soil nutrient patches in model tropical ecosystems. *Acta Oecologia* **18**: 367–376.

Berntson, G.M. 1994. Modeling root architecture: are there tradeoffs between efficiency and potential of resource acquisition? *New Phytologist* **127**: 483–493.

Berntson, G.M. and Bazzaz, F.A. 1998. Regenerating temperate forest mesocosms in elevated CO_2: belowground growth and nitrogen cycling. *Oecologia* **113**: 115–125.

De Graaff, M.-A., Van Kessel, C., and Six, J. 2009. Rhizodeposition-induced decomposition increases N availability to wild and cultivated wheat genotypes under elevated CO_2. *Soil Biology & Biochemistry* **41**: 1094–1103.

DeLucia, E.H., Callaway, R.M., Thomas, E.M., and Schlesinger, W.H. 1997. Mechanisms of phosphorus acquisition for ponderosa pine seedlings under high CO_2 and temperature. *Annals of Botany* **79**: 111–120.

Eissenstat, D.M., Wells, C.E., Yanai, R.D., and Whitbeck, J.L. 2000. Building roots in a changing environment: Implications for root longevity. *New Phytologist* **147**: 33–42.

Finzi, A.C. and Schlesinger, W.H. 2003. Soil-nitrogen cycling in a pine forest exposed to 5 years of elevated carbon dioxide. *Ecosystems* **6**: 444–456.

Grantz, D.A., Gunn, S., and Vu, H.-B. 2006. O_3 impacts on plant development: a meta-analysis of root/shoot allocation and growth. *Plant, Cell and Environment* **29**: 1193–1209.

Guo, D., Mitchell, R.J., Han, W., Hendricks, J.J., Fahey, T.J., and Hendrick, R.L. 2008. Fine root heterogeneity by branch order: exploring the discrepancy in root turnover estimates between minirhizotron and carbon isotopic methods. *New Phytologist* **177**: 443–456.

Janssens, I.A., Crookshanks, M., Taylor, G., and Ceulemans, R. 1998. Elevated atmospheric CO_2 increases fine root production, respiration, rhizosphere respiration and soil CO_2 efflux in Scots pine seedlings. *Global Change Biology* **4**: 871–878.

Johansson, E.M., Fransson, P.M.A., Finlay, R.D., and van Hees, P.A.W. 2009. Quantitative analysis of soluble exudates produced by ectomycorrhizal roots as a response to ambient and elevated CO_2. *Soil Biology & Biochemistry* **41**: 1111–1116.

Johnson, D.W., Hoylman, A.M., Ball, J.T., and Walker, R.F. 2006. Ponderosa pine responses to elevated CO_2 and nitrogen fertilization. *Biogeochemistry* **77**: 157–175.

Johnson, M.G., Phillips, D.L., Tingey, D.T., and Storm, M.J. 2000. Effects of elevated CO_2, N-fertilization, and season on survival of ponderosa pine fine roots. *Canadian Journal of Forest Research* **30**: 220–228.

Joslin, J.D., Gaudinski, J.B., Torn, M.S., Riley, W.J., and Hanson, P.J. 2006. Fine-root turnover patterns and their relationship to root diameter and soil depth in a ^{14}C-labeled hardwood forest. *New Phytologist* **172**: 523–535.

Norby, R.J., DeLucia, E.H., Gielen, B., Calfapietra, C., Giardina, C.P., King, S.J., Ledford, J., McCarthy, H.R., Moore, D.J.P., Ceulemans, R., De Angelis, P., Finzi, A.C., Karnosky, D.F., Kubiske, M.E., Lukac, M., Pregitzer, K.S., Scarasci-Mugnozza, G.E., Schlesinger, W.H., and Oren, R. 2005. Forest response to elevated CO_2 is conserved across a broad range of productivity. *Proceedings of the National Academy of Sciences USA* **102**: 18,052–18,056.

Norby, R.J., Ledford, J., Reilly, C.D., Miller, N.E., and O'Neill, E.G. 2004. Fine-root production dominates response of a deciduous forest to atmospheric CO_2 enrichment. *Proceedings of the National Academy of Sciences, USA* **101**: 9689–9693.

Phillips, D.L., Johnson, M.G., Tingey, D.T., and Storm, M.J. 2009. Elevated CO_2 and O_3 effects on fine-root survivorship in ponderosa pine mesocosms. *Oecologia* **160**: 827–837.

Phillips, D.L., Johnson, M.G., Tingey, D.T., Storm, M.J., Ball, J.T., and Johnson, D.W. 2006. CO_2 and N-fertilization effects on fine-root length, production, and mortality: a 4-year ponderosa pine study. *Oecologia* **148**: 517–525.

Pritchard, S.G., Davis, M.A., Mitchell, R.J., Prior, A.S., Boykin, D.L., Rogers, H.H., and Runion, G.B. 2001a. Root dynamics in an artificially constructed regenerating longleaf pine ecosystem are affected by atmospheric CO_2 enrichment. *Environmental and Experimental Botany* **46**: 35–69.

Pritchard, S.G., Rogers, H.H., Davis, M.A., Van Santen, E., Prior, S.A., and Schlesinger, W.H. 2001b. The influence of elevated atmospheric CO_2 on fine root dynamics in an intact temperate forest. *Global Change Biology* **7**: 829–837.

Pritchard, S.G., Strand, A.E., McCormack, M.L., Davis, M.A., Finzi, A.C., Jackson, R.B., Matamala, R., Rogers, H.H., and Oren, R. 2008. Fine root dynamics in a loblolly pine forest are influenced by free-air-CO_2-enrichment: a six-year-minirhizotron study. *Global Change Biology* **14**: 588–602.

Runion, G.B., Mitchell, R.J., Rogers, H.H., Prior, S.A., and Counts, T.K. 1997. Effects of nitrogen and water limitation and elevated atmospheric CO_2 on ectomycorrhiza of longleaf pine. *New Phytologist* **137**: 681–689.

Tingey, D.T., Johnson, M.G., Lee, E.H., Wise, C., Waschmann, R., Olszyk, D.M., Watrud, L.S., and Donegan, K.K. 2006. Effects of elevated CO_2 and O_3 on soil respiration under ponderosa pine. *Soil Biology & Biochemistry* **38**: 1764–1778.

Tingey, D.T., Johnson, M.G., and Phillips, D.L. 2005. Independent and contrasting effects of elevated CO_2 and N-fertilization on root architecture in *Pinus ponderosa*. *Trees* **19**: 43–50.

Wiemken, V., Ineichen, K., and Boller, T. 2001. Development of ectomycorrhizas in model beech-spruce ecosystems on siliceous and calcareous soil: a 4-year experiment with atmospheric CO_2 enrichment and nitrogen fertilization. *Plant and Soil* **234**: 99–108.

2.23.3.2 Deciduous

- Experimental findings indicate the ongoing rise in the air's CO_2 content, together with possible concurrent increases in air temperature and nitrogen deposition, will make Earth's deciduous woody plants increasingly robust and productive.

Although life-sustaining photosynthesis occurs aboveground in the presence of light, what happens in the darkness beneath the surface of the soil is equally important to the welfare of Earth's higher plants and the many benefits they provide for the rest of the biosphere. This section highlights the findings of some of the scientific literature germane to this subject, focusing on root responses of deciduous trees to atmospheric CO_2 enrichment.

Berntsen and Bazzaz (1998) removed intact chunks of soil from the Hardwood-White Pine-Hemlock forest region of New England and placed them in plastic containers within controlled environment glasshouses maintained at either 375 or 700 ppm CO_2 for two years to study the effects of elevated CO_2 on the regeneration of plants from seeds and rhizomes in the soil. At the conclusion of the study, total mesocosm plant biomass (more than 95% of which was supplied by yellow and white birch tree seedlings) was 31% higher in the elevated CO_2 treatment than in ambient air, with a mean enhancement of 23% aboveground and 62% belowground. The extra CO_2 also increased the mycorrhizal colonization of root tips by 45% in white birch and 71% in yellow birch, and the CO_2-enriched yellow birch seedlings exhibited 322% greater root length and 305% more root surface area than did the yellow birch seedlings growing in ambient air.

Kubiske *et al.* (1998) grew cuttings of four quaking aspen genotypes in open-top chambers for five months at atmospheric CO_2 concentrations of either 380 or 720 ppm and low or high soil nitrogen concentrations. The cuttings grown in elevated CO_2 displayed no discernible increases in aboveground growth. However, the extra CO_2 significantly increased fine-root length and root turnover rates at high soil nitrogen by increasing fine-root production, which would be expected to produce benefits, not the least of which would be a larger belowground water- and nutrient-gathering system, that would eventually lead to enhanced aboveground growth as well. The many positive aboveground growth responses of quaking aspen trees to atmospheric CO_2 enrichment are documented in Appendices 2 and 3 of this volume (see *Populus tremuloides* Michx.).

Expanding on this study, Pregitzer *et al.* (2000) grew six quaking aspen genotypes for 2.5 growing seasons in open-top chambers maintained at atmospheric CO_2 concentrations of 350 and 700 ppm with both adequate and inadequate supplies of soil nitrogen. The trees exposed to elevated CO_2 developed thicker and longer roots than the trees growing in ambient air, and the fine-root biomass of the CO_2-enriched trees was enhanced by 17% in the nitrogen-poor soils and by 65% in the nitrogen-rich soils.

Another study of quaking aspen, conducted by King *et al.* (2001), demonstrates trees exposed to an atmospheric CO_2 concentration 560 ppm in a FACE experiment produced 133% more fine-root biomass than trees grown in ambient air of 360 ppm, which roughly equates to 233% more fine-root biomass for the degree of CO_2 enrichment employed in the prior study of Pregitzer *et al* where the CO_2 concentration was 700 ppm. When simultaneously exposed to air of 1.5 times the normal ozone concentration, the degree of fine-root biomass stimulation produced by the extra CO_2 was still as great as 66%, or roughly 115% when extrapolated to the greater CO_2 enrichment employed by Pregitzer *et al.*

King *et al.* (1999) grew four clones at two temperature regimes (separated by 5°C) and two levels of soil nitrogen (N) availability (high and low) for 98 days, measuring photosynthesis, growth, biomass allocation, and root production and mortality. They found the higher of the two temperature regimes increased rates of photosynthesis by 65% and rates of whole-plant growth by 37%, simultaneously enhancing root production and turnover. They conclude, "trembling aspen has the potential for substantially greater growth and root turnover under conditions of warmer soil at sites of both high and low N-availability" and "an immediate consequence of this will be greater inputs of C and nutrients to forest soils."

These several findings pertaining to quaking aspen trees indicate increases in atmospheric CO_2 concentration, air temperature, and soil nitrogen content all enhance the trees' belowground growth, which positively affects their aboveground growth.

Regarding other deciduous trees, Gleadow *et al.* (1998) grew eucalyptus seedlings for six months in glasshouses maintained at atmospheric CO_2 concentrations of either 400 or 800 ppm, fertilizing them twice daily with low or high nitrogen solutions. The elevated CO_2 increased total plant biomass by 98 and 134% relative to plants grown at ambient CO_2 in the high and low nitrogen treatments, respectively. In addition, in the low nitrogen treatment, elevated CO_2 stimulated greater root growth, as indicated by a 33% higher root:shoot ratio.

Day *et al.* (1996) studied the effects of elevated CO_2 on fine-root production in open-top chambers erected over a regenerating oak-palmetto scrub ecosystem in Florida (USA). They found a 350-ppm increase in the atmosphere's CO_2 concentration increased fine-root length densities by 63% while enhancing the distribution of fine roots at the soil surface (0–12 cm) and at a depth of 50–60 cm. These findings suggest the ongoing rise in the atmosphere's CO_2 concentration likely will increase the distribution of fine roots near the soil surface, where the greatest concentrations of nutrients are located, and at a depth that coincides with the upper level of the site's water table, both of which should increase the trees' ability to acquire the nutrients and water they will need to support CO_2-enhanced biomass production in the future.

Uselman *et al.* (2000) grew seedlings of the nitrogen-fixing black locust tree for 100 days in controlled environments maintained at atmospheric CO_2 concentrations of 350 and 700 ppm and air temperatures of 26°C (ambient) and 30°C, with either some or no additional nitrogen fertilization. The extra CO_2 increased total seedling biomass by 14%, the elevated temperature increased it by 55%, and nitrogen fertilization increased it by 157%. Root exudation showed a similar pattern. Plants grown in elevated CO_2 exuded 20% more organic carbon compounds than plants grown in ambient air, and elevated temperature and fertilization increased root exudation by 71 and 55%, respectively. Hence, as the air's CO_2 content continues to rise, black locust trees likely will exhibit enhanced rates of biomass production and exudation of dissolved organic compounds from their roots. Moreover, if air temperature also rises, even by as much as 4°C, its positive effect on biomass production and root exudation likely will be even greater than that resulting from the increasing atmospheric CO_2 concentration. The same would appear to hold true for

anthropogenic nitrogen deposition, reinforcing what was learned about the impacts of these three environmental factors on the growth of quaking aspen trees.

McDowell *et al.* (1999) grew five-month-old seedlings of western hemlock in root boxes, subjecting them for several hours to various root-space CO_2 concentrations, ranging from approximately 90 to 7,000 ppm, to determine the effect of soil CO_2 concentration on growth, maintenance, and total root respiration. Although they could detect no effect of atmospheric CO_2 enrichment on growth respiration, it significantly affected maintenance and total respiration rates. At a soil CO_2 concentration of 1,585 ppm, for example, total and maintenance respiration rates were 55 and 60% lower, respectively, than they were at a soil CO_2 concentration of 395 ppm. The impact of elevated soil CO_2 on maintenance respiration (which comprised 85% of the total respiration in this study) was so strong it exhibited an exponential decline of about 37% for every doubling of the soil CO_2 concentration.

These several experimental findings allow confidence in the conclusion that the ongoing rise in the air's CO_2 content, together with possible concurrent increases in air temperature and nitrogen deposition, likely will make Earth's woody plants increasingly robust and productive.

References

Berntson, G.M. and Bazzaz, F.A. 1998. Regenerating temperate forest mesocosms in elevated CO_2: belowground growth and nitrogen cycling. *Oecologia* **113**: 115–125.

Day, F.P., Weber, E.P., Hinkle, C.R., and Drake, B.G. 1996. Effects of elevated atmospheric CO_2 on fine root length and distribution in an oak-palmetto scrub ecosystem in central Florida. *Global Change Biology* **2**: 143–148.

Gleadow, R.M., Foley, W.J., and Woodrow, I.E. 1998. Enhanced CO_2 alters the relationship between photosynthesis and defense in cyanogenic *Eucalyptus cladocalyx* F. Muell. *Plant, Cell and Environment* **21**: 12–22.

King, J.S., Pregitzer, K.S., and Zak, D.R. 1999. Clonal variation in above- and below-ground growth responses of *Populus tremuloides* Michaux: Influence of soil warming and nutrient availability. *Plant and Soil* **217**: 119–130.

King, J.S., Pregitzer, K.S., Zak, D.R., Sober, J., Isebrands, J.G., Dickson, R.E., Hendrey, G.R., and Karnosky, D.F. 2001. Fine-root biomass and fluxes of soil carbon in young stands of paper birch and trembling aspen as affected by elevated atmospheric CO_2 and tropospheric O_3. *Oecologia* **128**: 237–250.

Kubiske, M.E., Pregitzer, K.S., Zak, D.R., and Mikan, C.J. 1998. Growth and C allocation of *Populus tremuloides* genotypes in response to atmospheric CO_2 and soil N availability. *New Phytologist* **140**: 251–260.

McDowell, N.G., Marshall, J.D., Qi, J., and Mattson, K. 1999. Direct inhibition of maintenance respiration in western hemlock roots exposed to ambient soil carbon dioxide concentrations. *Tree Physiology* **19**: 599–605.

Pregitzer, K.S., Zak, D.R., Maziasz, J., DeForest, J., Curtis, P.S., and Lussenhop, J. 2000. Interactive effects of atmospheric CO_2 and soil-N availability on fine roots of *Populus tremuloides. Ecological Applications* **10**: 18–33.

Uselman, S.M., Qualls, R.G., and Thomas, R.B. 2000. Effects of increased atmospheric CO_2, temperature, and soil N availability on root exudation of dissolved organic carbon by a N-fixing tree (*Robinia pseudoacacia* L.). *Plant and Soil* **222**: 191–202.

2.23.4 Other

In reviewing the scientific literature pertaining to atmospheric CO_2 enrichment effects on belowground plant growth and development, Weihong *et al.* (2000) briefly summarize what was known about this subject at the turn of the century. They report atmospheric CO_2 enrichment typically enhances the growth rates of roots, especially those of fine roots, and CO_2-induced increases in root production eventually lead to increased carbon inputs to soils, due to enhanced root turnover and exudation of various organic carbon compounds, which can lead to greater soil carbon sequestration. In addition, they note, increased soil carbon inputs stimulate the growth and activities of soil microorganisms that utilize plant-derived carbon as their primary energy source, and they report subsequently enhanced activities of fungal and bacterial plant symbionts often lead to increased plant nutrient acquisition.

In a more narrowly focused study, Gouk *et al.* (1999) grew specimens of an orchid plantlet, Mokara Yellow, in plastic bags flushed with 350 and 10,000 ppm CO_2 for three months, in order to study the effects of elevated CO_2 on this epiphytic CAM species. The super-elevated CO_2 of their experiment enhanced the total dry weight of the orchid plantlets more than twofold, while increasing the growth of existing roots and stimulating the induction of new roots from internodes located on the orchid stems. Total chlorophyll content also was increased in CO_2-enriched air, by 64 percent in young leaves and by 118 percent in young roots. This phenomenon permit-

ted greater light harvesting during photosynthesis and likely led to the tissue starch contents of the CO_2-enriched plantlets rising nearly 20-fold higher than those of the control-plantlets. In spite of this large CO_2-induced accumulation of starch, however, no damage or disruption of chloroplasts was evident in the leaves and roots of the CO_2-enriched plants.

A final question that has periodically intrigued researchers is whether plants take up carbon through their roots in addition to through their leaves. Although a definitive answer remains elusive, Idso (1989) described various aspects of the issue a quarter-century ago:

"Although several investigators have claimed that plants should receive little direct benefit from dissolved CO_2 (Stolwijk *et al.*, 1957; Skok *et al.*, 1962; Splittstoesser, 1966), a number of experiments have produced significant increases in root growth (Erickson, 1946; Leonard and Pinckard, 1946; Geisler, 1963; Yorgalevitch and Janes, 1988), as well as yield itself (Kursanov *et al.*, 1951; Grinfeld, 1954; Nakayama and Bucks, 1980; Baron and Gorski, 1986), with CO_2-enriched irrigation water. Early on, Misra (1951) suggested that this beneficent effect may be related to CO_2-induced changes in soil nutrient availability; and this hypothesis may well be correct. Arteca *et al.* (1979), for example, have observed K, Ca and Mg to be better absorbed by potato roots when the concentration of CO_2 in the soil solution is increased; while Mauney and Hendrix (1988) found Zn and Mn to be better absorbed by cotton under such conditions, and Yurgalevitch and Janes (1988) found an enhancement of the absorption of Rb by tomato roots. In all cases, large increases in either total plant growth or yield accompanied the enhanced uptake of nutrients. Consequently, as it has been suggested that CO_2 concentration plays a major role in determining the porosity, plasticity and charge of cell membranes (Jackson and Coleman, 1959; Mitz, 1979), which could thereby alter ion uptake and organic acid production (Yorgalevitch and Janes, 1988), it is possible that some such suite of mechanisms may well be responsible for the plant productivity increases often observed to result from enhanced concentrations of CO_2 in the soil solution."

References

Arteca, R.N., Pooviah, B.W., and Smith, O.E. 1979. Changes in carbon fixation, tuberization, and growth induced by CO_2 applications to the root zones of potato plants. *Science* **205**: 1279–1280.

Baron, J.J. and Gorski, S.F. 1986. Response of eggplant to a root environment enriched with CO_2. *HortScience* **21**: 495–498.

Erickson, L.C. 1946. Growth of tomato roots as influenced by oxygen in the nutrient solution. *American Journal of Botany* **33**: 551–556.

Geisler, G. 1963. Morphogenetic influence of (CO_2 + HCO_3^-) on roots. *Plant Physiology* **38**: 77–80.

Gouk, S.S., He, J., and Hew, C.S. 1999. Changes in photosynthetic capability and carbohydrate production in an epiphytic CAM orchid plantlet exposed to super-elevated CO_2. *Environmental and Experimental Botany* **41**: 219–230.

Grinfeld, E.G. 1954. On the nutrition of plants with carbon dioxide through the roots. *Dokl. Akad. Nauk SSSR* **94**: 919–922.

Idso, S.B. 1989. *Carbon Dioxide and Global Change: Earth in Transition*. IBR Press, Tempe, AZ.

Jackson, W.A. and Coleman, N.T. 1959. Fixation of carbon dioxide by plant roots through phosphoenolpyruvate carboxylase. *Plant and Soil* **11**: 1–16.

Kursanov, A.L., Kuzin, A.M., and Mamul, Y.V. 1951. On the possibility for assimilation by plants of carbonates taken in with the soil solution. *Dokl. Akad. Nauk SSSR* **79**: 685–687.

Leonard, O.A. and Pinckard, J.A. 1946. Effect of various oxygen and carbon dioxide concentrations on cotton root development. *Plant Physiology* **21**: 18–36.

Mauney, J.R. and Hendrix, D.L. 1988. Responses of glasshouse grown cotton to irrigation with carbon dioxide-saturated water. *Crop Science* **28**: 835–838.

Misra, R.K. 1951. Further studies on the carbon dioxide factor in the air and soil layers near the ground. *Indian Journal of Meteorology and Geophysics* **2**: 284–292.

Mitz, M.A. 1979. CO_2 biodynamics: A new concept of cellular control. *Journal of Theoretical Biology* **80**: 537–551.

Nakayama, F.S. and Bucks, D.A. 1980. Using subsurface trickle system for carbon dioxide enrichment. In Jensen, M.H. and Oebker, N.F. (Eds.) *Proceedings of the 15th Agricultural Plastics Congress*, National Agricultural Plastics Association, Manchester, MO, pp. 13–18.

Skok, J., Chorney, W., and Broecker, W.S. 1962. Uptake of CO_2 by roots of Xanthium plants. *Botanical Gazette* **124**: 118–120.

Splittstoesser, W.E. 1966. Dark CO_2 fixation and its role in the growth of plant tissue. *Plant Physiology* **41**: 755–759.

Stolwijk, J.A.J. and Thimann, K.V. 1957. On the uptake of carbon dioxide and bicarbonate by roots and its influence on growth. *Plant Physiology* **32**: 513–520.

Weihong, L., Fusuo, Z., and Kezhi, B. 2000. Responses of plant rhizosphere to atmospheric CO_2 enrichment. *Chinese Science Bulletin* **45**: 97–101.

Yorgalevitch, C.M. and Janes, W.H. 1988. Carbon dioxide enrichment of the root zone of tomato seedlings. *Journal of Horticultural Science* **63**: 265–270.

2.24 Rubisco

Rubisco is the primary carboxylating enzyme used by C_3 plants during photosynthesis to incorporate CO_2 into sugars needed for growth and development. Even C_4 and CAM plants, which use PEP-carboxylase as their primary carboxylating enzyme, utilize rubisco during subsequent secondary CO_2 assimilation events. Thus rubisco is universally present in all the planet's vegetation and is, in fact, the most abundant plant enzyme on the face of the Earth, comprising 40 to 50% of total foliage protein and representing an enormous sink for nitrogen and other valuable resources within plants.

However, rubisco is a bifunctional enzyme that also possesses oxygenation activity, and when oxygenation reactions occur, photorespiration is enhanced, resulting in an increased loss of carbon from plant tissues. Thus, CO_2 and O_2 compete for active sites on rubisco in order to drive photosynthesis and photorespiration, respectively. The following subsections explore how these biochemical processes are affected by the rising CO_2 content of the atmosphere, as well as the implications of these changes for the content and/or activity of rubisco.

2.24.1 Agricultural Species

- There is a reduced need for nitrogen investment in leaf rubisco in agricultural crops growing in CO_2-enriched air because under such conditions plants typically reallocate some of their "surplus" nitrogen to other processes essential for optimal growth and development, without compromising enhanced carbon gains via photosynthesis.

Voluminous experimental data demonstrate atmospheric CO_2 enrichment favors the process of carboxylation over that of oxygenation, which thereby increases photosynthetic rates while decreasing photorespiratory rates. Thus the rising CO_2 content of the air invariably leads to greater rates of net photosynthesis and a more efficient process of carbon fixation, requiring less rubisco to obtain the carbon needed for plant growth and development under CO_2-enriched conditions.

As a consequence, plants grown in elevated CO_2 environments often, but not always (Farage *et al.*, 1998), exhibit a certain degree of photosynthetic acclimation or down-regulation, which is typically characterized by reduced amounts of rubisco (Sims *et al.*, 1998; Theobald *et al.*, 1998) and/or decreases in its activation state (Pritchard *et al.*, 2000; Reid *et al.*, 1998). However, in nearly every reported case of CO_2-induced photosynthetic acclimation, net photosynthetic rates displayed by CO_2-enriched plants have been significantly greater than those exhibited by plants growing at ambient CO_2 concentrations. This section briefly reviews the photosynthetic acclimation of rubisco within agricultural species subjected to elevated CO_2 concentrations.

Sicher and Bunce (1999) grew potato plants at atmospheric CO_2 concentrations of 350, 530, and 700 ppm over a three-year period, documenting 13 and 21% CO_2-induced reductions in rubisco concentrations at 530 and 700 ppm CO_2, respectively. Nevertheless, the rates of photosynthesis in the CO_2-enriched plants were still 28 and 49% greater than those observed in control plants grown in ambient air. Similarly, Maroco *et al.* (1999) report a tripling of the ambient air's CO_2 concentration increased photosynthetic rates in maize (a C_4 plant) by about 15%, in spite of foliar reductions in both rubisco and PEP-carboxylase concentrations. And Theobald *et al.* (1998) grew spring wheat at twice-ambient CO_2 concentrations, discovering the elevated CO_2 reduced the amount of rubisco required to sustain enhanced rates of photosynthesis, which consequently led to a significant increase in plant nitrogen-use efficiency.

Interestingly, when elevated CO_2 induces photosynthetic acclimation, the phenomenon generally does not occur in every leaf of the plant. Osborne *et al.* (1998), for example, grew wheat plants with an additional 200 ppm of CO_2 and reported CO_2-induced reductions in foliar rubisco concentrations occurred in a depth-dependent manner, with the reductions increasing with depth in the canopy. Sims *et al.* (1999) observed similar canopy-depth-dependent reductions in the rubisco content of sunflowers. Thus, because CO_2-induced reductions in rubisco typically occur within only a portion of a plant's total leaf area, most plants still exhibit biomass increases in response to elevated CO_2 exposure in spite of acclimation.

CO_2-induced photosynthetic acclimation also often results from insufficient plant sink strength, which can lead to carbohydrate accumulation in source leaves and the subsequent triggering of photosynthetic end-product feedback inhibition that reduces foliar rubisco concentrations. Gesch *et al.* (1998), for example, report rice plants—which have a relatively limited potential for developing additional carbon sinks—grown at an atmospheric CO_2 concentration of 700 ppm exhibited increased leaf carbohydrate contents, which likely reduced *rbcS* mRNA levels and ultimately leaf rubisco protein contents.

In another experiment, Gesch *et al.* (2000) took rice plants growing in ambient air and placed them in an atmospheric CO_2 concentration of 175 ppm, which reduced their photosynthesis rates by 45%. After five days of exposure to this sub-ambient CO_2 concentration, however, the plants manifested an up-regulation of rubisco, which stimulated photosynthetic rates by 35%. Thus, plant acclimation responses can involve both increases and decreases in specific enzymcs, depending on the nature of the change in atmospheric CO_2 concentration.

These observations demonstrate the reduced need for nitrogen investment in leaf rubisco in plants growing in CO_2-enriched environments. Under such conditions, plants are able to reallocate some of their "surplus" nitrogen to other processes essential to optimal growth and development without compromising enhanced carbon gains via photosynthesis. The end result, as almost always observed in well-run experiments, is increased biomass pro-duction in CO_2-enriched air (see Section 1.1.1, this volume).

References

Farage, P.K., McKee, I.F., and Long, S.P. 1998. Does a low nitrogen supply necessarily lead to acclimation of photosynthesis to elevated CO_2? *Plant Physiology* **118**: 573–580.

Gesch, R.W., Boote, K.J., Vu, J.C.V., Allen Jr., L.H., and Bowes, G. 1998. Changes in growth CO_2 result in rapid adjustments of ribulose-1,5-bisphosphate carboxylase/ oxygenase small subunit gene expression in expanding and mature leaves of rice. *Plant Physiology* **118**: 521–529.

Gesch, R.W., Vu, J.C.V., Boote, K.J., Allen Jr., L.H., and Bowes, G. 2000. Subambient growth CO_2 leads to increased Rubisco small subunit gene expression in developing rice leaves. *Journal of Plant Physiology* **157**: 235–238.

Maroco, J.P., Edwards, G.E., and Ku, M.S.B. 1999. Photosynthetic acclimation of maize to growth under elevated levels of carbon dioxide. *Planta* **210**: 115–125.

Osborne, C.P., LaRoche, J., Garcia, R.L., Kimball, B.A., Wall, G.W., Pinter Jr., P.J., LaMorte, R.L., Hendrey, G.R., and Long, S.P. 1998. Does leaf position within a canopy affect acclimation of photosynthesis to elevated CO_2? *Plant Physiology* **117**: 1037–1045.

Pritchard, S.G., Ju, Z., van Santen, E., Qiu, J., Weaver, D.B., Prior, S.A., and Rogers, H.H. 2000. The influence of elevated CO_2 on the activities of antioxidative enzymes in two soybean genotypes. *Australian Journal of Plant Physiology* **27**: 1061–1068.

Reid, C.D., Fiscus, E.L., and Burkey, K.O. 1998. Combined effects of chronic ozone and elevated CO_2 on rubisco activity and leaf components in soybean (*Glycine max*). *Journal of Experimental Botany* **49**: 1999–2011.

Sicher, R.C. and Bunce, J.A. 1999. Photosynthetic enhancement and conductance to water vapor of field-grown *Solanum tuberosum* (L.) in response to CO_2 enrichment. *Photosynthesis Research* **62**: 155–163.

Sims, D.A., Cheng, W., Luo, Y., and Seeman, J.R. 1999. Photosynthetic acclimation to elevated CO_2 in a sunflower canopy. *Journal of Experimental Botany* **50**: 645–653.

Sims, D.A., Luo, Y., and Seeman, J.R. 1998. Comparison of photosynthetic acclimation to elevated CO_2 and limited nitrogen supply in soybean. *Plant, Cell and Environment* **21**: 945–952.

Theobald, J.C., Mitchell, R.A.C., Parry, M.A.J., and Lawlor, D.W. 1998. Estimating the excess investment in ribulose-1,5-bisphosphate carboxylase/oxygenase in leaves of spring wheat grown under elevated CO_2. *Plant Physiology* **118**: 945–955.

2.24.2 Grassland Species

- The reduced need for nitrogen investment in leaf rubisco in grassland plants growing in CO_2-enriched environments enables them to reallocate some of this "surplus" nitrogen to other limiting processes required for optimal growth and development without compromising enhanced carbon gains via photosynthesis.

As is the case with agricultural plants, voluminous experimental data demonstrate atmospheric CO_2 enrichment also favors carboxylation over oxygenation in grassland species, which in turn increases their photosynthetic rates and decreases their photorespiratory rates. That means the rising CO_2 content of the air invariably leads to greater rates of net photosynthesis and a more efficient process of carbon fixation, where once again less rubisco is needed to obtain the carbon required for maximum plant growth and development under CO_2-enriched conditions.

Thus, plants grown in elevated atmospheric CO_2 environments often, but not always (Ziska *et al.*, 1999), exhibit some degree of photosynthetic acclimation or down-regulation, typically characterized by reduced amounts of rubisco and/or decreases in its activation state. However, in nearly every reported case of CO_2-induced photosynthetic acclimation, net photosynthetic rates displayed by CO_2-enriched plants were still significantly greater than those exhibited by plants growing in ambient air.

Cheng *et al.* (1998), for example, grew the herbaceous plant *Arabidopsis thaliana* at an atmospheric CO_2 concentration of 1,000 ppm for 40 days; they found the elevated CO_2 reduced foliar rubisco contents by 34%. However, the elevated CO_2 enhanced foliar contents of glucose and fructose more than twofold, and starch concentrations were increased more than 3.5-fold. Thus, although elevated CO_2 reduced the amount of rubisco in leaves, photosynthetically derived sugars and starch still accumulated.

Midgley *et al.* (1999) grew four *Leucadendron* species from South Africa in air of twice-ambient CO_2 concentrations, observing a 30% reduction in the activity of rubisco. However, rates of net photosynthesis in the CO_2-enriched plants were still about 40% greater than rates measured in ambiently grown plants. Bryant *et al.* (1998) reported similar results for chalk grassland species exposed to an atmospheric CO_2 concentration of 600 ppm for 14 months. They note elevated CO_2 caused an average reduction of 32% in the rubisco activity of two forbs and one C_3 grass, while still maintaining photosynthetic rates about 28% greater than those observed in ambiently growing plants. Likewise, after growing three grasslands species from the United Kingdom for two full years at 700 ppm CO_2, Davey *et al.* (1999) reported elevated CO_2 reduced rubisco activity by an average of 27% and increased photosynthetic rates from 12 to 74% in a nutrient-dependent manner.

In the illuminating study of Rogers *et al.* (1998), swards of perennial ryegrass grown in air containing an extra 240 ppm of CO_2 did not exhibit any reductions in rubisco content as long as they were supplied with high levels of soil nitrogen. In contrast, at low soil nitrogen contents the CO_2-enriched plants displayed a 25% reduction in rubisco levels prior to mechanical cutting. After cutting, however, which removed a large portion of the plants' leaf area, the CO_2-enriched plants in low nitrogen completely reversed their acclimation response and increased their levels of rubisco to facilitate greater carbon uptake to repair the damage.

The bottom-line message of these observations is that the reduced need for nitrogen investment in leaf rubisco in plants growing in CO_2-enriched environments enables them to reallocate some of this "surplus" nitrogen to other limiting processes required for optimal growth and development— without compromising enhanced carbon gains via photosynthesis.

References

Bryant, J., Taylor, G., and Frehner, M. 1998. Photosynthetic acclimation to elevated CO_2 is modified by source:sink balance in three component species of chalk grassland swards grown in a free air carbon dioxide enrichment (FACE) experiment. *Plant, Cell and Environment* **21**: 159–168.

Cheng, S.-H., Moore, B.D., and Seemann, J.R. 1998. Effects of short- and long-term elevated CO_2 on the expression of ribulose-1,5-bisphosphate carboxylase/oxygenase genes and carbohydrate accumulation in leaves of *Arabidopsis thaliana* (L.) Heynh. *Plant Physiology* **116**: 715–723.

Davey, P.A., Parsons, A.J., Atkinson, L., Wadge, K., and Long, S.P. 1999. Does photosynthetic acclimation to elevated CO_2 increase photosynthetic nitrogen-use efficiency? A study of three native UK grassland species in open-top chambers. *Functional Ecology* **13**: 21–28.

Midgley, G.F., Wand, S.J.E., and Pammenter, N.W. 1999. Nutrient and genotypic effects on CO_2-responsiveness: photosynthetic regulation in *Leucadendron* species of a nutrient-poor environment. *Journal of Experimental Botany* **50**: 533–542.

Rogers, A., Fischer, B.U., Bryant, J., Frehner, M., Blum, H., Raines, C.A., and Long, S.P. 1998. Acclimation of photosynthesis to elevated CO_2 under low-nitrogen nutrition is affected by the capacity for assimilate utilization. Perennial ryegrass under free-air CO_2 enrichment. *Plant Physiology* **118**: 683–689.

Ziska, L.H., Sicher, R.C. and Bunce, J.A. 1999. The impact of elevated carbon dioxide on the growth and gas exchange of three C_4 species differing in CO_2 leak rates. *Physiologia Plantarum* **105**: 74–80.

2.24.3 Tree Species

- Woody species growing in CO_2-enriched environments have a reduced need for nitrogen investment in rubisco, which enables them to reallocate some of the "surplus" nitrogen they might possess to other processes required for optimal growth and development without compromising enhanced carbon gains via photosynthesis.

Experimental data typically demonstrate atmospheric CO_2 enrichment favors carboxylation over oxygenation in rubisco, which increases photosynthetic rates while reducing photorespiratory rates. Thus the rising CO_2 content of the air usually leads to greater rates of net photosynthesis and more efficient carbon fixation, such that less rubisco is needed to obtain the carbon required for plant growth and development under CO_2-enriched conditions.

As a consequence, trees grown in elevated CO_2 environments often, but not always (Stylinski *et al.*, 2000; Beerling *et al.*, 1998), exhibit some degree of photosynthetic acclimation or down-regulation, which typically is characterized by reduced amounts of rubisco (Gleadow *et al.*, 1998) and/or decreases in its activation state (Hamerlynck *et al.*, 2002; Kubiske *et al.*, 2002). In nearly every reported case of CO_2-induced photosynthetic acclimation, however, the net photosynthetic rates displayed by CO_2-enriched plants have been significantly greater than those exhibited by plants growing in ambient-air CO_2 concentrations (Murray *et al.*, 2000).

Tjoelker *et al.* (1998), for example, found a 210-ppm increase in the air's CO_2 content increased the average rate of net photosynthesis in aspen and birch seedlings by 57% even while inducing a 24% reduction in foliar rubisco content. Similarly, Takeuchi *et al.* (2001) report aspen seedlings grown at an atmospheric CO_2 concentration of 560 ppm exhibited photosynthetic rates in upper-canopy leaves 26% greater than those displayed by upper-canopy leaves of control plants grown in ambient air, in spite of a 28% decrease in foliar rubisco concentrations. CO_2-induced reductions in foliar rubisco contents that did not offset CO_2-induced photosynthetic enhancements also have been reported in oak (Blaschke *et al.*, 2001) and pine (Turnbull *et al.*, 1998) trees.

In another manifestation of photosynthetic acclimation, Centritto *et al.* (1999) observe elevated CO_2 reduced the activity of rubisco without negating CO_2-induced increases in photosynthesis, and Centritto and Jarvis (1999) report twice-ambient atmospheric CO_2 concentrations reduced rubisco activity in Sitka spruce needles by 36% while enhancing photosynthetic rates by 62%. Similarly, Turnbull *et al.*, (1998) report pine seedlings grown at 650 ppm CO_2 displayed 40% reductions in rubisco activity while exhibiting photosynthetic rates 31% greater than those observed in ambiently grown control seedlings. Rey and Jarvis (1998) also documented this phenomenon in young silver birch trees.

These observations demonstrate the reduced need for nitrogen investment in rubisco in woody species growing in CO_2-enriched environments, which enables them to reallocate some of the resultant "surplus" nitrogen they might possess to other processes required for optimal growth and development without compromising enhanced carbon gains via photosynthesis.

References

Beerling, D.J., McElwain, J.C., and Osborne, C.P. 1998. Stomatal responses of the 'living fossil' *Ginkgo biloba* L. to changes in atmospheric CO_2 concentrations. *Journal of Experimental Botany* **49**: 1603–1607.

Blaschke, L., Schulte, M., Raschi, A., Slee, N., Rennenberg, H., and Polle, A. 2001. Photosynthesis, soluble and structural carbon compounds in two Mediterranean oak species (*Quercus pubescens* and *Q. ilex*) after lifetime growth at naturally elevated CO_2 concentrations. *Plant Biology* **3**: 288–297.

Centritto, M. and Jarvis, P.G. 1999. Long-term effects of elevated carbon dioxide concentration and provenance on four clones of Sitka spruce (*Picea sitchensis*). II. Photosynthetic capacity and nitrogen use efficiency. *Tree Physiology* **19**: 807–814.

Centritto, M., Magnani, F., Lee, H.S.J., and Jarvis, P.G. 1999. Interactive effects of elevated [CO_2] and drought on cherry (*Prunus avium*) seedlings. II. Photosynthetic capacity and water relations. *New Phytologist* **141**: 141–153.

Gleadow, R.M., Foley, W.J., and Woodrow, I.E. 1998. Enhanced CO_2 alters the relationship between photosynthesis and defense in cyanogenic *Eucalyptus cladocalyx* F. Muell. *Plant, Cell and Environment* **21**: 12–22.

Hamerlynck, E.P., Huxman, T.E., Charlet, T.N., and Smith, S.D. 2002. Effects of elevated CO_2 (FACE) on the functional ecology of the drought-deciduous Mojave Desert shrub, *Lycium andersonii*. *Environmental and Experimental Botany* **48**: 93–106.

Kubiske, M.E., Zak, D.R., Pregitzer, K.S., and Takeuchi, Y. 2002. Photosynthetic acclimation of overstory *Populus tremuloides* and understory *Acer saccharum* to elevated atmospheric CO_2 concentration: interactions with shade and soil nitrogen. *Tree Physiology* **22**: 321–329.

Murray, M.B., Smith, R.I., Friend, A., and Jarvis, P.G.

2000. Effect of elevated [CO_2] and varying nutrient application rates on physiology and biomass accumulation of Sitka spruce (*Picea sitchensis*). *Tree Physiology* **20**: 421–434.

Rey, A. and Jarvis, P.G. 1998. Long-term photosynthetic acclimation to increased atmospheric CO_2 concentration in young birch (*Betula pendula*) trees. *Tree Physiology* **18**: 441–450.

Stylinski, C.D., Oechel, W.C., Gamon, J.A., Tissue, D.T., Miglietta, F., and Raschi, A. 2000. Effects of lifelong [CO_2] enrichment on carboxylation and light utilization of *Quercus pubescens* Willd. examined with gas exchange, biochemistry and optical techniques. *Plant, Cell and Environment* **23**: 1353–1362.

Takeuchi, Y., Kubiske, M.E., Isebrands, J.G., Pregitzer, K.S., Hendrey, G., and Karnosky, D.F. 2001. Photosynthesis, light and nitrogen relationships in a young deciduous forest canopy under open-air CO_2 enrichment. *Plant, Cell and Environment* **24**: 1257–1268.

Tjoelker, M.G., Oleksyn, J., and Reich, P.B. 1998. Seedlings of five boreal tree species differ in acclimation of net photosynthesis to elevated CO_2 and temperature. *Tree Physiology* **18**: 715–726.

Turnbull, M.H., Tissue, D.T., Griffin, K.L., Rogers, G.N.D., and Whitehead, D. 1998. Photosynthetic acclimation to long-term exposure to elevated CO_2 concentration in *Pinus radiata* D. Don. is related to age of needles. *Plant, Cell and Environment* **21**: 1019–1028.

2.25 Seeds

Atmospheric CO_2 enrichment has been shown to increase amount, size, weight, carbohydrate content, lipid content, protein content, earlier production, earlier germination, and greater percent germination of various plant seeds, all of which bode well for the future of Earth's biosphere.

2.25.1 Crops

- Rising atmospheric CO_2 concentrations will confer several benefits on the seeds of crop plants, including an increase in seed quantity and improvements in seed quality.

When dealing with agricultural commodities such as grain crops, seeds comprise the yield, and in such cases the biomass of one (seeds) is the biomass of the other (yield). Therefore, when looking for effects of elevated CO_2 on the seeds of such crops, there is a natural interest in something more than just their final biomass. A number of pertinent papers are explored in this section that consider the sources of biomass production as well as seed properties that go beyond biomass.

In a greenhouse study of the various components of seed biomass production, Palta and Ludwig (2000) grew narrow-leafed lupine in pots filled with soil within Mylar-film tunnels maintained at either 355 or 700 ppm CO_2. They found the extra CO_2 increased the final number of pods and the number of pods that filled large seeds, while it reduced to zero the number of pods that had small seeds, reduced the number of pods with unfilled seeds from 16 to 1 pod per plant, and increased pod set and dry matter accumulation on the developing branches. These CO_2-induced improvements in key physiological processes resulted in 47 to 56% increases in dry matter per plant, which led to increases of 44 to 66% in seed yield per plant.

Sanhewe *et al.* (1996) grew winter wheat in polyethylene tunnels maintained at atmospheric CO_2 concentrations of 380 and 680 ppm from the time of seed germination to the time of plant maturity, maintaining a temperature gradient of approximately 4°C in each tunnel. In addition to the elevated CO_2 increasing seed yield per unit area, they found it also increased seed weight, but not seed survival or germination. Increasing air temperature, on the other hand, increased seed longevity across the entire range of temperatures investigated (14 to 19°C).

Thomas *et al.* (2003) grew soybean plants to maturity in sunlit controlled-environment chambers under sinusoidally varying day/night-max/min temperatures of 28/18, 32/22, 36/26, 40/30, and 44/34°C and two levels of atmospheric CO_2 concentration (350 and 700 ppm). The effect of temperature on seed composition and gene expression was "pronounced," but "there was no effect of CO_2." However, they note, "Heagle *et al.* (1998) observed a positive significant effect of CO_2 enrichment on soybean seed oil and oleic acid concentration," and Thomas *et al.* did find the latter parameters increased with rising temperature, from 28/18 to 44/34°C. In addition, they found, "32/22°C is optimum for producing the highest oil concentration in soybean seed," "the degree of fatty acid saturation in soybean oil was significantly increased by increasing temperature," and crude protein concentration increased with temperature to 40/30°C.

Thomas *et al.* note "the intrinsic value of soybean seed is in its supply of essential fatty acids and amino acids in the oil and protein, respectively." Thus the temperature-driven changes they identified in these parameters, as well as the CO_2 effect observed by Heagle *et al.*, bode well for the future production of this important crop and its value to society in a CO_2-enriched and warming world. They do note, however, "temperatures during the soybean-growing season in the southern USA are at, or slightly higher than, 32/22°C," and warming could negatively impact the soybean oil industry in this region. For the world as a whole, however, warming would be a positive development for soybean production, and in the southern United States, shifts in planting zones could accommodate changing weather patterns associated with this phenomenon.

Ziska *et al.* (2001) grew one modern and eight ancestral soybean genotypes in glasshouses maintained at atmospheric CO_2 concentrations of 400 and 710 ppm, finding the extra CO_2 increased photosynthetic rates by an average of 75%. This enhancement in photosynthetic sugar production led to increases in seed yield that averaged 40% for all cultivars, except for one ancestral variety that exhibited an 80% increase in seed yield. Hence, if plant breeders utilize the highly CO_2-responsive ancestral cultivar identified in this study in their breeding programs, soybean seed yields could rise even faster and higher in the future.

Fiscus *et al.* (2007) grew well-watered and well-fertilized soybean (*Glycine max* (L.) Merr. cv. Essex) plants from seed to maturity for one full growing season out-of-doors near Raleigh, North Carolina (USA) within open-top chambers, either rooted in the ground or in 21-liter pots (one plant per pot) at equal plant densities per unit ground area, while exposing the plants to charcoal-filtered air maintained at CO_2 concentrations of either 370 or 700 ppm.

Although seed yields in the container-grown plants were about 17% less than those of the plants rooted directly in the ground, the CO_2-induced enhancement ratios of both sets of plants were not significantly different from each other, averaging approximately 20%. In addition, the six researchers state, "there was a small (3–4%) but highly significant increase in the seed oil concentration due to elevated CO_2," and this increase was experienced in both rooting environments. Fiscus *et al.* note, "the 3 to 4% increase in oil per seed would amount to a very substantial increase in oil production on a regional, national, or international scale." For the year 2005, for example, they calculated "an increase of 3.5% of seed oil concentration could result in an additional 2.9 Tg of seed oil in a future climate with CO_2 concentrations well above current ambient levels."

Derner *et al.* (2004) determined above- and below-ground responses of three generations of two genotypes of spring wheat to atmospheric CO_2 enrichment to 336 ppm above ambient. This experiment was conducted in glasshouse bays, where the second- and third-generation plants were progeny of seeds produced by plants grown at either ambient or enriched atmospheric CO_2 concentrations under well-watered and high soil-nutrient conditions.

Neither genotype in the first generation exhibited enhanced growth in response to the increased concentration of atmospheric CO_2. However, Derner *et al.* report, "relative enhancement occurred in both the second and third generations for both above- and below-ground variables," and the "relative enhancement of measured variables was generally greater in the third than second generation when plants were in the seedling or vegetative stage." They also determined "intergenerational above- and below-ground responses of this C_3 annual plant to CO_2 enrichment are not driven by genetic change (selection) that occurred between generations, but rather CO_2-induced changes in seeds that affected seedling responses to CO_2 enrichment."

References

Derner, J.D., Tischler, C.R., Polley, H.W., and Johnson, H.B. 2004. Intergenerational above- and belowground responses of spring wheat (*Triticum aestivum* L.) to elevated CO_2. *Basic and Applied Ecology* **5**: 145–152.

Fiscus, E.L., Booker, F.L., Dubois, J.-J. B., Rufty, T.W., Burton, J.W., and Pursley, W.A. 2007. Carbon dioxide enhancement effects in container- versus ground-grown soybean at equal planting densities. *Crop Science* **47**: 2486–2494.

Heagle, A.S., Miller, J.E., and Pursley, W.A. 1998. Influence of ozone stress on soybean response to carbon dioxide enrichment: III. Yield and seed quality. *Crop Science* **38**: 128–134.

Palta, J.A. and Ludwig, C. 2000. Elevated CO_2 during pod filling increased seed yield but not harvest index in indeterminate narrow-leafed lupine. *Australian Journal of Agricultural Research* **51**: 279–286.

Sanhewe, A.J., Ellis, R.H., Hong, T.D., Wheeler, T.R., Batts, G.R., Hadley, P., and Morison, J.I.L. 1996. The effect of temperature and CO_2 on seed quality development in wheat (*Triticum aestivum* L.). *Journal of Experimental Botany* **47**: 631–637.

Thomas, J.M.G., Boote, K.J., Allen Jr., L.H., Gallo-Meagher, M., and Davis, J.M. 2003. Elevated temperature and carbon dioxide effects on soybean seed composition and transcript abundance. *Crop Science* **43**: 1548–1557.

Ziska, L.H., Bunce, J.A., and Caulfield, F.A. 2001. Rising atmospheric carbon dioxide and seed yields of soybean genotypes. *Crop Science* **41**: 385–391.

2.25.2 Grasslands

- Atmospheric CO_2 enrichment typically increases the amount, size, and weight of seeds produced and dispersed each year by various grassland species, as well as their carbon/nitrogen ratios and germination percentage. Concomitant increases in air temperature may result in advancements of flowering and fruiting phenology, which can increase spread rates of plant populations because wind conditions in spring tend to produce higher spread rates than wind conditions later in the year.

Steinger *et al.* (2000) collected seeds from *Bromus erectus* plants grown at atmospheric CO_2 concentrations of 360 and 650 ppm, and then germinated some of both groups of seeds under those same two sets of conditions. In the first part of their study, they found the elevated CO_2 treatment increased individual seed mass by about 9% and increased the seed carbon-to-nitrogen ratio by almost 10%. These changes in seed properties had little impact on subsequent seedling growth; when the seeds produced by ambient or CO_2-enriched plants were germinated and grown in ambient air, there was no significant size difference between the two groups of resultant seedlings after a period of 19 days. Likewise, when the seeds produced from the ambient and CO_2-enriched plants were germinated and grown in the high CO_2 treatment, there was no significant difference between the sizes of the seedlings derived from the two groups of seeds. However, the CO_2-enriched seedlings produced from both groups of seeds were almost 20% larger than the seedlings produced from both groups of seeds grown in ambient air, demonstrating the direct effects of atmospheric CO_2 enrichment on seedling growth and development were more important than the differences in seed characteristics produced by the elevated atmospheric CO_2 concentration in which their parent plants grew.

Edwards *et al.* (2001) employed a FACE experiment where daytime atmospheric CO_2 concentrations above a sheep-grazed pasture in New Zealand were increased by 115 ppm, in order to study the effects of elevated CO_2 on seed production, seedling recruitment, and species compositional changes. In the two years of their study, the extra daytime CO_2 increased seed production and dispersal in seven of the eight most abundant species, including the grasses *Anthoxanthum odoratum*, *Lolium perenne*, and *Poa pratensis*, the legumes *Trifolium repens* and *T. subterranean*, and the herbs *Hypochaeris radicata* and *Leontodon saxatilis*. In some of these plants, elevated CO_2 also increased the number of seeds per reproductive structure, and all exhibited CO_2-induced increases in the number of reproductive structures per unit of ground area. In addition, the CO_2-induced increases in seed production contributed to the increase in the numbers of species found within the CO_2-enriched plots.

In a five-year study of a nutrient-poor calcareous grassland in Switzerland, Thurig *et al.* (2003) used screen-aided CO_2 control (SACC) technology (Leadley *et al.*, 1997) to enrich the air over half of their experimental plots with an extra 300 ppm of CO_2. They found "the effect of elevated CO_2 on the number of flowering shoots (+24%) and seeds (+29%) at the community level was similar to above ground biomass response." In terms of species functional groups, there was a 42% increase in the mean seed number of graminoids and a 33% increase in the mean seed number of forbs, but no change in legume seed numbers. In most species, mean seed weight also tended to be greater in plants grown in CO_2-enriched air (+12%), and Thurig *et al.* note many studies have shown heavier seeds result in seedlings "more robust than seedlings from lighter seeds (Baskin and Baskin, 1998)."

Wang and Griffin (2003) grew dioecious white campion plants from seed to maturity in sand-filled pots maintained at optimum moisture and fertility conditions in environmentally controlled growth chambers in which the air was continuously maintained at CO_2 concentrations of either 365 or 730 ppm. In response to this doubling of the air's CO_2 content, the vegetative mass of both male and female plants rose by approximately 39%. Reproductive mass rose by 82% in male plants and by 97% in females. In the female plants, this was accomplished, in part, by increases of 36% and 44% in the number and mass of seeds per plant, and by a 15% increase in the mass of individual seeds, in harmony with the findings of Jablonski *et al.* (2002), which they derived from a meta-analysis of the results of 159 CO_2 enrichment experiments conducted on 79 species of agricultural and wild plants. Dioecious plants comprise nearly half of all angiosperm families, so their allocation of a greater proportion of plant biomass to reproduction in a high-CO_2 world of the future bodes well for the biodiversity of Earth's ecosystems.

Wang (2005) grew well-watered and -fertilized specimens of *Silene latifolia* from seed to maturity in pots within controlled environment chambers maintained at mean CO_2 concentrations of 386 and 696 ppm, documenting reproductive responses during growth and at final harvest. Then, the seeds produced by the plants in this experiment were used to grow a second generation of plants under the same environmental conditions in which the parent plants had been grown.

In the first experiment, the total reproductive biomass of the plants grown in CO_2-enriched air was 32% greater than that of the plants grown in ambient air, as was the total number of fruit produced. In the second experiment, for seeds from female plants grown in ambient air, 55% of all emergence occurred within six days of sowing, and for seeds from plants grown in CO_2-enriched air, 67% of total emergence occurred during the same period. In addition, 87% of the seeds from the elevated-CO_2-grown plants ultimately germinated, whereas only 67% of the seeds from the ambient-CO_2-grown plants did so. Finally, the plants produced a greater percentage of female progeny in the CO_2-enriched air than in ambient-air (56.3% vs. 52.7%).

The combined effect of a greater number of seeds being produced per female plant, a higher percentage of seed germination, and more female-biased seed production in CO_2-enriched air suggest white campion plants will fare well in a high-CO_2 world of the future, which might cause some to worry, as it is a rather cosmopolitan and somewhat weedy species. However, any plants of agricultural value with which it might compete also will be doing better in such conditions. Hence, the greater importance of this study is what it may imply about other dioecious species, especially in light of the fact that *Silene latifolia*, in the words of Wang, "has become a model system for studying sexual dimorphism and sex-determination mechanisms and is likely the most extensively studied dioecious species."

Kuparinen *et al.* (2009) investigated the effects of a warming-induced increase in local convective turbulence (caused by a postulated 3°C increase in local temperature) on the long-distance dispersal (LDD) of seeds and pollen based on mechanistic models of wind dispersal (Kuparinen *et al.*, 2007) and population spread (Clark *et al.*, 2001) in a boreal forest of southern Finland. For light-seeded herbs, the group of researchers report spread rates increased by 35–42 m/yr (6.3–9.2%), and for heavy-seeded herbs the increase was 0.01-0.06 m/yr (1.9–6.7%). In addition, they note, "climate change driven advancements of flowering and fruiting phenology can increase spread rates of plant populations because wind conditions in spring tend to produce higher spread rates than wind conditions later in the year."

The four researchers from France, Germany, Israel, and the United States conclude—in addition to the obvious benefits of greater LDD (being better able to move toward more hospitable locations)—the increased wind dispersal of seeds and pollen may "promote geneflow between populations, thus increasing their genetic diversity and decreasing the risk of inbreeding depression," citing Ellstrand (1992) and Aguilar et al. (2008). They further note, "increased gene flow between neighboring populations can accelerate adaptation to environmental change," citing Davis and Shaw (2001) and Savolainen et al. (2007). The scientists report the "dispersal and spread of populations are widely viewed as a means by which species can buffer negative effects of climate change."

References

Aguilar, R., Quesada, M., Ashworth, L., Herrerias-Diego, Y., and Lobo, J. 2008. Genetic consequences of habitat fragmentation in plant populations: susceptible signals in plant traits and methodological approaches. *Molecular Ecology* 17: 5177–5188.

Baskin, C.C. and Baskin, J.M. 1998. *Seeds: Ecology, Biogeography, and Evolution of Dormancy and Germination*. Academic Press, San Diego, CA.

Clark, J.S., Lewis, M., and Hovarth, L. 2001. Invasion by extremes; population spread with variation in dispersal and reproduction. *American Naturalist* 157: 537–544.

Davis, M.B. and Shaw, R.G. 2001. Range shifts and adaptive responses to quaternary climate change. *Science* 292: 673–679.

Edwards, G.R., Clark, H., and Newton, P.C.D. 2001. The effects of elevated CO_2 on seed production and seedling recruitment in a sheep-grazed pasture. *Oecologia* 127: 383–394.

Ellstrand, N.C. 1992. Gene flow by pollen: Implications for plant conservation genetics. *Oikos* 63: 77–86.

Jablonski, L.M., Wang, X., and Curtis, P.S. 2002. Plant reproduction under elevated CO_2 conditions: a meta-analysis of reports on 79 crop and wild species. *New Phytologist* 156: 9–26.

Kuparinen, A., Katul, G., Nathan, R., and Schurr, F.M. 2009. Increases in air temperature can promote wind-driven dispersal and spread of plants. *Proceedings of the Royal Society B* 276: 3081–3087.

Leadley, P.W., Niklaus, P.A., and Stocker, R., *et al.* 1997. Screen-aided CO_2 control (SACC): a middle ground between FACE and open-top chambers. *Acta Oecologica* 18: 39–49.

Savolainen, O., Pyhajarvi, T., and Knurr, T. 2007. Gene flow and local adaptation in trees. *Annual Review of Ecology, Evolution and Systematics* 38: 595–619.

Steinger, T., Gall, R., and Schmid, B. 2000. Maternal and direct effects of elevated CO_2 on seed provisioning, germination and seedling growth in *Bromus erectus*. *Oecologia* 123: 475–480.

Thurig, B., Korner, C., and Stocklin, J. 2003. Seed production and seed quality in a calcareous grassland in elevated CO_2. *Global Change Biology* 9: 873–884.

Wang, X. 2005. Reproduction and progeny of *Silene latifolia* (Caryophyllaceae) as affected by atmospheric CO_2 concentration. *American Journal of Botany* 92: 826–832.

Wang, X. and Griffin, K.L. 2003. Sex-specific physiological and growth responses to elevated atmospheric CO_2 in *Silene latifolia* Poiret. *Global Change Biology* 9: 612–618.

2.25.3 Trees

- Atmospheric CO_2 enrichment typically increases seed amount, size, weight, carbohydrate content, lipid content, and protein content, and also causes earlier production, earlier germination, and greater percent of germination.

LaDeau and Clark (2001) investigated how enriching the air with CO_2 impacts the reproductive capacity of trees by determining various responses of loblolly pines to atmospheric CO_2 enrichment at the Duke Forest in the Piedmont region of North Carolina (USA). In August 1996 three 30-m-diameter FACE rings had been set up around three groups of the 13-year-old trees to enrich the air about them to 200 ppm above the atmosphere's normal background concentration; three identical FACE rings served as control plots. The trees were not mature at the start of the experiment, so they did not produce any cones until a few rare ones appeared in 1998. By the fall of 1999, however, the scientists found the CO_2-enriched trees were twice as likely as trees growing in ambient air to be reproductively mature, and they produced three times more cones per tree. Similarly, the trees growing in the CO_2-enriched air produced 2.4 times more cones in the fall of 2000, and from August 1999 through July 2000, the scientists collected three times as many seeds in the CO_2-fertilized FACE rings as in the control rings.

Hussain *et al.* (2001) also worked on this aspect of the Duke Forest FACE study. They report seeds collected from the CO_2-enriched trees were 91% heavier than those collected from the trees growing in ambient air, and the CO_2-enriched seeds had a lipid content 265% greater than that of the seeds produced on the ambient-treatment trees. They also noted the germination success for seeds developed under atmospheric CO_2 enrichment was more than three times greater than for control seeds developed at ambient CO_2, regardless of germination CO_2 concentration. Seeds from the CO_2-enriched trees germinated approximately five days earlier than their ambiently produced counterparts, again regardless of germination CO_2 concentration, and seedlings developing from seeds collected from CO_2-enriched trees displayed significantly greater root lengths and needle numbers than seedlings developing from trees exposed to ambient air, also regardless of growth CO_2 concentration.

The propensity for elevated levels of atmospheric CO_2 to hasten the production of more plentiful seeds on the trees of this valuable timber species bodes well for naturally regenerating loblolly pine stands of the southeastern United States, where LaDeau and Clark report the trees "are profoundly seed-limited for at least 25 years." Hence, as the air's CO_2 content continues to climb, they conclude, "this period of seed limitation may be reduced." In addition, the observations of Hussain *et al.* suggest loblolly pine trees in a CO_2-enriched world of the future likely will display significant increases in their photosynthetic rates. Enhanced carbohydrate supplies resulting from this phenomenon likely will increase seed weight and lipid content. Such seeds consequently should exhibit significant increases in germination success, and their enhanced lipid supplies likely will lead to greater root lengths and needle numbers in developing seedlings. Consequently, when CO_2-enriched loblolly pine seedlings become photosynthetically active, they likely will produce biomass at greater rates than those exhibited by seedlings growing under current CO_2 concentrations.

Five years later, LaDeau and Clark (2006a) conducted a follow-up study extending this work. They found "carbon dioxide enrichment affected mean cone production both through early maturation and increased fecundity," so "trees in the elevated CO_2 plots produced twice as many cones between 1998 and 2004 as trees in the ambient plots." In addition, the trees grown in elevated CO_2 "made the transition to reproductive maturation at smaller [trunk] diameters," and they "not only reached reproductive maturation at smaller diameters, but also at younger ages." By 2004, for example, "roughly 50% of ambient trees and 75% of fumigated trees [had] produced cones." In addition, "22% of the trees in high CO_2 produced between 40 and 100 cones during the study, compared with only 9% of ambient trees."

"In this 8-year study," the two researchers write, they found "previous short-term responses indeed persist," in contradiction of those who downplay the immense biological benefits of atmospheric CO_2 enrichment. In addition, they note, "*P. taeda* trees that produce large seed crops early in their life span tend to continue to be prolific producers (Schultz, 1997)," and they conclude this fact, together with their findings, suggests "individual responses seen in this young forest may be sustained over their life span."

LaDeau and Clark (2006b) additionally analyzed the seed and pollen responses of the loblolly pines to atmospheric CO_2 enrichment, finding the "trees grown in high-CO_2 plots first began producing pollen while younger and at smaller sizes relative to ambient-grown trees." Cone pollen and airborne pollen grain abundances were significantly greater in the CO_2-enriched stands. They write, "by spring 2005, 63% of all trees growing in high CO_2 had produced both pollen and seeds vs. only 36% of trees in the ambient plots."

This propensity for elevated concentrations of atmospheric CO_2 to hasten and increase the production of pollen by this valuable timber species bodes well for naturally regenerated loblolly pine stands, which have a continuous range from Maryland south to Florida and west to Texas, where they currently are profoundly seed-limited for at least 25 years. In addition, the two researchers indicate precocious pollen production "could enhance the production of viable seeds by increasing the percentage of fertilized ovules," and "more pollen disseminated from multiple-source trees may also increase rates of gene flow among stands, and could further reduce rates of self-pollination, indirectly enhancing the production of viable seeds." Also of importance, in view of the negative twists some attempt to put on even overwhelmingly positive research findings, they state, "pine pollen is not a dangerous allergen for the public at large."

Another major study of the reproductive responses of trees to elevated levels of atmospheric CO_2 was conducted at the Kennedy Space Center, Florida (USA), where in 1996 researchers enclosed three species of scrub-oak (*Quercus myrtifolia, Q. chapmanii*, and *Q. geminata*) within 16 open-top chambers, half of which were maintained at 379 ppm CO_2 and half at 704 ppm. Five years later—in August, September, and October 2001—Stiling *et al.* (2004) counted the acorns on randomly selected twigs of each species, and in November they counted fallen acorns of each species within equal-size quadrates of ground area, additionally evaluating mean acorn weight, acorn germination rate, and degree of acorn infestation by weevils.

Acorn germination rate and degree of predation by weevils were unaffected by elevated CO_2, and acorn size was enhanced by a small amount: 3.6% for *Q. myrtifolia*, 7.0% for *Q. chapmanii*, and 7.7% for *Q. geminata*. Acorn number responses, on the other hand, were enormous, but for only two of the three species, as *Q. geminata* did not register any CO_2-induced increase in reproductive output, in harmony with its unresponsive overall growth rate. For *Q. myrtifolia*, however, Stiling *et al.* report, "there were four times as many acorns per 100 twigs in elevated CO_2 as in ambient CO_2 and for *Q. chapmanii* the increase was over threefold." On the ground, the enhancement was greater still, with the researchers reporting "the number of *Q. myrtifolia* acorns per meter squared in elevated CO_2 was over seven times greater than in ambient CO_2 and for *Q. chapmanii*, the increase was nearly sixfold."

Stiling *et al.* thus conclude "there will be large increases in seedling production in scrub-oak forests in an atmosphere of elevated CO_2," noting "this is important because many forest systems are 'recruitment-limited' (Ribbens *et al.*, 1994; Hubbell *et al.*, 1999)." This conclusion echoes that of LaDeau and Clark with respect to loblolly pines. Therefore, and if other trees behave similarly, the rising CO_2 content of Earth's atmosphere likely will be a great boon to the regenerative prowess of the planet's forests.

A third major study of CO_2 effects on seed production in trees was conducted at the FACE facility near Rhinelander, Wisconsin (USA), where young paper birch (*Betula papyrifera* Marsh.) seedlings were planted in 1997 and had been growing since 1998 in open-top chambers maintained at atmospheric CO_2 concentrations of either 360 or 560 ppm, as well as at atmospheric ozone (O_3) concentrations of either ambient or 1.5 times ambient. Darbah *et al.* (2007) collected many types of data pertaining to flowering, seed production, seed germination, and new seedling growth and development over the 2004–2006 growing seasons.

They found "elevated CO_2 had significant positive effect[s] on birch catkin size, weight, and germination success rate." Specifically, "elevated CO_2 increased germination rate of birch by 110%, compared to ambient CO_2 concentrations, decreased seedling mortality by 73%, increased seed weight by 17% [and] increased [new seedling] root length by 59%."

The six researchers found "the opposite was true of elevated O_3"; it "decreased the germination rate of birch by 62%, decreased seed weight by 25%, and increased [new seedling] root length by [only] 15%." In addition, they note, "the seeds produced under elevated O_3 had much less stored carbohydrate, lipids, and proteins for the newly developing seedling to depend on and, hence, the slow growth rate." They also report "the total number of trees that flowered increased by 139% under elevated CO_2 [but only] 40% under elevated O_3." Likewise, they state, "with respect to the quantity of flowers produced, elevated CO_2 had [a] 262% increase, while that of elevated O_3 had [only a] 75% increase compared to the control treatment."

Darbah *et al.* state their findings imply seedling recruitment in paper birch "will be enhanced under elevated CO_2 but reduced under elevated O_3."

References

Darbah, J.N.T., Kubiske, M.E., Nelson, N., Oksanen, E., Vaapavuori, E., and Karnosky, D.F. 2007. Impacts of elevated atmospheric CO_2 and O_3 on paper Birch (*Betula papyrifera*): Reproductive fitness. *The Scientific World Journal* **7**(S1): 240–246.

Hubbell, S.P., Foster, R.B., O'Brien, S.T., Harms, K.E., Condit, R., Wechsler, B., Wright, S.J., and Loo de Lao, S. 1999. Light-gap disturbances, recruitment limitation, and tree diversity in a neotropical forest. *Science* **283**: 554–557.

Hussain, M., Kubiske, M.E., and Connor, K.F. 2001. Germination of CO_2-enriched *Pinus taeda* L. seeds and subsequent seedling growth responses to CO_2 enrichment. *Functional Ecology* **15**: 344–350.

LaDeau, S.L. and Clark, J.S. 2001. Rising CO_2 levels and the fecundity of forest trees. *Science* **292**: 95–98.

LaDeau, S.L. and Clark, J.S. 2006a. Elevated CO_2 and tree fecundity: the role of tree size, interannual variability, and population heterogeneity. *Global Change Biology* **12**: 822–833.

LaDeau, S.L. and Clark, J.S. 2006b. Pollen production by *Pinus taeda* growing in elevated atmospheric CO_2. *Functional Ecology* **20**: 541–547.

Ribbens, E., Silander, J.A., and Pacala, S.W. 1994.

Seedling recruitment in forests: calibrating models to predict patterns of tree seedling dispersion. *Ecology* **75**: 1794–1806.

Schultz, R.P. 1997. *Loblolly Pine—The Ecology and Culture of Loblolly Pine (Pinus taeda L.).* USDA Forest Service Agricultural Handbook 713. USDA Forest Service, Washington, DC, USA.

Stiling, P., Moon, D., Hymus, G., and Drake, B. 2004. Differential effects of elevated CO_2 on acorn density, weight, germination, and predation among three oak species in a scrub-oak forest. *Global Change Biology* **10**: 228–232.

2.26 Starch

- As the air's CO_2 content rises, most of Earth's vegetation responds with enhanced rates of photosynthesis and greater production of carbohydrates. Many of these carbohydrates are exported from leaves and needles to provide energy or carbon skeletons to facilitate increased biomass production, after which remaining carbohydrates are generally converted into starch and stored within leaves or roots for future use.

CO_2-induced starch accumulation is occurring in a variety of plants. Janssens *et al.* (1998) found a six-month period of atmospheric CO_2 exposure of 700 ppm caused a 90% increase in root starch accumulation in Scots pine seedlings relative to control seedlings exposed to ambient CO_2 of 350 ppm. Studying the same species, Kainulainen *et al.* (1998) report a significant enhancement in needle starch concentrations after three years of atmospheric CO_2 enrichment to 300 ppm above ambient. Similar results have been reported in tropical trees, where 10 (Lovelock *et al.*, 1998) and four (Wurth *et al.*, 1998) species exhibited approximate doublings of their leaf starch contents in response to a doubling of the atmospheric CO_2 content. In other tree studies, Rey and Jarvis (1998) noted a 100% CO_2-induced increase in leaf starch contents of birch seedlings exposed to an atmospheric CO_2 concentration of 700 ppm, and Pan *et al.* (1998) report a 17-fold increase in this parameter for apple seedlings grown at an atmospheric CO_2 concentration of 1600 ppm.

Liu *et al.* (2005) found the combined effects of elevated CO_2 and ozone (O_3) produced a significant increase in leaf nonstructural carbohydrates of three- and four-year-old European beech (*Fagus sylvatica* L.) and Norway spruce (*Picea abies* (L.) Karst) seedlings under both mixed and monoculture conditions, which was similar to what was observed under CO_2 enrichment alone. Hence, they conclude, "since the responses to the combined exposure were more similar to elevated pCO_2 than to elevated pO_3, apparently elevated pCO_2 overruled the effects of elevated pO_3 on nonstructural carbohydrates."

Kostiainen *et al.* (2006) also studied the combined effects of elevated carbon dioxide and ozone, examining fast-growing silver birch (*Betula pendula* Roth) clones grown out-of-doors at Suonenjoki, Finland, in open-top chambers maintained at ambient and 1.9x ambient CO_2 concentrations in combination with ambient and 1.5x ambient O_3 concentrations.

Among other findings, the five researchers report the elevated CO_2 treatment increased trunk starch concentration by 7%. Recognizing "the concentration of nonstructural carbohydrates (starch and soluble sugars) in tree tissues is considered a measure of carbon shortage or surplus for growth (Korner, 2003)," the Finnish researchers state the "starch accumulation observed under elevated CO_2 in this study indicates a surplus of carbohydrates produced by enhanced photosynthesis of the same trees (Riikonen *et al.*, 2004)." In addition, they report, "during winter, starch reserves in the stem are gradually transformed to soluble carbohydrates involved in freezing tolerance (Bertrand *et al.*, 1999; Piispanen and Saranpaa, 2001), so the increase in starch concentration may improve acclimation in winter." The ongoing rise in the air's CO_2 content should be a boon to silver birch (and likely many other trees) in both summer and winter in both pristine and ozone-polluted air.

It should also be noted elevated CO_2 concentrations increase starch concentrations within non-woody herbaceous plants. Reid *et al.* (1998), for example, documented a doubling of the atmospheric CO_2 concentration led to a 148% increase in soybean leaf starch contents at both normal and elevated concentrations of ozone. Exposure to 1,000 ppm CO_2 caused a 10-fold increase in leaf starch concentrations of potato (Ludewig *et al.*, 1998).

It is therefore highly likely that rising atmospheric CO_2 concentrations will significantly boost starch production in plants, increasing the availability of an important raw material that can be metabolized to help sustain enhanced growth under a variety of stressful conditions.

References

Bertrand, A., Robitaille, G., Nadeau, P., and Castonguay,

Y. 1999. Influence of ozone on cold acclimation in sugar maple seedlings. *Tree Physiology* **19**: 527–534.

Janssens, I.A., Crookshanks, M., Taylor, G., and Ceulemans, R. 1998. Elevated atmospheric CO_2 increases fine root production, respiration, rhizosphere respiration and soil CO_2 efflux in Scots pine seedlings. *Global Change Biology* **4**: 871–878.

Kainulainen, P., Holopainen, J.K., and Holopainen, T. 1998. The influence of elevated CO_2 and O_3 concentrations on Scots pine needles: Changes in starch and secondary metabolites over three exposure years. *Oecologia* **114**: 455–460.

Korner, C. 2003. Carbon limitation in trees. *Journal of Ecology* **91**: 4–17.

Kostiainen, K., Jalkanen, H., Kaakinen, S., Saranpaa, P., and Vapaavuori, E. 2006. Wood properties of two silver birch clones exposed to elevated CO_2 and O_3. *Global Change Biology* **12**: 1230–1240.

Liu, X.-P., Grams, T.E.E., Matyssek, R., and Rennenberg, H. 2005. Effects of elevated pCO_2 and/or pO_3 on C-, N-, and S-metabolites in the leaves of juvenile beech and spruce differ between trees grown in monoculture and mixed culture. *Plant Physiology and Biochemistry* **43**: 147–154.

Lovelock, C.E., Winter, K., Mersits, R., and Popp, M. 1998. Responses of communities of tropical tree species to elevated CO_2 in a forest clearing. *Oecologia* **116**: 207–218.

Ludewig, F., Sonnewald, U., Kauder, F., Heineke, D., Geiger, M., Stitt, M., Muller-Rober, B.T., Gillissen, B., Kuhn, C., and Frommer, W.B. 1998. The role of transient starch in acclimation to elevated atmospheric CO_2. *FEBS Letters* **429**: 147–151.

Pan, Q., Wang, Z., and Quebedeaux, B. 1998. Responses of the apple plant to CO_2 enrichment: changes in photosynthesis, sorbitol, other soluble sugars, and starch. *Australian Journal of Plant Physiology* **25**: 293–297.

Piispanen, R. and Saranpaa, P. 2001. Variation of nonstructural carbohydrates in silver birch (*Betula pendula* Roth) wood. *Trees* **15**: 444–451.

Reid, C.D., Fiscus, E.L., and Burkey, K.O. 1998. Combined effects of chronic ozone and elevated CO_2 on rubisco activity and leaf components in soybean (*Glycine max*). *Journal of Experimental Botany* **49**: 1999–2011.

Rey, A. and Jarvis, P.G. 1998. Long-term photosynthetic acclimation to increased atmospheric CO_2 concentration in young birch (*Betula pendula*) trees. *Tree Physiology* **18**: 441–450.

Riikonen, J., Lindsberg, M.-M., Holopainen, T., Oksanen, E., Lappi, J., Peltonen, P., and Vapaavuori, E. 2004. Silver birch and climate change: variable growth and carbon

allocation responses to elevated concentrations of carbon dioxide and ozone. *Tree Physiology* **24**: 1227–1237.

Wurth, M.K.R., Winter, K., and Korner, C. 1998. Leaf carbohydrate responses to CO_2 enrichment at the top of a tropical forest. *Oecologia* **116**: 18–25.

2.27 Stomatal Density

2.27.1 Herbaceous Plants

- In addition to sequentially reducing the openness of their stomata to restrict unnecessary water loss via excessive transpiration as the air's CO_2 content rises, some plants also reduce the density (number per area) of stomates on their leaves, but only to a certain degree, beyond which this latter phenomenon would be counterproductive.

As the air's CO_2 content rises, many plants reduce their stomatal apertures, because with more CO_2 in the air they don't need to open their stomates as wide as they do at lower atmospheric CO_2 concentrations to allow for sufficient inward diffusion of CO_2 for use in photosynthesis. As a result, plants growing in CO_2-enriched air typically exhibit reduced rates of water loss via transpiration, smaller yield losses attributable to the indiscriminate uptake of air pollutants, and increased water-use efficiencies.

For much the same reason (and producing similar effects), many plants also reduce the density of stomates on the surfaces of their leaves at higher atmospheric CO_2 concentrations. This section reviews the findings of a few of the studies that have addressed this subject in non-woody herbaceous plants.

Case *et al.* (1998) collected 12 wild radish genotypes with a variety of stomatal indices and guard cell lengths in Maine (USA) and grew them to maturity in greenhouses maintained at atmospheric CO_2 concentrations of 370 and 680 ppm. They found the elevated CO_2 did not significantly affect stomatal index or guard cell length. Across all genotypes investigated, leaf surface characteristics essentially were unchanged by elevated CO_2.

In the case of C_4 maize plants grown for 30 days in plexiglass chambers maintained at ambient or triple-ambient concentrations of atmospheric CO_2, on the other hand, Maroco *et al.* (1999) determined the leaves of the CO_2-enriched plants displayed approximately 10% fewer stomates per unit leaf area than the leaves of control plants growing in ambient air.

Why one of these plants exhibited no change in stomatal density as the air's CO_2 content was increased above the current ambient value, while the other exhibited a decrease, may perhaps be explained by the results reported by Gray *et al.* (2000). They identified a gene of the small mustard plant *Arabidopsis thaliana* that prevents decreases in the number density of leaf stomata in response to atmospheric CO_2 enrichment above a certain critical value of atmospheric CO_2 concentration. It can readily be appreciated why this is so, because decreases in stomatal density and conductance in response to rising atmospheric CO_2 concentrations (which are typically beneficial) cannot go on indefinitely, for there would ultimately come a point (likely different for different species) where further decreases in these plant properties become counter-productive, leading to a situation where the enhanced air-to-leaf CO_2 concentration gradient could not overcome the increased resistance of CO_2 entry into the leaf, causing the plant to die of carbon starvation, or where transpiration is reduced so much that leaf evaporative cooling cannot prevent plant death due to increased thermal stress.

Viewed in this light, the difference between the stomatal density responses of wild radish and maize likely derives from genetically programmed species-specific differences in the critical value of atmospheric CO_2 concentration at which the decline in stomatal density with increasing atmospheric CO_2 concentration is genetically terminated. Serna and Fenoll (2000) note, "plants seem to be well armed to cope with a further enrichment in atmospheric CO_2," and genes such as the one discovered by Gray *et al.*— denoted HIC for high carbon dioxide—"should ensure that, at high CO_2 concentrations, changes in stomatal indices are kept to a minimum."

References

Case, A.L., Curtis, P.S., and Snow, A.A. 1998. Heritable variation in stomatal responses to elevated CO_2 in wild radish, *Raphanus raphanistrum* (Brassicaceae). *American Journal of Botany* **85**: 253–258.

Gray, J.E., Holroyd, G.H., van der Lee, F.M., Bahraml, A.R., Sijmons, P.C., Woodward, F.I., Schuch, W., and Hetherington, A.M. 2000. The HIC signaling pathway links CO_2 perception to stomatal development. *Nature* **408**: 713–716.

Maroco, J.P., Edwards, G.E., and Ku, M.S.B. 1999. Photosynthetic acclimation of maize to growth under elevated levels of carbon dioxide. *Planta* **210**: 115–125.

Serna, L. and Fenoll, C. 2000. Coping with human CO_2 emissions. *Nature* **408**: 656–657.

2.27.2 Woody Plants

- As the air's CO_2 content rises, leaf stomatal densities (number per area) of woody plants range from no change at all to double-digit percentage decreases that cease after a few hundred ppm increase in CO_2, beyond which this phenomenon becomes counterproductive.

As the air's CO_2 content rises, many plants reduce their stomatal apertures, because with more CO_2 in the air they don't need to open their stomates as wide as they do at lower atmospheric CO_2 concentrations to allow for sufficient inward diffusion of CO_2 for use in photosynthesis. As a result, plants growing in CO_2-enriched air typically exhibit reduced rates of transpirational water loss, smaller productivity losses attributed to the uptake of aerial pollutants, and increased water use efficiency.

For much the same reason (and producing similar effects), many plants also reduce the density of stomates on their leaf surfaces at higher atmospheric CO_2 concentrations. This section reviews the findings of studies that addressed this subject in woody plants such as trees and shrubs.

Apple *et al.* (2000) grew two-year-old Douglas fir seedlings for three years in controlled-environment chambers maintained at atmospheric CO_2 concentrations of either 350 or 550 ppm and ambient or elevated (ambient plus 4°C) air temperatures. They found neither elevated CO_2 nor elevated air temperature, acting alone or together, significantly affected needle stomatal density.

By contrast, in a study of the long-term effects of elevated CO_2 on various leaf properties of mature white oak trees growing at different distances from CO_2-emitting springs in central Italy, Paoletti *et al.* (1998) found elevated CO_2 significantly decreased leaf stomatal density by a factor of nearly 1.5 as the air's CO_2 concentration rose from 350 to 750 ppm. From that point on, however, there were no further reductions in stomatal density, even for CO_2 concentrations as great as 2600 ppm.

Evaluating the impact of a 350-to-750 ppm increase in the atmosphere's CO_2 concentration, Lin *et al.* (2001) grew seven-year-old Scots pine seedlings in the field in open-top chambers for four years, applying no additional nutrients or irrigation waters to the soils in which the young trees were rooted. After the fourth year of their experiment, a detailed analysis of their data revealed the extra CO_2 reduced needle stomatal density by an average of 7.4%, indicating Scots pines may be better able to conserve water and cope with periods of drought and water stress in a high-CO_2 world of the future.

Beerling *et al.* (1998) grew one-year old *Ginkgo biloba* saplings in greenhouses maintained at atmospheric CO_2 concentrations of 350 and 560 ppm for three years. They found the leaves of plants grown at 560 ppm CO_2 exhibited significant reductions in both stomatal density (number of stomates per leaf area) and stomatal index (ratio of stomata to epidermal cells). Interestingly, the stomatal density of the CO_2-enriched leaves was similar to that measured on fossilized *Ginkgo* leaves dating back to the Triassic and Jurassic time periods, and because the CO_2-induced reductions in stomatal density and index did not impact rates of photosynthesis, it can be inferred the water-use efficiencies of ancient *Ginkgo* species were much higher than those of their modern counterparts. Consequently, as the CO_2 content of the air continues to rise, it may, as Beerling *et al.* remark, "contribute to restoring the function of this 'living fossil' species back to that more representative of its long geological history."

Much like what has been learned about herbaceous plants, studies of the effects of atmospheric CO_2 enrichment on the leaf stomatal density of woody species reveal a wide range of responses, from no change at all to a double-digit percentage point decrease that ceases after a few hundred ppm increase in CO_2. These changes have been found to be beneficial to the species that exhibit them, including the cessation of the response at a species-specific critical atmospheric CO_2 concentration.

References

Apple, M.E., Olszyk, D.M., Ormrod, D.P., Lewis, J., Southworth, D., and Tingey, D.T. 2000. Morphology and stomatal function of Douglas fir needles exposed to climate change: elevated CO_2 and temperature. *International Journal of Plant Science* **161**: 127–132.

Beerling, D.J., McElwain, J.C., and Osborne, C.P. 1998. Stomatal responses of the 'living fossil' *Ginkgo biloba* L. to changes in atmospheric CO_2 concentrations. *Journal of Experimental Botany* **49**: 1603–1607.

Lin, J., Jach, M.E., and Ceulemans, R. 2001. Stomatal density and needle anatomy of Scots pine (*Pinus sylvestris*) are affected by elevated CO_2. *New Phytologist* **150**: 665–674.

Paoletti, E., Nourrisson, G., Garrec, J.P., and Raschi, A. 1998. Modifications of the leaf surface structures of *Quercus ilex* L. in open, naturally CO_2-enriched environments. *Plant, Cell and Environment* **21**: 1071–1075.

2.28 Sugars

- Atmospheric CO_2 enrichment typically increases plants' ability to produce greater amounts of various forms of sugar.

Plants grown in CO_2-enriched atmospheres nearly always exhibit increased photosynthetic rates, which typically lead to increased foliar concentrations of total nonstructural carbohydrates, including various sugars. Schortemeyer *et al.* (1999), for example, report significant increases in leaf total nonstructural carbohydrate contents in an Australian tree species exposed to twice-ambient atmospheric CO_2 concentrations for six weeks. Similarly, Wurth *et al.* (1998) found twice-ambient CO_2 levels increased leaf sugar concentrations by an average of 30% in four Panamanian tropical tree species. Just an eight-day exposure of apple seedlings to an atmospheric CO_2 concentration of 1,600 ppm led to a 38% increase in leaf sorbitol concentration.

In a study of *Pinus radiata* seedlings that had been growing for several years in open-top chambers maintained at atmospheric CO_2 concentrations of 360 and 650 ppm, Griffin *et al.* (2000) found needle sugar contents increased by 26%. Likewise, studying young spruce (*Picea abies*) seedlings for three years in growth chambers maintained at atmospheric CO_2 concentrations of 280, 420, and 560 ppm, Wiemken and Ineichen (2000) discovered that in late summer, fall, and winter, glucose concentrations in needles on the CO_2-enriched trees were 40 to 50% higher than those of needles on trees subjected to ambient and sub-ambient CO_2 concentrations (420 and 280 ppm, respectively).

Atmospheric CO_2 enrichment also has been documented to increase sugar contents in plant organs other than leaves. Lake and Hughes (1999), for example, found a doubling of the air's CO_2 concentration produced a 2.4-fold increase in nectar production in nasturtium flowers. And in the early flowering stage of *Cucumis melo* melons, Dag and Eisikowitch (2000) observed in a sector of a greenhouse maintained at a CO_2 concentration of 1,000 ppm throughout the morning, 400 ppm between 1300 and 1500 hours, and then 600 ppm until the next morning, nectar volumes per flower were significantly higher than in the control sector of the greenhouse, sometimes by as much as 100%.

De Souza *et al.* (2008) grew sugarcane (*Saccharum officinarum* L.), one of Earth's most important sugar-producing plants, in pots within open-top chambers maintained at either ambient (~370 ppm) or elevated (~720 ppm) atmospheric CO_2 concentrations in the field under natural conditions at Sao Paulo, Brazil over a period of 50 weeks, during which time and at the end of the season, various plant physiological parameters and properties were measured. The plants grown in the elevated CO_2 chambers exhibited "an increase of about 30% in photosynthesis and 17% in height, and accumulated 40% more biomass in comparison with the plants grown at ambient CO_2," and the CO_2-enriched plants "also had lower stomatal conductance and transpiration rates (-37 and -32%, respectively), and higher water use efficiency (c.a. 62%)." In addition, the sucrose concentration in the sugarcane leaves rose from 2.18% in the ambient-treatment plants to 2.82% in the CO_2-enriched plants, for a CO_2-induced increase of 29%.

References

Dag, A. and Eisikowitch, D. 2000. The effect of carbon dioxide enrichment on nectar production in melons under greenhouse conditions. *Journal of Apicultural Research* **39**: 88–89.

De Souza, A.P., Gaspar, M., da Silva, E.A., Ulian, E.C., Waclawovsky, A.J., Nishiyama Jr., M.Y., dos Santos, R.V., Teixeira, M.M., Souza, G.M., and Buckeridge, M.S. 2008. Elevated CO_2 increases photosynthesis, biomass and productivity, and modifies gene expression in sugarcane. *Plant, Cell and Environment* **31**: 1116–1127.

Griffin, K.L., Tissue, D.T., Turnbull, M.H., and Whitehead, D. 2000. The onset of photosynthetic acclimation to elevated CO_2 partial pressure in field-grown *Pinus radiata* D. Don. after 4 years. *Plant, Cell and Environment* **23**: 1089–1098.

Lake, J.C. and Hughes, L. 1999. Nectar production and floral characteristics of *Tropaeolum majus* L. grown in ambient and elevated carbon dioxide. *Annals of Botany* **84**: 535–541.

Pan, Q., Wang, Z., and Quebedeaux, B. 1998. Responses of the apple plant to CO_2 enrichment: changes in photosynthesis, sorbitol, other soluble sugars, and starch. *Australian Journal of Plant Physiology* **25**: 293–297.

Schortemeyer, M., Atkin, O.K., McFarlane, N., and Evans, J.R. 1999. The impact of elevated atmospheric CO_2 and nitrate supply on growth, biomass allocation, nitrogen partitioning and N2 fixation of *Acacia melanoxylon*. *Australian Journal of Plant Physiology* **26**: 737–774.

Wiemken, V. and Ineichen, K. 2000. Seasonal fluctuations of the levels of soluble carbohydrates in spruce needles exposed to elevated CO_2 and nitrogen fertilization and glucose as a potential mediator of acclimation to elevated CO_2. *Journal of Plant Physiology* **156**: 746–750.

Wurth, M.K.R., Winter, K., and Korner, C. 1998. Leaf carbohydrate responses to CO_2 enrichment at the top of a tropical forest. *Oecologia* **116**: 18–25.

2.29 Tannins

Atmospheric CO_2 enrichment significantly enhances the condensed tannin concentrations of the vast majority of Earth's trees and grasses, giving them stronger defenses against various herbivores both above and below ground. And by causing less methane to be released to the atmosphere via ruminants browsing on tree leaves and grass, this phenomenon should reduce the rate of rise of the air's methane concentration and thereby decrease methane-induced global warming.

Condensed tannins are naturally occurring secondary carbon compounds produced in the leaves of a number of different plants that often act to deter herbivorous insects. In New Zealand, the Legume Lotus is a good source of these substances, and scientists with the country's AgResearch Grasslands institute have determined sheep and cattle feeding on forage containing this plant may reduce their methane emissions by as much as 16%.

This latter finding is of special importance to New Zealanders, because the methane expelled by cattle and sheep, which is a by-product of the fermentation of feed in the rumen of these animals, accounts for close to 90% of the country's methane emissions. A significant reduction in such a large national source of one of the atmosphere's most potent greenhouse gases would go a long way toward reducing emissions of climate-altering substances, which would be, according to the press release that described this development, "very welcome." The release also stated consumption of tannins has "a variety of other animal-related benefits, such as improved milk yield, increased liveweight gain, decreased internal parasite burden and reduced occurrence of bloat, dags and fly strike."

It is also important to note ruminants, as they are called, comprise a great group of animals in addition to sheep and cattle. They are four-footed, hoofed, even-toed, cud-chewing mammals that have a stomach consisting of four divisions or chambers; the group includes antelope, bison, buffalo, camel, deer, giraffe, goat, llama, etc. These animals eat a number of other types of plants that may also experience increases in leaf tannin production as the air's CO_2 content rises. The following sections investigate this subject as it applies to other types of plants.

2.29.1 Aspen Trees

- Because the amount of methane expelled by ruminants is an inverse function of the amount of condensed tannins contained in the foliage they consume, the increased tannin concentrations likely to exist in aspen foliage in a high-CO_2 world of the future should result in less methane being released to the atmosphere via ruminants browsing on the trees' leaves. This should help decrease methane-induced global warming.

King et al. (2001) grew aspen (Populus tremuloides) seedlings for five months in open-top chambers maintained at atmospheric CO_2 concentrations of either 350 or 700 ppm; at the end of this period they collected and analyzed naturally senesced leaf litter. They found the elevated CO_2 of this particular study had no effect on the tannin concentration of leaf litter.

A substantially different result was obtained in an earlier study of aspen leaves conducted by McDonald et al. (1999), who grew aspen seedlings in controlled environment greenhouses maintained at either ambient (387 ppm) or elevated (696 ppm) CO_2 concentrations under conditions of either low or high light availability (half and full sunlight, respectively) for 31 days after the mean date of bud break. Under low light conditions the CO_2-enriched seedlings exhibited an approximate 15% increase in leaf condensed tannin concentration, and under high light conditions the CO_2-induced increase in leaf condensed tannin concentration was 175%.

In a much more complex study, Agrell et al. (2005) examined the effects of ambient and elevated concentrations of atmospheric CO_2 (360 and 560 ppm, respectively) and O_3 (35–60 ppb and 52–90 ppb, respectively) on the foliar chemistry of more mature aspen trees of two different genotypes (216 and 259) growing out-of-doors at the Aspen Free Air CO_2 Enrichment (FACE) facility near Rhinelander, Wisconsin (USA). They also studied the impacts of these effects on the host plant preferences of forest tent caterpillar larvae.

Agrell et al. report, "the only chemical component showing a somewhat consistent covariation with larval preferences was condensed tannins," noting "the tree becoming relatively less preferred as a result of CO_2 or O_3 treatment was in general also the one for which average levels of condensed tannins were most positively (or least negatively) affected by that treatment." The mean condensed tannin concentrations of the aspen 216 and 259 genotypes were 25% and 57% higher, respectively, under the elevated CO_2 and O_3 combination treatment compared to the ambient CO_2 and O_3 combination treatment.

In light of these findings, it is logical to presume that as atmospheric concentrations of CO_2 and O_3 continue to rise, the increase in condensed tannin concentration likely to occur in the foliage of aspen trees should lead to their leaves becoming less preferred for consumption by the forest tent caterpillar, which according to Agrell et al. is "an eruptive generalist defoliator in North American hardwood forests, causing extensive damage during outbreak years (Fitzgerald, 1995)." Also, because the amount of methane expelled by ruminants is an inverse function of the amount of condensed tannins in the foliage they consume, the increased aspen foliage tannin concentrations likely to exist in a high-CO_2 world of the future should result in less methane being released to the atmosphere via ruminants browsing on aspen foliage, thus decreasing an impetus for methane-induced global warming.

References

Agrell, J., Kopper, B., McDonald, E.P., and Lindroth, R.L. 2005. CO_2 and O_3 effects on host plant preferences of the forest tent caterpillar (Malacosoma disstria). Global Change Biology 11: 588–599.

Fitzgerald, T.D. 1995. The Tent Caterpillars. Comstock Publishing, Ithaca, New York, USA.

King, J.S., Pregitzer, K.S., Zak, D.R., Kubiske, M.E., Ashby, J.A., and Holmes, W.E. 2001. Chemistry and decomposition of litter from Populus tremuloides Michaux grown at elevated atmospheric CO_2 and varying N availability. Global Change Biology 7: 65–74.

McDonald, E.P., Agrell, J., and Lindroth, R.L. 1999. CO_2 and light effects on deciduous trees: growth, foliar chemistry, and insect performance. Oecologia 119: 389–399.

2.29.2 Birch Trees

- Elevated concentrations of atmospheric CO_2 tend to increase leaf and fine-root tannin concentrations of birch trees, which tends to protect the trees' foliage from predation by voracious insect herbivores, protect the trees' roots from soil-borne pathogens and herbivores, enhance the sequestration of carbon in forest soils, and reduce methane emissions from ruminants that might consume the trees' foliage.

This section reviews how condensed tannin concentrations in the leaves and roots of paper birch (*Betula papyrifera* Marsh.) and silver birch (*Betula pendula* Roth) trees respond to atmospheric CO_2 enrichment with and without concomitant increases in atmospheric temperature and ozone concentrations.

Peltonen *et al.* (2005) studied the effect of doubled atmospheric CO_2 and O_3 concentrations on the accumulation of 27 phenolic compounds, including soluble condensed tannins, in the leaves of two European silver birch clones in seven-year-old soil-grown trees in central Finland exposed in open-top chambers for three growing seasons to ambient and twice-ambient atmospheric CO_2 and O_3 concentrations singly and in combination. They found the elevated CO_2 increased the concentration of soluble condensed tannins in the leaves of the trees by 19% and protected the leaves from elevated O_3 because, as they describe it, "all the O_3-derived effects on the leaf phenolics and traits were prevented by elevated CO_2."

Kuokkanen *et al.* (2003) grew two-year-old silver birch seedlings in both ambient air of 350 ppm CO_2 and air enriched to a CO_2 concentration of 700 ppm under conditions of either ambient temperature or ambient temperature plus 3°C for one full growing season in the field in closed-top chambers at the Mekrijarvi Research Station of the University of Joensuu in eastern Finland. Then, during the middle of the summer, when carbon-based secondary compounds of birch leaves are fairly stable, they picked several leaves from each tree and determined their condensed tannin concentrations, along with the concentrations of a number of other physiologically important substances. The concentration of total phenolics, condensed tannins, and their derivatives significantly increased in the leaves produced in the CO_2-enriched air, as also was observed by Lavola and Julkunen-Titto (1994), Williams *et al.* (1994), Kinney *et al.* (1997), Bezemer and Jones (1998), and Kuokkanen *et al.* (2001). The extra 350 ppm of CO_2 nearly tripled condensed tannin concentrations in the

ambient-temperature air, while it increased their concentrations in the elevated-temperature air by a factor in excess of 3.5.

Parsons *et al.* (2003) grew two-year-old paper birch saplings in well-watered and fertilized 16-liter pots from early May until late August in glasshouse rooms maintained at either 400 or 700 ppm CO_2. They found the concentration of condensed tannins in the fine roots of the saplings was increased by 27% in the CO_2-enriched treatment. The researchers state, "the higher condensed tannin concentrations that were present in the birch fine roots may offer these tissues greater protection against soil-borne pathogens and herbivores."

Parsons *et al.* (2004) collected leaf litter samples from early September to mid-October beneath paper birch trees growing in ambient and CO_2-enriched (to 200 ppm above ambient) FACE plots in northern Wisconsin (USA), which also were maintained under ambient and O_3-enriched (to 19 ppb above ambient) conditions. Afterward, the leaf mass produced in each treatment was determined, sub-samples of the leaves were assessed for a number of chemical constituents (including nitrogen, which hastens leaf decay, and condensed tannins, which retard decay). The remaining leaves were placed in 1-mm-aperture litterbags made of fiberglass cloth and left to decay on the ground for the next 12 months under the same atmospheric conditions in which they were produced. At the conclusion of the one-year litter-exposure period, the researchers measured the mass of remaining litter and determined the time required to achieve 95% mass loss.

Under ambient O_3 conditions, the nitrogen concentrations of the leaves in the CO_2-enriched plots at the time of litterfall were 31% less than those of the leaves in the ambient-CO_2 plots, and condensed tannin concentrations were 64% greater in the CO_2-enriched plots. Similarly, under the O_3-enriched conditions, leaf nitrogen concentrations were 32% less, and concentrations of condensed tannins were 99% greater.

These observations suggest leaf decay rates in the CO_2-enriched plots should be lower than in the ambient-CO_2 plots, and the mass-loss rates determined at the end of the one-year exposure period bore out this expectation. Parsons *et al.* report, "for control litter, 5% of mass remained after 3.6 years, while CO_2-enriched litter took ~4.5 years to turn over 95% of its mass." Hence, it could take 25% more time (4.5 years / 3.6 years) to lose an equivalent percentage of paper birch leaf litter from CO_2-enriched forests, independent of the air's O_3 concentration. In addition, the CO_2-enriched trees "attained greater size, and a greater degree of canopy closure, and contributed more litterfall to the development of [the] forest floor than did trees in the control rings," making it clear the ongoing rise in the atmosphere's CO_2 concentration should greatly augment the sequestration of carbon by paper birch tree stands as the air's CO_2 content climbs.

Also working at the Wisconsin FACE site, Agrell *et al.* (2005) examined the effects of ambient and elevated concentrations of atmospheric CO_2 (360 and 560 ppm) and O_3 (35–60 ppb and 52–90 ppb) on the foliar chemistry of paper birch trees, as well as the impacts of these effects on the host plant preferences of forest tent caterpillar larvae. They found the mean condensed tannin concentration of the birch tree leaves was 18% greater in the elevated CO_2 and O_3 treatment than in the ambient CO_2 and O_3 treatment. In addition, "the only chemical component showing a somewhat consistent covariation with larval preferences was condensed tannins," and "the tree becoming relatively less preferred as a result of CO_2 or O_3 treatment was in general also the one for which average levels of condensed tannins were most positively (or least negatively) affected by that treatment."

In light of these findings, it is logical to presume the rising atmospheric concentrations of CO_2 and O_3 and consequent increase in condensed tannin concentration likely to occur in the foliage of birch trees should lead to their leaves becoming less preferred for consumption by the forest tent caterpillar, which according to Agrell *et al.* is "an eruptive generalist defoliator in North American hardwood forests, causing extensive damage during outbreak years (Fitzgerald, 1995)." Also, because the amount of methane expelled by ruminants is an inverse function of the condensed tannin concentration of the foliage they consume, the higher birch-foliage tannin concentrations likely to prevail in a high-CO_2 world of the future should result in less methane being released to the atmosphere via ruminants browsing on the foliage of birch trees, reducing that impetus for methane-induced global warming.

Elevated concentrations of atmospheric CO_2 tend to increase leaf and fine-root tannin concentrations of birch trees, which in turn tends to protect the trees' foliage from predation by voracious insect herbivores, protect the trees' roots from soil-borne pathogens and herbivores, enhance the sequestration of carbon in forest soils, and reduce methane emissions from ruminants that consume the trees' foliage.

References

Agrell, J., Kopper, B., McDonald, E.P., and Lindroth, R.L. 2005. CO_2 and O_3 effects on host plant preferences of the forest tent caterpillar (*Malacosoma disstria*). *Global Change Biology* **11**: 588–599.

Bezemer, T.M. and Jones, T.H. 1998. Plant-insect herbivore interactions in elevated atmospheric CO_2, quantitative analyses and guild effects. *Oikos* **82**: 212–222.

Fitzgerald, T.D. 1995. *The Tent Caterpillars*. Comstock Publishing, Ithaca, New York, USA.

Kinney, K.K., Lindroth, R.L., Jung, S.M., and Nordheim, E.V. 1997. Effects of CO_2 and NO_3 availability on deciduous trees, phytochemistry and insect performance. *Ecology* **78**: 215–230.

Kuokkanen, K., Julkunen-Titto, R., Keinanen, M., Niemela, P., and Tahvanainen, J. 2001. The effect of elevated CO_2 and temperature on the secondary chemistry of *Betula pendula* seedlings. *Trees* **15**: 378–384.

Kuokkanen, K., Yan, S., and Niemela, P. 2003. Effects of elevated CO_2 and temperature on the leaf chemistry of birch *Betula pendula* (Roth) and the feeding behavior of the weevil *Phyllobius maculicornis*. *Agricultural and Forest Entomology* **5**: 209–217.

Lavola, A. and Julkunen-Titto, R. 1994. The effect of elevated carbon dioxide and fertilization on primary and secondary metabolites in birch, *Betula pendula* (Roth). *Oecologia* **99**: 315–321.

Parsons, W.F.J., Kopper, B.J., and Lindroth, R.L. 2003. Altered growth and fine root chemistry of *Betula papyrifera* and *Acer saccharum* under elevated CO_2. *Canadian Journal of Forest Research* **33**: 842–846.

Parsons, W.F.J., Lindroth, R.L., and Bockheim, J.G. 2004. Decomposition of *Betula papyrifera* leaf litter under the independent and interactive effects of elevated CO_2 and O_3. *Global Change Biology* **10**: 1666–1677.

Peltonen, P.A., Vapaavuori, E., and Julkunen-Tiitto, R. 2005. Accumulation of phenolic compounds in birch leaves is changed by elevated carbon dioxide and ozone. *Global Change Biology* **11**: 1305–1324.

Williams, R.S., Lincoln, D.E., and Thomas, R.B. 1994. Loblolly pine grown under elevated CO_2 affects early instar pine sawfly performance. *Oecologia* **98**: 64–71.

2.29.3 Oak Trees

- The large increase of condensed tannin concentrations in oak tree foliage produced in CO_2-enriched air results in methane emissions from ruminants feeding on such foliage being lower than methane emissions from ruminants feeding on foliage grown in non-CO_2-enriched air, and foliage better able to resist herbivore attacks.

This section examines how rising air temperatures and atmospheric CO_2 concentrations affect the leaf tannin concentrations of several oak tree species, including myrtle oak (*Quercus myrtifolia* Wild.), pedunculate oak (*Quercus robur* L.), sand live oak (*Quercus geminata* Small), and Chapman's oak (*Quercus chapmanii* Sargent).

Dury *et al.* (1998) grew four-year-old pedunculate oak trees in pots within greenhouses maintained at ambient and twice-ambient atmospheric CO_2 concentrations in combination with ambient and elevated (ambient plus 3°C) air temperatures for approximately one year. The elevated CO_2 concentration had only minor and contrasting direct effects on leaf palatability, including a temporary increase in foliar phenolic concentrations and decreases in leaf toughness and nitrogen content. The elevated temperature treatment, on the other hand, significantly reduced leaf palatability, because oak leaf toughness increased as a consequence of temperature-induced increases in condensed tannin concentrations. Hence the five researchers conclude, "a 3°C rise in temperature might be expected to result in prolonged larval development, increased food consumption, and reduced growth" for herbivores feeding on oak leaves in a CO_2-enriched and warmer world of the future.

Cornelissen *et al.* (2003) studied fluctuating asymmetry in the leaves of two species of schlerophyllous oaks—myrtle oak (*Quercus myrtifolia*) and sand live oak (*Quercus geminata*)—that dominate a native scrub-oak community at the Kennedy Space Center, Titusville, Florida (USA), which has served as the base of operations for a number of important open-top-chamber investigations of the effects of a 350-ppm increase in the air's CO_2 concentration on this unique ecosystem. Fluctuating asymmetry is the terminology used to describe small variations from perfect symmetry in otherwise bilaterally symmetrical characters in an organism (Moller and Swaddle, 1997); such asymmetry is believed to arise as a consequence of developmental instabilities experienced during ontogeny that may result from various stresses, including both genetic and environmental factors (Moller and Shykoff, 1999).

Based on measurements of distances from the leaf midrib to the left and right edges of the leaf at its widest point and leaf areas on the left and right sides of the leaf midrib, Cornelissen *et al.* determined "asymmetric leaves were less frequent in elevated CO_2, and, when encountered, they were less asymmetric than leaves growing under ambient CO_2." In addition, they found "*Q. myrtifolia* leaves under elevated CO_2 were 15.0% larger than in ambient CO_2 and *Q. geminata* leaves were 38.0% larger in elevated CO_2 conditions." They also determined "elevated CO_2 significantly increased tannin concentration for both *Q. myrtifolia* and *Q. geminata* leaves" and "asymmetric leaves contained significantly lower concentrations of tannins than symmetric leaves for both *Q. geminata* and *Q. myrtifolia*."

Commenting on their two primary findings—reduced percentages of leaves experiencing asymmetry in the presence of elevated levels of atmospheric CO_2 and the lesser degree of asymmetry exhibited by affected leaves in the elevated CO_2 treatment—Cornelissen *et al.* write, "a possible explanation for this pattern is the fact that, in contrast to other environmental stresses, which can cause negative effects on plant growth, the predominant effect of elevated CO_2 on plants is to promote growth with consequent reallocation of resources (Docherty *et al.*, 1996)." Another possibility they discuss "is the fact that CO_2 acts as a plant fertilizer," and, as a result, "elevated CO_2 ameliorates plant stress compared with ambient levels of CO_2," which is one of the well-documented biological benefits of atmospheric CO_2 enrichment (Idso and Idso, 1994).

With respect to the ancillary finding of CO_2-induced increases in tannin concentrations in the leaves of both oak species (a mean increase of approximately 35% for *Q. myrtifolia* and 43% for *Q. geminata*), this phenomenon may provide the two species with greater protection against herbivores, and part of that protection may be associated with the observed CO_2-induced reductions in the amount and degree of asymmetry in the leaves of the CO_2-enriched trees. Consistent with this hypothesis, for example, Stiling *et al.* (1999, 2003) found higher abundances of leaf miners in the leaves of the trees in the ambient CO_2 chambers, where asymmetric leaves were more abundant, and in the current study it was determined leaf miners attacked asymmetric leaves more frequently than would be expected by chance alone in both CO_2 treatments.

In a subsequent study conducted at the Kennedy Space Center's scrub-oak community, Hall *et al.* (2005b) evaluated foliar quality and herbivore damage in three oaks (*Q. myrtifolia*, *Q. chapmanii*, and *Q. geminata*) plus the nitrogen-fixing legume

Galactia elliottii at three-month intervals from May 2001 to May 2003, at which times samples of undamaged leaves were removed from each of the four species in all chambers and analyzed for various chemical constituents, and 200 randomly selected leaves of each species in each chamber were scored for the presence of six types of herbivore damage. The data indicated for condensed tannins, hydrolyzable tannins, total phenolics and lignin, in all four species there were always greater concentrations of all four leaf constituents in the CO_2-enriched leaves, with across-species mean increases of 6.8% for condensed tannins, 6.1% for hydrolyzable tannins, 5.1% for total phenolics, and 4.3% for lignin. There also were large CO_2-induced decreases in all leaf damage categories among all species: chewing (-48%), mines (-37%), eye spot gall (-45%), leaf tier (-52%), leaf mite (-23%), and leaf gall (-16%). Hall *et al.* conclude the changes in leaf chemical constituents and herbivore damage "suggest that damage to plants may decline as atmospheric CO_2 levels continue to rise."

Largely overlapping the investigation of Hall *et al.* (2005b), Hall *et al.* (2005a) evaluated the effects of the Kennedy Space Center experiment's extra 350 ppm of CO_2 on litter quality and herbivore activity, and their interactions, over the three-year-period 2000–2002. They found "changes in litter chemistry from year to year were far larger than effects of CO_2 or insect damage, suggesting that these may have only minor effects on litter decomposition." The one exception to this finding was "condensed tannin concentrations increased under elevated CO_2 regardless of species, herbivore damage, or growing season," rising by 11% in 2000, 18% in 2001, and 41% in 2002 as a result of atmospheric CO_2 enrichment, as best as can be determined from the researchers' bar graphs. The five scientists also report "lepidopteran larvae can exhibit slower growth rates when feeding on elevated CO_2 plants (Fajer *et al.*, 1991) and become more susceptible to pathogens, parasitoids, and predators (Lindroth, 1996; Stiling *et al.*, 1999)," noting further that at their field site, "which hosts the longest continuous study of the effects of elevated CO_2 on insects, herbivore populations decline markedly under elevated CO_2 (Stiling *et al.*, 1999, 2002, 2003; Hall *et al.*, 2005b)."

The evidence thus suggests the large and continuous enhancement of condensed tannin concentrations in oak tree foliage produced in CO_2-enriched air will help reduce greenhouse gas-induced global warming because methane emissions from ruminants feeding on foliage rich in condensed tannins tend to be lower than when those ruminants feed on foliage of lower tannin concentration. In addition, the marked tannin-induced declines in herbivore populations observed in CO_2-enriched open-top-chamber studies indicate the ongoing increase in atmospheric CO_2 will improve plants' resistance to herbivore attacks, a highly beneficial outcome.

References

Cornelissen, T., Stiling, P., and Drake, B. 2003. Elevated CO_2 decreases leaf fluctuating asymmetry and herbivory by leaf miners on two oak species. *Global Change Biology* **10**: 27–36.

Docherty, M., Hurst, D.K., and Holopainem, J.K., *et al.* 1996. Carbon dioxide-induced changes in beech foliage cause female beech weevil larvae to feed in a compensatory manner. *Global Change Biology* **2**: 335–341.

Dury, S.J., Good, J.E.G., Perrins, C.M., Buse, A., and Kaye, T. 1998. The effects of increasing CO_2 and temperature on oak leaf palatability and the implications for herbivorous insects. *Global Change Biology* **4**: 55–61.

Fajer, E.D., Bowers, M.D., and Bazzaz, F.A. 1991. The effects of enriched CO_2 atmospheres on the buckeye butterfly, *Junonia coenia. Ecology* **72**: 751–754.

Hall, M.C., Stiling, P., Hungate, B.A., Drake, B.G., and Hunter, M.D. 2005a. Effects of elevated CO_2 and herbivore damage on litter quality in a scrub oak ecosystem. *Journal of Chemical Ecology* **31**: 2343–2356.

Hall, M.C., Stiling, P., Moon, D.C., Drake, B.G., and Hunter, M.D. 2005b. Effects of elevated CO_2 on foliar quality and herbivore damage in a scrub oak ecosystem. *Journal of Chemical Ecology* **31**: 267–285.

Idso, K.E. and Idso, S.B. 1994. Plant responses to atmospheric CO_2 enrichment in the face of environmental constraints: a review of the past 10 years' research. *Agricultural and Forest Meteorology* **69**: 153–203.

Lindroth, R.L. 1996. CO_2-mediated changes in tree chemistry and tree-Lepidoptera interactions. In: Koch, G.W. and Mooney, H.A. (Eds.) *Carbon Dioxide and Terrestrial Ecosystems*. Academic Press, San Diego, California, USA, pp. 105–120.

Moller, A.P. and Shykoff, P. 1999. Morphological developmental stability in plants: patterns and causes. *International Journal of Plant Sciences* **160**: S135–S146.

Moller, A.P. and Swaddle, J.P. 1997. *Asymmetry, Developmental Stability and Evolution*. Oxford University Press, Oxford, UK.

Stiling, P., Cattell, M., Moon, D.C., Rossi, A., Hungate, B.A., Hymus, G., and Drake, B.G. 2002. Elevated atmospheric CO$_2$ lowers herbivore abundance, but increases leaf abscission rates. *Global Change Biology* **8**: 658–667.

Stiling, P., Moon, D.C., Hunter, M.D., Colson, J., Rossi, A.M., Hymus, G.J., and Drake, B.G. 2003. Elevated CO$_2$ lowers relative and absolute herbivore density across all species of a scrub-oak forest. *Oecologia* **134**: 82–87.

Stiling, P., Rossi, A.M., Hungate, B., Dijkstra, P., Hinkle, C.R., Knot III, W.M., and Drake, B. 1999. Decreased leaf-miner abundance in elevated CO$_2$: Reduced leaf quality and increased parasitoid attack. *Ecological Applications* **9**: 240–244.

2.29.4 Other

- Atmospheric CO$_2$ enrichment significantly enhances the concentrations of condensed tannins in the vast majority of the planet's trees and grasses, providing them with stronger defenses against various herbivores both above and below ground. Increasing atmospheric CO$_2$ levels also may be helping to reduce the rate-of-rise of the air's methane concentration.

Ruminants—sheep, cattle, antelope, bison, buffalo, camel, deer, giraffe, goat, llama, and more—eat a wide variety of plants, many of which undergo increases in leaf tannin production as the air's CO$_2$ content rises, as has been found to be true for a number of different species, including both deciduous and evergreen trees, as described by Lindroth *et al.* (1993, 1995), Traw *et al.* (1996), and Hattenschwiler and Schafellner (1999), and a number of species of grass, as described by (Goverde *et al.*, 2002).

With respect to how widespread CO$_2$-induced increases in foliar phenolics and tannins are, and the magnitudes of their increases, almost all relevant knowledge initially came from studies of temperate-region trees, the leaf phenolic concentrations of which had been shown to rise by 20–60% in response to a doubling of the air's CO$_2$ content (Koricheva *et al.*, 1998; Peñuelas and Estiarte, 1998; McDonald *et al.*, 1999; Agrell *et al.*, 2000; Hartley *et al.*, 2000). This knowledge base was vastly enhanced by the experiment of Coley *et al.* (2002), which focused on nine species of tropical trees. The trees were rooted in the ground and grown in their natural environment (near the Smithsonian Tropical Research Institute's experiment site in central Panama), rather than being planted in pots and grown in greenhouses. This point is especially important because nonnatural environments can lead to results different from those obtained with open-top chambers or FACE facilities constructed around trees growing out-of-doors in the absence of artificial root restrictions (O'Neil and Norby, 1996).

Eight of the nine species studied in Coley *et al.*'s six-month open-top chamber experiment exhibited positive leaf phenolic/tannin responses to a doubling of the atmosphere's CO$_2$ content, the largest of which was a concentration increase of 119%. The single negative response was a 27% decline, and the mean response of all nine species was an increase of 48%. These results are comparable with those obtained for temperate-region trees, and they provide the basis for Coley *et al.*'s primary conclusion; i.e., that although "both temperate and tropical trees show large interspecific variation in the extent of their response to CO$_2$ ... the overwhelming pattern is for an increase in phenolics by approximately 50%."

For four years, Kelly *et al.* (2010) grew six-year-old quaking aspen (*Populus tremuloides)* clones, two-year-old white willow (*Salix alba*) clones, and two-year-old sugar maple (*Acer saccharum*) siblings out-of-doors at the University of Michigan Biological Station in northern Michigan (USA) in open-bottom root boxes enclosed within clear-plastic-wall open-top chambers continuously supplied throughout the growing season (from May until leaf senescence in November) with either ambient-CO$_2$-air (360 ppm) or elevated-CO$_2$-air (720 ppm). At the conclusion of the four-year period, fallen leaves were collected, dried, and analyzed for simple phenolic and condensed tannin concentrations. Kelly *et al.*'s tabular results indicate the 360-ppm CO$_2$ increase boosted the simple phenolics concentrations of the aspen, maple, and willow leaves by 16, 30, and 22%, respectively, and it boosted their condensed tannin concentrations by 60, 85, and 26%, respectively. And because both foliar phenolics and condensed tannins often enhance plant resistance to herbivore and pathogen attack, plus the fact that ruminants browsing on foliage containing condensed tannins seem to have a tendency to expel less methane to the atmosphere, the increased concentrations of these substances in the leaves of the trees grown in CO$_2$-enriched air bodes well for the health of the trees themselves and for some amelioration of CO$_2$- and methane-induced global warming.

These findings suggest many wild and domesticated animals may be participating in this important natural "program" for reducing methane emissions to the atmosphere. They may also be at least partially responsible for the reduced rate of rise of the atmosphere's methane concentration (as shown in Figure 2.29.4.1) over the past few decades. If so, one could expect to see more of the same as the air's CO_2 content continues to rise; for the biosphere appears to take care of its own, as demonstrated by this unique negative feedback phenomenon.

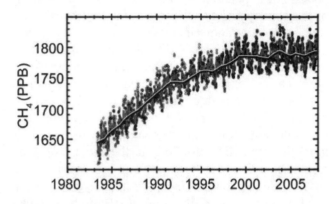

Figure 2.29.4.1. Trace gas mole fractions of methane (CH_4) as measured at Mauna Loa, Hawaii. Adapted from Schnell and Dlugokencky (2008).

References

Agrell, J., McDonald, E.P., and Lindroth, R.L. 2000. Effects of CO_2 and light on tree phytochemistry and insect performance. *Oikos* **88**: 259–272.

Coley, P.D., Massa, M., Lovelock, C.E., and Winter, K. 2002. Effect of elevated CO_2 on foliar chemistry of saplings of nine species of tropical tree. *Oecologia* **133**: 62–69.

Freeman, C., Ostle, N., and Kang, H. 2001. An enzymic 'latch' on a global carbon store. *Nature* **409**: 149.

Goverde, M., Bazin, A., Shykoff, J.A., and Erhardt, A. 1999. Influence of leaf chemistry of *Lotus corniculatus* (Fabaceae) on larval development of *Polyommatus icarus* (Lepidoptera, Lycaenidae): effects of elevated CO_2 and plant genotype. *Functional Ecology* **13**: 801–810.

Goverde, M., Erhardt, A., and Niklaus, P.A. 2002. In situ development of a satyrid butterfly on calcareous grassland exposed to elevated carbon dioxide. *Ecology* **83**: 1399–1411.

Hartley, S.E., Jones, C.G., Couper, G.C., and Jones, T.H. 2000. Biosynthesis of plant phenolic compounds in elevated atmospheric CO_2. *Global Change Biology* **6**: 497–506.

Hattenschwiler, S. and Schafellner, C. 1999. Opposing effects of elevated CO_2 and N deposition on *Lymantria*

monacha larvae feeding on spruce trees. *Oecologia* **118**: 210–217.

Kelly, J.J., Bansal, A., Winkelman, J., Janus, L.R., Hell, S., Wencel, M., Belt, P., Kuehn, K.A., Rier, S.T., and Tuchman, N.C. 2010. Alteration of microbial communities colonizing leaf litter in a temperate woodland stream by growth of trees under conditions of elevated atmospheric CO_2. *Applied and Environmental Microbiology* **76**: 4950–4959.

Koricheva, J., Larsson, S., Haukioja, E., and Keinanen, M. 1998. Regulation of woody plant metabolism by resource availability: hypothesis testing by means of a meta-analysis. *Oikos* **83**: 212–226.

Lindroth, R.L., Arteel, G.E., and Kinney, K.K. 1995. Responses of three saturniid species to paper birch grown under enriched CO_2 atmospheres. *Functional Ecology* **9**: 306–311.

Lindroth, R.L., Kinney, K.K., and Platz, C.L. 1993. Responses of deciduous trees to elevated atmospheric CO_2: Productivity, phytochemistry, and insect performance. *Ecology* **74**: 763–777.

McDonald, E.P., Agrell, J., and Lindroth, R.L. 1999. CO_2 and light effects on deciduous trees: growth, foliar chemistry and insect performance. *Oecologia* **119**: 389–399.

O'Neil, E.G. and Norby, R.J. 1996. Litter quality and decomposition rates of foliar litter produced under CO_2 enrichment. In: Koch, G.W. and Mooney, H.A. (Eds.) *Carbon Dioxide and Terrestrial Ecosystems*. Academic Press, San Diego, CA, pp. 87–103.

Peñuelas, J. and Estiarte, M. 1998. Can elevated CO_2 affect secondary metabolism and ecosystem function? *Trends in Ecology and Evolution* **13**: 20–24.

Peñuelas, J., Estiarte, M., and Llusia, J. 1997. Carbon-based secondary compounds at elevated CO_2. *Photosynthetica* **33**: 313–316.

Schnell, R.C. and Dlugokencky, E. 2008. Methane. In: Levinson, D.H. and Lawrimore, J.H. (Eds.) State of the Climate in 2007. *Special Supplement to the Bulletin of the American Meteorological Society* **89**: S27.

Traw, M.B., Lindroth, R.L., and Bazzaz, F.A. (1996) Decline in gypsy moth (*Lymantria dispar*) performance on an elevated CO_2 atmosphere depends upon host plant species. *Oecologia* **108**: 113–120.

2.30 Thylakoid Membranes

- Thylakoid membranes of chloroplasts perform a host of important functions that influence the process of carbon fixation in plants. In CO_2-

enriched air, they generally perform these functions more efficiently, enabling plants to overcome some of the deleterious effects of a host of plant stresses, including insufficient soil moisture, abnormally cold temperatures, abnormally hot temperatures, and ozone pollution.

Nearly all plants respond positively to increases in the air's CO_2 content by increasing their rates of photosynthesis, partly as a consequence of decreases in photorespiration and increases in the operating efficiency of the primary carboxylating enzyme rubisco. Less research has addressed the direct effects of elevated CO_2 on thylakoid membranes, the membranes within chloroplasts that contain chlorophyll and other pigments that absorb sunlight, together with the specialized protein complexes of photosystem II that play an integral role in the light-dependent reactions of photosynthesis that convert sunlight into usable cellular energy. This section reviews the findings of papers investigating how elevated CO_2 may impact thylakoid membranes and thereby influence the overall process of carbon fixation in plants.

After growing alfalfa in open-top chambers at ambient (340 ppm) and enriched (600 ppm) atmospheric CO_2 concentrations with ample soil moisture for 25 days, followed by inadequate levels of soil moisture for five additional days, Sgherri et al. (1998) determined the plants grown in the elevated CO_2 treatment maintained greater leaf chlorophyll contents and lipid-to-protein ratios in their thylakoid membranes, especially under conditions of water stress. When water was withheld, for example, leaf chlorophyll content dropped by a mere 6% at 600 ppm CO_2, whereas it plummeted by approximately 30% at 340 ppm. Leaf lipid contents in the plants grown in the CO_2-enriched air were about 22 and 83% higher than those measured in the plants grown in the ambient air treatment during the periods of ample and insufficient soil moisture, respectively. In addition, in the high CO_2 treatment the average degree of unsaturation of the two most important thylakoid membrane lipids was approximately 20 and 37% greater than it was in plants grown at 340 ppm CO_2 during times of adequate and inadequate soil moisture, respectively.

With respect to the implications of these observations, it is generally believed that the greater concentrations of thylakoid lipids typically observed at elevated atmospheric CO_2 concentrations, plus their enhanced degree of unsaturation, may allow thylakoid membranes to maintain a more fluid and stable environment, which is critical during periods of water stress in enabling plants to continue photosynthetic carbon uptake. These effects are so important, some researchers suggest adaptive plant responses such as these may allow plants to better cope with *any* altered environmental condition that produces stress.

The study of Tuba et al. (1998) provides a good example of this phenomenon as it pertains to extreme water stress. Detached leaves of *Xerophyta scabrida* (a woody shrub that grows in arid regions of east Africa) were rehydrated and regreened in air of 350 and 700 ppm CO_2, after which they were allowed to desiccate. The elevated CO_2 did not affect the amount of chlorophyll, the functioning of the thylakoid membranes, or the time to complete drying during desiccation. However, it allowed positive photosynthetic carbon gains to continue three times longer than in leaves exposed to ambient air, which resulted in the CO_2-enriched leaves gaining more than 10 times the amount of carbon over the period of desiccation than was gained by the leaves exposed to normal air.

Tuba et al. also studied the effects of desiccation on the carbon balance of a moss and a lichen under the same two atmospheric CO_2 concentrations, observing similar response patterns in both plants. Positive photosynthetic carbon gains were maintained 14% longer with atmospheric CO_2 enrichment, and total assimilation during the dry-down in elevated CO_2 was increased by 52 and 69% in the lichen and moss, respectively.

Investigating responses to chilling, Hugly and Somerville (1992) worked with wild-type *Arabidopsis thaliana* and two mutants deficient in thylakoid lipid unsaturation. They found "chloroplast membrane lipid polyunsaturation contributes to the low-temperature fitness of the organism" and "is required for some aspect of chloroplast biogenesis." When lipid polyunsaturation was low, for example, they observed "dramatic reductions in chloroplast size, membrane content, and organization in developing leaves." Furthermore, they found a positive correlation "between the severity of chlorosis in the two mutants at low temperatures and the degree of reduction in polyunsaturated chloroplast lipid composition."

Kodama et al. (1994) demonstrated the low-temperature-induced suppression of tobacco leaf growth and concomitant induction of chlorosis observed in wild-type plants was much less evident in transgenic plants containing a gene that allowed for greater expression of unsaturation in the fatty acids of leaf lipids. They conclude substantially unsaturated fatty acids "are undoubtedly an important factor contributing to cold tolerance."

Moon *et al.* (1995) found heightened unsaturation of the membrane lipids of chloroplasts stabilized the photosynthetic machinery of transgenic tobacco plants against low-temperature photoinhibition "by accelerating the recovery of the photosystem II protein complex." Also working with transgenic tobacco plants, Kodama *et al.* (1995) showed increased fatty acid desaturation is one of the prerequisites for normal leaf development at low, nonfreezing temperatures, and Ishizaki-Nishizawa *et al.* (1996) demonstrated transgenic tobacco plants with a reduced level of saturated fatty acids in most membrane lipids "exhibited a significant increase in chilling resistance."

These observations are laden with significance for Earth's agro-ecosystems because many economically important crops, such as rice, maize, and soybeans, are classified as chilling-sensitive; they experience injury or death at temperatures between 0 and 15°C (Lyons, 1973). But if atmospheric CO_2 enrichment enhances their production and degree-of-unsaturation of thylakoid lipids, as it does in alfalfa, a continuation of the ongoing rise in the air's CO_2 content could increase the abilities of these critically important agricultural species to withstand periodic exposure to debilitating low temperatures. This phenomenon could provide the extra boost in food production that will be needed to sustain the planet's increasing human population in the future (Wallace, 2000; Tilman *et al.*, 2001).

Earth's natural ecosystems also would benefit from a CO_2-induced increase in thylakoid lipids containing more-highly-unsaturated fatty acids. Many plants of tropical origin, for example, suffer cold damage when temperatures fall below 20°C (Graham and Patterson, 1982), and with the improved lipid characteristics provided by the ongoing rise in the air's CO_2 content, such plants would be able to expand their ranges both poleward and upward in a higher-CO_2 world, significantly increasing ecosystem biodiversity along the way.

At the other end of the biologically tolerable temperature spectrum is heat stress. Taub *et al.* (2000) note electron transport through photosystem II is the most heat-sensitive component of the photosynthetic process, and any reductions in electron transport through this thylakoid-membrane-bound protein complex invariably lead to reductions in photosynthetic carbon uptake and reduced growth potential. Hence, they conducted several experiments on herbaceous, woody, monocot, and dicot species (to assess the degree of universality of any response that might be detected) in controlled environment chambers, greenhouses, and FACE plots to examine the photosynthetic responses of this wide array of plants to acute heat stress under ambient and elevated CO_2 concentrations ranging from 550 to 1,000 ppm.

Of the 16 plant species studied, all but one displayed greater photochemical efficiencies of photosystem II when growing in CO_2-enriched air as opposed to ambient air when exposed to high air temperatures. The air temperatures that caused a 50% reduction in the maximum efficiency of photosystem II were nearly one degree Celsius higher for plants grown in elevated CO_2 air than for plants grown in ambient air. In other words, elevated CO_2 almost universally allowed more electrons to flow through photosystem II, thereby laying the foundation for greater photosynthetic rates. In an extended experiment, rates of net photosynthesis measured at 40°C in CO_2-enriched cucumbers were 3.2 times greater than those exhibited by plants grown in ambient air and exposed to the same air temperature.

Another stress to which many plants are routinely exposed is elevated atmospheric ozone concentrations. Oksanen *et al.* (2001) grew aspen clones with varying degrees of ozone tolerance together with sugar maple and paper birch trees for three years in 30-m diameter FACE plots maintained at atmospheric CO_2 concentrations of 360 and 560 ppm with and without exposure to elevated ozone concentrations (1.5 times ambient) to study the interactive effects of these two trace gases on leaf ultrastructure.

In the birch trees, the negative effects of ozone on leaf ultrastructure were minor, and injuries to thylakoid membranes were partially ameliorated by exposure to elevated CO_2. In the aspen clones, ozone exposure caused more significant structural injuries to thylakoid membranes and the stromal compartment within chloroplasts, but these injuries also were largely ameliorated by atmospheric CO_2 enrichment. Leaf thickness, mesophyll tissue thickness, the amount of chloroplasts per unit cell area, and the amount of starch in chloroplasts all were lower in the high ozone treatment, but simultaneous exposure of the ozone-stressed trees to elevated CO_2 more than compensated for the ozone-induced problems. As tropospheric ozone concentrations continue to rise, therefore, they likely will pose a problem for regenerating aspen and birch trees by negatively affecting chloroplast ultrastructure at the site of carbon fixation, which likely will decrease their productivity and growth. However, if the atmospheric CO_2 concentration also continues to rise, these negative effects will be either partly, completely, or more than completely ameliorated, thus stimulating productivity and growth to varying degrees within these species.

The studies reviewed above suggest atmospheric CO_2 enrichment may constitute a powerful remedy for all sorts of environmental ailments that afflict plants and have their origin in stress-induced problems associated with the functioning of the thylakoid membranes of the plants' chloroplasts.

References

Graham, D. and Patterson, B.D. 1982. Responses of plants to low, non-freezing temperatures: proteins, metabolism, and acclimation. *Annual Review of Plant Physiology* **33**: 347–372.

Hugly, S. and Somerville, C. 1992. A role for membrane lipid polyunsaturation in chloroplast biogenesis at low temperature. *Plant Physiology* **99**: 197–202.

Ishizaki-Nishizawa, O., Fujii, T., Azuma, M., Sekiguchi, K., Murata, N., Ohtani, T., and Toguri T. 1996. Low-temperature resistance of higher plants is significantly enhanced by a nonspecific cyanobacterial desaturase. *Nature Biotechnology* **14**: 1003–1006.

Kodama, H., Hamada, T., Horiguchi, G., Nishimura, M., and Iba, K. 1994. Genetic enhancement of cold tolerance by expression of a gene for chloroplast w-3 fatty acid desaturase in transgenic tobacco. *Plant Physiology* **105**: 601–605.

Kodama, H., Horiguchi, G., Nishiuchi, T., Nishimura, M., and Iba, K. 1995. Fatty acid desaturation during chilling acclimation is one of the factors involved in conferring low-temperature tolerance to young tobacco leaves. *Plant Physiology* **107**: 1177–1185.

Lyons, J.M. 1973. Chilling injury in plants. *Annual Review of Plant Physiology* **24**: 445–466.

Moon, B.Y., Higashi, S.-I., Gombos, Z., and Murata, N. 1995. Unsaturation of the membrane lipids of chloroplasts stabilizes the photosynthetic machinery against low-temperature photoinhibition in transgenic tobacco plants. *Proceedings of the National Academy of Sciences, USA* **92**: 6219–6223.

Oksanen, E., Sober, J., and Karnosky, D.F. 2001. Impacts of elevated CO_2 and/or O_3 on leaf ultrastructure of aspen (*Populus tremuloides*) and birch (*Betula papyrifera*) in the Aspen FACE experiment. *Environmental Pollution* **115**: 437–446.

Sgherri, C.L.M., Quartacci, M.F., Menconi, M., Raschi, A., and Navari-Izzo, F. 1998. Interactions between drought and elevated CO_2 on alfalfa plants. *Journal of Plant Physiology* **152**: 118–124.

Taub, D.R., Seeman, J.R., and Coleman, J.S. 2000. Growth in elevated CO_2 protects photosynthesis against high-temperature damage. *Plant, Cell and Environment* **23**: 649–656.

Tilman, D., Fargione, J., Wolff, B., D'Antonio, C., Dobson, A., Howarth, R., Schindler, D., Schlesinger, W.H., Simberloff, D., and Swackhamer, D. 2001. Forecasting agriculturally driven global environmental change. *Science* **292**: 281–284.

Tuba, Z., Csintalan, Z., Szente, K., Nagy, Z., and Grace, J. 1998. Carbon gains by desiccation-tolerant plants at elevated CO_2. *Functional Ecology* **12**: 39–44.

Wallace, J.S. 2000. Increasing agricultural water use efficiency to meet future food production. *Agriculture, Ecosystems & Environment* **82**: 105–119.

2.31 Transpiration

2.31.1 Herbaceous Plants

If the atmosphere's CO_2 content continues to rise as it has over the past few decades, the world's farmers should be able to produce substantially more food on each hectare of land with little or no change in per-hectare water requirements. In the case of C_4 crops, higher yields may be produced with smaller amounts of water, even in the face of higher temperatures. And most herbaceous non-crop plants should respond to increases in the air's CO_2 concentration in like manner, leading to greater soil moisture content in CO_2-enriched ecosystems and a positive effect on plant growth.

2.31.1.1 Crops

- If the atmosphere's CO_2 content continues to rise as it has over the past few decades, the world's farmers should be able to produce substantially more food on each hectare of land with little or no change in per-hectare water requirements. Higher yields of C_4 crops may be produced with smaller amounts of water, even in higher temperatures.

Most plants respond to increases in the atmosphere's CO_2 content by reducing their leaf stomatal conductances, which typically leads to reduced rates of transpirational water loss. The resultant water savings, in turn, often lead to greater soil moisture content in CO_2-enriched ecosystems, with positive effects on plant water status and growth. This section reviews the results of studies of both C_3 and C_4 crops that treat various aspects of this CO_2-induced multistage interaction.

Dong-Xiu *et al.* (2002) grew spring wheat in open-top chambers maintained at atmospheric CO_2 concentrations of 350 and 700 ppm and three levels of soil moisture (40, 60, and 80% of field capacity). In addition to increasing rates of net photosynthesis by 48, 120, and 97% at low, medium, and high soil water contents, this doubling of the air's CO_2 concentration reduced rates of transpiration by 56, 53, and 63%, respectively, in the three soil water treatments.

De Costa *et al.* (2003) grew two crops of rice in the field in Sri Lanka—from January to March (the *maha* season) and from May to August (the *yala* season)—in open-top chambers maintained at either ambient or ambient plus 200 ppm CO_2. Leaf net photosynthetic rates were significantly higher in the CO_2-enriched chambers than in the ambient-air chambers: 51–75% greater in the *maha* season and 22–33% greater in the *yala* season. In addition, leaf stomatal conductances exhibited CO_2-induced reductions of 15–52% in the *maha* season and 13–19% in the *yala* season. However, because of the significantly greater leaf area in the CO_2-enriched chambers, total canopy transpiration rate per unit land area did not differ significantly between the two CO_2 treatments. Nevertheless, leaf water potentials were higher (less negative, and therefore more beneficial) in the CO_2-enriched chambers.

Vu (2005) grew peanuts from seed to maturity in greenhouses maintained at atmospheric CO_2 concentrations of 360 and 720 ppm and at air temperatures 1.5 and 6.0°C above outdoor air temperatures. Although rubisco protein content and activity were down-regulated by elevated CO_2, the rubisco photosynthetic efficiency of the elevated-CO_2 plants "was 1.3- to 1.9-fold greater than that of the ambient-CO_2 plants at both growth temperatures." He also found "leaf soluble sugars and starch of plants grown at elevated CO_2 were 1.3- and 2-fold higher, respectively, than those of plants grown at ambient CO_2." Finally, the leaf transpirational water loss of the elevated-CO_2 plants compared to that of the ambient-CO_2 plants was 12% less at near-ambient temperatures and 17% less in the higher temperature regime.

Malmstrom and Field (1997) grew individual oat plants for two months in pots placed within phytocells having atmospheric CO_2 concentrations of 350 and 700 ppm. One-third of the plants were infected with the barley yellow dwarf virus that plagues more than 150 plant species, including all major cereal crops.

The elevated CO_2 stimulated rates of net photosynthesis in all plants, with the greatest percentage increase occurring in diseased individuals (48% vs. 34%), and it decreased stomatal conductance by 50% in infected plants and 34% in healthy ones, thus reducing transpirational water losses. Together, these phenomena contributed to a CO_2-induced doubling of the instantaneous water use efficiency in healthy plants and a 2.7-fold increase in diseased plants.

Leakey *et al.* (2004) grew corn in their SoyFACE facility in the heart of the U.S. Corn Belt while exposing different parts of the field to atmospheric CO_2 concentrations of 354 and 549 ppm during a year of summer rainfall "very close to the 50-year average for this site, indicating that the year was not atypical or a drought year." On five days during the growing season (11 and 22 July, 9 and 21 August, and 5 September), they measured diurnal patterns of photosynthesis, stomatal conductance, and micro-climatic conditions.

Contrary to what many people had long assumed would be the case for a C_4 crop such as corn growing under the best of natural conditions, Leakey *et al.* found "growth at elevated CO_2 significantly increased leaf photosynthetic CO_2 uptake rate by up to 41%." The highest whole-day increase was 21% (11 July) followed by 11% (22 July), during a period of low rainfall. Thereafter, however, during a period of greater rainfall, there were no significant differences between the photosynthetic rates of the plants in the two CO_2 treatments. Over the entire growing season, the CO_2-induced increase in leaf photosynthesis averaged 10%.

Additionally, on all but the first day of measurements, stomatal conductance was significantly lower (-23% on average) in the elevated CO_2 treatment, which led to reduced transpiration rates in the CO_2-enriched plants. And since "low soil water availability and high evaporative demand can both generate water stress and inhibit leaf net CO_2 assimilation in C_4 plants," as Leakey *et al.* note, they conclude the lower transpiration rates of the plants growing in the CO_2-enriched air "may have counteracted the development of water stress under elevated CO_2 and prevented the inhibition of leaf net CO_2 assimilation observed under ambient CO_2."

Therefore, they write, "contrary to expectations, this US Corn Belt summer climate appeared to cause sufficient water stress under ambient CO_2 to allow the ameliorating effects of elevated CO_2 to significantly enhance leaf net CO_2 assimilation." They conclude this response of corn to elevated CO_2 "indicates the potential for greater future crop biomass and harvestable yield across the US Corn Belt," due largely to the amelioration of water stress by CO_2-induced decreases in transpirational water loss.

Grant *et al.* (2004) adjusted the crop growth and water relations model *ecosys* to represent the C_4 crop sorghum and ran it for two growing seasons (1 May 1998 to 31 October 1999) under both wet and dry irrigation regimes at two atmospheric CO_2 concentrations (approximately 368 and 561 ppm), using hourly meteorological data measured at a field south of Phoenix, Arizona (USA). They used these simulated energy balances and water relations— verified by measurements of energy flux and water potential—to infer the effects of free-air atmospheric CO_2 enrichment on various plant parameters and processes.

The 12 researchers report "model results, corroborated by field measurements, showed elevated CO_2 raised canopy water potential and lowered latent heat fluxes under high irrigation [both of which responses are beneficial] and delayed water stress under low irrigation [which is also beneficial]." As they described it elsewhere, the elevated CO_2 "reduced transpiration and hence improved water status of sorghum [and] lowered the vulnerability of sorghum CO_2 fixation to soil or atmospheric water deficits, even when irrigation was high." Also, in applying their reality-tuned model to a scenario where the air's CO_2 content was 50% higher and air temperature was 3°C greater, they calculated sorghum yields would rise by about 13%, and "current high sorghum yields could be achieved with ~120 mm or ~20% less irrigation water if these rises in temperature and CO_2 were to occur."

The studies reviewed here suggest a continued rise of the atmosphere's CO_2 content should allow production of substantially more food on each hectare of land with little or no change in per-hectare water requirements. In the case of C_4 crops, it appears higher yields may be produced with smaller amounts of water, even in the face of higher temperatures.

References

De Costa, W.A.J.M., Weerakoon, W.M.W., Abeywardena, R.M.I., and Herath, H.M.L.K. 2003. Response of photosynthesis and water relations of rice (*Oryza sativa*) to elevated atmospheric carbon dioxide in the subhumid zone of Sri Lanka. *Journal of Agronomy and Crop Science* **189**: 71–82.

Dong-Xiu, W., Gen-Xuan, W., Yong-Fei, B., Jian-Xiong, L., and Hong-Xu, R. 2002. Response of growth and water use efficiency of spring wheat to whole season CO_2 enrichment and drought. *Acta Botanica Sinica* **44**: 1477-1483.

Grant, R.F., Kimball, B.A., Wall, G.W., Triggs, J.M., Brooks, T.J., Pinter Jr., P.J., Conley, M.M., Ottman, M.J., Lamorte, R.L., Leavitt, S.W., Thompson, T.L., and Matthias, A.D. 2004. Modeling elevated carbon dioxide effects on water relations, water use, and growth of irrigated sorghum. *Agronomy Journal* **96**: 1693–1705.

Leakey, A.D.B., Bernacchi, C.J., Dohleman, F.G., Ort, D.R., and Long, S.P. 2004. Will photosynthesis of maize (*Zea mays*) in the US Corn Belt increase in future $[CO_2]$ rich atmospheres? An analysis of diurnal courses of CO_2 uptake under free-air concentration enrichment (FACE). *Global Change Biology* **10**: 951–962.

Malmstrom, C.M. and Field, C.B. 1997. Virus-induced differences in the response of oat plants to elevated carbon dioxide. *Plant, Cell and Environment* **20**: 178–188.

Vu, J.C.V. 2005. Acclimation of peanut (*Arachis hypogaea* L.) leaf photosynthesis to elevated growth CO_2 and temperature. *Environmental and Experimental Botany* **53**: 85–95.

2.31.1.2 Other Plants

- Most herbaceous non-crop plants respond to increases in the air's CO_2 concentration by reducing their leaf stomatal conductances, which typically leads to reduced rates of evaporative water loss from them. The saved water, in turn, often leads to greater soil moisture content in CO_2-enriched ecosystems, with positive effects on plant growth.

This section examines the results of some studies of C_3 and C_4 grassland species that broach various aspects of this multifaceted subject.

Szente *et al.* (1998) grew four perennial C_3 plants (two grasses and two broad-leaved species) common to loess grasslands of Budapest in open-top chambers maintained at atmospheric CO_2 concentrations of 350 or 700 ppm for 231 days. They found this doubling of the air's CO_2 content significantly enhanced rates of net photosynthesis in all species studied, with the two grasses and the two broad-leaved species exhibiting average increases of 136 and 486%, respectively. The extra CO_2 increased transpiration rates for one of the grasses and one of the broad-leaved species, but it did not affect the water loss rates of the remaining species. Nevertheless, the two grasses exhibited an average CO_2-induced increase in water use efficiency of 72%, and the two broad-leaved species displayed an average increase of 366%,. These large improvements should allow them to cope better with the hot and dry summers they characteristically experience in this part of Hungary.

Engloner *et al.* (2003) removed grassland monoliths with their original soils to a depth of 40 cm from a xeric loess grassland and relocated them to open-top chambers outside Budapest, where they were exposed for seven years to either ambient air or air enriched to a CO_2 concentration of 700 ppm. Measurements of leaf photosynthesis and transpiration rates of a dominant member of this ecosystem (couch-grass) were conducted throughout the experiment according to protocols described by Tuba *et al.* (1994, 1996), and measurements of starch and soluble sugars were made as described by Tuba *et al.* (1994). Rates of net photosynthesis increased by an average of 194% in response to the ~90% increase in atmospheric CO_2 concentration, leading to starch and soluble sugar increases of approximately 50 and 72%, respectively. Leaf transpiration rates declined by about 18%, leading to a 345% increase in water use efficiency, which for a xeric grassland species is like manna from heaven, greatly fortifying it against the rigors of its xeric environment.

Turning to C_4 plants, Seneweera *et al.* (1998) grew a drought-resistant perennial grass (*Panicum coloratum*) for five weeks in controlled environment chambers having atmospheric CO_2 concentrations of 350 or 1,000 ppm and different vapor pressure deficits (VPDs) maintained by keeping the relative humidity of the air at either 50 or 80%. The plants were watered daily to 65, 80, or 100% of their potting soils' field capacities. Under favorable environmental conditions, characterized by a low VPD and high soil moisture (100% field capacity), atmospheric CO_2 enrichment failed to cause any significant increases in leaf or stem dry weight. However, when water-stressed conditions prevailed, due to either a high VPD, low field capacities of 65 or 80%, or combinations of both parameters, elevated CO_2 caused large, significant increases in growth. At the high VPD, for example, the percentage increases in leaf dry weight at field capacities of 65 and 80% were 117 and 112%, respectively, and the growth responses for stems under these conditions were 50 and 57%.

These growth increases resulted in part from the ability of elevated CO_2 to ameliorate the negative effects of water stress on growth. Under the most extreme water-stressed condition, for example, leaf water potential values were about 3.5 times more negative, i.e., more stressful, for plants grown in air

of 350 ppm CO_2 than for plants grown in air of 1,000 ppm, because transpirational water loss was always less for plants grown in elevated CO_2. For the most water-stressed condition investigated, which resulted from a high VPD and a field capacity of 65%, the transpiration rates of plants grown in ambient CO_2 were about 2.5 times greater than those of plants grown in elevated CO_2. Consequently, higher concentrations of atmospheric CO_2 likely will allow C_4 grasses to maintain better internal water relations by reducing transpirational water losses, resulting in greater water-use efficiencies and the likely expansion of the plants into hot and arid regions commonly subjected to drought.

In an extension of this work, Seneweera *et al.* (2001) grew *P. coloratum* in controlled environment chambers maintained at atmospheric CO_2 concentrations of 360 and 1,000 ppm for three weeks before withholding water from half the plants for 10 days, after which the plants were rewatered for five days to promote recovery. At the onset of water stress, shoot dry mass in the CO_2-enriched plants was 33% greater than in the plants grown in ambient air. Although water stress reduced shoot dry mass, the reductions were less severe for CO_2-enriched than ambiently grown plants. During the water stress treatment, leaf water potentials and leaf relative water contents dropped at much slower rates and to lesser degrees in the CO_2-enriched plants than in the ambiently grown plants. Similarly, transpiration rates of the CO_2-enriched plants were much less than those of plants growing in ambient air, and this phenomenon helped contribute to the greater soil moisture contents that were always present beneath the CO_2-enriched plants. At final harvest, the CO_2-induced enhancement of shoot dry mass was 44 and 70% for plants that had been subjected to well-watered and water-stressed treatments, respectively.

In a two-year experiment in an annual-dominated California grassland, Zavaleta *et al.* (2003) delivered extra heating to a number of FACE plots (enriched with an extra 300 ppm of CO_2) via IR heat lamps that warmed the surface of the soil beneath them by 0.8–1.0°C. The individual effects of atmospheric CO_2 enrichment and soil warming were of similar magnitude, and acting together they enhanced mean spring soil moisture content by about 15% over that of the control plots. The effect of CO_2 was produced primarily as a consequence of its ability to cause partial stomatal closure and thereby reduce season-long plant water loss via transpiration. With warming, there was an acceleration of canopy senescence that further increased soil moisture by reducing the period of time (the length of the growing season) over which transpiration losses occur, all without any decrease in total plant production.

The six researchers note their findings "illustrate the potential for organism-environment interactions to modify the direction as well as the magnitude of global change effects on ecosystem functioning." Whereas for the past several years there have been multiple predictions of vast reaches of agricultural land drying up and being lost to profitable production in a CO_2-enriched and warmed world of the future, this study suggests just the opposite could occur. As Zavaleta *et al*. describe it, "we suggest that in at least some ecosystems, declines in plant transpiration mediated by changes in phenology can offset direct increases in evaporative water losses under future warming."

For both C_3 and C_4 grassland plants, the reductions in leaf transpirational water loss that result from increases in the air's CO_2 concentration should significantly enhance their ability to withstand the rigors of periodic severe water stress in arid and semi-arid parts of the globe—even in the face of significant warming, which may induce its own beneficial feedback—while enhancing their productivities and thereby providing more forage for the various forms of animal life that inhabit these regions. In addition, these plants may reclaim great tracts of desert as their water use efficiencies rise to levels not experienced for millions of years.

References

Engloner, A.I., Kovacs, D., Balogh, J., and Tuba, Z. 2003. Anatomical and eco-physiological changes in leaves of couch-grass (*Elymus repens* L.), a temperate loess grassland species, after 7 years growth under elevated CO_2 concentration. *Photosynthetica* **41**: 185–189.

Seneweera, S.P., Ghannoum, O., and Conroy, J. 1998. High vapor pressure deficit and low soil water availability enhance shoot growth responses of a C_4 grass (*Panicum coloratum* cv. Bambatsi) to CO_2 enrichment. *Australian Journal of Plant Physiology* **25**: 287–292.

Seneweera, S., Ghannoum, O., and Conroy, J.P. 2001. Root and shoot factors contribute to the effect of drought on photosynthesis and growth of the C_4 grass Panicum coloratum at elevated CO_2 partial pressures. *Australian Journal of Plant Physiology* **28**: 451–460.

Szente, K., Nagy, Z., and Tuba, Z. 1998. Enhanced water use efficiency in dry loess grassland species grown at elevated air CO_2 concentration. *Photosynthetica* **35**: 637–640.

Tuba, Z., Szente, K., and Koch, J. 1994. Response of photosynthesis, stomatal conductance, water use efficiency and production to long-term elevated CO_2 in winter wheat. *Journal of Plant Physiology* **144**: 651–668.

Tuba, Z., Szente, K., Nagy, Z., Csintalan, Z., and Koch, J. 1996. Responses of CO_2 assimilation, transpiration and water use efficiency to long-term elevated CO_2 in perennial C_3 xeric loess steppe species. *Journal of Plant Physiology* **148**: 356–361.

Zavaleta, E.S., Thomas, B.D., Chiariello, N.R., Asner, G.P., Shaw, M.R., and Field, C.B. 2003. Plants reverse warming effect on ecosystem water balance. *Proceedings of the National Academy of Science USA* **100**: 9892–9893.

2.31.2 Woody Plants

As the air's CO_2 content rises, the water use efficiencies (amount of carbon gain per unit of water loss) of coniferous trees and dryland shrubs tend to rise as well. The same is true of most deciduous trees, enabling them to cope more effectively with the increased water stress they would otherwise experience in stressful conditions and locations.

2.31.2.1 Conifers

- As the air's CO_2 content rises, conifer water use efficiency (the amount of carbon gain at the needle level per unit of water loss) tends to rise as well.

Apple *et al*. (2000) grew two-year-old Douglas fir seedlings for three additional years in controlled environment chambers maintained at atmospheric CO_2 concentrations of either 350 or 550 ppm and ambient or elevated (ambient plus 4°C) air temperature. They found the 200-ppm increase in the air's CO_2 concentration and the 4°C increase in air temperature, when applied together, did not significantly affect seedling transpiration. When applied alone, however, the extra CO_2 reduced transpiration by 12%, and the elevated air temperature increased it by 66%.

After a one-year continuation of the same experiment, Lewis *et al*. (2002) report results obtained over its final 21 months. Once again, the extra CO_2 decreased transpiration by 12%, but the elevated air temperature increased it by 37%, considerably less than the 66% increase report by Apple *et al*. Adding more confusion, the combination of the identical CO_2 effect and a weaker temperature effect yielded a 19% increase in transpiration, whereas in the first three years of the study the identical CO_2 effect and a stronger temperature effect produced no change in transpiration.

In a one-year study in which closed-top chambers were constructed around 30-year-old Scots pine trees growing in Finland, Kellomaki and Wang (1998) applied doubled CO_2 to half the trees while studying the effect of a 4°C increase in air temperature. The elevated CO_2 reduced cumulative sap flow (a measure of transpiration) by 14% in the trees maintained at ambient temperatures, but when both air temperature and CO_2 concentration were increased together, cumulative sap flow exhibited no change.

In the studies cited above, atmospheric CO_2 enrichment consistently produced a small reduction in tree transpiration rates at ambient air temperatures, and the added effect of warming was inconsistent and confusing. Hence, it is instructive to consider the study of Saurer *et al.* (2004), who measured carbon isotope ratios in the rings of coniferous trees of northern Eurasia (including the genera *Larix*, *Picea* and *Pinus*) across a longitudinal transect that covered the entire supercontinent in the latitude range 59–71°N. Between the two 30-year periods 1861–1890 and 1961–1990, when air temperature and CO_2 concentration both rose significantly, they found intrinsic water use efficiency (Wi, the amount of carbon gain at the needle level per unit of water loss) rose significantly, such that "125 out of 126 trees showed increasing Wi from 1861–1890 to 1961–1990, with an average improvement of 19.2 ± 0.9%."

The three Swiss scientists say their results suggest the trees they studied "are able to produce the same biomass today [as they did 100 years ago] but with lower costs in terms of transpiration." This finding is very important because, they write, recent warming in other longitudinal segments of the same latitude belt "may be accompanied by increased drought stress (Lloyd and Fastie, 2002)" and the ongoing rise in the air's CO_2 content may be helping the trees in those areas to better cope with this environmental challenge, even in the face of increasing air temperatures.

References

Apple, M.E., Olszyk, D.M., Ormrod, D.P., Lewis, J., Southworth, D., and Tingey, D.T. 2000. Morphology and stomatal function of Douglas fir needles exposed to climate change: elevated CO_2 and temperature. *International Journal of Plant Science* **161**: 127–132.

Kellomaki, S. and Wang, K.-Y. 1998. Sap flow in Scots pines growing under conditions of year-round carbon dioxide enrichment and temperature elevation. *Plant, Cell and Environment* **21**: 969–981.

Lewis, J.D., Lucash, M., Olszyk, D.M., and Tingey, D.T. 2002. Stomatal responses of Douglas-fir seedlings to elevated carbon dioxide and temperature during the third and fourth years of exposure. *Plant, Cell and Environment* **25**: 1411–1421.

Lloyd, A.H. and Fastie, C.L. 2002. Spatial and temporal variability in the growth and climate response of treeline trees in Alaska. *Climatic Change* **52**: 481–509.

Saurer, M., Siegwolf, R.T.W., and Schweingruber, F.H. 2004. Carbon isotope discrimination indicates improving water use efficiency of trees in northern Eurasia over the last 100 years. *Global Change Biology* **10**: 2109–2120.

2.31.2.2 Dryland Plants

- As the air's CO_2 content rises, the water-use efficiencies of Earth's dryland plants usually tend to rise as well.

In a FACE experiment conducted in a chaparral region of southern California, Roberts *et al.* (1998) exposed *Adenostoma fassciculatum* shrubs to atmospheric CO_2 concentrations of 360 and 550 ppm. After six months of treatment, it was clear the elevated CO_2 had reduced the stomatal conductances of the shrubs' leaves and decreased their rates of evaporative water loss. The CO_2-enriched shrubs exhibited leaf water potentials significantly more positive (less stressful) than those of the plants growing in ambient air. This enhancement of internal water status should help this woody perennial better withstand the periods of drought that commonly occur throughout its southern California range.

Dugas *et al.* (2001) studied the response of whole-plant transpiration to atmospheric CO_2 enrichment in the woody legume *Acacia farnesiana*, which occurs throughout the south-central United States and is one of the most aggressive woody-plant invaders of grasslands worldwide. Plants of this species were grown for a full year in greenhouse bays continuously maintained at atmospheric CO_2 concentrations of either 385 or 980 ppm, and at the end of this time whole-plant transpiration was assessed via sap flow measurements. The mean transpiration rate of the plants grown at an atmospheric CO_2 concentration of 980 ppm was only about one-fourth of that exhibited by the plants grown at a concentration of 385 ppm.

The increase in water use efficiency implied by this result could explain *A. farnesiana*'s increasing ascendancy over dryland grasses as the air's CO_2 content has risen over the past century or more.

Peterson and Neofotis (2004) sprouted and grew velvet mesquite plants in small pots within controlled environment chambers maintained at atmospheric CO_2 concentrations of either 380 or 760 ppm. Although they did not see a large CO_2-induced increase in plant growth, by the end of their six-week study there was a highly significant 41% reduction in the volume of water transpired by the mesquite seedlings in the CO_2-enriched treatment. "This large reduction in whole-plant water use," they write, "occurred because the reduction in transpiration per unit leaf area at elevated CO_2 was not offset by a proportional increase in total leaf area."

The pair of scientists from the Biosphere 2 Center near Oracle, Arizona, state their findings suggest in a future high-CO_2 world, mesquite seedlings "may deplete soil moisture at a slower rate than they do currently," and "this could facilitate seedling survival between intermittent rain events." They also note their work "corroborates the conclusions of Polley *et al.* (1994, 1999, 2003) that increasing levels of atmospheric CO_2 may facilitate the establishment of mesquite seedlings through a reduction in soil water depletion." Peterson and Neofotis note "mesquites and other woody species in the semiarid southwestern United States have shown substantial increases in population density and geographic range since Anglo-American settlement of the region approximately 120 years ago," citing Van Auken and Bush (1990), Gibbens *et al.* (1992), Bahre and Shelton (1993), Archer (1995), Boutton *et al.* (1999), Van Auken (2000), Ansley *et al.* (2001), Wilson *et al.* (2001), and Biggs *et al.* (2002).

Just as nonagricultural herbaceous plants are encroaching on Earth's deserts as the air's CO_2 content rises, so too are woody dryland shrubs following in their "rootsteps," as the greening of Earth continues.

References

Ansley, R.J., Ben Wu, X., and Kramp, B.A. 2001. Observation: long-term increases in mesquite canopy cover in a north Texas savanna. *Journal of Range Management* **54**: 171–176.

Archer, S. 1995. Tree-grass dynamics in a *Prosopis*-thornscrub savanna parkland: reconstructing the past and predicting the future. *Ecoscience* **2**: 83–99.

Bahre, C.J. and Shelton, M.L. 1993. Historic vegetation change, mesquite increases, and climate in southeastern Arizona. *Journal of Biogeography* **20**: 489–504.

Biggs, T.H., Quade, J., and Webb, R.H. 2002. $\delta^{13}C$ values of soil organic matter in semiarid grassland with mesquite (*Prosopis*) encroachment in southeastern Arizona. *Geoderma* **110**: 109–130.

Boutton, T.W., Archer, S.R., and Midwood, A.J. 1999. Stable isotopes in ecosystem science: structure, function and dynamics of a subtropical savanna. *Rapid Communications in Mass Spectrometry* **13**: 1263–1277.

Dugas, W.A., Polley, H.W., Mayeux, H.S., and Johnson, H.B. 2001. Acclimation of whole-plant *Acacia farnesiana* transpiration to carbon dioxide concentration. *Tree Physiology* **21**: 771–773.

Gibbens, R.P., Beck, R.F., McNeely, R.P., and Herbel, C.H. 1992. Recent rates of mesquite establishment in the northern Chihuahuan desert. *Journal of Range Management* **45**: 585–588.

Peterson, A.G. and Neofotis, P.G. 2004. A hierarchical analysis of the interactive effects of elevated CO_2 and water availability on the nitrogen and transpiration productivities of velvet mesquite seedlings. *Oecologia* **141**: 629–640.

Polley, H.W., Johnson, H.B., and Mayeux, H.S. 1994. Increasing CO_2: comparative responses of the C_4 grass *Schizachyrium* and grassland invader *Prosopis*. *Ecology* **75**: 976–988.

Polley, H.W., Johnson, H.B., and Tischler, C.R. 2003. Woody invasion of grasslands: evidence that CO_2 enrichment indirectly promotes establishment of *Prosopis glandulosa*. *Plant Ecology* **164**: 85–94.

Polley, H.W., Tischler, C.R., Johnson, H.B., and Pennington, R.E. 1999. Growth, water relations, and survival of drought-exposed seedlings from six maternal families of honey mesquite (*Prosopis glandulosa*): responses to CO_2 enrichment. *Tree Physiology* **19**: 359–366.

Roberts, S.W., Oechel, W.C., Bryant, P.J., Hastings, S.J., Major, J., and Nosov, V. 1988. A field fumigation system for elevated carbon dioxide exposure in chaparral shrubs. *Functional Ecology* **12**: 708–719.

Van Auken, O.W. 2000. Shrub invasions of North American semiarid grasslands. *Annual Review of Ecological Systems* **31**: 197–215.

Van Auken, O.W. and Bush, J.K. 1990. Importance of grass density and time of planting on *Prosopis glandulosa* seedling growth. *Southwest Naturalist* **35**: 411–415.

Wilson, T.B., Webb, R.H., and Thompson, T.L. 2001. *Mechanisms of Range Expansion and Removal of Mesquite in Desert Grasslands of the Southwestern United States.* U.S. Department of Agriculture, Forest Service, Rocky Mountain Research Station.

2.31.2.3 Deciduous Trees

- Most deciduous trees exhibit modest reductions in transpirational water loss in CO_2-enriched air, enabling them to cope more effectively with the increased water stress they otherwise would experience under water-limiting conditions.

Wayne *et al.* (1998) grew yellow birch seedlings in controlled environment chambers maintained at atmospheric CO_2 concentrations of either 400 or 800 ppm and day/night air temperatures of either 26/21 or 31/26°C for two months. They determined the elevated CO_2 treatment stimulated net photosynthesis by 48% at both temperatures, and it increased seedling biomass by 60% and 227% at normal and high air temperatures, respectively. In addition, because the extra CO_2 reduced transpiration by 25 and 36% at the normal and high air temperatures, plant water use efficiency rose by 52 and 94% in these two situations, which suggests yellow birch may someday be able to expand into regions where high summer temperatures and limited rainfall currently discourage its presence.

In a FACE study established within a 10-year-old stand of sweetgum trees growing on a nutrient-rich soil in Tennessee (USA), Wullschleger and Norby (2001) measured CO_2-induced sap-flow reductions that averaged 13% over the growing season. The elevated CO_2 (540 vs. 390 ppm) also reduced growing-season transpiration rates by about the same amount, leading to a 28% increase in stand-level water use efficiency in the CO_2-enriched trees. In a second year of measurements, Wullschleger *et al.* (2002) found the CO_2-enriched air reduced the stomatal conductances of individual leaves by an average of 23% across the growing season. When extrapolated to the entire canopy, however, the reduction fell to 14%, and there was a 7% reduction in stand evapotranspiration.

Tognetti *et al.* (1998) studied the effects of naturally occurring elevated CO_2 concentrations (500 to 1,000 ppm) near a CO_2-emitting spring in central Italy on summer water relations of mature oak trees by measuring leaf stomatal conductances and trunk sap flow rates (a measure of transpiration) over a period of two years and comparing the results with those obtained from similar-age oaks (15 to 25 years old) growing in air of ambient CO_2 concentration at a site about three kilometers away. As both summers were characterized by severe drought, rates of water loss were relatively high in both sets of trees. Leaf stomatal conductances, however, were significantly lower in the trees growing near the CO_2 springs, as were trunk sap velocities. These findings suggest the trees near the CO_2-emitting springs experienced less water loss and maintained a more favorable internal water status than those growing in non-CO_2-enriched ambient air.

Tognetti *et al.* also determined the trees growing near the CO_2-emitting springs possessed less foliage area than the control trees, and this reduction in transpirational surface area allowed the CO_2-enriched trees to maintain a better internal water status than the control trees during periods of drought. The researchers state the reduction in foliage area was "equally, if not more, effective than stomatal closure in reducing transpiration and plant water use under elevated CO_2." Thus if drought situations continue to recur during future Italian summers, the rising CO_2 content of the atmosphere should provide oak, and perhaps other trees, with at least two different mechanisms for sustaining their growth during protracted periods of reduced water availability.

In a more broad-ranging study, Cech *et al.* (2003) enriched the air's CO_2 content within the canopy of a 30-meter-tall species-rich forest just south of Basel, Switzerland, using the web-FACE technique of Pepin and Korner (2002), to a mean value of 520 ppm for an entire growing season to test, they write, "whether elevated CO_2 reduces water use in mature forest trees." They took sap flow measurements of 14 broadleaved trees (three *Fagus*, four *Quercus*, four *Carpinus*, one *Tilia*, one *Acer*, and one *Prunus*) and their ambient-treatment counterparts via the constant heat-flow technique of Granier (1985, 1987) from 5 June to 1 October 2001.

Over the growing season, the extra 150 ppm of CO_2 reduced mean daily sap flow across all species by an average of 10.7%. At one end of the spectrum, the reductions were high (22%) when the evaporative demand of the air was low (mean daily vapor pressure deficits less than 5 hPa); but they were small (2%) at the other end, when the evaporative demand of the air was high (mean daily vapor pressure deficits greater than 10 hPa). The researchers conclude the "daily water savings by CO_2-enriched trees may have accumulated to [produce] a significantly improved water status by the time when control trees were short of soil moisture," so "CO_2-enriched trees would enter drier periods with a higher soil moisture capital, permitting prolonged gas exchange (for a few days)."

In light of these several experimental observations, it would appear most deciduous trees exhibit modest reductions in transpirational water loss in CO_2-enriched air. Consequently, if the planet continues to warm and experience increased dryness in some regions, Earth's deciduous trees may more effectively deal with the increased water stress they otherwise would experience in these places, if the air's CO_2 content continues to rise as well.

References

Cech, P.G., Pepin, S., and Korner, C. 2003. Elevated CO_2 reduces sap flux in mature deciduous forest trees. *Oecologia* **137**: 258–268.

Granier, A. 1985. A new method of sap flow measurement in tree stems. *Annales Des Sciences Forestieres* **42**: 193–200.

Granier, A. 1987. Evaluation of transpiration in a Douglas fir stand by means of sap flow measurements. *Tree Physiology* **3**: 309–320.

Pepin, S. and Korner, C. 2002. web-FACE: a new canopy free-air CO_2 enrichment system for tall trees in mature forests. *Oecologia* **133**: 1–9.

Tognetti, R., Longobucco, A., Miglietta, F., and Raschi, A. 1998. Transpiration and stomatal behaviour of *Quercus ilex* plants during the summer in a Mediterranean carbon dioxide spring. *Plant, Cell and Environment* **21**: 613–622.

Wayne, P.M., Reekie, E.G., and Bazzaz, F.A. 1998. Elevated CO_2 ameliorates birch response to high temperature and frost stress: implications for modeling climate-induced geographic range shifts. *Oecologia* **114**: 335–342.

Wullschleger, S.D., Gunderson, C.A., Hanson, P.J., Wilson. K.B., and Norby, R.J. 2002. Sensitivity of stomatal and canopy conductance to elevated CO_2 concentration—interacting variables and perspectives of scale. *New Phytologist* **153**: 485–496.

Wullschleger, S.D. and Norby, R.J. 2001. Sap velocity and canopy transpiration in a sweetgum stand exposed to free-air CO_2 enrichment (FACE). *New Phytologist* **150**: 489–498.

2.32 Vegetative Storage Proteins

- Atmospheric CO_2 enrichment appears to enhance the between-cuttings savings of vegetative storage proteins (VSPs) in the roots of alfalfa crops, as well as the between-years storage of

VSPs in the leaves of sour orange trees (and possibly other citrus species), giving first flush of foliage a tremendous head start when the next crop's or tree's growing season begins.

Maier *et al.* (2008) described how a soil nitrogen fertilizer application affected upper-canopy needle morphology and gas exchange in 20-meter-tall loblolly pine (*Pinus taeda* L.) trees previously exposed to elevated atmospheric CO_2 concentrations (200 ppm above ambient) for nine years at the Duke Forest FACE facility in Orange County, North Carolina (USA). During the tenth year of exposure to elevated CO_2, there was a strong enhancement (greater than 50%) of light-saturated net photosynthesis across all age classes of needles, and the stimulation was 28% greater in current-year foliage than in one-year-old foliage. In addition, current-year foliage incorporated the added nitrogen into photosynthetic components that increased the photosynthetic capacity of the current-year foliage, but the one-year-old foliage tended to simply store extra nitrogen, which subsequently served as "an important source of nitrogen for the development of current-year foliage" via "efficient retranslocation of nitrogen from senescing one-year-old foliage to developing foliage."

These findings echo those observed several years earlier in sour orange tree (*Citrus aurantium* L.) foliage in an open-top chamber experiment conducted at Phoenix, Arizona (USA) by Idso *et al.* (2001), where half the trees they studied had been grown from the seedling stage for the prior six years in air continuously enriched with an extra 300 ppm of CO_2. In the seventh year of that study, the Arizona researchers identified three putative vegetative storage proteins located within amorphous material in the vacuoles of leaf mesophyll cells that was rerouted, "starting at about day 25 of the new year, into developing foliage on the new branch buds of the CO_2-enriched trees." They speculate this phenomenon may have been "the key that allows the CO_2-enriched trees to temporarily stockpile the unusually large pool of nitrogen that is needed to support the large CO_2-induced increase in new-branch growth that is observed in the spring," citing Idso *et al.* (2000), who previously found 24 days after new-branch emergence in the spring, "the new branches of the CO_2-enriched trees were, on average, 4.4 times more massive than the new branches of the trees growing in ambient air," and "the total new-branch tissue produced on the CO_2-enriched trees to that point in time was over six times greater than that produced on the ambient-treatment trees."

If there is a common mechanism that links the results of the two groups, it could revolve around the hypothesized vacuolar storage proteins Idso *et al.*(2001) identified in the sour orange tree foliage, since they detected immunologically related proteins in a variety of other citrus species, but not in 20 different grasses, shrubs, and trees growing in the Biosphere 2 facility near Oracle, Arizona. This possibility merits further study because if it is found to have merit, Idso *et al.* (2001) further speculate the proteins in question "could possibly be genetically exploited to enhance the responses of other plant species to atmospheric CO_2 enrichment." This could prove to be a valuable property of agriculturally important plants in a high-CO_2 world of the future.

Erice *et al.* (2007) studied 30-day-old nodulated alfalfa (*Medicago sativa* L.) plants grown in two temperature-gradient greenhouses (one maintained at an atmospheric CO_2 concentration of 350 ppm and the other at a concentration of 700 ppm) in pots recessed into the ground in an alfalfa field under conditions of ambient temperature (TA) and elevated temperature (TE = TA + 4°C) and well-watered (to field capacity) and water-stressed (50% field capacity) conditions for one month, after which a first cutting took place, and for one additional month, after which a second cutting took place. After each cutting, the scientists determined plant dry matter production and analyzed taproots for vegetative storage protein contents.

At the time of first cutting, the alfalfa plants had had their dry matter production boosted by an average of about 30% in the well-watered treatment (averaged across both temperature treatments) over the first growth period, but by only about 10% in the water-stressed treatment. At the time of the second cutting, however, the well-watered plants had experienced an average dry matter production increase on the order of 20% over the second growth period, and the plants in the water-stressed treatment displayed a mean increase of fully 40%. In addition, Erice *et al.* report over the first growth period "taproot vegetative storage protein content increased in response to drought and elevated CO_2."

The researchers thus state, "it has been demonstrated that nitrogen pools in alfalfa taproot, especially vegetative storage proteins, condition new regrowing shoots," and that appears to be what happened in their study. At the end of the first growth period, for example, the enhanced taproot vegetative storage protein content in the water-stressed and CO_2-enriched treatment may have been the reason the elevated CO_2 was so effective in stimulating biomass production in the water-stressed treatment over the second growth period.

This finding is somewhat analogous to the observation of Idso *et al.* (2001), who found nitrogen reabsorbed from second-year leaves of sour orange trees (which hold most of their leaves for two years) during the process of senescence in the fall was stored over winter in much greater amounts in putative vegetative storage proteins in first-year leaves of CO_2-enriched trees than in first-year leaves of trees growing in ambient air. When the stored nitrogen was released in the spring to produce a flush of new leaves on the trees, leaf production on the CO_2-enriched trees vastly outpaced the production of new leaves on trees growing in ambient air. Taken together, these observations indicate yet another of the manifold benefits of atmospheric CO_2 enrichment.

References

Erice, G., Irigoyen, J.J., Sanchez-Diaz, M., Avice, J.-C., and Ourry, A. 2007. Effect of drought, elevated CO_2 and temperature on accumulation of N and vegetative storage proteins (VSP) in taproot of nodulated alfalfa before and after cutting. *Plant Science* **172**: 903–912.

Idso, C.D., Idso, S.B., Kimball, B.A., Park, H.-S., Hoober, J.K., and Balling Jr., R.C. 2000. Ultra-enhanced spring branch growth in CO_2-enriched trees: can it alter the phase of the atmosphere's seasonal CO_2 cycle? *Environmental and Experimental Botany* **43**: 91–100.

Idso, K.E., Hoober, J.K., Idso, S.B., Wall, G.W., and Kimball, B.A. 2001. Atmospheric CO_2 enrichment influences the synthesis and mobilization of putative vacuolar storage proteins in sour orange tree leaves. *Environmental and Experimental Botany* **48**: 199–211.

Maier, C.A., Palmroth, S., and Ward, E. 2008. Short-term effects of fertilization on photosynthesis and leaf morphology of field-grown loblolly pine following long-term exposure to elevated CO_2 concentration. *Tree Physiology* **28**: 597–606.

2.33 Water Use Efficiency

As the atmosphere's CO_2 concentration rises, most plants tend to exhibit increased rates of net photosynthesis and biomass production, and on a per-unit-leaf-area basis, plants exposed to elevated CO_2 concentrations are likely to lose less water via transpiration because they tend to exhibit lower stomatal conductances. Therefore, the amount of carbon gained per unit of water lost per unit leaf area—or water use efficiency—should increase significantly as the air's CO_2 content rises. The following three sub-sections present evidence for this phenomenon in agricultural crops, grasslands, and trees.

2.33.1 Agricultural Species

- As the CO_2 content of the air continues to rise, nearly all agricultural plants will respond favorably by exhibiting increases in water use efficiency. It is also thus likely food and fiber production will increase on a worldwide basis, even in areas where productivity is currently severely restricted by limited availability of soil moisture.

Serraj et al. (1999) found soybeans grown at 700 ppm CO_2 displayed 10 to 25% reductions in total water loss while simultaneously exhibiting dry weight increases of as much as 33%. Thus, elevated CO_2 significantly increased the water-use efficiencies of the plants. Likewise, Garcia et al. (1998) determined spring wheat grown at 550 ppm CO_2 exhibited a water use efficiency about one-third greater than that of plants grown at 370 ppm CO_2. Similarly, Hakala et al. (1999) report twice-ambient CO_2 concentrations increased the water use efficiency of spring wheat by 70 to 100%, depending on experimental air temperature. In addition, Hunsaker et al. (2000) report CO_2-induced increases in water use efficiency for field-grown wheat 20 and 10% higher than those displayed by ambiently grown wheat subjected to high and low soil nitrogen regimes, respectively. Also, pea plants grown for two months in growth chambers maintained at CO_2 concentrations of 700 ppm displayed an average water use efficiency 27% greater than that exhibited by ambiently grown control plants (Gavito et al., 2000).

In some cases, the water use efficiency increases caused by atmospheric CO_2 enrichment are spectacularly high. De Luis et al. (1999), for example, demonstrated alfalfa plants subjected to atmospheric CO_2 concentrations of 700 ppm had water-use efficiencies 2.6 and 4.1 times greater than those of control plants growing at 400 ppm CO_2 under water-stressed and well-watered conditions, respectively. Also, when grown at an atmospheric CO_2 concentration of 700 ppm, a 2.7-fold increase in water use efficiency was reported by Malmstrom and Field (1997) for oats infected with the barley yellow dwarf virus.

In addition to enhancing the water-use efficiencies of agricultural C_3 crops, elevated CO_2 also enhances the water-use efficiencies of crops possessing alternate carbon fixation pathways. Maroco et al. (1999), for example, demonstrated maize—a C_4 crop—grown for 30 days at an atmospheric CO_2 concentration of 1,100 ppm exhibited an intrinsic water use efficiency 225% higher than that of plants grown at 350 ppm CO_2. In addition, Conley et al. (2001) report a 200-ppm increase in the air's CO_2 content boosted the water use efficiency of field-grown sorghum by 9 and 19% under well-watered and water-stressed conditions, respectively. Also, Zhu et al. (1999) report pineapple—a CAM plant—grown at 700 ppm CO_2 exhibited water-use efficiencies always significantly greater than those of control plants grown at 350 ppm CO_2 over a wide range of growth temperatures.

Olivo et al. (2002) grew two potato species (Solanum curtilobum cv. Ugro Shiri, from high altitude, and S. tuberosum cv. Baronesa, from low altitude) in pots placed within open-top chambers maintained at atmospheric CO_2 concentrations of 350 and 700 ppm for 30 days following the onset of reproductive growth, to study the effects of elevated CO_2 on gas exchange and biomass production in these two species in the first-ever study of the CO_2 responsiveness of the high-altitude-adapted Solanum curtilobum, which is economically important in the highlands of the South American Andes. The elevated CO_2 treatment increased rates of net photosynthesis by 56 and 53% in the high- and low-altitude potato species, respectively, while reducing their stomatal conductances by 55 and 59% and thereby increasing their water-use efficiencies by 90 and 80%, respectively. Tuber dry mass production was increased by 85 and 40% in the high- and low-altitude potato species, respectively.

Dong-Xiu et al. (2002) grew spring wheat (Triticum aestivum L. cv. Gaoyuan 602) in open-top chambers maintained at atmospheric CO_2 concentrations of 350 and 700 ppm and three levels of soil moisture (40, 60, and 80% of field capacity), to study the interactive effects of these environmental variables on the productivity and growth of this variety of wheat. The elevated CO_2 treatment increased rates of net photosynthesis by 48, 120, and 97% at low, medium, and high soil water capacities, respectively, and it reduced rates of transpiration by 56, 53, and 63% in the same order. These changes led to CO_2-induced increases in plant water use efficiency of approximately 25, 15, and 30% under low, medium, and high soil moisture conditions, respectively.

Agrawal and Deepak (2003) grew two other cultivars of wheat (*Triticum aestivum* L. cv. Malviya 234 and HP1209) in open-top chambers maintained at atmospheric CO_2 concentrations of 350 and 600 ppm alone and in combination with 60 ppb of sulfur dioxide (SO_2), to study the interactive effects of elevated CO_2 and this major air pollutant on the growth and yield of this important crop. They found exposure to elevated CO_2 significantly increased photosynthetic rates by 58 and 48% in M234 and HP1209, respectively, and fumigation with elevated SO_2 did not significantly impact rates of photo-synthesis in either cultivar. However, plants grown in the combined treatment of elevated CO_2 and elevated SO_2 displayed photosynthetic rates significantly less-enhanced to values of 42 and 38% greater than those measured in control plants for M234 and HP1209, respectively.

Of more significance to the topic of this review, however, plants grown in elevated CO_2 also displayed an approximate 20% reduction in stomatal conduct-ance, and those grown in elevated SO_2 exhibited an average increase of 15%. But when exposed simul-taneously to both gases, the plants displayed an average 11% reduction in stomatal conductance, which resulted in a 32% increase in water use efficiency, whereas plants exposed to elevated SO_2 alone displayed an average decrease in water use efficiency of 16%.

Working with a very different type of crop, Kyei-Boahen *et al.* (2003) grew well-watered and well-fertilized plants of four carrot (*Daucus carota* var. sativus L.) cultivars (Cascade, Caro Choice, Oranza, and Red Core Chantenay) from seed in 15-cm-diameter plastic pots in a controlled environment facility for 30 days past emergence. Leaf net photo-synthetic rate (PN), stomatal conductance (Gs), and transpiration rate (E) were then measured at 100-ppm intervals of short-term (five-minute) atmospheric CO_2 enrichment yielding absolute CO_2 concentrations (Ca) stretching from 50 to 1,050 ppm. The five researchers found "an increase in Ca from 50 to 350 ppm produced a 100-fold increase in PN and the value increased by 43% when Ca was elevated from 350 to 650 ppm," but "only [a] 7% increase in PN was observed when Ca was increased from 650 to 1050 ppm."

They also found "increasing Ca from 50 to 350 ppm increased Gs to a maximum and thereafter Gs declined by 17% when Ca was increased to 650 ppm," and "a three-fold increase in Ca from 350 to 1050 ppm decreased Gs by 53%." They further

report, "E reached maximum values (0.9–1.1 mmol m^{-2} s^{-1}) at 350 ppm followed by a decline to 0.40–0.60 mmol m^{-2} s^{-1} when Ca was increased to 1050 ppm." Finally, "water use efficiency increased linearly with Ca due to increases in PN in addition to the decline in E at high Ca," so "increasing Ca from 350 to 650 ppm improved water use efficiency by 76%, whereas a three-fold increase in Ca from 350–1050 ppm resulted in a three-fold increase in water use efficiency" They conclude, "future enrichment in the atmospheric CO_2 may lead to adjustments in PN and Gs, which could improve carrot productivity and water utilization."

Triggs *et al.* (2004) grew sorghum (*Sorghum bicolor* (L.) Moench, a C_4 grain crop) for two full seasons in control CO_2 plots (about 370 ppm) and FACE plots (Control + 200 ppm) under both well-watered (Wet) and water-stressed (Dry, less than half the total water received by the Wet treatment via rainfall and irrigation) conditions near Maricopa, Arizona (USA), assessing evapotranspiration (ET) on a continuous basis by means of micrometeorological measurements designed to allow the calculation of all of the other elements (net radiation, sensible heat flux, and soil surface heat flux) of the energy balance of the crop-soil interface with the atmosphere.

Triggs *et al.* report, "In the Wet treatments, a reduction in ET of about 19%, combined with only a slight increase in total biomass (+4%), resulted in a 28% increase in WUE in elevated CO_2 conditions," and "in the Dry treatments, the relatively large increase in total biomass (+16% for both years) more than compensated for the approximate 5% increase in total ET, giving the FACE-Dry treatments an increase in WUE of 16% over both seasons." Based on these results, Triggs *et al.* conclude, "even if future climate change results in less water available for agriculture, higher atmospheric CO_2 concentrations will still benefit C_4 crops," but they note, "in regions with ample precipitation or irrigation, C_3 crops with higher growth responses may be preferable."

Grant *et al.* (2004) adjusted the crop growth and water relations model *ecosys* to represent sorghum (*Sorghum bicolor* (L.) Moench) and run for two growing seasons (1 May 1998 to 31 October 1999) under both wet and dry irrigation schedules at two atmospheric CO_2 concentrations (approximately 368 and 561 ppm) using hourly meteorological data measured at a field south of Phoenix, Arizona (USA), after which the crop's simulated energy balances and water relations—verified by measurements of energy flux and water potential—were used to infer the effects of free-air atmospheric CO_2 enrichment on various plant parameters and processes.

The 12 researchers write, "model results, corroborated by field measurements, showed that elevated CO_2 raised canopy water potential and lowered latent heat fluxes under high irrigation [both of which responses are beneficial] and delayed water stress under low irrigation [which is also beneficial]," such that the elevated CO_2 "reduced transpiration and hence improved water status of sorghum [and] lowered the vulnerability of sorghum CO_2 fixation to soil or atmospheric water deficits, even when irrigation was high." In applying their reality-tuned model to a scenario where the air's CO_2 content was 50% higher and air temperature was 3°C greater, they calculated that sorghum yields would rise by about 13%, and "current high sorghum yields could be achieved with ~120 mm or ~20% less irrigation water if these rises in temperature and CO_2 were to occur." Their real-world data and their analysis of those data indicate rising atmospheric CO_2 concentrations, even in the face of rising air temperatures, should be good for both sorghum and the people who grow it, in terms of both the higher yields that can be produced under these conditions and the smaller amounts of water required to produce them.

Yoshimoto *et al.* (2005) grew rice (*Oryza sativa* L. cv. Akita-Komachi) from hand-transplanting to harvest (May to September) under normal paddy culture near Shizukuishi, Iwate (Japan) within FACE rings maintained at either ambient or ambient + 200 ppm CO_2 for 24 hours per day. Over this period they measured a number of micrometeorological parameters and plant characteristics that enabled them to calculate both the amount of water lost directly from the paddy-water surface and that lost by plant transpiration, which together with the plant biomass data they obtained at harvest enabled them to calculate total growing-season crop water use efficiency.

Yoshimoto *et al.* determined "elevated CO_2 reduced stomatal conductance by 13% in upper leaves and by 40% in lower leaves at the panicle initiation stage," but the reduction declined thereafter. In addition, "stomata closed more in the elevated CO_2 plot as vapor pressure deficit increased," i.e., during drier conditions. In more common terms, and averaged over the entire growing season, the Japanese researchers determined the total water used by the crop was 268.7 mm in the ambient CO_2 treatment and 246.7 mm in the elevated CO_2 treatment. Combining this CO_2-induced reduction in total evaporative water loss (8.2%) with the CO_2-induced increase in total plant biomass that was observed (9.1%) indicated season-long crop water use efficiency rose by about

19% in response to the approximate 54% increase in atmospheric CO_2 concentration provided by the FACE apparatus. Thus, as world population continues to grow, the increase in rice-crop water use efficiency provided by the concomitant increase in the atmosphere's CO_2 concentration should be a great asset in helping to produce the extra food that will be needed to feed the planet's many newcomers, while sparing some of the precious water that will be needed to slake their thirst.

Kim *et al.* (2006) grew well-watered and fertilized maize (*Zea mays* L. cv. Pioneer 3733) plants from seed to developmental stage R3 (milky ripe stage, 70 days after planting) in sunlit soil-plant-atmosphere research (SPAR) chambers maintained at either 370 (ambient) or 750 (elevated) ppm CO_2 concentrations, while periodically measuring a number of plant physiological parameters. They discovered that at saturating photosynthetically active radiation (PAR, 2000 μmol m^{-2} s^{-1}), rates of leaf net photosynthesis in the elevated CO_2 chambers were only 4% greater than those in the ambient CO_2 chambers. However, upper-canopy leaves grown at elevated CO_2 exhibited reductions in excess of 50% in both leaf stomatal conductance and transpiration, and as a result of these changes, instantaneous leaf water use efficiency was more than doubled in the high-CO_2 treatment. Because of shading within the canopy, and because the difference in stomatal conductance between ambient and elevated CO_2 declines as PAR drops, the CO_2-induced reduction in canopy evapotranspiration was only a little over 20%.

Commenting on their findings, the seven scientists write, "although several previous studies report CO_2 enrichment enhanced the growth of maize under well watered and fertilized conditions," in their study "there was little evidence of increased biomass accumulation." On the other hand, they state the sizable CO_2-induced reduction in canopy evapotranspiration "is comparable to findings from other studies of C_4 plants." Although the maize plants of their study were somewhat anomalous in not undergoing a significant boost in growth in response to atmospheric CO_2 enrichment, their more characteristic transpiration response enabled them to produce their slightly enhanced biomass with a considerably smaller consumption of water than that of the plants growing in ambient air.

Cunniff *et al.* (2008) note, "early agriculture was characterized by sets of primary domesticates or 'founder crops' that were adopted in several independent centers of origin," all at about the same time; and they speculate, "this synchronicity suggests the involvement of a global trigger." Further noting Sage (1995) saw a causal link between this development and the rise in atmospheric CO_2 concentration that followed deglaciation (a jump from about 180 to 270 ppm), they hypothesize the aerial fertilization effect caused by the rise in CO_2 combined with its transpiration-reducing effect led to a large increase in the water use efficiencies of the world's major C_4 founder crops, and this development was the global trigger that launched the agricultural enterprise. To test this hypothesis, they designed "a controlled environment experiment using five modern day representatives of wild C_4 crop progenitors, all 'founder crops' from a variety of independent centers."

The five crops employed in their study were *Setaria viridis* (L.) P. *Beauv, Panicum miliaceum* var. *ruderale* (Kitag.), *Pennisetum violaceum* (Lam.) Rich., *Sorghum arundinaceum* (Desv.), and *Zea mays* subsp. *parviglumis* H.H. Iltis & Doebley. Each was grown individually in 6-cm x 6-cm x 6-cm pots filled with a 1:1 mix of washed sand and vermiculite for 40–50 days within growth chambers maintained at atmospheric CO_2 concentrations of 180, 280, and 380 ppm, characteristic of glacial, post-glacial, and modern times, respectively. The scientists found the "increase in CO_2 from glacial to postglacial levels [180 to 280 ppm] caused a significant gain in vegetative biomass of up to 40%," together with "a reduction in the transpiration rate via decreases in stomatal conductance of ~35%," which led to "a 70% increase in water use efficiency, and a much greater productivity potential in water-limited conditions."

The five researchers conclude, "these key physiological changes could have greatly enhanced the productivity of wild crop progenitors after deglaciation ... improving the productivity and survival of these wild C_4 crop progenitors in early agricultural systems." They note, "the lowered water requirements of C_4 crop progenitors under increased CO_2 would have been particularly beneficial in the arid climatic regions where these plants were domesticated."

For comparative purposes, the researchers also had included one C_3 species in their study—*Hordeum spontaneum* K. Koch—and they report it "showed a near-doubling in biomass compared with [the] 40% increase in the C_4 species under growth treatments equivalent to the postglacial CO_2 rise."

The civilizations of the past, which could not have existed without agriculture, were largely made possible by the increase in the air's CO_2 content that accompanied deglaciation. The peoples of Earth today are likewise indebted to this phenomenon, as well as to the additional 100 ppm of CO_2 the atmosphere has subsequently acquired. The ongoing rise in the air's CO_2 content is likely to play a pivotal role in enabling society to grow the food needed to sustain the still-expanding global population without usurping all the planet's remaining freshwater resources and much of its untapped arable land.

Morison *et al.* (2007) discuss at length the water use challenge, noting "agriculture accounts for 80–90% of all freshwater used by humans," "most of that is in crop production," and "in many areas, this water use is unsustainable." They also note "farmers in many countries are now faced with legislative restrictions on use of water," indicating the Chinese government has "set a target of a reduction of 20% in water use in agriculture by the year 2020," but "if food security for the region is not to be threatened, this must be achieved without a loss in production." How is this global food and water crisis to be overcome?

In their many pages of discussion of the subject, the four UK researchers examine underlying relationships that connect crop carbon uptake, growth, and water loss, noting "much effort is being made to reduce water use by crops and produce 'more crop per drop.'" Some of the topics they examine in the course of this discussion were designed to alter various crop characteristics that might increase their water use efficiency, such as genetic engineering, and others deal with crop management strategies, such as how and when to apply irrigation water. As reported by the studies discussed above, and additional studies discussed below, water use efficiencies driven by increasing levels of atmospheric CO_2 will help address the problem.

Fleisher *et al.* (2008) grew potato (*Solanum tuberosum* cv. Kennebec) plants from "seed tubers" in soil-plant-atmosphere research (SPAR) chambers maintained at daytime atmospheric CO_2 concentrations of either 370 or 740 ppm in a 75/25 mix of coarse sand and vermiculite at well-watered and progressively water-stressed conditions until they were harvested when canopy photosynthetic rates dropped to below 50% of their seasonal peak values, before and after which they measured a variety of plant physical properties and physiological parameters.

They write, "elevated CO_2 plants maintained a higher daily net assimilation rate throughout most of the growing season," and "at moderate and more severe levels of water stress, CO_2 enrichment appeared to encourage shifting of assimilate into tubers as opposed to additional vegetative growth." Hence, "total biomass, yield and water use efficiency increased under elevated CO_2, with the largest percent increases occurring at irrigations that induced the most water stress," and "water use efficiency was nearly doubled under enriched CO_2 when expressed on a tuber fresh weight basis." Overall, "the results indicate that increases in potato gas exchange, dry matter production and yield with elevated CO_2 are consistent at various levels of water stress as compared with ambient CO_2."

Ceusters *et al.* (2008) measured gas exchange and diel metabolite (e.g. malate, soluble sugars, starch) dynamics in the youngest fully expanded leaves of well-watered and well-fertilized CAM bromeliad *Aechmea* 'Maya' plants—a spineless cultivar resulting from a cross between *A. tessmannii* and *A. fasciata*—after exposure of half of the original seven-month-old plants to 700 ppm CO_2 for five more months in one of two controlled-environment compartments of a greenhouse, and the other compartment was maintained at the original atmospheric CO_2 concentration of 380 ppm. They report, "there was a 60% increase in 24-hour carbon gain under elevated CO_2 due to a stimulation of daytime C_3 and C_4 carboxylation," and they note water use efficiency was twofold higher during the night under elevated CO_2 and three- to four-fold higher during the day.

The six scientists state the great increase they observed in plant water use efficiency "could be a major physiological advantage to growth under elevated CO_2 in this CAM bromeliad," and this fact further suggests CAM species should "be considered in an agronomic context as potential sources of biomass production on arid, marginal lands."

Sanchez-Guerrero (2009) grew cucumber plants from seed to maturity in standard perlite bags within climate-controlled greenhouses at Almeria, Spain, and the plants were "fertigated" (fertilized and irrigated) via a nutrient-solution drip system regulated to maintain the same electrical conductivity in the leached solution draining from the perlite bags of each greenhouse. One of the greenhouses was supplied with extra CO_2 during daylight hours (through outlets below each plant) when the greenhouse side vents were closed or when the roof vent was less than 20% of full opening, resulting in a mean daytime concentration of about 450 ppm around the plants, approximately 100 ppm more than the CO_2 concentration around the plants in the other greenhouse.

The total season-long yield of the CO_2-enriched cucumber crop was increased by 19% by the extra 100 ppm of CO_2 supplied to it during daylight hours, and the overall water use efficiency of the CO_2-enriched plants, based on the amount of water supplied to them, was about 40% higher. The five Spanish scientists conclude their study "confirms the potential interest of using moderate CO_2 enrichment strategies in greenhouses located in areas such as the Mediterranean basin, where the agricultural sector is facing scarce and declining water resources, and needs to drastically reduce the contamination due to fertilizer emission to ensure the sustainability of greenhouse production."

Shimono *et al.* (2010) write, "by 2050, the world's population will have increased by about 37%, from the current level of 6.7 billion to an estimated 9.2 billion (UN, 2009), with a corresponding increase in global food demand." They also note "about 0.6 billion Mg of rice is produced annually from an area of 1.5 million km^2, making rice one of the most important crops for supporting human life," especially, as noted by Pritchard and Amthor (2005), since it supplies the planet's human population with an estimated 20% of its energy needs (on a caloric basis) and 14% of its protein requirements (on a weight basis).

The six scientists further note "rice production depends heavily on water availability," stating "irrigated lowlands account for 55% of the total area of harvested rice and typically produce two to three times the crop yield of rice grown under non-irrigated conditions (IRRI, 2002)." And because mankind's demand for ever-greater quantities of water will continue to rise, due to the need to adequately feed the world's growing numbers, they conclude, "efficient use of water will thus be essential for future rice production."

To determine how the ongoing rise in the air's CO_2 content may impact agriculture in this regard, the Japanese researchers conducted a two-year free-air CO_2 enrichment (FACE) study in fields at Shizukuishi, Iwate (Japan) to learn how elevated CO_2 may reduce crop water use via its impact on the leaf stomatal conductances (gs) of three varieties of rice (*Oryza sativa* L.): early maturing Kirara397, intermediate-maturing Akitakomachi, and latest-maturing Hitomebore.

In response to the 53% increase in daytime atmospheric CO_2 concentration employed in their experiments, Shimono *et al.* determined "the reduction in gs due to elevated CO_2 was similar across measurements, averaging around 20% in the morning, 24% around noon and 23% in the afternoon across all growth stages." In addition, "there was no significant CO_2 x cultivar interaction." Therefore, with the concomitant increase in grain yield that results from atmospheric CO_2 enrichment, a continuation of the historical and still-ongoing rise in the air's CO_2 content will play a major role in enabling the world to meet its food needs without having to lay claim to all of the planet's remaining freshwater resources and much of its undeveloped land.

Expanding on this thesis, Fereres *et al.* (2011) write, "forecasts on population growth and economic development indicate that there will be substantial increases in food demand for the forthcoming decades," and as a result, "food security has not only moved to the forefront of agricultural research, but is now perceived as an important topic for more fundamental research," citing numerous items published in *Nature* (2010) and *Science* (2010). They add, "the question of whether there will be enough food in the future should immediately be followed by the question: Will there be enough water to produce sufficient food?" They state, "given the competition for water faced by the agricultural sector, and the uncertainties associated with climate change, improving the efficiency of water use in both rain-fed and irrigated systems is the main avenue to face the challenge."

As to developing new sources of water, or transferring water from one place to another, in order to increase food production where water shortages exist, the three Spanish researchers state such measures have "limited potential in some areas" but are "no longer possible in other world regions." They do note, however, many agriculturalists have significantly increased crop water use efficiency "by reducing water losses (and some of the water consumed in evaporation from soil) through improved agronomy and engineering of irrigation systems." But they lament the fact, as they put it, "science has been much less successful so far in reducing the water consumed in transpiration."

Fortunately, mankind has had a measurable amount of success in this area, albeit unintentionally and unknowingly. The extraction of fossil fuels from the crust of the Earth has provided coal, gas, and oil to fuel the engines of industry, and the carbon dioxide emitted to the air in the combustion process has raised the atmosphere's CO_2 concentration by some 40% since the inception of the Industrial Revolution. That phenomenon has had two major effects on man's production of food: It has increased significantly the leaf photosynthetic rates of crops, and it has reduced significantly their transpiration rates, which has led to

significant increases in leaf water use efficiency, the amount of biomass produced per unit of water transpired in the process.

In spite of these well-documented facts, to quote Morgan *et al.* (2011), "many believe that CO_2-induced reductions in transpiration at the leaf level will be largely offset at the canopy level by increases in leaf area," and "global warming is predicted to induce desiccation in many world regions through increases in evaporative demand."

In a real-world test of these two potentially negative phenomena in a prairie heating and CO_2 enrichment (PHACE) experiment conducted in a native mixed-grass prairie in Wyoming (USA), Morgan *et al.* found the positive effects of elevated CO_2 prevailed, indicating, they write, "in a warmer, CO_2-enriched world, both soil water content and productivity in semi-arid grasslands may be higher than previously expected," providing what Baldocchi (2011) described as "one of the first and best views of how a mixed-grass ecosystem growing in a semi-arid climate will respond to future CO_2 and climatic conditions."

A full decade earlier, Robock *et al.* (2000) had already developed a massive collection of soil moisture data from more than 600 stations spread across a variety of climatic regimes, including the former Soviet Union, China, Mongolia, India, and the United States. In analyzing those observations, they determined, "in contrast to predictions of summer desiccation with increasing temperatures, for the stations with the longest records, summer soil moisture in the top one meter has increased while temperatures have risen."

Allen *et al.* (2011) write, "plants of the C_4 photosynthetic pathway have a CO_2-concentrating mechanism that overcomes limitations of low atmospheric CO_2" and thereby provides them with "a near-saturating photosynthetic capability at current atmospheric CO_2." In this circumstance, they note, "a rise in atmospheric CO_2 will theoretically have a limited direct impact on C_4 photosynthesis." However, "a number of C_4 crop plants express a positive response to elevated growth CO_2, although to a smaller extent compared to C_3 plants," citing the analyses of Kimball (1993) and Poorter *et al.* (1996).

To test plants' reaction to drought stress, the four researchers planted seeds of maize (*Zea mays* L. cv. Saturn Yellow) and grain sorghum (*Sorghum bicolor* L. cv. DeKalb 28E) in pots and grew them for 39 days in sunlit controlled-environment chambers at 360 and 720 ppm CO_2 concentrations. Throughout this period, canopy net photosynthesis and evapotranspiration were measured and summarized daily from 0800 to 1700 hours. Irrigation was withheld from matched pairs of treatments starting 26 days after sowing, and biomass determinations were made at 34 and 39 days after sowing for maize and grain sorghum, respectively.

The four researchers found for both maize and grain sorghum, there was a "maintenance of relatively high canopy photosynthetic rates in the face of decreased transpiration rates [that] resulted in enhanced water use efficiency when these plants were grown at elevated CO_2 of 720 ppm, but not at 360 ppm." Thus they demonstrated "both plants maintained growth better at double-ambient CO_2 than their counterparts at ambient CO_2 in the presence of drought," such that reductions in total above-ground biomass due to drought were 42% for maize and 36% for sorghum at ambient CO_2, but only 18% for maize and 14% for sorghum at double-ambient CO_2. In discussing their findings, Allen *et al.* state they "agree with Leakey (2009) that drought stress in C_4 crop plants can be ameliorated at elevated CO_2 as a result of lower stomatal conductance and sustained intercellular CO_2."

As the CO_2 content of the air continues to rise, nearly all agricultural plants will respond favorably by exhibiting increases in water use efficiency. It is thus likely food and fiber production will increase on a worldwide basis, even in areas where productivity is severely restricted by limited availability of soil moisture. Global agricultural productivity should rise in tandem with future increases in the atmosphere's CO_2 concentration.

References

Agrawal, M. and Deepak, S.S. 2003. Physiological and biochemical responses of two cultivars of wheat to elevated levels of CO_2 and SO_2, singly and in combination. *Environmental Pollution* **121**: 189–197.

Allen Jr., L.H., Kakani, V.G., Vu, J.C.V., and Boote, K.J. 2011. Elevated CO_2 increases water use efficiency by sustaining photosynthesis of water-limited maize and sorghum. *Journal of Plant Physiology* **168**: 1909–1918.

Baldocchi, D. 2011. The grass response. *Nature* **476**: 160–161.

Ceusters, J., Borland, A.M., Londers, E., Verdoodt, V., Godts, C., and de Proft, M.P. 2008. Diel shifts in carboxylation pathway and metabolite dynamics in the CAM Bromeliad *Aechmea* 'Maya' in response to elevated CO_2. *Annals of Botany* **102**: 389–397.

Conley, M.M., Kimball, B.A., Brooks, T.J., Pinter Jr., P.J., Hunsaker, D.J., Wall, G.W., Adams, N.R., LaMorte, R.L., Matthias, A.D., Thompson, T.L., Leavitt, S.W., Ottman, M.J., Cousins, A.B., and Triggs, J.M. 2001. CO_2 enrichment increases water use efficiency in sorghum. *New Phytologist* **151**: 407–412.

Cunniff, J., Osborne, C.P., Ripley, B.S., Charles, M., and Jones, G. 2008. Response of wild C_4 crop progenitors to subambient CO_2 highlights a possible role in the origin of agriculture. *Global Change Biology* **14**: 576–587.

De Luis, J., Irigoyen, J.J., and Sanchez-Diaz, M. 1999. Elevated CO_2 enhances plant growth in droughted N2-fixing alfalfa without improving water stress. *Physiologia Plantarum* **107**: 84–89.

Dong-Xiu, W., Gen-Xuan, W., Yong-Fei, B., Jian-Xiong, L., and Hong-Xu, R. 2002. Response of growth and water use efficiency of spring wheat to whole season CO_2 enrichment and drought. *Acta Botanica Sinica* **44**: 1477–1483.

Fereres, E., Orgaz, F., and Gonzalez-Dugo, V. 2011. Reflections on food security under water scarcity. *Journal of Experimental Botany* **62**: 4079–4086.

Fleisher, D.H., Timlin, D.J., and Reddy, V.R. 2008. Elevated carbon dioxide and water stress effects on potato canopy gas exchange, water use, and productivity. *Agricultural and Forest Meteorology* **148**: 1109–1122.

Garcia, R.L., Long, S.P., Wall, G.W., Osborne, C.P., Kimball, B.A., Nie, G.Y., Pinter Jr., P.J., LaMorte, R.L., and Wechsung, F. 1998. Photosynthesis and conductance of spring-wheat leaves: field response to continuous free-air atmospheric CO_2 enrichment. *Plant, Cell and Environment* **21**: 659–669.

Gavito, M.E., Curtis, P.S., Mikkelsen, T.N.. and Jakobsen, I. 2000. Atmospheric CO_2 and mycorrhiza effects on biomass allocation and nutrient uptake of nodulated pea (*Pisum sativum* L.) plants. *Journal of Experimental Botany* **52**: 1931–1938.

Grant, R.F., Kimball, B.A., Wall, G.W., Triggs, J.M., Brooks, T.J., Pinter Jr., P.J., Conley, M.M., Ottman, M.J., Lamorte, R.L., Leavitt, S.W., Thompson, T.L., and Matthias, A.D. 2004. Modeling elevated carbon dioxide effects on water relations, water use, and growth of irrigated sorghum. *Agronomy Journal* **96**: 1693–1705.

Hakala, K., Helio, R., Tuhkanen, E., and Kaukoranta, T. 1999. Photosynthesis and Rubisco kinetics in spring wheat and meadow fescue under conditions of simulated climate change with elevated CO_2 and increased temperatures. *Agricultural and Food Science in Finland* **8**: 441–457.

Hunsaker, D.J., Kimball. B.A., Pinter Jr., P.J., Wall, G.W., LaMorte, R.L., Adamsen, F.J., Leavitt, S.W., Thompson,

T.L., Matthias, A.D., and Brooks, T.J. 2000. CO_2 enrichment and soil nitrogen effects on wheat evapotranspiration and water use efficiency. *Agricultural and Forest Meteorology* **104**: 85–105.

IRRI (International Rice Research Institute). 2002. *Rice Almanac: Source Book for the Most Important Economic Activity on Earth.* CABI Publishing, Oxnon, United Kingdom.

Kim, S.-H., Sicher, R.C., Bae, H., Gitz, D.C., Baker, J.T., Timlin, D.J., and Reddy, V.R. 2006. Canopy photosynthesis, evapotranspiration, leaf nitrogen, and transcription profiles of maize in response to CO_2 enrichment. *Global Change Biology* **12**: 588–600.

Kimball, B.A. 1993. Effects of elevated CO_2 and climate variables on plants. *Journal of Soil and Water Conservation* **48**: 9–14.

Kyei-Boahen, S., Astatkie, T., Lada, R., Gordon, R., and Caldwell, C. 2003. Gas exchange of carrot leaves in response to elevated CO_2 concentration. *Photosynthetica* **41**: 597–603.

Leakey, A.D.B. 2009. Rising atmospheric carbon dioxide concentration and the future of C_4 crops for food and fuel. *Proceedings of the Royal Society B* **276**: 2333–2343.

Malmstrom, C.M. and Field, C.B. 1997. Virus-induced differences in the response of oat plants to elevated carbon dioxide. *Plant, Cell and Environment* **20**: 178–188.

Maroco, J.P., Edwards, G.E., and Ku, M.S.B. 1999. Photosynthetic acclimation of maize to growth under elevated levels of carbon dioxide. *Planta* **210**: 115–125.

Morgan, J.A., LeCain, D.R., Pendall, E., Blumenthal, D.M., Kimball, B.A., Carrillo, Y., Williams, D.G., Heisler-White, J., Dijkstra, F.A., and West, M. 2011. C_4 grasses prosper as carbon dioxide eliminates desiccation in warmed semi-arid grassland. *Nature* **476**: 202–205.

Morison, J.I.L., Baker, N.R., Mullineaux, P.M., and Davies, W.J. 2007. Improving water use in crop production. *Philosophical Transactions of the Royal Society B* **363**: 639–658.

Nature. 2010. Can science feed the world? http://www.nature.com/news/specials/food/index.html.

Olivo, N., Martinez, C.A., and Oliva, M.A. 2002. The photosynthetic response to elevated CO_2 in high altitude potato species (*Solanum curtilobum*). *Photosynthetica* **40**: 309–313.

Ottman, M.J., Kimball, B.A., Pinter Jr., P.J., Wall, G.W., Vanderlip, R.L., Leavitt, S.W., LaMorte, R.L., Matthias, A.D., and Brooks, T.J. 2001. Elevated CO_2 increases sorghum biomass under drought conditions. *New Phytologist* **150**: 261–273.

Poorter, H., Roumet, C., and Campbell, B.D. 1996. Interspecific variation in the growth response of plants to elevated CO_2: a search for functional types. In: Korner, C. and Bazzaz, F.A. (Eds.) *Carbon Dioxide, Populations, and Communities.* Academic Press, New York, New York, USA, pl 375–412.

Pritchard, S.G. and Amthor, J.S. 2005. *Crops and Environmental Change.* Food Production Press, New York, New York, USA.

Robock, A., Vinnikov, K.Y., Srinivasan, G., Entin, J.K., Hollinger, S.E., Speranskaya, N.A., Liu, S., and Namkhai, A. 2000. The global soil moisture data bank. *Bulletin of the American Meteorological Society* **81**: 1281–1299.

Sage, R.F. 1995. Was low atmospheric CO_2 during the Pleistocene a limiting factor for the origin of agriculture? *Global Change Biology* **1**: 93–106.

Sanchez-Guerrero, M.C., Lorenzo, P., Medrano, E., Baille, A., and Castilla, N. 2009. Effects of EC-based irrigation scheduling and CO_2 enrichment on water use efficiency of a greenhouse cucumber crop. *Agricultural Water Management* **96**: 429–436.

Science. 2010. Food security. http://www.sciencemag.org/site/special/foodsecurity/.

Serraj, R., Allen Jr., L.H., Sinclair, T.R. 1999. Soybean leaf growth and gas exchange response to drought under carbon dioxide enrichment. *Global Change Biology* **5**: 283–291.

Shimono, H., Okada, M., Inoue, M., Nakamura, H., Kobayashi, K., and Hasegawa, T. 2010. Diurnal and seasonal variations in stomatal conductance of rice at elevated atmospheric CO_2 under fully open-air conditions. *Plant, Cell and Environment* **33**: 322–331.

Triggs, J.M., Kimball, B.A., Pinter Jr., P.J., Wall, G.W., Conley, M.M., Brooks, T.J., LaMorte, R.L., Adam, N.R., Ottman, M.J., Matthias, A.D., Leavitt, S.W., and Cerveny, R.S. 2004. Free-air CO_2 enrichment effects on the energy balance and evapotranspiration of sorghum. *Agricultural and Forest Meteorology* **124**: 63–79.

UN (United Nations). 2009. *The 2006 World Population Prospects. The 2008 Revision Population Database.* United Nations, New York, New Your, USA. http://esa.un.org/unpp/.

Yoshimoto, M., Oue, H., and Kobayashi, K. 2005. Energy balance and water use efficiency of rice canopies under free-air CO_2 enrichment. *Agricultural and Forest Meteorology* **133**: 226–246.

Zhu, J., Goldstein, G., and Bartholomew, D.P. 1999. Gas exchange and carbon isotope composition of *Ananas comosus* in response to elevated CO_2 and temperature. *Plant, Cell and Environment* **22**: 999–1007.

2.33.2 Grasslands

- As the air's CO_2 content continues to rise, nearly all of Earth's grassland species likely will experience increases in both productivity and water use efficiency, even if available moisture decreases. The CO_2-induced increases in water use efficiency likely will allow grassland species to expand their ranges into desert areas where they previously could not survive due to lack of sufficient moisture, thereby contributing to a greater "greening of the globe."

As the air's CO_2 content rises, most plants exhibit increased rates of net photosynthesis and biomass production. Moreover, on a per-unit-leaf-area basis, they often lose less water via transpiration, as they tend to display lower stomatal conductances at elevated CO_2. Hence, the amount of carbon gained per unit of water lost per unit leaf area water use efficiency—should increase dramatically as the air's CO_2 content continues to rise. This section summarizes the results of recent studies of this phenomenon in grassland species.

Grunzweig and Korner (2001) grew model grasslands representative of the semi-arid Negev of Israel for five months at atmospheric CO_2 concentrations of 440 and 600 ppm. The grasslands exhibited cumulative water-use efficiencies 17 and 28% greater, respectively, than control communities grown at 280 ppm CO_2. Similarly, Szente et al. (1998) report a doubling of the atmospheric CO_2 concentration increased the water use efficiency two C_3 grasses and two broad-leaved species common to the loess grasslands of Budapest by 72 and 266%, respectively. Leymarie et al. (1999) calculated twice-ambient CO_2 concentrations increased the water use efficiency of the herbaceous weedy species *Arabidopsis thaliana* by 41 and 120% under well-watered and water-stressed conditions, respectively. Other CO_2-induced increases in C_3 plant water use efficiency were documented by Clark et al. (1999) for several New Zealand pasture species and by Roumet et al. (2000) for various Mediterranean herbs.

Elevated CO_2 also has been shown to increase the water use efficiency of C_4 grassland species. Adams et al. (2000), for example, report twice-ambient CO_2 concentrations enhanced the daily water use efficiency of a C_4 tallgrass prairie in Kansas (USA) dominated by *Andropogon gerardii*. LeCain and Morgan (1998) also documented enhanced water-use efficiencies for six C_4 grasses grown with twice-ambient CO_2 concentrations. Seneweera et al. (1998) report a 650-ppm increase in the air's CO_2 content dramatically increased the water use efficiency of the perennial C_4 grass *Panicum coloratum*.

As the air's CO_2 content continues to rise, nearly all of Earth's grassland species—including both C_3 and C_4 plants—likely will experience increases in water use efficiency. The productivity of the world's grasslands also should increase, even if available moisture decreases in certain areas. Such CO_2-induced increases in water use efficiency likely will allow grassland species to expand their ranges into desert areas where they previously could not survive due to lack of sufficient moisture, contributing to a greater "greening of the globe."

References

Adams, N.R., Owensby, C.E., and Ham, J.M. 2000. The effect of CO_2 enrichment on leaf photosynthetic rates and instantaneous water use efficiency of *Andropogon gerardii* in the tallgrass prairie. *Photosynthesis Research* **65**: 121–129.

Clark, H., Newton, P.C.D., and Barker, D.J. 1999. Physiological and morphological responses to elevated CO_2 and a soil moisture deficit of temperate pasture species growing in an established plant community. *Journal of Experimental Botany* **50**: 233–242.

Grunzweig, J.M. and Korner, C. 2001. Growth, water and nitrogen relations in grassland model ecosystems of the semi-arid Negev of Israel exposed to elevated CO_2. *Oecologia* **128**: 251–262.

LeCain, D.R. and Morgan, J.A. 1998. Growth, gas exchange, leaf nitrogen and carbohydrate concentrations in NAD-ME and NADP-ME C4 grasses grown in elevated CO_2. *Physiologia Plantarum* **102**: 297–306.

Leymarie, J., Lasceve, G., and Vavasseur, A. 1999. Elevated CO_2 enhances stomatal responses to osmotic stress and abscisic acid in *Arabidopsis thaliana*. *Plant, Cell and Environment* **22**: 301–308.

Roumet, C., Garnier, E., Suzor, H., Salager, J.-L., and Roy, J. 2000. Short and long-term responses of whole-plant gas exchange to elevated CO_2 in four herbaceous species. *Environmental and Experimental Botany* **43**: 155–169.

Seneweera, S.P., Ghannoum, O., and Conroy, J. 1998. High vapor pressure deficit and low soil water availability enhance shoot growth responses of a C_4 grass (*Panicum coloratum* cv. Bambatsi) to CO_2 enrichment. *Australian Journal of Plant Physiology* **25**: 287–292.

Szente, K., Nagy, Z., and Tuba, Z. 1998. Enhanced water use efficiency in dry loess grassland species grown at elevated air CO_2 concentration. *Photosynthetica* **35**: 637–640.

2.33.3 Trees

- As the air's CO_2 content continues to rise, nearly all the planet's trees will exhibit increases in water use efficiency, enabling them to expand into areas where they previously could not grow due to insufficient available moisture. Earth will gradually acquire a much greener terrestrial cover with a significantly greater carbon sequestering capacity over time.

When the atmosphere's CO_2 concentration is increased, most plants exhibit increased rates of net photosynthesis and biomass production. In addition, they often lose less water via transpiration, as they tend to exhibit lower leaf stomatal conductances. Therefore, the amount of carbon they gain per unit of water lost per unit leaf area—water use efficiency—should increase significantly as the air's CO_2 content rises, as is described in this review of experimental results pertaining to this phenomenon in trees.

The effect of elevated atmospheric CO_2 concentrations on the water use efficiencies of trees is clearly positive, having been documented in numerous single-species studies of longleaf pine (Runion et al., 1999), red oak (Anderson and Tomlinson, 1998), scrub oak (Lodge et al., 2001), silver birch (Rey and Jarvis, 1998), beech (Bucher-Wallin et al., 2000; Egli et al., 1998), sweetgum (Gunderson et al., 2002; Wullschleger and Norby, 2001), and spruce (Roberntz and Stockfors, 1998). In a multispecies study performed by Tjoelker et al. (1998), seedlings of quaking aspen, paper birch, tamarack, black spruce, and jack pine, grown at 580 ppm CO_2 for three months, displayed water use efficiencies 40 to 80% larger than those exhibited by their respective controls grown at 370 ppm CO_2.

Similar results also have been obtained when trees were exposed to different environmental stresses. In a study conducted by Centritto et al. (1999), for example, cherry seedlings grown at twice-ambient levels of atmospheric CO_2 displayed water use efficiencies 50% greater than their ambient controls, regardless of soil moisture status. In the study of Wayne et al. (1998), yellow birch seedlings grown at 800 ppm CO_2 had water use efficiencies 52 and 94% greater than their respective controls when subjected to uncharacteristically low and high air temperature regimes, respectively.

In some parts of the world, perennial woody species have been exposed to elevated atmospheric CO_2 concentrations for decades, due to their proximity to CO_2-emitting springs and vents in the

Earth, allowing scientists to assess the long-term effects of this phenomenon. In Venezuela, for example, the water use efficiency of a common tree exposed to a lifetime atmospheric CO_2 concentration of approximately 1,000 ppm rose twofold and 19-fold during the local wet and dry seasons, respectively (Fernandez et al., 1998). Similarly, Bartak et al. (1999) report 30-year-old *Arbutus unedo* trees growing in central Italy at a lifetime aerial CO_2 concentration around 465 ppm exhibited water use efficiencies 100% greater than control trees growing at a lifetime CO_2 concentration of 355 ppm. Also, two species of oak in central Italy that had been growing for 15 to 25 years at an atmospheric CO_2 concentration ranging from 500 to 1,000 ppm displayed "such marked increases in water use efficiency under elevated CO_2," the scientists who studied them declare, this phenomenon "might be of great importance in Mediterranean environments in the perspective of global climate change." The work of Blaschke et al. (2001) and Tognetti et al. (1998) suggest similar conclusions.

Some scientists also have looked to the past and determined the positive impact the historic rise in the air's CO_2 content already has had on plant water use efficiency. Duquesnay et al. (1998), for example, examined tree-ring data derived from beech trees and found the water use efficiency of such trees in northeastern France increased by about 33% over the past century. Similarly, Feng (1999) used tree-ring chronologies from trees in western North America to calculate a 10 to 25% increase in tree water use efficiency from 1750 to 1970, during which time the atmospheric CO_2 concentration rose by approximately 16%.

Knapp et al. (2001) developed tree-ring chronologies from western juniper stands located in Oregon (USA) for the past century, determining growth recovery from drought was much greater in the latter third of their chronologies (1964–1998) than in the first third (1896–1930). The researchers suggest the greater atmospheric CO_2 concentrations of the latter period allowed the trees to recover more quickly from water stress. Beerling et al. (1998) grew *Gingko* saplings at 350 and 650 ppm CO_2 for three years and found elevated atmospheric CO_2 concentrations reduced leaf stomatal densities to values comparable to those measured on fossilized *Gingko* leaves dating back to the Triassic and Jurassic periods, implying greater water use efficiencies for those times too.

Tognetti et al. (2001) grew five-year-old seedlings of two olive cultivars in pots placed within free-air CO_2 enrichment (FACE) arrays maintained at atmospheric CO_2 concentrations of 360 and 560 ppm for seven to eight months in a study designed to evaluate the effects of elevated CO_2 on gas exchange in this economically important tree species. The elevated CO_2 enhanced rates of net photosynthesis by an average of 38% in both cultivars while reducing stomatal conductances by an average of 30%. Instantaneous water use efficiency rose by approximately 80% in both cultivars, suggesting that as the air's CO_2 content continues to rise, olive trees growing in semi-arid Mediterranean-type climates should be able to cope with recurring drought conditions that are common in such areas.

Centritto *et al.* (2002) grew peach (*Prunus persica*) seedlings at atmospheric CO_2 concentrations of 350 and 700 ppm for one full year in two "growth tunnels," then transferred them to pots and placed them in open-top chambers having the same CO_2 concentrations for an additional three months, during the final four weeks of which half of the seedlings in each CO_2 treatment were allowed to "dry-down." This enabled the three researchers to investigate the interactive effects of elevated CO_2 and water stress on both photosynthesis and growth.

The elevated CO_2 stimulated net photosynthesis rates by about 60% in the well-watered seedlings. Under drought conditions, however, the relative photosynthetic stimulation increased to as much as 180%, ameliorating the negative effect of water stress. In addition, elevated CO_2 increased whole-plant water use efficiency by 51 and 63% in the well-watered and water-stressed seedlings, respectively. Thus, as the air's CO_2 content increases, peach seedlings likely will exhibit increased rates of both net photosynthesis and biomass production. In addition, they likely will be better able to deal with intermittent periods of water shortage without compromising overall productivity and growth. Peach production can be expected to increase as the atmospheric CO_2 concentration continues to rise.

Arneth *et al.* (2002) describe how they developed 20 tree-ring $^{13}C/^{12}C$ chronologies from *Pinus sylvestris* (Scots pine) trees at five locations along a 1,000-km north-south transect running through central Siberia they converted into plant isotopic discrimination ($\delta^{13}Cc$) values. Based on these data, they conclude in 17 of the 20 samples the trees' $\delta^{13}Cc$ had declined during the past 150 years, "particularly so during the second half of the twentieth century." Based on a model of stomatal behavior combined with a process-oriented photosynthesis model, they deduce "this trend indicates a long-term decrease in canopy stomatal conductance, probably in response to increasing atmospheric CO_2 concentrations." They conclude their observations suggest "increased water use efficiency for Scots pine in central Siberia over the last century."

Centritto (2002) grew peach seedlings for two years in pots placed within open-top chambers of either ambient or CO_2-enriched air (350 or 700 ppm, respectively) located inside a glasshouse, where they were continuously maintained at optimum soil fertility and, for the entire first growing season, at optimum soil water availability. In the second growing season, water was withheld from half the seedlings for four weeks.

At the end of the study, there were no CO_2-induced differences in the basal diameters of the seedlings. In terms of total dry weight, however, the elevated CO_2 treatment enhanced the growth of the water-stressed seedlings by 30% and the growth of the well-watered seedlings by 35%, which was largely a consequence of increased height growth. In addition, Centritto found no evidence of any downward acclimation of photosynthesis in the seedlings grown at elevated CO_2, nor was there any downward acclimation in rubisco carboxylation efficiency nor in the maximum RuBP regeneration capacity mediated by electron transport. There were also no significant effects of elevated CO_2 on stomatal conductance in either of the two water treatments. But the CO_2-induced increase in plant growth brought a complementary increase in seedling water use efficiency, even though there was no difference in total water uptake between the two CO_2 treatments. In a world of the future where atmospheric CO_2 concentration is approximately doubled, young peach trees likely will produce about a third more growth on the same amount of water as they did at the turn of the century.

As part of the long-term (November 1987 to January 2005) sour orange tree study conducted at the U.S. Water Conservation Laboratory in Phoenix, Arizona (Idso and Kimball, 2001; Kimball *et al.*, 2007), Leavitt *et al.* (2003) report the results of a multifaceted investigation of a phenomenon never before assessed in this long-term experiment: the effects of a 75% increase in the air's CO_2 content on the efficiency with which well-watered and well-fertilized sour orange trees utilize water. It was based, as the six scientists noted, "on the conceptual framework developed by Farquhar *et al.* (1982), who defined intrinsic water use efficiency (iWUE) as the ratio of the photosynthetic uptake of CO_2 through leaf stomata to the simultaneous transpirational loss of water vapor through the same [stomatal] openings."

This ratio may be experimentally evaluated by measuring stable-carbon isotopes of various plant tissues and the air to which those tissues were exposed during their development. In this study, the plant materials utilized were leaves that had been collected every two months throughout 1992 and on three occasions in 1994–95, plus wood samples extracted five years later from north-south- and east-west-oriented wood cores that passed through the centers of each of the eight trees' trunks at a height of 45 cm above the ground. The average result of these measurements, evaluated within the context described by Farquhar *et al.*, was, as Leavitt *et al.* report, "an 80% increase in [water use efficiency] in response to the [75%] increase in atmospheric CO_2 concentration employed in the study."

This result is interesting for a number of reasons. First, it suggests a doubling of the air's CO_2 content likely would bring more than a doubling of the trees' water use efficiency. Second, as the six scientists note, "this increase in sour orange tree iWUE is identical to the long-term CO_2-induced increase in the trees' production of wood and fruit biomass," as documented by Idso and Kimball (2001), suggesting a doubling of the air's CO_2 content should produce more than a doubling of the trees' total productivity, which further suggests the carbon sequestration potential of land planted to sour orange trees, and perhaps many other tree species, will increase dramatically in a CO_2-enriched world.

Third, Leavitt *et al.* note the CO_2-induced increase in sour orange tree water use efficiency is also identical "to the increase in the mean iWUE reported for 23 groups of naturally occurring trees scattered across western North America that was caused by the historical rise in the air's CO_2 content that occurred between 1800 and 1985," as documented by Feng (1999), who further noted these iWUE trends in trees "are largely caused by the anthropogenic increase of the atmospheric CO_2 concentration," concluding this phenomenon "would have caused natural trees in arid environments to grow more rapidly, acting as a carbon sink for anthropogenic CO_2." In addition, Leavitt *et al.* note "even greater water use efficiency responses have been observed in European tree-ring studies," citing Bert *et al.* (1997) with white fir and Hemming (1998) with beech, oak, and pine trees. With respect to what these observations portend for the decades ahead, Leavitt *et al.* state, "the ongoing rise in the air's CO_2 content could continue to do the same for Earth's trees in the future," dramatically increasing their productivity and the efficiency with which they utilize

water to achieve vastly enhanced growth rates.

As for how general this phenomenon could be expected to be, Saxe *et al.* (1998) determined in a comprehensive review of the scientific literature, "close to a doubling" of the air's CO_2 concentration leads to an approximate 50% increase in the biomass production of angiosperm trees and a 130% increase in the biomass production of coniferous species. With sour orange trees projected to experience just slightly more than a 100% increase in wood and fruit production in response to a doubling of the air's CO_2 concentration, the results of the Phoenix study fall well within the mid-range results typical of most other trees that have been similarly studied.

In light of these many empirical observations, one can confidently expect the growth rates of Earth's trees to increase dramatically as the air's CO_2 content continues to climb; this phenomenon, in turn, should enable them to sequester increasingly greater amounts of carbon. In addition, as the planet's trees become increasingly efficient at utilizing water, one could expect to see them rapidly expand into areas that are currently too dry to support their growth and reproduction, and this phenomenon also should increase the magnitude of carbon sequestration by Earth's trees. Hence, as time progresses, the planet's trees, if not destroyed by mankind's cutting and burning them, should provide an ever-increasing brake upon the rate of rise of the air's CO_2 content.

Waterhouse *et al.* (2004) determined the intrinsic water use efficiency (iWUE) responses of three tree species growing across northern Europe—pedunculate oak (*Quercus robur* L.), common beech (*Fagus sylvatica* L.), and Scots pine (*Pinus sylvestris* L.)—to the increase in the air's CO_2 concentration experienced between 1895 and 1994, using parameters derived from measurements of stable carbon isotope ratios of trunk cellulose. They report, "all species at all the sites show a long-term increase in their values of iWUE during the past century," and "the main cause of this common behavior is likely to be the increase in atmospheric CO_2 concentration."

Linearly extrapolating these responses, which occurred over a period of time when the air's CO_2 concentration rose by approximately 65 ppm, to what would be expected for the more common 300-ppm increase employed in the majority of atmospheric CO_2 enrichment experiments, the iWUE increases they derived amount to +158 ± 14% for the oak trees (mean ± standard error for the five sites studied), +195% for the pine trees, and +220% for the beech trees, as best as can be determined from the graphs of their results. These responses are huge and probably not due to rising CO_2 alone, but to the positive synergism that occurs when the air's CO_2 content and temperature rise together, as these parameters have done over the past century or so.

Peterson and Neofotis (2004) grew velvet mesquite (*Prosopis velutina* Woot.) seedlings for six weeks from their time of planting (as seeds) in small pots within environmentally controlled growth chambers maintained at atmospheric CO_2 concentrations of 380 and 760 ppm and two levels of water availability (high and low). Although they did not see a significant CO_2-induced increase in plant growth, they report by the end of their six-week study there was a highly significant reduction of approximately 41% in the volume of water transpired by *P. velutina* in response to the experimental doubling of the air's CO_2 content. "This large reduction in whole-plant water use," they write, "occurred because the reduction in transpiration per unit leaf area at elevated CO_2 was not offset by a proportional increase in total leaf area."

The two scientists from the Biosphere 2 Center near Oracle, Arizona (USA) state their findings suggest "under a future [high-CO_2] scenario, seedlings may deplete soil moisture at a slower rate than they do currently," and "this could facilitate seedling survival between intermittent rain events," noting their work "corroborates the conclusions of Polley *et al.* (1994, 1999, 2003) that increasing levels of atmospheric CO_2 may facilitate the establishment of mesquite seedlings through a reduction in soil water depletion." Peterson and Neofotis note, "mesquites and other woody species in the semiarid southwestern United States have shown substantial increases in population density and geographic range since Anglo-American settlement of the region approximately 120 years ago," citing Van Auken and Bush (1990), Gibbens *et al.* (1992), Bahre and Shelton (1993), Archer (1995), Boutton *et al.* (1999), Van Auken (2000), Ansley *et al.* (2001), Wilson *et al.* (2001), and Biggs *et al.* (2002).

Saurer *et al.* (2004), measured carbon isotope ratios in the rings of coniferous trees from northern Eurasia—including the three genera *Larix*, *Picea* and *Pinus*—across a longitudinal transect covering the entire super-continent in the latitude range from 59 to 71°N, to determine the change in intrinsic water use efficiency (Wi, the amount of water loss at the needle level per unit of carbon gain) experienced by the trees between the two 30-year periods 1861–1890 and 1961–1990.

They found the "increasing CO_2 in the atmosphere resulted in improved intrinsic water use efficiency," such that "125 out of 126 trees showed increasing Wi from 1861–1890 to 1961–1990, with an average improvement of $19.2 \pm 0.9\%$." The three Swiss scientists state their results suggest the trees they studied "are able to produce the same biomass today [as they did 100 years ago] but with lower costs in terms of transpiration." This finding is highly significant, because some data had indicated recent warming in other longitudinal segments of the same latitude belt "may be accompanied by increased drought stress (Lloyd and Fastie, 2002)." The historical increase in the air's CO_2 content may have been helping those trees better cope with the newly established drought conditions.

Syvertsen and Levy (2005) reviewed what was known about salinity stress in citrus trees and how it may be modified by atmospheric CO_2 enrichment. They note, for example, rapidly growing plants almost always use more water than slower growing plants, and "in citrus, many vigorous rootstocks that produce fast-growing trees also tend to have poor salt tolerance (Castle *et al.*, 1993)," possibly because they accumulate more salt in their tissues because of their greater uptake of water. When growing plants in CO_2-enriched air, however, plant stomatal conductance and water use often are decreased at the same time net photosynthesis and growth are increased, so, "elevated CO_2 almost always leads to higher water use efficiency as it disconnects rapid tree growth from high water use." Consequently, the two scientists explain, "if salt uptake is coupled with water uptake, then leaves grown at elevated CO_2 should have lower salt concentrations than leaves grown at ambient CO_2 (Ball and Munns, 1992)."

"As expected," Syvertsen and Levy write, "all citrus rootstock species studied increased growth and water use efficiency in response to elevated CO_2 that was twice ambient," and generally, but not always, "the salinity-induced accumulation of sodium (Na^+) in leaves was less when seedlings were grown at elevated CO_2 than at ambient CO_2." One exception, where Na^+ accumulation was not affected by elevated CO_2, was Rangpur lime (*Citrus reticulata*); the scientists note this citrus variety is relatively salt-tolerant and another variety of the same species (Cleopatra mandarin) had lower leaf chloride (Cl^-) concentrations in CO_2-enriched air than in ambient air.

All the citrus trees tested to that point in time had exhibited increased growth rates and water use efficiencies when growing in CO_2-enriched air. In addition, they generally experienced less salinity stress than when grown in lower-CO_2 ambient air. As a result, the ongoing rise in the atmosphere's CO_2 concentration bodes well for the future vitality and productivity of the many varieties of citrus trees, which in turn bodes well for humanity.

Hietz *et al.* (2005) collected samples of wood from 37 tropical cedar (*Cedrela odorata* L.) trees that were between 11 and 151 years old in 2001 and from 16 big-leaf mahogany (*Swietenia macrophylla* King) trees that were between 48 and 126 years old at that time, from a rain forest in Aripuana, Brazil. They measured the wood samples' cellulose $\delta^{13}C$ in 10-year growth increments. They found the cellulose $\delta^{13}C$ decreased by 1.3 per mil in *Cedrela* and by 1.1 per mill in *Swietenia* over the past century, with the largest changes occurring during the last 50 years. Based on these data and known trends in atmospheric CO_2 and $\delta^{13}CO_2$, they calculated the intrinsic water use efficiency of the trees increased by 34% in *Cedrela* and by 52% in *Swietenia* over this period, which they state is about the same as what had been deduced from similar measurements of the wood of temperate trees (Freyer, 1979; Bert *et al.*, 1997; Feng, 1999).

The three researchers note, since "water is probably not a strong limiting factor in tropical rain forest trees," the increase in water use efficiency they discovered likely "translates mostly to increased carbon assimilation, which may explain the observed increase in tree growth and turnover (Phillips, 1996; Laurance *et al.*, 2004)" in such forests.

Defining intrinsic water use efficiency (iWUE) as the ratio of the photosynthetic uptake of CO_2 through leaf stomata to the simultaneous transpirational loss of water vapor through the stomata, Liu *et al.* (2007) evaluated this parameter based on $\delta^{13}C$ measurements of cellulose extracted from the wood of tree-ring cores taken from living Qilian juniper (*Sabina przewalskii* Kom.) and Qinghai spruce (*Picea crassifolia* Kom.) trees, focusing on the period AD 1850–2000 at time resolutions of three years for juniper from the semi-arid Qilian Mountains, two years for juniper from the arid Qaidam Basin, and one year for spruce from both of the northwest China sites.

Overall, and based on means for the first and last decades of the study period, the seven Chinese researchers found "the iWUE values of the two species both showed long-term increases, by 33.6 and 37.4% for spruce in the arid and semi-arid areas, respectively, and by increases of 24.7 and 22.5% for juniper," noting "the main cause of this behavior is likely to be an increase in atmospheric CO_2 concentration," which for the start and end decades of

the study period rose from approximately 285 ppm to 362 ppm, about 27%.

Increases in the water use efficiencies of trees in arid and semi-arid regions must be considered a significant benefit. And in the case of the two species studied by Liu *et al.*, they note Qinghai spruce, in particular, "plays an important role in preventing soil erosion, regulating climate, and retaining ecological stability," citing Zhou and Li (1990) in this regard. This phenomenon is undoubtedly one of the chief reasons for the concomitant "greening of the Earth" that has been so evident in many historical studies of China and other parts of Asia.

Leal *et al.* (2008) obtained cores from eight to 20 black pine (*Pinus nigra*) trees growing at each of 28 sites within the Vienna basin of Austria in the European Eastern Alps during the summers of 1996 and 1997, focusing on trees possessing umbrella-like crowns (indicating water-limited conditions) growing on shallow and poor soils, in order to maximize their ring-width response to moisture availability. They discovered "a very clear change in the sensitivity of the growth rate of tree stems to water availability in the late 20th century," noting "trees previously sensitive to spring-summer drought show a lack of response to this climatic parameter in recent decades." Hence, they write, "tree-ring indices were larger in the second half of the 20th century than predicted given prevailing spring-summer drought conditions and the previous sensitivity of growth to these conditions." In addition, they found "a decrease in correspondence between the occurrence of extreme events in precipitation and rate of change of growth," such that "in the second half of the century this correspondence was not significant," and "recent extreme droughts did not result in the formation of very narrow rings, which means the droughts were not as limiting to tree growth as they had been in the past."

The five researchers suggest the greater atmospheric CO_2 concentrations of the latter decades of the twentieth century "induced improved water use efficiency enabling *P. nigra* growing in the Vienna basin to avoid the impact of recurrent dry conditions." This phenomenon also has been observed in many other parts of the world in a number of tree species.

Describing *Araucaria angustifolia* as "an indigenous conifer tree restricted to the southern region of South America that plays a key role in the dynamics of regional ecosystems where forest expansion over grasslands has been observed," Silva *et al.* (2009) studied various types of tree-ring data obtained from *A. angustifolia* trees growing in both forest and grassland sites of southern Brazil. They compared changes in iWUE with historical changes in temperature, precipitation, and atmospheric CO_2 concentration over the past century.

During the past several decades, they write, "iWUE increased over 30% in both habitats [forests and grasslands]," and "this increase was highly correlated with increasing levels of CO_2 in the atmosphere." However, tree growth remained rather stable over this latter period, due to lower-than-normal precipitation and higher-than-normal temperatures, which would normally tend to depress the growth of this species, as Katinas and Crisci (2008) described *A. angustifolia* as being "intolerant of dry seasons and requiring cool temperatures." Therefore, Silva *et al.* conclude, "climatic fluctuations during the past few decades," which normally would be expected to have been deleterious to the growth of *A. angustifolia*, seem to have had their growth-retarding effects "compensated by increases in atmospheric CO_2 and changes [i.e., increases] in iWUE."

Wyckoff and Bowers (2010) note, "with continued increases in global greenhouse gas emissions, climate models predict that, by the end of the 21st century, Minnesota [USA] summer temperature will increase by 4–9°C and summer precipitation will slightly decrease," citing Kling *et al.* (2003) and Christensen *et al.* (2007). They further note certain "forest models and extrapolations from the paleoecological record suggest that, in response to increased temperature and/or drought, forests may retreat to the extreme north-eastern parts of the state," citing Pastor and Post (1998), Hamilton and Johnson (2002), and Galatowitsch *et al.* (2009).

Working with bur oak (*Quercus macrocarpa*) trees, Wyckoff and Bowers explored the likelihood of the latter of these two projections coming to pass by "(i) using tree rings to establish the relationship between drought and *Q. macrocarpa* growth for three sites along Minnesota's prairie-forest border, (ii) calculating the current relationship between growth and mortality for adult *Q. macrocarpa* and (iii) using the distributions of current growth rates for *Q. macracarpa* to predict the susceptibility of current populations to droughts of varying strength." They also looked for "temporal trends in the correlation between *Q. macrocarpa* growth and climate, hypothesizing increases in CO_2 may lead to weaker relationships between drought and tree growth over time," because atmospheric CO_2 enrichment typically leads to increases in plant water use efficiency, which generally makes them less susceptible to the deleterious impact of drought on growth.

The two University of Minnesota researchers discovered "the sensitivity of annual growth rates to drought has steadily declined over time as evidenced by increasing growth residuals and higher growth rates for a given PDSI [Palmer Drought Severity Index] value after 1950 [when the atmosphere's CO_2 concentration rose by 57 ppm from 1950 to 2000] compared with the first half of the century [when the CO_2 increase was only 10 ppm]." Thus, they conclude, "for *Q. macrocarpa*, declining sensitivity of growth to drought translates into lower predicted mortality rates at all sites," and "at one site, declining moisture sensitivity yields a 49% lower predicted mortality from a severe drought (PDSI = -8, on a par with the worst 1930s 'American Dust Bowl' droughts)." Hence, "the decreasing drought sensitivity of established trees may act as a buffer and delay the movement of the prairie-forest ecotone for many decades even in the face of climate change."

Briencn *et al.* (2011) note water use efficiency is the ratio of photosynthesis (A) to transpiration (E), or the amount of carbon gained per unit of water used in the process of acquiring the carbon. They also define A/gs—where gs is stomatal conductance—to be intrinsic water use efficiency (Wi), and state, "an increase in *W*i in response to increasing CO_2 since the industrial revolution has been found in nearly all temperate trees that have been studied," citing Feng (1999), Saurer *et al.* (2004), and Nock *et al.* (2010). They decided to see if this is true also for tropical trees.

Noting "increases in *W*i have been observed in short-term experiments of tree responses to elevated CO_2 (Norby *et al.*, 1999), and over long-time periods using records of $\delta^{13}C$ in tree rings that reflect the global increase in atmospheric CO_2 (Feng, 1999; Waterhouse *et al.*, 2004)," Brienen *et al.* "analyzed carbon isotope ratios over the last 40 years in tree rings of *Mimosa acantholoba*, a tropical dry forest pioneer species," in a study conducted "on the Pacific slope of the isthmus of Tehuantepec, close to the village of Nizanda in the state of Oaxaca, South Mexico (16°39'N, 95°00'W)." The three researchers, representing Austria, Mexico, and the United Kingdom, report the dry-forest tropical *M. acantholoba* trees "responded strongly to the increase in atmospheric CO_2 over the last four decades," as their "*W*i increased dramatically by 40%."

Chen *et al.* (2011) write "Idso (1998) suggested that elevated CO_2 affects plant growth dependent upon plant water status: it has less effect on plants in the well-watered optimal growth phase, but exerts more effect under non-lethal dry conditions, and is most beneficial to plants under severe drought conditions." In a further assessment of this phenomenon, Chen *et al.* measured leaf transpiration rate (E) and net photosynthetic rate (PN) in *Populus euphratica* trees growing just within the northern edge of the Taklimakan Desert in Xinjiang, northwestern China, where the riparian trees dominate the indigenous vegetation because of their tolerance of severe drought and the high salinity and alkalinity of the region's soils. They did so in four locations, where mean soil water contents at groundwater depths of 4.12, 4.74, 5.54, and 7.74 meters were 10.9, 9.5, 3.5, and 1.3%, respectively, making their measurements at atmospheric CO_2 concentrations of either 360 or 720 ppm. They then calculated the trees' water use efficiencies (WUE = PN/E) when measured under the two atmospheric CO_2 concentrations.

In the case of each CO_2 concentration, the researchers found no statistical difference between the leaf water use efficiencies of the first three groundwater depths; but the mean WUE at the higher of the two CO_2 concentrations was 44% greater than the mean measured at the lower CO_2 concentration. The WUE of the lowest and driest of the four groundwater depths was statistically different from the WUEs of the other three groundwater depths, and the mean WUE of the trees growing under this most stressful condition when measured at the higher of the two CO_2 concentrations was 86% greater than the mean measured at the lower CO_2 concentration. Chen *et al.* conclude, with respect to the plant water use efficiency of *Populus euphratica* trees, those growing "under a mild water stress show a weak responsiveness, and those under a moderate drought stress display a strong responsiveness to CO_2 enrichment."

Soule and Knapp (2011) note, "in 2008, atmospheric CO_2 concentrations from the Mauna Loa, Hawaii, Observatory records exceeded 385 ppm, representing a 22% increase since 1959," and "as CO_2 has increased, most tree species have been able to use water more efficiently," as their "leaf stomatal apertures narrow during photosynthesis," resulting in "less transpirational water loss per biomass gained." The two researchers studied changes in and relationships among radial growth rates and the iWUE of ponderosa pine (*Pinus ponderosa*) trees, climate, and atmospheric CO_2 concentration in the western United States since the mid-nineteenth century, developing tree-ring chronologies for eight sites in three climate regions and using carbon isotope data to calculate pentadal values of iWUE. They examined relationships among radial growth, climate,

iWUE, and CO_2 via correlation and regression analyses.

Soule and Knapp report finding significant upward trends in iWUE at all sites, and they state, "despite an absence of climate changes that would favor growth," upward radial growth trends occurred at five sites. In addition, they discovered the highest iWUE values "were recorded in the last pentad at six of eight sites and follow a positive quadratic progression at all sites, suggesting that future increases in iWUE are likely for ponderosa pine within our study regions as CO_2 levels increase." They found "significant improvements in radial growth rates during drought years after 1950," when the air's CO_2 content rose at an accelerating rate.

The two U.S. researchers suggest "increased iWUE associated with rising CO_2 can positively impact tree growth rates in the western United States and are thus an evolving component of forest ecosystem processes." They conclude, "if potential climate changes lead to increasing aridity in the western United States, additional increases in iWUE associated with future increases in CO_2 might ameliorate growth declines associated with drought conditions."

Wang *et al.* (2012) introduce their treatment of the subject by noting iWUE "represents the ratio of photosynthetic assimilation (A) to stomatal conductance (gw)," and "higher iWUE can result from reducing gw, increasing A, or a combination of the two responses." They also state, "empirical evidence from lab studies with a controlled CO_2 concentration and from free-air CO_2 enrichment (FACE) experiments have revealed significantly increased iWUE in response to rising CO_2," as demonstrated by the studies of Luo *et al.* (1996), Ainsworth and Rogers (2007), and Niu *et al.* (2011). They also note "tree-ring stable carbon isotope ratios ($\delta^{13}C$) have proven to be an effective tool for evaluating variations in iWUE around the world," citing Farquhar *et al.* (1989), Saurer *et al.* (2004), Liu *et al.* (2007), and Andreu *et al.* (2011). In addition, they report "during the past 100–200 years, most of the sampled forests demonstrated a trend of increasing iWUE, which paralleled the increasing atmospheric CO_2," citing Peñuelas *et al.* (2011) and references therein.

In November 2009, Wang *et al.* extracted two cores from the trunks of each of 17 dominant living Qinghai spruce (*Picea crassifolia*) trees at a site in the Xinglong Mountains in the eastern part of northwestern China (35°40'N, 104°02'E), obtaining from those cores precise ring-width measurements they used to calculate yearly mean basal area growth increments. They used subsamples of the cores to conduct the stable carbon isotope analyses needed to obtain the $\delta^{13}C$ data required to calculate iWUE over the course of their study period: 1800–2009. By calibrating the $\delta^{13}C$ data against climatic data obtained at the nearest weather station over the period 1954–2009, they were able to extend the histories of major meteorological parameters back to 1800. And by comparing these weather data with the tree growth and water use efficiency data, they were able to interpret the impacts of climate change and atmospheric CO_2 enrichment on spruce tree growth and water use efficiency.

For the arid region of northwestern China in which the spruce trees they studied were growing, Wang *et al.* found iWUE increased by approximately 40% between 1800 and 2009, rising very slowly for the first 150 years but then more rapidly to about 1975, and then faster still until 1998, when it leveled off for the remaining 11 years of the record. Commenting on the main cause of the increasing trend in iWUE from 1800 to 1998, they state it "is likely to be the increase in atmospheric CO_2," because "regression analysis suggested that increasing atmospheric CO_2 explained 83.0% of the variation in iWUE from 1800 to 1998 ($p<0.001$)." Thereafter, they note, a substantial drought at the end of the record is probably what caused the leveling off of iWUE, which was also strong enough to cause a decline in yearly basal area growth increment, much like what occurred between 1923 and 1934, which they describe as "the most severe drought since 1800," citing Fang *et al.* (2009).

Wang *et al.*'s study suggests the historical increase in the air's CO_2 content over the course of the Industrial Revolution gradually but greatly enhanced the intrinsic water use efficiency of Qinghai spruce trees in northwest China, as well as their growth rates. During times of very severe drought stress, even this added help can fall short of what is needed to keep the trees from maintaining an exemplary rate of growth. Rising atmospheric CO_2 concentrations see them through the times of severe stress to where they can once again grow exceedingly well once the drought is past.

Battipaglia *et al.* (2013) combined tree ring analyses with carbon and oxygen isotope measurements made at three free-air CO_2 enrichment (FACE) sites—POP-EUROFACE in Italy, Duke FACE in North Carolina (USA), and ORNL in Tennessee (USA)—"to cover the entire life of the trees," which they accomplished by using $\delta^{13}C$ to assess carbon

isotope discrimination and changes in water use efficiency, while direct CO_2 effects on stomatal conductance were explored using $\delta^{18}O$ as a proxy.

The seven scientists report, "across all the sites, elevated CO_2 increased ^{13}C-derived water use efficiency on average by 73% for *Liquidambar styraciflua* [POP-EUROFACE, +200 ppm CO_2], 77% for *Pinus taeda* [Duke FACE, +200 ppm CO_2] and 75% for *Populus sp.* [ORNL, +153 ppm CO_2], but through different ecophysiological mechanisms." They state their findings provide "a robust means of predicting water use efficiency responses from a variety of tree species exposed to variable environmental conditions over time, and species-specific relationships that can help modeling elevated CO_2 and climate impacts on forest productivity, carbon and water balances."

As the CO_2 content of the air continues to rise, nearly all Earth's trees will respond favorably through increases in water use efficiency. Woody species are likely to expand into areas where they previously could not exist due to limiting amounts of available moisture. One can expect Earth to become a greener biospheric body with greater carbon-sequestering capacity as the air's CO_2 concentration continues to rise.

References

Ainsworth, E.A. and Rogers, A. 2007. The response of photosynthesis and stomatal conductance to rising [CO_2]: mechanisms and environmental interactions. *Plant, Cell and Environment* **30**: 258–270.

Anderson, P.D. and Tomlinson, P.T. 1998. Ontogeny affects response of northern red oak seedlings to elevated CO_2 and water stress. I. Carbon assimilation and biomass production. *New Phytologist* **140**: 477–491.

Andreu, L., Planells, O., Gutierrez, E., Muntan, E., Helle, G., Anchukaitis, K.J., and Schleser, G.H. 2011. Long tree-ring chronologies reveal 20th century increases in water use efficiency but no enhancement of tree growth at five Iberian pine forests. *Global Change Biology* **17**: 2095–2112.

Ansley, R.J., Ben Wu, X., and Kramp, B.A. 2001. Observation: long-term increases in mesquite canopy cover in a north Texas savanna. *Journal of Range Management* **54**: 171–176.

Archer, S. 1995. Tree-grass dynamics in a *Prosopis*-thornscrub savanna parkland: reconstructing the past and predicting the future. *Ecoscience* **2**: 83–99.

Arneth, A., Lloyd, J., Santruckova, H., Bird, M.,

Grigoryev, S., Kalaschnikov, Y.N., Gleixner, G., and Schulze, E.-D. 2002. Response of central Siberian Scots pine to soil water deficit and long-term trends in atmospheric CO_2 concentration. *Global Biogeochemical Cycles* **16**: 10.1029/2000GB001374.

Bahre, C.J. and Shelton, M.L. 1993. Historic vegetation change, mesquite increases, and climate in southeastern Arizona. *Journal of Biogeography* **20**: 489–504.

Ball, M.C. and Munns, R. 1992. Plant responses to salinity under elevated atmospheric concentrations of CO_2. *Australian Journal of Botany* **40**: 515–525.

Bartak, M., Raschi, A., and Tognetti, R. 1999. Photosynthetic characteristics of Sun and shade leaves in the canopy of *Arbutus unedo* L. trees exposed to *in situ* long-term elevated CO_2. *Photosynthetica* **37**: 1–16.

Battipaglia, G., Saurer, M., Cherubini, P., Calfapietra, C., McCarthy, H.R., Norby, R.J., and Cotrufo, M.F. 2013. Elevated CO_2 increases tree-level intrinsic water use efficiency: insights from carbon and oxygen isotope analyses in tree rings across three forest FACE sites. *New Phytologist* **197**: 544–554.

Beerling, D.J., McElwain, J.C., and Osborne, C.P. 1998. Stomatal responses of the 'living fossil' *Ginkgo biloba* L. to changes in atmospheric CO_2 concentrations. *Journal of Experimental Botany* **49**: 1603–1607.

Bert, D., Leavitt, S.W., and Dupouey, J.-L. 1997. Variations in wood $\delta^{13}C$ and water use efficiency of *Abies alba* during the last century. *Ecology* **78**: 1588–1595.

Biggs, T.H., Quade, J., and Webb, R.H. 2002. $\delta^{13}C$ values of soil organic matter in semiarid grassland with mesquite (*Prosopis*) encroachment in southeastern Arizona. *Geoderma* **110**: 109–130.

Blaschke, L., Schulte, M., Raschi, A., Slee, N., Rennenberg, H., and Polle, A. 2001. Photosynthesis, soluble and structural carbon compounds in two Mediterranean oak species (*Quercus pubescens* and *Q. ilex*) after lifetime growth at naturally elevated CO_2 concentrations. *Plant Biology* **3**: 288–298.

Boutton, T.W., Archer, S.R., and Midwood, A.J. 1999. Stable isotopes in ecosystem science: structure, function and dynamics of a subtropical savanna. *Rapid Communications in Mass Spectrometry* **13**: 1263–1277.

Brienen, R.J.W., Wanek, W., and Hietz, P. 2011. Stable carbon isotopes in tree rings indicate improved water use efficiency and drought responses of a tropical dry forest tree species. *Trees* **25**: 103–113.

Bucher-Wallin, I.K., Sonnleitner, M.A., Egli, P., Gunthardt-Goerg, M.S., Tarjan, D., Schulin, R., and Bucher, J.B. 2000. Effects of elevated CO_2, increased nitrogen deposition and soil on evapotranspiration and water use efficiency of spruce-beech model ecosystems. *Phyton* **40**: 49–60.

Castle, W.S., Tucker, D.P.H., Krezdorn, A.H., and Youtsey, C.O. 1993. *Rootstocks for Florida Citrus: Rootstock Selection, the First Step to Success*. University of Florida, Institute of Food and Agricultural Science, Gainesville, Florida, USA.

Centritto, M. 2002. The effects of elevated [CO_2] and water availability on growth and physiology of peach (*Prunus persica*) plants. *Plant Biosystems* **136**: 177–188.

Centritto, M., Lee, H.S.J., and Jarvis, P.G. 1999. Interactive effects of elevated [CO_2] and drought on cherry (*Prunus avium*) seedlings. I. Growth, whole-plant water use efficiency and water loss. *New Phytologist* **141**: 129–140.

Centritto, M., Lucas, M.E., and Jarvis, P.G. 2002. Gas exchange, biomass, whole-plant water use efficiency and water uptake of peach (*Prunus persica*) seedlings in response to elevated carbon dioxide concentration and water availability. *Tree Physiology* **22**: 699–706.

Chen, Y., Chen, Y., Xu, C., and Li, W. 2011. Photosynthesis and water use efficiency of *Populus euphratica* in response to changing groundwater depth and CO_2 concentration. *Environmental Earth Sciences* **62**: 119–125.

Christensen, J.H., Hewitson, B., Bisuioc, A., Chen, A., Gao, X., Held, I., Jones, R., Kolli, R.K., Kwon, W.-T., Laprise, R., Magana-Rueda, V., Mearns, L., Menendez, C.G., Raisanen, J., Rinke, A., Saar, A., and Whetton, P. 2007. Regional climate projections. In: Solomon, S., Qin, D., Manning, M., Chen, Z., Marquis, M., Avery, K.B., Tignor, M., and Miller, H.L. (Eds.) *Climate Change 2007: The Physical Science Basis. Contribution of Working Group I to the Fourth Assessment Report of the Intergovernmental Panel on Climate Change* (Cambridge University Press, Cambridge, UK/New York, New York, USA, pp. 847–940.

Duquesnay, A., Breda, N., Stievenard, M., and Dupouey, J.L. 998. Changes of tree-ring $\delta^{13}C$ and water use efficiency of beech (*Fagus sylvatica* L.) in north-eastern France during the past century. *Plant, Cell and Environment* **21**: 565–572.

Egli, P., Maurer, S., Gunthardt-Goerg, M.S., and Korner, C. 1998. Effects of elevated CO_2 and soil quality on leaf gas exchange and aboveground growth in beech-spruce model ecosystems. *New Phytologist* **140**: 185–196.

Fang, K., Gou, X., Chen, F., Yang, M., Li, J., He, M., Zhang, Y., Tian, Q., and Peng, J. 2009. Drought variations in the eastern part of Northwest China over the past two centuries: evidence from tree rings. *Climate Research* **38**: 129–135.

Farquhar, G.D., Ehleringer, J.R., and Hubick, K.T. 1989.

Carbon isotope discrimination and photosynthesis. *Annual Reviews of Plant Physiology and Plant Molecular Biology* **40**: 503–537.

Farquhar, G.D., O'Leary, M.H., and Baxter, J.A. 1982. On the relationship between carbon isotope discrimination and intercellular carbon dioxide concentration in leaves. *Australian Journal of Plant Physiology* **9**: 121–137.

Feng, X. 1999. Trends in intrinsic water use efficiency of natural trees for the past 100-200 years: A response to atmospheric CO_2 concentration. *Geochimica et Cosmochimica Acta* **63**: 1891–1903.

Fernandez, M.D., Pieters, A., Donoso, C., Tezara, W., Azuke, M., Herrera, C., Rengifo, E., and Herrera, A. 1998. Effects of a natural source of very high CO_2 concentration on the leaf gas exchange, xylem water potential and stomatal characteristics of plants of *Spatiphylum cannifolium* and *Bauhinia multinervia*. *New Phytologist* **138**: 689–697.

Galatowitsch, S., Frelich, L., and Phillips-Mao, L. 2009. Regional climate change adaptation strategies for biodiversity conservation in a mid-continental region of North America. *Biological Conservation* **142**: 2012–2022.

Gibbens, R.P., Beck, R.F., Mcneely, R.P., and Herbel, C.H. 1992. Recent rates of mesquite establishment in the northern Chihuahuan desert. *Journal of Range Management* **45**: 585–588.

Gunderson, C.A., Sholtis, J.D., Wullschleger, S.D., Tissue, D.T., Hanson, P.J., and Norby, R.J. 2002. Environmental and stomatal control of photosynthetic enhancement in the canopy of a sweetgum (*Liquidambar styraciflua* L.) plantation during 3 years of CO_2 enrichment. *Plant, Cell and Environment* **25**: 379–393.

Hamilton, J.D. and Johnson, S. 2002. *Playing with Fire: Climate Change in Minnesota*. Minnesotans for an Energy-Efficient Economy. St Paul, Minnesota, USA.

Hemming, D.L. 1998. Stable Isotopes in Tree Rings: Biosensors of Climate and Atmospheric Carbon-Dioxide Variations. Ph.D. Dissertation. University of Cambridge, Cambridge, UK.

Idso, S.B. 1998. Three phases of plant response to atmospheric CO_2 enrichment. *Plant Physiology* **87**: 5–7.

Idso, S.B. and Kimball, B.A. 2001. CO_2 enrichment of sour orange trees: 13 years and counting. *Environmental and Experimental Botany* **46**: 147–153.

Katinas, L. and Crisci, J.V. 2008. Reconstructing the biogeographical history of two plant genera with different dispersion capabilities. *Journal of Biogeography* **35**: 1374–1384.

Kimball, B.A., Idso, S.B., Johnson, S., and Rillig, M.C. 2007. Seventeen years of carbon dioxide enrichment of sour orange trees: final results. *Global Change Biology* **13**: 2171–2183.

Kling, G.W., Hayhoe, K., Johnson, L.B., Magnuson, J.J., Polasky, S., Robinson, S.K., Shuter, B.J., Wander, M.M., Wuebbles, D.J., and Zak, D.R. 2003. *Confronting Climate Change in the Great Lakes Region: Impacts on our Communities and Ecosystems*. Union of Concerned Scientists and Ecological Society of America, Washington, DC, USA.

Knapp, P.A., Soule, P.T., and Grissino-Mayer, H.D. 2001. Post-drought growth responses of western juniper (*Junipers occidentalis* var. *occidentalis*) in central Oregon. *Geophysical Research Letters* **28**: 2657–2660.

Leal, S., Eamus, D., Grabner, M., Wimmer, R., and Cherubini, P. 2008. Tree rings of *Pinus nigra* from the Vienna basin region (Austria) show evidence of change in climatic sensitivity in the late 20th century. *Canadian Journal of Forest Research* **38**: 744–759.

Leavitt, S.W., Idso, S.B., Kimball, B.A., Burns, J.M., Sinha, A., and Stott, L. 2003. The effect of long-term atmospheric CO_2 enrichment on the intrinsic water use efficiency of sour orange trees. *Chemosphere* **50**: 217–222.

Liu, X., Shao, X., Liang, E., Zhao, L., Chen, T., Qin, D., and Ren J. 2007. Species-dependent responses of juniper and spruce to increasing CO_2 concentration and to climate in semi-arid and arid areas of northwestern China. *Plant Ecology* **193**: 195–209.

Lloyd, A.H. and Fastie, C.L. 2002. Spatial and temporal variability in the growth and climate response of treeline trees in Alaska. *Climatic Change* **52**: 481–509.

Lodge, R.J., Dijkstra, P., Drake, B.G., and Morison, J.I.L. 2001. Stomatal acclimation to increased CO_2 concentration in a Florida scrub oak species *Quercus myrtifolia* Willd. *Plant, Cell and Environment* **24**: 77–88.

Luo, Y., Sims, D.A., Thomas, R.B., Tissue, D.T., and Ball, J.T. 1996. Sensitivity of leaf photosynthesis to CO_2 concentration is an invariant function for C_3 plants: a test with experimental data and global applications. *Global Biogeochemical Cycles* **10**: 209–222.

Niu, S., Xing, X., Zhang, Z., Xia, J., Zhou, X., Song, B., Li, L., and Wan, S. 2011. Water use efficiency in response to climate change: from leaf to ecosystem in a temperate steppe. *Global Change Biology* **17**: 1073–1082.

Nock, C.A., Baker, P.J., Wanek, W., Leis, A., Grabner, M., Bunyavejchewin, S., and Hietz, P. 2010. Long-term increases in intrinsic water use efficiency do not lead to increased stem growth in a tropical monsoon forest in western Thailand. *Global Change Biology* **17**: 1049–1063.

Norby, R.J., Wullschleger, S.D., Gunderson, C.A., Johnson, D.W., and Ceulemans, R. 1999. Tree responses to rising CO_2 in field experiments: implications for the future forest. *Plant, Cell and Environment* **22**: 683–714.

Pastor, J. and Post, W.M. 1988. Response of northern forests to CO_2-induced climate change. *Nature* **334**: 55–58.

Peñuelas, J., Canadell, J.G., and Ogaya, R. 2011. Increased water use efficiency during the 20th century did not translate into enhanced tree growth. *Global Ecology and Biogeography* **20**: 597–608.

Peterson, A.G. and Neofotis, P.G. 2004. A hierarchical analysis of the interactive effects of elevated CO_2 and water availability on the nitrogen and transpiration productivities of velvet mesquite seedlings. *Oecologia* **141**: 629–640.

Polley, H.W., Johnson, H.B., and Mayeux, H.S. 1994. Increasing CO_2: comparative responses of the C_4 grass *Schizachyrium* and grassland invader Prosopis. *Ecology* **75**: 976–988.

Polley, H.W., Johnson, H.B., and Tischler, C.R. 2003. Woody invasion of grasslands: evidence that CO_2 enrichment indirectly promotes establishment of *Prosopis glandulosa*. *Plant Ecology* **164**: 85–94.

Polley, H.W., Tischler, C.R., Johnson, H.B., and Pennington, R.E. 1999. Growth, water relations, and survival of drought-exposed seedlings from six maternal families of honey mesquite (*Prosopis glandulosa*): responses to CO_2 enrichment. *Tree Physiology* **19**: 359–366.

Rey, A. and Jarvis, P.G. 1998. Long-term photosynthetic acclimation to increased atmospheric CO_2 concentration in young birch (*Betula pendula*) trees. *Tree Physiology* **18**: 441–450.

Roberntz, P. and Stockfors, J. 1998. Effects of elevated CO_2 concentration and nutrition on net photosynthesis, stomatal conductance and needle respiration of field-grown Norway spruce trees. *Tree Physiology* **18**: 233–241.

Runion, G.B., Mitchell, R.J., Green, T.H., Prior, S.A., Rogers, H.H., and Gjerstad, D.H. 1999. Longleaf pine photosynthetic response to soil resource availability and elevated atmospheric carbon dioxide. *Journal of Environmental Quality* **28**: 880–887.

Saurer, M., Siegwolf, R.T.W., and Schweingruber, F.H. 2004. Carbon isotope discrimination indicates improving water use efficiency of trees in northern Eurasia over the last 100 years. *Global Change Biology* **10**: 2109–2120.

Saxe, H., Ellsworth, D.S., and Heath, J. 1998. Tree and forest functioning in an enriched CO_2 atmosphere. *New Phytologist* **139**: 395–436.

Silva, L.C.R., Anand, M., Oliveira, J.M., and Pillar, V.D. 2009. Past century changes in *Araucaria angustifolia*

(Bertol.) Kuntze water use efficiency and growth in forest and grassland ecosystems of southern Brazil: implications for forest expansion. *Global Change Biology* **15**: 2387–2396.

Soule, P.T. and Knapp, P.A. 2011. Radial growth and increased water use efficiency for ponderosa pine trees in three regions in the western United States. *The Professional Geographer* **63**: 370–391.

Syvertsen, J. and Levy, Y. 2005. Salinity interactions with other abiotic and biotic stresses in citrus. *HortTechnology* **15**: 100–103.

Tjoelker, M.G., Oleksyn, J., and Reich, P.B. 1998. Seedlings of five boreal tree species differ in acclimation of net photosynthesis to elevated CO_2 and temperature. *Tree Physiology* **18**: 715–726.

Tognetti, R., Johnson, J.D., Michelozzi, M., and Raschi, A. 1998. Response of foliar metabolism in mature trees of *Quercus pubescens* and *Quercus ilex* to long-term elevated CO_2. *Environmental and Experimental Botany* **39**: 233–245.

Tognetti, R., Sebastiani, L., Vitagliano, C., Raschi, A., and Minnocci, A. 2001. Responses of two olive tree (*Olea europaea* L.) cultivars to elevated CO_2 concentration in the field. *Photosynthetica* **39**: 403–410.

Van Auken, O.W. 2000. Shrub invasions of North American semiarid grasslands. *Annual Review of Ecological Systems* **31**: 197–215.

Van Auken, O.W. and Bush, J.K. 1990. Importance of grass density and time of planting on *Prosopis glandulosa* seedling growth. *Southwest Naturalist* **35**: 411–415.

Wang, W., Liu, X., An, W., Xu, G., and Zeng, X. 2012. Increased intrinsic water use efficiency during a period with persistent decreased tree radial growth in northwestern China: Causes and implications. *Forest Ecology and Management* **275**: 14–22.

Waterhouse, J.S., Switsur, V.R., Barker, A.C., Carter, A.H.C., Hemming, D.L., Loader, N.J., and Robertson, I. 2004. Northern European trees show a progressively diminishing response to increasing atmospheric carbon dioxide concentrations. *Quaternary Science Reviews* **23**: 803–810.

Wayne, P.M., Reekie, E.G., and Bazzaz, F.A. 1998. Elevated CO_2 ameliorates birch response to high temperature and frost stress: implications for modeling climate-induced geographic range shifts. *Oecologia* **114**: 335–342.

Wilson, T.B., Webb, R.H., and Thompson, T.L. 2001. *Mechanisms of Range Expansion and Removal of Mesquite in Desert Grasslands of the Southwestern United States*. U.S. Department of Agriculture, Forest Service, Rocky Mountain Research Station.

Wullschleger, S.D. and Norby, R.J. 2001. Sap velocity and canopy transpiration in a sweetgum stand exposed to free-air CO_2 enrichment (FACE). *New Phytologist* **150**: 489–498.

Wyckoff, P.H. and Bowers, R. 2010. Response of the prairie-forest border to climate change: impacts of increasing drought may be mitigated by increasing CO_2. *Journal of Ecology* **98**: 197–208.

Zhou, Y. and Li, S. 1990. *Forestry in China*. Science Press, Beijing, China.

2.34 Wood Density

- Atmospheric CO_2 enrichment tends to increase wood density in both seedlings and mature trees, increasing a number of strength properties of their branches and trunks. Different species of trees may respond somewhat differently to atmospheric CO_2 enrichment, and they can respond with still greater variety under different environmental conditions.

Numerous experiments have demonstrated trees grown in air enriched with CO_2 nearly always sequester more biomass in their trunks and branches than do trees grown in ambient air. Several studies also have looked at the effects of elevated CO_2 on the density of that sequestered biomass, some of which are summarized here.

Rogers *et al.* (1983) observed no difference in the wood density of loblolly pine (*Pinus taeda*) trees grown at 340 and 718 ppm CO_2 for 10 weeks; but they found a 33% CO_2-induced increase in the wood density of sweetgum (*Liquidambar styraciflua*) trees grown at these concentrations for only eight weeks. Doyle (1987) and Telewski and Strain (1987) studied the same two tree species over three growing seasons in air of 350 and 650 ppm CO_2, finding no effect of atmospheric CO_2 enrichment on the stem density of sweetgum, but a mean increase of 9% in the stem density of loblolly pine.

Conroy *et al.* (1990) grew seedlings of two *Pinus radiata* families at 340 and 660 ppm CO_2 for 114 weeks, finding CO_2-induced trunk density increases for the two families of 5.4 and 5.6% when soil phosphorus was less than adequate and increases of 5.6 and 1.2% when it was nonlimiting. In a similar study, Hattenschwiler *et al.* (1996) grew six genotypes of clonally propagated four-year-old Norway spruce (*Picea abies*) for three years at CO_2 concentrations of 280, 420, and 560 ppm at three rates of wet nitrogen deposition. On average, they found wood density was 12% greater in the trees grown at the two higher CO_2 concentrations than in the trees grown at 280 ppm.

Norby *et al.* (1996) grew yellow poplar or "tulip" trees (*Liriodendron tulipifera*) at ambient and ambient plus 300 ppm CO_2 for three years, during which time the wood density of the trees increased by approximately 7%. Tognetti *et al.* (1998) studied two species of oak tree—one deciduous (*Quercus pubescens*) and one evergreen (*Quercus ilex*)—growing in the vicinity of CO_2 springs in central Italy that raised the CO_2 concentration of the surrounding air by approximately 385 ppm. This increase in the air's CO_2 content increased the wood density of the deciduous oaks by 4.2% and that of the evergreen oaks by 6.4%.

Telewski *et al.* (1999) grew loblolly pine trees for four years at ambient and ambient plus 300 ppm CO_2. Wood density determined directly from mass and volume measurements was increased by 15% by the extra CO_2, and average ring density determined by X-ray densitometry was increased by 4.5%.

Beismann *et al.* (2002) grew different genotypes of spruce and beech (*Fagus sylvatica*) seedlings for four years in open-top chambers maintained at atmospheric CO_2 concentrations of 370 and 590 ppm in combination with low and high levels of wet nitrogen application on both rich calcareous and poor acidic soils, to study the effects of these factors on seedling toughness (fracture characteristics) and rigidity (bending characteristics such as modulus of elasticity). They found some genotypes of each species were sensitive to elevated CO_2 while others were not. Similarly, some were responsive to elevated nitrogen deposition, but others were not. Moreover, such responses often were dependent upon soil type. Averaged across all tested genotypes, atmospheric CO_2 enrichment increased wood toughness in spruce seedlings grown on acidic soils by 12 and 18% at low and high levels of nitrogen deposition, respectively. In addition, atmospheric CO_2 enrichment increased this same wood property in spruce seedlings grown on calcareous soils by about 17 and 14% with low and high levels of nitrogen deposition, respectively. In contrast, elevated CO_2 had no significant effects on the mechanical wood properties of beech seedlings, regardless of soil type.

Kilpelainen *et al.* (2003) erected 16 open-top chambers within a 15-year-old stand of Scots pines growing on a nutrient-poor sandy soil of low nitrogen content near the Mekrijarvi Research Station of the University of Joensuu, Finland. Over the next three years they maintained the trees within these chambers in a well-watered condition, while they enriched the air in half of the chambers to a mean daytime CO_2 concentration of approximately 580 ppm and maintained the air in half of each of the two CO_2 treatments at 2°C above ambient. In the ambient temperature treatment the 60% increase in the air's CO_2 concentration significantly increased latewood density by 27% and maximum wood density by 11%. In the elevated-temperature treatment the 60% increase in the air's CO_2 concentration significantly increased latewood density by 25% and maximum wood density by 15%. These changes led to mean overall CO_2-induced wood density increases of 2.8% in the ambient-temperature treatment and 5.6% in the elevated-temperature treatment.

Kostiainen et al. (2004) investigated the effects of elevated CO_2 (doubled concentration: 720 ppm vs. 360 ppm) and elevated nutrient input to soil (described as "heavy fertilization," i.e., "higher than used in forestry in practice") on a number of wood properties of 40-year-old Norway spruce (Picea abies L. Karst.) trees enclosed by open-top chambers for three years. They report previous data from this long-term study "showed fertilization decreased wood density (Makinen et al., 2002)," and in the presence of elevated CO_2, such was still found to be the case in the new study, but only for earlywood density (a mean decrease of 3.8% over the three years of the study). In the case of latewood density, the extra CO_2 supplied to the trees overrode the negative effect of heavy fertilization and increased mean wood density by 4.6%. Moreover, in the treatment where no extra nutrients were supplied to the trees, both earlywood and latewood density were increased by the doubling of the air's CO_2 concentration: by 4.8% in the case of earlywood density and by 2.0% in the case of latewood density. Thus, under normal growing conditions, a doubling of the air's CO_2 concentration likely would increase the wood density of Norway spruce trees by about 2–5%.

Buitenwerf et al. (2012) analyzed changes in woody-plant density at three sites in South African savannas where the normal disturbance regime (fire and herbivores) was kept constant for either 30 or 50 years, noting "if global drivers had significant effects on woody plants, we would expect significant increases in tree densities and biomass over time under the constant disturbance regime."

The four South African scientists report for the more arid savannas they analyzed there was no indication of global drivers promoting an increase in wood density over the period of their study. However, they found wood density tripled in a mesic savanna between the 1970s and 1990s; in another mesic savanna it doubled from the mid-1990s to 2010; and "aerial photograph analysis on adjacent non-cleared areas showed an accompanying 48% increase in woody cover." Buitenwerf et al. say their analysis "has shown significant increase in tree densities and stature that are consistent with global drivers promoting woody thickening." They conclude "the only plausible candidate in the experimental areas is increasing CO_2 since there were no significant temperature or rainfall trends over the last 50 years."

These observations make it clear different species of trees sometimes respond differently to atmospheric CO_2 enrichment, and they respond with still greater variety under different sets of environmental conditions. In general, however, atmospheric CO_2 enrichment tends to increase wood density in both seedlings and mature trees, thereby also increasing strength properties of their branches and trunks.

References

Beismann, H., Schweingruber, F., Speck, T., and Korner, C. 2002. Mechanical properties of spruce and beech wood grown in elevated CO_2. Trees 16: 511–518.

Buitenwerf, R., Bond, W.J., Stevens, N., and Trollope, W.S.W. 2012. Increased tree densities in South African savannas: >50 years of data suggests CO_2 as a driver. Global Change Biology 18: 675–684.

Conroy, J.P., Milham, P.J., Mazur, M., and Barlow, E.W.R. 1990. Growth, dry weight partitioning and wood properties of Pinus radiata D. Don after 2 years of CO_2 enrichment. Plant, Cell and Environment 13: 329–337.

Doyle, T.W. 1987. Seedling response to CO_2 enrichment under stressed and non-stressed conditions. In: Jacoby Jr., G.C. and Hornbeck, J.W. (Eds.) Proceedings of the International Symposium on Ecological Aspects of Tree-Ring Analysis. National Technical Information Service, Springfield, VA, pp. 501–510.

Hattenschwiler, S., Schweingruber, F.H., and Korner, C. 1996. Tree ring responses to elevated CO_2 and increased N deposition in Picea abies. Plant, Cell and Environment 19: 1369–1378.

Kilpelainen A., Peltola, H., Ryyppo, A., Sauvala, K., Laitinen, K., and Kellomaki, S. 2003. Wood properties of Scots pines (Pinus sylvestris) grown at elevated temperature and carbon dioxide concentration. Tree Physiology 23: 889–897.

Kostiainen, K., Kaakinen, S., Saranpaa, P., Sigurdsson, B.D., Linder, S., and Vapaavuori, E. 2004. Effect of elevated [CO_2] on stem wood properties of mature Norway spruce grown at different soil nutrient availability. Global Change Biology 10: 1526–1538.

Makinen, H., Saranpaa, P., and Linder, S. 2002. Wood-density variation of Norway spruce in relation to nutrient optimization and fiber dimensions. *Canadian Journal of Forest Research* **32**: 185–194.

Norby, R.J., Wullschleger, S.D., and Gunderson, C.A. 1996. Tree responses to elevated CO_2 and implications for forests. In: Koch, G.W. and Mooney, H.A. (Eds.) *Carbon Dioxide and Terrestrial Ecosystems*. Academic Press, New York, NY, pp. 1–21.

Rogers, H.H., Bingham, G.E., Cure, J.D., Smith, J.M., and Surano, K.A. 1983. Responses of selected plant species to elevated carbon dioxide in the field. *Journal of Environmental Quality* **12**: 569–574.

Telewski, F.W. and Strain, B.R. 1987. Densitometric and ring width analysis of 3-year-old *Pinus taeda* L. and *Liquidambar styraciflua* L. grown under three levels of CO_2 and two water regimes. In: Jacoby Jr., G.C. and Hornbeck, J.W. (Eds.) *Proceedings of the International Symposium on Ecological Aspects of Tree-Ring Analysis*. National Technical Information Service, Springfield, VA, pp. 494–500.

Telewski, F.W., Swanson, R.T., Strain, B.R., and Burns, J.M. 1999. Wood properties and ring width responses to long-term atmospheric CO_2 enrichment in field-grown loblolly pine (*Pinus taeda* L.). *Plant, Cell and Environment* **22**: 213–219.

Tognetti, R., Johnson, J.D., Michelozzi, M., and Raschi, A. 1998. Response of foliar metabolism in mature trees of *Quercus pubescens* and *Quercus ilex* to long-term elevated CO_2. *Environmental and Experimental Botany* **39**: 233–245.

3

Plants Under Stress

Key Findings

The key findings of this chapter are presented in the bullet points below.

- There is little experimental or real-world evidence to support the suggestion C_3 plants may out-compete C_4 plants and thereby replace them in a high-CO_2 environment. (A C_3 plant is one in which CO_2 is fixed into a compound containing three carbon atoms before entering the Calvin cycle of photosynthesis. A C_4 plant fixes CO_2 into a compound containing four carbon atoms.)

- N-fixing legumes are not likely to out-compete non-N-fixing plants in various ecosystems.

- Future increases in the air's CO_2 content may

313

increase the competitiveness of *non*-weeds over weeds.

- Atmospheric CO_2 enrichment asserts its greatest positive influence on diseased as opposed to healthy plants; it has the ability to significantly ameliorate the deleterious effects of stresses imposed on plants by numerous pathogenic invaders.

- Increases in the air's CO_2 content improve plants' ability to withstand the deleterious effects of heavy metals that may be present in soils at ordinarily toxic levels.

- Rising atmospheric CO_2 concentrations may reduce the frequency and severity of pest outbreaks detrimental to agriculture, while not seriously impacting herbivorous organisms found in natural ecosystems.

- Specific genetic alterations to crops may enable them to better withstand the assaults of insects pests, better bear the consequences of possible future increases in seasonal maximum air temperatures, and take advantage of the positive effects of atmospheric CO_2 enrichment on various plant properties and processes, while elevated CO_2 simultaneously reduces the severity of possible negative effects that could arise from the escape of transplanted genes into the natural environment.

- Data obtained from open experimental systems suggest herbivore damage to trees may decrease in a CO_2-enriched environment. If herbivore damage were to increase, other evidence suggests air of higher CO_2 concentration makes Earth's trees more capable of surviving severe defoliation.

- Higher CO_2 concentrations tend to reduce fluctuating asymmetry in plant leaves, leading to more symmetrical leaves that are less susceptible to attacks by herbivores, because they are under less stress of both genetic and environmental origin than leaves growing in less-CO_2-enriched air.

- Atmospheric CO_2 enrichment can stimulate biomass production in both iron-sufficient and iron-deficient plants, while it increases internal iron (Fe) use efficiency, stimulates root growth, and increases root exudation of Fe-mobilizing

phytosiderophores in sub-apical root zones, thereby increasing the competitiveness of plants with rhizosphere microorganisms such as barley in their quest for this trace element.

- Whether light intensity is high or low, or leaves are sunlit or shaded, when the CO_2 content of the air is increased, so are the various biological processes that lead to plant robustness. Less than optimal light intensities, therefore, do not negate the beneficial effects of atmospheric CO_2 enrichment. In fact, under low light conditions, the benefits of atmospheric CO_2 enrichment on plant growth are often relatively greater than when light conditions are ideal.

- The maximum benefits of elevated levels of atmospheric CO_2 for the growth and grain production of rice and wheat cannot be realized in soils that are highly deficient in nitrogen, but increasing nitrogen concentrations above what is considered adequate may not result in proportional gains in CO_2-induced growth and yield enhancement. Although there are significant exceptions to the rule, many agricultural crops experience increases in net photosynthesis and biomass production even when soil nitrogen concentrations are a limiting factor to growth.

- CO_2-induced stimulations of percent root infection by various fungi are generally greater under lower, rather than higher, soil nitrogen concentrations. This tendency implies elevated CO_2 will enhance fungal-plant interactions to a greater extent when soil nutrition is less-than-optimal for plant growth, which is the common state of most ecosystems not subjected to the fertilization practices typical of intensive agriculture.

- Atmospheric CO_2 enrichment stimulates photosynthesis and biomass production in grasses and grassland species when soil nitrogen avail-ability is high and/or moderate. Where nitrogen availability is low, grasslands given enough time still have the ability to overcome soil nitrogen limitations and produce positive CO_2-induced growth responses.

- Generally speaking, the degree of soil nitrogen availability positively impacts the aerial fertilization effect of atmospheric CO_2 enrichment on the growth of young aspen, pine, spruce, and other young tree species by promoting a greater CO_2-induced growth enhancement in soils of adequate, as opposed to insufficient, nitrogen content.

- Atmospheric CO_2 enrichment typically reduces—and more often than not completely overrides—the negative effects of ozone pollution on the photosynthesis, growth, and yield of essentially all agricultural crops that have been experimentally evaluated.

- Earth's trees, like much of the rest of the biosphere, are better equipped to live long and productive lives in CO_2-enriched air, even when experiencing the generally negative influence of atmospheric ozone pollution.

- Although labeled by the United Nations and the U.S. Environmental Protection Agency as a dangerous air pollutant, not only is CO_2 not a "pollutant," it is actually an anti-pollutant that helps plants overcome the negative effects of real air and soil pollutants and better enables their removal from polluted areas.

- Plants growing in CO_2-enriched air typically respond by increasing their biomass production, even under conditions of low soil phosphorus content, and this effect is especially strong among plants that possess the ability to increase root phosphatase activity.

- Contrary to the claim that low concentrations of soil nitrogen will curtail the ability of the productivity-enhancing effect of rising atmospheric CO_2 concentration to maintain increased plant growth and ecosystem carbon sequestration rates over the long term, real-world data from several multiyear experiments indicate additional CO_2-induced carbon input to the soil stimulates microbial decomposition and thus leads to more available soil nitrogen.

- Extensive experimentation on loblolly pine trees (plus several understory species) at the Duke Forest long-term free-air CO_2 enrichment (FACE) site has conclusively demonstrated the progressive nitrogen limitation hypothesis has been disproven, suggesting the growth-enhancing benefits of atmospheric CO_2 enrichment should continue as the air's CO_2 content rises.

- The buildup of soil salinity from repeated irrigations can produce growth stresses in agricultural plants, but these stresses can be overcome by the rise in the air's CO_2 concentration.

- As the atmosphere's CO_2 content rises, nearly all agricultural crops, grassland plants, and trees will exhibit enhanced rates of photosynthesis and biomass production that will not be diminished by any global warming that might accompany it. If ambient air temperatures rise concurrently, the growth-promoting effects of atmospheric CO_2 enrichment likely will rise even more as Earth gets "greener."

- The rise in the air's CO_2 content is a powerful antidote for the deleterious biological impacts that might be caused by an increase in the flux of UV-B radiation at the surface of Earth due to depletion of the planet's stratospheric ozone layer.

- The rise in the atmosphere's CO_2 content likely will lead to substantial increases in the photosynthetic rates and biomass production of the world's plants, even under stressful conditions imposed by less-than-optimum soil moisture conditions.

- Non-parasitic weeds likely will be no more competitive in high-CO_2 conditions than they are today, and many of them could be a little less competitive. Atmospheric CO_2 enrichment may provide non-weeds with greater protection against weed-induced decreases in productivity, thereby increasing the competitiveness of non-weeds over weeds. And although atmospheric CO_2 enrichment increases the growth of many weeds, the fraction helped is likely not as large as among non-weeds.

- The rising CO_2 content of the air appears to reduce the negative effects of parasitic weed infection, so that infected host plants continue to exhibit positive (but somewhat reduced) growth responses to elevated CO_2.

Introduction

As was discussed in Chapters 1 and 2, the aerial fertilization effect of Earth's rising atmospheric CO_2

concentration is conferring multiple benefits on terrestrial plants and soils. Such benefits are almost universally acknowledged to occur when growing conditions are ideal, but some have countered that under predicted future CO_2-induced global warming, growing conditions for many plants will be less than ideal. Such counteracting forces to growth, they claim, might negate the benefits of atmospheric CO_2 enrichment. The focus of the current chapter, therefore, is to investigate such claims by examining the responses of plants under various stresses to atmospheric CO_2 enrichment.

As demonstrated in the many sections and subsections below, atmospheric CO_2 enrichment has been shown to ameliorate the negative effects of a number of environmental stresses. The growth enhancement produced by an increase in the air's CO_2 concentration is generally greater under stressful and resource-limited conditions than when growing conditions are ideal.

The physical and environmental stresses addressed below include competition from weeds, diseases, herbivory, nitrogen insufficiency, ozone pollution, phosphorus and nitrogen insufficiency, salinity, higher temperatures, drought, and weeds. IPCC predicts many of these stresses can be expected to increase in a warmer world, but (a) this is not what is revealed by the record of the twentieth century, which IPCC claims experienced "unprecedented" global warming, and (b) in nearly every case, CO_2 enrichment is shown experimentally to immunize plants from these stresses or mitigate their consequences. For example, atmospheric CO_2 enrichment typically reduces—and more often than not completely overrides—the negative effects of ozone pollution on the photosynthesis, growth, and yield of essentially all agricultural crops that have been experimentally evaluated. And the buildup of soil salinity from repeated irrigations can produce growth stresses in agricultural plants, but these stresses can be overcome by the rise in the air's CO_2 concentration.

This chapter contains good news for those concerned about mankind's ability to feed a growing population in coming years, an issue addressed in depth in the following chapter. Importantly, none of the models used to forecast the impact of global warming on crops makes any provision for these positive effects of CO_2 enrichment. One can only conclude that this invalidates their overly pessimistic predictions.

3.1 Competition

One of the concerns about rising concentrations of atmospheric CO_2 is that some plants might benefit more than others, resulting in competitive advantages and ecological changes that could be judged as "bad" because of their effects on wildlife or plants that are beneficial to mankind. This section addresses this issue by surveying research on the different effects of atmospheric CO_2 enrichment on C_3 and C_4 plants, nitrogen-fixers and non-nitrogen-fixers, and weeds and crops.

3.1.1 C_3 vs. C_4 Plants

- There is little experimental or real-world evidence from natural systems to support the suggestion C_3 plants may out-compete C_4 plants and thereby replace them in a high-CO_2 environment. (A C_3 plant is one in which CO_2 is fixed into a compound containing three carbon atoms before entering the Calvin cycle of photosynthesis. A C_4 plant fixes CO_2 into a compound containing four carbon atoms.)

C_3 plants typically respond better to atmospheric CO_2 enrichment than do C_4 plants in increasing their rates of photosynthesis and biomass production. Thus it has been suggested rising atmospheric CO_2 concentrations may lead to C_3 plants out-competing C_4 plants and displacing them, thereby decreasing the biodiversity of certain ecosystems. The story is much more complex than suggested by this simple scenario.

Wilson *et al.* (1998) grew 36 species of perennial grass common to tallgrass prairie ecosystems with and without arbuscular mycorrhizal fungi, finding the dry matter production of the C_3 species colonized by the fungi was the same as the non-inoculated C_3 species, but the fungal-colonized C_4 species produced, on average, 85% more dry matter than the non-inoculated C_4 species. This finding is important with respect to the relative responsiveness of C_3 and C_4 plants to atmospheric CO_2 enrichment; elevated levels of atmospheric CO_2 tend to enhance the mycorrhizal colonization of plant roots, which is known to make soil minerals and water more available for plant growth. This CO_2-induced fungal-mediated growth advantage, which Wilson *et al.*'s work suggests is more readily available to C_4 plants than C_3 plants, could counter the inherently greater CO_2-induced biomass response of C_3 plants relative to C_4 plants, leveling the playing field relative to their competition for space in any given ecosystem.

BassiriRad et al. (1998) report elevated CO_2 enhanced the ability of the perennial C_4 grass *Bouteloua eriopoda* to increase its uptake of NO_3^- and PO_4^{3-} considerably more than the perennial C_3 shrubs *Larrea tridentata* and *Prosopis glandulosa*. And in an eight-year study of the effects of twice-ambient atmospheric CO_2 concentrations on a pristine tallgrass prairie in Kansas, Owensby et al. (1999) found the elevated CO_2 concentration did not affect the basal coverage of its C_4 species or their relative contribution to the composition of the ecosystem.

The anti-transpirant effect of atmospheric CO_2 enrichment discussed by Pospisilova and Catsky 1999) is also often more strongly expressed in C_4 plants than in C_3 plants, and it typically allows C_4 plants to better cope with water stress. In a study of the C_3 dicot *Abutilon theophrasti* and the C_4 dicot *Amaranthus retroflexus*, for example, Ward et al. (1999) found *Amaranthus retroflexus* exhibited a greater relative recovery from drought than did the C_3 species. This suggests, they write, "the C_4 species would continue to be more competitive than the C_3 species in regions receiving more frequent and severe droughts."

Morgan et al. (2001) published the results of an open-top chamber study of a native shortgrass steppe ecosystem in Colorado (USA), where they exposed the enclosed ecosystems to atmospheric CO_2 concentrations of 360 and 720 ppm for two six-month growing seasons. In spite of an average air temperature increase of 2.6°C caused by the presence of the open-top chambers, the elevated CO_2 increased above-ground biomass production by an average of 38% in both years of the study, and when 50% of the standing green plant biomass was defoliated to simulate grazing halfway through the growing season, atmospheric CO_2 enrichment still increased above-ground biomass by 36%. The communities enriched with CO_2 also tended to have greater amounts of moisture in their soils than communities exposed to ambient air. This phenomenon likely contributed to the less negative and, therefore, less stressful plant water potentials measured in the CO_2-enriched plants. The elevated CO_2 did not preferentially stimulate the growth of C_3 species over C_4 species in these communities, nor did it significantly alter the percentage composition of C_3 and C_4 species in the shortgrass steppe ecosystem.

This result was very similar to what Wand et al. (1999) found in an extensive review of the scientific literature published between 1980 and 1997.

Analyzing nearly 120 individual responses of C_3 and C_4 grasses to elevated CO_2, they found average photosynthetic enhancements of 33 and 25%, respectively, for C_3 and C_4 plants, along with biomass enhancements of 44 and 33%, respectively, for a doubling of the air's CO_2 concentration. These larger growth responses in the C_4 species suggest "it may be premature to predict that C_4 grass species will lose their competitive advantage over C_3 grass species in elevated CO_2."

Campbell et al. (2000) provided support for that conclusion. They reviewed research conducted between 1994 and 1999 by a worldwide network of 83 scientists associated with the Global Change and Terrestrial Ecosystems (GCTE) Pastures and Rangelands Core Research Project 1, published in more than 165 peer-reviewed scientific journal articles. After analyzing this body of research, the 17 scientists conclude the "growth of C_4 species is about as responsive to CO_2 concentration as [is that of] C_3 species when water supply restricts growth, as is usual in grasslands containing C_4 species." Thus this group of scientists provided no evidence for the suggestion C_3 plants may out-compete C_4 plants and thereby replace them in high-CO_2 conditions.

Derner et al. (2003) studied the effects of atmospheric CO_2 enrichment to 200 ppm above ambient in a FACE experiment conducted in the field at Maricopa, Arizona (USA) in which they evaluated the growth of C_3 cotton (*Gossypium hirsutum* L.) and C_4 sorghum (*Sorghum bicolor* (L.) Moench) in monocultures and low- and high-density mixtures under both optimum and less than optimum soil water conditions. They found no significant CO_2-soil water interactions, and the 14 researchers thus report the plant growth responses to atmospheric CO_2 enrichment as averages of the wet and dry treatment results.

When grown in monoculture for two months, the aboveground biomass of cotton was 85% greater in the CO_2-enriched treatment than in the ambient-air treatment, and the aboveground biomass of sorghum was 2% lower in the CO_2-enriched air than in the ambient air. In the low-density plant mixture, these responses were exacerbated: the aboveground biomass of sorghum was reduced by 14% in the CO_2-enriched air, and cotton was increased by 154%. In the high-density mixture, this trend continued: sorghum biomass was reduced by 16% in the CO_2-enriched air, and cotton was increased by 276%.

When grown in monoculture, C_3 cotton was significantly stimulated by atmospheric CO_2 enrichment, and C_4 sorghum experienced a small growth reduction. When grown in competition with each other, these positive and negative tendencies were both amplified, and more so when the crowding of the plants was greater.

This study merits careful attention. Importantly, soil water status did not impact the growth response of either species to atmospheric CO_2 enrichment, in contradiction of what had been observed in many earlier experiments (Idso and Idso, 1994). In addition, the negative response of sorghum to elevated CO_2 clashes with the results of several other studies of C_4 plants, where double-digit percentage increases in growth had been the rule (Poorter, 1993; Wand *et al.*, 1999). Thus it is necessary to consider still other experimental results.

Zeng *et al.* (2011) note, "among the 18 most harmful weeds in the world, 14 are C_4," and "by contrast, of the 86 plant species that supply most of the world's food, only 5 are C_4 (Patterson and Flint, 1995)." In addition, "studies comparing C_3 crops with C_4 weeds (Wary and Strain, 1987; Patterson *et al.*, 1984; Patterson, 1986; Patterson and Flint, 1990, 1995; Alberto *et al.*, 1996; Fround-Williams, 1996; Ziska, 2000) ... have demonstrated that elevated CO_2 favors the growth and development of C_3 over C_4 species."

Zeng *et al.* grew rice (*Oryza sativa* L., a C_3 crop) in competition with barnyard grass (*Echinochloa crusgalli* L., a C_4 weed) in a standard paddy-field experiment conducted in ambient air and in air enriched with an extra 200 ppm of CO_2 via FACE technology at Xiaoji Village, Yangzhou City in Eastern China over a period of 120 days. The eight Chinese scientists and their Norwegian colleague found the elevated CO_2 significantly enhanced rice biomass (straw +27.3%, ears +37.6%), tillers (+20%), leaf area index (+11.7%), and net assimilation rate (+50.1%), but they note it reduced all but the last of these characteristics of barnyard grass: biomass (straw -43.6%, ears -47.9%), tillers (-46.1%), leaf area index (-27.3%), and net assimilation rate (+14.1%, the only positive result, but much less than the +50.1% of the rice). In addition, "the absolute uptake of C, N, P, K by rice was increased while those of barnyard grass decreased." Zeng *et al.* write, "rising atmospheric CO_2 concentration could alter the competition between rice and barnyard grass in paddy fields in favor of rice."

These studies show there is little experimental or real-world evidence to support the suggestion C_3 plants may out-compete C_4 plants and thereby replace them in a high-CO_2 environment.

References

Alberto, M.P., Ziska, L.H., Cervancia, C.R., and Manalo, P.A. 1996. The influence of increasing carbon dioxide and temperature on competitive interactions between a C_3 crop and a C_4 weed. *Australian Journal of Plant Physiology* **23**: 795–802.

BassiriRad, H., Reynolds, J.F., Virginia, R.A., and Brunelle, M.H. 1998. Growth and root NO_3^- and PO_4^{3-} uptake capacity of three desert species in response to atmospheric CO_2 enrichment. *Australian Journal of Plant Physiology* **24**: 353–358.

Campbell, B.D., Stafford Smith, D.M., Ash, A.J., Fuhrer, J., Gifford, R.M., Hiernaux, P., Howden, S.M., Jones, M.B., Ludwig, J.A., Manderscheid, R., Morgan, J.A., Newton, P.C.D., Nosberger, J., Owensby, C.E., Soussana, J.F., Tuba, Z., and ZuoZhong, C. 2000. A synthesis of recent global change research on pasture and rangeland production: reduced uncertainties and their management implications. *Agriculture, Ecosystems and Environment* **82**: 39–55.

Derner, J.D., Johnson, H.B., Kimball, B.A., Pinter Jr., P.J., Polley, H.W., Tischler, C.R., Bouttons, T.W., LaMorte, R.L., Wall, G.W., Adam, N.R., Leavitt, S.W., Ottman, M.J., Matthias, A.D., and Brooks, T.J. 2003. Above- and below-ground responses of C_3-C_4 species mixtures to elevated CO_2 and soil water availability. *Global Change Biology* **9**: 452–460.

Fround-Williams, R.J. 1996. Weeds and climate change: Implications for their ecology and control. *Aspects of Applied Biology* **45**: 187–196.

Idso, K.E. and Idso, S.B. 1994. Plant responses to atmospheric CO_2 enrichment in the face of environmental constraints: a review of the past 10 years' research. *Agricultural and Forest Meteorology* **69**: 153–203.

Morgan, J.A., Lecain, D.R., Mosier, A.R., and Milchunas, D.G. 2001. Elevated CO_2 enhances water relations and productivity and affects gas exchange in C_3 and C_4 grasses of the Colorado shortgrass steppe. *Global Change Biology* **7**: 451–466.

Owensby, C.E., Ham, J.M., Knapp, A.K., and Auen, L.M. 1999. Biomass production and species composition change in a tallgrass prairie ecosystem after long-term exposure to elevated atmospheric CO_2. *Global Change Biology* **5**: 497–506.

Patterson, D.T. 1986. Response of soybean (*Glycine max*) and three C_4 grass weeds to CO_2 enrichment during drought. *Weed Science* **34**: 203–210.

Patterson, D.T. and Flint, E.P. 1990. Implications of increasing carbon dioxide and climate change for plant communities and competition in natural ecosystems. In:

Kimball, B.A. (Ed.) *Impact of Carbon Dioxide, Trace Gases and Climate Change on Global Agriculture.* American Society of Agronomy Special Publication 53. American Society of Agronomy, Madison, Wisconsin, USA, pp. 83–110.

Patterson, D.T. and Flint, E.P. 1995. Effect of environmental stress on weed/crop interactions. *Weed Science* **43**: 483–490.

Patterson, D.T., Flint, E.P., and Beyers, J.L. 1984. Effects of CO_2 enrichment on competition between a C_4 weed and a C_3 crop. *Weed Science* **32**: 101–105.

Poorter, H. 1993. Interspecific variation in the growth response of plants to an elevated ambient CO_2 concentration. *Vegetatio* **104/105**: 77–97.

Pospisilova, J. and Catsky, J. 1999. Development of water stress under increased atmospheric CO_2 concentration. *Biologia Plantarum* **42**: 1–24.

Wand, S.J.E., Midgley, G.F., Jones, M.H., and Curtis, P.S. 1999. Responses of wild C_4 and C_3 grass (Poaceae) species to elevated atmospheric CO_2 concentration: a meta-analytic test of current theories and perceptions. *Global Change Biology* **5**: 723–741.

Ward, J.K., Tissue, D.T., Thomas, R.B., and Strain, B.R. 1999. Comparative responses of model C_3 and C_4 plants to drought in low and elevated CO_2. *Global Change Biology* **5**: 857–867.

Wary, S.M. and Strain, B.R. 1987. Competition in old-field perennials under CO_2 enrichment. *Functional Ecology* **1**: 145–149.

Wilson, G.W.T. and Hartnett, D.C. 1998. Interspecific variation in plant responses to mycorrhizal colonization in tallgrass prairie. *American Journal of Botany* **85**: 1732–1738.

Zeng, Q., Liu, B., Gilna, B., Zhang, Y., Zhu, C., Ma, H., Pang, J., Chen, G., and Zhu, J. 2011. Elevated CO_2 effects on nutrient competition between a C_3 crop (*Oryza sativa* L.) and a C_4 weed (*Echinochloa crusgalli* L.). *Nutrient Cycling in Agroecosystems* **89**: 93–104.

Ziska, L.H. 2000. The impact of elevated CO_2 on yield loss from a C_3 and C_4 weed in field-grown soybean. *Global Change Biology* **6**: 899–905.

3.1.2 N-Fixers vs. Non-N-Fixers

- N-fixing legumes are not likely to out-compete non-N-fixing plants in various ecosystems.

This section investigates the concern nitrogen-fixing (N-fixing) plants might benefit more from atmospheric CO_2 enrichment than non-N-fixers and thus obtain a competitive advantage that could lead to some non-N-fixers being excluded from certain plant communities, thereby decreasing the biodiversity of those ecosystems.

In a two-year glasshouse study of simulated low-fertility ecosystems composed of grassland species common to Switzerland, Stocklin and Korner (1999) found atmospheric CO_2 enrichment gave nitrogen-fixing legumes an initial competitive advantage over non-N-fixers. However, it would be expected that over time a portion of the extra nitrogen fixed by these legumes would become available to neighboring non-N-fixing species, which would be able to use it to their own advantage, thereby preserving the species richness of the ecosystem over time. Thus, in a four-year study of an established (non-simulated) high grassland ecosystem located in the Swiss Alps, Arnone (1999) found no difference between the growth responses of N-fixing and non-N-fixing species to elevated levels of atmospheric CO_2.

In a study of mixed plantings of the grass *Lolium perenne* and the legume *Medicago sativa*, Matthies and Egli (1999) found elevated CO_2 did not influence competition between the two plants, either directly or indirectly via its effects on the root hemi-parasite *Rhinanthus alectorolophus*. And in a study of mixed plantings of two grasses and two legumes, Navas *et al.* (1999) observed plant responses to atmospheric CO_2 enrichment are more dependent on neighboring plant density than on neighboring plant identity.

The few studies of this question that have been conducted to date do not suggest N-fixing legumes will out-compete non-N-fixing plants in a world with higher CO_2 concentrations in the air.

References

Arnone III, J.A. 1999. Symbiotic N_2 fixation in a high Alpine grassland: effects of four growing seasons of elevated CO_2. *Functional Ecology* **13**: 383–387.

Matthies, D. and Egli, P. 1999. Response of a root hemiparasite to elevated CO_2 depends on host type and soil nutrients. *Oecologia* **120**: 156–161.

Navas, M.-L., Garnier, E., Austin, M.P., and Gifford, R.M. 1999. Effect of competition on the responses of grasses and legumes to elevated atmospheric CO_2 along a nitrogen gradient: differences between isolated plants, monocultures and multi-species mixtures. *New Phytologist* **143**: 323–331.

Stocklin, J. and Korner, C. 1999. Interactive effects of

elevated CO_2, P availability and legume presence on calcareous grassland: results of a glasshouse experiment. *Functional Ecology* **13**: 200–209.

3.1.3 Weeds vs. Non-Weeds

- Future increases in the air's CO_2 content may increase the competitiveness of non-weeds over weeds.

Elevated CO_2 typically stimulates the growth of nearly all plant species in monoculture, including those deemed undesirable by humans, i.e., weeds. Consequently, it is important to determine how future increases in the air's CO_2 content may influence relationships between weeds and non-weeds when they grow competitively in mixed-species stands.

Dukes (2002) grew model serpentine grasslands common to California (USA) in competition with the invasive forb *Centaurea solstitiali*s at atmospheric CO_2 concentrations of 350 and 700 ppm for one year. They found elevated CO_2 increased the biomass proportion of this weedy species in the community by a mere 1.2%, while total community biomass increased by 28%. Similarly, Gavazzi *et al.* (2000) grew loblolly pine seedlings for four months in competition with both C_3 and C_4 weeds at atmospheric CO_2 concentrations of 260 and 660 ppm, finding elevated CO_2 increased pine biomass by 22% while eliciting no response from either type of weed.

In a study of pasture ecosystems near Montreal, Canada, Taylor and Potvin (1997) found elevated CO_2 concentrations did not influence the number of native species returning after their removal (to simulate disturbance), even in the face of the introduced presence of the C_3 weed *Chenopodium album*, which normally competes quite effectively with several slower-growing crops in ambient air. Atmospheric CO_2 enrichment did not impact the growth of this weed in any measurable way.

Ziska *et al.* (1999) also studied the C_3 weed *C. album*, along with the C_4 weed *Amaranthus retroflexus*, in glasshouses maintained at atmospheric CO_2 concentrations of 360 and 720 ppm. They determined elevated CO_2 significantly increased the photosynthetic rate and total dry weight of the C_3 weed but had no effect on the C_4 weed. The growth response of the C_3 weed to a doubling of the air's CO_2 content was approximately 51%, about the same as the average 52% growth response tabulated by Idso (1992) and that obtained by Poorter (1993) for rapidly

growing wild C_3 species (54%). This finding suggests there is no enhanced dominance of the C_3 weed over other C_3 plants in a CO_2-enriched environment.

Wayne *et al.* (1999) studied another agricultural weed, field mustard (*Brassica kaber*), which was sown in pots at six densities, placed in atmospheric CO_2 concentrations of 350 and 700 ppm, and sequentially harvested during the growing season. Early in stand development, elevated CO_2 increased above-ground weed biomass in a density-dependent manner, with the greatest stimulation, 141%, occurring at the lowest density (corresponding to 20 plants per square meter) and the smallest stimulation, 59%, occurring at the highest density (corresponding to 652 plants per square meter). As stands matured, the density-dependence of the CO_2-induced growth response disappeared and CO_2-enriched plants exhibited an average above-ground biomass 34% greater than ambient-grown plants across a broad range of plant densities. This final growth stimulation was similar to most other herbaceous plants exposed to atmospheric CO_2 enrichment (30 to 50% biomass increases for a doubling of the air's CO_2 content), once again providing evidence atmospheric CO_2 enrichment confers no undue advantage on weeds at the expense of other plants.

In a study of a weed that affects both plants and animals, Caporn *et al.* (1999) grew bracken (*Pteridium aquilinum*)—which poses a serious weed problem and potential threat to human health in the United Kingdom and other regions—for 19 months in controlled-environment chambers maintained at atmospheric CO_2 concentrations of 370 and 570 ppm and normal or high levels of soil fertility. They found the high CO_2 treatment consistently increased rates of net photosynthesis by 30 to 70%, depending on soil fertility and time of year. However, the elevated CO_2 did not increase total plant dry mass or the dry mass of any plant organ, including rhizomes, roots, and fronds. The only significant effect of elevated CO_2 on bracken growth was observed in the normal nutrient regime, where elevated CO_2 reduced mean frond area.

In a study involving two parasitic species (*Striga hermonthica* and *Striga asiatica*), Watling and Press (1997) reported total parasitic biomass per host plant at an atmospheric CO_2 concentration of 700 ppm was 65% less than in ambient air. And in a related study, Dale and Press (1999) observed the presence of a parasitic plant (*Orobanche minor*) reduced its host's biomass by 47% in ambient air of 360 ppm CO_2 but by only 20% in air of 550 ppm CO_2.

These studies suggest, contrary to what IPCC has

claimed, the rise in the air's CO_2 content will not favor the growth of weedy species over crops and native plants. In fact, it may provide non-weeds greater protection against weed-induced decreases in their productivity and growth.

References

Caporn, S.J.M., Brooks, A.L., Press, M.C., and Lee, J.A. 1999. Effects of long-term exposure to elevated CO_2 and increased nutrient supply on bracken (*Pteridium aquilinum*). *Functional Ecology* **13**: 107–115.

Dale, H. and Press, M.C. 1999. Elevated atmospheric CO_2 influences the interaction between the parasitic angiosperm *Orobanche minor* and its host *Trifolium repens*. *New Phytologist* **140**: 65–73.

Dukes, J.S. 2002. Comparison of the effect of elevated CO_2 on an invasive species (*Centaurea solstitialis*) in monoculture and community settings. *Plant Ecology* **160**: 225–234.

Gavazzi, M., Seiler, J., Aust, W., and Zedaker, S. 2000. The influence of elevated carbon dioxide and water availability on herbaceous weed development and growth of transplanted loblolly pine (*Pinus taeda*). *Environmental and Experimental Botany* **44**: 185–194.

Idso, K.E. 1992. Plant responses to rising levels of carbon dioxide: a compilation and analysis of the results of a decade of international research into the direct biological effects of atmospheric CO_2 enrichment. *Climatological Publications Scientific Paper #23*, Office of Climatology, Arizona State University, Tempe, AZ.

Poorter, H. 1993. Interspecific variation in the growth response of plants to an elevated and ambient CO_2 concentration. *Vegetatio* **104/105**: 77–97.

Taylor, K. and Potvin, C. 1997. Understanding the long-term effect of CO_2 enrichment on a pasture: the importance of disturbance. *Canadian Journal of Botany* **75**: 1621–1627.

Watling, J.R. and Press, M.C. 1997. How is the relationship between the C_4 cereal *Sorghum bicolor* and the C_3 root hemi-parasites *Striga hermonthica* and *Striga asiatica* affected by elevated CO_2? *Plant, Cell and Environment* **20**: 1292–1300.

Wayne, P.M., Carnelli, A.L., Connolly, J., and Bazzaz, F.A. 1999. The density dependence of plant responses to elevated CO_2. *Journal of Ecology* **87**: 183–192.

Ziska, L.H., Teasdale, J.R., and Bunce, J.A. 1999. Future atmospheric carbon dioxide may increase tolerance to glyphosate. *Weed Science* **47**: 608–615.

3.2 Disease

3.2.1 Legumes

- Atmospheric CO_2 enrichment can ameliorate the deleterious effects of various stresses imposed on legumes by numerous pathogenic invaders, providing reason to conclude plants will gain the advantage as the air's CO_2 content rises in the future, enabling them to deal successfully with pathogenic organisms and the damage they inflict.

As the atmosphere's CO_2 content rises, nearly all plants should continue to exhibit increasing rates of photosynthesis and, as a result, increased biomass production. This section investigates whether such benefits are exhibited in legumes suffering from pathogenic diseases.

Chakraborty and Datta (2003) note a number of CO_2-induced changes in plant physiology, anatomy, and morphology have been implicated in increased plant resistance to disease and "can potentially enhance host resistance at elevated CO_2." Among these phenomena they list "increased net photosynthesis allowing mobilization of resources into host resistance (Hibberd *et al.*, 1996a.); reduced stomatal density and conductance (Hibberd *et al.*, 1996b); greater accumulation of carbohydrates in leaves; more waxes, extra layers of epidermal cells and increased fiber content (Owensby, 1994); production of papillae and accumulation of silicon at penetration sites (Hibberd *et al.*, 1996a); greater number of mesophyll cells (Bowes, 1993); and increased biosynthesis of phenolics (Hartley *et al.*, 2000), among others."

Chakraborty and Datta (2003) studied the aggressiveness of the fungal anthracnose pathogen *Colletotrichum gloeosporioides* by inoculating two isolates of it onto two cultivars of the tropical pasture legume *Stylosanthes scabra* (Fitzroy, which is susceptible to the fungal pathogen, and Seca, which is more resistant) over 25 sequential infection cycles in controlled-environment chambers filled with air of either 350 or 700 ppm CO_2. They determined the aggressiveness of the pathogen was reduced at the twice-ambient level of atmospheric CO_2, with aggressiveness defined as "a property of the pathogen reflecting the relative amount of damage caused to the host without regard to resistance genes (Shaner *et al.*, 1992)." They report "at twice-ambient CO_2 the overall level of aggressiveness of the two [pathogen] isolates was significantly reduced on both cultivars."

Simultaneously, however, pathogen fecundity

was found to increase at twice-ambient CO_2. Chakraborty and Datta say their results "concur with the handful of studies that have demonstrated increased pathogen fecundity at elevated CO_2 (Hibberd *et al.*, 1996a; Klironomos *et al.*, 1997; Chakraborty *et al.*, 2000)." The overall increase in fecundity at high CO_2 "is a reflection of the altered canopy environment," they write, in which "the 30% larger *S. scabra* plants at high CO_2 (Chakraborty *et al.*, 2000) makes the canopy microclimate more conducive to anthracnose development."

In light of the opposing changes in pathogen behavior induced by the elevated level of atmospheric CO_2 in this experiment—reduced aggressiveness but increased fecundity—it was difficult to determine the ultimate impact of atmospheric CO_2 enrichment on the pathogen-host relationship of this particular plant. One year later, however, the publication of new research provided more insight.

Pangga *et al.* (2004) grew well-watered and well-fertilized seedlings of the Fitzroy cultivar of *Stylosanthes scabra* in a controlled-environment facility maintained at atmospheric CO_2 concentrations of either 350 or 700 ppm, where they inoculated six-, nine- and 12-week-old plants with *C. gloeosporioides*. Ten days after inoculation, they counted the anthracnose lesions on the plants and classified them as either resistant or susceptible.

They found "the mean number of susceptible, resistant, and total lesions per leaf averaged over the three plant ages was significantly (P<0.05) greater at 350 ppm than at 700 ppm CO_2, reflecting the development of a level of resistance in susceptible cv. Fitzroy at high CO_2." With respect to the plants inoculated at 12 weeks of age, they write those grown "at 350 ppm had 60 and 75% more susceptible and resistant lesions per leaf, respectively, than those [grown] at 700 ppm CO_2."

In terms of infection efficiency (IE), the Australian scientists state their work "clearly shows that at 350 ppm overall susceptibility of the canopy increases with increasing age because more young leaves are produced on secondary and tertiary branches of the more advanced plants." They note, "at 700 ppm CO_2, IE did not increase with increasing plant age despite the presence of many more young leaves in the enlarged canopy"; this finding, they write, "points to reduced pathogen efficiency or an induced partial resistance to anthracnose in Fitzroy at 700 ppm CO_2." Consequently, as the air's CO_2 content rises, it would appear (at least for the Fitzroy cultivar of this pasture legume) *Stylosanthes scabra*

will acquire a greater intrinsic resistance to the devastating anthracnose disease.

Lau *et al.* (2008) measured the amounts of pathogen damage done to the common prairie plant *Lespedeza capitata* growing in ambient and elevated (560 ppm) CO_2 treatments in the seventh and eighth years (2004 and 2005) of the BioCON study (Reich *et al.*, 2001) conducted at the Cedar Creek Natural History Area in Minnesota (USA), where the CO_2 treatments were applied during the daylight hours of each growing season.

Lau *et al.* write, disease incidence "was lower in the elevated CO_2 environment, although this difference [10% less in 2004 and 53% less in 2005] was statistically significant only in 2005 ($P < 0.01$)." They point out, "because disease caused major reductions in reproductive output, the effects of CO_2 on disease incidence may be important for *L. capitata* evolution and population dynamics." In addition, they note, Strengbom and Reich (2006), "working in the same experimental site ... also found that elevated CO_2 ... reduced disease incidence on *Solidago rigida*."

Eastburn *et al.* (2010) note, "globally, soybean is the most widely planted dicot crop and has economic significance due to its wide variety of uses, ranging from food and health products to printing inks and biodiesel [fuels]," but "little to no work has evaluated the influence of future atmospheric conditions on soybean diseases," even though "worldwide yield losses to all soybean diseases combined are about 11% (Wrather *et al.*, 1997), which is equivalent to more than 24 million metric tons based on current production."

Eastburn *et al.* evaluated the individual and combined effects of elevated carbon dioxide (CO_2, 550 ppm) and ozone (O_3, 1.2 times ambient) on three economically important soybean diseases—downy mildew, *Septoria* brown spot, and sudden death syndrome (SDS)—over the three-year period 2005–2007 under natural field conditions at the soybean free-air CO_2-enrichment (SoyFACE) facility on the campus of the University of Illinois (USA). The five researchers found "elevated CO_2 alone or in combination with O_3 significantly reduced downy mildew disease severity by 39–66% across the three years of the study." They also report "elevated CO_2 alone or in combination with O_3 significantly increased brown spot severity in all three years," but "the increase was small in magnitude." Finally, "the atmospheric treatments had no effect on the incidence of SDS."

Braga *et al.* (2006) examined the effects of

atmospheric CO_2 enrichment on another soybean pathogen in three independent experiments. They grew well-watered soybean (*Glycine max* (L.) Merr) plants of two cultivars (IAC-14, susceptible to stem canker disease, and IAC-18, resistant to stem canker disease) from seed through the cotyledon stage in 5-liter pots placed in open-top chambers maintained at atmospheric CO_2 concentrations of either 360 or 720 ppm in a glasshouse. They measured various plant properties and processes, concentrating on the production of glyceollins (the major phytoalexins, or anti-microbial compounds, produced in soybeans) in response to the application of ß-glucan elicitor (derived from mycelial walls of *Phythophthora sojae*) to carefully created and replicated wounds in the surfaces of several soybean cotyledons.

The IAC-14 cultivar did not exhibit a CO_2-induced change in glyceollin production in response to elicitation—as Braga *et al.* had hypothesized would be the case, since this cultivar is susceptible to stem canker disease. But the IAC-18 cultivar, which has the potential to resist the disease to varying degrees, experienced a 100% CO_2-induced increase in the amount of glyceollins produced after elicitation, a response the researchers describe as remarkable. Braga *et al.* say the CO_2-induced response they observed "may increase the potential of the soybean defense since infection at early stages of plant development, followed by a long incubation period before symptoms appear, [as] is characteristic of the stem canker disease cycle caused by Dpm [*Diaporthe phaseolorum* (Cooke & Ellis) Sacc. f. sp. *Meridionalis* Morgan-Jones]." The response they observed "indicates that raised CO_2 levels forecasted for next decades may have a real impact on the defensive chemistry of the cultivars."

Kretzschmar *et al.* (2009) noted "isoflavonoids constitute a group of natural products derived from the phenylpropanoid pathway, which is abundant in soybeans," and "the inducible accumulation of low molecular weight antimicrobial pterocarpan phytoalexins, the glyceollins, is one of the major defense mechanisms implicated in soybean resistance." The authors evaluated "the effect of an elevated CO_2 atmosphere on the production of soybean defensive secondary chemicals induced by nitric oxide and a fungal elicitor." They grew soybeans from seed for nine days in a glasshouse in large, well-watered pots placed in open-top chambers maintained at atmospheric CO_2 concentrations of either 380 or 760 ppm, examining changes in the production of phytoalexins and some of their precursors in the

activity of three enzymes related to their biosynthetic pathways.

Kretzschmar *et al.* report "elevated CO_2 combined with nitric oxide resulted in an increase of intermediates and diverted end products (daidzein—127%, coumestrol—93%, genistein—93%, luteolin—89% and apigenin—238%) with a concomitant increase of 1.5–3.0 times in the activity of enzymes related to their biosynthetic routes." These findings, the four Brazilian researchers write, are evidence of "changes in the pool of defense-related flavonoids in soybeans due to increased carbon availability, which may differentially alter the responsiveness of soybean plants to pathogens in CO_2 atmospheric concentrations such as those predicted for future decades."

The studies reviewed here show elevated CO_2 can significantly ameliorate the deleterious effects of various stresses imposed on legume plants by numerous pathogenic invaders, but there remains a need to clarify some issues through further research. Nevertheless, the large number of ways in which elevated CO_2 has been demonstrated to increase plant resistance to pathogen attack gives reason to conclude plants will gain the advantage as the air's CO_2 content climbs, enabling them to deal successfully with pathogenic organisms and the damage they inflict.

References

Bowes, G. 1993. Facing the inevitable: Plants and increasing atmospheric CO_2. *Annual Review of Plant Physiology and Plant Molecular Biology* **44**: 309–332.

Braga, M.R., Aidar, M.P.M., Marabesi, M.A., and de Godoy, J.R.L. 2006. Effects of elevated CO_2 on the phytoalexin production of two soybean cultivars differing in the resistance to stem canker disease. *Environmental and Experimental Botany* **58**: 85–92.

Chakraborty, S. and Datta, S. 2003. How will plant pathogens adapt to host plant resistance at elevated CO_2 under a changing climate? *New Phytologist* **159**: 733–742.

Chakraborty, S., Pangga, I.B., Lupton, J., Hart, L., Room, P.M., and Yates, D. 2000. Production and dispersal of *Colletotrichum gloeosporioides* spores on *Stylosanthes scabra* under elevated CO_2. *Environmental Pollution* **108**: 381–387.

Eastburn, D.M., Degennaro, M.M., DeLucia, E.H., Dermody, O., and McElrone, A.J. 2010. Elevated atmospheric carbon dioxide and ozone alter soybean diseases at SoyFACE. *Global Change Biology* **16**: 320–330.

Hartley, S.E., Jones, C.G., and Couper, G.C. 2000. Biosynthesis of plant phenolic compounds in elevated atmospheric CO_2. *Global Change Biology* **6**: 497–506.

Hibberd, J.M., Whitbread, R., and Farrar, J.F. 1996a. Effect of elevated concentrations of CO_2 on infection of barley by *Erysiphe graminis*. *Physiological and Molecular Plant Pathology* **48**: 37–53.

Hibberd, J.M., Whitbread, R., and Farrar, J.F. 1996b. Effect of 700 μmol per mol CO_2 and infection of powdery mildew on the growth and partitioning of barley. *New Phytologist* **134**: 309–345.

Klironomos, J.N., Rillig, M.C., Allen, M.F., Zak, D.R., Kubiske, M., and Pregitzer, K.S. 1997. Soil fungal-arthropod responses to *Populus tremuloides* grown under enriched atmospheric CO_2 under field conditions. *Global Change Biology* **3**: 473–478.

Kretzschmar, F.S., Aidar, M.P.M., Salgado, I., and Braga, M.R. 2009. Elevated CO_2 atmosphere enhances production of defense-related flavonoids in soybean elicited by NO and a fungal elicitor. *Environmental and Experimental Botany* **65**: 319–329.

Lau, J.A., Strengbom, J., Stone, L.R., Reich, P.B., and Tiffin, P. 2008. Direct and indirect effects of CO_2, nitrogen, and community diversity on plant-enemy interactions. *Ecology* **89**: 226–236.

Owensby, C.E. 1994. Climate change and grasslands: ecosystem-level responses to elevated carbon dioxide. *Proceedings of the XVII International Grassland Congress.* Palmerston North, New Zealand: New Zealand Grassland Association, pp. 1119–1124.

Pangga, I.B., Chakraborty, S., and Yates, D. 2004. Canopy size and induced resistance in *Stylosanthes scabra* determine anthracnose severity at high CO_2. *Phytopathology* **94**: 221–227.

Reich, P.B., Tilman, D., Craine, J., Ellsworth, D., Tjoelker, M.G., Knops, J., Wedin, D., Naeem, S., Bahauddin, D., Goth, J., Bengston, W., and Lee, T.D. 2001. Do species and functional groups differ in acquisition and use of C, N, and water under varying atmospheric CO_2 and N availability regimes? A field test with 16 grassland species. *New Phytologist* **150**: 435–448.

Shaner, G., Stromberg, E.L., Lacy, G.H., Barker, K.R., and Pirone, T.P. 1992. Nomenclature and concepts of aggressiveness and virulence. *Annual Review of Phytopathology* **30**: 47–66.

Strengbom, J. and Reich, P.B. 2006. Elevated CO_2 and increased N supply reduce leaf disease and related photosynthetic impacts on *Solidago rigida*. *Oecologia* **149**: 519–525.

Wrather, J.A., Anderson, T.R., Arsyad, D.M., Gai, J., Ploper, L.D., Porta-Puglia, A., Ram, H.H., and Yourinori, J.T. 1997. Soybean disease loss estimates for the top 10 soybean producing countries in 1994. *Plant Disease* **81**: 107–110.

3.2.2 Other Agricultural Plants

• Atmospheric CO_2 enrichment asserts its greatest positive influence on infected as opposed to healthy plants because it can significantly ameliorate the deleterious effects of various stresses imposed on plants by pathogenic invaders.

As the air's CO_2 content rises, nearly all plants should continue to exhibit increasing rates of photosynthesis and increased biomass production. This section examines whether such benefits occur in plants that are suffering from various pathogen-induced diseases, specifically non-legume agricultural plants.

Plessl *et al.* (2007) write, "potato late blight caused by the oomycete *Phytophthora infestans* (Mont.) de Bary is the most devastating disease of potato worldwide," and "infection occurs through leaves and tubers followed by a rapid spread of the pathogen finally causing destructive necrosis." The five researchers grew individual well-watered and fertilized plants of the potato cultivar Indira in controlled-environment chambers maintained at atmospheric CO_2 concentrations of either 400 or 700 ppm. Four weeks after the start of the experiment, researchers cut the first three fully developed pinnate leaves from the plants and inoculated them with zoospores of *P. infestans* in Petri dishes containing water-agar. They evaluated the leaves' symptoms daily via comparison with control leaves similarly treated but unexposed to the pathogen.

The German scientists report the 400- to 700-ppm increase in CO_2 "dramatically reduced symptom development," including extent of necrosis (down by 44% four days after inoculation and 65% five days after inoculation), area of sporulation (down by 100% four days after inoculation and 61% five days after inoculation), and sporulation intensity (down by 73% four days after inoculation and 17% five days after inoculation). These findings, Plessl *et al.* write, "clearly demonstrated that the potato cultivar Indira, which under normal conditions shows a high susceptibility to *P. infestans*, develops resistance against this pathogen after exposure to 700 ppm CO_2," and "this finding agrees with results from Jwa *et al.* (1995), who reported an increased tolerance of tomato plants to *Phytophthora* root rot when grown at elevated CO_2."

Jwa and Walling (2001) grew tomato plants hydroponically for eight weeks in controlled-environment chambers maintained at atmospheric CO_2 concentrations of 350 and 700 ppm. At week five of their study, they infected half of all plants growing in each CO_2 concentration with the fungal pathogen *Phytophthora parasitica*, which attacks plant roots and induces a water stress that decreases growth and yield. At the end of the study, they found the pathogenic infection had reduced total plant biomass by nearly 30% at both atmospheric CO_2 concentrations. However, the elevated CO_2 treatment had increased the total biomass of the healthy and diseased plants by the same amount (+30%), with the result that the infected tomato plants grown at 700 ppm CO_2 had biomass values essentially identical to those of the healthy tomato plants grown at 350 ppm CO_2. Thus, the extra CO_2 counterbalanced the negative effect of the pathogenic infection on overall plant productivity.

Malmstrom and Field (1997) grew individual oat plants for two months in pots placed in phytocells maintained at atmospheric CO_2 concentrations of 350 and 700 ppm, and they infected one-third of the plants with the barley yellow dwarf virus (BYDV), which affects more than 150 plant species worldwide, including all major cereal crops. They found elevated CO_2 stimulated rates of net photosynthesis in all plants, regardless of pathogen infection. However, the greatest percentage increase occurred in diseased specimens (48% vs. 34%). Moreover, atmospheric CO_2 enrichment decreased stomatal conductance by 50% in infected plants but by only 34% in healthy ones, which led to a CO_2-induced doubling of the instantaneous water-use efficiency of the healthy plants but a 2.7-fold increase in the diseased plants.

After 60 days of growth under these conditions, the researchers determined the extra CO_2 increased total plant biomass by 36% in infected plants but 12% in healthy plants. In addition, whereas elevated CO_2 had little effect on root growth in the healthy plants, it increased root biomass in the infected plants by up to 60%. Malmstrom and Field conclude CO_2 enrichment "may reduce losses of infected plants to drought" and "may enable diseased plants to compete better with healthy neighbors."

Tiedemann and Firsching (2000) grew spring wheat plants from germination to maturity in controlled-environment chambers maintained at ambient (377 ppm) and elevated (612 ppm) concentrations of atmospheric CO_2 and at ambient (20 ppb) and elevated (61 ppb) concentrations of ozone (and combinations thereof); the latter gas is typically toxic to most plants. In addition, they inoculated half the plants in each treatment with a leaf rust-causing fungus. The elevated CO_2 increased the photosynthetic rates of the diseased plants by 20 and 42% at the ambient and elevated ozone concentrations, respectively, and it also enhanced the yield of the infected plants, increasing it by 57%, even in the presence of high ozone concentrations.

Matros *et al.* (2006) grew tobacco plants (*Nicotiana tabacum* L.) in 16-cm-diameter pots filled with quartz sand in controlled-climate chambers maintained at either 350 or 1,000 ppm CO_2 for eight weeks, where they were irrigated daily with a complete nutrient solution containing either 5 or 8 mM NH_4NO_3. Some of the plants in each treatment were mechanically infected with the potato virus Y (PVY) when they were six weeks old. At the end of the study, the researchers harvested the plants and identified and quantified a number of their chemical constituents.

The researchers report "plants grown at elevated CO_2 and 5 mM NH_4NO_3 showed a marked and significant decrease in content of nicotine in leaves as well as in roots," and at 8 mM NH_4NO_3 the same was found to be true of upper leaves but not of lower leaves and roots. With respect to the PVY part of the study, they further note the "plants grown at high CO_2 showed a markedly decreased spread of virus." Both these findings would likely be considered beneficial by most people because potato virus Y infects many crops and ornamental plants worldwide, and nicotine is widely acknowledged to have significant negative impacts on human health (Topliss *et al.*, 2002).

In a study conducted in the BioCON (Biodiversity, Carbon dioxide, and Nitrogen effects on ecosystem functioning) FACE facility located at the Cedar Creek Natural History Area in east-central Minnesota (USA), Strengbom and Reich (2006) evaluated the effects of an approximately 190 ppm increase in the air's daytime CO_2 concentration on leaf photosynthetic rates of stiff goldenrod (*Solidago rigida*) growing in monoculture for two full seasons, together with its concomitant effects on the incidence and severity of leaf spot disease. Although they found elevated CO_2 had no significant effect on plant photosynthetic rate in their study, they write, "both disease incidence and severity were lower on plants grown under elevated CO_2." Specifically, "disease incidence was on average more than twice as high under ambient as under elevated CO_2," and "disease severity (proportion of leaf area with lesions) was on average 67% lower under elevated CO_2 compared to ambient conditions."

Strengbom and Reich note the "indirect effects from elevated CO_2, i.e., lower disease incidence, had a stronger effect on realized photosynthetic rate than the direct effect of higher CO_2." They conclude, "it may be necessary to consider potential changes in susceptibility to foliar diseases to correctly estimate the effects on plant photosynthetic rates of elevated CO_2." In addition, they found the plants grown in CO_2-enriched air had lower leaf nitrogen concentrations than those grown in ambient air, as is often observed in studies of this type. They say their results "are, thus, also in accordance with other studies that have found reduced pathogen performance following reduced nitrogen concentration in plants grown under elevated CO_2 (Thompson and Drake, 1994)." In addition, they write, their results are "also in accordance with studies that have found increased [disease] susceptibility following increased nitrogen concentration of host plants (Huber and Watson, 1974; Nordin et al., 1998; Strengbom et al., 2002)."

Gamper et al. (2004) note arbuscular mycorrhizal fungi (AMF) are expected to modulate plant responses to elevated CO_2 by "increasing resistance/ tolerance of plants against an array of environmental stressors (Smith and Read, 1997)." Investigating this subject in a set of experiments conducted over a seven-year period of free-air CO_2-enrichment on two of the world's most extensively grown cool-season forage crops (*Lolium perenne* and *Trifolium repens*) at the Swiss FACE facility near Zurich, they determined "at elevated CO_2 and under [two] N treatments, AMF root colonization of both host plant species was increased," and "colonization levels of all three measured intraradical AMF structures (hyphae, arbuscules and vesicles) tended to be higher." They conclude these CO_2-induced benefits may lead to "increased protection against pathogens and/or herbivores."

Al-Kayssi (2009) notes soil solarization "is a method of heating the soil by using polyethylene sheets as mulching over moistened soil, to retain solar radiation during the hot season," so "soil-borne pathogens may be killed by lethal heat ($>40°C$) and weakened by sub-lethal heat ($<38–40°C$) to the extent that they are unable to cause damage to plants or they are more susceptible to chemical toxicants." This

technique "has been successfully used to control soil-borne pathogens and weeds (Katan et al., 1976; Mahrer, 1979; Grinstein et al., 1979; Katan, 1981; Mahrer et al., 1984; Avissar et al., 1986; Al-Karaghouli et al., 1990; Al-Kayssi and Al-Karaghouli, 1991)."

Al-Kayssi conducted a laboratory experiment where "clay soil samples infested with *Verticillium dahliae* were exposed to different CO_2 concentrations (350, 700, 1050, 1400, 1750 ppm air) and incubated in hot water baths at 35, 40, 45, 50 and 55°C," while "field plots were exposed to the same CO_2 levels during soil solarization in three periods (1st of July to 30th of September, 1st of August to 30th of September, and 1st to 30th of September)."

The Iraqi researcher found higher than normal CO_2 contents in the soil increased maximum soil temperatures while reducing the length of time required to kill 90% of the propagules of *V. dahliae* in natural field soil with moisture content at field capacity. He notes this killing time parameter in soil heated to 35°C was reduced from 24 days at the normal ambient CO_2 concentration to 15 days at 1,750 ppm CO_2, and sub-lethal soil temperatures were raised to lethal levels as the soil's CO_2 content was raised. This finding suggests a high-CO_2 environment could make soil solarization a more important method of controlling soil-borne pathogens and weeds than it is today.

These studies indicate atmospheric CO_2 enrichment asserts a relatively greater positive influence on infected as opposed to healthy plants. Moreover, they suggest elevated CO_2 can significantly ameliorate the deleterious effects of various stresses imposed on plants by pathogenic invaders. Consequently, as the atmosphere's CO_2 concentration continues its upward climb, Earth's vegetation should be increasingly better equipped to deal with pathogenic organisms and the damage they do.

References

Al-Karaghouli, A.A., Al-Kayssi, A.W., and Hasson, A.M. 1990. The photometric properties of different colored plastic mulches used for soil solarization. *Solar and Wind Technology* 7: 119–123.

Al-Kayssi, A.W. 2009. Impact of elevated CO_2 concentrations in the soil on soil solarization efficiency. *Applied Soil Ecology* 43: 150–158.

Al-Kayssi, A.W. and Al-Karaghouli, A.A. 1991. Influence

of different colored plastic mulches used for soil solarization on the effectiveness of soil heating. *Soil Solarization* **109**: 297–308.

Avissar, R., Mahrer, Y., Margulies, L., and Katan, J. 1986. Field aging of transparent polyethylene mulch: I. Photometric properties. *Soil Science Society of America Journal* **50**: 202–205.

Gamper, H., Peter, M., Jansa, J., Luscher, A., Hartwig, U.A., and Leuchtmann, A. 2004. Arbuscular mycorrhizal fungi benefit from 7 years of free air CO_2 enrichment in well-fertilized grass and legume monocultures. *Global Change Biology* **10**: 189–199.

Grinstein, A., Orion, D., Greenberger, A., and Katan, J. 1979. Solar heating of the soil for the control of *Verticillium dahliae* and *Pratylenchus thornei* in potatoes. In: Shippers, B. and Gams, W. (Eds.) *Soilborne Plant Pathogens*. Academic Press, London, UK, pp. 431–438.

Huber, D.M. and Watson, R.D. 1974. Nitrogen form and plant disease. *Annual Reviews of Phytopathology* **12**: 139–155.

Jwa, N.-S. and Walling, L.L. 2001. Influence of elevated CO_2 concentration on disease development in tomato. *New Phytologist* **149**: 509–518.

Jwa, N.S., Walling, L., and McCool, P.M. 1995. Influence of elevated CO_2 on disease development and induction of PR proteins in tomato roots by *Phytophthora parasitica*. *Plant Physiology* **85** (Supplement): 1139.

Katan, J. 1981. Solar heating (solarization) of soil for control of soilborne pests. *Annual Review of Phytopathology* **19**: 211–236.

Katan, J., Greenberger, A., Alon, H., and Grinstein, A. 1976. Solar heating by polyethylene mulching for the control of diseases caused by soilborne pathogens. *Phytopathology* **66**: 683–688.

Mahrer, Y. 1979. Prediction of soil temperatures of a soil mulched with transparent polyethylene. *Journal of Applied Meteorology* **18**: 1263–1267.

Mahrer, Y., Naot, O., Rawitz, E., and Katan, J. 1984. Temperature and moisture regimes in soils mulched with transparent polyethylene. *Soil Science Society of America Journal* **48**: 362–367.

Malmstrom, C.M. and Field, C.B. 1997. Virus-induced differences in the response of oat plants to elevated carbon dioxide. *Plant, Cell and Environment* **20**: 178–188.

Matros, A., Amme, S., Kettig, B., Buck-Sorlin, G.H., Sonnewald, U., and Mock, H.-P. 2006. Growth at elevated CO_2 concentrations leads to modified profiles of secondary metabolites in tobacco cv. SamsunNN and to increased

resistance against infection with *potato virus Y*. *Plant, Cell and Environment* **29**: 126–137.

Nordin, A., Nasholm, T., and Ericson, L. 1998. Effects of simulated N deposition on understory vegetation of a boreal coniferous forest. *Functional Ecology* **12**: 691–699.

Plessl, M., Elstner, E.F., Rennenberg, H., Habermeyer, J., and Heiser, I. 2007. Influence of elevated CO_2 and ozone concentrations on late blight resistance and growth of potato plants. *Environmental and Experimental Botany* **60**: 447–457.

Smith, S.E. and Read, D.J. 1997. *Mycorrhizal Symbioses*. Academic Press, London, UK.

Strengbom, J., Nordin, A., Nasholm, T., and Ericson, L. 2002. Parasitic fungus mediates change in nitrogen-exposed boreal forest vegetation. *Journal of Ecology* **90**: 61-67.

Strengbom, J. and Reich, P.B. 2006. Elevated [CO_2] and increased N supply reduce leaf disease and related photosynthetic impacts on *Solidago rigida*. *Oecologia* **149**: 519–525.

Thompson, G.B. and Drake, B.G. 1994. Insect and fungi on a C_3 sedge and a C_4 grass exposed to elevated atmospheric CO_2 concentrations in open-top chambers in the field. *Plant, Cell and Environment* **17**: 1161-1167.

Tiedemann, A.V. and Firsching, K.H. 2000. Interactive effects of elevated ozone and carbon dioxide on growth and yield of leaf rust-infected versus non-infected wheat. *Environmental Pollution* **108**: 357–363.

Topliss, J.G., Clark, A.M., and Ernst, E., *et al.* 2002. Natural and synthetic substances related to human health. *Pure and Applied Chemistry* **74**: 1957–1985.

3.2.3 Trees

- The balance of evidence obtained to date demonstrates trees are better able to withstand pathogen attacks in CO_2-enriched air as opposed to ambient-CO_2 air.

Plant pathogens reduce growth in agricultural and natural ecosystems worldwide; estimates of financial loss due to such reductions amount to more than $33 billion annually in the United States alone (Pimentel *et al.*, 2000). It is thus natural to wonder—and important to determine—how rising atmospheric CO_2 will affect plant-pathogen interactions. This section examines what researchers have learned about these phenomena from experiments conducted on various types of trees.

Leaf spot disease, which is characterized by chlorotic to necrotic localized leaf lesions, is caused by the *Cercospora* (a large genus of ascomycete fungi) that affect, in the words of McElrone *et al.* (2010), "numerous economically important plant species around the world, including grapes, cereals, soybeans, peanuts, orchids, coffee, alfalfa and potatoes (Sinclair *et al.*, 1987)," as well as redbud (*Cercis canadensis*) and sweetgum (*Liquidambar styraciflua*) trees, such as those growing at the Duke Forest FACE facility in Orange County, North Carolina (USA), where McElrone *et al.* studied the disease throughout the growing seasons of five years (2000–2003 and 2005).

The six scientists assessed how elevated CO_2 (to 200 ppm above the ambient air's CO_2 concentration) and natural interannual climatic variability affected the incidence and severity of leaf spot disease among the sweetgum and redbud trees growing in the several FACE rings at the Duke Forest site. In order "to determine how photosynthetic capacity surrounding pathogen damage was affected by CO_2 exposure, the spatial pattern of photosystem II operating efficiency was quantified on *C. canadensis* leaves still attached to plants with an imaging chlorophyll fluorometer," they write.

McElrone *et al.* determined "disease incidence and severity for both species were greater in years with above average rainfall," and "in years with above average temperatures, disease incidence for *Liquidambar styraciflua* was decreased significantly." They also note elevated CO_2 increased disease incidence and severity "in some years." However, they write, the "chlorophyll fluorescence imaging of leaves revealed that any visible increase in disease severity induced by elevated CO_2 was mitigated by higher photosynthetic efficiency in the remaining undamaged leaf tissue and in a halo surrounding lesions." Although atmospheric CO_2 enrichment was sometimes observed to increase the incidence and severity of leaf spot disease, the photosynthesis-enhancing effect of the extra CO_2 compensated for the photosynthetic productivity lost to the disease by enhancing productivity in healthy portions of diseased leaves and in leaves without lesions, with no net ill effect.

Fleischmann *et al.* (2010) grew well-watered European Beech (*Fagus sylvatica* L.) trees from seed for four years in growth chambers maintained at either 400 or 700 ppm CO_2 in a greenhouse. During this period, they gave the trees an adequate supply of

all essential nutrients, but in the case of nitrogen (N), there were low N and high N treatments, where they gave the high-N treatment twice as much nitrogen as the low-N treatment. In addition, half of the seedlings were infected with *Phytophthora citricola*—a root pathogen known to infest the roots and trunks of European Beech trees—in the early summer of the third year of the study, and half of the trees in each treatment were harvested and examined at the ends of the third and fourth years of the experiment.

The three German researchers write, "chronic elevation of atmospheric CO_2 increased the susceptibility of beech seedlings towards the root pathogen *P. citricola*, while additional nitrogen supply reduced susceptibility." They found 27% of the infected plants in the low-N high-CO_2 treatment had been killed by the pathogen by the end of their study, and only 9% of the infected plants in the high-N high-CO_2 treatment had died. Surviving beech seedlings of the low-N high-CO_2 treatment "managed to tolerate the root infection by (a) increasing their carbon gain, (b) improving their fine root functionality and (c) changing their allometric relation between below-ground and above-ground biomass."

Fleischmann *et al.* conclude infected beech seedlings in the low-N high-CO_2 treatment responded to the pernicious pathogen and "enhanced [their] primary production rates in the second year of the experiment and increased above-ground biomass significantly as compared to control trees."

Percy *et al.* (2002) grew the most widely distributed North American tree species—trembling aspen—in 12 30-m-diameter FACE rings near Rhinelander, Wisconsin (USA) in air maintained at ambient CO_2 and O_3 concentrations, ambient O_3 and elevated CO_2 (560 ppm during daylight hours), ambient CO_2 and elevated O_3 (46.4–55.5 ppb during daylight hours), and elevated CO_2 and O_3 over the period of each growing season from 1998 through 2001. Throughout the experiment they assessed several of the young trees' growth characteristics, as well as their responses to poplar leaf rust (*Melampsora medusae*), which they note "is common on aspen and belongs to the most widely occurring group of foliage diseases." They found elevated CO_2 alone did not alter rust occurrence, but elevated O_3 alone increased it by nearly fourfold. When applied together, the elevated CO_2 reduced the enhancement of rust development caused by elevated O_3 from nearly fourfold to just over twofold.

Parsons *et al.* (2003) grew two-year-old saplings of paper birch and three-year-old saplings of sugar maple in well-watered and -fertilized pots from early May until late August in glasshouse rooms maintained at either 400 or 700 ppm CO_2. They found the whole-plant biomass of paper birch was increased by 55% in the CO_2-enriched portions of the glasshouse, and sugar maple was increased by 30%. In addition, concentrations of condensed tannins were increased by 27% in the paper birch (but not the sugar maple) saplings grown in the CO_2-enriched air. Parsons *et al.* conclude "the higher condensed tannin concentrations present in the birch fine roots may offer these tissues greater protection against soil-borne pathogens and herbivores." Parsons *et al.* report CO_2-induced increases in fine root concentrations of total phenolics and condensed tannins also have been observed in warm temperate conifers by King *et al.* (1997), Entry *et al.* (1998), Gebauer *et al.* (1998), and Runion *et al.* (1999), and in cotton by Booker (2000).

McElrone *et al.* (2005) "assessed how elevated CO_2 affects a foliar fungal pathogen, *Phyllosticta minima*, of *Acer rubrum* [red maple] growing in the understory at the Duke Forest free-air CO_2 enrichment experiment in Durham, North Carolina, USA ... in the 6th, 7th, and 8th years of the CO_2 exposure." Surveys conducted in those years "revealed that elevated CO_2 [to 200 ppm above ambient] significantly reduced disease incidence, with 22%, 27% and 8% fewer saplings and 14%, 4%, and 5% fewer leaves infected per plant in the three consecutive years, respectively." They report the elevated CO_2 "also significantly reduced disease severity in infected plants in all years (e.g. mean lesion area reduced 35%, 50%, and 10% in 2002, 2003, and 2004, respectively)."

Hypothesizing these consequences could have resulted from a direct deleterious effect of elevated CO_2 on the fungal pathogen, McElrone *et al.* performed other experiments in controlled-environment chambers. These experiments revealed the elevated CO_2 benefited the fungal pathogen as well as the red maple saplings, as the authors report "exponential growth rates of *P. minima* were 17% greater under elevated CO_2." They obtained similar results when they repeated the *in vitro* growth analysis two additional times in different growth chambers.

When "scanning electron micrographs verified that conidia germ tubes of *P. minima* infect *A. rubrum* leaves by entering through the stomata," the researchers turned their attention to the pathogen's mode of entry into the saplings' foliage. In this investigation they report both stomatal size and

density were unaffected by atmospheric CO_2 enrichment, but "stomatal conductance was reduced by 21–36% under elevated CO_2, providing smaller openings for infecting germ tubes." They conclude the reduced disease severity under elevated CO_2 was also likely due to altered leaf chemistry, as elevated CO_2 increased total leaf phenolic concentrations by 15% and tannin concentrations by 14%.

Because the phenomena they found to be important in reducing the amount and severity of fungal pathogen infection (leaf spot disease) of red maple have been demonstrated to be operative in most other plants as well, McElrone *et al.* state these CO_2-enhanced leaf defensive mechanisms "may be prevalent in many plant pathosystems where the pathogen targets the stomata." They conclude their results "provide concrete evidence for a potentially generalizable mechanism to predict disease outcomes in other pathosystems under future climatic conditions."

Runion *et al.* (2010) write, obligate pathogens "have a more intimate relationship with their host and must have the host to survive," whereas facultative pathogens "live saprophytically and generally result in disease (or tend to be more severe) under conditions of plant stress such as low nutrition or water." They grew well-watered and well-fertilized seedlings of loblolly pine (*Pinus taeda*) and northern red oak (*Quercus rubra*) out-of-doors in open-top chambers constructed in large soil bins located at the USDA-ARS National Soil Dynamics Laboratory in Auburn, Alabama (USA), where they exposed the plants to atmospheric CO_2 concentrations of either 360 or 720 ppm with or without infecting them with the fusiform rust fungus (the obligate pathogen *Cronartium quercuum* f.sp. *fusiforme*), and with or without infecting them with the pitch canker fungus (the facultative pathogen *Fusarium circinatum*) for various lengths of time ranging from weeks to a year, with each of the three experiments being conducted twice.

With respect to the pine *Fusarium* rust study, Runion *et al.* state "percent infection was not significantly affected by CO_2 concentration," yet "the percentage of loblolly pine seedlings which died as a result of rust infection was generally significantly lower under elevated CO_2 in both runs of the experiment." With respect to the oak *Fusarium* rust study, they report "the percent of oak seedlings with uredia was consistently lower for seedlings exposed to elevated CO_2 in both runs," and "the percent of oak seedlings with telia was significantly lower for seedlings exposed to elevated CO_2 at the 16 and 19 days evaluations in both runs of the experiment." With respect to the pine pitch canker study, the four researchers say "the percent of loblolly pine seedlings which developed cankers following inoculation with the pitch canker fungus was consistently lower for seedlings grown under elevated CO_2 in both runs of the experiment ... with infection in elevated CO_2-grown seedlings remaining about half that of ambient-grown seedlings."

Runion *et al.* conclude "disease incidence—regardless of pathogen type—may be reduced as atmospheric CO_2 concentration continues to rise," which should significantly benefit the two species of trees in the high-CO_2 environment.

The balance of evidence obtained to date demonstrates an enhanced ability of trees to withstand pathogen attacks in CO_2-enriched as opposed to ambient-CO_2 air. As the atmosphere's CO_2 concentration rises, Earth's vegetation should fare better against the ravages inflicted on it by myriad debilitating plant diseases.

References

Booker, F.L. 2000. Influence of carbon dioxide enrichment, ozone and nitrogen fertilization on cotton (*Gossypium hirsutum* L.) leaf and root composition. *Plant, Cell and Environment* **23**: 573–583.

Entry, J.A., Runion, G.B., Prior, S.A., Mitchell, R.J., and Rogers, H.H. 1998. Influence of CO_2 enrichment and nitrogen fertilization on tissue chemistry and carbon allocation in longleaf pine seedlings. *Plant and Soil* **200**: 3–11.

Fleischmann, F., Raidl, S., and Osswald, W.F. 2010. Changes in susceptibility of beech (*Fagus sylvatica*) seedlings towards *Phytophthora citricola* under the influence of elevated atmospheric CO_2 and nitrogen fertilization. *Environmental Pollution* **158**: 1051–1060.

Gebauer, R.L., Strain, B.R., and Reynolds, J.F. 1998. The effect of elevated CO_2 and N availability on tissue concentrations and whole plant pools of carbon-based secondary compounds in loblolly pine. *Oecologia* **113**: 29–36.

King, J.S., Thomas, R.B., and Strain, B.R. 1997. Morphology and tissue quality of seedling root systems of *Pinus taeda* and *Pinus ponderosa* as affected by varying CO_2, temperature, and nitrogen. *Plant and Soil* **195**: 107–119.

McElrone, A.J., Hamilton, J.G., Krafnick, A.J., Aldea, M., Knepp, R.G., and DeLucia, E.H. 2010. Combined effects of elevated CO_2 and natural climatic variation on leaf spot diseases of redbud and sweetgum trees. *Environmental Pollution* **158**: 108–114.

McElrone, A.J., Reid, C.D., Hoye, K.A., Hart, E., and Jackson, R.B. 2005. Elevated CO_2 reduces disease incidence and severity of a red maple fungal pathogen via changes in host physiology and leaf chemistry. *Global Change Biology* **11**: 1828–1836.

Parsons, W.F.J., Kopper, B.J., and Lindroth, R.L. 2003. Altered growth and fine root chemistry of *Betula papyrifera* and *Acer saccharum* under elevated CO_2. *Canadian Journal of Forest Research* **33**: 842–846.

Percy, K.E., Awmack, C.S., Lindroth, R.L., Kubiske, M.E., Kopper, B.J., Isebrands, J.G., Pregitzer, K.S., Hendrey, G.R., Dickson, R.E., Zak, D.R., Oksanen, E., Sober, J., Harrington, R., and Karnosky, D.F. 2002. Altered performance of forest pests under atmospheres enriched by CO_2 and O_3. *Nature* **420**: 403–407.

Pimentel, D., Lach, L., and Zuniga, R., *et al.* 2000. Environmental and economic costs of nonindigenous species in the United States. *Bioscience* **50**: 53–65.

Runion, G.B., Entry, J.A., Prior, S.A., Mitchell, R.J., and Rogers, H.H. 1999. Tissue chemistry and carbon allocation in seedlings of *Pinus palustris* subjected to elevated atmospheric CO_2 and water stress. *Tree Physiology* **19**: 329–335.

Runion, G.B., Prior, S.A., Rogers, H.H., and Mitchell, R.J. 2010. Effects of elevated atmospheric CO_2 on two southern forest diseases. *New Forests* **39**: 275–285.

Sinclair, W.A., Lyon, H.H., and Johnson, W.T. 1987. *Diseases of Trees and Shrubs*. Cornell University Press, Ithaca, New York, USA.

3.3 Heavy Metal Toxicity

- Increases in the air's CO_2 content improve plants' ability to withstand the deleterious effects of heavy metals that may be present in soils at ordinarily toxic levels.

Noting copper (Cu) is "an essential micronutrient [that] plays a vital role in maintaining normal metabolism in higher plants," but "is toxic to plant cells at higher concentrations and causes the inhibition of plant growth or even death," Jia *et al.* (2007) grew a Japonica rice cultivar in control and Cu-contaminated soil for one full growing season at ambient and elevated atmospheric CO_2 concentrations (370 and 570 ppm), measuring leaf Cu concentrations at the tillering, jointing, heading, and ripening stages.

At the tillering stage of the plants' progression, leaf Cu concentrations in the plants growing in the Cu-contaminated soil of both CO_2 treatments were about 90% greater than those in the plants growing in the uncontaminated soil of both CO_2 treatments. By the time the plants had reached the jointing stage, the mean leaf Cu concentration in the plants growing in the Cu-contaminated soil in the CO_2-enriched air had dropped to the same level as the plants growing in uncontaminated soil in ambient air, and this equivalence was maintained throughout the plants' subsequent heading and ripening stages.

For the plants growing in contaminated soil in ambient air, leaf Cu concentrations remained 50% greater than those of the plants growing in contaminated soil in CO_2-enriched air at the end of the experiment. Thus the negative effect of a more-than-five-fold increase in soil Cu concentration, which increased leaf Cu concentration by approximately 90% at the crop tillering stage, was completely ameliorated throughout the rest of the crop's development by a 54% increase in the atmosphere's CO_2 concentration.

Jia *et al.* (2011a) note "mining and smelting, disposal of sewage sludge and use of cadmium (Cd) rich phosphate fertilizers have contaminated large areas throughout the world, causing an increase in the Cd content of the soil (Liu *et al.*, 2007)." This is, they note, an unfortunate development, because "cadmium is a non-essential element that negatively affects plant growth and development processes, such as respiration and photosynthesis (Vega *et al.*, 2006), water and mineral uptake (Singh and Tewari, 2003), cell division (Fojtova *et al.*, 2002) and cellular redox homoeostasis (Romero-Puertas *et al.*, 2004)."

Jia *et al.* studied the interactive effects of Cd contamination and atmospheric CO_2 enrichment on a perennial ryegrass (*Lolium perenne*), growing it from seed hydroponically in half-strength Hoagland solution for three days, followed by growth in full-strength Hoagland solution for five and 20 days and at a range of Cd concentrations ranging from 0 to 160 µmol/liter. Regardless of Cd treatment, the five researchers found "the Cd concentration was much lower under elevated CO_2 than under ambient CO_2," most likely due to the "fast growth triggered by elevated CO_2," such that in their experiment "the dry biomass increased by 81.2% for shoots and 55.2% for roots under non-Cd stress, and an average of 99.1% for shoots and 68.5% for roots under Cd stress, respectively." The five Chinese scientists conclude, "under elevated CO_2, *L. perenne* may be better protected against Cd stress with higher biomass, lower Cd concentration and better detoxification by phytochelatins." In addition, "lower Cd concentration in plants under elevated CO_2 may relieve the Cd toxicity to plants and reduce the risk of Cd transport in the food chain."

Jia *et al.* (2011b) obtained similar results when they hydroponically grew two important forage crops (*Lolium perenne* and *Lolium multiflorum*) at three different Cd (0, 4, and 16 mg/L) and two different atmospheric CO_2 (360 or 1,000 ppm) concentrations in individual pots in controlled-environment chambers for three weeks. They found "root morphological parameters, including root length, surface area, volume, tip number, and fine roots, all decreased under Cd exposure," whereas "by contrast, elevated levels of CO_2 significantly increased all those parameters in the presence of Cd, compared to the CO_2 control, suggesting that elevated levels of CO_2 had an ameliorating effect on Cd-induced stress." The extra 640 ppm of CO_2 also increased the shoot dry weight of *L. multiflorum* by 68%, 92%, and 90% and *L. perenne* by 65%, 61%, and 67% at low, medium, and high (0, 4, and 16 mg/L) cadmium concentrations. It increased the root dry weight of *L. multiflorum* by 65%, 54%, and 50% and *L. perenne* by 47%, 67%, and 10%. The researchers note, "total Cd uptake per pot, calculated on the basis of biomass, was significantly greater under elevated levels of CO_2 than under ambient CO_2," increasing by 42–73% in plant shoots. Meanwhile, elevated CO_2 resulted in a reduction of Cd concentration in the plants' tissues.

The seven scientists note the high Cd uptake under CO_2-enriched conditions for the two *Lolium* species indicate great potential for use in the phytoremediation of Cd-contaminated soils in a CO_2-enriched environment. Also, because of much greater biomass production, the reduction of Cd concentrations in the forage crops' tissues suggests the rise in the air's CO_2 content could improve the safety of these crops, as was demonstrated by Guo *et al.* (2006), who according to Jia *et al.* (2011b), "reported decreased Cd accumulation in leaves, stems, roots and grains of rice at elevated CO_2"; by Zheng *et al.* (2008), who "showed that *Pteridium revolutum* and *Pteridium aquilinum* grown on Cu-contaminated soils accumulated less Cu in plant tissues at elevated levels of CO_2 than at ambient CO_2", and by Li *et al.* (2010), who also "found that elevated levels of CO_2 diluted [rice] grain Cd concentration."

Tukaj *et al.* (2007) note cadmium has been demonstrated to cause "inhibition or inactivation of many enzymes, thereby disturbing the growth, respiration, or photosynthesis in plant cells and algae (Tukendorf and Baszynski, 1991; Sanita di Toppi and Gabbrielli, 1999; Prasad *et al.*, 2001; Faller *et al.*, 2005)." The four Polish scientists grew the unicellular green alga *Scenedesmus armatus* for periods of one, two, and three days in batch cultures that contained a 93μM concentration of cadmium and were continuously bubbled with air of either 0.1% or 2% (v/v) CO_2—equivalent to approximately 1,000 and 20,000 ppm CO_2, respectively—while making a number of measurements of algal properties and physiological processes.

The researchers found the density of the cultures grown for three days at 2% CO_2 "was markedly higher in comparison to cultures grown at 0.1% CO_2 concentration mainly due to the growth rate acceleration during the first day of culture." After 24 hours of cadmium exposure, for example, "growth was inhibited to about 49% at 0.1% CO_2, whereas at 2% CO_2 only to about 74% of the controls." In addition, "cadmium inhibited the rate of oxygen evolution (70% of control) of cells cultured at 0.1% CO_2 [but] had no effect on the rate of oxygen evolution of cells cultured at 2% CO_2."

The researchers state their results suggest the protective mechanism(s) directed against cadmium was (were) "more efficient in algae cultured under elevated CO_2 than algae cultured under low level of CO_2." They also note "the main detoxifying strategy of plants contaminated by heavy metals is the production of phytochelatins (PCs)," as described by Cobbett (2000), and they report "cells grown at 2% CO_2—after 24 hours of exposure—produced much more PCs than cells cultured at 0.1% CO_2." Their data indicate the CO_2-induced phytochelatin enhancement of their study was more than tenfold. They conclude, "algae living in conditions of elevated CO_2 are better protected against cadmium than those at ordinary CO_2 level."

Taken together, the studies reviewed here bode well for the ability of plants in a CO_2-enriched environment to better deal with the problem of heavy metal soil toxicity.

References

Cobbett, C.S. 2000. Phytochelatins and their roles in heavy metal detoxification. *Plant Physiology* **123**: 825–832.

Faller, P., Kienzler, K., and Krieger-Liszkay, A. 2005. Mechanism of Cd^{2+} toxicity: Cd^{2+} inhibits photoactivation of Photosystem II by competitive binding to the essential Ca^{2+} site. *Biochimica et Biophysica Acta* **1706**: 158–164.

Fojtova, M., Fulneckova, J., Fajkus, J., and Kovarik, A. 2002. Recovery of tobacco cells from cadmium stress is accompanied by DNA repair and increased telomerase activity. *Journal of Experimental Botany* **53**: 2151–2158.

Guo, H.Y., Jia, H.X., Zhu, J.G., and Wang, X.R. 2006. Influence of the environmental behavior and ecological effect of cropland heavy metal contaminants by CO_2 enrichment in atmosphere. *Chinese Journal of Geochemistry* **25**: 10.1007/BF02840155.

Jia, H.X., Guo, H.Y., Yin, Y., Wang, Q., Sun, Q., Wang, X.R., and Zhu, J.G. 2007. Responses of rice growth to copper stress under free-air CO_2 enrichment (FACE). *Chinese Science Bulletin* **52**: 2636–2641.

Jia, Y., Ju, X., Liao, S., Song, Z., and Li, Z. 2011a. Phytochelatin synthesis in response to elevated CO_2 under cadmium stress in *Lolium perenne* L. *Journal of Plant Physiology* **168**: 1723–1728.

Jia, Y., Tang, S.-r., Ju, X.-h., Shu, L.-n., Tu, S.-x., Feng, R.-w., and Giusti, L. 2011b. Effects of elevated CO_2 levels on root morphological traits and Cd uptakes of two *Lolium* species under Cd stress. *Journal of Zhejiang University—SCIENCE B (Biomedicine & Biotechnology)* **12**: 313–325.

Li, Z.Y., Tang, S.R., Deng, X.F., Wang, R.G., and Song, Z.G. 2010. Contrasting effects of elevated CO_2 on Cu and Cd uptake by different rice varieties grown on contaminated soils with two levels of metals: implication for phytoextraction and food safety. *Journal of Hazardous Materials* **177**: 352–361.

Liu, Y.G., Wang, X., Zeng, G.M., Qu, D., Gu, J.J., Zhou, M., and Chai, L. 2007. Cadmium-induced oxidative stress and response of the ascorbate-glutathione cycle in *Bechmeria nivea* (L.), Gaud. *Chemosphere* **69**: 99–107.

Prasad, M.N.V., Malec, P., Waloszek, A., Bojko, M., and Strzalka, K. 2001. Physiological responses of *Lemna trisulca* L. (duckweed) to cadmium and copper bioaccumulation. *Plant Science* **161**: 881–889.

Romero-Puertas, M.C., Rodriguez-Serrano, M., Corpas, F.J., and delRio, L.A. 2004. Cadmium-induced subcellular accumulation of O_2^{2-} and H_2O_2 in pea leaves. *Plant, Cell and Environment* **27**: 1122–1134.

Sanita di Toppi, L. and Gabbrielli, R. 1999. Response to cadmium in higher plants. *Environmental and Experimental Botany* **41**: 105–130.

Singh, P.K. and Tewari, R.K. 2003. Cadmium toxicity induced changes in plant water relations and oxidative metabolism of *Brassica juncea* L. plants. *Journal of Environmental Biology* **24**: 107–112.

Tukaj, Z., Bascik-Remisiewicz, A., Skowronski, T., and Tukaj, C. 2007. Cadmium effect on the growth, photosynthesis, ultrastructure and phytochelatin content of green microalga *Scenedesmus armatus*: A study at low and elevated CO$_2$ concentration. *Environmental and Experimental Botany* **60**: 291–299.

Tukendorf, A. and Baszynski, T. 1991. The *in vivo* effect of cadmium on photochemical activities in chloroplast of runner bean plants. *Acta Physiologiae Plantarum* **13**: 51–57.

Vega, J.M., Garbayo, I., Dominguez, M.J., and Vigar, J. 2006. Effect of abiotic stress on photosynthesis and respiration in *Chlamydomonas reinhardtii*: induction of oxidative stress. *Enzyme and Microbial Technology* **40**: 163–167.

Zheng, J.M., Wang, H.Y., Li, Z.Q., Tang, S.R., and Chen, Z.Y. 2008. Using elevated carbon dioxide to enhance copper accumulation in *Pteridium revolutum*, a copper-tolerant plant, under experimental conditions. *International Journal of Phytoremediation* **10**: 161–172.

3.4 Herbivory

By itself, a rising atmospheric CO$_2$ concentration may reduce the frequency and severity of pest outbreaks detrimental to agriculture, without seriously affecting herbivorous organisms found in natural ecosystems.

In addition, specific genetic alterations to crop plants may increase their resistance to assaults of insect pests, allow them to better bear the consequences of possible future increases in seasonal maximum air temperatures, and help them take advantage of the positive effects of atmospheric CO$_2$ enrichment on various plant properties and processes. At the same time, the elevated CO$_2$ would reduce the severity of possible negative effects that could arise from the escape of transplanted genes into the natural environment.

3.4.1 Herbaceous Plants

- Rising atmospheric CO$_2$ concentrations may reduce the frequency and severity of pest outbreaks detrimental to agriculture, without seriously impacting herbivorous organisms found in natural ecosystems.

Kerslake *et al.* (1998) grew five-year-old heather (*Calluna vulgaris*) plants collected from a Scottish moor in open-top chambers maintained at atmospheric CO$_2$ concentrations of 350 and 600 ppm. Twice during the study, they allowed larvae of the destructive winter moth *Operophtera brumata*—whose outbreaks periodically cause extensive damage to heather moorland—to feed on current-year shoots. Feeding on the high-CO$_2$-grown foliage did not affect larval growth rates, development, or final pupal weights; nor was moth survivorship significantly altered. The three researchers conclude their study provides "no evidence that increasing atmospheric CO$_2$ concentrations will affect the potential for outbreak of *Operophtera brumata* on this host."

Newman *et al.* (1999) inoculated tall fescue (*Festuca arundinacea*) plants growing in open-top chambers maintained at atmospheric CO$_2$ concentrations of 350 and 700 ppm with bird cherry-oat aphids (*Rhopalosiphum padi*). After nine weeks, the plants growing in the CO$_2$-enriched air had experienced a 37% increase in productivity and were covered with far fewer aphids than the plants growing in ambient air. The result was a "win" for the favored plants and a "loss" for the destructive insects.

Goverde *et al.* (1999) collected four genotypes of *Lotus corniculatus* near Paris and grew them in controlled-environment chambers kept at atmospheric CO$_2$ concentrations of 350 and 700 ppm. Larvae of the Common Blue Butterfly (*Polyommatus icarus*) the researchers allowed to feed on the foliage produced in the CO$_2$-enriched air ate more, grew larger, and experienced shorter development times than larvae feeding on the foliage in the ambient-air treatment, suggesting this butterfly species will become more robust and plentiful as the air's CO$_2$ content rises.

Brooks and Whittaker (1999) removed grassland monoliths containing eggs of the xylem-feeding spittlebug *Neophilaenus lineatus* from the UK's Great Dun Fell in Cumbria and placed them in glasshouses maintained at atmospheric CO$_2$ concentrations of 350 and 600 ppm for two years. Survival of the spittlebug's nymphal states was reduced by 24% in both of the generations produced in their experiment in the high-CO$_2$ treatment, suggesting this particular insect likely will cause less tissue damage to the plants of this species-poor grassland in a CO$_2$-enriched environment.

Joutci *et al.* (2000) grew bean (*Phaseolus vulgaris*) plants in controlled environments kept at atmospheric CO$_2$ concentrations of 350 and 700 ppm, into which they introduced the destructive agricultural mite *Tetranychus urticae*. They found female mites produced 34% and 49% fewer offspring in the CO_2-enriched chambers in their first and second generations, respectively. These reductions in the reproductive success of this mite, which attacks more than 150 crop species worldwide, has important agricultural implications in terms of crop production.

Peters *et al.* (2000) fed foliage derived from FACE plots of calcareous grasslands of Switzerland (maintained at 350 and 650 ppm CO_2) to terrestrial slugs, finding they exhibited no preference with respect to the CO_2 treatment from which the foliage was derived. Also, in a study that targeted no specific insect pest, Castells *et al.* (2002) found a doubling of the air's CO_2 content enhanced the total phenolic contents of two Mediterranean perennial grasses (*Dactylis glomerata* and *Bromus erectus*) by 15% and 87%, respectively; these compounds tend to enhance mechanisms that allow plants to defend against and resist attacks by herbivores and pathogens.

Coviella and Trumble (2000) determined toxins produced by *Bacillus thuringiensis* (Bt)—which are applied to crop plants by spraying as a means of combating various crop pests—were "more efficacious" in cotton grown in an elevated CO_2 environment than in ambient air, an important benefit for modern agriculture. In addition, Coviella *et al.* (2000) write, "elevated CO_2 appears to eliminate differences between transgenic [Bt-containing] and nontransgenic plants for some key insect developmental/fitness variables including length of the larval stage and pupal weight," which could prove significant for nature in the event of inadvertent Bt gene transference to wild relatives of transgenic crop lines.

Barbehenn *et al.* (2004b) note increases in the air's CO_2 content typically lead to greater decreases in the concentrations of nitrogen and, therefore, protein in the foliage of C_3 as compared to C_4 grasses, citing Wand *et al.* (1999). Barbehenn *et al.* write, "it has been predicted that insect herbivores will increase their feeding damage on C_3 plants to a greater extent than on C_4 plants (Lincoln *et al.*, 1984, 1986; Lambers, 1993)." The three researchers grew *Lolium multiflorum* Lam. (Italian ryegrass, a common C_3 pasture grass) and *Bouteloua curtipendula* (Michx.) Torr. (sideoats gramma, a native C_4 rangeland grass) in chambers maintained at either the ambient atmospheric CO_2 concentration of 370 ppm or 740 ppm for two months. They allowed newly molted sixth instar larvae of *Pseudaletia unipuncta* (a grass-specialist noctuid) and *Spodoptera frugiperda* (a generalist noctuid) to feed on the grasses' foliage.

As expected, foliage protein concentration decreased by 20% in the C_3 grass, but by only 1% in the C_4 grass, when they were grown in CO_2-enriched air, and "to the extent that protein is the most limiting of the macronutrients examined, these changes represent a decline in the nutritional quality of the C_3 grass," Barbehenn *et al.* write. However, and contrary to their expectations, they report "neither caterpillar species significantly increased its consumption rate to compensate for the lower concentration of protein in [the] C_3 grass," noting "this result does not support the hypothesis that C_3 plants will be subject to greater rates of herbivory relative to C_4 plants in future [high-CO_2] atmospheric conditions (Lincoln *et al.*, 1984)." In addition, and "despite significant changes in the nutritional quality of *L. multiflorum* under elevated CO_2," they note "no effect on the relative growth rate of either caterpillar species on either grass species resulted," and there were "no significant differences in insect performance between CO_2 levels." Barbehenn *et al.* suggest "post-ingestive mechanisms could provide a sufficient means of compensation for the lower nutritional quality of C_3 plants grown under elevated CO_2."

Barbehenn *et al.* conclude "there will not be a single pattern that characterizes all grass feeders" with respect to their feeding preferences and developmental responses under conditions where certain C_3 plants may experience foliar protein concentrations lower than those they exhibit today, nor will the changes that may occur necessarily impede herbivore development or damage the health and vigor of their host plants.

Barbehenn *et al.* (2004a) fed some of the identical foliage of the same experiment to grasshopper (*Melanoplus sanguinipes*) nymphs reared to the fourth instar stage. They note "*M. sanguinipes* did not significantly increase its consumption rate when feeding on the C_3 grass grown under elevated CO_2," which they say implies "post-ingestive mechanisms enable these grasshoppers to compensate for variable nutritional quality in their host plants." They further suggest some of these post-ingestive responses may include "changes in gut size, food residence time, digestive enzyme levels, and nutrient metabolism (Simpson and Simpson, 1990; Bernays and Simpson, 1990; Hinks *et al.*, 1991; Zanotto *et al.*, 1993; Yang and Joern, 1994a,b)." If anything, *M. sanguinipes* growth rates were increased, perhaps by as much as 12%, when they fed on the C_3 foliage produced in the CO_2-enriched, as compared to the ambient-air treatment.

Therefore, just as was found in Barbehenn *et al.*

(2004b), the CO_2-induced decrease in leaf protein concentration observed in this study did not induce an increase in consumption in the C_3 plant studied, nor did it reduce the growth rate of the herbivore studied. Therefore, the scientists state, "although compensatory feeding was commonly observed in early studies [of this subject], the absence of compensatory feeding on C_3 plants grown under elevated CO_2 has since been observed frequently among herbivorous insects (Bezemer and Jones, 1998)."

Bidart-Bouzat et al. (2005) grew three genotypes of mouse-ear cress (Arabidopsis thaliana) from seed in pots placed in controlled-environment chambers maintained at either ambient CO_2 (360 ppm) or elevated CO_2 (720 ppm). On each of half of the plants (the herbivory treatment) in each of the CO_2 treatments, they placed two second instar larvae of the diamondback moth (Plutella xylostella) at bolting time and removed them at pupation, which resulted in an average of 20% of each plant's total leaf area in the herbivory treatment being removed. Next, each pupa was placed in a gelatin capsule until adult emergence and ultimate death, after which insect gender was determined and the pupa's weight recorded. At the end of the herbivory trial, leaves of the control and larvae-infested plants were analyzed for concentrations of individual glucosinolates—a group of plant-derived chemicals that can act as herbivore deterrents, as reported by Mauricio and Rausher (1997)—after which the researchers determined total glucosinolate production by summation of the individual glucosinolate assays. Finally, they evaluated various influences of elevated CO_2 on moth performance and their association with plant defense-related traits.

Bidart-Bouzat et al. found herbivory by larvae of the diamondback moth did not induce any increase in the production of glucosinolates in the mouse-ear cress in the ambient CO_2 treatment. They report, "herbivory-induced increases in glucosinolate contents, ranging from 28% to 62% above basal levels, were found under elevated CO_2 in two out of the three genotypes studied." In addition, "elevated CO_2 decreased the overall performance of diamondback moths." And because "induced defenses can increase plant fitness by reducing subsequent herbivore attacks (Agrawal, 1999; Kessler and Baldwin, 2004)," the three researchers suggest "the pronounced increase in glucosinolate levels under CO_2 enrichment may pose a threat not only for insect generalists that are likely to be more influenced by rapid changes in the concentration of these chemicals,

but also for other insect specialists more susceptible than diamondback moths to high glucosinolate levels (Stowe, 1998; Kliebenstein et al., 2002)."

Ayres et al. (2008) reported the responses of belowground nematode herbivores to atmospheric CO_2 enrichment to approximately 350 ppm above ambient in experiments conducted on three grassland ecosystems in Colorado and California (USA) and Montpellier, France. They note "soil moisture increased in response to elevated CO_2 in the California, Colorado, and French stud[ies] (Hungate et al., 1997; Nijs et al., 2000; Morgan et al., 2004)." They also found "elevated CO_2 increased root biomass by approximately 3–32% in the first 5 years of the Coloradoan study (Pendall et al., 2004), by 23% after 6 years in the Californian study (Rillig et al., 1999), and by 31% after 6 months in the French study (Dhillion et al., 1996)." Regarding nematodes, they add, "CO_2 enrichment did not significantly affect the family richness, diversity, or PPI [plant parasitic nematode index] of herbivorous nematodes in the Colorado, California, or French study," noting "in each experiment, neutral effects were the most frequent response to CO_2 enrichment." The seven scientists conclude, "one consequence of increased root production, without changes in belowground herbivore populations, might be greater plant inputs to soil," which "may lead to greater soil organic matter pools in grassland ecosystems, potentially enhancing soil carbon sequestration."

Lau et al. (2008) measured the amounts of herbivore and pathogen damage done to the common prairie legume Lespedeza capitata growing in ambient and elevated (560 ppm) CO_2 treatments in the seventh and eighth years (2004 and 2005) of the BioCON study (Reich et al., 2001) conducted at the Cedar Creek Natural History Area in Minnesota (USA), where the CO_2 treatments were applied during the daylight hours of each growing season. In this setting, three types of pests inflicted herbivore damage—generalist chewers (primarily grasshoppers), Pachyschelus laevigatus (Coleoptera: Buprestidae), and Tortriedon sp. (Lepidoptera)—and pathogen damage was caused by Pythium or Fusarium spp.

Lau et al. say they detected "no evidence that the CO_2 treatments affected herbivore damage." As to pathogen damage, they found disease incidence "was lower in the elevated CO_2 environment, although this difference [10% less in 2004 and 53% less in 2005] was statistically significant only in 2005 ($P < 0.01$)." Therefore, and because "disease caused major reductions in reproductive output," the five researchers write, "the effects of CO_2 on disease incidence may be important for *L. capitata* evolution and population dynamics," and this phenomenon should significantly benefit this species in a high-CO_2 environment. In addition, they note Strengbom and Reich (2006), "working in the same experimental site ... also found that elevated CO_2 ... reduced disease incidence on *Solidago rigida*."

Coll and Hughes (2008) describe their work as "the first study that measured the effect of global atmospheric change on an omnivorous consumer," exploring the impacts of elevated atmospheric CO_2 on the behavior and performance of an omnivorous bug (*Oechalia schellenbergii*, Heteroptera: Pentatomidae) and its prey, a polyphagous chewing herbivorous pest (*Helicoverpa armigera*; Lepidoptera: Noctuidae), feeding on pea (*Pisum sativum*) foliage grown in controlled-environment cabinets maintained at atmospheric CO_2 concentrations of either 360 or 700 ppm. They found the *H. armigera* pests that fed on the elevated CO_2-grown pea plants were significantly smaller than those that fed on the ambient CO_2-grown pea plants, and the bigger *O. schellenbergii* bugs that fed on them "performed best when fed larvae from the elevated-CO_2 treatment," because the prey of that treatment "were smaller and thus easier to subdue." Only 13.3% of the predation attempts made on the larvae fed ambient-CO_2-grown foliage were successful, as compared to 78.2% for the larvae fed elevated-CO_2-grown foliage.

The two researchers conclude "elevated CO_2 may benefit generalist predators through increased prey vulnerability, which would put pest species under higher risk of predation." Consequently, and "since omnivory is widespread in agroecosystems," they argue "yield loss to most pest species will be lower under elevated atmospheric CO_2 levels, compared to the current condition."

The majority of evidence to date suggests rising atmospheric CO_2 concentrations may reduce the frequency and severity of pest outbreaks detrimental to agriculture, without seriously impacting herbivorous organisms found in natural ecosystems.

References

Agrawal, A.A. 1999. Induced-responses to herbivory in wild radish: effects on several herbivores and plant fitness. *Ecology* **80**: 1713–1723.

Ayres, E., Wall, D.H., Simmons, B.L., Field, C.B.,

Milchunas, D.G., Morgan, J.A., and Roy, J. 2008. Belowground nematode herbivores are resistant to elevated atmospheric CO_2 concentrations in grassland ecosystems. *Soil Biology & Biochemistry* **40**: 978–985.

Barbehenn, R.V., Karowe, D.N. and Chen, Z. 2004a. Performance of a generalist grasshopper on a C_3 and a C_4 grass: compensation for the effects of elevated CO_2 on plant nutritional quality. *Oecologia* **140**: 96–103.

Barbehenn, R.V., Karowe, D.N., and Spickard, A. 2004b. Effects of elevated atmospheric CO_2 on the nutritional ecology of C_3 and C_4 grass-feeding caterpillars. *Oecologia* **140**: 86–95.

Bernays, E.A. and Simpson, S.J. 1990. Nutrition. In: Chapman, R.F. and Joern, A. (Eds.) *Biology of Grasshoppers*. Wiley, New York, NY, pp. 105–127.

Bezemer, T.M. and Jones, T.H. 1998. Plant-insect herbivore interactions in elevated atmospheric CO_2: quantitative analyses and guild effects. *Oikos* **82**: 212–222.

Bidart-Bouzat, M.G., Mithen, R., and Berenbaum, M.R. 2005. Elevated CO_2 influences herbivory-induced defense responses of *Arabidopsis thaliana*. *Oecologia* **145**: 415–424.

Brooks, G.L. and Whittaker, J.B. 1999. Responses of three generations of a xylem-feeding insect, *Neophilaenus lineatus* (Homoptera), to elevated CO_2. *Global Change Biology* **5**: 395–401.

Castells, E., Roumet, C., Peñuelas, J., and Roy, J. 2002. Intraspecific variability of phenolic concentrations and their responses to elevated CO_2 in two Mediterranean perennial grasses. *Environmental and Experimental Botany* **47**: 205–216.

Coll, M. and Hughes, L. 2008. Effects of elevated CO_2 on an insect omnivore: A test for nutritional effects mediated by host plants and prey. *Agriculture, Ecosystems and Environment* **123**: 271–279.

Coviella, C.E., Morgan, D.J.W., and Trumble, J.T. 2000. Interactions of elevated CO_2 and nitrogen fertilization: Effects on production of *Bacillus thuringiensis* toxins in transgenic plants. *Environmental Entomology* **29**: 781–787.

Coviella, C.E. and Trumble, J.T. 2000. Effect of elevated atmospheric carbon dioxide on the use of foliar application of *Bacillus thuringiensis*. *BioControl* **45**: 325–336.

Dhillion, S.D., Roy, J., and Abrams, M. 1996. Assessing the impact of elevated CO_2 on soil microbial activity in a Mediterranean model ecosystem. *Plant & Soil* **187**: 333–342.

Goverde, M., Bazin, A., Shykoff, J.A., and Erhardt, A. 1999. Influence of leaf chemistry of *Lotus corniculatus*

(Fabaceae) on larval development of *Polyommatus icarus* (Lepidoptera, Lycaenidae): effects of elevated CO_2 and plant genotype. *Functional Ecology* 13: 801–810.

Hinks, C.R., Cheeseman, M.T., Erlandson, M.A., Olfert, O., and Westcott, N.D. 1991. The effects of kochia, wheat and oats on digestive proteinases and the protein economy of adult grasshoppers, *Malanoplus sanguinipes*. *Journal of Insect Physiology* 37: 417–430.

Hungate, B.A., Holland, E.A., Jackson, R.B., Chapin, F.S., Mooney, H.A., and Field, C.B. 1997. The fate of carbon in grasslands under carbon dioxide enrichment. *Nature* 388: 576–579.

Joutei, A.B., Roy, J., Van Impe, G., and Lebrun, P. 2000. Effect of elevated CO_2 on the demography of a leaf-sucking mite feeding on bean. *Oecologia* 123: 75–81.

Kerslake, J.E., Woodin, S.J., and Hartley, S.E. 1998. Effects of carbon dioxide and nitrogen enrichment on a plant-insect interaction: the quality of *Calluna vulgaris* as a host for *Operophtera brumata*. *New Phytologist* 140: 43–53.

Kessler, A. and Baldwin, I.T. 2004. Herbivore-induced plant vaccination. Part I. The orchestration of plant defenses in nature and their fitness consequences in the wild tobacco, *Nicotiana attenuata*. *Plant Journal* 38: 639–649.

Kliebenstein, D., Pedersen, D., Barker, B., and Mitchell-Olds, T. 2002. Comparative analysis of quantitative trait loci controlling glucosinolates, myrosinase and insect resistance in *Arabidopsis thaliana*. *Genetics* 161: 325–332.

Lambers, H. 1993. Rising CO_2, secondary plant metabolism, plant-herbivore interactions and litter decomposition. Theoretical considerations. *Vegetatio* 104/105: 263–271.

Lau, J.A., Strengbom, J., Stone, L.R., Reich, P.B., and Tiffin, P. 2008. Direct and indirect effects of CO_2, nitrogen, and community diversity on plant-enemy interactions. *Ecology* 89: 226–236.

Lincoln, D.E., Couvet, D., and Sionit, N. 1986. Responses of an insect herbivore to host plants grown in carbon dioxide enriched atmospheres. *Oecologia* 69: 556–560.

Lincoln, D.E., Sionit, N., and Strain, B.R. 1984. Growth and feeding response of *Pseudoplusia includens* (Lepidoptera: Noctuidae) to host plants grown in controlled carbon dioxide atmospheres. *Environmental Entomology* 13: 1527–1530.

Mauricio, R. and Rausher, M.D. 1997. Experimental manipulation of putative selective agents provides evidence for the role of natural enemies in the evolution of plant defense. *Evolution* 51: 1435–1444.

Morgan, J.A., Mosier, A.R., Milchunas, D.G., LeCain, D.R., Nelson, J.A., and Parton, W.J. 2004. CO_2 enhances productivity, alters species composition, and reduces digestibility of shortgrass steppe vegetation. *Ecological Applications* 14: 208–219.

Newman, J.A., Gibson, D.J., Hickam, E., Lorenz, M., Adams, E., Bybee, L., and Thompson, R. 1999. Elevated carbon dioxide results in smaller populations of the bird cherry-oat aphid *Rhopalosiphum padi*. *Ecological Entomology* 24: 486–489.

Nijs, I., Roy, J., Salager, J.-L., and Fabreguettes, J. 2000. Elevated CO_2 alters carbon fluxes in early successional Mediterranean ecosystems. *Global Change Biology* 6: 981–994.

Pendall, E., Mosier, A.R., and Morgan, J.A. 2004. Rhizodeposition stimulated by elevated CO_2 in a semiarid grassland. *New Phytologist* 162: 447–458.

Peters, H.A., Baur, B., Bazzaz, F., and Korner, C. 2000. Consumption rates and food preferences of slugs in a calcareous grassland under current and future CO_2 conditions. *Oecologia* 125: 72–81.

Reich, P.B., Tilman, D., Craine, J., Ellsworth, D., Tjoelker, M.G., Knops, J., Wedin, D., Naeem, S., Bahauddin, D., Goth, J., Bengston, W., and Lee, T.D. 2001. Do species and functional groups differ in acquisition and use of C, N, and water under varying atmospheric CO_2 and N availability regimes? A field test with 16 grassland species. *New Phytologist* 150: 435–448.

Rillig, M.C., Field, C.B., and Allen, M.F. 1999. Soil biota responses to long-term atmospheric CO_2 enrichment in two California annual grasslands. *Oecologia* 119: 572–577.

Simpson, S.J. and Simpson, C.L. 1990. The mechanisms of nutritional compensation by phytophagous insects. In: Bernays, E.A. (Ed.) *Insect-Plant Interactions*, Vol. 2. CRC Press, Boca Raton, FL, pp. 111–160.

Stowe, K.A. 1998. Realized defense of artificially selected lines of *Brassica rapa*: effects of quantitative genetic variation in foliar glucosinolate concentration. *Environmental Entomology* 27: 1166–1174.

Strengbom, J. and Reich, P.B. 2006. Elevated CO_2 and increased N supply reduce leaf disease and related photosynthetic impacts on *Solidago rigida*. *Oecologia* 149: 519–525.

Wand, S.J.E., Midgley, G.F., Jones, M.H., and Curtis, P.S. 1999. Responses of wild C_4 and C_3 grass (Poaceae) species to elevated atmospheric CO_2 concentration: a meta-analytic test of current theories and perceptions. *Global Change Biology* 5: 723–741.

Yang, Y. and Joern, A. 1994a. Gut size changes in relation to variable food quality and body size in grasshoppers. *Functional Ecology* 8: 36–45.

Yang, Y. and Joern, A. 1994b. Influence of diet quality, developmental stage, and temperature on food residence time in the grasshopper *Melanoplus differentialis*. *Physiological Zoology* **67**: 598–616.

Zanotto, F.P., Simpson, S.J., and Raubenheimer, D. 1993. The regulation of growth by locusts through post-ingestive compensation for variation in the levels of dietary protein and carbohydrate. *Physiological Entomology* **18**: 425–434.

3.4.2 Transgenic Plants

• Specific genetic alterations to crop plants may improve their ability to withstand the assaults of insects pests, bear the consequences of possible future increases in seasonal maximum air temperatures, and take advantage of the positive effects of atmospheric CO_2 enrichment on various plant properties and processes. Meanwhile, elevated CO_2 reduces the severity of possible negative effects that could arise from the escape of transplanted genes into the natural environment.

Toxins produced by *Bacillus thuringiensis* (Bt) supplied to crops via foliar application have been used as a means of combating crop pests for well over half a century. The effectiveness of this management technique depends primarily on the amount of Bt-produced toxins ingested by targeted insects. This section examines how atmospheric CO_2 enrichment might impact this phenomenon.

If atmospheric CO_2 concentrations are high but soil nitrogen levels are low, foliar concentrations of nitrogen are generally reduced from what they are at ambient CO_2 concentrations, suggesting insects would have to eat more foliage to get their normal requirement of nitrogen for proper growth and development in CO_2-enriched air. By consuming more foliage, the insects also would ingest more Bt-produced toxins, and would thus be more severely impacted by those substances.

To test this hypothesis, Coviella and Trumble (2000) grew cotton plants in each of six Teflon-film chambers in a temperature-controlled greenhouse, where three of the chambers were maintained at an atmospheric CO_2 concentration of 370 ppm and three were maintained at 900 ppm CO_2. In addition, half of the plants in each chamber were given high levels of nitrogen (N) fertilization, and half received low levels (30 vs. 130 mg N/kg soil/week). After 45 days of growth under these conditions, the researchers removed leaves from the plants and dipped them in a Bt solution, after which known amounts of treated leaf material were fed to *Spodoptera exigua* larvae and the responses measured and analyzed.

The two researchers determined the plants grown in the elevated CO_2 chambers did indeed have significantly lower foliar nitrogen concentrations than those grown in the ambient CO_2 chambers under the low N fertilization regime, but this was not the case under the high N regime. They also discovered older larvae fed with foliage grown in elevated CO_2 with low N fertilization consumed significantly more plant material than insects fed with foliage grown in ambient CO_2; but again, they found no differences with high N fertilization. Finally, and "consistent with the effect of higher Bt toxin intake due to enhanced consumption," they found "insects fed on low N plants had significantly higher mortality in elevated CO_2." They identified no such effect in the high N treatment. Consequently, with respect to pest management using Bt-produced toxins supplied to crops via foliar application, Coviella and Trumble conclude "increasing atmospheric CO_2 is making the foliar applications more efficacious."

Coviella *et al.* (2000) addressed what happens to transgenic plants into which the Bt gene for producing the toxin has been artificially inserted. They grew cotton plants in 12 Teflon-film chambers in a temperature-controlled greenhouse, where six chambers were maintained at an atmospheric CO_2 concentration of 370 ppm and six were maintained at 900 ppm CO_2. Half of the cotton plants in each of these chambers were of a transgenic line containing the Bt gene for the production of the Cry1Ac toxin, which is mildly toxic for *Spodoptera exigua*, and the other half were of a near isogenic line without the Bt gene. Half of the plants in each chamber received low and high levels of N fertilization. Between 40 and 45 days after leaves emerged, researchers removed leaves from the plants and fed them to the *S. exigua* larvae, measuring and analyzing a number of larval responses and various leaf properties.

They found the low-N plants in the elevated CO_2 treatment had lower foliar N concentrations than the low-N plants in the ambient CO_2 treatment, and the transgenic plants from the low-N, high CO_2 treatment produced lower levels of Bt toxin than the transgenic plants from the low-N, ambient CO_2 treatment. The high level of N fertilization only partially compensated for the latter high-CO_2 effect, and in the ambient CO_2 treatment there was also a significant increase in days to pupation for insects fed transgenic plants.

This difference was not evident in elevated CO_2. Pupal weight in ambient CO_2 was significantly higher in non-transgenic plants, and again, this difference was not observed in elevated CO_2.

The three researchers write, "these results support the hypothesis that the lower N content per unit of plant tissue caused by the elevated CO_2 will result in lower toxin production by transgenic plants when nitrogen supply to the plants is a limiting factor." They also note "elevated CO_2 appears to eliminate differences between transgenic and non-transgenic plants for some key insect developmental/fitness variables including length of the larval stage and pupal weight."

These findings suggest, in the case of inadvertent Bt gene transference to wild relatives of transgenic crop lines, elevated levels of atmospheric CO_2 will tend to negate certain of the negative effects the wayward genes might otherwise inflict. The rise in the air's CO_2 content could therefore constitute a buffer against this potential outcome.

Coviella *et al.*'s results also suggest transgenic crops designed to produce Bt-type toxins may become less effective in carrying out the objectives of their design as the air's CO_2 content rises. Coupling this possibility with the fact the foliar application of *Bacillus thuringiensis* to crops should become even more effective in a higher-CO_2 world, as Coviella and Trumble found, it can be argued the implantation of toxin-producing genes in crops is not viable in the face of the rise in the air's CO_2 content, which reduces that technique's effectiveness at the same time it increases the effectiveness of direct foliar applications.

Although it is difficult to predict the future of genetic modification of crops for pesticidal purposes, it is useful to know the rise in the atmosphere's CO_2 concentration will help both nature and agriculture, whatever the outcome of the current debate.

In a study of three different types of rice—a wild type (WT) and two transgenic varieties, one with 65% wild-type rubisco (AS-77) and one with 40% wild-type rubisco (AS-71)—Makino *et al.* (2000) grew plants from seed for 70 days in growth chambers maintained at 360 and 1,000 ppm CO_2. They harvested the plants and determined their biomass, finding the mean dry weights of the WT, AS-77, and AS-71 varieties grown in air of 360 ppm were, respectively, 5.75, 3.02, and 0.83 g. In air of 1,000 ppm CO_2, corresponding mean dry weights were 7.90, 7.40, and 5.65 g. Consequently, although the growth rates of the genetically engineered rice plants were far inferior to the wild type when grown in normal air of 360 ppm CO_2 (with AS-71 producing less than 15% as much biomass as the wild type), when grown in air of 1,000 ppm CO_2 they experienced far greater CO_2-induced increases in growth: a 145% increase in the case of AS-77 and a 581% increase for AS-71. Thus, whereas the transgenic plants were highly disadvantaged in normal air of 360 ppm CO_2, they were found to be pretty much on an equal footing in highly CO_2-enriched air..

Chen *et al.* (2005) grew well-watered and well-fertilized plants of two varieties of cotton—one expressing Cry1A (c) genes from *Bacillus thuringiensis* and a non-transgenic cultivar from the same recurrent parent—in pots placed in open-top chambers maintained at either 375 or 750 ppm CO_2 in Sanhe County, Hebei Province, China, from planting in mid-May to harvest in October. During this period, they collected several immature bolls and analyzed them for various chemical characteristics, and they refrigerated others for later feeding to cotton boll-worm larvae, whose growth characteristics they closely monitored. The five researchers found the elevated CO_2 treatment increased immature boll concentrations of condensed tannins by approximately 22% and 26% in transgenic and non-transgenic cotton, respectively. In addition, elevated CO_2 slightly decreased the body biomass of the cotton bollworms and reduced moth fecundity. The Bt treatment was even more effective in this regard, and the negative cotton bollworm responses were expressed most strongly in the combined Bt-high-CO_2 treatment. Chen *et al.* conclude the expected higher atmospheric CO_2 concentrations of the future will "either not change or only slightly enhance the efficacy of Bt technology against cotton bollworms."

Chen *et al.* (2007) report growing the same two cotton cultivars under the same conditions from the time of planting on 10 May 2004 until the plants were harvested in October, after which egg masses of the cotton bollworms were reared in a growth chamber under ambient-CO_2 conditions. They fed three successive generations of bollworms either transgenic or non-transgenic cotton bolls from plants grown in either ambient or twice-ambient atmospheric CO_2 concentrations, assessing a number of physiological characteristics of the bollworms. Chen *et al.* report "both elevated CO_2 and transgenic Bt cotton increased larval lifespan," but they decreased "pupal weight, survival rate, fecundity, frass output, relative and mean relative growth rates, and the efficiency of conversion of ingested and digested food." They write, "transgenic Bt cotton significantly decreased the population-trend index compared to non-transgenic cotton for the three successive bollworm generations, especially at elevated CO_2."

The four researchers conclude the negative effects of elevated CO_2 on cotton bollworm physiology and population dynamics "may intensify through successive generations," in agreement with the findings of Brooks and Whittaker (1998, 1999) and Wu *et al.* (2006). They conclude "both elevated CO_2 and transgenic Bt cotton are adverse environmental factors for cotton bollworm long-term population growth."

Fu *et al.* (2008) note "heat stress is a major constraint to wheat production and negatively impacts grain quality, causing tremendous economic losses, and may become a more troublesome factor due to global warming." They "introduced into wheat the maize gene coding for plastidal EF-Tu [protein synthesis elongation factor]" to assess "the expression of the transgene, and its effect on thermal aggregation of leaf proteins in transgenic plants," and "the heat stability of photosynthetic membranes (thylakoids) and the rate of CO_2 fixation in young transgenic plants following exposure to heat stress." They found "improved protection of leaf proteins against thermal aggregation, reduced damage to thylakoid membranes and enhanced photosynthetic capability following exposure to heat stress," and these results "support the concept that EF-Tu ameliorates negative effects of heat stress by acting as a molecular chaperone."

Fu *et al.* describe their work as "the first demonstration that a gene other than HSP [heat shock protein] gene can be used for improvement of heat tolerance," noting it also indicates "the improvement is possible in a species that has a complex genome," such as hexaploid wheat. They conclude their results "strongly suggest that heat tolerance of wheat, and possibly other crop plants, can be improved by modulating expression of plastidal EF-Tu and/or by selection of genotypes with increased endogenous levels of this protein."

It appears specific genetic alterations to crop plants may improve their ability to withstand the assaults of insects pests, bear the consequences of possible future increases in seasonal maximum air temperatures, and take advantage of the positive effects of atmospheric CO_2 enrichment on various plant properties and processes. Elevated CO_2 reduces the severity of any negative effects that could arise from the escape of transplanted genes into the natural environment.

References

Brooks, G.L. and Whittaker, J.B. 1998. Responses of multiple generations of *Gastrophysa viridula*, feeding on *Rumex obtusifolius*, to elevated CO_2. *Global Change Biology* **4**: 63–75.

Brooks, G.L. and Whittaker, J.B. 1999. Responses of three generations of a xylem-feeding insect, *Neophilaenus lineatus* (Homoptera), to elevated CO_2. *Global Change Biology* **5**: 395–401.

Chen, F., Wu, G., Ge, F., Parajulee, M.N., and Shrestha, R.B. 2005. Effects of elevated CO_2 and transgenic Bt cotton on plant chemistry, performance, and feeding of an insect herbivore, the cotton bollworm. *Entomologia Experimentalis et Applicata* **115**: 341–350.

Chen, F., Wu, G., Parajulee, M.N., and Ge, F. 2007. Long-term impacts of elevated carbon dioxide and transgenic Bt cotton on performance and feeding of three generations of cotton bollworm. *Entomologia Experimentalis et Applicata* **124**: 27–35.

Coviella, C.E., Morgan, D.J.W., and Trumble, J.T. 2000. Interactions of elevated CO_2 and nitrogen fertilization: Effects on production of *Bacillus thuringiensis* toxins in transgenic plants. *Environmental Entomology* **29**: 781–787.

Coviella, C.E. and Trumble, J.T. 2000. Effect of elevated atmospheric carbon dioxide on the use of foliar application of *Bacillus thuringiensis*. *BioControl* **45**: 325–336.

Fu, J., Momcilovic, I., Clemente, T.E., Nersesian, N., Trick, H.N., and Ristic, Z. 2008. Heterologous expression of a plastid EF-Tu reduces protein thermal aggregation and enhances CO_2 fixation in wheat (*Triticum aestivum*) following heat stress. *Plant Molecular Biology* **68**: 277–288.

Makino, A., Harada, M., Kaneko, K., Mae, T., Shimada, T., and Yamamoto, N. 2000. Whole-plant growth and N allocation in transgenic rice plants with decreased content of ribulose-1,5-bisphosphate carboxylase under different CO_2 partial pressures. *Australian Journal of Plant Physiology* **27**: 1–12.

Wu, G., Chen, J.F., and Ge, F. 2006. Response of multiple generations of cotton bollworm *Helicoverpa armigera* Hubner, feeding on spring wheat, to elevated CO_2. *Journal of Applied Entomology* **130**: 2–9.

3.4.3 Woody Plants

Data obtained from open experimental systems in the field suggest herbivore damage to trees may decrease in a CO_2-enriched environment. However, if the opposite circumstances were to occur, other evidence suggests air of higher CO_2 concentration would make trees more capable of surviving severe defoliation events. In addition, higher CO_2 concentrations tend to reduce fluctuating asymmetry in plant leaves, leading to more symmetrical leaves that are less susceptible to attacks by herbivores, because they are under less stress of both genetic and environmental origin than leaves growing in less-CO_2-enriched air.

3.4.3.1 Maple

- In contrast to the view herbivores will do more damage to trees, including maples, in CO_2-enriched air as a result of enhanced feeding on lower-quality foliage, data from open experimental systems suggest such damage may decrease in a CO_2-enriched environment. Evidence also suggests sugar maple may be more capable of surviving severe defoliation events that in the past have been implicated in the widespread decline of maples.

Insect pests have greatly affected trees in the past and likely will continue to do so in the future. The rise in the atmosphere's CO_2 concentration may affect this phenomenon. Here we review studies that have addressed this subject as it applies to three maple tree species.

Williams *et al.* (2003) studied *Acer rubrum* saplings beginning their fourth year of growth in open-top chambers maintained at four atmospheric CO_2/temperature combinations: ambient temperature, ambient CO_2; ambient temperature, elevated CO_2 (ambient + 300 ppm); elevated temperature (ambient + 3.5°C), ambient CO_2; and elevated temperature, elevated CO_2. They collected first instar gypsy moth larvae on various branches of the trees and observed their behavior. They report, "larvae feeding on CO_2-enriched foliage ate a comparably poorer food source than those feeding on ambient CO_2-grown plants, irrespective of temperature." Nevertheless, the "CO_2-induced reductions in foliage quality (e.g. nitrogen and water) were unrelated to insect mortality, development rate and pupal weight," and these and any other phytochemical changes that may have occurred "resulted in no negative effects on gypsy moth performance." They also write, "irrespective of CO_2 concentration, on average, male larvae pupated 7.5 days earlier and female larvae 8 days earlier at elevated temperature." They conclude the observed temperature-induced hastening of the insects'

development would likely expose the trees to less predation and parasitism risk.

Hamilton *et al.* (2004) note many single-species investigations suggest increases in atmospheric CO_2 will increase herbivory (Bezemer and Jones, 1998; Cannon, 1998; Coviella and Trumble, 1999; Hunter, 2001; Lincoln *et al.*, 1993; Whittaker, 1999). However, because there are so many feedbacks and complex interactions among the numerous components of real-world ecosystems, they warn one ought not put too much faith in these predictions until relevant real-world ecosystem-level experiments have been completed.

Hamilton *et al.* "measured the amount of leaf tissue damaged by insects and other herbivorous arthropods during two growing seasons in a deciduous forest understory continuously exposed to ambient (360 ppm) and elevated (560 ppm) CO_2 conditions." This forest, at the Duke Forest FACE facility near Chapel Hill, North Carolina (USA), was dominated by loblolly pine trees that accounted for fully 92% of the ecosystem's total woody biomass. It contained 48 species of other woody plants (trees, shrubs, and vines) that had naturally established themselves in the forest's understory. Hamilton *et al.* quantified the loss of foliage due to herbivory experienced by three deciduous tree species, one of which was *Acer rubrum*. They report, "we found that elevated CO_2 led to a trend toward reduced herbivory in [the] deciduous understory in a situation that included the full complement of naturally occurring plant and insect species." In 1999, for example, they determined "elevated CO_2 reduced overall herbivory by more than 40%," and in 2000 they say they observed "the same pattern and magnitude of reduction."

Hamilton *et al.* say they "found no evidence for significant changes in leaf nitrogen, C/N ratio, sugar, starch or total leaf phenolics in either year of [the] study." They note these findings agree with those of "another study performed at the Duke Forest FACE site that also found no effect of elevated CO_2 on the chemical composition of leaves of understory trees (Finzi and Schlesinger, 2002)."

Hamilton *et al.* conclude their landmark paper by emphasizing, "despite the large number of studies that predict increased herbivory, particularly from leaf chewers, under elevated CO_2, our study found a trend toward reduced herbivory two years in a row." In addition, they note their real-world results "agree with the only other large-scale field experiment that quantified herbivory for a community exposed to elevated CO_2 (Stiling *et al.*, 2003)."

Consequently, and contrary to the predictions of increased destruction of natural ecosystems by insects and other herbivorous arthropods in a CO_2-enriched environment, just the opposite would appear to be the more likely outcome: greater plant productivity plus less foliage consumption by herbivores, "whether expressed on an absolute or a percent basis," as Hamilton *et al.* found in their study.

Knepp *et al.* (2005) quantified leaf damage caused by insects chewing on saplings of seven species (including *Acer rubrum*) in 2001, 2002, and 2003, and five additional species (including *Acer barbatum*) in 2001 and 2003, also at the Duke Forest FACE site. They found, "across the seven species measured in each of the three years, elevated CO_2 caused a reduction in the percentage of leaf area removed by chewing insects," such that "the percentage of leaf tissue damaged by insect herbivores was 3.8% per leaf under ambient CO_2 and 3.3% per leaf under elevated CO_2." The greatest effects occurred in 2001, when "across 12 species the average damage per leaf under ambient CO_2 was 3.1% compared with 1.7% for plants under elevated CO_2," which is "indicative of a 46% decrease in the total area and total mass of leaf tissue damaged by chewing insects in the elevated CO_2 plots."

Knepp *et al.* write, "given the consistent reduction in herbivory under high CO_2 across species in 2001, it appears that some universal feature of chemistry or structure that affected leaf suitability was altered by the treatment." They also note "forest herbivory may decrease under elevated CO_2 because of a decline in the abundance of chewing insects," citing Stiling *et al.* (2003) and noting "slower rates of development under elevated CO_2 prolongs the time that insect herbivores are susceptible to natural enemies, which may be abundant in open-top chambers and FACE experiments but absent from greenhouse experiments." In addition, they suggest "decreased foliar quality and increased per capita consumption under elevated CO_2 may increase exposure to toxins and insect mortality," also noting "CO_2-induced changes in host plant quality directly decrease insect fecundity," citing Coviella and Trumble (1999) and Awmack and Leather (2002).

Knepp *et al.* conclude, "in contrast to the view that herbivore damage will increase under elevated CO_2 as a result of compensatory feeding on lower quality foliage, our results and those of Stiling *et al.* (2003) and Hamilton *et al.* (2004) in open experimental systems suggest that damage to trees may decrease."

Kruger *et al.* (1998) explored the consequences of an *increase* in herbivore-induced damage in a future CO_2-enriched world, although that is unlikely to occur. They grew well-watered and well-fertilized one-year-old *Acer saccharum* saplings in glasshouses maintained at atmospheric CO_2 concentrations of either 356 or 645 ppm for 70 days, to determine the effects of elevated CO_2 on photosynthesis and growth. On the 49th day of differential CO_2 exposure, they removed 50% of the saplings' leaf area from half of the trees in order to study the impact of concomitant simulated herbivory. They found the 70-day CO_2 enrichment treatment increased the total dry weight of the non-defoliated seedlings by about 10%. When the trees were stressed by simulated herbivory, the CO_2-enriched maples produced 28% more dry weight over the final phase of the study than the maples in the ambient-air treatment did. Kruger *et al.* conclude that in a high-CO_2 environment "sugar maple might be more capable of tolerating severe defoliation events which in the past have been implicated in widespread maple declines."

These studies indicate maple trees—and probably many, if not most, other trees—may fare much better against the periodic assaults of leaf-damaging herbivores as the air's CO_2 content continues to rise.

References

Awmack, C.S. and Leather, S.R. 2002. Host plant quality and fecundity in herbivorous insects. *Annual Review of Entomology* **47**: 817–844.

Bezemer, T.M. and Jones, T.H. 1998. Plant-insect herbivore interactions in elevated atmospheric CO_2: quantitative analyses and guild effects. *Oikos* **82**: 212–222.

Cannon, R.J. 1998. The implications of predicted climate change for insect pests in the UK, with emphasis on non-indigenous species. *Global Change Biology* **4**: 785–796.

Coviella, C.E. and Trumble, J.T. 1999. Effects of elevated atmospheric carbon dioxide on insect-plant interactions. *Conservation Biology* **13**: 700–712.

Finzi, A.C. and Schlesinger, W.H. 2002. Species control variation in litter decomposition in a pine forest exposed to elevated CO_2. *Global Change Biology* **8**: 1217–1229.

Hamilton, J.G., Zangerl, A.R., Berenbaum, M.R., Pippen, J., Aldea, M., and DeLucia, E.H. 2004. Insect herbivory in an intact forest understory under experimental CO_2 enrichment. *Oecologia* **138**: 10.1007/s00442-003-1463-5.

Hunter, M.D. 2001. Effects of elevated atmospheric carbon dioxide on insect-plant interactions. *Agricultural and Forest Entomology* **3**: 153–159.

Knepp, R.G., Hamilton, J.G., Mohan, J.E., Zangerl, A.R., Berenbaum, M.R., and DeLucia, E.H. 2005. Elevated CO_2 reduces leaf damage by insect herbivores in a forest community. *New Phytologist* **167**: 207–218.

Kruger, E.L., Volin, J.C., and Lindroth, R.L. 1998. Influences of atmospheric CO_2 enrichment on the responses of sugar maple and trembling aspen to defoliation. *New Phytologist* **140**: 85–94.

Lincoln, D.E., Fajer, E.D., and Johnson, R.H. 1993. Plant-insect herbivore interactions in elevated CO_2 environments. *Trends in Ecology and Evolution* **8**: 64–68.

Stiling, P., Moon, D.C., Hunter, M.D., Colson, J., Rossi, A.M., Hymus, G.J., and Drake, B.G. 2003. Elevated CO_2 lowers relative and absolute herbivore density across all species of a scrub-oak forest. *Oecologia* **134**: 82–87.

Whittaker, J.B. 1999. Impacts and responses at population level of herbivorous insects to elevated CO_2. *European Journal of Entomology* **96**: 149–156.

Williams, R.S., Lincoln, D.E., and Norby, R.J. 2003. Development of gypsy moth larvae feeding on red maple saplings at elevated CO_2 and temperature. *Oecologia* **137**: 114–122.

3.4.3.2 Oak

- Research suggests various insect pests will do decreasing amounts of damage to oak trees as the air's CO_2 concentration rises.

In order to determine whether the ongoing rise in the air's CO_2 content will exacerbate or ameliorate herbivore damage to oak trees, Dury *et al.* (1998) grew four-year-old *Quercus robur* seedlings in pots in greenhouses maintained at ambient and twice-ambient atmospheric CO_2 concentrations in combination with ambient and elevated (ambient plus 3°C) air temperatures for approximately one year, to study the interactive effects of elevated CO_2 and temperature on leaf nutritional quality. The researchers determined the elevated temperature treatment significantly reduced leaf palatability, and leaf toughness increased as a consequence of temperature-induced increases in condensed tannin concentrations. In addition, the imposition of higher temperatures significantly reduced leaf nitrogen content, as did elevated CO_2.

In one of the first attempts to move outside the laboratory/greenhouse and study the effects of atmospheric CO_2 enrichment on trophic food webs in a natural ecosystem, Stiling *et al.* (1999) enclosed portions of a native scrub-oak community in Florida (USA) in 3.6-m-diameter open-top chambers and fumigated them with air having CO_2 concentrations of either 350 or 700 ppm for approximately one year, to see whether elevated CO_2 would impact leaf miner densities, feeding rates, and mortality in this nutrient-poor ecosystem.

They discovered total leaf miner densities were 38% less on the foliage of trees growing in CO_2-enriched air than on that of trees growing in ambient air. Atmospheric CO_2 enrichment consistently reduced the absolute numbers of the study's six leaf miner species. At the same time, the elevated CO_2 treatment increased the leaf area consumed by the less-abundant herbivore miners by approximately 40% relative to the areas mined by the more-abundant herbivores present on the foliage exposed to ambient air. Despite this increase in feeding, the leaf miners in the CO_2-enriched chambers experienced significantly greater mortality than those in the ambient-air chambers. And although CO_2-induced reductions in leaf nitrogen content played a minor role in this phenomenon, the greatest factor contributing to increased herbivore mortality was a four-fold increase in parasitization by various wasps, which could more readily detect the more-exposed leaf miners on the CO_2-enriched foliage.

In another study conducted on five scrub-oak forest species at the same experimental facility, Stiling *et al.* (2003) investigated the effects of an approximate doubling of the air's CO_2 concentration on a number of characteristics of several insect herbivores. As before, they report, the "relative levels of damage by the two most common herbivore guilds, leaf-mining moths and leaf-chewers (primarily larval lepidopterans and grasshoppers), were significantly lower in elevated CO_2 than in ambient CO_2, for all five plant species," and "the response to elevated CO_2 was the same across all plant species." In addition, "more host-plant induced mortality was found for all miners on all plants in elevated CO_2 than in ambient CO_2." In addition to the relative densities of insect herbivores being reduced in the CO_2-enriched chambers, and "even though there were more leaves of most plant species in the elevated CO_2 chambers," the total densities of leaf miners in the high-CO_2 chambers were also lower for all plant species. Consequently, it would appear a high-CO_2 environment may improve plants' ability to better withstand various insect pests. Stiling *et al.* also note "reductions in herbivore loads in elevated CO_2 could boost plant growth beyond what might be expected based on pure plant responses to elevated CO_2."

Rossi *et al.* (2004) studied the same ecosystem, which was dominated by two species of scrub oak (*Quercus geminata* and *Q. myrtifolia*) that accounted for more than 90% of the ecosystem's biomass. They focused on the abundance of a guild of lepidopteran leafminers that attack the leaves of *Q. myrtifolia*, as well as on various leaf chewers, following 100 marked leaves in each of 16 open-top chambers (half exposed to ambient air and half exposed to air containing an extra 350 ppm of CO_2) for nine months, after which "differences in mean percent of leaves with leafminers and chewed leaves on trees from ambient and elevated chambers were assessed using paired *t*-tests."

The researchers write, "both the abundance of the guild of leafmining lepidopterans and damage caused by leaf chewing insects attacking myrtle oak were depressed in elevated CO_2." Leafminer abundance was 44% lower ($P = 0.096$) in the CO_2-enriched chambers compared to the ambient-air chambers, and the abundance of leaves suffering chewing damage was 37% lower ($P = 0.072$) in the CO_2-enriched air. Myrtle oak trees growing in their natural habitat likely will suffer far less damage from both leaf miners and leaf chewers as the air's CO_2 concentration rises in the years ahead.

Working in the same ecosystem, where atmospheric enrichment with an extra 350 ppm of CO_2 was begun in May 1996, Hall *et al.* (2005b) studied the four species that dominate the community and are present in every experimental chamber: the three oaks (*Quercus myrtifolia*, *Q. chapmanii,* and *Q. geminata*) plus the nitrogen-fixing legume *Galactia elliottii*. At three-month intervals from May 2001 to May 2003, they removed undamaged leaves from each of these species in all chambers and analyzed them for various chemical constituents, and they scored 200 randomly selected leaves of each species in each chamber for the presence of six types of herbivore damage.

Throughout the study they found no significant differences between the CO_2-enriched and ambient-treatment leaves of any single species in terms of condensed tannins, hydrolyzable tannins, total phenolics, or lignin. However, in all four species together there were always greater concentrations of four important leaf constituents in the CO_2-enriched leaves, with across-species mean increases of 6.8% for condensed tannins, 6.1% for hydrolyzable tannins,

5.1% for total phenolics, and 4.3% for lignin. In addition, the researchers found large and often significant CO_2-induced decreases in all leaf damage categories among all species: chewing (-48%, $P < 0.001$), mines (-37%, $P = 0.001$), eye spot gall (-45%, $P < 0.001$), leaf tier (-52%, $P = 0.012$), leaf mite (-23%, $P = 0.477$), and leaf gall (-16%, $P = 0.480$). Hall *et al.* conclude the changes in leaf chemical constituents and herbivore damage "suggest that damage to plants may decline as atmospheric CO_2 levels continue to rise."

In one final study of the Florida scrub-oak ecosystem, Hall *et al.* (2005a) examined the effects of an extra 350 ppm of CO_2 on litter quality, herbivore activity, and their interactions. Over the three years of this experiment (2000, 2001, 2002), they determined "changes in litter chemistry from year to year were far larger than the effects of CO_2 or insect damage, suggesting that these may have only minor effects on litter decomposition." The one exception to this finding, they write, was "condensed tannin concentrations[, which] increased under elevated CO_2 regardless of species, herbivore damage, or growing season," rising by 11% in 2000, 18% in 2001, and 41% in 2002 as a result of atmospheric CO_2 enrichment, as best as can be determined from their bar graphs.

The five researchers also report "lepidopteran larvae can exhibit slower growth rates when feeding on elevated CO_2 plants (Fajer *et al.*, 1991) and become more susceptible to pathogens, parasitoids, and predators (Lindroth, 1996; Stiling *et al.*, 1999)," noting further that at their field site, "which hosts the longest continuous study of the effects of elevated CO_2 on insects, herbivore populations decline[d] markedly under elevated CO_2 (Stiling *et al.*, 1999, 2002, 2003; Hall *et al.*, 2005b)."

The evidence accumulated to date with respect to herbivory in oak trees indicates various insect pests will do decreasing amounts of damage to such trees as the air's CO_2 concentration climbs ever-higher.

References

Dury, S.J., Good, J.E.G., Perrins, C.M., Buse, A., and Kaye, T. 1998. The effects of increasing CO_2 and temperature on oak leaf palatability and the implications for herbivorous insects. *Global Change Biology* **4**: 55–61.

Fajer, E.D., Bowers, M.D., and Bazzaz, F.A. 1991. The effects of enriched CO_2 atmospheres on the buckeye butterfly, *Junonia coenia*. *Ecology* **72**: 751–754.

Hall, M.C., Stiling, P., Hungate, B.A., Drake, B.G., and Hunter, M.D. 2005a. Effects of elevated CO_2 and herbivore damage on litter quality in a scrub oak ecosystem. *Journal of Chemical Ecology* **31**: 2343–2356.

Hall, M.C., Stiling, P., Moon, D.C., Drake, B.G., and Hunter, M.D. 2005b. Effects of elevated CO_2 on foliar quality and herbivore damage in a scrub oak ecosystem. *Journal of Chemical Ecology* **31**: 267–285.

Lindroth, R.L. 1996. CO_2-mediated changes in tree chemistry and tree-Lepidoptera interactions. In: Koch, G.W. and Mooney, H.A. (Eds.) *Carbon Dioxide and Terrestrial Ecosystems*. Academic Press, San Diego, California, USA, pp. 105–120.

Rossi, A.M., Stiling, P., Moon, D.C., Cattell, M.V., and Drake, B.G. 2004. Induced defensive response of myrtle oak to foliar insect herbivory in ambient and elevated CO_2. *Journal of Chemical Ecology* **30**: 1143–1152.

Stiling, P., Cattell, M., Moon, D.C., Rossi, A., Hungate, B.A., Hymus, G., and Drake, B.G. 2002. Elevated atmospheric CO_2 lowers herbivore abundance, but increases leaf abscission rates. *Global Change Biology* **8**: 658–667.

Stiling, P., Moon, D.C., Hunter, M.D., Colson, J., Rossi, A.M., Hymus, G.J., and Drake, B.G. 2003. Elevated CO_2 lowers relative and absolute herbivore density across all species of a scrub-oak forest. *Oecologia* **134**: 82–87.

Stiling, P., Rossi, A.M., Hungate, B., Dijkstra, P., Hinkle, C.R., Knot III, W.M., and Drake, B. 1999. Decreased leaf-miner abundance in elevated CO_2: Reduced leaf quality and increased parasitoid attack. *Ecological Applications* **9**: 240–244.

3.4.3.3 Miscellaneous

- Numerous studies of numerous insect pests of numerous species of trees indicate atmospheric CO_2 enrichment may contribute to reduced herbivory in forest ecosystems.

Insect pests have had enormous impacts on Earth's trees and shrubs in the past. Will the anticipated increase in the atmosphere's CO_2 concentration exacerbate or ameliorate their effects? This section describes and discusses the results of several studies that address this question.

Docherty *et al.* (1997) grew beech and sycamore saplings in glasshouses maintained at atmospheric CO_2 concentrations of 350 and 600 ppm and allowed groups of three sap-feeding aphid species and two sap-feeding leafhopper species to feed on them.

Overall, they report elevated CO_2 had few significant effects on the performance of these insects, although there was a non-significant tendency for elevated CO_2 to reduce the individual weights and population sizes of the aphids.

Gleadow *et al.* (1998) grew eucalyptus seedlings in glasshouses maintained at 400 and 800 ppm CO_2 for six months, observing biomass increases of 98% and 134% in high and low nitrogen treatments, respectively. They also studied a sugar-based compound called prunasin, which produces cyanide in response to tissue damage caused by foraging herbivores. Although elevated CO_2 caused no significant change in leaf prunasin content, the proportion of nitrogen allocated to prunasin increased by approximately 20% in the CO_2-enriched saplings, suggesting a potential for increased prunasin had the eucalyptus saplings been under attack by herbivores.

In a study of simulated herbivory, Kruger *et al.* (1998) grew seedlings of one-year-old maple (*Acer saccharum*) and two-year-old aspen (*Populus tremuloides*) trees in glasshouses with atmospheric CO_2 concentrations of 356 and 645 ppm for 70 days. At the 49-day point of the experiment, half of the leaf area on half of the trees in each treatment was removed, and this defoliation caused the final dry weights of both species growing in ambient air to decline. In the CO_2-enriched glasshouse, on the other hand, the defoliated maple trees ended up weighing just as much as the non-defoliated maple trees. The defoliated aspen trees ended up weighing a little less, but not significantly less, than their non-defoliated counterparts. Thus, atmospheric CO_2 enrichment improved both species' ability to recover from the debilitating effect of leaf removal, suggesting a future world of higher atmospheric CO_2 concentration may make these trees better able to deal with physical damage inflicted on them by herbivores.

Lovelock *et al.* (1999) grew seedlings of the tropical tree *Copaifera aromatica* for 50 days in pots placed in open-top chambers maintained at atmospheric CO_2 concentrations of 390 and 860 ppm. At the 14-day point of the experiment, half of the seedlings in each treatment had about 40% of their total leaf area removed. None of the defoliated trees of either CO_2 treatment fully recovered from this manipulation, but at the end of the experiment the total plant biomass of the defoliated trees in the CO_2-enriched treatment was 15% greater than that of the defoliated trees in the ambient-CO_2 treatment.

Hattenschwiler and Schafellner (1999) grew seven-year-old spruce (*Picea abies*) trees at atmospheric CO_2 concentrations of 280, 420, and 560 ppm and various nitrogen deposition treatments for three years, allowing nun moth larvae to feed on current-year needles for 12 days. Larvae placed on the CO_2-enriched foliage consumed less needle biomass than those placed on the ambient-grown foliage, regardless of nitrogen treatment. The larvae feeding on needles produced by the CO_2-enriched trees attained an average final biomass only two-thirds of that attained by the larvae that fed on needles produced at 280 ppm CO_2. The nun moth is a powerful defoliator that resides in most parts of Europe and East Asia between 40 and 60°N latitude; the results of this study suggest the rise in the air's CO_2 content likely will lead to significant reductions in damage to spruce and other coniferous trees by this insect pest.

Parsons *et al.* (2003) grew two-year-old saplings of paper birch (*Betula papyrifera* Marsh.) and three-year-old saplings of sugar maple (*Acer saccharum* Marsh.) in well-watered and -fertilized 16-L pots from early May until late August in glasshouse rooms maintained at either 400 or 700 ppm CO_2. The whole-plant biomass of paper birch was increased by 55% in the CO_2-enriched rooms, and the biomass of sugar maple was increased by 30%. Condensed tannins were unaltered in sugar maple but increased by 27% in paper birch in the CO_2-enriched treatment. The three researchers note, "the higher condensed tannin concentrations present in the birch fine roots may offer these tissues greater protection against soil-borne pathogens and herbivores." CO_2-induced increases in fine root concentrations of total phenolics and condensed tannins also have been observed in warm temperate conifers by King *et al.* (1997), Entry *et al.* (1998), Gebauer *et al.* (1998), and Runion *et al.* (1999), as well as in cotton by Booker (2000).

Holton *et al.* (2003) reared parasitized and non-parasitized forest tent caterpillars (*Malacosoma disstria*) on two quaking aspen (*Populus tremuloides*) genotypes (216, which is O_3-tolerant, and 259, which is O_3-sensitive) alone and in combination at the Aspen FACE site in northern Wisconsin (USA), in plots exposed to ambient air; ambient air + 200 ppm extra CO_2; ambient air + 50% extra ozone; and ambient air + 200 ppm extra CO_2 and 50% extra O_3. The researchers found "elevated CO_2 had little effect on both primary and secondary metabolites of aspen" and "had few biologically significant effects on forest tent caterpillar performance." Elevated O_3 altered foliar composition much more than did elevated CO_2, and it improved tent caterpillar

performance under ambient CO_2 conditions, but not in CO_2-enriched air. The extra CO_2 of this study totally thwarted the positive impact of the extra O_3 on caterpillar performance, thus possibly eliminating a major negative consequence for the trees.

Kuokkanen *et al.* (2003) grew two-year-old birch (*Betula pendula* Roth) seedlings in ambient air of 350 ppm CO_2 or air enriched to a CO_2 concentration of 700 ppm under conditions of either ambient temperature or ambient temperature plus 3°C for one full growing season in the field in closed-top chambers at the Mekrijarvi Research Station of the University of Joensuu in eastern Finland. During the middle of the summer, when carbon-based secondary compounds of birch leaves are fairly stable, they picked several leaves from each tree and determined their condensed tannin concentrations, along with the concentrations of other physiologically important substances.

The concentration of total phenolics, condensed tannins, and their derivatives significantly increased in the birch leaves produced in the CO_2-enriched air, as also was observed by Lavola and Julkunen-Titto (1994), Williams *et al.* (1994), Kinney *et al.* (1997), Bezemer and Jones (1998), and Kuokkanen *et al.* (2001). The extra 350 ppm of CO_2 nearly tripled condensed tannin concentrations in the ambient-temperature air, and it increased their concentrations in the elevated-temperature air by a factor greater than 3.5. The presence of condensed tannins in leaves tends to greatly reduce methane emissions from ruminants that feed on them, which in turn reduces the supposed global warming impact.

Mattson *et al.* (2004) write, "although there have been many studies on the effects of elevated CO_2 on the interaction between plants and their insect herbivores (see Bezemer and Jones, 1998; Hunter, 2001), comparable studies on mammalian herbivores are lacking altogether, even though mammals play important roles in dynamics of many ecosystems (McNaughton and Sabuni, 1988; Pastor and Naiman, 1992)." Mattson *et al.* grew one-year-old seedlings of silver birch (*Betula pendula*) in closed-top chambers for one summer and autumn in pots containing an unfertilized commercial peat maintained at three different soil nitrogen (N) levels (low = 0 kg N ha^{-1}, medium = 150 kg N ha^{-1}, high = 500 kg N ha^{-1}) and two temperature (T) levels (ambient and ambient + 3°C) in air of either 362 or 700 ppm CO_2 concentration. They carried out feeding trials with caged Eurasian hares (*Lepus timidus*) and performed chemical analyses of the tops of the seedlings and the basal parts of their stems.

In a second experiment, they grew paper birch (*Betula papyrifera*) from seed for two 140-day growing seasons in well-watered and well-fertilized pots placed in FACE rings maintained at atmospheric CO_2 concentrations of either 362 or 562 ppm, after which (in an unplanned aspect of the study) North American eastern cottontail rabbits (*Sylvilagus floridanus*) fed *ad libitum*, consuming bark tissue down to the wood and scoring it, on the basal third of the seedlings. These tissues were tested for the presence of various herbivore-deterring chemical constituents.

"As expected," the six scientists write, "elevated CO_2 substantially increased the above-ground woody biomass growth of both paper birch (63%) and silver birch (21%)." In addition, noting "numerous studies have shown that elevated atmospheric CO_2 often, but not always, elicits increases in carbon partitioning to carbon-based secondary plant compounds," which often act as deterrents to herbivory, they say their findings "confirm this general pattern in silver and paper birch." Finally, they report high CO_2 reduced hare feeding on silver birch shoots by as much as 48%, and it reduced rabbit feeding on paper birch stems by about 51%. Neither temperature nor severe early season defoliation (another treatment) affected tree resistance against these mammalian herbivores.

Calling the anti-herbivory effect of elevated CO_2 "remarkably strong," and noting rabbits "overwhelmingly preferred ambient CO_2 plants," Mattson *et al.* say their data "clearly suggest that the defensive biochemistry of paper birch twigs as well as the main stem were [positively] altered as the result of elevated CO_2."

Noting the "detrimental effects of ozone on plants are well known," and "carbon dioxide generally affects trees in opposite ways to ozone," Valcama *et al.* (2007) conducted a literature review they describe as "the first quantitative analysis of the interactive effects of elevated O_3 and elevated CO_2 on tree chemistry and herbivore performance," based on the results of "63 studies conducted on 22 tree species and 10 insect herbivore species and published between 1990 and 2005."

With respect to ways elevated O_3 may benefit insect herbivores that tend to damage trees, Valkama *et al.* say they determined "elevated O_3 significantly shortened development time of insect herbivores [when they are exposed and vulnerable to attack by various enemies] and increased their pupal mass in the overall dataset." In addition, they report the "relative growth rate of chewers was significantly increased by 3.5% under elevated O_3." However, "these effects were counteracted by elevated CO_2," such that "elevated O_3 in combination with CO_2 had no effect on herbivore performance"—except when elevated CO_2 was added to the O_3-enriched air, it not only counteracted the O_3-induced increase in pupal biomass, it actually reduced it by 7% below ambient air.

Valkama *et al.*'s analysis of much of the pertinent experimental data obtained prior to 2006 suggests in the interactions between insect herbivores and trees, the rise in the air's CO_2 content likely plays an important role in negating, and in some cases even more than negating, the damage otherwise capable of being done to Earth's forests by insect pests. Subsequent research has continued to demonstrate these effects.

Huttunen *et al.* (2007) grew silver birch (*Betula pendula* Roth) seedlings in pots filled with peat at three levels of nitrogen (N) fertility—no N, moderate N (130 kg N ha^{-1}) and high N (270 kg N ha^{-1})—in climate-controlled closed-top chambers from mid-June to October 2002 at the Mekrijarvi Research Station of the University of Joensuu, Finland. The chambers were maintained at atmospheric CO_2 concentrations of either 360 or 720 ppm and at either ambient air temperatures or elevated air temperatures 2°C above ambient from June to August and 4°C above ambient for the remainder of the growing season. The researchers mimicked larval and adult leaf-feeding patterns exhibited during real-world defoliation by manually damaging the leaves of the seedlings by tearing off the apical halves of either 25% or 50% of all leaves greater than 1 cm in length on 1 July (mid-season) and again on 29 July (late-season). They determined total plant shoot and root biomass once the plants had gone dormant in October.

As best as can be determined from the six scientists' bar graphs of their results, and averaged over all three defoliation treatments, the elevated CO_2 treatment increased the biomass of the seedlings in the moderate and high-N fertility treatments much more than it increased the biomass of the seedlings in the no-N fertility treatment (29 and 30%, respectively, vs. 13%). The same was also true of the combined elevated CO_2 and elevated temperature treatment, where the corresponding treatment-induced biomass increases were 34 and 36% vs. 20%, suggesting the heightened temperatures tended to augment the beneficial effects of the elevated CO_2 treatment, with the greatest amplification being manifest in the no-N fertility treatment (54% vs. 17 and 20% in the moderate- and high-N treatments, respectively).

Averaged over all three N fertility treatments, the effect of the elevated CO_2 was to increase the plant biomass of the undefoliated seedlings by approximately 25%, the 25%-defoliated seedlings by 24%, and the 50%-defoliated seedlings by 22%. The effect of the combined elevated CO_2 and elevated temperature treatment was to increase the plant biomass of the same three categories of seedlings by approximately 31%, 30%, and 29%, respectively. Huttunen et al. conclude, "climatic change"—which they specifically defined to mean elevated atmospheric temperature and CO_2—"will have a positive impact on the compensatory ability of defoliated silver birch seedlings."

In another study conducted with the same trees under the same conditions, Huttunen et al. (2008) studied leaf palatability to adult blue alder leaf beetles (Agelastica alni). They periodically measured a host of seedling parameters related to plant chemical and morphological defense properties. The researchers' findings were varied and complex, but their most basic finding was that the blue alder leaf beetle's "total leaf consumption was higher under the ambient climatic conditions than under elevated temperature, elevated CO_2, or the combination of elevated temperature and CO_2."

Nabity et al. (2012) write, "arthropod herbivory can reduce plant productivity by removing photosynthetic leaf area," noting Zangerl et al. (2002), Aldea et al. (2005, 2006), and Patankar et al. (2011) indicate, in some cases, "damage to leaf surfaces causes a reduction in the quantum efficiency of photosystem II fluorescence, which is highly correlated with the rate of carbon assimilation." Working at the Aspen FACE site in north-central Wisconsin (USA), the four researchers studied how different types of herbivore damage (leaf-chewing, gall-forming, and leaf-folding) altered component processes of photosynthesis under both ambient and elevated (ambient + 200 ppm) atmospheric CO_2 concentrations in aspen (Populus tremuloides, genotype 216) trees, as well as how the damage caused by leaf-chewing insects impacted photosynthesis in birch (Betula papyrifera) trees.

The four researchers found "growth under elevated CO_2 reduced the distance that herbivore-induced reductions in photosynthesis propagated away from the point of damage in aspen and birch," leading them to conclude, "at least for these species," elevated CO_2 "may reduce the impact of herbivory on photosynthesis," a very positive development.

Hamilton et al. (2012) noted "the response of complex plant and animal communities to global change is highly variable (Tylianakis et al., 2008)," but "recent studies have documented that loss of foliage to arthropod herbivores decreases under elevated CO_2 in woody communities (Hamilton et al., 2004; Knepp et al., 2005; Stiling and Cornelissen, 2007)." They also note the fitness and in some cases population size of herbivorous insects may decline in communities exposed to elevated CO_2 (Hillstrom and Lindroth, 2008; Hillstrom et al., 2010)," although the "effects of elevated CO_2 on naturally-occurring arthropod assemblages have not yet been widely characterized."

Working at the Duke Forest FACE facility in the Piedmont region of North Carolina (USA)—where three 30-meter-diameter plots of an expansive stand of loblolly pine had their atmospheric CO_2 concentrations boosted by about 200 ppm, and where three other such plots were maintained at the normal ambient CO_2 concentration—Hamilton et al. counted the numbers of arthropods found in each of the six plots every two weeks throughout June and July of 2005, assigning them to different feeding guilds. In addition, they analyzed stable isotope data for spiders collected in the ambient and elevated CO_2 plots in order to determine the extent herbivorous prey species moved into and out of the elevated CO_2 plots.

The seven U.S. scientists write their isotopic data "gave no indication that the treatment plots represented a 'boundary' to the movement of insects." In addition, they determined there was no detectable effect of elevated CO_2 on the total number of individual arthropods in the two sets of treatment plots. However, they write, "there was an increase in the numbers of individuals collected in primarily predaceous orders (Araneae and Hymenoptera; from 60% to more than 150%) under elevated CO_2 and a decrease in the numbers in primarily herbivorous orders (Lepidoptera and Coleoptera; from -30 to -45%)." Hamilton et al. conclude "decreases in herbivorous arthropods and increases in predaceous arthropods may contribute to reduced herbivory under elevated CO_2 in forest systems."

References

Aldea, M., Hamilton, J.G., Resti, J.P., Zangerl, A.R., Berenbaum, M.R., and DeLucia, E.H. 2005. Indirect effects of insect herbivory on leaf gas exchange in soybean. *Plant, Cell and Environment* **28**: 402–411.

Aldea, M., Hamilton, J.G., Resti, J.P., Zangerl, A.R., Berenbaum, M.R., Frank, T.D., and DeLucia, E.H. 2006. Comparison of photosynthetic damage from arthropod herbivory and pathogen infection in understory hardwood samplings. *Oecologia* **149**: 221–232.

Bezemer, T.M. and Jones, T.H. 1998. Plant-insect herbivore interactions in elevated atmospheric CO_2, quantitative analyses and guild effects. *Oikos* **82**: 212–222.

Booker, F.L. 2000. Influence of carbon dioxide enrichment, ozone and nitrogen fertilization on cotton (*Gossypium hirsutum* L.) leaf and root composition. *Plant, Cell and Environment* **23**: 573–583.

Docherty, M., Wade, F.A., Hurst, D.K., Whittaker, J.B., and Lea, P.J. 1997. Responses of tree sap-feeding herbivores to elevated CO_2. *Global Change Biology* **3**: 51–59.

Entry, J.A., Runion, G.B., Prior, S.A., Mitchell, R.J., and Rogers, H..H. 1998. Influence of CO_2 enrichment and nitrogen fertilization on tissue chemistry and carbon allocation in longleaf pine seedlings. *Plant and Soil* **200**: 3–11.

Gebauer, R.L., Strain, B.R., and Reynolds, J.F. 1998. The effect of elevated CO_2 and N availability on tissue concentrations and whole plant pools of carbon-based secondary compounds in loblolly pine. *Oecologia* **113**: 29–36.

Gleadow, R.M., Foley, W.J., and Woodrow, I.E. 1998. Enhanced CO_2 alters the relationship between photosynthesis and defense in cyanogenic *Eucalyptus cladocalyx* F. Muell. *Plant, Cell and Environment* **21**: 12–22.

Hamilton, J.G., Zangerl, A.R., Berenbaum, M.R., Pippen, J.S., Aldea, M., and DeLucia, E.H. 2004. Insect herbivory in an intact forest understory under experimental CO_2 enrichment. *Oecologia* **138**: 566–573.

Hamilton, J., Zangerl, A.R., Berenbaum, M.R., Sparks, J.P., Elich, L., Eisenstein, A., and DeLucia, E.H. 2012. Elevated atmospheric CO_2 alters the arthropod community in a forest understory. *Acta Oecologica* **43**: 80–85.

Hattenschwiler, S. and Schafellner, C. 1999. Opposing effects of elevated CO_2 and N deposition on *Lymantria monacha* larvae feeding on spruce trees. *Oecologia* **118**: 210–217.

Hillstrom, M.L. and Lindroth, R.L. 2008. Elevated atmospheric carbon dioxide and ozone alter forest insect abundance and community composition. *Insect Conservation and Diversity* **1**: 233–241.

Hillstrom, M.L., Vigue, L.M., Coyle, D.R., Raffa, K.F., and Lindroth, R.L. 2010. Performance of the invasive weevil *Polydrusus sericeus* is influenced by atmospheric CO_2 and host species. *Agricultural and Forest Entomology* **12**: 285–292.

Holton, M.K., Lindroth, R.L., and Nordheim, E.V. 2003. Foliar quality influences tree-herbivore-parasitoid interactions: effects of elevated CO_2, O_3, and plant genotype. *Oecologia* **137**: 233–244.

Hunter, M.D. 2001. Effects of elevated atmospheric carbon dioxide on insect-plant interactions. *Agricultural and Forest Entomology* **3**: 153–159.

Huttunen, L., Niemela, P., Julkunen-Titto, R., Heiska, S., Tegelberg, R., Rousi, M., and Kellomaki, S. 2008. Does defoliation induce chemical and morphological defenses in the leaves of silver birch seedlings under changing climate? *Chemoecology* **18**: 85–98.

Huttunen, L., Niemela, P., Peltola, H., Heiska, S., Rousi, M., and Kellomaki, S. 2007. Is a defoliated silver birch seedling able to over-compensate the growth under changing climate? *Environmental and Experimental Botany* **60**: 227–238.

King, J.S., Thomas, R.B., and Strain, B.R. 1997. Morphology and tissue quality of seedling root systems of *Pinus taeda* and *Pinus ponderosa* as affected by varying CO_2, temperature, and nitrogen. *Plant and Soil* **195**: 107–119.

Kinney, K.K., Lindroth, R.L., Jung, S.M., and Nordheim, E.V. 1997. Effects of CO_2 and NO_3 availability on deciduous trees, phytochemistry and insect performance. *Ecology* **78**: 215–230.

Knepp, R.G., Hamilton, J.G., Mohan, J.E., Zangerl, A.R., Berenbaum, M.R., and DeLucia, E.H. 2005. Elevated CO_2 reduces leaf damage by insect herbivores in a forest community. *New Phytologist* **167**: 207–218.

Kruger, E.L., Volin, J.C., and Lindroth, R.L. 1998. Influences of atmospheric CO_2 enrichment on the responses of sugar maple and trembling aspen to defoliation. *New Phytologist* **140**: 85–94.

Kuokkanen, K., Julkunen-Titto, R., Keinanen, M., Niemela, P., and Tahvanainen, J. 2001. The effect of elevated CO_2 and temperature on the secondary chemistry of *Betula pendula* seedlings. *Trees* **15**: 378–384.

Kuokkanen, K., Yan, S., and Niemela, P. 2003. Effects of elevated CO_2 and temperature on the leaf chemistry of birch *Betula pendula* (Roth) and the feeding behavior of the weevil *Phyllobius maculicornis*. *Agricultural and Forest Entomology* **5**: 209–217.

Lavola, A. and Julkunen-Titto, R. 1994. The effect of elevated carbon dioxide and fertilization on primary and secondary metabolites in birch, *Betula pendula* (Roth). *Oecologia* **99**: 315–321.

Lovelock, C.E., Posada, J., and Winter, K. 1999. Effects of elevated CO_2 and defoliation on compensatory growth and photosynthesis of seedlings in a tropical tree, *Copaifera aromatica. Biotropica* **31**: 279–287.

Mattson, W.J., Kuokkanen, K., Niemela, P., Julkunen-Tiitto, R., Kellomaki, S., and Tahvanainen, J. 2004. Elevated CO_2 alters birch resistance to Lagomorpha herbivores. *Global Change Biology* **10**: 1402–1413.

McNaughton, S.J. and Sabuni G.A. 1988. Large African mammals as regulators of vegetation structure. In: Werger, M.J.A., Van der Aart, P.J.M., During, H.J., and Verhoeven, J.T.A. (Eds.) *Plant Form and Vegetation Structure*. SPB Academic Publishing, The Hague, The Netherlands, pp. 339–354.

Nabity, P.D., Hillstrom, M.L., Lindroth, R.L., and DeLucia, E.H. 2012. Elevated CO_2 interacts with herbivory to alter chlorophyll fluorescence and leaf temperature in *Betula papyrifera* and *Populus tremuloides. Oecologia* **169**: 905–913.

Parsons, W.F.J., Kopper, B.J., and Lindroth, R.L. 2003. Altered growth and fine root chemistry of *Betula papyrifera* and *Acer saccharum* under elevated CO_2. *Canadian Journal of Forest Research* **33**: 842–846.

Pastor, J. and Naiman, R.J. 1992. Selective foraging and ecosystem processes in boreal forest. *American Naturalist* **139**: 690–705.

Patankar, R., Thomas, S.C., and Smith, S.M. 2011. A gall-inducing arthropod drives declines in canopy photosynthesis. *Oecologia* **167**: 701–709.

Runion, G.B., Entry, J.A., Prior, S.A., Mitchell, R.J., and Rogers, H.H. 1999. Tissue chemistry and carbon allocation in seedlings of *Pinus palustris* subjected to elevated atmospheric CO_2 and water stress. *Tree Physiology* **19**: 329–335.

Stiling, P. and Cornelissen, T. 2007. How does elevated carbon dioxide (CO_2) affect plant-herbivore interactions? A field experiment and meta-analysis of CO_2-mediated changes on plant chemistry and herbivore performance. *Global Change Biology* **13**: 1–20.

Tylianakis, J.M., Didham, R.K., Bascompte, J., and Wardle, D.A. 2008. Global change and species interactions in terrestrial ecosystems. *Ecology Letters* **11**: 1351–1363.

Valkama, E., Koricheva, J., and Oksanen, E. 2007. Effects of elevated O_3, alone and in combination with elevated CO_2, on tree leaf chemistry and insect herbivore performance: a meta-analysis. *Global Change Biology* **13**: 184–201.

Williams, R.S., Lincoln, D.E., and Thomas, R.B. 1994. Loblolly pine grown under elevated CO_2 affects early instar pine sawfly performance. *Oecologia* **98**: 64–71.

Zangerl, A.R., Hamilton, J.G., Miller, T.J., Crofts, A.R., Oxborough, K., Berenbaum, M.R., and DeLucia, E.H. 2002. Impact of folivory on photosynthesis is greater than the sum of its holes. *Proceedings of the National Academy of Sciences USA* **99**: 1088–1091.

3.4.3.4 Fluctuating Asymmetry

- Higher concentrations of atmospheric CO_2 tend to reduce fluctuating asymmetry in plant leaves, leading to more symmetrical leaves that appear to be less susceptible to attacks by herbivores.

Fluctuating asymmetry (FA) is the term used to describe small variations from perfect symmetry in otherwise bilaterally symmetrical characters in an organism (Moller and Swaddle, 1997). It is thought to arise in consequence of developmental instability experienced during ontogeny that is caused by various stresses, including both genetic and environmental factors (Martel *et al.*, 1999; Cornelissen and Stiling, 2005). It has been studied extensively in animals but less so in plants (Moller and Shykoff, 1999).

In the first study to address the effects of atmospheric CO_2 enrichment on leaf asymmetry and herbivore response, Cornelissen *et al.* (2004) studied native scrub-oak community at the Kennedy Space Center, Titusville, Florida (USA), which is dominated by myrtle oak (*Quercus myrtifolia*) and sand live oak (*Quercus geminata*), under atmospheric CO_2 concentrations of either 370 or 700 ppm. Based on measurements of distances from the leaf midrib to the left and right edges of the leaf at its widest point and leaf areas on the left and right sides of the leaf midrib, Cornelissen *et al.* determined "asymmetric leaves were less frequent in elevated CO_2, and, when encountered, they were less asymmetric than leaves growing under ambient CO_2." In addition, "*Q. myrtifolia* leaves under elevated CO_2 were 15.0% larger than in ambient CO_2 and *Q. geminata* leaves were 38.0% larger in elevated CO_2 conditions." They also report "elevated CO_2 significantly increased tannin concentration for both *Q. myrtifolia* and *Q. geminata* leaves," and "asymmetric leaves contained significantly lower concentrations of tannins than symmetric leaves for both *Q. geminata* and *Q. myrtifolia*."

Cornelissen *et al.* write, "a possible explanation for [reduced asymmetry in leaves under elevated CO_2] is the fact that, in contrast to other environmental stresses, which can cause negative effects on plant growth, the predominant effect of elevated CO_2 on plants is to promote growth with consequent reallocation of resources (Docherty *et al.*, 1996)." Another possibility, they say, "is the fact that CO_2 acts as a plant fertilizer," and, as a result, "elevated CO_2 ameliorates plant stress compared with ambient levels of CO_2," which is one of the well-documented biological benefits of atmospheric CO_2 enrichment documented by Idso and Idso (1994).

As to the ancillary finding of CO_2-induced increases in tannin concentrations in the leaves of both oaks (a mean increase of approximately 35% for *Q. myrtifolia* and 43% for *Q. geminata*), it should be noted this phenomenon may provide both species with greater protection against herbivores, and part of that protection may be associated with the observed CO_2-induced reductions in the amount and degree of asymmetry in the leaves of the CO_2-enriched trees. Consistent with this hypothesis, Stiling *et al.* (1999, 2003) found higher abundances of leaf miners in the leaves of the trees in the ambient CO_2 chambers, where asymmetric leaves were more abundant, and in the current study it was determined leaf miners attacked asymmetric leaves more frequently than would be expected by chance alone in both CO_2 treatments.

In further support of this CO_2-induced benefit, Cornelissen and Stiling (2005) evaluated patterns of asymmetry in 40 leaves from each of 30 trees of each of two species of oak—sand live oak (*Quercus geminata*) and turkey oak (*Q. laevis*)—at the University of South Florida Botanical Garden in Tampa, Florida (USA), well before any herbivores had begun to attack the trees that growing season. They examined patterns of leaf asymmetry, leaf quality, and herbivory for 30 individual trees of each of the two oak species from March to October of the same year.

The "before and after" measurements indicate differential herbivory patterns neither caused nor affected patterns of leaf FA. The authors write, "herbivores may use asymmetry as a cue to plant quality and suitable oviposition sites," as plants with a higher percentage of asymmetric leaves were attacked more frequently by various leaf miners, as were leaves on the same plant more asymmetric. Cornelissen and Stiling report, "asymmetric leaves of both plant species exhibited better nutritional quality for herbivores than symmetric leaves," with asymmetric leaves possessing "significantly lower concentrations of tannins [-22% for *Q. geminata* and -36% for *Q. laevis*] and higher nitrogen content [+8%

for both species]."

Kaligaric *et al.* (2008) measured the degree of FA in "undamaged (not grazed, not visibly attacked by herbivores or pathogens) fully developed leaves" of the Mediterranean shrub *Myrtus communis* L. growing along an atmospheric CO_2 gradient (570, 530, 490, 450, 410, and 370 ppm) moving away from a natural CO_2 spring, "I Borboi," near Lajatico (Pisa, Tuscany, Italy) at distances of 2, 18, 34, 50, 66, and 82 m, respectively, from the CO_2 source.

The four researchers report they found "a significant and negative correlation between CO_2 concentration and leaf FA," such that "with increased CO_2 concentration the leaf FA decreased." This result, they write, "confirms what was obtained by Cornelissen *et al.* (2004) on *Quercus myrtifolia* and *Quercus geminata* (in a short-term experiment)." In addition, they note "*Myrtus communis*, grown under elevated CO_2 concentration at 'I Borboi,' showed a reduction in xylem embolism and an increase in hydraulic efficiency (Tognetti *et al.*, 2001)," stating "improved water relations could represent a good explanation for the observed reduction in leaf FA [as the air's CO_2 content increased]."

Kaligaric *et al.* conclude "adaptation and selection could explain the tendency towards decreased leaf FA in plants from the CO_2 spring relative to ambient conditions," since "the more symmetrical leaves under long-term elevated CO_2 concentration were more developmentally stable in these conditions."

References

Cornelissen, T. and Stiling, P. 2005. Perfect is best: low leaf fluctuating asymmetry reduces herbivory by leaf miners. *Oecologia* **142**: 46–56.

Cornelissen, T., Stiling, P., and Drake, B. 2004. Elevated CO_2 decreases leaf fluctuating asymmetry and herbivory by leaf miners on two oak species. *Global Change Biology* **10**: 27–36.

Docherty, M., Hurst, D.K., Holopainem, J.K., Whittaker, J.B., Lea, P.J., and Watt, A.D. 1996. Carbon dioxide-induced changes in beech foliage cause female beech weevil larvae to feed in a compensatory manner. *Global Change Biology* **2**: 335–341.

Idso, K.E. and Idso, S.B. 1994. Plant responses to atmospheric CO_2 enrichment in the face of environmental constraints: a review of the past 10 years' research. *Agricultural and Forest Meteorology* **69**: 153–203.

Kaligaric, M., Tognetti, R., Janzekovic, F., and Raschi, A. 2008. Leaf fluctuating asymmetry of *Myrtus communis* L., affected by increases in atmospheric CO_2 concentration: Evidence from a natural CO_2 spring. *Polish Journal of Environmental Studies* **17**: 503–508.

Martel, J., Lempa, K., and Haukioja, E. 1999. Effects of stress and rapid growth on fluctuating asymmetry and insect damage in birch leaves. *Oikos* **86**: 208–216.

Moller, A.P. and Swaddle, J.P. 1997. *Asymmetry, Developmental Stability and Evolution.* Oxford University Press, Oxford, UK.

Moller, A.P. and Shykoff, P. 1999. Morphological developmental stability in plants: patterns and causes. *International Journal of Plant Sciences* **160**: S135–S146.

Stiling, P., Moon, D.C., Hunter, M.D., Colson, J., Rossi, A.M., Hymus, G.J., and Drake, B.G. 2003. Elevated CO_2 lowers relative and absolute herbivore density across all species of a scrub-oak forest. *Oecologia* **134**: 82–87.

Stiling, P., Rossi, A.M., Hungate, B., Dijkstra, P., Hinkle, C.R., Knot III, W.M., and Drake, B. 1999. Decreased leaf-miner abundance in elevated CO_2: Reduced leaf quality and increased parasitoid attack. *Ecological Applications* **9**: 240–244.

Tognetti, R., Longobucco, A., Raschi, A., and Jones, M.B. 2001. Stem hydraulic properties and xylem vulnerability to embolism in three co-occurring Mediterranean shrubs at a natural CO_2 spring. *Australian Journal of Plant Physiology* **28**: 257–268.

3.5 Iron Stress

- Atmospheric CO_2 enrichment can stimulate biomass production in both iron-sufficient and iron-deficient plants, and it increases internal iron (Fe) use efficiency, stimulates root growth, and increases root exudation of Fe-mobilizing phyto-siderophores in sub-apical root zones, thereby increasing the competitiveness of plants with rhizosphere microorganisms in their quest for this trace element.

Little is known about the interaction of CO_2 and iron stress on the growth of plants; few researchers have investigated this topic. In one study, Haase *et al.* (2008) grew barley (*Hordeum vulgare* L. cv. Europa) plants from seed for four weeks—both hydro-ponically in nutrient solution having adequate or less-than-adequate iron (Fe) concentrations (+Fe and -Fe, respectively), as well as in rhizobox microcosms filled with soil under the same two conditions of iron availability—in controlled-environment chambers maintained at atmospheric CO_2 concentrations of either ambient CO_2 (400 ppm) or elevated CO_2 (800 ppm). They found the elevated atmospheric CO_2 treatment stimulated biomass production in both the Fe-sufficient and Fe-deficient barley plants, in both hydroponics and soil culture. They also discovered three CO_2-induced modifications in plant activity: "(i) increased internal Fe use efficiency, (ii) stimulation of root growth, and (iii) increased root exudation of Fe-mobilizing phytosiderophores in the sub-apical root zones."

Since phytosiderophores act as metal chelators that mobilize sparingly soluble inorganic forms of iron and zinc and make them more readily available to plants, the eight researchers suggest atmospheric CO_2 enrichment increases the competitiveness of plants such as barley with rhizosphere micro-organisms in their quest for these often difficult-to-obtain trace elements, which helps to explain the strong growth response of barley to atmospheric CO_2 enrichment they observed, even when iron availability was low.

Jin *et al.* (2009) grew 20-day-old plants for an additional seven days in controlled-environment chambers maintained at atmospheric CO_2 concentrations of either 350 or 800 ppm in an iron (Fe)-sufficient medium with a soluble Fe source or under Fe-limited conditions in a medium containing the sparingly soluble hydrous Fe(III)-oxide. They found the elevated CO_2 increased plant growth in both the Fe-sufficient and Fe-limited media, with shoot fresh weight increasing by 22% and 44%, respectively, and root fresh weight increasing by 43% and 97%, respectively. Jin *et al.* report, "the elevated CO_2 under Fe-limited conditions enhance[d] root growth, root hair development, proton release, root FCR [ferric chelate reductase] activity, and expressions of LeFR01 and LeIRT1 genes [which respectively encode FCR and the Fe(II) transporter in tomato], all of which enable plants to access and accumulate more Fe." Also, as would be expected, "the associated increase in Fe concentrations in the shoots and roots alleviated Fe-deficiency-induced chlorosis."

Jin *et al.* state the bioavailability of iron to terrestrial plants "is often limited (Guerinot and Yi, 1994), particularly in calcareous soils, which represent 30% of the Earth's [land] surface (Imsande, 1998)." They conclude "Fe nutrition in plants is likely to be affected by the continued elevation of atmospheric CO_2, which, in turn, will affect crop production." As their work strongly suggests, those important effects should be highly beneficial, and Sasaki *et al.* (1998) suggest even wider biospheric benefits, demonstrating elevated CO_2 concentrations significantly enhanced both the ferric reductase activity and Fe uptake capacity of the marine alga *Chlorococcum littorale* cultured in Fe-limited media.

References

Guerinot, M.L. and Yi, Y. 1994. Iron: nutritious, noxious, and not readily available. *Plant Physiology* **104**: 815–820.

Haase, S., Rothe, A., Kania, A., Wasaki, J., Romheld, V., Engels, C., Kandeler, E., and Neumann, G. 2008. Responses to iron limitation in *Hordeum vulgare* L. as affected by the atmospheric CO_2 concentration. *Journal of Environmental Quality* **37**: 1254–1262.

Imsande, J. 1998. Iron, sulfur, and chlorophyll deficiencies: a need for an integrative approach in plant physiology. *Physiologia Plantarum* **103**: 139–144.

Jin, C.W., Du, S.T., Chen, W.W., Li, G.X., Zhang, Y.S., and Zheng, S.J. 2009. Elevated carbon dioxide improves plant iron nutrition through enhancing the iron-deficiency-induced responses under iron-limited conditions in tomato. *Plant Physiology* **150**: 272–280.

Sasaki, T., Kurano, N., and Miyachi, S. 1998. Induction of ferric reductase activity and of iron uptake capacity in *Chlorococcum littorale* cells under extremely high-CO_2 and iron-deficient conditions. *Plant & Cell Physiology* **39**: 405–410.

3.6 Light Stress

- Whether light intensity is high or low, or leaves are sunlit or shaded, an increase in the CO_2 content of the air increases the biological processes that lead to plant robustness. Less than optimal light intensities do not negate the beneficial effects of atmospheric CO_2 enrichment. In fact, under low light conditions, the benefits of atmospheric CO_2 enrichment on plant growth are often relatively greater than when light conditions are ideal.

Granados and Korner (2002) grew three tropical understory vines (*Gonolobus cteniophorus*, *Ceratophytum tetragonolobum*, and *Thinouia tomocarpa*) for seven months in controlled-environment chambers maintained at atmospheric CO_2 concentrations of 280, 420, 560, and 700 ppm in combination with low and high light intensities, to study the interactive effects of the two parameters on the vines' growth. Plant biomass was found to be 61% greater at high light than at low light. However, the greatest relative CO_2-induced growth response in each species occurred in the low light environment. Increasing the atmospheric CO_2 concentration from 280 to 420 ppm, for example, increased *Gonolobus* biomass by 86 and 32% in low and high light environments, respectively, *Ceratophytum* biomass by 249 and 24% in low and high light environments, respectively, and *Thinouia* biomass by 65% in low light.

Harnos *et al.* (2002) grew winter wheat (*Triticum aestivum* L. cv. Emma) in open-top chambers maintained at atmospheric CO_2 concentrations of 365 and 700 ppm. Among other things, they too report elevated CO_2 stimulated photosynthetic rates to a greater extent under light-limiting than under non-light-limiting conditions. Twice-ambient CO_2 concentrations increased net photosynthesis rates by approximately 100% in upper-canopy leaves and by about 770% further down in the canopy, where light intensity was 60% less than in the upper canopy. This indicates increasing atmospheric CO_2 concentrations likely will lead to enhanced photosynthesis rates by winter wheat plants, even in leaves deep in their canopies, where irradiance is severely reduced due to shading by upper-canopy leaves.

Louche-Tessandier *et al.* (1999) grew potato plantlets inoculated with an arbuscular mycorrhizal fungus at various light intensities and super CO_2 enrichment of approximately 10,000 ppm, finding the unusually high CO_2 concentration produced an unusually high degree of root colonization by the beneficial mycorrhizal fungus, which typically helps supply water and nutrients to plants. It did so irrespective of the degree of light intensity to which the potato plantlets were exposed.

Leakey *et al.* (2002) grew seedlings of *Shorea leprosula* (an under-story rainforest tree) in controlled environments maintained at atmospheric CO_2 concentrations of 376 and 711 ppm in combination with low irradiance treatments delivered in either a uniform or intermittent (sunfleck) manner for about seven months, to study the effects of elevated CO_2 and low light intensity on photosynthesis and growth in this species. They found the initial steady-state rates of photosynthesis measured in the shade in CO_2-enriched leaves were approximately 109% greater than those observed in ambient-grown leaves. In addition, seedlings in the sunfleck treatment grown in elevated CO_2 displayed post-irradiance rates of photosynthesis 14% greater than those observed in control seedlings. Taken together, these increases in photosynthesis led to CO_2-induced increases in carbon uptake 59 and 89% greater than those observed in control seedlings subjected to uniform and sunfleck light treatments, respectively. The seedlings subjected to uniform irradiance produced more biomass than those exposed to sunfleck irradiance, but the CO_2-induced percentage increase in biomass was greater under the sunfleck irradiance regime (60%) than under the uniform irradiance regime (25%).

Rasineni *et al.* (2011) write, "excess light limits photosynthesis by photoinhibition, resulting in reduced carbon gain and also causing photo-damage (Oquist and Huner, 1993; Pastenes *et al.*, 2003; Allakhverdiev and Murata, 2004; Nishiyama *et al.*, 2006)," and thus "plants grown in tropical climates usually experience significantly high irradiance leading to the strong midday depression of photosynthesis (Hymus *et al.*, 2001)." They utilized two open-top chambers in the Botanical Gardens of the University of Hyderabad, India—each of which contained four six-month-old specimens of the fast-growing tropical *Gmelina arborea* tree, which they maintained at optimum moisture and nutrient levels—to measure several plant physiological properties and processes related to leaf photosynthesis and photosystem II (PSII) photochemistry and photo-inhibition at both ambient and elevated CO_2 concentrations (360 and 460 ppm, respectively), working with "well-expanded and light-exposed leaves randomly chosen from the upper half of the plant canopy."

The three Indian scientists determined there were no significant differences in CO_2 assimilation rates between the ambient and elevated CO_2 grown plants during early morning hours, but thereafter "photosynthesis typically maximized between 0900 hours and 1000 hours in both ambient and elevated CO_2-grown plants," which experienced net photosynthetic rates of 20 and 32.5 μmol/m^2/s, respectively, for a CO_2-induced enhancement of 62%, which for the more standard CO_2 enrichment of 300 ppm would be an enhancement of roughly 180%. Subsequently, during the midday period of 1100–1300 hours, the net photosynthesis rate was still significantly enhanced by about 37% (roughly equivalent to a 300-ppm induced increase of more than 100%) in the elevated CO_2 treatment. After that, the difference between the net photosynthetic rates of the two CO_2 treatments once again became insignificant.

Noting the "elevated CO_2 treatment mitigated PSII-photoinhibition through enhanced electron trans-port rates and through efficient biochemical reactions in leaves of *G. arborea*," Rasineni *et al.* conclude their data "demonstrate that future increases in atmospheric CO_2 may have positive effects on photochemical efficiency in fast growing tropical tree species," allowing them to take great advantage of the high-light midday period of potential maximum growth in Earth's tropical regions.

Kerstiens (1998) provided further evidence elevated atmospheric CO_2 helps to ameliorate the stress of low light intensities in trees, analyzing the results of 15 previously published studies of trees having differing degrees of shade tolerance. He found elevated CO_2 caused greater relative biomass increases in shade-tolerant species than in shade-intolerant or sun-loving species. In more than half the studies he analyzed, shade-tolerant species experienced CO_2-induced relative growth increases two to three times greater than those of less shade-tolerant species.

In an extended follow-up review analyzing 74 observations from 24 studies, Kerstiens (2001) reports twice-ambient CO_2 concentrations increased the relative growth response of shade-tolerant and shade-intolerant woody species by an average of 51 and 18%, respectively. Similar results were reported by Poorter and Perez-Soba (2001), who performed a detailed meta-analysis of research results pertaining to this topic, and subsequently by Kubiske *et al.* (2002), who measured photosynthetic acclimation in aspen and sugar maple trees. Low light intensity, therefore, is by no means a barrier to the benefits of an increase in the air's CO_2 content.

Herrick and Thomas (1999) found a 200 ppm increase in the air's CO_2 concentration enhanced the photosynthetic rates of sunlit and shaded leaves of sweetgum trees by 92 and 54%, respectively, at one time of year, and by 166 and 68% at another time. Naumburg and Ellsworth (2000) report a 200 ppm increase in the air's CO_2 content boosted steady-state photosynthetic rates in leaves of four hardwood understory species by an average of 60 and 40% under high and low light intensities, respectively. Even though these photosynthetic responses were significantly less in shaded leaves, they were still substantial, with mean increases ranging from 40 to 68% for a 60% increase in atmospheric CO_2 concentration.

Under extremely low light intensities, the benefits arising from atmospheric CO_2 enrichment may be small, but oftentimes they are very important in terms of plant carbon budgeting. Hattenschwiler (2001), for example, found seedlings of five temperate forest species favored with an additional 200 ppm of CO_2 under light intensities only 3.4 and 1.3% of full sunlight exhibited CO_2-induced biomass increases ranging from 17 to 74%. Similarly, Naumburg *et al.* (2001) found a 200 ppm increase in the air's CO_2 content enhanced photosynthetic carbon uptake in three of four hardwood understory species more than twofold in three of the four species under light irradiances as low as 3% of full sunlight.

Sefcik *et al.* (2006) grew seedlings of two shade-tolerant northern hardwood tree species—sugar maple (*Acer saccharum* Marsh.) and American beech (*Fagus grandifolia* J.F. Ehrh.)—as well as seedlings of two shade-intolerant northern hardwood tree species—black cherry (*Prunus serotina* J.F. Ehrh.) and paper birch (*Betula papyrifera* Marsh.)—for two full growing seasons inside open-top chambers maintained at either ambient (383 ppm) or elevated (658 ppm) atmospheric CO_2 concentrations in an overarching 90-year-old nitrogen-limited northern hardwood forest in Michigan (USA). They determined the seedlings' responses to atmospheric CO_2 enrichment in two contrasting degrees of shade: moderate shade (14.2 μmol photons m^{-2} s^{-1} = 5.6% full sun) and deep shade (6.5 μmol photons m^{-2} s^{-1} = 2.2% full sun). Sefcik *et al.* state "the magnitude of enhancement from exposure to elevated CO_2 was similar for both shade-tolerance groups," with the elevated CO_2 treatment increasing the mean light-saturated net photosynthetic rate by 63% in the shade-tolerant species and by 67% in the shade-intolerant species. More important, they write, "seedlings grown in deep shade, regardless of shade-tolerance group, showed a greater long-term photosynthetic enhancement to elevated CO_2 than those grown in moderate shade," with the mean long-term enhancement being 47% in moderate shade and a much larger 97% in deep shade.

Noting the same type of photosynthetic response "has also been found in a number of other studies, suggesting that the impact of a CO_2-enriched atmosphere increases as light becomes more limiting (Hattenschwiler, 2001; Granados and Korner, 2002; Leakey *et al.*, 2002)," Sefcik *et al.* conclude, "if long-term enhancement of photosynthesis in elevated CO_2 and deep shade translates into greater survival, especially for shade-intolerant species, this could have profound successional implications for nitrogen-limited northern hardwood forest composition in a future higher CO_2 atmosphere."

Elevated CO_2 often reduces a plant's light compensation point, which is the light intensity at which the amount of carbon fixed by photosynthesis is equal to that lost by respiration. Above that particular light intensity, net photosynthesis is positive. Below it, net photosynthesis is negative, and if prolonged, the plant will ultimately die. This phenomenon is especially beneficial to vegetation growing in deep shade beneath forest canopies that block out much of the incoming sunlight (Kubiske and Pregitzer, 1996; Osborne *et al.*, 1997), and it also helps aquatic plants extend their life zones to greater depths (Zimmerman *et al.*, 1997).

Whether light intensity is high or low, or leaves are shaded or sunlit, an increase in the CO_2 content of the air increases the various biological processes that lead to plant robustness. Less than optimal light intensities do not negate the beneficial effects of atmospheric CO_2 enrichment.

References

Allakhverdiev, S.I. and Murata, N. 2004. Environmental stress inhibits the synthesis de novo of proteins involved in the photodamage-repair cycle of photosystem II in Synechocystis sp. PCC 6803. *Biochimica et Biophysica Acta* **1657**: 23–32.

Granados, J. and Korner, C. 2002. In deep shade, elevated CO_2 increases the vigor of tropical climbing plants. *Global Change Biology* **8**: 1109–1117.

Harnos, N., Tuba, Z., and Szente, K. 2002. Modelling net photosynthetic rate of winter wheat in elevated air CO_2 concentrations. *Photosynthetica* **40**: 293–300.

Hattenschwiler, S. 2001. Tree seedling growth in natural deep shade: functional traits related to interspecific variation in response to elevated CO_2. *Oecologia* **129**: 31–42.

Herrick, J.D. and Thomas, R.B. 1999. Effects of CO_2 enrichment on the photosynthetic light response of Sun and shade leaves of canopy sweetgum trees (*Liquidambar styraciflua*) in a forest ecosystem. *Tree Physiology* **19**: 779–786.

Hymus, G.J., Baker, N.R., and Long, S.P. 2001. Growth in elevated CO_2 can both increase and decrease photochemistry and photoinhibition of photosynthesis in a predictable manner. *Dactylis glomerata* growth in two levels of nitrogen nutrition. *Plant Physiology* **127**: 1204–1211.

Kerstiens, G. 1998. Shade-tolerance as a predictor of responses to elevated CO_2 in trees. *Physiologia Plantarum* **102**: 472–480.

Kerstiens, G. 2001. Meta-analysis of the interaction between shade-tolerance, light environment and growth response of woody species to elevated CO_2. *Acta Oecologica* **22**: 61–69.

Kubiske, M.E. and Pregitzer, K.S. 1996. Effects of elevated CO_2 and light availability on the photosynthetic response of trees of contrasting shade tolerance. *Tree Physiology* **16**: 351–358.

Kubiske, M.E., Zak, D.R., Pregitzer, K.S., and Takeuchi, Y. 2002. Photosynthetic acclimation of overstory *Populus tremuloides* and understory *Acer saccharum* to elevated atmospheric CO_2 concentration: interactions with shade and soil nitrogen. *Tree Physiology* **22**: 321–329.

Leakey, A.D.B., Press, M.C., Scholes, J.D., and Watling, J.R. 2002. Relative enhancement of photosynthesis and growth at elevated CO_2 is greater under sunflecks than uniform irradiance in a tropical rain forest tree seedling. *Plant, Cell and Environment* **25**: 1701–1714.

Louche-Tessandier, D., Samson, G., Hernandez-Sebastia, C., Chagvardieff, P., and Desjardins, Y. 1999. Importance of light and CO_2 on the effects of endomycorrhizal colonization on growth and photosynthesis of potato plantlets (*Solanum tuberosum*) in an in vitro tripartite system. *New Phytologist* **142**: 539–550.

Naumburg, E. and Ellsworth, D.S. 2000. Photosynthetic sunfleck utilization potential of understory saplings growing under elevated CO_2 in FACE. *Oecologia* **122**: 163–174.

Naumburg, E., Ellsworth, D.S., and Katul, G.G. 2001. Modeling dynamic understory photosynthesis of contrasting species in ambient and elevated carbon dioxide. *Oecologia* **126**: 487–499.

Nishiyama, Y., Allakhverdiev, S.I., and Murata, N. 2006. A new paradigm for the action of reactive oxygen species in the photoinhibition of photosystem II. *Biochimica et Biophysica Acta* **1757**: 742–749.

Oquist, G. and Huner, N.P.A. 1993. Cold-hardening-induced resistance to photoinhibition of photosynthesis in winter rye is dependent upon an increased capacity for photosynthesis. *Planta* **189**: 150–156.

Osborne, C.P., Drake, B.G., LaRoche, J., and Long, S.P. 1997. Does long-term elevation of CO_2 concentration increase photosynthesis in forest floor vegetation? *Plant Physiology* **114**: 337–344.

Pastenes, C., Santa-Maria, E., Infante, R., and Franck, N. 2003. Domestication of the Chilean guava (*Ugni molinae* Turcz.) a forest understory shrub, must consider light intensity. *Scientia Horticulturae* **98**: 71–84.

Poorter, H. and Perez-Soba, M. 2001. The growth response

of plants to elevated CO_2 under non-optimal environmental conditions. *Oecologia* **129**: 1–20.

Rasineni, G.K., Guha, A., and Reddy, A.R. 2011. Elevated atmospheric CO_2 mitigated photoinhibition in a tropical tree species, *Gmelina arborea*. *Journal of Photochemistry and Photobiology B: Biology* **103**: 159–165.

Sefcik, L.T., Zak, D.R., and Ellsworth, D.S. 2006. Photosynthetic responses to understory shade and elevated carbon dioxide concentration in four northern hardwood tree species. *Tree Physiology* **26**: 1589–1599.

Zimmerman, R.C., Kohrs, D.G., Steller, D.L., and Alberte, R.S. 1997. Impacts of CO_2-enrichment on productivity and light requirements of eelgrass. *Plant Physiology* **115**: 599–607.

3.7 Nitrogen Insufficiency

Numerous studies have investigated the effects of different soil nitrogen (N) concentrations on plant responses to increases in the air's CO_2 content, because some scientists have claimed a deficiency of soil nitrogen reduces the relative growth stimulation in plants that is typically provided by elevated concentrations of atmospheric CO_2. This section investigates that claim for various crops, fungi, grasses, and young trees.

The results of these experiments indicate some plants sometimes will not respond to atmospheric CO_2 enrichment at low levels of soil N, and others will. Some plants respond equally well to increases in the air's CO_2 content when growing in soils exhibiting a whole range of N concentrations. Most commonly, however, plants respond ever-better to rising atmospheric CO_2 concentrations as soil N concentrations rise. Interestingly, Earth's atmosphere and land surface are currently undergoing joint increases in CO_2 and N concentrations. Thus, the outlook is good for continually increasing terrestrial vegetative productivity as these trends continue.

3.7.1 Crops

The maximum benefits of elevated levels of atmospheric CO_2 for the growth and grain production of rice and wheat cannot be realized in soils that are highly deficient in nitrogen, but increasing nitrogen concentrations above what is considered adequate may not result in proportional gains in CO_2-induced growth and yield enhancement. Although there are significant exceptions to the rule, many agricultural crops experience increases in net photosynthesis and biomass production even when soil nitrogen concentrations are a limiting factor to growth.

3.7.1.1 Rice

- The maximum benefits of elevated levels of atmospheric CO_2 for the growth and grain production of rice cannot be realized in soils that are highly deficient in nitrogen, but increasing nitrogen concentrations above what is considered adequate may not result in proportional gains in CO_2-induced growth and yield enhancement.

Does a deficiency of soil nitrogen lessen the relative growth and yield stimulation of rice that is typically provided by elevated levels of atmospheric CO_2? In exploring this question, Weerakoon et al. (1999) grew seedlings of two rice cultivars for 28 days in glasshouses maintained at atmospheric CO_2 concentrations of 373, 545, 723, and 895 ppm under conditions of low, medium, and high soil nitrogen content. After four weeks of treatment, they found photosynthesis significantly increased with increasing nitrogen availability and atmospheric CO_2 concentration. Averaged across all nitrogen regimes, plants grown at 895 ppm CO_2 exhibited photosynthetic rates 50 percent greater than those observed in plants grown at ambient CO_2. Total plant dry weight also increased with increasing atmospheric CO_2. In addition, the percentage growth enhancement resulting from CO_2 enrichment increased with increasing soil nitrogen—from 21 percent at the lowest soil nitrogen concentration to 60 percent at the highest concentration.

Using a different CO_2 enrichment technique, Weerakoon et al. (2000) grew rice in open-top chambers maintained at atmospheric CO_2 concentrations of approximately 350 and 650 ppm during a wet and dry growing season and under a range of soil nitrogen contents. Early in both growing seasons, plants exposed to elevated atmospheric CO_2 concentrations intercepted significantly more sunlight than plants fumigated with ambient air, due to CO_2-induced increases in leaf area index. This phenomenon occurred regardless of soil nitrogen content, but it disappeared shortly after canopy closure in all treatments. Later, mature canopies achieved similar leaf area indexes at identical levels of soil nitrogen supply, but mean season-long radiation use efficiency—the amount of biomass

produced per unit of solar radiation intercepted—was 35 percent greater in CO_2-enriched vs. ambient-grown plants and tended to increase with increasing soil nitrogen content.

Utilizing a third approach to CO_2 enrichment, Kim et al. (2003) grew rice crops from the seedling stage to maturity at atmospheric CO_2 concentrations of ambient and ambient plus 200 ppm using FACE technology and three levels of applied nitrogen—low (LN, 4 g N m^{-2}), medium (MN, 8 and 9 g N m^{-2}), and high (HN, 15 g N m^{-2})—for three cropping seasons (1998–2000). They report "the yield response to elevated CO_2 in crops supplied with MN (+14.6%) or HN (+15.2%) was about twice that of crops supplied with LN (+7.4%)," confirming the importance of nitrogen availability to the response of rice to atmospheric CO_2 enrichment previously determined by Kim et al. (2001) and Kobaysahi et al. (2001).

These observations indicate the maximum benefits of elevated levels of atmospheric CO_2 for the growth and grain production of rice cannot be realized in soils highly deficient in nitrogen, but increasing nitrogen concentrations above what is considered adequate may not result in proportional gains in CO_2-induced growth and yield enhancement.

References

Kim, H.-Y., Lieffering, M., Kobayashi, K., Okada, M., Mitchell, M.W., and Gumpertz, M. 2003. Effects of free-air CO_2 enrichment and nitrogen supply on the yield of temperate paddy rice crops. *Field Crops Research* **83**: 261–270.

Kim, H.-Y., Lieffering, M., Miura, S., Kobayashi, K., and Okada, M. 2001. Growth and nitrogen uptake of CO_2-enriched rice under field conditions. *New Phytologist* **150**: 223–229.

Kobayashi, K., Lieffering, M., and Kim, H.-Y. 2001. Growth and yield of paddy rice under free-air CO_2 enrichment. In: Shiyomi, M. and Koizumi, H. (Eds.) *Structure and Function in Agroecosystem Design and Management*. CRC Press, Boca Raton, FL, USA, pp. 371–395.

Weerakoon, W.M.W., Ingram, K.T., and Moss, D.D. 2000. Atmospheric carbon dioxide and fertilizer nitrogen effects on radiation interception by rice. *Plant and Soil* **220**: 99–106.

Weerakoon, W.M., Olszyk, D.M., and Moss, D.N. 1999. Effects of nitrogen nutrition on responses of rice seedlings to carbon dioxide. *Agriculture, Ecosystems and Environment* **72**: 1–8.

3.7.1.2 Wheat

- The maximum benefits of elevated levels of atmospheric CO_2 for the growth and grain production of wheat cannot be realized in soils that are highly deficient in nitrogen, but increasing nitrogen concentrations above what is considered adequate may not result in proportional gains in CO_2-induced growth and yield enhancement.

Smart *et al.* (1998) grew wheat from seed for 23 days in controlled-environment chambers maintained at atmospheric CO_2 concentrations of 360 and 1,000 ppm and two concentrations of soil nitrate, finding the extra CO_2 increased average plant biomass by approximately 15 percent, irrespective of soil nitrogen content. In a more realistic FACE experiment, however, Brooks *et al.* (2000) grew spring wheat for two seasons at atmospheric CO_2 concentrations of 370 and 570 ppm at both high and low levels of nitrogen fertility, obtaining twice the yield enhancement (16 percent vs. 8 percent) in the high nitrogen treatment.

Vilhena-Cardoso and Barnes (2001) grew spring wheat for two months in environmental chambers fumigated with air containing atmospheric CO_2 concentrations of either 350 or 700 ppm at ambient and elevated (75 ppb) ozone levels, and supplied the plants with either low, medium, or high levels of soil nitrogen. With respect to biomass production, the elevated CO_2 treatment increased total plant dry weight by 44, 29, and 12 percent at the high, medium, and low soil nitrogen levels, respectively. Although elevated ozone by itself reduced plant biomass, the simultaneous application of elevated CO_2 completely ameliorated its detrimental effects on biomass production, irrespective of soil nitrogen supply.

Why do the plants of some studies experience a major reduction in the relative growth stimulation provided by atmospheric CO_2 enrichment under low soil nitrogen conditions, whereas other studies find the aerial fertilization effect of elevated CO_2 to be independent of root-zone nitrogen concentration? Based on studies of both potted and hydroponically grown plants, Farage *et al.* (1998) determined low root-zone nitrogen concentrations need not lead to photosynthetic acclimation (less than maximum potential rates of photosynthesis) in elevated CO_2, as long as root-zone nitrogen supply is adequate to meet plant nitrogen needs to maintain the enhanced relative growth rate that is made possible by atmospheric CO_2 enrichment. When supply cannot meet this need, as is often the case in soils with limited nitrogen reserves, the aerial fertilization effect of atmospheric CO_2 enrichment begins to be reduced and causes less-than-potential CO_2-induced growth stimulation. Nevertheless, the acclimation process is the plant's "first line of defense" to keep its productivity from falling even further than it otherwise would, as it typically mobilizes nitrogen from "excess" rubisco and sends it to other plant sink tissues to maintain growth and development (Theobald *et al.*, 1998).

Although atmospheric CO_2 enrichment tends to increase the growth and yield of wheat under a wide range of soil nitrogen concentrations, including some that are very low, considerably greater CO_2-induced enhancements are possible when more soil nitrogen is available. The response can saturate at high soil nitrogen levels, with excess nitrogen providing little or no extra yield.

References

Brooks, T.J., Wall, G.W., Pinter Jr., P.J., Kimball, B.A., LaMorte, R.L., Leavitt, S.W., Matthias, A.D., Adamsen, F.J., Hunsaker, D.J., and Webber, A.N. 2000. Acclimation response of spring wheat in a free-air CO_2 enrichment (FACE) atmosphere with variable soil nitrogen regimes. 3. Canopy architecture and gas exchange. *Photosynthesis Research* **66**: 97–108.

Farage, P.K., McKee, I.F., and Long, S.P. 1998. Does a low nitrogen supply necessarily lead to acclimation of photosynthesis to elevated CO_2? *Plant Physiology* **118**: 573–580.

Smart, D.R., Ritchie, K., Bloom, A.J., and Bugbee, B.B. 1998. Nitrogen balance for wheat canopies (*Triticum aestivum* cv. Veery 10) grown under elevated and ambient CO_2 concentrations. *Plant, Cell and Environment* **2**1: 753–763.

Theobald, J.C., Mitchell, R.A.C., Parry, M.A.J., and Lawlor, D.W. 1998. Estimating the excess investment in ribulose-1,5-bisphosphate carboxylase/oxygenase in leaves of spring wheat grown under elevated CO_2. *Plant Physiology* **118**: 945–955.

Vilhena-Cardoso, J. and Barnes, J. 2001. Does nitrogen supply affect the response of wheat (*Triticum aestivum* cv. Hanno) to the combination of elevated CO_2 and O_3? *Journal of Experimental Botany* **52**: 1901–1911.

3.7.1.3 Other Crops

- Agricultural crops generally experience greater

CO_2-induced percentage increases in net photosynthesis and biomass production even when soil nitrogen concentrations are a limiting factor, although there are some significant exceptions to the rule.

Zerihun et al. (2000) grew sunflowers for one month in pots of three different soil nitrogen concentrations placed in open-top chambers maintained at atmospheric CO_2 concentrations of 360 and 700 ppm. The extra CO_2 of the CO_2-enriched chambers reduced average rates of root nitrogen uptake by about 25%, which by itself would tend to reduce tissue nitrogen contents and the relative growth rates of the seedlings. However, the elevated CO_2 also increased photosynthetic nitrogen-use efficiency by an average of 50%, which tends to increase the relative growth rates of seedlings. The latter of these two competing effects was more powerful, leading to an increase in whole plant biomass. At the conclusion of the one-month study, the CO_2-enriched plants exhibited whole plant biomass values 44, 13, and 115 percent greater than those of the plants growing in ambient air at low, medium, and high levels of soil nitrogen, respectively. These findings demonstrate low tissue nitrogen contents do not necessarily preclude a growth response to atmospheric CO_2 enrichment, particularly if photosynthetic nitrogen-use efficiency is enhanced, which is typically the case, as it was in this study. Nevertheless, the greatest CO_2-induced growth increase of Zerihun et al.'s study was exhibited by the plants growing in the high soil nitrogen treatment.

Deng and Woodward (1998) grew strawberries in environment-controlled glasshouses maintained at atmospheric CO_2 concentrations of 390 and 560 ppm for nearly three months. The strawberries were supplied with fertilizers containing three levels of nitrogen. The extra CO_2 increased rates of net photosynthesis and total plant dry weight at all three nitrogen levels, but the increases were not significant. Nevertheless, they provided the CO_2-enriched plants with enough additional sugar and physical mass to support significantly greater numbers of flowers and fruits than the plants grown at 390 ppm CO_2. This effect ultimately led to total fresh fruit weights 42 and 17 percent greater in the CO_2-enriched plants that received the highest and lowest levels of nitrogen fertilization, respectively, once again indicating a greater growth response at higher nitrogen levels.

Newman et al. (2003) investigated the effects of two levels of nitrogen fertilization and an approximate doubling of the air's CO_2 concentration on the growth of tall fescue, an important forage crop. The plants were initially grown from seed in greenhouse flats, but after 16 weeks the researchers transplanted them into 19-liter pots filled with potting media given periodic applications of a slow-release fertilizer. Over the next two years of outdoor growth, the researchers periodically clipped, divided, and repotted the plants to ensure they did not become root-bound. At the end of that time, they placed the plants in 20 1.3-m-diameter open-top chambers, half of which were maintained at the ambient atmospheric CO_2 concentration and half of which received an approximately doubled CO_2 concentration of 700 ppm. In addition, half of the pots in each CO_2 treatment received 0.0673 kg N m^{-2} applied over a period of three consecutive days, and half received only one-tenth that amount. Researchers repeated the entire procedure three times during the 12-week study.

The researchers found the plants grown in the high-CO_2 air photosynthesized 15 percent more and produced 53 percent more dry matter (DM) under low N conditions and 61 percent more DM under high N conditions. The percent of organic matter (OM) was little changed, except under elevated CO_2 and high N, when %OM (as %DM) increased by 3 percent. In this study too, then, the greatest relative increase in productivity occurred under high soil N availability.

Demmers-Derks et al. (1998) grew sugar beets as an annual crop in controlled-environment chambers at atmospheric CO_2 concentrations of 360 and 700 ppm and air temperatures of ambient and ambient plus 3°C for three consecutive years. In addition to exposing the plants to these CO_2 and temperature combinations, the researchers supplied the sugar beets with solutions of low and high nitrogen content. Averaged across all three years and both temperature regimes, the extra CO_2 of this study enhanced total plant biomass by 13 and 25% in the low and high nitrogen treatments, respectively. In addition, it increased root biomass by 12 and 26%. As with sunflowers, strawberries, and tall fescue, elevated CO_2 produced the largest growth responses in the sugar beets that received a high supply of nitrogen.

Romanova et al. (2002) grew sugar beets from seed for one month in controlled-environment chambers maintained at atmospheric CO_2 concentrations of 350 and 700 ppm, fertilizing them with three levels of nitrate-nitrogen. The plants grown in CO_2-enriched air exhibited rates of net photosynthesis approximately 50% greater than those of the plants grown in ambient air, regardless of soil nitrate availability. These CO_2-induced increases in photosynthetic carbon uptake contributed to 60, 40, and 30% above-ground organ dry weight increases in plants receiving one-half, standard, and three-fold levels of soil nitrate, respectively. Root weights were less responsive to atmospheric CO_2 enrichment, displaying 10 and 30% increases in dry weight at one-half and standard nitrate levels but no increase at the high soil nitrate concentration. In this study, the role of soil nitrogen fertility was opposite that observed in the four prior studies in the case of above-ground biomass production, but mixed in the case of belowground biomass production.

Fangmeier *et al.* (2000) grew barley plants in containers in open-top chambers maintained at atmospheric CO_2 concentrations of either 360 or 650 ppm and either a high or low nitrogen fertilization regime. Te elevated CO_2 had the greatest relative impact on yield when the plants were grown under the less-than-optimum low-nitrogen regime—a 48 percent increase vs. 31 percent under high-nitrogen conditions.

Kimball *et al.* (2002) summarized the findings of most FACE studies conducted on agricultural crops since the introduction of that technology in the late 1980s. In response to a 300 ppm increase in the air's CO_2 concentration, rates of net photosynthesis in several C_3 grasses were enhanced by an average of 46% under conditions of ample soil nitrogen supply and by 44% when nitrogen was limiting to growth. The differential for above-ground biomass production was much larger, with the C_3 grasses wheat, rice, and ryegrass showing an average increase of 18% at ample nitrogen but only 4% at low nitrogen. As to belowground biomass production, they experienced an average increase of 70% at ample nitrogen and 58% at low nitrogen. Similarly, clover experienced a 38% increase in belowground biomass production at ample soil nitrogen and a 32% increase at low soil nitrogen. Finally, with respect to agricultural yield—the true indicator of food and fiber production—wheat and ryegrass showed an average increase of 18% at ample nitrogen, and wheat saw only a 10% increase at low nitrogen.

These results indicate most agricultural crops generally experience greater CO_2-induced relative (percentage) increases in net photosynthesis and biomass production even when soil nitrogen concentrations are a limiting factor, although there are some exceptions to the rule.

References

Demmers-Derks, H., Mitchell, R.A.G., Mitchell, V.J., and Lawlor, D.W. 1998. Response of sugar beet (*Beta vulgaris* L.) yield and biochemical composition to elevated CO_2 and temperature at two nitrogen applications. *Plant, Cell and Environment* **21**: 829–836.

Deng, X. and Woodward, F.I. 1998. The growth and yield responses of *Fragaria ananassa* to elevated CO_2 and N supply. *Annals of Botany* **81**: 67–71.

Fangmeier, A., Chrost, B., Hogy, P., and Krupinska, K. 2000. CO_2 enrichment enhances flag leaf senescence in barley due to greater grain nitrogen sink capacity. *Environmental and Experimental Botany* **44**: 151–164.

Kimball, B.A., Kobayashi, K., and Bindi, M. 2002. Responses of agricultural crops to free-air CO_2 enrichment. *Advances in Agronomy* **77**: 293–368.

Newman, J.A., Abner, M.L., Dado, R.G., Gibson, D.J., Brookings, A., and Parsons, A.J. 2003. Effects of elevated CO_2, nitrogen and fungal endophyte-infection on tall fescue: growth, photosynthesis, chemical composition and digestibility. *Global Change Biology* **9**: 425–437.

Romanova, A.K., Mudrik, V.A., Novichkova, N.S., Demidova, R.N., and Polyakova, V.A. 2002. Physiological and biochemical characteristics of sugar beet plants grown at an increased carbon dioxide concentration and at various nitrate doses. *Russian Journal of Plant Physiology* **49**: 204–210.

Zerihun, A., Gutschick, V.P., and BassiriRad, H. 2000. Compensatory roles of nitrogen uptake and photosynthetic N-use efficiency in determining plant growth response to elevated CO_2: Evaluation using a functional balance model. *Annals of Botany* **86**: 723–730.

3.7.2 Fungi

- CO_2-induced stimulation of root infection by various fungi (which tends to benefit the plants) is generally greater under lower soil nitrogen concentrations. This implies elevated CO_2 will enhance fungal-plant interactions to a greater extent when soil nutrition is less than optimal for plant growth, which is the common state of most ecosystems not subjected to fertilization practices typical of intensive agriculture.

Nearly all plants establish intimate relationships with different fungal species at one point or another in their life cycles, and these fungi commonly aid plants in the acquisition of water and nutrients. In addition, fungal-plant interactions are often affected by variations in atmospheric CO_2 and soil nitrogen concentrations.

In a one-year study conducted by Walker *et al.* (1998), ponderosa pine seedlings exposed to elevated atmospheric CO_2 concentrations of 525 and 700 ppm displayed total numbers of ectomycorrhizal fungi on their roots 170 and 85% greater, respectively, than those observed on roots of ambient-grown seedlings.

Rillig *et al.* (1998) found three grasses and two herbs fumigated with ambient air and air containing an extra 350 ppm CO_2 for four months displayed various root infection responses by arbuscular mycorrhizal fungi, which varied with soil nitrogen supply. At low soil nitrogen contents, elevated CO_2 increased the percent root infection by this type of fungi in all five annual grassland species. At high soil nitrogen, this trend was reversed in four of the five species.

Rillig and Allen (1998) made several important observations regarding the effects of elevated CO_2 and soil nitrogen status on fungal-plant interactions. First, after growing three-year-old shrubs at an atmospheric CO_2 concentration of 750 ppm for four months, they reported non-significant 19 and 9% increases in percent root infected by arbuscular mycorrhizal fungi at low and high soil nitrogen concentrations, respectively. In addition, elevated CO_2 significantly increased the percent root infection by arbuscules, which are the main structures involved in the symbiotic exchange of carbon and nutrients between a host plant and its associated fungi, by more than 14-fold at low soil nitrogen concentrations. In addition, the length of fungal hyphae more than doubled with atmospheric CO_2 enrichment in the low soil nitrogen regime, and in the high soil nitrogen treatment elevated CO_2 increased the percent root infection by vesicles, which are organs used by arbuscular mycorrhizal fungi for carbon storage, by approximately 2.5-fold.

These observations suggest elevated CO_2 affects fungal-plant interactions in positive ways that may depend on soil nitrogen status. Typically, it appears CO_2-induced stimulations of percent root infection by various fungal components is greater under lower soil nitrogen concentrations. This tendency implies elevated CO_2 will enhance fungal-plant interactions to a greater extent when soil nutrition is less than optimal for plant growth, which is commonly the case for most ecosystems not subjected to cultural fertilization practices typical of intensive agricultural production.

References

Rillig, M.C. and Allen, M.F. 1998. Arbuscular mycorrhizae of *Gutierrezia sarothrae* and elevated carbon dioxide: evidence for shifts in C allocation to and within the mycobiont. *Soil Biology and Biochemistry* **30**: 2001–2008.

Rillig, M.C., Allen, M.F., Klironomos, J.N., Chiariello, N.R., and Field, C.B. 1998. Plant species-specific changes in root-inhabiting fungi in a California annual grassland: responses to elevated CO_2 and nutrients. *Oecologia* **113**: 252–259.

Walker, R.F., Johnson, D.W., Geisinger, D.R., and Ball, J.T. 1998. Growth and ectomycorrhizal colonization of ponderosa pine seedlings supplied different levels of atmospheric CO_2 and soil N and P. *Forest Ecology and Management* **109**: 9–20.

3.7.3 Grasses

- Atmospheric CO_2 enrichment stimulates photosynthesis and biomass production in grasses and grassland species when soil nitrogen availability is high or moderate. Where nitrogen availability is low, grasslands are able to overcome soil nitrogen limitations and produce positive CO_2-induced growth responses, given enough time.

Perennial ryegrass (*Lolium perenne* L.) has been used as a model species in many experiments to help elucidate grassland responses to atmospheric CO_2 enrichment and soil nitrogen availability. In the FACE study of Rogers *et al.* (1998), for example, ryegrass plants exposed to 600 ppm CO_2 exhibited a 35% increase in their photosynthetic rates without regard to soil nitrogen availability. However, when ryegrass was grown in plastic ventilated tunnels at twice-ambient concentrations of atmospheric CO_2, the CO_2-induced photosynthetic response was about 3-fold greater in a higher soil nitrogen regime (Casella and Soussana, 1997).

Similarly, in an open-top chamber study Davey *et al.* (1999) found an atmospheric CO_2 concentration of 700 ppm stimulated photosynthesis by 30% in this species when it was grown with moderate, but not low, soil nitrogen availability. Thus, CO_2-induced photosynthetic stimulations in perennial ryegrass can be influenced by soil nitrogen content, with greater positive responses typically occurring under higher, as opposed to lower, soil nitrogen availability.

With respect to biomass production, van Ginkel and Gorissen (1998) report a doubling of the atmospheric CO_2 concentration increased shoot biomass of perennial ryegrass by 28%, regardless of soil nitrogen concentration. In the more revealing six-year FACE study of Daepp et al. (2000), however, plants grown at 600 ppm CO_2 and high soil nitrogen availability continually increased their dry matter production over that observed in ambient-treatment plots, from 8% more in the first year to 25% more at the close of year six. When grown at a low soil nitrogen availability, CO_2-enriched plants exhibited an initial 5% increase in dry matter production, which dropped to a negative 11% in year two. This negative trend was thereafter turned around, reaching a 9% stimulation at the end of the study. These data demonstrate elevated CO_2 increases perennial rye-grass biomass, even under conditions of low soil nitrogen availability, especially under conditions of long-term atmospheric CO_2 enrichment.

Lutze et al. (1998) report microcosms of the C_3 grass Danthonia richardsonii grown for four years in glasshouses fumigated with air containing 720 ppm CO_2 displayed total photosynthetic carbon gains 15–34% higher than those of ambient-grown microcosms, depending on the soil nitrogen concentration. And in a clearer depiction of photosynthetic responses to soil nitrogen, Davey et al. (1999) note the photosynthetic rates of Agrostis capillaries exposed to twice-ambient levels of atmospheric CO_2 for two years were 12 and 38% greater than rates measured in control plants grown at 350 ppm CO_2 under high and low soil nitrogen regimes, respectively. They also reported CO_2-induced photosynthetic stimulations of 25 and 74% for Trifolium repens subjected to high and low soil nitrogen regimes, respectively. Thus the greatest CO_2-induced percentage increase in photosynthesis occurred under the least favorable soil nitrogen conditions.

With respect to biomass production, Navas et al. (1999) state 60 days' exposure to 712 ppm CO_2 increased biomass production of Danthonia richardsonii, Phalaris aquatica, Lotus pedunculatus, and Trifolium repens across a large soil nitrogen gradient. With slightly more detail, Cotrufo and Gorissen (1997) reported average CO_2-induced increases in whole-plant dry weights of Agrostis capillaries and Festuca ovina 20% greater than those of their respective controls, regardless of soil nitrogen availability. And Ghannoum and Conroy (1998) report three Panicum grasses grown for two months at twice-ambient levels of atmospheric CO_2 and high soil nitrogen availability displayed similar increases in total plant dry mass about 28% greater than those

of their respective ambient-grown controls. At low nitrogen, however, elevated CO_2 had no significant effect on the dry mass of two of the species, and it decreased in the third species.

It is clear atmospheric CO_2 enrichment stimulates photosynthesis and biomass production in grasses and grassland species when soil nitrogen availability is high or moderate. Under lower soil nitrogen conditions, atmospheric CO_2 enrichment can have the same positive effect, but it also can have a reduced positive effect, no effect, or a negative effect. In light of the one long-term study that lasted six years, however, it is likely, given enough time, grasslands can overcome soil nitrogen limitations and produce positive CO_2-induced growth responses. Because the rising CO_2 content of the air is likely to continue for a long time to come, occasional nitrogen limitations on the aerial fertilization effect of atmospheric CO_2 enrichment of grasslands likely will become less restrictive as time goes on.

References

Casella, E. and Soussana, J-F. 1997. Long-term effects of CO_2 enrichment and temperature increase on the carbon balance of a temperate grass sward. Journal of Experimental Botany 48: 1309–1321.

Cotrufo, M.F. and Gorissen, A. 1997. Elevated CO_2 enhances below-ground C allocation in three perennial grass species at different levels of N availability. New Phytologist 137: 421–431.

Daepp, M., Suter, D., Almeida, J.P.F., Isopp, H., Hartwig, U.A., Frehner, M., Blum, H., Nosberger, J., and Luscher, A. 2000. Yield response of Lolium perenne swards to free air CO_2 enrichment increased over six years in a high N input system on fertile soil. Global Change Biology 6: 805–816.

Davey, P.A., Parsons, A.J., Atkinson, L., Wadge, K., and Long, S.P. 1999. Does photosynthetic acclimation to elevated CO_2 increase photosynthetic nitrogen-use efficiency? A study of three native UK grassland species in open-top chambers. Functional Ecology 13: 21–28.

Ghannoum, O. and Conroy, J.P. 1998. Nitrogen deficiency precludes a growth response to CO_2 enrichment in C_3 and C_4 Panicum grasses. Australian Journal of Plant Physiology 25: 627–636.

Lutze, J.L. and Gifford, R.M. 1998. Carbon accumulation, distribution and water use of Danthonia richardsonii swards in response to CO_2 and nitrogen supply over four years of growth. Global Change Biology 4: 851–861.

Navas, M.-L., Garnier, E., Austin, M.P., and Gifford, R.M. 1999. Effect of competition on the responses of grasses and legumes to elevated atmospheric CO_2 along a nitrogen gradient: differences between isolated plants, monocultures and multi-species mixtures. *New Phytologist* **143**: 323–331.

Rogers, A., Fischer, B.U., Bryant, J., Frehner, M., Blum, H., Raines, C.A., and Long, S.P. 1998. Acclimation of photosynthesis to elevated CO_2 under low-nitrogen nutrition is affected by the capacity for assimilate utilization. Perennial ryegrass under free-air CO_2 enrichment. *Plant Physiology* **118**: 683–689.

Van Ginkel, J.H. and Gorissen, A. 1998. In situ decomposition of grass roots as affected by elevated atmospheric carbon dioxide. *Soil Science Society of America Journal* **62**: 951–958.

3.7.4 Trees

3.7.4.1 Aspen

- Typically, the aerial fertilization effect of atmospheric CO_2 enrichment stimulates the growth of young aspen trees in soils of adequate and insufficient nitrogen content, although the stimulation is generally greater when nitrogen is not limiting.

Does a deficiency of soil nitrogen lessen the relative growth stimulation of young quaking aspen (*Populus tremuloides* Michx) trees that is typically provided by elevated concentrations of atmospheric CO_2? Kubiske *et al.* (1998) grew cuttings of four quaking aspen genotypes for five months at CO_2 concentrations of 380 or 720 ppm and low or high soil nitrogen in open-top chambers in the field in Michigan (USA). Elevated CO_2 significantly increased net photosynthesis, regardless of soil nitrogen content, although there were no discernible increases in above-ground growth in the five-month study period. Belowground, elevated CO_2 significantly increased fine root production, but only in the high soil nitrogen treatment.

Zak *et al.* (2000) and Curtis *et al.* (2000) grew six aspen genotypes from cuttings in open-top chambers for 2.5 growing seasons at atmospheric CO_2 concentrations of 350 and 700 ppm on soils containing either adequate or inadequate supplies of nitrogen. At the end of this period, Curtis *et al.* found the trees growing in the doubled-CO_2 treatment exhibited rates of net photosynthesis 128 and 31% greater than those of the trees growing in the ambient-air treatment on

the high- and low-nitrogen soils, respectively. Zak *et al.* also determined the CO_2-induced biomass increases of the trees in the high- and low-nitrogen soils to be 38 and 16%, respectively.

Mikan *et al.* (2000) grew aspen cuttings for two years in open-top chambers receiving atmospheric CO_2 concentrations of 367 and 715 ppm in soils of low and high soil nitrogen concentrations. They report elevated CO_2 increased the total biomass of the aspen cuttings by 50 and 26% in the high and low soil nitrogen treatments, respectively, and it increased coarse root biomass by 78 and 24% in the same respective treatments.

Wang and Curtis (2001) grew cuttings of two male and two female aspen trees for about five months in open-top chambers maintained at atmospheric CO_2 concentrations of 380 and 765 ppm on soils of high and low nitrogen content. The male cuttings exhibited a modest difference in the CO_2-induced increase in total biomass (58 and 66% in the high- and low-nitrogen soils, respectively), and the female cuttings showed a much greater difference (82 and 22% in the same respective treatments).

Taken together, these observations suggest the aerial fertilization effect of atmospheric CO_2 enrichment stimulates the growth of young aspen trees in soils of adequate and insufficient nitrogen content, although the stimulation is generally greater when nitrogen is not limiting.

References

Curtis, P.S., Vogel, C.S., Wang, X.Z., Pregitzer, K.S., Zak, D.R., Lussenhop, J., Kubiske, M., and Teeri, J.A. 2000. Gas exchange, leaf nitrogen, and growth efficiency of *Populus tremuloides* in a CO_2-enriched atmosphere. *Ecological Applications* **10**: 3–17.

Kubiske, M.E., Pregitzer, K.S., Zak, D.R., and Mikan, C.J. 1998. Growth and C allocation of *Populus tremuloides* genotypes in response to atmospheric CO_2 and soil N availability. *New Phytologist* **140**: 251–260.

Mikan, C.J., Zak, D.R., Kubiske, M.E., and Pregitzer, K.S. 2000. Combined effects of atmospheric CO_2 and N availability on the belowground carbon and nitrogen dynamics of aspen mesocosms. *Oecologia* **124**: 432–445.

Wang, X. and Curtis, P.S. 2001. Gender-specific responses of *Populus tremuloides* to atmospheric CO_2 enrichment. *New Phytologist* **150**: 675–684.

Zak, D.R., Pregitzer, K.S., Curtis, P.S., Vogel, C.S., Holmes, W.E., and Lussenhop, J. 2000. Atmospheric CO_2, soil-N availability, and allocation of biomass and nitrogen by *Populus tremuloides*. *Ecological Applications* **10**: 34–46.

3.7.4.2 Pine

- Typically, the aerial fertilization effect of atmospheric CO_2 enrichment stimulates the growth of young pine trees in soils of adequate and insufficient nitrogen content, although the stimulation is generally greater when nitrogen is not limiting.

In a review of 11 papers dealing with both loblolly pine (*Pinus taeda* L.) and ponderosa pine (*Pinus ponderosa* Dougl.), Johnson *et al.* (1998) report when soil nitrogen levels were extremely deficient or so high as to be toxic, growth responses to atmospheric CO_2 enrichment in both species were negligible. For moderate soil nitrogen deficiencies, however, a doubling of the air's CO_2 content sometimes boosted growth by as much as 1,000%. In addition, atmospheric CO_2 enrichment mitigated the negative growth response of ponderosa pine to extremely high soil nitrogen concentrations.

Walker *et al.* (1998) raised ponderosa pine tree seedlings for two growing seasons in open-top chambers having CO_2 concentrations of 350, 525 and 700 ppm on soils of low, medium, and high nitrogen content. They found elevated CO_2 had little effect on most growth parameters after the first growing season, the one exception being belowground biomass, which increased with both CO_2 and soil nitrogen. After two growing seasons, however, elevated CO_2 significantly increased all growth parameters, including tree height, stem diameter, shoot weight, stem volume, and root volume, with the greatest responses typically occurring at the highest CO_2 concentration in the highest soil nitrogen treatment. Root volume at 700 ppm CO_2 and high soil nitrogen, for example, exceeded all other treatments by at least 45%, as did shoot volume, by 42%. Similarly, at high CO_2 and soil nitrogen, coarse root and shoot weights exceeded those at ambient CO_2 and high nitrogen by 80 and 88%, respectively.

Walker *et al.* (2000) published another paper on the same trees and treatments after five years of growth. At this time, the trees exposed to the twice-ambient levels of atmospheric CO_2 had heights 43, 64, and 25% greater than those of trees exposed to ambient air and conditions of high, medium, and low

soil nitrogen, respectively. The trunk diameters of the 700 ppm trees were 24, 73, and 20% greater than the trunk diameters of the ambient-grown trees exposed to high, medium, and low levels of soil nitrogen.

Entry *et al.* (1998) grew one-year-old longleaf pine seedlings for 20 months in pots of high and low soil nitrogen content in open-top chambers maintained at atmospheric CO_2 concentrations of 365 or 720 ppm, finding the elevated CO_2 caused no overall change in whole-plant biomass at low soil nitrogen, but at high soil nitrogen, it increased it by 42%. After two years of these treatments, Runion *et al.* (1999) report rates of net photosynthesis were about 50% greater in the high CO_2 treatment, irrespective of soil nitrogen content and water content.

Finzi and Schlesinger (2003) measured and analyzed the pool sizes and fluxes of inorganic and organic nitrogen (N) in the floor and top 30 cm of the mineral soil of the Duke Forest at the five-year point of a long-term FACE study, where half of the experimental plots were enriched with an extra 200 ppm of CO_2. They had hypothesized "the increase in carbon fluxes to the microbial community under elevated CO_2 would increase the rate of N immobilization over mineralization," leading to a decline in the significant CO_2-induced stimulation of forest net primary production that developed over the first two years of the experiment (DeLucia *et al.*, 1999; Hamilton *et al.*, 2002). Quite to the contrary, however, they discovered "there was no statistically significant change in the cycling rate of N derived from soil organic matter under elevated CO_2." Neither was the rate of net N mineralization significantly altered by elevated CO_2, nor was there any statistically significant difference in the concentration or net flux of organic and inorganic N in the forest floor and top 30 cm of mineral soil after five years of CO_2 fumigation. Thus they found no support for their hypothesis of growth stimulation provided by elevated levels of atmospheric CO_2 gradually becoming insignificant before the stand reached its equilibrium biomass—although they continued to cling to this unsubstantiated belief.

Taken together, these observations indicate the aerial fertilization effect of atmospheric CO_2 enrichment stimulates the growth of young pine trees in soils of adequate and insufficient nitrogen content, although the stimulation is generally greater when nitrogen is not limiting. Evidence also suggests at some point the response to increasing soil nitrogen saturates, and beyond that point, higher N concentrations may reduce the growth response of young pine trees to elevated CO_2.

References

DeLucia, E.H., Hamilton, J.G., Naidu, S.L., Thomas, R.B., Andrews, J.A., Finzi, A., Lavine, M., Matamala, R., Mohan, J.E., Hendrey, G.R., and Schlesinger, W.H. 1999. Net primary production of a forest ecosystem with experimental CO_2 enrichment. *Science* **284**: 1177–1179.

Entry, J.A., Runion, G.B., Prior, S.A., Mitchell, R.J., and Rogers, H.H. 1998. Influence of CO_2 enrichment and nitrogen fertilization on tissue chemistry and carbon allocation in longleaf pine seedlings. *Plant and Soil* **200**: 3–11.

Finzi, A.C. and Schlesinger, W.H. 2003. Soil-nitrogen cycling in a pine forest exposed to 5 years of elevated carbon dioxide. *Ecosystems* **6**: 444–456.

Hamilton, J.G., DeLucia, E.H., George, K., Naidu, S.L., Finzi, A.C., and Schlesinger, W.H. 2002. Forest carbon balance under elevated CO_2. *Oecologia* **131**: 250–260.

Johnson, D.W., Thomas, R.B., Griffin, K.L., Tissue, D.T., Ball, J.T., Strain, B.R., and Walker, R.F. 1998. Effects of carbon dioxide and nitrogen on growth and nitrogen uptake in ponderosa and loblolly pine. *Journal of Environmental Quality* **27**: 414–425.

Runion, G.B., Mitchell, R.J., Green, T.H., Prior, S.A., Rogers, H.H., and Gjerstad, D.H. 1999. Longleaf pine photosynthetic response to soil resource availability and elevated atmospheric carbon dioxide. *Journal of Environmental Quality* **28**: 880–887.

Walker, R.F., Geisinger, D.R., Johnson, D.W., and Ball, J.T. 1998. Atmospheric CO_2 enrichment and soil N fertility effects on juvenile ponderosa pine: Growth, ecto-mycorrhizal development, and xylem water potential. *Forest Ecology and Management* **102**: 33–44.

Walker, R.F., Johnson, D.W., Geisinger, D.R., and Ball, J.T. 2000. Growth, nutrition, and water relations of ponderosa pine in a field soil as influenced by long-term exposure to elevated atmospheric CO_2. *Forest Ecology and Management* **137**: 1–11.

3.7.4.3 Spruce

- Typically, the aerial fertilization effect of CO_2 enrichment stimulates the growth of young spruce trees in soils of adequate and insufficient nitrogen content, although the stimulation is generally greater when nitrogen is not limiting.

Egli *et al.* (1998) rooted saplings of different genotypes of Norway spruce (*Picea abies* L. Karst.) directly into calcareous or acidic soils in open-top chambers and exposed them to atmospheric CO_2 concentrations of 370 or 570 ppm and low or high soil nitrogen contents. The authors report elevated CO_2 generally stimulated light-saturated rates of photosynthesis under all conditions by as much as 35%, regardless of genotype, which consistently led to increases in above-ground biomass production, also regardless of genotype without respect to soil type or nitrogen content.

Murray *et al.* (2000) grew Sitka spruce (*Picea sitchensis* (Bong.) Carr.) seedlings for two years in pots in open-top chambers maintained at atmospheric CO_2 concentrations of 355 and 700 ppm, where in the last year of the study, half of the seedlings received one-tenth of the optimal soil nitrogen supply recommended for this species and the other half received twice the optimal amount. The extra CO_2 increased the seedlings' light-saturated rates of net photosynthesis by 19 and 33% in the low- and high-nitrogen treatments, respectively, and it increased their total biomass by 0 and 37% in these same treatments. Murray *et al.* note there was a reallocation of biomass from above-ground organs (leaves and stems) into roots in the low-nitrogen treatment, and they remark this phenomenon "may provide a long-term mechanism by which Sitka spruce could utilize limited resources both more efficiently and effectively." This finding suggests although low soil nitrogen precluded a short-term CO_2-induced growth response in this tree species, it is possible the negative impact of nitrogen deficiency could be overcome in the course of much longer-term atmospheric CO_2 enrichment.

Liu *et al.* (2002) grew Sitka spruce seedlings in well-watered and -fertilized pots in open-top chambers maintained for three years at atmospheric CO_2 concentrations of either 350 or 700 ppm. They then planted the seedlings directly into native nutrient-deficient forest soil and maintained them at the same atmospheric CO_2 concentrations for two more years in larger open-top chambers either with or without extra nitrogen being supplied to the soil. After the first three years of the study, they determined the CO_2-enriched trees possessed 11.6% more total biomass than the ambient-treatment trees. At the end of the next two years, the CO_2-enriched trees supplied with extra nitrogen had 15.6% more total biomass than their similarly treated ambient-air counterparts, and the CO_2-enriched trees receiving no extra nitrogen had 20.5% more biomass than their ambient-treatment counterparts.

Typically, the aerial fertilization effect of atmospheric CO_2 enrichment stimulates the growth of young spruce trees in soils of adequate and insufficient nitrogen content, although the stimulation is generally greater when nitrogen is not limiting. Evidence also suggests at some point the response to increasing soil nitrogen saturates, and beyond that point, higher N concentrations may reduce the growth response of young spruce trees to elevated CO_2.

References

Egli, P., Maurer, S., Gunthardt-Goerg, M.S., and Korner, C. 1998. Effects of elevated CO_2 and soil quality on leaf gas exchange and aboveground growth in beech-spruce model ecosystems. *New Phytologist* **140**: 185–196.

Liu, S.R., Barton, C., Lee, H., Jarvis, P.G., and Durrant, D. 2002. Long-term response of Sitka spruce (*Picea sitchensis* (Bong.) Carr.) to CO_2 enrichment and nitrogen supply. I. Growth, biomass allocation and physiology. *Plant Biosystems* **136**: 189–198.

Murray, M.B., Smith, R.I., Friend, A., and Jarvis, P.G. 2000. Effect of elevated [CO_2] and varying nutrient application rates on physiology and biomass accumulation of Sitka spruce (*Picea sitchensis*). *Tree Physiology* **20**: 421–434.

3.7.4.4 Other

- Typically, the aerial fertilization effect of atmospheric CO_2 enrichment stimulates the growth of young tree species in soils of adequate and insufficient nitrogen content, although the stimulation is generally greater when nitrogen is not limiting.

Maillard *et al.* (2001) grew pedunculate oak seedlings for three to four months in greenhouses maintained at atmospheric CO_2 concentrations of either 350 or 700 ppm under conditions of either low or high soil nitrogen concentration. The elevated CO_2 of their study stimulated belowground growth in the seedlings growing in the nitrogen-poor soil, significantly increasing their root-to-shoot ratios. It increased both the below- and above-ground biomass of seedlings growing in nitrogen-rich soil. The CO_2-enriched seedlings growing in the nitrogen-rich soil produced 217 and 533% more stem and coarse-root biomass,

respectively, than their ambient-air counterparts growing in the same fertility treatment. Overall, the doubled CO_2 concentration of the air in their study enhanced total seedling biomass by approximately 30 and 140% under nitrogen-poor and nitrogen-rich soil conditions, respectively.

Schortemeyer *et al.* (1999) grew seedlings of *Acacia melanoxylon* (a leguminous nitrogen-fixing tree native to southeastern Australia) in hydroponic culture for six weeks in growth cabinets, where the air was maintained at CO_2 concentrations of either 350 or 700 ppm and the seedlings were supplied with water containing nitrogen in a number of concentrations ranging from 3 to 6,400 mmol m^{-3}. In the two lowest of these nitrogen concentration treatments, final biomass was unaffected by atmospheric CO_2 enrichment; but it was increased by 5- to 10-fold at the highest nitrogen concentration.

Temperton *et al.* (2003) measured total biomass production in another N_2-fixing tree—*Alnus glutinosa* (the common alder)—seedlings of which had been grown for three years in open-top chambers in either ambient or elevated (ambient + 350 ppm) concentrations of atmospheric CO_2 and one of two soil nitrogen regimes (full nutrient solution or no fertilizer). The trees growing under low soil nutrient conditions exhibited essentially the same growth enhancement as the well-fertilized trees.

Gleadow *et al.* (1998) grew eucalyptus seedlings for six months in glasshouses maintained at atmospheric CO_2 concentrations of either 400 or 800 ppm, fertilizing them twice daily with low or high nitrogen solutions. Their doubling of the air's CO_2 concentration increased total seedling biomass by 134% in the low nitrogen treatment and 98% in the high nitrogen treatment. In addition, the elevated CO_2 led to greater root growth in the low nitrogen treatment, as indicated by a 33% higher root:shoot ratio.

Different species of young trees respond differently to atmospheric CO_2 enrichment under conditions of low vs. high soil nitrogen fertility. The most common response is for the growth-promoting effects of atmospheric CO_2 enrichment to be expressed to a greater degree when soil nitrogen fertility is optimal as opposed to less than optimal.

References

Gleadow, R.M., Foley, W.J., and Woodrow, I.E. 1998. Enhanced CO_2 alters the relationship between photosynthesis and defense in cyanogenic *Eucalyptus cladocalyx* F. Muell. *Plant, Cell and Environment* **21**: 12–22.

Maillard, P., Guehl, J.-M., Muller, J.-F., and Gross, P. 2001. Interactive effects of elevated CO_2 concentration and nitrogen supply on partitioning of newly fixed ^{13}C and ^{15}N between shoot and roots of pedunculate oak seedlings (*Quercus robur* L.). *Tree Physiology* **21**: 163–172.

Schortemeyer, M., Atkin, O.K., McFarlane, N., and Evans, J.R. 1999. The impact of elevated atmospheric CO_2 and nitrate supply on growth, biomass allocation, nitrogen partitioning and N_2 fixation of *Acacia melanoxylon*. *Australian Journal of Plant Physiology* **26**: 737–774.

Temperton, V.M., Grayston, S.J., Jackson, G., Barton, C.V.M., Millard, P., and Jarvis, P.G. 2003. Effects of elevated carbon dioxide concentration on growth and nitrogen fixation in *Alnus glutinosa* in a long-term field experiment. *Tree Physiology* **23**: 1051–1059.

3.8 Ozone Pollution

3.8.1 Agricultural Species

- Atmospheric CO_2 enrichment typically reduces—and more often than not completely overrides—the negative effects of ozone pollution on the photosynthesis, growth, and yield of essentially all agricultural crops that have been experimentally evaluated.

3.8.1.1 Soybean

- The high ozone concentrations that will exist in many parts of the world in the future will have severe negative consequences for soybean production, all else being equal. However, the higher CO_2 concentration predicted for the future will have an important ameliorative effect on the adverse impact of this major air pollutant. It may compensate, or even more than compensate, for the potential negative consequences of elevated O_3.

Air pollution-induced productivity losses to agriculture are serious, especially to soybeans (*Glycine max* L.). Some appreciation for the magnitude of this problem can be gained by considering East Asia, which has 25% of the world's population but produces only 21% of humanity's cereal needs.

Wang and Mauzerall (2004) note air pollution, and especially that due to ozone (O_3), is an increasingly serious problem in this region, reducing agricultural productivity and exacerbating the problem of food security. The two researchers evaluates the impact of rising surface O_3 concentrations in East Asia on agricultural production in 1990 and its projected impact in 2020.

According to their "conservative estimates," the two scientists write, "due to O_3 concentrations in 1990, China, Japan and south Korea lost ... 23–27% of their yield of soybeans," and by 2020, the "loss due to increased levels of O_3 pollution is projected to increase to ... 28–35% for soybeans." As a result of these and other O_3-induced crop losses, Wang and Mauzerall conclude, "East Asian countries are presently on the cusp of substantial reductions in grain production," meaning they are also "on the cusp" of substantial reductions in food security.

Wahid *et al.* (2001) demonstrated the findings of Wang and Mauzerall are indeed "conservative." In a study of the effects of ozone pollution in the Punjab region of Pakistan, Wahid *et al.* periodically applied a powerful ozone protectant to soybeans growing in three locations near the city of Lahore—a suburban site, a remote rural site, and a rural roadside site—throughout two growing seasons (one immediately post-monsoon and one the following spring or pre-monsoon).

At the suburban site, application of the ozone protectant increased the weight of soybean seeds produced per plant by 47% in the post-monsoon season and by 113% in the pre-monsoon season. At the remote rural site, the corresponding yield increases were 94% and 182%, and at the rural roadside site, they were 170% and 285%. Averaged across all three sites and both seasons of the year, the mean increase in yield caused by countering the deleterious effects of this major air pollutant was nearly 150%, and because they found "the impacts of ozone on the yield of soybean are larger in the rural areas around Lahore than in suburban areas of the city," they conclude "there may be substantial impacts of oxidants on crop yield across large areas of the Punjab."

Clearly, whatever can be done to reduce O_3-induced crop losses—or eliminate them altogether—would be considered a benefit in areas where such pollution is commonplace. Rising atmospheric CO_2 concentrations can help to alleviate this problem.

Miller *et al.* (1998) grew soybeans for one season in pots in open-top chambers maintained at atmospheric CO_2 concentrations of 370, 482, 599, and 713 ppm in combination with atmospheric O_3 concentrations of 20, 50, and 79 ppb. By harvest time (113 days after planting), elevated CO_2 had significantly increased all biomass and growth variables measured, with the greatest enhancements occurring at the highest CO_2 and O_3 concentrations. Plants grown at 20 ppb O_3 and 713 ppm CO_2, for example, displayed total dry weights 48% greater than their ambient-air-grown counterparts, and plants grown at 79 ppb O_3 and 713 ppm CO_2 exhibited dry weights 53% greater than their ambient-air counterparts. Likewise, in the same experiment, Heagle *et al.* (1998) observed plants grown at 20 ppb O_3 and 713 ppm CO_2 displayed seed dry weights 20% greater than their ambient-air-grown counterparts, and plants grown at 79 ppb O_3 and 713 ppm CO_2 exhibited seed dry weights 74% greater.

Reid *et al.* (1998) grew soybeans in open-top chambers maintained at atmospheric CO_2 concentrations of 371 and 708 ppm and O_3 concentrations of 24 and 81 ppb. In the ambient-CO_2 air, the elevated O_3 exposure reduced the amount and activity of rubisco per unit leaf area, as well as leaf starch content. In the elevated-CO_2 air, elevated O_3 exposure had no effect on these three leaf parameters: the atmospheric CO_2 enrichment completely ameliorated potential O_3-induced damage.

Reid and Fiscus (1998) grew soybeans for a single season in pots placed in open-top chambers maintained at either ambient (365 ppm) or elevated (727 ppm) concentrations of atmospheric CO_2 and below-ambient (20 ppb) or 1.5 times ambient (74 ppb) levels of ozone. They found elevated CO_2 enhanced rates of photosynthesis regardless of the presence of ozone and typically ameliorated the negative effects of ozone on carbon assimilation.

In a literature review of O_3 and CO_2 effects on soybean photosynthesis, growth and yield, Morgan *et al.* (2003) write, "meta-analytic techniques were used to quantitatively summarize the response of soybean to an average, chronic ozone exposure of 70 ppb, from 53 peer-reviewed studies," after which they similarly derived the net effect of concurrently elevated O_3 and CO_2 (to unspecified concentrations described as being "above 400 ppm"). They found "when both O_3 and CO_2 are elevated, the mean decrease in photosynthesis is 7%," which "compares to a 20% loss for plants grown at elevated O_3 and the current ambient CO_2." The three researchers also report, "at maturity, the average shoot biomass was decreased 34% and seed yield was 24% lower" in

response to elevated O_3 alone, but "seed yield decreases for plants grown in elevated O_3 and elevated CO_2 are only half of those for plants grown in current ambient CO_2 and elevated O_3."

They also found "significant ozone responses in several plant parameters at low daily average concentrations (less than 60 ppb)," which is less than current concentrations in many locations. In studies where the O_3 treatment average was less than 60 ppb, they report, "seed yield, shoot and root dry weight were all significantly decreased by about 10%," which suggests the atmospheric CO_2 enrichment employed in the joint O_3/CO_2 experiments likely would have completely eradicated the O_3-induced losses in plant production.

The findings of Booker *et al.* (2005a) suggest this conclusion is robust. They grew well-watered and well-fertilized soybeans from seeds sown either directly in the ground or in 15-liter pots out-of-doors in open-top chambers maintained at all combinations of low (24 ppb) or high (75 ppb) O_3 concentrations and ambient (373 ppm) or elevated (699 ppm) CO_2 concentrations in 1999, and in 21-liter pots maintained at all combinations of low (24 ppb) or high (75 ppb) O_3 concentrations and ambient (369 ppm) or elevated (717 ppm) CO_2 concentrations in 2000.

In 1999, in the pot-grown plants, the 212% increase in atmospheric O_3 concentration decreased net photosynthesis by approximately 21%. When the air's CO_2 concentration was simultaneously increased by 87%, the negative impact of the O_3 increase was more than ameliorated, as the plants exposed to elevated concentrations of both gases exhibited net photosynthesis rates 26% greater than the plants growing in low O_3 and CO_2 air. Likewise, in the ground-grown plants, the 212% increase in atmospheric O_3 concentration decreased net photosynthesis by approximately 14%, but when the air's CO_2 concentration was simultaneously increased by 87%, the negative impact of the O_3 increase was more than ameliorated, as the plants exposed to elevated concentrations of both gases exhibited net photosynthesis rates 40% greater than the plants growing in low O_3 and CO_2 air.

With respect to seed yield in 1999, in the pot-grown plants the 212% increase in atmospheric O_3 concentration decreased total seed biomass by approximately 27%, but when the air's CO_2 concentration was boosted by 87%, the negative impact of the O_3 increase was also more than ameliorated, as the plants exposed to elevated concentrations of both gases produced 15% more total seed biomass than those growing in low O_3 and CO_2 air. Likewise, in the ground-grown plants, the 212% increase in atmospheric O_3 concentration decreased total seed biomass by approximately 24%, but when the air's CO_2 concentration was boosted by 87%, the negative impact of the O_3 increase was more than ameliorated, as the plants exposed to elevated concentrations of both gases produced 15% more total seed biomass than those in low O_3 and CO_2 air.

With respect to seed yield in 2000, in the pot-grown plants the 212% increase in atmospheric O_3 concentration decreased total seed biomass by approximately 41%, but when the air's CO_2 concentration was simultaneously boosted by 94%, the negative impact of the O_3 increase was more than ameliorated, as the plants exposed to elevated concentrations of both gases produced 18% more total seed biomass than those in low O_3 and CO_2 air. Likewise, in the ground-grown plants, the 212% increase in atmospheric O_3 concentration decreased total seed biomass by approximately 39%, but when the air's CO_2 concentration was boosted by 94%, the negative impact of the O_3 increase was more than ameliorated, as the plants exposed to elevated concentrations of both gases produced 9% more total seed biomass than those in low O_3 and CO_2 air. In all of the many situations investigated by Booker et al., slightly less than a doubling of the air's CO_2 concentration more than compensated for the deleterious effects of slightly more than a tripling of the atmosphere's O_3 concentration on both leaf net photosynthesis and total seed biomass production in soybeans.

In a similar two-year open-top chamber study of aboveground postharvest residue, Booker et al. (2005b) grew soybeans in reciprocal combinations of low and high atmospheric concentrations of O_3 (21 and 74 ppb, respectively) and CO_2 (370 and 714 ppm, respectively), finding residue mass input "is increased by elevated CO_2 and suppressed by O_3." They found elevated O_3 decreased aboveground postharvest residue by 15–46%, elevated CO_2 increased it by 28–56%, and in combination the CO_2 effect always predominated. In the case of leaves, for example, elevating the air's O_3 concentration dropped dry mass residue to only 54% of what it was under ambient conditions, and concurrently elevating the air's CO_2 concentration boosted it to 124% of what it was in ambient air. Corresponding results of 85% and 123% were obtained for petioles, 60% and 121% for stems, and 72% and 122% for husks. Consequently, as in the cases of net photosynthesis and seed yield investi-

gated by Booker et al. (2005a), the results of this study demonstrated a slightly less than doubling of the air's CO_2 concentration more than compensated for the deleterious effects of slightly more than a tripling of the air's O_3 concentration on the production of aboveground postharvest residue in soybeans.

Booker and Fiscus (2005) grew well-watered and well-fertilized soybean plants for two years (1998 and 1999) out-of-doors in 21-liter pots in open-top chambers from emergence to maturity and exposed them to either charcoal-filtered air, charcoal-filtered air plus an extra 336 ppm CO_2, charcoal-filtered air plus 1.5 times normal ambient O_3, or charcoal-filtered air plus an extra 336 ppm CO_2 and 1.5 times normal ambient O_3. They found the imposition of elevated CO_2 alone increased soybean pod biomass by 23.0%, the imposition of elevated O_3 alone decreased pod biomass by 13.3%, and the imposition of elevated CO_2 and O_3 together increased pod biomass by 23.0%.

Today's high ozone concentrations and the even-higher concentrations of the future have and will continue to have severe negative consequences for soybean production, all else being equal. But the atmosphere's current high CO_2 concentration, plus the higher concentration it will have in the future, ameliorates the adverse impacts of this major air pollutant and will continue to do so in the years to come. The anticipated concentrations of CO_2 may more than compensate for the negative effects of elevated O_3.

References

Booker, F.L. and Fiscus, E.L. 2005. The role of ozone flux and antioxidants in the suppression of ozone injury by elevated CO_2 in soybean. *Journal of Experimental Botany* **56**: 2139–2151.

Booker, F.L., Miller, J.E., Fiscus, E.L., Pursley, W.A., and Stefanski, L.A. 2005a. Comparative responses of container- versus ground-grown soybean to elevated carbon dioxide and ozone. *Crop Science* **45**: 883–895.

Booker, F.L., Prior, S.A., Torbert, H.A., Fiscus, E.L., Pursley, W.A., and Hu, S. 2005b. Decomposition of soybean grown under elevated concentrations of CO_2 and O_3. *Global Change Biology* **11**: 685–698.

Heagle, A.S., Miller, J.E., and Pursley, W.A. 1998. Influence of ozone stress on soybean response to carbon dioxide enrichment: III. Yield and seed quality. *Crop Science* **38**: 128–134.

Miller, J.E., Heagle, A.S., and Pursley, W.A. 1998. Influence of ozone stress on soybean response to carbon dioxide enrichment: II. Biomass and development. *Crop Science* **38**: 122–128.

Morgan, P.B., Ainsworth, E.A., and Long, S.P. 2003. How does elevated ozone impact soybean? A meta-analysis of photosynthesis, growth and yield. *Plant, Cell and Environment* **26**: 1317–1328.

Reid, C.D. and Fiscus, E.L. 1998. Effects of elevated [CO_2] and/or ozone on limitations to CO_2 assimilation in soybean (*Glycine max*). *Journal of Experimental Botany* **18**: 885–895.

Reid, C.D., Fiscus, E.L., and Burkey, K.O. 1998. Combined effects of chronic ozone and elevated CO_2 on rubisco activity and leaf components in soybean (*Glycine max*). *Journal of Experimental Botany* **49**: 1999–2011.

Wahid, A., Milne, E., Shamsi, S.R.A., Ashmore, M.R., and Marshall, F.M. 2001. Effects of oxidants on soybean growth and yield in the Pakistan Punjab. *Environmental Pollution* **113**: 271–280.

Wang, X. and Mauzerall, D.L. 2004. Characterizing distributions of surface ozone and its impact on grain production in China, Japan and South Korea: 1990 and 2020. *Atmospheric Environment* **38**: 4383–4402.

3.8.1.2 Wheat

- A number of studies conducted around the turn of the century demonstrate enriching the air with CO_2 substantially ameliorates a variety of negative influences of ozone pollution on the productivity of wheat plants.

Bender *et al.* (1999) analyzed the results of 13 open-top chamber studies in which spring wheat was grown at ambient and twice-ambient CO_2 concentrations in combination with ambient and elevated ozone (O_3) concentrations. They found the elevated O_3 treatment had little effect on growth and yield, suggesting either the O_3 concentrations employed in the studies were not high enough to elicit a negative response in the specific cultivar tested (Minaret) or the cultivar was highly tolerant of ozone. Consequently, elevated CO_2 was the primary variable influencing the growth and yield of the spring wheat. It proved very effective in this regard, increasing aboveground biomass by an average of 37% (with a range of 11 to 128%) and grain yield by an average of 35% (with a range of 11 to 121%).

Tiedemann and Firsching (2000) grew spring wheat from germination to maturity in controlled-environment chambers maintained at ambient (377 ppm) and enriched (612 ppm) atmospheric CO_2 concentrations and ambient (20 ppb) and enriched (61 ppb) atmospheric O_3 concentrations. The extra CO_2 increased mean photosynthetic rates at both O_3 concentrations, with the greatest absolute photosynthetic rates and the largest CO_2-induced percentage increases in photosynthesis being observed in the elevated CO_2/elevated O_3 treatment. Total grain yield was also greatest in the high CO_2/high O_3 treatment, with the elevated CO_2 increasing total grain yield at high O_3 by 38% relative to that observed at ambient CO_2 and elevated O_3. Moreover, the absolute value of total grain yield in the high CO_2/high O_3 treatment was not significantly different from that produced at ambient O_3, regardless of the atmospheric CO_2 concentration. Atmospheric CO_2 enrichment completely ameliorated the deleterious effects of ozone on photosynthesis and yield in this study.

Pleijel *et al.* (2000) grew spring wheat in open-top chambers maintained at atmospheric CO_2 concentrations of 340 and 680 ppm for three consecutive years. They exposed some plants in each CO_2 treatment to ambient, 1.5 x ambient, and 2 x ambient O_3 concentrations. These elevated O_3 concentrations negatively influenced wheat yield at both atmospheric CO_2 concentrations. Grain yield was always higher for the plants grown in the CO_2-enriched air, averaging 13% greater over the three years of the study and leading the scientists who conducted the work to conclude "the positive effect of elevated CO_2 could compensate for the yield losses due to O_3."

Vilhena-Cardoso and Barnes (2001) grew spring wheat for two months in environmental chambers fumigated with air containing atmospheric CO_2 concentrations of 350 and 700 ppm at ambient and elevated (75 ppb) O_3 concentrations in soils of low, medium, and high nitrogen content. The elevated O_3 treatment was shown to reduce photosynthetic rates in the ambient-CO_2-grown plants, but it had no effect on the CO_2-enriched plants, which maintained enhanced photosynthetic rates even in the high O_3 treatments. With respect to biomass production, elevated CO_2 increased total plant dry weight by 44, 29, and 12% at high, medium, and low soil nitrogen supply, respectively, and although elevated O_3 by itself reduced plant biomass, the simultaneous application of elevated CO_2 completely ameliorated this detrimental effect at all soil nitrogen concentrations.

Fangmeier and Bender (2002) analyzed mean

grain yields of spring wheat derived from the ESPACE-Wheat project of the European Stress Physiology and Climate Experiment—Project 1, which was conducted for three growing seasons at eight experimental field sites across Europe that employed atmospheric CO_2 concentrations of 380, 540, and 680 ppm and O_3 concentrations of 32.5 and 60.3 ppb for half-day periods (Jager et al., 1999). They found the high O_3 stress reduced wheat yields by an average of about 12% at the ambient CO_2 concentration. As the air's CO_2 concentration was increased to 540 and 680 ppm, there were no longer any significant reductions in yield due to the high O_3 stress. Whereas wheat yield in ambient-O_3 air increased by 34% over the entire CO_2 enrichment range investigated (380 to 680 ppm), it increased by 46% in the high-O_3 air, once again more than compensating for the O_3-alone-induced yield losses.

The results described above indicate enriching the air with CO_2 substantially ameliorates a variety of negative influences of ozone pollution on the productivity of wheat plants.

References

Bender, J., Herstein, U., and Black, C.R. 1999. Growth and yield responses of spring wheat to increasing carbon dioxide, ozone and physiological stresses: a statistical analysis of 'ESPACE-wheat' results. *European Journal of Agronomy* **10**: 185–195.

Fangmeier, A. and Bender, J. 2002. Air pollutant combinations—Significance for future impact assessments on vegetation. *Phyton* **42**: 65–71.

Jager, H.-J., Hertstein, U., and Fangmeier, A. 1999. The European stress physiology and climate experiments—Project 1—Wheat. *European Journal of Agronomy* **10**: 153–260.

Pleijel, H., Gelang, J., Sild, E., Danielsson, H., Younis, S., Karlsson, P.-E., Wallin, G., Skarby, L., and Sellden, G. 2000. Effects of elevated carbon dioxide, ozone and water availability on spring wheat growth and yield. *Physiologia Plantarum* **108**: 61–70.

Tiedemann, A.V. and Firsching, K.H. 2000. Interactive effects of elevated ozone and carbon dioxide on growth and yield of leaf rust-infected versus non-infected wheat. *Environmental Pollution* **108**: 357–363.

Vilhena-Cardoso, J. and Barnes, J. 2001. Does nitrogen supply affect the response of wheat (*Triticum aestivum* cv. Hanno) to the combination of elevated CO_2 and O_3? *Journal of Experimental Botany* **52**: 1901–1911.

3.8.1.3 Other Species

- Atmospheric CO_2 enrichment typically reduces, and more often than not completely counteracts, the negative effects of ozone pollution on the photosynthesis, growth, and yield of almost all agricultural crops that have been experimentally evaluated.

In addition to soybean and wheat, several studies have examined the effects of elevated CO_2 and ozone on photosynthesis and growth in other agricultural crops. The main findings of some of these studies are described below.

Cotton plants grown by Booker (2000) at elevated ozone concentrations exhibited 25 and 48 percent reductions in leaf mass per unit area and foliar starch concentration, respectively, relative to control plants grown in ambient air. When the cotton plants were simultaneously exposed to twice-ambient CO_2 concentrations, the reductions in these parameters were only 5 and 7 percent, respectively.

Wolf and van Oijen (2002) used a validated potato model to predict increases in European tuber production ranging from 1,000 to 3,000 kg of dry matter per hectare in spite of concomitant increases in ozone concentrations and air temperatures. In a field-based study, Vandermeiren et al. (2005) studied the impact of future increases in atmospheric ozone (O_3) and carbon dioxide (CO_2) concentrations on yield and tuber quality in potato (*Solanum tuberosum* L.). This research endeavor, they write, was "the first large-scale open-top chamber project to provide field-based data spanning a wide range of European climatic conditions and ozone concentrations for a widely used cultivar, cv. Bintje." After two years of intensive measurements made on potatoes growing throughout Europe—including Belgium, Finland, Germany, Ireland, Sweden, and the United Kingdom—they determined the relative yield losses expected to occur in response to O_3 concentrations projected to prevail in Europe at mid-century were a mere 5%. The four researchers also report "the prevailing conditions under climate scenarios for 2050 (including increases in temperature, solar radiation and CO_2 and O_3 concentrations) would increase the yield of irrigated potato crops by 2000–4000 kg ha^{-1} in most regions in Europe, primarily because of the beneficial influence of increased atmospheric CO_2," citing Wolf and Van Oijen (2003).

Plessl et al. (2005) grew well-watered and fertilized spring barley (*Hordeum vulgare* L. cv.

Scarlett) plants from seed for four weeks after emergence in containers located in controlled-environment chambers maintained at either ambient (400 ppm) or 1.75 x ambient (700 ppm) atmospheric CO_2 concentrations. They simultaneously exposed the plants to either ambient or 2 x ambient atmospheric O_3 concentrations, evaluating the individual and combined effects of the CO_2 and O_3 additions. The researchers report the "elevated CO_2 concentration significantly increased aboveground biomass [15%], root biomass [30%], and tiller number [41%], whereas double-ambient ozone significantly decreased these parameters." When applied together, the "ozone-induced reductions in growth parameters were strongly overridden by 700 ppm CO_2." In the doubled-ozone treatment, the 75% increase in the air's CO_2 content increased the barley's aboveground biomass by 42%, its root biomass by 75%, and its tiller number by 94%. Thus, a less than doubling of the air's CO_2 concentration more than compensated for a full doubling of the air's O_3 concentration, revealing the potential for the rise in the air's CO_2 content to more than overcome the negative growth effects of elevated O_3 concentrations on spring barley.

Yonekura et al. (2005) grew komatsuna (Brassica campestris cv. Rakuten) and radish (Raphanus sativus cv. Akamaru) plants from seed (one to a pot) in 1.4-L pots filled with "black soil" in controlled-climate chambers for 30 days in air of one of four different daylight O_3 concentrations—0–5 (charcoal-filtered), 60, 90, or 120 ppb—after which they destructively harvested the plants and determined their final dry weights. In the case of komatsuna (Japanese mustard spinach), where the edible portion of the vegetable is produced aboveground, the mean aboveground dry weights of the plants at the end of their 30-day growth cycle were 0.76, 0.63, 0.53, and 0.39 g in the 0–5, 60, 90, and 120 ppb O_3 treatments, respectively, when grown in ambient air of 380 ppm CO_2. When grown in air of 760 ppm CO_2, aboveground weights for the same set of O_3 concentrations were 1.19, 1.10, 0.98, and 0.85 g, representing CO_2-induced growth enhancements of 57%, 75%, 85%, and 118%. The doubling of the air's CO_2 concentration more than compensated for the negative impact caused by the highest of the four O_3 concentrations in ambient-CO_2 air, turning what would have been a 49% O_3-induced yield loss (from 0.76 to 0.39 g) into a 12% CO_2-induced yield gain (from 0.76 to 0.85 g).

In the case of radish, where the edible portion of the vegetable is produced belowground, the mean belowground dry weights of the plants at the end of their 30-day growth cycle were 0.63, 0.59, 0.39, and 0.36 g in the 0–5, 60, 90, and 120 ppb O_3 treatments, respectively, when grown in ambient air of 380 ppm CO_2. When grown in air of 760 ppm CO_2, however, belowground weights for the same set of O_3 concentrations were 1.45, 1.34, 1.15, and 0.88 g, which represent CO_2-induced growth enhancements of 132%, 127%, 195%, and 144%. Once again, the doubling of the air's CO_2 concentration more than compensated for the negative impact caused by the highest of the four O_3 concentrations in ambient-CO_2 air, turning what would have been a 43% O_3-induced yield loss (from 0.63 to 0.36 g) into a 40% CO_2-induced yield gain (from 0.63 to 0.88 g).

Burkey et al. (2007) grew peanuts (Arachis hypogaea L., cv NC-V11) in a field near Raleigh, North Carolina (USA) using standard agricultural practices for two years in open-top chambers maintained at all combinations of three CO_2 treatments (375, 548, and 730 ppm) and three O_3 treatments—charcoal-filtered air (CF, 22 ppb), non-filtered air (NF, 46 ppb), and O_3-enriched air (75 ppb)—after which they assessed peanut seed yields and qualities. They found "elevated CO_2 increased yield parameters 7 to 17% for plants grown in CF air and restored yield in NF air and elevated O_3 treatments to control or higher levels," while "market grade characteristics and seed protein and oil contents were not affected by elevated O_3 and CO_2."

The USDA Agricultural Research Service scientists conclude, in the case of peanuts, "the major impacts of rising atmospheric O_3 and CO_2 will be on productivity, not product quality," and as to productivity, their data indicate the positive effects of the rise in the air's CO_2 content should be able to compensate for concomitant future increases in tropospheric ozone concentrations. In fact, the continuing upward trend in atmospheric CO_2 concentration should more than compensate for any future increases in the air's O_3 content, because the latter will likely be relatively small due to the strong negative influence of elevated atmospheric CO_2 concentrations on vegetative isoprene emissions (Monson et al., 2007), which are responsible for increasing O_3 concentrations over land by perhaps 50% over what they would be in their absence (Poisson et al., 2000). Similarly, Arneth et al. (2007) calculated that when the effect of CO_2 on vegetative isoprene emissions is included, a properly forced model "maintains global isoprene emissions in ± 15% of present values," which should significantly temper the future rate-of-rise of the troposphere's ozone concentration.

Tu *et al.* (2009) grew *Arachis hypogaea* L. plants from seed to maturity out-of-doors near Raleigh, North Carolina (USA) in open-top chambers under adequately watered and fertilized conditions, exposing the plants to charcoal-filtered air, which was thus ozone-free, ambient air of unaltered ozone (O_3) concentration, and air containing 1.6 times the ambient O_3 concentration. All of these O_3 treatments were exposed to air of 376, 550, and 730 ppm CO_2. At the end of this period they harvested the crop and measured its final steam, leaf, and pod biomass.

They found "elevated CO_2 generally increased biomass production while O_3 suppressed it, and CO_2 ameliorated the O_3 effect." In terms of the season-long mean of midday net photosynthesis, for example, the 94% increase in the air's CO_2 concentration experienced in going from the lowest to the highest CO_2 treatment resulted in a 25% increase in net photosynthesis in the charcoal-filtered air, a 50% increase in the non-filtered air, and a 104% increase in the ozone-polluted air. As to the final aboveground biomass produced, the corresponding CO_2-induced increases were 10%, 41%, and 105%.

The four researchers also note "at mid-vegetative growth, elevated CO_2 significantly reduced leaf nitrogen concentrations by up to 44%," but "plant nitrogen concentrations only differed by 8% among CO_2 treatments at harvest while N_2 fixation was increased." They say their experiment suggests "symbiotic N_2 fixation is important for maintaining seed N concentrations and that CO_2 enhancement of symbiotic N_2 fixation may compensate for low soil N availability."

Tu *et al.* state a number of experiments, like theirs, "have shown that elevated CO_2 can offset the adverse effects of O_3 on crop biomass production and yield," citing Olszyk *et al.* (2000), Fuhrer (2003), and Fiscus *et al.* (2005). In addition, they note "the protective effect of elevated CO_2 against O_3 injury has been observed in a number of C_3 plant species, including cotton, peanut, rice, soybean, and wheat, due in large part to a reduction in O_3 uptake from reduced stomatal conductance and possibly from increases in photoassimilation rates and antioxidant metabolism," citing McKee *et al.* (2000), Booker and Fiscus (2005), Fiscus *et al.* (2005), and Booker *et al.* (2007).

Kumari *et al.* (2013) studied Palak (*Beta vulgaris* L. var Allgreen), "a cheap and popular leafy vegetable preferred mainly for iron content in the diet," which is "widely grown" and "suitable for all

seasons in north India." Recognizing the global growth in both atmospheric CO_2 (an aerial fertilizer) and tropospheric ozone (O_3, an aerial pollutant) over the past two centuries, plus their anticipated future increases, Kumari *et al.* examined the interactive effects of these contrasting atmospheric molecules on the growth of palak. The three Indian researchers utilized open-top chambers at the botanical garden of Banaras Hindu University in the eastern Gangetic plains of India during December 2008 and January 2009, measuring morphological, biochemical, and yield responses of palak to ambient (A) and elevated (E) levels of CO_2 and O_3, alone and in combination. The atmospheric CO_2 concentrations employed in this study were ambient (normal air) and 570 ppm, and the O_3 concentrations utilized were ambient and ambient + 20 ppb, with the elevated values selected to match predicted concentrations at the end of the century under the A1B scenario of IPCC (2007).

Their analysis revealed elevated CO_2 enhanced various plant growth parameters in palak, including root length, shoot length, number of leaves, leaf area, root biomass, shoot biomass, total plant biomass, and yield (compare the ECO_2 values in Table 3.8.1.3.1 with the ACO_2 values), and elevated concentrations of ozone had a negative effect (compare the EO_3 values in Table 3.8.1.3.1 with the $ACO_2 + AO_3$ values). When enhanced ozone and enhanced carbon dioxide were tested together, the growth-enhancing effects of CO_2 were sufficient in every instance to overpower the growth-retarding effects of ozone for every plant parameter measured (compare the $ECO_2 + EO_3$ values in Table 3.8.1.3.1 with the $ACO_2 + AO_3$ values).

Kumari *et al.* conclude, for IPCC-predicted atmospheric concentrations of CO_2 and O_3 at the end of the century, "palak is going to be benefited as biomass enhancement was more under $ECO_2 + EO_3$ compared to $ACO_2 + AO_3$."

These studies indicate atmospheric CO_2 enrichment reduces, and more often than not completely overrides, the negative effects of ozone pollution on plant photosynthesis, growth, and yield.

References

Arneth, A., Miller, P.A., Scholze, M., Hickler, T., Schurgers, G., Smith, B., and Prentice, I.C. 2007. CO_2 inhibition of global terrestrial isoprene emissions: Potential implications for atmospheric chemistry. *Geophysical Research Letters* **34**: 10.1029/2007GL030615.

Booker, F.L. 2000. Influence of carbon dioxide enrichment,

Parameters	50 DAG				
	ACO_2	$ACO_2 + AO_3$	ECO_2	EO_3	$ECO_2 + EO_3$
Root length (cm)	9.6	7.6	10.6	6.4	8.7
Shoot length (cm)	36.5	32.0	39.7	28.7	32.3
Number of leaves	13.66	10.00	22.66	7.66	11.33
Leaf area (cm^2)	626	496	983	390	589
Root biomass (g plant^{-1})	0.36	0.22	0.53	0.14	0.34
Shoot biomass (g plant^{-1})	2.1	1.5	3.3	1.2	2.5
Total biomass (g plant^{-1})	2.5	1.7	3.8	1.3	2.8
Yield (g plant^{-1})	38.2	30.0	51.9	22.5	34.8

ACO_2 = Ambient CO_2, $ACO_2 + AO_3$ = Ambient CO_2 + Ambient O_3, ECO_2 = Elevated CO_2, EO_3 = Elevated O_3 + Ambient CO_2, $ECO_2 + EO_3$ = Elevated CO_2 + Elevated O_3.

Table 3.8.1.3.1. Growth parameters of palak plants under different treatments of O_3 and CO_2, individually and in combination at 50 days after germination (DAG). Adapted from Kumari et al. (2013).

ozone and nitrogen fertilization on cotton (*Gossypium hirsutum* L.) leaf and root composition. *Plant, Cell and Environment* **23**: 573–583.

Booker, F.L., Burkey, K.O., Pursley, W.A., and Heagle, A.S. 2007. Elevated carbon dioxide and ozone effects on peanut: I. Gas-exchange, biomass, and leaf chemistry. *Crop Science* **47**: 1475–1487.

Booker, F.L. and Fiscus, E.L. 2005. The role of ozone flux and antioxidants in the suppression of ozone injury by elevated CO_2 in soybean. *Journal of Experimental Botany* **56**: 2139–2151.

Burkey, K.O., Booker, F.L., Pursley, W.A., and Heagle, A.S. 2007. Elevated carbon dioxide and ozone effects on peanut: II. Seed yield and quality. *Crop Science* **47**: 1488–1497.

Fiscus, E.L., Booker, F.L. and Burkey, K.O. 2005. Crop responses to ozone: Uptake, modes of action, carbon assimilation and partitioning. *Plant, Cell and Environment* **28**: 997–1011.

Fuhrer, J. 2003. Agroecosystem responses to combinations of elevated CO_2, ozone, and global climate change. *Agriculture, Ecosystems and Environment* **97**: 1–20.

IPCC. 2007. *Climate Change 2007. The Physical Science Basis.* Contribution of Working Group I to the Fourth Assessment Report of the Intergovernmental Panel on Climate Change, Cambridge University Press, Cambridge, United Kingdom.

Kumari, S., Agrawal, M., and Tiwari, S. 2013. Impact of elevated CO_2 and elevated O_3 on *Beta vulgaris* L.: Pigments, metabolites, antioxidants, growth and yield. *Environmental Pollution* **174**: 279–288.

McKee, I.F., Mulholland, B.J., Craigon, J., Black, C.R., and Long, S.P. 2000. Elevated concentrations of atmospheric CO_2 protect against and compensate for O_3 damage to photosynthetic tissues of field-grown wheat. *New Phytologist* **146**: 427–435.

Monson, R.K., Trahan, N., Rosenstiel, T.N., Veres, P., Moore, D., Wilkinson, M., Norby, R.J., Volder, A., Tjoelker, M.G., Briske, D.D., Karnosky, D.F., and Fall, R. 2007. Isoprene emission from terrestrial ecosystems in response to global change: minding the gap between models and observations. *Philosophical Transactions of the Royal Society A* **365**: 1677–1695.

Olszyk, D.M., Tingey, D.T., Watrud, L., Seidler, R., and Andersen, C. 2000. Interactive effects of O_3 and CO_2: Implications for terrestrial ecosystems. In Singh, S.N. (Ed.) *Trace Gas Emissions and Plants*. Kluwer Academic, Dordrecht, the Netherlands, pp. 97–136.

Plessl, M., Heller, W., Payer, H.-D., Elstner, E.F., Habermeyer, J., and Heiser, I. 2005. Growth parameters and resistance against *Drechslera teres* of spring barley (*Hordeum vulgare* L. cv. Scarlett) grown at elevated ozone and carbon dioxide concentrations. *Plant Biology* **7**: 694–705.

Poisson, N., Kanakidou, M., and Crutzen, P.J. 2000.

Impact of non-methane hydrocarbons on tropospheric chemistry and the oxidizing power of the global troposphere: 3-dimensional modeling results. *Journal of Atmospheric Chemistry* **36**: 157–230.

Tu, C., Booker, F.L., Burkey, K.O., and Hu, S. 2009. Elevated atmospheric carbon dioxide and O_3 differentially alter nitrogen acquisition in peanut. *Crop Science* **49**: 1827–1836.

Vandermeiren, K., Black, C., Pleijel, H., and De Temmerman, L. 2005. Impact of rising tropospheric ozone on potato: effects on photosynthesis, growth, productivity and yield quality. *Plant, Cell and Environment* **28**: 982–996.

Wolf, J. and van Oijen, M. 2002. Modelling the dependence of European potato yields on changes in climate and CO_2. *Agricultural and Forest Meteorology* **112**: 217–231.

Wolf, J. and van Oijen, M. 2003. Model simulation of effects of changes in climate and atmospheric CO_2 and O_3 on tuber yield potential of potato (cv. Bintje) in the European Union. *Agriculture, Ecosystems and Environment* **94**: 141–157.

Yonekura, T., Kihira, A., Shimada, T., Miwa, M., Aruzate, A., Izuta, T., and Ogawa, K. 2005. Impacts of O_3 and CO_2 enrichment on growth of Komatsuna (*Brassica campestris*) and radish (*Raphanus sativus*). *Phyton* **45**: 229–235.

3.8.2 Tree Species

3.8.2.1 Aspen

- Earth's aspen trees, like much of the rest of the biosphere, are better equipped to live long and productive lives in CO_2-enriched air, even when experiencing the generally negative influence of atmospheric ozone pollution.

Trees grown in CO_2-enriched air nearly always exhibit increased rates of photosynthesis and biomass production, and trees grown in ozone (O_3)-enriched air tend to experience the opposite effects. So what happens when both of these trace constituents of the atmosphere increase together? This question is explored below with respect to the most widely distributed tree species of North America: quaking aspen (*Populus tremuloides* Michx.).

Karnosky *et al.* (1999) describe how they grew O_3-sensitive and O_3-tolerant aspen clones in 30-m diameter plots at the Aspen FACE site near Rhinelander, Wisconsin (USA), where the young trees were maintained at atmospheric CO_2 concentrations of either 360 or 560 ppm either with or without exposure to elevated O_3 (1.5 times the ambient ozone concentration). After one year of growth at ambient CO_2, the researchers found elevated O_3 caused visible injury to leaves of both types of aspen, with the average percent damage in O_3-sensitive clones more than three times as great as observed in O_3-tolerant clones (55% vs. 17%, respectively). In combination with elevated CO_2, the O_3-induced damage to the leaves of these same clones was only 38% and 3%, respectively. Thus elevated CO_2 prevented much of the foliar damage that otherwise would have been induced by the high O_3 concentrations.

King *et al.* (2001) studied the same young trees for two years, concentrating on belowground growth, where elevated O_3 alone had no effect on fine-root biomass. When the two aspen clones were simultaneously exposed to elevated CO_2 and O_3, there was an approximate 66% increase in the fine-root biomass of both. Wustman *et al.* (2001) found the aspen clones exposed to both elevated ozone and CO_2 had 40% fewer visible foliar injuries than clones exposed to elevated ozone and ambient CO_2.

Noormets *et al.* (2001) studied the interactive effects of O_3 and CO_2 on photosynthesis in the aspen trees at the same facility, finding elevated CO_2 increased rates of photosynthesis in both clones at all leaf positions. Maximum rates of photosynthesis increased in the O_3-tolerant clone by averages of 33 and 49% due to elevated CO_2 alone and in combination with elevated O_3, respectively, and in the O_3-sensitive clone they increased by 38% in both cases. Elevated-CO_2-induced increases in maximal rates of net photosynthesis were typically maintained, and sometimes even increased, during simultaneous exposure to elevated O_3.

In another phase of the same experiment, Oksanen *et al.* (2001) found, after three years of treatment, ozone exposure caused significant structural injuries to thylakoid membranes and the stromal compartments in the chloroplasts of the trees' leaves, but they note these injuries were largely ameliorated by atmospheric CO_2 enrichment. Likewise, leaf thickness, mesophyll tissue thickness, the amount of chloroplasts per unit cell area, and the amount of starch in the leaf chloroplasts were all decreased in the high ozone treatment, but simultaneous exposure of the ozone-stressed trees to elevated CO_2 more than compensated for the ozone-induced reductions.

After four years of growing five aspen clones with varying degrees of tolerance to ozone under the same experimental conditions, McDonald *et al.* (2002) developed what they term a "competitive stress index," based on the heights of the four nearest neighbors of each tree, in order to study the influence of competition on the CO_2 growth response of the various clones as modified by ozone. This work showed elevated O_3 reduced aspen growth independent of competitive status, and the four researchers note an "apparent convergence of competitive performance responses in $+CO_2$ $+O_3$ conditions," which suggests "stand diversity may be maintained at a higher level" in such circumstances.

Percy *et al.* (2002) utilized the same experimental setting to assess a number of the aspen trees' growth characteristics and the responses of one plant pathogen and two insects with different feeding strategies that typically attack the trees. Of the plant pathogen studied, they write, "the poplar leaf rust, *Melampsora medusae*, is common on aspen and belongs to the most widely occurring group of foliage diseases." As for the two insects, they note "the forest tent caterpillar, *Malacosoma disstria*, is a common leaf-chewing lepidopteran in North American hardwood forests" and "the sap-feeding aphid, *Chaitophorus stevensis*, infests aspen throughout its range." Thus the rust and the two insect pests the scientists studied are widespread and have significant deleterious impacts on trembling aspen and other tree species. Percy *et al.* note "the forest tent caterpillar has defoliated more deciduous forest than any other insect in North America" and "outbreaks can reduce timber yield up to 90% in one year, and increase tree vulnerability to disease and environmental stress."

Percy *et al.* found elevated O_3 by itself decreased tree height and trunk diameter, increased rust occurrence by nearly fourfold, improved tent caterpillar performance by increasing female pupal mass by 31%, and had a strong negative effect on the natural enemies of aphids. The addition of the extra CO_2 completely ameliorated the negative effects of elevated O_3 on tree height and trunk diameter, reduced the O_3-induced enhancement of rust development from nearly fourfold to just over twofold, completely ameliorated the enhancement of female tent caterpillar pupal mass caused by elevated O_3, and also completely ameliorated the reduction in the abundance of natural enemies of aphids caused by elevated O_3.

Also studying the Aspen FACE site, Holton *et al.* (2003) raised parasitized and non-parasitized forest tent caterpillars on two quaking aspen genotypes (O_3-sensitive and O_3-tolerant) alone and in combination for one full growing season. They too found elevated O_3 improved tent caterpillar performance under ambient CO_2 conditions but not in CO_2-enriched air. Thus it is clear elevated ozone concentrations have significant negative impacts on the well-being of North America's most widely distributed tree species, and elevated carbon dioxide concentrations have significant positive impacts that often completely override the negative impacts of elevated O_3. Therefore, if the tropospheric O_3 concentration rises as expected (Percy *et al.* note "damaging O_3 concentrations currently occur over 29% of the world's temperate and subpolar forests but are predicted to affect fully 60% by 2100"), a concomitant rise in the air's CO_2 content will help to prevent damage to the planet's aspen trees.

Working at the same site, Oksanen *et al.* (2003) report they were able to "visualize and locate ozone-induced H_2O_2 [hydrogen peroxide] accumulation within leaf mesophyll cells, and relate oxidative stress with structural injuries in aspen." They discovered "H_2O_2 accumulation was found only in ozone-exposed leaves and not in the presence of elevated CO_2," leading them to conclude "CO_2 enrichment appears to alleviate chloroplastic oxidative stress."

King *et al.* (2005) evaluated the effect of CO_2 enrichment alone, O_3 enrichment alone, and the net effect of CO_2 and O_3 enrichment together after seven years of treatment at the Aspen FACE site. Relative to the ambient-air treatment, they found elevated CO_2 increased total biomass by 25%, whereas elevated O_3 decreased it by 23%. The combination of elevated CO_2 and O_3 resulted in a total biomass response of -7.8% relative to the control. King *et al.* thus conclude "exposure to even moderate levels of O_3 significantly reduces the capacity of net primary productivity to respond to elevated CO_2 in some forests." They suggest it makes sense to move forward with technologies that reduce anthropogenic precursors to photochemical O_3 formation, because their use would decrease an important constraint on the ability of forest ecosystems to benefit from the rise in the air's CO_2 concentration.

Kubiske *et al.* (2006) found individual tree and stand growth at the Aspen FACE site were significantly increased by the elevated CO_2 treatment but decreased by the elevated O_3 treatment, and the two effects essentially negated each other for no net change in the combined CO_2 plus O_3 treatment. They also state "growth in elevated CO_2 continued to increase each year but at a decreasing rate," such that "the annual growth increases under elevated CO_2 became smaller with each successive year." They examined several possible explanations for this phenomenon, including N limitations and water limitations.

The eight researchers write, "inter-annual variation in soil moisture did not modify the CO_2 or O_3 responses," and "N limitations on growth did not differ among treatments." In addition, they report "root-specific uptake of nitrate or ammonium was not affected by elevated CO_2 or O_3." The growth response to elevated CO_2 "paralleled decreasing July PPF [photosynthetic photon flux] from 2001 through 2004, and decreasing previous October temperatures from 2001 to 2003." Kubiske et al. conclude "a several-year trend of increasingly cloudy summers and cool autumns was responsible for the decrease in CO_2 growth response," explaining, "July PPF directly influences the amount of photosynthate available for stem volume growth," and "October temperature in the north-temperate latitudes is of major importance in the photosynthetic activity of trees before leaf senescence," the stored products of which are used "to support the determinate growth phase the following year."

Reporting the results of their study of the Wisconsin aspen trees during the eighth and ninth years of growing-season CO_2 enrichment, Riikonen et al. (2008) state elevated O_3 decreased net photosynthesis in aspen clone 42E by 30% and clone 271 by 13%, averaged over the growing season, and in aspen clone 216 by 42% in the late-season. Elevated CO_2 increased net photosynthesis in aspen clones 42E and 271 by 73 and 52%, respectively, averaged over the growing season, and in aspen clone 216, measured in the late-season only, elevated CO_2 enhanced net photosynthesis by 42%. They write, "elevated CO_2 delayed, and elevated O_3 tended to accelerate, leaf abscission in autumn." When both treatments were applied together, they report, "elevated CO_2 generally ameliorated the effects of elevated O_3," noting "leaf stomatal conductance was usually lowest in the combination treatment, which probably caused a reduction in O_3 uptake."

Kostiainen et al. (2008) studied interactive effects of elevated concentrations of CO_2 and O_3 on radial growth, wood chemistry, and structure of five 5-year-old trembling aspen clones at the Wisconsin FACE facility, where they had been exposed to four treatments—control, elevated CO_2 (560 ppm), elevated O_3 (1.5 x ambient), and their combination—

for five full growing seasons. The researchers report, "elevated CO_2 in the presence of ambient O_3 tended to increase, and elevated O_3 in the presence of ambient CO_2 tended to decrease, stem radial growth," whereas "stem radial growth of trees in the combined elevated CO_2 + O_3 treatment did not differ from controls." None of the structural variables of the aspen wood was affected by the elevated CO_2 treatment, but elevated O_3 tended to decrease vessel lumen diameter.

Reporting on another aspect of the long-term aspen study at the Wisconsin FACE facility, Udling et al. (2008) investigated how a 40% increase above ambient values in CO_2 and O_3, alone and in combination, affected tree water use where "measurements of sap flux and canopy leaf area index (L) were made during two growing seasons, when steady-state L had been reached after more than 6 years of exposure to elevated CO_2 and O_3." The 40% increase in atmospheric CO_2 increased tree size and L by 40%, and the 40% increase in O_3 concentration decreased tree size and L by 22%. The combined effect of the two trace gas increases was an 18% increase in maximum stand-level sap flux. In addition, elevated O_3 predisposed aspen stands to drought-induced sap flux reductions, whereas increased tree water use in response to elevated CO_2 did not result in lower soil water content in the upper soil or decreasing sap flux relative to control values during dry periods.

Thus the negative effects of O_3 enrichment on tree growth and leaf development were more than compensated by the positive effects of an equal percentage increase in atmospheric CO_2 concentration. And although the net effect on sap flux was positive (so that the trees transferred more water to the atmosphere), when the aspen stands needed moisture most (during times of drought), the water was available to them, possibly because they "were growing in soil with CO_2-induced increases in litter build-up and water-holding capacity of the upper soil," as these latter two benefits and the extra water they could supply to the trees were lacking when the trees were exposed to elevated ozone.

Pregitzer et al. (2008) write, "all root biomass sampling previous to 2002 showed that O_3 exposure, alone or in combination with elevated CO_2, consistently resulted in lower coarse root biomass." In analyzing more recent data, they determined the elevated O_3 treatment significantly increased fine-root biomass in the aspen trees and, in combination with elevated CO_2, increased coarse root biomass in them as well. They conclude "the amount of carbon being allocated to aspen fine-root biomass under elevated O_3 is increasing over time relative to the control, especially in the elevated CO_2 and elevated O_3 treatment," in contrast with most shorter-term results, including those of King *et al.* (2001). Consequently, they conclude "the positive effects of elevated CO_2 on belowground net primary productivity may not be offset by negative effects of O_3."

Andrew and Lilleskov (2009) note sporocarps (the reproductive structures of fungi) can be significant carbon sinks for the ectomycorrhizal fungi that develop symbiotic relationships with plants by forming sheaths around their root tips, where they are the last sinks for carbon in the long and winding pathway that begins at the source of carbon assimilation in plant leaves. The researchers say "it is critical to understand how ectomycorrhizal fungal sporocarps are affected by elevated CO_2 and O_3" because "sporocarps facilitate genetic recombination, permit long-distance dispersal and contribute to food webs."

They sampled aboveground sporocarps for four years at the Aspen FACE site, which provided, they write, a "unique opportunity to examine the effects of both elevated CO_2 and O_3 on a forested ecosystem." They conducted their examination during years 4 through 7 of the long-term study. They report total mean sporocarp biomass "was generally lowest under elevated O_3 with ambient CO_2," and it "was greatest under elevated CO_2, regardless of O_3 concentration." They state there was "a complete elimination of O_3 effects on sporocarp production when [extra] CO_2 was added," noting they "expect that the responses seen in the present study were conservative compared to those expected under regional to global changes in CO_2 and O_3."

By itself, or in combination with rising ozone concentrations, the rise in the air's CO_2 content appears destined to enhance the genetic recombination and long-distance dispersal of the ectomycorrhizal fungi that form symbiotic relationships with the roots of aspen and other trees, thereby positively contributing to various food webs that will be found in Earth's forests of the future.

Zak *et al.* (2011) noted how both insufficient soil nitrogen (N) and an overabundance of atmospheric ozone have been claimed to either partially or totally repress the many positive effects of elevated atmospheric CO_2 concentrations on plant growth and development, especially in the case of long-lived woody plants such as trees. However, they write, the combined effects of elevated CO_2 and elevated O_3 (eCO_2 and eO_3) "remain undocumented in the context of long-term, replicated field experiments." In 1997 the four researchers planted at the Rhinelander (Wisconsin, USA) FACE facility one-half of each of 12 FACE plots with various trembling aspen (*Populus tremuloides*) genotypes (8, 42, 216, 259, 271) of differing CO_2 and O_3 sensitivities. They planted one-quarter of each ring with a single aspen genotype (226) and paper birch (*Betula papyrifera*), and another quarter of each ring with the same single aspen genotype and sugar maple (*Acer saccharum*). The authors maintained each FACE plot for 12 years at either ambient CO_2 and O_3 (aCO_2 and aO_3), aCO_2 and eO_3, eCO_2 and aO_3, or eCO_2 and eO_3—where eCO_2 was 560 ppm, and where eO_3 was in the range of 50–60 nmol/mol—while they collected numerous types of pertinent data.

In reference to the progressive nitrogen limitation hypothesis, Zak *et al.* (2011) say they "found no evidence of this effect after 12 years of eCO_2 exposure." Relative to net primary production (NPP) under aCO_2, they found a 26% increase in NPP in the eCO_2 treatment over the last three years of the study, which for a more standard 300-ppm increase in atmospheric CO_2 concentration equates to an approximate 42% increase in NPP. The increase "was sustained by greater root exploration of soil for growth-limiting N, as well as more rapid rates of litter decomposition and microbial N release during decay."

With respect to the concomitant stress of O_3 pollution, the researchers report, "despite eO_3-induced reductions in plant growth that occurred early in the experiment (i.e., after three years of exposure), eO_3 had no effect on NPP during the 10th-12th years of exposure." This response, they write, "appears to result from the compensatory growth of eO_3-tolerant genotypes and species as the growth of eO_3-sensitive individuals declined over time (Kubiske *et al.*, 2007; Zak *et al.*, 2007), thereby causing NPP to attain equivalent levels under ambient O_3 and elevated O_3."

Zak *et al.* (2011) write, "NPP in the three plant communities responded similarly to the combined eCO_2 and eO_3 treatment." And "given the degree to which eO_3 has been projected to decrease global NPP (Felzer *et al.*, 2005), the compensatory growth of eO_3-tolerant plants in our experiment should be considered in future simulations and, depending on the generality of this response, could dramatically diminish the negative effect of eO_3 on NPP and carbon storage on land."

The four researchers ultimately conclude if forests of similar composition growing throughout northeastern North America respond in the same manner as those in their experiment (Cole *et al.*, 2009), enhanced forest NPP under eCO_2 may be sustained for a longer duration than previously had been thought possible. They conclude, "the negative effect of eO_3 may be diminished by compensatory growth of eO_3-tolerant plants as they begin to dominate forest communities (Kubiske *et al.*, 2007; Zak *et al.*, 2007), suggesting that aspects of biodiversity like genetic diversity and species composition are important components of ecosystem response to this agent of global change."

References

Andrew, C. and Lilleskov, E.A. 2009. Productivity and community structure of ectomycorrhizal fungal sporocarps under increased atmospheric CO_2 and O_3. *Ecology Letters* 12: 813–822.

Cole, C.T., Anderson, J.E., Lindroth, R.L., and Waller, D.M. 2009. Rising concentrations of atmospheric CO_2 have increased growth of natural stands of quaking aspen (*Populous tremuloides*). *Global Change Biology* 16: 2186–2197.

Felzer, B., Reilly, J., Melillo, J., Kicklighter, D., Sarofim, M., Wang, C., Prinn, R., and Zhuang, Q. 2005. Future effects of ozone on carbon sequestration and climate change policy using a global biogeochemical model. *Climatic Change* 73: 345–373.

Holton, M.K., Lindroth, R.L., and Nordheim, E.V. 2003. Foliar quality influences tree-herbivore-parasitoid interactions: effects of elevated CO_2, O_3, and plant genotype. *Oecologia* 137: 233–244.

Karnosky, D.F., Mankovska, B., Percy, K., Dickson, R.E., Podila, G.K., Sober, J., Noormets, A., Hendrey, G., Coleman, M.D., Kubiske, M., Pregitzer, K.S., and Isebrands, J.G. 1999. Effects of tropospheric O_3 on trembling aspen and interaction with CO_2: results from an O_3-gradient and a FACE experiment. *Water, Air, and Soil Pollution* 116: 311–322.

King, J.S., Kubiske, M.E., Pregitzer, K.S., Hendrey, G.R., McDonald, E.P., Giardina, C.P., Quinn, V.S., and Karnosky, D.F. 2005. Tropospheric O_3 compromises net primary production in young stands of trembling aspen, paper birch and sugar maple in response to elevated atmospheric CO_2. *New Phytologist* 168: 623–636.

King, J.S., Pregitzer, K.S., Zak, D.R., Sober, J., Isebrands, J.G., Dickson, R.E., Hendrey, G.R., and Karnosky, D.F. 2001. Fine-root biomass and fluxes of soil carbon in young stands of paper birch and trembling aspen as affected by elevated atmospheric CO_2 and tropospheric O_3. *Oecologia* 128: 237–250.

Kostiainen, K., Kaakinen, S., Warsta, E., Kubiske, M.E., Nelson, N.D., Sober, J., Karnosky, D.F., Saranpaa, P., and Vapaavuori, E. 2008. Wood properties of trembling aspen and paper birch after 5 years of exposure to elevated concentrations of CO_2 and O_3. *Tree Physiology* 28: 805–813.

Kubiske, M.E., Quinn, V.S., Heilman, W.E., McDonald, E.P., Marquardt, P.E., Teclaw, R.M., Friend, A.L., and Karnosky, D.F. 2006. Interannual climatic variation mediates elevated CO_2 and O_3 effects on forest growth. *Global Change Biology* 12: 1054–1068.

Kubiske, M.E., Quinn, V.S., Marquart, P.E., and Karnosky, D.F. 2007. Effects of elevated atmospheric CO_2 and/or O_3 on intra- and inter-specific competitive ability of aspen. *Plant Biology* 9: 342–355.

McDonald, E.P., Kruger, E.L., Riemenschneider, D.E., and Isebrands, J.G. 2002. Competitive status influences tree-growth responses to elevated CO_2 and O_3 in aggrading aspen stands. *Functional Ecology* 16: 792–801.

Noormets, A., Sober, A., Pell, E.J., Dickson, R.E., Podila, G.K., Sober, J., Isebrands, J.G., and Karnosky, D.F. 2001. Stomatal and non-stomatal limitation to photosynthesis in two trembling aspen (*Populus tremuloides* Michx.) clones exposed to elevated CO_2 and O_3. *Plant, Cell and Environment* 24: 327–336.

Oksanen, E., Haikio, E., Sober, J., and Karnosky, D.F. 2003. Ozone-induced H_2O_2 accumulation in field-grown aspen and birch is linked to foliar ultrastructure and peroxisomal activity. *New Phytologist* 161: 791–799.

Oksanen, E., Sober, J., and Karnosky, D.F. 2001. Impacts of elevated CO_2 and/or O_3 on leaf ultrastructure of aspen (*Populus tremuloides*) and birch (*Betula papyrifera*) in the Aspen FACE experiment. *Environmental Pollution* 115: 437–446.

Percy, K.E., Awmack, C.S., Lindroth, R.L., Kubiske, M.E., Kopper, B.J., Isebrands, J.G., Pregitzer, K.S., Hendrey, G.R., Dickson, R.E., Zak, D.R., Oksanen, E., Sober, J., Harrington, R., and Karnosky, D.F. 2002. Altered performance of forest pests under atmospheres enriched by CO_2 and O_3. *Nature* 420: 403–407.

Pregitzer, K.S., Burton, A.J., King, J.S., and Zak, D.R. 2008. Soil respiration, root biomass, and root turnover following long-term exposure of northern forests to elevated atmospheric CO_2 and tropospheric O_3. *New Phytologist* 180: 153–161.

Riikonen, J., Kets, K., Darbah, J., Oksanen, E., Sober, A.,

Vapaavuori, E., Kubiske, M.E., Nelson, N., and Karnosky, D.F. 2008. Carbon gain and bud physiology in *Populus tremuloides* and *Betula papyrifera* grown under long-term exposure to elevated concentrations of CO_2 and O_3. *Tree Physiology* **28**: 243–254.

Uddling, J., Teclaw, R.M., Kubiske, M.E., Pregitzer, K.S., and Ellsworth, D.S. 2008. Sap flux in pure aspen and mixed aspen-birch forests exposed to elevated concentrations of carbon dioxide and ozone. *Tree Physiology* **28**: 1231–1243.

Wustman, B.A., Oksanen, E., Karnosky, D.F., Noormets, A., Isebrands, J.G., Pregitzer, K.S., Hendrey, G.R., Sober, J., and Podila, G.K. 2001. Effects of elevated CO_2 and O_3 on aspen clones varying in O_3 sensitivity: Can CO_2 ameliorate the harmful effects of O_3? *Environmental Pollution* **115**: 473–481.

Zak, D.R., Holmes, W.E., Pregitzer, K.S., King, J.S., Ellsworth, D.S., and Kubiske, M.E. 2007. Belowground competition and the response of developing forest communities to atmospheric CO_2 and O_3. *Global Change Biology* **13**: 2230–2238.

Zak, D.R., Pregitzer, K.S., Kubiske, M.E., and Burton, A.J. 2011. Forest productivity under elevated CO_2 and O_3: positive feedbacks to soil N cycling sustain decade-long net primary productivity enhancement by CO_2. *Ecology Letters* **14**: 1220–1226.

3.8.2.2 Beech

- Even when faced with the generally negative influence of atmospheric ozone pollution on their leaves, shoot axes, coarse roots, and fine roots, as well as the carbohydrate (starch and soluble sugar) contents and concentrations of those plant parts, these adverse effects of ozone on beech trees are typically more than counteracted by atmospheric CO_2 enrichment.

In discussing the problem of elevated tropospheric ozone (O_3) concentrations, Liu *et al.* (2004) write, "ozone is considered to be one of the air pollutants most detrimental to plant growth and development in both urban and rural environments (Lefohn, 1992; Skarby *et al.*, 1998; Matyssek and Innes, 1999)," because it "reduces the growth and yield of numerous agronomic crops as well as fruit and forest trees (Retzlaff *et al.*, 1997; Fumagalli *et al.*, 2001; Matyssek and Sandermann, 2003)." In addition, they note ozone concentrations are "currently two to three times higher than in the early 1900s (Galloway, 1998;

Fowler *et al.*, 1999)," and likely "will remain high in the future (Elvingson, 2001)." This section addresses studies that have examined the effects of ozone on European beech (*Fagus sylvatica* L.) trees.

Liu *et al.* (2005) grew three- and four-year-old European beech seedlings for five months in well-watered and -fertilized soil in containers located in walk-in phytotrons maintained at either ambient or ambient + 300 ppm CO_2 (each subdivided into ambient and double-ambient O_3 concentration treatments, with maximum ozone levels restricted to <150 ppb), in both monoculture and in competition with Norway spruce. They examined the effects of each treatment on leaf non-structural carbohydrate levels (soluble sugars and starch), finding the effects of elevated O_3 alone on non-structural carbohydrate levels were small when the beech seedlings were grown in monoculture. When they were grown in mixed culture, the elevated O_3 slightly enhanced leaf sugar levels but reduced starch levels by 50%.

With respect to elevated CO_2 alone, for the beech seedlings grown in both monoculture and mixed culture, levels of sugar and starch were significantly enhanced. Thus, when elevated O_3 and CO_2 significantly affected non-structural carbohydrate levels, elevated CO_2 tended to enhance them, whereas elevated O_3 tended to reduce them. The combined effects of elevated CO_2 and O_3 acting together were such as to produce a significant increase in leaf non-structural carbohydrates in both mixed and mono-culture conditions. The researchers conclude "since the responses to the combined exposure were more similar to elevated pCO_2 than to elevated pO_3, apparently elevated pCO_2 overruled the effects of elevated pO_3 on non-structural carbohydrates."

Grams *et al.* (1999) grew European beech seedlings in glasshouses maintained at average atmospheric CO_2 concentrations of either 367 or 667 ppm for one year. Throughout the following year, in addition to being exposed to the same set of CO_2 concentrations, the seedlings were exposed to either ambient or twice-ambient levels of O_3. Elevated O_3 significantly reduced photosynthesis in beech seedlings grown at ambient CO_2 concentrations by a factor of approximately three. In the CO_2-enriched air, the seedlings did not exhibit any photosynthetic reduction due to the doubled O_3 concentration. The photosynthetic rates of the CO_2-enriched seedlings rose by 8% when simultaneously fumigated with elevated O_3, leading the five researchers to conclude long-term acclimation to elevated CO_2 supply does indeed counteract the O_3-induced decline of photosynthetic light and dark reactions.

Liu *et al.* (2004) grew three- and four-year-old beech seedlings for two growing seasons under the same experimental conditions as Liu *et al.* (2005) after the seedlings had been pre-acclimated for one year to either the ambient or elevated CO_2 treatment. At the end of the study, the plants were harvested and fresh weights and dry biomass values were determined for leaves, shoot axes, coarse roots, and fine roots, as were carbohydrate (starch and soluble sugar) contents and concentrations for the same plant parts. The results falsified the hypothesis that "prolonged exposure to elevated CO_2 does not compensate for the adverse ozone effects on European beech," instead revealing all "adverse effects of ozone on carbohydrate concentrations and contents were counteracted when trees were grown in elevated CO_2."

These results add more evidence of the ability of increased CO_2 concentrations to fight—and overpower—the deleterious consequences of one of the world's most devastating air pollutants.

References

Elvingson, P. 2001. For the most parts steadily down. *Acid News* **3**: 20–21.

Fowler, D., Cape, J.N., Coyle, M., Flechard, C., Kuylenstrierna, J., Hicks, K., Derwent, D., Johnson, C., and Stevenson, D. 1999. The global exposure of forests to air pollutants. In: Sheppard, L.J. and Cape, J.N. (Eds.) *Forest Growth Responses to the Pollution Climate of the 21st Century.* Kluwer Academic Publisher, Dordrecht, The Netherlands.

Fumagalli, I., Gimeno, B.S., Velissariou, D., De Temmerman, L., and Mills, G. 2001. Evidence of ozone-induced adverse effects on crops in the Mediterranean region. *Atmospheric Environment* **35**: 2583–2587.

Galloway, J.N. 1998. The global nitrogen cycle: changes and consequences. *Environmental Pollution* **102**: 15–24.

Grams, T.E.E, Anegg, S., Haberle, K.-H., Langebartels, C., and Matyssek, R. 1999. Interactions of chronic exposure to elevated CO_2 and O_3 levels in the photosynthetic light and dark reactions of European beech (*Fagus sylvatica*). *New Phytologist* **144**: 95–107.

Lefohn, A.S. 1992. *Surface Level Ozone Exposure and Their Effects on Vegetation.* Lewis Publishers, Chelsea, UK.

Liu, X.-P., Grams, T.E.E., Matyssek, R., and Rennenberg, H. 2005. Effects of elevated pCO_2 and/or pO_3 on C-, N-, and S-metabolites in the leaves of juvenile beech and spruce differ between trees grown in monoculture and mixed culture. *Plant Physiology and Biochemistry* **43**: 147–154.

Liu, X., Kozovits, A.R., Grams, T.E.E., Blaschke, H., Rennenberg, H., and Matyssek, R. 2004. Competition modifies effects of ozone/carbon dioxide concentrations on carbohydrate and biomass accumulation in juvenile Norway spruce and European beech. *Tree Physiology* **24**: 1045–1055.

Matyssek, R. and Innes, J.L. 1999. Ozone—a risk factor for trees and forests in Europe? *Water, Air and Soil Pollution* **116**: 199–226.

Matyssek, R. and Sandermann, H. 2003. Impact of ozone on trees: an ecophysiological perspective. *Progress in Botany* **64**: 349–404.

Retzlaff, W.A., Williams, L.E., and DeJong, T.M. 1997. Growth and yield response of commercial bearing-age "Casselman" plum trees to various ozone partial pressures. *Journal of Environmental Quality* **26**: 858–865.

Skarby, L., Ro-Poulsen, H., Wellburn, F.A.M., and Sheppard, L.J. 1998. Impacts of ozone on forests: a European perspective. *New Phytologist* **139**: 109–122.

3.8.2.3 Birch

- Birch trees are generally harmed by rising ozone concentrations, but when the air's CO_2 concentration is also rising, these negative effects are generally eliminated and replaced by positive responses.

At the free-air CO_2 enrichment (FACE) facility located near Rhinelander, Wisconsin (USA), King *et al.* (2001) grew a mixture of paper birch and quaking aspen trees in 30-m-diameter plots maintained at atmospheric CO_2 concentrations of 360 and 560 ppm with and without exposure to elevated O_3 (1.5 times the ambient O_3 concentration) for two years. The extra O_3 had no effect on the growth of fine roots over that period, but elevated O_3 and CO_2 together increased the fine-root biomass of the mixed stand by 83%.

At the same FACE facility, Oksanen *et al.* (2001) observed O_3-induced injuries in the thylakoid membranes of the chloroplasts of the birch trees' leaves, but the injuries were partially ameliorated in the elevated CO_2 treatment. And in a study conducted two years later, Oksanen *et al.* (2003) "were able to visualize and locate ozone-induced H_2O_2 accumulation within leaf mesophyll cells, and relate oxidative stress with structural injuries." They report "H_2O_2 accumulation was found only in ozone-exposed leaves and not in the presence of elevated CO_2," adding "CO_2 enrichment appears to alleviate chloroplastic oxidative stress."

In Finland, Kull *et al.* (2003) constructed open-top chambers around two clones (V5952 and K1659) of silver birch saplings rooted in the ground and growing there for the past seven years. These chambers were then fumigated with air containing 360 and 720 ppm CO_2 in combination with 30 and 50 ppb O_3 for two growing seasons, after which it was reported the extra O_3 had significantly decreased branching in the trees' crowns. This effect was almost completely ameliorated by a doubling of the air's CO_2 content. In addition, after one more year of study, Eichelmann *et al.* (2004) report the increase in the air's CO_2 content by itself increased the average net photosynthetic rates of both clones by approximately 16%, whereas the increased O_3 by itself caused a 10% decline in the average photosynthetic rate of clone V5952, although not of clone K1659. When both gases were simultaneously increased, the photosynthetic rate of clone V5952 once again experienced a 16% increase in net photosynthesis, as if the extra O_3 had had no effect when applied in the presence of the extra CO_2.

Riikonen *et al.* (2004) harvested the same trees and reported "the negative effects of elevated O_3 were found mainly in ambient CO_2, not in elevated CO_2." Doubling the air's O_3 concentration decreased total biomass production by 13% across both clones, but simultaneously doubling the air's CO_2 concentration increased total biomass production by 30%, more than compensating for the deleterious consequences of doubling the atmospheric ozone concentration.

The Finnish scientists say this ameliorating effect of elevated CO_2 "may be associated with either increased detoxification capacity as a consequence of higher carbohydrate concentrations in leaves grown in elevated CO_2, or decreased stomatal conductance and thus decreasing O_3 uptake in elevated CO_2 conditions (e.g., Rao *et al.*, 1995)." They also note "the ameliorating effect of elevated CO_2 is in accordance with the results of single-season open-top chamber and growth chamber studies on small saplings of various deciduous tree species (Mortensen 1995; Dickson *et al.*, 1998; Loats and Rebbeck, 1999) and long-term open-field and open-OTC studies with aspen and yellow-poplar (Percy *et al.*, 2002; Rebbeck and Scherzer, 2002)."

Peltonen *et al.* (2005) evaluated the impacts of doubled atmospheric CO_2 and O_3 concentrations on the accumulation of 27 phenolic compounds in the leaves of the silver birch trees, finding elevated CO_2 increased the concentration of phenolic acids (+25%), myricetin glycosides (+18%), catechin derivatives (+13%), and soluble condensed tannins (+19%). Elevated O_3 increased the concentration of one glucoside by 22%, chlorogenic acid by 19%, and flavone aglycons by 4%. Peltonen *et al.* say this O_3-induced production of antioxidant phenolic compounds "did not seem to protect the birch leaves from detrimental O_3 effects on leaf weight and area, but may have even exacerbated them." In the combined elevated CO_2 and O_3 treatment, they write, "elevated CO_2 did seem to protect the leaves from elevated O_3 because all the O_3-derived effects on the leaf phenolics and traits were prevented by elevated CO_2."

At the Rhinelander, Wisconsin (USA) FACE facility, Agrell *et al.* (2005) examined the effects of ambient and elevated concentrations of atmospheric CO_2 and O_3 on the foliar chemistry of birch and aspen trees, plus the consequences of these effects for host plant preferences of forest tent caterpillar larvae. They note "the only chemical component showing a somewhat consistent co-variation with larval preferences was condensed tannins," and they report "the tree becoming relatively less preferred as a result of CO_2 or O_3 treatment was in general also the one for which average levels of condensed tannins were most positively (or least negatively) affected by that treatment."

The researchers found the mean condensed tannin concentration of birch leaves was 18% higher in the elevated CO_2 and O_3 treatment. Consequently, as atmospheric concentrations of CO_2 and O_3 continue to rise, the increases in condensed tannin concentrations likely to occur in the foliage of birch trees should lead to their leaves becoming less preferred for consumption by the forest tent caterpillar, which according to Agrell *et al.* is "an eruptive generalist defoliator in North American hardwood forests, causing extensive damage during outbreak years (Fitzgerald, 1995)."

King *et al.* (2005) evaluated the effect of CO_2 enrichment alone, O_3 enrichment alone, and the net effect of both CO_2 and O_3 enrichment together on the growth of the Rhinelander birch trees. In the ambient-air control treatment, elevated CO_2 increased total biomass by 45% in the aspen-birch community; elevated O_3 caused a 13% reduction in total biomass relative to the control. The combination of elevated

CO_2 and O_3 resulted in a total biomass increase of 8.4% relative to the control aspen-birch community. King et al. conclude "exposure to even moderate levels of O_3 significantly reduces the capacity of net primary productivity to respond to elevated CO_2 in some forests."

Kostiainen et al. (2006) studied the effects of elevated CO_2 and O_3 on various wood properties of silver birch. They found the elevated CO_2 treatment had no effect on wood structure but increased annual ring width by 21%, woody biomass by 23%, and trunk starch concentration by 7%. Elevated O_3 decreased stem vessel percentage in one of the clones by 10% but had no effect on vessel percentage in the presence of elevated CO_2.

Kostiainen et al. note, "in the xylem of angiosperms, water movement occurs principally in vessels (Kozlowski and Pallardy, 1997)," and "the observed decrease in vessel percentage by elevated O_3 may affect water transport." They continue, "elevated CO_2 ameliorated the O_3-induced decrease in vessel percentage." In addition, they note "the concentration of nonstructural carbohydrates (starch and soluble sugars) in tree tissues is considered a measure of carbon shortage or surplus for growth (Korner, 2003)." They conclude "starch accumulation observed under elevated CO_2 in this study indicates a surplus of carbohydrates produced by enhanced photosynthesis of the same trees (Riikonen et al., 2004)." In addition, they report, "during winter, starch reserves in the stem are gradually transformed to soluble carbohydrates involved in freezing tolerance (Bertrand et al., 1999; Piispanen and Saranpaa, 2001)," so "the increase in starch concentration may improve acclimation in winter."

At the Rhinelander FACE studies of paper birch, Darbah et al. (2007) found the total number of trees that flowered increased by 139% under elevated CO_2 but only 40% under elevated O_3. With respect to the quantity of flowers produced, elevated CO_2 led to a 262% increase and elevated O_3 led to only a 75% increase. They also determined elevated CO_2 had significant positive effects on birch catkin size, weight, and germination success rate, with elevated CO_2 increasing the germination rate of birch by 110%, decreasing seedling mortality by 73%, increasing seed weight by 17%, and increasing new seedling root length by 59%. Just the opposite was true of elevated O_3, as it decreased the germination rate of birch by 62%, decreased seed weight by 25%, and increased new seedling root length by only 15%.

Darbah et al. report "the seeds produced under elevated O_3 had much less stored carbohydrate, lipids, and proteins for the newly developing seedlings to depend on and, hence, the slow growth rate." They conclude, "seedling recruitment will be enhanced under elevated CO_2 but reduced under elevated O_3," another important reason to hope the atmosphere's CO_2 concentration continues to climb as long as the air's O_3 content is doing so as well.

Riikonen et al. (2008) studied physiological consequences of increases in the atmospheric concentrations of CO_2 (+36%) and O_3 (+39%)—both alone and in combination—in paper birch trees during the eighth and ninth years of growing-season CO_2 enrichment at the Rhinelander FACE site. They determined elevated O_3 decreased net photosynthesis in birch short-shoot leaves by 27%, averaged over the growing season, and in birch long-shoot leaves by 23% in the late season, whereas elevated CO_2 increased net photosynthesis in birch short-shoot leaves by 49% averaged over the growing season. They also report, for birch long-shoot leaves, measured in the late-season only, elevated CO_2 enhanced net photosynthesis by 42%. In addition, "elevated CO_2 delayed, and elevated O_3 tended to accelerate, leaf abscission in autumn." When both treatments were applied together, the scientists note, "elevated CO_2 generally ameliorated the effects of elevated O_3," adding "leaf stomatal conductance was usually lowest in the combination treatment, which probably caused a reduction in O_3 uptake."

Darbah et al. (2008) at various times over the 2004–2007 growing seasons collected many types of data pertaining to flowering, seed production, seed germination, and new seedling growth and development of young paper birch trees at the Rhinelander FACE site. Giving results for O_3 elevation first and CO_2 enrichment second (as best can be determined from Darbah et al.'s graphs and text), the following percentage changes were derived for:

- number of trees producing male flowers: (+86%, +140%) in 2006, (+70%, +70%) in 2007,

- total number of male flowers produced (+58%, +260%) in 2006, (+68%, +82%) in 2007,

- mean catkin or flower cluster mass (-8%, +12%) in 2004,

- mean seed mass (-22%, +10%) in 2004, (-24%, +17%) in 2005, (-22%, -2%) in 2006,

- mean seed germination success (-70%, +70%) in 2004, (-60%, +110%) in 2005, (-50%, +20%) in 2006,

- mean seedling mortality, where the greatest reductions represent the greatest benefits, (-9%, -73%) in 2004,

- mean seedling root length (+15%, +59%) in 2004,

- mean seedling shoot length (-7%, +21%) in 2004,

- mean seedling cotyledon length (-5%, +13%) in 2004, and

- mean seedling dry mass after approximately five months growth in ambient air (-38%, +69%) in 2004.

Summarizing their findings, the six researchers write, "in this study, we found that elevated CO_2 enhances and elevated O_3 decreases birch reproduction and early seedling growth," while in the concluding sentence of their abstract, they write, "the evidence from this study indicates that elevated CO_2 may have a largely positive impact on forest tree reproduction and regeneration while elevated O_3 will likely have a negative impact."

Kostiainen *et al.* (2008) investigated the interactive effects of elevated concentrations of CO_2 and O_3 on the wood chemistry of paper birch saplings at the FACE facility in Rhinelander, where the saplings had been exposed to four treatments—control, elevated CO_2 (560 ppm), elevated O_3 (1.5 x ambient), and their combination—for five growing seasons. They found the paper birch saplings exhibited a tendency for increased stem diameter in elevated CO_2, that also caused "an increase in extractives," such as fats, waxes, triterpenoids, and steroids, that have important roles to play in defense against pathogens and other biotic attacks. The nine researchers conclude the increased growth they observed in response to elevated CO_2 "can be foreseen to shorten rotation lengths, with only moderate changes in wood properties," which is good. However, "in response to elevated O_3, stem wood production decreased and was accompanied by changes in vessel properties, which may indicate decreasing efficiency of water and nutrient transport," which is not good. Here, too, the major negative effects of the elevated O_3 concentration were reversed by the positive effects of the elevated CO_2 concentration.

Uddling *et al.* (2008) studied how a 40% increase in CO_2 and O_3, alone and in combination, affected tree water use of mixed aspen-birch forests in the Rhinelander FACE study, where sap flux and canopy leaf area index (L) were measured during two growing seasons, when steady-state L had been reached after more than six years of exposure to elevated CO_2 and O_3. The 40% increase in atmospheric CO_2 concentration increased tree size and L by 40%, and the 40% increase in O_3 concentration decreased tree size and L by 22%. The combined effect of the two trace gas increases was an 18% increase in maximum stand-level sap flux in the mixed tree stands.

Pregitzer *et al.* (2008) write, "all root biomass sampling [at the Rhinelander FACE facility] previous to 2002 showed that O_3 exposure, alone or in combination with elevated CO_2, consistently resulted in lower coarse root biomass for all plant communities." In their analysis of subsequent data, however, they found $+O_3$ in combination with $+CO_2$ increased coarse root biomass in birch/aspen communities, leading them to conclude the amount of carbon being allocated to fine-root biomass under elevated O_3 was increasing over time relative to the control, especially in the $+CO_2$ $+O_3$ treatment, in contrast with most shorter-term results. They conclude, "the positive effects of elevated CO_2 on belowground net primary productivity may not be offset by negative effects of O_3."

For three years (1999–2001) Vapaavuori *et al.* (2009) grew 20 initially seven-years-old individual trees of each of two different silver birch (*Betula pendula* Roth) clones—4 and 80 (V5952 and K1659, respectively, in the Finnish forest genetic register)—out-of-doors at the Suonenjoki Research Unit site of the Finnish Forest Research Institute in individual open-top chambers maintained at all combinations of ambient CO_2 and ambient O_3, ambient CO_2 and double O_3, double CO_2 and ambient O_3, and double CO_2 and double O_3, where CO_2 treatments were imposed 24 hours per day and O_3 treatments were imposed for 12, 12, and 14 hours per day in 1999, 2000, and 2001, respectively. Throughout the course of the experiment they measured a variety of plant physiological responses to the four treatments, including net photosynthesis, leaf stomatal conductance, leaf soluble proteins, leaf phenolic compounds, leaf nutrient concentrations, trunk and branch growth, physiology of the foliage and root systems, crown structure, wood properties, and interactions with folivorous insects.

The 12 scientists report the negative effects of elevated O_3 on the various growth parameters and properties of the trees "were mainly found in ambient CO_2," noting elevated CO_2 typically "reversed or diminished the effects of elevated O_3."

References

Agrell, J., Kopper, B., McDonald, E.P., and Lindroth, R.L. 2005. CO_2 and O_3 effects on host plant preferences of the forest tent caterpillar (*Malacosoma disstria*). *Global Change Biology* **11**: 588–599.

Bertrand, A., Robitaille, G., Nadeau, P., and Castonguay, Y. 1999. Influence of ozone on cold acclimation in sugar maple seedlings. *Tree Physiology* **19**: 527–534.

Darbah, J.N.T., Kubiske, M.E., Nelson, N., Oksanen, E., Vaapavuori, E., and Karnosky, D.F. 2007. Impacts of elevated atmospheric CO_2 and O_3 on paper birch (*Betula papyrifera*): Reproductive fitness. *The Scientific World Journal* **7**(S1): 240–246.

Darbah, J.N.T., Kubiske, M.E., Nelson, N., Oksanen, E., Vapaavuori, E., and Karnosky, D.F. 2008. Effects of decadal exposure to interacting elevated CO_2 and/or O_3 on paper birch (*Betula papyrifera*) reproduction. *Environmental Pollution* **155**: 446–452.

Dickson, R.E., Coleman, M.D., Riemenschneider, D.E., Isebrands, J.G., Hogan, G.D., and Karnosky, D.F. 1998. Growth of five hybrid poplar genotypes exposed to interacting elevated [CO_2] and [O_3]. *Canadian Journal of Forest Research* **28**: 1706–1716.

Eichelmann, H., Oja, V., Rasulov, B., Padu, E., Bichele, I., Pettai, H., Mols, T., Kasparova, I., Vapaavuori, E., and Laisk, A. 2004. Photosynthetic parameters of birch (*Betula pendula* Roth) leaves growing in normal and in CO_2- and O_3-enriched atmospheres. *Plant, Cell and Environment* **27**: 479–495.

Fitzgerald, T.D. 1995. *The Tent Caterpillars*. Comstock Publishing, Ithaca, New York, USA.

King, J.S., Kubiske, M.E., Pregitzer, K.S., Hendrey, G.R., McDonald, E.P., Giardina, C.P., Quinn, V.S., and Karnosky, D.F. 2005. Tropospheric O_3 compromises net primary production in young stands of trembling aspen, paper birch and sugar maple in response to elevated atmospheric CO_2. *New Phytologist* **168**: 623–636.

King, J.S., Pregitzer, K.S., Zak, D.R., Sober, J., Isebrands, J.G., Dickson, R.E., Hendrey, G.R., and Karnosky, D.F. 2001. Fine-root biomass and fluxes of soil carbon in young stands of paper birch and trembling aspen as affected by elevated atmospheric CO_2 and tropospheric O_3. *Oecologia* **128**: 237–250.

Korner, C. 2003. Carbon limitation in trees. *Journal of Ecology* **91**: 4–17.

Kostiainen, K., Jalkanen, H., Kaakinen, S., Saranpaa, P., and Vapaavuori, E. 2006. Wood properties of two silver birch clones exposed to elevated CO_2 and O_3. *Global Change Biology* **12**: 1230–1240.

Kostiainen, K., Kaakinen, S., Warsta, E., Kubiske, M.E., Nelson, N.D., Sober, J., Karnosky, D.F., Saranpaa, P., and Vapaavuori, E. 2008. Wood properties of trembling aspen and paper birch after 5 years of exposure to elevated concentrations of CO_2 and O_3. *Tree Physiology* **28**: 805–813.

Kozlowski, T.T. and Pallardy, S.G. 1997. *Physiology of Woody Plants*. Academic Press, San Diego, CA, USA.

Kull, O., Tulva, I., and Vapaavuori, E. 2003. Influence of elevated CO_2 and O_3 on *Betula pendula* Roth crown structure. *Annals of Botany* **91**: 559–569.

Loats, K.V. and Rebbeck, J. 1999. Interactive effects of ozone and elevated carbon dioxide on the growth and physiology of black cherry, green ash, and yellow-poplar seedlings. *Environmental Pollution* **106**: 237–248.

Mortensen, L.M. 1995. Effects of carbon dioxide concentration on biomass production and partitioning in *Betula pubescens* Ehrh. seedlings at different ozone and temperature regimes. *Environmental Pollution* **87**: 337–343.

Oksanen, E., Haikio, E., Sober, J., and Karnosky, D.F. 2003. Ozone-induced H_2O_2 accumulation in field-grown aspen and birch is linked to foliar ultrastructure and peroxisomal activity. *New Phytologist* **161**: 791–799.

Oksanen, E., Sober, J., and Karnosky, D.F. 2001. Impacts of elevated CO_2 and/or O_3 on leaf ultrastructure of aspen (*Populus tremuloides*) and birch (*Betula papyrifera*) in the Aspen FACE experiment. *Environmental Pollution* **115**: 437–446.

Peltonen, P.A., Vapaavuori, E., and Julkunen-Tiitto, R. 2005. Accumulation of phenolic compounds in birch leaves is changed by elevated carbon dioxide and ozone. *Global Change Biology* **11**: 1305–1324.

Percy, K.E., Awmack, C.S., Lindroth, R.L., Kubiske, M.E., Kopper, B.J., Isebrands, J.G., Pregitzer, K.S., Hendrey, G.R., Dickson, R.E., Zak, D.R., Oksanen, E., Sober, J., Harrington, R., and Karnosky, D.F. 2002. Altered performance of forest pests enriched by CO_2 and O_3. *Nature* **420**: 403–407.

Piispanen, R. and Saranpaa, P. 2001. Variation of non-structural carbohydrates in silver birch (*Betula pendula* Roth) wood. *Trees* **15**: 444–451.

Pregitzer, K.S., Burton, A.J., King, J.S., and Zak, D.R. 2008. Soil respiration, root biomass, and root turnover following long-term exposure of northern forests to elevated atmospheric CO_2 and tropospheric O_3. *New Phytologist* **180**: 153–161.

Rao, M.V., Hale, B.A., and Ormrod, D.P. 1995. Amelioration of ozone-induced oxidative damage in wheat plants grown under high carbon dioxide. *Plant Physiology* **109**: 421–432.

Rebbeck, J. and Scherzer, A.J. 2002. Growth responses of yellow-poplar (*Liriodendron tulipifera* L.) exposed to 5 years of $[O_3]$ alone or combined with elevated $[CO_2]$. *Plant, Cell and Environment* **25**: 1527–1537.

Riikonen, J., Kets, K., Darbah, J., Oksanen, E., Sober, A., Vapaavuori, E., Kubiske, M.E., Nelson, N., and Karnosky, D.F. 2008. Carbon gain and bud physiology in *Populus tremuloides* and *Betula papyrifera* grown under long-term exposure to elevated concentrations of CO_2 and O_3. *Tree Physiology* **28**: 243–254.

Riikonen, J., Lindsberg, M.-M., Holopainen, T., Oksanen, E., Lappi, J., Peltonen, P., and Vapaavuori, E. 2004. Silver birch and climate change: variable growth and carbon allocation responses to elevated concentrations of carbon dioxide and ozone. *Tree Physiology* **24**: 1227–1237.

Uddling, J., Teclaw, R.M., Kubiske, M.E., Pregitzer, K.S., and Ellsworth, D.S. 2008. Sap flux in pure aspen and mixed aspen-birch forests exposed to elevated concentrations of carbon dioxide and ozone. *Tree Physiology* **28**: 1231–1243.

Vapaavuori, E., Holopainen, J.K., Holopainen, T., Julkunen-Titto, R., Kaakinen, S., Kasurien, A., Kontunen-Soppela, S., Kostiainen, K., Oksanen, E., Peltonen, P., Riikonen, J., and Tulva, I. 2009. Rising atmospheric CO_2 concentration partially masks the negative effects of elevated O_3 in silver birch (*Betula pendula* Roth). *Ambio* **38**: 418–424.

3.8.2.4 Yellow Poplar

- As the air's CO_2 content rises, yellow-poplar trees likely will display substantial increases in photosynthetic rate and biomass production, even under conditions of elevated O_3 concentrations, and the soils in which the trees grow should therefore sequester increasing quantities of carbon.

Scherzel *et al.* (1998) grew yellow-poplar seedlings in open-top chambers for four years at three combinations of atmospheric O_3 and CO_2—ambient O_3 and ambient CO_2, doubled O_3 and ambient CO_2, and doubled O_3 and doubled CO_2—to study the interactive effects of these gases on leaf-litter decomposition. This experiment revealed decomposition rates of yellow-poplar leaves were similar for all three treatments for nearly five months, after which time litter produced in the elevated O_3 and elevated CO_2 air decomposed at a significantly slower rate, such that even after two years of decomposition, litter from the elevated O_3 and elevated CO_2 treatment still contained about 12% more biomass than litter produced in the other two treatments. This reduced rate of decomposition under elevated O_3 and CO_2 conditions likely will result in greater carbon sequestration in soils supporting yellow-poplar trees in the future.

Loats and Rebbeck (1999) grew yellow-poplar seedlings for 10 weeks in pots placed in growth chambers filled with ambient air, air with twice the ambient CO_2 concentration, air with twice the ambient O_3 concentration, and air with twice the ambient CO_2 and O_3 concentrations, to determine the effects of elevated CO_2 and O_3 on photosynthesis and growth in this deciduous tree species. They found doubling the air's CO_2 concentration increased the rate of net photosynthesis by 55% in ambient O_3 air; at twice the ambient level of O_3 it stimulated net photosynthesis by an average of 50%. The doubled CO_2 concentration significantly increased total biomass by 29%, and the doubled O_3 concentration had little impact on growth.

Rebbeck *et al.* (2004) grew yellow poplar seedlings for five years in open-top chambers in a field plantation at Delaware, Ohio (USA), exposing them continuously from mid-May through mid-October of each year to charcoal-filtered air to remove ambient O_3, ambient O_3, 1.5 times ambient O_3, or 1.5 times ambient O_3 plus 350 ppm CO_2 above ambient CO_2. The trees were never fertilized during the study, and they received no supplemental water beyond some given in the first season.

Averaged over the experiment's five growing seasons, the midseason net photosynthetic rate of upper canopy foliage at saturating light intensities declined by 10% when the trees were grown in ambient O_3-air and by 14% when grown in elevated O_3-air, compared to the trees grown in the charcoal-filtered air. Seasonal net photosynthesis of foliage grown in the combination of elevated O_3 and elevated CO_2 was 57–80% higher than it was in the trees exposed to elevated O_3 alone. There was no evidence of any photosynthetic down-regulation in the trees exposed to the elevated O_3 and CO_2 air, with some of the highest rates being observed during the final growing season. Rebbeck *et al.* conclude "elevated CO_2 may ameliorate the negative effects of increased tropospheric O_3 on yellow-poplar." Their results suggest a nominally doubled atmospheric CO_2 concentration more than compensates for the deleterious effects of a 50% increase in ambient O_3 levels, and by several times over.

References

Loats, K.V. and Rebbeck, J. 1999. Interactive effects of ozone and elevated carbon dioxide on the growth and physiology of black cherry, green ash, and yellow-poplar seedlings. *Environmental Pollution* **106**: 237–248.

Rebbeck, J., Scherzer, A.J., and Loats, K.V. 2004. Foliar physiology of yellow-poplar (*Liriodendron tulipifera* L.) exposed to O_3 and elevated CO_2 over five seasons. *Trees* **18**: 253–263.

Scherzel, A.J., Rebbeck, J., and Boerner, R.E.J. 1998. Foliar nitrogen dynamics and decomposition of yellow-poplar and eastern white pine during four seasons of exposure to elevated ozone and carbon dioxide. *Forest Ecology and Management* **109**: 355–366.

3.8.2.5 Miscellaneous

- The positive effects of atmospheric CO_2 enrichment generally more than compensate for the negative effects of elevated ozone concentrations on tree growth.

Ozone (O_3) is the primary air pollutant responsible for visible foliar injury and reduced growth in trees the world over. Most studies of the subject suggest it gains entrance to leaves through their stomata, where it interferes with the process of photosynthesis and thereby reduces plant productivity. Fowler *et al.* (1999) described the global significance of the phenomenon in some detail by estimating O_3 to have been negatively affecting a quarter of Earth's forests at the close of the twentieth century, and calculating it to have the potential to negatively affect one-half of the planet's forests by 2100.

In one of the earlier studies of the subject, Kainulainen *et al.* (1998) constructed open-top chambers around Scots pine (*Pinus sylvestris* L.) trees about 20 years old and fumigated them with combinations of ambient or CO_2-enriched air (645 ppm) and ambient or twice-ambient (20 to 40 ppb) ozone-enriched air for three growing seasons, to study the interactive effects of these gases on starch and secondary metabolite production. They discovered elevated CO_2 and O_3 had no significant impact on the trees' starch production, even after two years of treatment exposure. Near the end of the third year, elevated CO_2 alone significantly enhanced starch production in current-year needles. But neither elevated CO_2 nor O_3, acting alone or together, had any significant effects on the concentrations of the secondary metabolites the researchers investigated.

Kainulainen *et al.*'s paper made clear the need for long-term studies of tree responses to atmospheric CO_2 enrichment. Whereas no effects of elevated CO_2 on starch production were found after two years of treatment exposure, starch concentrations in needles ultimately increased significantly in the CO_2-enriched trees late into the third year of the study. It's hardly surprising that long-lived perennial plants, such as trees, require long-term CO_2-enrichment studies to reveal how they will respond to the rising concentration of atmospheric CO_2. This study suggests over time, Scots pine trees may respond to the rising CO_2 content of the air with increases in starch concentration, which can be mobilized to provide carbohydrates for active plant sinks to increase total tree size and biomass. In addition, if ozone continues to accumulate in the lower atmosphere, Scots pine may not display any adverse response to it, as atmospheric CO_2 enrichment seems able to protect against O_3-induced harm.

Broadmeadow *et al.* (1999) studied several species of young trees, including sessile oak (*Quercus petraea*), European beech (*Fagus sylvatica*), and sweet chestnut (*Castanea sativa*), to determine how their responses to ozone exposure are affected by elevated CO_2 and other environmental variables. They found elevated CO_2 generally reduced the amount of ozone damage by inducing stomatal closure, which decreased the uptake of this air pollutant. This study suggests, as the air's CO_2 concentration continues to rise, many tree species likely will exhibit reductions in stomatal conductance, which should reduce the negative effects of tropospheric ozone on their growth and development.

Herman *et al.* (2001) note air pollution by SO_2, Pb, NOx, and NH_3 had been significantly reduced in central Europe over the two decades prior to their study, but ozone levels were still on the rise, based on trends derived from European databases that included ozone measurements from about 100 stations in Austria and Germany. The parameter Herman *et al.*

used to express the significance of these ozone trends was the *AOT40* Critical Level set by the UN-ECE (1994), which had a value of 10 ppm.h and was defined as accumulated ozone exposure above a threshold of 40 ppb 24 hours per day over the six-month growing season of April–September, which in controlled experiments had been documented to cause approximate 10% reductions in tree biomass production.

As a measure of how bad ozone pollution had become in central Europe, in most of the grid plots of the Austrian Forest Inventory Grid, and based on 1993 ozone data, Herman *et al.* report "the Critical Level of 10 ppm.h had been exceeded up to sevenfold," and "where standards had been exceeded to such an alarming extent, serious damage of forest trees should be expected."

So what did the trees in these highly ozone-polluted grid plots look like? Were they absolutely devastated? Or dead? Herman *et al.* report, "the results of the Austrian monitoring surveys did not reflect such damage." They note, for example, "neither the general evaluation of the foliage losses in the context of the crown condition inventories nor the development of the growing stock reflect a dramatic situation." Not only were there no "dramatic" reductions in tree health and productivity, there were typically none at all, and in many areas there were actually improvements, such as crown conditions in Austria looking slightly better and the growing stock increasing.

Herman *et al.* acknowledge that although ozone-related losses of biomass could not be confirmed on old trees, under the ozone levels of that day they did show some reductions in photosynthetic CO_2 uptake. This phenomenon was particularly evident in old trees at high altitudes, where AOT40 values were much more extreme, and in trees experiencing "additional climatic stress." But the researchers were careful to add "the reductions of the CO_2 uptake were in no proportion to the massive excess of the AOT40."

Ozone exposures more than sevenfold greater than the Critical Level (which Critical Level alone should have decreased tree productivity by 10%) were occurring all across the Austrian Forest Inventory Grid, and such conditions could have been expected to reduce the growth rates of the exposed trees by 70% or more. Yet there was no evidence of any widespread damage or productivity reduction. In fact, growth conditions seemed to have improved almost everywhere, except at high altitudes and under conditions of more-than-usual climatic stress.

Herman *et al.* suggest these observations imply the once-adequate Critical Level of ozone exposure was no longer suitable for application. Why? Because "the significant parameter for the assessment of the risk" is not the atmospheric concentration of ozone, but "the absorbed dose." Therefore, they advise the creation of a new Critical Level that "takes into account leaf conductance and the environmental parameters influencing it."

This latter statement is an example of the proper approach to risk assessment, for there are many concurrent and ongoing changes in Earth's atmosphere and the net result of all of them acting in concert must be considered when predicting the consequences of changes in any individual factor. In the case of Earth's climate, for example, the surface air temperature effects of an increase in the air's CO_2 content cannot be adequately evaluated without considering the effects of concurrent changes in atmospheric aerosol quantities and properties. Likewise, in the case of ozone and forest health, the biological consequences of rising tropospheric ozone concentrations cannot be adequately evaluated without considering the effects of the concurrent rise in the air's CO_2 content, which is known to have a significant impact on leaf conductance and, hence, largely determines a tree's critical "absorbed dose" of ozone. When this more rational approach has been followed, numerous laboratory and field experiments have shown realistically scaled concurrent increases in atmospheric CO_2 and ozone concentrations typically lead to very little change in plant net productivity. The lack of substantial negative ozone-induced impacts on the forests of central Europe, as described by Herman *et al.*, may have been the result of the compensatory beneficial impacts of the historical and still-ongoing rise in the air's CO_2 content.

King *et al.* (2005) note preindustrial concentrations of tropospheric O_3 were estimated to have been less than 10 ppb, but subsequently rose to the 30–40 ppb background levels of their day, referencing Levy *et al.* (1997). In addition, they report the rising boundary-layer O_3 concentration caused by increasing industrialization around the globe has had negative continent-scale implications for carbon sequestration (Felzer *et al.*, 2004). Thus they sought to evaluate the net effect of the positive CO_2 and negative O_3 impacts of possible future increases in these trace atmospheric gases on the productivity of the most widespread tree species found in North America—trembling aspen (*Populus tremuloides* Michx.)—and two-member mixed communities of trembling aspen-paper birch (*Betula papyrifera* Marsh.) and trembling aspen-sugar maple (*Acer saccharum* Marsh.).

Working at the Aspen FACE site (Dickson *et al.*, 2000) near Rhinelander, Wisconsin (USA), King *et al.* allowed pure stands of aspen and mixed stands of aspen-birch and aspen-maple to grow for seven years in ambient air, air enriched with an extra 200 ppm of CO_2, air enriched with an extra 50% O_3, or air thus enriched by both CO_2 and O_3. Relative to the ambient-air control treatment, the eight researchers found elevated CO_2 increased "total biomass 25, 45, and 60% in the aspen, aspen-birch and aspen-maple communities, respectively," while elevated O_3 "caused 23, 13, and 14% reductions in total biomass relative to the control in the respective communities." The combination of elevated CO_2 and O_3 "resulted in total biomass responses of -7.8, +8.4, and +24.3% relative to the control in the aspen, aspen-birch and aspen-sugar maple communities, respectively."

King *et al.* conclude "exposure to even moderate levels of O_3 significantly reduces the capacity of net primary productivity to respond to elevated CO_2 in some forests."

Gardner *et al.* (2005) grew pre-flushed hardwood stem cuttings of the inter-American (*Populus trichocarpa* Torr. & Gray ex Hook. *x P. deltoides* Bartr. ex Marsh) hybrid poplar clone 'Boelare' out-of-doors in eight open-top chambers for two growing seasons of 132 and 186 days (first and second years, respectively), measuring a number of plant properties and physiological processes. Two of the eight chambers were maintained at ambient carbon dioxide (350 ppm) and ozone concentrations (A), two at ambient CO_2 with daily O_3 episodes rising to a mid-day peak of 100 ppb (AO), two at elevated CO_2 (700 ppm) and ambient O_3 (E), and two at elevated CO_2 and O_3 (EO) throughout the first year of the study. Only CO_2 was elevated during the second year.

With respect to the effect of CO_2 alone, Gardner *et al.* write mainstem dry weight "was increased by 38% in 700-ppm CO_2 compared with that in 350-ppm CO_2 at the end of the first growing season," and "during year 2 mainstem dry weight increased by about 5-fold and the relative effect of elevated CO_2 remained similar in magnitude (32%) to that seen in the first year." During the first season of exposure, mainstem dry mass was decreased by 45% in the O_3-episode treatment in 350-ppm CO_2, and by 34% in the O_3-episode treatment in 700-ppm CO_2. Because of the strong growth-promoting effect of the extra CO_2, the O_3-induced change in growth when going from the ambient-CO_2-ambient-O_3 treatment to the elevated-CO_2-elevated-O_3 treatment was only a reduction of 10%, as compared to the O_3-induced reduction of 45% when CO_2 was not increased concurrently.

The British researchers conclude "elevated levels of CO_2 can play a key role in ameliorating the worst effects of severe ozone episodes on a relatively sensitive tree species," and "O_3 episodes are less likely to be detrimental to *P. trichocarpa x P. deltoides* in the CO_2 concentrations of the future."

Noting the "detrimental effects of ozone on plants are well known" and "CO_2 generally affects trees in opposite ways to ozone," Valkama *et al.* (2007) conducted a literature review they describe as "the first quantitative analysis of the interactive effects of elevated O_3 and elevated CO_2 on tree chemistry and herbivore performance," based on the results of 63 studies conducted on 22 tree species and 10 insect herbivore species published between 1990 and 2005.

With respect to the ways elevated O_3 may benefit insect herbivores that tend to damage trees, Valkama *et al.* write, "elevated O_3 significantly shortened development time of insect herbivores [when they are exposed and vulnerable to attack by various enemies] and increased their pupal mass in the overall dataset." In addition, the "relative growth rate of chewers was significantly increased by 3.5% under elevated O_3." They report "these effects were counteracted by elevated CO_2," such that "elevated O_3 in combination with CO_2 had no effect on herbivore performance," with the exception that when elevated CO_2 was added to the O_3-enriched air, it not only counteracted the O_3-induced increase in pupal biomass, but reduced it below what it was in ambient air by 7%. This analysis of the vast majority of experimental data obtained prior to 2006 suggests in the interaction between insect herbivores and trees, the rise in the air's CO_2 content likely plays an extremely important role in negating, and in some cases even more than negating, the damage insect pests would otherwise do to forests.

Wittig *et al.* (2007) calculated the increase in the atmosphere's O_3 concentration since the start of the Industrial Revolution had caused a mean decrease of 11% in the leaf photosynthetic CO_2 uptake of temperate and boreal forests. Based on projections derived from the A2 storyline of the *Special Report on Emissions Scenarios* included in IPCC's Fourth Assessment Report (which indicate atmospheric O_3 concentrations could rise 20–25% between 2015 and 2050, and could further increase by 40–60% by 2100 if current emission trends continue), they calculate temperate and boreal forest photosynthetic rates could decline by an additional 8–16% by the end of the century.

Fortunately, the stomatal-aperture-constricting effect of concomitant past increases and anticipated future increases in the air's CO_2 content tend to counter the negative influence of rising O_3 concentrations by retarding O_3 entry into plant leaves. In addition, the CO_2-induced increase in leaf photosynthesis (its "aerial fertilization effect") has been shown to often more than compensate for the negative influence of ozone on leaf photosynthesis rates. These welcome findings comprise only half of the good news about rising CO_2 concentrations and their impact on the ozone problem.

It is a well-established fact that vegetative isoprene emissions are responsible for the production of vast amounts of tropospheric ozone (Chameides *et al.*, 1988; Harley *et al.*, 1999). Poisson *et al.* (2000) calculated current levels of non-methane hydrocarbon (NMHC) emissions (the vast majority of which are isoprene, accounting for more than twice as much as all other NMHCs combined) likely increase surface ozone concentrations from what they would be in their absence by up to 50–60% over land. In addition, although little appreciated, it has been known for some time that atmospheric CO_2 enrichment typically leads to large reductions in isoprene emissions from plants. This phenomenon typically has not been factored into projections of future atmospheric O_3 concentrations.

Arneth *et al.* (2007) addressed this issue, noting future vegetative isoprene emissions typically have been modeled to rise in tandem with projected increases in vegetative biomass and productivity driven by projected changes in various environmental factors. This protocol, in an anticipated warmer and CO_2-enriched environment, generally has led to predictions of significant increases in isoprene emissions and, therefore, significant increases in future atmospheric O_3 concentrations, as Wittig *et al* predicted. However, Arneth *et al.* convincingly demonstrate "a quite different result is obtained when the direct CO_2 effect on isoprene emissions is included," noting in this more-realistic situation a properly forced model "maintains global isoprene emissions within ± 15% of present values."

The seven Swedish and UK researchers thus conclude "predictions of high future tropospheric O_3 concentrations partly driven by isoprene emissions may need to be revised."

Xu *et al.* (2012) report "levels of atmospheric CO_2 and O_3 have increased rapidly in the last five decades," and "it is predicted that at the end of this century, the average levels of CO_2 and O_3 in Earth's atmosphere are going to reach 700 ppm and 80 ppb, respectively (IPCC, 2007)." Thus, in an experiment designed to evaluate the opposing effects of these two atmospheric trace gases on Chinese pine (*Pinus tabulaeformis*) trees at the year AD 2100, they grew four-year-old trees in loamy soil with no extra fertilizer in 12 open-top chambers in May 2006 in the populated central area of Shenyang city in northeastern China, where the trees were exposed to either current ambient air of about 400 ppm CO_2 and 40 ppb O_3 or 700 ppm CO_2 and 80 ppm O_3, plus all combinations thereof.

This study revealed elevated CO_2 by itself increased growth but "did not significantly affect net photosynthetic rate, stomatal conductance, chlorophyll content, the maximum quantum yield of photosystem II, or the effective quantum yield of photosystem II electron transport after 90 days of gas exposure." Elevated O_3 by itself "decreased growth, net photosynthetic rate and stomatal conductance after 90 days of exposure," but Xu *et al.* note "its negative effects were alleviated by elevated CO_2."

References

Arneth, A., Miller, P.A., Scholze, M., Hickler, T., Schurgers, G., Smith, B., and Prentice, I.C. 2007. CO_2 inhibition of global terrestrial isoprene emissions: Potential implications for atmospheric chemistry. *Geophysical Research Letters* **34**: 10.1029/2007GL030615.

Broadmeadow, M.S.J., Heath, J., and Randle, T.J. 1999. Environmental limitations to O_3 uptake—Some key results from young trees growing at elevated CO_2 concentrations. *Water, Air, and Soil Pollution* **116**: 299–310.

Chameides, W.L., Lindsay, R.W., Richardson, J., and Kiang, C.S. 1988. The role of biogenic hydrocarbons in urban photochemical smog: Atlanta as a case study. *Science* **241**: 1473–1475.

Dickson, R.E., Lewin, K.F., Isebrands, J.G., Coleman, M.D., Heilman, W.E., Riemenschneider, D.E., Sober, J, Host, G.E., Zak, D.R., Hendrey, G.R., Pregitzer, K.S., and Karnosky, D.F. 2000. *Forest Atmosphere Carbon Transfer and Storage (FACTS-II): The Aspen Free-Air CO_2 and O_3 Enrichment (FACE) Project: An Overview.* USDA Forest Service NCRS, St. Paul, Minnesota, USA.

Felzer, B., Kicklighter, D., Mellilo, J., Wang, C., Zhuang, Q., and Prinn, R. 2004. Effects of ozone on net primary production and carbon sequestration in the conterminous United States using a biogeochemistry model. *Tellus* **56B**: 230–248.

Fowler, D., Cape, J.N., Coyle, M., Flechard, C., Kuylenstierna, J., Hicks, K., Derwent, D., Johnson, C., and Stevenson, D. 1999. The global exposure of forests to air pollutants. *Water, Air & Soil Pollution* **116**: 5–32.

Gardner, S.D.L., Freer-Smith, P.H., Tucker, J., and Taylor, G. 2005. Elevated CO_2 protects poplar (*Populus trichocarpa x P. deltoides*) from damage induced by O_3: identification of mechanisms. *Functional Plant Biology* **32**: 221–235.

Harley, P.C., Monson, R.K., and Lerdau, M.T. 1999. Ecological and evolutionary aspects of isoprene emission from plants. *Oecologia* **118**: 109–123.

Herman, F., Smidt, S., Huber, S., Englisch, M., and Knoflacher, M. 2001. Evaluation of pollution-related stress factors for forest ecosystems in central Europe. *Environmental Science & Pollution Research* **8**: 231–242.

IPCC. 2007. *Climate Change 2007*. Working Group I Report: The Physical Basis of Climate Change. IPCC, Geneva, Switzerland.

Kainulainen, P., Holopainen, J.K., and Holopainen, T. 1998. The influence of elevated CO_2 and O_3 concentrations on Scots pine needles: Changes in starch and secondary metabolites over three exposure years. *Oecologia* **114**: 455–460.

King, J.S., Kubiske, M.E., Pregitzer, K.S., Hendrey, G.R., McDonald, E.P., Giardina, C.P., Quinn, V.S., and Karnosky, D.F. 2005. Tropospheric O_3 compromises net primary production in young stands of trembling aspen, paper birch and sugar maple in response to elevated atmospheric CO_2. *New Phytologist* **168**: 623–636.

Levy, H.II., Kasibhatla, P.S., Moxim, W.J., Klonecki, A.A., Hirsch, A.I., Oltmans, S.J., and Chameides, W.L. 1997. The global impact of human activity on tropospheric ozone. *Geophysical Research Letters* **24**: 791–794.

Poisson, N., Kanakidou, M., and Crutzen, P.J. 2000. Impact of non-methane hydrocarbons on tropospheric chemistry and the oxidizing power of the global troposphere: 3-dimensional modeling results. *Journal of Atmospheric Chemistry* **36**: 157–230.

UN-ECE. 1994. *Critical Levels for Ozone*. A UN-ECE Workshop Report. Fuhrer, J. and Achermann, B. (Eds.) Swiss Federal Research Station of Agricultural Chemistry and Environmental Health, No. 16. ISSN-1013-154X.

Valkama, E., Koricheva, J., and Oksanen, E. 2007. Effects of elevated O_3, alone and in combination with elevated CO_2, on tree leaf chemistry and insect herbivore performance: a meta-analysis. *Global Change Biology* **13**: 184–201.

Wittig, V.E., Ainsworth, E.A., and Long, S.P. 2007. To what extent do current and projected increases in surface ozone affect photosynthesis and stomatal conductance of trees? A meta-analytic review of the last 3 decades of experiments. *Plant, Cell and Environment* **30**: 1150–1162.

Xu, S., Chen, W., Huang, Y., and He, X. 2012. Responses of growth, photosynthesis and VOC emissions of *Pinus tabulaeformis* Carr. exposure to elevated CO_2 and/or elevated O_3 in an urban area. *Bulletin of Environmental Contamination and Toxicology* **88**: 443–448.

3.9 Non-Ozone Air Pollutants

- Despite being labeled by the United Nations and U.S. Environmental Protection Agency as a dangerous air pollutant, not only is CO_2 not a "pollutant," as those entities claim it is; it is actually an anti-pollutant that helps plants overcome the negative effects of real air and soil pollutants and better enables their removal from polluted areas.

In addition to ozone, many other airborne substances can damage plant life. This section explores the scientific literature pertaining to the negative effects of some of these other harmful components of the planet's atmosphere and how these negative effects can be alleviated by atmospheric CO_2 enrichment.

Lee *et al.* (1997) note, "several studies using controlled-environment chambers have shown that CO_2 may compensate for sulfur dioxide (SO_2)-induced leaf injury (Black, 1982; Carlson and Bazzaz, 1982; Darrall, 1989; Sandhu *et al.*, 1992; Rao and De Kok, 1994; Niewiadomska and Miszalski, 1995; Tausz *et al.*, 1996)." They conducted a similar study out-of-doors using open-top chambers placed over soybeans (*Glycine max* L. Merr. cv. Essex) growing in a typical field situation, to determine whether the positive effects of atmospheric CO_2 enrichment would compensate for the negative effects of elevated SO_2 concentrations on soybean photosynthetic rates. They exposed the soybeans to either ambient (350 ppm) or elevated (500 ppm) atmospheric CO_2 concentrations in combination with atmospheric SO_2 concentrations of either 0.00 or 0.12 ppm. They describe the latter concentration as being sufficient to produce "potentially toxic effects over long term exposure."

They found, throughout the period of pod filling, the mean photosynthetic rate of plants growing in ambient-CO_2 but elevated-SO_2 air was 17.2% lower than the mean rate of plants growing in ambient-CO_2 and SO_2-free air, and the mean photosynthetic rate of plants growing in CO_2-enriched but SO_2-free air was 25.1% higher than the mean rate of plants growing in ambient-CO_2 and SO_2-free air. The mean photosynthetic rate of plants growing in CO_2-enriched and elevated-SO_2 air was 33.4% greater than the mean rate of plants growing in ambient-CO_2 and SO_2-free air. Enriching the air with CO_2 more than compensated for the negative effects of the elevated SO_2 on the photosynthetic rates of the soybeans the five researchers studied.

Deepak and Agrawal (2001) grew two cultivars of soybeans (*Glycine max* L. Merr. Cv. PK472 and Bragg) in open-top chambers at atmospheric CO_2 concentrations of either 350 or 600 ppm, both alone and in combination with 60 ppb SO_2, to determine the individual and interactive effects of elevated CO_2 and SO_2 on the growth and yield of this important crop. Exposure to the elevated SO_2 significantly reduced total plant biomass and grain yield by approximately 18% in both cultivars. In contrast, elevated CO_2 significantly increased total plant biomass and grain yield in both cultivars by averages of 30 and 34%, respectively. When the plants were exposed simultaneously to elevated SO_2 and CO_2, the negative effects of SO_2 were completely ameliorated.

Agrawal and Deepak (2003) conducted a similar study of two cultivars of wheat (*Triticum aestivum* L. cv. Malviya 234 and HP1209) in open-top chambers maintained at atmospheric CO_2 concentrations of 350 and 600 ppm both alone and in combination with 60 ppb SO_2, to study the individual and interactive effects of elevated CO_2 and SO_2 on another of the world's major crops. They found exposure to elevated CO_2 boosted photosynthetic rates by 58 and 48% in M234 and HP1209, respectively, and fumigation with elevated SO_2 had no significant impact on rates of photosynthesis in either cultivar. Plants grown in the combined treatment of elevated CO_2 and elevated SO_2 displayed slightly lower photosynthetic rates, but they were still 42 and 38% greater than those measured in control plants for M234 and HP1209, respectively.

The plants grown in elevated CO_2 in this experiment also displayed an approximate 20% reduction in stomatal conductance, and those grown in elevated SO_2 exhibited an average conductance increase of 15%. When exposed simultaneously to both gases, the plants displayed an average 11% reduction in stomatal conductance. This phenomenon contributed to an approximate 32% increase in water-use efficiency (plant growth per unit of water used) for plants simultaneously exposed to increased concentrations of both gases, whereas plants exposed

to elevated SO_2 alone displayed an average decrease in water-use efficiency of 16%. In addition, plant exposure to elevated SO_2 caused an average 13% decrease in foliar protein concentrations in both cultivars, but when the plants were concurrently exposed to an atmospheric CO_2 concentration of 600 ppm, leaf protein levels decreased by only 3% in HP1209 and increased by 4% in M234.

As the air's CO_2 content rises, it likely will reduce the stress and growth reductions of these specific wheat cultivars and others as a consequence of SO_2 pollution. Agrawal and Deepak's study demonstrates CO_2-induced increases in photosynthesis will be only partially offset by elevated SO_2 concentrations, which should allow greater wheat yields to be produced in the future under similar conditions. In addition, since SO_2-induced reductions in plant water-use efficiency were essentially eliminated by concurrent plant exposure to elevated CO_2, these cultivars should be able to grow better in areas with limited water availability and in areas close to industrial complexes emitting large quantities of SO_2. Also, wheat plants growing in SO_2-polluted air should not suffer as large a reduction in foliar protein content in a future high-CO_2 world as they do today.

Izrael *et al.* (2002) evaluated the effects of sulfur dioxide pollution on Russian forests. Among other things, the five researchers report "sulfur dioxide (SO_2) causes widespread damage to plants, because it can spread through large distances, and its emissions into the atmosphere are large." In 1996, for example, they found "total SO_2 emission from the industrial areas of Russia comprised 5866.76 thousand tons, or 42.2% of the total emission of liquid and gaseous pollutants." They determined 1.3 million hectares of Russian forest land had been adversely affected by SO_2 pollution. They estimated total forest destruction occurs on 2–5% of this area, and heavy, moderate, and slight damage occur on 10–15%, 30–40%, and 40–50% of this area, respectively.

These results indicate the seriousness of SO_2 pollution for forest health, and they highlight the fact that atmospheric CO_2 enrichment can significantly alleviate SO_2's adverse biological consequences. Hallgren (1984), for example, demonstrated a 300 ppm increase in the air's CO_2 concentration stimulated the photosynthetic rate of Scots pine trees by 64% in unpolluted air and by 77% in air with abnormally high SO_2 concentrations. Hallgren also found a 600-ppm increase in atmospheric CO_2 stimulated photosynthetic rates in this important forest species by 85% in unpolluted air and 110% in air of high SO_2 concentration. Similarly, Carlson (1983) found a 900-ppm increase in the air's CO_2 concentration boosted photosynthetic rates of soybeans by 87% in unpolluted air and 715% in high-SO_2 air. Thus the rise in the air's CO_2 content can do much to prevent or significantly alleviate the adverse consequences of SO_2 pollution.

Several studies have been conducted at naturally occurring CO_2 springs in Tuscany, Italy, providing a unique opportunity to examine the effects of long-term atmospheric CO_2 enrichment on plant growth and development. These springs also emit elevated concentrations of the major phytotoxic air pollutants H_2S and SO_2 (Schulte et al., 1999). Consequently, the springs provide a suitable setting in which to study the relative strengths of two competing phenomena: the growth-promoting effect of elevated CO_2 and the growth-retarding effects of elevated H_2S and SO_2.

Grill et al. (2004) analyzed various properties of leaves and acorns produced on two species of oak tree (Quercus ilex L. and Quercus pubescens L.) growing in air of double-to-triple the normal atmospheric CO_2 concentration near the CO_2 springs, and the same characteristics of leaves and acorns growing on similar trees located some distance away in ambient-CO_2 air. They also analyzed several characteristics of seedlings they sprouted from acorns produced by the CO_2-enriched and ambient-treatment trees, and they used chromosome stress tests "to investigate whether alterations in sulfur-regime have negative consequences for seedlings."

The six scientists report "acorns from CO_2 springs contained significantly higher sulphur concentrations than controls (0.67 vs. 0.47 mg g^{-1} dry weight in Q. ilex cotyledons and 1.10 vs. 0.80 in Q. pubescens)," indicating the trees were indeed significantly affected by the H_2S- and SO_2-enriched air in the vicinity of the CO_2-emitting springs. They also note Q. ilex seedlings grown from CO_2-spring acorns showed elevated rates of chromosomal aberrations in root tips, suggestive of a permanent stress. Nevertheless, as demonstrated by the results of several studies conducted on mature trees from these sites, the CO_2-enriched air—even in the presence of significantly elevated concentrations of phytotoxic H_2S and SO_2—significantly enhanced the trees' photosynthetic capacity: by 26–69% (Blaschke et al., 2001), 36–77% (Stylinski et al., 2000), and 175–510% (Tognetti et al., 1998).

Jia et al. (2010) note "mining and smelting, disposal of sewage sludge and the use of cadmium rich phosphate fertilizers (Wagner, 1993; Liu et al., 2007) have contaminated a large proportion of the agricultural land throughout the world, causing an increase in the soil concentration of many heavy metals." They further note, "as one of the most toxic environmental pollutants (Zhang et al., 2009) cadmium (Cd) has a strong influence on metabolic activities of crop plants by inducing a number of physiological changes, such as growth inhibition, changes in water and ion metabolism, photosynthesis inhibition, enzyme activity changes, and free radical formation (Ekmekci et al., 2008)," stating "even at relatively low concentrations cadmium can exert strong toxic effects on crops (Seregin and Ivanov, 2001)."

The seven scientists grew Italian and perennial ryegrass (Lolium mutiflorum and L. perenne) in pots filled with soil from a long-term experimental rice field in Guangdong Province, China, which they treated to contain either 0, 25, or 100 mg Cd per kg soil. They fertilized the soils to contain 150 mg N/kg, 100 mg P/kg, and 150 mg K/kg, after which (once the ryegrass seeds had sprouted) the pots were taken outdoors and distributed among six open-top chambers. Three of these (one each for the three soil cadmium concentrations) were maintained at the ambient atmospheric CO_2 concentration of 375 ppm, and three were maintained at an elevated CO_2 concentration of 810 ppm from 0800 to 1700 hours throughout all 58 days of the summer study. During this time and at the conclusion of the study, they measured a number of plant physiological processes and parameters.

Jia et al. found elevated CO_2 significantly increased both net photosynthesis and plant water use efficiency, which led to increases in both shoot and root biomass at harvest. "When compared with the ambient CO_2 control, the increase in total biomass due to elevated CO_2 was about 32 and 31% for L. multiflorum and L. perenne, respectively, grown on the control soil; 37 and 45% on soil amended with 25 mg/kg Cd; [and] 46 and 52% on soil spiked with 100 mg/kg Cd, respectively." In addition to these very positive results, compared to the ambient CO_2 control, under elevated CO_2 both Lolium species had decreased Cd concentrations in their shoots and roots, where "the decreased magnitude of Cd concentration in L. multiflorum and L. perenne grown on soil spiked with 25 mg/kg Cd was 10.3 and 3.8% for the shoots, and 18.6 and 14.7% for the roots, respectively; for those [plants] grown on soil spiked with 100 mg/kg Cd, it was 8.4 and 8.9% for the shoots, and 12.5 and 13.9% for the roots, respectively."

Thus atmospheric CO_2 enrichment not only spurred both ryegrass species to produce more root and shoot biomass, but this greater amount of plant material contained reduced concentrations of a toxic soil pollutant. Jia *et al.* conclude, "given expected global increases in CO_2 concentration, elevated CO_2 may help plants better survive in contaminated soil and reduce the food safety risk due to CO_2-induced reduction and dilution in heavy metal concentration."

Not only is carbon dioxide not a "pollutant," as the United Nations and U.S. Environmental Protection Agency claim, it is actually an *anti*-pollutant that helps plants overcome the negative effects of real air and soil pollutants and remove them from polluted areas.

References

Agrawal, M. and Deepak, S.S. 2003. Physiological and biochemical responses of two cultivars of wheat to elevated levels of CO_2 and SO_2, singly and in combination. *Environmental Pollution* **121**: 189–197.

Black, V.J. 1982. Effects of sulphur dioxide on physiological processes in plants. In: Unsworth, M.H. and Ormrod, O.P. (Eds.) *Effects of Gaseous Pollution in Agriculture and Horticulture*, Butterworth, London, UK, pp. 67–91.

Blaschke, L., Schulte, M., Raschi, A., Slee, N., Rennenberg, H., and Polle, A. 2001. Photosynthesis, soluble and structural carbon compounds in two Mediterranean oak species (*Quercus pubescens* and *Q. ilex*) after lifetime growth at naturally elevated CO_2 concentrations. *Plant Biology* **3**: 288–297.

Carlson, R.W. 1983. The effect of SO_2 on photosynthesis and leaf resistance at varying concentrations of CO_2. *Environmental Pollution Series A* **30**: 309–321.

Carlson, R.W. and Bazzaz, F.A. 1982. Photosynthetic and growth responses to fumigation with SO_2 at elevated CO_2 for C_3 and C_4 plants. *Oecologia* **54**: 50–54.

Darrall, N.M. 1989. The effect of air pollutants on physiological processes in plants. *Plant, Cell and Environment* **12**: 1–30.

Deepak, S.S. and Agrawal, M. 2001. Influence of elevated CO_2 on the sensitivity of two soybean cultivars to sulphur dioxide. *Environmental and Experimental Botany* **46**: 81–91.

Ekmekci, Y., Tanyolac, D., and Ayhan, B. 2008. Effects of cadmium on antioxidant enzyme and photosynthetic activities in leaves of two maize cultivars. *Journal of Plant Physiology* **165**: 600–611.

Grill, D., Muller, M., Tausz, M. Strnad, B., Wonisch, A., and Raschi, A. 2004. Effects of sulphurous gases in two CO_2 springs on total sulphur and thiols in acorns and oak seedlings. *Atmospheric Environment* **38**: 3775–3780.

Hallgren, J.-E. 1984. Photosynthetic gas exchange in leaves affected by air pollutants. In: Koziol, M.J. and Whatley, F.R. (Eds.) *Gaseous Air Pollutants and Plant Metabolism*. Butterworths, London, UK, pp. 147–159.

Izrael, Y.A., Gytarsky, M.L., Karaban, R.T., Lelyakin, A.L., and Nazarov, I.M. 2002. Consequences of climate change for forestry and carbon dioxide sink in Russian forests. *Isvestiya, Atmospheric and Oceanic Physics* **38**: S84-S98.

Jia, Y., Tang, S., Wang, R., Ju, X., Ding, Y., Tu, S., and Smith, D.L. 2010. Effects of elevated CO_2 on growth, photosynthesis, elemental composition, antioxidant level, and phytochelatin concentration in *Lolium mutiflorum* and *Lolium perenne* under Cd stress. *Journal of Hazardous Materials* **180**: 384–394.

Lee, E.H., Pausch, R.C., Rowland, R.A., Mulchi, C.L., and Rudorff, B.F.T. 1997. Responses of field-grown soybean (cv. Essex) to elevated SO_2 under two atmospheric CO_2 concentrations. *Environmental and Experimental Botany* **37**: 85–93.

Liu, Y., Wang, X., Zeng, G., Qu, D., Gu, J., Zhou, M., and Chai, L. 2007. Cadmium-induced oxidative stress and response of the ascorbate-glutathione cycle in *Bechmeria nivea* (L.), Gaud. *Chemosphere* **69**: 99–107.

Niewiadomska, E. and Miszalski, Z. 1995. Does CO_2 modify the effect of SO_2 on variegated leaves of *Chlorophytum comosum* (Thunb) Bak? *New Phytologist* **130**: 461–466.

Rao, M.V. and De Kok, L.J. 1994. Interactive effects of high CO_2 and SO_2 on growth and antioxidant levels in wheat. *Phyton (Horn)* **34**: 279–290.

Sandhu, R., Li, Y., and Gupta, G. 1992. Sulphur dioxide and carbon dioxide induced changes in soybean physiology. *Plant Science* **83**: 31–34.

Schulte, M., Raiesi, F.G., Papke, H., Butterbach-Bahl, K., van Breemen, N., and Rennenberg, H. 1999. CO_2 concentration and atmospheric trace gas mixing ratio around natural CO_2 vents in different Mediterranean forests in central Italy. In: Raschi, A., Vaccori, F.P., and Miglietta, F. (Eds.) *Ecosystem Response to CO_2: The Maple Project Results*. European Communities, Brussels, Belgium, pp. 168–188.

Seregin, I.V. and Ivanov, V.B. 2001. Physiological aspects of cadmium and lead toxic effects on higher plants. *Russian Journal of Plant Physiology* **48**: 523–544.

Stylinski, C.D., Oechel, W.C., Gamon, J.A., Tissue, D.T., Miglietta, F., and Raschi, A. 2000. Effects of lifelong [CO_2] enrichment on carboxylation and light utilization of *Quercus pubescens* Willd. examined with gas exchange, biochemistry and optical techniques. *Plant, Cell and Environment* **23**: 1353–1362.

Tausz, M., De Kok, L., Stulen, I., and Grill, D. 1996. Physiological responses of Norway spruce trees to elevated CO_2 and SO_2. *Journal of Plant Physiology* **148**: 362–376.

Tognetti, R., Johnson, J.D., Michelozzi, M., and Raschi, A. 1998. Response of foliar metabolism in mature trees of *Quercus pubescens* and *Quercus ilex* to long-term elevated CO_2. *Environmental and Experimental Botany* **39**: 233–245.

Wagner, G.J. 1993. Accumulation of cadmium in crop plants and its consequences to human health. *Advances in Agronomy* **51**: 173–212.

Zhang, F.Q., Zhang, H.X., Wang, G.P., Xu, L.L., and Shen, Z.G. 2009. Cadmium-induced accumulation of hydrogen peroxide in the leaf apoplast of *Phaseolus aureus* and *Vicia sativa* and the roles of different antioxidant enzymes. *Journal of Hazardous Materials* **168**: 76–84.

3.10 Phosphorus Insufficiency

- Plants growing in CO_2-enriched air typically respond by increasing their biomass production, even under conditions of low soil phosphorus content, especially if the plants possess the ability to increase root phosphatase activity.

Under current ambient conditions, plant growth and development are typically carbon-limited, which is why plants generally exhibit increased growth and biomass production in response to atmospheric CO_2 enrichment. Next to carbon, nitrogen is usually the second-most-limiting nutrient to plant growth, followed by phosphorus. Although it is a less-significant component of plant tissues than carbon and nitrogen, phosphorus is still required for successful life-cycle completion in many plant species. It is thus important to investigate aspects of plant phosphorus acquisition and biomass production in response to atmospheric CO_2 enrichment when phosphorus concentrations in soils are less than optimal.

In an early study of the subject, Barrett *et al.* (1998) demonstrated a doubling of the air's CO_2 content under continuous phosphorus deficiency increased wheat root phosphatase activity by 30 to 40%, thus increasing the inorganic phosphorus supply available for plant utilization. As phosphatase is the primary enzyme responsible for the mineralization of organic phosphate, which thereby makes phosphorus available for plant use, an increase in its activity with elevated CO_2 could facilitate sustained plant growth responses to the rise in the air's CO_2 content, even in areas where growth is currently limited by phosphorous deficiencies. And because these increases in phosphatase activity also were observed under sterile growing conditions, this response can be mediated directly by plant roots without involving soil micro-organisms, which are known to aid in phosphorus mineralization.

As the air's CO_2 content continues to rise, phosphatase activity in wheat roots should increase, increasingly converting organic phosphorus into inorganic forms that support the increased plant growth and development stimulated by higher CO_2 concentrations. As a similar increase in phosphatase activity at elevated CO_2 already has been reported for a native Australian pasture grass, these results may be applicable to most of the planet's vegetation. If that turns out to be true, plants that are currently phosphorus-limited in their growth might increase their phosphorous acquisition from soil organic supplies as the atmosphere's CO_2 concentration rises, and this phenomenon, in turn, may allow them to sequester even greater amounts of carbon from the air.

Other studies also have investigated plant bio-mass responses to atmospheric CO_2 enrichment under conditions of limiting phosphorus supply. Staddon *et al.* (1999), for example, found *Plantago lanceolata* and *Trifolium repens* effectively increased their phosphorus-use efficiency under elevated CO_2 conditions by reducing shoot phosphorus content as a component of CO_2-induced photosynthetic acclimation. Walker *et al.* (1998) found ponderosa pine seedlings grown for a year at atmospheric CO_2 concentrations of 525 and 700 ppm exhibited significantly greater root, shoot, and total dry weights than control plants grown at ambient CO_2, with little influence of a superimposed phosphorus treatment (low vs. high).

Niklaus *et al.* (1998) explored the effects of elevated CO_2, nitrogen, and phosphorus supply on calcareous grassland communities. At low phosphorus concentrations, biomass nitrogen contents were unaffected by elevated CO_2 (600 ppm), whereas at high phosphorus concentrations, community biomass-nitrogen increased by 28%, suggesting community biomass nitrogen will increase in the future if soil phosphorus contents are increased. A companion study of these grasslands published by Stocklin and Korner (1999) showed community total biomass (the actual dry weight of plant material, not the amount of nitrogen in the plant material) increased with atmospheric CO_2 enrichment even under low phosphorus concentrations, with or without nitrogen-fixing legumes present in the grassland swards.

Nguyen *et al.* (2006) grew seedlings of two N-fixing woody plants (*Acacia auriculiformis* Cunn. ex Benth and *Acacia mangium* Willd) well irrigated and fertilized—except for phosphorus (P), of which there were three treatments (low, medium, and high) composing 10, 50, and 100 mg P/liter of soil mixture—in growth chambers maintained at atmospheric CO_2 concentrations of either ambient or ambient + 800 ppm. They found plant biomass of *A. auriculiformis* was enhanced by 19%, 21%, and 57%, respectively, at high, medium, and low P. Biomass in *A. mangium* was enhanced by 5%, 32%, and 47%, respectively. Nguyen *et al.* also note, "in both species the increase in plant growth [caused] by elevated CO_2 was accompanied by increased P use efficiency," "increased N use efficiency[,] and total N accumulation." In addition, they write, "elevated CO_2 also increased P use efficiency for N_2 fixation." Consequently, under ambient CO_2, "plant growth and the amount of N fixed symbiotically in N_2-fixing seedlings decreased with the decrease of supplied P," but "this relationship did not occur under elevated CO_2," because "elevated CO_2 alleviated [the] low P-induced reduction in plant growth," mainly by "increasing the use efficiency of internal P for plant growth and N_2 fixation."

Nguyen *et al.* note in many parts of the world "*Acacia* species are grown for environmental protection and energy plantations on degraded soils," and their findings indicate these soils' low nutrient levels may not impede the growth of these important plants.

Khan *et al.* (2008) note the faster and more vigorous plant growth typically observed in CO_2-enriched air "has to be sustained by a sufficient nutrient supply," because "if increased biomass production is to continue, [nutrient] availability in the soil has to match increasing demand for major nutrients," such as nitrogen (N) and phosphorus (P), two of the elements "often considered to limit productivity in terrestrial ecosystems." Khan *et al.* set out to test this hypothesis as it pertains to phosphorus

at the EuroFACE facility near Viterbo in central Italy. They grew three genotypes of *Populus*—*P. alba, P nigra,* and *P. x euroamericana*—under ambient and elevated (ambient + 200 ppm) atmospheric CO_2 concentrations for five years.

The four UK researchers report "increased tree growth under elevated CO_2 has not resulted in the depletion of phosphorus pools in soils as originally hypothesized, but rather in the replenishment and increased storage of P in the rooting zone," and thus "P may not, therefore, limit tree growth in a high CO_2 world." Kahn *et al.* conclude "biogenically driven weathering of primary minerals in the rooting zone is sufficient to maintain the replenishment of plant available inorganic P," and "since future levels of elevated CO_2 may stimulate biomass production in a diverse range of forests (Norby *et al.*, 2005), this increase of P availability is of global consequence."

Kahn *et al.* (2010) report similar findings in the same EuroFACE experiment, writing, "the availability of P can actually increase in elevated CO_2, forming a positive feedback with increased biomass production on P limited soils." They conclude "phosphorus limitation may therefore not reduce tree growth in a high CO_2 world."

Plants growing in CO_2-enriched air likely will respond by increasing their biomass production, even under conditions of low soil phosphorus concentration, especially if plants have the ability to increase root phosphatase activity, as Barrett *et al.* (1998) observed regarding wheat.

References

Barrett, D.J., Richardson, A.E., and Gifford, R.M. 1998. Elevated atmospheric CO_2 concentrations increase wheat root phosphatase activity when growth is limited by phosphorus. *Australian Journal of Plant Physiology* **25**: 87–93.

Khan, F.N., Lukac, M., Miglietta, F., Khalid, M., and Godbold, D.L. 2010. Tree exposure to elevated CO_2 increases availability of soil phosphorus. *Pakistan Journal of Botany* **42**: 907–916.

Khan, F.N., Lukac, M., Turner, G., and Godbold, D.L. 2008. Elevated atmospheric CO_2 changes phosphorus fractions in soils under a short rotation poplar plantation (EuroFACE). *Soil Biology & Biochemistry* **40**: 1716–1723.

Nguyen, N.T., Mohapatra, P.K., and Fujita, K. 2006. Elevated CO_2 alleviates the effects of low P on the growth of N_2-fixing *Acacia auriculiformis* and *Acacia mangium*. *Plant and Soil* **285**: 369–379.

Niklaus, P.A., Leadley, P.W., Stocklin, J., and Korner, C. 1998. Nutrient relations in calcareous grassland under elevated CO_2. *Oecologia* **116**: 67–75.

Norby, R.J., DeLucia, E.H., Gielen, B., Calfapietra, C., Giardina, C.P., King J.S., Ledford, J., McCarthy, H.R., Moore, D.J.P., Ceulemans, R., Angelis, P.D., Finzi, A.C., Karnosky, D.F., Kubiske, M.E., Lukac, M., Pregitzer, K.S., Scarascia-Mugnozza, G.E., Schlesinger, W.H., and Oren, R. 2005. Forest response to elevated CO_2 is conserved across a broad range of productivity. *Proceedings of the National Academy of Sciences USA* **102**: 18,052–18,056.

Staddon, P.L., Fitter, A.H., and Graves, J.D. 1999. Effect of elevated atmospheric CO_2 on mycorrhizal colonization, external mycorrhizal hyphal production and phosphorus inflow in *Plantago lanceolata* and *Trifolium repens* in association with the arbuscular mycorrhizal fungus *Glomus mosseae*. *Global Change Biology* **5**: 347–358.

Stocklin, J. and Korner, Ch. 1999. Interactive effects of elevated CO_2, P availability and legume presence on calcareous grassland: results of a glasshouse experiment. *Functional Ecology* **13**: 200–209.

Walker, R.F., Johnson, D.W., Geisinger, D.R., and Ball, J.T. 1998. Growth and ectomycorrhizal colonization of ponderosa pine seedlings supplied different levels of atmospheric CO_2 and soil N and P. *Forest Ecology and Management* **109**: 9–20.

3.11 The Progressive Nitrogen Limitation Hypothesis

The progressive nitrogen limitation hypothesis suggests low concentrations of soil nitrogen will impede the productivity-enhancing and carbon-sequestering effects of rising atmospheric CO_2 concentrations over the long term. The following three sections explore this possibility as it pertains to Earth's grasslands, loblolly pine trees, and other types of vegetation.

3.11.1 Grasslands

• Real-world data from several multiyear experiments indicate CO_2-induced increases in carbon input to the soil stimulate microbial decomposition and thus lead to more available soil nitrogen, contrary to the progressive nitrogen limitation hypothesis.

Richter *et al.* (2003) measured gross rates of N mineralization, NH_4^+ consumption, and N immobil-ization in soils on which monocultures of *Lolium perenne* and *Trifolium repens* had been exposed to ambient (360 ppm) and elevated (600 ppm) concentrations of atmospheric CO_2 for seven years in the Swiss FACE study conducted near Zurich. After seven years of exposure to elevated CO_2, "gross mineralization, NH_4^+ consumption and N immobilization in both the *L. perenne* and the *T. repens* swards did not show significant differences," and the size of the microbial N pool and immob-ilization of applied mineral ^{15}N were not significantly affected by elevated CO_2. The five researchers conclude their observations "did not support the initial hypothesis," which was "that increased below-ground translocation of photoassimilates at elevated pCO_2 would lead to an increase in immobilization of N due to an excess supply of energy to the roots and rhizosphere" and would ultimately lead to a reduction in the size of the growth-promoting effect of elevated atmospheric CO_2.

After five years of exposure of a nutrient-poor low-productivity calcareous grassland in northwestern Switzerland to atmospheric CO_2 concentrations of 360 and 660 ppm via screen-aided CO_2 control or SACC technology (Leadley *et al.*, 1997), Thurig *et al.* (2003) measured the vegetative and reproductive responses of the plants comprising the ecosystem. They write, "the effect of elevated CO_2 on the number of flowering shoots (+24%, P < 0.01) and seeds (+29%, P = 0.06) at the community level was similar to [the] above ground biomass response." They also found a 42% (P < 0.01) increase in the mean seed number of graminoids and a 33% (P = 0.07) increase in the mean seed number of forbs, and in most species mean seed weight also tended to be greater (+12%, P < 0.01). Atmospheric CO_2 enrichment significantly increased both vegetative and reproductive biomass production. The researchers note many studies have shown heavier seeds result in seedlings that "are more robust than seedlings from lighter seeds (Baskin and Baskin, 1998)." Thus the continued rise of the air's CO_2 content would bode well for these and other nutrient-poor, low-productivity grasslands.

Reich *et al.* (2006) described the first six years' results of a FACE study of perennial grassland species conducted at the Cedar Creek Natural History Area in central Minnesota (USA). On natural ambient-N soil (where N limits growth) or natural soil receiving an extra 4 g N m^{-2} yr^{-1} (applied as NH_4NO_3), they planted 296 field plots to support the growth of either 1, 4, 9, or 16 grassland species (four C_3 grasses, four C_4 grasses, four N-fixing legumes, and four non-leguminous forbs). The plots were fumigated with either ambient air of ~370 ppm CO_2 or air enriched to a CO_2 concentration of 560 ppm throughout each year's growing season. The nine researchers conclude "low availability of N progressively suppresses the positive response of plant biomass to elevated CO_2."

Their data, however, do not support this conclusion. As best as can be determined from their graph of total plant biomass vs. time in their ambient-N plots (see Figure 3.11.1.1), the percent increase in plant biomass production induced by the extra ~190 ppm of CO_2 supplied to the CO_2-enriched plots progressed from 15% in year 1 to 16% in year 2, 13% in year 3, 0% in year 4, 8% in year 5, and 12% in year 6. Over the first three years of the study, it is difficult to claim there is any meaningful trend in the data, but in year 4 it is clear something happened, as the CO_2-induced growth stimulation dropped to zero. The CO_2-induced growth stimulation reappeared in year 5, rising from 0% to 8%, and it continued its upward climb in year 6, rising from 8% to 12%. The latter value is probably not significantly different from the 13% biomass stimulation recorded in year 3.

The behavior illustrated in Figure 3.11.1.1 is not a low-soil-N-induced "progressive limitation" of the aerial fertilization effect of elevated CO_2. The percent growth enhancement experienced in year 6 of Reich *et al.*'s study was essentially the same as that experienced in year 3, and the record ends with the aerial fertilization effect in a strong ascending mode. As for years 1 and 2, where the CO_2-induced growth stimulation was slightly higher, Reich *et al.* state, "the positive response to CO_2 enrichment observed under ambient N during the first two years of the experiment may also be more characteristic of seedlings or juvenile plants than of mature well-established plants." This phenomenon (initial large CO_2-induced growth stimulation in the juvenile plant stage which subsequently decreases with time) has been observed in a number of experiments, indicating just how risky it is to predict the course of the CO_2-induced aerial fertilization effect of atmospheric CO_2 enrichment on the basis of even multiple years of data.

These observations indicate there is no compelling reason to believe, as Reich *et al.* concluded, "low availability of N progressively suppresses the positive response of plant biomass to elevated CO_2." There is not even a weak reason for doing so, as their data depict no such phenomenon. And even if the trend they postulate were apparent, the long-term sour orange tree study of Idso and Kimball (2001; see section 1.1.3.2.3 Sour Orange, this volume) shows six years of data are simply not sufficient to predict the ultimate equilibrium response of a long-lived plant or ecosystem to a large step-increase in atmospheric CO_2 concentration in either N-limiting or non-N-limiting situations. In addition, in the real world of nature the air's CO_2 concentration rises gradually, by only a ppm or two per year, a much easier situation for plants to cope with than that employed in essentially all CO_2 enrichment experiments that have been conducted to date, where a CO_2 concentration increase fully two orders of magnitude greater than that experienced each year in nature is typically imposed on the plants being studied. Thus it is important to

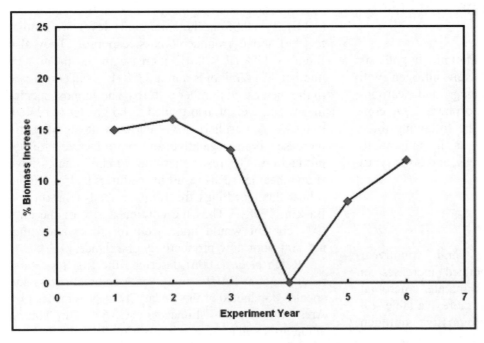

Figure 3.11.1.1. Percent increase in biomass production by the plants in the ambient-N soil plots of Reich *et al.* since the start of their long-term experiment, as a result of enriching the CO_2 concentration of the air above the plots by 190 ppm. Adapted from Reich *et al.* (2006)

conduct experiments for as long a period of time as possible—the answer is out there, but it could be far out there, several years in the future.

Zavaleta and Kettley (2006) studied an annual grassland at the Jasper Ridge Biological Preserve in the interior foothills of the central coast mountain range south of San Francisco, California (USA). They examined patterns of production, standing biomass, carbon and nitrogen storage, community composition, and soil moisture along a 25-year chronosequence of sites in various stages of invasion by the woody shrub *Baccharis pilularis*. They sought evidence for the hypothesis "*Baccharis*-invaded sites would experience increasing nitrogen limitation as nitrogen was immobilized in biomass and litter," and whether this phenomenon would preclude further increases in ecosystem biomass.

In progressing from initial grassland conditions to conditions that prevailed 25 years after shrub invasion began, the two researchers report, "net increases in biomass and tissue and soil C:N [carbon to nitrogen ratio] contributed to increases in total ecosystem carbon storage of over 125%." Even more stunning was their discovery the increases in ecosystem biomass "drove increases in ecosystem nitrogen sequestration of ~700%." In the soil alone, nitrogen content also "increased rapidly with shrub age," as the increase in soil nitrogen "was much larger than the increase in nitrogen immobilization in biomass and litter over time."

What was the source of the extra nitrogen? The two researchers mention several possibilities but say they could not be sure of them. Nevertheless, their observations repudiate the progressive nitrogen limitation hypothesis, making it clear a soil of low initial nitrogen status need not constrain long-term positive ecosystem responses to biomass-enhancing phenomena such as woody plant invasions and atmospheric CO_2 enrichment. Zavaleta and Kettley state, "while many climate models now incorporate the effects of short-term energy and resource exchanges between the atmosphere and the biosphere, most do not consider feedbacks associated with long-term vegetation changes." They also say their findings "illustrate the potential for important vegetation-mediated ecosystem responses and feedbacks to atmospheric CO_2 and climate change," while additionally noting many of the changes they observed "were progressive and did not saturate with time."

Drissner *et al.* (2007) measured soil microbial biomass and the activities of associated enzymes covering cycles of the most important elements (C, N, and P) for nine years in a FACE study conducted near Zurich, Switzerland, on three types of grassland (monocultures and mixed cultures of *Trifolium repens* L. and *Lolium perenne* L.) under two nitrogen treatments (low N = 14 g N m^{-2} year^{-1}; high N = 56 g N m^{-2} year^{-1}) and maintained at atmospheric CO_2 concentrations of either 350 or 600 ppm. They write, "the enrichment in CO_2 increased soil microbial biomass (+48.1%) as well as activities of invertase (+36.2%), xylanase (+22.9%), urease (+23.8%), protease (+40.2%) and alkaline phosphomonoesterase (+54.1%) in spring," and "in autumn, the stimulation of microbial biomass was 25% less and that of enzymes 3–12% less than in spring." All of these increases, the researchers write, "were most likely stimulated by increase in roots under enriched CO_2."

Drissner *et al.* report in their nine-year-long FACE experiment, "stimulation of enzyme activities in the enriched CO_2 indicated enhanced C, N and P cycling and greater availabilities of nutrients for microbial and plant growth." They conclude their results "support the hypothesis of positive feedback proposed by Zak *et al.* (1993), who stated that additional C stimulates microbial decomposition and thus leads to more available N under enriched CO_2." Their results and others thus contradict periodic claims that the future availability of nitrogen will be too low to support large CO_2-induced increases in plant growth over the long term.

References

Baskin, C.C. and Baskin, J.M. 1998. *Seeds: Ecology, Biogeography, and Evolution of Dormancy and Germination*. Academic Press, San Diego, CA.

Drissner, D., Blum, H., Tscherko, D., and Kandeler, E. 2007. Nine years of enriched CO_2 changes the function and structural diversity of soil microorganisms in a grassland. *European Journal of Soil Science* **58**: 260–269.

Hungate, B.A., Dukes, J.S., Shaw, M.R., Luo, Y., and Field, C.B. 2003. Nitrogen and climate change. *Science* **302**: 1512–1513.

Idso, S.B. and Kimball, B.A. 2001. CO_2 enrichment of sour orange trees: 13 years and counting. *Environmental and Experimental Botany* **46**: 147-153.

Leadley, P.W., Niklaus, P.A., and Stocker, R., *et al.* 1997. Screen-aided CO_2 control (SACC): a middle ground between FACE and open-top chambers. *Acta Oecologica* **18**: 39–49.

Luo, Y., Su, B., Currie, W.S., Dukes, J.S., Finzi, A., Hartwig, U., Hungate, B., McMurtrie, R.E., Oren, R., Parton, W.J., Pataki, D.E., Shaw, M.R., Zak, D.R., and Field, C.B. 2004. Progressive nitrogen limitation of ecosystem responses to rising atmospheric carbon dioxide. *BioScience* **54**: 731–739.

Reich, P.B., Hobbie, S.E., Lee, T., Ellsworth, D.S., West, J.B., Tilman, D., Knops, J.M.H., Naeem, S., and Trost, J. 2006. Nitrogen limitation constrains sustainability of ecosystem response to CO_2. *Nature* **440**: 922–925.

Richter, M., Hartwig, U.A., Frossard, E., Nosberger, J., and Cadisch, G. 2003. Gross fluxes of nitrogen in grassland soil exposed to elevated atmospheric pCO_2 for seven years. *Soil Biology & Biochemistry* **35**: 1325–1335.

Thurig, B., Korner, C., and Stocklin, J. 2003. Seed production and seed quality in a calcareous grassland in elevated CO_2. *Global Change Biology* **9**: 873–884.

Zak, D.R., Pregitzer, K.S., Curtis, P.S., Teeri, J.A., Fogel, R., and Randlett, D.L. 1993. Elevated atmospheric CO_2 and feedback between carbon and nitrogen cycles. *Plant and Soil* **151**: 105–117.

Zavaleta, E.S. and Kettley, L.S. 2006. Ecosystem change along a woody invasion chronosequence in a California grassland. *Journal of Arid Environments* **66**: 290–306.

3.11.2 Loblolly Pine

- Extensive experimentation on loblolly pine trees (plus several understory species) at the Duke Forest long-term free-air CO_2 enrichment (FACE) site has conclusively disproven the progressive nitrogen limitation hypothesis, instead suggesting the growth-enhancing benefits of atmospheric CO_2 enrichment should continue as the air's CO_2 content rises.

The progressive nitrogen limitation (PNL) hypothesis posits low concentrations of soil nitrogen will inhibit the productivity-enhancing effect of atmospheric CO_2 enrichment, meaning increases in plant growth and ecosystem carbon sequestration rates will not be sustained over long periods of time. In this section this possibility is explored as it pertains to loblolly pine (*Pinus taeda* L.) trees.

Finzi and Schlesinger (2003) measured and analyzed pool sizes and fluxes of inorganic and organic nitrogen in the forest floor and top 30 cm of mineral soil during the first five years of differential atmospheric CO_2 treatment of a stand of initially 13-year-old loblolly pine trees at the Duke Forest FACE facility in the Piedmont region of North Carolina (USA), where half of the experimental plots were maintained at an atmospheric CO_2 concentration approximately 200 ppm above ambient. The extra CO_2 significantly increased the input of carbon (C) and nitrogen (N) to the forest floor, as well as to the mineral soil in which the trees were growing. Finzi and Schlesinger report "there was no statistically significant change in the cycling rate of N derived from soil organic matter under elevated CO_2," and "neither the rate of net N mineralization nor gross $^{15}NH_4^+$ dynamics were significantly altered by elevated CO_2." They found "no statistically significant difference in the concentration or net flux of organic and inorganic N in the forest floor and top 30-cm of mineral soil after 5 years of CO_2 fumigation," adding, "microbial biomass was not a larger sink for N." Based on these findings, they rejected their original hypothesis, which was essentially the PNL hypothesis: that the extra CO_2 provided to the experimental plots would significantly increase the rate of nitrogen immobilization by the soil microbial communities found in the CO_2-enriched FACE arrays and thereby lead to a reduction in the magnitude of the growth stimulation initially manifest in the CO_2-enriched treatment.

Schafer *et al.* (2003) measured net ecosystem exchange (NEE) and net ecosystem production (NEP) at the Duke Forest FACE facility during the third and fourth years of the long-term CO_2 enrichment study conducted there. They found the extra 200 ppm of CO_2 supplied to the loblolly pine trees in the CO_2-enriched FACE arrays increased the entire canopy's net uptake of CO_2 (NEE) by 41%, and canopy NEP was increased by 44%. They note 87% of the extra NEP "was sequestered in a moderately long-term C pool in wood." This large increase in solidly sequestered carbon is remarkable, especially given that, as noted by Finzi and Schlesinger (2003), the soil at the Duke Forest FACE site at that time was in "a state of acute nutrient deficiency that can only be reversed with fertilization," which was not provided.

Finzi *et al.* (2006) again tested the PNL concept "using data on the pools and fluxes of C and N in tree biomass, microbes and soils" obtained from the first six years of the Duke Forest FACE study. As was the case three years earlier, "there was no reduction in the average stimulation of net primary production by elevated CO_2," even though "significantly more N was immobilized in tree biomass and in the O [soil] horizon under elevated CO_2." Also, and "in contrast to the PNL hypothesis," they write, "microbial-N immobilization did not increase under elevated CO_2, and although the rate of net N mineralization declined through time, the decline was not significantly more rapid under elevated CO_2." The 12 researchers also report, "mass balance calculations demonstrated a large accrual of ecosystem N capital," and the rate of the extra N accrual was "much greater than the estimated rate of N input via atmospheric deposition or heterotrophic N fixation." Noting "there are no plant species capable of symbiotic N fixation in this ecosystem," they say some other mechanism enabled the loblolly pine trees to obtain the extra N they needed to stave off the negative effects predicted by the PNL hypothesis; possibly, Finzi *et al.* write, by roots "actively taking up N and redistributing N from deeper in the soil profile."

Moore *et al.* (2006) report finding "a sustained increase in basal area increment over the first 8 years of [their] experiment," which varied between 13 and 27% in harmony with variations in weather and the timing of growth. They also report, "there was no evidence of a decline in the relative enhancement of tree growth by elevated CO_2 as might be expected if soil nutrients were becoming progressively more limiting," which normally would be expected, considering the unfertilized state of the soil in which the experiment was conducted.

Pritchard *et al.* (2008a) published the results they obtained from minirhizotrons employed to characterize the influence of the extra 200 ppm of CO_2 on the fine roots of the Duke Forest loblolly pines over the six-year period 1998–2004. Averaged over all six years, they found the extra CO_2 increased average fine-root standing crop by 23%, which compared well with the overall stimulation of tree net primary productivity of 18–24% observed over the period 1996–2002. They noted "the positive effects of CO_2 enrichment on fine root growth persisted 6 years following minirhizotron tube installation (8 years following initiation of the CO_2 fumigation)," finding no evidence of progressive nitrogen limitation to the stimulatory effect of atmospheric CO_2 enrichment. As a possible explanation for their findings, Pritchard *et al.* point out the distal tips of fine roots are "the primary site for initiation of mycorrhizal partnerships which are critical for resource acquisition and could also influence whether or not forests can sustain higher productivity in a CO_2-enriched world."

Pritchard *et al.* (2008b) focused their attention on the role played by ectomycorrhizal (ECM) fungi over five years, based on minirhizotron observations of fungal dynamics at the Duke Forest FACE site.

Summed across all years of the study, the five researchers found the extra 200 ppm of CO_2 provided to the trees in the high-CO_2 treatment did not influence mycorrhizal production in the top 15 cm of the forest soil, but it increased mycorrhizal root-tip production by 194% throughout the 15–30 cm depth interval. Production of soil rhizomorph length was 27% greater in the CO_2-enriched plots than in the ambient-air plots.

Pritchard *et al.* state the CO_2-induced "stimulation of carbon flow into soil has increased the intensity of root and fungal foraging for nutrients," and "the shift in distribution of mycorrhizal fungi to deeper soils may enable perennial plant systems to acquire additional soil nitrogen to balance the increased availability of ecosystem carbohydrates in CO_2-enriched atmospheres." This additional acquisition of nitrogen in the CO_2-enriched plots of the Duke Forest FACE study was determined to be approximately 12 g N per m^2 per year.

Pritchard *et al.* also write, "the notion that CO_2 enrichment expands the volume of soil effectively explored by roots and fungi, and that foraging in a given volume of soil also seems to intensify, provides compelling evidence to indicate that CO_2 enrichment has the potential to stimulate productivity (and carbon sequestration) in N-limited ecosystems more than previously expected." While they also speculate "it is unlikely that ecosystem productivity will be stimulated by CO_2 enrichment indefinitely," nature had to this point in time proven such speculations invalid.

Summarizing their nine years of work at the Duke Forest FACE facility, Lichter *et al.* (2008) once again warn progressive nitrogen limitation may "accompany carbon sequestration in plants and soils stimulated by CO_2 fertilization, gradually attenuating the CO_2 response." They describe what they had learned about the PNL hypothesis over the prior nine years.

The nine scientists first note their data pertaining to forest-floor carbon pools indicate the existence of "a long-term steady-state sink" of about 30 g C per m^2 per year, which represents, they write, "a substantial increase in forest-floor C storage under elevated CO_2 (i.e. 29%)," which they attribute to "increased litter-fall and root turnover during the first 9 years of the study." Second, below the forest floor, they say, "approximately 20% [of the mineral soil carbon formed during the prior nine years] has been allocated to stable pools that will likely remain protected from microbial activity and associated release as CO_2."

A third important finding was "a significant

widening of the C/N ratio of soil organic matter in the upper mineral soil under both elevated and ambient CO_2," which suggests, as they describe it, "enhanced rates of soil organic matter decomposition are increasing mineralization and uptake to provide the extra N required to support the observed increase in primary productivity under elevated CO_2." And at the Duke Forest FACE site, Pritchard *et al.* (2008b) say this CO_2-induced increase in productivity amounted to approximately 30% annually, adding there is "little evidence to indicate a diminished response through time." They cite Finzi *et al.* (2007), who found the same to be true at the long-term forest FACE studies at Rhinelander, Wisconsin (USA), Oak Ridge National Laboratory (USA), and Tuscania (Italy).

Contrary to the early expectations of many scientists, many forests thought to have had access to less-than-adequate soil nitrogen supplies appear to be able to acquire the extra nitrogen they need to maintain the sizable increases in their growth rates driven by elevated concentrations of atmospheric CO_2. In North Carolina's Duke Forest, for example, "even after nine years of experimental CO_2 fertilization," as Lichter *et al.* (2008) note, "attenuation of the CO_2-induced productivity enhancement has not been observed," as Finzi *et al.* (2006) also found. This finding at this location is extremely significant because the growth of pine-hardwood forests in the southeastern United States often removes so much nitrogen from the soil they induce what Finzi and Schlesinger (2003) describe as "a state of acute nutrient deficiency that can only be reversed with fertilization," which, as noted earlier in this section, was not employed at the Duke Forest FACE study.

Jackson *et al.* (2009) describe new belowground data they obtained at the Duke Forest Face site, then present a synthesis of these and other results obtained from 1996 through 2008 to determine which variables may have shown a decrease in their response to atmospheric CO_2 enrichment during that period. Among many other things, they found, "on average, in elevated CO_2, fine-root biomass in the top 15 cm of soil increased by 24%," and in recent years the fine-root biomass increase "grew stronger, averaging ~30% at high CO_2." Regarding coarse roots with diameters greater than 2 mm and extending to a soil depth of 32 cm, they report, biomass sampled in 2008 was "twice as great in elevated CO_2." The graphical representation of their results indicates the coarse-root biomass was 130% greater, quite extraordinary given that the extra 200 ppm of CO_2 supplied to the air

surrounding the CO_2-enriched trees represented an enhancement of only about 55% above ambient conditions. They conclude, "overall, the effect of elevated CO_2 belowground shows no sign of diminishing."

The four researchers also remark, "if progressive nitrogen limitation were occurring in this system, we would expect differences in productivity to diminish for trees in the elevated vs. ambient CO_2 plots," but "there is little evidence from estimates of aboveground or total net primary productivity in the replicated Duke experiment that progressive nitrogen limitation is occurring there or at other forest FACE experiments," citing Finzi *et al.* (2007).

McCarthy *et al.* (2010) analyzed data from the Duke Forest FACE experiment for the years 1996–2004, calculating the net primary productivity (NPP) of the entire ecosystem—including the loblolly pines' understory of various broadleaf species (*Liriodendron tulipifera, Liquidambar styraciflua, Acer rubrum, Ulmus alata, Cornus florida*) plus various other trees, shrubs, and vines—as "the sum of the production of coarse wood (stems, branches, coarse roots), leaf litter (lagged for pines), fine roots and reproductive structures."

They report "elevated CO_2 increased pine biomass production, starting in 1997 and continuing every year thereafter"; "the CO_2-induced enhancement remained fairly consistent as the stand developed"; and "elevated CO_2 increased stand (pine plus all other species) biomass production every year from 1997 onwards with no trend over time." They also noted the average yearly increase in NPP caused by the approximate 54% increase in the air's CO_2 content was 28%. In contradiction of the PNL hypothesis, the trees, bushes, and shrubs constituting the Duke Forest has continued to maintain the extra CO_2-enabled vitality it exhibited from the start of the study, with no subsequent sign of it tapering off.

Drake *et al.* (2011) described how the CO_2-induced enhanced rates of net primary production at the Duke Forest FACE site likely were sustained by a carbon cascade through the root-microbe-soil system. They write, "increases in the flux of carbon belowground under elevated CO_2 stimulated microbial activity" that in turn "accelerated the rate of soil organic matter decomposition and stimulated tree uptake of nitrogen bound to this soil organic matter." This process "set into motion a positive feedback maintaining greater carbon gain under elevated CO_2 as a result of increases in canopy nitrogen content and higher photosynthetic nitrogen-use efficiency," the consequence of which was "the dominance of carbon storage in tree biomass."

Drake *et al.* write, "the long-term increase in forest productivity under elevated CO_2 at the Duke FACE site appears to be maintained by a belowground exchange of tree carbon for soil nitrogen, with the quantity of carbon allocated belowground set by the availability of nitrogen in the soil and the demand for nitrogen to meet growth requirements." They note, "all of the belowground carbon fluxes thought to increase decomposition rates increased under elevated CO_2, including root production and mortality (Pritchard *et al.*, 2008a), root exudation (Phillips *et al.*, 2011), fungal rhizomorph production (Pritchard *et al.*, 2008b) and allocation of carbon to mycorrhizal fungi (Garcia *et al.*, 2008)." They conclude, "the preponderance of the evidence points to increased decomposition [of organic matter] in surface soils as the primary source of additional nitrogen taken up by the trees growing under elevated CO_2."

Phillips *et al.* (2011) opine "increased root exploration alone is unlikely to sustain plant nitrogen requirements under rising CO_2 unless accompanied by the concomitant stimulation of soil microbial activity and the release of nutrients from soil organic matter." Despite the presumed importance of root exudates in this scenario, they note no studies had yet quantified the effects of CO_2 enrichment on exudation by mature trees. They set out to do so in order to understand why progressive nitrogen limitation was not observed in some long-term studies of trees growing on nutrient-poor soil (Langley *et al.*, 2009; McCarthy *et al.*, 2010). Working at the Duke Forest FACE facility, the three researchers examined plant-microbe interactions in the rhizospheres and bulk soils of the various treatments, measuring differences in rhizosphere microbial activity and root exudation rates.

On an annual basis, Phillips *et al.* state, "exudation increased by *c.* 50% for trees enriched with CO_2 in non-fertilized plots," but trees were unaffected in this manner by CO_2 enrichment in fertilized plots, demonstrating "increased root carbon efflux from CO_2-enriched trees stimulates rhizosphere N cycling in low fertility soils." Their work provides additional evidence that "rhizosphere microbes such as actinomycetes, which produce NAGase enzymes and respond strongly to CO_2 at this site (Billings and Ziegler, 2008), are using energy derived from exudates to synthesize enzymes that release nitrogen from soil organic matter (Cheng and Kuzyakov,

2005)." They emphasize "this dramatic contrast between the fertilized and unfertilized treatments provides evidence that enhanced exudation is a mechanism trees employ for increasing nitrogen availability."

Phillips *et al.* write "the enhanced carbon flux from roots to soil in low fertility forests exposed to elevated CO_2 creates hotspots for microbial activity that are associated with faster rates of soil organic matter turnover and N cycling." This phenomenon provides the trees the extra nitrogen they need to take full advantage of the enhanced potential for growth provided by atmospheric CO_2 enrichment, contrary to the incorrect implications of the progressive nitrogen limitation hypothesis. Phillips *et al.* state their results "provide field-based empirical support suggesting that sustained growth responses of forests to elevated CO_2 in low fertility soils are maintained by enhanced rates of microbial activity and N cycling fueled by inputs of root-derived carbon."

Hofmockel *et al.* (2011) write, "several free-air CO_2 enrichment (FACE) experiments in North America have shown a continual stimulation in forest productivity under elevated CO_2 over time scales nearly reaching a decade (Finzi *et al.*, 2006; Norby and Iversen, 2006; Zak *et al.*, 2007; McCarthy *et al.*, 2010)." In their own examination of the effects of elevated CO_2 on nitrogen (N) cycling in the Duke Forest, where elevated atmospheric CO_2 concentrations "consistently stimulated forest productivity" throughout the decade-long experiment being conducted there, Hofmockel *et al.* provide "an integrated understanding" of this phenomenon that serves as "a basis for inferring how C and N cycling in this forest may respond to elevated CO_2 beyond the decadal time scale."

"Using natural-abundance measures of nitrogen isotopes together with an ecosystem-scale ^{15}N tracer experiment," as the six scientists describe it, they "quantified the cycling of ^{15}N in plant and soil pools under ambient and elevated CO_2 over three growing seasons to determine how elevated CO_2 changed nitrogen cycling between plants, soil and microorganisms," after having first measured natural abundances of ^{15}N in plant and soil pools in the two CO_2 treatments over the prior year. They discovered "at the Duke FACE site, the rate at which N is being sequestered in plant biomass is greater than the rate of atmospheric deposition and heterotrophic N fixation," a finding also established by Finzi *et al.* (2002), Hofmockel and Schlesinger (2007), and Sparks *et al.* (2008). These findings suggest, they write, "soil organic matter decomposition supplies a significant fraction of plant N in both ambient and elevated-CO_2 conditions, but that this is greater under elevated CO_2."

Hofmockel *et al.* conclude, "in pine forests of the southeastern United States, rising CO_2 may elicit shifts in the mechanisms by which plants acquire nitrogen, allowing a sustained increase in net primary productivity for decades," further stating, "increased mineralization of nitrogen in the organic and 0–15 cm mineral horizon and deeper rooting are likely sustaining the elevated CO_2 enhancement of net primary productivity."

Ellsworth *et al.* (2012) "compiled a comprehensive dataset measured over ten years for a temperate pine forest of *Pinus taeda*, but also including deciduous species, primarily *Liquidambar styraciflua*," derived from "over one thousand controlled-response curves of photosynthesis as a function of environmental drivers (light, atmospheric CO_2 concentration [Ca] and temperature) measured at canopy heights up to 20 meters over eleven years (1996–2006)." From that data they generated "parameterizations for leaf-scale models for the Duke free-air CO_2 enrichment (FACE) experiment."

They found the enhancement of light-saturated leaf net photosynthesis (Anet) in *P. taeda* trees produced by an elevated Ca of +200 ppm was 67% for current-year needles in the upper crown of the trees in summer conditions over the 10-year period, and previous-year foliage Anet was enhanced by 30%. They note "the mean stimulation in light-saturated Anet averaged over the growing season of all years and across canopy positions and needle age classes was 53 ± 7%." In addition, "the photosynthetic enhancement responses to elevated Ca are mirrored in part by the pine biomass accumulation responses to elevated Ca across different years."

The eight researchers also report "co-dominant and sub-canopy *L. styraciflua* trees showed Anet enhancement of 62%," and "various understory deciduous tree species showed an average Anet enhancement of 42%." In addition, "the photosynthetic responses of shaded, understory leaves suggest a capacity to increase photosynthetic carbon capture in elevated Ca in shade-grown plants when measured in sunflecks," citing DeLucia and Thomas (2000). They note this response suggests "a competitive advantage to shade-tolerant species adapted for carbon capture in high sunlight or sunflecks in the understory over less shade-tolerant species."

This comprehensive set of photosynthesis measurements compiled over the course of the Duke Forest FACE study rebuts the progressive nitrogen limitation hypothesis, which posits the initial growth stimulation of atmospheric CO_2 enrichment will dwindle away as time progresses, especially in the case of the pine-hardwood forests of the southeastern United States, which often remove so much nitrogen from the soils in which they grow as to induce what Finzi and Schlesinger (2003) once described as "a state of acute nutrient deficiency that can only be reversed with fertilization." Ellsworth *et al.*'s work demonstrates this is simply not true. In another implication of their findings, the eight researchers conclude the observed "differences in photosynthetic responses between the over-story pines and deciduous tree sub-canopy suggest that increased Ca may have the potential to enhance the mixed-species composition of planted pine stands," and, by extension, "naturally regenerating pine-dominated stands."

Rounding out this review of the progressive nitrogen limitation hypothesis are Phillips *et al.* (2012), who write, "after nearly two decades of research on forest ecosystem responses to global change, uncertainty about the role of roots and rhizosphere processes in soil C and N retention and loss has limited our ability to predict biogeochemical feedbacks to long-term forest productivity." Working at the Duke Forest FACE site, where eight 30-meter-diameter plots of loblolly pine (*Pinus taeda* L.) trees were enriched with an extra 200 ppm of CO_2 from 1996 to 2010, and four similar plots were maintained under then-current ambient-air conditions, Phillips *et al.* measured root-induced changes in soil C dynamics of trees exposed to CO_2 and nitrogen enrichment by combining stable isotope analyses, molecular characterizations of soil organic matter, and microbial assays.

The six scientists conclude the CO_2-enriched trees "may be both enhancing the availability of N by stimulating microbial decomposition of soil organic matter via priming and increasing the rate at which N cycles through the microbial pools owing to the rapid turnover of N-rich fungal tissues," noting "the accelerated turnover of hyphal tissues under elevated CO_2 may represent an important source of N to plants and microbes." Referring to this CO_2-induced phenomenon as the Rhizo-Accelerated Mineralization and Priming, or RAMP, hypothesis, Phillips *et al.* suggest it may have "important consequences for N availability and forest productivity," which could be expected to sustain CO_2-enhanced tree growth over their lifetimes.

References

Billings, S.A. and Ziegler, S.E. 2008. Altered patterns of soil carbon substrate usage and heterotrophic respiration in a pine forest with elevated CO_2 and N fertilization. *Global Change Biology* 14: 1025–1036.

Cheng, W. and Kuzyakov, Y. 2005. Root effects on soil organic matter decomposition. In: Zobel, R. and Wright, S. (Eds.) *Roots and Soil Management: Interactions Between Roots and the Soil.* American Society of Agronomy, Crop Science Society of America, Soil Science Society of America, Madison, Wisconsin, USA, pp. 119–143.

DeLucia, E.H. and Thomas, R.B. 2000. Photosynthetic responses to CO_2 enrichment of four hardwood species in a forest understory. *Oecologia* 122: 11–19.

Drake, J.E., Gallet-Budynek, A., Hofmockel, K.S., Bernhardt, E.S., Billings, S.A., Jackson, R.B., Johnsen, K.S., Lichter, J., McCarthy, H.R., McCormack, M.L., Moore, D.J.P., Oren, R., Palmroth, S., Phillips, R.P., Pippen, J.S., Pritchard, S.G., Treseder, K.K., Schlesinger, W.H., DeLucia, E.H., and Finzi, A.C. 2011. Increases in the flux of carbon belowground stimulate nitrogen uptake and sustain the long-term enhancement of forest productivity under elevated CO_2. *Ecology Letters* 14: 349–357.

Ellsworth, D.S., Thomas, R., Crous, K.Y., Palmroth, S., Ward, E., Maier, C., DeLucia, E., and Oren, R. 2012. Elevated CO_2 affects photosynthetic responses in canopy pine and subcanopy deciduous trees over 10 years: a synthesis from Duke FACE. *Global Change Biology* 18: 223–242.

Finzi, A.C., Delucia, E.H., Hamilton, J.G., Richter, D.D., and Schlesinger, W.H. 2002. The nitrogen budget of a pine forest under free air CO_2 enrichment. *Oecologia* 132: 567–578.

Finzi, A.C., Moore, D.J.P., DeLucia, E.H., Lichter, J., Hofmockel, K.S., Jackson, R.B., Kim, H.-S., Matamala, R., McCarthy, H.R., Oren, R., Pippen, J.S., and Schlesinger, W.H. 2006. Progressive nitrogen limitation of ecosystem processes under elevated CO_2 in a warm-temperate forest. *Ecology* 87: 15–25.

Finzi, A.C., Norby, R.J., Calfapietra, C., Gallet-Budynek, A., Gielen, B., Holmes, W.E., Hoosbeek, M.R., Iversen, C.M., Jackson, R.B., Kubiske, M.E., Ledford, J., Liberloo, M., Oren, R., Polle, A., Pritchard, S., Zak, D.R., Schlesinger, W.H., and Ceulemans, R. 2007. Increases in nitrogen uptake rather than nitrogen-use efficiency support higher rates of temperate forest productivity under elevated CO_2. *Proceedings of the National Academy of Sciences, USA* 104: 14,014–14,019.

Finzi, A.C. and Schlesinger, W.H. 2003. Soil-nitrogen cycling in a pine forest exposed to 5 years of elevated carbon dioxide. *Ecosystems* 6: 444–456.

Garcia, M.O., Ovaspyan, T., Greas, M., and Treseder, K.K. 2008. Mycorrhizal dynamics under elevated CO_2 and nitrogen fertilization in a warm temperate forest. *Plant and Soil* 303: 301–310.

Hofmockel, K.S., Gallet-Budynek, A., McCarthy, H.R., Currie, W.S., Jackson, R.B., and Finzi, A. 2011. Sources of increased N uptake in forest trees growing under elevated CO_2: results of a large-scale ^{15}N study. *Global Change Biology* 17: 3338–3350.

Hungate, B.A., Dukes, J.S., Shaw, M.R., Luo, Y., and Field, C.B. 2003. Nitrogen and climate change. *Science* 302: 1512–1513.

Jackson, R.B., Cook, C.W., Pippen, J.S., and Palmer, S.M. 2009. Increased belowground biomass and soil CO_2 fluxes after a decade of carbon dioxide enrichment in a warm-temperate forest. *Ecology* 90: 3352–3366.

Langley, J.A., McKinley, D.C., Wolf, A.A., Hungate, B.A., Drake, B.G., and Megonigal, J.P. 2009. Priming depletes soil carbon and releases nitrogen in a scrub-oak ecosystem exposed to elevated CO_2. *Soil Biology and Biochemistry* 41: 54–60.

Lichter, J., Billings, S.A., Ziegler, S.E., Gaindh, D., Ryals, R., Finzi, A.C., Jackson, R.B., Stemmler, E.A., and Schlesinger, W.H. 2008. Soil carbon sequestration in a pine forest after 9 years of atmospheric CO_2 enrichment. *Global Change Biology* 14: 2910–2922.

McCarthy, H.R., Oren, R., Johnsen, K.H., Gallet-Budynek, A., Pritchard, S.G., Cook, C.W., LaDeau, S.L., Jackson, R.B., and Finzi, A.C. 2010. Re-assessment of plant carbon dynamics at the Duke free-air CO_2 enrichment site: interactions of atmospheric [CO_2] with nitrogen and water availability over stand development. *New Phytologist* 185: 514–528.

Moore, D.J.P., Aref, S., Ho, R.M., Pippen, J.S., Hamilton, J.G., and De Lucia, E.H. 2006. Annual basal area increment and growth duration of *Pinus taeda* in response to eight years of free-air carbon dioxide enrichment. *Global Change Biology* 12: 1367–1377.

Norby, R.J. and Iversen, C.M. 2006. Nitrogen uptake, distribution, turnover, and efficiency of use in a CO_2-enriched sweetgum forest. *Ecology* 87: 5–14.

Phillips, R.P., Finzi, A.C., and Bernhardt, E.S. 2011. Enhanced root exudation induces microbial feedbacks to N cycling in a pine forest under long-term CO_2 fumigation. *Ecology Letters* 14: 187–194.

Phillips, R.P., Meier, I.C., Bernhardt, E.S., Grandy, A.S., Wickings, K., and Finzi, A.C. 2012. Roots and fungi accelerate carbon and nitrogen cycling in forests exposed to elevated CO_2. *Ecology Letters* 15: 1042–1049.

Pritchard, S.G., Strand, A.E., McCormack, M.L., Davis, M.A., Finzi, A.C., Jackson, R.B., Matamala, R., Rogers, H.H., and Oren, R. 2008a. Fine root dynamics in a loblolly pine forest are influenced by free-air-CO_2-enrichment: a six-year-minirhizotron study. *Global Change Biology* **14**: 588–602.

Pritchard, S.G., Strand, A.E., McCormack, M.L., Davis, M.A., and Oren, R. 2008b. Mycorrhizal and rhizomorph dynamics in a loblolly pine forest during 5 years of free-air-CO_2-enrichment. *Global Change Biology* **14**: 1–13.

Schafer, K.V.R., Oren, R., Ellsworth, D.S., Lai, C.-T., Herrick, J.D., Finzi, A.C., Richter, D.D., and Katul, G.G. 2003. Exposure to an enriched CO_2 atmosphere alters carbon assimilation and allocation in a pine forest ecosystem. *Global Change Biology* **9**: 1378–1400.

Sparks, J.P., Walker, J., Turnipseed, A., and Guenther, A. 2008. Dry nitrogen deposition estimates over a forest experiencing free air CO_2 enrichment. *Global Change Biology* **14**: 768–781

Zak, D.R., Holmes, W.E., and Pregitzer, K.S. 2007. Atmospheric CO_2 and O_3 alter the flow of N-15 in developing forest ecosystems. *Ecology* **88**: 2630–2639.

3.11.3 Other Plants

- Although the progressive nitrogen limitation hypothesis initially was embraced by many scientists, a vast array of observational data has subsequently shown it dos not explain changes in real ecosystems.

The progressive nitrogen limitation (PNL) hypothesis—which contends low concentrations of soil nitrogen will gradually inhibit the aerial fertilization effect of atmospheric CO_2 enrichment—had its origins in the writings of Hungate *et al.* (2003) and Luo *et al.* (2004). Interestingly, the first of these papers contains considerable evidence that argues against its authors' contentions, as does a subsequent publication (Luo *et al.*, 2006), the senior author of which was also senior author of the second paper.

Hungate *et al.* (2003) report the C:N ratio of tree biomass increases with increases in the air's CO_2 concentration, citing Hungate (1999) and Rastetter *et al.* (1992). This indicates increasing amounts of carbon can be stored in tree tissues per unit of nitrogen stored therein as the air's CO_2 content rises; as Hungate and his coauthors state, "soil C:N could also increase with rising atmospheric CO_2 concentration, allowing soil carbon accumulation without additional nitrogen."

Lou *et al.* (2006) conducted a meta-analysis of various C and N processes in plants and soils in response to atmospheric CO_2 enrichment based on experimentally derived data contained in 104 scientific publications. In response to atmospheric CO_2 enrichment, the carbon and nitrogen contents in all the plant and soil pools studied significantly increased, "leading to more net C and N accumulations in ecosystems at elevated than ambient CO_2." They found the mean CO_2-induced increases in C pools of shoot, root, whole plant, litter, and soil were 22.4%, 31.6%, 23.0%, 20.6%, and 5.6%, respectively, and the corresponding CO_2-induced increases in N pools were 4.6%, 10.0%, 10.2%, 25.4%, and 11.2%. In addition, "N accumulations in ecosystems have long been documented in association with C accumulations during both primary and secondary successions (Crocker and Major, 1955; Binkley *et al.*, 2000; Vitousek, 2004)." They conclude, "the net C and N accumulations revealed in this study," which were produced by atmospheric CO_2 enrichment, "together with studies of C and N dynamics during succession over hundreds to millions of years, suggest that ecosystems may have intrinsic capabilities to stimulate N accumulation by C input," which is typically increased by atmospheric CO_2 enrichment. They further conclude "net N accumulation likely supports long-term C sequestration in response to rising atmospheric CO_2 concentration." They state "concomitant increases in C and N contents in plant and soil pools at elevated CO_2 as shown in this study point toward a long-term trend of terrestrial C sequestration in response to rising atmospheric CO_2 concentration," just the opposite of what the PNL hypothesis predicts.

Norby and Iverson (2006) reviewed what they had learned about the PNL hypothesis from "a six-year record of N dynamics of a sweetgum (*Liquidambar styraciflua*) stand exposed to elevated CO_2 in the free-air CO_2 enrichment (FACE) experiment at Oak Ridge, Tennessee, USA," focusing on N uptake, content, distribution, turnover, and N-use efficiency. They write, "net primary productivity in this stand has been significantly higher in CO_2-enriched plots, and the response has been sustained through time, thereby meeting one of the criteria for the development of PNL." They further report, "none of the measured responses of plant N dynamics in this ecosystem indicated the occurrence of PNL."

Hungate *et al.* (2006) tested the PNL hypothesis against what they had observed over seven years in an open-top chamber study of a scrub oak woodland dominated by *Quercus myrtifolia, Q. geminate,* and *Q. chapmanii* on an island in NASA's Kennedy Space Center on the coast of central Florida (USA). Their experiment commenced just a few months after a complete burning of the ecosystem located on well-drained but nutrient-poor soil. They report "litterfall production (one measure of aboveground primary productivity) increased initially in response to elevated CO_2, but the CO_2 stimulation declined during years five through seven, concurrent with the accumulation of N in the O [soil] horizon and the apparent restriction of plant N availability." They state these changes in N cycling were "likely to reduce the response of plant production to elevated CO_2." However, they acknowledge, "at the level of aboveground plant biomass (estimated by allometry), progressive N limitation was less apparent." In fact, there was a persistent CO_2-induced increase in aboveground plant carbon, which led them to conclude "some mechanisms are partially alleviating progressive N limitation," as Finzi *et al.* (2006) also concluded in their study of loblolly pines, where by some unknown means the pines obtained the extra nitrogen they needed.

Idso and Kimball (2001) also observed a large initial CO_2-induced increase in aboveground biomass production, followed by a rapid but slowing decline in this parameter, in their long-term sour orange tree study. Because the trees of their experiment were periodically fertilized so as never to lack nitrogen, the similar productivity vs. time pattern Hungate *et al.* observed may have had nothing to do with "restriction of plant N availability," which they characterized as being merely "apparent." It is also important to note the slow decline in the CO_2-induced growth stimulation of the sour orange trees came to a halt at the ten-year point of the experiment, when the declining growth stimulation finally leveled out at an essentially constant value that was maintained to the end of the 17-year study—a 69% increase in yearly total biomass production in response to a 75% increase in the air's CO_2 content (Kimball *et al.*, 2007).

Consequently, as Norby and Iverson (2006) and Finzi *et al.* (2006) both found, the pattern of CO_2-induced growth stimulation in the scrub oak ecosystem Hungate *et al.* studied provides no evidence for the PNL hypothesis. In fact, it and others of their observations point to one or more unknown means of ecosystem N acquisition that allow the aerial fertilization effect of atmospheric CO_2

enrichment to continue, albeit at a level of impact lower than its peak manifestation, even with "apparent" N limitations.

Johnson *et al.* (2006) studied the effects of elevated CO_2 (ambient, +175, +350 ppm) and N fertilization (unfertilized, +100, +200 kg N ha^{-1} yr^{-1}, provided as ammonium sulfate) on C and N accumulations in the biomass of ponderosa pines (*Pinus ponderosa* Laws, grown from seed) and the soils that supported them, in a six-year open-top chamber experiment conducted near Placerville, California (USA). This study, like several others according to Johnson *et al.*, "showed that growth response to elevated CO_2 more than offset declines in tissue N concentrations, necessitating increased N uptake by trees," which led them to ask, "How did the trees manage to obtain this 'extra' N in an N-limited environment?"

In the fertilized treatments, the four researchers suggest, the extra N could readily have been supplied by the added fertilizer, but in the unfertilized treatments they opine a substantial amount of the N uptake "probably came from the soil," as both wet and dry deposition were not great enough to have supplied all of the extra N, and "no symbiotic N fixer was present in the study plots." Citing other investigators' results as supplying circumstantial evidence for what they finally concluded, they write, "the additional N needed to respond to elevated CO_2 came from the soil and was facilitated by greater root exploration under elevated CO_2." Acknowledging they could not "provide an accurate prediction from the results of this study," Johnson *et al.* nevertheless state they could "see no evidence that either growth or additional N uptake at the +350 ppm CO_2 level are being inhibited by PNL as of year 6 in this study."

Studying the same trees, Phillips *et al.* (2006) collected video images every two months of roots growing against the surfaces of three minirhizotron tubes installed in each chamber. Yearly values of fine-root standing crop, production, and mortality were consistently higher in the elevated CO_2 treatments throughout the study, and they write, "in this same study, Johnson *et al.* (2000) found that elevated CO_2 increased fine-root life span." Because elevated CO_2 also increased fine-root length, Phillips *et al.* note, "the amount of root length dying per year was actually greater." Therefore, they write, "the higher rates of mortality in absolute terms for elevated CO_2 are driven by increased standing crop and not reduced life spans." In addition, they report Tingey *et al.* (2005) found "in the elevated CO_2

treatments, fine roots explored the soil more extensively and deeper, and filled in the explored areas more intensively." With respect to the PNL hypothesis, therefore, Phillips *et al.* state "the increased fine-root length reported here explains how additional N was provided to support the increased whole plant growth in elevated CO_2 treatments, and corresponds with the increased extent and intensity of the root system architecture discussed by Tingey *et al.* (2005)." This "mining of soil N," they continue, "can in some cases go on for substantial lengths of time, and there is no evidence that PNL occurred during the course of this study."

Barnard *et al.* (2006) injected ^{15}N-labelled NH_4 into the soil of mesocosms of *Holcus lanatus* (L.) grown for more than 15 months at either ambient or elevated atmospheric CO_2 concentrations to determine whether the uptake capacity of soil micro-organisms had remained higher at elevated CO_2, and to shed further light on the short-term (48 hours) partitioning of N between plants and soil micro-organisms. Their results and data from other plant-microbial ^{15}N partitioning experiments at elevated CO_2 suggest "the mechanisms controlling the effects of CO_2 on short- vs. long-term N uptake and turnover differ." They state "short-term immobilization of added N by soil micro-organisms at elevated CO_2 does not appear to lead to long-term increases in N in soil microbial biomass," noting the increased soil microbial C:N ratios they observed at elevated CO_2 "suggest that long-term exposure to CO_2 alters either the functioning or structure of these microbial communities." Barnard *et al.* conclude "short-term immobilization of inorganic soil nitrogen or exploitation of nutrient pulses may be altered under conditions of elevated atmospheric CO_2 concentration," and this alteration undermines the PNL hypothesis, likely allowing long-lived plants and ecosystems to maintain positive growth responses to atmospheric CO_2 enrichment.

Noting the photosynthetic down-regulation posited by the PNL hypothesis "may occur in ecosystems that have a low soil N availability, such as piedmont loblolly pine forests"—the setting in which the long-term Duke Forest FACE study was being conducted—Springer and Thomas (2007) tested the validity of the hypothesis on some of the site's understory tree species. They "hypothesized that after seven years of exposure to elevated CO_2, significant photosynthetic down-regulation would be observed in these tree species," which included red maple (*Acer rubrum* L.), hickory (*Carya glabra* Mill.), redbud (*Cercis canadensis* L.), and sweetgum (*Liquidambar styraciflua* L.).

During the first year of the Duke Forest FACE experiment, DeLucia and Thomas (2000) examined the photosynthetic responses of these particular saplings to the 200 ppm increase in atmospheric CO_2 concentration employed in that study. Subsequently, Springer and Thomas "reexamined the photosynthetic responses of saplings of the same four understory species to determine whether the enhancement of photosynthesis observed during the first year of exposure to elevated CO_2 was sustained in the seventh year of the experiment." They found "no evidence of photosynthetic down-regulation in any species in either early or late summer." Not only did their measurements reveal no down-regulation of photo-synthesis, they observed "a small increase in the photosynthetic capacity of all of the study species in response to elevated CO_2," which they say "has been demonstrated in several studies (Campbell *et al.*, 1988; Ziska and Teramura, 1992; Idso *et al.*, 1991)."

Springer and Thomas note "the progressive N limitation hypothesis predicts a diminished response of plant productivity to elevated CO_2 as N availability decreases because of the increased nutrient demands of greater plant biomass production (Luo *et al.*, 2004)." They go on to reiterate their own finding: "after seven years of elevated CO_2 treatment in the Duke Forest FACE experiment, we see little evidence of progressive N limitation in the leaf level processes of these four species of understory trees."

Working at the EUROFACE facility in central Italy near Viterbo, Liberloo *et al.* (2007) grew three species of poplar trees—robusta poplar (*Populus x euramericana*), white poplar (*P. alba*), and black poplar (*P. nigra*)—for two three-year periods, between which times the trees were coppiced and allowed to regrow, in either ambient air or air enriched with an extra 180 ppm of CO_2 (an approximate 49% enhancement). They applied no fertilization to any of the plots over the first growth cycle, then fertilized half of the trees over the second growth cycle. During the last year of the last cycle, they measured a number of plant processes and parameters and compared them with similar observations made throughout earlier years of the experiment.

The five researchers discovered, after six years of growth under elevated atmospheric CO_2, the poplar trees did not experience any down-regulation of leaf net photosynthesis, and the long-term stimulation was substantial. In response to the 49% increase in the atmosphere's CO_2 concentration, the CO_2-induced stimulation of net photosynthesis, averaged over the three species, was 49%. In addition, they found no difference in CO_2-induced net photosynthetic stimulation between Sun and shade leaves, nor was there any difference in CO_2 effects between the fertilized and non-fertilized trees.

After thus finding "photosynthetic stimulation of poplar leaves was sustained in elevated CO_2 after six years of fumigation, even under non-fertilized conditions," Liberloo *et al.* state "these results give optimistic perspectives for the future, as the maintained enhancement of photosynthesis in poplar trees is likely to continue over several rotations, thereby providing more carbon for growth in a closed canopy forest."

Finzi *et al.* (2007) evaluated the PNL hypothesis based on data obtained from four well-known FACE experiments conducted on forests—the Rhinelander, Duke, and Oak Ridge National Laboratory (ORNL) studies in the United States and the POP-EUROFACE study in Europe—where previous research described by Norby *et al.* (2005) showed net primary production (NPP) increased by $23 \pm 2\%$ in response to a CO_2 concentration increase of 174 ppm (46%) above the mean ambient-air concentration. Finzi *et al.* found the CO_2-induced increase in forest productivity at the POP-EUROFACE site, which they note was "located on former agricultural land where soil nitrogen availability was high and not limiting," not to have been supported by greater nitrogen uptake from the soil but instead by an increase in nitrogen use efficiency (NUE). At the other three sites, however, the CO_2-induced increase in forest productivity was supported by greater N uptake from the soil, with no change in NUE. They state this result was "unexpected," especially for the Duke and ORNL sites, where they say "tree growth is demonstrably N-limited."

Focusing on the findings of the three U.S. studies, Finzi *et al.* state "the response of N uptake and NUE in these young temperate forests exposed to FACE is the opposite of that predicted by the current generation of biogeochemical models," meaning those based on the PNL hypothesis. After discussing how these forests might be obtaining the seemingly impossible-to-obtain nitrogen they needed to maintain their significantly CO_2-enhanced growth rates, the scientists conclude, "regardless of the specific mechanism, this analysis demonstrates that larger quantities of carbon entering the below-ground system under elevated CO_2 result in greater N uptake,

even in N-limited ecosystems."

Zak *et al.* (2007) initiated a year-long ecosystem-level ^{15}N tracer experiment at the Rhinelander, Wisconsin (USA) FACE facility at the seven-year point of a long-term study of aspen (*Populus tremuloides*) and aspen-birch (*P. tremuloides-Betula papyrifera*) communities exposed to treatments of CO_2 (ambient and elevated to 200 ppm above ambient) and O_3 (ambient and elevated to 30–40 ppb above ambient). One year after adding tracer amounts of $^{15}NH_4^+$ to the forest floor of the young tree stands, they found "both forest communities exposed to elevated CO_2 obtained greater amounts of ^{15}N (29%) and N (40%) from soil, despite no change in soil N availability or plant N-use efficiency." They attribute this to greater belowground root growth and a more thorough exploration of the soil for nitrogen in the CO_2-enriched treatment. In contrast, they note the elevated O_3 treatment "decreased the amount of ^{15}N (-15%) and N (-29%) in both communities." These decreases were significantly smaller than the corresponding CO_2-induced increases. Consequently, Zak *et al.* conclude "progressive nitrogen limitation is presently not a factor governing plant growth response to elevated CO_2 in these young, developing forest communities." In addition, they state their findings "are consistent with those in young sweet gum (*Liquidambar styraciflua*) and loblolly pine (*Pinus taeda*) forests exposed to elevated CO_2 (Finzi *et al.*, 2006; Norby and Iversen, 2006)."

Langley *et al.* (2009) "employed an acid-hydrolysis-incubation method and a net nitrogen-mineralization assay to assess stability of soil carbon pools and short-term nitrogen dynamics in a Florida scrub-oak ecosystem after six years of exposure to elevated CO_2" at the multiple open-top-chamber facility at NASA's Kennedy Space Center. Their research showed elevated atmospheric CO_2 (to 350 ppm above ambient concentrations) tended to increase net N mineralization in the top 10 cm of the soil, but it also decreased total soil organic carbon content there by 21%. That loss of carbon mass was equivalent only to "roughly one-third of the increase in plant biomass that occurred in the same experiment." They found the strongest increases in net N mineralization were in the 10–30 cm depth increment, and "release of N from this depth may have allowed the sustained CO_2 effect on productivity in this scrub-oak forest," which over the four years leading up to their study "increased litterfall by 19–59%."

Thus yet another experiment demonstrates

atmospheric CO_2 enrichment generally enables plants to find the extra nitrogen they need to take full advantage of the aerial fertilization effect of elevated atmospheric CO_2 concentrations, thus increasing total ecosystem carbon content. Although the PNL hypothesis sounds logical enough and many scientists initially embraced it as a fact, a vast array of observational data has subsequently proven it unfounded.

References

Barnard, R., Barthes, L., and Leadley, P.W. 2006. Short-term uptake of ^{15}N by a grass and soil micro-organisms after long-term exposure to elevated CO_2. *Plant and Soil* **280**: 91–99.

Binkley, D., Son, Y., and Valentine, D.W. 2000. Do forests receive occult inputs of nitrogen? *Ecosystems* **3**: 321–331.

Campbell, W.J., Allen, L.H., and Bowes, G. 1988. Effects of CO_2 concentration on rubisco activity, amount, and photosynthesis in soybean leaves. *Plant Physiology* **88**: 1310–1316.

Crocker, R.L. and Major, J. 1955. Soil development in relation to vegetation and surface age at Glacier Bay, Alaska. *Journal of Ecology* **43**: 427–448.

DeLucia, E.H. and Thomas, R.B. 2000. Photosynthetic responses to CO_2 enrichment of four hardwood species in a forest understory. *Oecologia* **122**: 11–19.

Finzi, A.C., Moore, D.J.P., DeLucia, E.H., Lichter, J., Hofmockel, K.S., Jackson, R.B., Kim, H.-S., Matamala, R., McCarthy, H.R., Oren, R., Pippen, J.S., and Schlesinger, W.H. 2006. Progressive nitrogen limitation of ecosystem processes under elevated CO_2 in a warm-temperate forest. *Ecology* **87**: 15–25.

Finzi, A.C., Norby, R.J., Calfapietra, C., Gallet-Budynek, A., Gielen, B., Holmes, W.E., Hoosbeek, M.R., Iversen, C.M., Jackson, R.B., Kubiske, M.E., Ledford, J., Liberloo, M., Oren, R., Polle, A., Pritchard, S., Zak, D.R., Schlesinger, W.H., and Ceulemans, R. 2007. Increases in nitrogen uptake rather than nitrogen-use efficiency support higher rates of temperate forest productivity under elevated CO_2. *Proceedings of the National Academy of Sciences, USA* **104**: 14,014–14,019.

Hungate, B.A. 1999. Ecosystem responses to rising atmospheric CO_2: Feedbacks through the nitrogen cycle. In: Luo, Y. and Mooney, H. (Eds.) *Carbon Dioxide and Environmental Stress*. Academic Press, San Diego, CA, USA., pp. 265–285.

Hungate, B.A., Dukes, J.S., Shaw, M.R., Luo, Y., and Field, C.B. 2003. Nitrogen and climate change. *Science* **302**: 1512–1513.

Hungate, B.A., Johnson, D.W., Dijkstra, P., Hymus, G., Stiling, P., Megonigal, J.P., Pagel, A.L., Moan, J.L., Day, F., Li, J., Hinkle, C.R., and Drake, B.G. 2006. Nitrogen cycling during seven years of atmospheric CO_2 enrichment in a scrub oak woodland. *Ecology* **87**: 26–40.

Idso, S.B. and Kimball, B.A. 2001. CO_2 enrichment of sour orange trees: 13 years and counting. *Environmental and Experimental Botany* **46**: 147–153.

Idso, S.B., Kimball, B.A., and Allen, S.G. 1991. CO_2 enrichment of sour orange trees: 2.5 years into a long-term experiment. *Plant, Cell and Environment* **14**: 351–353.

Johnson, D.W., Hoylman, A.M., Ball, J.T., and Walker, R.F. 2006. Ponderosa pine responses to elevated CO_2 and nitrogen fertilization. *Biogeochemistry* **77**: 157–175.

Johnson, M.G., Phillips, D.L., Tingey, D.T., and Storm, M.J. 2000. Effects of elevated CO_2, N-fertilization, and season on survival of ponderosa pine fine roots. *Canadian Journal of Forest Research* **30**: 220–228.

Kimball, B.A., Idso, S.B., Johnson, S., and Rillig, M.C. 2007. Seventeen years of carbon dioxide enrichment of sour orange trees: final results. *Global Change Biology* **13**: 2171–2183.

Langley, J.A., McKinley, D.C., Wolf, A.A., Hungate, B.A., Drake, B.G., and Megonigal, J.P. 2009. Priming depletes soil carbon and releases nitrogen in a scrub-oak ecosystem exposed to elevated CO_2. *Soil Biology & Biochemistry* **41**: 54–60.

Liberloo, M., Tulva, I., Raim, O., Kull, O., and Ceulemans, R. 2007. Photosynthetic stimulation under long-term CO_2 enrichment and fertilization is sustained across a closed *Populus* canopy profile (EUROFACE). *New Phytologist* **173**: 537–549.

Luo, Y., Hui, D., and Zhang, D. 2006. Elevated CO_2 stimulates net accumulations of carbon and nitrogen in land ecosystems: A meta-analysis. *Ecology* **87**: 53–63.

Luo, Y., Su, B., Currie, W.S., Dukes, J.S., Finzi, A., Hartwig, U., Hungate, B., McMurtrie, R.E., Oren, R., Parton, W.J., Pataki, D.E., Shaw, M.R., Zak, D.R., and Field, C.B. 2004. Progressive nitrogen limitation of ecosystem responses to rising atmospheric carbon dioxide. *BioScience* **54**: 731–739.

Norby, R.J., DeLucia, E.H., Gielen, B., Calfapietra, C., Giardina, C.P., King, S.J., Ledford, J., McCarthy, H.R., Moore, D.J.P., Ceulemans, R., De Angelis, P., Finzi, A.C., Karnosky, D.F., Kubiske, M.E., Lukac, M., Pregitzer, K.S., Scarasci-Mugnozza, G.E., Schlesinger, W.H., and Oren, R. 2005. Forest response to elevated CO_2 is conserved across a broad range of productivity. *Proceedings of the National Academy of Sciences* **102**: 10.1073/pnas.0509478102.

Norby, R.J. and Iversen, C.M. 2006. Nitrogen uptake, distribution, turnover, and efficiency of use in a CO_2-enriched sweetgum forest. *Ecology* **87**: 5–14.

Phillips, D.L., Johnson, M.G., Tingey, D.T., Storm, M.J., Ball, J.T., and Johnson, D.W. 2006. CO_2 and N-fertilization effects on fine-root length, production, and mortality: a 4-year ponderosa pine study. *Oecologia* **148**: 517–525.

Rastetter, E.B., McKane, R.B., Shaver, G.R., Melillo, J.M., Nadelhoffer, K.J., Bobbie, J.E., and Aber, J. D. 1992. Changes in C storage by terrestrial ecosystems: how C-N interactions restrict responses to CO_2 and temperature. *Water, Air and Soil Pollution* **64**: 327–344.

Springer, C.J. and Thomas, R.B. 2007. Photosynthetic responses of forest understory tree species to long-term exposure to elevated carbon dioxide concentration at the Duke Forest FACE experiment. *Tree Physiology* **27**: 25–32.

Tingey, D.T., Johnson, M.G., and Phillips, D.L. 2005. Independent and contrasting effects of elevated CO_2 and N-fertilization of root architecture in *Pinus ponderosa*. *Trees* **19**: 43–50.

Vitousek, P.M. 2004. *Nutrient Cycling and Limitation: Hawaii as a Model System*. Princeton University Press, Princeton, New Jersey, USA.

Zak, D.R., Holmes, W.E., and Pregitzer, K.S. 2007. Atmospheric CO_2 and O_3 alter the flow of ^{15}N in developing forest ecosystems. *Ecology* **88**: 2630–2639.

Ziska, L.H. and Teramura, A.H. 1992. Intraspecific variation in the response of rice (*Oryza sativa*) to increased CO_2 concentration—photosynthetic, biomass, and reproductive characteristics. *Physiologia Plantarum* **84**: 269–274.

3.12 Salinity Stress

- The buildup of soil salinity from repeated irrigation can produce growth stresses in agricultural plants, but the rise in the air's CO_2 concentration can overcome these stresses.

In agricultural enterprises the buildup of soil salinity from repeated irrigations can reduce crop yields. Similarly, in unmanaged ecosystems where exposure to brackish or salty water is commonplace, saline soils can induce growth stresses in plants not adapted to these conditions. It is important to understand how rising atmospheric CO_2 concentrations may interact with soil salinity to affect plant growth. Experiments addressing this issue are discussed below.

Ball *et al.* (1997) grew two Australian mangrove species—*Rhizophora stylosa* and *Rhizophora apiculata*, the former of which has a slower relative growth rate than the latter but a greater salt tolerance—for 14 weeks in glasshouses with different combinations of atmospheric CO_2 (340 and 700 ppm), relative humidity (43 and 86%), and salinity (25 and 75% of seawater), to determine the effects of these variables on their development and growth. Averaged across the entire experiment, the elevated CO_2 treatment significantly increased the rates of net photosynthesis in both species, but only at the lower salinity level.

Mavrogianopoulos *et al.* (1999) grew parnon melons (*Cucumis melo*) in greenhouses subjected to atmospheric CO_2 concentrations of 400, 800, and 1,200 ppm for the first five hours of each day, irrigating them with nutrient solutions containing 0, 25, and 50 mM NaCl to determine the interactive effects of elevated CO_2 and salinity on plant growth and yield. Exposure to CO_2 concentrations of 800 and 1,200 ppm increased net photosynthetic rates by averages of 75 and 120%, respectively—regardless of salinity—relative to rates measured at 400 ppm CO_2. The CO_2 enrichment partially reversed the negative effects of salinity on shoot growth, leaf growth, and leaf chlorophyll content, and although melon yields were significantly increased with atmospheric CO_2 enrichment at all salinity levels, the greatest CO_2-induced enhancement was observed at the lowest salinity level.

Also working in the agricultural sector, Maggio *et al.* (2002) grew tomato (*Lycopersicon esculentum* Mill.) plants in controlled-environment chambers maintained at atmospheric CO_2 concentrations of either 400 or 900 ppm in combination with varying degrees of soil salinity for one month. They found plants grown in the elevated CO_2 treatment tolerated an average root-zone salinity threshold value about 60% greater than plants grown in the low CO_2 treatment, and the water-use of the CO_2-enriched plants was about half the low-CO_2 plants. In addition, the amount of chloride in the leaves of the CO_2-enriched plants was significantly lower than in the leaves of the low-CO_2 plants.

Poorter and Perez-Soba (2001) reported very similar findings in a review paper. They found the positive effects of elevated CO_2 on the growth responses of most plants over a wide range of soil salinities remained the same, which concurred with the earlier findings of Idso and Idso (1994) in their review. Hence, there is abundant evidence indicating plants respond positively to increases in the air's CO_2 content, even where high soil salinity levels present mild to moderate stresses.

Syvertsen and Levy (2005) reviewed what was known about salinity stress in citrus trees and how atmospheric CO_2 enrichment might modify it. They note rapidly growing plants almost always use more water than slower-growing plants, and "in citrus, many vigorous rootstocks that produce fast-growing trees also tend to have poor salt tolerance (Castle et al., 1993)," possibly because they accumulate more salt in their tissues because of their greater uptake of water. When growing plants in CO_2-enriched air, however, plant stomatal conductance and water use are often decreased at the same time net photosynthesis and growth are increased, so, in the words of the two scientists, "elevated CO_2 almost always leads to higher water use efficiency as it disconnects rapid tree growth from high water use." They explain, "if salt uptake is coupled with water uptake, then leaves grown at elevated CO_2 should have lower salt concentrations than leaves grown at ambient CO_2 (Ball and Munns, 1992)."

"As expected," Syvertsen and Levy continue, "all citrus rootstock species studied increased growth and water use efficiency in response to elevated CO_2 that was twice ambient," and generally, but not always, "the salinity-induced accumulation of sodium (Na^+) in leaves was less when seedlings were grown at elevated CO_2 than at ambient CO_2." One exception—where Na^+ accumulation was not affected by elevated CO_2—was Rangpur lime (Citrus reticulata), but they report this citrus variety was already relatively salt-tolerant, and another variety of the same species (Cleopatra mandarin) had lower leaf chloride concentrations in CO_2-enriched air than in ambient air.

Rasse et al. (2005) reported on the long-term effects of atmospheric CO_2 enrichment on the net CO_2 exchange, shoot density, and shoot biomass of the wetland sedge, Scirpus olneyi, as well as how those effects were influenced by salinity (one of the main environmental stressors of the wetlands), in one of the longest (17 years) in situ atmospheric CO_2 enrichment experiments ever conducted—in a natural wetland located at the Smithsonian Environmental Research Center on the Chesapeake Bay (USA). In every year of that period, the net CO_2 exchange rate and shoot biomass and density of the plants growing in the CO_2-enriched (ambient +340 ppm) air were greater than they were among the plants growing in ambient air. In the case of the net CO_2 exchange rate, for example,

the extra CO_2 boosted it by 80% in the first year of the study, but the enhancement declined to about 35% by the end of the third year and remained relatively constant at that value over the following 15 years. Shoot biomass and density also increased; while the CO_2-induced stimulation of the net CO_2 exchange rate remained essentially constant over the past 15 years, the CO_2-induced stimulations of shoot biomass and density increased over time. After five years of a nearly constant stimulation of 16%, for example, shoot density increased in near-linear fashion to a value 128% above the ambient-air value at the end of year 17. The response of shoot biomass to CO_2 enrichment was also nearly linear, reaching a value approximately 70% above ambient at year 17. The trends in shoot density and biomass did not appear to be leveling off.

Net CO_2 exchange, shoot density, and shoot biomass were also closely correlated with salinity—the higher the salinity, the more detrimental were its effects on these variables. But even at the highest levels of salinity reported, atmospheric CO_2 enrichment was able to produce a positive, albeit reduced, stimulation of net CO_2 exchange. For shoot biomass and density, the responses were better still. Not only did atmospheric CO_2 enrichment essentially eradicate the detrimental effects of salinity, there was, Rasse et al. write, "evidence suggesting that salinity stress increased the stimulation of shoot density by elevated atmospheric CO_2 concentration."

This experiment demonstrated several important facts. First, as the researchers state, their results "leave no doubt as to the sustained response of the salt marsh sedge to elevated atmospheric CO_2 concentration." Second, as the initial responses of the three growth variables declined or remained low during the first few years of the study, but leveled out or increased thereafter, it is clear long-term research must be carried out to ascertain the full and correct impacts of atmospheric CO_2 enrichment on plants. In the wetland sedge of this study, for example, it took about 10 growing seasons before an increasing trend in the shoot density could be recognized. Finally, there is what the researchers called their "most important finding": "a species response to elevated atmospheric CO_2 concentration can continually increase when [it] is under stress and declining in its natural environment."

Garcia-Sanchez and Syvertsen (2006) grew well-watered and -fertilized three-month-old rootstock seedlings of Cleopatra mandarin (Citrus reticulata Blanco) and Carrizo citrange (Citrus sinensis (L.)

Osb. x *Poncirus trifoliata* L.), with or without salt stress (an additional 50 mM NaCl), for eight additional weeks, one plant each in 1.5-liter containers located in controlled-environment greenhouses maintained at either 360 or 700 ppm CO_2. During that time and at the end of the experiment, they measured a number of plant properties and physiological processes that allowed them to determine whether "salinity tolerance of citrus rootstock seedlings would be increased when grown in elevated CO_2."

The two researchers found "elevated CO_2 increased plant growth, shoot/root ratio, leaf dry weight per area, net assimilation of CO_2, chlorophyll, and water-use efficiency." The increase in the last parameter was caused by a decrease in transpiration and an increase in plant biomass. In Cleopatra mandarin, biomass received a 27% CO_2-induced boost in the salt-stress treatment and a 40% boost in the non-salt-stress treatment; in Carrizo citrange, biomass received a 49% boost in the salt-stress treatment and 43% in the non-salt-stress treatment. They note "elevated CO_2 increased salinity tolerance in the relatively salt-sensitive Carrizo more than in the salt-tolerant Cleopatra."

Takagi *et al.* (2008) grew well-watered and well-fertilized *Solanum lycopersicum* (formerly *Lycopersicon esculentum*) tomato plant seedlings for two weeks at two levels of irrigation-water salinity (0 or 100 mM NaCl) in 3-L pots inside the greenhouse of Hiroshima University (Japan), at atmospheric CO_2 concentrations of either 370 or 1,000 ppm, measuring various plant properties and physiological responses. They report the "salt-stress treatment severely decreased whole-plant biomass" and "leaf photosynthesis and transport of carbon assimilates," but "the impact of stress on these activities was alleviated under elevated CO_2 concentration." This alleviation, they write, "was promoted when sink activity relative to source activity was higher," which they say was "probably owing to improvement of oxidative stress," due "at least partially to the higher constitutive antioxidant enzymes' activities" as well as improved water status "through stomatal closure at high CO_2 concentration." They conclude their study "corroborates earlier reports that the interaction between salinity stress and CO_2 concentration results in the alleviative effect of elevated CO_2 on the negative effects of salinity on plant growth."

Geissler *et al.* (2009a) note, "desertification is often accompanied by soil salinization ... leading to growth conditions unacceptable for most conventional crops." They suggest "a promising solution" to the problem is "the desalinization and reclamation of degraded land by making sustainable use of naturally salt-tolerant halophytes under seawater irrigation (including drainage mechanisms which avoid salt accumulation in the soil)."

The three researchers grew well-fertilized two-month-old *Aster tripolium* plants in a hydroponic system maintained at seawater salinity (sws) levels of 0, 50, and 100% in open-top chambers at atmospheric CO_2 concentrations of either 380 ppm (ambient) or 520 ppm (elevated), during which time they measured several plant properties and processes. Growing the plants with water of 100% sws (as opposed to 0% sws) resulted in "a significant decrease in photosynthesis and water use efficiency and to an increase in oxidative stress." When they raised the air's CO_2 concentration by 37% (from 380 to 520 ppm), there was a subsequent increase of 84% in photosynthesis and 60% in water use efficiency. The researchers note "the improved water and energy supply was used to increase the investment in mechanisms reducing water loss and oxidative stress." They conclude, because "elevated CO_2 concentration enhances the energy and water supply of *Aster tripolium*, ameliorates oxidative stress, and thus enhances the survival of this plant in saline habitats," it "can help in desalinizing and reclaiming degraded land and sequestering CO_2, thus counteracting the greenhouse effect."

Geissler *et al.* (2009b) write halophytes are "naturally salt tolerant plants which are able to complete their life cycle on a substrate rich in NaCl," and cash-crop halophytes "can be used for various economical and ecological purposes, e.g. for food, fodder, for obtaining timber, fibers, reeds or chemicals, as ornamental plants, for coastal protection, land reclamation or greenification of deserts." They note *Aster tripolium*, in particular, "can be used for food (the leaves have a high nutritional value and can be eaten as salad or vegetable), for fodder and as an ornamental plant."

The three scientists state the 40% increase in the air's CO_2 content in their experiment increased the light-saturated rate of net photosynthesis by 56%, 82%, and 71%, respectively, in the plants irrigated with water of 0, 50, and 100% sws, and it increased their water use efficiencies by 14, 26, and 61%, respectively. Other positive impacts of the CO_2-enriched air were "an enhanced synthesis of proline, carbohydrates and proteins," and "these mechanisms led to a higher survival rate under saline conditions, i.e. to an improved salt tolerance." Thus, they conclude "*A. tripolium* is a promising cash crop halophyte which will probably benefit from rising atmospheric CO_2 concentrations in the future," and "its sustainable use can help feeding the growing world population."

Working with a more common crop, Perez-Lopez *et al.* (2009a) grew two barley (*Hordeum vulgare* L.) cultivars, Alpha and Iranis, in controlled-environment growth chambers at either ambient (350 ppm) or elevated (700 ppm) atmospheric CO_2 concentrations in a 3:1 perlite:vermiculite mixture watered with Hoagland's solution every two days (until the first leaf was completely expanded at 14 days), after which they administered a salinity treatment by adding 0, 80, 160, or 240 mM NaCl to the Hoagland's solution every two days for 14 more days. After a total of 28 days, the primary leaf of each barley plant was harvested and assessed for a number of biochemical properties.

In the various ambient-air salinity treatments, the deleterious effects of reactive oxygen species on barley leaves were made apparent through ion leakage and increases in thiobarbituric acid reactive substances (TBARS), which rose as salt concentrations rose. "On the other hand," the seven scientists continue, "when [the] salinity treatment was imposed under elevated CO_2 conditions, lower solute leakage and TBARS levels were observed, suggesting that the oxidative stress caused by salinity was lower." They conclude "elevated CO_2 protects barley cultivars from oxidative stress," noting "the relief of oxidative stress damage observed in our barley leaves grown under a CO_2 enriched atmosphere has also been observed in alfalfa (Sgherri *et al.*, 1998), pine (Vu *et al.*, 1999) and oak (Schwanz and Polle, 2001)."

Working with the same plants in the same experiment, but focusing on different phenomena, Perez-Lopez *et al.* (2009b) measured relative water content, water potential and its components, transpiration rate, hydraulic conductance, and water use efficiency, computed as plant dry weight produced per unit of water transpired. They found "elevated CO_2 improves barley water relations under saline conditions because elevated CO_2 permits a greater osmotic adjustment, most likely due to a greater carbon supply from increased photosynthesis, and a lower passive dehydration due to reductions in stomatal conductance and hydraulic conductance." Specifically, by the end of their study the water use efficiency of salt-stressed plants grown in the elevated CO_2 treatment was 61% greater in Alpha and 43%

greater in Iranis than that of plants grown in the ambient CO_2 treatment. The five researchers conclude, "elevated CO_2 will mitigate the negative impact of salinity on barley growth and will enable plants to remain turgid and functional for a longer period and for a higher salt concentration," noting "these facts open the possibility of a future successful development of this species in saline areas in which nowadays growth is not possible." This finding has enormous implications, as Frommer *et al.* (1999) have estimated approximately one-third of the world's irrigated land is currently unsuitable for crop production because of its high salinity.

Also working with barley plants grown in the same experiment, Perez-Lopez *et al.* (2010) measured midday leaf water potential, osmotic potential, osmotic potential at full turgor, dehydration, and osmotic adjustment; they subsequently harvested the primary leaf of each plant and made assessments of its concentrations of various minerals and organic compounds. They write, "elevated CO_2 permitted plant metabolism to be maintained at a better status under salt stress than did ambient CO_2," and "growth was reduced more at ambient than at elevated CO_2." They also report, "elevated CO_2 widens the range of salt concentrations at which osmotic adjustment continues to be efficient by providing a greater supply of carbon and Adenosine-5'-triphosphate," a multifunctional nucleotide that transports chemical energy in cells for metabolism and is "needed to perform the energetically expensive salt tolerance mechanisms." Thus, they conclude—as they had in their earlier papers—"under future environmental conditions, barley species will be able to succeed in salinized areas in which growth is not currently possible."

Azam *et al.* (2005) note "in agro-ecosystems, green manuring legumes occupy a key position in maintaining/improving soil fertility and productivity," and the important role of these plants as a source of nitrogen has increased further due to economic and pollution concerns associated with nitrogen supplied by chemical fertilizers. They state, "species of sesbania have generally been considered as most important for green manuring, especially in wheat-rice rotation systems."

In many situations, the growth of sesbania is suppressed by varying degrees of water stress and salinity, but the five Pakistani scientists state "elevated CO_2 favors different physiological processes of plants, thereby leading to increased biomass production and ecosystem functioning," citing Drake and Leadley (1991), Idso and Idso

(1994), and Azam and Farooq (2001). They report this effect is more pronounced for plants facing stresses imposed through the soil or atmosphere, citing the collection of papers compiled and edited by Koch and Mooney (1996). They hypothesized rising atmospheric CO_2 concentrations might mitigate salinity stress in sesbania, enabling the rotation cover-crop to more effectively "fix" atmospheric nitrogen and deposit the plant-usable form of it in the soil, where it could help promote the growth of such important agricultural staples as wheat and rice.

Conducting greenhouse experiments designed to assess the effects of elevated atmospheric CO_2 concentrations on growth and nitrogen fixation in *Sesbania aculeata* exposed to different salinity and water regimes, Azam *et al.* report "elevated CO_2 favored N_2 fixation leading to a greater contribution of fixed N to the total plant N." In addition, "biological nitrogen fixation decreased with salinity" but "elevated CO_2 arrested the decrease to a significant extent."

Perez-Lopez *et al.* (2012) write, "salt stress has a threefold effect on plant health" because it reduces water availability, causes ion imbalance, and causes toxicity, all of which phenomena, they write, "curtail growth, photosynthesis, protein synthesis, energy storage, and lipid metabolism," as described in detail by Munns (2005) and Parida and Das (2005). In a study designed to explore the negative consequences of potentially greater salt stress in a CO_2-enriched environment, they grew barley (*Hordeum vulgare*) plants in pots containing a 3:1 mix of perlite: vermiculite in controlled-environment chambers maintained at either ambient or elevated atmospheric CO_2 concentrations (350 or 700 ppm) for the last 14 days of a 28-day post-planting period. They also instituted four salt-stress treatments on the 15th day by supplying the plants then and thereafter with water of one of four degrees of saltiness (0, 80, 160, or 240 mM NaCl). At the end of the 28-day period they measured a number of plant physiological properties and processes related to the maximal rate of net photosynthesis (Amax) exhibited by the first fully expanded attached leaf of each plant.

The five Spanish scientists report, "in the zero-saline treatment, elevated CO_2 increased the Amax by 49% compared with the Amax measured at ambient CO_2," whereas "under ambient CO_2 conditions, saline treatments (80-, 160- and 240-mM NaCl) reduced the Amax by 18, 32 and 39%, respectively." They add, "these reductions were lower at elevated CO_2: 8, 22 and 28% for 80-, 160-, and 240-mM NaCl." Based on

the graphical representations of their results, the CO_2-induced enhancements of Amax in the four saline treatments (0-, 80-, 160-, and 240-mM NaCl) appear to have been, respectively, 49%, 68%, 71%, and 76%, revealing the greater the salinity-induced percentage reduction in barley Amax becomes, the greater the CO_2-induced percentage increase in barley Amax becomes.

Also investigating salt stress in barley, Perez-Lopez *et al.* (2013) write, "soil salinization is an important growth limiting factor for most plants," citing the United Nations' Food and Agriculture Organization (FAO, 2007) and noting "around 20% of the irrigated land and one third of the world's arable soil are affected by a progressive salinization." They note "barley is one of the most extensively cultivated crops worldwide" but "salt stress reduces its productivity."

Perez-Lopez *et al.* analyzed "the effect of salinity on nitrogen acquisition, distribution and assimilation, the consequences of these effects on growth in barley (*Hordeum vulgare* L., cv. Iranis), and the possible effects on these processes provoked by elevated CO_2 levels." They sowed six barley seeds in each of several 2.5-liter pots containing a 3:1 mix of perlite: vermiculite in controlled-environment chambers maintained at either ambient (350 ppm) or elevated (700 ppm) CO_2 concentrations and watered the plants with 250 ml of Hoagland's solution containing 0, 80, 160, or 240 mM concentrations of NaCl every two days until the end of the 28-day study.

The six Spanish scientists report, "under ambient CO_2 conditions, 80, 160, and 240 mM NaCl reduced the total plant biomass by 12%, 30%, and 44%, respectively." By contrast, "growth at elevated CO_2 levels led to 24%, 20%, and 33% higher total biomass than under ambient CO_2 levels for 80, 160, and 240 mM NaCl, respectively." And because "the relative stimulation of total plant biomass in response to elevated CO_2 levels was higher in salt-stressed plants than in non-stressed ones," they conclude, "barley plants subjected to elevated CO_2 levels will likely overcome mild saline conditions."

References

Azam, F., Aziz, F., Sial, M.H., Ashraf, M., and Farooq, S. 2005. Mitigation of salinity effects on *Sesbania aculeata* L., through enhanced availability of carbon dioxide. *Pakistan Journal of Botany* **37**: 959–967.

Azam, F. and Farooq, S. 2001. Impact of elevated

atmospheric CO_2 on crop plants—an overview. *Pakistan Journal of Biological Sciences* **4**: 220–22.

Ball, M.C., Cochrane, M.J., and Rawson, H.M. 1997. Growth and water use of the mangroves *Rhizophora apiculata* and *R. stylosa* in response to salinity and humidity under ambient and elevated concentrations of atmospheric CO_2. *Plant, Cell and Environment* **20**: 1158–1166.

Ball, M.C. and Munns, R. 1992. Plant responses to salinity under elevated atmospheric concentrations of CO_2. *Australian Journal of Botany* **40**: 515–525.

Castle, W.S., Tucker, D.P.H., Krezdorn, A.H., and Youtsey, C.O. 1993. *Rootstocks for Florida Citrus: Rootstock Selection, the First Step to Success*. University of Florida, Institute of Food and Agricultural Science, Gainesville, Florida, USA.

Drake, B.G. and Leadley, P.W. 1991. Canopy photosynthesis of crops and native plant communities exposed to long-term elevated CO_2. *Plant, Cell & Environment* **14**: 853–860.

FAO, 2007. Global Network on Integrated Soil Management for Sustainable Use of Salt-affected Soils. http:/www.fao.org/nr/land/soils/.

Frommer, W.B., Ludewig, U., and Rentsch, D. 1999. Taking transgenic plants with a pinch of salt. *Science* **285**: 1222–1223.

Garcia-Sanchez, F. and Syvertsen, J.P. 2006. Salinity tolerance of Cleopatra mandarin and Carrizo citrange citrus rootstock seedlings is affected by CO_2 enrichment during growth. *Journal of the American Society of Horticultural Science* **131**: 24–31.

Geissler, N., Hussin, S., and Koyro, H.-W. 2009a. Elevated atmospheric CO_2 concentration ameliorates effects of NaCl salinity on photosynthesis and leaf structure of *Aster tripolium* L. *Journal of Experimental Botany* **60**: 137–151.

Geissler, N., Hussin, S., and Koyro, H.-W. 2009b. Interactive effects of NaCl salinity and elevated atmospheric CO_2 concentration on growth, photosynthesis, water relations and chemical composition of the potential cash crop halophyte *Aster tripolium* L. *Environmental and Experimental Botany* **65**: 220–231.

Idso, K.E. and Idso, S.B. 1994. Plant responses to atmospheric CO_2 enrichment in the face of environmental constraints: A review of the past 10 years' research. *Agricultural and Forest Meteorology* **69**: 153–203.

Koch, G.W. and Mooney, H.A. (Eds.) 1996. *Carbon Dioxide and Terrestrial Ecosystems*. Academic Press, San Diego, California, USA.

Maggio, A., Dalton, F.N., and Piccinni, G. 2002. The effects of elevated carbon dioxide on static and dynamic indices for tomato salt tolerance. *European Journal of Agronomy* **16**: 197–206.

Mavrogianopoulos, G.N., Spanakis, J., and Tsikalas, P. 1999. Effect of carbon dioxide enrichment and salinity on photosynthesis and yield in melon. *Scientia Horticulturae* **79**: 51–63.

Munns, R. 2005. Genes and salt tolerance: bringing them together. *New Phytologist* **167**: 645–663.

Parida, A.K. and Das, A.B. 2005. Salt tolerance and salinity effects on plants: a review. *Ecotoxicology and Environmental Safety* **60**: 324–349

Perez-Lopez, U., Robredo, A., Lacuesta, M., Mena-Petite, A., and Munoz-Rueda, A. 2009b. The impact of salt stress on the water status of barley plants is partially mitigated by elevated CO_2. *Environmental and Experimental Botany* **66**: 463–470.

Perez-Lopez, U., Robredo, A., Lacuesta, M., Mena-Petite, A., and Munoz-Rueda, A. 2012. Elevated CO_2 reduces stomatal and metabolic limitations on photosynthesis caused by salinity in *Hordeum vulgare*. *Photosynthesis Research* **111**: 269–283.

Perez-Lopez, U., Robredo, A., Lacuesta, M., Munoz-Rueda, A., and Mena-Petite, A. 2010. Atmospheric CO_2 concentration influences the contributions of osmolyte accumulation and cell wall elasticity to salt tolerance in barley cultivars. *Journal of Plant Physiology* **167**: 15–22.

Perez-Lopez, U., Robredo, A., Lacuestra, M., Sgherri, C., Munoz-Rueda, A., Navari-Izzo, F., and Mena-Petite, A. 2009a. The oxidative stress caused by salinity in two barley cultivars is mitigated by elevated CO_2. *Physiologia Plantarum* **135**: 29–42.

Perez-Lopez, U., Robredo, A., Miranda-Apodaca, J., Lacuesta, M., Munoz-Rueda, A., and Mena-Petite, A. 2013. Carbon dioxide enrichment moderates salinity-induced effects on nitrogen acquisition and assimilation and their impact on growth in barley plants. *Environmental and Experimental Botany* **87**: 148–158.

Poorter, H. and Perez-Soba, M. 2001. The growth response of plants to elevated CO_2 under non-optimal environmental conditions. *Oecologia* **129**: 1–20.

Rasse, D.P., Peresta, G., and Drake, B.G. 2005. Seventeen years of elevated CO_2 exposure in a Chesapeake Bay Wetland: sustained but contrasting responses of plant growth and CO_2 uptake. *Global Change Biology* **11**: 369–377.

Schwanz, P. and Polle, A. 2001. Differential stress responses of antioxidative systems to drought in pedunculate oak (*Quercus robur*) and maritime pine (*Pinus pinaster*) grown under high CO_2 concentrations. *Journal of Experimental Botany* **52**: 133–143.

Sgherri, C., Quartacci, M., Menconi, M., Raschi, A., and Navari-Izzo, F. 1998. Interactions between drought and elevated CO_2 on alfalfa plants. *Journal of Plant Physiology* **152**: 118–124.

Syvertsen, J. and Levy, Y. 2005. Salinity interactions with other abiotic and biotic stresses in citrus. *HortTechnology* **15**: 100–103.

Takagi, M., El-Shemy, H.A., Sasaki, S., Toyama, S., Kanai, S., Saneoka, H., and Fujita, K. 2008. Elevated CO_2 concentration alleviates salinity stress in tomato plant. *Acta Agriculturae Scandinavica Section B—Soil and Plant Science:* 10.1080/09064710801932425.

Vu, J.C., Gesch, R., Allen, L.H., Boote, K., and Bowes, G. 1999. CO_2 enrichment delays a rapid, drought induced decrease in Rubisco small subunit transcript abundance. *Journal of Plant Physiology* **155**: 139–142.

3.13 Temperature Stress

As the atmosphere's CO_2 content rises, nearly all agricultural crops, grassland plants, and trees will exhibit enhanced rates of photosynthesis and biomass production that will not be diminished by any global warming that might accompany it. If ambient air temperatures rise concurrently, the growth-promoting effects of atmospheric CO_2 enrichment likely will rise even more, as the Earth gets "greener."

3.13.1 Agricultural Crops

- As the air's CO_2 concentration rises, nearly all agricultural crops will exhibit enhanced rates of photosynthesis and biomass production that will not be diminished by any concomitant global warming. If air temperatures rise concurrently, the growth-promoting effects of atmospheric CO_2 enrichment likely will rise even more.

As the air's CO_2 content rises, most plants exhibit increased rates of photosynthesis and biomass production (see Chapter 1), which should increase the amount of food, fiber, and timber production that can be utilized to feed, clothe, and shelter the expanding human population. However, some researchers argue the growth-promoting effects of atmospheric CO_2 enrichment may be largely negated by the global warming predicted to occur in the near future by a number of state-of-the-art climate models. Such an outcome could compromise the planet's ability to sustain a greater human population without increasing use of land for agriculture. This section examines the scientific literature to see whether plants will continue to exhibit CO_2-induced growth increases under conditions of predicted future warming, reviewing what has been learned about the photosynthetic and growth responses of CO_2-enriched agricultural crops grown at both current and projected future growing-season temperatures.

The optimum growth temperatures of several plants have been shown to rise substantially with increasing levels of atmospheric CO_2 (Berry and Bjorkman, 1980; Stuhlfauth and Fock, 1990; McMurtrie *et al.*, 1992; McMurtrie and Wang, 1993). This phenomenon was explained by Long (1991), who calculated from well-established plant physiological principles that most C_3 plants should increase their optimum growth temperatures by approximately 5°C for a 300 ppm increase in the air's CO_2 concentration. Thus plant photosynthetic rates should rise in response to concomitant increases in both the air's CO_2 concentration and temperature, as Idso and Idso (1994) and Cowling (1999) have shown to be typically the case. These positive CO_2 x temperature interactions have been observed in subsequent scientific studies, as indicated below.

Zhu *et al.* (1999) report pineapples grown at 700 ppm CO_2 assimilated 15, 97, and 84% more total carbon than pineapples grown at the current ambient CO_2 concentration in day/night air temperature regimes of 30/20 (which is optimal for pineapple growth at ambient CO_2), 30/25, and 35/25 °C, respectively. Similarly, Taub *et al.* (2000) demonstrated net photosynthetic rates of cucumbers grown at twice-ambient levels of atmospheric CO_2 and air temperatures of 40°C were 3.2 times greater than those of control plants grown at ambient CO_2 and this same elevated air temperature. Thus, at air temperatures normally considered to be deleterious to plant growth, rates of photosynthesis are typically considerably greater for CO_2-enriched vs. ambient-grown plants.

Reddy *et al.* (1999) reported similar results when they grew cotton plants at air temperatures ranging from 2°C below to 7°C above ambient air temperature, finding the plants simultaneously exposed to 720 ppm CO_2 had photosynthetic rates 137 to 190% greater than those of plants exposed to ambient CO_2 concentrations across this temperature range. Cowling and Sage (1998) found a 200 ppm increase in the air's CO_2 concentration boosted photosynthetic rates of young bean plants by 58 and 73% at growth temperatures of 25 and 36°C, respectively. Bunce (1998) grew wheat and barley at 350 and 700 ppm CO_2 across a wide range of temperatures and found elevated CO_2 stimulated photosynthesis in these species by 63 (wheat) and 74% (barley) at an air temperature of 10°C and by 115 (wheat) and 125% (barley) at 30°C. These studies show the percentage increase in photosynthetic rate resulting from atmospheric CO_2 enrichment often increases substantially with increasing air temperature.

Elevated CO_2 also helps plants recover from high-temperature- and drought-induced reductions in photosynthetic capacity, as Ferris et al. (1998) demonstrated. They grew soybeans for 52 days under normal air temperatures and soil water conditions at atmospheric CO_2 concentrations of 360 and 700 ppm, then subjected the plants to an eight-day period of high temperature and water stress. When the researchers restored normal air temperatures and soil water conditions, the CO_2-enriched plants attained photosynthetic rates 72% of their unstressed controls, and the plants grown at ambient CO_2 attained photosynthetic rates only 52% of their controls. At the end of the growing season, Ferris et al. (1999) report, plants growing in the elevated CO_2 treatment exhibited an average biomass 24% greater than plants grown in ambient CO_2, and a seed yield 32% greater.

CO_2-induced increases in plant growth under high air temperatures also have been observed in other agricultural plants. In the previously mentioned study of Cowling and Sage (1998), for example, the 200 ppm increase in the air's CO_2 content boosted total plant biomass for wheat and barley by a combined average of 59 and 200% at air temperatures of 25 and 36°C. Similarly, Ziska (1998) found a doubling of the atmospheric CO_2 concentration increased the total dry weight of soybeans by 36 and 42% at root zone temperatures of 25 and 30°C, respectively, and Hakala (1998) noted spring wheat grown at 700 ppm CO_2 attained total biomass values 17 and 23% greater than those attained by ambient-grown plants exposed to ambient and elevated (ambient plus 3°C) air temperatures. After inputting various observed CO_2-induced growth responses of winter wheat into plant growth models, Alexandrov and Hoogenboom (2000) predicted 12 to 49% increases in wheat yield in Bulgaria, even if air temperatures were to ultimately rise by as much as 4°C. And Reddy et al. (1998) found elevated CO_2 (700 ppm) increased total cotton biomass by 31 to

78% across an air temperature range of 20 to 40°C.

These studies make it clear elevated air temperatures often significantly enhance the beneficial effects of elevated atmospheric CO_2 on agricultural crop yields. In some cases, however, rising air temperatures do not interact with rising atmospheric CO_2 concentrations to further increase the growth-promoting effects of atmospheric CO_2 enrichment. Instead, they simply do not interfere with the status quo.

Demmers-Derks et al. (1998) found sugar beets grown at 700 ppm CO_2 produced 25% more biomass than ambient-grown plants, regardless of air temperature, which was increased by 3°C. Similarly, Fritschi et al. (1999) found significant warming (4.5°C above ambient) had no impact on the growth of rhizoma peanut, whereas a 300 ppm increase in the air's CO_2 content increased the plant's total biomass by 52% regardless of air temperature. In the unlikely event the air's CO_2 content were to cease rising or have no effect on the productivity of certain plants, it is possible the temperature increase itself may promote plant growth and development, as was found in the experiment conducted by Wurr et al. (2000), where elevated CO_2 had essentially no effect on the yield of French beans but a 4°C increase in air temperature increased their yield by approximately 50%.

Aloni et al. (2001) grew bell pepper (Capsicum annuum L. cv. Mazurka) plants under optimal conditions until eight days prior to anthesis, then placed the plants in greenhouses maintained at atmospheric CO_2 concentrations of either 350 or 800 ppm and normal (28/22°C) or elevated (32/26°C) day/night air temperatures to determine the effects of these two environmental changes on reproductive parameters associated with pollen, which is extremely sensitive to high temperatures. The high temperature stress reduced pollen germination by 75% at ambient CO_2, but atmospheric CO_2 enrichment completely ameliorated this negative effect. The high temperature treatment also reduced the number of seeds produced per fruit by 68%, but the elevated CO_2 treatment nearly compensated for this deleterious effect, reducing the warming-induced seed-per-fruit reduction to only 9%.

Tako et al. (2001) grew rice (Oryza sativa L. cv. Mutsu-homare) plants hydroponically in controlled-environment chambers having atmospheric CO_2 concentrations of 350 and 700 ppm and day/night air temperatures of 24/17 (ambient) and 26/19°C (elevated), to study the interactive effects of elevated

CO_2 and temperature on the growth of this important crop. After 18 weeks, elevated CO_2 had no effect on whole-plant biomass at ambient growth temperatures, but with the additional 2°C of warming, atmospheric CO_2 enrichment produced a whole-plant biomass enhancement of 22%.

Bunce (2001) grew strawberry (*Fragaria x ananassa* Duchesne cv. Honeoye) plants in the field in open-top chambers maintained at atmospheric CO_2 concentrations of 350, 650, and 950 ppm for two years to study the effects of elevated CO_2 on photosynthesis in this important fruit crop. They took measurements weekly to evaluate the temperature dependence of the photosynthetic stimulation resulting from the two levels of atmospheric CO_2 enrichment. Plants grown at 650 and 950 ppm CO_2 exhibited mean photosynthetic rates 77 and 106% greater, respectively, than those of control plants exposed to ambient air.

Prasad *et al.* (2003) grew peanuts (*Arachis hypogaea* L. cv. Georgia Green, of the Virginia Runner type) from seed to maturity in sunlit controlled-environment growth chambers maintained at atmospheric CO_2 concentrations of 350 and 700 ppm and daytime-maximum/nighttime-minimum air temperatures of 32/22, 36/26, 40/30, and 44/34°C. During this study, leaf photosynthetic rates were unaffected by air temperatures over the range studied, but they rose by approximately 27% in response to the experimental doubling of the air's CO_2 content. Vegetative biomass increased by 51% and 54% in ambient air and CO_2-enriched air, respectively, as temperatures rose from 32/22 to 40/30°C. A further temperature increase to 44/34°C caused moderate to slight declines in vegetative biomass in ambient and CO_2-enriched air, respectively, so the final biomass increase over the entire temperature range investigated was 27% in the ambient air and 53% in the CO_2-enriched air. Going from the lowest-temperature, ambient CO_2 treatment to the highest-temperature, elevated CO_2 treatment led to a 106% increase in vegetative biomass.

In contrast, seed yields in both the ambient and CO_2-enriched air dropped dramatically with each of the three temperature increases studied, declining at the highest temperature regime to but a small percentage of what they were at the lowest temperature regime. Nevertheless, Prasad *et al.* report, "seed yields at 36.4/26.4°C under elevated CO_2 were similar to those obtained at 32/22°C under ambient CO_2," describing the latter pair of temperatures as "present-day seasonal temperatures."

Even an unrealistically large warming of 4.4°C above present-day growing temperatures for peanut production would have essentially no effect on peanut seed yields, as long as the atmosphere's CO_2 concentration rose concurrently by something on the order of 350 ppm. And more realistic values of CO_2-induced global warming—temperature increases on the order of 0.4°C or less for a doubling of the air's CO_2 content (Idso, 1998)—likely would lead to a significant increase in peanut production.

Vu (2005) grew peanut plants of the cultivar Florunner from seed to maturity in greenhouses maintained at atmospheric CO_2 concentrations of 360 and 720 ppm and at air temperatures 1.5 and 6.0°C above outdoor air temperatures, measuring a number of parameters related to the plants' photosynthetic performance. They report rubisco photosynthetic efficiency—the ratio of midday light-saturated carbon exchange rate to rubisco initial or total activity—of the elevated-CO_2 plants was 1.3- to 1.9-fold greater than rubisco efficiency of the ambient-CO_2 plants at both growth temperatures. In addition, leaf soluble sugars and starch of plants grown at elevated CO_2 were 1.3- and 2-fold higher, respectively, than those of plants grown at ambient CO_2. Leaf transpiration of the elevated-CO_2 plants relative to the ambient-CO_2 plants was 12% less at near-ambient temperatures and 17% less in the higher temperature regime, and the water use efficiency of the elevated-CO_2 plants relative to the ambient-CO_2 plants was 56% greater at near-ambient temperatures and 41% greater in the higher temperature environment. Because less rubisco protein was required by the elevated-CO_2 plants, the subsequent redistribution of excess leaf nitrogen "would increase the efficiency of nitrogen use for peanut under elevated CO_2," just as the optimization of inorganic carbon acquisition and greater accumulation of the primary photosynthetic products in the CO_2-enriched plants "would be beneficial for peanut growth at elevated CO_2," Vu writes. Consequently, in the absence of other stresses, "peanut photosynthesis would perform well under rising atmospheric CO_2 and temperature predicted for this century," Vu concludes.

Crafts-Brandner and Salvucci (2004) explored the concurrent effects of elevated atmospheric CO_2 concentration and temperature on photosynthetic CO_2 fixation in cotton (*Gossypium hirsutum* L. cv. Coker 100A-glandless), using "intact plants and biochemical measurements to directly determine how environmental change impacts specific physiological mechanisms important to plant productivity." They report "net photosynthesis of cotton leaves at ambient levels of CO_2 was inhibited at leaf temperatures above about 32°C." At a leaf internal CO_2 concentration 4.3 times greater than ambient, however, net photosynthesis did not begin to decline until leaf temperatures rose above 40°C. Viewed another way, the net photosynthetic rate of cotton leaves exposed to ambient air declined by approximately 77% as leaf temperature rose from 32 to 40°C, whereas in leaves exposed to the CO_2-enriched air it rose by about 9%, indicating the increase in atmospheric CO_2 concentration more than compensated for the dramatic decrease in photosynthetic rate that would ordinarily result from the 8°C increase in temperature.

Aranjuelo *et al.* (2005) grew the forage crop alfalfa (*Medicago sativa* L.) in 13-L pots for three consecutive June–July periods (2001–2003) out-of-doors in polyethylene-covered temperature gradient tunnels maintained at atmospheric CO_2 concentrations that averaged 405 and 730 ppm at ambient (AT) and elevated (ET) temperatures (ET = AT + 4°C) and at high (HW) and low (LW) soil water contents (LW = 0.5HW). They fed all of the plants adequate nutrients except for nitrogen, to ensure the only source of nitrogen for the plants was that which was fixed by their nodules in response to inoculation with *Sinorhizobium meliloti* strain 102F78. The researchers report "the effect of elevated CO_2 on plant growth interacted positively with temperature," and "higher dry mass production of plants grown under elevated CO_2 and temperature was a consequence of enhanced photosynthetic rates." Mean CO_2-induced increases in leaf net photosynthesis over the entire experiment were found to be: +5% (HW, AT), +50% (HW, ET), +17% (LW, AT), and +42% (LW, ET), as best as can be determined from the bar graphs in the paper describing their study. Mean CO_2-induced increases in leaf biomass were +4% (HW, AT), +54% (HW, ET), +23% (LW, AT), and +58% (LW, ET), with the same caveat.

For both leaf net photosynthesis and biomass production, Aranjuelo *et al.* found the stimulatory effect of the elevated CO_2 was about 2.5 times greater in the warmer of the two temperature treatments in the low soil water regime and 10 times greater in the high soil water regime. In addition, the extra CO_2 benefited plant water loss via transpiration, which declined by 25% (HW, AT), 41% (HW, ET), 31% (LW, AT), and 31% (LW, ET). Under both well-watered and droughty conditions in this study, atmospheric CO_2 enrichment enhanced photosynthesis and biomass production in alfalfa, and

simultaneously decreased transpirational water losses.

Bencze *et al.* (2005) grew specimens of three varieties (Emma, Martina, and Mezofold) of winter wheat (*Triticum aestivum*) in controlled-environment chambers under ambient (375 ppm) and elevated (750 ppm) CO_2 at minimum, maximum, and mean temperature regimes of 10,12, and 10.7°C, respectively. Twelve days after the average date of heading, they subjected several plants of each variety to 15 more days of elevated temperatures (min/max/mean of 20, 35, and 25.2°C) to assess the independent effects of both elevated CO_2 and temperature on wheat growth and yield.

They found the temperature treatment accelerated the aging process in the three wheat varieties, and concurrent atmospheric CO_2 enrichment generally helped them maintain a higher and longer level of photosynthetic activity during grain-filling and maturation. Bencze *et al.* report the CO_2-enriched plants "suffered less damage from heat stress and produced a higher yield than at the ambient level." In addition, the extra CO_2 supplied to the Emma cultivar plants meant the difference between life and premature death, since by the end of the 15-day high-temperature treatment the plants growing in ambient air were dead, whereas those growing in elevated CO_2 survived for a few more days. In a future world of higher atmospheric CO_2 concentrations, wheat crops should be better able to withstand the stress of potentially higher temperatures, suffering less damage and producing greater yields.

Cen and Sage (2005) grew well-watered and well-fertilized sweet potato (*Ipomoea batatas* L.) plants in 20-L pots of soil in a greenhouse, periodically measuring light-saturated rates of net photosynthesis in new but fully expanded leaves in response to short-term changes in air temperature and atmospheric CO_2 concentration. In response to an approximate 370 ppm increase in the air's CO_2 concentration, the optimum leaf temperature for net photosynthesis—the leaf temperature at which net photosynthesis proceeds at its maximum rate—rose by approximately 4.5°C, and its maximal rate of net photosynthesis rose by about 75%. The doubling of the air's CO_2 concentration had no impact on net photosynthesis at a leaf temperature of 15°C but boosted it by 28% at 21°C, by 43% at 27°C, by 56% at 33°C, and by 70% at 39°C. In order for the net photosynthetic rate of sweet potatoes growing in air of 740 ppm CO_2 to drop below the maximum rate exhibited by plants growing in air of 370 ppm CO_2 (which occurred at a leaf temperature of 30°C), leaf temperature would have to rise by 12°C to a value of 42°C.

De Costa *et al.* (2006) write, "doubts have been expressed whether the expected yield increases [of rice] in response to increased CO_2 could be sustained under high temperature regimes." The investigators set out to learn whether this might happen in sub-humid Sri Lanka, where weekly maximum temperatures during both the maha (January to March) and yala (May to August) growing seasons typically range from 30 to 33°C. They grew two crops of rice (one in the maha season and one in the yala season) in open-top chambers maintained at atmospheric CO_2 concentrations of either 363 or 567 ppm under normal field conditions at the Rice Research and Development Institute of Sri Lanka, measuring a number of meteorological and plant physiological parameters throughout both seasons, as well as total biomass production and grain yield at the times of final harvest. They found the CO_2-induced increase in total plant biomass at the time of final harvest was 23% in the maha season and 37% in the yala season, and final grain yields were enhanced by 24% and 39% in the maha and yala seasons, respectively. These increases occurred even though air temperatures in the CO_2-enriched chambers were on average 1.6°C higher than air temperatures in the ambient-air chambers.

Borjigidai *et al.* (2006) grew rice (cv Akitakomachi) plants from seed in greenhouses maintained at atmospheric CO_2 concentrations of 370 and 570 ppm and then transplanted them to the field and grew them in a well-fertilized paddy culture in a FACE study at the same CO_2 concentrations under which the seeds were sprouted in both 2003 and 2004. At various times throughout the two growing seasons during the field portion of the experiments, the researchers made photosynthetic measurements of the most recently fully expanded leaves in full sunlight at a variety of different leaf temperatures. They report "the optimal temperature of photosynthesis (T_{opt}, the value where the photosynthetic rate was maximum) was significantly higher at elevated CO_2: it ranged from 22 to 34.5°C with an average value of 28.9°C at ambient CO_2, and from 29.5 to 37°C with an average value of 33.5°C at elevated CO_2."

Bernacchi *et al.* (2006) grew soybeans (*Glycine max* (L.) Merr.) for three years at the SoyFACE facility of the University of Illinois at Urbana-Champaign, Illinois (USA) at atmospheric CO_2 concentrations of either 375 or 550 ppm under natural field conditions, measuring a number of weather and plant physiological parameters from pre-dawn to post-dusk on several days during the three growing seasons. They found the mean daily integral of leaf-level net photosynthesis (A) was enhanced by nearly 25% in the CO_2-enriched air. In addition, the 11 scientists write, "there was a strong positive correlation between daytime maximum temperatures and mean daily integrated A at elevated CO_2." Their graphical representation of this relationship indicates at a daily maximum temperature of approximately 26.5°C, the CO_2-enriched air stimulated leaf-level net photosynthesis by about 14%, and at a daily maximum temperature of approximately 34.5°C, CO_2 enrichment stimulated photosynthesis by about 35%.

Koti *et al.* (2007) used Soil-Plant-Atmosphere-Research (SPAR) chambers at Mississippi State University (USA) to investigate the effects of doubled atmospheric CO_2 concentration (720 vs. 360 ppm) on the growth and development of six well-watered and well-fertilized soybean genotypes they grew from seed in pots filled with fine sand and exposed to the dual stresses of high day/night temperatures (38/30°C vs. 30/22°C) and high UV-B radiation levels (10 vs. 0 kJ/m²/day). They found the elevated CO_2 partially compensated for the damaging effects on vegetative growth and physiology caused by high temperatures and enhanced UV-B radiation levels, and elevated CO_2 had a positive influence on plant height, leaf area, total biomass, net photosynthesis, total chlorophyll content, phenolic content, and wax content, as well as relative plant injury.

Mishra *et al.* (2008) documented the positive impact of atmospheric CO_2 enrichment on the photosynthetic rates of field-grown soybean plants subjected to the simultaneous negative effects of acute heat stress and elevated atmospheric ozone (O_3) concentrations at the SoyFACE facility of the University of Illinois. The seven scientists discovered elevated ozone exacerbated heat-related decreases in photosynthetic electron transport, but "elevated CO_2 minimized or prevented light-dependent O_3-related decreases in electron transport (and thus photoinhibition) during heat stress."

Alonso *et al.* (2009) sequentially grew well-watered and well-fertilized plants of the wheat cultivar Alcala in 16-liter pots of perlite (sown at a rate of 35 seeds per pot) in a controlled-environment growth chamber—first at an atmospheric CO_2 concentration of 370 ppm and then at 700 ppm—from sowing through anthesis. They measured gas exchange in flag leaves at ear emergence to obtain the values of various plant physiological parameters required for the biochemical photosynthesis model developed by Farquhar *et al.* (1980), along with the responses of those parameters to changes in temperature. They found "photosynthesis response to temperature was negative at low air CO_2 concentrations and became progressively positive as CO_2 increased," which might have been expected "from the increase in photorespiration with temperature and the gradual inhibition of this process as CO_2 increases (Long, 1991)." In addition, "at high chloroplastic CO_2, photosynthesis in elevated growth CO_2 was lower at 15–25°C and higher at 30–35°C, than in ambient growth CO_2, implying an enhanced photosynthesis response to temperature in plants grown in elevated CO_2."

In 2004 and 2005, Gutierrez *et al.* (2009) grew well-watered and well-fertilized spring wheat (*Triticum aestivum* L. cv. Gazul) plants from seed to maturity out-of-doors in Salamanca, Spain in temperature-gradient chambers maintained at ambient (370 ppm) and elevated (700 ppm) atmospheric CO_2 concentrations and ambient air temperature (TA) and elevated air temperature (TE = TA plus 4°C). They titled their paper, "Acclimation to future atmospheric CO_2 levels increases photochemical efficiency and mitigates photochemistry inhibition by warm temperatures in wheat." They report net photosynthesis was increased by 62–72% in both years in the CO_2-enriched chambers; at the conclusions of the two growing seasons, total plant biomass production in the CO_2-enriched chambers was increased by 12–18%. They conclude, "future increases in atmospheric CO_2 and temperature may have a positive effect on photochemical efficiency," noting their work "provides evidence that with air CO_2 enrichment a reallocation of resources favoring light capture may occur."

Xiao *et al.* (2010) note "the impact of future climate change on crop production has been widely predicted by modeling the interaction between crops and climate change," adding it is currently thought "overall crop yields will decrease by 5–10% in China by 2030 as a result of climatic changes, and that the yields of wheat, rice and maize will be greatly reduced." They further note "the direct fertilization effect of rising CO_2 will offset these losses," citing Ewert *et al.* (2002) and Long *et al.* (2006). In addition, they remark, few real-world observations of the impacts of climate change on crop production have been reported.

The seven scientists conducted two sets of field experiments to evaluate the effects of warming on the productivity of winter wheat from 2006 to 2008 in the semiarid northwestern part of China: one set of experiments at the Tongwei County station located at the foot of Lulu Mountain (35°13'N, 105°14'E) at an altitude of 1,798 meters above sea level, and another set at the mountain's summit at an altitude of 2,351 meters. At each of these locations, they established four air temperature treatments (ambient and ambient plus 0.6, 1.4, and 2.2°C), which they created by placing electric heating wires on the surface of the soil between the rows of wheat, which induced the 0.6–2.2°C air temperature increases they measured at a height of 20 cm above the tops of the wheat canopies. They found this increase in temperature "will lead to a significant change in the growth stages and water use of winter wheat," and "crop yields at both high and low altitudes will likely increase," by 2.6% at low altitudes and 6.0% at high altitudes. Even without the benefits of the aerial fertilization and anti-transpiration effects of the rise in the air's CO_2 content, the increase in temperature predicted by climate models for the year 2050 likely will lead to increases in winter wheat production in the northwestern part of China, not the decreases some modeling studies have predicted.

Yoon *et al.* (2009) grew well-watered and well-fertilized cotton plants from seed to maturity—one plant to each container of washed sand, with spacing between plants similar to the plant spacing found in typical cotton fields—in the Georgia Envirotron at the University of Georgia Griffin Campus. They placed the containers with their plants in chambers maintained at all combinations of two day/night air temperatures regimes (25/15°C and 35/25°C) and three atmospheric CO_2 concentrations (400, 600, and 800 ppm). At the lower of the two air temperature regimes, the authors found "final boll weight at harvest was 1.59 times (at 600 ppm) and 6.3 times (at 800 ppm) higher compared to ambient CO_2." Further increasing the temperature tremendously increased this difference, as "the final boll weight was 34.1 times (at 600 ppm) and 23.3 times (at 800 ppm) higher compared to ambient CO_2." In addition, "the response of final lint yield to CO_2 was more or less similar to the response of boll weight."

Thus a significant body of scientific literature suggests a continuation of the rise in the air's CO_2 content likely will lead to enhanced rates of photosynthesis and biomass production by agricultural crops, which will not be diminished by any global warming that might occur concurrently. If the ambient air temperature rises, the growth-promoting effects of atmospheric CO_2 enrichment likely will rise right along with it, in agreement with the experimental observations reviewed by Idso and Idso (1994). The biosphere will continue producing the food and fiber needed for an increasing population.

Beyond this natural phenomenon, Meerburg *et al.* (2009) describe how crop yields will continue to increase in the future because of "the development and adoption of new technologies and improved farm management," citing Ewert *et al.* (2005), who demonstrated continuing advances in agricultural technology historically have been the most important drivers of productivity change. Between 1961 and 2007, Meerburg *et al.* report, "average US corn yields increased by 240%, from 3.9 tons per hectare per year to 9.4 tons per hectare per year," citing the FAO (2009) and noting some researchers have predicted "advances in agronomics, breeding, and biotechnology will lead to an average corn yield in the US of just over 20 tons per hectare per year in 2030," citing Duvick (2005).

Meerburg *et al.* also note farmers in Brazil successfully increased the productivity of soybeans, maize, and cotton during the past decade even though the cumulative number of days of exposure to temperatures above the three crops' optimum values "is far greater than in the US." In the Brazilian state of Mato Grosso, for example, "maximum average day temperature exceeds 35°C for 118 days per year, of which 75 days are in the average soybean-growing season." Nevertheless, they report the average production of soybeans in 2008 was about 3.1 tons per hectare per year in Mexico, and the average yield in the United States was 2.8 tons per hectare per year. Similarly, they note the mean cotton yield in Brazil in 2006/2007 was 1.4 tons per hectare per year, while in the United States it was 0.9 tons per hectare per year.

The seven scientists thus conclude "temperatures higher than currently experienced in the US do not necessarily need to coincide with lower crop yields and … already existing technology and future advances (new varieties, optimized farm management, biotechnology, etc.) can overrule the negative effect of increasing temperatures on yield."

References

Alexandrov, V.A. and Hoogenboom, G. 2000. The impact of climate variability and change on crop yield in Bulgaria. *Agricultural and Forest Meteorology* **104**: 315–327.

Aloni, B., Peet, M., Pharr, M., and Karni, L. 2001. The effect of high temperature and high atmospheric CO_2 on carbohydrate changes in bell pepper (*Capsicum annuum*) pollen in relation to its germination. *Physiologia Plantarum* **112**: 505–512.

Alonso, A., Perez, P., and Martinez-Carrasco, R. 2009. Growth in elevated CO_2 enhances temperature response of photosynthesis in wheat. *Physiologia Plantarum* **135**: 109–120.

Aranjuelo, I., Irigoyen, J.J., Perez, P., Martinez-Carrasco, R., and Sanchez-Diaz, M. 2005. The use of temperature gradient tunnels for studying the combined effect of CO_2, temperature and water availability in N_2 fixing alfalfa plants. *Annals of Applied Biology* **146**: 51–60.

Bencze, S., Veisz, O., and Bedo, Z. 2005. Effect of elevated CO_2 and high temperature on the photosynthesis and yield of wheat. *Cereal Research Communications* **33**: 385–388.

Bernacchi, C.J., Leakey, A.D.B., Heady, L.E., Morgan, P.B., Dohleman, F.G., McGrath, J.M., Gillespie, K.M., Wittig, V.E., Rogers, A., Long, S.P., and Ort, D.R. 2006. Hourly and seasonal variation in photosynthesis and stomatal conductance of soybean grown at future CO_2 and ozone concentrations for 3 years under fully open-air field conditions. *Plant, Cell and Environment* 10.1111/j.1365-3040.2006.01581.x

Berry, J. and Bjorkman, O. 1980. Photosynthetic response and adaptation to temperature in higher plants. *Annual Review of Plant Physiology* **31**: 491–543.

Borjigidai, A., Hikosaka, K., Hirose, T., Hasegawa, T., Okada, M., and Kobayashi, K. 2006. Seasonal changes in temperature dependence of photosynthetic rate in rice under a free-air CO_2 enrichment. *Annals of Botany* **97**: 549–557.

Bunce, J.A. 1998. The temperature dependence of the stimulation of photosynthesis by elevated carbon dioxide in wheat and barley. *Journal of Experimental Botany* **49**: 1555–1561.

Bunce, J.A. 2001. Seasonal patterns of photosynthetic response and acclimation to elevated carbon dioxide in field-grown strawberry. *Photosynthesis Research* **68**: 237–245.

Cen, Y.-P. and Sage, R.E. 2005. The regulation of Rubisco activity in response to variation in temperature and atmospheric CO_2 partial pressure in sweet potato. *Plant Physiology* **139**: 979–990.

Cowling, S.A. 1999. Plants and temperature—CO_2 uncoupling. *Science* **285**: 1500–1501.

Cowling, S.A. and Sage, R.F. 1998. Interactive effects of low atmospheric CO_2 and elevated temperature on growth, photosynthesis and respiration in *Phaseolus vulgaris*. *Plant, Cell and Environment* 21: 427–435.

Crafts-Brandner, S.J. and Salvucci, M.E. 2004. Analyzing the impact of high temperature and CO_2 on net photosynthesis: biochemical mechanisms, models and genomics. *Field Crops Research* 90: 75–85.

De Costa, W.A.J.M., Weerakoon, W.M.W., Herath, H.M.L.K., Amaratunga, K.S.P., and Abeywardena, R.M.I. 2006. Physiology of yield determination of rice under elevated carbon dioxide at high temperatures in a subhumid tropical climate. *Field Crops Research* 96: 336–347.

Demmers-Derks, H., Mitchell, R.A.G., Mitchell, V.J., and Lawlor, D.W. 1998. Response of sugar beet (*Beta vulgaris* L.) yield and biochemical composition to elevated CO_2 and temperature at two nitrogen applications. *Plant, Cell and Environment* 21: 829–836.

Duvick, D.N. 2005. The contribution of breeding to yield advances in maize (*Zea mays* L.). *Advances in Agronomy* 86: 83–145.

Ewert, F., Rodriguez, D., Jamieson, P., Semenov, M.A., Mitchell, R.A.C., Goudriaan, J., Porter, J.R., Kimball, B.A., Pinter Jr., P.J., Manderscheid, R., Weigel, H.J., Fangmeier, A., Fereres, E., and Villalobos, F. 2002. Effects of elevated CO_2 and drought on wheat: testing crop simulation models for different experimental and climatic conditions. *Agriculture, Ecosystems and Environment* 93: 249–266.

Ewert, F., Rounsevell, M.D.A., Reginster, I., Metzger, M.J., and Leemans, R. 2005. Future scenarios of European agricultural land use: I. Estimating changes in crop productivity. *Agriculture, Ecosystems and Environment* 107: 101–116.

FAO. 2009. FAOSTAT Database. United Nations Food and Agriculture Organization. Available at www.fao.org. Accessed 8 September 2009.

Farquhar, G.D., von Caemmerer, S., and Berry, J.A. 1980. A biochemical model of photosynthetic CO_2 assimilation in leaves of C_3 species. *Planta* 149: 78–90.

Ferris, R., Wheeler, T.R., Ellis, R.H., and Hadley, P. 1999. Seed yield after environmental stress in soybean grown under elevated CO_2. *Crop Science* 39: 710–718.

Ferris, R., Wheeler, T.R., Hadley, P., and Ellis, R.H. 1998. Recovery of photosynthesis after environmental stress in soybean grown under elevated CO_2. *Crop Science* 38: 948–955.

Fritschi, F.B., Boote, K.J., Sollenberger, L.E., Allen Jr., L.H., and Sinclair, T.R. 1999. Carbon dioxide and temperature effects on forage establishment: photosynthesis and biomass production. *Global Change Biology* 5: 441–453.

Gutierrez, D., Gutierrez, E., Perez, P., Morcuende, R., Verdejo, A.L., and Martinez-Carrasco, R. 2009. Acclimation to future atmospheric CO_2 levels increases photochemical efficiency and mitigates photochemistry inhibition by warm temperatures in wheat under field chambers. *Physiologia Plantarum* 137: 86–100.

Hakala, K. 1998. Growth and yield potential of spring wheat in a simulated changed climate with increased CO_2 and higher temperature. *European Journal of Agronomy* 9: 41–52.

Idso, K.E. and Idso, S.B. 1994. Plant responses to atmospheric CO_2 enrichment in the face of environmental constraints: A review of the past 10 years' research. *Agricultural and Forest Meteorology* 69: 153–203.

Idso, S.B. 1998. CO_2-induced global warming: a skeptic's view of potential climate change. *Climate Research* 10: 69–82.

Koti, S., Reddy, K.R., Kakani, V.G., Zhao, D., and Gao, W. 2007. Effects of carbon dioxide, temperature and ultraviolet-B radiation and their interactions on soybean (*Glycine max* L.) growth and development. *Environmental and Experimental Botany* 60: 1–10.

Long, S.P. 1991. Modification of the response of photosynthetic productivity to rising temperature by atmospheric CO_2 concentrations: Has its importance been underestimated? *Plant, Cell and Environment* 14: 729–739.

Long, S.P., Ainsworth, E.A., Leakey, A.D.B., Nosberger, J., and Ort, D.R. 2006. Food for thought: lower-than-expected crop yield simulation with rising CO2 concentrations. *Science* 312: 1918–1921.

McMurtrie, R.E., Comins, H.N., Kirschbaum, M.U.F., and Wang, Y.-P. 1992. Modifying existing forest growth models to take account of effects of elevated CO_2. *Australian Journal of Botany* 40: 657–677.

McMurtrie, R.E. and Wang, Y.-P. 1993. Mathematical models of the photosynthetic response of tree stands to rising CO_2 concentrations and temperatures. *Plant, Cell and Environment* 16: 1–13.

Meerburg, B.G., Verhagen, A., Jongschaap, R.E.E., Franke, A.C., Schaap, B.F., Dueck, T.A., and van der Werf, A. 2009. Do nonlinear temperature effects indicate severe damages to US crop yields under climate change? *Proceedings of the National Academy of Sciences USA* 106: 10.1073 pnas.0910618106.

Mishra, S., Heckathorn, S.A., Barua, D., Wang, D., Joshi, P., Hamilton III, E.W., and Frantz, J. 2008. Interactive effects of elevated CO_2 and ozone on leaf thermotolerance in field-grown *Glycine max*. *Journal of Integrative Plant Biology* 50: 1396–1405.

Prasad, P.V.V., Boote, K.J., Allen Jr., L.H., and Thomas, J.M.G. 2003. Super-optimal temperatures are detrimental to peanut (*Arachis hypogaea* L.) reproductive processes and yield at both ambient and elevated carbon dioxide. *Global Change Biology* **9**: 1775–1787.

Reddy, K.K., Davidonis, G.H., Johnson, A.S., and Vinyard, B.T. 1999. Temperature regime and carbon dioxide enrichment alter cotton boll development and fiber properties. *Agronomy Journal* **91**: 851–858.

Reddy, K.R., Robana, R.R., Hodges, H.F., Liu, X.J., and McKinion, J.M. 1998. Interactions of CO_2 enrichment and temperature on cotton growth and leaf characteristics. *Environmental and Experimental Botany* **39**: 117–129.

Stuhlfauth, T. and Fock, H.P. 1990. Effect of whole season CO_2 enrichment on the cultivation of a medicinal plant, *Digitalis lanata. Journal of Agronomy and Crop Science* **164**: 168–173.

Tako, Y., Arai, R., Otsubo, K., and Nitta, K. 2001. Application of crop gas exchange and transpiration data obtained with CEEF to global change problem. *Advances in Space Research* **27**: 1541–1545.

Taub, D.R., Seeman, J.R., and Coleman, J.S. 2000. Growth in elevated CO_2 protects photosynthesis against high-temperature damage. *Plant, Cell and Environment* **23**: 649–656.

Vu, J.C.V. 2005. Acclimation of peanut (*Arachis hypogaea* L.) leaf photosynthesis to elevated growth CO_2 and temperature. *Environmental and Experimental Botany* **53**: 85–95.

Wurr, D.C.E., Edmondson, R.N., and Fellows, J.R. 2000. Climate change: a response surface study of the effects of CO_2 and temperature on the growth of French beans. *Journal of Agricultural Science* **135**: 379–387.

Xiao, G., Zhang, Q., Li, Y., Wang, R., Yao, Y., Zhao, H., and Bai, H. 2010. Impact of temperature increase on the yield of winter wheat at low and high altitudes in semiarid northwestern China. *Agricultural Water Management* **97**: 1360–1364.

Yoon, S.T., Hoogenboom, G., Flitcroft, I., and Bannayan, M. 2009. Growth and development of cotton (*Gossypium hirsutum* L.) in response to CO_2 enrichment under two different temperature regimes. *Environmental and Experimental Botany* **67**: 178–187.

Zhu, J., Goldstein, G., and Bartholomew, D.P. 1999. Gas exchange and carbon isotope composition of *Ananas comosus* in response to elevated CO_2 and temperature. *Plant, Cell and Environment* **22**: 999–1007.

Ziska, L.H. 1998. The influence of root zone temperature on photosynthetic acclimation to elevated carbon dioxide concentrations. *Annals of Botany* **81**: 717–721.

3.13.2 Grasslands

• As the air's CO_2 content rises, grassland plants likely will exhibit enhanced rates of photosynthesis and biomass production that will not be diminished by any global warming that might occur. If the ambient air temperature does rise, the growth-promoting effects of atmospheric CO_2 enrichment likely will rise also. Grasslands are likely to produce increasingly greater amounts of forage and perhaps reclaim areas of barren ground in certain environments.

As the atmosphere's CO_2 content rises, most plants, including those of various grassland ecosystems, will exhibit increased rates of photosynthesis and biomass production. This increase in productivity should increase the amount of forage available for grazing animals and possibly reduce the land area occupied by bare soil in certain environments. However, some researchers claim global warming will negate the growth-promoting effects of atmospheric CO_2 enrichment and cause the opposite to occur. This section reviews the results of experimental studies of the photosynthetic and growth responses of grassland plants to atmospheric CO_2 enrichment when exposed to higher-than normal-temperatures.

The optimum growth temperatures of many plants have been demonstrated to rise substantially with increasing concentrations of atmospheric CO_2 (Berry and Bjorkman, 1980; Stuhlfauth and Fock, 1990; McMurtrie *et al.*, 1992; McMurtrie and Wang, 1993), as has been described in more detail by Long (1991), Idso and Idso (1994), and Cowling and Sykes (1999). These previously observed positive CO_2 x temperature interactions have continued to appear in more recent studies of the subject for grassland species.

Lilley *et al.* (2001) grew swards of subterranean clover (*Trifolium subterraneum*) at 380 and 690 ppm CO_2 in combination with simultaneous exposure to ambient and elevated (ambient plus 3.4°C) air temperatures. After one year of these treatments, they found elevated CO_2 increased foliage growth by 19% at ambient air temperatures. At elevated air temperatures, the CO_2-enriched plants displayed a growth enhancement of only 8%, but the plants grown at ambient CO_2 exhibited a 28% reduction in foliage growth. Similarly, Morgan *et al.* (2001) determined twice-ambient levels of atmospheric CO_2 increased aboveground biomass in native shortgrass steppe ecosystems by an average of 38%, despite an average air temperature increase of 2.6°C. And when bahiagrass was grown across a temperature gradient of 4.5°C, Fritschi *et al.* (1999) found a 275 ppm increase in the air's CO_2 content boosted photosynthesis and aboveground biomass by 22 and 17%, respectively, independent of air temperature.

Greer *et al.* (2000) grew five pasture species at 18 and 28°C and found plants concomitantly exposed to 700 ppm CO_2 displayed average photosynthetic rates 36 and 70% greater, respectively, than average rates of control plants grown in air of ambient CO_2 concentration. The average CO_2-induced biomass increase for the five species rose dramatically with increasing air temperature, from only 8% at 18°C to 95% at 28°C.

Stirling *et al.* (1998) had found much the same thing. They nurtured five fast-growing native annual species in glasshouses maintained at two combinations of CO_2 (ambient and ambient plus 340 ppm) and temperature (ambient and ambient plus 3°C) for eight weeks, to assess their growth responses to elevated CO_2 and temperature. Elevated CO_2 significantly increased photosynthetic rates, by 18–36% for all species, independent of growth temperature, for the entire eight weeks of the experiment. The persistence of this photosynthetic enhancement led to total plant biomass increases for CO_2-enriched plants, on average, 25% greater than those of control plants grown in ambient-CO_2 air. And although elevated CO_2 and elevated temperature together had few significant interactive effects on the various metrics of growth, the overall CO_2 growth response was generally slightly larger at elevated than at ambient temperatures.

In a similar study with similar findings, Newman *et al.* (2001) grew two perennial grassland species (rhizoma peanut-*Arachis glabrata* and bahiagrass-*Paspalum notatum*) native to South America and common to Florida (USA) in greenhouses fumigated with air of either 360 or 700 ppm CO_2 for three full growing seasons. The C_3 and C_4 grasses were simultaneously exposed to air temperatures ranging from ambient to 4.5°C above ambient. Averaged across the three growing seasons, elevated CO_2 increased dry matter production in rhizoma peanut and bahiagrass by 25 and 15%, respectively. Here too, the researchers found no significant interactive effects of elevated CO_2 and temperature on dry mass production in these species, and on their own, air temperatures 4.5°C above ambient increased dry matter production in both species by an average of 13% across all three years.

Niklaus *et al.* (2001) established experimental plots in a nutrient-poor calcareous grassland in northwestern Switzerland that contained either 31, 12, or five species, removing selected species from some of the plots so the proportion of plant functional types in each of the plots remained unchanged (55% graminoids, 15% legumes, and 30% non-legume forbs). They fumigated the plots with air of either 360 or 600 ppm CO_2 for four years, to determine the ecological effects of elevated CO_2 across a biodiversity gradient in this grassland community. As plant community diversity decreased at ambient CO_2, soil nitrate concentrations increased, the scientists report. Elevated CO_2, however, reduced soil nitrate concentrations at all the studied levels of plant diversity. In addition, nitrification—a biological process that yields nitrate—increased with decreasing species diversity at ambient CO_2, and at elevated CO_2, rates of nitrification were 25% lower than those observed at ambient CO_2 at all levels of community diversity, suggesting a CO_2-enriched environment would reduce the risk of nitrate pollution of groundwater.

Hakala and Mela (1996) grew field-sown meadow fescue (*Festuca pratensis* cv. Kalevi) in open-top chambers and glasshouses maintained at atmospheric CO_2 concentrations of 350 and 700 ppm in combination with ambient and elevated (ambient plus 3°C) air temperatures for four consecutive years to determine the effects on aboveground biomass production in this important forage crop. They found elevated CO_2 significantly increased aboveground biomass by an average of 18% in each of the four study years, but the effect occurred only when plants were concomitantly exposed to elevated air temperatures.

Sinclair *et al.* (2007) note it has long been assumed global warming would be bad for plants that appear to be adapted to cool temperatures and typically exhibit reduced growth rates in warmer environments. Using climate-controlled mini-greenhouses, the five researchers tested this assumption by examining the interacting effects of air temperature and vapor pressure deficit (VPD) on the growth of tall fescue (*Festuca arundinacea* Schreb), a cool-season grass that from past studies was expected to show declining growth with warmer temperatures over the range of 18.5 to 27°C. They grew well-watered and -fertilized plants in two sets of six-week-long experiments, one in which air VPD was held constant at 1.2 kPa while air temperature was maintained at either 18.5, 21, 24, or 27°C, and one in which air temperature was held constant at 22°C while air VPD was maintained at either 0.9, 1.2, 1.4, or 1.7 kPa.

In the experiment where the air VPD was held constant, they write, "in direct contrast to the anticipated results, the weekly growth of the tall fescue was substantially increased with increased temperature," as "growth at 24 and 27°C was about 2.3 times that at 18.5°C and 1.4 times that at 21°C." In the experiment where air temperature was held constant, "there was a strong, negative influence of increasing VPD on plant growth." In addition, "transpiration rates were similar across treatments," indicating "water movement through the plants did not increase in response to increasing VPD." This led them to conclude limitation of water movement through the plant "is likely a result of stomatal closure in response to elevated VPD (Bunce, 2006)." This phenomenon also would restrict the CO_2 diffusion pathway into the plants and result in a decrease in photosynthesis, which is likely what caused the decreased growth at increased VPD. Nonetheless, their results indicate as long as the air VPD does not rise concurrently, increasing temperatures do not lead to growth reductions in this cool-season plant. In fact, they observe just the opposite to be true—warming dramatically increased tall fescue growth.

Sinclair *et al.* note, "during the past 50 years, VPD has remained virtually constant (Szilagyi *et al.*, 2001) due to an increase in atmospheric dew point temperature (Gaffen and Ross, 1999)," even in the face of what IPCC describes as unprecedented global warming. In a future warmer world, they conclude, "tall fescue, and perhaps other cool season species, could experience a substantial benefit with temperature increases expected in temperate zones if VPD were to remain unchanged."

Wolfe-Bellin *et al.* (2006) write, "nocturnal temperatures are predicted to increase more than diurnal temperatures," as has been observed in the real world over much of the twentieth century, and it might be expected "increased nocturnal temperature would increase dark respiration rate" and thereby "diminish the positive effects of elevated CO_2 on whole-plant growth, as measured by total biomass." In an experiment designed to explore this hypothesis, they grew the C_3 forb *Phytolacca americana* L. from the four-leaf stage to maturity under well-watered and well-fertilized conditions in 6.2-L containers filled with a general purpose growing medium in controlled-environment glass chambers maintained at either 370 or 740 ppm CO_2 at diurnal/nocturnal

temperatures of either 26°/20°C or 26°/24°C. They periodically measured the plants' light-saturated photosynthetic rates and whole-plant biomass. They found "plant photosynthetic rate was greater under elevated CO_2 [+69% during the first part of the growing season], and dark respiration rate, predicted to increase under higher nocturnal temperatures, exhibited no response to the nocturnal temperature treatment." In contrast to their prediction, the forb they studied "exhibited no diminishment of total plant size in response to elevated nocturnal temperature," and "time to flowering decreased and biomass allocation to reproduction increased under conditions of elevated nocturnal temperatures." They conclude, "elevated CO_2 and high nocturnal temperatures of the future could have a neutral or even positive effect on the growth of northern *P. americana* populations," even to the extent of "increasing population sizes, at least for plants growing at the northern edge of the species' range."

Niu *et al.* (2010) note, "most modeling studies predict ecosystem carbon storage will decrease as respiration is stimulated more than photosynthesis by rising temperature, with a consequent positive feedback to climate warming." Working in a tallgrass prairie in McClain County, Oklahoma (USA) dominated by C_4 grasses and C_3 forbs that had not been grazed for the prior 40 years, they conducted a warming experiment in which they used infrared heaters to elevate soil temperature at a depth of 2.5 cm by an average of 1.96°C from 2000 to 2008, and "yearly biomass clipping mimicked hay or biofuel feedstock harvest."

They found the experimental warming "significantly stimulated carbon storage in aboveground plant, root, and litter pools by 17%, 38%, and 29%, respectively, averaged over the nine years," but it "did not change soil carbon content or nitrogen content in any pool." They conclude increased plant nitrogen use efficiency played a more important role than soil nitrogen availability in regulating carbon cycling in this ecosystem, as the tallgrass prairie experienced a significant increase in productivity caused solely by the warming of its soil and not promoted by any addition of nitrogen to it. They explain this result by stating, "increased inputs of more recalcitrant [higher carbon:nitrogen ratio] material into soil counterbalanced any direct warming stimulation of carbon release, leading to little change in soil carbon stock and no apparent feedback to climate warming."

Morgan *et al.* (2011) write, "global warming is

predicted to induce desiccation in many world regions through increases in evaporative demand," but "rising CO_2 may counter that trend by improving plant water-use efficiency." However, they note, "it is not clear how important this CO_2-enhanced water use efficiency might be in offsetting warming-induced desiccation because higher CO_2 also leads to higher plant biomass, and therefore greater transpirational surface."

Morgan *et al.* conducted a prairie heating and CO_2 enrichment (PHACE) experiment in which they evaluated the productivity of native mixed-grass prairie west of Cheyenne, Wyoming (USA) to two levels of atmospheric CO_2 concentration (385 and 600 ppm, supplied via standard FACE technology) and two temperature regimes—ambient and elevated (ambient plus 1.5/3.0°C warmer day/night temperatures) for three full growing seasons (2007–2009) by means of T-FACE technology (Kimball *et al.*, 2008)—after first having measured grassland productivity under unmodified conditions for one growing season (2005) and with CO_2 enrichment alone for a second season (2006).

The 10 researchers report their warming treatment reduced annual soil water content by 13.1%, but their elevated CO_2 treatment increased annual soil water content by 17.3%, demonstrating "the water conservation effects of elevated CO_2 can completely cancel the desiccating effects of moderately warmer temperatures." In addition, they write, "exposure of the prairie to 600 ppm CO_2 increased peak total above-ground biomass by an average 33% in the first 3 years of the experiment when annual precipitation amounts were in 7% of the site's 132-year average of 388 mm," but "CO_2 enrichment had no effect on above-ground biomass in 2009," when "annual precipitation was 17% higher than the long-term mean." They speculate the "higher soil water content in 2009 minimized the potential water-relations benefit of CO_2 enrichment on plant productivity."

Morgan *et al.* write, "many believe that CO_2-induced reductions in transpiration at the leaf level will be largely offset at the canopy level by increases in leaf area," citing McNaughton and Jarvis (1991), Piao *et al.* (2007), Frelich and Reich (2010), and Seager and Vecchi (2010). They say their results "clearly illustrate the importance of compensating CO_2 and warming effects in semi-arid ecosystems" and "indicate that in a warmer, CO_2-enriched world, both soil water content and productivity in semi-arid grasslands may be higher than previously expected." In an accompanying commentary on their paper,

Baldocchi (2011) writes, "Morgan and colleagues provide one of the first and best views of how a mixed-grass ecosystem growing in a semi-arid climate will respond to future CO_2 and climatic conditions." Morgan *et al.*'s findings help explain the great CO_2-induced greening of the Earth phenomenon (see section 4.2, this volume), especially as manifested in semi-arid regions of the planet.

Even if the air's CO_2 content were to cease rising or have no effect on plants, it is still possible temperature increases alone would promote plant growth and development in some situations. Norton *et al.* (1999) found this to be the case. Elevated CO_2 had essentially no effect on the growth of the perennial grass *Agrostis curtisii* after two years of fumigation, whereas a 3°C increase in air temperature increased the growth of the species considerably.

The recent scientific literature indicates grassland plants likely will exhibit enhanced rates of photosynthesis and biomass production as the air's CO_2 content rises, and those benefits will not be diminished by any global warming that might occur. If the ambient air temperature does rise, the growth-promoting effects of atmospheric CO_2 enrichment likely will rise right along with it, becoming increasingly robust in agreement with the experimental observations reviewed by Idso and Idso (1994). As long as the air's CO_2 content continues to rise, grasslands will likely produce increasingly great amounts of forage, and perhaps reclaim areas of barren ground in certain environments.

References

Baldocchi, D. 2011. The grass response. *Nature* **476**: 160–161.

Berry, J. and Bjorkman, O. 1980. Photosynthetic response and adaptation to temperature in higher plants. *Annual Review of Plant Physiology* **31**: 491–543.

Bunce, J.A. 2006. How do leaf hydraulics limit stomatal conductance at high water vapor pressure deficits? *Plant, Cell and Environment* **29**: 1644–1650.

Cowling, S.A. and Sykes, M.T. 1999. Physiological significance of low atmospheric CO_2 for plant-climate interactions. *Quaternary Research* **52**: 237–242.

Frelich, L.E. and Reich, P.B. 2010. Will environmental changes reinforce the impact of global warming on the prairie-forest border of central north America? *Frontiers in Ecology and the Environment* **8**: 371–378.

Fritschi, F.B., Boote, K.J., Sollenberger, L.E., Allen Jr.,

L.H., and Sinclair, T.R. 1999. Carbon dioxide and temperature effects on forage establishment: photosynthesis and biomass production. *Global Change Biology* **5**: 441–453.

Gaffen, D.J. and Ross, R.J. 1999. Climatology and trends of U.S. surface humidity and temperature. *Journal of Climate* **12**: 811–828.

Greer, D.H., Laing, W.A., Campbell, B.D., and Halligan, E.A. 2000. The effect of perturbations in temperature and photon flux density on the growth and photosynthetic responses of five pasture species. *Australian Journal of Plant Physiology* **27**: 301–310.

Hakala, K. and Mela, T. 1996. The effects of prolonged exposure to elevated temperatures and elevated CO_2 levels on the growth, yield and dry matter partitioning of field-sown meadow fescue. *Agriculture and Food Science in Finland* **5**: 285–298.

Idso, K.E. and Idso, S.B. 1994. Plant responses to atmospheric CO_2 enrichment in the face of environmental constraints: A review of the past 10 years' research. *Agricultural and Forest Meteorology* **69**: 153–203.

Kimball, B.A., Conley, M., Wang, S., Xingwu, L., Morgan, J., and Smith, D. 2008. Infrared heater arrays for warming ecosystem field plots. *Global Change Biology* **14**: 309–320.

Lilley, J.M., Bolger, T.P., and Gifford, R.M. 2001. Productivity of *Trifolium subterraneum* and *Phalaris aquatica* under warmer, higher CO_2 conditions. *New Phytologist* **150**: 371–383.

Long, S.P. 1991. Modification of the response of photosynthetic productivity to rising temperature by atmospheric CO_2 concentrations: Has its importance been underestimated? *Plant, Cell and Environment* **14**: 729–739.

McMurtrie, R.E., Comins, H.N., Kirschbaum, M.U.F., and Wang, Y.-P. 1992. Modifying existing forest growth models to take account of effects of elevated CO_2. *Australian Journal of Botany* **40**: 657–677.

McMurtrie, R.E. and Wang, Y.-P. 1993. Mathematical models of the photosynthetic response of tree stands to rising CO_2 concentrations and temperatures. *Plant, Cell and Environment* **16**: 1–13.

McNaughton, K.G. and Jarvis, P.G. 1991. Effects of spatial scale on stomatal control of transpiration. *Agricultural and Forest Meteorology* **54**: 279–301.

Morgan, J.A., LeCain, D.R., Mosier, A.R., and Milchunas, D.G. 2001. Elevated CO_2 enhances water relations and productivity and affects gas exchange in C_3 and C_4 grasses of the Colorado shortgrass steppe. *Global Change Biology* **7**: 451–466.

Morgan, J.A., LeCain, D.R., Pendall, E., Blumenthal, D.M., Kimball, B.A., Carrillo, Y., Williams, D.G., Heisler-White, J., Dijkstra, F.A., and West, M. 2011. C4 grasses prosper as carbon dioxide eliminates desiccation in warmed semi-arid grassland. *Nature* **476**: 202–205.

Newman, Y.C., Sollenberger, L.E., Boote, K.J., Allen Jr., L.H., and Littell, R.C. 2001. Carbon dioxide and temperature effects on forage dry matter production. *Crop Science* **41**: 399–406.

Niklaus, P.A., Kandeler, E., Leadley, P.W., Schmid, B., Tscherko, D., and Korner, C. 2001. A link between plant diversity, elevated CO_2 and soil nitrate. *Oecologia* **127**: 540–548.

Niu, S., Sherry, R.A., Zhou, X., Wan, S., and Luo, Y. 2010. Nitrogen regulation of the climate-carbon feedback: evidence from a long-term global change experiment. *Ecology* **91**: 3261–3273.

Norton, L.R., Firbank, L.G., Gray, A.J., and Watkinson, A.R. 1999. Responses to elevated temperature and CO_2 in the perennial grass *Agrostis curtisii* in relation to population origin. *Functional Ecology* **13**: 29–37.

Piao, S., Friedlingstein, P., Ciais, P., de Noblet-Ducoudre, N., Labat, D., and Zaehle, S. 2007. Changes in climate and land use have a larger direct impact than rising CO_2 on global river runoff trends. *Proceedings of the National Academy of Sciences USA* **104**: 15,242–15,247.

Seager, R. and Vecchi, G.A. 2010. Greenhouse warming and the 21st century hydroclimate of southwestern North America. *Proceedings of the National Academy of Sciences USA* **107**: 21,277–21,282.

Sinclair, T., Fiscus, E., Wherley, B., Durham, M., and Rufty, T. 2007. Atmospheric vapor pressure deficit is critical in predicting growth response of "cool-season" grass *Festuca arundinacea* to temperature change. *Planta* **227**: 273–276.

Stirling, C.M., Heddell-Cowie, M., Jones, M.L., Ashenden, T.W., and Sparks, T.H. 1998. Effects of elevated CO_2 and temperature on growth and allometry of five native fast-growing annual species. *New Phytologist* **140**: 343–354.

Stuhlfauth, T. and Fock, H.P. 1990. Effect of whole season CO_2 enrichment on the cultivation of a medicinal plant, *Digitalis lanata*. *Journal of Agronomy and Crop Science* **164**: 168–173.

Szilagyi, J., Katul, G.G., and Parlange, M.B. 2001. Evapotranspiration intensifies over the conterminous United States. *Journal of Water Resources Planning and Management* **127**: 354–362.

Wolfe-Bellin, K.S., He, J.-S., and Bazzaz, F.A. 2006. Leaf-level physiology, biomass, and reproduction of *Phytolacca americana* under conditions of elevated carbon dioxide and increased nocturnal temperature. *International Journal of Plant Science* **167**:1011–1020.

3.13.3 Woody Plants

- As the air's CO_2 content rises, trees likely will exhibit enhanced rates of photosynthesis and biomass production that will not be counteracted by any global warming that might occur. If the ambient air temperature rises, the growth-promoting effects of atmospheric CO_2 enrichment likely will rise also. Trees are likely to produce greater amounts of biomass and, therefore, more timber products to meet the increasing needs of Earth's growing human population in the future.

As the air's CO_2 content rises, most trees likely will exhibit increased rates of photosynthesis and biomass production, which can help meet human demands for wood products. However, some researchers claim global warming will negate the growth-promoting effects of atmospheric CO_2 enrichment and actually reduce tree growth. To determine whether this claim has any validity, this section examines the results of several studies designed to reveal the net effect of both elevated CO_2 and air temperature on the growth of trees and other woody plants.

The optimum growth temperature for several plants already has been shown to rise substantially with increasing levels of atmospheric CO_2 (Berry and Bjorkman, 1980; Stuhlfauth and Fock, 1990; McMurtrie *et al.*, 1992; McMurtrie and Wang, 1993). Long (1991) described this phenomenon at length, having calculated from well-established plant physiological principles that most C_3 plants should increase their optimum growth temperature by approximately 5°C in response to a 300 ppm increase in the atmosphere's CO_2 concentration. In a subsequent review of the pertinent scientific literature, Cowling and Sykes (1999) demonstrated this was true for a number of plants. The photosynthetic rates of woody plants also are likely to rise in tandem with increases in the air's CO_2 concentration and temperature, as previously documented by Idso and Idso (1994) and by more recent studies for various trees and shrubs.

Kellomaki and Wang (2001) grew birch seedlings at atmospheric CO_2 concentrations of 350 and 700 ppm in combination with ambient and elevated (ambient plus 3°C) air temperatures. After five

months, the photosynthetic rates of the CO_2-enriched seedlings were 21 and 28% greater than their ambient-grown counterparts at ambient and elevated air temperatures, respectively. Carter *et al.* (2000) report a 300 ppm increase in the air's CO_2 content allowed leaves of sugar maple seedlings to remain green and non-chlorotic when exposed to air temperatures 3°C above ambient air temperature, and seedlings fumigated with ambient air exhibited severe foliar chlorosis when exposed to the same elevated air temperatures. At elevated air temperatures, rates of photosynthesis are greater and foliar health is typically better in CO_2-enriched as opposed to ambient air.

Many other studies report similar results. Sheu *et al.* (1999), for example, grew a subtropical tree at day/night temperatures of 25/20 (ambient) and 30/25°C (elevated) for six months, reporting seedlings exposed to 720 ppm CO_2 displayed photosynthetic rates 20 and 40% higher, respectively, than those of their ambient-grown controls. The CO_2-induced increases in total dry weight for this species were 14 and 49%, respectively, at the ambient and elevated air temperatures. Similarly, Maherali *et al.* (2000) report a 5°C increase in ambient air temperature increased the CO_2-induced biomass enhancement resulting from a 750 ppm CO_2 enrichment of ponderosa pine seedlings from 42 to 62%. In addition, Wayne *et al.* (1998) observed that a 5°C increase in the optimal growth temperature of yellow birch seedlings fumigated with an extra 400 ppm of CO_2 increased the CO_2-induced increase in biomass from 60% to 227%. The beneficial effects of elevated CO_2 on tree photosynthesis and growth are often further enhanced by elevated air temperatures, a fact also observed during natural seasonal temperature changes, as documented by Hymus *et al.* (1999) for loblolly pine and Roden *et al.* (1999) for snow gum seedlings.

In some cases, however, there appear to be few interactive effects between elevated CO_2 and temperature on photosynthesis and growth in trees. For example, when Tjoelker *et al.* (1998a) grew seedlings of quaking aspen, paper birch, tamarack, black spruce, and jack pine at atmospheric CO_2 concentrations of 580 ppm, they reported an average increase in photosynthetic rates of 28%, irrespective of air temperature, which varied from 18 to 30°C. And after analyzing the CO_2-induced increases in dry mass for these seedlings, Tjoelker *et al.* (1998b) further reported dry mass values were about 50 and 20% greater for the deciduous and coniferous species, respectively, again irrespective of air temperature.

The list of recent studies of woody plants that experience a CO_2-induced enhancement of growth in response to environmental warming is extensive, starting with Hamerlynck *et al.* (2000), who grew seedlings of the evergreen perennial shrub *Larrea tridentata* in glasshouses maintained at atmospheric CO_2 concentrations of 360, 550, and 700 ppm for one year. The researchers withheld water from half of the seedlings for three months prior to a nine-day high-temperature treatment. Elevated CO_2 largely offset the detrimental effects of drought and high temperature on water relations and photosynthesis in this species. Averaged across the entire experiment, the photosynthetic rates of seedlings grown at 550 and 700 ppm CO_2 were 31 and 90% greater, respectively, than the rates of the ambient-grown control plants.

Usami *et al.* (2001) grew two-year-old saplings of *Quercus myrsinaefolia*, an evergreen broad-leaved oak species, in controlled-environment chambers having various atmospheric CO_2 concentrations and air temperatures for approximately one year, to study the interactive effects of elevated CO_2 and temperature on the development and growth of this important tree, which is widely distributed throughout Laos, Vietnam, China, Taiwan, South Korea, and southwestern Japan. In ambient air, 3 and 5°C increases in air temperature boosted final sapling biomass by 53 and 47%, respectively. At elevated CO_2 concentrations 1.5 or 2 times greater than the ambient CO_2 concentration, the same 3 and 5°C increases in air temperature enhanced final biomass by 110 and 140%, respectively.

Turbull *et al.* (2002) manipulated day/night air temperatures around 4-m-tall cottonwood (*Populus deltoides* Bartr. Ex Marsh) trees growing in large experimental enclosures, to study the effects of temperature on carbon relations. A 6°C increase in daytime temperature, coupled with a 10°C increase in nighttime temperature, enhanced rates of net photosynthesis by 64% and rates of dark respiration by 77%. On an absolute scale, the photosynthetic carbon gains due to the daytime temperature increase were nearly an order of magnitude greater than the nocturnal carbon losses caused by the greater increase in nighttime temperature. Consequently, if Earth were to begin to warm again, carbon uptake by cottonwood trees should increase significantly.

Peltola *et al.* (2003) constructed closed chambers around 20-year-old Scots pine (*Pinus sylvestris* L.) trees growing on a low-nitrogen-containing soil, and for three years thereafter they fumigated the trees in the chambers with air containing either 350 or 700 ppm CO_2 at either ambient or elevated air temperatures (about 4°C above ambient temperatures), to study the effects of elevated CO_2 and air temperature on stem development in this coniferous species when growing on a soil low in nitrogen. After three years, they found cumulative stem diameter growth in the CO_2-enriched trees grown at ambient air temperature was 57% greater than that of control trees grown at ambient CO_2 and ambient air temperature. The trees subjected to elevated CO_2 and elevated air temperature exhibited cumulative stem-diameter growth 67% greater than trees grown in ambient air at ambient air temperatures.

Sallas *et al.* (2003) grew seedlings of Scots pine and Norway spruce (*Picea abies* (L.) Karst.) for 50 days in computer-controlled environmental growth chambers in air of ambient or twice-ambient CO_2 concentration (normal or elevated (EC) treatments) at day/night temperature combinations of 19/12°C or 23/16°C (normal or elevated (ET) treatments), making a host of measurements. Seedlings of both species were shown to accumulate the most biomass in the combined EC + ET treatment.

Hymus *et al.* (2003) studied net ecosystem exchange (NEE) of CO_2 in a scrub-oak ecosystem— 85–90% of the aboveground biomass of which was comprised of three oak species (*Quercus myrtifolia*, *Quercus geminate,* and *Quercus chapmanii*)—on Merritt Island in NASA's Kennedy Space Center on the coast of central Florida (USA). This ecosystem was completely burned in January 1996, after which 16 open-top chambers (OTCs) were placed on it in the spring of that year, half of which were maintained at the ambient atmospheric CO_2 concentration while the other half were maintained at ambient plus 350 ppm, with routine measurements being started in June 1999 and continuing for 25 months through July 2001. The scientists found the extra CO_2 supplied to the CO_2-enriched OTCs "increased maximum NEE and the apparent quantum yield of the NEE during the photoperiod," and the magnitude of the stimulation of maximum NEE, expressed per unit ground area, "was seasonal, rising from 50% in the winter to 180% in the summer," in accord with what is known about the interactive effects of atmospheric CO_2 enrichment and daily, seasonal, and multiyear warming.

Turnbull *et al.* (2004) studied four- to five-meter-tall cottonwood trees (*Populus deltoides* Bartr.) grown for three years in air of different CO_2 concentrations (420, 800, and 1,200 ppm) in the three bays of the Biosphere 2 facility near Tucson, Arizona (USA). They maintained the trees at three nocturnal temperatures (15, 20, or 25°C) and a single constant daytime temperature (31 ± 1°C) in a short-term experiment in which they routinely measured maximum photosynthesis (Amax) rates at growth CO_2 concentrations. As nocturnal air temperature rose from 15 to 25°C, the researchers observed subsequent daytime Amax increased by 16% in air of 420 ppm CO_2, 12% in air of 800 ppm CO_2, and 4% in air of 1,200 ppm CO_2, leading them to conclude "at future elevated night temperatures suggested by global climate monitoring and modeling, net photosynthesis at elevated CO_2 may be increased." It appears the response could saturate at a CO_2 partial pressure of somewhat more than 1,200 ppm CO_2, but that value is far greater than anyone is suggesting will ever be reached as a consequence of mankind's burning of fossil fuels.

But what if air temperatures get *really* hot, for some as-yet-unknown reason? Idso *et al.* (1995) grew well-watered and -fertilized sour orange (*Citrus aurantium* L.) trees from the seedling stage out-of-doors at Phoenix, Arizona (USA) in clear-plastic-wall open-top chambers continuously maintained at mean atmospheric CO_2 concentrations of either approximately 400 or 700 ppm for 5.5 years. During the warmest parts of some of the hottest days of summer, the scientists measured the temperatures and rates of net photosynthesis of fully expanded outer-canopy sunlit leaves.

Figure 3.13.3.1 portrays the results of plotting their net photosynthesis measurements against leaf temperature. Based on the linear regression lines fit to the data, it can be determined the 75% increase in the air's CO_2 content led to a 75% enhancement of leaf net photosynthesis at a leaf temperature of 31°C, a 100% enhancement at a leaf temperature of 35°C, and a 200% enhancement at 42°C. At higher leaf temperatures, the net photosynthetic rate of the foliage growing in ambient air dropped to zero at

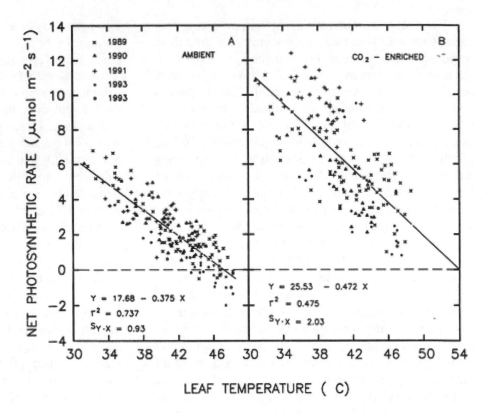

Figure 3.13.3.1. Leaf net photosynthetic rate vs. leaf temperature for the foliage of sour orange trees growing in air of either 400 or 700 ppm CO_2. Adapted from Idso *et al.* (1995).

47°C (making the CO_2-induced enhancement of photosynthesis at that point essentially infinite), and it became negative thereafter (which condition, if prolonged, would ultimately lead to plant death).

In the CO_2-enriched trees, by contrast, the net photosynthetic rate of the foliage was still substantial at 47°C, and the regression line for those trees suggests their mean rate of foliage net photosynthesis likely would not have declined to zero until leaf temperature reached 54°C, approximately 7°C above the upper-limiting temperature for positive net photosynthesis in the trees grown in ambient air.

These findings show if Earth's air temperature continues to rise significantly in the future, a concomitant rise in the air's CO_2 content would serve as a powerful antidote for the ill—and sometimes deadly—effects of temperature stress.

Lewis *et al.* (2001) reached somewhat similar conclusions when they grew Douglas fir (*Pseudotsuga menziesii* (Mirb.) Franco) seedlings in sunlit chambers programmed to track either ambient atmospheric CO_2 concentration or ambient + 200 ppm CO_2, as well as either ambient air temperature or ambient + 4°C, over a 21-month period, measuring light-saturated rates of net photosynthesis at approximately monthly intervals. The extra CO_2 they supplied to the seedlings "increased net photosynthetic rates by an average of 21% across temperature treatments during both the 1996 hydrologic year, the third year of exposure, and the 1997 hydrologic year," and "elevated mean annual temperature increased net photosynthetic rates by an average of 33% across CO_2 treatments during both years." In addition, "between February and August 1996, the short-term temperature optima for photosynthesis shifted by approximately 10°C higher in both CO_2 treatments," and the elevated CO_2 treatment "increased the short-term (minutes to hours) temperature optima for photosynthesis, as has been observed in other tree species (Idso and Idso, 1994; Eamus *et al.*, 1995)." The four researchers conclude "an increase of 200 ppm above current atmospheric CO_2 concentrations may shift temperature optima upward 3 4°C, paralleling the increase in mean annual temperatures predicted to occur during the next century," and "by shifting temperature optima upward, elevated CO_2 may 'acclimate' photosynthetic processes to future temperature regimes."

Huang *et al.* (2007) compared, synthesized, and evaluated the scientific literature to that point in time, describing atmospheric CO_2 enrichment experiments conducted on trees and empirical tree-ring studies designed to ascertain whether the growth-promoting effects of rising atmospheric CO_2 concentrations occur in natural forests. They found numerous CO_2-enrichment experiments have "demonstrated significantly positive physiological and growth responses of trees to CO_2, providing strong evidence to support the direct CO_2 fertilization effect (increased photosynthesis, water use efficiency, above- and below-ground growth) and thus allowing prediction of which ecosystems might be most responsive to CO_2." They suggest the latter will be "warm, moderately drought-stressed ecosystems with an ample nitrogen supply," because "drought-stressed trees could benefit from increased water use efficiency to enhance growth." They note tree-ring studies on the cold and arid Tibetan Plateau also "showed significant growth enhancements as well as increased water use efficiency (24.7% and 33.6% for each species, respectively) in Qilian juniper and Qinghai spruce since the 1850s," citing Zhang *et al.* (2003), Shao *et al.* (2005), Liang *et al.* (2006), Huang and Zhang (2007), and Zhang and Qiu (2007).

Hickler *et al.* (2008) evaluated the process-based LPJ-GUESS model of vegetation dynamics and biogeochemistry (Smith *et al.*, 2001; Hickler *et al.*, 2004) via a site-by-site comparison with the results of four temperate forest FACE experiments (Norby *et al.*, 2005). After demonstrating the model simulations adequately reproduced the magnitude of the FACE site measurements—a mean model-derived net primary productivity (NPP) increase of 25.9% for CO_2 raised to a value of 550 ppm vs. a mean measured NPP increase of 27.8% for the same CO_2 increase—they conducted what they called a "global forest FACE experiment" to see what the reality-tested model suggested about CO_2 enrichment effects on the NPP of boreal and tropical forests, as well as its temperate forests.

For the world as a whole, the model suggests raising the air's CO_2 concentration to 550 ppm would increase the NPP of temperate forests by an average of 25.7%. The NPP of boreal forests would be raised by 15.1%, and tropical forests would experience an NPP increase of 35.1%. Hickler *et al.* note warming "is likely to increase NPP more in cold northern regions than close to the equator because of a greater proportional growing season extension in temperature-limited environments."

Martinez-Vilalta *et al.* (2008) describe their use of tree-ring data from the Catalan Ecological and Forest Inventory "to study the temporal variability of Scots pine stem radial growth (period 1901–1997) across a relatively large region (Catalonia, NE Spain) situated close to the southern limit of the distribution of the species." This inventory, they write, "included a total of 10,664 plots randomly distributed throughout the forested area of Catalonia," where Scots pine was present in 30.2% of the plots and dominant in 18.4% of them. They found "an overall increase of 84% in Scots pine BAI [basal area increment] during the 20th century, consistent with most previous studies for temperate forests." They state, "this trend was associated with increased atmospheric CO_2 concentration," which they interpret to be "a fertilization effect." Over the same period, the five researchers note, "there was also a marked increase in temperature across the study region (0.19°C per decade on average)," and "this warming had a negative impact on radial growth, particularly at the drier sites." They add "its magnitude was not enough to counteract the fertilization effect."

Darbah *et al.* (2010) measured the effects of a natural and prolonged heat wave on the photosynthetic rates of quaking aspen (*Populus tremuloides* Michx) and paper birch (*Betula papyrifera*) trees grown from the seedling stage for an additional nine years in the free-air CO_2-enrichment (FACE) facility near Rhinelander, Wisconsin (USA), where from 0700 to 1900 hours each day throughout the growing season half of the trees were exposed to an extra ~190 ppm of CO_2. For the aspen trees, the heat wave produced "no visible symptoms of stress," but the birch trees exhibited "leaf curling and then yellowing of leaves and finally leaf shedding," with trees in the control treatment dropping 33% of their leaves and those in the CO_2-enriched treatment dropping 20%. Aspen clone 42E exhibited a 30% CO_2-induced increase in the rate of photosynthesis at saturating light intensities in the 32–35°C temperature range, and 218% in the 36–39°C range. Similarly, aspen clone 271 exhibited a 38% CO_2-induced increase in the 32–35°C range and a 199% increase in the 36–39°C range. The birch trees exhibited a 95% CO_2-induced increase in photosynthetic rates in the 32–35°C range and a 297% increase in the 36–39°C range.

The four researchers say their findings agree with those of Idso and Kimball (1992), who reported elevated CO_2 (ambient + 300 ppm) increased net photosynthetic rates in sour orange tree (*Citrus aurantium* L.) leaves exposed to full sunlight by 75, 100, and 200% compared to leaves in ambient CO_2 air at temperatures of 31, 35, and 42°C, respectively, suggesting "elevated CO_2 ameliorates heat stress in tree leaves." They also note their observations "agree with Veteli *et al.* (2007), who reported that elevated CO_2 ameliorated the negative effects of high temperature in three deciduous tree species," and "Wayne *et al.* (1998) reported that elevated CO_2 ameliorated high temperature stress in yellow birch trees (*Betula alleghaniensis*)." They conclude, "in the face of rising atmospheric CO_2 and temperature (global warming), trees will benefit from elevated CO_2 through increased thermotolerance."

Ghannoum, *et al.* (2010b) grew individual well-watered and -fertilized plants of two species of Australian eucalypts—faster-growing *Eucalyptus saligna* and slower-growing *E. sideroxylon*—from seed in 10-L pots filled with 9 kg of loamy sand in naturally lit glasshouse compartments maintained at either ambient or ambient + 4°C air temperature and three different CO_2 concentrations (280, 400, or 650 ppm) for 140 days, measuring various plant responses throughout the course of the experiment. They found light-saturated net photosynthesis (Asat) increased by ~50% with each step-increase in the air's CO_2 concentration—going from 280 to 400 ppm, and going from 400 to 650 ppm—and in the higher of the

two temperature treatments the optimal temperature for Asat increased by 2–7°C across the three CO_2 treatments. They note these results "partly explain the strong growth responses to elevated CO_2 and temperature observed in a previous study with the same eucalypt seedlings," citing Ghannoum *et al.* (2010a).

Keenan *et al.* (2011) note climate models consistently project significant increases in temperature and decreases in precipitation in the Mediterranean basin, and they state these changes may have a large impact on current Mediterranean forests and the related ecosystem services they provide. They say niche-based models—also known as bioclimatic envelope models or habitat models—are the most commonly used method for predicting potential species distribution responses to future climatic changes, and they note these models typically predict significant negative consequences for terrestrial plants and animals in the face of increasing atmospheric CO_2 concentrations.

Keenan *et al.* say they prefer process-based models, which describe eco-physiological processes ranging from purely empirical relationships to mechanistic descriptions based on physical laws. These models, supported by experiments and growth and yield surveys, "suggest that global warming will have a positive impact on forest productivity (van der Meer *et al.*, 2002; Nigh *et al.*, 2004; Norby and Luo, 2004; Briceño-Elizondo *et al.*, 2006; Gaucharel *et al.*, 2008), due to the direct fertilization effect of increased CO_2 and indirect effects such as lengthening of the growing period." To elucidate the difference in results obtained by employing these two approaches, the five researchers assessed and compared the projections when applied to stands of three forest species (*Quercus ilex, Pinus halepensis,* and *Pinus sylvestris*) that have widely contrasting distributions in continental Spain.

Keenan *et al.* found CO_2 fertilization tends to show an increase in forest productivity in mechanistic process-based models (despite increased drought and presumed temperature stress) by up to three times the non-CO_2 fertilization scenario by the period 2050–2080, in stark contrast to projections of reduced habitat suitability based on niche-based models for the same period. Their results show "previous reports of species decline in continental Spain (e.g. Benito-Garzon *et al.*, 2008) may be overestimated due to two reasons." One of these is the use of only one predictive niche-based model, and the other is the failure to account for positive effects of CO_2

fertilization in a warming world. They note similar studies in other regions that do not consider these two aspects are also potentially overestimating species decline due to climate change, because "niche-based model results also likely overestimate the decline in [habitat] suitability." They conclude, "an organism's niche must be modeled mechanistically if we are to fully explain distribution limits," citing Kearney (2006).

Osorio *et al.* (2011) investigated the impacts of drought and high-temperature stresses on photosynthesis, energy partitioning, and membrane lipids—as well as the potential ability of Carob or St. John's (*Ceratonia siliqua*) trees to attenuate oxidative damage. They studied seedlings growing in controlled-environment chambers and rooted in 3-dm^3 pots filled with a 2:1 mixture of a fertilized substrate and natural soil, maintained under two thermal regimes—low and high temperature (LT: 25/18°C; HT: 32/21°C)—and three soil water conditions (control, water stress, and rewetting), monitoring numerous physiological and biochemical plant properties and processes. The decrease in net photosynthesis (P_N) caused by drought was 33% in the LT chamber and 84% in the HT chamber. They note, "the negative effects of soil drying on P_N and stomatal conductance of HT plants were no longer detected 36 hours following rewatering." Also, "although *C. siliqua* seedlings exhibit clear signs of oxidative stress under drought and high temperature, they retain a remarkable ability to quickly restore normal physiological activity on rehydration." This ability was so strong the five Portuguese scientists say they "can state that although *C. siliqua* seedlings exhibit clear signs of oxidative stress under drought and high temperature, they retain a remarkable ability to quickly restore normal physiological activity on rehydration, which let us believe that they can satisfactorily deal with predicted climate warming and increased soil drying in the Mediterranean area."

Wertin *et al.* (2012) examined the influence of elevated temperature (ambient + 2°C) and atmospheric CO_2 concentration (700 ppm), applied singly and in combination, on biomass accumulation and the temperature response of net photosynthesis (Anet) and leaf respiration (Rd) of loblolly pine (*Pinus taeda* L.) seedlings grown simultaneously at a northern and a southern site in the species' range, where the long-term mean growing season temperature (from February through October) at the cool site was 15.2°C and at the warm site was 21.5°C. They grew the well-watered and -fertilized seedlings over two con-secutive years in half-cylindrical polyfilm-enclosed chambers located in open fields.

Wertin *et al.* determined "biomass accumulation was substantially greater at the warmer site compared with the cooler site regardless of treatment," and "at each site, biomass accumulation was greater in the elevated temperature treatment compared with the ambient treatment." They also found "elevated CO_2 increased biomass accumulation and Anet at both sites and in both temperature treatments." The five University of Georgia (USA) researchers conclude their study "provides an indication that future projected increases in CO_2 and air temperature of 700 ppm and +2°C, respectively, are likely to increase loblolly pine growth in most, if not all, of its current range." And they state, "the large number of studies that have reported an increase in tree growth in elevated growth temperatures compared with current ambient temperature (Way and Oren, 2010) suggest that other species may respond similarly."

Ameye *et al.* (2012) note that in studies where the air's CO_2 content was doubled, "increases in net photosynthesis were reported ranging from 43% to 192% in *Pinus taeda* (Teskey, 1997; Tissue *et al.*, 1997; Ellsworth, 1999; Wertin *et al.*, 2010; Frenck *et al.*, 2011) and from 30% to 256% in *Quercus rubra* (Kubiske and Pregitzer, 1996; Anderson and Tomlinson, 1998; Cavender-Bares *et al.*, 2000)." Moreover, "generally, an increase in air temperature also has a positive effect on net photosynthesis and growth," citing Sage and Kubien (2007) and Way and Oren (2010).

Investigating how loblolly pine and northern red oak trees might respond to the extreme heat waves often predicted to occur in a future CO_2-enriched world, the scientists examined the most recent fully developed leaves of well-watered and -fertilized seedlings of *Pinus taeda* and *Quercus rubra* grown in 7.6-L pots out-of-doors at Athens, Georgia (USA) in polyethylene chambers maintained at ambient and elevated air temperatures (T_{amb} and T_{amb} + 3°C), as well as seven-day heat waves consisting of a biweekly +6°C heat wave or a monthly +12°C heat wave. These treatments were maintained throughout the growing season, and Ameye *et al.* measured rates of net photosynthesis before, during, and after the many midsummer heat waves they created. They report "an immediate and significant decline in net photosynthesis was observed in seedlings subjected to a +12°C heat wave, but not in seedlings subjected to a +6°C heat wave." They also state, "after the third day of the +12°C heat wave, net photosynthesis values stabilized at positive values and did not show signs of further reduction, indicating that the photosynthetic apparatus did not accrue additional stress or damage as the heat wave continued." Therefore, they conclude, "if soil moisture is adequate, trees will experience negative effects in photosynthetic performance only with the occurrence of extreme heat waves." Also, as "elevated CO_2 diminished these negative effects," they conclude "the future climate may not be as detrimental to plant communities as previously assumed."

In concluding this literature review, it is instructive to consider the Paleocene-Eocene Thermal Maximum (PETM) of some 56 million years ago. According to Jaramillo et al. (2010), it "was one of the most abrupt global warming events of the past 65 million years (Kennett and Stott, 1991; Zachos et al., 2003; Westerhold et al., 2009)." It was presumed to have been driven, they write, by "a massive release of ^{13}C-depleted carbon (Pagani et al., 2006; Zeebe et al., 2009)" that led to "an approximate 5°C increase in mean global temperature in about 10,000 to 20,000 years (Zachos et al., 2003)." Earth's tropical ecosystems "suffered extensively because mean temperatures are surmised to have exceeded the ecosystems' heat tolerance (Huber, 2008)," according to many scientists, Jaramillo et al. write.

To ascertain whether the ancient warming of the world truly constituted a major problem for the planet's rainforests, the 29 researchers from eight countries analyzed pollen and spore contents and the stable carbon isotopic composition of organic materials obtained from three tropical terrestrial PETM sites in eastern Colombia and western Venezuela. Contrary to the prevailing wisdom of the recent past, they found the onset of the PETM was "concomitant with an increase in diversity produced by the addition of many taxa (with some representing new families) to the stock of preexisting Paleocene taxa." They determined this increase in biodiversity "was permanent and not transient."

Jaramillo et al. write, "today, most tropical rainforests are found at mean annual temperatures below 27.5°C," and several scientists have argued "higher temperatures could be deleterious to the health of tropical ecosystems," citing Stoskopf (1981), Bassow et al. (1994), Lewis et al. (2004), Huber (2008, 2009), and Tewksbury et al. (2008). They report tropical warming during the PETM is actually thought to have produced intolerable conditions for tropical ecosystems, citing Huber (2008, 2009). Nevertheless, Jaramillo et al. reiterate

that at the sites that they studied, "tropical forests were maintained during the warmth of the PETM (~31° to 34°C)." Thus they conclude, "it is possible that higher Paleocene CO_2 levels (Royer, 2010) contributed to their success."

Their conclusion is supported by what is now the well-established fact that most woody plants tend to exhibit their greatest photosynthetic rates at increasingly warmer temperatures as the air's CO_2 content rises. It is becoming increasingly clear that greater warmth and atmospheric CO_2 concentrations are not as detrimental as IPCC and others typically make them out to be. Quite to the contrary, they are likely to make ecosystems both more stable and more productive.

The scientific literature of the past few decades indicates a continuing rise in the air's CO_2 content likely will lead to enhanced rates of photosynthesis and biomass production that will not be negated by any global warming that might occur. If the ambient air temperature rises, the growth-promoting effects of atmospheric CO_2 enrichment likely will rise right along with it. Trees are likely to produce greater amounts of biomass and, therefore, more timber products to meet the increasing needs of Earth's expanding human population.

References

Ameye, M., Wertin, T.M., Bauweraerts, I., McGuire, M.A., Teskey, R.O., and Steppe, K. 2012. The effect of induced heat waves on *Pinus taeda* and *Quercus rubra* seedlings in ambient and elevated CO_2 atmospheres. *New Phytologist* **196**: 448–461.

Anderson, P.D. and Tomlinson, P.T. 1998. Ontogeny affects response of northern red oak seedlings to elevated CO_2 and water stress. I. Carbon assimilation and biomass production. *New Phytologist* **140**: 477–491.

Bassow, S.L., McConnaughay, K.D., and Bazzaz, F.A. 1994. The Response of temperate tree seedlings grown in elevated CO_2 to extreme temperature events. *Ecological Applications* **4**: 593–603.

Benito-Garzon, M., Sanchez de Dios, R., and Sainz Ollero, H. 2008. Effects of climate change on the distribution of Iberian tree species. *Applied Vegetation Science* **11**: 169–178.

Berry, J. and Bjorkman, O. 1980. Photosynthetic response and adaptation to temperature in higher plants. *Annual Review of Plant Physiology* **31**: 491–543.

Briceño-Elizondo, R., Garcia-Gonzalo, J., Peltola, H.,

Matala, J., and Kellomaki, S. 2006. Sensitivity of growth of Scots pine, Norway spruce and silver birch to climate change and forest management in boreal conditions. *Forest Ecology and Management* **232**: 152–167.

Carter, G.A., Bahadur, R., and Norby, R.J. 2000. Effects of elevated atmospheric CO_2 and temperature on leaf optical properties in *Acer saccharum*. *Environmental and Experimental Botany* **43**: 267–273.

Cavender-Bares, J., Potts, M., Zacharias, E., and Bazzaz, F.A. 2000. Consequences of CO_2 and light interactions for leaf phenology, growth, and senescence in *Quercus rubra*. *Global Change Biology* **6**: 877–887.

Cowling, S.A. and Sykes, M.T. 1999. Physiological significance of low atmospheric CO_2 for plant-climate interactions. *Quaternary Research* **52**: 237–242.

Darbah, J.N.T., Sharkey, T.D., Calfapietra, C., and Karnosky, D.F. 2010. Differential response of aspen and birch trees to heat stress under elevated carbon dioxide. *Environmental Pollution* **158**: 1008–1014.

Eamus, D., Duff, G.A., and Berryman, C.A. 1995. Photosynthetic responses to temperature, light flux-density, CO_2 concentration and vapor pressure deficit in *Eucalyptus tetrodonia* grown under CO_2 enrichment. *Environmental Pollution* **90**: 41–49.

Ellsworth, D.S. 1999. CO_2 enrichment in a maturing pine forest: are CO_2 exchange and water status in the canopy affected? *Plant, Cell and Environment* **22**: 461–472.

Frenck, G., van der Linden, L., Mikkelsen, T.N., Brix, H., and Jorgensen, R.B. 2011. Increased CO_2 does not compensate for negative effects on yield caused by higher temperature and O_3 in *Brassica napus* L. *European Journal of Agronomy* **35**: 127–134.

Gaucharel, C., Guiot, J., and Misson, L. 2008. Changes of the potential distribution area of French Mediterranean forests under global warming. *Biogeosciences* **5**: 1493–1503.

Ghannoum, O., Phillips, N.G., Conroy, J.P., Smith, R.A., Attard, R.D., Woodfield, R., Logan, B.A., Lewis, J.D., and Tissue, D.T. 2010a. Exposure to preindustrial, current and future atmospheric CO_2 and temperature differentially affects growth and photosynthesis in Eucalyptus. *Global Change Biology* **16**: 303–319.

Ghannoum, O., Phillips, N.G., Sears, M.A., Logan, B.A., Lewis, J.D., Conroy, J.P., and Tissue, D.T. 2010b. Photosynthetic responses of two eucalypts to industrial-age changes in atmospheric [CO_2] and temperature. *Plant, Cell and Environment* **33**: 1671–1681.

Hamerlynck, E.P., Huxman, T.E., Loik, M.E., and Smith, S.D. 2000. Effects of extreme high temperature, drought and elevated CO_2 on photosynthesis of the Mojave Desert evergreen shrub, *Larrea tridentata*. *Plant Ecology* **148**: 183–193.

Hickler, T., Smith, B., Prentice, I.C., Mjofors, K., Miller, P., Arneth, A., and Sykes, M.T. 2008. CO_2 fertilization in temperate FACE experiments not representative of boreal and tropical forests. *Global Change Biology* **14**: 1531–1542.

Hickler, T., Smith, B., Sykes, M.T., Davis, M., Sugita, S., and Walker, K. 2004. Using a generalized vegetation model to simulate vegetation dynamics in northeastern USA. *Ecology* **85**: 519–530.

Huang, J.-G., Bergeron, Y., Denneler, B., Berninger, F., and Tardif, J. 2007. Response of forest trees to increased atmospheric CO_2. *Critical Reviews in Plant Sciences* **26**: 265–283.

Huang, J.G. and Zhang, Q.B. 2007. Tree-rings and climate for the last 680 years in Wulan area of northeastern Qinghai-Tibctan Platcau. *Climatic Change* **80**: 369 377.

Huber, M. 2008. A hotter greenhouse? *Science* **321**: 353–354.

Huber, M. 2009. Snakes tell a torrid tale. *Nature* **457**: 669–670.

Hymus, G.J., Ellsworth, D.S., Baker, N.R., and Long, S.P. 1999. Does free-air carbon dioxide enrichment affect photochemical energy use by evergreen trees in different seasons? A chlorophyll fluorescence study of mature loblolly pine. *Plant Physiology* **120**: 1183–1191.

Hymus, G.J., Johnson, D.P., Dore, S., Anderson, H.P., Hinkle, C.R., and Drake, B.G. 2003. Effects of elevated atmospheric CO_2 on net ecosystem CO_2 exchange of a scrub-oak ecosystem. *Global Change Biology* **9**: 1802–1812.

Idso, K.E. and Idso, S.B. 1994. Plant responses to atmospheric CO_2 enrichment in the face of environmental constraints: A review of the past 10 years' research. *Agricultural and Forest Meteorology* **69**: 53–203.

Idso, S.B., Idso, K.E., Garcia, R.L., Kimball, B.A., and Hoober, J.K. 1995. Effects of atmospheric CO_2 enrichment and foliar methanol application on net photosynthesis of sour orange tree (*Citrus aurantium*; Rutaceae) leaves. *American Journal of Botany* **82**: 26–30.

Idso, S.B. and Kimball, B.A. 1992. Effects of atmospheric CO_2 enrichment on photosynthesis, respiration and growth of sour orange trees. *Plant Physiology* **99**: 341–343.

Jaramillo, C., Ochoa, D., Conteras, L., Pagani, M., Carvajal-Ortiz, H., Pratt, L.M., Krishnan, S., Cardona, A., Romero, M., Quiroz, L., Rodriguez, G., Rueda, M.J., de la

Parra, F., Moron, S., Green, W., Bayona, G., Montes, C., Quintero, O., Ramirez, R., Mora, G., Schouten, S., Bermudez, H., Navarrete, R., Parra, F., Alvaran, M., Osorno, J., Crowley, J.L., Valencia, V., and Vervoort, J. 2010. Effects of rapid global warming at the Paleocene-Eocene boundary on neotropical vegetation. *Science* **330**: 957–961.

Kearney, M. 2006. Habitat, environment and niche: what are we modeling? *Oikos* **115**: 186–191.

Keenan, T., Serra, J.M., Lloret, F., Ninyerola, M., and Sabate, S. 2011. Predicting the future of forests in the Mediterranean under climate change, with niche- and process-based models: CO_2 matters! *Global Change Biology* **17**: 565–579.

Kellomaki, S. and Wang, K.-Y. 2001. Growth and resource use of birch seedlings under elevated carbon dioxide and temperature. *Annals of Botany* **87**: 669–682.

Kennett, J.P. and Stott, L.D. 1991. Abrupt deep-sea warming, palaeoceanographic changes and benthic extinctions at the end of the Palaeocene. *Nature* **353**: 225–229.

Kubiske, M.E. and Pregitzer, K.S. 1996. Effects of elevated CO_2 and light availability on the photosynthetic response of trees of contrasting shade tolerance. *Tree Physiology* **16**: 351–358.

Lewis, J.D., Lucash, M., Olszyk, D., and Tingey, D.T. 2001. Seasonal patterns of photosynthesis in Douglas fir seedlings during the third and fourth year of exposure to elevated CO_2 and temperature. *Plant, Cell and Environment* **24**: 539–548.

Lewis, S.L., Malhi, Y., and Phillips, O.L. 2004. Fingerprinting the impacts of global change on tropical forests. *Philosophical Transactions of the Royal Society B* **359**: 437–462.

Liang, E.Y., Shao, X.M., Eckstein, D., Huang, L., and Liu, X.H. 2006. Topography- and species-dependent growth response of *Sabina przewalskii* and *Picea crassifolia* to climate on the northeast Tibetan Plateau. *Forest Ecology and Management* **236**: 268–277.

Long, S.P. 1991. Modification of the response of photosynthetic productivity to rising temperature by atmospheric CO_2 concentrations: Has its importance been underestimated? *Plant, Cell and Environment* **14**: 729–739.

Maherali, H. and DeLucia, E.H. 2000. Interactive effects of elevated CO_2 and temperature on water transport in ponderosa pine. *American Journal of Botany* **87**: 243–249.

Martinez-Vilalta, J., Lopez, B.C., Adell, N., Badiella, L., and Ninyerola, M. 2008. Twentieth century increase of Scots pine radial growth in NE Spain shows strong climate interactions. *Global Change Biology* **14**: 2868–2881.

McMurtrie, R.E., Comins, H.N., Kirschbaum, M.U.F., and Wang, Y.-P. 1992. Modifying existing forest growth models to take account of effects of elevated CO_2. *Australian Journal of Botany* **40**: 657–677.

McMurtrie, R.E. and Wang, Y.-P. 1993. Mathematical models of the photosynthetic response of tree stands to rising CO_2 concentrations and temperatures. *Plant, Cell and Environment* **16**: 1–13.

Nigh, G.D., Ying, C.C., and Qian, H. 2004. Climate and productivity of major conifer species in the interior of British Columbia, Canada. *Forest Science* **50**: 659–671.

Norby, R.J., DeLucia, E.H., Gielen, B., Calfapietra, C., Giardina, C.P., King, S.J., Ledford, J., McCarthy, H.R., Moore, D.J.P., Ceulemans, R., De Angelis, P., Finzi, A.C., Karnosky, D.F., Kubiske, M.E., Lukac, M., Pregitzer, K.S., Scarasci-Mugnozza, G.E., Schlesinger, W.H., and Oren, R. 2005. Forest response to elevated CO_2 is conserved across a broad range of productivity. *Proceedings of the National Academy of Sciences* **102**: 18,052–18,056.

Norby, R.J. and Luo, Y. 2004. Evaluating ecosystem responses to rising atmospheric CO_2 and global warming in a multi-factor world. *New Phytologist* **162**: 281–293.

Osorio, M.L., Osorio, J., Vieira, A.C., Goncalves, S., and Romano, A. 2011. Influence of enhanced temperature on photosynthesis, photooxidative damage, and antioxidant strategies in *Ceratonia siliqua* L. seedlings subjected to water deficit and rewatering. *Photosynthetica* **49**: 3–12.

Pagani, M., Caldeira, K, Archer, D., and Zachos, J.C. 2006. An ancient carbon mystery. *Science* **314**: 1556–1557.

Peltola, H., Kilpelainen, A., and Kellomaki, S. 2002. Diameter growth of Scots pine (*Pinus sylvestris*) trees grown at elevated temperature and carbon dioxide concentration under boreal conditions. *Tree Physiology* **22**: 963–972.

Roden, J.S., Egerton, J.J.G., and Ball, M.C. 1999. Effect of elevated [CO_2] on photosynthesis and growth of snow gum (*Eucalyptus pauciflora*) seedlings during winter and spring. *Australian Journal of Plant Physiology* **26**: 37–46.

Royer, D.L. 2010. Fossil soils constrain ancient climate sensitivity. *Proceedings of the National Academy of Sciences, USA* **107**: 517–518.

Sage, R.F. and Kubien, D.S. 2007. The temperature response of C_3 and C_4 photosynthesis. *Plant, Cell and Environment* **30**: 1086–1106.

Sallas, L., Luomala, E.-M., Utriainen, J., Kainulainen, P., and Holopainen, J.K. 2003. Contrasting effects of elevated carbon dioxide concentration and temperature on Rubisco activity, chlorophyll fluorescence, needle ultrastructure and secondary metabolites in conifer seedlings. *Tree Physiology* **23**: 97–108.

Shao, X.M., Huang, L., Liu, H.B., Liang, E.Y., Fang, X.Q., and Wang, L.L. 2005. Reconstructions of precipitation variation from tree-rings in recent 1000 years in Delingha, Qinghai. *Science in China (Series D)* **48**: 939–949.

Sheu, B.-H. and Lin, C.-K. 1999. Photosynthetic response of seedlings of the sub-tropical tree *Schima superba* with exposure to elevated carbon dioxide and temperature. *Environmental and Experimental Botany* **41**: 57–65.

Smith, B., Prentice, I.C., and Sykes, M.T. 2001. Representation of vegetation dynamics in the modeling of terrestrial ecosystems: comparing two contrasting approaches within European climate space. *Global Ecology & Biogeography* **10**: 621–637.

Stoskopf, N. 1981. *Understanding Crop Production.* Prentice-Hall, Upper Saddle River, New Jersey, USA.

Stuhlfauth, T. and Fock, H.P. 1990. Effect of whole season CO_2 enrichment on the cultivation of a medicinal plant, *Digitalis lanata. Journal of Agronomy and Crop Science* **164**: 168–173.

Teskey, R.O. 1997. Combined effects of elevated CO_2 and air temperature on carbon assimilation of *Pinus taeda* trees. *Plant, Cell and Environment* **20**: 373–380.

Tewksbury, J.J., Huey, R.B., and Deutsch, C.A. 2008. Putting the heat on tropical animals. *Science* **320**: 1296–1297.

Tissue, D.T., Thomas, R.B., and Strain, B.R. 1997. Atmospheric CO_2 enrichment increases growth and photosynthesis of *Pinus taeda*: a 4-year experiment in the field. *Plant, Cell and Environment* **20**: 1123–1134.

Tjoelker, M.G., Oleksyn, J., and Reich, P.B. 1998a. Seedlings of five boreal tree species differ in acclimation of net photosynthesis to elevated CO_2 and temperature. *Tree Physiology* **18**: 715–726.

Tjoelker, M.G., Oleksyn, J., and Reich, P.B. 1998b. Temperature and ontogeny mediate growth response to elevated CO_2 in seedlings of five boreal tree species. *New Phytologist* **140**: 197–210.

Turnbull, M.H., Murthy, R., and Griffin, K.L. 2002. The relative impacts of daytime and night-time warming on photosynthetic capacity in *Populus deltoides. Plant, Cell and Environment* **25**: 1729–1737.

Turnbull, M.H., Tissue, D.T., Murthy, R., Wang, X., Sparrow, A.D., and Griffin, K.L. 2004. Nocturnal warming increases photosynthesis at elevated CO_2 partial pressure in *Populus deltoides. New Phytologist* **161**: 819–826.

Usami, T., Lee, J., and Oikawa, T. 2001. Interactive effects of increased temperature and CO_2 on the growth of *Quercus myrsinaefolia* saplings. *Plant, Cell and Environment* **24**: 1007–1019.

van der Meer, P.J., Jorritsma, I.T.M., and Kramer, J.K. 2002. Assessing climate change effects on long-term forest development: adjusting growth, phenology and seed production in a gap model. *Forest Ecology and Management* **162**: 39–52.

Veteli, T.O., Mattson, W.J., Niemela, P., Julkunen-Tiitto, R., Kellomaki, S., Kuokkanen, K., and Lavola, A. 2007. Do elevated temperature and CO_2 generally have counteracting effects on phenolic phytochemistry of boreal trees? *Journal of Chemical Ecology* **33**: 287–296.

Way, D.A. and Oren, R. 2010. Differential responses to changes in growth temperature between trees from different functional groups and biomes: a review and synthesis of data. *Tree Physiology* **30**: 669–688.

Wayne, P.M., Reekie, E.G., and Bazzaz, F.A. 1998. Elevated CO_2 ameliorates birch response to high temperature and frost stress: implications for modeling climate-induced geographic range shifts. *Oecologia* **114**: 335–342.

Wertin, T.M., McGuire, M.A., and Teskey, R.O. 2010. The influence of elevated temperature, elevated atmospheric CO_2 concentration and water stress on net photosynthesis of loblolly pine (*Pinus taeda* L.) at northern, central and southern sites in its native range. *Global Change Biology* **16**: 2089–2103.

Wertin, T.M., McGuire, M.A., van Iersel, M., Ruter, J.M., and Teskey, R.O. 2012. Effects of elevated temperature and [CO_2] on photosynthesis, leaf respiration, and biomass accumulation of *Pinus taeda* seedlings at a cool and a warm site within the species' current range. *Canadian Journal of Forest Research* **42**: 943–957.

Westerhold, T., Rohl, U., McCarren, H.K., and Zachos, J.C. 2009. Latest on the absolute age of the Paleocene-Eocene Thermal Maximum (PETM): New insights from exact stratigraphic position of key ash layers + 19 and - 17. *Earth and Planetary Science Letters* **287**: 412–419.

Zachos, J.C., Wara, M.W., Bohaty, S., Delaney, M.L., Petrizzo, M.R., Brill, A., Bralower, T.J., and Premoli-Silva, I. 2003. A transient rise in tropical sea surface temperature during the Paleocene-Eocene Thermal Maximum. *Science* **302**: 1551–1554.

Zeebe, R.E., Zachos, J.C., and Dickens, G.R. 2009. Carbon dioxide forcing alone insufficient to explain Palaeocene-Eocene Thermal Maximum warming. *Nature Geoscience* **2**: 576–580.

Zhang, Q.B., Cheng, G.D., Yao, T.D., Kang, X.C., and Huang, J.G. 2003. A 2,326-year tree-ring record of climate variability on the northeastern Qinghai-Tibetan Plateau. *Geophysical Research Letters* **30**: 10.1029/2003GL017425.

Zhang, Q.B. and Qiu, H.Y. 2007. A millennium-long tree-ring chronology of *Sabina przewalskii* on northeastern Qinghai-Tibetan Plateau. *Dendrochronologia* **24**: 91–95.

3.14 UV-B Radiation Stress

- The rise in the air's CO_2 content is a powerful antidote to the deleterious biological impacts that might be caused by an increase in the flux of UV-B radiation at the surface of Earth due to depletion of the planet's stratospheric ozone layer.

Zhao *et al.* (2004) state "as a result of stratospheric ozone depletion, UV-B radiation (280–320 nm) levels are still high at the Earth's surface and are projected to increase in the near future (Madronich *et al.*, 1998; McKenzie *et al.*, 2003)," noting, "increased levels of UV-B radiation are known to affect plant growth, development and physiological processes (Dai *et al.*, 1992; Nogues *et al.*, 1999)." High UV-B levels often result in "inhibition of photosynthesis, degradation of protein and DNA, and increased oxidative stress (Jordan *et al.*, 1992; Stapleton, 1992)." In light of these observations, it is only natural to wonder how the rise in the air's CO_2 content might affect the deleterious effects of UV-B radiation on vegetation.

Zhao *et al.* grew well-watered and -fertilized cotton plants in sunlit controlled-environment chambers maintained at atmospheric CO_2 concentrations of 360 or 720 ppm from emergence until three weeks past first-flower stage under three levels of UV-B radiation (0, 8, and 16 kJ m^{-2} d^{-1}). On five dates between 21 and 62 days after emergence, they measured a number of plant physiological processes and parameters. Over the course of the experiment, the mean net photosynthetic rate of the upper-canopy leaves in the CO_2-enriched chambers was increased relative to that in the ambient-air chambers by 38.3% in the low UV-B treatment (from 30.3 to 41.9 m m^{-2} s^{-1}), 41.1% in the medium UV-B treatment (from 28.7 to 40.5 m m^{-2} s^{-1}), and 51.5% in the high UV-B treatment (from 17.1 to 25.9 m m^{-2} s^{-1}).

In the medium UV-B treatment, the growth stimulation from the elevated CO_2 was sufficient to raise net photosynthesis rates 33.7% above the rates experienced in the ambient air and no UV-B treatment (from 30.3 to 40.5 m m^{-2} s^{-1}). In the high UV-B treatment, however, the radiation damage was so great the 51.5% increase in net photosynthesis provided by the doubled-CO_2 air could not prevent the destruction, and the mean net photosynthesis rate of the cotton leaves was 14.5% less than in the

ambient air and no UV-B treatment (dropping from 30.3 to 25.9 m m^{-2} s^{-1}).

The medium UV-B treatment of this study was chosen to represent the intensity of UV-B radiation presently received on a clear summer day in the major cotton production region of Mississippi (USA) under current stratospheric ozone conditions, and the high UV-B treatment was chosen to represent what might be expected there following a 30% depletion of the ozone layer, which has been predicted to double the region's reception of UV-B radiation from 8 to 16 kJ m^{-2} d^{-1}. Thus doubling the current CO_2 concentration and current UV-B radiation level would reduce the net photosynthetic rate of cotton leaves by just under 10% (from 28.7 to 25.9 m m^{-2} s^{-1}), whereas in the absence of a doubling of the air's CO_2 content, a doubling of the UV-B radiation level would reduce cotton net photosynthesis by just over 40% (from 28.7 to 17.1 m m^{-2} s^{-1}). Doubling the current atmospheric CO_2 concentration thus would compensate for more than three-fourths of the loss of cotton photosynthetic capacity caused by a doubling of the current UV-B radiation intensity. And it might do even better than that: Zhao *et al.* (2003) reported both Adamse and Britz (1992) and Rozema *et al.* (1997) found a doubling of CO_2 fully compensated for the negative effects of equally high UV-B radiation.

Deckmyn *et al.* (2001) grew white clover plants for four months in four small greenhouses, in two of which they allowed 88% of the incoming UV-B radiation to pass through the roofs and walls and two of which allowed 82% to pass through. They maintained one of the two greenhouses in each of the UV-B treatments at ambient CO_2 (371 ppm) and the other at elevated CO_2 (521 ppm). At the midseason point of their study, the 40% increase in atmospheric CO_2 concentration stimulated the production of flowers in the low UV-B treatment by 22% and in the slightly higher UV-B treatment by 43%. At the end of the season, the extra CO_2 provided no stimulation of biomass production in the low UV-B treatment but stimulated biomass production by 16% in the high UV-B treatment.

The results of this study indicate the positive effects of atmospheric CO_2 enrichment on flower and biomass production in white clover are greater at more realistic or natural values of UV-B radiation than those found in many greenhouses. Deckmyn *et al.* state their results "clearly indicate the importance of using UV-B transmittant greenhouses or open-top chambers when conducting CO_2 studies," lest the results obtained significantly underestimate the magnitude of the benefits provided by the rise in the air's CO_2 content.

Qaderi and Reid (2005) grew well-watered and well-fertilized canola plants (*Brassica napus*) from seed to maturity in pots in controlled-environment chambers maintained at either 370 or 740 ppm CO_2 with and without a daily dose of UV-B radiation in the amount of 4.2 kJ m^{-2}, measuring a number of plant parameters at various times throughout the growing season. The final seed yield was 0.98 g/plant in the control treatment (ambient CO_2, with UV-B). Doubling the CO_2 concentration increased yield by 25.5% to 1.23 g/plant, and removing the UV-B radiation flux increased yield by 91.8% to 1.88 g/plant. Doing both (doubling the CO_2 concentration while simultaneously removing the UV-B flux) increased final seed yield by 175.5% to 2.7 g/plant. Hence, doubling the air's CO_2 concentration in the presence of the UV-B radiation flux enhanced final seed yield by 25.5%, and doubling CO_2 in the absence of the UV-B radiation flux increased seed yield by 43.6%. Qaderi and Reid conclude, "elevated CO_2 may have a positive effect on plants by mitigating the detrimental effects caused by UV-B radiation."

In a follow-up paper, Qaderi *et al.* (2007) examined the effects of elevated CO_2 and UVB radiation on the photosynthetic rates and water use efficiency of the maturing husks (siliquas) that surround the canola plant's seeds. For the plants exposed to 4.2 kJ m^{-2} d^{-1} of UVB radiation, the experimental doubling of the air's CO_2 concentration led to a 29% increase in siliqua net photosynthesis, an 18% decrease in siliqua transpiration, and a 58% increase in siliqua water use efficiency. For the plants exposed to no UVB radiation, siliqua net photosynthesis was increased by 38%, transpiration was decreased by 22%, and water use efficiency was increased by 87% in the CO_2-enriched air.

Tohidimoghadam *et al.* (2011) grew two varieties (Okapi and Talaye) of canola out-of-doors over the 2008 and 2009 growing seasons beneath rigid frames covered with polyethylene plastic film in air maintained at ambient and elevated atmospheric CO_2 concentrations of 400 and 900 ppm, at ambient and elevated levels of UV radiation, and under well-watered and deficit-watered conditions, measuring numerous plant properties during and after the growing period. They found "water stress significantly decreased yield and yield components, oil yield, protein percentage, height, specific leaf area and the number of branches." Elevated CO_2

"increased the final yield, 1000-seed weight, oil percentage, oil yield, height, specific leaf area and number of branches." UV radiation "decreased the yield, yield components, oil and protein percentages and growth parameters." They also note "the highest seed weight was obtained from the 'Talaye' cultivar treated with compete irrigation and elevated CO_2 and grown under sunlight radiation," whereas "the seed weights of both cultivars visibly decreased due to UV-B, UV-C and water stress under an ambient CO_2 concentration." The three Iranian researchers who conducted the study state, "an increase in UV exposure deceases plant growth and development," but "elevated CO_2 ameliorate(s) the adverse effects of UV radiation in the final yield, seed weight, oil percentage, oil yield, plant height, specific leaf area and number of branches per plant." They conclude an increase in the atmosphere's CO_2 concentration "could improve yield, yield components and growth parameters for plants subjected to elevated levels of UV radiation."

In a study of UV-B and CO_2 effects on a natural ecosystem, conducted at the Abisko Scientific Research Station in Swedish Lapland, Johnson *et al.* (2002) studied plots of subarctic heath composed of open canopies of downy birch and dense dwarf-shrub layers containing herbs and grasses. For five years, they exposed the plots to factorial combinations of UV-B radiation (ambient and that expected to result from a 15% stratospheric ozone depletion) and atmospheric CO_2 concentration (ambient, around 365 ppm, and enriched, around 600 ppm), after which they determined the amounts of microbial carbon (C_{mic}) and nitrogen (N_{mic}) in the soils of the plots.

When the plots were exposed to the enhanced UV-B radiation, the amount of C_{mic} in the soil was reduced to only 37% of what it was at the ambient UV-B level when the air's CO_2 content was maintained at the ambient concentration. When the UV-B increase was accompanied by the CO_2 increase, however, there was no decrease in C_{mic} but an increase of 37%. When the plots were exposed to the enhanced level of UV-B radiation, the amount of N_{mic} in the soil showed a 69% increase when the air's CO_2 content was maintained at the ambient concentration, and when the UV-B increase was accompanied by the CO_2 increase, N_{mic} rose by 138%.

These findings, Johnson *et al.* write, "may have far-reaching implications ... because the productivity of many semi-natural ecosystems is limited by N (Ellenberg, 1988)." Thus, the 138% increase in soil microbial N observed in this study to accompany a

15% reduction in stratospheric ozone and a 64% increase in atmospheric CO_2 concentration should significantly enhance the input of plant litter to the soils of these ecosystems, which represents the first half of the carbon sequestration process—the carbon input stage.

As to the second stage—keeping as much of that carbon as possible in the soil—Johnson *et al.* note "the capacity for subarctic semi-natural heaths to act as major sinks for fossil fuel-derived carbon dioxide is [also] likely to be critically dependent on the supply of N," as indicated in the literature review of Berg and Matzner (1997). The latter report the presence of additional nitrogen in the soil significantly enhances the long-term storage of carbon, as more litter is chemically transformed into humic substances when nitrogen is more readily available, and these more recalcitrant carbon compounds can be successfully stored in the soil for many millennia.

Koti *et al.* (2007) investigated the interactive effects of elevated atmospheric CO_2 (720 vs. 360 ppm), UV-B radiation levels (0 vs. 10 kJ/m^2/day), and temperature (38/30°C vs. 30/22°C day/night) on the growth and development of six well-watered and well-fertilized soybean (*Glycine max* L.) genotypes. They found "elevated CO_2 partially compensated [for] the damaging effects on vegetative growth and physiology caused by negative stressors such as high temperatures and enhanced UV-B radiation levels in soybean." The authors note CO_2's positive influence on plant height, leaf area, total biomass, net photosynthesis, total chlorophyll content, phenolic content, and wax content, as well as relative plant injury. Thus, with respect to almost all of the ways high air temperatures and high UV-B radiation levels retard the growth and development of soybeans, elevated atmospheric CO_2 concentrations appear to provide significant ameliorative relief.

Estiarte *et al.* (1999) grew spring wheat in FACE plots in Arizona (USA) at atmospheric CO_2 concentrations of 370 and 550 ppm and two levels of soil moisture (50 and 100% of potential evapotranspiration). Under those conditions, leaves of plants growing in elevated CO_2 had 14% higher total flavonoid concentrations than those of plants grown in ambient air, and soil water content did not affect the relationship. One of the functions of flavonoids in plant leaves is to protect them against UV-B radiation. Hence, more studies of this nature should be conducted to see how general this beneficial response may be throughout the plant world.

These findings indicate the rise in the air's CO_2 content is a powerful counterbalance against the deleterious biological impacts that could be caused by an increase in the flux of UV-B radiation at the surface of Earth due to depletion of the planet's stratospheric ozone layer.

References

Adamse, P. and Britz, S.J. 1992. Amelioration of UV-B damage under high irradiance. I. Role of photosynthesis. *Photochemistry and Photobiology* **56**: 645–650.

Berg, B. and Matzner, E. 1997. Effect of N deposition on decomposition of plant litter and soil organic matter in forest ecosystems. *Environmental Reviews* **5**: 1–25.

Dai, Q., Coronal, V.P., Vergara, B.S., Barnes, P.W., and Quintos, A.T. 1992. Ultraviolet-B radiation effects on growth and physiology of four rice cultivars. *Crop Science* **32**: 1269–1274.

Deckmyn, G., Caeyenberghs, E., and Ceulemans, R. 2001. Reduced UV-B in greenhouses decreases white clover response to enhanced CO_2. *Environmental and Experimental Botany* **46**: 109–117.

Ellenberg, H. 1988. *Vegetation Ecology of Central Europe.* Cambridge University Press, Cambridge, UK.

Estiarte, M., Peñuelas, J., Kimball, B.A., Hendrix, D.L., Pinter Jr., P.J., Wall, G.W., LaMorte, R.L., and Hunsaker, D.J. 1999. Free-air CO_2 enrichment of wheat: leaf flavonoid concentration throughout the growth cycle. *Physiologia Plantarum* **105**: 423–433.

Johnson, D., Campbell, C.D., Lee, J.A., Callaghan, T.V., and Gwynn-Jones, D. 2002. Arctic microorganisms respond more to elevated UV-B radiation than CO_2. *Nature* **416**: 82–83.

Jordan, B.R., Chow, W.S., and Anderson, J.M. 1992. Changes in mRNA levels and polypeptide subunits of ribulose 1,5-bisphosphate carboxylase in response to supplementary ultraviolet-B radiation. *Plant, Cell and Environment* **15**: 91–98.

Koti, S., Reddy, K.R., Kakani, V.G., Zhao, D., and Gao, W. 2007. Effects of carbon dioxide, temperature and ultraviolet-B radiation and their interactions on soybean (*Glycine max* L.) growth and development. *Environmental and Experimental Botany* **60**: 1–10.

Madronich, S., McKenzie, R.L., Bjorn, L.O., and Caldwell, M.M. 1998. Changes in biologically active ultraviolet radiation reaching the Earth's surface. *Journal of Photochemistry and Photobiology B: Biology* **46**: 5–19.

McKenzie, R.L., Bjorn, L.O., Bais, A., and Ilyasd, M. 2003. Changes in biologically active ultraviolet radiation reaching the Earth's surface. *Photochemical and Photobiological Sciences* **2**: 5–15.

Nogues, S., Allen, D.J., Morison, J.I.L., and Baker, N.R. 1999. Characterization of stomatal closure caused by ultraviolet-B radiation. *Plant Physiology* **121**: 489–496.

Qaderi, M.M. and Reid, D.M. 2005. Growth and physiological responses of canola (*Brassica napus*) to UV-B and CO_2 under controlled environment conditions. *Physiologia Plantarum* **125**: 247–259.

Qaderi, M.M., Reid, D.M., and Yeung, E.C. 2007. Morphological and physiological responses of canola (*Brassica napus*) siliquas and seeds to UVB and CO_2 under controlled environment conditions. *Environmental and Experimental Botany* **60**: 428–437.

Rozema, J., Lenssen, G.M., Staaij, J.W.M., Tosserams, M., Visser, A.J., and Brockman, R.A. 1997. Effects of UV-B radiation on terrestrial plants and ecosystems: interaction with CO_2 enrichment. *Plant Ecology* **128**: 182–191.

Stapleton, A.E. 1992. Ultraviolet radiation and plants: Burning questions. *The Plant Cell* **105**: 881–889.

Tohidimoghadam, H.R., Ghooshchi, F., and Zahedi, H. 2011. Effect of UV radiation and elevated CO_2 on morphological traits, yield and yield components of canola (*Brassica napus* L.) grown under water deficit. *Notulae Botanicae Horti Agrobotanici Cluj-Napoca* **39**: 213–219.

Zhao, D., Reddy, K.R., Kakani, V.G., Mohammed, A.R., Read, J.J., and Gao, W. 2004. Leaf and canopy photosynthetic characteristics of cotton (*Gossypiuym hirsutum*) under elevated CO_2 concentration and UV-B radiation. *Journal of Plant Physiology* **161**: 581–590.

Zhao, D., Reddy, K.R., Kakani, V.G., Read, J.J., and Sullivan, J.H. 2003. Growth and physiological responses of cotton (*Gossypium hirsutum* L.) to elevated carbon dioxide and ultraviolet-B radiation under controlled environmental conditions. *Plant, Cell and Environment* **26**: 771–782.

3.15 Water Stress

As the CO_2 content of the air rises, nearly all plants will exhibit increases in photosynthesis and biomass production, but some researchers claim water stress will negate these benefits. This section examines the results of several CO_2-enrichment studies designed to show the net effect of elevated CO_2 and water stress on the growth of Earth's vegetation.

3.15.1 Agricultural Crops

- The rise in the atmosphere's CO_2 content likely will lead to substantial increases in the photosynthetic rates and biomass production of the world's chief agricultural crops, even in stressful situations imposed by less-than-optimum soil moisture.

As the air's CO_2 content rises, nearly all plants will exhibit increases in photosynthesis and biomass production, but some researchers claim elevated concentrations of atmospheric CO_2 will lead to more droughty conditions in many parts of the world and thereby significantly reduce or totally negate these CO_2-induced benefits. This section reviews the results of numerous studies that show atmospheric CO_2 enrichment may help important food crops cope with periods of less-than-optimal water availability.

One way atmospheric CO_2 enrichment helps plants in this regard is by stimulating them to develop larger-than-usual and more robust root systems that enable them to probe greater volumes of soil for moisture. Wechsung *et al.* (1999), for example, observed a 70% increase in lateral root dry weights of water-stressed wheat grown at 550 ppm CO_2, and De Luis *et al.* (1999) reported a 269% increase in root-to-shoot ratio of water-stressed alfalfa growing at 700 ppm CO_2. Thus, elevated CO_2 may often elicit stronger-than-usual positive root responses in agricultural species under conditions of water stress.

Elevated levels of atmospheric CO_2 also tend to reduce the openness of stomatal pores on leaves, thus decreasing plant stomatal conductance. This phenomenon, in turn, reduces the amount of water lost to the atmosphere by transpiration and, consequently, lowers overall plant water use. Serraj *et al.* (1999), for example, reported water-stressed soybeans grown at 700 ppm CO_2 reduced their total seasonal water loss by 10% relative to water-stressed control plants grown at 360 ppm CO_2. And Conley *et al.* (2001) found a 200 ppm increase in the air's CO_2 concentration reduced cumulative evapotranspiration in water-stressed sorghum by about 4%.

Atmospheric CO_2 enrichment thus increases plant water acquisition by stimulating root growth, and it reduces plant water loss by constricting stomatal apertures. These two phenomena typically enhance plant water-use efficiency, even under conditions of less-than-optimal soil water content. They have other implications as well.

CO_2-induced increases in root development

together with CO_2-induced reductions in stomatal conductance often improve plant water status during times of drought. Sgherri et al. (1998), for example, found leaf water potential, which is a good indicator of overall plant water status, was 30% higher (less negative and therefore more favorable) in water-stressed alfalfa grown at an atmospheric CO_2 concentration of 600 ppm versus 340 ppm. Wall (2001) found leaf water potentials were similar in CO_2-enriched water-stressed plants and ambient-grown well-watered control plants, which implies a complete CO_2-induced amelioration of water stress in the CO_2-enriched plants. Lin and Wang (2002) demonstrated elevated CO_2 caused a several-day delay in the onset of the water stress-induced production of the highly reactive oxygenated compound H_2O_2 in spring wheat. Also, they found plants grown in elevated CO_2 maintained higher enzymatic activities of superoxide dismutase and catalase—two important antioxidants—relative to those observed in ambient-grown plants, following the induction of water stress.

If atmospheric CO_2 enrichment allows plants to maintain a better water status during times of water stress, it is only logical to surmise they would exhibit greater rates of photosynthesis than plants growing in similarly water-deficient soil in non-CO_2-enriched air. With the onset of experimentally induced water stress in India Mustard (*Brassica juncea*), Rabha and Uprety (1998) observed photosynthetic rates dropped by 40% in plants growing in ambient air, while plants growing in air containing 600 ppm CO_2 experienced only a 30% reduction in net photosynthesis. Ferris et al. (1998) imposed water-stress conditions on soybeans and allowed them to recover following complete rewetting of the soil, finding plants grown in air containing 700 ppm CO_2 reached pre-stressed rates of photosynthesis after six days, whereas plants grown in ambient air never recovered to pre-stressed photosynthetic rates.

Analogously, it is also to be expected that elevated CO_2 concentrations would enhance plant biomass production under drought conditions. Ferris et al. (1999) report water-stressed soybeans grown at 700 ppm CO_2 attained seed yields 24% greater than those of similarly water-stressed plants grown at ambient CO_2 concentrations, and Hudak et al. (1999) determined water stress had no detrimental effect on yield in CO_2-enriched spring wheat. Many studies have found the CO_2-induced biomass increase to be greater for water-stressed plants than for well-watered plants, as demonstrated in the review of the subject by

Idso and Idso (1994).

Li et al. (2000), reported a 180 ppm increase in the air's CO_2 content increased final grain weights in the upper and lower sections of the main stems of the spring wheat they studied by 10 and 24%, respectively, under water-stressed conditions, but under well-watered conditions elevated CO_2 increased final grain weights only in the lower sections of the main stems and by only 14%. Thus elevated CO_2 had a greater positive impact on final grain weights of spring wheat under water-stressed field conditions than in non-water-stressed field conditions, once again demonstrating atmospheric CO_2 enrichment is often more important to stressed plants than to non-stressed plants.

Similarly, spring wheat grown in air containing an additional 280 ppm CO_2 exhibited 57 and 40% increases in grain yield under water-stressed and well-watered conditions, respectively (Schutz and Fangmeier, 2001). Ottman et al. (2001) found elevated CO_2 increased plant biomass in water-stressed sorghum by 15%, but no biomass increase occurred in well-watered sorghum. In predicting maize and winter wheat yields in Bulgaria under future scenarios of increased air temperature and decreased precipitation, Alexandrov and Hoogenboom (2000) note yield losses were likely to occur if the air's CO_2 content remained unchanged, but if the atmospheric CO_2 concentration doubled, maize and winter wheat yields likely would increase, even under the combined stresses of elevated temperature and reduced rainfall.

Widodo et al. (2003) grew rice (*Oryza sativa* [L.] cv. IR-72) in eight outdoor, sunlit, controlled-environment chambers at daytime atmospheric CO_2 concentrations of 350 and 700 ppm for an entire season. In one pair of chambers the plants were continuously flooded, in a second pair drought stress was imposed during panicle initiation, in a third pair it was imposed during anthesis, and in a fourth pair it was imposed at both stages. In the elevated CO_2 treatment, midday leaf photosynthetic CO_2 exchange rates (CER) and chlorophyll concentrations were higher at most sampling dates. In addition, the CO_2-enriched plants exhibited enhanced midday leaf sucrose and starch accumulation during early reproductive phases.

Near the end of the imposed drought periods, water deficits caused substantial decreases in midday leaf CER and chlorophyll concentrations, along with concomitant reductions in the primary products of photosynthesis. These drought-induced effects,

Widodo *et al.* note, "were more severe for plants grown at ambient than at elevated CO_2." They report, for example, "plants grown under elevated CO_2 were able to maintain midday leaf photosynthesis, and to some extent other photosynthetic-related parameters, longer into the drought period than plants grown at ambient CO_2," as also has been observed for a number of other plants (Rogers *et al.*, 1984; Jones *et al.*, 1985; Idso, 1988; Bhattacharya *et al.*, 1990; Chaves and Pereira, 1992; Clifford *et al.*, 1993; Baker *et al.*, 1997; Vu *et al.*, 1998).

Recovery from drought-induced water stress was more rapid in the elevated CO_2 treatment. At panicle initiation, for example, Widodo *et al.* write, "as water was added back following a drought induction, it took more than 24 days for the ambient CO_2-[water] stressed plants to recuperate in midday leaf CER, compared with only 6–8 days for the elevated CO_2-[water] stressed plants." Similarly, they note, "for the drought imposed during anthesis, midday leaf CER of the elevated CO_2-[water] stressed plants was fully recovered after 16 days of re-watering, whereas those of the ambient CO_2-[water] stressed plants were still 21% lagging behind their unstressed controls at that date." The five researchers conclude, "rice grown under future rising atmospheric CO_2 should be better able to tolerate drought situations."

Triggs *et al.* (2004) grew sorghum (*Sorghum bicolor* (L.) Moench, a C_4 grain crop) for two full seasons in control CO_2 plots (about 370 ppm) and FACE plots (Control + 200 ppm) under both well-watered (Wet) and water-stressed (Dry, less than half the total water received by the Wet treatment via rainfall and irrigation) conditions near Maricopa, Arizona (USA). They assessed evapotranspiration (ET) on a continuous basis by means of micro-meteorological measurements designed to allow the calculation of all the other elements (net radiation, sensible heat flux, and soil surface heat flux) of the energy balance of the crop-soil interface with the atmosphere. Sorghum water use efficiency (WUE) was calculated using final grain yield data obtained by Ottman *et al.* (2001).

Triggs *et al.* write, "in the Wet treatments, a reduction in ET of about 19%, combined with only a slight increase in total biomass (+4%), resulted in a 28% increase in WUE in elevated CO_2 conditions," whereas "in the Dry treatments, the relatively large increase in total biomass (+16% for both years) more than compensated for the approximate 5% increase in total ET, giving the FACE-Dry treatments an increase in WUE of 16% over both seasons." They conclude,

"even if future climate change results in less water available for agriculture, higher atmospheric CO_2 concentrations will still benefit C_4 crops," although "in regions with ample precipitation or irrigation, C_3 crops with higher growth responses may be preferable."

Kaddour and Fuller (2004) grew three commercial cultivars of durum wheat (*Triticum durum* Desf.) registered in Syria (Cham 1, Cham 3, and Cham 5) from seed in 10-liter pots in different compartments of a phytotron. Half of the compartments were maintained at an atmospheric CO_2 concentration of approximately 400 ppm and half were maintained at a concentration of approximately 1,000 ppm. Half of each of these treatments were further subdivided into two soil water treatments: well-watered, where available water content (AWC) was replenished to 90% of full capacity when it dropped to 60%, and water-stressed, where AWC was replenished to 70% of full capacity when it dropped to 45%. Averaged over the three cultivars, the extra 600 ppm of CO_2 supplied to the CO_2-enriched compartments led to total plant biomass increases of 62% in the well-watered treatment and 60% in the water-stressed treatment. The extra CO_2 also led to increases in the nitrogen concentrations of stems and ears. Nitrogen concentration of the ears was increased by 22% in the well-watered plants and by 16% in the water-stressed plants.

Kaddour and Fuller write their results "have important implications for the production of durum wheat in the future." They state "yields can be expected to rise as atmospheric CO_2 levels rise," and "this increase in yield can be expected under both water restricted and well irrigated conditions." Therefore, "where water availability is a prime limiting economic resource, it can be distributed more effectively under higher CO_2 conditions," and "for countries such as Syria where average national production is well below the physiological maximum due largely to drought stress, the predicted rise in atmospheric CO_2 could have a positive effect on production."

Richter and Semenov (2005) note, "with global warming, evapotranspiration is likely to increase and, with more variable rainfall, droughts could occur more often." They evaluated the impact of potential climate change on drought indicators and yields of winter wheat in England and Wales using a crop simulation model (*Sirius*) that also incorporates the effects of elevated atmospheric CO_2 concentration and temperature on crop growth and development, where the CO_2 scenario driving the model was of medium to high anthropogenic emissions that raise the air's CO_2 concentration from 334 ppm (the 1961–1990 baseline) to 554 ppm in the 2050s. Probability distributions derived from multiple simulations using representative weather, soil types, and sowing dates indicate maximum soil moisture deficit "is likely to increase in the future, especially on shallow soils, and the probability of potential yield reductions exceeding 25% will increase by 10% until the 2050s." Nevertheless, they write, "average wheat yields are likely to increase by 1.2 to 2 t/ha (15–23%) by the 2050s because of a CO_2-related increase in radiation use efficiency."

Bernacchi *et al.* (2006) grew soybeans (*Glycine max* (L.) Merr.) for three years at the SoyFACE facility of the University of Illinois at Urbana-Champaign, Illinois (USA) at atmospheric CO_2 concentrations of either 375 or 550 ppm under natural field conditions with and without a 23% increase in ambient atmospheric ozone concentration, measuring a number of weather and plant physiological parameters from pre-dawn to post-dusk on several days during the three growing seasons. They determined the mean daily integral of leaf-level net photosynthesis (A) was enhanced by nearly 25% in the CO_2-enriched air under ambient ozone concentrations, but by a slightly smaller 20% in the high-ozone air. In addition, "there was a strong positive correlation between daytime maximum temperatures and mean daily integrated A at elevated CO_2." From their graphical depiction of this relationship, it appears at a daily maximum temperature of approximately 26.5°C, A was stimulated by about 14%, and at a daily maximum temperature of approximately 34.5°C, it was stimulated by about 35%. The 11 researchers report "the effect of elevated CO_2 on photosynthesis tended to be greater under water stress conditions," rising from an approximate 17% enhancement of A at the most favorable soil moisture condition encountered to an enhancement close to 30% under the driest of the conditions experienced by the crop.

Robredo *et al.* (2007) grew well-watered and well-fertilized barley (*Hordeum vulgare* L.) seedlings (seven per each 2.5-liter pot filled with perlite and vermiculite) in controlled-environment chambers maintained at atmospheric CO_2 concentrations of either 350 or 700 ppm. At the conclusion of the 18th day after seedling emergence, the treatments were split, with one continuing to be watered three times a week and the other treatment receiving no further

water. At that time and on several following dates, researchers measured a number of soil and plant water parameters, along with rates of leaf transpiration and net photosynthesis. They found "during the period of drought, elevated CO_2 delayed by 3–4 days the depletion of soil water content," because of "the lower rates of transpiration in plants grown under CO_2 enrichment." As a result, "under elevated CO_2, plant water stress developed more slowly," thanks to "a slower rate of soil water depletion," They report "the stimulation of carbon assimilation by elevated CO_2 was even greater in droughted compared to well-watered plants," even though "elevated CO_2 caused stomata closure."

The seven Spanish researchers write, "exposure to high carbon dioxide concentration resulted in an increase in photosynthesis and in a reduction in whole plant transpiration, contributing to an increase in water use efficiency that was more noticeable when plants were subjected to elevated CO_2 in conjunction with drought." They conclude, "growing plants under [an] elevated CO_2 environment mitigates or delays the effects of water stress in barley."

Li *et al.* (2007) employed open-top chambers to determine net ecosystem CO_2 exchange (NEE) before, during, and after the severe Central Florida drought of 1998 in a scrub-oak ecosystem in ambient-CO_2 (AC) air and in elevated-CO_2 (EC) air enriched with an extra 350 ppm of CO_2 since May 1996. They focused on the ecosystem's dominant species (*Quercus myrtifolia* Willd.), for which they measured net photosynthetic rate (PN) throughout the daylight hours of several days. They found EC air generally increased PN, whereas drought decreased it. Under droughty conditions, PN peaked at around 0830 each day, after which it declined in a fairly steady fashion until solar noon and typically remained at a relatively low level throughout the remainder of the daylight hours. The scientists assessed the interactive impacts of elevated CO_2 and drought on tree PN by comparing the percentage reduction in PN from 0830 to 1230 in the two CO_2 treatments. They found in May 1998, PN was reduced by 77% from 0830 to 1230 at AC but by only 48% at EC, and in July 1998, when the drought had further intensified, PN was reduced by 82% at AC but by a lesser 69% at EC.

NEE responded in much the same way. In May and June 1998, for example, NEE's midday depression was 58% and 60% less at EC than at AC, and in July 1999 it was 66% less. In addition, Li *et al.* note, "the mitigation of the effects of water stress by EC was reflected in the aboveground biomass growth," such that "the relative effect of EC on biomass accumulation of the dominant species *Q. myrtifolia* was higher during the drought year (210% for 1998) compared to the non-drought years (67% for 1997)."

Manderscheid and Weigel (2007) grew spring wheat (*Triticum aestivum* cv. Minaret) in open-top chambers on an experimental field of the Federal Agricultural Research Center in Braunschweig, Germany, in two growing seasons at either current or future (current + 280 ppm) atmospheric CO_2 concentrations and under sufficient-water-supply (WET) or drought-stress (DRY) conditions. They imposed the latter just after the crop first-node stage was reached (approximately 35 days after emergence), by halving the subsequent water supplied to the plants. The researchers found, "in both years, biomass and grain yield were decreased by drought and increased by CO_2 enrichment," with the positive CO_2 effect being greater under drought conditions. Averaged over both years, "CO_2 enrichment increased biomass and grain yield under WET conditions by <=10% and under DRY conditions by >=44%." The CO_2-induced increase in crop water-use efficiency was 20% in the sufficient-water-supply treatment and 43% in the drought-stress treatment.

Veisz *et al.* (2008) grew seven cereal grain crops—winter barley (*Hordeum vulgare*, cv. Petra), winter wheat (*Triticum aestivum*, cvs. Libellula, Mv Regiment, Mv Mambo), winter durum wheat (*Triticum durum*, cv. Mv Makaroni), spring wheat (*Triticum aestivum*, cv Lona), and spring oats (*Avena sativa*, cv. Mv Pehely)—in a phytotron at the Agricultural Research Institute of the Hungarian Academy of Sciences at ambient and enriched atmospheric CO_2 concentrations (380 and 750 ppm, respectively) under both well-watered and drought conditions. For the latter condition they withheld water beginning at the 10th day after heading, and soil volumetric water content dropped from approximately 25% to 6%. They measured a number of crop characteristics at harvest.

Under the experimental conditions, the plants grown in the CO_2-enriched air "produced more organic matter, being taller, with more spikes and a higher grain number per plant than those grown at the present CO_2 level," and "thanks to the more intensive incorporation of carbohydrate, there was an increase in the mean grain mass and in the grain yield per plant" in the CO_2-enriched air. However, there was a concomitant decrease in the protein concentration of the grains produced in the high-CO_2 treatment.

Nevertheless, the net effect was positive because, for the several cereal varieties averaged together, grain yield under the well-watered conditions rose by 12.37% (from 2.83 to 3.18 g/plant) in response to atmospheric CO_2 enrichment, and grain protein concentration dropped from 17.04% to 16.23%, resulting in a net increase of 7% in total grain protein production. Likewise, grain yield under the water-stressed conditions rose by 30.68% (from 1.76 to 2.30 g/plant) in response to atmospheric CO_2 enrichment, and the concentration of the grain protein dropped from 21.63% to 19.70%, leading to a net increase of 19% in total grain protein production.

Chun *et al.* (2011) grew corn plants from seed in naturally sunlit soil-plant-atmosphere-research (SPAR) units in which temperature, humidity, and CO_2 concentration were precisely controlled, the latter at either 400 ppm (ambient) or 800 ppm (elevated), beginning 21 days after emergence (DAE). These units were placed atop soil bins (2.0 m long by 0.5 m wide by 1.0 m deep) filled with a mixture of 75% coarse sand and 25% vermiculate, where soil water contents were monitored hourly by a time domain reflectometry (TDR) system that consisted of 15 TDR probes per chamber placed in three rows at depths of 0, 15, 30, 50, and 75 cm from the soil surface. By means of this system of soil water content assessment, combined with nightly "fertigation," Chun *et al.* were able to provide the plants with the nitrogen they needed while maintaining four soil water stress levels—control, mild, moderate, and severe—which were also initiated at 21 DAE. Thereafter, the height, number of leaves, leaf lengths, and growth states of the corn plants were determined twice weekly, and samples of the plants were collected, dried, and analyzed for biomass accumulation at 21 and 60 DAE (the beginning and end of the different CO_2 and soil water content treatments).

The five researchers did not find the elevated CO_2 treatment had a strong effect on plant height, leaf area, or above-ground biomass. But under both well-watered and water-stressed conditions, higher soil water contents were maintained in the elevated CO_2 treatment, even though 20–49% less water was applied to the soil of the elevated CO_2 treatment. The five researchers conclude, "under increased CO_2 concentrations as generally predicted in the future, less water will be required for corn plants than at present."

Robredo *et al.* (2011) write, "barley, an economically important and extensively cultivated cereal worldwide, increases its yield in parallel with an increase in CO_2," but "responds to drought stress through altered nitrogen metabolism and reduced productivity." They explored these complexities by growing barley (*Hordeum vulgare* L. cv. Iranis) seedlings in 2.5-L pots containing a 3:1 mix of perlite:vermiculite in a controlled-environment growth chamber, first at ambient and then at elevated atmospheric CO_2 concentrations (350 and 700 ppm, respectively). Initially, they watered the pots twice a week with a complete Hoagland solution and with deionized water between each Hoagland solution application. They initiated drought when the seedlings were 18 days old, withholding water for intervals of 9, 13, and 16 days. They analyzed the effects of these actions at the end of each drought period and analyzed water recovery three days after rewatering the 13-day droughted plants, with each complete experiment being replicated three times.

The six Spanish scientists state their barley plants showed a reduction in water use, even though under elevated CO_2 the plants had a larger leaf area, much as others also have found (Owensby *et al.*, 1997; Niklaus *et al.*, 1998). In addition, "during the period of drought, the depletion of soil water content was delayed by 3–4 days in plants grown under elevated CO_2 conditions," and in the CO_2-enriched plants "water stress also developed more slowly than at ambient CO_2 because of a slower rate of water depletion." They report, "leaf water potential in plants subjected to drought but grown at elevated CO_2 was less negative than in their ambient CO_2 grown counterparts."

Robredo *et al.* also note "absolute values for nitrogen uptake by barley plants were higher under elevated CO_2 compared to ambient CO_2." In addition, they "observed high nitrate reductase activity in plants grown at elevated CO_2, which should parallel an increase in photosynthesis (Robredo *et al.*, 2007) and sugar content (Perez-Lopez *et al.*, 2010)." Also, "under ambient CO_2 conditions, protein content decreased as the water stress progressed," but "when plants grew under elevated CO_2 conditions, the rate of photosynthesis was higher [and] drought had less effect on the protein content." They report the barley plants "showed a greater content of proteins under elevated CO_2," in harmony with Geiger *et al.* (1999), who they say "reported a similar outcome in tobacco with the same supra-optimal nitrogen concentration." They further remark these findings also mesh with the results of studies reviewed by Idso and Idso (2001), who conclude any negative effects of elevated CO_2 on

crop protein content "could be ameliorated by increased use of nitrogen fertilizer." Robredo *et al.* conclude "elevated CO_2 mitigates many of the effects of drought on nitrogen metabolism and allows more rapid recovery following water stress."

Tohidimoghadam *et al.* (2011) grew two varieties (Okapi and Talaye) of canola (*Brassica napus* L.) plants over the 2008 and 2009 growing seasons out-of-doors at 35°59'N, 50°75'E beneath rigid frames covered with polyethylene plastic film in air maintained at ambient and elevated atmospheric CO_2 concentrations of 400 and 900 ppm, at ambient and elevated levels of UV radiation, and under well-watered and deficit-watered conditions, during and after which periods they measured numerous plant properties. They found "water stress significantly decreased yield and yield components, oil yield, protein percentage, height, specific leaf area and the number of branches," but elevated CO_2 "increased the final yield, 1000-seed weight, oil percentage, oil yield, height, specific leaf area and number of branches." They also found elevated UV radiation "decreased the yield, yield components, oil and protein percentages and growth parameters," but elevated CO_2 once again ameliorated "the adverse effects of UV radiation in the final yield, seed weight, oil percentage, oil yield, plant height, specific leaf area and number of branches per plant."

Varga *et al.* (2012) write, "as well as damaging numerous physiological functions, abiotic stress [such as drought] also leads to higher concentrations of reactive oxygen species, which are present in nature in all plants, but which may damage cell components and disturb metabolic processes when present in larger quantities," citing Omran (1980), Larson (1988), and Dat *et al.* (2000). They note, "many authors have demonstrated that the [atmosphere's] CO_2 concentration has a substantial influence on the stress sensitivity of plants via changes in antioxidant enzyme activity," citing Fernandez-Trujillo *et al.* (2007), Ali *et al.* (2008), and Varga and Bencze (2009).

In an experiment designed to explore this subject further, Varga *et al.* grew two varieties of winter wheat in phytotrons maintained at either 380 or 750 ppm CO_2, where the potted plants were watered daily and supplied with nutrient solution twice a week until the start of drought treatments. They induced drought in three phases—at first node appearance, heading, and grain filling—by completely withholding water for seven days, which ultimately dropped the volumetric soil water content in the pots from 20–25% to 3–5%. These actions, the four Hungarian researchers report, led to "changes in enzyme activity" that "indicated that enhanced CO_2 concentration delayed the development of drought stress up to first node appearance, and stimulated antioxidant enzyme activity when drought occurred during ripening, thus reducing the unfavorable effects of [drought] stress." They conclude the increases in the antioxidant enzymes they analyzed "may help to neutralize the reactive oxygen species induced by stress during various parts of the vegetation period," and this phenomenon should help crops cope with extremes of moisture insufficiency.

These peer-reviewed, scientific studies of the effects of water insufficiency on the productivity of the world's major agricultural crops strongly support the earlier work of Idso and Idso (1994), who concluded the rise in the air's CO_2 content likely will lead to substantial increases in the photosynthetic rates and biomass production of the world's major agricultural crops, even in less-than-optimum soil moisture conditions.

References

Alexandrov, V.A. and Hoogenboom, G. 2000. The impact of climate variability and change on crop yield in Bulgaria. *Agricultural and Forest Meteorology* **104**: 315–327.

Ali, M.B., Dewir, Y.H., Hahn, E., and Peak, K. 2008. Effect of carbon dioxide on antioxidant enzymes and ginsenoside production in root suspension cultures of *Panax ginseng*. *Environmental and Experimental Botany* **63**: 297–304.

Baker, J.T., Allen Jr., L.H., Boote, K.J., and Pickering, N.B. 1997. Rice responses to drought under carbon dioxide enrichment. 2. Photosynthesis and evapotranspiration. *Global Change Biology* **3**: 129–138.

Bernacchi, C.J., Leakey, A.D.B., Heady, L.E., Morgan, P.B., Dohleman, F.G., McGrath, J.M., Gillespie, K.M., Wittig, V.E., Rogers, A., Long, S.P., and Ort, D.R. 2006. Hourly and seasonal variation in photosynthesis and stomatal conductance of soybean grown at future CO_2 and ozone concentrations for 3 years under fully open-air field conditions. *Plant, Cell and Environment* 10.1111/j.1365-3040.2006.01581.x.

Bhattacharya, N.C., Hileman, D.R., Ghosh, P.P., Musser, R.L., Bhattacharya, S., and Biswas, P.K. 1990. Interaction of enriched CO_2 and water stress on the physiology of and biomass production in sweet potato grown in open-top chambers. *Plant, Cell and Environment* **13**: 933–940.

Chaves, M.M. and Pereira, J.S. 1992. Water stress, CO_2 and climate change. *Journal of Experimental Botany* **43**: 1131–1139.

Chun, J.A., Wang, Q., Timlin, D., Fleisher, D., and Reddy, V.R. 2011. Effect of elevated carbon dioxide and water stress on gas exchange and water use efficiency in corn. *Agricultural and Forest Meteorology* **151**: 378–384.

Clifford, S.C., Stronach, I.M., Mohamed, A.D., Azam-Ali, S.N., and Crout, N.M.J. 1993. The effects of elevated atmospheric carbon dioxide and water stress on light interception, dry matter production and yield in stands of groundnut (*Arachis hypogaea* L.). *Journal of Experimental Botany* **44**: 1763–1770.

Conley, M.M., Kimball, B.A., Brooks, T.J., Pinter Jr., P.J., Hunsaker, D.J., Wall, G.W., Adams, N.R., LaMorte, R.L., Matthias, A.D., Thompson, T.L., Leavitt, S.W., Ottman, M.J., Cousins, A.B., and Triggs, J.M. 2001. CO_2 enrichment increases water-use efficiency in sorghum. *New Phytologist* **151**: 407–412.

Dat, J., Vandenabeele, S., Vranova, A., Van Montagu, M., Inze, D., and Van Breusegem, F. 2000. Dual action of the active oxygen species during plant stress responses. *Cellular and Molecular Life Sciences* **57**: 779–995.

De Luis, J., Irigoyen, J.J., and Sanchez-Diaz, M. 1999. Elevated CO_2 enhances plant growth in droughted N_2-fixing alfalfa without improving water stress. *Physiologia Plantarum* **107**: 84–89.

Ferris, R., Wheeler, T.R., Ellis, R.H., and Hadley, P. 1999. Seed yield after environmental stress in soybean grown under elevated CO_2. *Crop Science* **39**: 710–718.

Ferris, R., Wheeler, T.R., Hadley, P., and Ellis, R.H. 1998. Recovery of photosynthesis after environmental stress in soybean grown under elevated CO_2. *Crop Science* **38**: 948–955.

Fernandez-Trujillo, J.P., Nock, J.F., and Watkins, C.B. 2007. Antioxidant enzyme activities in strawberry fruit exposed to high carbon dioxide atmospheres during cold storage. *Food Chemistry* **104**: 1425–1429.

Geiger, M., Haake, V., Ludewig, F., Sonnewald, U., and Stitt, M. 1999. The nitrate and ammonium nitrate supply have a major influence on the response of photosynthesis, carbon metabolism, nitrogen metabolism, and growth to elevated carbon dioxide in tobacco. *Plant, Cell and Environment* **22**: 1177–1199.

Hudak, C., Bender, J., Weigel, H.-J., and Miller, J. 1999. Interactive effects of elevated CO_2, O_3, and soil water deficit on spring wheat (*Triticum aestivum* L. cv. Nandu). *Agronomie* **19**: 677–687.

Idso, K.E. and Idso, S.B. 1994. Plant responses to

atmospheric CO_2 enrichment in the face of environmental constraints: A review of the past 10 years' research. *Agricultural and Forest Meteorology* **69**: 153–203.

Idso, S.B. 1988. Three phases of plant response to atmospheric CO_2 enrichment. *Plant Physiology* **87**: 5–7.

Idso, S.B. and Idso, K.E. 2001. Effects of atmospheric CO_2 enrichment on plant constituents related to animal and human health. *Environmental and Experimental Botany* **45**: 179–199.

Jones, P., Jones, J.W., and Allen Jr., L.H. 1985. Seasonal carbon and water balances of soybeans grown under stress treatments in sunlit chambers. *Transactions of the American Society of Agricultural Engineers* **28**: 2021–2028.

Kaddour, A.A. and Fuller, M.P. 2004. The effect of elevated CO_2 and drought on the vegetative growth and development of durum wheat (*Triticum durum* Desf.) cultivars. *Cereal Research Communications* **32**: 225–232.

Larson, R.A. 1988. The antioxidants of higher plants. *Phytochemistry* **27**: 969–978.

Li, A.-G., Hou, Y.-S., Wall, G.W., Trent, A., Kimball, B.A., and Pinter Jr., P.J. 2000. Free-air CO_2 enrichment and drought stress effects on grain filling rate and duration in spring wheat. *Crop Science* **40**: 1263–1270.

Li, J.H., Johnson, D.P., Dijkstra, P., Hungate, B.A., Hinkle, C.R., and Drake, B.G. 2007. Elevated CO_2 mitigates the adverse effects of drought on daytime net ecosystem CO_2 exchange and photosynthesis in a Florida scrub-oak ecosystem. *Photosynthetica* **45**: 51–58.

Lin, J.-S and Wang, G.-X. 2002. Doubled CO_2 could improve the drought tolerance better in sensitive cultivars than in tolerant cultivars in spring wheat. *Plant Science* **163**: 627–637.

Manderscheid, R. and Weigel, H.-J. 2007. Drought stress effects on wheat are mitigated by atmospheric CO_2 enrichment. *Agronomy for Sustainable Development* **27**: 79–87.

Niklaus, P.A., Spinnler, D., and Korner, C. 1998. Soil moisture dynamics of calcareous grassland under elevated CO_2. *Oecologia* **117**: 201–208.

Omran, R.G. 1980. Peroxide levels and the activities of catalase, peroxidase and indoleacetic acid oxidase during and after chilling cucumber seedlings. *Plant Physiology* **65**: 407–408.

Ottman, M.J., Kimball, B.A., Pinter Jr., P.J., Wall, G.W., Vanderlip, R.L., Leavitt, S.W., LaMorte, R.L., Matthias, A.D., and Brooks, T.J. 2001. Elevated CO_2 increases sorghum biomass under drought conditions. *New Phytologist* **150**: 261–273.

Owensby, C.E., Ham, J.M., Knapp, A.K., Breemer, D., and Auen, L.M. 1997. Water vapor fluxes and their impact under elevated CO_2 in a C_4-tallgrass prairie. *Global Change Biology* **3**: 189–195.

Perez-Lopez, U., Robredo, A., Lacuesta, M., Munoz-Rueda, A., and Mena-Petite, A. 2010. Atmospheric CO_2 concentration influences the contributions of osmolyte accumulation and cell wall elasticity to salt tolerance in barley cultivars. *Journal of Plant Physiology* **167**: 15–22.

Rabha, B.K. and Uprety, D.C. 1998. Effects of elevated CO_2 and moisture stress on *Brassica juncea*. *Photosynthetica* **35**: 597–602.

Richter, G.M. and Semenov, M.A. 2005. Modeling impacts of climate change on wheat yields in England and Wales: assessing drought risks. *Agricultural Systems* **84**: 77–97.

Robredo, A., Perez-Lopez, U., Miranda-Apodaca, J., Lacuesta, M., Mena-Petite, A., and Munoz-Rueda, A. 2011. Elevated CO_2 reduces the drought effect on nitrogen metabolism in barley plants during drought and subsequent recovery. *Environmental and Experimental Botany* **71**: 399–408.

Robredo, A., Perez-Lopez, U., Sainz de le Maza, H., Gonzalez-Moro, B., Lacuesta, M., Mena-Petite, A., and Munoz-Rueda, A. 2007. Elevated CO_2 alleviates the impact of drought on barley improving water status by lowering stomatal conductance and delaying its effects on photosynthesis. *Environmental and Experimental Botany* **59**: 252–263.

Rogers, H.H., Sionit, N., Cure, J.D., Smith, H.M., and Bingham, G.E. 1984. Influence of elevated CO_2 on water relations of soybeans. *Plant Physiology* **74**: 233–238.

Schutz, M. and Fangmeier, A. 2001. Growth and yield responses of spring wheat (*Triticum aestivum* L. cv. Minaret) to elevated CO_2 and water limitation. *Environmental Pollution* **114**: 187–194.

Serraj, R., Allen Jr., L.H., and Sinclair, T.R. 1999. Soybean leaf growth and gas exchange response to drought under carbon dioxide enrichment. *Global Change Biology* **5**: 283–291.

Sgherri, C.L.M., Quartacci, M.F., Menconi, M., Raschi, A., and Navari-Izzo, F. 1998. Interactions between drought and elevated CO_2 on alfalfa plants. *Journal of Plant Physiology* **152**: 118–124.

Tohidimoghadam, H.R., Ghooshchi, F., and Zahedi, H. 2011. Effect of UV radiation and elevated CO_2 on morphological traits, yield and yield components of canola (*Brassica napus* L.) grown under water deficit. *Notulae Botanicae Horti Agrobotanici Cluj-Napoca* **39**: 213–219.

Triggs, J.M., Kimball, B.A., Pinter Jr., P.J., Wall, G.W.,

Conley, M.M., Brooks, T.J., LaMorte, R.L., Adam, N.R., Ottman, M.J., Matthias, A.D., Leavitt, S.W., and Cerveny, R.S. 2004. Free-air CO_2 enrichment effects on the energy balance and evapotranspiration of sorghum. *Agricultural and Forest Meteorology* **124**: 63–79.

Varga, B. and Bencze, Sz. 2009. Comparative study of drought stress resistance in two winter wheat varieties raised at ambient and elevated CO_2 concentration. *Cereal Research Communications* **37**: 209–212.

Varga, B., Janda, T., Laszlo, E., and Veisz, O. 2012. Influence of abiotic stresses on the antioxidant enzyme activity of cereals. *Acta Physiologiae Plantarum* **34**: 849–858.

Veisz, O., Bencze, S., Balla, K., Vida, G., and Bedo, Z. 2008. Change in water stress resistance of cereals due to atmospheric CO_2 enrichment. *Cereal Research Communications* **36**: 10.1556/CRC.36.2008.Suppl.1.

Vu, J.C.V., Baker, J.T., Pennanen, A.H., Allen Jr., L.H., Bowes, G., and Boote, K.J. 1998. Elevated CO_2 and water deficit effects on photosynthesis, ribulose bisphosphate carboxylase-oxygenase, and carbohydrate metabolism in rice. *Physiologia Plantarum* **103**: 327–339.

Wall, G.W. 2001. Elevated atmospheric CO_2 alleviates drought stress in wheat. *Agriculture, Ecosystems and Environment* **87**: 261–271.

Wechsung, G., Wechsung, F., Wall, G.W., Adamsen, F.J., Kimball, B.A., Pinter Jr., P.J., LaMorte, R.L., Garcia, R.L., and Kartschall, Th. 1999. The effects of free-air CO_2 enrichment and soil water availability on spatial and seasonal patterns of wheat root growth. *Global Change Biology* **5**: 519–529.

Widodo, W., Vu, J.C.V., Boote, K.J., Baker, J.T., and Allen Jr., L.H. 2003. Elevated growth CO_2 delays drought stress and accelerates recovery of rice leaf photosynthesis. *Environmental and Experimental Botany* **49**: 259–272.

3.15.2 Grasslands

• The peer-reviewed scientific literature demonstrates the historical and still-ongoing rise in the air's CO_2 content has led and likely will continue to lead to substantial increases in the photosynthetic rates and biomass production of various grassland plants, even under stressful environmental conditions imposed by less-than-optimum soil moisture.

As the air's CO_2 content rises, nearly all plants should exhibit increases in photosynthesis and biomass production, but some researchers have claimed water stress will negate these benefits. In reviewing the scientific literature for 1983–1994, Idso and Idso (1994) concluded water stress will not in fact negate the CO_2-induced stimulation of plant productivity. They discovered the CO_2-induced percentage increase in plant productivity was nearly always greater under water-stressed conditions than when plants were well-watered. Seven years later, Poorter and Perez-Soba (2001) conducted a similar literature review and reached the same conclusion. This section provides background for this phenomenon and highlights some of the more important work that subsequently has been done in this area.

Elevated levels of atmospheric CO_2 tend to reduce the area of open stomatal pore space on leaf surfaces, thus reducing plant stomatal conductance. This phenomenon, in turn, effectively reduces the amount of water lost to the atmosphere via transpiration. Leymarie et al. (1999), for example, found twice-ambient levels of atmospheric CO_2 caused significant reductions in the stomatal conductance of water-stressed *Arabidopsis thaliana*. Similarly, Volk et al. (2000) reported several calcareous grassland species exposed to elevated atmospheric CO_2 concentrations (600 ppm) consistently exhibited reduced stomatal conductance, regardless of soil moisture availability.

In addition, CO_2-induced increases in root development and CO_2-induced reductions in leaf stomatal conductance often combine to maintain a more favorable plant water status during times of drought. In the case of four grassland species comprising a pasture characteristic of New Zealand, for example, Clark et al. (1999) report leaf water potential, a good indicator of plant water status, was consistently higher (less negative and, therefore, less stressful) under elevated atmospheric CO_2 concentrations. Leaf water potentials of the water-stressed C_4 grass *Panicum coloratum* grown at 1,000 ppm CO_2 were always higher than those of their water-stressed counterparts growing in ambient air (Seneweera et al., 2001). Seneweera et al. (1998) had earlier reported leaf water potentials observed in CO_2-enriched water-stressed plants were three-and-a-half times greater than those observed in control plants grown at 350 ppm during drought conditions (Seneweera et al., 1998).

If atmospheric CO_2 enrichment thus allows grassland plants to maintain better water status during times of water stress, it is logical to infer such plants will exhibit greater photosynthetic rates than similar plants growing in ambient air. In a severe test of this concept, Ward *et al.* (1999) found extreme water stress caused 93 and 85% reductions in the photosynthetic rates of two CO_2-enriched grassland species, yet their rates of carbon fixation were still greater than those observed under ambient CO_2 conditions.

These observations demonstrate elevated CO_2 nearly always enhances photosynthetic rates during times of water stress. One thus would expect plant biomass production to be enhanced by elevated CO_2 concentrations under drought conditions.

On the American prairie, Owensby *et al.* (1999) observed tallgrass ecosystems exposed to twice-ambient concentrations of atmospheric CO_2 for eight years exhibited significant increases in above- and below-ground biomass only during years of less-than-average rainfall. Derner *et al.* (2001) observed a 150 ppm increase in the CO_2 content of the air increased shoot biomass in two C_4 grasses by 57%, regardless of soil water content. Seneweera *et al.* (2001) reported a 640 ppm increase in the air's CO_2 content increased shoot dry mass in a C_4 grass by 44 and 70% under well-watered and water-stressed conditions, respectively. Volk *et al.* (2000) grew calcareous grassland assemblages at 360 and 600 ppm CO_2 and documented 18 and 40% CO_2-induced increases in whole-community biomass under well-watered and water-stressed conditions, respectively.

Nelson *et al.* (2004) reported on a five-year study (1997–2001) conducted on the semi-arid shortgrass steppe (SGS) of Colorado (USA). Working at the USDA-ARS Central Plains Experimental Range in the northern portion of the SGS about 60 km northeast of Fort Collins, Colorado, they used large (15.5 m^2) open-top chambers to examine the effects of elevated CO_2 (720 vs. 360 ppm) on plant water relations, ecosystem water use efficiency, soil moisture dynamics, and root distributions of the ecosystem's dominant C_3 (*Pascopyrum smithii* and *Stipa comata*) and C_4 (*Bouteloua gracilis*) grasses.

The five Agricultural Research Service scientists and their collaborator from Colorado State University report "seasonal average soil moisture throughout the soil profile (0–15, 15–45, 45–75, 75–105 cm) was increased under elevated CO_2 compared to ambient CO_2 for much of the study period," with the greatest relative increase (16.4%) occurring in the 75–105 cm depth increment. This finding of "increased soil moisture under elevated CO_2 at the deepest soil depth suggests that water percolated deeper into the soil profile and that less moisture was lost to evapotranspiration under elevated CO_2." Noting "this

phenomenon enhances water storage in the deep fine sandy loam soils underlying large portions of the SGS," they state, "this increase in soil moisture has been shown to be the major controlling factor in improved carbon assimilation rates and increased total aboveground biomass in this system (LeCain *et al.*, 2003) and will likely decrease the susceptibility of the SGS to drought."

The Colorado researchers also found, when averaged over the study period, "leaf water potential was enhanced 24–30% under elevated CO_2 in the major warm- and cool-season grass species of the SGS (*Bouteloua gracilis*, C_4, 28.5%; *Pascopyrum smithii*, C_3, 24.7%; *Stipa comata*, C_3, 30.4%)." They report these results are similar to those of "studies involving other C_3 and C_4 grass species (Owensby *et al.*, 1993; Jackson *et al.*, 1994)," and they say the enhanced leaf water potential—"which reflects improved plant water status and increased drought tolerance (Tyree and Alexander, 1993)"—may lead to increased leaf turgor and allow the grasses "to continue growth further into periods of drought." Averaged over the five years of the study, Nelson *et al.* report, "water-use efficiency (grams aboveground biomass harvested / kilogram water consumed) was 43% higher in elevated than ambient CO_2 plots."

Nelson *et al.* say their results "suggest that a future, elevated CO_2 environment may result not only in increased plant productivity due to improved water use efficiency, but also lead to increased water drainage and deep soil moisture storage in this semi-arid grassland ecosystem." They add, "this, along with the ability of the major grass species to maintain a favorable water status under elevated CO_2, should result in the SGS being less susceptible to prolonged periods of drought."

Nelson *et al.* note their findings are common, writing, "previous studies have reported increased soil moisture under elevated CO_2 in semi-arid C_3 annual grasslands in California (Fredeen *et al.*, 1997), mesic C_3/C_4 perennial tallgrass prairie in Kansas (Owensby *et al.*, 1993, 1999; Ham *et al.*, 1995; Bremer *et al.*, 1996), and mesic C_3 perennial grasslands in Switzerland (Niklaus *et al.*, 1998) and Sweden (Sindhoj *et al.*, 2000)." Taken together, these studies indicate the benefits of atmospheric CO_2 enrichment will apply to grasslands generally, as the air's CO_2 content rises to double-and-beyond its current concentration.

If air temperature rises concurrently, things could get even better. Nelson *et al.* note, for example, "air temperature was on average 2.6°C higher inside the chambers than outside," and this warming "was implicated in the 36% enhanced biomass production observed in chambered-ambient compared to non-chambered plots." Consequently, since this already-enhanced biomass production was the starting point from which the 41% increase in biomass arising from the doubling of the air's CO_2 content was calculated, the increase in biomass caused by the concurrent actions of both factors (increasing air temperature and CO_2 concentration) could be on the order of 90%.

The 15-member team of Morgan *et al.* (2004) reviewed the scientific literature on the role of water relations in the response of grassland and desert ecosystems to elevated levels of atmospheric CO_2. They found it suggests "atmospheric CO_2 enrichment may stimulate plant growth either directly through (1) enhanced photosynthesis or indirectly through (2) reduced plant water consumption and hence slower soil moisture depletion, or the combination of both." They performed an analysis to determine "gas exchange, plant biomass and species responses of five native or semi-native temperate and Mediterranean grasslands and three semi-arid ecosystems to CO_2 enrichment, with an emphasis on water relations."

The team found "increasing CO_2 led to decreased leaf conductance for water vapor, improved plant water status, altered seasonal evapotranspiration dynamics, and in most cases, periodic increases in soil water content." As a result, "across the grasslands of the Kansas tallgrass prairie, Colorado shortgrass steppe and Swiss calcareous grassland, increases in aboveground biomass from CO_2 enrichment were relatively greater in dry years." In contrast, they report, "CO_2-induced aboveground biomass increase in the Texas C_3/C_4 grassland and the New Zealand pasture seemed little or only marginally influenced by yearly variation in soil water, and plant growth in the Mojave Desert was stimulated by CO_2 in a relatively wet year." In addition, "Mediterranean grasslands sometimes failed to respond to CO_2-related increased late-season water, whereas semiarid Negev grassland assemblages profited."

Although they state "vegetative and reproductive responses to CO_2 were highly varied among species and ecosystems, and did not generally follow any predictable pattern in regard to function groups," considered in their entirety, they conclude the literature results they reviewed (many of which they themselves had been instrumental in collecting) "suggest that the indirect effects of CO_2 on plant and soil water relations may contribute substantially to experimentally induced CO_2-effects."

Lazzarotto *et al.* (2010) write, "white clover (*Trifolium repens* L.) is the most important pasture legume grown in temperate climates in association with a variety of grasses, notably perennial ryegrass (*Lolium perenne* L.)," adding, "white clover improves the nutritional quality and digestibility of the herbage" and "contributes substantially to the nitrogen status of the sward through biological nitrogen fixation." They note some researchers have expressed concern future drought, such as is predicted by climate models to occur in tandem with CO_2-induced global warming, will damage clover more than the grass with which it is intermingled, thereby degrading the nutritional quality and digestibility of pasture swards.

Lazzarotto *et al.* conducted a study in which "mechanisms controlling transient responses to elevated CO_2 concentration and climate change in an unfertilized grassland on the Swiss Plateau were examined in light of simulations with PROGRASS." They used a process-based model of grass-clover interactions developed by Lazzarotto *et al.* (2009), in which "daily weather for a series of transient climate scenarios spanning the 21st century were developed for the study site with the help of the LARS-WG weather generator," as described by Semenov and Barrow (1997) and Semenov *et al.* (1998), and "changes in the length of dry and wet spells, temperature, precipitation and solar radiation defining the scenarios were obtained from regional climate simulations carried out in the framework of the PRUDENCE project," as described by Christensen and Christensen (2007).

"Compared to 1961–1990," the Swiss and UK scientists write, the climate scenarios they developed for a CO_2 increase from 370 to 860 ppm "indicated that for 2071–2100 there would be a noticeable increase in temperature (roughly 3°C in winter and 5°C in summer), a significant drop in summer precipitation (of the order of -30%) and a nearly 2-fold increase in the length of dry spells." They report "clover abundance did not decline even in the absence of CO_2 stimulation." When the atmospheric CO_2 concentration was programmed to gradually rise from an initial value of 370 ppm to a final value of 860 ppm, "clover development benefited from the overall positive effects of CO_2 on nitrogen acquisition," which they note was "the reason for increasing productivity of the [entire] sward."

These findings indicate the rather large increases in temperature and decreases in precipitation projected for the remainder of the twenty-first century, even if they come to pass, will not have much of an effect on Swiss grass-clover swards, but the concomitant increase in the air's CO_2 content will benefit them considerably. Lazzarotto *et al.* opine it is likely "technical progress in the management of grasslands and pastures," which will surely occur, will help such pastures even more.

Noting "grassland communities constitute an important fraction of the green surface of the Earth, and are worldwide an important source of cattle-food (Carlier *et al.*, 2009; Ciais *et al.*, 2011)," Farfan-Vignolo and Asard (2012) investigated several physiological and molecular (antioxidant) responses to water deficit in two major grassland species (*Lolium perenne* L. and *Medicago lupulina* L.) under current ambient (A) and future elevated (E) atmospheric CO_2 concentrations and air temperatures (T), where $ECO_2 = ACO_2 + 375$ ppm, and $ET = AT + 3°C$. The researchers found "drought caused significant increases in oxidative damage, i.e., in protein oxidation and lipid peroxidation levels." They also report, "in both species the impact of drought on protein oxidation was reduced in future climate conditions [ECO_2 and ET]." As to the stress-reducing effect of ECO_2, they state "this 'CO_2-protection effect' is reported for a variety of abiotic stress conditions and species," citing Schwanz and Polle (1998), Sgherri *et al.* (2000), Geissler *et al.* (2009), Perez-Lopez *et al.* (2009), Vurro *et al.* (2009), and Salazar-Parra *et al.* (2012). They say they too "find support for this effect at the level of oxidative cell damage and protein oxidation in water-deficit responses of *L. perenne* and *M. lupulina*." Even under drought stress, they note, "elevated CO_2 significantly affected shoot production in *L. perenne* (increase by 27–32%)," and "also in *M. lupulina* a biomass increase was observed (26–38%)."

Thus the conclusions of Idso and Idso (1994), based on the pre-1994 literature, are well supported by the subsequent peer-reviewed scientific literature, which indicates the rise in the air's CO_2 content likely will lead to substantial increases in plant photosynthetic rates and biomass production, even with stressful environmental conditions imposed by less-than-optimum soil moisture conditions.

References

Bremer, D.J., Ham, J.M., and Owensby C.E. 1996. Effect of elevated atmospheric carbon dioxide and open-top chambers on transpiration in a tallgrass prairie. *Journal of Environmental Quality* **25**: 691–701.

Carlier, L., Rotar, I., Vlahova, M., and Vidican, R. 2009. Importance and functions of grasslands. *Notulae Botanicae Horti Agrobotanici Cluj-Napoca* **37**: 25–30.

Christensen, J.H. and Christensen, O.B. 2007. A summary of the PRUDENCE model projections of changes in European climate by the end of this century. *Climatic Change* **81**: 7–30.

Ciais, P., Gervois, S., Vuichard, N., Piao, S.L., and Viovy, N. 2011. Effects of land use change and management on the European cropland carbon balance. *Global Change Biology* **17**: 320–338.

Clark, H., Newton, P.C.D., and Barker, D.J. 1999. Physiological and morphological responses to elevated CO_2 and a soil moisture deficit of temperate pasture species growing in an established plant community. *Journal of Experimental Botany* **50**: 233–242.

Derner, J.D., Polley, H.W., Johnson, H.B., and Tischler, C.R. 2001. Root system response of C_4 grass seedlings to CO_2 and soil water. *Plant and Soil* **231**: 97–104.

Farfan-Vignolo, E.R. and Asard, H. 2012. Effect of elevated CO_2 and temperature on the oxidative stress response to drought in *Lolium perenne* L. and *Medicago sativa* L. *Plant Physiology and Biochemistry* **59**: 55–62.

Fredeen, A.L., Randerson, J.T., Holbrook, N.M., and Field, C.B. 1997. Elevated atmospheric CO_2 increases water availability in a water-limited grassland ecosystem. *Journal of the American Water Resources Association* **33**: 1033–1039.

Geissler, N., Hussin, S., and Koyro, H.-W. 2009. Elevated atmospheric CO_2 concentration ameliorates effects of NaCl salinity on photosynthesis and leaf structure of *Aster tripolium* L. *Journal of Experimental Botany* **60**: 137–151.

Ham, J.M., Owensby, C.E., Coyne, P.I., and Bremer, D.J. 1995. Fluxes of CO_2 and water vapor from a prairie ecosystem exposed to ambient and elevated atmospheric CO_2. *Agricultural and Forest Meteorology* **77**: 73–93.

Idso, K.E. and Idso, S.B. 1994. Plant responses to atmospheric CO_2 enrichment in the face of environmental constraints: A review of the past 10 years' research. *Agricultural and Forest Meteorology* **69**: 153–203.

Jackson, R.B., Sala, O.E., Field, C.B., and Mooney, H.A. 1994. CO_2 alters water use, carbon gain, and yield for the dominant species in a natural grassland. *Oecologia* **98**: 257–262.

Lazzarotto, P., Calanca, P., and Fuhrer, J. 2009. Dynamics of grass-clover mixtures—an analysis of the response to management with the PROductive GRASsland Simulator (PROGRASS). *Ecological Modeling* **220**: 703–724.

Lazzarotto, P., Calanca, P., Semenov, M., and Fuhrer, J.

2010. Transient responses to increasing CO_2 and climate change in an unfertilized grass-clover sward. *Climate Research* **41**: 221–232.

LeCain, D.R., Morgan, J.A., Mosier, A.R., and Nelson, J.A. 2003. Soil and plant water relations determine photosynthetic responses of C_3 and C_4 grasses in a semi-arid ecosystem under elevated CO_2. *Annals of Botany* **92**: 41–52.

Leymarie, J., Lasceve, G., and Vavasseur, A. 1999. Elevated CO_2 enhances stomatal responses to osmotic stress and abscisic acid in *Arabidopsis thaliana*. *Plant, Cell and Environment* **22**: 301–308.

Morgan, J.A., Pataki, D.E., Korner, C., Clark, H., Del Grosso, S.J., Grunzweig, J.M., Knapp, A.K., Mosier, A.R., Newton, P.C.D., Niklaus, P.A., Nippert, J.B., Nowak, R.S., Parton, W.J., Polley, H.W., and Shaw, M.R. 2004. Water relations in grassland and desert ecosystems exposed to elevated atmospheric CO_2. *Oecologia* **140**: 11–25.

Nelson, J.A., Morgan, J.A., LeCain, D.R., Mosier, A.R., Milchunas, D.G., and Parton, B.A. 2004. Elevated CO_2 increases soil moisture and enhances plant water relations in a long-term field study in semi-arid shortgrass steppe of Colorado. *Plant and Soil* **259**: 169–179.

Niklaus, P.A., Spinnler, D., and Korner, C. 1998. Soil moisture dynamics of calcareous grassland under elevated CO_2. *Oecologia* **117**: 201–208.

Owensby, C.E., Coyne, P.I., Ham, J.H., Auen, L.M., and Knapp, A.K. 1993. Biomass production in a tallgrass prairie ecosystem exposed to ambient and elevated CO_2. *Ecological Applications* **3**: 644–653.

Owensby, C.E., Ham, J.M., Knapp, A.K., and Auen, L.M. 1999. Biomass production and species composition change in a tallgrass prairie ecosystem after long-term exposure to elevated atmospheric CO_2. *Global Change Biology* **5**: 497–506.

Perez-Lopez, U., Robredo, A., Lacuestra, M., Sgherri, C., Munoz-Rueda, A., Navari-Izzo, F., and Mena-Petite, A. 2009. The oxidative stress caused by salinity in two barley cultivars is mitigated by elevated CO_2. *Physiologia Plantarum* **135**: 29–42.

Poorter, H. and Perez-Soba, M. 2001. The growth response of plants to elevated CO_2 under non-optimal environmental conditions. *Oecologia* **129**: 1–20.

Salazar-Parra, C., Aguirreolea, J., Sanchez-Diaz, M., Irigoyen, J.J., and Morales, F. 2012. Climate change (elevated CO_2, elevated temperature and moderate drought) triggers the antioxidant enzymes' response of grapevine cv. Tempranillo, avoiding oxidative damage. *Physiologia Plantarum* **144**: 99–110.

Schwanz, P. and Polle, A. 1998. Antioxidative systems, pigment and protein contents in leaves of adult Mediterranean oak species (*Quercus pubescens* and *Q. ilex*) with lifetime exposure to elevated CO_2. *New Phytologist* **140**: 411–423.

Semenov, M.A. and Barrow, E.M. 1997. Use of a stochastic weather generator in the development of climate change scenarios. *Climatic Change* **35**: 397–414.

Semenov, M.A., Books, R.J., Barrow, E.M., and Richardson, C.W. 1998. Comparison of the WGEN and LARS-WG stochastic weather generators for diverse climates. *Climate Research* **10**: 95–107.

Seneweera, S.P., Ghannoum, O., and Conroy, J. 1998. High vapor pressure deficit and low soil water availability enhance shoot growth responses of a C_4 grass (*Panicum coloratum* cv. Bambatsi) to CO_2 enrichment. *Australian Journal of Plant Physiology* **25**: 287–292.

Seneweera, S., Ghannoum, O., and Conroy, J.P. 2001. Root and shoot factors contribute to the effect of drought on photosynthesis and growth of the C_4 grass *Panicum coloratum* at elevated CO_2 partial pressures. *Australian Journal of Plant Physiology* **28**: 451–460.

Sgherri, C.L.M., Salvateci, P., Menconi, M., Raschi, A., and Navari-Izzo, F. 2000. Interaction between drought and elevated CO_2 in the response of alfalfa plants to oxidative stress. *Journal of Plant Physiology* **156**: 360–366.

Sindhoj, E., Hansson, A.C., Andren, O., Katterer, T., Marissink, M., and Pettersson, R. 2000. Root dynamics in a semi-natural grassland in relation to atmospheric carbon dioxide enrichment, soil water and shoot biomass. *Plant and Soil* **223**: 253–263.

Tyree, M.T. and Alexander, J.D. 1993. Plant water relations and the effects of elevated CO_2: A review and suggestions for future research. *Vegetatio* **104/105**: 47–62.

Volk, M., Niklaus, P.A., and Korner, C. 2000. Soil moisture effects determine CO_2 responses of grassland species. *Oecologia* **125**: 380–388.

Vurro, E., Bruni, R., Bianchi, A., and di Toppi, L.S. 2009. Elevated atmospheric CO_2 decreases oxidative stress and increases essential oil yield in leaves of *Thymus vulgaris* grown in a mini-FACE system. *Environmental and Experimental Botany* **65**: 99–106.

Ward, J.K., Tissue, D.T., Thomas, R.B., and Strain, B.R. 1999. Comparative responses of model C_3 and C_4 plants to drought in low and elevated CO_2. *Global Change Biology* **5**: 857–867.

3.15.3 Woody Plants

- The rise in the air's CO_2 concentration likely will lead to substantial increases in the photosynthetic rates and biomass production of trees and shrubs, even with stressful environmental conditions imposed by suboptimal soil moisture availability.

It is widely acknowledged that as the CO_2 content of the air rises, nearly all plant types will exhibit increases in photosynthesis and biomass production, but some researchers claim future water stress will negate these benefits of atmospheric CO_2 enrichment. Much of the pertinent scientific literature of the 10-year period 1983–1994, reviewed by Idso and Idso (1994), calls that claim into question, showing water stress will generally not negate the CO_2-induced stimulation of plant growth. Idso and Idso's literature review found the CO_2-induced percentage increase in plant productivity was nearly always greater under water-stressed conditions than when plants were well-watered. This section discusses subsequent relevant literature as it pertains to woody species.

It is well-known that during times of water stress, atmospheric CO_2 enrichment often stimulates the development of larger-than-usual and more robust root systems in woody plants, enabling them to probe greater volumes of soil for scarce and much-needed moisture. Tomlinson and Anderson (1998), for example, found greater root development in water-stressed red oak seedlings grown at 700 ppm CO_2 helped them effectively deal with the reduced availability of moisture, and these trees eventually produced just as much biomass as well-watered controls exposed to air containing 400 ppm CO_2. Polley et al. (1999) report water-stressed honey mesquite trees exposed to an atmospheric CO_2 concentration of 700 ppm produced 37% more root biomass than water-stressed seedlings in air of 370 ppm.

Elevated levels of atmospheric CO_2 also tend to reduce the area of open stomatal pore space on leaf surfaces, thus reducing plant stomatal conductance. This phenomenon, in turn, reduces the amount of water lost to the atmosphere via transpiration. Tognetti et al. (1998) determined the stomatal conductances of mature oak trees growing near natural CO_2 springs in central Italy were significantly lower than those of similar trees growing farther away from the springs during periods of severe summer drought, which allowed the CO_2-enriched trees to better conserve what little water was available to them.

Working together, CO_2-induced increases in root development and CO_2-induced reductions in stomatal conductance often contribute to the maintenance of a more favorable plant water status during times of drought. In the case of three Mediterranean shrubs, for example, Tognetti et al. (2002) found leaf water potential, a good indicator of plant water status, was consistently higher (less negative and, hence, less stressful) under twice-ambient CO_2 concentrations. Polley et al. (1999) observed leaf water potentials of water-stressed mesquite seedlings grown at 700 ppm CO_2 were 40% higher than those of their water-stressed counterparts growing in ambient air, comparable to the values of -5.9 and -3.4 MPa observed in water-stressed evergreen shrubs (Larrea tridentata) exposed to 360 and 700 ppm CO_2, respectively, as documented by Hamerlynck et al. (2000).

If atmospheric CO_2 enrichment allows plants to maintain a better water status during times of water stress, it is only logical to surmise plants growing under such conditions will exhibit CO_2-induced increases in photosynthesis. Palanisamy (1999) found water-stressed Eucalyptus seedlings grown at 800 ppm CO_2 had greater net photosynthetic rates than their ambient-grown and water-stressed counterparts. Runion et al. (1999) found the CO_2-induced photosynthetic stimulation of water-stressed pine seedlings grown at 730 ppm CO_2 was nearly 50% greater than similar water-stressed pine seedlings grown at 365 ppm CO_2. Similarly, Centritto et al. (1999a) report water-stressed cherry trees grown at 700 ppm CO_2 displayed net photosynthetic rates 44% greater than those of water-stressed trees grown at 350 ppm CO_2. And Anderson and Tomlinson (1998) determined a 300-ppm increase in the air's CO_2 concentration boosted photosynthetic rates in well-watered and water-stressed red oak seedlings by 34 and 69%, respectively, demonstrating the CO_2-induced enhancement in net photosynthesis in this species was essentially twice as great in water-stressed seedlings as in well-watered ones.

Nevertheless, plants sometimes suffer drastically when subjected to extreme water stress, but the addition of CO_2 to the air often induces plants to react better to stress than plants growing in normal air. Tuba et al. (1998), for example, reported leaves of a water-stressed woody shrub exposed to an atmospheric CO_2 concentration of 700 ppm continued to maintain positive rates of net carbon fixation for a period that lasted three times longer than did leaves of equally water-stressed control plants growing in ambient air. Fernandez *et al.* (1998) discovered herb and tree species growing near natural CO_2 vents in Venezuela continued to maintain positive rates of net photosynthesis during that location's dry season, and the same species growing some distance away from the CO_2 source displayed net losses of carbon during this stressful time. Likewise, Fernandez *et al.* (1999) note that after four weeks of drought, the deciduous Venezuelan shrub *Ipomoea carnea* continued to exhibit positive carbon gains under elevated CO_2 conditions, whereas ambient-growing plants displayed net carbon losses. Polley *et al.* (2002) reported seedlings of five woody species grown at twice-ambient CO_2 concentrations survived 11 days longer (on average) than control seedlings when subjected to maximum drought conditions.

Since elevated CO_2 enhances photosynthetic rates during times of water stress, one would expect tree and shrub biomass production to be enhanced by elevated CO_2 concentrations under drought conditions. That was demonstrated by Arp *et al.* (1998), who reported six perennial plants common to the Netherlands increased their biomass under CO_2-enriched conditions even when suffering from lack of water. In some cases, the CO_2-induced percentage biomass increase is greater for water-stressed plants than for well-watered plants. Catovsky and Bazzaz (1999), for example, reported the CO_2-induced biomass increase for paper birch was 27% and 130% for well-watered and water-stressed seedlings, respectively. Schulte *et al.* (1998) noted the CO_2-induced biomass increase of oak seedlings was greater under water-limiting conditions than under well-watered conditions (128% vs. 92%), as did Centritto *et al.* (1999b) for basal trunk area in cherry seedlings (69% vs. 22%).

Knapp *et al.* (2001) developed tree-ring index chronologies from western juniper stands in Oregon (USA), finding the trees recovered better from the effects of drought in the 1990s, when the air's CO_2 concentration was around 340 ppm, than they did in 1900–1930, when the atmospheric CO_2 concentration was around 300 ppm.

In a loosely related study, Osborne *et al.* (2000) looked at the warming and reduced precipitation experienced in Mediterranean shrublands over the last century and concluded primary productivity should have been negatively impacted in those areas. However, when the concurrent increase in atmospheric CO_2 concentration was factored into their mechanistic model, a 25% increase in primary productivity was projected.

Centritto (2002) grew peach seedlings for two growing seasons in pots in open-top chambers of either ambient or CO_2-enriched air (350 or 700 ppm, respectively) inside a glasshouse, where all plants were continuously maintained at optimum soil fertility and, for the entire first growing season, at optimum soil water availability. In the second growing season, half of the seedlings had water withheld from them for four weeks. At the end of the study, there was no evidence of any downward acclimation of photosynthesis in the seedlings grown at elevated CO_2, nor was there any downward acclimation in rubisco carboxylation efficiency or in the maximum RuBP regeneration capacity mediated by electron transport.

Xiao *et al.* (2005) experimented with *Caragana intermedia* Kuanget H.C. Fu, a deciduous shrub of semi-arid northern China that occurs primarily in the country's Maowusu sandland as well as parts of Inner Mongolia, where they state it is "used by local people as feed for livestock, and as shelter for protection of soils (Zhang, 1994)," noting "it is one of the dominant shrubs that fix soil and reduce wind speed, thus actively mitigating desertification." The five Chinese scientists grew seedlings of this species for 3.5 months in 10-cm-diameter by 10-cm-deep pots filled with sand and maintained at three water regimes—well-watered (60–70% field capacity), moderate-watered (45–55% field capacity), and drought-stressed (30–40% field capacity)—in greenhouse compartments maintained at atmospheric CO_2 concentrations of either 350 or 700 ppm. Near the end of this period, they measured leaf water potentials and several plant growth parameters.

Xiao *et al.* found, "elevated CO_2 significantly increased leaf water potential" while also increasing tree height, basal diameter, shoot biomass, root biomass, and total biomass, which was increased by 79% under the well-watered condition, by 61% under the moderate-watered condition, and by 53% under the drought-stressed condition. They report the Canopy Productivity Index (CPI, total growth per unit leaf area) was also "significantly increased by elevated CO_2, and the increase in CPI became stronger as the level of drought stress increased." They conclude their study "confirmed the beneficial effects of elevated CO_2 on *C. intermedia* seedlings exposed to drought-stressed conditions," and these findings "suggest that elevated CO_2 may enhance drought avoidance and improved water relations, thus weakening the effect of drought stress on growth of

C. intermedia seedlings."

Soule and Knapp (2006) write, "two major environmental issues have arisen regarding the increasingly CO_2-rich world of the late 20th and early 21st centuries: climatic change, and plant responses to the environment," and they note, "while the implications of atmospheric CO_2 for potential climatic change have received the majority of attention, the potential role of atmospheric CO_2 fertilization in plant growth and subsequent ecosystem dynamics may be equally important." They studied ponderosa pine trees growing at eight sites in the Pacific Northwest of the United States to see how they may have responded to the increase in the atmosphere's CO_2 concentration that occurred after 1950.

The two geographers say they chose study sites that "fit several criteria designed to limit potential confounding influences associated with anthropogenic disturbance," with "a variety of climatic and topo-edaphic conditions, ranging from extremely water-limiting environments ... to areas where soil moisture should be a limiting factor for growth only during extreme drought years." They note all their study sites were located in areas "where ozone concentrations and nitrogen deposition are typically low."

At each of the eight sites, Soule and Knapp obtained core samples from about 40 mature trees that included "the potentially oldest trees on each site," so their results would indicate "the response of mature, naturally occurring ponderosa pine trees that germinated before anthropogenically elevated CO_2 levels, but where growth, particularly post-1950, has occurred under increasing and substantially higher atmospheric CO_2 concentrations." Utilizing meteorological evaluations of the Palmer Drought Severity Index, they compared ponderosa pine (*Pinus ponderosa* Laws. var. *ponderosa*) radial growth rates during matched wet and dry years pre- and post-1950.

The two researchers report finding a post-1950 radial growth enhancement "more pronounced during drought years compared with wet years," and they add, "the greatest response occurred at the most stressed site." They write, "the relative change in growth [was] upward at seven of our [eight] sites, ranging from 11 to 133%."

Soule and Knapp state their results, "showing that radial growth has increased in the post-1950s period ... while climatic conditions have generally been unchanged, suggest that nonclimatic driving forces are operative." In addition, "these radial growth responses are generally consistent with what has been shown in long-term open-top chamber (Idso and Kimball, 2001) and FACE studies (Ainsworth and Long, 2005)." They state their findings suggest "elevated levels of atmospheric CO_2 are acting as a driving force for increased radial growth of ponderosa pine, but that the overall influence of this effect may be enhanced, reduced or obviated by site-specific conditions."

Soule and Knapp recount how they "hypothesized that ponderosa pine ... would respond to gradual increases in atmospheric CO_2 over the past 50 years, and that these effects would be most apparent during drought stress and on environmentally harsh sites," and in the following sentence they state their results "support these hypotheses." They conclude it is likely "an atmospheric CO_2-driven growth-enhancement effect exists for ponderosa pine growing under specific natural conditions in the [USA's] interior Pacific Northwest."

Wang *et al.* (2006) conducted a similar study, seeking to ascertain how the historical increase in atmospheric CO_2 concentration had affected the growth of trees in the real world rather than experimental settings. They examined ring-width development in cohorts of young and old white spruce (*Picea glauca*) trees in a mixed grass-prairie ecosystem in southwestern Manitoba, Canada, where a 1997 wildfire killed most of the older trees growing in high-density spruce islands, but where younger trees slightly removed from the islands were not affected by the flames. "Within each of a total of 24 burned islands," the three researchers write, "the largest dominant tree (dead) was cut down and a disc was then sampled from the stump height," and "adjacent to each sampled island, a smaller, younger tree (live) was also cut down, and a disc was sampled from the stump height."

After removing size-, age-, and climate-related trends in radial growth from the ring-width histories of the trees, Wang *et al.* plotted the residuals as functions of time for the 30-year periods for which both the old and young trees would have been approximately the same age: 1900–1929 for the old trees and 1970–1999 for the young trees. During the first of these periods, the atmosphere's CO_2 concentration averaged 299 ppm, and during the second it averaged 346 ppm. The mean rate-of-rise of the atmosphere's CO_2 concentration was 0.37 ppm/year for the first period and 1.43 ppm/year for the second.

In comparison to the 1900–1929 period, the slope of the linear regression describing the rate-of-growth of the ring-width residuals for the 1970–1999 period (when the air's CO_2 concentration was 15% greater and its rate-of-rise was 285% greater) was more than twice the linear regression describing the rate-of-growth of the ring-width residuals for the 1900–1929 period. As the researchers observe, these results show "at the same developmental stage, a greater growth response occurred in the late period when atmospheric CO_2 concentration and the rate of atmospheric CO_2 increase were both relatively high," and "these results are consistent with expectations for CO_2-fertilization effects." They write, "the response of the studied young trees can be taken as strong circumstantial evidence for the atmospheric CO_2-fertilization effect."

Wang *et al.* also learned "postdrought growth response was much stronger for young trees (1970–1999) compared with old trees at the same development stage (1900–1929)." They add, "higher atmospheric CO_2 concentration in the period from 1970–1999 may have helped white spruce recover from severe drought." Similarly, young trees showed a weaker relationship to precipitation than did old trees, noting "more CO_2 would lead to greater water-use efficiency, which may be dampening the precipitation signal in young trees." Wang *et al.*'s unique study provides an exciting real-world example of the benefits the historical rise in the air's CO_2 content likely has conferred on long-lived woody species.

Davi *et al.* (2006) used a meteorological model following "a moderate CO_2 emission scenario" (B2 of IPCC) to calculate a 1960–2100 average temperature increase of 3.1°C and a mean summer rainfall decrease of 27%, which they used as input to a physiologically based multilayer process-based ecosystem productivity model (which contained a carbon allocation sub-model coupled with a soil model) to evaluate net productivity changes of six French forest ecosystems representative of oceanic, continental, and Mediterranean climates dominated, respectively, by deciduous species (*Fagus sylvatica*, *Quercus robur*), coniferous species (*Pinus pinaster*, *Pinus sylvestris*), and sclerophyllous evergreen species (*Quercus ilex*). These ecosystems, they write, "are representative of a significant proportion of forests in western Europe."

"By comparing runs with and without CO_2 effects," according to the researchers, they found "CO_2 fertilization is responsible from 1960 to 2100 for an NEP [net ecosystem productivity] enhancement of about 427 g(C) on average for all sites (= 3.05 g(C) m^{-2} $year^{-1}$)," and "the CO_2 fertilization effect" turns a warming- and drying-induced "decrease of NEP into an increase." In addition, they report, "no saturation of this effect on NEP is found because the differences between the simulations with and without CO_2 fertilization continuously increase with time." Consequently, the real-world physiological effects of atmospheric CO_2 enrichment included in the ecosystem productivity model employed by Davi *et al.* are able to more than compensate for the deleterious effects of the dramatic climate-change scenario on the productivity of major European forests.

Pardos *et al.* (2006) grew seedlings of cork oak (*Quercus suber* L., which they describe as "a typical Mediterranean species") germinated from acorns they collected from trees near Toledo, Spain, and maintained for five months, one per each 3-L pot filled with a mixture of fine sand and peat. The seedlings were maintained at either high (83%) or low (32–34%) growing medium moisture, under either high (600 μmol m^{-2} s^{-1}) or low (60 μmol m^{-2} s^{-1}) light intensity, in growth chambers maintained at either ambient (360 ppm) or elevated (700 ppm) atmospheric CO_2 concentrations. The four Spanish researchers state "elevated CO_2 caused the cork oak seedlings to improve their performance in dry and high light environments to a greater extent than under well-irrigated and low-light conditions, thus ameliorating the effects of soil water stress and high light loads on growth." Consequently, and because they assume these latter two stressful conditions are what "global change is likely to produce in the Mediterranean basin in the next decades," the rise in the air's CO_2 concentration should help the cork oak species deal successfully with those stresses, if and when they occur.

Saleska *et al.* (2007) note "large-scale numerical models that simulate the interactions between changing global climate and terrestrial vegetation predict substantial carbon loss from tropical ecosystems, including the drought-induced collapse of the Amazon forest and conversion to savanna." They used Terra satellite data—Enhanced Vegetation Index (EVI) derived from the Moderate Resolution Imaging Spectroradiometer (MODIS)—to determine whether the widespread Amazon drought of 2005, which peaked during the dry season onset (July–September), did indeed reduce whole-canopy forest photosynthesis as predicted, which they said "should have been especially observable during this period, when anomalous interannual drought coincided with the already seasonally low precipitation."

Strongly contradicting the model predictions, the

four researchers found intact forest "greenness" in the region was "dominated by a significant increase (P<0.0001), not a decline." They say the trees of the Amazon forest may be utilizing deep roots to "access and sustain" water availability during drought. Another possibility is the historical increase in the air's CO_2 content has significantly enhanced the trees' water use efficiency, enabling them to produce considerably more biomass per unit of water transpired and thereby conserve water. And yet another possibility is the phenomenon described in Soule and Knapp (2006), Wang et al. (2006), Davi et al. (2006), and Pardos et al. (2006), discussed above.

Huang et al. (2007) compared, synthesized, and evaluated the scientific literature describing atmospheric CO_2 enrichment experiments conducted on trees and empirical tree-ring studies designed to ascertain whether the growth-promoting effects of rising atmospheric CO_2 concentrations occur in natural forests. They found numerous CO_2-enrichment experiments have "demonstrated significantly positive physiological and growth responses of trees to CO_2, providing strong evidence to support the direct CO_2 fertilization effect (increased photosynthesis, water use efficiency, above- and belowground growth) and thus allowing prediction of which ecosystems might be most responsive to CO_2." They conclude the latter will be "warm, moderately drought-stressed ecosystems with an ample nitrogen supply," because "drought-stressed trees could benefit from increased water use efficiency to enhance growth." They also note tree-ring studies on the cold and arid Tibetan Plateau "showed significant growth enhancements as well as increased water use efficiency (24.7% and 33.6% for each species, respectively) in Qilian juniper and Qinghai spruce since the 1850s," citing Zhang et al. (2003), Shao et al. (2005), Liang et al. (2006), Huang and Zhang (2007), and Zhang and Qiu (2007).

Wyckoff and Bowers (2010) note, "with continued increases in global greenhouse gas emissions, climate models predict that, by the end of the 21st century, Minnesota [USA] summer temperature will increase by 4–9°C and summer precipitation will slightly decrease," citing Kling et al. (2003) and Christensen et al. (2007). They state certain "forest models and extrapolations from the paleoecological record suggest that, in response to increased temperature and/or drought, forests may retreat to the extreme north-eastern parts of the state," citing Pastor and Post (1998), Hamilton and Johnson (2002), and Galatowitsch et al. (2009). Working with bur oak

(Quercus macrocarpa) trees, Wyckoff and Bowers explored the likelihood of this scenario by: "(i) using tree rings to establish the relationship between drought and Q. macrocarpa growth for three sites along Minnesota's prairie-forest border, (ii) calculating the current relationship between growth and mortality for adult Q. macrocarpa and (iii) using the distributions of current growth rates for Q. macrocarpa to predict the susceptibility of current populations to droughts of varying strength." In addition, they looked for "temporal trends in the correlation between Q. macrocarpa growth and climate, hypothesizing that increases in CO_2 may lead to weaker relationships between drought and tree growth over time," because atmospheric CO_2 enrichment typically leads to increases in plant water use efficiency, which generally makes them less susceptible to the deleterious impact of drought on growth.

The two University of Minnesota researchers report "the sensitivity of annual growth rates to drought has steadily declined over time as evidenced by increasing growth residuals and higher growth rates for a given PDSI [Palmer Drought Severity Index] value after 1950 [when the atmosphere's CO_2 concentration rose by 57 ppm from 1950 to 2000] compared with the first half of the century [when the CO_2 increase was only 10 ppm]." They state "for Q. macrocarpa, declining sensitivity of growth to drought translates into lower predicted mortality rates at all sites," and at one such site, "declining moisture sensitivity yields a 49% lower predicted mortality from a severe drought (PDSI = -8, on a par with the worst 1930s 'American Dust Bowl' droughts)." Wyckoff and Bowers conclude "the decreasing drought sensitivity of established trees may act as a buffer and delay the movement of the prairie-forest ecotone for many decades even in the face of climate change."

Noting climate models "consistently project significant increases in temperature and decreases in precipitation in the Mediterranean basin," Keenan et al. (2011) report these changes may have a large impact on current Mediterranean forests and the related ecosystem services they provide. They note niche-based models—also known as bioclimatic envelope models or habitat models—are the most commonly used method for predicting potential species distribution responses to future climatic changes. These models typically predict significant negative consequences for terrestrial plants and animals in the face of continued increases in atmospheric CO_2 concentrations.

Keenan et al. say they preferred process-based models, which describe eco-physiological processes ranging from purely empirical relationships to mechanistic descriptions based on physical laws. These models—supported by experiments and growth and yield surveys—"suggest that global warming will have a positive impact on forest productivity (van der Meer et al., 2002; Nigh et al., 2004; Norby and Luo, 2004; Briceño-Elizondo et al., 2006; Gaucharel et al., 2008), due to the direct fertilization effect of increased CO_2 and indirect effects such as lengthening of the growing period."

To demonstrate the difference in results obtained by these two approaches to forecasting, the five researchers assessed and compared the projections of each when applied to stands of three common forest species (Quercus ilex, Pinus halepensis, and Pinus sylvestris) with widely contrasting distributions in continental Spain. This procedure revealed, they write, "CO_2 fertilization through projected increased atmospheric CO_2 concentrations is shown to increase forest productivity in the mechanistic process-based model (despite increased drought stress) by up to three times the non-CO_2 fertilization scenario by the period 2050–2080, which is in stark contrast to projections of reduced habitat suitability from the niche-based models by the same period."

Thus the Spanish and U.S. scientists write, "previous reports of species decline in continental Spain (e.g. Benito-Garzon et al., 2008) may be overestimated due to two reasons: the use of only one predictive niche-based model, and the failure to account for possible effects of CO_2 fertilization." They add, "similar studies in other regions, which do not consider these two aspects, are also potentially overestimating species decline due to climate change." They note, "niche-based model results also likely overestimate the decline in [habitat] suitability," and they therefore conclude "an organism's niche must be modeled mechanistically if we are to fully explain distribution limits," citing Kearney (2006).

Osorio et al. (2011) write, "water deficits and high temperature are major abiotic stress factors restricting plant growth and productivity in many regions," and "the impact of climate change on temperature and rainfall patterns is of great importance in determining the future response of tree crops to new environmental conditions." They studied the Carob or St. John's tree (Ceratonia siliqua), which grows in the Mediterranean, where they contend water stress will be the most important factor limiting plant growth throughout the remainder of this century. They investigated the impacts of drought and high-temperature stresses on photosynthesis, energy partitioning, and membrane lipids, as well as the potential ability of Carob trees to attenuate oxidative damage, in young seedlings growing in controlled-environment chambers. They rooted the plants in 3-dm^3 pots filled with a 2:1 mixture of a fertilized substrate and natural soil and maintained them under two thermal regimes—low and high temperature (LT: 25/18°C; HT: 32/21°C)—and three soil water conditions (control, water stress, and rewetting), monitoring numerous physiological and biochemical plant properties and processes.

Osorio et al. report the decrease in net photosynthesis (PN) caused by drought was 33% in the LT chamber and 84% in the HT chamber. They say "the negative effects of soil drying on PN and stomatal conductance of HT plants were no longer detected 36 hours following rewatering." The five Portuguese scientists remark, "although C. siliqua seedlings exhibit clear signs of oxidative stress under drought and high temperature, they retain a remarkable ability to quickly restore normal physiological activity on rehydration, which let us believe that they can satisfactorily deal with predicted climate warming and increased soil drying in the Mediterranean area."

Soule and Knapp (2011) write, "in 2008, atmospheric CO_2 concentrations from the Mauna Loa, Hawaii, Observatory records exceeded 385 ppm, representing a 22% increase since 1959." They note, "as CO_2 has increased, most tree species have been able to use water more efficiently" as their "leaf stomatal apertures narrow during photosynthesis," resulting in "less transpirational water loss per biomass gained." The parameter representing this phenomenon is referred to as intrinsic water-use efficiency (iWUE), defined as the ratio of net CO_2 assimilation to stomatal conductance, and it has been documented, they write, "for various tree species in many parts of the world," citing Bert et al. (1997), Feng (1999), Tang et al. (1999), Arneth et al. (2002), Saurer et al. (2004), Waterhouse et al. (2004), and Liu et al. (2007).

They examined changes in, and relationships between, radial growth rates and the iWUE of ponderosa pine (Pinus ponderosa) trees, climate, and atmospheric CO_2 concentration in the western United States since the mid-nineteenth century, developing tree-ring chronologies for eight sites in three climate

461

regions, and using carbon isotope data to calculate pentadal values of iWUE. They examined relationships among radial growth, climate, iWUE, and CO_2 via correlation and regression analyses.

Soule and Knapp report finding significant upward trends in iWUE at all sites, and they state "despite an absence of climate changes that would favor growth," upward radial growth trends occurred at five sites. The highest iWUE values "were recorded in the last pentad at six of eight sites and follow a positive quadratic progression at all sites, suggesting that future increases in iWUE are likely for ponderosa pine within our study regions as CO_2 levels increase." They also found "significant improvements in radial growth rates during drought years after 1950," when the air's CO_2 content rose at an accelerating rate.

The two researchers say their findings suggest "increased iWUE associated with rising CO_2 can positively impact tree growth rates in the western United States and are thus an evolving component of forest ecosystem processes." They conclude, "if potential climate changes lead to increasing aridity in the western United States, additional increases in iWUE associated with future increases in CO_2 might ameliorate growth declines associated with drought conditions."

The peer-reviewed scientific studies described in this section support the earlier conclusions of Idso and Idso (1994), who found the rise in the air's CO_2 content likely will lead to substantial increases in photosynthetic rates and biomass production in Earth's many woody species, even under stressful conditions imposed by suboptimal soil moisture.

References

Ainsworth, E.A. and Long, S.P. 2005. What have we learned from 15 years of free-air CO_2 enrichment (FACE)? A meta-analytic review of the responses of photosynthesis, canopy properties and plant production to rising CO_2. *New Phytologist* **165**: 351–372.

Anderson, P.D. and Tomlinson, P.T. 1998. Ontogeny affects response of northern red oak seedlings to elevated CO_2 and water stress. I. Carbon assimilation and biomass production. *New Phytologist* **140**: 477–491.

Arneth, A., Lloyd, J., Santruckova, H., Bird, M., Girgoryev, S., Kalaschnikov, Y.N., Gleixner, G., and Schulze, E. 2002. Response of central Siberian Scots pine to soil water deficit and long-term trends in atmospheric CO_2 concentration. *Global Biogeochemical Cycles* **16**: 10.1029/2000GB001374.

Arp, W.J., Van Mierlo, J.E.M., Berendse, F., and Snijders, W. 1998. Interactions between elevated CO_2 concentration, nitrogen and water: effects on growth and water use of six perennial plant species. *Plant, Cell and Environment* **21**: 1–11.

Benito-Garzon, M., Sanchez de Dios, R., and Sainz Ollero, H. 2008. Effects of climate change on the distribution of Iberian tree species. *Applied Vegetation Science* **11**: 169–178.

Bert, D., Leavitt, S., and Dupouey, J.-L. 1997. Variations of wood $\delta^{13}C$ and water-use efficiency of Abies alba during the last century. *Ecology* **78**: 1588–1596.

Briceño-Elizondo, R., Garcia-Gonzalo, J., Peltola, H., Matala, J., and Kellomaki, S. 2006. Sensitivity of growth of Scots pine, Norway spruce and silver birch to climate change and forest management in boreal conditions. *Forest Ecology and Management* **232**: 152–167.

Catovsky, S. and Bazzaz, F.A. 1999. Elevated CO_2 influences the responses of two birch species to soil moisture: implications for forest community structure. *Global Change Biology* **5**: 507–518.

Centritto, M. 2002. The effects of elevated [CO_2] and water availability on growth and physiology of peach (*Prunus persica*) plants. *Plant Biosystems* **136**: 177–188.

Centritto, M., Lee, H.S.J., and Jarvis, P.G. 1999b. Interactive effects of elevated [CO_2] and drought on cherry (*Prunus avium*) seedlings. I. Growth, whole-plant water use efficiency and water loss. *New Phytologist* **141**: 129–140.

Centritto, M., Magnani, F., Lee, H.S.J., and Jarvis, P.G. 1999a. Interactive effects of elevated [CO_2] and drought on cherry (*Prunus avium*) seedlings. II. Photosynthetic capacity and water relations. *New Phytologist* **141**: 141–153.

Christensen, J.H., Hewitson, B., Bisuioc, A., Chen, A., Gao, X., and Held, I. *et al.* 2007. Regional climate projections. In: Solomon, S., Qin, D., Manning, M., Chen, Z., Marquis, M., Avery, K.B., Tignor, M., and Miller, H.L. (Eds.) *Climate Change 2007: The Physical Science Basis.* Contribution of Working Group I to the Fourth Assessment Report of the Intergovernmental Panel on Climate Change (Cambridge University Press, Cambridge, UK/New York, New York, USA, pp. 847–940.

Davi, H., Dufrene, E., Francois, C., Le Maire, G., Loustau, D., Bosc, A., Rambal, S., Granier, A., and Moors, E. 2006. Sensitivity of water and carbon fluxes to climate changes from 1960–2100 in European forest ecosystems. *Agricultural and Forest Meteorology* **141**: 35–56.

Feng, X. 1999. Trends in intrinsic water-use efficiency of natural trees for the past 100–200 years: A response to atmospheric CO_2 concentration. *Geochimica et Cosmochimica Acta* **63**: 1891–1903.

Fernandez, M.D., Pieters, A., Azuke, M., Rengifo, E., Tezara, W., Woodward, F.I., and Herrera, A. 1999. Photosynthesis in plants of four tropical species growing under elevated CO_2. *Photosynthetica* 37: 587–599.

Fernandez, M.D., Pieters, A., Donoso, C., Tezara, W., Azuke, M., Herrera, C., Rengifo, E., and Herrera, A. 1998. Effects of a natural source of very high CO_2 concentration on the leaf gas exchange, xylem water potential and stomatal characteristics of plants of *Spatiphylum cannifolium* and *Bauhinia multinervia*. *New Phytologist* 138: 689–697.

Galatowitsch, S., Frelich, L., and Phillips-Mao, L. 2009. Regional climate change adaptation strategies for biodiversity conservation in a mid-continental region of North America. *Biological Conservation* 142: 2012–2022.

Gaucharel, C., Guiot, J., and Misson, L. 2008. Changes of the potential distribution area of French Mediterranean forests under global warming. *Biogeosciences* 5: 1493–1503.

Hamerlynck, E.P., Huxman, T.E., Loik, M.E., and Smith, S.D. 2000. Effects of extreme high temperature, drought and elevated CO_2 on photosynthesis of the Mojave Desert evergreen shrub, *Larrea tridentata*. *Plant Ecology* 148: 183–193.

Hamilton, J.D. and Johnson, S. 2002. *Playing with Fire: Climate Change in Minnesota.* Minnesotans for an Energy-Efficient Economy. St Paul, Minnesota, USA.

Huang, J.-G., Bergeron, Y., Denneler, B., Berninger, F., and Tardif, J. 2007. Response of forest trees to increased atmospheric CO_2. *Critical Reviews in Plant Sciences* 26: 265–283.

Huang, J.G. and Zhang, Q.B. 2007. Tree-rings and climate for the last 680 years in Wulan area of northeastern Qinghai-Tibetan Plateau. *Climatic Change* 80: 369–377.

Idso, K.E. and Idso, S.B. 1994. Plant responses to atmospheric CO_2 enrichment in the face of environmental constraints: A review of the past 10 years' research. *Agricultural and Forest Meteorology* 69: 153–203.

Idso, S.B. and Kimball, B.A. 2001. CO_2 enrichment of sour orange trees: 13 years and counting. *Environmental and Experimental Botany* 46: 147–153.

Kearney, M. 2006. Habitat, environment and niche: what are we modeling? *Oikos* 115: 186–191.

Keenan, T., Serra, J.M., Lloret, F., Ninyerola, M., and Sabate, S. 2011. Predicting the future of forests in the Mediterranean under climate change, with niche- and process-based models: CO_2 matters! *Global Change Biology* 17: 565–579.

Kling, G.W., Hayhoe, K., Johnson, L.B., Magnuson, J.J., Polasky, S., and Robinson, S.K., *et al.* 2003. *Confronting Climate Change in the Great Lakes Region: Impacts on our Communities and Ecosystems.* Union of Concerned Scientists and Ecological Society of America, Washington, DC, USA.

Knapp, P.A., Soule, P.T., and Grissino-Mayer, H.D. 2001. Post-drought growth responses of western juniper (*Juniperus occidentalis* var. *occidentalis*) in central Oregon. *Geophysical Research Letters* 28: 2657–2660.

Liang, E.Y., Shao, X.M., Eckstein, D., Huang, L., and Liu, X.H. 2006. Topography- and species-dependent growth response of *Sabina przewalskii* and *Picea crassifolia* to climate on the northeast Tibetan Plateau. *Forest Ecology and Management* 236: 268–277.

Liu, X., Shao, X., Liang, E., Zhao, L., Chen, T., Qin, D., and Ren, J. 2007. Species dependent responses of juniper and spruce to increasing CO_2 concentration and to climate in semi-arid and arid areas of northwestern China. *Plant Ecology* 193: 195–209.

Nigh, G.D., Ying, C.C., and Qian, H. 2004. Climate and productivity of major conifer species in the interior of British Columbia, Canada. *Forest Science* 50: 659–671.

Norby, R.J. and Luo, Y. 2004. Evaluating ecosystem responses to rising atmospheric CO_2 and global warming in a multi-factor world. *New Phytologist* 162: 281–293.

Osorio, M.L., Osorio, J., Vieira, A.C., Goncalves, S., and Romano, A. 2011. Influence of enhanced temperature on photosynthesis, photooxidative damage, and antioxidant strategies in *Ceratonia siliqua* L. seedlings subjected to water deficit and rewatering. *Photosynthetica* 49: 3–12.

Osborne, C.P., Mitchell, P.L., Sheehy, J.E., and Woodward, F.I. 2000. Modeling the recent historical impacts of atmospheric CO_2 and climate change on Mediterranean vegetation. *Global Change Biology* 6: 445–458.

Palanisamy, K. 1999. Interactions of elevated CO_2 concentration and drought stress on photosynthesis in *Eucalyptus cladocalyx* F. Muell. *Photosynthetica* 36: 635–638.

Pardos, M., Puertolas, J., Aranda, I., and Pardos, J.A. 2006. Can CO_2 enrichment modify the effect of water and high light stress on biomass allocation and relative growth rate of cork oak seedlings? *Trees* 20: 713–724.

Pastor, J. and Post, W.M. 1988. Response of northern forests to CO_2-induced climate change. *Nature* 334: 55–58.

Polley, H.W., Tischler, C.R., Johnson, H.B., and Derner, J.D. 2002. Growth rate and survivorship of drought: CO_2 effects on the presumed tradeoff in seedlings of five woody legumes. *Tree Physiology* 22: 383–391.

Polley, H.W., Tischler, C.R., Johnson, H.B., and Pennington, R.E. 1999. Growth, water relations, and survival of drought-exposed seedlings from six maternal families of honey mesquite (*Prosopis glandulosa*): responses to CO_2 enrichment. *Tree Physiology* **19**: 359–366.

Runion, G.B., Mitchell, R.J., Green, T.H., Prior, S.A., Rogers, H.H., and Gjerstad, D.H. 1999. Longleaf pine photosynthetic response to soil resource availability and elevated atmospheric carbon dioxide. *Journal of Environmental Quality* **28**: 880–887.

Saleska, S.R., Didan, K., Huete, A.R., and da Rocha, H.R. 2007. Amazon forests green-up during 2005 drought. *Sciencexpress*: 10.1126/science.1146663.

Saurer, M., Siegwolf, R., and Schweingruber, F. 2004. Carbon isotope discrimination indicates improving water-use efficiency of trees in northern Eurasia over the last 100 years. *Global Change Biology* **10**: 2109–2120.

Schulte, M., Herschbach, C., and Rennenberg, H. 1998. Interactive effects of elevated atmospheric CO_2, mycorrhization and drought on long-distance transport of reduced sulfur in young pedunculate oak trees (*Quercus robur* L.). *Plant, Cell and Environment* **21**: 917–926.

Shao, X.M., Huang, L., Liu, H.B., Liang, E.Y., Fang, X.Q., and Wang, L.L. 2005. Reconstructions of precipitation variation from tree-rings in recent 1000 years in Delingha, Qinghai. *Science in China* **48**: 939–949.

Soule, P.T. and Knapp, P.A. 2006. Radial growth rate increases in naturally occurring ponderosa pine trees: a late-20th century CO_2 fertilization effect? *New Phytologist* **doi**: 10.1111/j.1469-8137.2006.01746.x.

Soule, P.T. and Knapp, P.A. 2011. Radial growth and increased water-use efficiency for ponderosa pine trees in three regions in the western United States. *The Professional Geographer* **63**: 370–391.

Tang, K., Feng, X., and Funkhouser, G. 1999. The $\delta^{13}C$ of trees in full-bark and strip-bark bristlecone pine trees in the White Mountains of California. *Global Change Biology* **5**: 33–40.

Tognetti, R., Longobucco, A., Miglietta, F., and Raschi, A. 1998. Transpiration and stomatal behaviour of *Quercus ilex* plants during the summer in a Mediterranean carbon dioxide spring. *Plant, Cell and Environment* **21**: 613–622.

Tognetti, R., Raschi, A., and Jones M.B. 2002. Seasonal changes in tissue elasticity and water transport efficiency in three co-occurring Mediterranean shrubs under natural long-term CO_2 enrichment. *Functional Plant Biology* **29**: 1097–1106.

Tomlinson, P.T. and Anderson, P.D. 1998. Ontogeny affects response of northern red oak seedlings to elevated CO_2 and water stress. II. Recent photosynthate distribution and growth. *New Phytologist* **140**: 493–504.

Tuba, Z., Csintalan, Z., Szente, K., Nagy, Z., and Grace, J. 1998. Carbon gains by desiccation-tolerant plants at elevated CO_2. *Functional Ecology* **12**: 39–44.

van der Meer, P.J., Jorritsma, I.T.M., and Kramer, J.K. 2002. Assessing climate change effects on long-term forest development: adjusting growth, phenology and seed production in a gap model. *Forest Ecology and Management* **162**: 39–52.

Wang, G.G., Chhin, S. and Bauerle, W.L. 2006. Effect of natural atmospheric CO_2 fertilization suggested by open-grown white spruce in a dry environment. *Global Change Biology* **12**: 601–610.

Waterhouse, J., Switsur, V., Barker, A., Carter, A., Hemming, D., Loader, N., and Robertson, I. 2004. Northern European trees show a progressively diminishing response to increasing atmospheric carbon dioxide concentrations. *Quaternary Science Reviews* **23**: 803–810.

Wyckoff, P.H. and Bowers, R. 2010. Response of the prairie-forest border to climate change: impacts of increasing drought may be mitigated by increasing CO_2. *Journal of Ecology* **98**: 197–208.

Xiao, C.-W., Sun, O.J., Zhou, G.-S., Zhao, J.-Z., and Wu, G. 2005. Interactive effects of elevated CO_2 and drought stress on leaf water potential and growth in *Caragana intermedia*. *Trees* **19**: 711–720.

Zhang, Q.B., Cheng, G.D., Yao, T.D., Kang, X.C., and Huang, J.G. 2003. A 2,326-year tree-ring record of climate variability on the northeastern Qinghai-Tibetan Plateau. *Geophysical Research Letters* **30**: 10.1029/2003GL017425.

Zhang, Q.B. and Qiu, H.Y. 2007. A millennium-long tree-ring chronology of *Sabina przewalskii* on northeastern Qinghai-Tibetan Plateau. *Dendrochronologia* **24**: 91–95.

Zhang, X.S. 1994. The ecological background of the Maowusu sandland: the principles and optimal models for grass land management. *Acta Photoecologica Sinica* **18**: 1–6.

3.16 Weeds

Some researchers suggest weeds will become more aggressive as the air's CO_2 content climbs, making them greater threats to the wellbeing of natural ecosystems and farming operations. The subsections below investigate the merits of this claim regarding non-parasitic and parasitic weeds.

3.16.1 Non-Parasitic

- Non-parasitic weeds likely will be no more competitive in a high-CO_2 environment than they are today, and many could become less competitive. Atmospheric CO_2 enrichment may provide non-weeds with greater protection against weed-induced decreases in productivity, thereby increasing the competitiveness of non-weeds over weeds. And although atmospheric CO_2 enrichment increases the growth of many weeds, the fraction helped is probably not as large as non-weeds.

3.16.1.1 Competitiveness

- Non-parasitic weeds likely will be no more competitive in a high-CO_2 environment than they are today, and many could become less competitive.

Wayne *et al.* (1999) grew a common agricultural weed (field mustard) at six densities in pots exposed to atmospheric CO_2 concentrations of 350 and 700 ppm, sequentially harvesting them during the growing season. Early in stand development, the extra CO_2 increased above-ground biomass in a density-dependent manner; with the greatest stimulation (141%) occurring at the lowest weed density (20 plants per square meter) and the smallest stimulation (59%) occurring at the highest weed density (652 plants per square meter), the authors report. As the stands matured, the density-dependence of the growth response disappeared, and the CO_2-enriched weeds exhibited an average above-ground biomass 34% greater than those grown in ambient air. That response is similar to those of most herbaceous plants (a 30 to 50% increase for a doubling of the air's CO_2 content) and less than those of most woody species (50% and up). Consequently, in currently farmed or abandoned agricultural fields, as well as in regenerating forests, it is unlikely field mustard plants will benefit relative to other plants from Earth's rising atmospheric CO_2 concentration.

Caporn *et al.* (1999) grew bracken—a serious weed and potential threat to human health in the United Kingdom and elsewhere—for 19 months in controlled-environment chambers maintained at atmospheric CO_2 concentrations of 370 and 570 ppm and normal or high levels of fertilization. They found the extra 200 ppm of CO_2 increased rates of net photosynthesis by 30 to 70%, depending on soil fertility and time of year. The elevated CO_2 did not increase total plant biomass, nor did it increase the biomass of any plant organs, including rhizomes, roots, and fronds. The only significant effect of elevated CO_2 on plant growth was observed in the normal nutrient regime, where it reduced average frond area.

Gavazzi *et al.* (2000) grew one-year-old loblolly pine seedlings for four months in pots seeded with a variety of C_3 and C_4 weeds and maintained at adequate and inadequate levels of soil moisture in growth chambers maintained at atmospheric CO_2 concentrations of 360 and 660 ppm. The elevated CO_2 increased pine seedling biomass by 22%, decreased total weed biomass by 22%, and reduced the percentage of weed biomass composed of C_4 species from 53 to 35%. The additional CO_2 induced an increase in root-to-shoot ratio under water-stressed conditions in the pine seedlings, which Gavazzi *et al.* opine could "contribute to an improved ability of loblolly pine to compete against weeds on dry sites under elevated CO_2 levels."

Ziska (2003) grew Canada thistle, "the most frequently listed noxious weed species in surveys of the continental United States and southern Canada," in pots watered to the drip point daily with one of three complete nutrient solutions that differed only in nitrogen (N) concentration (3.0, 6.0, or 14.5 mM) in controlled-environment chambers maintained at 287 and 373 ppm CO_2 from seeding until flowering, which occurred at 77 days after seeding (DAS). He reports, "N supply did not affect the relative response to CO_2 for any measured vegetative parameter up to 77 DAS." Averaged across the three nitrogen treatments, the 86 ppm increase in atmospheric CO_2 concentration increased total plant biomass by 65.5%, which for the full 100 ppm CO_2 increase experienced over the course of the Industrial Revolution (initial value ~275 ppm, current value ~375 ppm) translates into an approximate 76% biomass increase.

To assess the significance of this CO_2-induced increase in weed biomass, it is necessary to compare it with what would have been expected for crops with which Canada thistle competes. Mayeux *et al.* (1997) obtained data indicating the 100-ppm increase in atmospheric CO_2 concentration experienced over the course of the Industrial Revolution should have produced yield increases of 70 and 74% in the two wheat varieties they studied when grown under well-watered conditions comparable to those studied by Ziska. In addition, based on the voluminous data Idso and Idso (2000) summarized, we can scale these results to derive comparable CO_2-induced growth enhancements of 84% for other C_3 cereals, 74% for legumes, and 80% for root and tuber crops. Thus the CO_2-induced growth enhancement likely experienced by Canada thistle over the course of the Industrial Revolution was not much different from the growth enhancements of most of the crops with which it competes, suggesting the competitive ability of this noxious weed against these crops has remained largely unaffected by the historical increase in the air's CO_2 content.

Ziska and Goins (2006) grew genetically modified (Round-up Ready) soybean plants in the field in aluminum chambers maintained at ambient and ambient + 250 ppm atmospheric CO_2 concentrations for two full growing seasons under conditions allowing a variety of different weed densities to develop among the soybeans. The elevated CO_2 conditions advanced soybean seed yields by 25, 33, 50, 90, and 250% when chamber weed biomass densities were 0, 200, 400, 600, and 800 gm^{-2}, respectively. Soybean seed yield in the ambient-air treatment fell to a value of zero at a weed density of approximately 920 gm^{-2}, whereas calculations reveal it would not drop that far in the CO_2-enriched treatment until a weed density of approximately 1,250 gm^{-2} was reached. Consequently, the atmospheric CO_2 enrichment of this study boosted crop yield by an increasing percentage as the stress of the expanding weed population grew larger, benefiting the soybean plants most when they needed it most. This phenomenon also has been shown to be true of other environmental stressors, such as plant diseases, lack of water, and high temperatures.

Kao-Kniffin and Balser (2007) grew invasive reed canary grass from seed for four months in well-watered mesocosms located in greenhouses maintained at atmospheric CO_2 concentrations of either 365 or 600 ppm in soils of either low or high nitrogen (N) supply (5 mg N l^{-1} or 30 mg N l^{-1}) under conditions where the invading species was either dominant (high invasion: >90% cover) or sub-dominant (low invasion: <50% cover), and where the remaining surface portions of the mesocosms were covered with native graminoids (grasses, sedges, and bulrushes) and native forbs also grown from seed. Elevating the air's CO_2 content increased below-ground biomass only in the plant communities moderately invaded by reed canary grass, and the only plants to show a significant increase in above-ground biomass were the native graminoids in the

moderately invaded low N treatment. The scientists conclude, "when CO_2 concentrations rise in the future, wetland plant communities comprised of native graminoids may be better able to hinder reed canary grass invasion, particularly under low N environments."

Williams et al. (2007) studied the impacts of a 170 ppm increase in atmospheric CO_2 concentration and a 2°C rise in air temperature at the Tasmanian free-air CO_2 enrichment (TasFACE) facility, located in a native lowland grassland in the southern midlands region of Tasmania, Australia. Between spring 2003 and summer 2006, they documented annual seed production, seedling emergence, seedling survival, and adult survival of four abundant perennial species, including the two most dominant invading weeds: Hypochaeris radicata L. and Leontodon taraxacoides (Vill.) Merat, members of the Asteraceae family. They found no significant CO_2-induced differences in the population growth rates of either weed species, but the population growth rates of both "were substantially reduced by warming." The six researchers conclude "global warming may be a more important determinant of the success of invasive species than CO_2 concentration," and both the invading weed species they studied "are likely to be excluded from the grassland community by increasing temperatures."

McPeek and Wang (2007) collected seeds from a single dandelion plant in Speedway, Indiana (USA), which they allowed to sprout and grow until reaching reproductive maturity in pots placed in each of two controlled-environment chambers, one continually flushed with ambient air of 370 ppm CO_2 and the other maintained at an elevated atmospheric CO_2 concentration of 730 ppm. After harvesting the plants and measuring numerous parameters of reproductive fitness, the two scientists conducted a second experiment in which they measured various parameters of the germination of the seeds produced in the two CO_2 treatments, along with the physical characteristics of the second-generation plants 35 days after planting.

McPeek and Wang state the dandelion plants "produced 83% more inflorescences and 32% more achenes, i.e., single-seed fruits, per plant at elevated than at ambient CO_2," and the "seeds from elevated CO_2-grown plants were significantly heavier and had a higher germination percentage, leading to larger seedlings and earlier establishment in the subsequent generation." Furthermore, "achenes from plants grown at elevated CO_2 had characteristics, such as higher stalks at seed maturity, longer beaks, and larger pappi, which would increase the distance of seed dispersal by wind."

The two researchers conclude "dandelion can potentially become more widespread and noxious as atmospheric CO_2 continues to rise."

References

Caporn, S.J.M., Brooks, A.L., Press, M.C., and Lee, J.A. 1999. Effects of long-term exposure to elevated CO_2 and increased nutrient supply on bracken (*Pteridium aquilinum*). *Functional Ecology* **13**: 107–115.

Gavazzi, M., Seiler, J., Aust, W., and Zedaker, S. 2000. The influence of elevated carbon dioxide and water availability on herbaceous weed development and growth of transplanted loblolly pine (*Pinus taeda*). *Environmental and Experimental Botany* **44**: 185–194.

Idso, C.D. and Idso, K.E. 2000. Forecasting world food supplies: The impact of the rising atmospheric CO_2 concentration. *Technology* **7S**: 33–56.

Kao-Kniffin, J. and Balser, T.C. 2007. Elevated CO_2 differentially alters belowground plant and soil microbial community structure in reed canary grass-invaded experimental wetlands. *Soil Biology & Biochemistry* **39**: 517–525.

Mayeux, H.S., Johnson, H.B., Polley, H.W., and Malone, S.R. 1997. Yield of wheat across a subambient carbon dioxide gradient. *Global Change Biology* **3**: 269–278.

McPeek, T.M. and Wang, X. 2007. Reproduction of dandelion (*Taraxacum officinale*) in a higher CO_2 environment. *Weed Science* **55**: 334–340.

Wayne, P.M., Carnelli, A.L., Connolly, J., and Bazzaz, F.A. 1999. The density dependence of plant responses to elevated CO_2. *Journal of Ecology* **87**: 183–192.

Williams, A.L., Wills, K.E., Janes, J.K., Vander Schoor, J.K., Newton, P.C.D., and Hovenden, M.J. 2007. Warming and free-air CO_2 enrichment alter demographics in four co-occurring grassland species. *New Phytologist* **176**: 365–374.

Ziska, L.H. 2003. The impact of nitrogen supply on the potential response of a noxious, invasive weed, Canada thistle (*Cirsium arvense*) to recent increases in atmospheric carbon dioxide. *Physiologia Plantarum* **119**: 105–112.

Ziska, LH. and Goins, E.W. 2006. Elevated atmospheric carbon dioxide and weed populations in glyphosate treated soybean. *Crop Science* **46**: 1354–1359.

3.16.1.2 Biodiversity Impacts

- Rising atmospheric CO_2 concentrations will not favor the growth of non-parasitic weeds over crops and native plants. A CO_2 increase may provide the latter with greater protection against weed-induced decreases in productivity, thereby increasing the competitiveness of non-weeds over weeds.

Elevated CO_2 typically stimulates the growth of nearly all plant species in monoculture, including weeds. Consequently, it is important to determine how future increases in the air's CO_2 content may influence relationships between weeds and non-weeds when they grow competitively in mixed-species stands.

Dukes (2002) grew model serpentine grasslands common to California (USA) in competition with the invasive forb *Centaurea solstitialis* at atmospheric CO_2 concentrations of 350 and 700 ppm for one year. They found elevated CO_2 increased the biomass proportion of this weedy species in the community by 1.2%, while total community biomass increased by 28%. Similarly, Gavazzi *et al.* (2000) grew loblolly pine seedlings for four months in competition with C_3 and C_4 weeds at atmospheric CO_2 concentrations of 260 and 660 ppm, reporting elevated CO_2 increased pine biomass by 22% while eliciting no response from either type of weed. In a study of pasture ecosystems near Montreal, Canada, Taylor and Potvin (1997) determined elevated CO_2 concentrations did not influence the number of native species returning after their removal (to simulate disturbance), even in the face of the introduced presence of the C_3 weed *Chenopodium album*, which normally competes quite effectively with several slower-growing crops in ambient air. Atmospheric CO_2 enrichment did not impact the growth of this weed in any measurable way.

Ziska *et al.* (1999) studied the C_3 weed *C. album*, along with the C_4 weed *Amaranthus retroflexus*, in glasshouses maintained at atmospheric CO_2 concentrations of 360 and 720 ppm. Elevated CO_2 significantly increased the photosynthetic rate and total dry weight of the C_3 weed but had no effect on the C_4 weed. They report the growth response of the C_3 weed to a doubling of the air's CO_2 content was approximately 51%, about the same as the average 52% growth response tabulated by Idso (1992) and by Poorter (1993) for rapidly growing wild C_3 species (54%), suggesting a CO_2-enriched environment does not cause enhanced dominance of the C_3 weed over other C_3 plants.

Wayne *et al.* (1999) studied another agricultural weed, field mustard (*Brassica kaber*), which they sowed in pots at six densities, placed in atmospheric CO_2 concentrations of 350 and 700 ppm, and sequentially harvested during the growing season. Early in stand development, elevated CO_2 increased aboveground weed biomass in a density-dependent manner, with the greatest stimulation (141%) occurring at the lowest density (20 plants per square meter) and the smallest stimulation (59%) occurring at the highest density (652 plants per square meter). As these stands matured, the density-dependence of the CO_2-induced growth response disappeared, and CO_2-enriched plants exhibited an average aboveground biomass 34% greater than ambient-grown plants across a broad range of plant densities. This final growth stimulation was similar to those of most other herbaceous plants exposed to atmospheric CO_2 enrichment (30 to 50% biomass increases for a doubling of the air's CO_2 content), demonstrating atmospheric CO_2 enrichment confers no undue advantage on weeds at the expense of other plants.

In a study of a weed that affects both plants and animals, Caporn *et al.* (1999) examined bracken (*Pteridium aquilinum*), which poses a serious weed problem and potential threat to human health in the United Kingdom and other regions, growing specimens for 19 months in controlled-environment chambers maintained at atmospheric CO_2 concentrations of 370 and 570 ppm and normal or high levels of soil fertility. The high-CO_2 treatment consistently increased rates of net photosynthesis by 30 to 70%, depending on soil fertility and time of year. Elevated CO_2 did not increase total plant dry mass or the dry mass of any plant organ, including rhizomes, roots, and fronds. The only significant effect of elevated CO_2 on bracken growth was observed in the normal nutrient regime, where elevated CO_2 reduced mean frond area.

These studies suggest atmospheric CO_2 enrichment will not favor the growth of non-parasitic weeds over crops and native plants.

References

Caporn, S.J.M., Brooks, A.L., Press, M.C., and Lee, J.A. 1999. Effects of long-term exposure to elevated CO_2 and increased nutrient supply on bracken (*Pteridium aquilinum*). *Functional Ecology* **13**: 107–115.

Dale, H. and Press, M.C. 1999. Elevated atmospheric CO_2 influences the interaction between the parasitic angiosperm *Orobanche minor* and its host *Trifolium repens*. *New Phytologist* **140**: 65–73.

Dukes, J.S. 2002. Comparison of the effect of elevated CO_2 on an invasive species (*Centaurea solstitialis*) in monoculture and community settings. *Plant Ecology* **160**: 225–234.

Gavazzi, M., Seiler, J., Aust, W., and Zedaker, S. 2000. The influence of elevated carbon dioxide and water availability on herbaceous weed development and growth of transplanted loblolly pine (*Pinus taeda*). *Environmental and Experimental Botany* **44**: 185–194.

Idso, K.E. 1992. Plant responses to rising levels of carbon dioxide: A compilation and analysis of the results of a decade of international research into the direct biological effects of atmospheric CO_2 enrichment. *Climatological Publications Scientific Paper #23*, Office of Climatology, Arizona State University, Tempe, AZ.

Poorter, H. 1993. Interspecific variation in the growth response of plants to an elevated and ambient CO_2 concentration. *Vegetatio* **104/105**: 77–97.

Taylor, K. and Potvin, C. 1997. Understanding the long-term effect of CO_2 enrichment on a pasture: the importance of disturbance. *Canadian Journal of Botany* **75**: 1621–1627.

Wayne, P.M., Carnelli, A.L., Connolly, J., and Bazzaz, F.A. 1999. The density dependence of plant responses to elevated CO_2. *Journal of Ecology* **87**: 183–192.

Ziska, L.H., Teasdale, J.R., and Bunce, J.A. 1999. Future atmospheric carbon dioxide may increase tolerance to glyphosate. *Weed Science* **47**: 608–615.

3.16.1.3 Miscellaneous Weeds

- Atmospheric CO_2 enrichment tends to increase the growth of many weeds, but possibly not by quite as great a percentage as it does for non-weeds.

Lewis *et al.* (2002) grew the common cocklebur (*Xanthium strumarium* L.) in controlled-environment growth chambers maintained at atmospheric CO_2 concentrations of 365 and 730 ppm for 70 days post-emergence. During the weed's vegetative growth phase, the photosynthetic rates of the CO_2-enriched plants were 30% greater than those of the plants growing in ambient air. During the flowering period that ensued shortly thereafter, this stimulation was reduced to 10%, after which it rose to 20% during the weed's fruiting period.

Gibeaut *et al.* (2001) grew the common weed *Arabidopsis thaliana* for seven weeks in controlled-environment chambers maintained at atmospheric CO_2 concentrations of 360 and 1,000 ppm, finding the 640 ppm increase in the air's CO_2 concentration increased the relative growth rate of the plants by about 20% during the first three weeks of the study. The extra CO_2 also increased the activity of the enzyme UDP-glucose dehydrogenase (an important enzyme involved in cell wall biosynthesis) by approximately 25%. Thereafter, relative growth rates were the same in both CO_2 treatments. Nevertheless, by the end of the study the CO_2-enriched plants had produced 2.3 times more biomass than the ambient-grown plants.

Ziska (2002) grew Canadian thistle (*Cirsium arvense* L. Scop.) plants in controlled-environment chambers maintained at atmospheric CO_2 concentrations of 280, 380, and 720 ppm for about two months. They determined the first increment of extra CO_2 enhanced photosynthesis rates and total plant biomass production by 45 and 126%, respectively, and the second CO_2 increment enhanced these two parameters by 49 and 69%.

Leishman *et al.* (1999) grew four weedy C_3 plants common to European grasslands (*Cardamine hirsute, Spergula arvensis, Senecio vulgaris,* and *Poa annua*) from seed to senescence in glasshouses maintained at atmospheric CO_2 concentrations of 350 and 550 ppm at two light intensities: full light and 67% of full light. The extra 200 ppm of CO_2 did not significantly impact vegetative growth in three of the species. For *Spergula arvensis*, it increased maximum leaf length by an average of 15%, regardless of light treatment, and total dry weight by 20 and 68% at full and reduced light levels, respectively. It significantly enhanced reproductive success in only one of the species, increasing the number of seeds in *Poa annua* by 50 and 26% at full and reduced light levels, respectively.

Nagashima *et al.* (2003) established even-aged stands of the summer annual *Chenopodium album* (a weed commonly found in open habitats, such as abandoned fields and flood plains) at ambient and twice-ambient atmospheric CO_2 concentrations and low and high levels of soil nutrient availability in open-top chambers in the experimental garden of Tohoku University, Sendai, Japan. They monitored the growth of individual plants every week until flowering. At the conclusion of the experiment, they could detect no significant effect of elevated CO_2 on aboveground biomass in the low nutrient regime; in

the high nutrient regime, the extra CO_2 increased aboveground biomass by 50%. The CO_2-induced enhancement of growth in the high nutrient regime gradually waned and ultimately disappeared altogether in smaller subordinate individuals but continued in larger dominants throughout the experiment.

Ziska and Bunce (1999) grew four C_4 plants in controlled-environment chambers maintained continuously at atmospheric CO_2 concentrations of 350 and 700 ppm or at a nocturnal CO_2 concentration of 700 ppm and 350 ppm during the day for approximately three weeks. They found continuous CO_2 enrichment caused a significant increase in photosynthesis (+13%) and total dry mass (+21%) in only one of the four species, *Amaranthus retroflexus*. Nocturnal CO_2 enrichment provided no significant effects in this species, indicating the CO_2-induced increase in biomass was not facilitated by a reduction in dark respiration rate. Plants exposed to continuous CO_2 enrichment did not increase their biomass due to improved internal water balance, as leaf water potentials were not significantly different among plants of any CO_2 treatment.

Ziska *et al.* (1999) grew broad-leaved C_3 (*Chenopodium album*) and C_4 (*Amaranthus retroflexus*) weeds in glasshouses maintained at atmospheric CO_2 concentrations of 360 and 720 ppm. Both young and mature plants of each species were sprayed with one-tenth and full-strength solutions of the chemical glyphosate ("Roundup"). The elevated CO_2 significantly increased the photosynthetic rate and total dry weight (by 51%) of the unsprayed C_3 weed, regardless of maturity stage, but it had no effect on these parameters in the case of the C_4 weed. Spraying both young and mature *A. retroflexus* plants with full-strength herbicide resulted in their death, regardless of atmospheric CO_2 concentration; spraying *C. album* plants with full-strength glyphosate severely reduced, but did not eliminate, growth in the elevated-CO_2 air, whereas chemically treated plants died in ambient CO_2 air. Consequently, farmers who use glyphosate to control *A. retroflexus* should not have to modify their current chemical practices in the future, but better control of *C. album* may require application of glyphosate earlier in the season when the weeds are smaller or, if applied later, at higher concentrations, as elevated CO_2 slightly increases the glyphosate tolerance of this particular C_3 weed.

These studies suggest although atmospheric CO_2 enrichment tends to increase the growth of many weeds, it may not do so by as great a percentage as for non-weeds. (See, for example, the results of the many non-weed plants listed in Tables 1.1.1 and 1.1.2 in Appendices 3 and 4.)

References

Gibeaut, D.M., Cramer, G.R., and Seemann, J.R. 2001. Growth, cell walls, and UDP-glucose dehydrogenase activity of *Arabidopsis thaliana* grown in elevated carbon dioxide. *Journal of Plant Physiology* **158**: 569–576.

Leishman, M.R., Sanbrooke, K.J., and Woodfin, R.M. 1999. The effects of elevated CO_2 and light environment on growth and reproductive performance of four annual species. *New Phytologist* **144**: 455–462.

Lewis, J.D., Wang, X.Z., Griffin, K.L., and Tissue, D.T. 2002. Effects of age and ontogeny on photosynthetic responses of a determinate annual plant to elevated CO_2 concentrations. *Plant, Cell and Environment* **25**: 359–368.

Nagashima, H., Yamano, T., Hikosaka, K., and Hirose, T. 2003. Effects of elevated CO_2 on the size structure in even-aged monospecific stands of *Chenopodium album*. *Global Change Biology* **9**: 619–629.

Ziska, L. 2002. Influence of rising atmospheric CO_2 since 1900 on early growth and photosynthetic response of a noxious invasive weed, Canada thistle (*Cirsium arvense*). *Functional Plant Biology* **29**: 1387–1392.

Ziska, L.H. and Bunce, J.A. 1999. Effect of elevated carbon dioxide concentration at night on the growth and gas exchange of selected C_4 species. *Australian Journal of Plant Physiology* **26**: 71–77.

Ziska, L.H., Teasdale, J.R., and Bunce, J.A. 1999. Future atmospheric carbon dioxide may increase tolerance to glyphosate. *Weed Science* **47**: 608–615.

3.16.2 Parasitic

- Rising atmospheric CO_2 concentrations appear to reduce the negative effects of parasitic weed infection so infected host plants continue to exhibit positive (but somewhat reduced) growth responses to elevated CO_2.

Parasitic plants obtain energy, water, and nutrients from their host plants and cause widespread reductions in harvestable yields. This brief section examines how increasing atmospheric CO_2 concentrations may impact the growth of parasitic weeds and the relationships that exist between them and their host plants.

Dale and Press (1999) infected white clover (*Trifolium repens*) plants with *Orobanche minor*, a parasitic weed that primarily infects leguminous crops in the United Kingdom and the Middle East, and exposed them to atmospheric CO_2 concentrations of either 360 or 550 ppm for 75 days in controlled-environment growth cabinets. The elevated CO_2 had no effect on the total biomass of parasite per host plant, nor did it affect the number of parasites per host plant or the time to parasitic attachment to host roots. While infected host plants growing in ambient air produced 47% less biomass than uninfected plants growing in ambient air, infected plants growing at 550 ppm CO_2 exhibited final dry weights only 20% less than those of uninfected plants growing in the CO_2-enriched air, indicating a significant CO_2-induced partial alleviation of parasite-induced biomass reductions in the white clover host plants.

Watling and Press (1997) infected several C_4 sorghum plants with *Striga hermonthica* and *Striga asiatica* (parasitic C_3 weeds of the semi-arid tropics that infest many grain crops) and grew them, along with uninfected control plants, for approximately two months in controlled-environment cabinets maintained at atmospheric CO_2 concentrations of 350 and 700 ppm. In the absence of parasite infection, the extra 350 ppm of CO_2 increased sorghum biomass by approximately 36%. When infected with *S. hermonthica*, the sorghum plants grown at ambient and elevated CO_2 concentrations produced only 32 and 43% of the biomass displayed by their respective uninfected controls. Infection with *S. asiatica* was somewhat less stressful and led to host biomass production of about half that of uninfected controls in both ambient and CO_2-enriched air. Therefore, the doubling of the air's CO_2 content employed in this study increased sorghum biomass by 79% and 35% in the C_4 sorghum plants infected with *S. hermonthica* and *S. asiatica*, respectively.

Watling and Press (2000) grew upland rice (*Oryza sativa* L.) in pots in controlled-environment chambers maintained at 350 and 700 ppm CO_2 in either the presence or absence of the root parasite *S. hermonthica* for 80 days after sowing, after which they harvested and weighed the plants. In ambient air, the presence of the parasite reduced the biomass of the rice to only 35% of what it was in the absence of the parasite. In air enriched with CO_2 the presence of the parasite reduced the biomass of infected plants to 73% of what it was in the absence of the parasite.

These few observations suggest rising atmospheric CO_2 concentrations generally tend to reduce the negative effects of parasitic weed infection so infected host plants continue to exhibit positive growth responses to elevated CO_2. It is likely host plants infected by parasitic weeds will fare better under higher atmospheric CO_2 conditions than they do currently.

References

Dale, H. and Press, M.C. 1999. Elevated atmospheric CO_2 influences the interaction between the parasitic angiosperm *Orobanche minor* and its host *Trifolium repens*. *New Phytologist* **140**: 65–73.

Watling, J.R. and Press, M.C. 1997. How is the relationship between the C_4 cereal *Sorghum bicolor* and the C_3 root hemi-parasites *Striga hermonthica* and *Striga asiatica* affected by elevated CO_2? *Plant, Cell and Environment* **20**: 1292–1300.

Watling, J.R. and Press, M.C. 2000. Infection with the parasitic angiosperm *Striga hermonthica* influences the response of the C_3 cereal *Oryza sativa* to elevated CO_2. *Global Change Biology* **6**: 919–930.

4

Earth's Vegetative Future

Key Findings

The key findings of this chapter are listed below.

- Rising atmospheric CO_2 and warming temperatures, both of which IPCC claims constitute a significant threat to the biosphere, benefited agriculture in the ancient past and in the twentieth century.

- Empirical studies suggest a future warming of the climate coupled with rising atmospheric CO_2 levels will boost global agricultural production and help meet the food needs of the planet's growing population.

- When model-based studies fully account for the growth-enhancing and water-conserving benefits of atmospheric CO_2 enrichment, they project significant gains for future agricultural production.

- The vigor of the terrestrial biosphere has been increasing with time, revealing a great greening of the planet that extends across the globe.

- Satellite-based analyses of net terrestrial primary productivity (NPP) reveal an increase of around 6–13% since the 1980s.

- There is no empirical evidence to support the model-based claim that future carbon uptake will diminish on a global scale due to rising temperatures.

- Earth's land surfaces were a net *source* of CO_2-carbon to the atmosphere until about 1940. From 1940 onward, the terrestrial biosphere has become, in the mean, an increasingly greater *sink* for CO_2-carbon.

- Over the past 50 years, global carbon uptake has doubled from 2.4 ± 0.8 billion tons in 1960 to 5.0 ± 0.9 billion tons in 2010.

- The observed greening of the Earth has occurred in spite of the many real and imagined assaults on the planet's vegetation over this time period, including fires, disease, outbreaks of pests, deforestation, and climatic changes (primarily in temperature and precipitation).

- The atmosphere's rising CO_2 content—which IPCC considers to be the chief culprit behind its concerns about the future of the biosphere—is most likely the primary cause of the observed greening trends.

- In the future, plants should be able to adjust their physiology to accommodate a warming of the magnitude and rate of rise typically predicted by climate models to accompany the projected future increase in atmospheric CO_2 content.

- The rise in the air's CO_2 concentration and its anti-transpiration effect, which improves plant water-use efficiency, are enhancing and will continue to enhance the vegetative productivity of Africa.

- The rise of the air's CO_2 concentration and temperature to their highest values of the past century enhanced the terrestrial vegetative productivity of all parts of Asia, including deserts, forests, grasslands, and the Tibetan Plateau.

- Evergreen vegetation, woody plants, and other plant life have increased across Australia over the past 200 years as a result of CO_2 enrichment.

- Over the last two decades of the twentieth century, Europe as a whole became greener and much of it is seeing an increase in woodlands due to the recent rise in atmospheric CO_2, which has tended to offset the detrimental effects of climate change in the region.

- Opposite the forecasts promulgated by the models used by IPCC, land-based plants of the Arctic and near-Arctic regions of North America are thriving, thanks in large part to the ongoing rise in the atmosphere's CO_2 concentration and global warming.

- Late twentieth-century increases in air temperature and atmospheric CO_2 concentration did not negatively affect plant communities in the eastern United States. Rather, the temperature and CO_2 increases significantly enhanced local and regional productivity, and there is little reason to think such enhancements will not continue throughout the foreseeable future.

- The late twentieth-century rise in temperature and atmospheric CO_2 concentrations improved the productivity of plant communities in the central region of the United States, notwithstanding model-based concerns to the contrary.

- The late twentieth-century rise in temperature and atmospheric CO_2 improved the productivity of plant communities in the western region of the United States, notwithstanding model-based projections of unprecedented ecological disaster due to rising temperatures and drought.

- Warmer temperatures and higher CO_2 concentrations are resulting in net primary productivity increasing across tropical South America, overcoming the effects of deforestation, forest fires, and incursions by human civilization into natural areas.

- It is likely the greening of the planet will continue in the future, even if the largest temperature increases predicted by the models occur, because the optimum temperature for plant growth and development typically rises with increasing levels of atmospheric CO_2. This response, coupled with expected increases in plant photosynthetic rates from the rise in the air's CO_2 concentration, is more than enough to compensate for any temperature-induced plant stress caused by global warming.

- Real-world observations reveal plants have many ways of adjusting to changes in climate in addition to their ability to spread from places of rising warmth to cooler habitats, and these observations suggest the planet's current assemblage of plants is likely to be around a good deal longer than many theoretical models have predicted.

- A major cause of biodiversity reductions is not rising atmospheric CO_2 concentrations, but instead the direct encroachment of man upon the world of nature. Anthropogenic global warming, to whatever extent it exists, is helping plants overcome these assaults and thrive despite the growing human presence.

- As good as things currently are for world agriculture, and as much better as they are expected to become as the atmospheric CO_2 content continues to rise, there may be additional substantial room for both natural selection and bioengineering to remove the constraints of low CO_2 adaptation in several important agricultural crops and thereby create novel genotypes able to exploit high CO_2 conditions to their—and our—advantage.

- The ongoing rise in atmospheric CO_2 content is likely exerting significant selection pressure on Earth's naturally occurring terrestrial plants, which should improve their performance in the face of various environmental stressors via the process of microevolution. Plants may be much better prepared than most scientists once thought to meet whatever climatic challenges, including global warming, the future may pose for them.

- Evidence continues to accumulate for substantial heritable variation of ecologically important plant traits, including root allocation, drought tolerance, and nutrient plasticity, which suggests rapid evolution based on epigenetic variation alone should be possible.

Introduction

A remarkable global phenomenon occurred throughout much of the twentieth century that the authors of IPCC's reports pretend never occurred despite hundreds of scholarly studies documenting its extent, causes, and consequences. The phenomenon is a gradual yet dramatic increase in biospheric productivity, or more simply, the greening of the Earth. According to IPCC's assumptions, theories, and models, this should not be occurring, indeed *cannot* be occurring. And yet, as this chapter will document, the evidence is overwhelming.

The aerial fertilization effect caused by the rise in CO_2 following the last deglaciation, combined with its transpiration-reducing effect that in turn led to a large increase in the water use efficiencies of the world's major C_4 founder crops, was the global trigger that made human agriculture possible. By dramatically increasing the yields of the first crops, that natural rise in CO_2 made modern civilization possible. Far from being a crisis, it was a miracle.

Fast-forward to the modern era and we are witnessing a rise in CO_2 levels similar to what occurred some 22,000 to 7,000 years ago. Once again, agricultural production is increasing throughout the world and across all types of landscapes, including plants and areas where improvements in human cultivation techniques cannot explain the improvement. Could global warming be good? In China, home to a fifth of all of humanity, Liu *et al.* (2004) report "all of China would benefit from climate change in most scenarios." Julien *et al.* (2006) say of the last two decades of the twentieth century, "Europe as a whole has a tendency to greening," and much of it is "seeing an increase in its wood land proportion." Extensive research has found the benefits of global warming on agriculture are occurring globally, across Asia, North America, and South America.

Nor is there evidence this greening is soon to end. Ballantyne *et al.* (2012) conclude, "although present predictions indicate diminished C uptake by the land and oceans in the coming century, with potentially serious consequences for the global climate, as of 2010 there is no empirical evidence that C uptake has started to diminish on the global scale." Their results clearly indicate just the opposite appears to be the case, with global carbon uptake doubling over the past half-century. Their research refutes the hypothesis of Canadell *et al.* (2007) and Raupach *et al.* (2008), who claimed to have detected a decreasing trend in the efficiency of the planet's carbon sinks, and it vindicates the many studies revealing an increasing greening of planet Earth.

IPCC feigns ignorance of this reality. Its authors seem still to be in the thrall of two authors who, two decades ago, wrote CO_2-induced changes in global climate were expected to occur "too fast for evolutionary processes such as natural selection to keep pace," and this phenomenon "could substantially enhance the probability of extinction of numerous species" (Root and Schneider (1993)). This famous but unsubstantiated declaration has pervaded the publications of IPCC ever since … but it never has been proven correct. It is more likely to be incorrect.

This chapter begins, in Section 4.1, with a

discussion of how the rise in CO_2 levels boosted food production globally in the past and how models that include the fertilizing effects of CO_2 suggest a future warming of the climate coupled with rising CO_2 levels will boost future global agricultural production, helping to meet the food needs of the planet's growing population. Section 4.2 surveys the extensive literature on the greening of the Earth, first presenting global studies and then studies focusing on specific continents, and finally studies that ask whether rising temperatures could check or offset the greening trend.

Section 4.3 reviews evidence on the impact of the rise in CO_2 levels on biodiversity and finds that impact to be positive. Similarly, Section 4.4. looks at the impact of the rise in CO_2 levels on plant extinctions and finds CO_2 makes extinctions less likely to occur. Finally, Section 4.5 asks whether plants can in fact evolve fast enough to adapt to a world with higher levels of CO_2, higher temperatures, and more drought. The evidence is clear that many plant species can make significant adaptations to changes in their environment in just a few generations.

References

Ballantyne, A.P., Alden, C.B., Miller, J.B., Tans, P.P., and White, J.W. 2012. Increase in observed net carbon dioxide uptake by land and oceans during the past 50 years. *Nature* **488**: 70–72.

Canadell, J.G., LeQuere, C., Raupach, M.R., Field, C.B., Buitenhuis, E.T,., Ciais, P., Conway, T.J., Gillett, N.P., Houghton, R.A., and Marland, G. 2007. Contributions to accelerating atmospheric CO_2 growth from economic activity, carbon intensity, and efficiency of natural sinks. *Proceedings of the National Academy of Sciences of the United States of America* **104**: 18,866–18,870.

Julien, Y., Sobrino, J.A., and Verhoef, W. 2006. Changes in land surface temperatures and NDVI values over Europe between 1982 and 1999. *Remote Sensing of Environment* **103**: 43–55.

Liu, H., Li, X., Fischer, G., and Sun, L. 2004. Study on the impacts of climate change on China's agriculture. *Climatic Change* **65**: 125–148.

Raupach, M.R., Canadell, J.G., and LeQuere, C. 2008. Anthropogenic and biophysical contributions to increasing atmospheric CO_2 growth rate and airborne fraction. *Biogeosciences* **5**: 1601–1613.

Root, T.L. and Schneider, S.H. 1993. Can large-scale climatic models be linked with multiscale ecological studies? *Conservation Biology* **7**: 256–270.

4.1 Agricultural and Food Production

According to IPCC, over the past century or so the atmosphere's temperature and CO_2 concentration have risen at rates (and to levels) not seen for millennia in the case of temperature and millions of years in the case of CO_2. Section 4.1.1 examines how the modern increase in temperature and CO_2 affected agriculture and food production in the past, and Section 4.1.2 provides an appraisal of how they might affect them in the future.

4.1.1 The Past

- Rising atmospheric CO_2 and warming temperatures, both of which IPCC claims constitute a significant threat to the biosphere, benefited agriculture in the ancient past and in the twentieth century.

According to Cunniff *et al.* (2008), "early agriculture was characterized by sets of primary domesticates or 'founder crops' that were adopted in several independent centers of origin," all at about the same time, and "this synchronicity suggests the involvement of a global trigger." Further noting Sage (1995) saw a causal link between this development and the rise in atmospheric CO_2 concentration that followed deglaciation (a jump from about 180 to 270 ppm), they hypothesized the aerial fertilization effect caused by the rise in CO_2 combined with its transpiration-reducing effect led to a large increase in the water use efficiencies of the world's major C_4 founder crops, and that this development was the global trigger that launched the agricultural enterprise.

To test this hypothesis, Cunniff *et al.* designed "a controlled environment experiment using five modern day representatives of wild C_4 crop progenitors, all 'founder crops' from a variety of independent centers." The five C_4 crops employed in their study were *Setaria viridis*, *Panicum miliaceum* var. *ruderale*, *Pennisetum violaceum*, *Sorghum arundinaceum*, and *Zea mays* subsp. *parviglumis*. They were grown individually in small pots filled with a 1:1 mix of washed sand and vermiculite for 40–50 days in growth chambers maintained at atmospheric CO_2 concentrations of either 180, 280, or 380 ppm, characteristic of glacial, post-glacial, and modern times, respectively.

Cunniff *et al.* report the "increase in CO_2 from glacial to postglacial levels [180 to 280 ppm] caused a significant gain in vegetative biomass of up to 40%," together with "a reduction in the transpiration rate via decreases in stomatal conductance of ~35%," which led to "a 70% increase in water use efficiency, and a much greater productivity potential in water-limited conditions." The five researchers write, "these key physiological changes could have greatly enhanced the productivity of wild crop progenitors after deglaciation ... improving the productivity and survival of these wild C_4 crop progenitors in early agricultural systems." They further note "the lowered water requirements of C_4 crop progenitors under increased CO_2 would have been particularly beneficial in the arid climatic regions where these plants were domesticated."

Expanding on their work two years later, Cunniff et al. (2010) conducted a second set of experiments designed to further study the physiological and yield responses to glacial and post-glacial atmospheric CO_2 concentrations of modern representatives of the wild crop progenitors, but this time they included an analysis of C_3 and C_4 cereals. Once again, their experimental work was conducted in the laboratory in controlled-environment chambers maintained at atmospheric CO_2 concentrations of either 180 or 280 ppm. Cunniff et al. report "both the C_3 and C_4 species responded positively to rising CO_2 from the glacial to post-glacial level," with vegetative biomass near-doubling and yield rising by 50% in the C_3 species, consistent with the findings of Polley et al. (1992) and Dippery et al. (1995), and with a 10–15% yield enhancement under well-watered conditions in the C_4 species, consistent with the findings of Polley et al. (1996), Ziska and Bunce (1997), and Ward et al. (1999). In the case of the C_4 species, which typically are found in semi-arid environments, they discovered the transpiration-reducing effect of atmospheric CO_2 enrichment had a considerably larger positive impact on plant growth and yield. They write, "this stronger response of photosynthesis to soil drying in the C_4 species could represent an important route for rising CO_2 to stimulate biomass accumulation in a semi-arid environment," citing Cunniff (2009).

Cunniff et al. state the data described in their paper "provide experimental support for Sage's CO_2 limitation hypothesis, showing that atmospheric conditions of the last glacial period would have placed direct and indirect limitations on the productivity of crop progenitors." Although they also note the hypothesis does not explain why the domestication of crops occurred, they opine "it does offer evidence-based explanations of why agriculture did not begin earlier." It is logical to conclude civilizations of the past, which could not have existed without agriculture, were largely made possible by the increase in the atmospheric CO_2 content that accompanied deglaciation, and that people of today are likewise indebted to this phenomenon as well as to the additional 100 ppm of CO_2 the atmosphere has subsequently acquired.

A number of studies reveal the important role of temperature in agricultural production. Following the centuries-long cold period of the Little Ice Age (sixteenth through nineteenth centuries), global agriculture production has benefited from the warmer climate of the twentieth and twenty-first centuries.

Shen et al. (2005), for example, derived and analyzed long-term (1901–2002) temporal trends in the agroclimate of Alberta, Canada, reporting "an earlier last spring frost, a later first fall frost, and a longer frost-free period are obvious all over the province." They also say May–August precipitation in Alberta increased 14% from 1901 to 2002, and annual precipitation exhibited a similar increasing trend, with most of the increase coming in the form of low-intensity events. They note "the area with sufficient corn heat units for corn production, calculated according to the 1973–2002 normal, had extended to the north by about 200–300 km, when compared with the 1913–32 normal, and by about 50–100 km, when compared with the 1943–72 normal."

These changes, Shen et al. write, "imply that Alberta agriculture has benefited from the last century's climate change" and "the potential exists to grow crops and raise livestock in more regions of Alberta than was possible in the past." They also state the increase in the length of the frost-free period "can greatly reduce the frost risks to crops and bring economic benefits to Alberta agricultural producers." In addition, they note the northward extension of the corn heat unit boundary sufficient for corn production "implies that Alberta farmers now have a larger variety of crops to choose from than were available previously." Shen et al. say "there is no hesitation for us to conclude that the warming climate and increased precipitation benefit agriculture in Alberta."

Qian et al. (2010) derived a set of agroclimatic indices representing Canadian climatic conditions, which they analyzed for trends sure to prove useful for agricultural production planning for many years to come. They used a homogenized temperature dataset consisting of daily maximum and minimum air temperatures obtained from 210 meteorological stations distributed across Canada that cover the period 1895–2007, along with an adjusted precipitation dataset developed at the Climate Research Division of Environment Canada. They found "a significant lengthening of the growing season due to a significantly earlier start and a significantly later end of the growing season," adding, "significant positive trends are also observed for effective growing degree-days and crop heat units at most locations across the country." Qian *et al.* report "the occurrence of extremely low temperatures had become less frequent during the non-growing season, implying a more favorable climate for overwinter survival," and "the total numbers of cool days, frost days, and killing-frost days within a growing season had a decreasing trend," so "crops may also be less vulnerable to cold stress and injury during the growing season." Their work revealed "extreme daily precipitation amounts and 10-day precipitation totals during the growing season have been increasing" and "significant trends associated with increased availability of water during the growing season are identified."

Clearly, the global warming that brought an end to the debilitating cold of the Little Ice Age and ushered the planet into the Current Warm Period is proving to be a benefit to Canada.

Hicke and Lobell (2004) calculated cropland net primary production (NPP) in the central part of the United States (South Dakota, Nebraska, Kansas, Missouri, Iowa, Minnesota, Wisconsin, and Illinois) using U.S. Department of Agriculture information together with crop-specific parameters that convert agronomic data into carbon fluxes for the period 1972–2001. Total cropland area exhibited no temporal trend over the study period, but "both NPP (flux per unit area) and P (spatially aggregated flux) increased during the study period (46 and 51%, respectively)."

These results indicate agricultural productivity in the central United States increased, and dramatically so, over the last three decades of the twentieth century, contrary to frequent claims that rising air temperatures and CO_2 concentrations will have negative effects on agriculture. Possible drivers of this increased agricultural productivity, according to Hicke and Lobell, include "improved cultivars, better fertilizer and pest management, more favorable climate, shifts to productive crop types, and economic influences (Duvick and Cassman, 1999; Evans, 1997; Lobell and Asner, 2003)."

Moonen *et al.* (2002) studied agriculturally important data collected from 1878 to 1999 on the outskirts of Pisa, Italy. Meteorological parameters routinely measured over this period were daily maximum, minimum, and mean air temperature plus daily rainfall. Agrometeorological parameters included the date of first autumn frost, date of last spring frost, length of growing season, number of

frost days, lengths of dry spells, potential evapotranspiration, reference evapotranspiration, soil moisture surplus, theoretical irrigation requirement, number of days with soil moisture surplus, and number of days with soil moisture deficit.

Moonen *et al.*'s analysis found "extremely cold temperature events have decreased and extremely warm temperature events have remained unchanged." They suggest these observations may be attributed to the increase in cloud cover that would be expected to occur in a warming world, since more clouds would reduce midday heating and thereby offset much, if not all, of the impetus for global warming during the hottest part of the day. At night, the increased cloud cover would enhance the atmosphere's greenhouse effect, thereby adding to the long-term warming trend. Moonen *et al.* conclude, "no negative effects can be expected on crop production from this point of view." They found a real "silver lining" in the latter of these cloud feedback phenomena: "the number of frost days per year had decreased significantly resulting in a decrease in risk of crop damage." Hence, they say the time of planting spring crops could be safely advanced by many days, noting the length of the growing season increased by fully 47 days during the period they studied.

With respect to rainfall, Moonen *et al.* found a somewhat analogous situation. On an annual basis, the incidence of extremely high rainfall events did not appear to have changed, but there was an increase in the incidence of very low rainfall events. The one exception to this rule on a seasonal basis was a decrease in high rainfall events in the spring, which might be expected to increase drought risk at that time of year. However, when the maximum length of dry spells was assessed on a seasonal basis, the only significant change observed was a lengthening of this parameter in the autumn. Autumn is the wettest season of the year in Pisa, Italy; the researchers conclude "no increased drought risk is to be expected."

The bottom line with respect to water in agriculture is the balance between what is received via rainfall and what is lost via evapotranspiration, as this difference is what determines the soil moisture balance. Although there was a downward trend in yearly rainfall at Pisa over the past 122 years (due to the decrease of high rainfall events in the spring), there also was a nearly offsetting downward trend in evapotranspiration (possibly induced by enhanced daytime cloud cover), so there were "no significant changes in soil water surplus or deficit on an annual basis." The scientists noted a significant decrease in the number of surplus soil moisture days in the autumn, but because autumn is the wettest season of the year, they write, "this indicates a reduced flooding risk in autumn, which could have positive effects on workability of the soil and imply a reduction of erosion."

Thus Moonen et al. conclude, concomitant with the warming of the Northern Hemisphere over the past 122 years, "extreme events in Pisa have not changed in a way that is likely to negatively affect crop production." More often than not, the changes demonstrated to have occurred seem to have had positive impacts on agriculture. Moonen et al. say "there is no doubt regarding the reality of the observed changes."

Fengjin and Lianchun (2011) write, "the damage from extreme low temperature events during the warm season in Northeast China is one of the major disasters that affect agriculture in China," noting "rice, sorghum, corn, soybeans, and other major crops are all vulnerable to low-temperature damage." They computed temporal trends in the frequency of occurrence of extreme minimum temperatures during Northeast China's warm season (May to September) during the years 1956–2005, concurrently calculating trends in the region's annual average near-surface air temperature, after which they compared the former dependent trend with the latter independent trend.

The two Beijing Climate Center researchers found for the 1956–2005 period, the overall rate of increase in the annual average temperature was 0.32°C per decade. But from 1970 to 2005 it was 0.49°C per decade, and "from 1990, the increasing trend in the annual average temperature has become much more significant." They further report, "the average number of extreme minimum temperature days during the warm season in the 1950s was 15.8 days; in the 1960s, the average was 16.5 days; in the 1970s, the average increased to 17.3 days, and this was similar in the 1980s." In the 1990s, the average number of extreme minimum temperature days "decreased sharply to 13.3 days," and since 2000 the number of extreme minimum temperature days has been "decreasing constantly with an average of 11.4 days."

As warming accelerated across Northeast China over the latter part of the past half-century, there was a concomitant decrease in the number of extreme minimum temperature events during that region's warm season. Fengjin and Lianchun state a "decreased frequency of extreme low temperatures over the past few decades has also been reported in other regions, e.g., Australia and New Zealand (Salinger et al., 2000; Stone et al., 1996)." The two Chinese scientists say the decrease in extreme minimum temperature events in response to the warmer temperatures of the past few decades has enabled farmers in Northeast China to harvest greater amounts of rice, sorghum, corn, soybeans, and other major crops than would otherwise have been possible.

Chen et al. (2011) report corn acreage in Northeast China—specifically Heilongjiang, Jilin, and Liaoning provinces—"accounts for 26.3% of the corn area in the country and accounts for about 29.4% of Chinese total corn grain production." They note the corn production of this region "plays a significant role in ensuring Chinese food security," and "knowledge of the potential effects of climate change on corn production in Northeast China will be highly valuable, not only for China but also for the world." Chen et al. "performed a multiple regression analysis to study the relationship between corn growth and the key climatic factors of temperature and precipitation during the crop growing season and during specific months in Northeast China from 1965 to 2008," to learn "which variables of climate change and which month in the crop growing season were associated with yield variability over this 44-year period."

The six scientists determined the major climatic factor affecting corn yield in Northeast China is daily minimum temperature, particularly in the months of May and September. They found a warming of 1.0°C in the mean daily minimum temperature of either of these months may enhance corn yield by 303 kg/ha (May) or 284 kg/ha (September). They report growth duration—defined as the period from sowing to harvest (days to maturity)—rose by six days in Liaoning province and by seven days in Jilin and Heilongjiang provinces during the years 1950–2008, which encompassed the period of 1965–2008, when daily minimum temperature rose at a rate of 0.44°C per decade. They conclude, "in order to fully exploit the positive effects of global warming on corn production, new varieties should be adapted to the longer growing season." This adjustment could be described as a good example of man and nature working together to ensure maximum food security for a significant portion of humanity.

Magrin et al. (2005) evaluated twentieth-century changes in climate and the yields of the chief crops (soybean, wheat, maize, and sunflower) of nine areas of contrasting environment in Argentina's Pampas region, which accounts for more than 90% of the country's grain production. After determining low-frequency upward trends in yield due to improvements in crop genetics and management techniques, as well as the aerial fertilization effect of the historical increase in the air's CO_2 concentration, they used annual yield anomalies and concomitant climatic anomalies to develop relations describing the effects of precipitation, temperature, and solar radiation on crop yields, to determine the effects of long-term changes in these climatic parameters on Argentina's agriculture.

Although noting "technological improvements account for most of the observed changes in crop yields during the second part of the 20th century"—which totaled 110% for maize, 56% for wheat, and 102% for sunflower—Magrin *et al.* report changes in climate between the periods 1950–1970 and 1970–1999 led to yield increases of 38% in soybean, 18% in maize, 13% in wheat, and 12% in sunflower.

These studies suggest rising atmospheric CO_2 concentrations and warmer temperatures—both of which IPCC claims to constitute significant threats to the biosphere, having reached levels IPCC describes as unprecedented over the past one to two millennia—were far from problematic for agriculture.

References

Chen, C., Lei, C., Deng, A., Qian, C., Hoogmoed, W., and Zhang, W. 2011. Will higher minimum temperatures increase corn production in northeast China? An analysis of historical data over 1965–2008. *Agricultural and Forest Meteorology* **151**: 1580–1588.

Cunniff, J. 2009. The Roles of Atmospheric Carbon Dioxide and Plant Ecological Traits in the Origin of Agriculture. PhD Thesis, University of Sheffield, United Kingdom.

Cunniff, J., Charles, M., Jones, G., and Osborne, C.P. 2010. Was low atmospheric CO_2 a limiting factor in the origin of agriculture? *Environmental Archaeology* **15**: 113–123.

Cunniff, J., Osborne, C.P., Ripley, B.S., Charles, M., and Jones, G. 2008. Response of wild C_4 crop progenitors to subambient CO_2 highlights a possible role in the origin of agriculture. *Global Change Biology* **14**: 576–587.

Dippery, J.K., Tissue, D.T., Thomas, R.B., and Strain, B.R. 1995. Effects of low and elevated CO_2 on C_3 and C_4 annuals. I. Growth and biomass allocation. *Oecologia* **101**: 13–20.

Duvick, D.N. and Cassman, K.G. 1999. Post-green revolution trends in yield potential of temperate maize in the north-central United States. *Crop Science* **39**: 1622–1630.

Evans, L.T. 1997. Adapting and improving crops: The endless task. *Philosophical Transactions of the Royal Society of London, Series B* **352**: 901–906.

Fengjin, X. and Lianchun, S. 2011. Analysis of extreme low-temperature events during the warm season in Northeast China. *Natural Hazards* **58**: 1333–1344.

Hicke, J.A. and Lobell, D.B. 2004. Spatiotemporal patterns of cropland area and net primary production in the central United States estimated from USDA agricultural information. *Geophysical Research Letters* **31**: 10.1029/ 2004GL 020927.

Lobell, D.B. and Asner, G.P. 2003. Climate and management contributions to recent trends in US agricultural yields. *Science* **299**: 1032.

Magrin, G.O., Travasso, M.I., and Rodriguez, G.R. 2005. Changes in climate and crop production during the 20th century in Argentina. *Climatic Change* **72**: 229–249.

Moonen, A.C., Ercoli, L., Mariotti, M., and Masoni, A. 2002. Climate change in Italy indicated by agro-meteorological indices over 122 years. *Agricultural and Forest Meteorology* **111**: 13–27.

Polley, H.W., Johnson, H.B., and Mayeux, H.S. 1992. Growth and gas-exchange of oats (*Avena sativa*) and wild mustard (*Brassica kaber*) at sub-ambient CO_2 concentrations. *International Journal of Plant Sciences* **153**: 453–461.

Polley, H.W., Johnson, H.B., Mayeux, H.S., Brown, D.A., and White, J.W.C. 1996. Leaf and plant water use efficiency of C4 species grown at glacial to elevated CO_2 concentrations. *International Journal of Plant Sciences* **157**: 164–170.

Qian, B., Zhang, X., Chen, K., Feng, Y., and O'Brien, T. 2010. Observed long-term trends for agroclimatic conditions in Canada. *Journal of Applied Meteorology and Climatology* **49**: 604–618.

Sage, R.F. 1995. Was low atmospheric CO_2 during the Pleistocene a limiting factor for the origin of agriculture? *Global Change Biology* **1**: 93–106.

Salinger, M.J., Stigter, C.J., and Das, H.P. 2000. Agrometeorological adaptation strategies to increasing climate variability and climate change. *Agricultural and Forest Meteorology* **103**: 167-184.

Shen, S.S.P., Yin, H., Cannon, K., Howard, A., Chetner, S., and Karl, T.R. 2005. Temporal and spatial changes of the agroclimate in Alberta, Canada, from 1901 to 2002. *Journal of Applied Meteorology* **44**: 1090–1105.

Stone, R., Nicholls, N., and Hammer, G. 1996. Frost in NE Australia: trends and influence phases of Southern Oscillation. *Journal of Climate* **9**: 1896-1909.

Ward, J.K., Tissue, D.T., Thomas, R.B., and Strain, B.R.

1999. Comparative responses of model C_3 and C_4 plants to drought in low and elevated CO_2. *Global Change Biology* **5**: 857–867.

Ziska, L.H. and Bunce, J.A. 1997. Influence of increasing carbon dioxide concentration on the photosynthetic and growth stimulation of selected C_4 crops and weeds. *Photosynthesis Research* **54**: 199–208.

4.1.2 The Future

Several researchers have expressed concerns about a looming food production crisis on the horizon, suggesting just a few decades from now the ever-growing human population of the planet will need a near-doubling of present-day agricultural production. One example is the brief Perspective article published in *Science*, where Running (2012) resurrected shades of Meadows *et al.*'s 1972 treatise on *The Limits to Growth*.

Noting "terrestrial plant production is the foundation of the biospheric carbon cycle" and that "water and atmospheric CO_2 are transformed into plant carbohydrate matter with the help of solar energy," Running states this plant matter "sustains the global food web and becomes the source of food, fiber and fuel for humanity." A problem Running sees, however, is that for more than 30 years, global net primary production (NPP) has "stayed near 53.6 Pg per year, with only ~1 Pg of inter-annual variability," citing two studies of which he was a coauthor (Nemani *et al.*, 2003; Zhao and Running, 2010). He thus speculates, "if global NPP is fixed by planetary constraints, then no substantial increase in plant growth may be possible."

If true, this would indeed have catastrophic consequences, for it is almost universally agreed, as Running writes, "the projected 40% increase in human population by 2050 CE, combined with goals to substantially improve standards of living for the poorest 5 billion people on Earth, implies at least a doubling of future resource demand by 2050." The most important of these resources is food.

But is a doubling of food production by mid-century realistic? Agriculture already consumes 38% of the world's land surface, and Running notes "many analyses now conclude that freshwater use for irrigation has already reached a planetary boundary." Furthermore, with "massive river pollution and ocean anaerobic dead zones," he states, "if anything, future increases in NPP must be achieved with less, not more, irrigation and fertilizer use." Others have noted additional challenges, such as Tilman *et al.* (2009)

noting "land previously allocated to food production is transformed to bioenergy production, raising food prices for the people who can least afford it."

Has the planet reached a limit to its growth? In a 2012 paper published in *Nature*, titled "Increase in observed net carbon dioxide uptake by land and oceans during the past 50 years," Ballantyne *et al.* (2012) suggest it has not. The five U.S. scientists state their mass balance analysis shows "net global carbon uptake has increased significantly by about 0.05 billion tonnes of carbon per year and that global carbon uptake doubled, from 2.4 ± 0.8 to 5.0 ± 0.9 billion tonnes per year, between 1960 and 2010." They conclude, "there is no empirical evidence that carbon uptake has started to diminish on the global scale." In fact, as their results indicate, just the opposite appears to be the case, with global carbon uptake actually *doubling* over the past half-century.

There are many reasons why this doubling has occurred: breeding of better crop varieties that are higher-yielding, more competitive with weeds, less tasty to insect pests, more nutritious, and more drought-resistant, as well as smarter ways of farming, improved technologies, and the worldwide aerial fertilization and transpiration-reducing effects of the historical and still-ongoing rise in the atmosphere's CO_2 content. The latter two phenomena benefit agriculture and nature simultaneously.

Also concerned about adequately meeting the food needs of a growing world population, Parry and Hawkesford (2010) note "food production needs to increase 50% by 2030 and double by 2050 to meet projected demands." They say while the demand for food is increasing, production is progressively being limited by "non-food uses of crops and cropland," such as the production of biofuels. In their UK homeland, for example, they note, "by 2015 more than a quarter of wheat grain may be destined for bioenergy production," which is both sad and puzzling, as they also point out "currently, at least one billion people are chronically malnourished and the situation is deteriorating," with more people "hungrier now than at the start of the millennium."

The two researchers turn their discussion to photosynthesis, the all-important process by which plants "convert light energy into chemical energy, which is used in the assimilation of atmospheric CO_2 and the formation of sugars that fuel growth and yield." These phenomena make this natural and life-sustaining process "a major target for improving crop productivity both via conventional breeding and biotechnology," they write.

Next to a plant's need for carbon dioxide is its

need for water, the availability of which, in the words of Parry and Hawkesford, "is the major constraint on world crop productivity." They state, "since more than 80% of the [world's] available water is used for agricultural production, there is little opportunity to use additional water for crop production," because as populations increase, "the demand to use water for other activities also increases." Hence they conclude, "a real and immediate challenge for agriculture is to increase crop production with less available water."

They provide an example of a success story: the Australian wheat variety Drysdale, which gained fame "because it uses water more efficiently." This valued characteristic was achieved "by slightly restricting stomatal aperture and thereby the loss of water from the leaves." They note this ability "reduces photosynthetic performance slightly under ideal conditions," but it enables plants to "have access to water later in the growing season thereby increasing total photosynthesis over the life of the crop."

Of course, Drysdale is but one variety of one crop, and the ideal goal would be to get nearly all varieties of all crops to use water more efficiently. That goal in fact can be reached without doing anything new, because allowing atmospheric CO_2 concentrations to rise will cause the vast majority of plants to reduce the apertures of their stomata and thereby lower the rate at which water vapor escapes from them into the air. The result is even better than that produced by the breeding of Drysdale, because the extra CO_2 in the air more than overcomes the photosynthetic reduction that results from the partial closure of plant stomatal apertures, allowing even more yield to be produced per unit of water transpired in the process.

Human ingenuity can make the situation better still, by breeding and selecting crop varieties that perform better under higher atmospheric CO_2 concentrations than the varieties people currently rely upon, and by employing various technological means of altering them. Humanity can succeed even though "the United Nations Millennium Development Goal of substantially reducing the world's hungry by 2015 will not be met," as Parry and Hawkesford conclude. This truly seems to be the path to take, as they write "at least one billion people are chronically malnourished and the situation is deteriorating," with more people "hungrier now than at the start of the millennium."

Ainsworth *et al.* (2008) argue for breeding major crop varieties upon which the world depends for food to best take advantage of the ongoing rise in the atmospheric CO_2 content. The international consortium of 32 scientists from 12 countries notes, "the growing world population, increasing demands for grains for animal feeds, land loss to urban expansion and demand for bioenergy production are exerting more and more pressure on global agricultural productivity." They state, "a major challenge for plant biologists, agronomists and breeders will be to provide germplasm and seed material that maximize future crop production," particularly in the context of rising atmospheric CO_2 concentrations that provide "a unique opportunity to increase the productivity of C_3 crops." They say "only a fraction of available germplasm of crops has been tested for CO_2 responsiveness," and "further research is needed to elucidate the mechanisms of yield response to CO_2, to assess the genetic diversity available for improving responsiveness and to devise efficient schemes for selection for adaptation to rising ambient CO_2, whether based on conventional plant breeding or systems biology approaches for selecting and engineering improved genetics."

The first step in meeting these objectives, according to the researchers, "is to create facilities for field screening the yield response to elevated CO_2 across a wide range of germplasm," and doing so under "conditions and management that reflect dominant agronomic practices and provide as natural an environment as possible." They recommend free air CO_2 enrichment (FACE) experimentation, which these scientists say meets many of these criteria and presents a minimally obtrusive interaction with the natural environment.

Although FACE systems are often considered expensive to construct and operate, Ainsworth *et al.* note "the net cost is compensated for by economies of scale, and the cost per unit ground area is considerably less than alternative systems." This is very important, as they explain, because "the new research requires investigating large numbers of genotypes," and "to investigate the association of CO_2 responsiveness with a single quantitative trait locus mapping population, approximately 150 inbred lines would need to be investigated."

The world-renowned group of scientists concludes, "because it may take 10–15 years to move from discovery of new advantaged genetics to commercial cultivars of annual grain crops, developing a robust strategy and supporting the planned work with the best possible facilities should be an urgent priority."

Zhu *et al.* (2010) embrace an alternative strategy for boosting agricultural production. They say meeting the global increase in agricultural demand during this century "is predicted to require a doubling of global production," but "the world has limited capacity to sustainably expand cropland," and this capacity is actually "shrinking in many developed countries." The three researchers contend, "meeting future increases in demand will have to come from a near doubling of productivity on a land area basis." They suggest "a large contribution will have to come from improved photosynthetic conversion efficiency," for which they estimate "at least a 50% improvement will be required to double global production."

The researchers focus on photosynthetic conversion efficiency because experimental evidence has found increases in the atmosphere's CO_2 concentration boost the photosynthetic rates of nearly all plants, and those rate increases generally lead to equivalent increases in plant productivity on a land-area basis. They examined the prospects for boosting photosynthetic conversion efficiency in an entirely different way: genetically, without increasing the atmosphere's CO_2 content.

The three scientists write, "Improving photosynthetic conversion efficiency will require a full suite of tools including breeding, gene transfer, and synthetic biology in bringing about the designed alteration to photosynthesis." For some of these "near-term" endeavors, they write, "implementation is limited by technical issues that can be overcome by sufficient investment." But a number of "mid-term" goals could take 20 years to achieve, and "even when these improvements are achieved, it may take an additional 10–20 years to bring such innovations to farms in commercial cultivars at adequate scale." And they write of still longer-term goals for which "too little of the science has been undertaken to identify what needs to be altered to effect an increase in yield." They acknowledge some of what they envision may not even be possible, such as developing a form of rubisco that exhibits a significant decrease in oxygenation activity, or designing C_3 crops to utilize the C_4 form of photosynthetic metabolism. The focus of Ainsworth et al. (2008) appears to be a far better path to pursue: conducting research to "elucidate the mechanisms of yield response to CO_2, to assess the genetic diversity available for improving responsiveness and to devise efficient schemes for selection for adaptation to rising ambient CO_2, whether based on conventional plant breeding or systems biology approaches for selecting and engineering improved genetics."

Godfray et al. (2010) note, "more than one in seven people today still do not have access to sufficient protein and energy from their diet and even more suffer some form of micronutrient malnourishment," citing the FAO (2009). They write, although "increases in production will have an important part to play" in correcting this problem and keeping it from worsening in the future, mankind "will be constrained by the finite resources provided by the Earth's lands, oceans and atmosphere." This set of difficulties they describe at the end of their review as a "perfect storm."

The first question they ask in regard to how mankind might successfully navigate this highly restricted terrain is: "How can more food be produced sustainably?" They say the primary solution to food shortages of the past had been "to bring more land into agriculture and to exploit new fish stocks," but they quickly note there is precious little remaining of either of these resources. They conclude, "the most likely scenario is that more food will need to be produced from the same or less land," because "we must avoid the temptation to sacrifice further the Earth's already hugely depleted biodiversity for easy gains in food production, not only because biodiversity provides many of the public goods upon which mankind relies, but also because we do not have the right to deprive future generations of its economic and cultural benefits."

The key to meeting these diverse requirements simultaneously is in Godfray et al.'s statement, "greater water and nutrient use efficiency, as well as tolerance of abiotic stress, are likely to become of increasing importance." As discussed previously, rising carbon dioxide can bring about all of these changes in mankind's crops. Rising concentrations of atmospheric CO_2 increase the photosynthetic prowess of essentially all plants, while generally reducing the rate at which they transfer water from the soil to the air. In addition, an increase of CO_2 in the atmosphere tends to enhance the efficiency with which plants utilize nutrients in constructing their tissues and producing the edible portions that essentially all of Earth's animals and humans depend on.

Each of the important benefits noted above has been discussed in great detail in the preceding chapters of this volume. In the material that follows, we limit our discussion to studies that directly imply general trends regarding these global benefits. Section 4.1.2.1 examines the findings of several empirical studies from which trends in future agricultural production can be inferred, and Section 4.1.2.2 presents a review of several model-based studies that shed additional light on the subject.

References

Ainsworth, E.A., Beier, C., Calfapietra, C., Ceulemans, R., Durand-Tardif, M., Farquhar, G.D., Godbold, D.L., Hendrey, G.R., Hickler, T., Kaduk, J., Karnosky, D.F., Kimball, B.A., Korner, C., Koornneef, M., LaFarge, T., Leakey, A.D.B., Lewin, K.F., Long, S.P., Manderscheid, R., McNeil, D.L., Mies, T.A., Miglietta, F., Morgan, J.A., Nagy, J., Norby, R.J., Norton, R.M., Percy, K.E., Rogers, A., Soussana, J.-F., Stitt, M., Weigel, H.-J., and White, J.W. 2008. Next generation of elevated [CO₂] experiments with crops: a critical investment for feeding the future world. *Plant, Cell and Environment* **31**: 1317–1324.

Ballantyne, A.P., Alden, C.B., Miller, J.B., Tans, P.P., and White, J.W. 2012. Increase in observed net carbon dioxide uptake by land and oceans during the past 50 years. *Nature* **488**: 70–72.

FAO. 2009. *State of Food Insecurity in the World 2009*. Food and Agriculture Organization, Rome, Italy.

Godfray, H.C.J., Beddington, J.R., Crute, I.R., Haddad, L., Lawrence, D., Muir, J.F., Pretty, J., Robinson, S., Thomas, S.M., and Toulmin, C. 2010. Food security: The challenge of feeding 9 billion people. *Science* **327**: 812–818.

Meadows, D.H., Meadows, D.L., Randers, J., and Behrens III, W.W. 1972. *The Limits to Growth*. Universe Books, New York, New York, USA.

Nemani, R.R., Keeling, C.D., Hashimoto, H., Jolly, W.M., Piper, S.C., Tucker, C.J., Myneni, R.B., and Running. S.W. 2003. Climate-driven increases in global terrestrial net primary production from 1982 to 1999. *Science* **300**: 1560–1563.

Parry, M.A.J. and Hawkesford, M.J. 2010. Food security: increasing yield and improving resource use efficiency. *Proceedings of the Nutrition Society* **69**: 592–600.

Running, S.W. 2012. A measurable planetary boundary for the biosphere. *Science* **337**: 1458–1459.

Tilman, D., Socolow, R., Foley, J.A., Hill, J., Larson, E., Lynd, L., Pacala, S., Reilly, J., Searchinger, T., Somerville, C., and Williams, R. 2009. Beneficial biofuels: The food, energy, and environment trilemma. *Science* **325**: 270–271.

Zhao, M. and Running, S.W. 2010. Drought-induced reduction in global terrestrial net primary production from 2000 through 2009. *Science* **329**: 940–943.

Zhu, X.-G., Long, S.P., and Ort, D.R. 2010. Improving photosynthetic efficiency for greater yield. *Annual Review of Plant Biology* **61**: 235–261.

4.1.2.1 Empirical Studies

- Empirical studies suggest a future warming of the climate coupled with rising atmospheric CO_2 levels will boost global agricultural production and help meet the food needs of the planet's growing population.

As discussed in the preceding chapters of this volume, numerous studies attest to the growth-enhancing, water-conserving, and stress-alleviating benefits of CO_2 enrichment for plants. In the present subsection, therefore, we limit our discussion to studies from which we can infer general trends in future agricultural production.

According to Tian *et al.* (2012), "more than 20% of the world's food consumers depend on wheat (*Triticum aestivum* L.), which is produced on an area of over 200 million hectares worldwide (Ortiz *et al.*, 2008)." They note "winter wheat area accounts for more than 80% of this total," and "it is typically grown in the seasons of winter and spring where warming is mainly anticipated." China, the writers note, is the world's largest producer of winter wheat, and more than 70% of the crop is sown in the country's eastern provinces on the Yangtze Delta Plain.

Tian *et al.* "conducted a five-year field warming experiment since 2004 with a facility of Free Air Temperature Increase (FATI) in Nanjing, Jiangsu province," in which their objectives were "to investigate the actual responses of winter wheat phenophase, biomass production and grain yield to anticipated warming [~1.5°C] under field conditions" where "there were no water and nitrogen limitations for winter wheat growth, which is common in East China." They studied *Triticum aestivum* L. cv Yangmai 11, a local cultivar having a "high yield potential."

The 1.5°C increase in temperature significantly advanced crop phenophases, leading to a reduction in the length of the entire growth period of about 10 days, with the result that grain yields rose due to "the mitigation of low temperature limitation during the pre-anthesis phase and to the avoidance of hot-dry stress during the post-anthesis phase." The researchers found the areas of flag leaves and total green leaves at anthesis, as well as the 1,000-grain weight of the plants, were 36.0, 19.2, and 5.9% higher in the warmed plots than in the unaltered control, respectively. The net effect of these warmth-induced changes was a mean grain yield increase of 16.3%, and they therefore conclude "anticipated warming may facilitate winter wheat production in East China."

Ortiz *et al.* (2008) reviewed some of the approaches for ameliorating the oft-predicted negative impacts climate change may have on wheat production in some of the most important wheat growing areas of the world. They write, "to adapt and mitigate the climate change effects on wheat supplies for the poor, germplasm scientists and agronomists are developing heat-tolerant wheat germplasm, as well as cultivars better adapted to conservation agriculture," noting these encouraging results include "identifying sources of alleles for heat tolerance and their introgression into breeding populations through conventional methods and biotechnology." They report "wheat geneticists and physiologists are also assessing wild relatives of wheat as potential sources of genes with inhibitory effects on soil nitrification." This activity could lead to significantly reduced emissions of nitrous oxide from agricultural soils and thereby shrink the impetus for global warming provided by this powerful trace greenhouse gas, which molecule-for-molecule is about 300 times more radiatively active than CO_2. Ortiz *et al.* conclude important technology and knowledge will ultimately flow to farmers and enable them "to face the risks associated with climate change."

Bunce (2008) grew adequately fertilized plants of four varieties of the common garden bean (*Phaseolus vulgaris*)—Matterhorn (a great northern bean), Jaguar (a black bean), Red Hawk (a kidney bean), and Brown Beauty (a snap bean)—from seed to maturity under standard field conditions at Beltsville, Maryland (USA) in open-top chambers. They made photosynthetic measurements of mature upper-canopy leaves in full sunlight at midday during the pod-filling stages of four growing seasons and determined final seed yields and other plant characteristics at harvest. They found an extra 180 ppm of CO_2 in the CO_2-enriched chambers (a concentration increase of close to 50% during daylight hours) resulted in a mean long-term stimulation of midday net photosynthesis of approximately 18% in the Matterhorn and Jaguar bean varieties, and an increase of twice that much (36%) in the Red Hawk and Brown Beauty cultivars. In terms of dry mass seed yield, the Matterhorn variety experienced a CO_2-induced increase of about 39%, followed by Red Hawk at 21%, Brown Beauty at 18%, and Jaguar with a 10% decline in seed yield. As Bunce reports, "the highest yielding variety at ambient CO_2 [Jaguar] was out-yielded by a different variety at elevated CO_2 [Matterhorn]."

These observations make it clear there is significant variability in seed yield response to atmospheric CO_2 enrichment among the four bean varieties tested by Bunce. In addition, it is equally clear there was no *a priori* way of knowing which of the four cultivars would respond best to an increase in atmospheric CO_2 concentration, or that one would actually respond negatively. Bunce's experiment demonstrates the great need to perform a host of such studies on the planet's most important crop plants, to identify which of their many varieties should be selected for additional crop breeding work. That is the only way to take full advantage of the significant increase in the atmosphere's CO_2 concentration that will occur over the next several decades.

In a standard paddy-culture FACE experiment conducted at Yangzhou, Jiangsu, China, during the years 2004–2006, Yang *et al.* (2009) grew a two-line inter-subspecific hybrid rice variety (Liangyoupeijiu) at ambient and elevated atmospheric CO_2 concentrations of 376 and 568 ppm, respectively, at two levels of field nitrogen (N) application—low N (12.5 g N m^{-2}) and high N (25 g N m^{-2})—while measuring numerous aspects of crop growth, development, and final yield. The eight Chinese scientists found the 51% increase in atmospheric CO_2 concentration increased the final grain yield of the low N rice crop by 28% and that of the high N rice crop by 32%. As a result, and in light of the findings of two prior rice FACE experiments (Kim *et al.*, 2003; Yang *et al.*, 2006), they conclude "hybrid rice appears to profit much more from CO_2 enrichment than inbred rice cultivars (c. +13%)." Yang *et al.* describe Liangyoupeijiu as "one of the most popular 'super' hybrid rice varieties in China (Peng *et al.*, 2004)."

Shimono *et al.* (2007) say lodging—the environmental beating down of a crop—"can occur under heavy rains and strong winds," and this phenomenon "decreases canopy photosynthesis due to self-shading (Setter *et al.*, 1997) and disturbs the translocation of carbon and nutrients to the rice grains (Hitaka and Kobayashi, 1961), resulting in lower yield and poor grain quality." They note Setter *et al.* (1997) found a moderate degree of lodging reduced canopy height by 35% and decreased yield by about 20%, whereas severe lodging reduced canopy height by 75% and decreased yield by up to 50%.

Shimono *et al.* designed a free-air CO_2-enrichment experiment to determine what effect the ongoing rise in the atmosphere's CO_2 content might have on lodging in rice plants, growing the cultivar Akitakomachi in paddy fields under three nitrogen (N) fertilization regimes—low N (6 g N m^{-2}), medium N (9 g N m^{-2}), and high N (15 g N m^{-2})—at two season-long 24-hour mean CO_2 concentrations—375 ppm (ambient) and 562 ppm (enriched)—measuring the degree of naturally occurring lodging at the time of grain maturity on a scale of 0–5, based on the bending angles of the stems at 18° intervals, where 0 = 0° from the vertical, 1 = 1°–18°, 2 = 19°–36°, 3 = 37°–54°, 4 = 55°–72°, and 5 = 73°–90°.

The six scientists report lodging was significantly higher under high N than under medium and low N. The lodging experienced in the high N treatment "was alleviated by elevated CO_2," because the lowest internodes of the rice stems "became significantly shorter and thicker under elevated CO_2," which likely "strengthened the rice culms against the increased lodging that occurred under high N." They note the reduced lodging experienced under elevated CO_2 in the high N treatment increased the grain-ripening percentage of the rice by 4.5% per one-unit decrease in lodging score.

Shimono *et al.* note there is concern that in order "to increase rice yield under projected future CO_2 levels, N fertilization must be increased to meet increased plant demand for this nutrient as a result of increased growth rates," but greater N fertilization might enhance lodging, thereby defeating the purpose of the fertilization. Their study found "elevated CO_2 could significantly decrease lodging under high N fertilization, thereby increasing the ripening percentage and grain yield," in what amounts to another CO_2-induced success story for what the researchers called "the most important crop for feeding the world's population."

Lou *et al.* (2008) note there is a pressing need to identify genotypes that produce maximum grain yields under projected future atmospheric CO_2 levels. They grew four different rice cultivars—Dular (a traditional indica variety), IR72 (an improved indica variety), Koshihikari (a temperate japonica variety), and IR65598 (a new variety not yet released to farmers at that time)—in Japan in growth chambers in submerged pots filled with a fertilized soil at two atmospheric CO_2 concentrations: ambient (~370 ppm) and elevated (~570 ppm). They found the extra 200 ppm of CO_2 reduced the ultimate grain yield of Dular (by 0.7%) and increased it for IR72 (by 8.0%), Koshihikari (by 13.4%), and IR65598 (by 17.7%).

Roy *et al.* (2012) write "an average annual increase in grain production of 44 million metric tons is required to meet the food demands of the world by 2050," citing Tester and Langridge (2010), and they note "the predicted 2.0°C increase in air temperature by the end of 2050 (IPCC, 2007) might lead to a 20–40% decrease in cereal yields," citing Lele (2010). To assess this situation from an experiment-based perspective, the five researchers from the Central Rice Research Institute of India conducted a three-year open-top-chamber field study to observe the effects of elevated atmospheric CO_2 concentration (550 vs. ambient 390 ppm), as well as elevated temperature (T, 2°C above ambient temperature), on dry matter production, carbon (C), and nitrogen (N) concentrations and their allocation in a tropical rice cultivar (cv. *Naveen*).

In the elevated CO_2/normal temperature treatment, their experiment revealed: dry matter accumulation in the aboveground portion of the rice plants was enhanced by 17.7% at maturity; root biomass, leaf area index, and net carbon assimilation rates increased by 28, 19, and 40%, respectively; grain yield was significantly higher (22.6%); the net carbon yield increased by 23.3%; and nitrogen allocation increased significantly in leaf (13%), stem (14%), and panicle (17%) at maturity.

In the elevated CO_2/elevated temperature treatment, the found: dry matter accumulation in the aboveground portion of the rice plants was enhanced by 18.1% at maturity; root biomass, leaf area index, and net carbon assimilation rates also increased significantly; grain yield was significantly higher (19.6%); the net carbon yield increased by 24.2%; and nitrogen allocation increased significantly in leaf (13%), stem (14%), and panicle (17%) at maturity.

Jin *et al.* (2009) conducted a CO_2 enrichment study in three pairs of greenhouses placed over a uniform soil surface, in which they planted celery (*Apium graveolens* L.), leaf lettuce (*Lactuca virosa* L.), stem lettuce (*Lactuca saiva* L.), oily sowthistle (*Sonchus oleraceus* L.), and Chinese cabbage (*Brassica chinensis* L.). In response to a slightly more-than-doubling of atmospheric CO_2 content, "the average percentage of yield increases of all three sites were 270%, 257%, 87%, 140% and 227% for celery, leaf lettuce, stem lettuce, oily sowthistle, and Chinese cabbage, respectively." The extra CO_2 also increased the concentration of vitamin C in all five species, "by 13%, 39%, 25%, 72%, and 37% for celery, leaf lettuce, stem lettuce, oily sowthistle, and Chinese cabbage, respectively."

Vanaja *et al.* (2010) write, "food grain requirements of India (both human and cattle) are estimated at 300 Mt in 2020," citing Sinha *et al.* (1998), and they note "grain legumes are one of the mainstays of the drylands, as these crops provide much needed nutritional security in the form of proteins to the predominant vegetarian populations of India and also the world." They further state legumes—of which pigeon peas are an important example—"have the potential to maximize the benefit of elevated CO_2 by matching [CO_2-]stimulated photosynthesis with increased N_2 fixation," citing Rogers *et al.* (2009).

Vanaja *et al.* grew pigeon peas (*Cajanus cajan* L. Millsp.) from seed to maturity out-of-doors at Hyderabad (India) in open-top chambers maintained at atmospheric CO_2 concentrations of either 370 or 700 ppm (ambient or enriched, respectively), after which they harvested them and measured a number of pertinent productivity parameters. The team of nine Indian scientists from the country's Central Research Institute for Dryland Agriculture report "total biomass recorded an improvement of 91.3%, grain yield 150.1% and fodder yield 67.1%." They write, "the major contributing components for improved grain yield under elevated CO_2 were number of pods, number of seeds and test weight," which exhibited increases of 97.9%, 119.5%, and 7.2%, respectively. In addition, the found "a significant positive increase of harvest index at elevated CO_2 with an increment of 30.7% over ambient values," which they attribute to the crop's "improved pod set and seed yield under enhanced CO_2 concentration." These findings, Vanaja *et al.* conclude, illustrate the importance of pigeon peas for "sustained food with nutritional security under a climate change scenario."

Rosenthal *et al.* (2012) write, "given the projections that future food production will need to double to meet the global demand by 2050 (Lobell *et al.*, 2008; Godfray *et al.*, 2010; Tilman *et al.*, 2011), there is an urgent need to assess the impact of climate drivers on crops of food insecure regions." They note, "more than 900 million people are undernourished and nearly 90% live in Sub-Saharan Africa, Asia, and the Pacific," citing the United Nations Food and Agriculture Organization (FAO, 2010). The eight researchers also write, "in Sub-Saharan Africa, the starchy root tuber crop cassava accounts for almost two-thirds of the direct human caloric intake," and in areas where drought is recurrent, "cassava is harvested when other crops fail (FAO, 2005)," adding, cassava "provides food security during armed conflicts when above-ground crops are destroyed, as the cassava tuber remains viable below ground for up to three years (Cock, 1982; Lebot, 2009)."

Rosenthal *et al.* report a recent greenhouse study on cassava found decreased yields at elevated CO_2, and the smaller yields were accompanied by increases in leaf, but not tuber, cyanide content (Gleadow *et al.*, 2009). This finding alarmed them because, they write, "cassava leaves are eaten for their protein, and a higher leaf cyanide content suggests increased

toxicity at elevated CO_2." But since this study was conducted in a greenhouse, they opted to conduct a study to determine whether increases in cassava biomass or leaf toxicity would occur in plants grown under natural field conditions, employing free-air CO_2 enrichment (FACE) technology at the SoyFACE facility located at the Experimental Research Station of the University of Illinois in Urbana-Champaign (USA), where the air of four plots was enriched with CO_2 to approximately 200 ppm above what was measured in four ambient-treatment plots.

The U.S. and Australian researchers report, after three-and-a-half months of growth at elevated CO_2, the above-ground biomass of cassava was 30% greater and cassava tuber dry mass was more than 100% greater than in plants grown in ambient air. This result, they write, "surpasses all other C_3 crops and thus exceeds expectations." In contrast to the greenhouse study they cited, they find "no evidence" of increased leaf or total cyanide concentrations in the plants grown in the elevated CO_2 plots.

Vanuytrecht *et al.* (2012) acquired peer-reviewed publications reporting the results of free-air CO_2-enrichment (FACE) studies via searches of the ISI Web of Science citation database (Thomson) and the ScienceDirect citation database (Elsevier BV). They conducted a meta-analysis of 529 independent observations of various plant growth responses to elevated CO_2 obtained from 53 papers containing relevant data in graphical or numerical format pertaining to wheat (*Triticum aestivum* L.), barley (*Hordeum vulgare* L.), rice (*Oryza sativa* L.), soybean (*Glycine max* L.), potato (*Solanum tuberosum* L.), sugar beet (*Beta vulgaris* L.), cotton (*Gossypium hirsutum* L.), maize (*Zea mays* L.), and sorghum (*Sorghum bicolor* L.), as well as the two major pasture species of perennial ryegrass (*Lolium perenne* L.) and white clover (*Trifolium repens* L.).

Considered *en masse*, Vanuytrecht *et al.* report an approximate 200 ppm increase in the air's CO_2 concentration (the mean enhancement employed in the studies they analyzed) led to water productivity improvements of 23% in terms of aboveground biomass production per unit of water lost to evapotranspiration, and 27% in terms of aboveground yield produced per unit of water lost to evapo-transpiration. These two productivity increases would roughly correspond to enhancements of 34% and 40% for a 300 ppm increase in the air's CO_2 concentration.

Although "the FACE technique avoids the potential limitations of (semi-) closed systems by studying the influence of elevated CO_2 on crop growth in the field without chamber enclosure," the team of Belgian researchers writes, other studies have demonstrated a significant problem caused by the rapid (sub-minute) fluctuations of CO_2 concentration about a target mean common to most FACE experiments, as described by Bunce (2011, 2012). The latter found total shoot biomass of vegetative cotton plants in a typical FACE study averaged 30% less than in a constantly elevated CO_2 treatment at 27 days after planting, and wheat grain yields were 12% less in a fluctuating CO_2 treatment compared with a constant elevated CO_2 concentration treatment.

The results of the empirical studies described above suggest a future warming of the climate, coupled with rising atmospheric CO_2 levels, will boost global agricultural production and help to meet the food needs of the planet's growing population.

References

Bunce, J.A. 2008. Contrasting responses of seed yield to elevated carbon dioxide under field conditions within *Phaseolus vulgaris*. *Agriculture, Ecosystems and Environment* **128**: 219–224.

Bunce, J.A. 2011. Performance characteristics of an area distributed free air carbon dioxide enrichment (FACE) system. *Agricultural and Forest Meteorology* **151**: 1152–1157.

Bunce, J.A. 2012. Responses of cotton and wheat photosynthesis and growth to cyclic variation in carbon dioxide concentration. *Photosynthetica* **50**: 395–400.

Cock, J.H. 1982. Cassava—a basic energy source in the tropics. *Science* **218**: 755–762.

FAO. 2005. A Review of Cassava in Africa. Preface. *Proceedings on the Validation Forum on the Global Cassava Development Strategy*. International Fund for Agricultural Development and the Food and Agriculture Organization. Rome, Italy.

FAO. 2010. *The State of Food Insecurity in the World*. United Nations Food and Agriculture Organization. Rome, Italy, pp. 10–11.

Gleadow, R.M., Evans, J.R., Mccaffery, S., and Cavagnaro, T.R. 2009. Growth and nutritive value of cassava (*Manihot esculenta* Cranz.) are reduced when grown in elevated CO_2. *Plant Biology* **11**: 76–82.

Godfray, H.C.J., Beddington, J.R., Crute, I.R., Haddad, L., Lawrence, D., Muir, J.F., Pretty, J., Robinson, S., Thomas, S.M., and Toulmin, C. 2010. Food security: The challenge of feeding 9 billion people. *Science* **327**: 812–818.

Hitaka, H. and Kobayashi, H. 1961. Studies on the lodging of rice plants. (II) Source of decreasing yield due to lodging. *Japanese Journal of Crop Science* **32**: 270–276.

IPCC. 2007. *Climate Change 2007: Impacts, Adaptation and Vulnerability*. IPCC Secretariat, Geneva, Switzerland.

Jin, C., Du, S., Wang, Y., Condon, J., Lin, X., and Zhang, Y. 2009. Carbon dioxide enrichment by composting in greenhouses and its effect on vegetable production. *Journal of Plant Nutrition and Soil Science* **172**: 418–424.

Kim, H.Y., Lieffering, M., Kobayashi, K., Okada, M., Mitchell, M.W., and Gumpertz, M. 2003. Effects of free-air CO_2 enrichment and nitrogen supply on the yield of temperate paddy rice crops. *Field Crops Research* **83**: 261–170.

Lebot, V. 2009. Tropical Root and Tuber Crops: Cassava, Sweet Potato, Yams and Aroids. CABI, Oxfordshire, United Kingdom.

Lele, U. 2010. Food security for a billion poor. *Science* **326**: 1554.

Lobell, D.B., Burke, M.B., Tebaldi, C., Mastrandrea, M.D., Falcon, W.P., and Naylor, R.L. 2008. Prioritizing climate change adaptation needs for food security in 2030. *Science* **319**: 607–610.

Lou, Y., Inubushi, K., Mizuno, T., Hasegawa, T., Lin, Y., Sakai, H., Cheng, W., and Kobayashi, K. 2008. CH_4 emission with differences in atmospheric CO_2 enrichment and rice cultivars in a Japanese paddy soil. *Global Change Biology* **14**: 2678–2687.

Ortiz, R., Sayre, K.D., Govaerts, B., Gupta, R., Subbarao, G.V., Ban, T., Hodson, D., Dixon, J.M., Ortiz-Monasterio, J.I., and Reynolds, M. 2008. Climate change: Can wheat beat the heat? *Agriculture, Ecosystems and Environment* **126**: 46–58.

Peng, S., Laza, R.C., Visperas, R.M., Khush, G.S., Virk, P., and Zhu, D. 2004. Rice: Progress in breaking the yield ceiling. In: *New Directions for a Diverse Planet: Proceedings of the Fourth International Crop Science Congress*, 26 Sep–1 Oct 2004, Brisbane, Australia.

Rogers, A., Ainsworth, E.A., and Leakey A.D.B. 2009. Will elevated carbon dioxide concentration amplify the benefits of nitrogen fixation in legumes? *Plant Physiology* **151**: 1009–1016.

Rosenthal, D.M., Slattery, R.A., Miller, R.E., Grennan, A.K., Cavagnaro, T.R., Fauquet, C.M., Gleadow, R.M., and Ort, D.R. 2012. Cassava about-FACE: Greater than expected yield stimulation of cassava (*Manihot esculenta*) by future CO_2 levels. *Global Change Biology* **18**: 2661–2675.

Roy, K.S., Bhattacharyya, P., Neogi, S., Rao, K.S., and Adhya, T.K. 2012. Combined effect of elevated CO_2 and temperature on dry matter production, net assimilation rate, C and N allocations in tropical rice (*Oryza sativa* L.). *Field Crops Research* **139**: 71–79.

Setter, T.L., Laureles, E.V., and Mazaredo, A.M. 1997. Lodging reduces yield of rice by self-shading and reductions in canopy photosynthesis. *Field Crops Research* **49**: 95–106.

Shimono, H., Okada, M., Yamakawa, Y., Nakamura, H., Kobayashi, K., and Hasegawa, T. 2007. Lodging in rice can be alleviated by atmospheric CO_2 enrichment. *Agriculture, Ecosystems and Environment* **118**: 223–230.

Sinha, S.K., Kulshreshtha, S.M., Purohit, A.N., and Singh, A.K. 1998. Base Paper. *Climate Change and Perspective for Agriculture*. National Academy of Agricultural Sciences, 20.

Tester, M. and Langridge, P. 2010. Breeding technologies to increase crop production in a changing world. *Science* **327**: 818–822.

Tian, Y., Chen, J., Chen, C., Deng, A., Song, Z., Zheng, C., Hoogmoed, W., and Zhang, W. 2012. Warming impacts on winter wheat phenophase and grain yield under field conditions in Yangtze Delta Plain, China. *Field Crops Research* **134**: 193–199.

Tilman, D., Balzer, C., Hill, J., and Befort, B.L. 2011. Global food demand and the sustainable intensification of agriculture. *Proceedings of the National Academy of Sciences USA* **108**: 20,260–20,264.

Vanaja, M., Reddy, P.R.R., Lakshmi, N.J., Razak, S.K.A., Vagheera, P., Archana, G., Yadav, S.K., Maheswari, M., and Venkateswarlu, B. 2010. Response of seed yield and its components of red gram (*Cajanus cajan* L. Millsp.) to elevated CO_2. *Plant, Soil and Environment* **56**: 458–462.

Vanuytrecht, E., Raes, D., Willems, P., and Geerts, S. 2012. Quantifying field-scale effects of elevated carbon dioxide concentration on crops. *Climate Research* **54**: 35–47.

Yang, L.X., Huang, J.Y., Yang, H.J., Zhu, J.G., Liu, H.J., Dong, G.C., Liu, G., Han, Y., and Wang, Y.L. 2006. The impact of free-air CO_2 enrichment (FACE) and N supply on yield formation of rice crops with large panicle. *Field Crops Research* **98**: 141–150.

Yang, L., Liu,. H., Wang, Y., Zhu, J., Huang, J., Liu, G., Dong, G., and Wang, Y. 2009. Yield formation of CO_2-enriched inter-subspecific hybrid rice cultivar Liangyoupeijiu under fully open-air condition in a warm sub-tropical climate. *Agriculture, Ecosystems and Environment* **129**: 193–200.

4.1.2.2 Model-based Studies

- When model-based studies fully account for the growth-enhancing and water-conserving benefits of atmospheric CO_2 enrichment, they project

significant gains for future agricultural production.

Bootsma *et al.* (2005) derived relationships between agroclimatic indices and average grain yields of corn, soybeans, and barley obtained from field trials conducted in the eastern part of Canada and used them to estimate the impacts of projected climate change scenarios on the yields of these commodities for the years 2040–2069. Based on a range of heat units projected by multiple climate model simulations, they report average yields achievable in field trials could increase by 40–115% for corn and 21–50% for soybeans by 2040–2069, "not including the direct effect of increased atmospheric CO_2 concentrations." Adding the expected CO_2 increase into the mix, along with gains in yield anticipated to be achieved through breeding and improved technology, these numbers rose to 114–186% for corn and 117–157% for soybeans.

Initial yields of barley, in contrast, were projected to decline, by as much as 25% in areas with significant water deficits, but after reviewing the scientific literature on the subject, the Canadian researchers conclude the direct effect of increased CO_2 alone "would more than offset the yield reductions anticipated due to effects of rising temperature and changes in water deficit." All things considered, they conclude, "barley yields would increase by an average of about 15% under this scenario." Bootsma *et al.* predict a "switch to high-energy and high-protein-content crops (corn and soybeans) better adapted to the warmer climate," but say "there will likely still be a considerable area of land seeded to barley and other small grain cereals, as these are very desirable in rotation with potatoes."

Liu *et al.* (2004) made detailed calculations of the economic impact of predicted climate changes for the year 2050 (a mean countrywide temperature increase of 3.0°C and a mean precipitation increase of 3.9%) on agriculture in China, using the methodology of Mendelsohn *et al.* (1994) and agricultural, climate, social, economic, and edaphic data for 1,275 agricultural counties for the period 1985–1991. In the mean, Liu *et al.* report "all of China would benefit from climate change in most scenarios." In addition, they write, "the effects of CO_2 fertilization should be included, for some studies indicate that this may produce a significant increase in yield," an increase that is well-established (see Chapter 1, this volume) and was not included in their analysis. Liu *et al.* note "China's agriculture has to feed more than one-fifth of the world's population, and, historically, China has been famine prone," noting, "as recently as the late

1950s and early 1960s a great famine claimed about thirty million lives (Ashton *et al.*, 1984; Cambridge History of China, 1987)."

Chavas *et al.* (2009) also showed the importance of including the effects of CO_2 fertilization in projecting agricultural trends, studying potential climate change impacts on the productivity of five major crops (canola, corn, potato, rice, and winter wheat) of eastern China (30 to 42°N, 108 to 123°E). They conducted full-domain simulations of the EPIC agro-ecosystem model for the baseline period 1961–1990 and the future period 2071–2100 under IPCC's A2 scenario for projected atmospheric CO_2 concentrations and accompanying climate change. They found, "without the enhanced CO_2-fertilization effect, potential productivity declines in all cases ranging from 2.5 to 12%." When the CO_2-fertilization effect was included, "aggregate potential productivity (i.e. if the crop is grown everywhere) increases 6.5% for rice, 8.3% for canola, 18.6% for corn, 22.9% for potato, and 24.9% for winter wheat." In addition, "similar results are reported at the national scale in the work of Lin *et al.* (2005) using alternative RCM output and the CERES crop simulation model."

Thus, despite the supposedly deleterious climate changes predicted to occur over the rest of the twenty-first century, when the seven scientists factored into the yield model the aerial fertilization effect of the projected increase in atmospheric CO_2, they found the net productivities of all five crops rose over the entire study region.

Noting "rice is an essential component of the diet in more than half the world's population" and "the most socially and economically important crop in China," where it "contributes 43.7% of total national grain production," Xiong *et al.* (2009) assessed the effect of greenhouse gas-induced climate change and the direct fertilization effect of CO_2 on rice yields and production in China by coupling "the regional climate model PRECIS (Providing Regional Climates for Impacts Studies) with the CERES (Crop Environment Resources Synthesis) rice crop model to simulate current (1961–1990) and future (2011–2100) rice yields and production under [IPCC's] A2 and B2 climate change scenarios."

They found "single rice cropping may expand further north in China, and double rice cropping may move to the northern portion of the Yangtze River basin." In addition, "the national mean rice production is estimated to increase by 2.7 to 19.2% considering the combined effects of climate change, CO_2 and shifting rice-producing areas." Consequently, even considering the inflated temperature

increases predicted by IPCC, the estimated net effect of global warming and concomitant growth in anthropogenic CO_2 emissions results in a significant increase in rice production in the world's most populous country, where it is the people's most important food source.

Tao *et al.* (2013) introduce their work by writing "future climate change is projected to be one of the major challenges for regional agricultural production in broad regions of the world," noting Tao *et al.* (2009a,b) and Tao and Zhang (2010) developed "a new process-based Model to capture the Crop-Weather relationship over a Large Area (MCWLA) and a new super-ensemble-based probabilistic projection (Super EPPS) to account for the uncertainties not only from greenhouse gas emission scenarios and climate change scenarios but also from biophysical processes in crop models, and to assess the impacts of climate change (variability) on regional crop productivity and water use in a probabilistic framework." These model projections "have been demonstrated," they continue, "in addressing the probabilistic responses and adaptations of maize production to climate change in the North China Plain (NCP)."

Tao and Zhang state the crop model MCWLA-Wheat was first developed "by adapting the process-based general crop model, MCWLA, to winter wheat," after which "Bayesian probability inversion and a Markov chain Monte Carlo (MCMC) technique were applied to the MCWLA-Wheat to analyze uncertainties in parameter estimations, and to optimize parameters." Ensemble hindcasts show "the MCWLA-Wheat could capture the inter-annual variability of detrended historical yield series fairly well, especially over a large area." Based on the MCWLA-Wheat, they developed a Super EPPS and applied it to project the probabilistic responses of wheat productivity and water use in the NCP to future climate change. The scientists used 10 climate scenarios "consisting of the combinations of five global climate models and two greenhouse gases emission scenarios (A1F1 and B1), the corresponding atmospheric CO_2 concentration range, and multiple sets of crop model parameters representing the biophysical uncertainties from crop models."

The Chinese researchers found a high probability that future climate change would increase winter wheat yields in the NCP during the 2020s, 2050s, and 2080s, with (and without) CO_2 fertilization effects and relative to 1961–1990 levels, by, on average, 37.3% (18.6%), 67.8% (23.1%), and 87.2% (34.4%), respectively, over 80% of the study area.

These findings are encouraging in light of the analysis of Schmidhuber and Tubiello (2007), who suggest global food production may need to rise by as much as 70% by the year 2050 in order to adequately feed the nine billion people (compared to today's seven billion) they project to be inhabiting the planet at that midcentury point.

Trnka et al. (2004) used the crop growth model CERES-Barley version 2.1 (Otter-Nacke et al., 1991) to assess the direct biological effect of a doubling of the air's CO_2 concentration (from 350 to 700 ppm) on the growth and yield of spring barley in the Czech Republic, along with the indirect effect on growth and yield produced by the climate changes predicted to accompany such a CO_2 increase, as simulated by several GCMs, including ECHAM4, HadCM2, NCAR-DOE, and seven other GCMs available from IPCC. They report the indirect effect on spring barley yield caused by changed weather conditions was mostly negative, ranging from -19% to +5% for the several climate scenarios applied to three different production regions of the Czech Republic.

CO2 enrichment made a positive difference in these results. Trnka et al. write, "the magnitude of the direct [and positive] effect of doubled CO_2 on the stressed yields for the three test sites is 35–55% in the present climate and 25–65% in the 2 x CO_2 climates," and "the stressed yields would increase in 2 x CO_2 conditions by 13–52% when both direct [biological] and indirect [climatic] effects were considered." In addition, "the decrease of the mean yields due to the indirect [climatic] effect of doubled CO_2 may be reduced, and it might be even turned to increase, if the spring barley is planted 45–60 days sooner." They conclude, "application of the earlier planting date would result thus in an additional 15–22% increase of the yields in 2 x CO_2 conditions." They conclude, "the positive direct effect of doubled CO_2 dominates over the negative effect of changed weather conditions," and they note the results they obtained "might be applied to vast regions of Central Europe with similar environmental characteristics."

Kvalvik et al. (2011) state the consequences of predicted climate change "are not straightforward, but dependent on the interaction between different weather and biological elements, as well as political, economic and social conditions." In their interdisciplinary study of this complex situation, the six Norwegian scientists "assessed biological and agronomic effects of climate change, and their interaction with political, economic and social factors to identify farmers' vulnerability and adaptive capacity to climate change," based on "downscaled climate change scenarios and interviews with local farmers in the three northernmost counties in Northern Norway (latitude 65.5° to 70°N)."

The scientists found "the farmers themselves are willing to use the opportunities afforded by a more favorable climate," and "a warmer climate is generally regarded as favorable by the farmers in our study region." However, they report their study of farmers in northern Norway shows they are "vulnerable to a changing climate, not because of the direct effect of changing growing conditions, but because these changes are an added factor to an already tenuous situation created by Norwegian agricultural policy and the socio-economic development in general," which "poses a greater challenge to farming and is likely to reduce the farmers' adaptive capacity."

Kvalvik et al. conclude farmers in northern Norway "are highly adaptive, to both changing growing conditions and changing agricultural policies." They note "changes in policy are currently a greater challenge to farmers than climate change," and "such changes are therefore a more salient driver of vulnerability," implying the Norwegian government's presumptive cure for the disease of global warming (which is described in some detail in their paper) is probably no cure at all, and possibly worse than the disease itself.

Cullen et al. (2012) introduce their study by noting "climate change projections for southern Australia indicate the region is likely to become warmer and drier," noting "there is considerable variation in the projections from different climate models and emission pathways." They point out "there is some uncertainty about how rapidly warming will occur" and "projections for rainfall change vary widely." Given the large uncertainty in climate change projections from global circulation models, Cullen et al. conclude an alternative approach would be "to explore the sensitivity of agricultural systems to a range of likely future temperature, carbon dioxide and rainfall combinations, thereby creating a three-dimensional surface of response."

The three Australian researchers report the simulated changes in pasture production and the approach adopted in their study highlight when and where possible adaptation options may be required, adding this approach "clearly demonstrates the resistance of pasture production over a range of climate changes." Cullen et al. conclude that for south-eastern Australia, "annual pasture production is resistant to climatic changes of up to 2°C warming," thanks to the collective wisdom of farmers, who learned from experience how to cope with various degrees of temperature and precipitation change, and of scientists who had studied the subject in considerable detail.

Marin *et al.* (2013) evaluated the effects of climate change on sugarcane yield, water use efficiency, and irrigation needs in southern Brazil, based on downscaled outputs of two general circulation models (PRECIS and CSIRO) and a sugarcane growth model (DSSAT/CANEGRO) calibrated for the main cultivar currently grown in Brazil. They used data from five field experiments conducted under several soil and climate conditions, analyzing the sensitivities of simulated stalk fresh mass (SFM) to air temperature, CO_2 concentration, and rainfall, to identify increases in simulated SFM and water use efficiency (WUE) for all scenarios investigated.

On average, this analysis revealed, "for the current sugarcane area in the State of Sao Paulo, SFM would increase 24% and WUE 34% for rain-fed sugarcane." The authors write, "considering the current technological improvement rate, projected yields for 2050 ranged from 96 to 129 tons per hectare, which are respectively 15 and 59% higher than the current state average yield." They say their simulations suggest "the WUE increase due to higher CO_2 seems to be the main cause for the positive simulated yield response."

When model-based studies fully account for the growth-enhancing and water-conserving benefits of atmospheric CO_2 enrichment, they project significant gains for future agricultural production.

References

Ashton, B., Hill, K., Piazza, A., and Zeitz, R. 1984. Famine in China, 1958-1961. *Population and Development Review* **10**: 613-615.

Bootsma, A., Gameda, S., and McKenney, D.W. 2005. Potential impacts of climate change on corn, soybeans and barley yields in Atlantic Canada. *Canadian Journal of Plant Science* **85**: 345–357.

Cambridge History of China. 1987. Volume 14. Cambridge University Press, Cambridge, UK.

Chavas, D.R., Izaurralde, R.C., Thomson, A.M., and Gao, X. 2009. Long-term climate change impacts on agricultural productivity in eastern China. *Agricultural and Forest Meteorology* **149**: 1118–1128.

Cullen, B.R., Eckard, R.J., and Rawnsley, R.P. 2012. Resistance of pasture production to projected climate changes in south-eastern Australia. *Crop and Pasture Science* **63**: 77–86.

Kvalvik, I., Dalmannsdottir, S., Dannevig, H., Hovelsrud, G., Ronning, L., and Uleberg, E. 2011. Climate change vulnerability and adaptive capacity in the agricultural sector in Northern Norway. *Acta Agriculturae Scandinavica, Section B—Soil & Plant Science* **61**, Supplement 1: 27–37.

Lin, E., Xiong, W., Ju, H., Xu, Y., Li, Y., Bai, L., and Liyong, X. 2005. Climate change impacts on crop yield and quality with CO_2 fertilization in China. *Philosophical Transactions of the Royal Society B* **360**: 2149–2154.

Liu, H., Li, X., Fischer, G., and Sun, L. 2004. Study on the impacts of climate change on China's agriculture. *Climatic Change* **65**: 125–148.

Marin, F.R., Jones, J.W., Singels, A., Royce, F., Assad, E.D., Pellegrino, G.Q., and Justino, F. 2013. Climate change impacts on sugarcane attainable yield in southern Brazil. *Climatic Change* **117**: 227–239.

Mendelsohn, R., Nordhaus, W.D., and Shaw, D. 1994. The impact of global warming on agriculture: A Ricardian analysis. *American Economic Review* **84**: 753–771.

Otter-Nacke, S., Ritchie, J.T., Godwin, D.C., and Singh, U. 1991. *A User's Guide to CERES Barley—V2.10*, Manual IFDC-SM-3, International Fertilizer Development Center Simulation.

Schmidhuber, J. and Tubiello, F.N. 2007. Global food security under climate change. *Proceedings of the National Academy of Sciences USA* **104**: 19,703–19,708.

Tao, F., Yokozawa, M., and Zhang, Z. 2009a. Modeling the impacts of weather and climate variability on crop productivity over a large area: a new process-based model development, optimization, and uncertainties analysis. *Agricultural and Forest Meteorology* **149**: 831–850.

Tao, F. and Zhang, Z. 2010. Adaptation of maize production to climate change in North China Plain: quantify the relative contributions of adaptation options. *European Journal of Agronomy* **33**: 103–116.

Tao, F. and Zhang, Z. 2013. Climate change, wheat productivity and water use in the North China Plain: A new super-ensemble-based probabilistic projection. *Agricultural and Forest Meteorology* **170**: 146–165.

Tao, F., Zhang, Z., Liu, J., and Yokozawa, M. 2009b. Modeling the impacts of weather and climate variability on crop productivity over a large area: a new super-ensemble-based probabilistic projection. *Agricultural and Forest Meteorology* **149**: 1266–1278.

Trnka, M., Dubrovsky, M., and Zalud, Z. 2004. Climate change impacts and adaptation strategies in spring barley production in the Czech Republic. *Climatic Change* **64**: 227–255.

Xiong, W., Conway, D., Lin, E., and Holman, I. 2009. Potential impacts of climate change and climate variability on China's rice yield and production. *Climate Research* **40**: 23–35.

4.2 Biospheric Productivity: The Greening of the Earth

Since 1980, some parts of the world registered three of the warmest decades in the instrumental temperature record, intense and persistent El Niño events, large-scale deforestation, "unprecedented" forest fires, and the eruption of several volcanoes. Concurrently, the atmosphere's CO_2 content increased by 16% and the human population grew by 55%. How badly is the biosphere suffering in response to these much-feared events? Is it even suffering at all?

As reviewed in the subsections below, several research groups have explored those questions. This section begins with a discussion of what has been learned about the terrestrial biosphere as a whole, followed by a regional analysis exploring terrestrial productivity trends on continental and subcontinental scales.

4.2.1 Global Terrestrial

- The vigor of Earth's terrestrial biosphere has been increasing with time, revealing a great greening of the planet that extends across the globe. Satellite-based analyses of net terrestrial primary productivity (NPP) reveal an increase of 6–13% since the 1980s. There is no empirical evidence to support the model-based claim that future carbon uptake will diminish on a global scale due to rising temperatures.

Reichenau and Esser (2003) investigated the individual influences of the El Niño-Southern Oscillation (ENSO), volcanic eruptions, and the North Atlantic Oscillation (NAO) on the 1958–1994 time series of anomalous CO_2 fluxes using the High Resolution Biosphere Model of Esser *et al.* (1994) and real-world CO_2 measurements. Although the two researchers could conclude nothing about the NAO, other than to say "the influence of the NAO remain[s] unclear," they determined periods of anomalous rising atmospheric CO_2 concentrations coincided with El Niño periods, and times of anomalous declining atmospheric CO_2 concentrations coincided with periods of significant volcanism.

They write, "the globally averaged effect of [the

El Niño] circulation pattern on the terrestrial biosphere is a net release of carbon," in agreement with the results of earlier investigations of the subject (Bacastow, 1976; Bacastow *et al.*, 1980), which in turn "confirms earlier findings that the terrestrial biosphere is mainly responsible for atmospheric CO_2 variations on the ENSO timescale (Keeling *et al.*, 1995; Lee *et al.*, 1998; Feely *et al.*, 1999; Gerard *et al.*, 1999; Rayner and Law, 1999; Battle *et al.*, 2000; Bousquet *et al.*, 2000; Houghton, 2000; Knorr, 2000, LeQuere *et al.*, 2000; Langenfelds *et al.*, 2002)." At the other end of the spectrum, Reichenau and Esser report "volcanic eruptions with considerable aerosol production may create disturbances of the (biospheric) carbon cycle by increasing the photosynthetic carbon uptake due to the enhanced diffuse fraction of the incoming [solar] radiation." This accords with the findings of Roderick *et al.* (2001), Cohan *et al.* (2002), Law *et al.* (2002), and Gu *et al.* (2002, 2003).

The many published studies of anomalous CO_2 fluxes between Earth's surface and its atmosphere indicate warm El Niño conditions tend to reduce biospheric productivity, whereas cool volcanic conditions tend to enhance that productivity. At first glance, this appears to support claims of "cool is good" and "warm is bad" for the planet's plants. But there is much more to the story.

For one thing, the productivity-enhancing effect of volcanic eruptions arises not from their cooling influence, but from their increasing the amount of diffuse solar radiation received at Earth's surface, which allows for an enhanced penetration of solar radiation deeper into plant canopies, which reduces within-canopy shade and boosts rates of canopy net photosynthesis. As for the productivity-reducing effect of El Niños, it could be more a consequence of changes in global precipitation patterns than a direct effect of the temperature increases. Indermuhle *et al.* (1999), for example, demonstrated the pattern of biospheric productivity over the last 7,000 years of the Holocene was essentially that of a slow monotonic decline from the peak growth conditions of the interglacial's Climatic Optimum, and this productivity decline, they write, was "due to a change from the warmer and wetter mid-Holocene climate to colder and drier conditions."

Additional evidence of the benefits of long-term warming on plants comes from the study of Lin *et al.* (2010), who conducted a meta-analysis of data from 127 individual studies, reporting for the totality of terrestrial plants included in their analysis, "warming significantly increased biomass by 12.3%" and there was a "significantly greater stimulation of woody (+26.7%) than herbaceous species (+5.2%)." They also state the warming effects on plant biomass production "did not change with mean annual precipitation or experimental duration," and "other treatments, including CO_2 enrichment, nitrogen addition, drought and water addition, did not alter warming responses of plant biomass." Thus the Chinese researchers conclude, "results in this and previous meta-analyses (Arft et al., 1999; Rustad et al., 2001; Dormann and Woodin, 2002; Walker et al., 2006) have revealed that warming generally increases terrestrial plant biomass, indicating enhanced terrestrial carbon uptake via plant growth and net primary productivity."

These studies indicate long-term global warming tends to increase biospheric productivity. Deviations from this basic relationship evident in variations of CO_2 fluxes between Earth's surface and atmosphere are likely to be short-lived and anomalous.

Langenfelds et al. (1999) analyzed O_2/N_2 measurements of the contents of a suite of tanks filled with background air collected at Cape Grim, Tasmania between April 1978 and January 1997. The rates of carbon storage in the world's oceans and the terrestrial biosphere they derived from these data indicate the terrestrial biosphere was essentially in balance with respect to surface fluxes of carbon throughout this 19-year interval. However, other studies have established tropical deforestation produced a huge net loss of carbon during each of those years. Langenfelds et al. necessarily acknowledge the existence of a terrestrial carbon sink of like magnitude. They suggest this "compensating growth of the [terrestrial] biosphere" is due to "reforestation, higher rates of net production in response to climatic trends, fertilisation by elevated levels of atmospheric CO_2 or nitrogen deposition or a combination of these factors." Thus, the biosphere appears to be re-sequestering the carbon man takes out of it.

In a broad review of the scientific literature, Idso and Idso (2011) described a number of biological consequences of the "fertilization of elevated levels of atmospheric CO_2." The best-known of these impacts is probably CO_2's aerial fertilization effect, which works on plants that utilize all three of the major biochemical pathways of photosynthesis (C_3, C_4, and CAM). In the case of herbaceous plants, this phenomenon typically boosts their productivities by about a third in response to a 300-ppm increase in atmospheric CO_2 content, and it enhances the growth of woody plants by 50% or more, as demonstrated in literally thousands of laboratory and field experiments (Idso and Singer, 2009) (see Chapter 1, this volume).

Plant water use efficiency, which may be defined as the amount of organic matter produced per unit of water transpired to the atmosphere, is directly enhanced by the aerial fertilization effect of atmospheric CO_2 enrichment and its anti-transpirant effect, which is produced by CO_2-induced decreases in the number density and degree of openness of leaf stomatal apertures that occur at higher atmospheric CO_2 concentrations (see Chapter 2). CO_2-induced percentage increases as large as, or even larger than, those exhibited by plant productivity are commonplace.

An important ramification of this CO_2-induced increase in plant water use efficiency is that it enables plants to grow and reproduce in areas previously too dry for them. The consequent increases in ground cover in these regions reduce the adverse effects of wind- and water-induced soil erosion. This creates a tendency to reverse desertification and make vast tracts of previously unproductive land able to support more abundant animal life, both above- and below-ground.

In addition to helping vegetation overcome the stress of limited water supplies, elevated levels of atmospheric CO_2 help plants better cope with other environmental stresses, such as low soil fertility, low light intensity, high soil and water salinity, high air temperature, various oxidative stresses, and the stress of herbivory (see Chapter 3). When confronted with the specter of global warming, for example, many experiments have revealed concomitant enrichment of the air with CO_2 tends to increase the temperature at which plants function at their optimum, often making them even better suited to the warmer environment than they were to the cooler environment to which they were originally adapted. Under the most stressful of such conditions, extra CO_2 can be the deciding factor in determining whether a plant lives or dies.

These benefits of atmospheric CO_2 enrichment apply to both agricultural and natural ecosystems. As Wittwer (1995) has noted, "the rising level of atmospheric CO_2 could be the one global natural resource that is progressively increasing food production and total biological output in a world of otherwise diminishing natural resources of land, water, energy, minerals, and fertilizer." This phenomenon is thus a means, he says, "of inadvertently increasing the productivity of farming systems and other photosynthetically active ecosystems," and "the effects know no boundaries and both developing and developed countries are, and will be, sharing equally."

In light of these observations and the rising CO_2 content of Earth's atmosphere, especially since 1950, one would expect to see some evidence of a greening of the Earth (Idso, 1986). As indicated in the papers described below, a growing number of researchers have joined Langenfelds *et al.* in acknowledging these stimulatory effects on Earth's biosphere.

Idso (1995) laid out the evidence for a worldwide increase in the growth rates of Earth's forests coeval with the progression of the Industrial Revolution and the rising CO_2 content of the atmosphere. The development of this concept begins with the study of LaMarche *et al.* (1984), who analyzed annual growth rings of two species of pine tree growing near the timberline in California, Colorado, Nevada, and New Mexico (USA), discovering large increases in growth rate between 1859 and 1983, rates that exceeded what might have been expected from climatic trends but were consistent with the global trend of atmospheric CO_2. A further development was provided by a study of ring-width measurements of Douglas fir trees in British Columbia, Canada, which also revealed a marked increase in growth in the trees' latter decades (Parker, 1987), leading the principal investigator of the project to state "environmental influences other than increased CO_2 have not been found that would explain this [phenomenon]." West (1988) reports much the same thing with respect to long-leaf pines in Georgia—their annual growth increments began to rise at an unusual rate about 1920, increasing by approximately 30% by the mid-1980s—and he too states "the increased growth cannot be explained by trends in precipitation, temperature, or Palmer Drought Severity Index," leaving the rising CO_2 content of the atmosphere as the likely cause of the increase in productivity.

Hari *et al.* (1984) and Hari and Arovaara (1988) reported stands of Scots pines in northern Finland were found to have experienced growth increases ranging from 15 to 43% between 1950 and 1983. The researchers state "CO_2 seems to be the only environ-mental factor that has been changing systematically during this century in the remote area under study."

Graybill and Idso (1993) found very long ring-width chronologies (some stretching back nearly 1,800 years) of high-altitude long-lived bristlecone, foxtail, and limber pine trees in Arizona, California, Colo-rado, and Nevada (USA) showed an unprecedented upward growth trend in the 1850s that continued as far toward the present as the records extended. Comparisons of the chronologies with temperature and precipitation records ruled out the possibility either of these climatic variables played a significant role in enhancing the trees' growth rates, strongly implicating the historical rise in atmospheric CO_2 content as the factor responsible for their ever-increasing productivity over the prior century and a half.

Phillips and Gentry (1994) provided perhaps the most striking evidence for the significant twentieth-century growth enhancement of Earth's forests by the historical increase in the air's CO_2 concentration. Noting turnover rates of mature tropical forests correlate well with measures of net productivity (Weaver and Murphy, 1990), the two scientists assessed the turnover rates of 40 tropical forests from around the world in order to test the hypothesis global forest productivity was increasing *in situ*. They found the turnover rates of these highly productive forests had indeed been continually rising since at least 1960, with an apparent pan-tropical acceleration since 1980 (see Figure 4.2.1.1). They note "the accelerating increase in turnover coincides with an accelerating buildup of CO_2," and as Pimm and Sugden (1994)

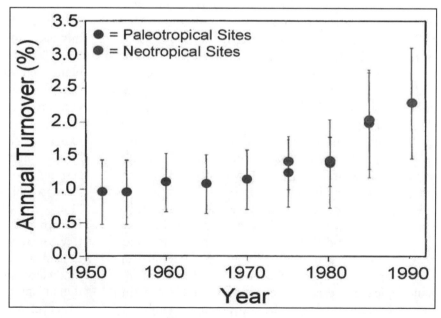

Figure 4.2.1.1. Average annual turnover rates (a surrogate for net productivity) for various tropical forests around the world since 1950. Adapted from Phillips and Gentry (1994).

note in a companion article, it was "the consistency and simultaneity of the changes on several continents that [led] Phillips and Gentry to their conclusion that enhanced productivity induced by increased CO_2 is the most plausible candidate for the cause of the increased turnover."

Four years later, a team of 11 researchers headed by Phillips (Phillips et al., 1998) reported another impressive finding. Working with data on tree basal area (a surrogate for tropical forest biomass) for the years 1958–1996, which they obtained from several hundred plots of mature tropical trees around the world, they report average forest biomass for the tropics as a whole increased substantially. They calculate the increase amounted to approximately 40% of the missing terrestrial carbon sink of the globe. Hence they suggest "intact forests may be helping to buffer the rate of increase in atmospheric CO_2, thereby reducing the impacts of global climate change," as Idso (1991a,b) had earlier suggested, and they identify the aerial fertilization effect of the ongoing rise in the atmospheric CO_2 content as one of the factors responsible for this phenomenon. Other contemporary studies support their findings (Grace et al., 1995; Malhi et al., 1998), verifying that neo-tropical forests were indeed accumulating ever-more carbon, and Phillips et al. (2002) state this phenomenon was occurring "possibly in response to the increasing atmospheric concentrations of carbon dioxide (Prentice et al., 2001; Malhi and Grace, 2000)."

The conclusions of Phillips and company were repeatedly challenged (Sheil, 1995; Sheil and May, 1996; Condit, 1997; Clark, 2002; Clark et al., 2003). In response to those challenges, Phillips and 17 other researchers (Lewis et al., 2004c), including one who had earlier criticized his and his colleagues' conclusions, published a new analysis that vindicated Phillips et al.'s earlier thoughts on the subject.

One of the primary criticisms of Phillips et al.'s work was their meta-analyses included sites with a wide range of tree census intervals (two–38 years), which critics claimed could be confounding or "perhaps even driving conclusions from comparative studies," as Lewis et al. (2004c) write. In Lewis et al.'s detailed study of this potential problem, which they conclude was indeed real, they state a re-analysis of Phillips et al.'s published results "shows that the pan-tropical increase in stem turnover rates over the late 20th century cannot be attributed to combining data with differing census intervals." Or as they state in another place, "the conclusion that turnover rates have increased in tropical forests over the late 20th

century is robust to the charge that this is an artifact due to the combination of data that vary in census interval (cf. Sheil, 1995)."

Lewis et al. (2004c) additionally note "Sheil's (1995) original critique of the evidence for increasing turnover over the late twentieth century also suggests that the apparent increase could be explained by a single event, the 1982–83 El Niño Southern Oscillation (ENSO), as many of the recent data spanned this event." However, they continue, "recent analyses from Amazonia have shown that growth, recruitment and mortality rates have simultaneously increased within the same plots over the 1980s and 1990s, as has net above-ground biomass, both in areas largely unaffected, and in those strongly affected, by ENSO events (Baker et al., 2004; Lewis et al., 2004a; Phillips et al., 2004)."

In a review of these global forest studies and many others (which led to their citing 186 scientific journal articles), Boisvenue and Running (2006) examined reams of "documented evidence of the impacts of climate change trends on forest productivity since the middle of the 20th century." They write, "globally, based on both satellite and ground-based data, climatic changes seemed to have a generally positive impact on forest productivity when water was not limiting," which was most of the time, because they report "less than 7% of forests are in strongly water-limited systems." Thus there has been what Boisvenue and Running call a significant "greening of the biosphere" in recent years, the world's forests in particular.

In another review of the scientific literature on this issue of global biospheric productivity, Lewis et al. (2009a) evaluated tropical forest inventory data, plant physiology experiments, ecosystem flux observations, Earth observations, atmospheric measurements, and dynamic global vegetation models. The five researchers report both theory and experiments suggest that over the past several decades "plant photosynthesis should have increased in response to increasing CO_2 concentrations, causing increased plant growth and forest biomass." They find "long-term plot data collectively indicate an increase in carbon storage, as well as significant increases in tree growth, mortality, recruitment, and forest dynamism." They also say satellite measurements "indicate increases in productivity and forest dynamism," and five Dynamic Global Vegetation Models, incorporating plant physiology, competition, and dynamics, predict "increasing gross primary productivity, net primary productivity, and carbon storage when forced using late-twentieth century climate and atmospheric CO_2 concentration data." They write, "the predicted increases in carbon storage via the differing methods are all of similar magnitude (0.2% to 0.5% per year)."

Another indication these CO_2- and temperature-induced biological benefits are indeed occurring in the real world of nature comes from the decline in the air's diurnal temperature range (DTR), evident in many parts of the world (Easterling *et al.*, 1997). Collatz *et al.* (2000) employed a simple land surface subroutine in a general circulation model of the atmosphere that included parameterizations of canopy physiological responses to various environmental changes, and by running the model with and without the vegetation subroutine, they were able to determine the degree of influence the planet's plant life may have on near-surface air temperature in a world of rising temperature and atmospheric CO_2 concentration.

They found realistic changes in the amount and physiological activity of Earth's plant life can produce changes in DTR of the order observed in the real world. The researchers state their results "suggest that reported increases in vegetation cover in the Northern Hemisphere during the 1980s [Myneni *et al.*, 1997] could have contributed to the lowered DTR." Thus, whereas some scientists have viewed the declining diurnal temperature range near the surface of Earth as a "fingerprint" of deleterious CO_2-induced global warming, evidence suggests the declining DTR may instead be an indication of beneficial CO_2-induced "global greening."

Alexandrov and Oikawa (2002) constructed a model of biospheric productivity based on empirical observations. Applied to the period 1980–1990, it suggests the total terrestrial carbon sink induced by the aerial fertilization effect of the contemporaneous increase in atmospheric CO_2 was approximately 1.3 Pg C yr^{-1}. This result compares well with estimates of up to 1.1 Pg C yr^{-1} derived from independent empirical observations of same-period anthropogenic CO_2 emissions, changes in land use, CO_2 uptake by the world's oceans, and increases in the air's CO_2 concentration.

Gurney and Eckles (2011) reported similar findings nearly a decade later. They state, "projections of atmospheric CO_2 concentrations and the resulting climate change rely to a significant degree on projections about future land and ocean uptake," citing Friedlingstein *et al.* (2006) and Sitch *et al.* (2008). To investigate how CO_2 uptake by Earth's terrestrial surfaces has varied over the past three decades, they examined the results of atmospheric CO_2 inversions—constrained by observed atmospheric CO_2 concentrations (Tans *et al.*, 1990) and simulated atmospheric transport—to estimate trends in air-to-land carbon fluxes, as per Enting (2002). They did so, they write, "at spatial scales down to the continents using the results of the TransCom 3 international atmospheric CO_2 inversion inter-comparison (Gurney *et al.*, 2002, 2008)," which involved 13 participating modeling groups. Their analyses indicate the global land carbon sink is intensifying (see Figure 4.2.1.2) at a rate of 0.057 PgC/year/year, resulting in 1.65 PgC of additional uptake over the period examined (1980–2008). This finding, they write, "is consistent with related findings in recent years," citing Cao *et al.* (2002), Cao *et al.* (2005), LeQuere *et al.* (2009), and Piao *et al.* (2009).

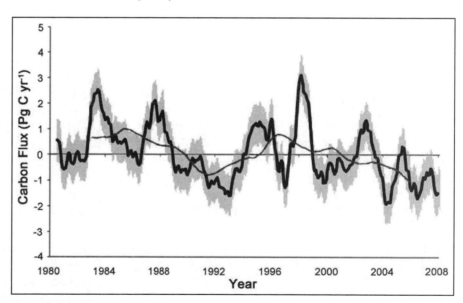

Figure 4.2.1.2. Global terrestrial biosphere net carbon exchange (positive from land to air, negative from air to land) during the years 1980–2008 (blue line), as calculated by Gurney and Eckles (2011). Also shown is the five-yr running mean (red line) and total 1σ flux uncertainty (light blue shading).

Other studies have produced additional evidence for a worldwide increase in vegetative productivity dating back to the inception of the Industrial Revolution. Joos and Bruno (1998), for example, used ice core data and direct observations of atmospheric CO_2 and ^{13}C to reconstruct the histories of terrestrial and oceanic uptake of anthropogenic carbon over the past two centuries. They discovered the biosphere typically acted as a source of CO_2 during the nineteenth century and the first decades of the twentieth century, but it subsequently "turned into a sink." Lloyd (1999) calculated that from 1730 to the early 1980s the increase in temperate deciduous forest net primary productivity (NPP) due solely to the historical increase in the atmosphere's CO_2 concentration was approximately 7%, and the increase in NPP due to a modest proportional increase in nitrogen deposition over the same time period would have been about 25%. However, when CO_2 and nitrogen increased together in Lloyd's model, the NPP stimulation was 40%, more than the sum of the individual contributions of the extra CO_2 and nitrogen.

Tans (2009) employed measurements of atmospheric and oceanic carbon contents, along with reasonably constrained estimates of global anthropogenic CO_2 emissions, to calculate the residual fluxes of carbon (in the form of CO_2) from the terrestrial biosphere to the atmosphere (+) or from the atmosphere to the terrestrial biosphere (-), obtaining the results depicted in Figure 4.2.1.3.

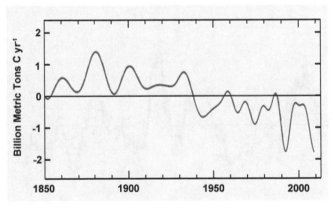

Figure 4.2.1.3. Five-year smoothed rates of carbon transfer from land to air (+) or from air to land (-) vs. time. Adapted from Tans (2009).

As the figure illustrates, Earth's land surfaces were a net *source* of CO_2-carbon to the atmosphere until about 1940, primarily because of the felling of forests and the plowing of grasslands to make way for expanded agricultural activities. From 1940 onward, however, the terrestrial biosphere has become, in the mean, an increasingly greater *sink* for CO_2-carbon, and it has done so despite increasing temperatures, massive global deforestation, and rising atmospheric

CO_2, more than compensating for any negative effects these phenomena have on the global biosphere.

Such findings, which do "not depend on models" but "only on the observed atmospheric increase and estimates of fossil fuel emissions," led Tans to conclude "suggestions that the carbon cycle is becoming less effective in removing CO_2 from the atmosphere (e.g., LeQuere *et al.*, 2007; Canadell *et al.*, 2007) can perhaps be true locally, but they do not apply globally, not over the 50-year atmospheric record, and not in recent years." Tans continues, "to the contrary," and "despite global fossil fuel emissions increasing from 6.57 GtC in 1999 to 8.23 in 2006, the five-year smoothed global atmospheric growth rate has not increased during that time, which requires more effective uptake [of CO_2] either by the ocean or by the terrestrial biosphere, or both, to satisfy atmospheric observations." The results portrayed in Figure 4.2.1.3, adapted from Tans' paper, clearly indicate this "more effective uptake" of CO_2-carbon has occurred primarily over land.

Many researchers also have examined trends in biospheric productivity using satellite data. Nemani *et al.* (2003), for example, discovered the terrestrial biosphere is growing ever more robust (see Figure 4.2.1.4). Globally, the group of eight scientists found terrestrial net primary production (NPP) increased by 6.17%, or 3.42 PgC, over the 18 years between 1982 and 1999. In addition, they observed net positive responses over all latitude bands studied: 4.2% (47.5–22.5°S), 7.4% (22.5°S–22.5°N), 3.7% (22.5–47.5°N), and 6.6% (47.5–90.0°N).

Nemani *et al.* mention a number of likely contributing factors to these significant NPP increases: nitrogen deposition and forest regrowth in northern mid and high latitudes; wetter rainfall regimes in water-limited regions of Australia, Africa, and the Indian subcontinent;, increased solar radiation reception over radiation-limited parts of Western Europe and the equatorial tropics; warming in many parts of the world; and the aerial fertilization effect of rising atmospheric CO_2 concentrations.

Regarding the latter factor, Nemani *et al.* remark, "an increase in NPP of only 0.2% per 1-ppm increase in CO_2 could explain all of the estimated global NPP increase of 6.17% over 18 years and is within the range of experimental evidence." However, they report NPP increased by more than 1% per year in Amazonia alone, noting "this result cannot be explained solely by CO_2 fertilization."

Although Nemani *et al.*'s conclusion may be correct, the aerial fertilization effect of atmospheric CO_2 enrichment is most pronounced at higher tem-

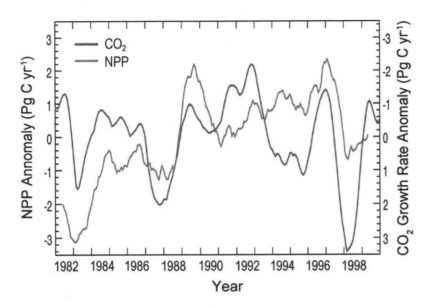

Figure 4.2.1.4. Interannual variations in global Net Primary Productivity (NPP) in relation to atmospheric CO_2 growth rate during the years 1982 to 1999. Adapted from Nemani *et al.* (2003).

peratures, rising from next to nothing at a mean temperature of 10°C to a 0.33% NPP increase per 1-ppm increase in CO_2 at a mean temperature of 36°C for a mixture of plants comprised predominantly of herbaceous species (Idso and Idso, 1994). For woody plants, this number could likely be two (Idso, 1999) or even three (Saxe *et al.*, 1998; Idso and Kimball, 2001; Leavitt *et al.*, 2003) times larger, yielding a 0.7% to 1% NPP increase per 1-ppm increase in CO_2, which would indeed represent the lion's share of the growth stimulation Nemani *et al.* observed in tropical Amazonia.

Chen *et al.* (2004) utilized the monthly satellite-derived normalized difference vegetation index (NDVI) dataset of 1987–1997 obtained from the advanced very high resolution radiometer (AVHRR) to calculate an 11-year history of global (75°N to 55°S) terrestrial NPP, deriving three results based on the three "NPP coefficient sets" of Whittaker and Likens (1975), Atjay *et al.* (1979), and Olson *et al.* (1983). Calculating from the beginning and end points of the graphical presentations of Chen *et al.*'s results, global terrestrial NPP increased by approximately 6.6% between 1987 and 1997 when the Atjay *et al.* coefficients were used, 9.9% when the Olson *et al.* coefficients were used, and 13.8% when the Whittaker and Likens coefficients were used, for a mean NPP increase of about 10% over the 11-year period.

Cao *et al.* (2004) derived net primary production

(NPP) values at 8-km and 10-day resolutions for the years 1981–2000 using variables based almost entirely on satellite observations, as described in the Global Production Efficiency Model (GLO-PEM). The model consists, they write, "of linked components that describe the processes of canopy radiation absorption, utiliza-tion, autotrophic respiration, and the regulation of these processes by environmental factors (Prince and Goward, 1995; Goetz *et al.*, 2000)." Over the last two decades of the twentieth century, "there was an increasing trend toward enhanced terrestrial NPP," which they say was "caused mainly by increases in atmospheric carbon dioxide and precipitation.

Cao *et al.* (2005) used the CEVSA (Carbon Exchanges in the Vegetation-Soil-Atmosphere sys-tem) model (Cao and Woodward, 1998; Cao *et al.*, 2002), forced by observed variations in climate and atmospheric CO_2, to quantify changes in NPP, soil heterotrophic respiration (HR), and net ecosystem production (NEP) from 1981 to 1998. As an independent check on the NPP estimate of CEVSA, they also estimated 10-day NPP for 1981–2000 with the GLO-PEM model that uses data almost entirely from remote sensing, including both the normalized difference vegetation index and meteorological variables (Prince and Goward, 1995; Cao *et al.*, 2004).

Cao *et al.* found "global terrestrial temperature increased by 0.21°C from the 1980s to the 1990s, and this alone increased HR more than NPP and hence reduced global annual NEP." They write, "combined changes in temperature and precipitation increased global NEP significantly," and "increases in atmospheric CO_2 produced further increases in NPP and NEP." They also note "the CO_2 fertilization effect [was] particularly strong in the tropics, compensating for the negative effect of warming on NPP."

They write, "the response of photosynthetic biochemical reactions to increases in atmospheric CO_2 is greater in warmer conditions, so the CO_2 fertilization effect will increase with warming in cool regions and be high in warm environments." They found global NEP increased "from 0.25 Pg C yr^{-1} in the 1980s to 1.36 Pg C yr^{-1} in the 1990s."

Commenting on their findings, Cao *et al.* note "the NEP that was induced by CO_2 fertilization and climatic variation accounted for 30% of the total terrestrial carbon sink implied by the atmospheric carbon budget (Schimel *et al.*, 2001), and the fraction changed from 13% in the 1980s to 49% in the 1990s," which indicates the growing importance of the CO_2 fertilization effect. Moreover, "the increase in the terrestrial carbon sink from the 1980s to the 1990s was a continuation of the trend since the middle of the twentieth century, rather than merely a consequence of short-term climate variability," suggesting as long as the atmosphere's CO_2 content continues to rise, so too will its stimulation of the terrestrial biosphere likely increase.

Using a newly developed satellite-based vegetation index (Version 3 Pathfinder NDVI) in conjunction with a gridded global climate dataset (global monthly mean temperature and precipitation at 0.5° resolution from New *et al.*, 2000), Xiao and Moody (2005) analyzed trends in global vegetative activity from 1982 to 1998. The greening trends exhibited substantial latitudinal and longitudinal variability, with the most intense greening of the globe located in high northern latitudes, portions of the tropics, southeastern North America, and eastern China. Temperature correlated strongly with greening trends in Europe, eastern Eurasia, and tropical Africa. Precipitation, in contrast, was not a significant driver of increases in greenness, except for isolated and spatially fragmented regions. Some decreases in greenness also were observed, mainly in the Southern Hemisphere in southern Africa, southern South America, and central Australia, and these trends were associated with concomitant increases in temperature and decreases in precipitation. Large regions of the globe showed no trend in greenness over the 17-year period, and large areas underwent strong greening that showed no association with trends of either temperature or precipitation. These greening trends, the scientists conclude, must have resulted from other factors, such as "CO_2 fertilization, reforestation, forest regrowth, woody plant proliferation and trends in agricultural practices."

Young and Harris (2005) investigated, for the majority of Earth's land surface, a near 20-year time series (1982–1999) of NDVI data, based on measurements obtained from the advanced very high resolution radiometer (AVHRR) carried aboard U.S. National Oceanic and Atmospheric Administration satellites. They employed two datasets derived from the sensor: the Pathfinder AVHRR Land (PAL) dataset and the Global Inventory Modeling and Mapping Studies (GIMMS) dataset.

Based on their analysis of the PAL data, the two researchers report "globally more than 30% of land pixels increased in annual average NDVI greater than 4% and more than 16% persistently increased greater than 4%," while "during the same period less than 2% of land pixels declined in NDVI and less than 1% persistently declined." Regarding the GIMMS dataset, they report "even more areas were found to be persistently increasing (greater than 20%) and persistently decreasing (more than 3%)." All told, they report "between 1982 and 1999 the general trend of vegetation change throughout the world has been one of increasing photosynthesis."

As for what has been responsible for the worldwide increase in photosynthesis, the researchers mention global warming and "associated precipitation change and increases in atmospheric carbon dioxide," citing Myneni *et al.* (1997) and Ichii *et al.* (2002). In addition, they write, "many of the areas of decreasing NDVI are the result of human activity," primarily deforestation (Skole and Tucker, 1993; Steininger *et al.*, 2001) and urbanization Seto *et al.* (2000).

Piao *et al.* (2006a) note "enhanced terrestrial vegetation growth in the middle and high latitudes of the Northern Hemisphere over the past two decades has been well documented (Zhou *et al.*, 2001; Nemani *et al.*, 2003)," but "the mechanisms for this phenomenon are still under debate." Using a leaf area index dataset for the years 1981–2000, created from satellite-derived observations of the normalized difference vegetation index parameter for land areas above 25°N latitude, the authors investigated "spatial patterns of mechanisms controlling current enhanced vegetation growth in the Northern Hemisphere," focusing on "how recent changes in precipitation, temperature [and] atmospheric CO_2 concentration have influenced vegetation growth."

Over the final two decades of the twentieth century, the researchers found, the mean rate of increase in growing-season leaf area index was 0.0041/year. They report 13% of that increase was provided by increases in precipitation, 31% by increases in temperature, and 49% by the increase in the atmosphere's CO_2 concentration.

Liu *et al.* (2010) looked for, and computed changes in, leaf area index (LAI) data derived from satellite observations for six latitude bands (50–90°N, 30–50°N, 10–30°N, 10°N–10°S, 10–30°S, and 30–63°S) that included all of Earth's continents but Antarctica. They report LAI "prominently increased" during the period July 1981 through December 2006 throughout Europe, Siberia, the Indian Peninsula, America and south Canada, the south region of the Sahara, the southwest corner of Australia, and the

Kgalagadi Basin, while it declined in southeast Asia, southeastern China, central Africa, central and southern South America, and arctic areas in North America. Despite the latter negative results, they found all six of the latitudinal bands they analyzed showed positive trends. Consequently, for the globe as a whole (the conglomerate of the six latitude bands they analyzed), they note, "LAI has increased at a rate of 0.0013 per year during July 1981–December 2006," while for the middle and high northern latitudes (north of 30°N), the linear LAI trend was 0.0032 per year.

Some researchers have expressed doubts the positive trends in global biospheric productivity are real or sustainable in a CO_2-induced globally warmed world of the future. Gloor *et al.* (2010) note the ratio of CO_2 accumulating in the atmosphere to the CO_2 flux into the atmosphere due to human activities—known as the airborne fraction (AF)—is central to predicting changes in Earth's surface temperature due to greenhouse gas-induced warming. This ratio has remained remarkably constant over the past five decades. However, they report Canadell *et al.* (2007) and Raupach *et al.* (2008) claim to have detected a long-term increasing trend in the airborne fraction, which they interpret as being indicative of "a decreasing trend in the efficiency of the ocean and land carbon sinks."

Gloor *et al.* report Knorr (2009) has challenged Canadell *et al.* and Raupach *et al.* regarding their detection of a positive AF trend, "arguing that given the noise in the data, the trend is not detectable." They then challenge the second claim of Canadell *et al.* and Raupach *et al.*—their contention a positive AF trend indicates a decreasing planetary carbon sink efficiency—by investigating "the question of what controls trends and decadal scale variations in CO_2 airborne fraction using simple linear models describing the evolution of an atmospheric perturbation in CO_2."

The three researchers first determined there is no one-to-one association between positive trends in CO_2 flux (due to fossil fuel emissions and changes in land use) to the atmosphere and negative trends in Earth's carbon sink efficiency. Second, they report in order to detect trends in sink efficiencies from the time of fossil fuel-derived CO_2 emissions and temporal changes in land use, "it is necessary to disentangle the spin-up time and fossil fuel growth rate variation signatures in the airborne fraction from signatures due to other causes." They make the pertinent

calculations for fossil-fuel and land-use changes and state they "do indeed find a positive trend in the residuals," but they argue this trend "is not statistically significant after correcting for known events such as the temporal distribution of the extrinsic forcings and likely omissions in the emissions (particularly from land-use change)." They note their analysis suggests "trends in airborne fraction are not a very good diagnostic to detect changes in carbon sink efficiency because variations in the signal are complex and the signal-to-noise ratio is small."

In describing another doubt about the recent greening of the Earth, Zhao and Running (2010) state "previous studies have shown that climate constraints were relaxing with increasing temperature and solar radiation, allowing an upward trend in NPP [net primary production] from 1982–1999," but over the past decade (2000–2009), satellite data "suggest a reduction in the global NPP." This finding caused some alarm in the scientific community. Zhao and Running demonstrate there is likely no cause for concern.

The graphical representation of this trend (Figure 4.2.1.5) illustrates that apart from the starting point of the initial year (2000) of their study, there is only one other year (2004) in which the global NPP was greater than it was at the end of the study (2009). Since global NPP was on the rise in 1982–1999, the more recent data would more accurately be described as a leveling off of that prior upward trend. Zhao and Running report the leveling off of global NPP over the past decade was induced by drought, and climate models have long predicted more frequent and more intense droughts would accompany global warming.

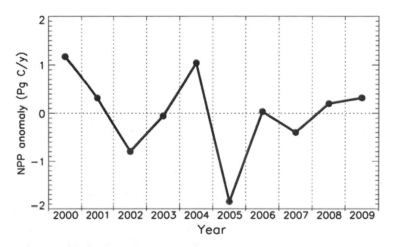

Figure 4.2.1.5. Interannual variations from the mean of global NPP over the past ten years. Adapted from Zhao and Running (2010).

The two researchers write, "NPP in the tropics explains 93% of variations in the global NPP," and "tropical rainforests explain 61% of global NPP variations." These findings are especially important because of the work of Coelho and Goddard (2009), who studied El Niño-induced tropical droughts as portrayed in climate models.

Coelho and Goddard write, "the majority of drought-related hazards and the attendant economic losses and mortality risks reside in the tropics," citing Dilley *et al.* (2005); They further note "changes in climate variability, including more frequent and damaging extreme events such as drought, is one of many anticipated impacts of climate change." More specifically (and germane to the subject at hand), they write, "El Niño brings widespread drought (i.e., precipitation deficit) to the tropics," and "stronger or more frequent El Niño events in the future" would "exacerbate drought risk in highly vulnerable tropical areas."

The two researchers evaluated "the patterns, magnitude, and spatial extent of El Niño-induced tropical droughts during a control period in the twentieth century in climate simulations, which have realistic evolution of greenhouse gases," after which they examined "the projected changes in the characteristics of El Niño and in the strength of the identified patterns of El Niño-induced tropical drought in the twenty-first century." That information allowed them to examine patterns of mean precipitation changes in order to "assess whether those changes exacerbate or ameliorate the risk of El Niño-induced drought conditions in the twenty-first century."

In the first instance, Coelho and Goddard say the models they studied "exhibit realistic patterns, magnitude, and spatial extent of El Niño-induced drought patterns in the twentieth century," and "the teleconnections are not projected to change in the twenty-first century." They add, "a possible slight reduction in the spatial extent of droughts is indicated over the tropics as a whole." They also report "all model groups investigated show similar changes in mean precipitation for the end of the twenty-first century, with increased precipitation projected between 10°S and 10°N."

De Jong *et al.* (2012) employed "detection of trend changes in normalized difference vegetation index (NDVI) satellite data between 1982 and 2008,"

based on "time series of 648 fortnightly images [that] were analyzed using a trend breaks analysis procedure," for 14 classes of land cover (biomes). The four researchers found short-term greening and browning trends in portions of the studied period for almost 15% of Earth's land surface, but for the entire time period, "net greening was detected in all biomes," and "the net global figure—considered over the full length of the time series—showed greening since the 1980s."

Ballantyne *et al.* (2012) used "global-scale atmospheric CO_2 measurements, CO_2 emission inventories and their full range of uncertainties to calculate changes in global CO_2 sources and sinks during the past fifty years." The five U.S. scientists say their mass balance analysis shows "net global carbon uptake has increased significantly by about 0.05 billion tonnes of carbon per year and that global carbon uptake doubled, from 2.4 ± 0.8 to 5.0 ± 0.9 billion tonnes per year, between 1960 and 2010" (see Figure 4.2.1.6).

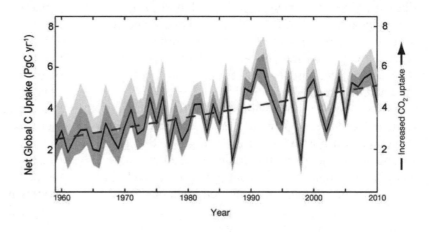

Figure 4.2.1.6. Annual global net carbon (C) uptake by Earth's lands and oceans (solid blue line) for 1959–2010, adapted from Ballantyne *et al.* (2012). The linear trend (dashed red line) and 1σ (dark shaded bands) and 2σ (light shaded bands) uncertainties are also shown.

They conclude, "although present predictions indicate diminished C uptake by the land and oceans in the coming century, with potentially serious consequences for the global climate, as of 2010 there is no empirical evidence that C uptake has started to diminish on the global scale." Their results clearly indicate just the opposite appears to be the case, with global carbon uptake doubling over the past half-century. This most recent effort refutes the hypothesis of Canadell *et al.* (2007) and Raupach *et al.* (2008), who claimed to have detected a decreasing trend in the efficiency of the planet's carbon sinks, and it vindicates the many studies described above revealing an increasing greening of planet Earth.

The above-described research demonstrates the terrestrial biomass of the globe has been rising, and it appears to be doing so at a remarkable rate. It is also clear recent increases in atmospheric CO_2 and temperature have positively affected those trends, likely responsible for the lion's share of the observed increase. This remarkable increase in biospheric productivity and observed greening of the Earth has occurred in spite of several real assaults on the globe's vegetation, such as deforestation and other land-use changes.

References

Alexandrov, G. and Oikawa, T. 2002. TsuBiMo: a biosphere model of the CO_2-fertilization effect. *Climate Research* **19**: 265–270.

Arft, A.M., Walker, M.D., Gurevitch, J., Alatalo, J.M., Bret-Harte, M.S., Dale, M., Diemer, M., Gugerli, F., Henry, G.H.R., Jones, M.H., Hollister, R.D., Jonsdottir, I.S., Laine, K., Levesque, E., Marion, G.M., Molau, U., Molgaard, P., Nordenhall, U., Raszhivin, V., Robinson, C.H., Starr, G., Stenstrom, A., Stenstrom, M., Totland, O., Turner, P.L., Walker, L.J., Webber, P.J., Welker, J.M., and Wookey, P.A. 1999. Responses of tundra plants to experimental warming: meta-analysis of the international tundra experiment. *Ecological Monographs* **69**: 491–511.

Atjay, G.L., Ketner, P., and Duvigneaud, P. 1979. Terrestrial primary production and photomass. In: Bolin, B., Degens, E., Kempe, S., and Ketner, P. (Eds.) *The Global Carbon Cycle, SCOPE 13*, Wiley, Chichester, pp. 129–182.

Bacastow, R.B. 1976. Modulation of atmospheric carbon dioxide by the Southern Oscillation. *Nature* **261**: 116–118.

Bacastow, R.B., Adams, J.A., Keeling, C.D., Moss, D.J., Whorf, T.P., and Wong, C.S. 1980. Atmospheric carbon dioxide, the Southern Oscillation and the weak 1975 El Niño. *Science* **210**: 66–68.

Baker, T.R., Phillips, O.L., Malhi, Y., Almeida, S., Arroyo, L., Di Fiore, A., Erwin, T., Higuchi, N., Killeen, T.J., Laurance, S.G., Laurance, W.F., Lewis, S.L., Monteagudo, A., Neill, D.A., Núñez Vargas, P., Pitman, N.C.A., Silva, J.N.M., and Vásquez Martínez, R. 2004. Increasing biomass in Amazonian forest plots. *Philosophical Transactions of the Royal Society of London Series B—Biological Sciences* **359**: 353–365.

Ballantyne, A.P., Alden, C.B., Miller, J.B., Tans, P.P., and White, J.W. 2012. Increase in observed net carbon dioxide uptake by land and oceans during the past 50 years. *Nature* **488**: 70–72.

Battle, M., Bender, M.L., Tans, P.P., White, J.W.C., Ellis, J.T., Conway, T., and Francey, R.J. 2000. Global carbon sinks and their variability inferred from atmospheric O_2 and ^{13}C. *Science* **287**: 2467–2470.

Boisvenue, C. and Running, S.W. 2006. Impacts of climate change on natural forest productivity—evidence since the middle of the 20th century. *Global Change Biology* **12**: 862–882.

Bousquet, P., Ciais, P., Monfray, P., Balkanski, Y., Ramonet, M., and Tans, P. 1996. Influence of two atmospheric transport models on inferring sources and sinks of atmospheric CO_2. *Tellus Series B* **48**: 568–582.

Canadell, J.G., LeQuere, C., Raupach, M.R., Field, C.B., Buitenhuis, E.T,., Ciais, P., Conway, T.J., Gillett, N.P., Houghton, R.A., and Marland, G. 2007. Contributions to accelerating atmospheric CO_2 growth from economic activity, carbon intensity, and efficiency of natural sinks. *Proceedings of the National Academy of Sciences of the United States of America* **104**: 18,866–18,870.

Cao, M.K., Prince, S.D., and Shugart, H.H. 2002. Increasing terrestrial carbon uptake from the 1980s to the 1990s with changes in climate and atmospheric CO_2. *Global Biogeochemical Cycles* **16**: 10.1029/2001GB001553.

Cao, M., Prince, S.D., Small, J., and Goetz, S.J. 2004. Remotely sensed interannual variations and trends in terrestrial net primary productivity 1981–2000. *Ecosystems* **7**: 233–242.

Cao, M., Prince, S.D., Tao, B., Small, J., and Kerang, L. 2005. Regional pattern and interannual variations in global terrestrial carbon uptake in response to changes in climate and atmospheric CO_2. *Tellus B* **57**: 210–217.

Cao, M.K. and Woodward, F.I. 1998. Dynamic responses of terrestrial ecosystem carbon cycling to global climate change. *Nature* **393**: 249–252.

Chen, Z.M., Babiker, I.S., Chen, Z.X., Komaki, K., Mohamed, M.A.A., and Kato, K. 2004. Estimation of interannual variation in productivity of global vegetation using NDVI data. *International Journal of Remote Sensing* **25**: 3139–3159.

Clark, D.A. 2002. Are tropical forests an important carbon sink? Reanalysis of the long-term plot data. *Ecological Applications* **12**: 3–7.

Clark, D.A., Piper, S.C., Keeling, C.D., and Clark, D.B. 2003. Tropical rain forest tree growth and atmospheric carbon dynamics linked to interannual temperature variation during 1984–2000. *Proceedings of the National Academy of Sciences, USA* **100**: 10.1073/pnas.0935903100.

Coelho, C.A.S. and Goddard, L. 2009. El Niño-induced tropical droughts in climate change projections. *Journal of Climate* **22**: 6456–6476.

Cohan, D.S., Xu, J., Greenwald, R., Bergin, M.H., and Chameides, W.L. 2002. Impact of atmospheric aerosol light scattering and absorption on terrestrial net primary productivity. *Global Biogeochemical Cycles* **16**: 10.1029/ 2001GB001441.

Collatz, G.J., Bounoua, L., Los, S.O., Randall, D.A., Fung, I.Y., and Sellers, P.J. 2000. A mechanism for the influence of vegetation on the response of the diurnal temperature range to changing climate. *Geophysical Research Letters* **27**: 3381–3384.

Condit, R. 1997. Forest turnover, density, and CO_2. *Trends in Ecology and Evolution* **12**: 249–250.

De Jong, R., Verbesselt, J., Schaepman, M.E., and De Bruin, S. 2012. Trend changes in global greening and browning: contribution of short-term trends to longer-term change. *Global Change Biology* **18**: 642–655.

Dilley, M., Chen, R.S., Deichmann, U., Lerner-Lam, A.L., and Arnold, M. 2005. *Natural Disaster Hotspots: A Global Risk Analysis*. World Bank, 145 pp.

Dormann, C.F. and Woodin, S.J. 2002. Climate change in the arctic: using plant functional types in a meta-analysis of field experiments. *Functional Ecology* **16**: 4–17.

Easterling, D.R., Horton, B., Jones, P.D., Peterson, T.C., Karl, T.R., Parker, D.E., Salinger, M.J., Razuvayev, V., Plummer, N., Jamason, P., and Folland, C.K. 1997. Maximum and minimum temperature trends for the globe. *Science* **277**: 364–367.

Enting, I. 2002. *Inverse Problems in Atmospheric Constituent Transport*. Cambridge University Press, Cambridge, United Kingdom.

Esser, G., Hoffstadt, J., Mack, F., and Wittenberg, U. 1994. High Resolution Biosphere Model-Documentation of Model Version 3.00.00. Institute fur Pflanzenokologie der Justus-Liebig-Universitat, Giessen.

Feely, R.A., Wanninkhof, R., Takahashi, T., and Tans, P. 1999. Influence of El Niño on the equatorial Pacific contribution to atmospheric CO_2 accumulation. *Nature* **398**: 597–601.

Friedlingstein, P., Cox, P., Betts, R., Bopp, L., von Bloh, W., Brovkin, V., Cadule, P., Doney, S., Eby, M., Fung, I., Bala, G., John, J., Jones, C., Joos, F., Kato, T., Kawamiya, M., Knorr, W., Lindsay, K., Matthews, H.D., Raddatz, T., Rayner, P., Reick, C., Roeckner, E., Schnitzler, K.-G., Schnur, R., Strassmann, K., Weaver, A.J., Yoshikawa, C., and Zeng, N. 2006. Climate-carbon cycle feedback analysis: Results from the (CMIP)-M-4 model inter-comparison. *Journal of Climate* **19**: 3337–3353.

Gerard, J.C., Nemry, B., Francois, L.M., and Warnant, P. 1999. The interannual change of atmospheric CO_2: Contribution of subtropical ecosystems? *Geophysical Research Letters* **26**: 243–246.

Gloor, M., Sarmiento, J.L., and Gruber, N. 2010. What can be learned about carbon cycle climate feedbacks from the CO_2 airborne fraction? *Atmospheric Chemistry and Physics* **10**: 7739–7751.

Goetz, S.J., Prince, S.D., Small, J., Gleason, A.C.R., and Thawley, M.M. 2000. Interannual variability of global terrestrial primary production: reduction of a model driven with satellite observations. *Journal of Geophysical Research* **105**: 20,007–20,091.

Grace, J., Lloyd, J., McIntyre, J., Miranda, A.C., Meir, P., Miranda, H.S., Nobre, C., Moncrieff, J., Massheder, J., Malhi, Y., Wright, I., and Gash, J. 1995. Carbon dioxide uptake by an undisturbed tropical rain-forest in Southwest Amazonia, 1992–1993. *Science* **270**: 778–780.

Graybill, D.A. and Idso, S.B. 1993. Detecting the aerial fertilization effect of atmospheric CO_2 enrichment in tree-ring chronologies. *Global Biogeochemical Cycles* **7**: 81–95.

Gu, L., Baldocchi, D., Verma, S.B., Black, T.A., Vesala, T., Falge, E.M., and Dowty, P.R. 2002. Advantages of diffuse radiation for terrestrial ecosystem productivity. *Journal of Geophysical Research* **107**: 10.1029/ 2001JD001242.

Gu, L., Baldocchi, D.D., Wofsy, S.C., Munger, J.W., Urbanski, S.P., and Boden, T.A. 2003. Response of a deciduous forest to the mount Pinatubo eruption: Enhanced photosynthesis. *Science* **299**: 2035–2038.

Gurney, K.R., Baker, D., Rayner, P., Denning, A.S., and TransCom 3 L2 modelers. 2008. Interannual variations in continental-scale net carbon exchange and sensitivity to observing networks estimated from atmospheric CO_2 inversions for the period 1980 to 2005. *Global Biogeochemical Cycles* **22**: 10.1029/2007GB003082.

Gurney, K.R. and Eckels, W.J. 2011. Regional trends in terrestrial carbon exchange and their seasonal signatures. *Tellus* **63B**: 328–339.

Gurney, K.R., Law, R.M., Denning, A.S., Rayner, P.J., Baker, D., Bousquet, P., Bruhwiler, L., Chen, Y.-H., Ciais, P., Fan, S., Fung, I.Y., Gloor, M., Heimann, M., Higuchi, K., John, J., Maki, T., Maksyutov, S., Masarie, K., Peylin, P., Prather, M., Pak, B.C., Randerson, J., Sarmiento, J., Taguchi, S., Takahashi, T., and Yuen, C.-W. 2002. Towards robust regional estimates of CO_2 sources and sinks using atmospheric transport models. *Nature* **415**: 626–630.

Hari, P. and Arovaara, H. 1988. Detecting CO_2 induced enhancement in the radial increment of trees. Evidence from the northern timberline. *Scandinavian Journal of Forest Research* **3**: 67–74.

Hari, P., Arovaara, H., Raunemaa, T., And Hautojarvi, A. 1984. Forest growth and the effects of energy production: A method for detecting trends in the growth potential of trees. *Canadian Journal of Forest Research* **14**: 437–440.

Houghton, R.A. 2000. Interannual variability in the global carbon cycle. *Journal of Geophysical Research* **105**: 20,121–20,130.

Ichii, K., Kawabata, A., and Yamaguchi, Y. 2002. Global correlation analysis for NDVI and climatic variables and NDVI trends: 1982–1990. *International Journal of Remote Sensing* **23**: 3873–3878.

Idso, C.D. and Idso, S.B. 2011. *The Many Benefits of Atmospheric CO_2 Enrichment*. Vales Lakes Publishing, Inc., Pueblo, Colorado, USA.

Idso, C.D. and Singer, S.F. 2009. *Climate Change Reconsidered: 2009 Report of the Nongovernmental Panel on Climate Change (NIPCC)*. The Heartland Institute, Chicago, IL.

Idso, K.E. and Idso, S.B. 1994. Plant responses to atmospheric CO_2 enrichment in the face of environmental constraints: A review of the past 10 years' research. *Agricultural and Forest Meteorology* **69**: 153–203.

Idso, S.B. 1986. Industrial age leading to the greening of the Earth? *Nature* **320**: 22.

Idso, S.B. 1991a. The aerial fertilization effect of CO_2 and its implications for global carbon cycling and maximum greenhouse warming. *Bulletin of the American Meteorological Society* **72**: 962–965.

Idso, S.B. 1991b. Reply to comments of L.D. Danny Harvey, Bert Bolin, and P. Lehmann. *Bulletin of the American Meteorological Society* **72**: 1910–1914.

Idso, S.B. 1995. *CO_2 and the Biosphere: The Incredible Legacy of the Industrial Revolution*. Department of Soil, Water & Climate, University of Minnesota, St. Paul, Minnesota, USA.

Idso, S.B. 1999. The long-term response of trees to atmospheric CO_2 enrichment. *Global Change Biology* **5**: 493–495.

Idso, S.B. and Kimball, B.A. 2001. CO_2 enrichment of sour orange trees: 13 years and counting. *Environmental and Experimental Botany* **46**: 147–153.

Indermuhle, A., Stocker, T.F., Joos, F., Fischer, H., Smith, H.J., Wahlen, M., Deck, B., Mastroianni, D., Tschumi, J., Blunier, T., Meyer, R., and Stauffer, B. 1999. Holocene carbon-cycle dynamics based on CO_2 trapped in ice at Taylor Dome, Antarctica. *Nature* **398**: 121–126.

Joos, F. and Bruno, M. 1998. Long-term variability of the terrestrial and oceanic carbon sinks and the budgets of the carbon isotopes ^{13}C and ^{14}C. *Global Biogeochemical Cycles* **12**: 277–295.

Keeling, C.D., Whorf, T.P., Wahlen, M., and van der Pflicht, J. 1995. Interannual extremes in the rate of rise of atmospheric carbon dioxide since 1980. *Nature* **375**: 666–670.

Knorr, W. 2000. Annual and interannual CO_2 exchanges of the terrestrial biosphere: Process-based simulations and uncertainties. *Global Ecology and Biogeography* **9**: 225–252.

Knorr, W. 2009. Is the airborne fraction of anthropogenic CO_2 emissions increasing? *Geophysical Research Letters* **36**: 10.1029/2009GL040613.

LaMarche Jr., V.C., Graybill, D.A., Fritts, H.C., and Rose, M.R. 1984. Increasing atmospheric carbon dioxide: Tree ring evidence for growth enhancement in natural vegetation. *Science* **223**: 1019–1021.

Langenfelds, R.L., Francey, R.J., Pak, B.C., Steele, L.P., Lloyd, J., Trudinger, C.M., and Allison, C.E. 2002. Interannual growth rate variations of atmospheric CO_2 and its ^{13}C, H_2, CH_4, and CO between 1992 and 1999 linked to biomass burning. *Global Biogeochemical Cycles* **16**: 10.1029/2001GB001466.

Langenfelds, R.L., Francey, R.J., and Steele, L.P. 1999. Partitioning of the global fossil CO_2 sink using a 19 year trend in atmospheric O_2. *Geophysical Research Letters* **26**: 1897–1900.

Law, B.E., Falge, E., Gu,. L., Baldocchi, D.D., Bakwin, P., Berbigier, P., Davis, K., Dolman, A.J., Falk, M., Fuentes, J.D., Goldstein, A., Granier, A., Grelle, A., Hollinger, D., Janssens, I.A., Jarvis, P., Jensen, N.O., Katul, G., Mahli, Y., Matteucci, G., Meyers, T., Monson, R., Munger, W., Oechel, W., Olson, R., Pilegaard, K., Paw U, K.T., Thorgeirsson, H., Valentini, R., Verma, S., Vesala, T., Wilson, K., and Wofsy, S. 2002. Environmental controls over carbon dioxide and water vapor exchange of terrestrial vegetation. *Agricultural and Forest Meteorology* **113**: 97–120.

LeQuere, C., Orr, J.C., Monfray, P., Aumont, O., and Madec, G. 2000. Interannual variability of the oceanic sink of CO_2 from 1979 through 1997. *Global Biogeochemical Cycles* **14**: 1247–1265.

LeQuere, C., Raupach, M.R., Canadell, J.G., Marland, G., Bopp, L., Ciais, P., Conway, T.J., Doney, S.C., Feely, R.A., Foster, P., Friedlingstein, P., Gurney, K., Houghton, R.A., House, J.I., Huntingford, C., Levy, P.E., Lomas, M.R., Majkut, J., Metzl, N., Ometto, J.P., Peters, G.P., Prentice, I.C., Randerson, J.T., Running, S.W., Sarmiento, J.L., Schuster, U., Sitch, S., Takahashi, T., Viovy, N., van der Werf, G.R., and Woodward, F.I. 2009. Trends in the sources and sinks of carbon dioxide. *Nature Geoscience* **2**: 831–836.

LeQuere, C., Rodenbeck, C., Buitenhuis, E.T., Conway, T.J., Langenfelds, R., Gomez, A., Labuschagne, C., Ramonet, M., Nakazawa, T., Metzl, N., Gillett, N., and Heimann, M. 2007. Saturation of the Southern Ocean CO_2 sink due to recent climate change. *Science* **316**: 1735–1738.

Leavitt, S.W., Idso, S.B., Kimball, B.A., Burns, J.M.,

Sinha, A., and Stott, L. 2003. The effect of long-term atmospheric CO_2 enrichment on the intrinsic water-use efficiency of sour orange trees. *Chemosphere* **50**: 217–222.

Lee, K., Wanninkhof, R., Takahashi, T., Doney, S.C., and Feely, R.A. 1998. Low interannual variability in recent oceanic uptake of carbon dioxide. *Nature* **396**: 155–159.

Lewis, S.L., Lloyd, J., Sitch, S., Mitchard, E.T.A., and Laurance, W.F. 2009a. Changing ecology of tropical forests: Evidence and drivers. *Annual Review of Ecology, Evolution, and Systematics* **40**: 529–549.

Lewis, S.L., Phillips, O.L., Baker, T.R., Lloyd, J., Malhi, Y., Almeida, S., Higuchi, N., Laurance, W.F., Neill, D.A., Silva, J.N.M., Terborgh, J., Lezama, A.T., Vásquez Martinez, R., Brown, S., Chave, J., Kuebler, C., Núñez Vargas, P., and Vinceti, B. 2004a. Concerted changes in tropical forest structure and dynamics: evidence from 50 South American long-term plots. *Philosophical Transactions of the Royal Society of London Series B—Biological Sciences* **359**: 421–436.

Lewis, S.L., Phillips, O.L., Sheil, D., Vinceti, B., Baker, T.R., Brown, S., Graham, A.W., Higuchi, N., Hilbert, D.W., Laurance, W.F., Lejoly, J., Malhi, Y., Monteagudo, A., Vargas, P.N., Sonke, B., Nur Supardi, M.N., Terborgh, J.W., and Vasquez, M.R. 2004c. Tropical forest tree mortality, recruitment and turnover rates: calculation, interpretation and comparison when census intervals vary. *Journal of Ecology* **92**: 929–944.

Lin, D., Xia, J., and Wan, S. 2010. Climate warming and biomass accumulation of terrestrial plants: a meta-analysis. *New Phytologist* **188**: 187–198.

Liu, S., Liu, R., and Liu, Y. 2010. Spatial and temporal variation of global LAI during 1981–2006. *Journal of Geographical Sciences* **20**: 323–332.

Lloyd, J. 1999. The CO_2 dependence of photosynthesis, plant growth responses to elevated CO_2 concentrations and their interaction with soil nutrient status, II. Temperate and boreal forest productivity and the combined effects of increasing CO_2 concentrations and increased nitrogen deposition at a global scale. *Functional Ecology* **13**: 439–459.

Malhi Y. and Grace, J. 2000. Tropical forests and atmospheric carbon dioxide. *Trends in Ecology and Evolution* **15**: 332–337.

Malhi, Y., Nobre, A.D., Grace, J., Kruijt, B., Pereira, M.G.P., Culf, A., and Scott, S. 1998. Carbon dioxide transfer over a Central Amazonian rain forest. *Journal of Geophysical Research* **103**: 31,593–31,612.

Myneni, R.B., Keeling, C.D., Tucker, C.J., Asrar, G., and Nemani, R.R. 1997. Increased plant growth in the northern high latitudes from 1981 to 1991. *Nature* **386**: 698–702.

Nemani, R.R., Keeling, C.D., Hashimoto, H., Jolly, W.M., Piper, S.C., Tucker, C.J., Myneni, R.B., and Running. S.W. 2003. Climate-driven increases in global terrestrial net primary production from 1982 to 1999. *Science* **300**: 1560–1563.

New, M., Hulme, M., and Jones, P.D. 2000. Global monthly climatology for the twentieth century (New *et al.*). Dataset. Available online (http://www.daac.ornl.gov) from Oak Ridge National Laboratory Distributed Active Archive Center, Oak Ridge, Tennessee, USA.

Olson, J.S., Watts, J., and Allison, L. 1983. *Carbon in Live Vegetation of Major World Ecosystems.* Environmental Sciences Division, Oak Ridge National Laboratory, Oak Ridge, TN, USA.

Parker, M.L. 1987. Recent abnormal increase in tree-ring widths: A possible effect of elevated atmospheric carbon dioxide. In: Jacoby Jr., G.C. and Hornbeck, J.W. (Eds.) *Proceedings of the International Symposium on Ecological Aspects of Tree-Ring Analysis.* U.S. Department of Energy, Washington, DC, pp. 511–521.

Phillips, O.L., Baker, T.R., Arroyo, L., Higuchi, N., Killeen, T.J., Laurance, W.F., Lewis, S.L., Lloyd, J., Malhi, Y., Monteagudo, A., Neill, D.A., Núñez Vargas, P., Silva, J.N.M., Terborgh, J., Vásquez Martínez, R., Alexiades, M., Almeida, S., Brown, S., Chave, J., Comiskey, J.A., Czimczik, C.I., Di Fiore, A., Erwin, T., Kuebler, C., Laurance, S.G., Nascimento, H.E.M., Olivier, J., Palacios, W., Patiño, S., Pitman, N.C.A., Quesada, C.A., Saldias, M., Torres Lezama, A.B., and Vinceti, B. 2004. Pattern and process in Amazon tree turnover: 1976–2001. *Philosophical Transactions of the Royal Society of London Series B—Biological Sciences* **359**: 381–407.

Phillips, O.L. and Gentry, A.H. 1994. Increasing turnover through time in tropical forests. *Science* **263**: 954–958.

Phillips, O.L., Malhi, Y., Higuchi, N., Laurance, W.F., Nunez, P.V., Vasquez, R.M., Laurance, S.G., Ferreira, L.V., Stern, M., Brown, S., and Grace, J. 1998. Changes in the carbon balance of tropical forests: Evidence from long-term plots. *Science* **282**: 439–442.

Phillips, O.L., Malhi, Y., Vinceti, B., Baker, T., Lewis, S.L., Higuchi, N., Laurance, W.F., Vargas, P.N., Martinez, R.V., Laurance, S., Ferreira, L.V., Stern, M., Brown, S., and Grace, J. 2002. Changes in growth of tropical forests: Evaluating potential biases. *Ecological Applications* **12**: 576–587.

Piao, S., Ciais, P., Friedlingstein, P., de Noblet-Ducoudre, N., Cadule, P., Viovy, N., and Wang, T. 2009. Spatio-temporal patterns of terrestrial carbon cycle during the 20th century. *Global Biogeochemical Cycles* **23**: 10.1029/2008GB003339.

Piao, S., Friedlingstein, P., Ciais, P., Zhou, L., and Chen, A. 2006a. Effect of climate and CO_2 changes on the greening of the Northern Hemisphere over the past two decades. *Geophysical Research Letters* **33**: 10.1029/2006GL028205.

Pimm, S.L. and Sugden, A.M. 1994. Tropical diversity and global change. *Science* **263**: 933–934.

Prentice, I.C., Farquhar, G.D., Fasham, M.J.R., Goulden, M.L., Heimann, M., Jaramillo, V.J., Kheshgi, H.S., Le Quere, C., Scholes, R.J., Wallace, D.W.R., Archer, D., Ashmore, M.R., Aumont, O., Baker, D., Battle, M., Bender, M., Bopp, L.P., Bousquet, P., Caldeira, K., Ciais, P., Cox, P.M., Cramer, W., Dentener, F., Enting, I.G., Field, C.B., Friedlingstein, P., Holland, E.A., Houghton, R.A., House, J.I., Ishida, A., Jain, A.K., Janssens, I.A., Joos, F., Kaminski, T., Keeling, C.D., Keeling, R.F., Kicklighter, D.W., Hohfeld, K.E., Knorr, W., Law, R., Lenton, T., Lindsay, K., Maier-Reimer, E., Manning, A.C., Matear, R.J., McGuire, A.D., Melillo, J.M., Meyer, R., Mund, M., Orr, J.C., Piper, S., Plattner, K., Rayner, P.J., Sitch, S., Slater, R., Taguchi, S., Tans, P.P., Tian, H.Q., Weirig, M.F., Whorf, T., and Yool, A. 2001. The carbon cycle and atmospheric carbon dioxide. Chapter 3 of the Third Assessment Report of the Intergovernmental Panel on Climate Change. *Climate Change 2001: The Scientific Basis.* Cambridge University Press, Cambridge, UK, pp. 183–238.

Prince, S.D. and Goward, S.N. 1995. Global primary production: a remote sensing approach. *Journal of Biogeography* **22**: 815–835.

Raupach, M.R., Canadell, J.G., and Le Quere, C. 2008. Anthropogenic and biophysical contributions to increasing atmospheric CO_2 growth rate and airborne fraction. *Biogeosciences* **5**: 1601–1613.

Rayner, P.J. and Law, R.M. 1999. The interannual variability of the global carbon cycle. *Tellus Series B* **51**: 210–212.

Reichenau, T.G. and Esser, G. 2003. Is interannual fluctuation of atmospheric CO_2 dominated by combined effects of ENSO and volcanic aerosols? *Global Biogeochemical Cycles* **17**: 10.1029/2002GB002025.

Roderick, M.L., Farquhar, G.D., Berry, S.L., and Noble, I.R. 2001. On the direct effect of clouds and atmospheric particles on the productivity and structure of vegetation. *Oecologia* **129**: 21–30.

Rustad, L., Campbell, J.L., Marion, G.M., Norby, R.J., Mitchell, M.J., Hartley, A.E., Cornelissen, J.H.C., Gurevitch, J., and GCTE-NEWS. 2001. A meta-analysis of the response of soil respiration, net nitrogen mineralization, and aboveground plant growth to experimental ecosystem warming. *Oecologia* **126**: 543–562.

Saxe, H., Ellsworth, D.S., and Heath, J. 1998. Tree and forest functioning in an enriched CO_2 atmosphere. *New Phytologist* **139**: 395–436.

Schimel, D.S., House, J.I., Hibbard, J.I., Bousquet, P., Ciais, P., Peylin, P., Braswell, B.H., Apps, M.J., Baker, D., Bondeau, A., Canadell, J., Churkina, G., Cramer, W., Denning, A.S., Field, C.B., Friedlingstein, P., Goodale, C., Heimann, M., Houghton, R.A., Melillo, J.M., Moore III, B., Murdiyarso, D., Noble, I., Pacala, S.W., Prentice, I.C., Raupach, M.R., Rayner, P.J., Scholes, R.J., Steffen, W.L., and Wirth, C. 2001. Recent patterns and mechanisms of carbon exchange by terrestrial ecosystems. *Nature* **414**: 169–172.

Seto, K.C., Kaufman, R.K., and Woodcock, C.E. 2000. Landsat reveals China's farmland reserves, but they're vanishing fast. *Nature* **406**: 121.

Sheil, D. 1995. Evaluating turnover in tropical forests. *Science* **268**: 894.

Sheil, D. and May, R.M. 1996. Mortality and recruitment rate evaluations in heterogeneous tropical forests. *Journal of Ecology* **84**: 91–100.

Sitch, S., Huntingford, C., Gedney, N., Levy, P.E., Lomas, M., Piao, S.L., Betts, R., Ciais, P., Cox, P., Friedlingstein, P., Jones, C.D., Prentice, I.C., and Woodward, F.I. 2008. Evaluation of the terrestrial carbon cycle, future plant geography and climate-carbon cycle feedbacks using five Dynamic Global Vegetation Models (DGVMs). *Global Change Biology* **14**: 2015–2039.

Skole, D. and Tucker, C.J. 1993. Tropical deforestation and habitat fragmentation in the Amazon: satellite data from 1978 to 1988. *Science* **260**: 1905–1909.

Steininger, M.K., Tucker, C.J., Ersts, P., Killen, T.J., Villegas, Z., and Hecht, S.B. 2001. Clearance and fragmentation of tropical deciduous forest in the Tierras Bajas, Santa Cruz, Bolivia. *Conservation Biology* **15**: 856–866.

Tans, P. 2009. An accounting of the observed increase in oceanic and atmospheric CO_2 and an outlook for the future. *Oceanography* **22**: 26–35.

Tans, P.P., Fung, I.Y., and Takahashi, T. 1990. Observational constraints on the global atmospheric CO_2 budget. *Science* **247**: 1431–1438.

Walker, M.D., Wahren, C.H., Hollister, R.D., Henry, G.H.R., Ahlquist, L.E., Alatalo, J.M., Bret-Harte, M.S., Calef, M.P., Callaghan, T.V., Carroll, A.B., Epstein, H.E., Jonsdottir, I.S., Klein, J.A., Magnusson, B., Molaug, U., Oberbauer, S.F., Rewan, S.P., Robinson, C.H., Shaver, G.R., Suding, K.N., Thompson, C.C., Tolvanen, A., Totland, O., Turner, P.L., Tweedie, C.E., Webber, P.J., and Wookey, P.A. 2006. Plant community responses to experimental warming across the tundra biome. *Proceedings of the National Academy of Sciences USA* **103**: 1342–1346.

Weaver, P.L. and Murphy, P.G. 1990. Forest structure and

productivity in Puerto Rico's Luquillo Mountains. *Biotropica* **22**: 69–82.

West, D.C. 1988. Detection of forest response to increased atmospheric carbon dioxide. In: Koomanoff, F.A. (Ed.) *Carbon Dioxide and Climate: Summaries of Research in FY 1988*. U.S. Department of Energy, Washington, D.C., p. 57.

Whittaker, R.H. and Likens, G.E. 1975. The biosphere and man. In: Leith, H. and Whittaker, R.H. (Eds.) *Primary Productivity and the Biosphere, Ecological Studies 14*, Springer-Verlag, Berlin, Germany, pp. 305–328.

Wittwer, S.H. 1995. *Food, Climate, and Carbon Dioxide: The Global Environment and World Food Production.* Lewis Publishers, Boca Raton, FL.

Xiao, J. and Moody, A. 2005. Geographical distribution of global greening trends and their climatic correlates: 1982–1998. *International Journal of Remote Sensing* **26**: 2371–2390.

Young, S.S. and Harris, R. 2005. Changing patterns of global-scale vegetation photosynthesis, 1982–1999. *International Journal of Remote Sensing* **26**: 4537–4563.

Zhao, M. and Running, S.W. 2010. Drought-induced reduction in global terrestrial net primary production from 2000 through 2009. *Science* **329**: 940–943.

Zhou, L.M., Tucker, C.J., Kaufmann, R.K., Slayback, D., Shabanov, N.V., and Myneni, R.B. 2001. Variations in northern vegetation activity inferred from satellite data of vegetation index during 1981 to 1999. *Journal of Geophysical Research* **106**: 20,069–20,083.

4.2.2 Continental Terrestrial

The following subsections analyze terrestrial productivity trends on continental and subcontinental scales, detailing what researchers have reported for Africa, Asia, Australia, Europe, North America, and South America.

4.2.2.1 Africa

- The ongoing rise in the air's CO_2 concentration and its anti-transpiration effect, which improves plant water-use efficiency, are enhancing and will continue to enhance the vegetative productivity of Africa.

According to a 2002 *New Scientist* article by Fred Pearce, "Africa's deserts are in 'spectacular' retreat," as vegetation is reclaiming great tracts of barren land across the entire southern edge of the Sahara. He notes, "the southern Saharan desert is in retreat, making farming viable again in what were some of the most arid parts of Africa." He writes, "Burkina Faso, one of the West African countries devastated by drought and advancing deserts 20 years ago, is growing so much greener that families who fled to wetter coastal regions are starting to go home."

"Vegetation," Pearce writes, "is ousting sand across a swathe of land stretching from Mauritania on the shores of the Atlantic to Eritrea 6000 kilometers away on the Red Sea coast." In addition to being widespread geographically, the greening was widespread in time, occurring since at least the mid-1980s.

Quoting Chris Reij of the Free University of Amsterdam, Pearce writes, "aerial photographs taken in June show 'quite spectacular regeneration of vegetation' in northern Burkina Faso." The data indicate the presence of more trees for firewood and more grassland for livestock. In addition, a survey Reij was collating showed, according to Pearce, "a 70 percent increase in yields of local cereals such as sorghum and millet in one province in recent years."

Kjeld Rasmussen of the University of Copenhagen studied the same area, reporting that since the 1980s there has been a "steady reduction in bare ground" with "vegetation cover, including bushes and trees, on the increase on the dunes."

Pearce also reports on the work of a team of geographers from Britain, Sweden, and Denmark who spent much of the summer of 2001 analyzing archived satellite images of the Sahel. Citing Andrew Warren of University College London as a source of information on this study, he says the results show "that 'vegetation seems to have increased significantly' in the past 15 years, with major regrowth in southern Mauritania, northern Burkina Faso, north-western Niger, central Chad, much of Sudan and parts of Eritrea."

In a study of a series of satellite images of the Central and Western Sahel taken from 1980 to 1995, Nicholson *et al.* (1998) found no evidence of any overall expansion of deserts and no drop in the rainfall use efficiency of native vegetation. Prince *et al.* (1998) further observed, in a satellite study of the Sahel from 1982 to 1990, a steady rise in rainfall use efficiency, suggesting plant productivity and coverage of the desert increased during this period.

Eklundh and Olsson (2003) provide further evidence. They analyzed normalized difference vegetation index (NDVI) data obtained from the U.S. National Oceanic and Atmospheric Administration's satellite-borne advanced very high resolution radiometer (AVHRR) whenever it passed over the African Sahel for the years 1982–2000. They write, "strong positive change in NDVI occurred in about 22% of the area, and weak positive change in 60% of the area," and "weak negative change occurred in 17% of the area, and strong negative change in 0.6% of the area." In addition, "integrated NDVI has increased by about 80% in the areas with strong positive change," whereas in areas with weak negative change, "integrated NDVI has decreased on average by 13%." The primary story these data tell, therefore, is of strong positive trends in NDVI for large areas of the African Sahel over the last two decades of the twentieth century, and Eklundh and Olsson conclude the "increased vegetation, as suggested by the observed NDVI trend, could be part of the proposed tropical sink of carbon."

Many more scientists subsequently confirmed the recent stunning increase in African vegetation. In 2005, Africa was featured in a special issue of the *Journal of Arid Environments,* "The 'Greening' of the Sahel." In that issue, Anyamba and Tucker (2005) describe their development of an NDVI history of the region for the years 1981–2003. Comparing this history with the precipitation history of the Sahel developed by Nicholson (2005), they report, "the persistence and spatial coherence of drought conditions during the 1980s is well represented by the NDVI anomaly patterns and corresponds with the documented rainfall anomalies across the region during this time period." In addition, "the prevalence of greener than normal conditions during the 1990s to 2003 follows a similar increase in rainfall over the region during the last decade."

In another analysis of NDVI and rainfall data in the same issue of the *Journal of Arid Environments,* Olsson *et al.* (2005) report finding "a consistent trend of increasing vegetation greenness in much of the region," which they describe as "remarkable." They say increasing rainfall "is certainly one reason" for the greening phenomenon but "does not fully explain" the increase in greenness.

The three Swedish scientists note, "only eight out of 40 rainfall observations showed a statistically significant increase between 1982–1990 and 1991–1999." In addition, "further analysis of this relationship does not indicate an overall relationship between rainfall increase and vegetation trend." Olsson *et al.* suggest "another potential explanation could be improved land management, which has been shown to cause similar changes in vegetation response elsewhere (Runnstrom, 2003)." However, in more

detailed analyses of Burkina Faso and Mali, where production of millet rose by 55% and 35%, respectively, since 1980, they could find "no clear relationship" between agricultural productivity and NDVI, which argues against the land management explanation.

Olsson *et al.* then suggest the greening of the Sahel could be caused by increasing rural-to-urban migration. In this scenario, widespread increases in vegetation occur as a result of "reduced area under cultivation," due to a shortage of rural laborers, and/or "increasing inputs on cropland," such as seeds, machinery, and fertilizers made possible by an increase in money sent home to rural households by family members working in cities. Olsson *et al.* note, "more empirical research is needed to verify this [hypothesis]."

Ichii *et al.* (2005) "simulated and analyzed 1982–1999 Amazonian, African, and Asian carbon fluxes using the Biome-BGC prognostic carbon cycle model driven by National Centers for Environmental Prediction reanalysis daily climate data," after which they "calculated trends in gross primary productivity (GPP) and net primary productivity (NPP)." They found solar radiation variability to be the primary factor responsible for interannual variations in GPP, followed by temperature and precipitation variability. As to GPP trends, the authors report, "recent changes in atmospheric CO_2 and climate promoted terrestrial GPP increases with a significant linear trend in all three tropical regions." In the African region, the rate of GPP increase was about 0.3 PgC year^{-1} per decade. In identifying the major cause of the increased growth, Ichii *et al.* favored carbon dioxide, reporting "CO_2 fertilization effects strongly increased recent NPP trends in regional totals."

Herrmann *et al.* (2005) investigated the "temporal and spatial patterns of vegetation greenness and rainfall variability in the African Sahel and their interrelationships based on analyses of Normalized Difference Vegetation Index (NDVI) time series for the years 1982–2003 and gridded satellite rainfall estimates." The three researchers determined "the overall trend in monthly maximum NDVI [was] positive over a large portion of the Sahel region, reaching up to 50% increase in the average NDVI in parts of Mali, Mauritania and Chad" (see Figure 4.2.2.1.1). In addition, they report, "rainfall emerges as the dominant causative factor in the dynamics of vegetation greenness in the Sahel at an 8 km spatial resolution," but "the presence of spatially coherent and significant long-term trends in the residuals suggests that there might be another, weaker,

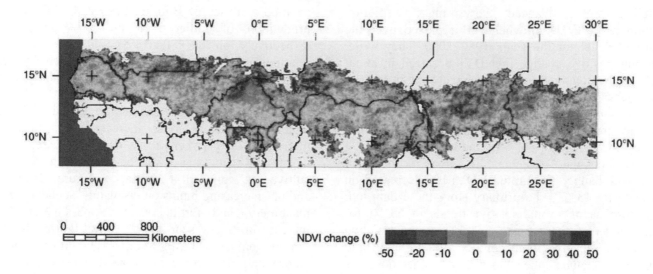

Figure 4.2.2.1.1. Percent change in vegetation greenness throughout the African Sahel during the years 1982–2003 based on monthly AVHRR NDVI time series data. Percentages indicate changes in average NDVI between 1982 and 2003. Adapted from Herrmann *et al.* (2005).

causative factor," as the "recovery of vegetation greenness [was] beyond what would be expected from the recovery of rainfall conditions alone."

Herrmann *et al.* state their study "confirms previous regional-scale findings for the years 1982–1999 by Eklundh and Olsson (2003) and Olsson *et al.* (2005), who observed widespread positive trends of both time-integrated NDVI and NDVI amplitudes, and Anyamba and Tucker (2005), who [observed] increases in growing season NDVI across most parts of the region." They conclude, "a greening of the Sahel expressed in positive trends in NDVI indicates a net increase in biomass production during the period 1982–2003, which challenges the notion of irreversible desertification in the Sahel."

Midgley and Seydack (2006) note "present and predicted future impacts of global environmental change on intact forests are both alarming and contentious," and "some local models have predicted the demise of South Africa's only significant extent of indigenous forest, the Knysna forest, by 2050," as reported by Midgley *et al.* (2001). To see how bad things had become by the end of the twentieth century, the authors measured and analyzed the growth of all trees greater than 10 cm in diameter at breast height in 108 0.04-ha plots distributed throughout an unharvested nature reserve in the Knysna forest for the years 1991–2001.

Following a protocol that provided what they say is "probably an under-estimate," the two researchers state, "net basal area and aboveground biomass increased over the 10-year study period by 2% and

there was a 1.2% increase in stem numbers, distributed almost equally amongst all size-classes." Because of the nature of the Knysna forest, Midgley and Seydack say "over relatively short periods such as our decade, the aboveground biomass of this forest is more sensitive to negative/stressful conditions that would increase mortality, than to factors which may increase growth." Nevertheless, they found "biomass increased." And because "precipitation over the period 1991–2001 was some 5% less than the long-term average," they conclude the observed increase in growth rate "may have been the effect of the increase in global atmospheric carbon dioxide."

Seaquist *et al.* (2006) provided important new details about the "greening up" of the African Sahel. Using a satellite data-driven light-use efficiency model to assess changes in absolute amounts of net primary production (NPP), expressed as carbon content, and its interannual variability in the African Sahel for the years 1982–1999, Seaquist *et al.* report they found an extensive, albeit discontinuous, east-west band of NPP increase (>10 g C m^{-2} year^{-1}). The band extends up to about 17°N and includes several hotspots (>20 g C m^{-2} year^{-1}) in central Senegal, south-western Mali, southern Chad, southern Sudan, and the Ivory Coast and southern Benin. For the Sahel in its entirety, the researchers calculate the mean rate of change per pixel was 8.4 g C m^{-2} year^{-1}, yielding a total mean rate of change of 51.0 Mt C year^{-1} and an absolute net gain in NPP over the 18-year period of 918.0 Mt C. In addition, they report, "this increase is associated with a decrease in the inter-annual variability of NPP for the 1990s compared to the 1980s," such that "overall, the increase in NPP through time appears to be associated with an increase in the stability of this ecosystem," with the changes in carbon capture and increase in stability being driven primarily by rainfall "followed by atmospheric CO_2."

Lewis *et al.* (2009a) documented changes in aboveground carbon storage in "79 permanent sample plots spanning 40 years (1968–2007), located in closed-canopy moist forest, spanning West, Central and Eastern Africa," based on data on more than 70,000 individual trees in 10 countries. They found "aboveground carbon storage in live trees increased by 0.63 Mg C ha^{-1} year^{-1} between 1968 and 2007," and "extrapolation to unmeasured forest components (live roots, small trees, necromass) and scaling to the continent implies a total increase in carbon storage in African tropical forest trees of 0.34 Pg C year^{-1}."

The 33 researchers say the observed changes in carbon storage "are similar to those reported for Amazonian forests per unit area, providing evidence that increasing carbon storage in old-growth forests is a pan-tropical phenomenon," and "combining all standardized inventory data from this study and from tropical America and Asia together yields a comparable figure of 0.49 Mg C ha^{-1} year^{-1}," which equates to "a carbon sink of 1.3 Pg C year^{-1} across all tropical forests during recent decades." That can account for roughly half of the so-called missing carbon sink.

Lewis *et al.* conclude, "taxon-specific analyses of African inventory and other data suggest that widespread changes in resource availability, such as increasing atmospheric carbon dioxide concentrations, may be the cause of the increase in carbon stocks, as some theory (Lloyd and Farquhar, 1996) and models (Friedlingstein *et al.*, 2006; Stephens *et al.*, 2007; Ciais *et al.*, 2008) predict."

Ciais *et al.* (2009) modeled the terrestrial carbon balance of Africa over the past century (1901–2002) using a spatially resolved process-based vegetation model (ORCHIDEE), which is forced by changing climate, human-induced changes in land use, and a parameterization of natural fires. They found the African net terrestrial carbon (C) balance increased "from a net CO_2 source to the atmosphere of 0.14 Pg C per year in the 1980s to a net sink of 0.15 Pg C per year in the 1990s." In addition, the land use flux due to deforestation was "a source of 0.13 Pg C per year," and "this implies that climatic trends (mainly increasing precipitation) and CO_2 increase (the fertilization effect), are causing a sink of 0.28 Pg C per year which

offsets the land-use source."

The five researchers write, "the trend of gross primary production is closely matching the trend in satellite observed NDVI." They state their simulated trend in gross primary production "is also consistent with an increased vegetation activity over [the] Sahel reported by Eklundh and Olsson (2003) and Olsson *et al.* (2005)." At the continental scale, they say the gross primary production trend can be largely (70%) explained by the CO_2 fertilization effect.

Doherty *et al.* (2010) modeled future changes in land biogeochemistry and biogeography in the region bounded by 12.5°N, 12.5°S, 25°E, and 42.5°E, representing most of East Africa (Kenya, Tanzania, Uganda, Rwanda, Burundi, Ethiopia, and Somalia) and portions of Central Africa (the Democratic Republic of Congo and Southern Sudan). They used 18 future climate projections derived from nine general circulation models that figured prominently in IPCC's *Fourth Assessment Report*, employing the projections as input to the Lund-Potsdam-Jena dynamic global vegetation model that simulates changes in vegetation and ecosystem carbon cycling under future climate conditions, based on what they describe as "a coupled photosynthesis-hydrological scheme [that] computes gross primary productivity, plant respiration, and evapotranspiration on a daily time step based on the current climate, atmospheric CO_2 concentration, vegetation structure and phenological state, and soil water content."

Doherty *et al.* report "all simulations showed future increases in tropical woody vegetation over the region at the expense of grasslands," noting "regional increases in net primary productivity (18–36%) and total carbon storage (3–13%) by 2080–2099 compared with the present-day were common to all simulations," and "seven out of nine simulations continued to show an annual net land carbon sink in the final decades of the 21st century because vegetation biomass continued to increase." They write, "overall, our model results suggest that East Africa, a populous and economically poor region, is likely to experience some ecosystem service benefits through increased precipitation, river runoff and fresh water availability," and "resulting enhancements in net primary productivity may lead to improved crop yields in some areas." They note their results "stand in partial contradiction of other studies that suggest possible negative consequences for agriculture, biodiversity and other ecosystem services caused by temperature increases."

Scheiter and Higgins (2009) write, "recent IPCC projections suggest that Africa will be subject to particularly severe changes in atmospheric conditions" in the future, and these changes could have equally severe repercussions for its flora and fauna. How the continent's "grassland-savanna-forest complex will respond to these changes has rarely been investigated," they note, and "most studies on global carbon cycles use vegetation models that do not adequately account for the complexity of the interactions that shape the distribution of tropical grasslands, savannas and forests."

The two scientists developed a new vegetation model—the adaptive dynamic global vegetation model (aDGVM)—that employs established sub-models for photosynthesis, respiration, canopy scaling, competition for water, competition for light, reproduction, and mortality. Their model also contains novel elements: dynamic carbon allocation and phenology functions, as well as a fire model that estimates fire intensity as a function of fuel biomass, fuel moisture, and wind speed, and which simulates topkill (stem mortality) as a function of individual tree size and fire intensity. All of these phenomena are related to the individual plant's physiological state and the environmental conditions surrounding it.

Simulations to the year 2100 with this model suggest "grasslands will spread into the Sahara and into the horn of Africa, such that the total area covered by deserts or bare soil decreases by 5.7%." In addition, "it is predicted that 34.6% of today's grasslands are transformed into savannas," and "45.3% of today's savannas are transformed into deciduous woodlands." As a result, "the total biomass stored in each of the biomes increases, with high relative changes in grasslands and savannas (by 256% and 241%, respectively)," with a 102% increase in tree biomass.

Heubes *et al.* (2011) modeled the future spatial distribution of desert, grassland, savanna, and deciduous and evergreen forests in West Africa using six bioclimatic models. None of the models accounted for the photosynthetic-enhancing and transpiration-reducing effects of projected increases in atmospheric CO_2 concentration, as they were based solely on the climatic projections of 17 general circulation models of the atmosphere for emissions scenario A2a, as described in the *Fourth Assessment Report* of IPCC (2007). These projections were downscaled to 0.1 degree of latitude and longitude as described by Ramirez and Jarvis (2008).

Heubes *et al.* report finding "a climate-driven greening trend," with "northward spread of grassland into the Sahara and the replacement of savannas by deciduous forest." These results, they write, "are

concordant with results from Cramer *et al.* (2001), Scholze *et al.* (2006) and Scheiter and Higgins (2009)," although they add the latter investigators "attributed the greening to increased CO_2 levels." They say the models they used "indicate climatic change alone can yield this pattern," where "the expected 'greening' of the Sahara is primarily driven by increasing precipitation," as they note Hickler *et al.* (2005) also suggested.

Using satellite images that reflect the region's current vegetation state, Heubes *et al.* additionally modeled "real" as opposed to "potential" vegetation, which enabled them to "clearly show," as they describe it, "effects of human activity negatively affecting tree cover, as also demonstrated by other case studies, e.g. in Senegal (Vincke *et al.*, 2010) and Mali (Ruelland *et al.*, 2010)." They report, in West Africa, "agricultural expansion, sometimes facilitated by other human activities such as wood extraction, has been identified as major drivers of forest loss and degradation," citing Norris *et al.* (2010).

"Considering climate change alone," Heubes *et al.* write, "the model results of potential vegetation (biomes) show a 'greening' trend by 2050," although "the modeled effects of human impact suggest future forest degradation."

The research presented here indicates the ongoing rise in the air's CO_2 concentration and its anti-transpiration effect, which improves plant water-use efficiency, are enhancing and will continue to enhance the vegetative productivity of Africa.

References

Anyamba, A. and Tucker, C.J. 2005. Analysis of Sahelian vegetation dynamics using NOAA-AVHRR NDVI data from 1981–2003. *Journal of Arid Environments* **63**: 596–614.

Ciais, P., Piao, S.-L., Cadule, P., Friedlingstein, P., and Chedin, A. 2008. Variability and recent trends in the African carbon balance. *Biogeosciences Discussions* **5**: 3497–3532.

Ciais, P., Piao, S.-L., Cadule, P., Friedlingstein, P., and Chedin, A. 2009. Variability and recent trends in the African terrestrial carbon balance. *Biogeosciences* **6**: 1935–1948.

Cramer, W., Bondeau, A., Woodward, F.I., Prentice, I.C., Betts, R.A., Brovkin, V., Cox, P.M., Fisher, V., Foley, J.A., Friend, A.D., Kucharik, C., Lomas, M.R., Ramankutty, N., Sitch, S., Smith, B., White, A., and Young-Molling, C. 2001. Global response of terrestrial ecosystem structure and function to CO_2 and climate change: results from six dynamic global vegetation models. *Global Change Biology* **7**: 357–373.

Doherty, R.M., Sitch, S., Smith, B., Lewis, S.L., and Thornton, P.K. 2010. Implications of future climate and atmospheric CO_2 content for regional biogeochemistry, biogeography and ecosystem services across East Africa. *Global Change Biology* **16**: 617–640.

Eklundh, L. and Olssson, L. 2003. Vegetation index trends for the African Sahel 1982–1999. *Geophysical Research Letters* **30**: 10.1029/2002GL016772.

Friedlingstein, P., Cox, P., Betts, R., Bopp, L., von Bloh, W., Brovkin, V., Cadule, P., Doney, S., Eby, M., Fung, I., Bala, G., John, J., Jones, C., Joos, F., Kato, T., Kawamiya, M., Knorr, W., Lindsay, K., Matthews, H.D., Raddatz, T., Rayner, P., Reick, C., Roeckner, E., Schnitzler, K.-G., Schnur, R., Strassmann, K., Weaver, A.J., Yoshikawa, C., and Zeng, N. 2006. Climate-carbon cycle feedback analysis: Results from the (CMIP)-M-4 model inter-comparison. *Journal of Climate* **19**: 3337–3353.

Herrmann, S.M., Anyamba, A., and Tucker, C.J. 2005. Recent trends in vegetation dynamics in the African Sahel and their relationship to climate. *Global Environmental Change* **15**: 394–404.

Heubes, J., Kuhn, I., Konig, K., Wittig, R., Zizka, G., and Hahn, K. 2011. Modelling biome shifts and tree cover change for 2050 in West Africa. *Journal of Biogeography* **38**: 2248–2258.

Hickler, T., Eklundh, L., Seaquist, J.W., Smith, B., Ardo, J., Olsson, L., Sykes, M.T., and Sjostrom, M. 2005. Precipitation controls Sahel greening trend. *Geophysical Research Letters* **32**: 10.1029/2005GL024370.

Ichii, K., Hashimoto, H., Nemani, R., and White, M. 2005. Modeling the interannual variability and trends in gross and net primary productivity of tropical forests from 1982 to 1999. *Global and Planetary Change* **48**: 274–286.

IPCC. 2007. *Climate Change 2007: Impacts, Adaptation and Vulnerability*. IPCC Secretariat, Geneva, Switzerland.

Lewis, S.L., Lloyd, J., Sitch, S., Mitchard, E.T.A., and Laurance, W.F. 2009a. Changing ecology of tropical forests: Evidence and drivers. *Annual Review of Ecology, Evolution, and Systematics* **40**: 529–549.

Lloyd, J. and Farquhar, G.D. 1996. The CO_2 dependence of photosynthesis, plant growth responses to elevated atmospheric CO_2 concentrations and their interaction with soil nutrient status. 1. General principles and forest ecosystems. *Functional Ecology* **10**: 4–32.

Midgley, G.F., Rutherford, M., and Bond, W.J. 2001. *The Heat Is On: Impacts of Global Change on Plant Diversity in South Africa*. National Botanical Institute, Cape Town, South Africa.

Midgley, J.J. and Seydack, A. 2006. No adverse signs of the effect of environmental change on tree biomass in the Knysna forest during the 1990s. *South African Journal of Science* **102**: 96–97.

Nicholson, S. 2005. On the question of the 'recovery" of the rains in the West African Sahel. *Journal of Arid Environments* **63**: 615–641.

Nicholson, S.E., Tucker, C.J., and Ba, M.B. 1998. Desertification, drought, and surface vegetation: An example from the West African Sahel. *Bulletin of the American Meteorological Society* **79**: 815–829.

Norris, K., Asase, A., Collen, B., Gockowksi, J., Mason, J., Phalan, B., and Wade, A. 2010. Biodiversity in a forest-agriculture mosaic—The changing face of West African rainforests. *Biological Conservation* **143**: 2341–2350.

Olsson, L., Eklundh, L., and Ardo, J. 2005. A recent greening of the Sahel—trends, patterns and potential causes. *Journal of Arid Environments* **63**: 556–566.

Prince, S.D., Brown De Colstoun, E., and Kravitz, L.L. 1998. Evidence from rain-use efficiencies does not indicate extensive Sahelian desertification. *Global Change Biology* **4**: 359–374.

Ramirez, J. and Jarvis, A. 2008. *High Resolution Statistically Downscaled Future Climate Surfaces*. International Centre for Tropical Agriculture, Cali, Colombia.

Ruelland, D., Levavasseur, F., and Tribotte, A. 2010. Patterns and dynamics of land-cover changes since the 1960s over three experimental areas in Mali. *International Journal of Applied Earth Observation and Geoinformation* **12**: S11-S17.

Runnstrom, M. 2003. Rangeland development of the Mu Us Sandy Land in semiarid China: an analysis using Landsat and NOAA remote sensing data. *Land Degradation & Development Studies* **14**: 189–202.

Scheiter, S. and Higgins, S.I. 2009. Impacts of climate change on the vegetation of Africa: an adaptive dynamic vegetation modeling approach. *Global Change Biology* **15**: 2224–2246.

Scholze, M., Knorr, W., Arnell, N.W., and Prentice, I.C. 2006. A climate-change risk analysis for world ecosystems. *Proceedings of the National Academy of Sciences USA* **103**: 13,116–13,120.

Seaquist, J.W., Olsson, L., Ardo, J., and Eklundh, L. 2006. Broad-scale increase in NPP quantified for the African Sahel, 1982–1999. *International Journal of Remote Sensing* **27**: 5115–5122.

Stephens, B.B., Gurney, K.R., Tans, P.P., Sweeney, C., Peters, W., Bruhwiler, L., Ciais, P., Ramonet, M., Bousquet, P., Nakazawa, T., Aoki, S., Machida, T., Inoue,

G., Vinnichenko, N., Lloyd, J., Jordan, A., Heimann, M., Shibistova, O., Langenfelds, R.L., Steele, L.P., Francey, R.J., and Denning, A.S. 2007. Weak northern and strong tropical land carbon uptake from vertical profiles of atmospheric CO_2. *Science* **316**: 1732–1735.

Vincke, C., Diedhiou, I., and Grouzis, M. 2010. Long term dynamics and structure of woody vegetation in the Ferlo (Senegal). *Journal of Arid Environments* **74**: 268–276.

4.2.2.2 Asia

- The rise of the air's CO_2 concentration and temperature to their highest values of the past century enhanced the terrestrial vegetative productivity of all parts of Asia, including deserts, forests, grasslands, and the Tibetan Plateau.

Many scientists have examined terrestrial productivity trends in Asia, with a vast majority of those studies focusing on locations in China. The material below is arranged into two sub-headings: *China* and *All Other Asian Countries*. In addition, given the sheer number of studies conducted in China, that subsection is further divided into five sub-regions: *Country-wide*, *Deserts*, *Forests*, *Grasslands*, and the *Tibetan Plateau*.

4.2.2.2.1 China

4.2.2.2.1.1 Country-wide

Liu *et al.* (2004) derived detailed estimates of the economic impact of predicted climate change on agriculture in China. They used county-level agricultural, climate, social, economic, and edaphic data for 1,275 agriculture-dominated counties for the years 1985–1991, together with the outputs of three general circulation models of the atmosphere based on five scenarios of anthropogenic CO_2-induced climate change that yielded a mean countrywide temperature increase of 3.0°C and a mean precipitation increase of 3.9% for the 50-year period ending in AD 2050. They determined "all of China would benefit from climate change in most scenarios." They also note, "the effects of CO_2 fertilization should be included, for some studies indicate that this may produce a significant increase in yield."

Fang *et al.* (2003) also looked at the whole of China, finding its terrestrial NPP increased by 18.7%

between 1982 and 1999. Referring to this result as "an unexpected aspect of biosphere dynamics," they say this increase "is much greater than would be expected to result from the fertilization effect of elevated CO_2, and also greater than expected from climate, based on broad geographic patterns." They may be wrong in that assessment. From 1982 to 1999 the atmosphere's CO_2 concentration rose by approximately 27.4 ppm, which could be expected to have increased the NPP of the forest types found in China by about 7.3% (see http://www.co2science.org/articles/V5/N38/EDIT.php for an explanation of this calculation).

And this increase is only part of the total NPP increase one could expect, for Fang *et al.* note "much of the trend in NPP appeared to reflect a change towards an earlier growing season," which was driven by the 1.1°C increase in temperature they found in their region of study between 1982 and 1999. White *et al.* (1999) analyzed 88 years of data (1900–1987) from 12 locations in the eastern U.S. deciduous forest that stretches from Charleston, South Carolina to Burlington, Vermont, finding a 1°C increase in mean annual air temperature increases the length of the forest's growing season by approximately five days. They further report a one-day extension in growing season increased the mean forest NPP of the 12 sites they studied by an average of 1.6%.

Applying White *et al.*'s results to Fang *et al.*'s findings suggests there could easily be an additional increase in the NPP of China's forests due to the warming-induced growing season expansion experienced there from 1982 to 1999: 1.6%/day x 5 days = 8.0%, bringing the total CO_2-induced plus warming-induced increase in NPP for China to 15.3%.

Moreover, as noted previously in this chapter, there is a well-documented positive synergy between increasing air temperature and CO_2 concentration (Idso and Idso, 1994), so the 1°C increase in temperature experienced in China between 1982 and 1999 could easily boost the initial CO_2-induced 7.3% NPP enhancement to 10.7% . That, when combined with the 8.0% enhancement caused by the warming-induced increase in growing season length, would produce the 18.7% increase in NPP Fang *et al.* detected in the satellite data.

Piao *et al.* (2005a) found "terrestrial NPP in China increased at a rate of 0.015 Pg C yr^{-1} over the period 1982–1999, corresponding to a total increase of 18.5%, or 1.03% annually." They also report, "during the past 2 decades the amplitude of the seasonal curve of NPP has increased and the annual peak NPP has advanced," which "may indirectly explain the enhanced amplitude and advanced timing of the seasonal cycle of atmospheric CO_2 concentration (Keeling *et al.*, 1996)." They further suggest the enhanced amplitude of the seasonal CO_2 cycle "was probably due to the rise in atmospheric CO_2 concentration, elevated temperature, and increased atmospheric N and P deposition," and they attribute the advanced timing of the seasonal cycle to "advanced spring onset and extended autumn growth owing to climate warming."

Citing 20 scientific papers, Piao *et al.* conclude "results from observed atmospheric CO_2 and O_2 concentrations, inventory data, remote sensing data, and carbon process models have all suggested that terrestrial vegetation NPP of the Northern Hemisphere has increased over the past 2 decades and, as a result, the northern terrestrial ecosystems have become important sinks for atmospheric CO_2."

Zhu *et al.* (2007a) analyzed 18 years (1982–1999) of climatic data and satellite observations of normalized difference vegetation index (NDVI) throughout China, calculating terrestrial vegetative net primary productivity (NPP) using the revised light-use efficiency model of Zhu *et al.* (2006) and Zhu *et al.* (2007b). They find "climatic changes in China have eased some critical climatic constraints on plant growth." They note, for example, "water availability most strongly limits vegetation growth over 28% of the whole country surface, whereas temperature limits growth over 43% and radiation over 29%," but "from 1982 to 1999, modeled NPP increased by 1.42% per year in water-limited regions of Northwest China, 1.46% per year in temperature-limited regions of Northeast China and Tibet Plateau, and 0.99% per year in radiation-limited regions of South China and East China." Summed over the 18-year period, total Chinese terrestrial vegetation NPP increased by 24.2%. They report "interannual variations of NPP in Chinese terrestrial vegetation are positively correlated with global increases in atmospheric CO_2 growth rate, indicating that NPP in Chinese terrestrial vegetation will increase with the global increases in atmospheric CO_2 growth rate."

Peng *et al.* (2011) report, "using satellite-derived normalized difference vegetation index (NDVI) datasets, previous studies have found that vegetation growth significantly increased in most areas of China during the period 1982–99 and that the increased vegetation growth was significantly correlated with increased temperature (e.g., Zhou *et al.*, 2001; Piao *et al.*, 2003)." In addition, "the increased temperature boosted vegetation growth through an increase in

growing season length and enhanced photosynthesis (e.g., Zhou *et al.*, 2001; Slayback *et al.*, 2003; Piao *et al.*, 2006b)."

Peng *et al.* used NOAA/AVHRR NDVI composites at a spatial resolution of 0.083° and 15-day intervals produced by the Global Inventory Modeling and Mapping Studies (GIMMS) program, Tucker *et al.* (2005), to explore vegetation activity over China for the years 1982–2010. They note "the GIMMS NDVI datasets have been corrected to minimize the effects of volcanic eruptions, solar angle and sensor errors and shifts," as described by Zhou *et al.* (2001) and Slayback *et al.* (2003), and state these datasets also have proved to be "one of the best products to depict the temporal change of vegetation growth," as Beck *et al.* (2011) demonstrated.

At the national scale and for the average growing season (April–October) a linear regression model predicts a significant increasing NDVI trend of 0.0007/year from 1982 to 2010, with an R^2 value of 0.40 and $P < 0.001$ (see Figure 4.2.2.2.1.1.1). They also found increasing trends for all three subsets of the growing season: April–May, June–August, and September–October.

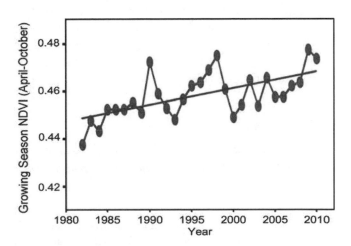

Figure 4.2.2.2.1.1.1. Interannual variations in growing season (April-October) NDVI for China during the years 1982–2010. The linear trend in the data, as mentioned in the text, is also shown. Adapted from Peng *et al.* (2011).

Mao *et al.* (2009) used a modified version of the Sheffield Dynamic Global Vegetation Model described by Woodward and Lomas (2004) to study changes in the structure, composition, and carbon storage of vegetation and soils throughout China in response to changes in climate and atmospheric CO_2 concentration between 1901 and 2000. They report their modeling exercise indicates "during the past

100 years a combination of increasing CO_2 with historical temperature and precipitation variability in continental China have caused the total vegetation carbon storage to increase by 2.04 Pg C, with 2.07 Pg C gained in the vegetation biomass but 0.03 Pg C lost from the organic soil carbon matter." They also found "the increasing CO_2 concentration in the 20th century is primarily responsible for the increase of the total potential vegetation carbon."

Mu *et al.* (2008) used "a well-documented daily ecosystem process model Biome-BGC (Running and Hunt, 1993; White *et al.*, 2000; Thornton *et al.*, 2002) to differentiate the effects of changing climate and increasing CO_2 on the carbon cycle for terrestrial China for two time periods, 1961–2000 (present conditions), and future (2071–2110) conditions with projected climate change under doubled CO_2." The five researchers write, "during 1961–2000 at the national scale, changes in climate reduced carbon storage in China's ecosystems, but increasing CO_2 compensated for these adverse effects of climate change, resulting in an overall increase in the carbon storage of China's ecosystems." They continue, "under the future scenario (2071–2110), with a doubling [of] CO_2, China will experience higher precipitation and temperature," but "the concomitant doubling of CO_2 will continue to counteract the negative effects of climate change on carbon uptake in the future, leading to an increase in carbon storage relative to current levels."

References

Ashton, B., Hill, K., Piazza, A., and Zeitz, R. 1984. Famine in China, 1958–1961. *Population and Development Review* **10**: 613–615.

Beck, H.E., McVicar, T.R., van Dijk, A.I.J.M., Schellekens, J., de Jeu, R.A.M., and Bruijnzeel, L.A. 2011. Global evaluation of four AVHRR-NDVI data sets: intercomparison and assessment against Landsat imagery. *Remote Sensing of the Environment* **115**: 2547–2563.

Cambridge History of China. 1987. Volume 14. Cambridge University Press, Cambridge, UK.

Fang, J., Piao, S., Field, C.B., Pan, Y., Guo, Q., Zhou, L., Peng, C., and Tao, S. 2003. Increasing net primary production in China from 1982 to 1999. *Frontiers in Ecology and the Environment* **1**: 293–297.

Idso, K.E. and Idso, S.B. 1994. Plant responses to atmospheric CO_2 enrichment in the face of environmental constraints: A review of the past 10 years' research. *Agricultural and Forest Meteorology* **69**: 153–203.

Keeling, C.D., Chin, J.F.S., and Whorf, T.P. 1996. Increased activity of northern vegetation inferred from atmospheric CO_2 measurements. *Nature* **382**: 146–149.

Liu, H., Li, X., Fischer, G., and Sun, L. 2004. Study on the impacts of climate change on China's agriculture. *Climatic Change* **65**: 125–148.

Mao, J., Wang, B., and Yongjiu, D. 2009. Sensitivity of the carbon storage of potential vegetation to historical climate variability and CO_2 in continental China. *Advances in Atmospheric Sciences* **26**: 87–100.

Mu, Q., Zhao, M., Running, S.W., Liu, M., and Tian, H. 2008. Contribution of increasing CO_2 and climate change to the carbon cycle in China's ecosystems. *Journal of Geophysical Research* **113**: 10.1029/2006JG000316.

Peng, S., Chen, A., Xu, L., Cao, C., Fang, J., Myneni, R.B., Pinzon, J.E., Tucker, C.J., and Piao, S. 2011. Recent change of vegetation growth trend in China. *Environmental Research Letters* **6**: 10.1088/1748–9326/6/4/044027.

Piao, S., Fang, J.Y., Zhou, L.M., Ciais, P., and Zhu, B. 2006b. Variations in satellite-derived phenology in China's temperate vegetation. *Global Change Biology* **12**: 672–685.

Piao, S.L., Fang, J.Y., Zhou, L.M., Guo, Q.H., Henderson, M., Ji, W., Li, Y., and Tao, S. 2003. Interannual variations of monthly seasonal normalized difference vegetation index (NDVI) in China from 1982 to 1999. *Journal of Geophysical Research* **108**: 4401–4413.

Piao, S.L., Fang, J.Y., Zhou, L.M., Zhu, B., Tan, K., and Tao, S. 2005a. Changes in vegetation net primary productivity from 1982 to 1999 in China. *Global Biogeochemical Cycles* **19**: 10.1029/2004GB002274.

Running, S.W. and Hunt, E.R. 1993. Generalization of a forest ecosystem process model for other biomes, Biome-BGC, and an application for global-scale models. In Ehleringer, J.R. and Field, C.B. (Eds.) *Scaling Physiological Processes: Leaf to Globe*. Academic Press, San Diego, California, USA, pp. 141–158.

Slayback, D.A., Pinzon, J.E., Los, S.O., and Tucker, C.J. 2003. Northern Hemisphere photosynthetic trends 1982–99. *Global Change Biology* **9**: 1–15.

Thornton, P.E., Law, B.E., Gholz, H.L., Clark, K.L., Falge, E., Ellsworth, D.S., Goldstein, A.H., Monson, R.K., Hollinger, D., Falk, M., Chen, J., and Sparks, J.P. 2002. Modeling and measuring the effects of disturbance history and climate on carbon and water budgets in evergreen needleleaf forests. *Agricultural and Forest Meteorology* **113**: 185–222.

Tucker, C.J., Pinzon, J.E., Brown, M.E., Slayback, D.A., Pak, E.W., Mahoney, R., Vermote, E.F., and El Saleous, N. 2005. An extended AVHRR 8-km NDVI dataset compatible with MODIS and SPOT vegetation NDVI data. *International Journal of Remote Sensing* **26**: 4485–4498.

White, M.A., Running, S.W., and Thornton, P.E. 1999. The impact of growing-season length variability on carbon assimilation and evapotranspiration over 88 years in the eastern US deciduous forest. *International Journal of Biometeorology* **42**: 139–145.

White, M.A., Thornton, P.E., Running, S.W., and Nemani, R.R. 2000. Parameterization and sensitivity analysis of the BIOME-BGC terrestrial ecosystem model: Net primary production controls. *Earth Interactions* **4**: 1–84.

Woodward, F.I. and Lomas, M.R. 2004. Vegetation dynamics—Simulation responses to climatic change. *Biological Reviews* **79**: 643–670.

Zhou, L.M., Tucker, C.J., Kaufmann, R.K., Slayback, D., Shabanov, N.V., and Myneni, R.B. 2001. Variations in northern vegetation activity inferred from satellite data of vegetation index during 1981 to 1999. *Journal of Geophysical Research* **106**: 20,069–20,083.

Zhu, W.Q., Pan, Y.Z., He, H., Yu, D., and Hu, H. 2006. Simulation of maximum light use efficiency for some typical vegetation types in China. *Chinese Science Bulletin* **51**: 457–463.

Zhu, W.Q., Pan, Y.Z., Yang, X.Q., and Song, G.B. 2007a. Comprehensive analysis of the impact of climatic changes on Chinese terrestrial net primary productivity. *Chinese Science Bulletin* **52**: 3253–3260.

Zhu, W.Q., Pan, Y.Z., and Zhang, J.S. 2007b. Estimation of net primary productivity of Chinese terrestrial vegetation based on remote sensing. *Journal of Plant Ecology* **31**: 413–424.

4.2.2.2.1.2 Deserts

Brogaard *et al.* (2005) examined the dry northern and northwestern regions of China, including the Inner Mongolia Autonomous Region (IMAR), which had been thought to have experienced declining vegetative productivity over the past few decades due to "increasing livestock numbers, expansion of cultivated land on erosive soils and the gathering of fuel wood and herb digging." These practices were believed to have been driven by rising living standards that, in combination with a growing population, increased the pressure on these marginal lands. Brogaard *et al.* note the total number of livestock in the IMAR increased from approximately 46 million head in 1980 to about 71 million in 1997.

To better assess the seriousness of this "ongoing land degradation process," as they describe it, the researchers adapted a satellite-driven parametric model, originally developed for Sahelian conditions, to the central Asian steppe region of the IMAR by including "additional stress factors and growth efficiency computations." The applied model, they write, "uses satellite sensor-acquired reflectance in combination with climate data to generate monthly estimates of gross primary production." They found, "despite a rapid increase in grazing animals on the steppes of the IMAR for the 1982–1999 period," their model estimates did "not indicate declining biological production."

Clearly, some strong positive influence compensated for the increased human and animal pressures on the lands of the IMAR over the period of Brogaard *et al.*'s study. They mention the possibility of increasing productivity on the agricultural lands of the IMAR, but crops are grown on "only a small proportion of the total land area." They also mention "an increase in precipitation, as well as afforestation projects." Two things they do not mention are the aerial fertilization and transpiration-reducing effects of the increase in the air's CO_2 concentration over the study period. Applied together, these positive influences, and possibly others that remain unknown, are demonstrably sufficient to keep plant productivity from declining in the face of greatly increasing animal and human pressures.

Yang *et al.* (2011) studied *Caragana microphylla* plantations established five to 40 years ago in the semi-arid Loess Plateau of northwestern Shanxi, China in efforts to combat desertification, which in the 1960s had claimed 48.5% of the region's surface area. These perennial leguminous and sand-binding shrubs have well-developed stems with many clustered branches and large root systems capable of adapting to poor nutrient conditions, and they were positioned in groups to act as sand barriers and windbreaks.

The establishment and development of the *C. microphylla* shrubs, in the words of the five Chinese scientists, "improved soil texture, enhanced soil organic matter (SOM), total nitrogen (TN), and cation exchange capacity (CEC)." In addition, "SOM, TN, and CEC were significantly higher at the center than at the outside of the shrub canopies and were higher at the 0–5 cm depth than at the 5–10 cm depth." They report "the differences in SOM, TN, and CEC from the center to the outside of shrub canopies were greater under 30- and 40-year-old shrubs than under 10- and 5-year-old shrubs." They found the spatiotemporal heterogeneity of the soil properties "facilitated the development of herbaceous species diversity and the restoration of the [region's] natural ecosystem," which had been lost to desertification.

Peng *et al.* (2010) used snow-depth measurements collected at 279 meteorological stations across China, plus co-located satellite-derived normalized difference vegetation index (NDVI) data, to investigate spatio-temporal changes in snow depth for the years 1980–2006 and the effects of those changes on vegetative growth the following spring and summer. The five researchers report, "over the past three decades, winter snow depth overall increased in northern China, particularly in the most arid and semiarid regions of western China where desert and grassland are mainly distributed." In those areas they found positive correlations between mean winter snow depth and spring NDVI data. They also note Piao *et al.* (2005b) determined the net primary productivity of the same desert and grasslands during 1982–1999 "increased by 1.6% per year and 1.1% per year, respectively," and "desertification has been reversed in some areas of western China since the 1980s," citing Runnstrom (2000), Wu (2001), Zhang *et al.* (2003), and Piao *et al.* (2005b).

Peng *et al.* state the "increase in vegetation coverage in arid and semiarid regions of China, possibly driven by winter snow, will likely restore soil and enhance its anti-wind-erosion ability, reducing the possibility of released dust and mitigating sand-dust storms," noting the frequency of sand-dust storms has indeed "declined in China since the early 1980s (Qian *et al.*, 2002; Zhao *et al.*, 2004)."

Piao *et al.* (2005b) used a time series of NDVI data from 1982 to 1999, together with precipitation and temperature data, to investigate variations of desert area in China by "identifying the climatic boundaries of arid area and semiarid area, and changes in NDVI in these areas." They discovered "average rainy season NDVI in arid and semiarid regions both increased significantly during the period 1982–1999." They report the NDVI increased for 72.3% of total arid regions and for 88.2% of total semiarid regions, such that the area of arid regions decreased by 6.9% and the area of semiarid regions decreased by 7.9% (see Figure 4.2.2.2.1.2.1). They also report, by analyzing Thematic Mapper satellite images, "Zhang *et al.* (2003) documented that the process of desertification in the Yulin area, Shannxi Province showed a decreased trend between 1987 and 1999," and "according to the national monitoring data on desertification in western China (Shi, 2003), the annual desertification rate decreased from 1.2% in the 1950s to -0.2% at present."

Further noting "variations in the vegetation coverage of these regions partly affect the frequency of sand-dust storm occurrence (Zou and Zhai, 2004)," Piao *et al.* conclude "increased vegetation coverage in these areas will likely fix soil, enhance its anti-wind-erosion ability, reduce the possibility of released dust, and consequently cause a mitigation of sand-dust storms." They report, "recent studies have suggested

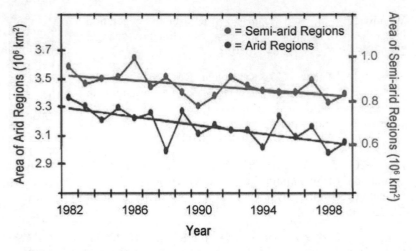

Figure 4.2.2.2.1.2.1. Interannual variation in area of arid (brown line) and semiarid region (green line) in China during the years 1982 to 1999. Adapted from Piao *et al.* (2005b).

that the frequencies of strong and extremely strong sand-dust storms in northern China have significantly declined from the early 1980s to the end of the 1990s (Qian *et al.*, 2002; Zhao *et al.*, 2004)."

Zhao *et al.* (2011) note "many studies based on analyses of satellite images have detected a greening trend at global (Myneni *et al.*, 1997; Nemani *et al.*, 2003; Potter *et al.*, 2007; Zhou *et al.*, 2001) and regional scales (Donohue *et al.*, 2009; Fang *et al.*, 2004; Herrmann *et al.*, 2005)," and they point out "the response of vegetation to climatic changes widely differed by biome (Fang *et al.*, 2005; Piao *et al.*, 2006c) and bioregion (Verbyla, 2008)." Focusing on the grassland-oasis-desert complex of northwest China, the four Chinese researchers "investigated spatio-temporal changes in vegetation growth and their responses to a changing climate by biome and bioregion, using satellite-sensed Normalized Difference Vegetation Index (NDVI) data from 1982 to 2003, along with corresponding climate data."

Over the 22 years of their study, during which annual mean temperature increased by 0.06°C/year, "about 30% of the total vegetated area showed an annual increase of 0.7% in growing season NDVI," they write. This trend "occurred in all biomes and all bioregions except Sawuer, a sub-region of the study area with no significant climate change." They report the NDVI increase was remarkable during 1982–1988, then tended to be slight, and finally declined a bit from 1998 to 2003. This pattern largely resembles the concomitant pattern of global air temperature change, which could have been responsible for the shifts in regional precipitation that appeared to be driving the observed shifts in NDVI. Zhao *et al.* note "previous analyses of satellite-measured vegetation growth suggested a greening trend of vegetation in the central United States (Wang *et al.*, 2001, 2003) and the Sahel (Anyamba and Tucker, 2005; Herrmann *et al.*, 2005) due to the effects of increasing precipitation at seasonal or annual scales."

The findings presented above indicate the vegetation in China's deserts has fared well in response to what has been called the most dramatic global warming and CO_2 rise of the past two millennia.

References

Anyamba, A. and Tucker, C.J. 2005. Analysis of Sahelian vegetation dynamics using NOAA-AVHRR NDVI data from 1981–2003. *Journal of Arid Environments* **63**: 596–614.

Brogaard, S., Runnstrom, M., and Seaquist, J.W. 2005. Primary production of Inner Mongolia, China, between 1982 and 1999 estimated by a satellite data-driven light use efficiency model. *Global and Planetary Change* **45**: 313–332.

Donohue, R.J., McVicar, T.R., and Roderick, M.L. 2009. Climate-related trends n Australian vegetation cover as inferred from satellite observations, 1981–2006. *Global Change Biology* **15**: 1025–1039.

Fang, J.Y., Piao, S.L., He, J.S., and Ma, W.H. 2004. Increasing terrestrial vegetation activity in China, 1982–1999. *Science in China Series C: Life Sciences* **47**: 229–240.

Fang, J.Y., Piao, S.L., Zhou, L.M., He, J.S., Wei, F.Y., Myneni, R.B., Tucker, C.J., and Tan, K. 2005. Precipitation patterns alter growth of temperate vegetation. *Geophysical Research Letters* **32**: 10.1029/2005GL024231.

Herrmann, S.M., Anyamba, A., and Tucker, C.J. 2005. Recent trends in vegetation dynamics in the African Sahel and their relationship to climate. *Global Environmental Change* **15**: 394–404.

Myneni, R.B., Keeling, C.D., Tucker, C.J., Asrar, G., and Nemani, R.R. 1997. Increased plant growth in the northern high latitudes from 1981 to 1991. *Nature* **386**: 698–702.

Nemani, R.R., Keeling, C.D., Hashimoto, H., Jolly, W.M., Piper, S.C., Tucker, C.J., Myneni, R.B., and Running. S.W. 2003. Climate-driven increases in global terrestrial net primary production from 1982 to 1999. *Science* **300**: 1560–1563.

Peng, S., Piao, S., Ciais, P., Fang, J., and Wang, X. 2010. Change in winter snow depth and its impacts on vegetation in China. *Global Change Biology* **16**: 3004–3013.

Piao, S., Fang, J.Y., Liu, H.Y., and Zhu, B. 2005b. NDVI-indicated decline in desertification in China in the past two decades. *Geophysical Research Letters* **32**: 10.1029/2004GL021764.

Piao, S., Mohammat, A., Fang, J.Y., Cai, Q., and Feng, J.M. 2006c. NDVI-based increase in growth of temperate grasslands and its responses to climate changes in China. *Global Environmental Change* **16**: 340–348.

Potter, C., Kumar, V., Klooster, S., and Nemani, R. 2007. Recent history of trends in vegetation greenness and large-scale ecosystem disturbances in Eurasia. *Tellus B—Chemical and Physical Meteorology* **59**: 260–272.

Qian, Z.A., Song, M.H., and Li, W.Y. 2002. Analysis on distributive variation and forecast of sand-dust storms in recent 50 years in north China. *Journal of Desert Research* **22**: 106–111.

Runnstrom, M. 2000. Is northern China winning the battle against desertification? Satellite remote sensing as a tool to study biomass trends on the Ordos plateau in semiarid China. *Ambio* **29**: 468–476.

Shi, Y.F. (Ed.) 2003. *An Assessment of the Issues of Climatic Shift from Warm-Dry to Warm-Wet in Northwest China*. China Meteorology, Beijing.

Verbyla, D. 2008. The greening and browning of Alaska based on 1982–2003 satellite data. *Global Ecology and Biogeography* **17**: 547–555.

Wang, J., Price, K.P., and Rich, P.M. 2001. Spatial patterns of NDVI in response to precipitation and temperature in the central Great Plains. *International Journal of Remote Sensing* **22**: 3827–3844.

Wang, J., Rich, P.M., and Price, K.P. 2003. Temporal responses of NDVI to precipitation and temperature in the central Great Plains, USA. *International Journal of Remote Sensing* **24**: 2345–2364.

Wu, W. 2001. Study on process of desertification in Mu Us sandy land for last 50 years, China. *Journal of Desert Research* **21**: 164–169.

Yang, Z.P., Zhang, Q., Wang, Y.L., Zhang, J.J., and Chen, M.C. 2011. Spatial and temporal variability of soil properties under *Caragana microphylla* shrubs in the northwestern Shanxi Loess Plateau, China. *Journal of Arid Environments* **75**: 538–544.

Zhang, L., Yue, L.P., and Xia, B. 2003. The study of land desertification in transitional zones between the UM US desert and the Loess plateau using RS and GIS—a case study of the Yulin region. *Environmental Geology* **44**: 530–534.

Zhao, C.S., Dabu, X., and Li, Y. 2004. Relationship between climatic factors and dust storm frequency in inner Mongolia of China. *Geophysical Research Letters* **31**: 10.1029/ 2003GL018351.

Zhao, X., Tan, K., Zhao, S., and Fang, J. 2011. Changing climate affects vegetation growth in the arid region of the northwestern China. *Journal of Arid Environments* **75**: 946–952.

Zhou, L.M., Tucker, C.J., Kaufmann, R.K., Slayback, D., Shabanov, N.V., and Myneni, R.B. 2001. Variations in northern vegetation activity inferred from satellite data of vegetation index during 1981 to 1999. *Journal of Geophysical Research* **106**: 20,069–20,083.

Zou, X.K. and Zhai P.M. 2004. Relationship between vegetation coverage and spring dust storms over northern China. *Journal of Geophysical Research* **109**: 10.1029/ 2003JD003913.

4.2.2.2.1.3 Forests

Ren *et al.* (2011) note, "in recent decades, there has been increased concern that elevated tropospheric ozone (O_3) and climate change have [negatively] influenced the ability of China's ecosystems to provide people with essential goods and services." They investigated "the potential effects of elevated O_3 along with climate change/variability on NPP [net primary production] and NCE [net carbon exchange] in China's forest ecosystems for the period 1961–2005 using a process-based dynamic land ecosystem model (DLEM, Tian *et al.*, 2005, 2010a,b)," while also considering "other environmental factors such as land-cover/land-use change (LCLUC), increasing [atmospheric] CO_2 and nitrogen deposition."

Ren *et al.* report O_3 pollution had consistent negative effects on forest production, reducing total NPP by 0.2 to 1.6% from the 1960s to 2000–2005; without O_3 pollution, carbon uptake rates would have increased by 3.5% in the 1960s and 12.6% in the six years of 2000–2005. Climate change had both negative and positive effects on NPP and NCE, and it was thus the major factor controlling the interannual variability of these two productivity parameters.

LCLUC also had negative impacts on NPP and NCE, but Ren *et al.* note "nitrogen deposition alone could compensate for the combined negative effects of O_3 and LCLUC in China." They also report an increase in NPP occurred in the CO_2-N combination simulation, which they write, "was consistent with previous studies (e.g., Ollinger *et al.*, 2002; Felzer *et al.*, 2004; Hanson *et al.*, 2005)." They suggest CO_2 and nitrogen deposition working together "could offset the combined negative effects of O_3 pollution, climate change and LCLUC on annual NCE." It would appear the combination of atmospheric CO_2 enrichment and nitrogen deposition provide powerful antidotes for the negative effects of ozone pollution, land-cover/land-use change, and various deleterious climatic phenomena on NPP and NCE in China and, by inference, other parts of the world as well.

Su and Sang (2004) used an ecosystem process model to explore the sensitivity of the net primary productivity (NPP) of an oak forest near Beijing to the global climate changes projected to result from a doubling of the atmosphere's CO_2 concentration from 355 to 710 ppm. They found the aerial fertilization effect of the increase in the atmospheric CO_2 content would raise the forest's NPP by 14.0%; a concomitant temperature increase of 2°C would boost the NPP increase to 15.7%; and adding a 20% increase in precipitation would push the NPP increase to 25.7%. They also calculate a 20% increase in precipitation and a 4°C increase in temperature would boost the forest's NPP by 25.7%.

Su *et al.* (2007) used a process-based model (BIOME-BGC) "to investigate the response of *Picea schrenkiana* forest to future climate changes and atmospheric carbon dioxide concentration increases in the Tianshan Mountains of northwestern China," which they "validated by comparing simulated net primary productivity (NPP) under current climatic conditions with independent field-measured data." They modeled a double-CO_2-induced temperature increase of 2.6°C and a precipitation increase of 25%.

When they considered the predicted precipitation increase by itself, Su *et al.* found the NPP of the *P. schrenkiana* forest increased by 14.5%. The predicted temperature increase by itself increased forest NPP by 6.4%, and the CO_2 increase by itself boosted NPP by only 2.7%. When the predicted increases in precipitation and temperature occurred together, forest NPP increased by 18.6%, just slightly less than the sum of the two individual effects. When the CO_2 concentration increase was added to the mix and all three factors increased together, the Chinese researchers report forest NPP "increased dramatically, with an average increase of about 30.4%."

Su *et al.* conclude the results derived from the various scenarios of their study indicate "the effects of precipitation and temperature change were simply additive, but that the synergy between the effects of climate change and doubled CO_2 was important," as it made the whole response much larger than the sum of its separate responses, because "feedback loops associated with the water and nitrogen cycles [which may be influenced significantly by atmospheric CO_2 enrichment] ultimately influence the carbon assimilation response."

References

Felzer, B.S., Kicklighter, D.W., Melillo, J.M., Wang, C., Zhuang, Q., and Prinn, R. 2004. Effects of ozone on net primary production and carbon sequestration in the conterminous United States using a biogeochemistry model. *Tellus* **56B**: 230–248.

Hanson, P.J., Wullschleger, S.D., Norby, R.J., Tschaplinski, T.J., and Gunderson, C.A. 2005. Importance of changing CO_2, temperature, precipitation, and ozone on carbon and water cycles of an upland-oak forest: incorporating experimental results into model simulations. *Global Change Biology* **11**: 1402–1423.

Ollinger, S.V., Aber, S.D., Reich, P.B., and Freuder, R.J. 2002. Interactive effects of nitrogen deposition, tropospheric ozone, elevated CO_2 and land use history on the carbon dynamics of northern hardwood forests. *Global Change Biology* **8**: 545–562.

Ren, W., Tian, H., Tao, B., Chappelka, A., Sun, G., Lu, C., Liu, M., Chen, G., and Xu, X. 2011. Impacts of tropospheric ozone and climate change on net primary productivity and net carbon exchange of China's forest ecosystems. *Global Ecology and Biogeography* **20**: 391–406.

Su, H.-X. and Sang, W.-G. 2004. Simulations and analysis of net primary productivity in *Quercus liaotungensis* forest of Donglingshan Mountain Range in response to different climate change scenarios. *Acta Botanica Sinica* **46**: 1281–1291.

Su, H.-X., Sang, W.-G., Wang, Y., and Ma, K. 2007. Simulating *Picea schrenkiana* forest productivity under climatic changes and atmospheric CO_2 increase in Tianshan Mountains, Xinjiang Autonomous Region, China. *Forest Ecology and Management* **246**: 273–284.

Tian, H., Chen, G.S., Liu, M.L., Zhang, C., Sun, G., Lu, C.Q., Xu, X.F., Ren, W., Pan, S.F., and Chappelka, A. 2010a. Model estimates of net primary productivity, evapotranspiration, and water use efficiency in the terrestrial ecosystems of the southern United States during 1895–2007. *Forest Ecology and Management* **259**: 1311–1327.

Tian, H.Q., Liu, M.L., Zhang, C., Ren, W., Chen, G.S., Xu, X.F., and Lu, C.Q. 2005. *DLEM—the Dynamic Land Ecosystem Model, user manual.* Ecosystem Science and Regional Analysis Laboratory, Auburn University, Auburn, Alabama, USA.

Tian, H., Xu, S., Liu, M., Ren, W., Zhang, C., Chen, G., and Lu, C.Q. 2010b. Spatial and temporal patterns of CH_4 and N_2O fluxes in terrestrial ecosystems of North America during 1979–2008: application of a global biogeochemistry model. *Biogeochemistry* **7**: 1–22.

4.2.2.2.1.4 Grasslands

Noting the climate of China's temperate grasslands "experienced dramatic change in the past several decades," Piao *et al.* (2006) investigated the impact of that climate change on the productivity of the country's grasslands. They analyzed normalized difference vegetation index (NDVI) data from the U.S. National Oceanic and Atmospheric Administration's very high-resolution radiometer at a spatial resolution of 8 x 8 km and at 15-day intervals from January 1982 to December 1999, comparing those results with temperature, precipitation, and Thornthwaite (1948) moisture index data generated from 680 well-distributed climate stations across China.

Piao *et al.* found little or no increase in precipitation and moisture index over the period of their study. For temperature, they found a least-squares linear warming of 0.89°C between 1982 and 1999 with $R = 0.59$ and $P = 0.009$, which they describe as "dramatic." Even more dramatic, "mean growing season NDVI increased significantly ($R = 0.73$, $P = 0.001$) from 0.25 in 1982 to 0.28 in 1999," or by approximately 12%.

At first glance it would appear the dramatic increase in temperature is what drove the dramatic increase in grassland productivity. But more detailed analyses revealed "the positive effect of temperature on the growth of grassland decreased as temperature rose." Piao *et al.* suggest the "atmospheric CO_2 fertilization effect, increased nutrient deposition, and human activity such as grazing management [and] land abandonment due to migration into urban areas" may have compensated for the decreasing strength of the growth enhancement provided by the region's warming.

One year later, using national grassland resource inventory data, a normalized difference vegetation index (NDVI) time series dataset, and a satellite-based statistical model, Piao *et al.* (2007) identified changes in the size and distribution of the aboveground biomass carbon (C) stocks of China's grasslands between 1982 and 1999. The authors report "aboveground biomass C stocks ... significantly increased from 136.3 Tg C in the early 1980s to 154.0 Tg C in the late 1990s," for a total increase of 13% (Figure 4.2.2.2.1.4.1). They note "growing season average temperature for the study area increased by 0.052°C per year and growing season precipitation also tended to increase," which led them to conclude "increased temperature may be associated with increasing C stocks and interannual changes in precipitation may be a factor in the fluctuations of C stocks." In addition, the "atmospheric CO_2 fertilization effect and human activity such as land management may also partly account for the observed increase in biomass C stocks of China's grassland."

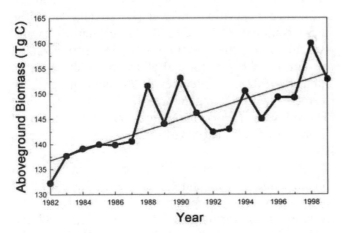

Figure 4.2.2.2.1.4.1. Interannual variations in aboveground biomass for China's grassland during the years 1982–1999. Adapted from Piao *et al.* (2007).

Peng *et al.* (2010) used snow-depth measurements collected at 279 meteorological stations across China, plus collocated satellite-derived normalized difference vegetation index (NDVI) data, to investigate spatio-temporal changes in snow depth during the years 1980–2006 and the effects of those changes on vegetative growth the following spring and summer. The five researchers report, "over the past three decades, winter snow depth overall increased in northern China, particularly in the most arid and semiarid regions of western China where desert and grassland are mainly distributed," and in those areas there were positive correlations between mean winter snow depth and spring NDVI data. They note Piao *et al.* (2005) determined the net primary productivity of the same desert and grasslands during 1982–1999 "increased by 1.6% per year and 1.1% per year, respectively," and "desertification has been

reversed in some areas of western China since the 1980s," citing Runnstrom (2000), Wu (2001), Zhang *et al.* (2003), and Piao *et al.* (2005).

Peng *et al.* write, the "increase in vegetation coverage in arid and semiarid regions of China, possibly driven by winter snow, will likely restore soil and enhance its antiwind-erosion ability, reducing the possibility of released dust and mitigating sand-dust storms," noting the frequency of sand-dust storms has indeed "declined in China since the early 1980s (Qian *et al.*, 2002; Zhao *et al.*, 2004)."

As the world warmed over the past three decades, a climatic change across China above 40°N latitude (an increase in winter snow depth) has prompted a biological change (increased vegetative growth in desert areas and grasslands) that has prompted yet another climatic change (a reduction in sand-dust storms). All of these changes are positive developments.

References

Peng, S., Piao, S., Ciais, P., Fang, J., and Wang, X. 2010. Change in winter snow depth and its impacts on vegetation in China. *Global Change Biology* **16**: 3004–3013.

Piao, S.L., Fang, J.Y., Liu, H.Y., and Zhu, B. 2005. NDVI-indicated decline in desertification in China in the past two decades. *Geophysical Research Letters* **32**: 10.1029/2004GL021764.

Piao, S.L., Fang, J.Y., Zhou, L., Tan, K., and Tao, S. 2007. Changes in biomass carbon stocks in China's grasslands between 1982 and 1999. *Global Biogeochemical Cycles* **21**: 10.1029/2005GB002634.

Piao, S.L., Mohammat, A., Fang, J., Cai, Q., and Feng, J. 2006. NDVI-based increase in growth of temperate grasslands and its responses to climate changes in China. *Global Environmental Change* **16**: 340–348.

Qian, Z.A., Song, M.H., and Li, W.Y. 2002. Analysis on distributive variation and forecast of sand-dust storms in recent 50 years in north China. *Journal of Desert Research* **22**: 106–111.

Runnstrom, M.C. 2000. Is northern China winning the battle against desertification? Satellite remote sensing as a tool to study biomass trends on the Ordos plateau in semiarid China. *Ambio* **29**: 468–476.

Thornthwaite, C.W. 1948. An approach toward a rational classification of climate. *Geographical Review* **38**: 55–94.

Wu, W. 2001. Study on process of desertification in Mu Us sandy land for last 50 years, China. *Journal of Desert Research* **21**: 164–169.

Zhang, L., Yue, L.P., and Xia, B. 2003. The study of land desertification in transitional zones between the UM US desert and the Loess plateau using RS and GIS—a case study of the Yulin region. *Environmental Geology* **44**: 530–534.

Zhao, C.S., Dabu, X., and Li, Y . 2004. Relationship between climatic factors and dust storm frequency in inner Mongolia of China. *Geophysical Research Letters* **31**: 10.1029/2003GL018351.

4.2.2.2.1.5 Tibetan Plateau

Taking a long temporal view of how vegetative productivity has fared in this region of China, Herzschuh *et al.* (2011) "critically review possible driving forces for early- to mid-Holocene vegetation shifts on the upper Tibetan Plateau (including precipitation, growing season length, radiation, human impact) with particular emphasis on changing CO_2 concentrations to better predict future environmental change and impacts on the Tibetan Plateau in a rapidly changing world."

The four researchers report, "numerous pollen records from across the upper Tibetan Plateau indicate that *Kobresia*-dominated high-alpine meadow invaded alpine steppes during the mid- to late-Holocene." Their investigation, which employed a pollen-moisture transfer function, indicates "this marked vegetation change cannot be satisfactorily explained by climate change." In addition, they note "a literature review did not reveal convincing evidence for any widespread human impact on mid-Holocene vegetation." They propose the reconstructed vegetation changes likely were "a response to Holocene CO_2 concentration changes," with values rising from approximately 260 ppm in the early Holocene to near-present-day values on the order of 375 ppm.

Their conclusion is based on four lines of evidence: (1) "high-elevation vegetation is particularly sensitive to CO_2 changes due to lowered CO_2 partial pressure"; (2) "water conservation of steppe vegetation in response to experimental CO_2 enrichment was of the same order of magnitude as inferred from mid- to late-Holocene Tibetan pollen records"; (3) "modern remote sensing-aided vegetation monitoring of the Central Tibetan Plateau yielded an increase in biomass, most probably as a response to modern CO_2 increase," even in spite of "increasing land-use by herding"; and (4) "experimental CO_2 fertilization of dry grassland and desert vegetation performed in several regions world-wide has stimulated plant growth directly through enhanced photosynthesis and indirectly through enhanced water-use efficiency (Morgan *et al.*, 2004)."

Zhuang *et al.* (2010) used a process-based biogeochemistry model—the Terrestrial Ecosystem Model or TEM, which also employed a soil thermal model—to examine permafrost dynamics and their effects on the carbon dynamics of the Tibetan Plateau. They accomplished this by "parameterizing and verifying" the TEM using real-world data for soil temperature, permafrost distribution, and carbon and nitrogen distributions throughout the region, and then extrapolating the model and its parameters to the whole of the plateau.

The six scientists report, "during the 20th century, the Tibetan Plateau changed from a small carbon source or neutral in the early part of the century to a sink later" (Figure 4.2.2.2.1.5.1), noting "net primary production and soil respiration increased by 0.52 and 0.22 Tg C/year, respectively, resulting in a regional carbon sink increase of 0.3 Tg C/year," so "by the end of the century, the regional carbon sink reached 36 Tg C/year and carbon storage in vegetation and soils is 32 and 16 Pg C, respectively."

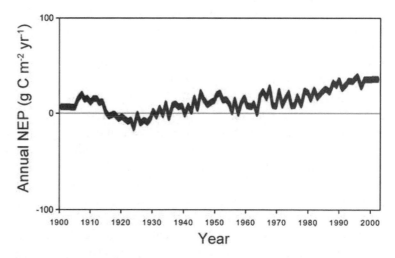

Figure 4.2.2.2.1.5.1. Five year running average of Net Ecosystem Production (NEP) on the Tibetan Plateau during the years 1901–2002. Negative values reveal the region to be a carbon source, positive values indicate it is a carbon sink. Adapted from Zhuang *et al.* (2010).

Zhuang *et al.* say the "increasing soil temperature and deepening active layer depth enhanced soil respiration, increasing the net nitrogen mineralization rate," and "together with the [positive] effects of warming air temperature and rising CO_2 concentrations on photosynthesis, the stronger plant nitrogen uptake due to the enhanced available nitrogen stimulate[d] plant carbon uptake, thereby strengthening the regional carbon sink as the rate of increase in net primary production was faster than that of soil respiration." They say their study implies "future warming will increase thawing of the permafrost, increase soil temperature and dry up soil moisture," and "these physical dynamics may enhance [the] future strength of the regional carbon sink, since the rate of increase of net primary production is higher than that of soil respiration on the Tibetan Plateau."

Satellite-based measurements taken over the past three decades provide further evidence the productivity of the Tibetan Plateau's vegetation has recently increased. Piao *et al.* (2006), for example, investigated net primary production (NPP) derived from a carbon model (Carnegie-Ames-Stanford approach, CASA) and its interannual change in the Qinghai-Xizang (Tibetan) Plateau using 1982–1999 NDVI data and paired ground-based information on vegetation, climate, soil, and solar radiation. Over the study period, NPP rose at a mean annual rate of 0.7%. Piao *et al.* report, "the NPP trends in the plateau over the two decades were divided into two distinguished periods: without any clear trend from 1982 to 1990 and significant increase from 1991 to 1999."

The three researchers say their findings indicate "vegetation growth on the plateau in the 1990s has been much enhanced compared to that in [the] 1980s, consistent with the trend in the northern latitudes indicated by Schimel *et al.* (2001)." They write, "previous observational and NPP modeling studies have documented substantial evidence that terrestrial photosynthetic activity has increased over the past two to three decades in the middle and high latitudes in the Northern Hemisphere," and "satellite-based NDVI data sets for the period of 1982–1999 also indicate consistent trends of NDVI increase," citing multiple references. Piao *et al.*'s findings add to the growing body of evidence that reveals a significant greening of the Earth in response to the ongoing recovery of the planet from the growth-inhibiting chill of the Little Ice Age, which was likely the coldest period of the current interglacial; the aerial fertilization effect of the historical and still-ongoing rise in the atmosphere's CO_2 concentration; and the growth-promoting effect of anthropogenic nitrogen deposition.

Zhou *et al.* (2007) investigated interannual variations of Tibetan Plateau vegetative productivity using a 21-year (1982–2002) normalized difference vegetation index (NDVI) dataset to quantify the consequences of changes in temperature and precipitation for the regional ecosystem. They report, "the maximum, minimum and mean temperature fluctuations all present an increasing trend over the 21 years." They note "the NDVI is comparatively large during the warm years, such as 1988, 1994, 1998, and 1999," and "relatively small NDVI values are well coupled with the cold extreme and mean temperature in 1982, 1983 and 1997." This relationship, they continue, "suggests a positive correlation between vegetation activity and surface air temperature on the plateau." They report, "the correlation coefficient between the NDVI and the maximum, minimum and mean temperature reaches 0.674 (significant at the 99% level), 0.53 (significant at the 95% level) and 0.55 (significant at the 99% level), respectively." In contrast, "the precipitation fluctuation does not show a detectable trend, and therefore its correlation with DNVI is not obvious."

Zhou *et al.* conclude, "vegetation variability on the Tibetan Plateau might be mostly driven by thermal impacts (i.e., surface air temperature), whereas precipitation impact is less clear." Overall, "vegetation activity demonstrates a gradual enhancement in an oscillatory manner during 1982–2002," suggesting a significant positive impact of what IPCC calls "unprecedented" global warming on the Tibetan Plateau, which Zhou *et al.* describe as "one of the most prominent features on Earth."

References

Herzschuh, U., Ni, J., Birks, H.J.B., and Bohner, J. 2011. Driving forces of mid-Holocene vegetation shifts on the upper Tibetan Plateau, with emphasis on changes in atmospheric CO_2 concentrations. *Quaternary Science Reviews* **30**: 1907–1917.

Morgan, J.A., Pataki, D.E., Korner, C., Clark, H., Del Grosso, S.J., Grunzweig, J.M., Knapp, A.K., Mosier, A.R., Newton, P.C.D., Niklaus, P.A., Nippert, J.B., Nowak, R.S., Parton, W.J., Polley, H.W., and Shaw, M.R. 2004. Water relations in grassland and desert ecosystems exposed to elevated atmospheric CO_2. *Oecologia* **140**: 11–25.

Piao, S., Fang, J., and He, J. 2006. Variations in vegetation net primary production in the Qinghai-Xizang Plateau, China, from 1982–1999. *Climatic Change* **74**: 253–267.

Schimel, D.S., House, J.I., Hibbard, J.I., Bousquet, P., Ciais, P., Peylin, P., Braswell, B.H., Apps, M.J., Baker, D., Bondeau, A., Canadell, J., Churkina, G., Cramer, W., Denning, A.S., Field, C.B., Friedlingstein, P., Goodale, C., Heimann, M., Houghton, R.A., Melillo, J.M., Moore III, B., Murdiyarso, D., Noble, I., Pacala, S.W., Prentice, I.C.,

Raupach, M.R., Rayner, P.J., Scholes, R.J., Steffen, W.L., and Wirth, C. 2001. Recent patterns and mechanisms of carbon exchange by terrestrial ecosystems. *Nature* **414**: 169–172.

Zhou, D., Fan, G., Huang, R., Fang, Z., Liu, Y., and Li, H. 2007. Interannual variability of the normalized difference vegetation index on the Tibetan Plateau and its relationship with climate change. *Advances in Atmospheric Sciences* **24**: 474–484.

Zhuang, Q., He, J., Lu, Y., Ji, L., Xiao, J., and Luo, T. 2010. Carbon dynamics of terrestrial ecosystems on the Tibetan Plateau during the 20th century: an analysis with a process-based biogeochemical model. *Global Ecology and Biogeography* **19**: 649–662.

4.2.2.2.2 All Other Asian Countries

This section examines how vegetative productivity has fared in Asian countries other than China over the past few decades.

Grunzweig *et al.* (2003) studied the Yatir forest, a 2,800-hectare stand of Aleppo and other pine trees, planted some 35 years earlier at the edge of the Negev Desert in Israel. They characterize the forest as growing in poor soil of only 0.2 to 1.0 meter's depth above chalk and limestone. Although it is located in an arid part of Asia that receives less annual precipitation than all of the other stations in the FluxNet global network of micrometeorological tower sites (Baldocchi *et al.*, 2001), the forest's annual net ecosystem CO_2 exchange was just as high as that of many high-latitude boreal forests and actually higher than those of most temperate forests.

Grunzweig *et al.* note the increase in atmospheric CO_2 concentration that has occurred since pre-industrial times should have improved water use efficiency (WUE) in most plants by increasing the ratio of CO_2 fixed to water lost via evapo-transpiration. That this hypothesis is correct has been demonstrated by Leavitt *et al.* (2003) in the context of the long-term atmospheric CO_2 enrichment experiment of Idso and Kimball (2001) on sour orange trees. It also has been confirmed in nature by Feng (1999), who obtained results identical to the study of Leavitt *et al.* for 23 groups of naturally occurring trees across western North America for the years 1800–1985; a response,

Feng concludes, that "would have caused natural trees in arid environments to grow more rapidly, acting as a carbon sink for anthropogenic CO_2," which is what Grunzweig *et al.* found in the Yatir forest on the edge of the Negev Desert. Grunzweig *et al.* also report, "reducing water loss in arid regions improves soil moisture conditions, decreases water stress and extends water availability," which "can indirectly increase carbon sequestration by influencing plant distribution, survival and expansion into water-limited environments."

Singh *et al.* (2011) used U.S. National Oceanic and Atmospheric Administration (NOAA) satellite-derived advanced very high resolution radiometer (AVHRR) data, together with the Global Production Efficiency Model (GloPEM) developed by Prince and Goward (1995), to calculate annual NPP over India for the years 1981–2000 (Figure 4.2.2.2.2.1). According to the five researchers, regression analysis of the 20-year NPP database showed a significant increase in the temporal trend of NPP over India (r=0.7, p<0.001), with the mean rate of increase being 10.43 gC/m^2/year, which yields a mean rate-of-increase in carbon fixation of 34.3 TgC/year for the country, including its arid and semi-arid regions, its forests, and its dry-land and irrigated agricultural regions.

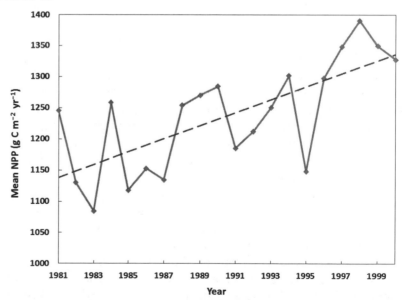

Figure 4.2.2.2.2.1. Average annual NPP estimated for India during the years 1981–2000 using NOAA-AVHRR data, as per Singh *et al.* (2011).

In Russia, in an area extending from 72°02'N to 72°40'N and from 101°15'E to 102°06' E—a total of approximately 36,000 ha that includes the Ary-Mas forest (the northernmost forest on the planet) plus larch forests on southeastern slopes descending to the Khatanga River—Kharuk *et al.* (2006) analyzed remote-sensing images made by Landsat satellites in 1973 and 2000. They found "the most significant changes were observed in the class of normal larch stands (canopy density > 0.3): their area increased by 66%," and "the areas of open and sparse forests (0.1 < canopy density < 0.3, and canopy density < 0.1) increased by 16 and 8%, respectively, whereas the background area became 19% smaller." They report the rates of expansion of larch onto tundra "for sparse, open, and normal stands were estimated at 3, 9, and 11 m per year, respectively." They remark, "since sparse stands are at the forefront of advancement to the tundra, the rate for this class (approximately 3 m per year) should be regarded as the rate of larch expansion in general," and "the above rates reflect not only the expansion of trees into the tundra, but also an increase in the density of sparse and open stands."

Kharuk *et al.* suggest the changes they reported were "induced by climatic trends" and the continuation of this process "will result in the expansion of larch to the Arctic coast," which they describe as a "phenomenon that took place in the Holocene." Thus the Ary Mas forest evidently is reclaiming what previously had been lost due to the progressive cooling of the planet after the Holocene Climatic Optimum, as this cooling culminated in the record interglacial cold of the Little Ice Age from which Earth and its biosphere are now recovering.

Lapenis *et al.* (2005) analyzed trends in forest biomass in all 28 ecoregions of the Russian territory, based on data collected from 1953 to 2002 in 3,196 sample plots comprising about 50,000 entries. This database, they write, "contains all available archived and published data." Over the period 1961–1998, they write, "aboveground wood, roots, and green parts increased by 4%, 21%, and 33%, respectively," such that "the total carbon density of the living biomass stock of the Russian forests increased by ~9%." They also report a concomitant increase of ~11% in the land area of Russian forests. In addition, the U.S., Austrian, and Russian scientists note, "within the range of 50–65° of latitude [the range of 90% of Russian forests], the relationship between biomass density and the area-averaged NDVI is very close to a linear function, with a slope of ~1," citing Myneni *et al.* (2001). They continue, "changes in the carbon density of live biomass in Russian forests occur at about the same rate as the increase in the satellite-based estimate in the seasonally accumulated NDVI."

Acknowledging remote sensing data suggest tundra vegetation in North America may be responding to recent warming via enhanced photosynthetic activity (Goetz *et al.*, 2005; Verbyla , 2008), Forbes *et al.* (2010) write, "at a circumpolar scale, the highest photosynthetic activity and strongest growth trends are reported in locations characterized by erect shrub tundra (Reynolds *et al.*, 2006)," noting "live leaf phytomass from deciduous shrubs, shown to have increased in northern Alaska during the second half of the last century (Sturm *et al.*, 2001; Tape *et al.*, 2006), is believed to be a key driver of the observed trends (Jia *et al.*, 2003; Goetz *et al.*, 2005; Verbyla, 2008)." Forbes *et al.* analyzed annual ring growth for 168 stem slices of 2- to 3-cm thickness they collected from 40 *Salix lanata* L. (*sensu latu*)—an abundant deciduous dioecious willow with nearly circumpolar geographic distribution from the northern boreal forest of Russia to the northern limits of the Low Arctic. Their samples were taken from 15 sites in an area of approximately 3 x 2.3 km located at about 68°40'N, 58°30'E.

The three researchers found "a clear relationship with photosynthetic activity for upland vegetation at a regional scale for the years 1981–2005, confirming a parallel 'greening' trend reported for similarly warming North American portions of the tundra biome," and they write, "the standardized growth curve suggests a significant increase in shrub willow growth over the last six decades." Noting "the quality of the chronology as a climate proxy is exceptional," Forbes *et al.* state their findings "are in line with field and remote sensing studies that have assigned a strong shrub component to the reported greening signal since the early 1980s," adding the growth trend agrees with the qualitative observations of nomadic reindeer herders, which suggest there have been "recent increases in willow size in the region." Forbes *et al.* say their analysis "provides the best proxy assessment to date that deciduous shrub phytomass has increased significantly in response to an ongoing summer warming trend."

Lioubimtseva *et al.* (2005) describe a number of findings generally not available to the international scientific community because of their publication in Russian. According to the four-member team of Russian and American scientists, "there has been a general warming trend in Central Asian republics on the order of 1–2°C since the beginning of the 20th century." They note the trend is expressed most strongly in winter and "the amplitude of this trend seems to be comparable with Holocene climate variability," suggesting it is nothing unusual nor does it require an anthropogenic explanation. Citing IPCC

(2001), they report precipitation has remained basically unchanged throughout the twentieth century, stating "there were no discernible trends in annual precipitation during 1900–95 for the region as a whole, nor in most parts of this region."

In the face of unchanging precipitation and significant warming, it might be expected the aridity of Central Asia would have increased significantly in recent years, especially throughout the 1990s, when IPCC purports the world had its most oppressive heat of both the twentieth century and the past two millennia. However, Lioubimtseva *et al.* report, "analyses of the NOAA AVHRR temporal series since the 1980s showed a decrease in aridity from 1991–2000 compared to 1982–1990 in the northern part of the region and a southward shift of the northern boundary of the desert zone in Central Asia," citing Zolotokrylin (2002). Lioubimtseva *et al.* suggest the cause of this unexpected development may have been the historical rise in the atmospheric CO_2 content.

The scientists note "an increased atmospheric CO_2 concentration has direct and relatively immediate effects on two important physiological processes in plants: it increases the photosynthetic rate, but decreases stomatal opening and therefore the rate at which plants lose water," so "the combination of these two factors, increased photosynthesis and decreased water loss, implies a significant increase of water [use] efficiency (the ratio of carbon gain per unit water loss) and ... a reduction in the sensitivity to drought stress in desert vegetation as a result of elevated atmospheric CO_2," citing Smith *et al.* (2000). They note these effects could "increase productivity and biomass of natural desert vegetation," which would make the land less arid.

Buttressing this reasoning with experimental evidence from the region, Lioubimtseva *et al.* report, "CO_2-enrichment experiments (both chamber and free-air) conducted in the Kara Kum (Voznesensky, 1997) and Kyzyl Kum (Voznesensky, 1997; Zelensky, 1977) deserts showed a 2–4 times increase in the photosynthetic rate under the saturating CO_2 concentrations," and "three Kara Kum species (*Eminium lehmanii*, *Rhemum turkestanuikum* and *Ephedra stobilacea*) responded with a six-fold increase in photosynthetic rate (Nechaeva, 1984)." They report, "the CO_2 fertilization effects included not only higher vegetation but also microphytic communities including mosses, lichens, fungi, algae, and cyanobacteria"; these communities, they write, "form biogenic crusts on the soil surface varying from a few millimeters to several centimeters in thickness

and play a significant role in the desert ecosystems controlling such processes as water retention and carbon and nitrogen fixation in soils."

Zhou *et al.* (2001) analyzed satellite-derived normalized difference vegetation index (NDVI) data from July 1981 to December 1999, between 40 and 70° N latitude. They found a persistent increase in growing season vegetative productivity in excess of 12% over this broad contiguous swath of Asia stretching from Europe through Siberia to the Aldan plateau, where almost 58% of the land is forested. In a companion study, Bogaert *et al.* (2002) determined this productivity increase occurred at a time when this vast Asian region showed an overall warming trend "with negligible occurrence of cooling."

Ichii *et al.* (2005) simulated and analyzed carbon fluxes during the years 1982–1999 "using the Biome-BGC prognostic carbon cycle model driven by National Centers for Environmental Prediction re-analysis daily climate data," after which they "calculated trends in gross primary productivity (GPP) and net primary productivity (NPP)." They found solar radiation variability to be the primary factor responsible for inter-annual variations in GPP, followed by temperature and precipitation variability. In terms of GPP trends, the authors report, "recent changes in atmospheric CO_2 and climate promoted terrestrial GPP increases with a significant linear trend in all three tropical regions." The rate of GPP increase for Asia was about 0.3 PgC year^{-1} per decade. Ichii *et al.* favor carbon dioxide as the likely cause, reporting "CO_2 fertilization effects strongly increased recent NPP trends in regional totals."

In a study examining a large portion of the Northern Hemisphere (East Asia, including China, Japan, Korea, and Mongolia), Piao *et al.* (2011) used three process-based ecosystem models—the Lund-Potsdam-Jena Dynamic Global Vegetation Model (LPJ-DGVM) described by Sitch *et al.* (2003), the ORganizing Carbon and Hydrology In Dynamic Ecosystems (ORCHIDEE) model described by Krinner *et al.* (2005), and the Sheffield model (SDGVM) described by Woodward and Lomas (2004)—to investigate East Asia's net primary productivity (NPP) response to the climatic change and rising atmospheric CO_2 concentration of the past century. They ran each of the three models for the years 1901 to 2002, using observed values of monthly climatology and annual global atmospheric CO_2 concentrations (Figure 4.2.2.2.2.2).

Between 1901 and 2002, modeled NPP "significantly increased by 5.5–8.5 Tg C per year (15–20% growth)," the authors write, and this

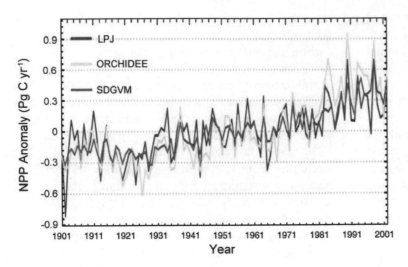

Figure 4.2.2.2.2.2. Terrestrial Net Primary Productivity anomalies for East Asia for the years 1901–2002 as determined from the three process-based ecosystem models described in the text (LPJ, ORCIDEE, and SDGVM). Adapted from Piao *et al.* (2011).

increase in NPP "caused an increased cumulated terrestrial carbon storage of about 5–11 Pg C," about 50–70% of which "is located in vegetation biomass." In addition, "40–60% of the accumulated carbon uptake of the 20th century is credited to the period of 1980–2002," the warmest two-decade interval of that century-long period, according to IPCC.

Thus Piao *et al.* demonstrate the rise of the air's CO_2 concentration and temperature to their highest values of the past century enhanced the terrestrial vegetative productivity of East Asia. This and the many other observations described above indicate plant productivity in Asia is increasing as atmospheric CO_2 concentrations and temperatures rise.

References

Baldocchi, D., Falge, E., Gu, L.H., Olson, R., Hollinger, D., Running, S., Anthoni, P., Bernhofer, C., Davis, K., Evans, R., Fuentes, J., Goldstein, A., Katul, G., Law B., Lee, X.H., Malhi, Y., Meyers, T., Munger, W., Oechel, W., Paw U, K.T., Pilegaard, K., Schmid, H.P., Valentini, R., Verma, S., Vesala, T., Wilson, K., and Wofsy, S. 2001. FLUXNET: A new tool to study the temporal and spatial variability of ecosystem-scale carbon dioxide, water vapor, and energy flux densities. *Bulletin of the American Meteorological Society* **82**: 2415–2434.

Bogaert, J., Zhou, L., Tucker, C.J, Myneni, R.B., and Ceulemans, R. 2002. Evidence for a persistent and extensive greening trend in Eurasia inferred from satellite vegetation index data. *Journal of Geophysical Research* **107**: 10.1029/2001JD001075.

Feng, X. 1999. Trends in intrinsic water-use efficiency of natural trees for the past 100–200 years: A response to atmospheric CO_2 concentration. *Geochimica et Cosmochimica Acta* **63**: 1891–1903.

Forbes, B.C., Fauria, M.M., and Zetterberg, P. 2010. Russian Arctic warming and 'greening' are closely tracked by tundra shrub willows. *Global Change Biology* **16**: 1542–1554.

Goetz, S.J., Bunn, A.G., Fiske, G.J., and Houghton, R.A. 2005. Satellite-observed photosynthetic trends across boreal North America associated with climate and fire disturbance. *Proceedings of the National Academy of Sciences USA* **102**: 13,521–13,525.

Grunzweig, J.M., Lin, T., Rotenberg, E., Schwartz, A., and Yakir, D. 2003. Carbon sequestration in arid-land forest. *Global Change Biology* **9**: 791–799.

Ichii, K., Hashimoto, H., Nemani, R., and White, M. 2005. Modeling the interannual variability and trends in gross and net primary productivity of tropical forests from 1982 to 1999. *Global and Planetary Change* **48**: 274–286.

Idso, S.B. and Kimball, B.A. 2001. CO_2 enrichment of sour orange trees: 13 years and counting. *Environmental and Experimental Botany* **46**: 147–153.

Jia, G.J., Epstein, H.E., and Walker, D.A. 2003. Greening of arctic Alaska, 1981–2001. *Geophysical Research Letters* **30**: 31–33.

Kharuk, V.I., Ranson, K.J., Im, S.T., and Naurzbaev, M.M. 2006. Forest-tundra larch forests and climatic trends. *Russian Journal of Ecology* **37**: 291–298.

Krinner, G., Viovy, N., de Noblet-Ducoudre, N., Ogee, J., Polcher, J., Friedlingstein, P., Ciais, P., Sitch, S., and Prentice, I.C. 2005. A dynamic global vegetation model for studies of the coupled atmosphere-biosphere system. *Global Biogeochemical Cycles* **19**: 10.1029/2003GB002199.

Lapenis, A., Shvidenko, A., Shepaschenko, D., Nilsson, S., and Aiyyer, A. 2005. Acclimation of Russian forests to recent changes in climate. *Global Change Biology* **11**: 2090–2102.

Leavitt, S.W., Idso, S.B., Kimball, B.A., Burns, J.M., Sinha, A., and Stott, L. 2003. The effect of long-term atmospheric CO_2 enrichment on the intrinsic water-use efficiency of sour orange trees. *Chemosphere* **50**: 217–222.

Lioubimtseva, E., Cole, R., Adams, J.M., and Kapustin, G. 2005. Impacts of climate and land-cover changes in arid lands of Central Asia. *Journal of Arid Environments* **62**: 285–308.

Myneni, R.B., Dong, J., Tucker, C.J., Kaufmann, R.K., Kauppi, P.E., Liski, J., Zhou, L., Alexeyev, V., and Hughes, M.K. 2001. A large carbon sink in the woody biomass of Northern forests. *Proceedings of the National Academy of Sciences, USA* **98**: 14,784–14,789.

Nechaeva, N.T. (Ed.) 1984. *Resursy biosphery pustin Srednei Azii i Kazakhstana*. Nauka, Moscow, Russia.

Piao, S., Ciais, P., Lomas, M., Beer, C., Liu, H., Fang, J., Friedlingstein, P., Huang, Y., Muraoka, H., Son, Y., and Woodward, I. 2011. Contribution of climate change and rising CO_2 to terrestrial carbon balance in East Asia: A multi-model analysis. *Global and Planetary Change* **75**: 133–142.

Prince, S.D. and Goward, S.J. 1995. Global primary production: A remote sensing approach. *Journal of Biogeography* **22**: 316–336.

Reynolds, M.K., Walker, D.A., and Maier, H.A. 2006. NDVI patterns and phytomass distribution in the circumpolar Arctic. *Remote Sensing of Environment* **102**: 271–281.

Singh, R.P., Rovshan, S., Goroshi, S.K., Panigrahy, S., and Parihar, J.S. 2011. Spatial and temporal variability of net primary productivity (NPP) over terrestrial biosphere of India using NOAA-AVHRR based GloPEM model. *Journal of the Indian Society of Remote Sensing* **39**: 345–353.

Sitch, S., Smith, B., Prentice, I.C., Arneth, A., Bondeau, A., Cramer, W., Kaplan, J.O., Levis, S., Lucht, W., Sykes, M.T., Thonicke, K., and Venevsky, S. 2003. Evaluation of ecosystem dynamics, plant geography and terrestrial carbon cycling in the LPJ dynamic global vegetation model. *Global Change Biology* **9**: 161–185.

Smith, S.D., Huxman, T.E., Zitzer, S.F., Charlet, T.N., Housman, D.C., Coleman, J.S., Fenstermaker, L.K., Seemann, J.R., and Nowak, R.S. 2000. Elevated CO_2 increases productivity and invasive species success in an arid ecosystem. *Nature* **408**: 79–82.

Sturm, M., Racine, C., and Tape, K. 2001. Increasing shrub abundance in the Arctic. *Nature* **411**: 546–547.

Tape, K., Sturm, M., and Racine, C.H. 2006. The evidence for shrub expansion in northern Alaska and the Pan-Arctic. *Global Change Biology* **32**: 686–702.

Verbyla, D. 2008. The greening and browning of Alaska based on 1982–2003 satellite data. *Global Ecology and Biogeography* **17**: 547–555.

Voznesensky, V.L. 1977. *Fotosyntez pustinnih rastenij*. Nauka, Leningrad, Russia.

Woodward, F.I. and Lomas, M.R. 2004. Vegetation dynamics-simulating responses to climatic change. *Biological Reviews* **79**: 643–670.

Zelensky, O.B. 1977. *Ecologo-fisiologicheskije aspekti izuchenija fotosinteza*. Nauka, Leningrad, Russia.

Zhou, L., Tucker, C.J., Kaufmann, R.K., Slayback, D., Shabanov, N.V., and Myneni, R.B. 2001. Variations in northern vegetation activity inferred from satellite data of vegetation index during 1981–1999. *Journal of Geophysical Research* **106**: 20,069–20,083.

Zolotokrylin, A.N. 2002. The indicator of climate aridity. *Arid Ecosystems* **8**: 49–57.

4.2.2.3 Australia

- Evergreen vegetation, woody plants, and other plant life have increased across Australia over the past 200 years as a result of CO_2 enrichment.

Banfai and Bowman (2006) note "a number of processes are thought to be threatening the ecological integrity of monsoon rainforests in Northern Australia," testing this retracting-rainforest claim with a comprehensive repeat aerial photography study of the Northern Territory's Kakadu National Park, where monsoon rainforest exists as an archipelago of hundreds of small patches within a larger eucalypt savanna matrix. The two Australian researchers from Charles Darwin University's School for Environmental Research assessed changes to the boundaries of 50 monsoon rainforest patches using temporal sequences of digitized aerial photography taken in 1964, 1984, 1991, and 2004, to ascertain the relative importance of factors driving any change.

They found "rainforest patches increased in size between 1964 and 2004 by an average of 28.8%" (see Figure 4.2.2.3.1). After lengthy analyses of several phenomena that might have been responsible for the range increases, the two researchers conclude "the expansion is likely to have been primarily driven by increases in variables such as rainfall and atmospheric CO_2." They note, "the average [area] change for dry rainforests from 1964 to 2004 was an increase of 42.1%, whereas for wet rainforests [the increase] was one-third of this at 13.1%." With respect to dry rainforests, they found "an almost linear increase in rainforest area over the study period."

In further support of the validity of their findings, and "contrary to the view that monsoon rainforests are contracting," the two researchers note other repeat aerial photography studies conducted in Northern Australia also have revealed rainforest "expansion at the expense of more open vegetation." These studies include those of monsoon rainforests in Litchfield

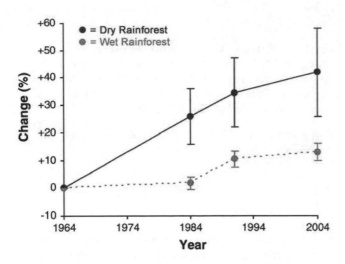

Figure 4.2.2.3.1. Average percentage change in rainforest area in Kakadu National Park, Northern Territory of Australia, relative to 1964 for dry rainforest (brown line) and wet rainforest (green dashed line). Standard errors are indicated. Adapted from Banfai and Bowman (2006).

National Park near Darwin (Bowman *et al.*, 2001)—where forest patches nearly doubled in size between 1941 and 1994—and in the Gulf of Carpentaria (Bowman *et al.*, 2006). Banfai and Bowman write, "these changes parallel the observed expansion of tropical rainforest on the east coast of Australia (Harrington and Sanderson, 1994; Russell-Smith *et al.*, 2004)."

Macinnis-Ng *et al.* (2011) note, "woody thickening" is typically defined as "the increase in woody standing biomass in a landscape already containing woody biomass." Both it and woody plant invasion, they continue, "are global phenomena commonly observed in arid and semi-arid regions, including Australia (Bowman *et al.*, 2001; Burrows *et al.*, 2002; Asner *et al.*, 2003; Fensham *et al.*, 2005; Scott *et al.*, 2006; Witt *et al.*, 2009)," the "tropical rainforests of Central and South America (Phillips *et al.*, 1998), and temperate forests globally (Birdsey *et al.*, 1993)." Although "the cause of woody thickening remains debated," they write, "there is an increasing awareness of potential roles for climate and changes in atmospheric CO_2 concentration in causing woody thickening (and woody invasion)," citing Fensham *et al.* (2005), Berry and Roderick (2006), Davis *et al.* (2007), and Sankaran *et al.* (2008).

The four researchers examined the responses of gross primary production (GPP) and water use of a typical Australian woodland using the soil-plant atmosphere (SPA) model of Williams *et al.* (1996), which they applied to the functioning of a temperate

open woodland in Australia (Zeppel *et al.*, 2008) that provided a methodology for testing the conceptual model of Eamus and Palmer (2007), which posits increasing atmospheric CO_2 concentration and declining evaporative demand "may explain the global phenomenon of woody thickening."

Macinnis-Ng *et al.* demonstrate that as the atmosphere's CO_2 content rises, plant stomatal conductance decreases, such that water use per tree decreases and, therefore, soil water content increases, leading to increases in leaf area index that allow more light to be intercepted, enabling existing trees to grow bigger, even in the case of photosynthetic acclimation. This set of phenomena constitutes the complex process of woody thickening. Noting their results "provide a valid mechanism for the conclusion of Berry and Roderick (2002) that evergreen vegetation has increased across Australia over the past 200 years as a result of CO_2 enrichment," they conclude "woody thickening in Australia and probably globally can be explained by the changes in landscape GPP and soil moisture balance arising principally from the increased atmospheric CO_2 concentration."

References

Asner, G.P., Archer, S., Hughes, R.F., and Ansleys, R.J. 2003. Net changes in regional woody vegetation cover and carbon storage in Texas Drylands, 1937–1999. *Global Change Biology* 9: 316–335.

Banfai, D.S. and Bowman, D.M.J.S. 2006. Forty years of lowland monsoon rainforest expansion in Kakadu national Park, Northern Australia. *Biological Conservation* 131: 553–565.

Berry, S.L. and Roderick, M.L. 2002. CO_2 and land-use effects on Australian vegetation over the last two centuries. *Australian Journal of Botany* 50: 511–531.

Berry, S.L. and Roderick, M.L. 2006. Changing Australian vegetation from 1788 to 1988: effects of CO_2 and land-use change. *Australian Journal of Botany* 54: 325–338.

Birdsey, R., Plantinga, A., and Heath, L. 1993. Past and prospective carbon storage in United States forests. *Forest Ecology & Management* 58: 33–40.

Bowman, D.M.J.S., McIntyre, D., and Brook, B.W. 2006. Is the Carpentarian Rock-rat (*Zyzomys palatalis*) critically endangered? *Pacific Conservation Biology* 12: 134–139.

Bowman, D.M.J.S., Walsh, A., and Milne, D.J. 2001. Forest expansion and grassland contraction within a Eucalyptus savanna matrix between 1941 and 1994 at Litchfield National Park in the Australian monsoon tropics. *Global Ecology and Biogeography* 10: 535–548.

Burrows, W.H., Henry, B.K., and Back, P.V. 2002. Growth and carbon stock change in eucalypt woodlands in northeast Australia: ecological and greenhouse sink implications. *Global Change Biology* **8**: 769–784.

Davis, M.A., Reich, P.B., Knoll, M.J.B., Dooley, L., Hundtoft, M., and Attleson, I. 2007. Elevated atmospheric CO_2: a nurse plant substitute for oak seedlings establishing in old fields. *Global Change Biology* **13**: 2308–2316.

Eamus, D. and Palmer, A.R. 2007. Is climate change a possible explanation for woody thickening in arid and semi-arid regions? *Research Letters in Ecology* doi: 10.1155/2007/37364.

Fensham, R.J., Fairfax, R.J., and Archer, S.R. 2005. Rainfall, land use and woody vegetation cover change in semi-arid Australian savanna. *Journal of Ecology* **93**: 596–606.

Harrington, G.N. and Sanderson, K.D. 1994. Recent contraction of wet sclerophyll forest in the wet tropics of Queensland due to invasion by rainforest. *Pacific Conservation Biology* **1**: 319–327.

Macinnis-Ng, C., Zeppel, M., Williams, M., and Eamus, D. 2011. Applying a SPA model to examine the impact of climate change on GPP of open woodlands and the potential for woody thickening. *Ecohydrology* **4**: 379–393.

Phillips, O.L., Malhi, Y., Higuchi, N., Laurance, W.F., Nunez, P.V., Vasquez, R.M., Laurance, S.G., Ferreira, L.V., Stern, M., Brown, S., and Grace, J. 1998. Changes in the carbon balance of tropical forests: Evidence from long-term plots. *Science* **282**: 439–442.

Russell-Smith, J., Stanton, P.J., Edwards, A.C., and Whitehead, P.J. 2004. Rain forest invasion of eucalypt-dominated woodland savanna, Iron Range, north-eastern Australia: II. Rates of landscape change. *Journal of Biogeography* **31**: 1305–1316.

Sankaran, M., Ratnam, J., and Hanan, N. 2008. Woody cover in African savannas: the role of resources, fire and herbivory. *Global Ecology and Biogeography* **17**: 236–245.

Scott, R.L., Huxman, T.E., Cable, W.L., and Emmerich, W.E. 2006. Partitioning of evapotranspiration and its relation to carbon dioxide exchange in a Chihuahuan Desert shrubland. *Hydrological Processes* **20**: 3227–3243.

Williams, M., Rastetter, E.B., and Fernandes, D.N. 1996. Modeling the soil-plant-atmosphere continuum in a Quercus-Acer stand at Harvard forest: the regulation of stomatal conductance by light, nitrogen and soil-plant hydraulic properties. *Plant, Cell & Environment* **19**: 911–927.

Witt, G.B., Harrington, R.A., and Page, M.J. 2009. Is 'vegetation thickening' occurring in Queensland's mulga lands—a 50-year aerial photographic analysis. *Australian Journal of Botany* **57**: 572–582.

Zeppel, M., Macinnis-Ng, C., Palmer, A., Taylor, A., Whitley, R., Fuentes, S., Yunusa, J., Williams, M., and Eamus, D. 2008. An analysis of the sensitivity of sap flux to soil and plant variables assessed for an Australian woodland using a soil-plant-atmosphere model. *Functional Plant Biology* **35**: 509–520.

4.2.2.4 Europe

- Over the last two decades of the twentieth century, Europe became greener and much of it is seeing an increase in its woodlands due to the recent rise in atmospheric CO_2, which has tended to offset the detrimental effects of climate change in the region.

- Opposite the forecasts promulgated by the models used by IPCC, land-based plants of the Arctic and near-Arctic regions of North America are thriving, thanks in large part to the ongoing rise in the atmosphere's CO_2 concentration and global warming.

Using an empirically based mechanistic model of Mediterranean shrub vegetation, Osborne *et al.* (2000) set out to address two important questions: Has recent climate change, especially increased drought, negatively impacted Mediterranean shrublands? And has the historical increase in the air's CO_2 concentration modified this impact?

The data-based model they employed suggests the warming and reduced precipitation experienced in the Mediterranean area over the past century should have had negative impacts on net primary production and leaf area index. When the measured increase in atmospheric CO_2 concentration experienced over the period was factored into the calculation, however, these negative influences were overpowered: net primary productivity increased by 25% and leaf area index by 7%. These results, they write, "indicate that the recent rise in atmospheric CO_2 may already have had significant impacts on productivity, structure and water relations of sclerophyllous shrub vegetation, which tended to offset the detrimental effects of climate change in the region."

Model-predicted changes in Earth's precipitation regime indicate a doubling of the atmosphere's CO_2 content will lead to a modest intensification of the planet's hydrologic cycle. In the Mediterranean region over the past century, however, there has been a recent tendency toward drier conditions. Hence the specific case Osborne *et al.* investigated represents a much-worse scenario than what is predicted by current climate models for Earth as a whole, yet the area's vegetation has grown even better than it did before the climatic change, thanks to the over-powering beneficial biological effects of the concurrent rise in atmospheric CO_2.

Cheddadi *et al.* (2001) employed a standard biogeochemical model (BIOME3)—which uses monthly temperature and precipitation data, certain soil characteristics, cloudiness, and atmospheric CO_2 concentration as inputs—to simulate the responses of various biomes in the region surrounding the Mediterranean Sea to changes in both climate (temperature and precipitation) and atmospheric CO_2 content. They first validated the model for two test periods, the present and 6,000 years before present (BP). They used recent instrumental records for atmospheric CO_2, temperature, and precipitation data for the present period; for 6,000 years BP, they used pollen data to reconstruct monthly temperature and precipitation values and ice core records to determine the atmospheric CO_2 concentration. They determined winter temperatures 6,000 years ago were about 2°C cooler than temperatures today, annual rainfall was approximately 200 mm less than today, and the air's CO_2 concentration averaged 280 ppm, considerably less than the 345 ppm the researchers used to represent the present—the midpoint of the period used for calculating 30-year climate normals at the time they wrote their paper. Applying the model to these two sets of conditions, they demonstrated "BIOME3 can be used to simulate ... the vegetation distribution under ... different climate and CO_2 conditions than today."

Cheddadi *et al.* used their validated model to explore the vegetative consequences of an increase in anthropogenic CO_2 emissions that pushes the air's CO_2 concentration to a value of 500 ppm and its mean annual temperature to a value 2°C higher than today's mean value. The basic response of the vegetation to this change in environmental conditions was "a substantial southward shift of Mediterranean vegetation and a spread of evergreen and conifer forests in the northern Mediterranean."

They write, "when precipitation is maintained at its present-day level, an evergreen forest spreads in the eastern Mediterranean and a conifer forest in Turkey." Current xerophytic woodlands in this scenario become "restricted to southern Spain and southern Italy and they no longer occur in southern France." In northwest Africa, "Mediterranean xerophytic vegetation occupies a more extensive territory than today and the arid steppe/desert boundary shifts southward," as each vegetation zone becomes signifi-

cantly more verdant than it is today.

In identifying the cause of these positive developments, Cheddadi *et al.* write, "the replacement of xerophytic woodlands by evergreen and conifer forests could be explained by the enhancement of photosynthesis due to the increase of CO_2." They also note, "under a high CO_2 stomata will be much less open which will lead to a reduced evapotranspiration and lower water loss, both for C_3 and C_4 plants," adding "such mechanisms may help plants to resist long-lasting drought periods that characterize the Mediterranean climate."

Contrary to what IPCC predicts for much of the world's moisture-challenged lands, the authors report, "an increase of CO_2, jointly with an increase of *ca.* 2°C in annual temperature would not lead to desertification on any part of the Mediterranean unless annual precipitation decreased drastically," defining a drastic decrease as a decline of 30% or more. Equally important in this context, Hennessy *et al.* (1997) found a doubling of atmospheric CO_2 content would lead to a 5 to 10% increase in annual precipitation at Mediterranean latitudes, which is also what is predicted for most of the rest of the world. Thus the results of Cheddadi *et al.*'s study, where precipitation was held constant, may be considered a worst-case scenario, with the true vegetative response being even better than they projected.

Bellassen *et al.* (2011) write, "several parties to the United Nations Framework Convention on Climate Change (UNFCCC) are calling for 'forward-looking baselines'" to develop country-specific scenarios based on forest age structure that can be used "to credit only the part of the forest sink going beyond business-as-usual practices." They derived such a baseline for Europe.

Using ORCHIDEE-FM—a process-based vegetation model that differs from earlier versions of ORCHIDEE by "its explicit representation of stand growth and idealized forest management"—Bellassen *et al.* applied the model on a grid across Europe to "simulate changes in the net ecosystem productivity (NEP) of forests with and without changes in climate, CO_2 and age structure." The six scientists report the model they used "simulates carbon stocks and volume increments comparable ... with inventory-derived estimates at country level for 20 European countries," providing "an upwards trend of forest NEP of 1 ± 0.5 g C/m^2/year between 1950 and 2000 across the EU 25," ending with "a mean European forest NEP of 175 ± 52 g C/m^2/year in the 1990s" (see Figure 4.2.2.4.1). They write, "61% of the change in NEP [over the last half of the 20th century] was attributed

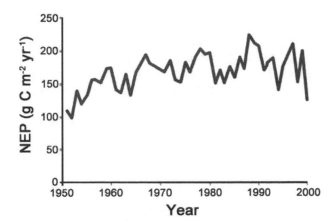

Figure 4.2.2.4.1. Simulated reconstruction of Net Ecosystem Productivity (NEP) in European forests for the years 1951–2000. Adapted from Bellassen *et al.* (2011).

to changes in CO_2, 26% to changes in climate, and 13% to changes in forest age structure."

As intriguing as these model-based studies are, it is important to examine the issue through the lens of real-world data to see how plant productivity has actually responded to modern warming, which IPCC claims is unprecedented over the past one to two thousand years. A number of scientists have done just that.

Allen *et al.* (1999) analyzed sediment cores from a lake in southern Italy and from the Mediterranean Sea, developing high-resolution climate and vegetation datasets for this region over the past 102,000 years. They found rapid changes in vegetation were well-correlated with rapid changes in climate, such that complete shifts in natural ecosystems would sometimes occur over periods of less than 200 years. Over the warmest portion of the record (the Holocene), the total organic carbon content of the vegetation reached its highest level, more than doubling values experienced over the rest of the record. Other proxy indicators reveal the increased vegetative cover also led to less soil erosion during the more-productive woody-plant period of the Holocene. This study thus demonstrates the biosphere can respond successfully to rapid changes in climate. As the 15 researchers write, "the biosphere was a full participant in these rapid fluctuations, contrary to widely held views that vegetation is unable to change with such rapidity." Their work also reveals warmer was always better in terms of plant growth, suggesting future warming in this region may return it to a level of biological productivity higher than it currently achieves.

Bert *et al.* (1997) calculated a 120-year (1860–

1980) history of intrinsic water-use efficiency (defined as the ratio of CO_2 assimilation rate to stomatal conductance for water vapor) for silver fir (*Abies alba* Mill.) trees, based on $\delta^{13}C$ data obtained from cores extracted from individual trees that grew within 208 pure stands in the Jura Mountains near the border that separates France and Switzerland. They found little net change in silver fir water-use efficiency from 1860 to 1930, but over the next half-century (1930 to 1980), when the atmosphere's CO_2 concentration rose at a rate more than three times faster than its rate of rise over the earlier period, this important tree physiological property rose by approximately 30% (see Figure 4.2.2.4.2). The three researchers state their results—which were "obtained at the level of mature trees"—are "consistent with the physiological effects of increasing CO_2 concentrations as observed in controlled experiments on young seedlings" and are also "consistent with the strong increases in radial growth observed for *Abies alba* in western Europe over the past decades."

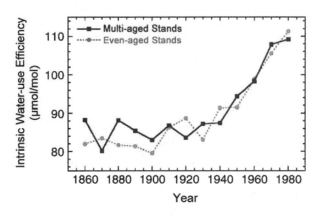

Figure 4.2.2.4.2. Intrinsic water-use efficiency (the ratio of CO_2 assimilation rate to stomatal conductance for water vapor) calculated from tree rings sampled in multi-aged and even-aged forest stands from the Jura Mountains in Eastern France for the years 1860–1980. Adapted from Bert *et al.* (1997).

Jandl *et al.* (2007) evaluated the growth rates of two Norway spruce (*Picea abies*) stands in the Bohemian Massif of Northern Austria over the prior four decades by analyzing the stem characteristics (height and diameter) of several trees they felled at two sites, and by comparing their results with data obtained from control plots of other experiments conducted there over an even longer period of time. The three researchers found "forest productivity is currently about two yield classes higher than it is in the regionally valid yield tables," which were derived from data collected at the end of the nineteenth century, and "the height and diameter of dominant stems exceed expectations." Jandl *et al.* conclude, "the sites are in a steady process of aggradation and that site productivity is rising."

The Austrian researchers contend climate was unlikely to be the main driver of the elevated growth rates of the forest stands they studied, because neither air temperature nor precipitation were strong predictors of the increment rates at their experimental sites. In addition, they state the "ongoing improvement" was "not the mere consequence of a nitrogen-enriching effect." Hence, they considered "the enriching effect of increasing CO_2 concentrations" and possibly changes in management practices (such as the abandonment of forest litter raking) to be the only viable alternative explanations for the steady historical increase in Norway spruce productivity at the sites they studied.

Leal *et al.* (2008) discovered "a very clear change in the sensitivity of the growth rate of [black pine (*Pinus nigra*)] tree stems to water availability in the late 20th century" in the Vienna basin of Austria in the European Eastern Alps, noting "trees previously sensitive to spring-summer drought show a lack of response to this climatic parameter in recent decades." They explain "tree-ring indices were larger in the second half of the 20th century than predicted given prevailing spring-summer drought conditions and the previous sensitivity of growth to these conditions." They also found "a decrease in correspondence between the occurrence of extreme events in precipitation and rate of change of growth," such that "in the second half of the century this correspondence was not significant" and "recent extreme droughts did not result in the formation of very narrow rings, which means the droughts were not as limiting to tree growth as they had been in the past."

The five researchers conclude by suggesting the greater atmospheric CO_2 concentrations of the latter decades of the twentieth century "induced improved water-use efficiency enabling *P. nigra* growing in the Vienna basin to avoid the impact of recurrent dry conditions." This phenomenon also has been observed in many other parts of the world in a number of different tree species, another indication of the propensity of the ongoing rise in the atmospheric CO_2 content to promote a greening of the Earth.

Martinez-Vilalta *et al.* (2008) used tree-ring data from the Catalan Ecological and Forest Inventory "to study the temporal variability of Scots pine stem radial growth (period 1901–1997) across a relatively large region (Catalonia, NE Spain) situated close to the southern limit of the distribution of the species." This inventory "included a total of 10,664 plots randomly distributed throughout the forested area of Catalonia." Scots pine was present in 30.2% of the plots and was the dominant tree species in 18.4%.

The researchers found "an overall increase of 84% in Scots pine BAI [basal area increment] during the 20th century (see Figure 4.2.2.4.3), consistent with most previous studies for temperate forests." They state "this trend was associated with increased atmospheric CO_2 concentration," which they characterize as "a fertilization effect." The five scientists note over the same time period there was "a marked increase in temperature across the study region (0.19°C per decade on average)," and "this warming had a negative impact on radial growth, particularly at the drier sites." However, they found "its magnitude was not enough to counteract the fertilization effect."

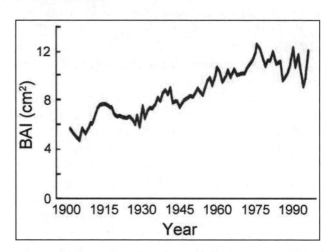

Figure 4.2.2.4.3. Basal area increment (BAI) for Scots pine trees growing in NE Spain during the years 1901–1997. Adapted from Martinez-Vilalta *et al.* (2008).

Noting "protected areas provide excellent opportunities for [determining] baseline descriptions and trends that ... can be used to evaluate the impact of global environmental change on terrestrial ecosystem functioning," Alcaraz-Segura *et al.* (2008) employed satellite-derived normalized difference vegetation index (NDVI) data—which provide a measure of net primary production, "the most integrative indicator of ecosystem functioning"—to "evaluate the impact of global environmental change on terrestrial ecosystem functioning of [Spain's] national parks." This information provides a sound basis for determining what could have been expected to have occurred throughout the rest of the country and much of Europe (Julien *et al.*, 2006) independent of confounding effects not related to global environmental change.

The four researchers from Argentina, Spain, and the United States report, "most parks showed areas with positive NDVI trends that tended to have higher proportions of Mediterranean coniferous and mixed forests, oro-Mediterranean scrublands, heathlands, maquis and garrigues," whereas "negative trends were scarce." Alcaraz-Segura *et al.* conclude "protected areas are changing in the short term and, at least in terms of vegetation greenness, they are changing in a directional way," such that "a large part of the Spanish National Parks is intercepting more photosynthetically active radiation than in the past."

Hallinger *et al.* (2010) studied male plants of the medium-sized *Juniperus nana* shrub at a site just three kilometers from the Abisko Scientific Research Station (68°21'N, 18°49'E) in the Northern Swedish Scandes. They collected the main stems of five to eight shrubs every hundred meters of elevation until the shrub zone ended. Ring-width measurements on these stems were then performed, they write, "to measure radial and vertical growth, to track growth changes over time, to age the shrub individuals and to correlate annual shrub growth with climate," the characteristics of which were derived from records of the nearby Abisko Station.

The three researchers say their analysis "documented a distinct increase in radial and vertical growth rates of *J. nana* shrubs during recent decades in the subalpine zone of North Sweden" (see Figure 4.2.2.4.4), and "the age structure of shrubs along the elevational gradient provides evidence that an upslope advance of the altitudinal shrubline is underway." They "observed significant, strong and stable correlations between annual ring width and summer temperatures (June, July, August)," and "the acceleration of radial and vertical growth since 1970 also coincides with the recent three decades of rising arctic air temperatures and the warming trend of 0.2°C per decade for the average temperature since 1956 at Abisko." These findings, they write, add to the "mounting evidence that shrubs are expanding into alpine and arctic areas because of climate warming," and "this expansion occurs in both evergreen and deciduous shrub types," citing Forbes *et al.* (2009).

Kullman (2010a) presents "an integrative review of results from long-term monitoring of subalpine/alpine vegetation" in the Swedish Scandes, from which he derives "tentative projections of landscape transformations in a potentially warmer future," based

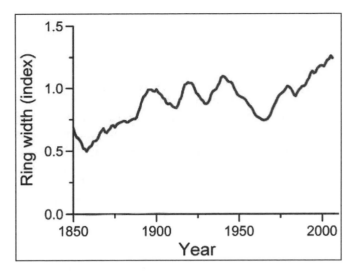

Figure 4.2.2.4.4. Indexed radial growth of juniper trees in the northern Swedish Scandes during the years 1850–2006, smoothed with a 10-year filter. Adapted from Hallinger *et al.* (2010).

on "actual observations and paleoecological data (Kullman and Kjallgren, 2006; Kullman 2006)." The professor of physical geography at Sweden's Umea University writes post-Little Ice Age warming has broken "a multi-millennial trend of plant cover retrogression" and "floristic and faunal impoverishment, all imposed by progressive and deterministic neoglacial climate cooling." He reports the "upper range margin rise of trees and low-altitude (boreal) plant species, expansion of alpine grasslands and dwarf-shrub heaths are the modal biotic adjustments during the past few decades, after a century of substantial climate warming." Currently, "alpine plant life is proliferating, biodiversity is on the rise and the mountain world appears more productive and inviting than ever." Kullman notes "in contrast to model predictions, no single alpine plant species has become extinct, neither in Scandinavia nor in any other part of the world in response to climate warming over the past century," citing, in addition to his own studies, Pauli *et al.* (2001, 2007), Theurillat and Guisan (2001), and Birks (2008).

In a contemporaneous study published in the *Nordic Journal of Botany*, Kullman describes how extensive the recent proliferation of plant life has been (Kullman, 2010c). He reports the findings of species inventories he conducted on the uppermost 20 meters of four high-mountain summits in the Swedish Scandes (Kullman 2007a,b), the results of which he compared with the findings of "historical species inventories from the early 1950s, executed by a highly competent and experienced botanist (Kilander,

1955)," which "can be seen as an evaluation of a full-scale 'natural experiment' (cf. Grabherr *et al.*, 2001)."

Kullman (2010c) writes the species pools at the tops of the studied mountains have "increased by 60–170% since the 1950s," "some of the invading species are new to the alpine tundra, with more silvine and thermophilic properties than the extant alpine flora," and "not a single species of the original flora has disappeared from any of the summits." Kullman concludes, "the alpine flora appears to be more adaptive and responsive to climate change than generally believed," and "overall, a richer, greener and more productive alpine world has emerged in the wake of the recent climate warming episode (Kullman, 2010a, 2010b)."

Rundqvist *et al.* (2011) documented "rapid and substantial increases in the abundance of prominent tree and shrub species near [the] tree-line and forest-line in sub-Arctic Sweden," on an east-facing slope of the Slattatjakka/Njulla mountains (68°21'N, 18°49'W) in the Abisko Valley about 200 km north of the Arctic Circle in Sweden. They "recorded an invasion by a thermophilic tree species not present in the plots 34 years ago."

The seven Swedish scientists say their observations mesh well with those of many other researchers, noting "there is an indication that the shrub layer near the tree-line has expanded, since the 1930s, in the Abisko area (Enquist *et al.*, 1933; Sandberg, 1963)," and "data from Canada, Fennoscandia, Alaska and Russia reveal that there is a Pan-Arctic expansion of shrubs and trees in progress (e.g. Kullman, 2002; Tommervik *et al.*, 2004; ACIA, 2005; Tape *et al.*, 2006; Karlsson *et al.*, 2007; Olofsson *et al.*, 2009; Hallinger *et al.*, 2010; Hendenas *et al.*, 2011)." They state the change in shrubs and small trees they observed is "consistent with anticipated changes due to climate change and reduced herbivory," and this change "could be interpreted as an ongoing natural re-establishment of plants at higher altitudes due to a natural increase in the temperature since the 'Little Ice Age' (Kammer *et al.*, 2007)."

Hedenas *et al.* (2011) state, "during the last 15 years, there has been an increasing focus on how climate change has and will affect the distribution and extent of ecosystems around the globe including alpine and Arctic areas (e.g., Callaghan *et al.*, 2005)." They report, "field studies and remote sensing have revealed a recent increase in altitude of the tree line (e.g., Kullman, 2002)," as well as "an extension and increased cover of mountain birch forest (Tommervik *et al.*, 2009; Rundqvist *et al.*, 2011)." They say Tommervik *et al.* determined "tree biomass has doubled over a 43-year period, within an area of Finnmarksvidda, and Rundqvist *et al.* have observed an increased density and cover of mountain birch in the treeline over the last three decades, within an area near Abisko village."

Hedenas *et al.* in 2010 re-surveyed shrub, tree, and vegetation data at 549 plots grouped into 61 clusters originally surveyed in 1997 in two areas close to the Abisko village approximately 200 km north of the Arctic Circle at 68°20'N, 18°50'E. They found "tree basal area and biomass increased by 19% between 1997 and 2010 with the main increase occurring in established birch forest" (see Figure 4.2.2.4.5), and this result "concurs with the results of other studies which suggest that there has been a general increase in cover and biomass of trees and shrubs in sub-Arctic and Arctic areas," citing Sturm *et al.* (2001), Tape *et al.* (2006), Danby and Hik (2007), Forbes *et al.* (2010), Hallinger *et al.* (2010), and Van Bogaert *et al.* (2011). They found the 19% net

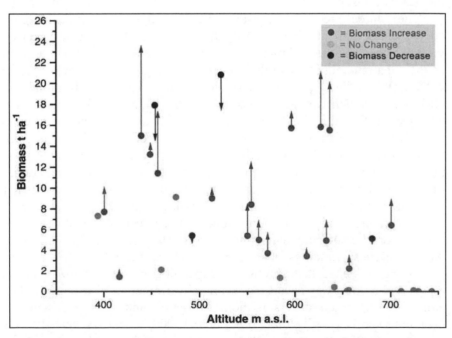

Figure 4.2.2.4.5. Change in mean tree biomass by altitude during the years 1997–2010 from various locations throughout the Swedish sub-Arctic. Colors reveal the direction of the change (green = biomass increase, yellow = no change, and red = biomass decrease), and arrows indicate the magnitude of the change over the 13-year period. Adapted from Hedenas *et al.* (2010).

increase in biomass occurred in spite of the increased browsing pressure provided by a growing reindeer population over the period of their study, as well as periodic outbursts of geometrid moths, which severely defoliated the birch trees in their study area in 2004 (Babst *et al.*, 2010). They write, "it has been suggested that increased nutrient availability associated with higher soil temperatures, and a longer growing season could underpin increased tree and shrub abundance and biomass in the Arctic (e.g., Chapin, 1983; Weih and Karlsson, 1997; Hartley *et al.*, 1999)," as a result of "a delayed re-expansion of shrubs and trees following the 'Little Ice Age,'" as suggested by Grubb (2008).

Noting forests are exposed to a changing environment and "responses to recent climate change start to become visible if observation periods become long enough," Pilegaard *et al.* (2011) present the results of continuous CO_2 flux measurements they made above a mature Danish beech stand in the Lille Bogeskov forest located near Soro on the island of Zealand (55°29'13"N, 11°38'45"E) during the years 1996–2009, describing the long-term changes they observed and relating them to possible causes.

They report observing "significant linear trends of increasing gross ecosystem exchange (GEE: 29 g C/m^2/year) and increasing net ecosystem exchange (NEE: 23 g C/m^2/year), while the positive trend for ecosystem respiration (RE: 5 g C/m^2/year) was not significant." They also state, "the length of the carbon uptake period increased by 1.9 day/year, whereas there was a non-significant increase of 0.3 day/year in the leafed period," which means, they write, "the leaves stay active longer." They say "the increase in the carbon uptake period explained only part of the increasing NEE (9 gC/m^2/year)." And noting "the maximum rate of photosynthetic assimilation increased by 15% during the 14-year period," they speculate the increase in canopy carbon uptake capacity "could be due to a combination of [the] increase in atmospheric CO_2, higher summer precipitation, and increased availability of nitrogen."

Lopatin *et al.* (2006) collected discs and cores from 151 Siberian spruce trees and 110 Scots pines in the Komi Republic in the northeast European sector of Russia, from which they developed ring-width chronologies that revealed yearly changes in forest productivity. They developed satellite-based time series of NDVI for the months of June, July, and August of the years 1982–2001, correlated their site-specific ring-width-derived productivity histories with same-site NDVI time series, and used the resulting relationship to establish six regional forest pro-

ductivity histories for the years 1982–2001. They compared the six regional productivity trends over this period with corresponding-region temperature and precipitation trends. For all six vegetation zones of the Komi Republic, this work indicates the 1982–2001 trends of integrated NDVI values from June to August were positive, and the "increase in productivity reflected in [the] NDVI data [was] maximal on the sites with increased temperature and decreased precipitation."

The three scientists write, "several studies (Riebsame *et al.*, 1994; Myneni *et al.*, 1998; Vicente-Serrano *et al.*, 2004) have shown a recent increase in vegetation cover in different world ecosystems." What is special about their study, as they describe it, is "in Europe, most forests are managed, except for those in north-western Russia [the location of their work], where old-growth natural forests are dominant (Aksenov *et al.*, 2002)." They conclude "productivity during recent decades also increased in relatively untouched forests," where non-management-related "climate change with lengthening growing season, increasing CO_2 and nitrogen deposition" are the primary determinants of changes in forest productivity.

Julien *et al.* (2006) "used land surface temperature (LST) algorithms and NDVI [normalized difference vegetation index] values to estimate changes in vegetation on the European continent between 1982 and 1999 from the Pathfinder AVHRR [advanced very high resolution radiometer] Land (PAL) dataset." This analysis revealed arid and semi-arid areas (Northern Africa, Southern Spain, and the Middle East) have seen their mean LST increase and NDVI decrease, and temperate areas (Western and Central Europe) have suffered a slight decrease in LST but a more substantial increase in NDVI, especially in Germany, the Czech Republic, Poland, and Belarus. In addition, parts of continental and Northern Europe experienced either slight increases or decreases in NDVI while LST values have decreased. The Dutch and Spanish researchers conclude, over the last two decades of the twentieth century, "Europe as a whole has a tendency to greening," and much of it is "seeing an increase in its wood land proportion."

References

ACIA. 2005. *Arctic Climate Impact Assessment*. Cambridge University Press, Cambridge, United Kingdom.

Aksenov, D., Dobrynin, D., Dubinin, M., Egorov, A.,

Isaev, A., Karpachevskiy, M., Laestadius, L., Potapov, P., Purekhovskiy, P., Turubanova, S., and Yaroshenko, A. 2002. *Atlas of Russia's Intact Forest Landscapes.* Global Forest Watch Russia, Moscow.

Alcaraz-Segura, D., Cabello, J., Paruelo, J.M., and Delibes, M. 2008. Trends in the surface vegetation dynamics of the national parks of Spain as observed by satellite sensors. *Applied Vegetation Science* **11**: 431–440.

Allen, J.R.M., Brandt, U., Brauer, A., Hubberten, H.-W., Huntley, B., Keller, J., Kraml, M., Mackensen, A., Mingram, J., Negendank, J.F.W., Nowaczyk, N.R., Oberhansli, H., Watts, W.A., Wulf, S., and Zolitschka, B. 1999. Rapid environmental changes in southern Europe during the last glacial period. *Nature* **400**: 740–743.

Babst, F., Esper, J., and Parlow, E. 2010. Landsat TM/ETM plus and tree-ring based assessment of spatiotemporal patterns of the autumnal moth (*Epirrita autumnata*) in northernmost Fennoscandia. *Remote Sensing of Environment* **114**: 637–646.

Bellassen, V., Viovy, N., Luyssaert, S., Le Marie, G., Schelhaas, M.-J., and Ciais, P. 2011. Reconstruction and attribution of the carbon sink of European forests between 1950 and 2000. *Global Change Biology* **17**: 3274–3292.

Bert, D., Leavitt, S.W., and Dupouey, J.-L. 1997. Variations of wood $\delta^{13}C$ and water-use efficiency of *Abies alba* during the last century. *Ecology* **78**: 1588–1596.

Birks, H.H. 2008. The late-quaternary history of arctic and alpine plants. *Plant Ecology and Diversity* **1**: 135–146.

Callaghan, T.V., Bjorn, L.O., Chapin, T., Chernov, Y., Christensen, T.R., Huntley, B., Ims, R.A., Johansson, M., Riedlinger, D.J., Jonasson, S., Matveyeva, N., Oechel, W., Panikov, N., Shaver, G., Elster, J., Henttonen, H., Jónsdóttir, I.S., Laine, K., Schaphoff, S., Sitch, S., Taulavuori, E., Taulavuori, K., and Zöckler, C. 2005. Arctic tundra and polar desert ecosystems. In: *Arctic Climate Impact Assessment (ACIA).* ACIA Scientific Report: Cambridge University Press, Cambridge, United Kingdom, pp. 243–352.

Chapin III, F.S. 1983. Direct and indirect effects of temperature on Arctic plants. *Polar Biology* **2**: 47–52.

Cheddadi, R., Guiot, J., and Jolly, D. 2001. The Mediterranean vegetation: what if the atmospheric CO_2 increased? *Landscape Ecology* **16**: 667–675.

Danby, R.K. and Hik, D.S. 2007. Variability, contingency and rapid change in recent subarctic alpine tree line dynamics. *Journal of Ecology* **95**: 352–363.

Enquist, F. 1933. Trädgränsundersökningar. *Svenska Skogsvårdsföreningens Tidskrift* **31**: 145–191.

Forbes, B.C., Fauria, M.M., and Zetterberg, P. 2009. Russian Arctic warming and greening are closely tracked by tundra shrub willows. *Global Change Biology* **15**: 1–13.

Forbes, B.C., Fauria, M.M., and Zetterberg, P. 2010. Russian Arctic warming and 'greening' are closely tracked by tundra shrub willows. *Global Change Biology* **16**: 1542–1554.

Grabherr, G., Gottfried, M., and Pauli, H. 2001. Long-term monitoring of mountain peaks in the Alps. In: Burga, C.A. and Kratochwil, A. (Eds.) *Biomonitoring: General and Applied Aspects on Regional and Global Scales. Tasks for Vegetation Science.* Kluwer, Dordrecht, Germany, pp. 153–177.

Grubb, H. 2008. Tornetrask tree-ring width and density AD 500–2004: A test of climatic sensitivity and a new 1500-year reconstruction of north Fennoscandian summers. *Climate Dynamics* **31**: 843–857.

Hallinger, M., Manthey, M., and Wilmking, M. 2010. Establishing a missing link: warm summers and winter snow cover promote shrub expansion into alpine tundra in Scandinavia. *New Phytologist* **186**: 890–899.

Hartley, A.E., Neil, C., Melillo, J.M., Crabtree, R., and Bowles, F.P. 1999. Plant performance and soil nitrogen mineralization in response to simulated climate change in subarctic dwarf shrub heath. *Oikos* **86**: 331–343.

Hedenas, H., Olsson, H., Jonasson, C., Bergstedt, J., Dahlberg, U., and Callaghan, T.V. 2011. Changes in tree growth, biomass and vegetation over a 13-year period in the Swedish Sub-Arctic. *Ambio* **40**: 672–682.

Hennessy, K.J., Gregory, J.M., and Mitchell, J.F.B. 1997. Changes in daily precipitation under enhanced greenhouse conditions. *Climate Dynamics* **13**: 667–680.

Jandl, R., Neumann, M., and Eckmullner, O. 2007. Productivity increase in Northern Austria Norway spruce forests due to changes in nitrogen cycling and climate. *Journal of Plant Nutrition and Soil Science* **170**: 157–165.

Julien, Y., Sobrino, J.A., and Verhoef, W. 2006. Changes in land surface temperatures and NDVI values over Europe between 1982 and 1999. *Remote Sensing of Environment* **103**: 43–55.

Kammer, P.M., Schob, C., and Choler, P. 2007. Increasing species richness on mountain summits: Upward migration due to anthropogenic climate change or re-colonization? *Journal of Vegetation Science* **18**: 301–306.

Karlsson, H., Hornberg, G., Hannon, G., and Nordstrom, E.-M. 2007. Long-term vegetation changes in the northern Scandinavian forest limit: A human impact-climate synergy? *The Holocene* **17**: 37–49.

Kilander, S. 1955. Karlvaxternas ovre granser pa fjall i sydvastra Jamtland samt angransande delar av Harjedalen och Norge. *Acta Phytogeogr. Suec.* **35**: 1–198.

Kullman, L. 2002. Rapid recent range-margin rise of tree and shrub species in the Swedish Scandes. *Journal of Ecology* **90**: 68–77.

Kullman, L. 2006. Transformation of alpine and subalpine vegetation in a potentially warmer future, the Anthropocene era. Tentative projections based on long-term observations and paleovegetation records. *Current Trends in Ecology* 1: 1–16.

Kullman, L. 2007a. Long-term geobotanical observations of climate change impacts in the Scandes of west-central Sweden. *Nordic Journal of Botany* 24: 445–467.

Kullman, L. 2007b. Modern climate change and shifting ecological states of the subalpine/alpine landscape in the Swedish Scandes. *Geo-Oko* 28: 187–221.

Kullman, L. 2010b. One century of treeline change and stability—experiences from the Swedish Scandes. *Landscape Online* 17: 1–31.

Kullman, L. 2010a. A richer, greener and smaller alpine world—review and projection of warming-induced plant cover change in the Swedish Scandes. *Ambio* 39: 159–169.

Kullman, L. 2010c. Alpine flora dynamics—a critical review of responses to climate change in the Swedish Scandes since the early 1950s. *Nordic Journal of Botany* 28: 398–408.

Kullman, L. and Kjallgren, L. 2006. Holocene tree-line evolution in the Swedish Scandes: Recent tree-line rise and climate change in a long-term perspective. *Boreas* 35: 159–168.

Leal, S., Eamus, D., Grabner, M., Wimmer, R., and Cherubini, P. 2008. Tree rings of *Pinus nigra* from the Vienna basin region (Austria) show evidence of change in climatic sensitivity in the late 20th century. *Canadian Journal of Forest Research* 38: 744–759.

Lopatin, E., Kolstrom, T., and Spiecker, H. 2006. Determination of forest growth trends in Komi Republic (northwestern Russia): combination of tree-ring analysis and remote sensing data. *Boreal Environment Research* 11: 341–353.

Martinez-Vilalta, J., Lopez, B.C., Adell, N., Badiella, L., and Ninyerola, M. 2008. Twentieth century increase of Scots pine radial growth in NE Spain shows strong climate interactions. *Global Change Biology* 14: 2868–2881.

Myneni, R.B., Tucker, C.J., Asrar, G., and Keeling, C.D. 1998. Interannual variations in satellite-sensed vegetation index data from 1981 to 1991. *Journal of Geophysical Research* 103: 6145–6160.

Olofsson, J., Oksanen, L., Callaghan, T., Hulme, E.P., Oksanen, T., and Suominen, O. 2009. Herbivores inhibit climate-driven shrub expansion on the tundra. *Global Change Biology* 15: 2681–2693.

Osborne, C.P., Mitchell, P.L., Sheehy, J.E., and Woodward, F.I. 2000. Modelling the recent historical impacts of atmospheric CO_2 and climate change on Mediterranean vegetation. *Global Change Biology* 6: 445–458.

Pauli, H., Gottfried, M., and Grabherr, G. 2001. High summits of the Alps in a changing climate. In: Walther, G.-R., Burga, C.A., and Edwards, P.J. (Eds.) *Fingerprints of Climate Change.* Kluwer, New York, New York, USA., pp. 139–149.

Pauli, H., Gottfried, M., Reiter, K., Klettner, C., and Grabherr, G. 2007. Signals of range expansions and contractions of vascular plants in the high Alps: Observations (1994–2004) at the GLORIA master site Schrankogel, Tyrol, Austria. *Global Change Biology* 13: 147–156.

Pilegaard, K., Ibrom, A., Courtney, M.S., Hummelshoj, P., and Jensen, N.O. 2011. Increasing net CO_2 uptake by a Danish beech forest during the period from 1996 to 2009. *Agricultural and Forest Meteorology* 151: 934–946.

Riebsame, W.E., Meyer, W.B., and Turner, B.L. 1994. Modeling land-use and cover as part of global environmental-change. *Climatic Change* 28: 45–64.

Rundqvist, S., Hedenas, H., Sandstrom, A., Emanuelsson, U., Eriksson, H., Jonasson, C., and Callaghan, T.V. 2011. Tree and shrub expansion over the past 34 years at the tree-line near Abisko, Sweden. *Ambio* 40: 683–692.

Sandberg, G. 1963. Vaxtvarlden I Abisko nationalpark. In: Curry-Lindahl, K. (Ed.) *Natur i Lappland*, II. Bokforlaget Svensk Natur, Uppsala, Sweden.

Sturm, M., Racine, C., and Tape, K. 2001. Climate change—increasing shrub abundance in the Arctic. *Nature* 411: 546–547.

Tape, K., Sturm, M., and Racine, C. 2006. The evidence for shrub expansion in Northern Alaska and the Pan-Arctic. *Global Change Biology* 12: 686–702.

Theurillat, J.-P. and Guisan, A. 2001. Potential impacts of climate change on vegetation in the European Alps: A review. *Climatic Change* 50: 77–109.

Tommervik, H., Johansen, B., Riseth, J.A., Karlsen, S.R., Solberg, B., and Hogda, K.A. 2009. Above ground biomass changes in the mountain birch forests and mountain heaths of Finnmarksvidda, northern Norway, in the period 1957–2006. *Forest Ecology and Management* 257: 244–257.

Tommervik, H., Johansen, B., Tombre, I., Thannheiser, D., Hogda, K., and Gaare, E. 2004. Vegetation changes in the Nordic mountain birch forest: The influence of grazing and climate change. *Arctic, Antarctic, and Alpine Research* 36: 323–332.

Van Bogaert, R., Haneca, K., Hoogestger, J., Jonasson, C., De Dapper, M., and Callaghan, T.V. 2011. A century of tree line changes in sub-Arctic Sweden show local and regional variability and only a minor role of 20th century climate warming. *Journal of Biogeography* 38: 907–921.

Vicente-Serrano, S.M., Lasanta, T., and Romo, A. 2004. Analysis of spatial and temporal evolution of vegetation cover in the Spanish central Pyrenees: Role of human management. *Environmental Management* **34**: 802–818.

Weih, M. and Karlsson, P.S. 1997. Growth and nitrogen utilization in seedlings of mountain birch (*Betula pubescens* ssp. tortuosa) as related to plant nitrogen status and temperature: A two-year study. *Ecoscience* **4**: 365–373.

4.2.2.5 North America

As in Asia, a significant amount of terrestrial productivity research has been conducted for locations in North America. We group that research into these subsections: *Entire Continent, High Latitude Regions, Eastern USA, Central USA,* and *Western USA.*

4.2.2.5.1 Entire Continent

Zhou *et al.* (2001) determined the satellite-derived normalized difference vegetation index (NDVI) rose by 8.44% over the North American continent between 1981 and 1999. Noting the NDVI "can be used to proxy the vegetation's responses to climate changes because it is well correlated with the fraction of photosynthetically active radiation absorbed by plant canopies and thus leaf area, leaf biomass, and potential photosynthesis," Zhou *et al.* suggest the increases in plant growth and vitality implied by their NDVI data were driven primarily by increases in near-surface air temperature. Ahlbeck (2002) suggests the observed upward trend in NDVI was primarily driven by the rise in atmospheric CO_2 content over the period, since warming was rather muted in North America and in the United States in particular, where temperatures may have declined throughout the eastern part of the country over the period of the study. It is likely both parameters played a role in the observed productivity increase, although the CO_2 increase was more likely the predominant one given the lack of temperature increase over the period of time under study.

Hicke *et al.* (2002) computed net primary productivity (NPP) over North America for the years 1982–1998 using the Carnegie-Ames-Stanford Approach (CASA) carbon cycle model driven by a satellite NDVI record at 8 km spatial resolution. They found NPP increases of 30% or more occurred across the continent from 1982 to 1998. During this period,

the air's CO_2 concentration rose by 25.74 ppm, as calculated from the Mauna Loa data of Keeling and Whorf (1998), which is 8.58% of the 300 ppm increase often used as a reference for expressing plant growth responses to atmospheric CO_2 enrichment. Consequently, for herbaceous plants that display NPP increases of 30–40% in response to a 300 ppm increase in atmospheric CO_2 concentration, the CO_2-induced NPP increase experienced between 1982 and 1998 would have been 2.6–3.4%. Similarly, for woody plants that display NPP increases of 60–80% in response to a 300 ppm increase in atmospheric CO_2 (Saxe *et al.*, 1998; Idso and Kimball, 2001), the expected increase in productivity between 1982 and 1998 would have been 5.1–6.9%. As both of these NPP increases are considerably less than the 30% or more observed by Hicke *et al.*, additional factors must have helped to stimulate NPP over this period. Those factors may have included concomitant increases in precipitation and air temperature, the tendency for warming to lengthen growing seasons and enhance the aerial fertilization effect of rising CO_2 concentrations, increasingly intensive crop and forest management, increasing use of genetically improved plants, the regrowth of forests on abandoned cropland, and improvements in agricultural practices such as irrigation and fertilization.

Lim *et al.* (2004) correlated the monthly rate of relative change in NDVI, derived from advanced very high resolution radiometer (AVHRR) data, with the rate of change in atmospheric CO_2 concentration during the natural vegetation growing season in three eco-region zones of North America (Arctic and sub-Arctic zone, humid temperate zone, and dry and desert zone, which they further subdivided into 17 regions) during the years 1982–1992. They explored the temporal progression of annual minimum NDVI during the years 1982–2001 throughout the eastern humid temperate zone of North America. In all of the regions but one, according to the researchers, "δCO_2 was positively correlated with the rate of change in vegetation greenness in the following month, and most correlations were high," which they say is "consistent with a CO_2 fertilization effect" of the type observed in "experimental manipulations of atmospheric CO_2 that report a stimulation of photosynthesis and above-ground productivity at high CO_2." They determined the yearly "minimum vegetation greenness increased over the period 1982–2001 for all the regions of the eastern humid temperate zone in North America."

Lim *et al.* say rising CO_2 could "increase minimum greenness by stimulating photosynthesis at the beginning of the growing season," citing Idso *et al.* (2000), who discovered that although new spring branch growth of sour orange trees began on exactly the same day of the year in both ambient (400 ppm) and CO_2-enriched (700 ppm) open-top chambers, the rate of new-branch growth was initially vastly greater in the CO_2-enriched trees. Three weeks after branch growth began in the spring, for example, new branches on the CO_2-enriched trees were typically more than four times more massive than their counterparts on the ambient-treatment trees, and on a per-tree basis, more than six times more new-branch biomass was produced on the CO_2-enriched trees, before declining to an approximate 80% stimulation typical of the bulk of the growing season.

By looking for a manifestation of the CO_2 fertilization effect at the time of year it is apt to be most strongly expressed, Lim *et al.* may have found it. Between 1982 and 2001, the air's CO_2 concentration rose by approximately 30 ppm. From Idso *et al.*'s findings of more than a 300% initial increase in the biomass of new sour orange tree branches for a 300 ppm increase in the air's CO_2 concentration and more than a 500% initial increase in per-tree new-branch biomass, it can be calculated yearly minimum greenness should have increased by an amount between just over 30% and just over 50%, if other woody plants respond to atmospheric CO_2 enrichment as sour orange trees do. When the mean 19-year increase in NDVI for the seven regions for which Lim *et al.* present data is calculated, the result is an increase of just over 40%, indicating Lim *et al.*'s data are not only qualitatively consistent with their hypothesis but on the mark quantitatively as well.

Xiao and Moody (2004) examined the responses of the normalized difference vegetation index integrated over the growing season (gNDVI) to annual and seasonal precipitation, maximum temperature (T_{max}), and minimum temperature (T_{min}) over an 11-year period (1990–2000) for six biomes in the conterminous United States (evergreen needleleaf forest, deciduous broadleaf forest, mixed forest, open shrubland, woody savanna, and grassland), focusing on within- and across-biome variance in long-term average gNDVI and emphasizing the degree to which this variance is explained by spatial gradients in long-term average seasonal climate. They found the greatest positive climate-change impacts on biome productivity were caused by increases in spring, winter, and fall precipitation and increases in fall and spring temperature, especially T_{min}, which historically has increased at roughly twice the rate of T_{max} in the United States. They write, "if historical climatic

trends and the biotic responses suggested in this analysis continue to hold true, we can anticipate further increases in productivity for both forested and non-forested ecoregions in the conterminous US, with associated implications for carbon budgets and woody proliferation."

References

Ahlbeck, J.R. 2002. Comment on "Variations in northern vegetation activity inferred from satellite data of vegetation index during 1981–1999" by L. Zhou *et al. Journal of Geophysical Research* **107**: 10.1029/2001389.

Hicke, J.A., Asner, G.P., Randerson, J.T., Tucker, C., Los, S., Birdsey, R., Jenkins, J.C., and Field, C. 2002. Trends in North American net primary productivity derived from satellite observations, 1982–1998. *Global Biogeochemical Cycles* **16**: 10.1029/2001GB001550.

Idso, C.D., Idso, S.B., Kimball, B.A., Park, H., Hoober, J.K., and Balling Jr., R.C. 2000. Ultra-enhanced spring branch growth in CO_2-enriched trees: can it alter the phase of the atmosphere's seasonal CO_2 cycle? *Environmental and Experimental Botany* **43**: 91–100.

Idso, S.B. and Kimball, B.A. 2001. CO_2 enrichment of sour orange trees: 13 years and counting. *Environmental and Experimental Botany* **46**: 147–153.

Keeling, C.D. and Whorf, T.P. 1998. *Atmospheric CO_2 Concentrations—Mauna Loa Observatory, Hawaii, 1958–1997* (revised August 2000). NDP-001. Carbon Dioxide Information Analysis Center, Oak Ridge National Laboratory, Oak Ridge, Tennessee.

Lim, C., Kafatos, M., and Megonigal, P. 2004. Correlation between atmospheric CO_2 concentration and vegetation greenness in North America: CO_2 fertilization effect. *Climate Research* **28**: 11–22.

Saxe, H., Ellsworth, D.S., and Heath, J. 1998. Tree and forest functioning in an enriched CO_2 atmosphere. *New Phytologist* **139**: 395–436.

Xiao, J. and Moody, A. 2004. Photosynthetic activity of US biomes: responses to the spatial variability and seasonality of precipitation and temperature. *Global Change Biology* **10**: 437–451.

Zhou, L., Tucker, C.J., Kaufmann, R.K., Slayback, D., Shabanov, N.V., and Myneni, R.B. 2001. Variations in northern vegetation activity inferred from satellite data of vegetation index during 1981–1999. *Journal of Geophysical Research* **106**: 20,069–20,083.

4.2.2.5.2 High Latitude Regions

- Opposite the forecasts promulgated by the models used by IPCC, land-based plants of the Arctic and near-Arctic regions of North America are thriving, thanks in large part to the ongoing rise in the atmosphere's CO_2 concentration and global warming.

For many years, some researchers argued rising temperatures would change the Arctic from a carbon sink to a carbon source, further exacerbating the cause of ecosystem change—regional warming—by adding to the atmosphere's burden of greenhouse gases and hastening that portion of the biosphere's inevitable degradation (Oechel *et al.*, 1993, 1995).

In the early to mid-1970s, for example, when the first carbon balance studies of Alaskan Arctic ecosystems were conducted, wet-sedge communities and moist-tussock tundra were observed to be net sinks of carbon. By the mid-1980s and early 1990s, however, following significant increases in air temperature and surface water deficit, both ecosystems had become net sources of carbon. Then, between 1992 and 1996, in response to further warming and drying that resulted, Oechel *et al.* (2000a) write, in "the highest average summer temperature and surface water deficit observed for the entire 39-year period," both ecosystems' net summer releases of CO_2 to the atmosphere declined, and they became CO_2 sinks.

How did it happen? Oechel *et al.* say their observations indicated "a previously undemonstrated capacity for ecosystems to metabolically adjust to long-term (decadal or longer) changes in climate."

But how did *that* happen? Was there help along the way from the concomitant rise in atmospheric CO_2 content and its aerial fertilization and anti-transpirant effects? Although these well-documented consequences of atmospheric CO_2 enrichment are known to enable plants to better respond to the environmental challenges of warming and drying, Oechel *et al.* downplayed these effects, instead noting other plausible possibilities.

First, there is the likelihood that during the initial stages of warming and soil drying, younger and more labile carbon would be rapidly decomposed, shifting the net summer carbon balance of the ecosystems from carbon sequestration to carbon evolution. After this initial perturbation, Oechel *et al.* suggest "enhanced rates of net nitrogen-mineralization should eventually stimulate rates of gross primary production and atmospheric CO_2 sequestration."

Another possibility is a gradual shift in plant species towards more productive types that would further reduce the large initial carbon losses over time. The researchers state, "there is evidence that the relative abundance of deciduous shrubs has increased in response to climate change over the past 1–2 decades in Alaskan moist-tussock tundra ecosystems," which is also expected to occur as a consequence of the ongoing rise in atmospheric CO_2 content. Capers and Stone (2011), for example, report, in response to rising air temperatures, "trees have established where they did not previously occur, both in alpine areas (Wardle and Coleman, 1992; Peterson, 1994; Kullman, 2001, 2002), and in arctic tundra (Lescop-Sinclair and Payette, 1995; Danby and Hik, 2007)," while "increasing shrub abundance also has been reported in alpine (Klanderud and Birks, 2003) and arctic locations (Sturm *et al.*, 2001; Tape *et al.*, 2006; Wilson and Nilsson, 2009)."

Noting "canopy-forming shrubs are reported to be increasing at sites around the circumpolar Arctic," Myers-Smith *et al.* (2011) examined historic photographs, repeated vegetation surveys, and conducted monitoring of long-term plots on Canada's Herschel Island (69.57°N, 138.91°W) to see what had occurred over the past century on this 100-km^2 parcel of land just off the western Arctic coast of Canada's Yukon Territory. They "found evidence of increases of each of the dominant canopy-forming willow species (*Salix richardsonii*, *Salix glauca* and *Salix pulchra*), during the twentieth century," along with evidence "the majority of willow patches for each of these species became established between 1910 and 1960," "with stem ages and maximum growth rates indicating that some patches could have established as late as the 1980s."

The seven scientists note their observations are an example of the twentieth-century greening of the Circumpolar Arctic, noting "recent evidence indicates an expansion of canopy-forming shrubs at sites on the North Slope of Alaska (Sturm *et al.*, 2001; Tape *et al.*, 2006), on the coast of the Northwest Territories (Lantz *et al.*, 2009), in Northern Quebec (B. Tremblay *et al.*, personal communication), and in northern Russia (Forbes *et al.*, 2010a)." They write, "in Arctic Alaska, canopy cover of alder shrubs has increased by 14–20% on average within the last 40 years, with increases of up to 80% in some areas (Tape *et al.*, 2006)." Also, they note, "studies of population structures of shrub and tree species indicate advancing of shrubs up slopes in alpine tundra ecosystems in subarctic Sweden (Hallinger *et al.*, 2010)," as well as in sites in Norway (Hofgaard *et al.*, 2009), further noting "local indigenous Nenets people in the western Russian Arctic report increasing willow shrubs (Forbes *et al.*, 2010b)" and "similar observations of vegetation change by Inuit have been reported in Arctic Canada (Thorpe *et al.*, 2002)."

The team of Canadian researchers also states "pollen records indicate willows were widespread in Arctic ecosystems during warmer periods after the last glacial maximum (Brubaker *et al.*, 1983; Bigelow *et al.* (2003)." These observations seem to suggest the entire Circumpolar Arctic is in the process of returning to conditions of an earlier period when that part of the planet was a good deal greener—and a good deal livelier—than it has been for a long, long time.

Goetz *et al.* (2005) also documented increased plant growth in the high latitudes of North America. They transformed satellite-derived NDVI data obtained across boreal North America (Canada and Alaska) for the years 1982–2003 into photosynthetically active radiation absorbed by green vegetation and treated the result as a proxy for relative June–August gross photosynthesis (Pg), stratifying the results by vegetation type and comparing them with spatially matched concomitant trends in surface air temperature data. They found area-wide tundra experienced a significant increase in Pg in response to a similar increase in air temperature, and "this observation is supported by a wide and increasing range of local field measurements characterizing elevated net CO_2 uptake (Occhel *et al.*, 2000b), greater depths of seasonal thaw (Goulden *et al.*, 1998), changes in the composition and density of herbaceous vegetation (Chapin *et al.*, 2000; Epstein *et al.*, 2004), and increased woody encroachment in the tundra areas of North America (Sturm *et al.*, 2001)." For interior forest, they found no significant increase in air temperature and essentially no change in Pg, with the last data point of the series being essentially indistinguishable from the first. This seemingly aberrant observation is in harmony with the fact that at low temperatures the growth-promoting effects of increasing atmospheric CO_2 levels are often very small or even nonexistent (Idso and Idso, 1994), which is what appears to have been the case with North American boreal forests over that time period. As a result, the tundra ecosystems of Canada and Alaska exhibited increasing productivity over the past couple of decades, but their boreal forests did not.

Ropars and Boudreau (2012) state, "Myneni *et al.* (1997, 1998) were the first to report evidence of the pan-Arctic increase in vegetation cover," noting, "by analyzing worldwide NDVI [normalized difference vegetation index] trends between 1981 and 1991, they showed that the greatest increase in photosynthetic activity occurred in regions above 50°N," and "since then, this phenomenon has been observed for different regions," including Alaska (Silapaswan *et al.*, 2001; Jia *et al.*, 2003; Verbyla, 2008), Russia (Forbes *et al.*, 2010a), and Western Canada (Olthof and Pouliot, 2010), over a longer time span (Jia *et al.*, 2003; Goetz *et al.*, 2005; Verbyla, 2008; Forbes *et al.*, 2010a; Olthof and Pouliot, 2010), and at a better resolution (Jia *et al.*, 2003; Olthof and Pouliot, 2010). Focusing on an area near the Boniface River research station 35 km east of Hudson Bay and 10 km south of the treeline in subarctic Quebec (Canada), Ropars and Boudreau (2012) evaluated changes in shrub cover over a half-century, comparing two aerial photographs taken in July 1957 and a satellite image of the same area obtained in July 2008.

They found "both hilltops and terraces recorded an increase in shrub cover" (Figure 4.2.2.5.2.1), and "the increase was significantly greater on terraces than on hilltops (21.6% versus 11.6%)," further noting "this finding corroborates other studies using a similar method conducted in different regions of the Arctic," including Alaska (Sturm *et al.*, 2001; Tape *et al.*, 2006), northern Quebec (Tremblay, 2010), and Russia (Forbes *et al.*, 2010), and studies that revealed a major increase of the NDVI over the past few decades (Jia *et al.*, 2003; Verbyla, 2008). Ropars and Boudreau conclude, "according to ground truthing, the shrub cover densification is associated mainly with an increase of *Betula glandulosa* Michx"—more commonly known as dwarf birch—and "the

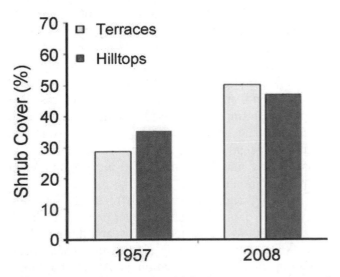

Figure 4.2.2.5.2.1. Percent shrub cover on terraces and hilltops in subarctic Quebec, Canada in 1957 and 2008. Adapted from Ropars and Boudreau (2012).

numerous seedlings observed during the ground truthing suggest that shrub densification should continue in the future."

Hudson and Henry (2009) note the Arctic has warmed by about 1.6°C over the past four decades, citing McBean *et al.* (2005), and this temperature increase has "led the Arctic Climate Impact Assessment (ACIA) and Intergovernmental Panel on Climate Change (IPCC) to predict tundra ecosystems will be particularly threatened by climate change [i.e., warming] over the next century." To provide real-world data with which to judge those predictions, Hudson and Henry measured biomass and composition changes in a heath community dominated by several vascular plants and bryophytes at an 8-km^2 coastal lowland adjacent to Alexandra Fiord on the east-central coast of Ellesmere Island, Nunavut, Canada. They did so over a period of 13 years (1995–2007), using a point-intercept method in permanent plots, and over a period of 27 years (1981–2008) using a biomass harvest comparison.

"Results from both methods," the Canadian scientists write, "indicate the community became more productive over time," that "bryophyte and evergreen shrub abundances increased," and "deciduous shrub, forb, graminoid, and lichen cover did not change," so "species diversity also remained unchanged." Hudson and Henry further report, "satellite-based remote sensing models, such as green trends derived from the normalized difference vegetation index (NDVI; e.g., Myneni *et al.*, 1997; Zhou *et al.*, 2001; Stow *et al.*, 2004; Verbyla, 2008), and global vegetation and ecosystem process simulations of the terrestrial carbon cycle (e.g., Kimball *et al.*, 2006; Zhang *et al.*, 2008), indicate increasing trends in vegetation photosynthetic activity and net primary production in the Arctic over the past several decades." They write, "it is likely that warming directly increased plant growth and reproduction and indirectly increased resource supply," noting "increased temperatures also lengthened the growing season, increased soil temperature, deepened the active [soil] layer, and consequently may have influenced nutrient uptake in the plant community."

Hudson and Henry (2010) used open-top chambers to passively warm an evergreen-shrub heath by 1.0–1.3°C over a period of 15 years, during which time there was also a significant background warming, at the same location at Alexandra Fiord, Nunavut, Canada (79°N), an effort they describe as "the longest-running passive warming experiment in the Canadian Arctic." They report, "experimental warming did not strongly affect vascular plant cover, canopy height or species diversity, but it did increase bryophyte cover by 6.3% and decrease lichen cover by 3.5%," although "temporal changes in plant cover were more frequent and of greater magnitude than changes due to experimental warming," as pointed out in their study published the year prior and highlighted above.

Madsen *et al.* (2011) compared the aboveground biomass of the graminoid marsh vegetation observed on Jameson Land, low Arctic, East Greenland in surveys conducted in 1982–1984 with similar surveys conducted in 2008, to see what had happened over the intervening period of significant global—and local—warming. The five researchers say the data they obtained in 2008 yielded a standing crop biomass of 98.2 g/m^2, which was 2.34 times greater than what had been measured in the same location in 1984. They note, "on Bylot Island, northeast Canada, graminoid above-ground production in wetlands has increased by 84% between 1990 and 2007, most likely as a consequence of climate warming," citing Cadieux *et al.* (2008), adding "on Svalbard, it is known that early snow melt has a dramatic positive effect on the density of nesting geese and their fecundity," citing Madsen *et al.* (2007) and noting "the climate in East Greenland has been warming during the last 30 years."

Villarreal *et al.* (2012) write, "climate warming is pronounced at high northern latitudes (ACIA, 2005; Serreze, 2010)," and "time series analysis of satellite remote sensing between 1982 and 2008 suggests that there has been a greening of arctic landscapes," citing Bhatt *et al.* (2010). They note "remotely detected changes in the normalized difference vegetation index (NDVI) of the arctic coastal plain near Barrow, Alaska, appear to be among the most dramatic recorded for much of the Arctic," again citing Bhatt *et al.* (2010).

Noting "there is a general scarcity of ground-based studies that examine vegetation change in the Arctic over decade time scales," Villarreal *et al.* in 1999, 2008, and 2010 resampled for species cover and presence 330 marked plots at 33 sites established in 1972, as part of the International Biological Program, in an area near Barrow at the northernmost point of the Alaskan Coastal Plain (71°18'N, 156°40'W).

Over the 38-year study period, they found, ecosystem diversity "increased for most plant communities, and wetter communities changed more than dry and moist plant communities." These findings, they say, support other observational studies, such as Wilson and Nilsson (2009). Of the 19 species that made up more than 80% of the overall relative cover, they say five had higher relative cover in 2010 than in 1972. Their results for changes in shrub cover "are somewhat consistent with other long-term observations and experimental studies that report increased shrub abundance (Myers-Smith *et al.*, 2011; Tape *et al.*, 2006; Walker *et al.*, 2006; Sturm *et al.*, 2001)," as well as warming-induced "treeline advancement (Lloyd, 2005; Danby and Hik, 2007)."

Tape *et al.* (2006) analyzed repeat photography data from a photo study of the Colville River, Alaska conducted between 1945 and 1953, plus 202 new photos of the same sites obtained between 1999 and 2002, to determine the nature of shrub expansion in that region over the past half-century. They found "large shrubs have increased in size and abundance over the past 50 years, colonizing areas where previously there were no large shrubs." They say their review of plot and remote sensing studies confirms "shrubs in Alaska have expanded their range and grown in size" and "a population of smaller, inter-tussock shrubs not generally sampled by the repeat photography, is also expanding and growing." They conclude, "these three lines of evidence allow us to infer a general increase in tundra shrubs across northern Alaska."

Tape *et al.* are inclined to attribute their findings to large-scale pan-Arctic warming, and from analyses of logistic growth curves, they estimate the expansion began about 1900, "well before the current warming in Alaska (which started about 1970)." Hence, they conclude "the expansion predates the most recent warming trend and is perhaps associated with the general warming since the Little Ice Age." These inferences appear reasonable, although the 80 ppm increase in the atmosphere's CO_2 concentration since 1900 likely played a role in the shrub expansion as well.

Elmendorf *et al.* (2012) note, "remote-sensing data indicate contemporary climate warming has already resulted in increased productivity over much of the Arctic," and "normalized difference vegetation index (NDVI) values have increased over the tundra biome in recent years, indicating a greening of the tundra ecosystem coincident with climate warming trends," citing Pouliot *et al.* (2009) and Bhatt *et al.* (2010). Because "plot-based evidence for vegetation transformation is not widespread," they analyzed "change in tundra vegetation surveyed between 1980 and 2010 in 158 plant communities spread across 46 locations throughout the Arctic," the majority of

which were in North America.

The 47 researchers from 12 countries found "biome-wide trends of increased height of the plant canopy and maximum observed plant height for most vascular growth forms; increased abundance of litter; increased abundance of evergreen, low-growing and tall shrubs, and decreased abundance of bare ground." These data confirm the findings of prior satellite assessments of the vegetative transformation of Earth's northernmost collection of landscapes over the past three decades, attributable not only to global warming but also to the aerial-fertilization and water-use-efficiency-enhancing effects of atmospheric CO_2 enrichment.

Wang *et al.* (2006) examined ring-width development in cohorts of young and old white spruce trees in a mixed grass-prairie ecosystem in southwestern Manitoba, Canada, where a 1997 wildfire killed most of the older trees growing in high-density spruce islands but younger trees slightly removed from the islands survived. "Within each of a total of 24 burned islands," the three researchers write, "the largest dominant tree (dead) was cut down and a disc was then sampled from the stump height," while "adjacent to each sampled island, a smaller, younger tree (live) was also cut down, and a disc was sampled from the stump height."

After removing size-, age-, and climate-related trends in radial growth from the ring-width histories of the trees, Wang *et al.* plotted the residuals as functions of time for the 30-year periods for which the old and young trees would have been approximately the same age: 1900–1929 for the old trees and 1970–1999 for the young trees. During the first of these periods, the atmosphere's CO_2 concentration averaged 299 ppm, and during the second it averaged 346 ppm. The mean rate of rise of the atmosphere's CO_2 concentration was 0.37 ppm/year for the first period and 1.43 ppm/year for the second.

The researchers found the slope of the linear regression describing the rate of growth of the ring-width residuals for the later period (when the air's CO_2 concentration was 15% greater and its rate-of-rise 285% greater) was more than twice that of the earlier period. The researchers say these results show, "at the same developmental stage, a greater growth response occurred in the late period when atmospheric CO_2 concentration and the rate of atmospheric CO_2 increase were both relatively high." They note, "these results are consistent with expectations for CO_2-fertilization effects," saying "the response of the studied young trees can be taken as strong circumstantial evidence for the atmospheric CO_2-fertilization effect."

Wang *et al.* also learned the "postdrought growth response was much stronger for young trees (1970–1999) compared with old trees at the same development stage (1900–1929)," and the "higher atmospheric CO_2 concentration in the period from 1970–1999 may have helped white spruce recover from severe drought." They report young trees showed a weaker relationship to precipitation than did old trees, noting "more CO_2 would lead to greater water-use efficiency, which may be dampening the precipitation signal in young trees."

The results presented here for the high latitude region of North America paint a picture of the planet's terrestrial vegetation opposite of that promulgated by the models used by IPCC. Instead of a world heading toward environmental degradation and extinction, land-based plants of the Arctic and near-Arctic regions of North America are thriving, thanks in large part to the ongoing rise in the atmosphere's CO_2 concentration and global warming.

References

ACIA. 2005. *Arctic Climate Impact Assessment—Scientific Report*, 1st edition. Cambridge University Press, Cambridge, United Kingdom.

Bhatt, U.S., Walker, D.A., Raynolds, M.K., Comiso, J.C., Epstein, H.E., Jia, G.J., Gens, R., Pinzon, J.E., Tucker, C.J., Tweedie, C.E., and Webber, P.J. 2010. Circumpolar Arctic tundra vegetation change is linked to sea ice decline. *Earth Interactions* **14**: 1–20.

Bigelow, N.H., Brubaker, L.B., Edwards, M.E., Harrison, S.P., Prentice, I.C., Anderson, P.M., Andreev, A.A., Bartlein, P.J., Christensen, T.R., Cramer, W., Kaplan, J.O., Lozhkin, A.V., Matveyeva, N.V., Murray, D.F., McGuire, A.D., Volodya Y., Razzhivin, V.Y., Ritchie, J.C., Smith, B., Walker, D.A., Gajewski, K., Wolf, V., Holmqvist, B.H., Igarashi, Y., Kremenetskii, K., Paus, A., Pisaric, M.F.J. and Volkova, V.S. 2003. Climate change and Arctic ecosystems: 1. Vegetation changes north of 55 N between the last glacial maximum, mid-Holocene, and present. *Journal of Geophysical Research* **108**: 10.1029/2002JD002558.

Brubaker, L.B., Garfinkee, H.L., and Edwards, M.E. 1983. A late Wisconsin and Holocene vegetation history from the central brooks range: Implications for Alaskan palaeoecology. *Quaternary Research* **20**: 194–214.

Cadieux, M.C., Gauthier, G., Gagnon, C.A., Bety, J., and Berteaux, D. 2008. *Monitoring the Environmental and Ecological Impacts of Climate Change on Bylot Island, Sirmilik National Park*. Universite Laval, Quebec, Canada.

Capers, R.S. and Stone, A.D. 2011. After 33 years, trees more frequent and shrubs more abundant in northeast U.S. alpine community. *Arctic, Antarctic, and Alpine Research* **43**: 495–502.

Chapin III, F.S., McGuire, A.D., Randerson, J., Pielke, R., Baldocchi, D., Hobbie, S.E., Roulet, N., Eugster, W., Kasischke, E., Rastetter, E.B., Zimov, S.A., and Running, S.W. 2000. Arctic and boreal ecosystems of western North America as components of the climate system. *Global Change Biology* **6**: 211–223.

Danby, R.K. and Hik, D.S. 2007. Variability, contingency and rapid change in recent subarctic alpine tree line dynamics. *Journal of Ecology* **95**: 352–363.

Elmendorf, S.C., Henry, G.H.R., Hollister, R.D., Bjork, R.G., Boulanger-Lapointe, N., Cooper, E.J., Cornelissen, J.H.C., Day, T.A., Dorrepaal, E., Elumeeva, T.G., Gill, M., Gould, W.A., Harte, J., Hik, D.S., Hofgaard, A., Johnson, D.R., Johnstone, J.F., Jonsdottir, I.S., Jorgenson, J.C., Klanderud, K., Klein, J.A., Koh, S., Kudo, G., Lara, M., Levesque, E., Magnusson, B., May, J.L., Mercado-Diaz, J.A., Michelsen, A., Molau, U., Myers-Smith, I.H., Oberbauer, S.F., Onipchenko, V.G., Rixen, C., Schmidt, N.M., Shaver, G.R., Spasojevic, M.J., Porhallsdottir, P.E., Tolvanen, A., Troxler, T., Tweedie, C.E., Villareal, S., Wahren, C.-H., Walker, X., Webber, P.J., Welker, J.M., and Wipf, S. 2012. Plot-scale evidence of tundra vegetation change and links to recent summer warming. *Nature Climate Change* **2**: 453–457.

Epstein, H.E., Calef, M.P., Walker, M.D., Chapin III, F.S., and Starfield, A.M. 2004. Detecting changes in arctic tundra plant communities in response to warming over decadal time scales. *Global Change Biology* **10**: 1325–1334.

Forbes, B.C., Fauria, M.M., and Zetterberg, P. 2010a. Russian Arctic warming and 'greening' are closely tracked by tundra shrub willows. *Global Change Biology* **16**: 1542–1554.

Forbes, B.C., Stammler, F., Kumpula, T., Meschtyb, N., Pajunen, A., and Kaarlejarvia, E. 2010b. High resilience in the Yamal-Nenets social-ecological system, West Siberian Arctic, Russia. *Proceedings of the National Academy of Science USA* **106**: 22,041–22,048.

Goetz, S.J., Bunn, A.G., Fiske, G.J., and Houghton, R.A. 2005. Satellite-observed photosynthetic trends across boreal North America associated with climate and fire disturbance. *Proceedings of the National Academy of Sciences* **102**: 13,521–13,525.

Goulden, M.L., Wofsy, S.C., Harden, J.W., Trumbore, S.E., Crill, P.M., Gower, S.T., Fries, T., Daube, B.C., Fan, S.M., Sutton, D.J., Bazzaz, A., and Munger, J.W. 1998. Sensitivity of boreal forest carbon balance to soil thaw. *Science* **279**: 214–217.

Hallinger, M., Manthey, M., and Wilmking, M. 2010. Establishing a missing link: Warm summers and winter snow cover promote shrub expansion into alpine tundra in Scandinavia. *New Phytologist* **186**: 890–899.

Hofgaard, A., Dalen, L., and Hytteborn, J. 2009. Tree recruitment above the treeline and potential for climate-driven treeline change. *Journal of Vegetation Science* **20**: 1133–1144.

Hudson, J.M.G. and Henry, G.H.R. 2009. Increased plant biomass in a High Arctic heath community from 1981 to 2008. *Ecology* **90**: 2657–2663.

Hudson, J.M.G. and Henry, G.H.R. 2010. High Arctic plant community resists 15 years of experimental warming. *Journal of Ecology* **98**: 1035–1041.

Idso, K.E. and Idso, S.B. 1994. Plant responses to atmospheric CO_2 enrichment in the face of environmental constraints: a review of the past 10 years' research. *Agricultural and Forest Meteorology* **69**: 153–203.

Jia, G.S.J., Epstein, H.E., and Walker, D.A. 2003. Greening of Arctic Alaska, 1981–2001. *Geophysical Research Letters* **30**: 10.1029/2003GL018268.

Kimball, J.S., Zhao, M., Mcguire, A.D., Heinsch, F.A., Clein, J., Calef, M.P., Jolly, W.M., Kang, S., Euskirchen, S.E., McDonald, K.C., and Running, S.W. 2006. Recent climate-driven increases in vegetation productivity for the Western Arctic: evidence for an acceleration of the northern terrestrial carbon cycle. *Earth Interactions* **11**: 1–23.

Klanderud, K. and Birks, H.J.B. 2003. Recent increases in species richness and shifts in altitudinal distributions of Norwegian mountain plants. *Holocene* **13**: 1–6.

Kullman, L. 2001. 20th century climate warming and tree-limit rise in the southern Scandes of Sweden. *Ambio* **30**: 72–80.

Kullman, L. 2002. Rapid recent range-margin rise of tree and shrub species in the Swedish Scandes. *Journal of Ecology* **90**: 68–77.

Lantz, T.C., Kokelj, S.V., Gergel, S.E., and Henry, G.H.R. 2009. Relative impacts of disturbance and temperature: Persistent changes in microenvironment and vegetation in retrogressive thaw slumps. *Global Change Biology* **15**: 1664–1675.

Lescop-Sinclair, K. and Payette, S. 1995. Recent advance of the arctic treeline along the eastern coast of Hudson Bay. *Journal of Ecology* **83**: 929–936.

Lloyd, A.H. 2005. Ecological histories from Alaskan tree lines provide insight into future change. *Ecology* **86**: 1687–1695.

Madsen, J., Jaspers, C., Tamstorf, M., Mortensen, C.E., and

Riget, F. 2011. Long-term effects of grazing and global warming on the composition and carrying capacity of graminoid marshes for moulting geese in East Greenland. *Ambio* **40**: 638–649.

Madsen, J., Tamstorf, M., Klaassen, M., Eide, N., Glahder, C., Riget, F., Nyegaard, H., and Cottaar, F. 2007. Effects of snow cover on the timing and success of reproduction in high-Arctic pink-footed geese *Anser brachyrhynchus*. *Polar Biology* **30**: 1363–1372.

McBean, G., Alekseev, G., Chen, D., Forland, E., Fyfe, J., Groisman, P.Y., King, R., Melling, H., Vose, R., and Whitfield, P.H. 2005. Arctic climate: past and present. In: *Arctic Climate Impact Assessment: Scientific Report*. Cambridge University Press, Cambridge, UK, pp. 21–60.

Myers-Smith, I.H., Hik, D.S., Kennedy, C., Cooley, D., Johnstone, J.F., Kenney, A.J., and Krebs, C.J. 2011. Expansion of canopy-forming willows over the twentieth century on Herschel Island, Yukon Territory, Canada. *Ambio* **40**: 610–623.

Myneni, R.B., Keeling, C.D., Tucker, C.J., Asrar, G., and Nemani, R.R. 1997. Increased plant growth in the northern high latitudes from 1981 to 1991. *Nature* **386**: 698–702.

Myneni, R.B., Tucker, C.J., Asrar, G., and Keeling, C.D. 1998. Interannual variations in satellite-sensed vegetation index data from 1981 to 1991. *Journal of Geophysical Research* **103**: 6145–6160.

Oechel, W.C., Hastings, S.J., Vourlitis, G., Jenkins, M., Riechers, G., and Grulke, N. 1993. Recent change of Arctic tundra ecosystems from a net carbon dioxide sink to a source. *Nature* **361**: 520–523.

Oechel, W.C., Vourlitis, G.L., Hastings, S.J., and Bochkarev, S.A. 1995. Change in Arctic CO_2 flux over two decades: Effects of climate change at Barrow, Alaska. *Ecological Applications* **5**: 846–855.

Oechel, W.C., Vourlitis, G.L., Hastings, S.J., Zulueta, R.C., Hinzman, L., and Kane, D. 2000a. Acclimation of ecosystem CO_2 exchange in the Alaskan Arctic in response to decadal climate warming. *Nature* **406**: 978–981.

Oechel, W.C., Vourlitis, G.L., Verfaillie, J., Crawford, T., Brooks, S., Dumas, E., Hope, A., Stow, D., Boynton, B., Nosov, V., and Zulueta, R. 2000b. A scaling approach for quantifying the net CO_2 flux of the Kuparuk River Basin, Alaska. *Global Change Biology* **6**: 160–173.

Olthof, I. and Pouliot, D. 2010. Treeline vegetation composition and change in Canada's western Subarctic from AVHRR and canopy reflectance modeling. *Remote Sensing of the Environment* **114**: 805–815.

Peterson, D.L. 1994. Recent changes in the growth and establishment of subalpine conifers in western North America. In: Beniston, M. (Ed.) *Mountain Environments in*

Changing Climates. Routeledge, London, United Kingdom, pp. 234–243.

Pouliot, D., Latifovic, R., and Olthof, I. 2009. Trends in vegetation NDVI from 1 km AVHRR data over Canada for the period 1985–2006. *International Journal of Remote Sensing* 30: 149–168.

Ropars, P. and Boudreau, S. 2012. Shrub expansion at the forest-tundra ecotone: spatial heterogeneity linked to local topography. *Environmental Research Letters* 7: 10.1088/1748-9326/7/1/015501.

Serreze, M.C. 2010. Understanding recent climate change. *Conservation Biology* 24: 10–17.

Silapaswan, C.S., Verbyla, D.L., and McGuire, A.D. 2001. Land cover change on the Seward Peninsula: the use of remote sensing to evaluate the potential influences of climate warming on historical vegetation dynamics. *Canadian Journal of Remote Sensing* 27: 542–554.

Stow, D.A. *et al.* 2004. Remote sensing of vegetation and land-cover change in Arctic tundra ecosystems. *Remote Sensing of Environment* 89: 281–308.

Sturm, M., Racine, C.H., and Tape, K.D. 2001. Increasing shrub abundance in the Arctic. *Nature* 411: 546–547.

Tape, K., Sturm, M., and Racine, C. 2006. The evidence for shrub expansion in Northern Alaska and the Pan-Arctic. *Global Change Biology* 12: 686–702.

Thorpe, N., Eyegetok, S., Hakongak, N., and Elders, K. 2002. Nowadays it is not the same: Inuit Quajimaja-tuqangit, climate caribou in the Kitikmeot region of Nunavut, Canada. In: Krupnik, I. and Jolly, D. (Eds.) *The Earth is Faster Now: Indigenous Observations of Arctic Environmental Change*, Arctic Research Consortium of the United States/Smithsonian Institution, Fairbanks/Washington, DC., pp. 198–239.

Tremblay, B. 2010. Augmentation recente du couvert ligneux erige dans les environs de Kangiqsualujjuaq (Nunavik, Quebec). Master Thesis, Universite du Quebec a Trois-Rivieres, Quebec, Canada.

Verbyla, D. 2008. The greening and browning of Alaska based on 1982–2003 satellite data. *Global Ecology and Biogeography* 17: 547–555.

Villarreal, S., Hollister, R.D., Johnson, D.R., Lara, M.J., Webber, P.J., and Tweedie, C.E. 2012. Tundra vegetation change near Barrow, Alaska (1972–2010). *Environmental Research Letters* 7: 10.1088/1748-9326/7/1/015508.

Walker, M.D., Wahren, C.H., Hollister, R.D., Henry, G.H.R., Ahlquist, L.E., Alatalo, J.M., Bret-Harte, M.S., Calef, M.P., Callaghan, T.V., Carroll, A.B., Epstein, H.E., Jónsdóttir, I.S., Klein, J.A. , Magnússon, B.ó., Molau, U., Oberbauer, S.F., Rewa, S.P., Robinson, C.H., Shaver, G.R., Suding, K.N., Thompson, C.C., Tolvanen, A., Totland, Ø.,

Turner, P.L., Tweedie, C.E., Webber, P.J., and Wookey, P.A. 2006. Plant community responses to experimental warming across the tundra biome. *Proceedings of the National Academy of Sciences USA* 103: 1342–1346.

Wang, G.G., Chhin, S., and Bauerle, W.L. 2006. Effect of natural atmospheric CO_2 fertilization suggested by open-grown white spruce in a dry environment. *Global Change Biology* 12: 601–610.

Wardle, P. and Coleman, M.C. 1992. Evidence for rising upper limits of four native New Zealand forest trees. *New Zealand Journal of Botany* 30: 303–314.

Wilson, S.D. and Nilsson, C. 2009. Arctic alpine vegetation change over 20 years. *Global Change Biology* 15: 1676–1684.

Zhang, K., Kimball, J.S., Hogg, E.H., Zhao, M.S., Oechel, W.C., Cassano, J.J., and Running, S.W. 2008. Satellite-based model detection of recent climate-driven changes in northern high-latitude vegetation productivity. *Journal of Geophysical Research-Biogeosciences* 113: G03033.

Zhou, L.M., Tucker, C.J., Kaufmann, R.K., Slayback, D., Shabanov, N.V., and Myneni, R.B. 2001. Variations in northern vegetation activity inferred from satellite data of vegetation index during 1981 to 1999. *Journal of Geophysical Research* 106: 20,069–20,083.

4.2.2.5.3 Eastern USA

- Late twentieth-century increases in air temperature and atmospheric CO_2 concentration did not negatively affect plant communities in the eastern United States. Rather, the temperature and CO_2 increases significantly enhanced local and regional productivity, and there is little reason to think such enhancements will not continue throughout the foreseeable future.

Pan *et al.* (2009) examined "how changes in atmospheric composition (CO_2, O_3 and N deposition), climate and land-use affected carbon dynamics and sequestration in Mid-Atlantic temperate forests during the 20th century," modifying and applying "a well-established process-based ecosystem model with a strong foundation of ecosystem knowledge from experimental studies." They validated the model "using the U.S. Forest Inventory and Analysis (FIA) data."

For previously harvested and currently regrowing forests, the calibrated model produced changes in net ecosystem productivity (NEP) due to observed changes in N deposition (+32%), CO_2 (+90%), O_3

(-40%), CO_2 + O_3 (+60%), CO_2 + N deposition (+184%), and CO_2 + N deposition + O_3 (+138%). Corresponding changes in NEP for undisturbed forests were +18%, +180%, -75%, +78%, +290%, and +208%. They report "the 'fertilization' effect of N deposition mainly stimulates carbon allocation to short-lived tissues such as foliage and fine roots," but "the 'fertilization' effect by elevated CO_2 likely enhances more sustainable carbon storage such as woody biomass (including coarse roots)."

The four USDA Forest Service scientists say their findings indicate "the change in atmospheric composition, particularly elevated CO_2, will gradually account for more of the carbon sink of temperate forests in the Mid-Atlantic region," and "such a significant 'fertilization effect' on the forest carbon sequestration could eventually result in a 'greener world' after a long period of chronic change in atmospheric composition and cumulative impact."

Westfall and Amateis (2003) used mean height measurements made at three-year intervals over a period of 15 years from dominant stands of loblolly pine plantations growing at 94 locations across the southeastern United States to calculate a site index related to the mean growth rate for each of the five three-year periods. They expected the index would increase monotonically if growth rates were being enhanced above normal by some monotonically increasing factor that promotes growth. The researchers found, the "mean site index over the 94 plots consistently increased at each re-measurement period," suggesting "loblolly pine plantations are realizing greater than expected growth rates." They found the growth rate increases grew larger with each succeeding three-year period.

Westfall and Amateis considered attributing their findings to increases in temperature and precipitation in addition to rising atmospheric CO_2 concentrations, but they report a review of annual precipitation amounts and mean ground surface temperatures showed no trends in these factors over the period of their study. They also say if increased nitrogen deposition were the cause, "such a factor would have to be acting on a regional scale to produce growth increases over the range of study plots." Hence, they favor the aerial fertilization effect of atmospheric CO_2 enrichment as being responsible for the accelerating pine tree growth rates.

McMahon et al. (2010) state, "there are indications that forest biomass accumulation may be accelerating where nutrients and water are not limiting," citing Myneni et al. (1997), Lewis et al. (2004), Lewis et al. (2009), Boisvenue and Running (2006), Delpierre et al. (2009), Salzer et al. (2009), and Chave et al. (2008). They further investigated the subject because of the great significance such growth portends for the planet's carbon balance and the future course of potential CO_2-induced global warming.

Using unique datasets of tree biomass collected from 55 temperate forest plots with known land-use histories and stand ages ranging from five to 250 years (which were derived from knowledge of when the stands had begun to regrow following major disturbances such as significant logging, various natural disasters that had decimated large patches of trees, or the clearing of trees to make room for agriculture that was ultimately abandoned), McMahon et al. "estimated biomass change, while controlling for stand regeneration" (see Figure 4.2.2.5.3.1) in parts of a temperate deciduous forest in the vicinity of the Smithsonian Environmental Research Center, Edgewater, Maryland (USA). They compared recent (the prior 22 years or less) rates of biomass accumulation of the various stands with rates predicted for those age intervals by the overall growth function derived from the combined data of all of the stands. They compared their findings with "over 100 years of local weather measurements and 17 years of on-site atmospheric CO_2 measurements."

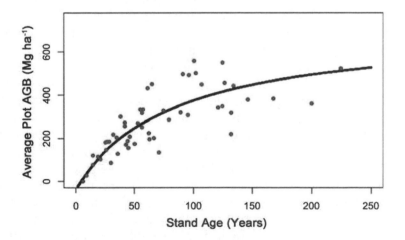

Figure 4.2.2.5.3.1. Graphic showing the relationship between above-ground biomass (AGB) and stand age of multiple-censused forest plots in a temperate deciduous forest in and near the Smithsonian Environmental Research Center in Edgewater, MD. The plot indicates younger trees are growing faster than older ones. Adapted from McMahon et al. (2010).

The authors report the results of their analysis reveal "recent biomass accumulation greatly exceeded the expected growth caused by natural recovery," and they note in stands younger than 50 years the observed rate increase was generally at least one-third of total growth, and in older stands it typically was "the majority of growth," even though past experience and the ensemble relationship of growth vs. age derived from their data suggest "old forests should grow very little as they approach equilibrium."

The Smithsonian scientists write, "increases in temperature, growing season [which is largely driven by temperature], and atmospheric CO_2 have documented influences on tree physiology, metabolism, and growth," and they state these factors may have been "critical to changing the rate of stand growth observed across stands."

Capers and Stone (2011) "studied a community in western Maine, comparing the frequency and abundance of alpine plants in 2009 with frequency and abundance recorded in 1976," noting "the 2009 survey was designed to provide a fair comparison with that of 1976," which was conducted and described by Stone (1980). The two researchers found the 2009 survey "provided evidence of the increasing importance of woody plants—both trees and shrubs—in the alpine community" (Figure 4.2.2.5.3.2), commenting, "the most widespread tree species increased dramatically." They "recorded an increase in total species richness of the community with the addition of four lower montane species that had not been recorded previously" and "found no evidence that species with high-arctic distributions had declined more than other species."

Capers and Stone write the changes they recorded "are consistent with those reported in tundra communities around the world." And although there is some concern the observed increase in species richness could turn out to be temporary if alpine species were to disappear because of competition from new species, they state, "species losses resulting from competition have not typically been found with rising richness in high alpine areas, possibly because newly arriving species occupy different micro-habitats," citing Walther *et al.* (2005).

Ziska *et al.* (2004) characterized the gradual changes that occur in a number of environmental variables as one moves from a rural location (a farm approximately 50 km from the center of the city of

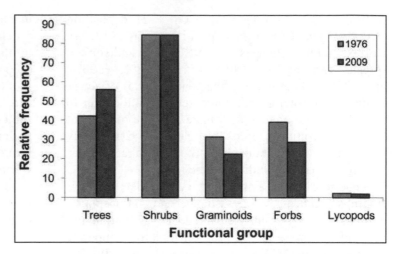

Figure 4.2.2.5.3.2. The relative frequency of five functional plant groups from surveys taken in 1976 and 2009 in a Northeast United States alpine plant community. The relative frequency of trees increased by a significant 14%, whereas the changes in forbs and graminoids were only marginally significant. Adapted from Capers and Stone (2011).

Baltimore, Maryland (USA)) to a suburban location (a park approximately 10 km from the city center) to an urban location (the Baltimore Science Center approximately 0.5 km from the city center). At each of these locations, four 2 x 2 m plots were excavated to a depth of about 1.1 m and filled with identical soils, the top layers of which contained seeds of naturally occurring plants of the general area. These seeds sprouted in the spring, and the plants they produced were allowed to grow until they senesced in the fall, after which all were cut at ground level, removed, dried, and weighed.

Along the rural to suburban to urban transect, the only consistent differences in the environmental variables Ziska *et al.* measured were a rural to urban increase of 21% in average daytime atmospheric CO_2 concentration and increases of 1.6 and 3.3°C in maximum (daytime) and minimum (nighttime) daily temperatures, respectively. These changes, they write, "were consistent with most short-term (~50 year) global change scenarios regarding CO_2 concentration and air temperature." They write, "productivity, determined as final above-ground biomass, and maximum plant height were positively affected by daytime and soil temperatures as well as enhanced CO_2, increasing 60 and 115% for the suburban and urban sites, respectively, relative to the rural site."

The three researchers say their results suggest "urban environments may act as a reasonable surrogate for investigating future climatic change in vegetative communities," and those results demonstrate rising air temperatures and CO_2 concentrations tend to produce dramatic increases in the productivity of the natural ecosystems typical of the greater Baltimore area and, by inference, probably those of many other areas as well.

The studies discussed above find late twentieth-century increases in air temperature and atmospheric CO_2 concentration did not negatively affect plant communities in the eastern United States. Rather, the temperature and CO_2 increases significantly enhanced local and regional productivity, and there is little reason to think such enhancements will not continue throughout the foreseeable future.

References

Boisvenue, C. and Running, S. 2006. Impacts of climate change on natural forest productivity—evidence since the middle of the 20th century. *Global Change Biology* **12**: 862–882.

Capers, R.S. and Stone, A.D. 2011. After 33 years, trees more frequent and shrubs more abundant in northeast U.S. alpine community. *Arctic, Antarctic, and Alpine Research* **43**: 495–502.

Chave, J., Condit, R., Muller-Landau, H.C., Thomas, S.C., Ashton, P.S., Bunyavejchewin, S., Co, L.L., Dattaraja, H.S., Davies, S.J., Esufali, S., Ewango, C.E.N., Feeley, K.J., Foster, R.B., Gunatilleke, N., Gunatilleke, S., Hall, P., Hart, T.B., Hernández, C., Hubbell, S.P., Itoh, A., Kiratiprayoon, S., LaFrankie, J.V., de Lao, S.L., Makana, J.-R., Noor, Md.N.S., Kassim, A.R., Samper, C., Sukumar, R., Suresh, H.S., Tan, S., Thompson, J., Tongco, Ma.D.C., Valencia, R., Vallejo, M., Villa, G., Yamakura, T., Zimmerman, J.K., and Losos, E.C. 2008. Assessing evidence for a pervasive alteration in tropical tree communities. *PLoS Biology* **6**: 10.1371/journal.pbio.0060045.

Delpierre, N., Soudani, K., Francois, C., Kostner, B., Pontailler, J.-Y., Nikinmaa, E., Misson, L., Aubinet, M., Bernhofer, C., Granier, A., Grunwald, T., Heinesch, B., Longdoz, B., Ourcival, J.-M., Rambal, S., Vesala, T., and Dufrene, E. 2009. Exceptional carbon uptake in European forests during the warm spring of 2007: A data-model analysis. *Global Change Biology* **15**: 1455–1474.

Lewis, S.L., Lopez-Gonzalez, G., Sonke, B., Affum-Baffoe, K., Baker, T.R., Ojo, L.O., Phillips, O.L., Reitsma, J.M., White, L., Comiskey, J.A., Djuikouo K., M.-N., Ewango, C.E.N., Feldpausch, T.R., Hamilton, A.C., Gloor, M., Hart, T., Hladik, A., Lloyd, J., Lovett, J.C., Makana, J.-R., Malhi, Y., Mbago, F.M., Ndangalasi, H.J., Peacock, J., Peh, K.S.-H., Sheil, D., Sunderland, T., Swaine, M.D., Taplin, J., Taylor, D., Thomas, S.C., Votere, R., and Woll, H. 2009. Increasing carbon storage in intact African tropical forests. *Nature* **457**: 1003–1006.

Lewis, S.L., Phillips, O.L., Baker, T.R., Lloyd, J., Malhi, Y., Almeida, S., Higuchi, N., Laurance, W.F., Neill, D.A., Silva, J.N.M., Terborgh, J., Lezama, A.T., Vásquez Martinez, R., Brown, S., Chave, J., Kuebler, C., Núñez Vargas, P., and Vinceti, B. 2004. Concerted changes in tropical forest structure and dynamics: evidence from 50 South American long-term plots. *Philosophical Transactions of the Royal Society of London Series B—Biological Sciences* **359**: 421–436.

McMahon, S.M., Parker, G.G., and Miller, D.R. 2010. Evidence for a recent increase in forest growth. *Proceedings of the National Academy of Sciences USA*: 10.1073/pnas.0912376107.

Myneni, R., Keeling, C., Tucker, C., Asrar, G., and Nemani, R. 1997. Increased plant growth in the northern high latitudes from 1981 to 1991. *Nature* **386**: 698–702.

Pan, Y., Birdsey, R., Hom, J., and McCullough, K. 2009. Separating effects of changes in atmospheric composition, climate and land-use on carbon sequestration of U.S. Mid-Atlantic temperate forests. *Forest Ecology and Management* **259**: 151–164.

Salzer, M., Hughes, M., Bunn, A., and Kipfmueller, K. 2009. Recent unprecedented tree-ring growth in bristlecone pine at the highest elevations and possible causes. *Proceedings of the National Academies of Science USA* **106**: 20,346–20,353.

Stone, A. 1980. Avery Peak on Bigelow Mountain, Maine: The Flora and Vegetation Ecology of a Subalpine Heathland. M.S. Thesis. University of Vermont, Burlington, Vermont, USA.

Walther, G.-R., Beissner, S., and Burga, C.A. 2005. Trends in the upward shift of alpine plants. *Journal of Vegetation Science* **16**: 541–548.

Westfall, J.A. and Amateis, R.L. 2003. A model to account for potential correlations between growth of loblolly pine and changing ambient carbon dioxide concentrations. *Southern Journal of Applied Forestry* **27**: 279–284.

Ziska, L.H., Bunce, J.A., and Goins, E.W. 2004. Characterization of an urban-rural CO_2/temperature gradient and associated changes in initial plant productivity during secondary succession. *Oecologia* **139**: 454–458.

4.2.2.5.4 Central USA

- The late twentieth-century rise in temperature and CO_2 has improved the productivity of plant communities in the central region of the United States, notwithstanding model-based concerns to the contrary.

Voelker *et al.* (2006) studied two species of oak (*Quercus velutina* Lam. and *Quercus coccinea* Muench.) and one of pine (*Pinus echinata* Mill.) in the Ozark Mountains of Missouri (USA). They report since 1850 the stem growth of the three species has risen "coincidently with increases in atmospheric CO_2," such that the overall trend in ring-width in recent years is "nearly two times that" experienced prior to 1850 (Figure 4.2.2.5.4.1). They note "long-term increases in radial growth appear unrelated to historical disturbance levels for the region, to long-term changes in relevant climatic variables, or to productivity of sites sampled." The four Department of Forestry researchers from the University of Missouri suggest a continual rise in the atmosphere's CO_2 concentration, aided by continued nitrogen deposition, likely will "stimulate further increases in the rates of stand development and carbon storage."

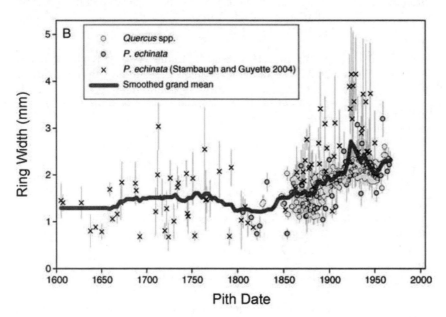

Figure 4.2.2.5.4.1. Mean ring width responses by pith date calculated across 11 equally spaced cambial ages from 1 to 50, for randomly sampled oak and pine trees in the Ozark Mountains of Missouri, USA. The means for P. echinata (Stambaugh and Guyette 2004) were calculated from three cambial ages but were shifted to the pith date for accurate intercomparisons among datasets (see Voelker *et al.*, 2006). The smoothed grand mean was calculated across each of the closest 14 ring widths. Adapted from Voelker *et al.* (2006).

Cole *et al.* (2010) note quaking aspen (*Populus tremuloides* Michx.) is a dominant forest type in north-temperate, montane, and boreal regions of North America, "the most widely distributed tree species on the continent," and aspen and related poplars are "quintessential foundation species (Ellison *et al.*, 2005), shaping the structure and function of the communities and ecosystems in which they occur

(Whitham *et al.*, 2006; Schweitzer *et al.*, 2008; Madritch *et al.*, 2009)." They sought to determine how this keystone species may have responded to the increase in atmospheric CO_2 concentration that has occurred over the past several decades, especially in light of the climatic changes that occurred concurrently.

The four researchers collected branches from 919 trees after their leaves had dropped in the fall, obtaining samples that represented 189 genets or clones (five trees per clone) at 11 sites distributed throughout three regions of Wisconsin (USA). The sampled trees ranged from five to 76 years of age and came from second-growth unmanaged forests south of the areas defoliated by forest tent caterpillars in 1980–1982, 1989–1990, and 2001–2002. In addition, the scientists recorded trunk diameter at breast height for each sampled tree, a parameter, they write, "is very highly correlated with total biomass in aspen," citing Bond-Lamberty *et al.* (2002).

The Minnesota and Wisconsin scientists report, "age-specific ring width increased over time" and "the greatest increase occurred for relatively young trees, so young trees grew faster in recent years than did young trees several decades ago." During the past half-century, for example, they found the growth of trees 11–20 years old rose by 60% (Figure 4.2.2.5.4.2). They write, "rising CO_2 causes ring width to increase at all moisture levels, apparently resulting from improved water use efficiency," so "the overall increase results from historical increases in both CO_2 and water availability." When they separated out the impacts of the two factors, they found "the effect of rising CO_2 had been to increase ring width by about 53%" as a result of "a 19.2% increase in ambient CO_2 levels during the growing season, from 315.8 ppm in 1958 (when CO_2 records began) to 376.4 ppm in 2003."

Cole *et al.* comment "the magnitude of the growth increase uncovered by this analysis raises the question of how much other major forest species have responded to the joint effects of long-term changes in CO_2 and precipitation."

Woody plants in the U.S. Northern Great Plains

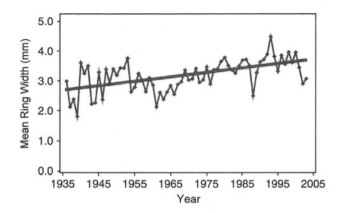

Figure 4.2.2.5.4.2. Mean ring width of quaking aspen trees sampled in Wisconsin, USA. Adapted from Cole *et al.* (2010).

also have responded positively to the twentieth-century increase in atmospheric CO_2 by expanding their ranges, and that expansion has led to greater benefits beneath the soil as well. Springsteen *et al.* (2012) note, "changes in soil attributes under woody vegetation have been documented in the arid grasslands of the southern Great Plains, including increases in soil carbon and nitrogen," citing Reynolds *et al.* (1999), Hibbard *et al.* (2001, 2003), McCulley *et al.* (2004), Schade and Hobbie (2005), and Liao *et al.* (2006). In their own investigation, Springsteen *et al.* examined near-surface (upper 15 cm) soil biogeochemistry along a 42-year (1963–2005) chronosequence, which encompassed grassland, woodland, and grassland-woodland transition zones in a northern Great Plains grassland at the USDA-ARS Northern Great Plains Research Laboratory near Mandan, North Dakota (USA), to determine the influence of woody plant expansion on soil carbon and nitrogen contents.

The four researchers report total soil carbon content rose by 26% across the chronosequence from grassland to woodland within the 0–15 cm soil depth, and total soil nitrogen content rose by 31%. The rate of woody shrub expansion from 1963 to 1988 (25 years) was ~1,800 m^2 per year at their study site, and from 1988 to 2005 (17 years) it was ~3,800 m^2 per year, just a little more than doubled. Soil carbon sequestration driven by woody-plant invasions of grasslands, which are driven to a significant degree by the ongoing rise in the atmospheric CO_2 content, as well as the increases in soil nitrogen content required to sustain them, are growing with the passage of time.

In a vastly different type of study based on a 48-year record derived from an average of 17 measurements per year, Raymond and Cole (2003) demon-

strated the export of alkalinity, in the form of bicarbonate ions, from the USA's Mississippi River to the Gulf of Mexico had increased by approximately 60% since 1953. "This increased export," they write, was "in part the result of increased flow resulting from higher rainfall in the Mississippi basin," which had led to a 40% increase in annual Mississippi River discharge to the Gulf of Mexico over the period. The remainder of the increased export of alkalinity had to have been due to increased rates of chemical weathering of soil minerals.

The two researchers note the mechanisms potentially responsible for this phenomenon include "an increase in atmospheric CO_2, an increase [in] rainwater throughput, or an increase in plant and microbial production of CO_2 and organic acids in soils due to biological responses to increased rainfall and temperature." They don't mention as a mechanism, but should have, the increase in terrestrial plant productivity produced by the increase in the aerial fertilization effect of the atmosphere's rising CO_2 content, which also leads to an increase in plant and microbial production of CO_2 and organic acids in soils.

The findings presented above indicate the late twentieth-century rise in temperature and CO_2 has improved the productivity of plant communities in the central region of the United States, notwithstanding model-based concerns to the contrary.

References

Bond-Lamberty, B., Wang, C., and Gower, S.T. 2002. Aboveground and belowground biomass and sapwood area allometric equations for six boreal tree species of northern Manitoba. *Canadian Journal of Forest Research* **32**: 1441–1450.

Cole, C.T., Anderson, J.E., Lindroth, R.L., and Waller, D.M. 2010. Rising concentrations of atmospheric CO_2 have increased growth in natural stands of quaking aspen (*Populus tremuloides*). *Global Change Biology* **16**: 2186–2197.

Ellison, A.M., Bank, M.S., Clinton, B.D., Colburn, E.A., Elliott, K., Ford, C.R., Foster, D.R., Kloeppel, B.D., Knoepp, J.D., Lovett, G.M., Mohan, J., Orwig, D.A., Rodenhouse, N.L., Sobczak, W.V., Stinson, K.A., Stone, J.K., Swan, C.M., Thompson, J., Holle, B.V., and Webster, JR. 2005. Loss of foundation species: consequences for the structure and dynamics of forested ecosystems. *Frontiers in Ecology and the Environment* **3**: 479–486.

Hibbard, K.A., Archer, S., Schimel, D.S., and Valentine, D.W. 2001. Biogeochemical changes accompanying woody plant encroachment in a subtropical savanna. *Ecology* **82**: 1999–2011.

Hibbard, K.A., Schimel, D.S., Archer, S., Ojima, D.S., and Parton, W. 2003. Grassland to woodland transitions: integrating changes in landscape structure and biogeochemistry. *Ecological Applications* **13**: 911–926.

Liao, J.D., Boutton, T.W., and Jastrow, J.D. 2006. Storage and dynamics of carbon and nitrogen in soil physical fractions following woody plant invasion of grassland. *Soil Biology and Biochemistry* **38**: 3184–3196.

Madritch, M.D., Greene, S.G., and Lindroth, R.L. 2009. Genetic mosaics of ecosystem functioning across aspen-dominated landscapes. *Oecologia* **160**: 119–127.

McCulley, R.L., Archer, S.R., Boutton, T.W., Hons, F.M., and Zuberer, D.A. 2004. Soil respiration and nutrient cycling in wooded communities developing in grassland. *Ecology* **85**: 2804–2817.

Raymond, P.A. and Cole, J.J. 2003. Increase in the export of alkalinity from North America's largest river. *Science* **301**: 88–91.

Reynolds, J.F., Virginia, R.A., Kemp, P.R., de Soyza, A.G., and Tremmel, D.C. 1999. Impact of drought on desert shrubs: effects of seasonality and degree of resource island development. *Ecological Monographs* **69**: 69–106.

Schade, J.D. and Hobbie, S.E. 2005. Spatial and temporal variation in islands of fertility in the Sonoran Desert. *Biogeochemistry* **73**: 541–553.

Schweitzer, J.A., Madritch, M.D., Bailey, J.K., LeRoy, C.J., Fischer, D.G., Rehill, B.J., Lindroth, R.L., Hagerman, A.E., Wooley, S.C., Hart, S.C., and Whitham, T.G. 2008. The genetic basis of condensed tannins and their role in nutrient regulation in a *Populus* model system. *Ecosystems* **11**: 1005–1020.

Springsteen, A., Loya, W., Liebig, M., and Hendrickson, J. 2010. Soil carbon and nitrogen across a chronosequence of woody plant expansion in North Dakota. *Plant and Soil* **328**: 369–379.

Voelker, S.L., Muzika, R.-M., Guyette, R.P., and Stambaugh, M.C. 2006. Historical CO_2 growth enhancement declines with age in *Quercus* and *Pinus*. *Ecological Monographs* **76**: 549–564.

Whitham, T.G., Bailey, J.K., and Schweitzer, J.A. 2006. A framework for community and ecosystem genetics from genes to ecosystems. *Nature Reviews Genetics* **7**: 510–523.

4.2.2.5.5 Western USA

- The late twentieth-century rise in temperature and CO_2 has improved the productivity of plant communities in the western region of the United States, notwithstanding model-based projections of unprecedented ecological disaster due to rising temperatures and drought.

Baron *et al.* (2000) used an empirically based hydro-ecological simulation model to evaluate the consequences of a doubling of atmospheric CO_2 content and 2 to 4°C increases in air temperature on ecosystem performance in a high-elevation Rocky Mountain watershed. They found "both photosynthesis and transpiration were highly responsive to doubled CO_2." They also determined the positive effects of the 4°C temperature increase "were additive, so a warmer and carbon-rich environment increased plant growth by 30%." The authors conclude, "forests will expand at the expense of tundra in a warmer, wetter, and enriched CO_2 world," and observed increases in tree height and density in recent decades illustrate "the rapidity with which vegetation can respond to climate change."

Because urban environments are affected by urban heat islands, carbon dioxide domes, and high-level nitrogen deposition, Shen *et al.* (2008) write, "to some extent they portend the future of the global ecosystem," and they "provide a unique 'natural laboratory' to study potential ecosystem responses to anthropogenic environmental changes." The team of four authors used a version of the Patch Arid Land Simulator-Functional Types (PALS-FT) process-based ecosystem model—originally developed for the Chihuahuan Desert but modified to represent the *Larrea tridentata*-dominated ecosystem characteristic of the Sonoran Desert in which Phoenix, Arizona (USA) is located—to investigate the impacts of previously documented city-to-desert gradients of atmospheric CO_2 concentration, air temperature (TA), and nitrogen deposition (N_{dep}) on aboveground net primary productivity (ANPP) and soil organic matter (SOM).

In response to the mean maximum rural-to-urban increases in CO_2 (160 ppm), N_{dep} (24 kg per ha/year) and TA (4.0°C) characteristic of Phoenix, mean ANPP changes of +52.5, +42.7 and -7.8 g dry matter (DM) per m^2/year were obtained, respectively, from the 76.3 g DM per m^2/year characteristic of desert conditions, when each of the three factors was increased individually. When all three parameters were increased together, the researchers found the net increase in ANPP was even greater than the sum of the three individual results: 108 vs. 87.4 g DM per m^2/year, translating to respective percentage increases of 142% vs. 115%. In the case of SOM, increases of 18.5, 12.3, and 1.2 g C per m^2/year were obtained for mean maximum individual increases in CO_2, N$_{dep}$, and TA, respectively, and the combined increase was 30.9 g C per m^2/year. These findings indicate that even in a desert region as hot as Phoenix, the types of CO_2, temperature, and nitrogen deposition increases predicted for the years ahead portend huge increases in indigenous ecosystem productivity and soil organic matter buildup.

Zavaleta and Kettley (2006) examined patterns of production, standing biomass, carbon (C) and nitrogen (N) storage, community composition, and soil moisture along a 25-year chronosequence of sites in an annual, exotic-dominated grassland at Stanford University's Jasper Ridge Biological Preserve in the interior foothills of the central coast range south of San Francisco, California (USA), various parts of which had been invaded at a number of different times over the past quarter-century by *Baccharis pilularis* shrubs.

The two researchers report increasing above- and below-ground biomass along the chronosequence "drove increases in ecosystem N sequestration of ~700% and in C storage of over 125%," including a 32% increase in total soil C over the 25-year period. They write, "increases in carbon storage also did not appear to be saturating at 25 years after shrub establishment in any pool, suggesting the potential for additional carbon gains beyond 25 years." *Baccharis* shrubs began to decline in prominence after about 20 years, as native oaks "with life spans of centuries" and the potential to drive even larger ecosystem changes began to grow in the shrub-dominated areas.

Zavaleta and Kettley note they "initially hypothesized *Baccharis*-invaded sites would experience increasing N limitation as N was immobilized in biomass and litter." However, they found "total soil N increased rapidly with shrub age" and "the magnitude of increase in total soil nitrogen was much larger than the increase in nitrogen immobilization in biomass and litter over time." They say their findings "illustrate the potential for important vegetation-mediated ecosystem responses and feedbacks to atmospheric CO_2 and climate change." In particular, they highlight the great potential for a CO_2-induced range expansion of trees, and they pretty much lay to rest the claim (Hungate *et al.*, 2003) that the availability of nitrogen, in forms usable by plants, will probably be too low for large future increases in carbon storage driven by CO_2-induced increases in plant growth and development.

Peterson and Neofotis (2004) grew velvet

mesquite (*Prosopis velutina* Woot.) seedlings for six weeks from their time of planting (as seeds) in small pots in environmentally controlled growth chambers maintained in a laboratory setting at atmospheric CO_2 concentrations of 380 and 760 ppm and two levels of water availability (high and low). Although they did not see a significant CO_2-induced increase in plant growth, by the end of their six-week study they observed a significant reduction of approximately 41% in the volume of water transpired by *P. velutina* in response to the experimental doubling of the atmospheric CO_2 content. "This large reduction in whole-plant water use," they write, "occurred because the reduction in transpiration per unit leaf area at elevated CO_2 was not offset by a proportional increase in total leaf area."

The pair of scientists from the Biosphere 2 Center near Oracle, Arizona (USA) say their findings suggest "under a future [high-CO_2] scenario, seedlings may deplete soil moisture at a slower rate than they do currently," and "this could facilitate seedling survival between intermittent rain events." They note their work "corroborates the conclusions of Polley *et al*. (1994, 1999, 2003) that increasing levels of atmospheric CO_2 may facilitate the establishment of mesquite seedlings through a reduction in soil water depletion." They note "mesquites and other woody species in the semiarid southwestern United States have shown substantial increases in population density and geographic range since Anglo-American settlement of the region approximately 120 years ago," citing Van Auken and Bush (1990), Gibbens *et al*. (1992), Bahre and Shelton (1993), Archer (1995), Boutton *et al*. (1999), Van Auken (2000), Ansley *et al*. (2001), Wilson *et al*. (2001), and Biggs *et al*. (2002).

Among such studies could also be listed the work of Feng (1999), who derived variations in plant intrinsic water-use efficiency over the preceding two centuries from 23 carbon isotope tree-ring chronologies. Their results were nearly identical to the historical trend in the atmospheric CO_2 content, with plant intrinsic water-use efficiency rising by 10 to 25% from 1750 to 1970, during which time the air's CO_2 concentration rose by approximately 16%. Feng concludes, "in arid environments where moisture limits the tree growth, biomass may have increased with increasing transpiration efficiency," noting the enhanced growth of trees in arid environments may "have operated as a carbon sink for the anthropogenic CO_2" emitted during that period.

Soule and Knapp (2006) studied ponderosa pine trees at eight sites in the Pacific Northwest of the

United States to see how they may have responded to the increase in the atmosphere's CO_2 concentration that occurred after 1950. The two geographers say the sites they chose "fit several criteria designed to limit potential confounding influences associated with anthropogenic disturbance." They selected locations with "a variety of climatic and topo-edaphic conditions, ranging from extremely water-limiting environments ... to areas where soil moisture should be a limiting factor for growth only during extreme drought years." They also note all sites were located in areas "where ozone concentrations and nitrogen deposition are typically low."

At all eight of the sites, Soule and Knapp obtained core samples from about 40 mature trees that included "the potentially oldest trees on each site," so their results would indicate, as they put it, "the response of mature, naturally occurring ponderosa pine trees that germinated before anthropogenically elevated CO_2 levels, but where growth, particularly post-1950, has occurred under increasing and substantially higher atmospheric CO_2 concentrations." Utilizing meteorological evaluations of the Palmer Drought Severity Index, they compared ponderosa pine radial growth rates during matched wet and dry years pre- and post-1950.

Overall, the two researchers discovered a post-1950 radial growth enhancement "more pronounced during drought years compared with wet years, and the greatest response occurred at the most stressed site" (see Figure 4.2.2.5.5.1). As for the magnitude of the response, they write, "the relative change in growth [was] upward at seven of our [eight] sites, ranging from 11 to 133%."

Soule and Knapp say their results show "radial growth has increased in the post-1950s period ... while climatic conditions have generally been unchanged," which suggests "nonclimatic driving forces are operative." They say the "radial growth responses are generally consistent with what has been shown in long-term open-top chamber (Idso and Kimball, 2001) and FACE studies (Ainsworth and Long, 2005)." They conclude their findings "suggest that elevated levels of atmospheric CO_2 are acting as a driving force for increased radial growth of ponderosa pine, but the overall influence of this effect may be enhanced, reduced or obviated by site-specific conditions."

Soule and Knapp note they "hypothesized that ponderosa pine ... would respond to gradual increases in atmospheric CO_2 over the past 50 years, and that these effects would be most apparent during drought stress and on environmentally harsh sites," and they report their results "support these hypotheses." They conclude, "an atmospheric CO_2-driven growth-enhancement effect exists for ponderosa pine growing under specific natural conditions within the interior Pacific Northwest."

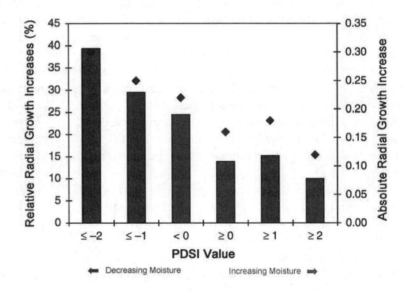

Figure 4.2.2.5.5.1. Relative and absolute radial growth increases of Ponderosa pine (Pinus ponderosa) in the Pacific Northwest, USA, post-1950 compared with pre-1950 during years falling into various Palmer Drought Severity Index (PDSI) categories of drought (moist) severity. Adapted from Soule and Knapp (2006).

The studies in this section document the late twentieth-century rise in temperature and CO_2 has improved the productivity of plant communities in the western region of the United States, notwithstanding model-based projections of unprecedented ecological disaster due to rising temperatures and drought.

References

Ainsworth, E.A. and Long, S.P. 2005. What have we learned from 15 years of free-air CO_2 enrichment (FACE)? A meta-analytic review of the responses of photosynthesis, canopy properties and plant production to rising CO_2. *New Phytologist* **165**: 351–372.

Ansley, R.J., Ben Wu, X., and Kramp, B.A. 2001. Observation: long-term increases in mesquite canopy cover in a north Texas savanna. *Journal of Range Management* **54**: 171–176.

Archer, S. 1995. Tree-grass dynamics in a *Prosopis*-thornscrub savanna parkland: reconstructing the past and predicting the future. *Ecoscience* **2**: 83–99.

Bahre, C.J. and Shelton, M.L. 1993. Historic vegetation change, mesquite increases, and climate in southeastern Arizona. *Journal of Biogeography* **20**: 489–504.

Baron, J.S., Hartman, M.D., Band, L.E., and Lammers, R.B. 2000. Sensitivity of a high-elevation Rocky Mountain watershed to altered climate and CO_2. *Water Resources Research* **36**: 89–99.

Biggs, T.H., Quade, J., and Webb, R.H. 2002. $\delta^{13}C$ values of soil organic matter in semiarid grassland with mesquite (*Prosopis*) encroachment in southeastern Arizona. *Geoderma* **110**: 109–130.

Boutton, T.W., Archer, S.R., and Midwood, A.J. 1999. Stable isotopes in ecosystem science: structure, function and dynamics of a subtropical savanna. *Rapid Communications in Mass Spectrometry* **13**: 1263–1277.

Feng, X. 1999. Trends in intrinsic water-use efficiency of natural trees for the past 100–200 years: A response to atmospheric CO_2 concentration. *Geochimica et Cosmochimica Acta* **63**: 1891–1903.

Gibbens, R.P., Beck, R.F., Mcneely, R.P., and Herbel, C.H. 1992. Recent rates of mesquite establishment in the northern Chihuahuan desert. *Journal of Range Management* **45**: 585–588.

Hungate, B.A., Dukes, J.S., Shaw, M.R., Luo, Y., and Field, C.B. 2003. Nitrogen and climate change. *Science* **302**: 1512–1513.

Idso, S.B. and Kimball, B.A. 2001. CO_2 enrichment of sour orange trees: 13 years and counting. *Environmental and Experimental Botany* **46**: 147–153.

Peterson, A.G. and Neofotis, P.G. 2004. A hierarchical analysis of the interactive effects of elevated CO_2 and water availability on the nitrogen and transpiration productivities of velvet mesquite seedlings. *Oecologia* **141**: 629–640.

Polley, H.W., Johnson, H.B., and Mayeux, H.S. 1994. Increasing CO_2: comparative responses of the C_4 grass *Schizachyrium* and grassland invader *Prosopis*. *Ecology* **75**: 976–988.

Polley, H.W., Johnson, H.B., and Tischler, C.R. 2003. Woody invasion of grasslands: evidence that CO_2 enrichment indirectly promotes establishment of *Prosopis glandulosa*. *Plant Ecology* **164**: 85–94.

Polley, H.W., Tischler, C.R., Johnson, H.B., and Pennington, R.E. 1999. Growth, water relations, and survival of drought-exposed seedlings from six maternal families of honey mesquite (*Prosopis* glandulosa): responses to CO_2 enrichment. *Tree Physiology* **19**: 359–366.

Shen, W., Wu,. J., Grimm, N.B., and Hope, D. 2008. Effects of urbanization-induced environmental changes on ecosystem functioning in the Phoenix metropolitan region, USA. *Ecosystems* **11**: 138–155.

Soule, P.T. and Knapp, P.A. 2006. Radial growth rate increases in naturally occurring ponderosa pine trees: a late-20th century CO_2 fertilization effect? *New Phytologist* doi: 10.1111/j.1469-8137.2006.01746.x.

Van Auken, O.W. 2000. Shrub invasions of North American semiarid grasslands. *Annual Review of Ecological Systems* **31**: 197–215.

Van Auken, O.W. and Bush, J.K. 1990. Importance of grass density and time of planting on *Prosopis glandulosa* seedling growth. *Southwest Naturalist* **35**: 411–415.

Wilson, T.B., Webb, R.H., and Thompson, T.L. 2001. *Mechanisms of Range Expansion and Removal of Mesquite in Desert Grasslands of the Southwestern United States.* U.S. Department of Agriculture, Forest Service, Rocky Mountain Research Station.

Zavaleta, E.S. and Kettley, L.S. 2006. Ecosystem change along a woody invasion chronosequence in a California grassland. *Journal of Arid Environments* **66**: 290–306.

4.2.2.6 South America

- Warmer temperatures and higher CO_2 concentrations are resulting in net primary productivity increasing across tropical South America, overcoming the effects of deforestation, forest fires, and incursions by human civilization into natural areas.

Beerling and Mayle (2006) investigated the Amazonian ecosystem's response to the large-scale environmental changes experienced during glacial-interglacial cycles via a series of 21,000-year simulations. They used a dynamic process-based ecosystem model for three scenarios: real-world glacial-to-interglacial changes in CO_2 concentration and climate, the real-world change in CO_2 with a constant preindustrial climate, and the real-world change in climate with a constant preindustrial CO_2 concentration.

During the last glacial maximum, the model suggests "total above-ground carbon storage in Amazonia was half preindustrial values, indicative of rain forests with markedly lower canopy densities and simpler structures due to lowered CO_2 levels, corroborating modeling studies by Cowling (2004) and Cowling *et al.* (2001)." Thereafter, they write, "biome shifts in ecotonal areas since the last glacial maximum ["the competitive replacement of drought-adapted vegetation (e.g. savanna or deciduous/semideciduous dry forest) by rain forest"] were driven predominantly by climate change, while coincident, increased ecosystem carbon storage throughout the Amazon Basin was driven largely by CO_2."

As to the contemporary relevance of these findings, Beerling and Mayle write, "the underlying cause for the observed trend of increasing biomass in long-term Amazonian forest plots over recent years, despite drought-induced El Niño events (Phillips *et al.*, 1998; Baker *et al.*, 2004a), has been a subject of considerable debate (Baker *et al.*, 2004a; Wright, 2005)," and they conclude "this biomass increase is part of a long-term historical trend driven by anthropogenically induced rising CO_2 levels since the 19th century."

Ichii *et al.* (2005) "simulated and analyzed 1982–1999 Amazonian, African, and Asian carbon fluxes using the Biome-BGC prognostic carbon cycle model driven by National Centers for Environmental Prediction reanalysis daily climate data" and "calculated trends in gross primary productivity (GPP) and net primary productivity (NPP)." They found solar radiation variability to be the primary factor responsible for inter-annual variations in GPP, followed by temperature and precipitation variability. In terms of GPP trends, they report, "recent changes in atmospheric CO_2 and climate promoted terrestrial GPP increases with a significant linear trend in all three tropical regions." In the Amazonian region, the rate of GPP increase was highest, at 0.67 PgC year^{-1} per decade, and in Africa and Asia it was about 0.3 PgC year^{-1} per decade. As Beerling and Mayle found, Ichii *et al.* say carbon dioxide was the major cause of increased growth, reporting, "CO_2 fertilization effects strongly increased recent NPP trends in regional totals."

This finding is especially interesting because many scientists over the past century believed old-growth forests, such as those of Amazonia, were close to dynamic equilibrium. Just the opposite, however, has been observed repeatedly by several groups of researchers over the past two decades.

Phillips and Gentry (1994) analyzed the turnover rates—close correlates of net productivity (Weaver and Murphy, 1990)—of 40 tropical forests from around the world. They report the growth rates of

these already highly productive forests have been rising since at least 1960, and they have undergone an apparent acceleration in growth rate sometime after 1980. Pimm and Sugden (1994) report the consistency and simultaneity of the forest growth trends Phillips and Gentry documented on several continents led them to conclude "enhanced productivity induced by increased CO_2 is the most plausible candidate for the cause of the increased turnover."

Phillips *et al.* (1998) analyzed forest growth rate data for the years 1958 to 1996 for several hundred plots of mature tropical trees around the world, finding tropical forest biomass, as a whole, increased substantially over the period of record (Figure 4.2.2.6.1). The increase in the neotropics (tropical Central and South America) was equivalent to approximately 40% of the missing terrestrial carbon sink of the entire globe. They identify the aerial fertilization effect of the ongoing rise in atmospheric CO_2 content as one of the primary factors likely to be responsible for this phenomenon.

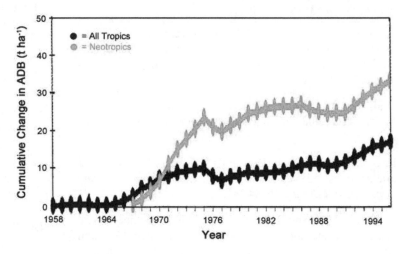

Figure 4.2.2.6.1. Cumulative aboveground dry biomass change (ADB) per year in humid forests in the entire Tropics since 1958 and in the Neotropics (tropical Central and South America) since 1967. Adapted from Phillips *et al.* (1998).

Laurance *et al.* (2004a) reported accelerated growth in the 1990s relative to the 1980s for the large majority (87%) of tree genera in 18 one-hectare plots spanning an area of about 300 km^2 in central Amazonia, and Laurance *et al.* (2004b) observed similarly accelerated tree community dynamics in the 1990s relative to the 1980s. Laurance *et al.* (2005) suggest these "pervasive changes in central Amazonian tree communities were most likely caused by global- or regional-scale drivers, such as increasing atmospheric CO_2 concentrations (Laurance et al., 2004a,b)." They "interpreted these changes as being consistent with an ecological 'signature' expected from increasing forest productivity (cf., Phillips and Gentry, 1994; Lewis et al. 2004a,b; Phillips et al., 2004)." Noting Nelson (2005) challenged this conclusion, they considered his arguments in some detail, dismantling each one.

Lewis (2006) reports the increasing dynamism and productivity of intact tropical forests has had a long history, noting "across the paleotropics forest dynamism has been steadily increasing for five decades (Phillips and Gentry, 1994)." Among 50 old-growth plots across tropical South America, for example, he notes "stem recruitment, stem mortality, and biomass growth, and loss, all increased significantly (Lewis et al., 2004a)." He reports "over approximately the last 20 years, long-term monitoring of 59 plots showed that above-ground biomass increased by 0.6 ± 0.2 tonnes C ha^{-1} a^{-1}, or a relative increase of $0.50 \pm 0.17\%$ a^{-1} (mean $\pm$ 95% confidence interval; Baker et al., 2004a)." This rate of increase "is slightly higher than that documented by Phillips et al. (1998)." Lewis concludes there is no question "over the past two decades these forests have shown concerted changes in their ecology, becoming, on average, faster growing—more productive—and more dynamic, and showing a net increase in above-ground biomass."

Lewis states "the results appear to show a coherent fingerprint of increasing net primary productivity across tropical South America, caused by a long-term increase in resource availability (Lewis et al., 2004a,b)." The four resources he identifies are increases in solar radiation, air temperature, nutrient deposition, and atmospheric CO_2 concentration. After analyzing each of them in detail, he concludes "the most parsimonious explanation is the increase in atmospheric CO_2, because of the undisputed long-term historical increase in CO_2 concentrations, the key role of CO_2 in photosynthesis, and the demonstrated positive effects of CO_2 fertilization on plant growth rates including experiments on whole temperate-forest stands (Ainsworth and Long, 2005)." He writes, the explanation is in "the anthropogenic increase in atmospheric carbon dioxide concentrations, increasing forest net primary productivity leading to accelerated forest growth and dynamics."

In spite of the forest growth optimism inherent in the studies cited above, some pessimists remained. Gloor et al. (2009) write, "analysis of earlier tropical plot data has suggested that large-scale changes in forest dynamics are currently occurring in Amazonia (Phillips and Gentry, 1994; Phillips et al., 2004a), and

an increase in aboveground biomass has occurred, with increases in mortality tending to lag increases in growth (Phillips et al., 1998; Baker et al., 2004a,b; Lewis et al., 2004a)." They state this conclusion had been challenged by an overzealous application of the "Slow in, Rapid out" dictum, which relates to the fact that forest growth is a slow process, whereas mortality can be dramatic and singular in time, so sampling over relatively short observation periods may miss the more severe events, leading to positively biased estimates of aboveground biomass trends when either no trend or negative trends actually exist.

Gloor et al. statistically characterized the disturbance process in Amazon old-growth forests as recorded in 135 forest plots of the RAINFOR network up to 2006, as well as other independent research programs, exploring the consequences of sampling artifacts using a data-based stochastic simulator. The authors report, "over the observed range of annual aboveground biomass losses, standard statistical tests show that the distribution of biomass losses through mortality follow an exponential or near-identical Weibull probability distribution and not a power law as assumed by others." They write, "the simulator was parameterized using both an exponential disturbance probability distribution as well as a mixed exponential-power law distribution to account for potential large-scale blow-down events," and "in both cases, sampling biases turn out to be too small to explain the gains detected by the extended RAINFOR plot network." Gloor et al. conclude their results lend "further support to the notion that currently observed biomass gains for intact forests across the Amazon are actually occurring over large scales at the current time, presumably as a response to climate change."

Bonal et al. (2011) write, "the impact of global change during the last century on the biology of tropical rainforest trees is largely unknown," but "an increase in tree radial growth increment over recent decades in Amazonian tropical rainforests has been observed, leading to increased above-ground biomass at most study sites," citing Phillips et al. (1998, 2009) and Malhi et al. (2004). They note "the stimulating impact on photosynthesis of increased CO_2 concentrations in the air (Ca) could explain these growth patterns (Lloyd and Farquhar, 2008)."

Bonal et al. assessed the impacts of historical environmental changes "on leaf morphological (stomatal density, stomatal surface, leaf mass per unit area) and physiological traits (carbon isotope composition, $\delta^{13}C$leaf, and discrimination, $\Delta^{13}C$leaf, oxygen isotope composition, $\delta^{18}O$leaf) of two tropical rainforest species (*Dicorynia guianensis*; *Humiria balsamifera*) that are abundant in the Guiana shield (Northern Amazonia)," working with leaf samples from different international herbariums that covered a 200-year period (AD 1790–2004).

The 11 researchers found "a clear response of leaf physiological characteristics to increasing Ca for both species," consistent with the findings of previous studies "from different ecosystems (Penuelas and Azcon-Bieto, 1992; Beerling *et al.*, 1993; Van de Water *et al.*, 1994; Pedicino *et al.*, 2002; Penuelas *et al.*, 2008), and with data from tree rings in Europe (Bert *et al.*, 1997; Duquesnay *et al.*, 1998; Saurer *et al.*, 2004), Africa (Gebrekirstos *et al.*, 2009) and in tropical rainforests (Hietz *et al.*, 2005; Silva *et al.*, 2009; Nock *et al.*, 2011)." They say their results indicate "an increase in water-use efficiency over recent decades of about 23.1 and 26.6% for *Humiria* and *Dicorynia*, respectively," driven mostly by increases in leaf photosynthesis. They write, "the range of change in water-use efficiency for these two species was consistent with many results observed not only in tropical forests (Hietz *et al.*, 2005; Nock *et al.*, 2011), but in boreal (Saurer *et al.*, 2004) and temperate forests (Francey and Farquhar, 1982; Penuelas and Azcon-Bieto, 1992; Bert *et al.*, 1997; Duquesnay *et al.*, 1998)." Bonal *et al.* further state the responses of the two tree species to increasing Ca appear to be "simply related to the availability of CO_2 in the air (fertilization effect)," and they note "this trend seems to be consistent with recent tree growth patterns in the Amazonian region."

Silva *et al.* (2009) studied tree-ring data obtained from *A. angustifolia* trees growing in forest and grassland sites in southern Brazil, comparing changes in intrinsic water use efficiency—iWUE, defined as the ratio of the rate of CO_2 assimilation by the trees' needles to their stomatal conductance—with concomitant historical changes in temperature, precipitation, and atmospheric CO_2 concentration over the past century. During the past several decades, the four researchers report, "iWUE increased over 30% in both habitats" (see Figure 4.2.2.6.2), and "this increase was highly correlated with increasing levels of CO_2 in the atmosphere." Over the latter period, tree growth remained rather stable because of lower-than-normal precipitation and higher-than-normal temperatures, which would normally tend to depress the growth of this species; Katinas and Crisci (2008) describe *A. angustifolia* as being "intolerant of dry seasons and requiring cool temperatures." Silva *et*

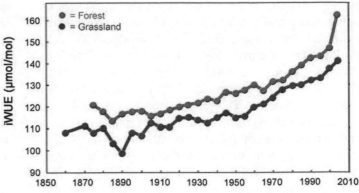

Figure 4.2.2.6.2. Intrinsic water-use efficiency (iWUE) in Araucaria angustifolia trees established into forest and grassland in southern Brazil (means of individuals per site in five-year total values). Adapted from Silva *et al.* (2009).

al. conclude the "climatic fluctuations during the past few decades," which would normally be expected to have been deleterious to the growth of *A. angustifolia*, seem to have had their growth-retarding effects "compensated by increases in atmospheric CO_2 and changes [i.e., increases] in iWUE."

Phillips *et al.* (2009) investigated what effect a severe drought might have on South America's surprisingly spry-for-its-age tropical mega-forest, especially a drought of the type the models predict will occur if anthropogenic CO_2 emissions are not significantly abated. The international team of scientists sought to determine whether such a decline in the availability of water might wipe out the super ecosystem's biomass gains of prior decades, thereby fulfilling one of the worst-case catastrophic scenarios of the models.

Focusing their attention on the Amazonian drought of 2005, which they describe as "one of the most intense droughts of the past 100 years" and "a possible analog of future events," the 66 researchers (who had monitored a host of forest plots across the Amazon basin over the prior quarter-century) utilized tree diameter, wood density, and allometric models to compute the basin's woody biomass at each time of measurement, both before and after the drought. They derived the results plotted in Figure 4.2.2.6.3.

As Figure 4.2.2.6.3. shows, the Amazonian drought of 2005 only slightly impacted the strong upward trend of tree biomass accumulation that was exhibited over the prior two decades, which had occurred, as Phillips *et al.* note, through a multi-decadal period spanning both wet and dry episodes, the latter of which are not even detectable in their wood biomass data. Hence it would appear that

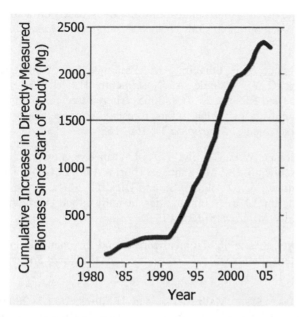

Figure 4.2.2.6.3. The post-1980 cumulative biomass increase of Amazon trees ≥10 cm in diameter as a function of the mid-date of each forest-plot census interval, portrayed as a 50-interval moving mean. Adapted from Phillips *et al.* (2009).

although extremely severe drought conditions can indeed stop biomass accumulation in old-growth tropical forests—and sometimes even lead to minor reductions in biomass due to selective tree mortality—the vast majority of the aged trees are able to regain their photosynthetic prowess and add to their prior store of biomass once the moisture stress subsides, thanks in large measure to the enhanced growth (Lin et al., 1998) and water use efficiency (Hietz *et al.*, 2005) of nearly all woody plants as the atmospheric CO_2 content rises.

Lloyd and Farquhar (2008) provide additional support for this attribution, concluding, "the magnitude and pattern of increases in forest dynamics across Amazonia observed over the last few decades are consistent with a CO_2-induced stimulation of tree growth." Phillips *et al.* (2008) add still more support for the premise, concluding the simplest explanation for the phenomenon is "improved resource availability has increased net primary productivity, in turn increasing growth rates," and "the only change for which there is unambiguous evidence that the driver has widely changed and that such a change should accelerate forest growth is the increase in atmospheric CO_2," because of "the undisputed long-term increase in [its] concentration, the key role of CO_2 in photosynthesis, and the demonstrated effects of CO_2 fertilization on plant growth rates."

The voluminous and undeniable real-world observations reported in the studies described above indicate forest productivity has been increasing along with the increasing CO_2 content of the air wherever tropical forests have not been decimated by the direct destructive actions of man, such as the felling and burning of trees. This productivity increase has persisted in spite of all concomitant changes in atmospheric, soil, and water chemistry and the twentieth-century global warming. Real-world evidence suggests the anthropogenic-induced increase in the atmospheric CO_2 content is primarily responsible for this beneficial state of affairs.

References

Ainsworth, E.A. and Long, S.P. 2005. What have we learned from 15 years of free-air CO_2 enrichment (FACE)? A meta-analytic review of the responses of photosynthesis, canopy properties and plant production to rising CO_2. *New Phytologist* **165**: 351–372.

Baker, T.R., Phillips, O.L., Malhi, Y., Almeida, S., Arroyo, L., Di Fiore, A., Erwin, T., Higuchi, N., Killeen, T.J., Laurance, S.G., Laurance, W.F., Lewis, S.L., Monteagudo, A., Neill, D.A., Núñez Vargas, P., Pitman, N.C.A., Silva, J.N.M., and Vásquez Martínez, R. 2004a. Increasing biomass in Amazonian forest plots. *Philosophical Transactions of the Royal Society of London Series B—Biological Sciences* **359**: 353–365.

Baker, T.R., Phillips, O.L., Malhi, Y., Almeida, S., Arroyo, L., Di Fiore, A., Erwin, T., Killeen, T.J., Laurance, S.G., Laurance, W.F., Lewis, S.L., Lloyd, J., Monteagudo, A., Neil, D.A., Patiño, S., Pitman, N.C.A., Silva, J.N.M., and Vásquez Martínez, R. 2004b. Variation in wood density determines spatial patterns in Amazonian forest biomass. *Global Change Biology* **10**: 545–562.

Beerling, D.J., Mattey, D.P., and Chaloner, W.G. 1993. Shifts in the $\delta^{13}C$ composition of *Salix herbacea* L. leaves in response to spatial and temporal gradients of atmospheric CO_2 concentration. *Proceedings of the Royal Society of London* **253**: 53–60.

Beerling, D.J. and Mayle, F.E. 2006. Contrasting effects of climate and CO_2 on Amazonian ecosystems since the last glacial maximum. *Global Change Biology* **12**: 1977–1984.

Bert, D., Leavitt, S.W., and Dupouey, J.L. 1997. Variations of wood $\delta^{13}C$ and water-use efficiency of *Abies alba* during the last century. *Ecology* **78**: 1588–1596.

Bonal, D., Ponton, S., Le Thiec, D., Richard, B., Ningre, N., Herault, B., Ogee, J., Gonzalez, S., Pignal, M., Sabatier, D., and Guehl, J.-M. 2011. Leaf functional response to increasing atmospheric CO_2 concentrations over the last century in two northern Amazonian tree species: a historical $\delta^{13}C$ and $\delta^{18}O$ approach using herbarium samples. *Plant, Cell and Environment* **34**: 1332–1344.

Cowling, S.A. 2004. Tropical forest structure: a missing dimension to Pleistocene landscapes. *Journal of Quarternary Science* **19**: 733–743.

Cowling, S.A., Maslin, M.A., and Sykes, M.T. 2001. Paleovegetation simulations of lowland Amazonia and implications for neotropical allopatry and speciation. *Quaternary Research* **55**: 140–149.

Duquesnay, A., Breda, N., Stievenard, M., and Dupouey, J.L. 1998. Changes of tree-ring $\delta^{13}C$ and water-use efficiency of beech (*Fagus sylvatica* L.) in north-eastern France during the past century. *Plant, Cell and Environment* **21**: 565–572.

Francey, R.J. and Farquhar, G.D. 1982. An explanation of $^{13}C/^{12}C$ variations in tree rings. *Nature* **297**: 28–31.

Gebrekirstos, A., Worbes, M., Teketay, D., Fetene, M., and Mitlohner, R. 2009. Stable carbon isotope ratios in tree rings of co-occurring species from semi-arid tropics in Africa: patterns and climatic signals. *Global and Planetary Change* **66**: 253–260.

Gloor, M., Phillips, O.L., Lloyd, J.J., Lewis, S.L., Malhi, Y., Baker, T.R., Lopez-Gonzalez, G., Peacock, J., Almeida, S., Alves de Oliveira, A.C., Alvarez, E., Amaral, I., Arroyo, L, Aymard, G., Banki, O., Blanc, L., Bonal, D., Brando, P., Chao, K.-J., Chave, J., Davila, N., Erwin, T., Silva, J., DiFiore, A., Feldpausch, T.R., Freitzs, A., Herrera, R., Higuchi, N., Honorio, E., Jimenez, E., Killeen, T., Laurance, W., Mendoza, C., Monteagudo, A., Andrade, A. Neill, D., Nepstad, D., Nunez Vargas, P., Peñuela, M.C., Pena Cruz, A., Prieto, A., Pitman, N., Quesada, C., Salomao, R., Silveira, M., Schwarz, M., Stropp, J., Ramirez, F., Ramirez, H., Rudas, A., ter Steege, H., Silva, N., Torres, A., Terborgh, J., Vasquez, R., and van der Heijden, G. 2009. Does the disturbance hypothesis explain the biomass increase in basin-wide Amazon forest plot data? *Global Change Biology* **15**: 2418–2430.

Hietz, P., Wanek, W., and Dunisch, O. 2005. Long-term trends in cellulose $\delta^{13}C$ and water-use efficiency of tropical Dedrela and Swietenia from Brazil. *Tree Physiology* **25**: 745–752.

Ichii, K., Hashimoto, H., Nemani, R., and White, M. 2005. Modeling the interannual variability and trends in gross and net primary productivity of tropical forests from 1982 to 1999. *Global and Planetary Change* **48**: 274–286.

Katinas, L. and Crisci, J.V. 2008. Reconstructing the biogeographical history of two plant genera with different dispersion capabilities. *Journal of Biogeography* **35**: 1374–1384.

Laurance, W.F., Nascimento, H.E.M., Laurance, S.G., Condit, R., D'Angelo, S., and Andrade, A. 2004b. Inferred longevity of Amazonian rainforest trees based on a long-term demographic study. *Forest Ecology and Management* **190**: 131–143.

Laurance, W.F., Oliveira, A.A., Laurance, S.G., Condit, R., Dick, C.W., Andrade, A., Nascimento, H.E.M., Lovejoy, T.E., and Ribeiro, J.E.L.S. 2005. Altered tree communities in undisturbed Amazonian forests: A consequence of global change? *Biotropica* **37**: 160–162.

Laurance, W.F., Oliveira, A.A., Laurance, S.G., Condit, R., Nascimento, H.E.M., Sanchez-Thorin, A.C., Lovejoy, T.E., Andrade, A., D'Angelo, S., and Dick, C. 2004a. Pervasive alteration of tree communities in undisturbed Amazonian forests. *Nature* **428**: 171–175.

Lewis, S.L. 2006. Tropical forests and the changing earth system. *Philosophical Transactions of the Royal Society B* **361**: 195–210.

Lewis, S.L., Malhi, Y., and Phillips, O.L. 2004b. Fingerprinting the impacts of global change on tropical forests. *Philosophical Transactions of the Royal Society of London Series B—Biological Sciences* **359**: 437–462.

Lewis, S.L., Phillips, O.L., Baker, T.R., Lloyd, J., Malhi, Y., Almeida, S., Higuchi, N., Laurance, W.F., Neill, D.A., Silva, J.N.M., Terborgh, J., Lezama, A.T., Vásquez Martinez, R., Brown, S., Chave, J., Kuebler, C., Núñez Vargas, P., and Vinceti, B. 2004a. Concerted changes in tropical forest structure and dynamics: evidence from 50 South American long-term plots. *Philosophical Transactions of the Royal Society of London Series B—Biological Sciences* **359**: 421–436.

Lin, G., Marino, B.D.V., Wei, Y., Adams, J., Tubiello, F., and Berry, J.A. 1998. An experimental and modeling study of responses in ecosystems carbon exchanges to increasing CO_2 concentrations using a tropical rainforest mesocosm. *Australian Journal of Plant Physiology* **25**: 547–556.

Lloyd, J. and Farquhar, G.D. 2008. Effects of rising temperatures and [CO_2] on the physiology of tropical forest trees. *Philosophical Transactions of the Royal Society B* **363**: 1811–1817.

Malhi, Y., Baker, T.R., Phillips, O.L., Almeida, S., Alvarez, E., Arroyo, L., Chave, J., Czimczik, C.I., Di Fiore, A., Higuchi, N., Killeen, T.J., Laurance, S.G., Laurance, W.F., Lewis, S.L., Montoya, L.M.M., Agudo, A., Neill, D.A., Vargas, P.N., Patino, S., Pitman, N.C.A., Quesadah, C.A., Salomao, R., Silva, J.N.M., Lezama, A.T., Martinez, R.V., Terborgh, J., Vinceti, B., and Lloyd, J. 2004. The above-ground coarse wood productivity of 104 Neotropical forest plots. *Global Change Biology* **10**: 563–591.

Nelson, B.W. 2005. Pervasive alteration of tree communities in undisturbed Amazonian forests. *Biotropica* **37**: 158–159.

Nock, C.A., Baker, P.J., Wanek, W., Albrecht, L., Grabner,

M., Bunyavejchewin, S., and Hietz, P. 2011. Long-term increases in intrinsic water-use efficiency do not lead to increased stem growth in a tropical monsoon forest in western Thailand. *Global Change Biology* **17**: 1049–1063.

Pedicino, L., Leavitt, S.W., Betancourt, J.L., and Van De Water, P.K. 2002. Historical variations in $\delta^{13}C$ leaf of herbarium specimens on the Southwestern U.S. *Western North American Naturalist* **62**: 348–359.

Peñulas, J. and Azcon-Bieto, J. 1992. Changes in leaf $\delta^{13}C$ of herbarium plant species during the last 3 centuries of CO_2 increase. *Plant, Cell and Environment* **15**: 485–489.

Peñuelas, J., Hunt, J.M., Ogaya, R., and Jump, A.S. 2008. Twentieth century changes of tree-ring $\delta^{13}C$ at the southern range-edge of *Fagus sylvatica*: increasing water-use efficiency does not avoid the growth decline induced by warming at low altitudes. *Global Change Biology* **14**: 1076–1088.

Phillips, O.L., Aragao, L., Lewis, S.L., Fisher, J.B., Lloyd, J., Lopez-Gonzalez, G., Malhi, Y., Monteagudo, A., Peacock, J., Quesada, C.A., van der Heijden, G., Almeida, S., Amaral, I., Arroyo, L., Aymard, G., Baker, T.R., Banki, O., Blanc, L., Bonal, D., Brando, P., Chave, J., de Oliveira, A.C.A., Cardozo, N.D., Czimczik, C.I, Feldpausch, T.R., Freitas, M.A., Gloor, E., Higuchi, N., Jimenez, E., Lloyd, G., Meir, P., Mendoza, C., Morel, A., Neill, D.A., Nepstad, D., Patino, S., Penuela, M.C., Prieto, A., Ramirez, F., Schwarz, M., Silva, J., Silveira, M., Thomas, A.S., ter Steege, H., Stropp, J., Vasquez, R., Zelazowski, P., Davila, E.A., Andelman, S., Andrade, A., Chao, K.-J., Erwin, T., Di Fiore, A., Honorio C., E., Keeling, H., Killeen, T.J., Laurance, W.F., Cruz, A.P., Pitman, N.C.A., Vargas, P.N., Ramirez-Angulo, H., Rudas, A., Salamao, R., Silva, N., Terborgh, J., and Torres-Lezama, A. 2009. Drought sensitivity of the Amazon rainforest. *Science* **323**: 1344–1347.

Phillips, O.L., Baker, T.R., Arroyo, L., Higuchi, N., Killeen, T.J., Laurance, W.F., Lewis, S.L., Lloyd, J., Malhi, Y., Monteagudo, A., Neill, D.A., Núñez Vargas, P., Silva, J.N.M., Terborgh, J., Vásquez Martínez, R., Alexiades, M., Almeida, S., Brown, S., Chave, J., Comiskey, J.A., Czimczik, C.I., Di Fiore, A., Erwin, T., Kuebler, C., Laurance, S.G., Nascimento, H.E.M., Olivier, J., Palacios, W., Patiño, S., Pitman, N.C.A., Quesada, C.A., Saldias, M., Torres Lezama, A., and Vinceti, B. 2004. Pattern and process in Amazon tree turnover: 1976–2001. *Philosophical Transactions of the Royal Society of London Series B—Biological Sciences* **359**: 381–407.

Phillips, O.L. and Gentry, A.H. 1994. Increasing turnover through time in tropical forests. *Science* **263**: 954–958.

Phillips, O.L., Lewis, S.L., Baker, T.R., Chao, K.-J., and Higuchi, N. 2008. The changing Amazon forest. *Philosophical Transactions of the Royal Society B* **363**: 1819–1827.

Phillips, O.L., Malhi, Y., Higuchi, N., Laurance, W.F., Nunez, P.V., Vasquez, R.M., Laurance, S.G., Ferreira, L.V., Stern, M., Brown, S., and Grace, J. 1998. Changes in the carbon balance of tropical forests: Evidence from long-term plots. *Science* **282**: 439–442.

Pimm, S.L. and Sugden, A.M. 1994. Tropical diversity and global change. *Science* **263**: 933–934.

Saurer, M., Siegwolf, R.T.W., and Schweingruber, F.H. 2004. Carbon isotope discrimination indicates improving water-use efficiency of trees in northern Eurasia over the last 100 years. *Global Change Biology* **10**: 2109–2120.

Silva, L.C.R., Anand, M., Oliveira, J.M., and Pillar, V.D. 2009. Past century changes in *Araucaria angustifolia* (Bertol.) Kuntze water use efficiency and growth in forest and grassland ecosystems of southern Brazil: implications for forest expansion. *Global Change Biology* **15**: 2387–2396.

Van de Water, P.K., Leavitt, S.W., and Betancourt, J.L. 1994. Trends in stomatal density and $^{13}C/^{12}C$ ratios of *Pinus flexilis* needles during last glacial-interglacial cycle. *Science* **264**: 239–243.

Weaver, P.L. and Murphy, P.G. 1990. Forest structure and productivity in Puerto Rico's Luquillo Mountains. *Biotropica* **22**: 69–82.

Wright, S.J. 2005. Tropical forests in a changing environment. *Trends in Ecology and Evolution* **20**: 553–560.

4.2.3 Rising Temperatures and Biospheric Productivity

- It is likely the greening of the planet will continue in the future, even if the largest temperature increases predicted by the models occur, because the optimum temperature for plant growth and development typically rises with increasing levels of atmospheric CO_2. This response, coupled with expected increases in plant photosynthetic rates from the rise in the air's CO_2 concentration, is more than enough to compensate for any temperature-induced plant stress caused by global warming.

In spite of the overwhelming amount of evidence, presented in Section 4.2 of this report, demonstrating rising atmospheric CO_2 concentrations and warmer temperatures have enhanced the productivity of the biosphere, some scientists have expressed concern these trends will gradually decline—and eventually reverse—if temperatures rise toward the upper limits projected in model-based scenarios of future global warming.

It is more likely, however, that the greening of the planet will continue in the future, even if the largest temperature increases predicted by the models do occur. This is because the optimum temperature for plant growth and development typically rises with increasing levels of atmospheric CO_2. This response, coupled with expected increases in plant photosynthetic rates from the rise in the air's CO_2 concentration, is more than enough to compensate for any temperature-induced plant stress caused by global warming.

Jurik *et al.* (1984) exposed bigtooth aspen leaves to atmospheric CO_2 concentrations of 325 and 1,935 ppm and measured their photosynthetic rates at a number of temperatures. Figure 4.2.3.1 below reproduces their results and slightly extends the two relationships defined by their data to warmer and cooler conditions.

where the net photosynthetic rate of the leaves exposed to 1,935 ppm CO_2 is maximal, the extra CO_2 boosts the net photosynthetic rate of the foliage by 450%. The extra CO_2 increases the optimum temperature for net photosynthesis in this species by about 11°C: from 25°C in air of 325 ppm CO_2 to 36°C in air of 1935 ppm CO_2.

The warm-temperature extensions of the two relationships at the right-hand side of the figure show the transition from positive to negative net photosynthesis—which denotes a change from life-sustaining to life-depleting conditions—likely occurs somewhere in the vicinity of 39°C in air of 325 ppm CO_2 but somewhere in the vicinity of 50°C in air of 1935 ppm CO_2. Thus not only was the optimum temperature for the growth of bigtooth aspen greatly increased by the extra CO_2 of this experiment, so too was the temperature above which life cannot be sustained also increased, and by about the same amount: 11°C.

Other researchers have documented this important CO_2-induced plant benefit in other agricultural, grassland, and woody plant species. Nearly all of these studies indicate a 300 ppm increase in the atmospheric CO_2 content increases a plant's optimum temperature for growth and development by a mean of approximately 6°C (Bjorkman *et al.*, 1978; Berry and Bjorkman, 1980; Nilsen *et al.*, 1983; Jurik *et al.*, 1984; Seeman *et al.*, 1984; Harley *et al.*, 1986; Stuhlfauth and Fock, 1990; McMurtrie *et al.*, 1992; McMurtrie and Wang, 1993; Idso *et al.*, 1995; Cowling and Sykes, 1999; Gutierrez *et al.*, 2009). This response is more than enough to compensate fully for any temperature-induced plant stress caused by the worst-case scenario of climate-model-predicted CO_2-induced global warming. Additional research indicates plants may be able to boost their optimum temperature for photosynthesis as the temperature warms, even in the absence of a concurrent increase in atmospheric CO_2.

Gunderson *et al.* (2010) investigated the "photosynthetic sensitivity to temperature and the

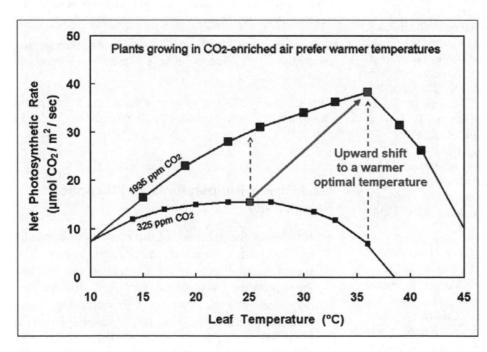

Figure 4.2.3.1. Net photosynthesis of big tooth aspen leaves growing under two concentrations of atmospheric carbon dioxide at various temperatures. Adapted from Jurik *et al.* (1984).

As the figure illustrates, at 10°C, elevated CO_2 has essentially no effect on net photosynthesis in this particular species, as Idso and Idso (1994) have demonstrated is characteristic of plants in general. At 25°C, however, where the net photosynthetic rate of the leaves exposed to 325 ppm CO_2 is maximal, the extra CO_2 of this study boosts the net photosynthetic rate of the foliage by nearly 100%, and at 36°C, potential for acclimation in relation to the climatic provenance of five species of deciduous trees, *Liquidambar styraciflua* [sweetgum], *Quercus rubra* [northern red oak], *Quercus falcata* [southern red oak], *Betula alleghaniensis* [yellow birch] and *Populus grandidentata* [bigtooth aspen]." They conducted their experiment out-of-doors in open-top chambers at three temperature regimes—ambient, ambient plus 2°C, and ambient plus 4°C—for three years. The five scientists report, "warming treatments resulted in a shift in the temperature response curves for CO_2 assimilation, such that leaves in warmer treatments had higher temperature optima [T_{opt}]." An example of this phenomenon is depicted in Figure 4.2.3.2 for *Q. rubra* seedlings during one specific month.

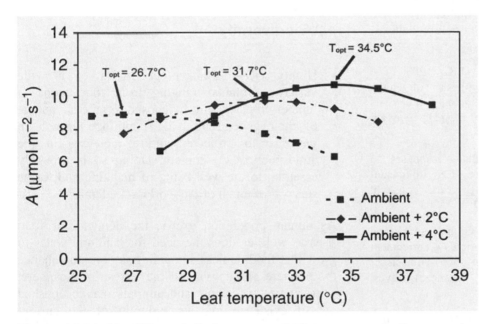

Figure 4.2.3.2. Net CO_2 assimilation rate vs. leaf temperature in Quercus rubra seedlings during June of 2003 in the ambient (A) and elevated (A+2°C and A+4°C) temperature treatments. Adapted from Gunderson *et al.* (2010).

As Figure 4.2.3.2 illustrates, the trees growing in progressively warmer environments had progressively higher T_{opt} values, and there was a tendency for the net CO_2 assimilation rates at those higher T_{opt} values to be a bit higher as well. Gunderson *et al.* found this adjustment in photosynthetic response was typically accomplished over a period of as little as two days, noting "others have found all or most acclimation within 2–6 days (Veres and Williams, 1984; Hill *et al.*, 1988; Battaglia *et al.*, 1996; Turnbull *et al.*, 2002; Froux *et al.*, 2004)." They state a similar "adjustment of thermal optima was confirmed in all species, whether temperatures varied with season or treatment,

and regardless of climate in the species' range or provenance of the plant material," and the "responses to the temperature manipulation were not different from the seasonal acclimation observed in mature indigenous trees."

These observations indicate plants will be able to adjust their physiology to accommodate a warming of the magnitude and rate of rise IPCC predicts to accompany the projected future increase in atmospheric CO_2 content. If the planet's flora can adjust their physiology to not only survive a modest instantaneous warming of 2–4°C, but to actually benefit from it, as has been demonstrated to be true of several trees examined by Gunderson *et al.*, there is every reason to believe they would respond to a similar warming projected to develop over a century or more. When one factors in the aerial fertilization effect of rising atmospheric CO_2 concentrations, plus the transpiration-reducing effect that boosts plant water use efficiency, plus CO_2's ability to also raise the T_{opt} values of most plants, it is clear the world's vegetation is well-prepared for future warming. The recent greening of the planet should continue in the years and decades to come, notwithstanding model-based concerns to the contrary.

References

Battaglia, M., Beadle, C., and Loughhead, S. 1996. Photosynthetic temperature responses of *Eucalyptus globulus* and *Eucalyptus nitens*. *Tree Physiology* **16**: 81–89.

Berry, J. and Bjorkman, O. 1980. Photosynthetic response and adaptation to temperature in higher plants. *Annual Review of Plant Physiology* **31**: 491–543.

Bjorkman, O., Badger, M., and Armond, P.A. 1978. Thermal acclimation of photosynthesis: Effect of growth temperature on photosynthetic characteristics and components of the photosynthetic apparatus in Nerium oleander. *Carnegie Institution of Washington Yearbook* **77**: 262–276.

Cowling, S.A. and Sykes, M.T. 1999. Physiological significance of low atmospheric CO_2 for plant-climate interactions. *Quaternary Research* **52**: 237–242.

Froux, F., Ducrey, M., Epron, D., and Dreyer, E. 2004. Seasonal variations and acclimation potential of the thermostability of photochemistry in four Mediterranean conifers. *Annals of Forest Science* **61**: 235–236.

Gunderson, C.A., O'Hara, K.H., Campion, C.M., Walker, A.V., and Edwards, N.T. 2010. Thermal plasticity of photosynthesis: the role of acclimation in forest responses to a warming climate. *Global Change Biology* **16**: 2272–2286.

Gutierrez, D., Gutierrez, E., Perez, P., Morcuende, R., Verdejo, A.L., and Martinez-Carrasco, R. 2009. Acclimation to future atmospheric CO_2 levels increases photochemical efficiency and mitigates photochemistry inhibition by warm temperatures in wheat under field chambers. *Physiologia Plantarum* **137**: 86–100.

Harley, P.C., Tenhunen. J.D., and Lange, O.L. 1986. Use of an analytical model to study the limitations on net photosynthesis in *Arbutus unedo* under field conditions. *Oecologia* **70**: 393–401.

Hill, R.S., Read, J., and Busby, J.R. 1988. The temperature-dependence of photosynthesis of some Australian temperate rainforest trees and its biogeographical significance. *Journal of Biogeography* **15**: 431–449.

Idso, K.E. and Idso, S.B. 1994. Plant responses to atmospheric CO_2 enrichment in the face of environmental constraints: A review of the past 10 years' research. *Agricultural and Forest Meteorology* **69**: 153–203.

Idso, S.B., Idso, K.E., Garcia, R.L., Kimball, B.A., and Hoober, J.K. 1995. Effects of atmospheric CO_2 enrichment and foliar methanol application on net photosynthesis of sour orange tree (*Citrus aurantium*; Rutaceae) leaves. *American Journal of Botany* **82**: 26–30.

Jurik, T.W., Webber, J.A., and Gates, D.M. 1984. Short-term effects of CO_2 on gas exchange of leaves of bigtooth aspen (*Populus grandidentata*) in the field. *Plant Physiology* **75**: 1022–1026.

McMurtrie, R.E. and Wang, Y.-P. 1993. Mathematical models of the photosynthetic response of tree stands to rising CO_2 concentrations and temperatures. *Plant, Cell and Environment* **16**: 1–13.

McMurtrie, R.E., Comins, H.N., Kirschbaum, M.U.F., and Wang, Y.-P. 1992. Modifying existing forest growth models to take account of effects of elevated CO_2. *Australian Journal of Botany* **40**: 657–677.

Nilsen, S., Hovland, K., Dons, C., and Sletten, S.P. 1983. Effect of CO_2 enrichment on photosynthesis, growth and yield of tomato. *Scientia Horticulturae* **20**: 1–14.

Seeman, J.R., Berry, J.A., and Downton, J.S. 1984. Photosynthetic response and adaptation to high temperature in desert plants. A comparison of gas exchange and fluorescence methods for studies of thermal tolerance. *Plant Physiology* **75**: 364–368.

Stuhlfauth, T. and Fock, H.P. 1990. Effect of whole season CO_2 enrichment on the cultivation of a medicinal plant, *Digitalis lanata*. *Journal of Agronomy and Crop Science* **164**: 168–173.

Turnbull, M.H., Murthy, R., and Griffin, K.L. 2002. The relative impacts of daytime and nighttime warming on photosynthetic capacity in *Populus deltoides*. *Plant, Cell and Environment* **25**: 1729–1737.

Veres, J.S. and Williams III, G.J. 1984. Time course of photosynthetic temperature acclimation in *Carex eleocharis* Bailey. *Plant, Cell and Environment* **7**: 545–547.

4.3 Biodiversity

- Highly CO_2-responsive genotypes of a wide variety of plants—ranging from food crops to lumber crops—could be chosen to take advantage of their genetic ability to optimize growth in response to projected future increases in the atmospheric CO_2 content. Doing so is probably essential to the well-being of mankind and to the survival of much of the world's wildlands.

As human population grows, the demand for food rises as well, as does the need for land and water to grow that food. Unless something is done to enhance the per-acre productivity of the terrestrial biosphere, some species of plants and animals may be pushed out of existence by the midpoint of the current century.

A number of real-world experiments demonstrate many of Earth's food- and lumber-producing plants possess the genetic potential to grow better while using less water as atmospheric CO_2 content rises. In an important paper by 32 researchers from 12 countries, Ainsworth *et al.* (2008) made the case for breeding varieties of major food crops to best take advantage of the ongoing rise in the atmospheric CO_2 content. They note, "the growing world population, increasing demands for grains for animal feeds, land loss to urban expansion and demand for bioenergy production are exerting more and more pressure on global agricultural productivity," so "a major challenge for plant biologists, agronomists and breeders will be to provide germplasm and seed material that maximize future crop production," particularly in the context of rising atmospheric CO_2 concentrations that provide, in their words, "a unique opportunity to increase the productivity of C_3 crops."

The scientists point out "only a fraction of available germplasm of crops has been tested for CO_2 responsiveness" and "further research is needed to elucidate the mechanisms of yield response to CO_2, to assess the genetic diversity available for improving responsiveness and to devise efficient schemes for selection for adaptation to rising ambient CO_2, whether based on conventional plant breeding or systems biology approaches for selecting and engineering improved genetics." They conclude, "because it may take 10–15 years to move from discovery of new advantaged genetics to commercial cultivars of annual grain crops, developing a robust strategy and supporting the planned work with the best possible facilities should be an urgent priority."

Ziska *et al.* (1996) grew well-watered and well-fertilized plants of 17 cultivars of rice (*Oryza sativa* L.) from seed to maturity in glasshouses maintained at atmospheric CO_2 concentrations of either 373 ppm (ambient) or 664 ppm (elevated) in 24-L pots filled with local soil at two sets of day/night temperatures (29/21°C and 37/29°C), afterwards measuring total plant biomass and grain biomass. They found the degree of CO_2-induced enhancement of total plant biomass and the number of cultivars showing significant yield enhancement with elevated CO_2 decreased at the higher and more stressful set of growth temperatures, dropping from 12 of 17 cultivars with a mean biomass stimulation of 70% at the lower set of temperatures to eight of 17 cultivars with a mean biomass stimulation of 23% at the higher set of temperatures.

At the lower set of temperatures, a few cultivars exhibited no significant changes in response to the atmospheric CO_2 enrichment employed in the study, but the most responsive cultivar—a tropical japonica type from Brazil—exhibited a 265% increase in total plant biomass and a 350% increase in grain biomass.

The wide range of productivity enhancement exhibited in response to atmospheric CO_2 enrichment by the 17 cultivars of rice examined in this experiment indicates the tremendous potential in selecting rice varieties to take advantage of the aerial fertilization effect of atmospheric CO_2. That endeavor, Ziska *et al.* write, "could maximize productivity as CO_2 concentration increases." Such a selection process likely will be an essential element of the race to feed humanity in the year 2050 without usurping vast tracts of tropical and temperate forests, savannas, and grasslands or commandeering all of the planet's remaining freshwater resources and destroy-ing most of the world's remaining wildlands.

Bunce (2008) grew adequately fertilized plants of four varieties of the common garden bean (*Phaseolus vulgaris* L.)—Matterhorn (a great northern bean), Jaguar (a black bean), Red Hawk (a kidney bean), and Brown Beauty (a snap bean)—from seed to maturity under standard field conditions at Beltsville, Maryland (USA) in open-top chambers, making photosynthetic measurements of mature upper-canopy leaves in full sunlight at midday during the pod-filling stages of four growing seasons and assessing final seed yields and other plant characteristics at harvest. They found the extra 180 ppm of CO_2 in the CO_2-enriched chambers (a concentration increase of close to 50% during daylight hours) resulted in a mean long-term stimulation of midday net photosynthesis of approximately 18% in the Matterhorn and Jaguar bean varieties and an increase of 36% in the Red Hawk and Brown Beauty cultivars. The Matterhorn variety increased dry mass seed yield by about 39%, followed by Red Hawk at 21%, Brown Beauty at 18%, and Jaguar with a 10% decline in seed yield. As Bunce reported, "the highest yielding variety at ambient CO_2 [Jaguar] was out-yielded by a different variety at elevated CO_2 [Matterhorn]."

These findings demonstrate there is significant variability in seed yield response to atmospheric CO_2 enrichment among the four bean varieties Bunce tested. There was no *a priori* way of knowing which of the four cultivars would respond best, or that one of them would respond negatively. Bunce's work demonstrates the need to perform experiments on the world's most important crop plants to identify which of their many varieties should be selected for crop breeding work, to take full advantage of the increase in the atmosphere's CO_2 concentration likely to occur over the next several decades.

Yang *et al.* (2009) write, "rice (*Oryza sativa* L.) is unequivocally one of the most important food crops that feed the largest proportion of the world's population" and "the demand for rice production will continue to increase in the coming decades, especially in the major rice-consuming countries of Asia, Africa and Latin America, due to the population explosion and cropland reduction." They note, "as sufficient intraspecific variation in yield response exists under field conditions, there is a pressing need to identify genotypes which would produce maximum grain yield under projected future CO_2 levels."

Working at the National Institute for Agro-Environmental Sciences in Tsukuba, Japan, Lou *et al.* (2008) grew plants of four rice cultivars—Dular (a traditional indica variety), IR72 (an improved indica variety), Koshihikari (a temperate japonica variety), and IR65598 (a new variety not yet released to farmers)—in growth chambers in submerged pots filled with a fertilized soil collected from the plough layer of a paddy field in Chiba Prefecture, Japan, at two atmospheric CO_2 concentrations: ambient (~370 ppm) and elevated (~570 ppm). They found the extra 200 ppm of CO_2 reduced the ultimate grain yield of Dular (by 0.7%) and increased the final grain yield of IR72 by 8.0%, of Koshihikari by 13.4%, and of IR65598 by 17.7%.

Yang et al. (2009) focused on a single two-line inter-subspecific hybrid rice variety (Liangyoupeijiu) produced as part of "a nationwide mega project" to develop what they called "super" hybrid cultivars that would "further break the yield ceiling." In their three-year CO_2-enrichment study at the FACE facility at Yangzhou City, Jiangsu Province, China, which employed the same CO_2 levels as the study of Lou et al., they found a much greater grain yield stimulation: a 28.4% CO_2-induced increase under a low nitrogen fertility treatment of 12.5 g N m^{-2} and a 31.7% CO_2-induced increase under a high nitrogen fertility treatment of 25 g N m^{-2}.

Yang et al. state their hybrid cultivar "appears to profit much more from elevated CO_2 than inbred japonica cultivars." Both the Japanese and Chinese FACE studies of inbred japonica cultivars found CO_2-induced grain yield enhancements on the order of only 13% for a 200 ppm increase in the air's CO_2 concentration. Noting "there is a pressing need to identify genotypes which could optimize harvestable yield as atmospheric CO_2 increases," Yang et al. conclude, "on the basis of available FACE data on rice," the hybrid rice cultivar Liangyoupeijiu appeared "to be particularly promising."

Mycroft et al. (2009) grew seedlings of 29 well-watered and fertilized white spruce (Picea glauca (Moench) Voss) tree genotypes in 2.83-liter pots filled with a mixture of peat and vermiculite between 10 May and 23 September 2006 in glasshouse compartments maintained at either ambient (370 ppm) or elevated (740 ppm) atmospheric CO_2 concentrations. They assessed plant performance by measuring final plant height, basal stem diameter, and total biomass production, including roots.

They found, "depending upon genotype, the increase in biomass at elevated CO_2 as a percentage of that at ambient CO_2 ranged from 23% to 108%, while increases in height ranged from 4% to 48%," and "in the case of stem diameter, the effect of elevated CO_2 varied from a non-significant decrease of 6% to an increase of 32% depending upon

genotype." The four researchers write, "similar to previous studies (e.g. Bazzaz et al., 1995; Lindroth et al., 2001; Moya et al., 1998; Steinger et al., 1997; Volk and Korner, 2001)," they discovered "significant genotype x CO_2 interactions for size-related traits." They note their CO_2-induced biomass increases (+23% to +108%) were of a range similar to those Mohan et al. (2004) obtained for red maple (0% to +93%) and Wang et al. (2000) found for quaking aspen (-29% to +94%).

These observations demonstrate highly CO_2-responsive genotypes of a wide variety of plants, ranging from food crops to lumber crops, could be selected to take advantage of their genetic ability to optimize growth in response to projected future increases in atmospheric CO_2 content. Such measures probably will prove essential to the well-being of mankind and to the survival of much of the world's wildlands.

References

Ainsworth, E.A., Beier, C., Calfapietra, C., Ceulemans, R., Durand-Tardif, M., Farquhar, G.D., Godbold, D.L., Hendrey, G.R., Hickler, T., Kaduk, J., Karnosky, D.F., Kimball, B.A., Korner, C., Koornneef, M., LaFarge, T., Leakey, A.D.B., Lewin, K.F., Long, S.P., Manderscheid, R., McNeil, D.L., Mies, T.A., Miglietta, F., Morgan, J.A., Nagy, J., Norby, R.J., Norton, R.M., Percy, K.E., Rogers, A., Soussana, J.-F., Stitt, M., Weigel, H.-J., and White, J.W. 2008. Next generation of elevated [CO_2] experiments with crops: a critical investment for feeding the future world. *Plant, Cell and Environment* **31**: 1317–1324.

Bazzaz, F.A., Jasienski, M., Thomas, S.C., and Wayne, P. 1995. Micro-evolutionary responses in experimental populations of plants to CO_2-enriched environments: Parallel results from two model systems. *Proceedings of the National Academy of Sciences USA* **92**: 8161–8165.

Bunce, J.A. 2008. Contrasting responses of seed yield to elevated carbon dioxide under field conditions within *Phaseolus vulgaris*. *Agriculture, Ecosystems and Environment* **128**: 219–224.

Lindroth, R.L., Roth, S., and Nordheim, E.V. 2001. Genotypic variation in response of quaking aspen (*Populus tremuloides*) to atmospheric CO_2 enrichment. *Oecologia* **126**: 371–379.

Lou, Y., Inubushi, K., Mizuno, T., Hasegawa, T., Lin, Y., Sakai, H., Cheng, W., and Kobayashi, K. 2008. CH_4 emission with differences in atmospheric CO_2 enrichment and rice cultivars in a Japanese paddy soil. *Global Change Biology* **14**: 2678–2687.

Mohan, J.E., Clark, J.S., and Schlesinger, W.H. 2004.

Genetic variation in germination, growth and survivorship of red maple in response to sub-ambient through elevated atmospheric CO_2. *Global Change Biology* **10**: 233–247.

Moya, T.B., Ziska, L.H., Namuco, O.S., and Olszyk, D. 1998. Growth dynamics and genotypic variation in tropical, field-grown paddy rice (*Oryza sativa* L.) in response to increasing carbon dioxide and temperature. *Global Change Biology* **4**: 645–656.

Mycroft, E.E., Zhang, J., Adams, G., and Reekie, E. 2009. Elevated CO_2 will not select for enhanced growth in white spruce despite genotypic variation in response. *Basic and Applied Ecology* **10**: 349–357.

Steinger, T., Lavigne, C., Birrer, A., Groppe, K., and Schmid, B. 1997. Genetic variation in response to elevated CO_2 in three grassland perennials—a field experiment with two competition regimes. *Acta Oecologica* **18**: 263–268.

Volk, M. and Korner, C. 2001. Genotype x elevated CO_2 interaction and allocation in calcareous grassland species. *New Phytologist* **151**: 637–645.

Wang, X., Curtis, P.S., Pregitzer, K.S., and Zak, D.R. 2000. Genotypic variation in physiological and growth responses of *Populus tremuloides* to elevated atmospheric CO_2 concentration. *Tree Physiology* **20**: 1019–1028.

Yang, L., Liu, H., Wang, Y., Zhu, J., Huang, J., Liu, G., Dong, G., and Wang, Y. 2009. Yield formation of CO_2-enriched inter-subspecific hybrid rice cultivar Liangyoupeijiu under fully open-air condition in a warm sub-tropical climate. *Agriculture, Ecosystems and Environment* **129**: 193–200.

Ziska, L.H., Manalo, P.A., and Ordonez, R.A. 1996. Intraspecific variation in the response of rice (*Oryza sativa* L.) to increased CO_2 and temperature: growth and yield response of 17 cultivars. *Journal of Experimental Botany* **47**: 1353–1359.

4.4 Extinction

Real-world observations reveal plants have many ways of adjusting to changes in climate in addition to their ability to spread from places of rising warmth to cooler habitats, and these observations suggest the planet's current assemblage of plants is likely to be around a good deal longer than many theoretical models have predicted. One of the great horror stories associated with predictions of CO_2-induced global warming is of warming so fast and furious that many species of plants will not be able to migrate towards cooler regions—poleward in latitude, or upward in elevation—quickly enough to avoid extinction. Real-world observations of plants show they have many

ways of adjusting to changes in climate in addition to their ability to move from places of rising warmth to cooler habitats. These observations suggest the planet's current assemblage of plants is likely to be around longer than many theoretical models have predicted.

Under-yielding species appear to be buffered from extinction because growth enhancements of smaller plants tend to diminish the relative biomass advantages of larger plants in crowded conditions, and when species are rare in a local area, they have a higher survival rate than when they are common, resulting in the enrichment of rare species and increasing diversity with age and size class in complex ecosystems. In addition, diversity should increase as a group of individuals ages, because more common species are selectively removed by pathogens and predators, especially those commonly associated with them.

Also, individuals of a species compete more intensively with conspecifics than with individuals of other species, and diversity may increase if an individual benefits nearby non-conspecifics, as such facilitation makes interspecific interactions more positive than intraspecific interactions and thus provides an advantage to locally rare species. Similarly, common trees growing closer together are more prone to deadly infections, and they may also face stiffer competition for certain resources, whereas rarer trees, by depending on slightly different sets of resources, may not have this problem.

4.4.1 Migrating Plants

If Earth warms by a significant amount, for whatever reason, the best thing that could happen to the planet would be for the air's CO_2 concentration to rise concurrently, or shortly thereafter, because that would obviate the need for plants to migrate to cooler regions or at least reduce the required rate of migration and/or distance of travel well below what overly simplistic coupled climate-biology models have suggested. In a CO_2-enriched world, as air temperature increases, so too would the temperature at which most plants function at their optimum. Plants thus would be able to grow and reproduce in close proximity to where they grew when the air temperature first began to increase.

This is exactly how nature appears to operate during and after a glacial-to-interglacial transition. In response to the air temperature increase during such transitions, Earth's atmospheric CO_2 concentration typically has risen by an amount sufficient to enable plants to cope with the warming of the globe. Cowling and Sage (1998) indicate a typical 180 ppm rise in atmospheric CO_2 concentration from a base level characteristic of glacial conditions can raise plant optimum growth temperature by about 4°–5°C, the temperature increase typically experienced during glacial terminations.

Cowling and Sykes (1999) conducted a review of the literature on the interactive effects of concurrent increases in atmospheric CO_2 and air temperature on plant growth and development. They report, "increases in CO_2 from 350 to 650 ppm are estimated to result in up to a 5°C rise in T_{opt} [plant optimal growth temperature], primarily because of a reduction in the rate of photorespiration at high temperatures." They also state, "experiments with *Phaseolus vulgaris* [common garden bean] exposed to low CO_2 T_{opt} can decrease by approximately 4°–5°C with a reduction in CO_2 from 380 to 200 ppm," citing Cowling and Sage (1998).

Cannariato et al. (1999) investigated the character, magnitude, and speed of biotic responses of benthic foraminifera to millennial-scale climate oscillations reconstructed from data obtained from a northeast Pacific Ocean sediment core that extended back in time some 60,000 years. This history revealed a number of rapid climatic switches throughout the record, representing periods of what they call "extreme environmental variability." They report they observed no extinctions, and the benthic ecosystems "appear to be both resilient and robust in response to rapid and often extreme [changes in] environmental conditions." They report faunal turnovers occurred within decades throughout the record "without extinction or speciation," which led them to conclude "broad segments of the biosphere are well adapted to rapid climate change."

Allen et al. (1999) examined an even longer period of time. After analyzing sediment cores from a lake in southern Italy and from the Mediterranean Sea, they developed high-resolution climate and vegetation datasets for this region covering the last 102,000 years. Their efforts revealed rapid changes in vegetation correlated well with rapid changes in climate, such that complete shifts in natural ecosystems would sometimes occur over periods of less than 200 years. They also report, over the warmest portion of the record (the Holocene), the total organic carbon content of the vegetation reached its highest level, more than doubling values experienced over the rest of the record, and during the more productive woody-plant period of the Holocene,

the increased vegetative cover also led to less soil erosion. As the 15 researchers state, "the biosphere was a full participant in these rapid fluctuations, contrary to widely held views that vegetation is unable to change with such rapidity." They learned warmer was always better in terms of vegetative productivity.

Other studies based on more modern data have continued to demonstrate the unlikelihood of warming-induced plant extinctions. In July/August 2003, for example, Walther et al. (2005) resurveyed the floristic composition of the uppermost 10 meters of 10 mountain summits in the Swiss Alps, applying the same methodology used in earlier surveys of the same mountain tops by Rubel (1912), conducted in 1905, and Hofer (1992), conducted in 1985. Their analyses covered the bulk of the Little Ice Age-to-Current Warm Period transition (1905–2003), the warming IPCC claims to have been unprecedented over the past millennium or more in terms of both the rate of temperature rise and the level to which Earth's temperature rose.

Whereas the mean increase in species numbers recorded by Hofer (1992) for the time interval 1905 to 1985 was 86%, "species numbers recorded in 2003 were generally more than double (138%) compared to the results by Rubel (1912) and 26% higher than those reported by Hofer (1992)." Walther et al. write, "the rate of change in species richness (3.7 species per decade) was significantly greater in the later period compared to the Hofer resurvey (1.3 species per decade)." They note "the observed increase in species numbers does not entail the replacement of high alpine specialists by species from lower altitudes, but rather has led to an enrichment of the overall summit plant diversity."

In spite of the apparent reasonableness of the global warming extinction hypothesis, in which high-altitude species are expected to be "squeezed out of existence"—or "pushed off the planet," as NASA's James Hansen once described it, by other species migrating upwards from lower altitudes to escape the increasing stress of rising temperatures, Walther et al. could find no sign of this dire consequence over a century of supposedly unprecedented warming in the Swiss Alps.

Kullman (2007) analyzed the changing behavior of alpine and subalpine plants, together with shifts in their geographical patterns over the past century (when air temperatures rose by about 1°C in the Scandes of west-central Sweden), based on "repeat photography, individual age determinations and analyses of permanent plots." Kullman reports, "at all levels, from trees to tiny herbs, and from high to low altitudes," as he describes it, "the results converge to indicate a causal association between temperature rise and biotic evolution," indicating "this appears to be an ecosystem on the brink of profound and imminent transformation."

Kullman reports treeline advance since the early twentieth century varied between 75 and 130 meters, depending on species and site, and subalpine and alpine plant species shifted upslope by an average of 200 meters. He writes, "present-day repetitions of floristic inventories on two alpine mountain summits reveal increases in plant species richness of 58 and 67%, respectively, since the early 1950s," and "no species have yet become extinct from the highest elevations." He states his results "converge with observations in other high-mountain regions world-wide," citing Grabherr et al. (1994), Keller et al. (2000), Kullman (2002), Virtanen et al. (2003), Klanderud and Birks (2003), Walther et al. (2005), and Lacoul and Freedman (2006).

Kullman concludes the rapidity with which the observed ecosystem transformations occurred "contrasts with earlier assumptions and theoretical generalizations, stressing significant time-lags or inertial adaptations to changed climatic conditions." His results demonstrate the capacity for vegetation to respond rapidly to climate change in dramatic ways that avert species extinctions and in fact can lead to increases in ecosystem species richness.

Three years later, Kullman reaffirmed his findings in additional works (Kullman, 2010a, 2010b, 2010c). In one of these (Kullman, 2010b), he describes how the post-Little Ice Age warming has broken "a multi-millennial trend of plant cover retrogression" and "floristic and faunal impoverish-ment, all imposed by progressive and deterministic neoglacial climate cooling." He says "alpine plant life is proliferating, biodiversity is on the rise and the mountain world appears more productive and inviting than ever."

Similar observations led Kullman to conclude (Kullman, 2010c), "the alpine flora appears to be more adaptive and responsive to climate change than generally believed," and "overall, a richer, greener and more productive alpine world has emerged in the wake of the recent climate warming episode (Kullman, 2010a, 2010b)." He makes it very clear that "in contrast to model predictions, no single alpine plant species has become extinct, neither in Scandinavia nor in any other part of the world in response to climate warming over the past century" (Kullman, 2010b), citing, in addition to his own prior

studies, Pauli et al. (2001, 2007), Theurillat and Guisan (2001), and Birks (2008). As for the future, Kullman opines, "continued modest warming over the present century will likely be beneficial to alpine biodiversity, geological stability, resilience, sustainable reindeer husbandry and aesthetic landscape qualities" (Kullman, 2010b).

Holzinger et al. (2008) revisited areas of 12 mountains with summits between elevations of 2,844 and 3,006 meters in the canton of Grisons (Switzerland). In 2004 they made complete inventories of all vascular plant species they encountered, which they compared with similar inventories made by other researchers in 1885, 1898, 1912, 1913, and 1958, following the ascension paths of the earlier investigators "as accurately as possible." The four researchers report mean summer temperatures in the studied region increased by at least 0.6°C between the time of the first study and the one they conducted in 2004.

Holzinger et al. detected plant upward migration rates of several meters per decade, and their data suggest vascular plant species richness increased by 11% per decade over the past 120 years on the mountain summits (defined as the upper 15 meters of the mountains) in the alpine-nival ecotone. This finding, they write, "agrees well with other investigations from the Alps, where similar changes have been detected (Grabherr et al., 1994; Pauli et al., 2001; Camenisch, 2002; Walther, 2003; Walther et al., 2005)." Regarding the ominous prediction of "the extinction of a considerable number of high-alpine species" in "the context of climate warming," they conclude this "outstanding threat for species to become out-competed 'beyond the summits' can neither be confirmed nor rejected with our data," suggesting the threat may not be quite as outstanding as the climate models have typically made it out to be.

Erschbamer et al. (2009) documented and analyzed changes (from 2001 to 2006) in plant species number, frequency, and composition along an altitudinal gradient crossing four summits from the treeline ecotone to the subnival zone in the South Alps (Dolomites, Italy), where minimum temperatures increased by 1.1–2.0°C during the past century with a marked rise over the last decades. The four researchers report, "after five years, a re-visitation of the summit areas revealed a considerable increase of species richness at the upper alpine and subnival zone (10% and 9%, respectively) and relatively modest increases at the lower alpine zone and the treeline ecotone (3% and 1%, respectively)." They note, "during the last five years, the endemic species of the research area were hardly affected," and "at the highest summit, one endemic species was even among the newcomers." The Austrian scientists conclude, "at least in short to medium time scales, the southern alpine endemics of the study area should not be seriously endangered."

Kelly and Goulden (2008) compared two vegetation surveys (one made in 1977 and the other in 2006–2007) of the Deep Canyon Transect in Southern California's (USA) Santa Rosa Mountains that spans several plant communities and climates, rising from an elevation of 244 meters to 2,560 meters over a distance of 16 km "through desert scrub, pinyon-juniper woodland, chaparral shrubland, and conifer forest." They found "the average elevation of the dominant plant species rose by ~65 meters," The 30-year mean temperature measured at seven stations around Deep Canyon rose by 0.41°C between 1947–1976 and 1977–2006, and the same metric rose by 0.63°C in the climate regions straddled by the transect, and by 0.77°C at the two weather stations nearest Deep Canyon. They conclude "surprisingly rapid shifts in the distribution of plants can be expected with climate change."

Alsos *et al.* (2007) analyzed DNA fingerprinting (amplified fragment-length polymorphism) of 4,439 samples from most of the geographic ranges of nine plant species native to the Arctic, studying the Svalbard Archipelago—the islands of which were almost entirely glaciated during the last glacial maximum of 20,000 years ago. They used the genetic data thereby obtained to reconstruct past plant colonization patterns, determining "the frequency of effective long-distance dispersal events, [identifying] the source areas, and [assessing] whether dispersal ability is more limiting than establishment in a new area."

The nine researchers found long-distance colonization of the Svalbard Archipelago "has occurred repeatedly and from several source regions," with probable propagule dispersal vectors being "wind, drift wood and drifting sea ice, birds, and mammals." They write, "the genetic effect of restricted colonization was strongly correlated with the temperature requirements of the species, indicating that establishment limits distribution more than dispersal."

Given that dispersal mechanisms in existence during the early and mid-Holocene (from 9,500 to 4,000 years before present, when "the climate was 1 to 2°C warmer than today," as Alsos *et al.* report) are probably "still operating," they conclude "Arctic species seem to be able to track their potential niche

and ... unlimited dispersal models may be appropriate to estimate long-term range shifts for Arctic regions."

Le Roux and McGeoch (2008) examined patterns of altitudinal range changes in the entire native vascular flora of sub-Antarctic Marion Island (46°54'S, 37°45'E) in the southern Indian Ocean, which warmed by 1.2°C between 1965 and 2003. Between 1966 and 2006, there was "a rapid expansion in altitudinal range," with species expanding their upper elevational boundaries by an average of 70 meters. Because "the observed upslope expansion was not matched by a similar change in lower range boundaries," they emphasize "the flora of Marion Island has undergone range expansion rather than a range shift." They note "the expansion of species distributions along their cooler boundaries in response to rising temperatures appears to be a consistent biological consequence of recent climate warming," citing several other studies that have observed the same type of response.

Another consequence of the stability of lower range boundaries together with expanding upper range boundaries is a greater overlapping of ranges, resulting in greater local biodiversity. Le Roux and McGeoch report, "the present species composition of communities at higher altitudes is not an analogue of past community composition at lower altitudes, but rather constitutes a historically unique combination of species," indicating a world significantly richer, ecologically speaking, than the old one.

Stocklin *et al.* (2009) provide some insight into why plants in the real world tend to undergo a proliferation of species instead of extinction as temperature and atmospheric CO_2 concentration rise. They studied the consequences of the Swiss Alps' highly structured alpine landscape for evolutionary processes in four plants (*Epilobium fleischeri, Geum reptans, Campanula thyrsoides,* and *Poa alpina*), testing for whether genetic diversity within their populations was related to altitude and land use while also seeking to determine whether genetic differentiation among populations was more related to different land use or to geographic distances.

The three Swiss scientists found within-population genetic diversity of the four species was high and mostly unrelated to altitude or population size. They also report genetic differentiation among populations was pronounced and strongly increased with distance, implying "considerable genetic drift among populations of alpine plants." Stocklin *et al.* conclude "phenotypic plasticity is particularly pronounced in alpine plants," and "because of the high heterogeneity of the alpine landscape, the pronounced capacity of a single genotype to exhibit variable phenotypes is a clear advantage for the persistence and survival of alpine plants." They write, "the evolutionary potential to respond to global change is mostly intact in alpine plants, even at high altitude." These results make it much easier to understand why, despite significant twentieth-century global warming, no species of plants have been observed to have been pushed off the planet, especially in alpine regions.

In an invited paper in *Quaternary Science Reviews*, Vegas-Vilarrubia *et al.* (2011) write, "current extinction estimates for the near-future should be revised in light of palaeoecological information," which in their view "shows that spatial reorganizations and persistence in suitable micro-refugia have been more common than extinction during the Quaternary." The four researchers conclude "an interesting consequence is the possibility of new unknown species combinations with no modern analogues."

Vegas-Vilarrubia *et al.* (2011) note the global warming that occurred at the end of the Younger Dryas (~13,000 to 11,500 years ago) is one of the more powerful analogues of projected future global warming "because both magnitude and rates of change parallel those predicted for the present century." Although this prior real-world transformation "seems to have consisted of ecological reorganizations and changes in community composition because of differential species migration patterns and rates," the four researchers point out "so far, it has not been possible to associate large-scale extinctions to the Younger Dryas climatic reversal." Instead of a model-inspired increase in atmospheric CO_2 triggering catastrophic changes in climate, real-world data from the past suggest rising atmospheric CO_2 will help plants avoid climatic-induced extinctions.

Two phenomena come into play in these ecosystem transformations, according to the Spanish scientists: acclimation and adaptation, "with the first relying on phenotypic plasticity and the second involving genetic changes of potential evolutionary significance," which have been proposed as "possible reactions to future global warming and as alternatives to extinction by habitat loss." Vegas-Vilarrubia *et al.* note "some authors propose that spatial reorganizations without extinction will be the dominant biotic response to the near-future global changes." They add, "it is also possible that ecosystems never attain equilibrium," and "transient states perpetuate because of the recurrent action of environmental change." They suggest "one of the main lessons to be learned from these considerations is that ecosystems may

express their resilience when confronted with environmental shifts by attaining several possible equilibrium states, as manifested in changes in biodiversity and/or composition, without losing their ecological functions."

Willis and MacDonald (2011) note key research efforts have focused on extinction scenarios derived from "a suite of predictive species distribution models (e.g., Guisan and Thuiller, 2005)"—most often referred to as bioclimatic envelope models—that "predict current and future range shifts and estimate the distances and rates of movement required for species to track the changes in climate and move into suitable new climate space." They report one of the most-cited studies of this type—that of Thomas *et al.* (2004)—"predicts that, on the basis of mid-range climatic warming scenarios for 2050, up to 37% of plant species globally will be committed to extinction owing to lack of suitable climate space."

In contrast, Willis and MacDonald write, "biotic adaptation to climate change has been considered much less frequently." This phenomenon— sometimes referred to as evolutionary resilience—they describe as "the ability of populations to persist in their current location and to undergo evolutionary adaptation in response to changing environmental conditions," citing Sgro *et al.* (2010). They note this approach to the subject "recognizes that ongoing change is the norm in nature and one of the dynamic processes that generates and maintains biodiversity patterns and processes," citing MacDonald *et al.* (2008) and Willis *et al.* (2009).

Willis and MacDonald examined the effects of significant and rapid warming on plants during several previous intervals of the planet's climatic history that were as warm as, or even warmer than, what climate models typically predict for the next century. These intervals included the Paleocene-Eocene Thermal Maximum, the Eocene climatic optimum, the mid-Pliocene warm interval, the Eemian interglacial, and the Holocene.

In stark contrast to what IPCC typically does, this approach relies on empirical (as opposed to theoretical), data-based (as opposed to model-based) reconstructions (as opposed to projections) of the past (as opposed to the future). Willis and MacDonald found "persistence and range shifts (migrations) seem to have been the predominant terrestrial biotic response (mainly of plants) to warmer intervals in Earth's history," and "the same responses also appear to have occurred during intervals of rapid climate change." They note "evidence for global extinctions or extinctions resulting from reduction of population sizes on the scale predicted for the next century owing to loss of suitable climate space (Thomas *et al.*, 2004) is not apparent." They report an increase in local biodiversity sometimes has been observed.

Feurdean *et al.* (2012) note species distribution models run at finer scales (Trivedi *et al.*, 2008; Randin *et al.*, 2009) or including representations of plant demography (Hickler *et al.*, 2009) and more accurate dispersal capability (Engler and Guisan, 2009) tend to predict much smaller habitat and species loss in response to climate model predictions than do more coarse-scale models (Thomas *et al.*, 2004; Thuiller *et al.*, 2005; Araujo *et al.*, 2008).

The German and Romanian researchers analyzed "seven fossil pollen sequences from Romania situated at different elevations … to examine the effects of climate change on community composition and biodiversity between 15,000 and 10,500 cal. yr BP in this biogeographically sensitive region of Europe." This period "was characterized by large-amplitude global climate fluctuations occurring on decadal to millennial time scales (Johnsen *et al.*, 1992; Jouzel *et al.*, 2007)," which enabled them to explore "how repeated temperature changes have affected patterns of community composition and diversity" and to analyze "recovery processes following major disruptions of community structure."

The four scientists report "community composition at a given time was not only the product of existing environmental conditions, but also the consequence of previous cumulative episodes of extirpation and recolonization." They found "many circumpolar woody plants were able to survive when environmental conditions became unfavorable," and "these populations acted as sources when the climate became more favorable again." The latter behavior, they write, "is in agreement with modeling results at the local scale, predicting the persistence of suitable habitats and species survival within large-grid cells in which they were predicted to disappear by coarse-scale models."

The findings of Feurdean *et al.* thus add to the growing number of studies demonstrating the shortcomings of "climate envelope" models of both vegetation and animal responses to rising temperatures, which are often used to predict massive species extinctions as a result of the "unprecedented" CO_2-induced global warming predicted by equally deficient climate models.

Dobrowski *et al.* (2013) write, "anthropogenic climate change is considered a threat to ecosystem services and to global biodiversity because of its magnitude, the potential for novel climatic conditions (Williams *et al.*, 2007), and the rate at which it is occurring (Parmesan and Yohe, 2003; Montoya and Rafaelli, 2010)." They note, "species have always been subject to changing climatic regimes and have responded through adaptation (Davis and Shaw, 2001; Hoffman and Sgro, 2011), changes in phenology (Cleland *et al.*, 2007), range shifts (Davis and Shaw, 2001), and the use of climate refugia (Dobrowski, 2011; Hampe and Jump, 2011)." They write, "the fossil record suggests that widespread extinctions of plant species were rare during periods of rapid warming (~2–10°C/century) such as the Pleistocene-Holocene transition (Willis and MacDonald, 2011)," noting instead of species disappearing, "ecological turnover and range shifts were common responses to rapid climate changes of the past (Botkin *et al.*, 2010; Hof *et al.*, 2011; Willis and MacDonald, 2011)."

The seven U.S. scientists assessed "climate velocity (both climate displacement rate and direction) for minimum temperature, actual evapotranspiration, and climatic water deficit over the contiguous U.S. during the 20th century (1916–2005)." They discovered "a complex picture of the climate in the contiguous U.S.," where "velocity vectors vary regionally, show variable and opposing directions among the variables considered, and shift direction through time."

Dobrowski *et al.* found "T_{min} vectors calculated over decadal and century scales demonstrate complex dynamics (e.g. northerly and southerly directions, direction reversal through time) that vary regionally," and "climate displacement vectors for metrics of the water balance were predominantly oriented toward the west and south, showing regional variability." They report "divergent climate vectors between temperature and water balance may help explain why roughly 10–30% of species assessed in previous climate change studies have not shifted their ranges whereas nearly 25% of species have shifted their ranges in a direction counter to expectations (Parmesan and Yohe, 2003; Chen *et al.*, 2011; Crimmins *et al.*, 2011)."

Dobrowski *et al.* say these results "suggest that the expectation of poleward and upward shifts associated with all taxa, previously referred to as a 'globally coherent fingerprint' (Parmesan and Yohe, 2003), may be derived from an oversimplification of the climate dynamics that have been observed over the 20th century." They conclude their findings imply "a more full understanding of changes in multiple climatic factors, in addition to temperature, may help explain unexpected or conflicting observational evidence of climate-driven species range shifts." They say "moving away from viewing climate as simple monotonic changes in temperature is a necessary step in advancing our understanding of how species have and will respond to climate shifts."

References

Allen, J.R.M., Brandt, U., Brauer, A., Hubberten, H.-W., Huntley, B., Keller, J., Kraml, M., Mackensen, A., Mingram, J., Negendank, J.F.W., Nowaczyk, N.R., Oberhansli, H., Watts, W.A., Wulf, S., and Zolitschka, B. 1999. Rapid environmental changes in southern Europe during the last glacial period. *Nature* **400**: 740–743.

Alsos, I.G., Eidesen, P.B., Ehrich, D., Skrede, I., Westergaard, K., Jacobsen, G.H., Landvik, J.Y., Taberlet, P., and Brochmann, C. 2007. Frequent long-distance plant colonization in the changing Arctic. *Science* **316**: 1606–1609.

Araujo, M.B., Nogues-Bravo, D., Reginster, I., Rounsevell, M., and Whittaker, R.J. 2008. Exposure of European biodiversity to changes in human-induced pressures. *Environmental Science and Policy* **11**: 38–45.

Birks, H.H. 2008. The late-quaternary history of arctic and alpine plants. *Plant Ecology and Diversity* **1**: 135–146.

Camenisch, M. 2002. Veranderungen der Gipfelflora im Bereich des Schweizerischen Nationalparks: Ein Vergleich uber die letzen 80 Jahre. *Jahresber nat forsch Ges Graubunden* **111**: 27–37.

Cannariato, K.G., Kennett, J.P., and Behl, R.J. 1999. Biotic response to late Quaternary rapid climate switches in Santa Barbara Basin: Ecological and evolutionary implications. *Geology* **27**: 63–66.

Cowling, S.A. and Sage, R.F. 1998. Interactive effects of low atmospheric CO_2 and elevated temperature on growth, photosynthesis, and respiration in *Phaseolus vulgaris*. *Plant, Cell and Environment* **21**: 427–435.

Cowling, S.A. and Sykes, M.T. 1999. Physiological significance of low atmospheric CO_2 for plant-climate interactions. *Quaternary Research* **52**: 237–242.

Engler, R. and Guisan, A. 2009. MIGCLIM: predicting plant distribution and dispersal in a changing climate. *Diversity and Distributions* **15**: 590–601.

Erschbamer, B., Kiebacher, T., Mallaun, M., and Unterluggauer, P. 2009. Short-term signals of climate change along an altitudinal gradient in the South Alps. *Plant Ecology* **202**: 79–89.

Feurdean, A., Tamas, T., Tantau, I., and Farcas, S. 2012. Elevational variation in regional vegetation responses to late-glacial climate changes in the Carpathians. *Journal of Biogeography* **39**: 258–271.

Grabherr, G., Gottfried, M., and Pauli, H. 1994. Climate effects on mountain plants. *Nature* **369**: 448.

Guisan, A. and Thuiller, W. 2005. Predicting species distribution: offering more than simple habitat models. *Ecology Letters* **8**: 993–1009.

Hickler, T., Fronzek, S., Araujo, M.B., Schweiger, O., Thuiller, W., and Sykes, M.T. 2009. An ecosystem-model-based estimate of changes in water availability differs from water proxies that are commonly used in species distribution models. *Global Ecology and Biogeography* **18**: 304–313.

Hofer, H.R. 1992. Veranderungen in der Vegetation von 14 Gipfeln des Berninagebietes zwischen 1905 und 1985. *Ber. Geobot. Inst. Eidgenoss. Tech. Hochsch. Stift. Rubel Zur* **58**: 39–54.

Holzinger, B., Hulber, K., Camenisch, M., and Grabherr, G. 2008. Changes in plant species richness over the last century in the eastern Swiss Alps: elevational gradient, bedrock effects and migration rates. *Plant Ecology* **195**: 179–196.

Johnsen, S.J., Clausen, H.B., Dansgaard, W., Fuhrer, K., Gundestrup, N., Hammer, C.U., Iversen, P., Jouzel, J., Stauffer, B., and Steffensen, J.P. 1992. Irregular glacial interstadials recorded in a new Greenland ice core. *Nature* **359**: 311–313.

Jouzel, J., Stievenard, M., Johnsen, S.J., Landais, A., Masson-Delmotte, V., Sveinbjornsdottir, A., Vimeux, F., von Grafenstein, U., and White, J.W.C. 2007. The GRIP deuterium-excess record. *Quaternary Science Reviews* **26**: 1–17.

Keller, F., Kienast, F., and Beniston, M. 2000. Evidence of response of vegetation to environmental change on high-elevation sites in the Swiss Alps. *Regional Environmental Change* **1**: 70–77.

Kelly, A.E. and Goulden, M.L. 2008. Rapid shifts in plant distribution with recent climate change. *Proceedings of the National Academy of Sciences, USA* **105**: 11,823–11,826.

Klanderud, K. and Birks, H.J.B. 2003. Recent increases in species richness and shifts in altitudinal distributions of Norwegian mountain plants. *Holocene* **13**: 1–6.

Kullman, L. 2002. Rapid recent range-margin rise of tree and shrub species in the Swedish Scandes. *Journal of Ecology* **90**: 68–77.

Kullman, L. 2007. Long-term geobotanical observations of climate change impacts in the Scandes of West-Central Sweden. *Nordic Journal of Botany* **24**: 445–467.

Kullman, L. 2010a. One century of treeline change and stability—experiences from the Swedish Scandes. *Landscape Online* **17**: 1–31.

Kullman, L. 2010b. A richer, greener and smaller alpine

world—review and projection of warming-induced plant cover change in the Swedish Scandes. *Ambio* **39**: 159–169.

Kullman, L. 2010c. Alpine flora dynamics—a critical review of responses to climate change in the Swedish Scandes since the early 1950s. *Nordic Journal of Botany* **28**: 398–408.

Lacoul, P. and Freedman, B. 2006. Recent observation of a proliferation of *Ranunculus trichophyllus* Chaix. in high-altitude lakes of Mount Everest Region. *Arctic, Antarctic and Alpine Research* **38**: 394–398.

Le Roux, P.C. and McGeoch, M.A. 2008. Rapid range expansion and community reorganization in response to warming. *Global Change Biology* **14**: 2950–2962.

MacDonald, G.M., Bennett, K.D., Jackson, S.T., Parducci, L., Smith, F.A., Smol, J.P., and Willis, K.J. 2008. Impacts of climate change on species, populations and communities: palaeobiogeographical insights and frontiers. *Progress in Physical Geography* **32**: 139–172.

Pauli, H., Gottfried, M., and Grabherr, G. 2001. High summits of the Alps in a changing climate. The oldest observation series on high mountain plant diversity in Europe. In: Walther, G.R., Burga, C.A., and Edwards, P.J. (Eds.) *Fingerprints of Climate Change—Adapted Behaviour and Shifting Species Ranges.* Kluwer Academic Publisher, New York, New York, USA, pp. 139–149.

Pauli, H., Gottfried, M., Reiter, K., Klettner, C., and Grabherr, G. 2007. Signals of range expansions and contractions of vascular plants in the high Alps: Observations (1994–2004) at the GLORIA master site Schrankogel, Tyrol, Austria. *Global Change Biology* **13**: 147–156.

Randin, C., Engler, R., Normans, S., Zappa, M., Zimmermann, N.E., Perman, P.B., Vittoz, P., Thuiller, W., and Guisan, A. 2009. Climate change and plant distribution: local models predict high-elevation persistence. *Global Change Biology* **15**: 1557–1569.

Rubel, E. 1912. Pflanzengeographische Monographie des Berninagebietes. Engelmann, Leipzig, DE.

Sgro, C.M., Lowe, A.J., and Hoffmann, A.A. 2010. Building evolutionary resilience for conserving biodiversity under climate change. *Evolutionary Applications* **4**: 326–337.

Stocklin, J., Kuss, P., and Pluess, A.R. 2009. Genetic diversity, phenotypic variation and local adaptation in the alpine landscape: case studies with alpine plant species. *Botanica Helvetica* **119**: 125–133.

Theurillat, J.-P. and Guisan, A. 2001. Potential impacts of climate change on vegetation in the European Alps: A review. *Climatic Change* **50**: 77–109.

Thomas, C.D., Cameron, A., Green, R.E., Bakkenes, M.,

Beaumont, L.J., Collingham, Y.C., Barend, F., Erasmus, N., Ferreira de Siqueira, M., Grainger, A., Hannah, L., Hughes, L., Huntley, B., van Jaarsveld, A.S., Midgley, G.F., Miles, L., Ortega-Huerta, M.A., Peterson, A.T., Phillips, O.L., and Williams, S.E. 2004. Extinction risk from climate change. *Nature* **427**: 145–148.

Thuiller, W., Lavorel, S., Araujo, M.B., Sykes, M.T., and Prentice, I.C. 2005. Climate change threats to plant diversity in Europe. *Proceedings of the National Academy of Sciences USA* **102**: 8245–8250.

Trivedi, M.R., Berry, P.M., Morecroft, M.D., and Dawson, T.P. 2008. Spatial scale affects bioclimate model projections of climate change impacts on mountain plants. *Global Change Biology* **14**: 1089–1103.

Vegas-Vilarrubia, T., Rull, V., Montoya, E., and Safont, E. 2011. Quaternary palaeoecoloogy and nature conservation: a general review with examples from the neotropics. *Quaternary Science Reviews* **30**: 2361–2388.

Virtanen, R., Eskelinen, A., and Gaare, E. 2003. Long-term changes in alpine plant communities in Norway and Finland. In: Nagy, L., Grabherr, G., Korner, C., and Thompson, D.B.A. (Eds.)*Alpine Biodiversity in Europe.* Springer, Berlin, Germany, pp. 411–422.

Walther, G.R. 2003. Plants in a warmer world. *Perspectives in Plant Ecology, Evolution and Systematics* **6**: 169–185.

Walther, G.-R., Beissner, S., and Burga, C.A. 2005. Trends in the upward shift of alpine plants. *Journal of Vegetation Science* **16**: 541–548.

Willis, K.J., Bennett, K.D., and Birks, H.J.B. 2009. Variability in thermal and UV-B energy fluxes through time and their influence on plant diversity and speciation. *Journal of Biogeography* **36**: 1630–1644.

Willis, K.J. and MacDonald, G.M. 2011. Long-term ecological records and their relevance to climate change predictions for a warmer world. *Annual Review of Ecology, Evolution, and Systematics* **42**: 267–287.

4.4.2 Stationary Plants

- A major cause of biodiversity reductions is not rising atmospheric CO_2 concentrations, but instead the direct encroachment of man upon the world of nature. Anthropogenic global warming, to whatever extent it exists, is helping plants overcome these assaults and thrive despite the growing human presence.

The "acid test" for any extinction hypothesis is to examine what appears to be happening—or to have happened—in the real world. Here we discuss studies of plants fighting to survive under experimental settings or real-world locations where they periodically face threats to their survival and are unable to spread to other areas to escape competition, predation, high temperatures, or other threats.

An experiment that broached the subject of plants threatened by external biological and climatic factors was established in spring 1994 at the Cedar Creek Natural History Area in central Minnesota (USA), where a decade later Lambers et al. (2004) quantified the temporal evolution of the productivity and "staying power" of 14 species of plants across an experimental grassland diversity gradient. Over the course of that long-term study, the five researchers learned certain species were over-yielders—plants that grow better and produce more biomass when grown in competition with other species than when grown by themselves. They found six such species: a C_3 grass, three C_4 grasses, and two legumes. The five researchers note these "over-yielding species were either superior N competitors (C_4 grasses) or N fixers (legumes)." They also found five under-yielding species, four of which were forbs that typically grew less robustly when in the presence of other species. The scientists report the over-yielding species were not displacing the under-yielding species over time.

Lambers et al. conclude diversity-promoting interactions played a role in this experiment, and "under-yielding species appear to be buffered from extinction." No one knows how common this phenomenon is, but its operation in this study suggests plants may be much better "buffered from extinction" than many have long supposed. More research should be directed toward elucidating the "diversity-promoting interactions" that maintain the existence of under-yielding species in the face of what might logically be presumed to be significant competitive pressure from average and over-yielding species.

Stinson and Bazzaz (2006) grew well-watered stands of ragweed (Ambrosia artemisiifolia) out-of-doors in open-top-chambers maintained at either 360 or 720 ppm CO_2 from their seedling stage to the onset of senescence, then harvested the plants and determined the dry masses of their shoots, roots, and reproductive structures. Prior to this time—at 14, 33, and 52 days after the start of the experiment—they also measured the heights and numbers of leaves of all the plants. The scientists found doubling the atmosphere's CO_2 concentration increased the mean stand-level biomass of the shoots of the ragweed plants by 44% and increased the biomass of their roots and reproductive structures by 46% and 94%, respectively, for a total CO_2-induced biomass increase of 70%. They also found the extra CO_2 "reduced the coefficients of variation for all aspects of plant growth, especially reproductive biomass," so the CO_2-induced growth enhancements were "more pronounced in small, rather than large plants." They report, "growth enhancements to smaller plants diminished the relative biomass advantages of larger plants in increasingly crowded conditions," and "CO_2-induced growth gains of subordinate A. artemisiifolia plants minimize differences in the reproductive output of small and large plants."

The Harvard University scientists conclude, "more homogeneous reproduction between subordinates and dominants also implies that a larger number of individuals will contribute propagules to future generations." This phenomenon, they write, "could in turn affect evolutionary and population dynamics."

An international team of 33 researchers (Wills et al., 2006) analyzed seven forest dynamics plots located throughout the New and Old World tropics, with a wide range of species richness and tree densities, all of which had been visited and "censused" more than once over the past few decades. For all of the plots they studied, they found "rare species survive preferentially, which increases diversity as the ages of the individuals increase" and "when species were rare in a local area, they had a higher survival rate than when they were common, resulting in enrichment for rare species and increasing diversity with age and size class in these complex ecosystems."

The researchers offer several explanations for their findings. They note "diversity should increase as a group of individuals ages, because more common species are selectively removed by pathogens and predators," especially those commonly associated with them. They also note "individuals compete more intensively with conspecifics than with individuals of other species" and "diversity may increase if an individual facilitates (benefits) nearby non-conspecifics." This facilitation may have "the effect of making interspecific interactions more positive than intraspecific interactions and thus provides an advantage to locally rare species."

Similarly, in a commentary on these important findings and the phenomena underpinning them, Pennisi (2006) write, "being closer together, common trees are more prone to deadly infections," and "they may also face stiffer competition for certain resources," whereas "rarer trees, by depending on slightly different sets of resources, may not have this problem." Pennisi quotes Scott Armbruster of the UK's University of Portsmouth as saying the fact "these patterns are found to be so consistent across so many distant tropical forests suggests to me that the conclusion may eventually be found to hold for other diverse ecosystems as well."

Londre and Schnitzer (2006) write, woody vines (lianas) around the globe are "competing intensely with trees and reducing tree growth, establishment, fecundity, and survivorship," possibly because "increasing levels of CO_2 may enhance growth and proliferation of temperate lianas more than of competing growth forms (e.g., trees)," and possibly because "warmer winter temperatures may also increase the abundance and distribution of temperate lianas, which are limited in their distribution by their vulnerability to freezing-induced xylem embolism in cold climates." The two researchers investigated whether these phenomena had impacted liana abundance and distribution over the prior 45 years in 14 temperate deciduous forests of southern Wisconsin (USA), during which time (1959–1960 to 2004–2005) the atmosphere's CO_2 concentration rose by 65 ppm, mean annual air temperature in the study region rose by 0.94°C, mean winter air temperature rose by 2.40°C, and mean annual precipitation did not change.

Contrary to their initial hypothesis, the researchers found "liana abundance and diameter did not increase in the interiors of Wisconsin (USA) forests over the last 45 years." They report *Toxicodendron radicans*—a liana popularly known as poison ivy, which "grew markedly better under experimentally elevated CO_2 conditions than did competing trees (Mohan *et al.*, 2006)"—decreased in abundance over this period, and did so significantly.

Londre and Schnitzer write, "the lack of change in overall liana abundance and diameter distribution in [the] study suggests that lianas are limited in the interiors of deciduous forests of Wisconsin by factors other than increased levels of CO_2," suggesting it was likely the interior-forest lianas were limited by the enhanced tree growth provided by the CO_2 increase, which likely resulted in the trees becoming more competitive with the vines because of CO_2-induced increases in tree leaf numbers, area, and thickness. These factors would have reduced the amount of light being transmitted to the lianas growing beneath the forest canopy, negating the enhanced propensity for growth provided to the vines by the historical increase in the atmosphere's CO_2 concentration.

In support of this net-zero competing effects hypothesis, Londre and Schnitzer found, "compared to the forest interior, lianas were >4 times more abundant within 15 m of the forest edge and >6 times more abundant within 5 m of the forest edge," and this "strong gradient in liana abundance from forest edge to interior was probably due to light availability." They report their results "are similar to findings in tropical forests, where liana abundance is significantly higher along fragmented forest edges and within tree fall gaps," and where the interior tropical trees have not suffered what some have claimed would be the negative consequences of CO_2-induced increases in liana growth, as described in the review of the study of Phillips *et al.* (2002).

Londre and Schnitzer write, because "forest fragmentation (and thus edge creation) has increased significantly over the last half-century, particularly in the northeastern and midwestern United States (e.g., Ritters and Wickham, 2003; Radeloff *et al.*, 2005), liana abundance has likely increased in temperate forests due to forest fragmentation." Consequently, "as forest fragmentation continues, liana abundance will also likely continue to increase, and the effects of lianas on temperate forests, such as intense competition with trees (Schnitzer *et al.*, 2005), reduced tree growth rates and biomass sequestration (Laurance *et al.*, 2001), and the incidence of arrested gap-phase regeneration (Schnitzer *et al.*, 2000) may become even more pronounced."

These latter observations remind us that a major cause of biodiversity reductions is not rising atmospheric CO_2 concentrations, but instead the direct encroachment of man upon the world of nature (Waggoner, 1995; Tilman *et al.*, 2001, 2002; Raven, 2002). Such encroachment could deplete the globe's forests and drive innumerable species of both plants and animals to extinction, unless we can dramatically increase the water use efficiency of our crop plants so we are not forced to encroach further upon forests to obtain the additional land and water resources (Wallace, 2000) we will otherwise need to grow the greater quantities of food required to sustain the growing human population.

Regarding this challenge, Feeley and Silman (2009) write, "ongoing development of the Amazon, including natural gas and oil production, large-scale cattle ranching, soy farming, extended networks of improved roads, and the various synergistic activities that invariably accompany increased access, is causing the rapid loss and degradation of natural habitat," which can lead to the extinctions of species that live there. The two researchers used various collections of pertinent data to map the potential ecoregion-based distributions of the more than 40,000 vascular plant species for which collections were available from the Amazon. They estimated rates of habitat loss due to future land-use changes, based on projections made by Soares-Filho *et al.* (2006) of areas that will be deforested by 2050 under business-as-usual and more-optimistic governance scenarios, which they translated into estimated extinction risks for the year 2050.

By AD 2050, they found, human land-use practices will have reduced the habitat available to Amazonian plants by approximately 12–24%, resulting in 5–9% of species becoming "committed to extinction" at that time.

Some regions will suffer more than others. For the largest Amazonian ecoregion—the seasonal Cerrado savannahs of southwestern Brazil that cover about two million square kilometers—Feeley and Silman calculated a habitat loss of 1.5%/year as characteristic of the past three decades, but "habitat loss in the Cerrado has actually accelerated to 3.1–4.3%/year." They state if they include "historic habitat loss and use a contemporary habitat loss rate of 3.7%, extinction risk for Cerrado species rises to more than 2 times greater than for non-Cerrado species."

The Cerrado has been losing "natural habitat to agricultural and pastoral land over the past three decades," Feeley and Silman note, and with the push for greater biofuel production, those habitat losses will accelerate. These incursions, not the ongoing rise in atmospheric CO_2 content, are the great threat to the Amazon's biodiversity.

Short *et al.* (2011) write about a different species of plants facing extinction threats. They write, "seagrasses, a functional group of marine flowering plants rooted in the world's coastal oceans, support marine food webs and provide essential habitat for many coastal species, playing a critical role in the equilibrium of coastal ecosystems and human livelihoods." Seagrasses are also "a component of more complex ecosystems within marine coastal zones, contributing to the health of coral reefs and mangroves, salt marshes and oyster reefs," they write, citing Dorenbosch *et al.* (2004), Duke *et al.* (2007), Heck *et al.* (2008) and Unsworth *et al.* (2008).

They report that for the first time, "the probability of extinction [has been] determined for the world's seagrass species under the Categories and Criteria of the International Union for the Conservation of Nature (IUCN) Red List of Threatened Species." They describe this effort as "a four-year process involving seagrass experts internationally, compilation of data on species' status, populations, and distribution, and review of the biology and ecology of each of the world's seagrass species."

The 26 seagrass experts from 11 countries determined 10 seagrass species (comprising 14% of all seagrass species) are at elevated risk of extinction, with three other species qualifying as endangered. They identified several possible causes of the problem, including suspended sediments and siltation (Dennison *et al.*, 1993; de Boer, 2007), coastal construction, land reclamation, shoreline hardening, and dredging (Erftemeijer and Lewis, 2006), damaging fisheries practices such as trawling and aquaculture (Pergent-Martini *et al.*, 2006), mechanical damage from boats, boat moorings and docks (Burdick and Short, 1999; Kenworthy *et al.*, 2002), introduced species (Williams, 2007) that compete for space and resources (Heck *et al.*, 2000), and certain diseases (Rasmussen, 1997). They conclude "the most common threat to seagrasses is human activity," not CO_2-induced global warming or ocean acidification.

Mosses offer another example of species under threat of extinction due to human activity, but not CO_2. Gerdol and Vicentini (2011) write, "*Sphagnum* mosses are a fundamental component of bog vegetation in northern regions, where these plants play a major role in controlling important ecosystem processes." Noting "heat waves are expected to become increasingly intense and frequent, especially in cold territories," they attempted to ascertain the ability of the mosses to survive such conditions.

The two researchers collected cores of two *Sphagnum* species—*S. fuscum* and *S. magellanicum*—from three mountain heights in the southeastern Alps of the Italian province of Bolzano above sea level: low (1,090 m), intermediate (1,780 m), and high (2,100 m). The locations spanned, they write, "almost the whole altitudinal range known for these species in mountainous regions of central-southern Europe." In the laboratory, they grew portions of the six cores for four consecutive days at three 12-hour daytime temperature levels—ambient temperature (AT, 25°C), medium temperature (MT, 36°C), and high temperature (HT, 43°C)—and measured net CO_2 exchange and chlorophyll *a* fluorescence, as well as plant tissue chemistry.

The two Italian scientists report normalized net CO_2 exchange rates did not vary among species nor with altitude. Net CO_2 exchange rates in the plants under the MT treatment declined during treatment but recovered noticeably six days after treatment stopped. Despite receiving "severe damage," the plants experiencing the HT treatment also exhibited a capacity to recover six days after the conclusion of the temperature treatment. Noting their study suggests "the two *Sphagnum* species possess moderate altitudinal plasticity to increased temperature," they conclude, "heat waves, even stronger than ever recorded, will unlikely bring about die-off of *Sphagnum* mosses in bog ecosystems unless high temperatures are coupled with drought."

References

Burdick, D.M. and Short, F.T. 1999. The effects of boat docks on eelgrass beds in coastal waters of Massachusetts. *Environmental Management* **23**: 231–240.

de Boer, W.F. 2007. Seagrass-sediment interactions, positive feedbacks and critical thresholds for occurrence: a review. *Hydrobiologia* **591**: 5–24.

Dennison, W.C., Orth, R.J., Moore, K.A., Stevenson, J.C., Carter, V., Kollar, S., Bergstrom, P.W., and Batiuk, R.A. 1993. Assessing water quality with submersed aquatic vegetation. *BioScience* **43**: 86–94.

Dorenbosch, M., van Riel, M.C., Nagelkerken, I., and van der Velde, G. 2004. The relationship of reef fish densities to the proximity of mangrove and seagrass nurseries. *Estuarine and Coastal Shelf Science* **60**: 37–48.

Duke, N.C., Meynecke, J.-O., Dittmann, S., Ellison, A.M., Anger, K., Berger, U., Cannicci, S., Diele, K., Ewel, K.C., Field, C.D., Koedam, N., Lee, S.Y., Marchand, C., Nordhaus, I., and Dahdouh-Guebas, F. 2007. A world without mangroves. *Science* **317**: 41–42.

Erftemeijer, P.L.A. and Lewis, R.R.R. 2006. Environmental impacts of dredging on seagrasses: a review. *Marine Pollution Bulletin* **52**: 1553–1572.

Feeley, K.J. and Silman, M.R. 2009. Extinction risks of Amazonian plant species. *Proceedings of the National Academy of Sciences, USA* **106**: 12,382–12,387.

Gerdol, R. and Vicentini, R. 2011. Response to heat stress of populations of two *Sphagnum* species from alpine bogs at different altitudes. *Environmental and Experimental Botany* **74**: 22–30.

Heck, K.L., Carruthers, T.J., Duarte, C.M., Hughes, A.R., Kendrick, G.A., Orth, R.J., and Williams, S.L. 2008. Trophic transfers from seagrass meadows subsidize diverse marine and terrestrial consumers. *Ecosystems* **11**: 1198–1210.

Heck, K.L., Pennock, J., Valentine, J., Coen, L., and Sklenar, S.S. 2000. Effects of nutrient enrichment and large predator removal on seagrass nursery habitats: an experimental assessment. *Limnology and Oceanography* **45**: 1041–1057.

Kenworthy, W.J., Fonseca, M.S., Whitfield, P.E., and Hammerstrom, K.K. 2002. Analysis of seagrass recovery in experimental excavations and propeller-scar disturbances in the Florida Keys National Marine Sanctuary. *Journal of Coastal Research* **37**: 75–85.

Lambers, J.H.R., Harpole, W.S., Tilman, D., Knops, J., and Reich, P.B. 2004. Mechanisms responsible for the positive diversity-productivity relationship in Minnesota grasslands. *Ecology Letters* **7**: 661–668.

Laurance, W.F., Perez-Salicrup, D., Delamonica, F., Fearnside, P.M., Agra, S., Jerozolinski, A., Pohl, L., and Lovejoy, T.E. 2001. Rainforest fragmentation and the structure of Amazonian liana communities. *Ecology* **82**: 105–116.

Londre, R.A. and Schnitzer, S.A. 2006. The distribution of lianas and their change in abundance in temperate forests over the past 45 years. *Ecology* **87**: 2973–2978.

Mohan, J.E., Ziska, L.H., Schlesinger, W.H., Thomas, R.B., Sicher, R.C., George, K., and Clark, J.S. 2006. Biomass and toxicity responses of poison ivy (*Toxicodendron radicans*) to elevated atmospheric CO_2. *Proceedings of the National Academy of Sciences, USA* **103**: 9086–9089.

Pennisi, E. 2006. Rare tree species thrive in local neighborhoods. *Science* **311**: 452–453.

Pergent-Martini, C., Boudouresque, C.F., Pasqualini, V., and Pergent, G. 2006. Impact of fish farming facilities on *Posidonia oceanica* meadows: a review. *Marine Ecology* **27**: 310–319.

Phillips, O.L., Martinez, R.V., Arroyo, L., Baker, T.R., Killeen, T., Lewis, S.L., Malhi, Y., Mendoza, A.M., Neill, D., Vargas, P.N., Alexiades, M., Ceron, C., Di Fiore, A., Erwin, T., Jardim, A., Paiacios, W., Saidias, M., and Vinceti, B. 2002. Increasing dominance of large lianas in Amazonian forests. *Nature* **418**: 770–774.

Radeloff, V.C., Hammer, R.B., and Stewart, S.I. 2005. Rural and suburban sprawl in the U.S. Midwest from 1940 to 2000 and its relation to forest fragmentation. *Conservation Biology* **19**: 793–805.

Rasmussen, E. 1977. The wasting disease of eelgrass (*Zostera marina*) and its effects on environmental factors and fauna. In: McRoy, C.P. and Helfferich, C. (Eds.) *Seagrass Ecosystems*. Marcel Dekker Inc., New York, New York, USA, pp. 1–51.

Raven, P.H. 2002. Science, sustainability, and the human prospect. *Science* **297**: 954–959.

Ritters, K.H. and Wickham, J.D. 2003. How far to the nearest road? *Frontiers in Ecology and the Environment* **1**: 125–129.

Schnitzer, S.A., Dalling, J.W., and Carson, W.P. 2000. The

impact of lianas on tree regeneration in tropical forest canopy gaps: evidence for an alternative pathway of gap-phase regeneration. *Journal of Ecology* **88**: 655–666.

Schnitzer, S.A., Kuzee, M.E., and Bongers, F. 2005. Disentangling above- and below-ground competition between lianas and trees in a tropical forest. *Journal of Ecology* **93**: 1115–1125.

Short, F.T., Polidoro, B., Livingstone, S.R., Carpenter, K.E., Bandeira, S., Bujang, J.S., Calumpong, H.P., Carruthers, T.J.B., Coles, R.G., Dennison, W.C., Erftemeijer, P.L.A., Fortes, M.D., Freeman, A.S., Jagtap, T.G., Kamal, A.H.M., Kendrick, G.A., Kenworthy, W.J., La Nafie, Y.A., Nasution, I.M., Orth, R.J., Prathep, A., Sanciangco, J.C., van Tussenbroek, B., Vergara, S.G., Waycott, M., and Zieman, J.C. 2011. Extinction risk assessment of the world's seagrass species. *Biological Conservation* **144**: 1961–1971.

Soares-Filho, B.S., Nepstad, D.C., Curran, L.M., Cerqueira, G.C., Garcia, R.A., Ramos, C.A., Voll, E., McDonald A., Lefebvre, P., and Schlesinger, P. 2006. Modelling conservation in the Amazon basin. *Nature* **440**: 520–523.

Stinson, K.A. and Bazzaz, F.A. 2006. CO_2 enrichment reduces reproductive dominance in competing stands of *Ambrosia artemisiifolia* (common ragweed). *Oecologia* **147**: 155–163.

Tilman, D., Cassman, K.G., Matson, P.A., Naylor, R., and Polasky, S. 2002. Agricultural sustainability and intensive production practices. *Nature* **418**: 671–677.

Tilman, D., Fargione, J., Wolff, B., D'Antonio, C., Dobson, A., Howarth, R., Schindler, D., Schlesinger, W.H., Simberloff, D., and Swackhamer, D. 2001. Forecasting agriculturally driven global environmental change. *Science* **292**: 281–284.

Unsworth, R.K.F., DeLeon, P.S., Garrard, S.L., Jompa, J., Smith, D.J., and Bell, J.J. 2008. High connectivity of Indo-Pacific seagrass fish assemblages with mangrove and coral reef habitats. *Marine Ecology Progress Series* **353**: 213–224.

Waggoner, P.E. 1995. How much land can ten billion people spare for nature? Does technology make a difference? *Technology in Society* **17**: 17–34.

Williams, S.L. 2007. Introduced species in seagrass ecosystems: status and concerns. *Journal of Experimental Marine Biology and Ecology* **350**: 89–110.

Wills, C., Harms, K.E., Condit, R., King, D., Thompson, J., He, F., Muller-Landau, H.C., Ashton, P., Losos, E., Comita, L., Hubbell, S., LaFrankie, J., Bunyavejchewin, S., Dattaraja, H.S., Davies, S., Esufali, S., Foster, R., Gunatilleke, N., Gunatilleke, S., Hall, P., Itoh, A., John, R., Kiratiprayoon, S., de Lao, S.L., Massa, M., Nath, C., Noor,

M.N.S., Kassim, A.R., Sukumar, R., Suresch, H.S., Sun, I.-F., Tan, S., Yamakura, T., and Zimmerman, J. 2006. Nonrandom processes maintain diversity in tropical forests. *Science* **311**: 527–531.

4.5 Evolution

- As good as things currently are for world agriculture, and as significantly better as they are expected to become as the atmosphere's CO_2 content continues to rise, there may be additional substantial room for natural selection and bio-engineering to remove the remaining constraints of low CO_2 adaptation in several important agricultural crops and thereby create novel genotypes able to exploit high CO_2 conditions.

4.5.1 A Major Opportunity

Sage and Coleman (2001) reviewed what is known about plant responses to increases and decreases in atmospheric CO_2 content. They note plants generally photosynthesize at reduced rates and produce less biomass at lower-than-current atmospheric CO_2 levels, and they photosynthesize at enhanced rates and produce more biomass at higher-than-current CO_2 concentrations. At optimal temperatures for C_3-plant photosynthesis, for example, the two researchers write, "reducing atmospheric CO_2 from the current level to 180 ppm [an approximate 50% reduction at that time] reduces photosynthetic capacity by approximately half" and "causes biomass to decline by 50%." Doubling the atmosphere's CO_2 concentration typically increases photosynthesis and biomass production by 30 to 50%.

Sage and Coleman also report, "high CO_2 concentrations reduce the impact of moderate drought, salinity and temperature stress, and can indirectly reduce low nutrient stress by promoting root growth, nitrogen fixation and mycorrhizal infection." These phenomena boost the basic CO_2-induced productivity increase still more, as Idso and Idso (1994) noted in an earlier review of the literature. These observations are common knowledge among plant biologists and serve merely as intro-ductory material for Sage and Coleman's hypothesis that modern bioengineering techniques might help make plants even more responsive to increases in atmospheric CO_2 content.

Their reasoning is as follows. During the peak of the last ice age, and throughout the bulk of all prior ice ages of the past two million years, atmospheric

CO_2 concentrations tended to be approximately 180 ppm. This value, according to Sage and Coleman, might not be much above the "critical CO_2 threshold at which catastrophic interactions occur." Thus they speculated plants of the late Pleistocene "might have been adapted to lower CO_2 concentrations than currently exist." And in light of the short period of evolutionary time that has elapsed since the last of these low-CO_2 conditions prevailed, the two researchers suggest "many if not most plants might still be adapted to CO_2 levels much lower than those that exist today."

Literally thousands of laboratory and field experiments have demonstrated Earth's vegetation responds in dramatic positive fashion to atmospheric CO_2 enrichment far above what is characteristic of the CO_2 conditions of the present. Hence Sage and Coleman conclude as good as things currently are, and as significantly better as they are expected to become as the atmospheric CO_2 content continues to rise, there may be additional "substantial room for natural selection and bioengineering to remove the constraints [of low CO_2 adaptation], thereby creating novel genotypes able to exploit high CO_2 conditions to best advantage."

That such is possible and even probable is borne out by Ziska *et al.* (1996), who grew well-watered and well-fertilized plants of 17 cultivars of rice from seed to maturity in glasshouses maintained at atmospheric CO_2 concentrations of either 373 or 664 ppm in soil-filled pots kept at two different sets of day/night temperatures (29/21°C and 37/29°C), after which they measured total plant biomass and grain biomass. They report the degree of CO_2-induced enhancement of total plant biomass and the number of cultivars showing significant enhancement with elevated CO_2 decreased at the higher and more stressful set of growth temperatures, dropping from 12 of 17 cultivars with an average biomass stimulation of 70% at the lower set of temperatures to eight of 17 cultivars with a mean biomass stimulation of 23% at the higher set of temperatures. A few cultivars exhibited no significant changes in response to the atmospheric CO_2 enrichment employed in the study, while the most responsive cultivar exhibited a 265% increase in total plant biomass and a 350% increase in grain biomass. The variability in productivity enhancement exhibited by the 17 rice cultivars clearly demonstrates the selection of rice varieties has tremendous potential to take advantage of the aerial fertilization effect of rising atmospheric CO_2 content, which "could maximize productivity as CO_2 concentration increases," Ziska *et al.* write.

Also noting there is "considerable variability among current rice cultivars in their responses to CO_2 and temperature (Ziska and Teramura, 1992; Ziska *et al.*, 1996; Moya *et al.*, 1998) leading to the possibility of selecting rice cultivars against these two environmental variables for yield increases and/or stability in a possibly warmer, but almost certainly higher future CO_2 world," Baker (2004) grew the Southern United States rice cultivars Cocodrie, Jefferson, and Cypress for an entire season in outdoor, naturally sunlit, controlled-environment chambers at a constant day/night temperature of 28°C at CO_2 concentrations of 350 and 700 ppm. In the following year he grew the cultivar Lamont under the same conditions, but at day/night temperatures of 27/23°C, as a main crop and ratoon (stubble) crop.

In the first of these experiments, grain yield per plant rose by 46%, 57%, and 71% in response to the doubling of the atmospheric CO_2 content in the Cocodrie, Jefferson, and Cypress cultivars, respectively. In the second experiment, with the Lamont cultivar, it rose by 12% when the rice was grown as a main crop but by 104% when it was grown as a ratoon crop. Baker concludes, "the wide range in grain yield responsiveness to CO_2 enrichment found among these four US rice cultivars points to the potential for selecting or developing high yielding US rice cultivars with the ability to take advantage of expected future global increases in CO_2," noting "CO_2 enrichment could have potentially large positive effects on ratoon crop yields."

Sage and Coleman note the low CO_2 levels of the past "could have had significant consequences for much of the Earth's biota." They suggest the origin of agriculture itself "might have been impeded by reduced ecosystem productivity during low CO_2 episodes of the late Pleistocene." Since then, the increase in atmospheric CO_2 content has essentially doubled the biological prowess of the planet's vegetation, and projected increases in atmospheric CO_2 content could readily lead to a tripling of the productivity of Earth's ice-age past. In addition, the three studies reviewed above suggest there may be other opportunities to improve plant performance even more by using modern bioengineering techniques to overcome genetic constraints linked to adaptations to low levels of CO_2 that may persist in many plants. For agriculture, Sage and Coleman suggest, "this could be a major opportunity to improve crop productivity and the efficiency of fertilizer and water use."

These studies demonstrate we are living in an age of unparalleled biological promise. The fullness of that promise has yet to be achieved, and how effectively we exploit the opportunities to do so, as Sage and Coleman write, "will depend on our ability to conduct the basic research [needed] to identify the genes controlling acclimation and adaptation to CO_2 variation."

References

Baker, J.T. 2004. Yield responses of southern US rice cultivars to CO_2 and temperature. *Agricultural and Forest Meteorology* **122**: 129–137.

Idso, K.E. and Idso, S.B. 1994. Plant responses to atmospheric CO_2 enrichment in the face of environmental constraints: a review of the past 10 years' research. *Agricultural and Forest Meteorology* **69**: 153–203.

Moya, T.B., Ziska, L.H., Namuco, O.S., and Olszky, D. 1998. Growth dynamics and genotypic variation in tropical, field-grown paddy rice (*Oryza sativa* L.) in response to increasing carbon dioxide and temperature. *Global Change Biology* **4**: 645–656.

Sage, R.F. and Coleman, J.R. 2001. Effects of low atmospheric CO_2 on plants: more than a thing of the past. *TRENDS in Plant Science* **6**: 18–24.

Ziska, L.H., Manalo, P.A., and Ordonez, R.A. 1996. Intraspecific variation in the response of rice (*Oryza sativa* L.) to increased CO_2 and temperature: growth and yield response of 17 cultivars. *Journal of Experimental Botany* **47**: 1353–1359.

Ziska, L.H. and Teramura, A.H. 1992. Intraspecific variation in response of rice (*Oryza sativa*) to increased CO_2—photosynthetic, biomass and reproductive characteristics. *Physiologia Plantarum* **84**: 269–276.

4.5.2 CO_2-Induced

- The ongoing rise in atmospheric CO_2 content likely is exerting significant selection pressure on Earth's naturally occurring terrestrial plants, which should improve their resistance to various environmental stressors via the process of micro-evolution as the air's CO_2 concentration continues to rise in the years and decades ahead.

The ongoing rise in atmospheric CO_2 content likely is exerting significant selection pressure on Earth's naturally occurring terrestrial plants, which should improve their resistance to various environmental stressors via the process of micro-evolution. Plants may be much better prepared than we have commonly believed to meet whatever climatic challenges, including global warming, the future may pose for them. Moreover, evidence continues to accumulate for substantial heritable variation of ecologically important plant traits, including root allocation, drought tolerance, and nutrient plasticity, which suggests rapid evolution based on epigenetic variation alone should be possible.

Two decades ago, Root and Schneider (1993) wrote CO_2-induced changes in global climate were expected to occur "too fast for evolutionary processes such as natural selection to keep pace," and this phenomenon "could substantially enhance the probability of extinction of numerous species." This famous but unsubstantiated declaration has pervaded the publications of IPCC ever since ... but it never has been proven correct. It is more likely to be incorrect, especially as it pertains to CO_2-induced changes in natural (i.e., non-agricultural) terrestrial vegetation, the topic examined in the scientific studies reviewed below.

Rae *et al.* (2007) note various studies "are beginning to identify genes that appear sensitive to elevated CO_2 (Gupta *et al.*, 2005; Taylor *et al.*, 2005; Ainsworth *et al.*, 2006)," while "leaf growth responses to elevated CO_2 have been found in *Populus*" and "quantitative trait loci (QTL) for this response [have been] determined (Rae *et al.*, 2006)." Continuing this endeavor, they studied a three-generation *Populus* pedigree generated by the hybridization of two contrasting *Populus* species—where two full-siblings from the resulting F1 family were crossed to form an F2 family—growing cuttings of the different generations for 152 days out-of-doors in open-top chambers maintained at either the ambient CO_2 concentration or concentrations on the order of 600 ppm. They measured various plant properties and physiological processes and determined QTL for above- and below-ground growth and genotype-by-environment interactions.

The four UK researchers report, "in the F2 generation, both above- and below-ground growth showed a significant increase in elevated CO_2," and "three areas of the genome on linkage groups I, IX and XII were identified as important in determining above-ground growth response to elevated CO_2, while an additional three areas of the genome on linkage groups IV, XVI and XIX appeared important in determining root growth response to elevated CO_2." Consequently, stating their results "quantify and identify genetic variation in response to elevated CO_2 and provide an insight into genomic response to the changing environment," they conclude further work in this area "should lead to an understanding of micro-evolutionary response to elevated CO_2," as subsequent studies have further demonstrated.

Springer *et al.* (2008) grew well-watered and well-fertilized plants of two closely related out-crossed genotypes (SG and CG) of *Arabidopsis thaliana*, generated via artificial selection, in controlled-environment chambers maintained at atmospheric CO_2 concentrations of either 380 or 700 ppm. They selected genotype SG for high seed number at elevated CO_2 over five generations, and they randomly chose genotype CG to serve as a control. They measured time to flowering, number of leaves at flowering, and total biomass at flowering, as well as foliar sugar concentrations. In a second experiment conducted under the same growing conditions, they characterized the expression patterns of several floral-initiation genes.

They found "SG delayed flowering by 7–9 days, and flowered at a larger size (122% higher biomass) and higher leaf number (81 more leaves) when grown at elevated versus current CO_2 concentration," but "flowering time, size and leaf number at flowering were similar for CG plants grown at current and elevated CO_2." They note "SG plants had 84% higher foliar sugar concentrations at the onset of flowering when grown at elevated versus current CO_2, whereas foliar sugar concentrations of CG plants grown at elevated CO_2 only increased by 38% over plants grown at current CO_2." They report, "SG exhibited changes in the expression patterns of floral-initiation genes in response to elevated CO_2, whereas CG plants did not."

Noting "delayed flowering increases production of vegetative resources that can be subsequently allocated to reproductive structures," the researchers conclude "such evolutionary responses may alter total carbon gain of annual plants if the vegetative stage is extended, and may potentially counteract some of the accelerations in flowering that are occurring in response to increasing temperatures." Their results demonstrate the ability of elevated CO_2 to alter the expression of plant genes in ways that may enable plants to take better advantage of the ongoing rise in atmospheric CO_2 content.

Lau *et al.* (2008) measured the amount of pathogen damage caused by *Pythium* or *Fusarium* spp. to the common prairie legume *Lespedeza capitata* growing in ambient and elevated (560 ppm) CO_2 treatments in the seventh and eighth full years (2004 and 2005) of the BioCON study (Reich *et al.*, 2001) conducted at the Cedar Creek Natural History Area in Minnesota (USA), where they applied the CO_2 treatments during the daylight hours of each growing season. They found disease incidence was lower in the elevated CO_2 environment (down by 10% in 2004 and 53% in 2005). "Because disease caused major reductions in reproductive output," the five researchers conclude, "the effects of CO_2 on disease incidence may be important for *L. capitata* evolution and population dynamics." They note Strengbom and Reich (2006), "working in the same experimental site ... also found that elevated CO_2 ... reduced disease incidence on *Solidago rigida*."

Kaligaric *et al.* (2008) investigated fluctuating asymmetry (FA), which describes the magnitude of random deviations from perfect symmetry in morphological traits of both plants and animals that "offers a unique tool for comparative studies of developmental stability (Moller and Swaddle, 1997)" and has been used as "an indicator of genetic and environmental stress (Martel *et al.*, 1999; Cornelissen and Stiling, 2004)" in plants. They measured the degree of FA in "undamaged (not grazed, not visibly attacked by herbivores or pathogens) fully developed leaves" of the Mediterranean shrub *Myrtus communis* growing along an atmospheric CO_2 gradient (570, 530, 490, 450, 410, and 370 ppm) moving away from a natural CO_2 spring (I Borboi) near Lajatico (Pisa, Tuscany, Italy) at distances of 2, 18, 34, 50, 66, and 82 meters, respectively, from the CO_2 source.

The four researchers found "a significant and negative correlation between CO_2 concentration and leaf FA," such that "with increased CO_2 concentration the leaf FA decreased." This result, they write, "confirms what was obtained by Cornelissen *et al.* (2004) on *Quercus myrtifolia* and *Quercus geminata* (in a short-term experiment)." They report, "*Myrtus communis*, grown under elevated CO_2 concentration at 'I Borboi,' showed a reduction in xylem embolism and an increase in hydraulic efficiency (Tognetti *et al.*, 2001)," stating "improved water relations could represent a good explanation for the observed reduction in leaf FA" as the atmospheric CO_2 content increased. They conclude "adaptation and selection could explain the tendency towards decreased leaf FA in plants from the CO_2 spring relative to ambient conditions," because "the more symmetrical leaves under long-term elevated CO_2 concentration were more developmentally stable in these conditions."

Onoda *et al.* (2009) write the ongoing rise in atmospheric CO_2 content "is likely to act as a selective agent" among plants, citing Woodward *et al.* (1991), Thomas and Jasienski (1996), Ward *et al.* (2000), Kohut (2003), Ward and Kelly (2004), and Lau *et al.* (2007). They report, "evolutionary responses have been found in selection experiments with short-lived organisms, such as *Arabidopsis thaliana* (e.g. development rate and biomass production; Ward *et al.*, 2000) and *Chlamydomonas reinhardtii* (e.g. photosynthesis and cell size; Collins and Bell, 2004)." They add, "the evolutionary response of wild plants (especially long-lived plants) is, in general, difficult to evaluate using growth experiments," because of the long time spans needed to evaluate the phenomenon properly. They avoid this problem by studying plants growing around natural CO_2 springs, where they "have been exposed to a CO_2-enriched atmosphere over many generations," providing what the researchers call "a unique opportunity to explore the micro-evolutionary response of wild plants to elevated CO_2."

Onoda *et al.* write, "the adaptation of leaf photosynthesis to elevated CO_2 was tested by a common garden experiment with herbaceous species originating from three different natural CO_2 springs in Japan: Nibu, Ryuzin-numa and Yuno-kawa," where "several genotypes were collected from each high-CO_2 area (spring population) and nearby control areas (control population), and each genotype was propagated or divided into two ramets, and grown in pots at 370 and 700 ppm CO_2." They assessed the plants' photosynthetic nitrogen use efficiency (PNUE), water use efficiency (WUE), and the degree of carbohydrate accumulation in the plants' leaves, which if too large can lead to down-regulation of photosynthesis.

Onoda *et al.* report, "high CO_2 concentration directly and greatly increased PNUE and WUE, suggesting that plants will show higher growth rates at a given resource availability." They also identify "a significant reduction in stomatal conductance, which contributed to higher WUE, and a trend of reduced down-regulation of photosynthesis with a lower starch accumulation," and they note these results suggest "there is substantial room for plant evolution in high-CO_2 environments." They write, a molecular study "also found relatively large genetic differentiation across the CO_2 gradient in these plants." As a result of their own work and "the increasing number of studies on CO_2 springs (e.g. Fordham *et al.*, 1997; Polle *et al.*, 2001; Schulte *et al.* 2002) and selection experiments (Ward *et al.*, 2000; Collins and Bell, 2004)," Onoda *et al.* conclude "high CO_2 will act as a selection agent" as atmospheric CO_2 content continues to rise. This phenomenon should enable plants to fare even better in the CO_2-enriched air of the future than they do today.

Cseke *et al.* (2009) note certain perceived "genetic and environmental bottlenecks" may limit a plant's capacity to allocate assimilated carbon to greater biomass production. However, it is plausible that numerous species may possess the genetic diversity needed to overcome these potential roadblocks and thereby benefit more than is commonly anticipated from the enhanced growth known to be possible in a CO_2-enriched atmosphere.

Working at the Aspen FACE site near Rhinelander, Wisconsin (USA), Cseke *et al.* grew two quaking aspen (*Populus tremuloides* Michx.) clones (216 and 271) from the seedling stage in replicate plots maintained at either 372 or 560 ppm CO_2 throughout each year's growing season (May–September), assessing their stem volume (a surrogate for biomass) annually for a period of eight years. They measured the trees' maximum light-saturated rates of leaf net photosynthesis, the transcriptional activity of leaf elevated-CO_2-responsive genes, and numerous leaf primary and secondary carbon-based compounds. The CO_2-induced increase in the maximum light-saturated rate of leaf net photosynthesis in clone 216 was more than twice as great as that of clone 271 (37% vs. 17%, as best as can be determined from Cseke *et al.*'s bar graphs); they found just the opposite relationship in the CO_2-induced increases in the trees' stem volumes, which increased only 0–10% for clone 216 but. 40–50% for clone 271.

The researchers' transcript abundance and carbon/nitrogen biochemistry data suggest "the CO_2-responsive clone (271) partitions carbon into pathways associated with active defense/response to stress, carbohydrate/starch biosynthesis and subsequent growth," whereas "the CO_2-unresponsive clone (216) partitions carbon into pathways associated with passive defense and cell wall thickening." The seven scientists conclude there was "significant variation in expression patterns between different tree genotypes in response to long-term exposure to elevated CO_2," and "future efforts to improve productivity or other advantageous traits for carbon sequestration should include an examination of genetic variability in CO_2 responsiveness." As the atmosphere's CO_2 concentration continues to rise, manifestations of these fitness-promoting traits will appear on their own, brought forth naturally by the changing environment, as plants appear to be genetically programmed to respond positively to atmospheric CO_2 enrichment. Plants are innately well-prepared to use the ongoing rise in the air's CO_2 concentration to their advantage.

Nakamura *et al.* (2011) suggest "evolutionary responses to elevated CO_2 in wild plants are, in general, difficult to detect using growth experiments, because the duration of experiments is often too short

585

compared to the time required for evolution." They note areas around natural CO_2 springs—and locations nearby but beyond the influence of the additional CO_2—provide ideal sources of plants for such studies, as the plants near the springs have "been exposed to high CO_2 over an evolutionary time scale," citing Miglietta *et al.* (1993) and Raschi *et al.* (1999).

Nakamura *et al.* conducted experiments designed to reveal numerous characteristics of *Plantago asiatica* plants (a C_3 rosette perennial herb) acquired from locations at different distances from a stream emerging from a CO_2-emitting spring situated at the foot of Mount Gassan (Japan), where the plants had been exposed to normal ambient (370 ppm) and several elevated (726, 771, 1,044, and 5,339 ppm) CO_2 concentrations, as measured in late August and early September in two years presumed to have been typical of CO_2 concentrations at those locations over what they called "an evolutionary time scale."

The six scientists "found phenotypic differences between populations in areas with high and normal CO_2, some of which were heritable," indicating "an evolutionary differentiation occurred in the *P. asiatica* population across a CO_2 gradient." One of these differences was in plant relative growth rate, which, they write, "was higher in parent plants that originated in areas with higher CO_2, suggesting that plants from higher-CO_2 populations had an inherent potential for higher productivity." They conclude "a higher potential of biomass production contributes to fitness and has selective advantages."

Noting their results are "consistent with those of previous experiments, wherein artificial selection increased seed production under the respective CO_2 condition compared to non-selected plants (Ward *et al.*, 2000; Ward and Kelly, 2004)," Nakamura *et al.* conclude their study "clearly shows that phenotypic and genetic differences have occurred between high and normal CO_2 populations."

The scientific findings described above indicate the ongoing rise in atmospheric CO_2 content is exerting significant selection pressure on naturally occurring terrestrial plants, which should improve their resistance to environmental stressors via the process of micro-evolution as atmospheric CO_2 concentrations continue to rise.

References

Ainsworth, E.A., Rogers, A., Vodkin, L.O., Walter, A., and Schurr, U. 2006. The effects of elevated CO_2 concentration on soybean gene expression. An analysis of growing and mature leaves. *Plant Physiology* **142**: 135–147.

Collins, S. and Bell, G. 2004. Phenotypic consequences of 1000 generations of selection at elevated CO_2 in a green alga. *Nature* **431**: 566–569.

Cornelissen, T. and Stiling, P. 2004. Perfect is best: how leaf fluctuating asymmetry reduces herbivory by leaf miners. *Oecologia* **142**: 46–56.

Cornelissen, T., Stiling, P., and Drake, B. 2004. Elevated CO_2 decreases leaf fluctuating asymmetry and herbivory by leaf miners on two oak species. *Global Change Biology* **10**: 27–36.

Cseke, L.J., Tsai, C.-J., Rogers, A., Nelsen, M.P., White, H.L., Karnosky, D.F., and Podila, G.K. 2009. Transcriptomic comparison in the leaves of two aspen genotypes having similar carbon assimilation rates but different partitioning patterns under elevated [CO_2]. *New Phytologist* **182**: 891–911.

Fordham, M., Barnes, J.D., Bettarini, I., Polle, A., Slee, N., Raines, C., Miglietta, F., and Raschi, A. 1997. The impact of elevated CO_2 on growth and photosynthesis in *Agrostis canina* L ssp. *monteluccii* adapted to contrasting atmospheric CO_2 concentrations. *Oecologia* **110**: 169–178.

Gupta, P., Duplessis, S., White, H., Karnosky, D.F., Martin, F., and Podila, G.K. 2005. Gene expression patterns of trembling aspen trees following long-term exposure to interacting elevated CO_2 and tropospheric O_3. *New Phytologist* **167**: 129–142.

Kaligaric, M., Tognetti, R., Janzekovic, F., and Raschi, A. 2008. Leaf fluctuating asymmetry of *Myrtus communis* L., affected by increases in atmospheric CO_2 concentration: Evidence from a natural CO_2 spring. *Polish Journal of Environmental Studies* **17**: 503–508.

Kohut, R. 2003. The long-term effects of carbon dioxide on natural systems: issues and research needs. *Environment International* **29**: 171–180.

Lau, J.A., Shaw, R.G., Reich, P.B., Shaw, F.H., and Tiffin, P. 2007. Strong ecological but weak evolutionary effects of elevated CO_2 on a recombinant inbred population of *Arabidopsis thaliana*. *New Phytologist* **175**: 351–362.

Lau, J.A., Strengbom, J., Stone, L.R., Reich, P.B., and Tiffin, P. 2008. Direct and indirect effects of CO_2, nitrogen, and community diversity on plant-enemy interactions. *Ecology* **89**: 226–236.

Martel, J., Lempa, K., and Haukioja, E. 1999. Effects of stress and rapid growth on fluctuating asymmetry and insect damage in birch leaves. *Oikos* **86**: 208–216.

Miglietta, F., Raschi, A., Bettarini, I., Resti, R., and Selvi, F. 1993. Natural CO_2 springs in Italy: a resource for examining long-term response of vegetation to rising atmospheric CO_2 concentrations. *Plant, Cell and Environment* **16**: 873–878.

Moller, A. and Swaddle, J.P. 1997. *Asymmetry, Developmental Stability and Evolution.* Oxford University Press, Oxford, UK.

Nakamura, I., Onoda, Y., Matsushima, N., Yokoyama, J., Kawata, M., and Hikosaka, K. 2011. Phenotypic and genetic differences in a perennial herb across a natural gradient of CO_2 concentration. *Oecologia* **165**: 809–818.

Onoda, Y., Hirose, T., and Hikosaka, K. 2009. Does leaf photosynthesis adapt to CO_2-enriched environments? An experiment on plants originating from three natural CO_2 springs. *New Phytologist* **182**: 698–709.

Polle, A., McKee, I., and Blaschke, L. 2001. Altered physiological and growth responses to elevated [CO_2] in offspring from holm oak (*Quercus ilex* L.) mother trees with lifetime exposure to naturally elevated [CO_2]. *Plant, Cell & Environment* **24**: 1075–1083.

Rae, A.M., Ferris, R., Tallis, M.J., and Taylor, G. 2006. Elucidating genomic regions determining enhanced leaf growth and delayed senescence in elevated CO_2. *Plant, Cell & Environment* **29**: 1730–1741.

Rae, A.M., Tricker, P.J., Bunn, S.M., and Taylor, G. 2007. Adaptation of tree growth to elevated CO_2: quantitative trait loci for biomass in *Populus*. *New Phytologist* **175**: 59–69.

Raschi, A., Miglietta, F., Tognetti, R., and van Gardingen, P.R. 1999. *Plant Responses to Elevated CO_2. Evidence from Natural Springs.* Cambridge University Press, Cambridge, UK.

Reich, P.B., Tilman, D., Craine, J., Ellsworth, D., Tjoelker, M.G., Knops, J., Wedin, D., Naeem, S., Bahauddin, D., Goth, J., Bengston, W., and Lee, T.D. 2001. Do species and functional groups differ in acquisition and use of C, N, and water under varying atmospheric CO_2 and N availability regimes? A field test with 16 grassland species. *New Phytologist* **150**: 435–448.

Root, T.L. and Schneider, S.H. 1993. Can large-scale climatic models be linked with multiscale ecological studies? *Conservation Biology* **7**: 256–270.

Schulte, M., Von Ballmoos, P., Rennenberg, H., and Herschbach, C. 2002. Life-long growth of *Quercus ilex* L. at natural CO_2 springs acclimates sulphur, nitrogen and carbohydrate metabolism of the progeny to elevated pCO_2. *Plant, Cell & Environment* **25**: 1715–1727.

Springer, C.J., Orozco, R.A., Kelly, J.K., and Ward, J.K. 2008. Elevated CO_2 influences the expression of floral-initiation genes in *Arabidopsis thaliana*. *New Phytologist* **178**: 63–67.

Strengbom, J. and Reich, P.B. 2006. Elevated CO_2 and increased N supply reduce leaf disease and related photosynthetic impacts on *Solidago rigida*. *Oecologia* **149**: 519–525.

Taylor, G., Street, N.R., Tricker, P.J., Sjodin, A., Graham, L., Skogstrom, O., Calfapietra, C., Scarascia-Mugnozza, G., and Jansson, S. 2005. The transcriptome of *Populus* in elevated CO_2. *New Phytologist* **167**: 143–154.

Thomas, S.C. and Jasienski, M. 1996. Genetic variability and the nature of micro-evolutionary response to elevated CO_2. In: Korner, C. and Bazzaz, F.A. (Eds.) *Carbon Dioxide, Populations and Communities.* Academic Press, Inc., San Diego, California, USA, pp. 51–81.

Tognetti, R., Longobucco, A., Raschi, A., and Jones, M.B. 2001. Stem hydraulic properties and xylem vulnerability to embolism in three co-occurring Mediterranean shrubs at a natural CO_2 spring. *Australian Journal of Plant Physiology* **28**: 257–268.

Ward, J.K., Antonovics, J., Thomas, R.B., and Strain, B.R. 2000. Is atmospheric CO_2 a selective agent on model C_3 annuals? *Oecologia* **123**: 330–341.

Ward, J.K. and Kelly, J.K. 2004. Scaling up evolutionary responses to elevated CO_2: lessons from *Arabidopsis*. *Ecology Letters* **7**: 427–440.

Woodward, F.I., Thompson, G.B., and McKee, I.F. 1991. The effects of elevated concentrations of carbon dioxide on individual plants, populations, communities and ecosystems. *Annals of Botany* **67**: 23–38.

4.5.3 Warming-Induced

- Plants may exhibit a rapid evolutionary response to temperature modifications, making them much better prepared than scientists have long believed to meet whatever possible challenge higher temperatures might pose.

IPCC contends CO_2-induced global warming will result in mass plant extinctions because many species will not be able to migrate poleward in latitude or upward in altitude fast enough to find temperature regimes suitable for their continued existence. That scenario assumes plants cannot evolve quickly enough to increase their ranges to keep up with the effects of warming, and that they cannot adjust their inner workings to be able to tolerate more heat than they seem capable of enduring at present. The papers reviewed below explore those possibilities.

Gunter *et al.* (2000) note many models of actual or attempted range shifts in response to global warming lack a thorough understanding of "the role that acclimation and genetic adaptation may have in a species' response to predicted climate regimes," stating if populations "have a greater capacity for adjustment to higher temperatures, and if they are not constrained by complete genetic isolation from other populations, then the effects of global warming will probably be less severe than what may be predicted from a simple temperature-response curve applied without regard to spatial or temporal genetic variation."

The four researchers employed random amplified polymorphic DNA markers to evaluate population-level genetic structure as an indirect indicator of the capacity for response to environmental change by sugar maple trees from three geographical locations representing a north-south gradient of that species' current distribution. They found "genetic diversity, as indicated by estimates of percent polymorphic loci, expected heterozygosity, fixation coefficients, and genetic distance, is greatest in the southern region, which consists of populations with the maximum potential risk due to climate change effects." They say "the high degree of variation within sugar maple implies that it may contain genetic mechanisms for adaptation."

Gunter *et al.* note sugar maple range shift potentials derived by the Goddard Institute for Space Studies (Hansen *et al.*, 1983) and NASA's Geophysical Fluid Dynamics Laboratory (Manabe and Wetherald, 1987)—as described by Davis and Zabinski (1992)—"assume that a species grows only in a climate with temperature and precipitation identical to its current range." In a significant rebuff of those studies and their alarmist implications, Gunter *et al.* note existing "high levels of genetic variation among families indicate that vegetational models designed to predict species' responses to global-scale environmental change may need to consider the degree and hierarchical structure of genetic variation when making large-scale inferences." The ability of species to adapt to a changing environment may be far greater than what is presumed by the outdated climate envelope approach.

Hamrick (2004) also noted concerns that "expected changes may be of such an extent that tree species will not have adequate genetic variation to adapt to the modified conditions (Critchfield, 1984; Davis and Zabinski, 1992)"; "environmental changes may occur at such a rapid rate that trees, with their long generation times, could not adapt quickly enough to keep pace with predicted changes (Davis and Shaw, 2001)"; and trees "may not be capable of dispersing into newly available habitats quickly enough to match the rate of environmental change (Clark, 1998)."

In reviewing the findings of several studies that focused on the responses of trees to conditions analogous to those of computer-generated simulations of rapid global warming, Hamrick found "trees combine life-history traits and levels of genetic diversity that will allow them to adapt relatively quickly to environmental changes," noting they have high genetic mobility via pollen. The plant biology and genetics professor also notes "tree species have faced large-scale global environmental changes many times during their evolutionary histories," and even though these changes "occurred quite quickly, most tree species have survived," maintaining traits that "may allow many tree species to survive predicted global climatic changes while preserving much of their genetic diversity."

Jump *et al.* (2006) write, "one of the basic assumptions in the study of plant adaptation to environment (genecology) is that natural selection in different environments generates genetic clines that correlate with environmental clines." They point out "temperature is of major importance as a selective agent causing population differentiation over altitudinal and latitudinal clines (Saxe *et al.*, 2001)," and "temporal changes in gene frequency that result from global warming should therefore mirror spatial changes observed with decreasing altitude and latitude." These changes, they write, are typically manifest in particular alleles that "may be confined to, or occur preferentially in, different sites with contrasting environmental conditions."

The four researchers "combined population genomic and correlative approaches to identify adaptive genetic differentiation linked to temperature within a natural population of the tree species *Fagus sylvatica* L. [European beech] in the Montseny Mountains of Catalonia, northeastern Spain," concentrating on three areas: the upper treeline (high *Fagus* limit, HFL), the lower limit of *F. sylvatica* forest (low *Fagus* limit, LFL), and an area of the forest interior.

Jump *et al.* note the 648-meter altitudinal difference that separates the HFL and LFL locations "equates to a mean temperature difference of 3°C ... based on the altitudinal lapse rate of 0.51°C per 100 meters reported by Peñuelas and Boada (2003) for Montseny." Regarding the change in temperature due to the region's manifestation of twentieth-century global warming, they write, "by 2003, temperatures had increased by approximately 1.65°C when compared with the 1952–1975 mean," and this temperature change, they remark, was "likely to represent a strong selection pressure."

Numerous tests conducted by Jump *et al.* on the data they collected reveal the frequency of a particular *F. sylvatica* allele shows a predictable response to both altitudinal and temporal variations in temperature, with a declining frequency and probability of presence at the HFL site the Spanish research team determined to be "in parallel with rising temperatures in the region over the last half-century." They say their work "demonstrates that adaptive climatic differentiation occurs between individuals within populations, not just between populations throughout a species geographic range," which further suggests "some genotypes in a population may be 'pre-adapted' to warmer temperatures (Davis and Shaw, 2001)."

Jump *et al.* also contend "the increase in frequency of these genotypes," which occurred in their study in parallel with rising temperatures, "shows that current climatic changes are now imposing directional selection pressure on the population," and "the change in allele frequency that has occurred in response to this selection pressure also demonstrates that a significant evolutionary response can occur on the same timescale as current changes in climate," citing Davis *et al.* (2005), Jump and Peñuelas (2005), and Thomas (2005).

Jump *et al.* conclude an evolutionary response to global warming of the type they describe is likely already "underway," which further suggests many species of plants probably will not be forced to migrate either poleward in latitude or upward in altitude in response to global warming, as climate models suggest they will be forced to do. Instead, they will adjust their ranges (meaning, expand them) at the cold-limited boundaries of their ranges, and they may not be forced to make any major changes at the heat-limited boundaries of their ranges.

Keller *et al.* (2011) note "studies on the evolution of plant populations during historical fluctuations in climate can reveal the capacity for and constraints on adaptive evolution and may help inform predictions about evolutionary responses to future environments." They tested for adaptive variation in 13 ecophysiology and phenology traits on clonally propagated genotypes of balsam poplar (*Populus balsamifera* L.) trees originating from a range-wide sample of 20 sub-populations that developed during the warming of climate conditions that marked the end of the last glacial maximum (~18 thousand years ago), when there was a rapid environmental change that increased population sizes and led to range expansions in many plant species. This "wave of migrations," they write, "affected genomic diversity within populations, as colonists sub-sampled alleles from the ancestral gene pool during the process of expansion," as described

by Lascoux *et al.* (2004), Petit *et al.* (2004), and Savolainen and Pyhajarvi (2007). The six scientists report, "evidence for divergence in excess of neutral expectations was present for eight of thirteen traits," noting "strong correlations were present between traits, geography [extending across the whole of Canada from the Atlantic to Pacific Oceans], and climate." These results, they conclude, reveal "a general pattern of northern subpopulations adapted to shorter, drier growing seasons compared with populations in the center or eastern regions of the range."

Keller *et al.* say their study "demonstrates pronounced adaptive variation in ecophysiology and phenology among balsam poplar populations," suggesting "as this widespread forest tree species expanded its range since the end of the last glacial maximum, it evolved rapidly in response to geographically variable selection." It is likely to do so again if circumstances warrant; as they conclude, "balsam poplar is both highly variable and capable of a broad range of adaptive physiological responses to a changing climate."

Niu *et al.* (2012) write, "it is well documented that plants (Mooney *et al.*, 1978; Berry and Bjorkman, 1980; Atkin and Tjoelker, 2003), animals (Parmesan, 2006), and microbes (Bradford *et al.*, 2008) acclimate and/or adapt to prevailing environmental conditions in a way that can optimize their functioning under varying temperatures, which is collectively termed optimality (Parker and Maynard Smith, 1990)." They hypothesize "the integrated response of an ecosystem, as an assemblage of interacting organisms, might also demonstrate thermal optimality under temperature change," citing Loreau (2010).

Niu *et al.* "compiled data from 169 globally distributed sites of eddy covariance and quantified the temperature response functions of net ecosystem exchange (NEE), an ecosystem-level property, to determine whether NEE shows thermal optimality and to explore the underlying mechanisms."

The team of 68 researchers from 19 countries writes, "the temperature response of NEE followed a peak curve, with the optimum temperature (corresponding to the maximum magnitude of NEE) being positively correlated with annual mean temperature over years and across sites." They state, "shifts of the optimum temperature of NEE were mostly a result of temperature acclimation of gross primary productivity (upward shift of optimum temperature) rather than changes in the temperature sensitivity of ecosystem respiration." They report, "extended growing seasons, increased nitrogen mineralization, and enhanced root growth (Peñuelas and Filella, 2001; Churkina *et al.*, 2005; Luo *et al.*, 2009) may also have contributed to the increased CO_2 uptake under higher temperatures, leading to the upward shift in the optimum temperature of gross primary productivity in warmer years."

Pluess and Weber (2012) write, "with increasing temperatures and dryer summers [as predicted by various climate models], areas nowadays covered by beech forests are expected to shrink tremendously," but "if individuals at the dry distribution limits [of the species: *Fagus sylvatica* L.] are adapted to lower moisture availability, *F. sylvatica* might contain the genetic variation for the continuation of beech forests under climate change," even in areas predicted to become devoid of the trees.

The two researchers used an AFLP (amplified fragment length polymorphism) genome scan approach designed to explore the "neutral and potentially adaptive genetic variation in *Fagus sylvatica* in three regions [in the lowland forests of Switzerland] containing a dry and mesic site each," after which they "linked this dataset with dendrochronological growth measures and local moisture availabilities based on precipitation and soil characteristics." They found a "potential for adaptation to water availability" reflected in observed outlier alleles that "indicated micro-evolutionary changes between mesic and dry stands." They also note, "while Rose *et al.* (2009) found adaptation to drought in a common garden experiment with seedlings originating from provenances which were more than 1000 km apart," their own work found genetic differentiation in relation to water availability in neighboring stands. Pluess and Weber conclude "dispersal across large distances is thereby not needed for the spread of 'pre-adapted' genes in *F. sylvatica*," for the trees apparently have the genetic material needed for "the continuation of beech forests under climate change," even in areas that have been predicted to become too dry for *F. sylvatica* trees to survive.

Hahn *et al.* (2012) note "altitudinal gradients comprise an assemblage of environmental, especially climatic, variables which influence the distribution of plant species and, potentially, population genetic variation." They also note some scientists argue climate change may alter species distributions such that, locally, certain species "might become extinct," citing Sala *et al.* (2000) and Thomas *et al.* (2004). The basis for this prediction, the six scientists write, are the observations, "habitat suitability typically decreases at the upper edge of the altitudinal range where population size might decline," and "in small populations genetic diversity is often reduced and inbreeding may increase (Lynch *et al.*, 1995; Young *et al.*, 1996)," with the result that "low genetic diversity and high inbreeding potentially cause loss of fitness due to fixation of deleterious alleles and inbreeding depression (Ouborg *et al.*, 1991; Lynch *et al.*, 1995; Young *et al.*, 2002), which could affect future population persistence."

Hahn *et al.* investigated patterns of population genetic variation in three common plants of semi-dry grasslands—*Briza media*, a wind-pollinated grass, and *Trifolium montanum* and *Ranunculus bulbosus*, two insect-pollinated herbs—at upper peripheral and lower more central altitudes in the Swiss Alps using the AFLP technique. The Swiss researchers determined, contrary to what many had long supposed, altitude had not affected genetic diversity in the grassland species they studied. They report their results indicate "populations at the upper periphery are not genetically depauperate or isolated" and thus may be "important populations for migration under climate change." Hahn *et al.* conclude what they call the "potentially pre-adapted genes" of the three plant species might "spread easily across altitudes," which would help to prevent their local extinction in a warming world.

Thompson *et al.* (2013) write, "in addition to changes in distribution and plasticity, an evolutionary response to climate change may occur if species evolve a genetically-based adaptation to climate change," citing Chevin *et al.* (2010) and Hoffmann and Sgro (2011). They note "it is important to distinguish this genetic response from a plastic response of individuals if we are to fully understand the evolutionary potential of species to evolve with climate change," as has been described by Gienapp *et al.* (2008).

To test the hypothesis that phenolic chemotypes (thymol and carvacrol) of Mediterranean wild thyme (*Thymus vulgaris*) now occur in sites where they were previously absent or have increased their frequency in transitional sites due to a relaxation of selection normally associated with extreme early winter freezing, the team of eight researchers compared the chemotype composition of populations observed in the early 1970s (Vernet *et al.*, 1977) to that found in 2009–2010 for 36 populations sampled along six transects in and around the Saint Martin-de-Londres basin, which covers an area of about 80 km^2 with southern limits about 20 km north of Montpellier in the Mediterranean climate region of southern France.

The eight French researchers discovered "a rapid

and probably ongoing spatial reorganization of a genetic polymorphism that is closely associated with a warming of extreme winter freezing events on a highly localized spatial scale," observing "both a significant appearance of freezing-sensitive phenolic chemotypes in sites where they were historically absent and an increase in their frequency in previously mixed populations." Thompson *et al.* conclude their study, "done over a similar time span as work reporting ecological changes in plant species distribution, illustrates that a rapid evolutionary response to temperature modifications can occur where genetic variation is combined with a change in a previously strong selection pressure, even for a perennial woody plant."

Matter *et al.* (2013) write, "gene flow connects populations, maintains genetic diversity, prevents inbreeding and facilitates the spread of adaptive genes across a species range," citing Slatkin (1985, 1987) and Ellstrand and Elam (1993). They further state, "understanding how plant populations are connected by gene flow, particularly across altitudinal gradients in mountain regions, will improve our understanding of how they will respond to future environmental change." The four Swiss scientists studied patterns of historic gene flow, flowering phenology, and contemporary pollen flow in two common herbs (*Ranunculus bulbosus* and *Trifolium montanum*) along an altitudinal gradient of 1200–1,800 meters a.s.l. over a distance of 1 km among five alpine meadows in Switzerland.

"Historic gene flow was extensive," they write, with their data suggesting "contemporary pollen flow is not limited across altitudes in either species." They conclude "high levels of pollen flow among altitudes in both *R. bulbosus* and *T. montanum* should facilitate exchange of genes which may enhance adaptive responses to rapid climate change."

The observations discussed above suggest plants may be much better prepared to meet upcoming climatic challenges than most scientists once believed.

References

Atkin, O.K. and Tjoelker, M.G. 2003. Thermal acclimation and the dynamic response of plant respiration to temperature. *Trends in Plant Science* 8: 343–351.

Berry, J. and Bjorkman, O. 1980. Photosynthetic response and adaptation to temperature in higher-plants. *Annual Review of Plant Physiology and Plant Molecular Biology* 31: 491–543.

Bradford, M.A., Davies, C.A., Frey, S.D., Maddox, T.R., Melillo, J.M., Mohan, J.E., Reynolds, J.F., Treseder, K.K., and Wallenstein, M.D. 2008. Thermal adaptation of soil microbial respiration to elevated temperature. *Ecology Letters* 11: 1316–1327.

Chevin, L.-M., Lande, R., and Mace, G.M. 2010. Adaptation, plasticity, and extinction in a changing environment: Towards a predictive theory. *PLoS Biology* 8: 10.1371/journal.pbio.1000357.

Churkina, G., Schimel, D., Braswell, B.H., and Xiao, X.M. 2005. Spatial analysis of growing season length control over net ecosystem exchange. *Global Change Biology* 11: 1777–1787.

Clark, J.S. 1998. Why trees migrate so fast: confronting theory with dispersal biology and the paleo-record. *American Naturalist* 152: 204–224.

Critchfield, W.B. 1984. Impact of the Pleistocene on the genetic structure of North American conifers. In: Tanner, R.M. (Ed.) *Proceedings of the Eighth North American Forest Biology Workshop*. Logan, Utah, USA, pp. 70–118.

Davis, M.B. and Shaw, R.G. 2001. Range shifts and adaptive responses to Quaternary climate change. *Science* 292: 673–679.

Davis, M.B., Shaw, R.G., and Etterson, J.R. 2005. Evolutionary responses to changing climate. *Ecology* 86: 1704–1714.

Davis, M.B. and Zabinski, C. 1992. Changes in geographical range resulting from greenhouse warming: Effects on biodiversity of forests. In: *Global Warming and Biological Diversity*, Peters, R.L. (Ed.) Yale University Press, New Haven, Connecticut, USA, pp. 297–308.

Ellstrand, N.C. and Elam, D.R. 1993. Population genetic consequences of small population size: implications for plant conservation. *Annual Review of Ecology and Systematics* 24: 217–242.

Gienapp, P., Teplitsky, C., Alho, J.S., Mills, J.A., and Merila, J. 2008. Climate change and evolution: Disentangling environmental and genetic responses. *Molecular Ecology* 17: 167–178.

Gunter, L.E., Tuskan, G.A., Gunderson, C.A., and Norby, R.J. 2000. Genetic variation and spatial structure in sugar maple (*Acer saccharum* Marsh.) and implications for predicted global-scale environmental change. *Global Change Biology* 6: 335–344.

Hahn, T., Kettle, C.J., Ghazoul, J., Frei, E.R., Matter, P., and Pluess, A.R. 2012. Patterns of genetic variation across altitude in three plant species of semi-dry grasslands. *PLoS ONE* 7: e41608.

Hamrick, J.L. 2004. Response of forest trees to global environmental changes. *Forest Ecology and Management* 197: 323–335.

Hansen, J., Russell, G., Rind, D., Stone, P., Lacis, A., Lebedeff, S., Ruedy, R., and Travis, L. 1983. Efficient three-dimensional global models for climate studies: Models I and II. *Monthly Weather Review* 111: 609–662.

Hoffmann, A.A. and Sgro, C.M. 2011. Climate change and evolutionary adaptation. *Nature* 470: 479–485.

Jump, A.S., Hunt, J.M., Martinez-Izquierdo, J.A., and Peñuelas, J. 2006. Natural selection and climate change: temperature-linked spatial and temporal trends in gene frequency in *Fagus sylvatica*. *Molecular Ecology* 15: 3469–3480.

Jump, A.S. and Peñuelas, J. 2005. Running to stand still: adaptation and the response of plants to rapid climate change. *Ecology Letters* 8: 1010–1020.

Keller, S.R., Soolanayakanahally, R.Y., Guy, R.D., Silim, S.N., Olson, M.S., and Tiffin, P. 2011. Climate-driven local adaptation of ecophysiology and phenology in balsam poplar, *Populus balsamifera* L. (Salicaceae). *American Journal of Botany* 98: 99–108.

Lascoux, M., Palme, A.E., Cheddadi, R., and Latta, R.G. 2004. Impact of ice ages on the genetic structure of trees and shrubs. *Philosophical Transactions of the Royal Society of London B, Biological Sciences* 359: 197–207.

Loreau, M. 2010. Evolution of ecosystems and ecosystem properties. In: Loreau, M. (Ed.) *From Populations to Ecosystems, Theoretical Foundations for a New Ecological Synthesis.* Princeton University Press, Princeton, New Jersey, USA, pp. 225–259.

Luo, Y., Sherry, R., Zhou, X., and Wan, S. 2009. Terrestrial carbon-cycle feedback to climate warming: experimental evidence on plant regulation and impacts of biofuel feedstock harvest. *Global Change Biology Bioenergy* 1: 62–74.

Lynch, M., Conery, J., and Burger, R. 1995. Mutation accumulation and the extinction of small populations. *The American Naturalist* 146: 489–518.

Manabe, S. and Wetherald, R.T. 1987. Large-scale changes in soil wetness induced by an increase in carbon dioxide. *Journal of Atmospheric Sciences* 44: 1211–1235.

Matter, P., Kettle, C.J., Ghazoul, J., and Pluess, A.R. 2013. Extensive contemporary pollen-mediated gene flow in two herb species, *Ranunculus bulbosus* and *Trifolium montanum*, along an altitudinal gradient in a meadow landscape. *Annals of Botany* 111: 611–621.

Mooney, H.A., Bjorkman, O., and Collatz, G.J. 1978. Photosynthetic acclimation to temperature in desert shrub, *Larrea-divaricata*. 1. Carbon-dioxide exchange characteristics of intact leaves. *Plant Physiology* 61: 406–410.

Niu, S., Luo, Y., Fei, S., Yuan, W., Schimel, D., Law, B.E., Ammann, C., Arain, M.A., Arneth, A., Aubinet, M., Barr, A., Beringer, J., Bernhofer, C., Black, T.A., Buchmann, N., Cescatti, A., Chen, J., Davis, K.J., Dellwik, E., Desai, A.R., Etzold, S., Francois, L., Gianelle, D., Gielen, B., Goldstein, A., Groenendijk, M., Gu, L., Hanan, N., Helfter, C., Hirano, T., Hollinger, D.Y., Jones, M.B., Kiely, G., Kolb, T.E., Kutsch, W.L., Lafleur, P., Lawrence, D.M., Li, L., Lindroth, A., Litvak, M., Loustau, D., Lund, M., Marek, M., Martin, T.A. Matteucci, G., Migliavacca, M., Montagnani, L., Moors, E., Munger, J.W., Noormets, A., Oechel, W., Olejnik, J., Paw U, K.T., Pilegaard, K., Rambal, S., Raschi, A., Scott, R.L., Seufert, G., Spano, D., Stoy, P., Sutton, M.A., Varlagin, A., Vesala, T., Weng, E., Wohlfahrt, G., Yang, B., Zhang, Z., and Zhou, X. 2012. Thermal optimality of net ecosystem exchange of carbon dioxide and underlying mechanisms. *New Phytologist* 194: 775–783.

Ouborg, N.J., Treuren, R., and Damme, J.M.M. 1991. The significance of genetic erosion in the process of extinction. *Oecologia* 86: 359–367.

Parker, G.A. and Maynard Smith, J. 1990. Optimality theory in evolutionary biology. *Nature* 348: 27–33.

Parmesan, C. 2006. Ecological and evolutionary responses to recent climate change. *Annual Review of Ecology, Evolution and Systematics* 37: 637–669.

Peñuelas, J. and Boada, M. 2003. A global change-induced biome shift in the Montseny Mountains (NE Spain). *Global Change Biology* 9: 131–140.

Peñuelas, J. and Filella, I. 2001. Phenology—Responses to a warming world. *Science* 294: 793–795.

Petit, R.J., Bialozyt, R., Garnier-Gere, P., and Hampe, A. 2004. Ecology and genetics of tree invasions: From recent introductions to Quaternary migrations. *Forest Ecology and Management* 197: 117–137.

Pluess, A.R. and Weber, P. 2012. Drought-adaptation potential in *Fagus sylvatica*: Linking moisture availability with genetic diversity and dendrochronology. *PLoS ONE* 7: 10.1371/journal.pone.0033636.

Rose, L., Leuschner, C., Kockemann, B., and Buschmann, H. 2009. Are marginal beech (*Fagus sylvatica* L.) provenances a source for drought tolerant ecotypes? *European Journal of Forest Research* 128: 335–343.

Sala, O.E., Chapin, F.S., Armesto, J.J., Berlow, E., Bloomfield, J., Dirzo, R., Huber-Sanwald, E., Huenneke, L.F., Jackson, R.B., Kinzig, A., Leemans, R., Lodge, D.M., Mooney, H.A., Oesterheld, M., Poff, N.L., Sykes, M.T., Walker, B.H., Walker, M., and Wall, D.H. 2000. Global biodiversity scenarios for the year 2100. *Science* 287: 1770–1774.

Savolainen, O. and Pyhajarvi, T. 2007. Genomic diversity in forest trees. *Current Opinion in Plant Biology* 10: 162–167.

Saxe, H., Cannell, M.G.R., Johnsen, B., Ryan, M.G., and Vourlitis, G. 2001. Tree and forest functioning in response to global warming. *New Phytologist* **149**: 369–399.

Slatkin, M. 1985. Gene flow in natural populations. *Annual Review of Ecology and Systematics* **16**: 393–430.

Slatkin, M. 1987. Gene flow and the geographic structure of natural populations. *Science* **236**: 787–792.

Thomas, C.D. 2005. Recent evolutionary effects of climate change. In: Lovejoy, T.E. and Hannah, L. (Eds.) *Climate Change and Biodiversity*, Yale University Press, New Haven, Connecticut, USA, pp. 75–88.

Thomas, C.D., Cameron, A., Green, R.E., Bakkenes, M., Beaumont, L.J., Collingham, Y.C., Barend, F., Erasmus, N., Ferreira de Siqueira, M., Grainger, A., Hannah, L., Hughes, L., Huntley, B., van Jaarsveld, A.S., Midgley, G.F., Miles, L., Ortega-Huerta, M.A., Peterson, A.T., Phillips, O.L., and Williams, S.E. 2004. Extinction risk from climate change. *Nature* **427**: 145–148.

Thompson, J., Charpentier, A., Bouguet, G., Charmasson, F., Roset, S., Buatois, B., Vernet, P., and Gouyon, P.-H. 2013. Evolution of a genetic polymorphism with climate change in a Mediterranean landscape. *Proceedings of the National Academy of Sciences* **110**: 2893–2897.

Vernet, P, Guillerm, J.L., and Gouyon, P.H. 1977. Le polymorphisme chimique de *Thymus vulgaris* L. (Labiee) I. Repartition des forms chimiques en relation aver certains facteurs ecologiques. *Oecologia Plantarum* **12**: 159–179.

Young, A.G., Boyle, T.J.B., and Brown, A.H.D. 1996. The population genetic consequences of habitat fragmentation for plants. *Trends in Ecology and Evolution* **11**: 413–418.

Young, A.G., Hill, J.H., Murray, B.G., and Peakall, R. 2002. Breeding system, genetic diversity and clonal structure in the sub-alpine forb *Rutidosis leiolepis* F. Muell. (Asteraceae). *Biological Conservation* **106**: 71–78.

4.5.4 Drought-Induced

- Evidence continues to accumulate for substantial heritable variation of ecologically important plant traits, including root allocation, drought tolerance, and nutrient plasticity, which suggests plants should be capable of rapid evolution based on epigenetic variation alone.

One generally thinks of evolution as acting over very long spans of time. This section explores whether evolution can occur more quickly to help plants cope with the rapid climatic changes IPCC predicts will be caused by continued increases in the atmosphere's CO_2 content.

Franks *et al.* (2007) compared "phenotypic and fitness values of ancestral, descendant, and ancestral x descendant hybrid genotypes [of field mustard (*Brassica rapa*)] grown simultaneously" under conditions that mimicked those before and after a real-world switch from above-average to below-average precipitation in southern California (USA), which led to abbreviated growing seasons from 2000 to 2004. They had "collected *B. rapa* seed in 1997, before the drought, and then again in 2004 from two populations," a dry site and a wet site. Hence they could grow—at the same time and under the same circumstances, in a new set of experiments—plants that had experienced extended drought conditions (descendants) and plants that had not experienced such conditions (ancestors), as well as hybrids of the two, and thus could see whether flowering times (FT) differed, as is likely from life history theory, which "predicts that the optimal FT in annual plants will be shorter with shorter growing seasons," such as those that were imposed by the extended drought that occurred between the two times of their seed collecting.

The three researchers found, as predicted, "the abbreviated growing seasons caused by drought led to the evolution of earlier onset of flowering," as plant descendants "bloomed earlier than ancestors, advancing first flowering by 1.9 days in one study population and 8.6 days in another." They state, "the intermediate flowering time of ancestor x descendant hybrids supports an additive genetic basis for divergence." They conclude, "natural selection for drought escape thus appears to have caused adaptive evolution in just a few generations," further noting, "abundant evidence has accumulated over the past several decades showing that natural selection can cause evolutionary change in just a few generations (Kinnison and Hendry, 2001; Reznick and Ghalambor, 2001)."

Franks *et al.* write their findings "provide evidence for a rapid, adaptive evolutionary shift in flowering phenology after a climatic fluctuation," which "adds to the growing evidence that evolution is not always a slow, gradual process but can occur on contemporary time scales in natural populations" and in response to real-world climatic changes.

In a follow-up study conducted with the same plant material, Franks and Weis (2008) report several life-history traits "differed between the ancestral genotypes collected before and descendant genotypes collected after the natural drought," stating "this shows directly that an evolutionary change in the life-history traits has occurred during a 5-year drought."

They also report "the evolutionary changes in trait levels following the drought are consistent with predictions from life-history theory" because "the drought selected for individuals that flowered earlier, continued to flower for longer given sufficient resources, and produced a more consistent, evenly distributed pattern of flowering over time." These changes, they write, constitute "a true genetically based evolutionary change rather than an expression of phenotypic plasticity."

Jump *et al.* (2008) studied *Fumana thymifolia* (a small shrub that occurs around the Mediterranean Basin) at Spain's Garraf Natural Park, seeking to determine whether reduced seedling establishment observed as a consequence of climate manipulation is a random or selective process, in an attempt to answer what they called "the key question": Does climate change provoke evolutionary change within natural populations?

As an unaltered control treatment, the seven scientists' study had a drought treatment that employed automatically activated transparent plastic shields that covered a third of the plots in response to rainfall and retreated when rainfall stopped (which decreased soil moisture by approximately 20%), and a warming treatment employing reflective covers that reduced nighttime re-radiation of energy received from the Sun during the prior daylight hours from another one-third of the plots (which increased temperature by about 1°C).

Over the seven-year period 1999–2005, Jump *et al.* report, mean yearly seedling density per treatment was significantly reduced in the drought and warming treatments compared with the control treatment, and "when compared against control samples, high single-locus genetic divergence occurred in drought and warming treatment samples, with genetic differentiation up to 37 times higher than background (mean neutral locus) genetic differentiation."

The researchers say the significant reduction in seedling survival in the drought and warming treatments "results from an episode of selection for individuals tolerant of the modified climatic conditions and is not due simply to a random reduction in plant establishment." This implication, they write, "reinforces results reported by other authors that show that genetic variability for climate-related traits exists within natural plant populations (Hamrick and Holden, 1979; Cobb *et al.*, 1994; Kelly *et al.*, 2003; Mitton and Duran, 2004; Franks *et al.*, 2007)."

Jump *et al.* conclude contemporary climate change "is driving changes in gene frequency within natural plant populations," and these changes "are occurring on the same time scale as current climatic changes, based on preexisting genetic variability within populations," citing Jump and Peñuelas (2005), Thomas (2005), Jump *et al.* (2006), and Reusch and Wood (2007). They state this ability to adapt rapidly to rapid climate change may increase the persistence of species "beyond that predicted under a species-based climate envelope approach," such as IPCC typically uses to justify predictions of impending extinctions of species.

In a conclusion that clearly repudiates the catastrophic extinction scenario, Jump *et al.* state their results demonstrate "that rapid evolution in response to climate change may be widespread in natural populations, based on genetic variation already present within the population." The accumulating evidence suggests plants are likely to be much more resilient to rising temperatures and reductions in precipitation than people have long been led to believe.

Franks and Weis (2009) write, "one rigorous way to determine if evolution has occurred in a natural population is to collect propagules before and after an environmental change and raise them under common conditions," noting "this approach was used previously to show that *Brassica rapa* [a self-incompatible weedy winter annual] evolved drought escape through earlier flowering following a series of recent dry years in Southern California, and that early flowering results in higher fitness under drought conditions (Franks *et al.*, 2007)," and "a related study showed that multiple phenological traits and their interactions evolved in response to the drought (Franks and Weis, 2008)."

Working with the same pre- and post-drought collection lines as were used in the Franks *et al.* (2007) experiment, the two researchers set out to estimate the amount of assortative mating within, and the degree of phenological isolation between, two *B. rapa* populations. They found "climate change can alter plant phenology, which can change patterns of assortative mating within populations," and "this assortative mating can directly change genotype frequencies and can also increase the rate of evolution by interacting with selection." Their work demonstrates "climatically driven changes in phenology can potentially influence gene flow among populations due to changes in overlap in flowering schedules," and "these changes in gene flow can also influence both the rate and pattern of evolutionary change."

The two scientists conclude "the high degree of

interdependence of flowering time, assortative mating, selection and gene flow make predicting evolutionary responses to changes in climate particularly complex and challenging." This great degree of complexity suggests that among the multiplicity of outcomes there is a good chance one or more will be just what plants need to respond successfully to the climate change that elicited the changes.

Vigouroux et al. (2001) write, "one important phenomenon that is often overlooked and is poorly documented is the ability of agro-systems to rapidly adapt to environmental variations." Such adaptations, they note, can occur by the adoption of new varieties or by the adaptation of existent varieties to a changing environment. Working in "one of the driest agro-ecosystems in Africa, the Sahel," they "analyzed samples of pearl millet landraces collected in the same villages in 1976 and 2003 throughout the entire cultivated area of Niger," to see how the agro-system had responded to recurrent drought over that time. They studied "phenological and morphological differences in the 1976 and 2003 collections by comparing them over three cropping seasons in a common garden experiment."

The 15 researchers write, "compared to the 1976 samples, samples collected in 2003 displayed a shorter lifecycle and a reduction in plant and spike size." They also report an early flowering allele "increased in frequency between 1976 and 2003," and this increase "exceeded the effect of drift and sampling, suggesting a direct effect of selection for earliness on this gene." Vigouroux et al. conclude "recurrent drought can lead to selection for earlier flowering in a major Sahelian crop," reinforcing the earlier findings of Franks et al. (2007), Franks and Weis (2008, 2009), and Jump et al. (2008).

Pluess and Weber (2012) note, "with increasing temperatures and dryer summers [as predicted by various climate models], areas nowadays covered by beech forests are expected to shrink tremendously," but "if individuals at the dry distribution limits [of the species: Fagus sylvatica L.] are adapted to lower moisture availability, F. sylvatica might contain the genetic variation for the continuation of beech forests under climate change," even in areas predicted to become devoid of the trees.

Pluess and Weber employed an AFLP genome scan approach designed to explore the "neutral and potentially adaptive genetic variation in Fagus sylvatica in three regions [within the lowland forests of Switzerland] containing a dry and mesic site each." They "linked this dataset with dendrochronological growth measures and local moisture availabilities based on precipitation and soil characteristics."

The two Swiss scientists report a "potential for adaptation to water availability" was reflected in observed outlier alleles that "indicated micro-evolutionary changes between mesic and dry stands." They note, "while Rose et al. (2009) found adaptation to drought in a common garden experiment with seedlings originating from provenances which were more than 1000 km apart," Pluess and Weber found genetic differentiation in relation to water availability in neighboring stands. They conclude, "dispersal across large distances is thereby not needed for the spread of 'preadapted' genes in F. sylvatica," for the trees apparently contain the genetic material needed for "the continuation of beech forests under climate change," even in areas predicted to become too dry for F. sylvatica trees to survive.

Zhang et al. (2012) note "a key question in ecology and evolution is to what degree variation in ecologically important traits is heritable, because heritability determines the potential for evolutionary change of traits (Fisher, 1930; Falconer and MacKay, 1996)," and this phenomenon significantly enhances the ability of a species "to adapt to changing environments (Visser, 2008; Hoffmann and Sgro, 2011)." Zhang et al. conducted a glasshouse experiment in which they tested the response of a large number of epigenetic recombinant inbred lines, or epiRILs (lines that are nearly isogenic but highly variable at the level of DNA methylation, which can stably alter the gene expression pattern in cells) of Arabidopsis thaliana to drought and increased nutrient conditions.

The four researchers found "significant heritable variation among epiRILs both in the means of several ecologically important plant traits and in their plasticities to drought and nutrients." They state the significant selection gradients of the several mean traits and plasticities they discovered "suggest that selection could act on this epigenetically based phenotypic variation." They conclude their study "provides evidence that variation in DNA methylation can cause substantial heritable variation of ecologically important plant traits, including root allocation, drought tolerance and nutrient plasticity, and that rapid evolution based on epigenetic variation alone should thus be possible."

These findings bode well for the future of terrestrial plants, even if a significant degree of global warming resumes after its ongoing decade-and-a-half hiatus.

References

Cobb, N., Mitton, J.B., and Whitham, T.G. 1994. Genetic variation associated with chronic water and nutrient stress in pinyon pine. *American Journal of Botany* **81**: 936–940.

Falconer, D.S. and MacKay, T.F.C. 1996. *Introduction to Quantitative Genetics, 4th Edition*. Longman, New York, New York, USA.

Fisher, R.A. 1930. *The Genetical Theory of Natural Selection*. Oxford University Press, Oxford, United Kingdom.

Franks, S.J., Sim, S., and Weis, A.E. 2007. Rapid evolution of flowering time by an annual plant in response to a climate fluctuation. *Proceedings of the National Academy of Sciences USA* **104**: 1278–1282.

Franks, S.J. and Weis, A.E. 2008. A change in climate causes rapid evolution of multiple life-history traits and their interactions in an annual plant. *Journal of Evolutionary Biology* **21**: 1321–1334.

Franks, S.J. and Weis, A.E. 2009. Climate change alters reproductive isolation and potential gene flow in an annual plant. *Evolutionary Applications* **2**: 481–488.

Hamrick, J.L. and Holden, L.R. 1979. Influence of microhabitat heterogeneity on gene frequency distribution and gametic phase disequilibrium in *Avena barbata*. *Evolution* **33**: 707–711.

Hoffmann, A.A. and Sgro, C.M. 2011. Climate change and evolutionary adaptation. *Nature* **470**: 479–485.

Jump, A.S., Hunt, J.M., Martinez-Izquierdo, J.A., and Peñuelas, J. 2006. Natural selection and climate change: temperature-linked spatial and temporal trends in gene frequency in *Fagus sylvatica*. *Molecular Ecology* **15**: 3469–3480.

Jump, A.S. and Peñuelas, J. 2005. Running to stand still: adaptation and the response of plants to rapid climate change. *Ecology Letters* **8**: 1010–1020.

Jump, A.S., Peñuelas, J., Rico, L., Ramallo, E., Estiarte, M., Martinez-Izquierdo, J.A., and Lloret, F. 2008. Simulated climate change provokes rapid genetic change in the Mediterranean shrub *Fumana thymifolia*. *Global Change Biology* **14**: 637–643.

Kelly, C.K., Chase, M.W., de Bruijn, A., Fay, M.F., and Woodward, F.I. 2003. Temperature-based population segregation in birch. *Ecology Letters* **6**: 87–89.

Kinnison, M.T. and Hendry, A.P. 2001. The pace of modern life II: from rates of contemporary microevolution to pattern and process. *Genetica* **112**: 145–164.

Mitton, J.B. and Duran, K.L. 2004. Genetic variation in pinon pine, *Pinus edulis*, associated with summer precipitation. *Molecular Ecology* **13**: 1259–1264.

Pluess, A.R. and Weber, P. 2012. Drought-adaptation potential in *Fagus sylvatica*: Linking moisture availability with genetic diversity and dendrochronology. *PLoS ONE* **7**: 10.1371/journal.pone.0033636.

Reusch, T.B.H. and Wood, T.E. 2007. Molecular ecology of global change. *Molecular Ecology* **16**: 3973–3992.

Reznick, D.N. and Ghalambor, C.K. 2001. The population ecology of contemporary adaptations: what empirical studies reveal about the conditions that promote adaptive evolution. *Genetica* **112**: 183–198.

Rose, L., Leuschner, C., Kockemann, B., and Buschmann, H. 2009. Are marginal beech (*Fagus sylvatica* L.) provenances a source for drought tolerant ecotypes? *European Journal of Forest Research* **128**: 335–343.

Thomas, C.D. 2005. Recent evolutionary effects of climate change. In: Lovejoy, T.E. and Hannah, L. (Eds.) *Climate Change and Biodiversity*, Yale University Press, Cambridge, Massachusetts, USA, pp. 75–88.

Vigouroux, Y., Mariac, C., De Mita, S., Pham, J.-L., Gerard, B., Kapran, I., Sagnard, F., Deu, M., Chantereau, J., Ali, A., Ndjeunga, J., Luong, V., Thuillet, A.-C., Saidou, A.-A., and Bezancon, G. 2001. Selection for earlier flowering crop associated with climatic variations in the Sahel. *PLos ONE* **6**: 10.1371/journal.pone.0019563.

Visser, M.E. 2008. Keeping up with a warming world: assessing the rate of adaptation to climate change. *Proceedings of the Royal Society B—Biological Sciences* **275**: 649–659.

Zhang, Y.-Y., Fischer, M., Colot, V., and Bossdorf, O. 2012. Epigenetic variation creates potential for evolution of plant phenotypic plasticity. *New Phytologist* **197**: 314–322.

5

Terrestrial Animals

Key Findings

The following bullet points summarize the main findings of this chapter:

- The Intergovernmental Panel on Climate Change's (IPCC's) view of future species extinction relies on a narrow view of the literature that is highly selective and based almost entirely on model projections as opposed to real-world observations. The latter often contradict the former.

- Numerous shortcomings are inherent in the models used to predict the impact of climate on the health and distributions of animal species. Assumptions and limitations make those models unreliable in projecting the future in this regard.

- As in past species extinctions, future species losses are unlikely to be directly attributable to climate changes that act over long terms and to which species are well adapted. Species losses in the future are more likely to be attributable to the novel, relatively rapid twentieth and twenty-first century anthropogenic processes of habitat loss and the transportation-mediated dispersal of pathogens and predators (including man) into previously isolated populations.

- The planet's animal species have inherent abilities enabling them to cope with climate changes over a period of a few generations, a single generation, or even in real time.

- Research suggests amphibian populations will

suffer little, if any, harm from projected CO_2-induced global warming, and they may even benefit from it.

- Enhanced plant productivity driven by elevated levels of atmospheric CO_2 tends to support greater abundance of soil microarthropods.

- Although some changes in bird populations and their habitat areas have been documented in the literature, linking such changes to CO_2-induced global warming remains elusive. Also, when there have been changes, they often are positive, as many species have adapted and are thriving in response to rising temperatures of the modern era.

- Published research indicates rising temperatures will not likely increase, and may decrease, plant damage from leaf-eating herbivores, as rising atmospheric CO_2 boosts the production of certain defensive compounds in plants that are detrimental to animal pests.

- Global warming is creating opportunities for butterflies to expand their populations and ranges, just the opposite of alarmist projections of range contractions and butterfly species demise in response to a CO_2-induced warming of Earth.

- The warming-induced extinctions of mammals that have been predicted to occur are highly unlikely to be realized in nature, and warming in fact opens new territories for mammal range expansions. In addition, rising atmospheric CO_2 concentrations may produce changes in the palatability of the trunk and branch tissues of certain trees that may protect them from being killed by hares and rabbits.

- The likely net effect of climate change on the spread of parasitic and vector-borne diseases is complex and at this time difficult to predict. Rising temperatures increase the mortality rates as well as the development rates of many parasites, and temperature is only one of many variables that influence the range of viruses and other sources of diseases.

- Polar bears have survived historic changes in climate that have exceeded those of the twentieth century or are forecast by computer models to occur in the future. In addition, some populations of polar bears appear to be stable despite rising

temperatures and summer sea ice declines. The biggest threat they face is not from global warming, but commercial hunting by humans, which historically has taken a huge toll on polar bear populations.

- Studies of the effects of rising temperatures on reptiles find they often are able to tolerate a greater range of environmental conditions than they have been exposed to in the recent past, demonstrate abilities to thermo-regulate to achieve body temperatures close to their preferred temperatures, and often benefit from warmer temperatures.

- It appears earthworms and soil nematodes respond to increases in the air's CO_2 content, via a number of plant-mediated phenomena, in ways that further enhance the positive effects of atmospheric CO_2 enrichment on plant growth and development, while helping to sequester more carbon more securely in the soil and thereby reducing the potential for CO_2-induced global warming.

Introduction

The draft Summary for Policymakers from the Intergovernmental Panel on Climate Change's (IPCC) Working Group II contribution to the *Fifth Assessment Report* makes the following claims about the impact of climate change on species:

> In response to ongoing climate change, terrestrial and marine species have shifted their ranges, seasonal activities, migration patterns, and abundance, have demonstrated altered species interaction (*high confidence*). Increased tree mortality, observed in many places worldwide, has been attributed to climate change in some regions. While recent warming contributed to the extinction of many species of Central American amphibians (*medium confidence*), most recent observed terrestrial-species extinctions have not been attributed to recent climate change, despite some speculative efforts (*high confidence*). Natural climate change at rates much slower than current anthropogenic change has led to significant ecosystem shifts, including species emergences and extinctions, in the past million years (IPCC-II, 2014, p. 3).

While this language is somewhat more nuanced than

past IPCC reports, the necessary qualifications and uncertainties are missing from this language appearing later in the same draft report:

> A large fraction of terrestrial and freshwater species faces increased extinction risk under projected climate change during and beyond the 21st century, especially as climate change interacts with other pressures, such as habitat modification, over-exploitation, pollution, and invasive species (*high confidence*). Extinction risk is increased under all RCP scenarios, with risk increasing with both magnitude and rate of climate change. Many species will be unable to move fast enough during the 21st century to track suitable climates under mid- and high-ranges rates of climate change (i.e., RCP4.5, 6.0, and 8.5) (*medium confidence*). See Figure SPM.5. Management actions can reduce, but not eliminate, risks to ecosystems and can increase ecosystem adaptability, for example through reduction of other stresses and habitat (Ibid., pp. 8–9).

These conclusions are overly alarmist and unsupported by scientific research. The primary error made by IPCC's authors is to ignore the growing anomaly between climate model simulations and real-world observations of global temperature. The world in fact is not warming as fast as IPCC predicts, the twentieth century warming was not as "unprecedented" as IPCC previously thought, transient climate response is likely to be less than once thought, the risk of damaging increases in drought or tropical cyclones is lower, and so on (Idso *et al.*, 2013a; Idso *et al.*, 2013b). All of these concessions and walk-backs have implications for the impacts of climate change on terrestrial animals, all of them seemingly positive, yet Working Group II's Summary for Policymakers makes no concessions. A large body of research thus must be treated with considerable caution because of the resulting exaggeration of species range shifts and erroneous climate projections at regional scales.

Even assuming IPCC climate models were unbiased and reasonably accurate at regional scales, the material presented in this chapter reveals IPCC's view of future species extinction relies on a narrow view of the literature that is highly selective. It is based almost entirely on "climate envelope" model projections that often contradict real-world observations. It is clear the SAR-based (species-area-relationship) extinction estimates pioneered by Thomas *et al.* (2005) exaggerate future extinction rates due to the inherent bias of structural errors (He and Hubbell, 2012) and by systematically disregard-

ing any species that benefit from climate change (Stockwell, 2004). IPCC also improperly characterizes the adaptive responses (e.g., range shifts, phenotypic or genetic adaptations) of many species as supporting its model-based extinction claims. In reality such adaptive responses provide documentary evidence of species *resilience*, proving their ability to cope with present and future climate changes as they have so often done throughout the historic and geologic past.

The findings cited in this chapter make it clear that when confronted with climate change or other challenges, terrestrial animals ranging from amphibians and arthropods to insects, polar bears, and worms exhibit opportunistic and highly adaptive behaviors. Ranges do not suddenly shrink as wildlife passively endures changes to its habitat, as is often projected in model-based studies. Instead, the species fortify themselves against the possibility of extinction, behaving as resilient evolutionary survivors and colonizing new habitat as it becomes available, strengthening their populations against the myriad challenges associated with environmental change.

This chapter begins with a review and analysis of the IPCC-based species extinction claim, highlighting many of the problems inherent in the models on which such claims are based and examples from the paleoecological record where species responded to and survived climate changes similar to or greater than those forecast by IPCC. Model projections are then evaluated against real-world observations of how various animal species responded to what IPCC has called the unprecedented rise in atmospheric CO_2 and temperature of the twentieth and twenty-first centuries. Although there likely will be some changes in species population dynamics in the decades and centuries ahead, few if any species are likely to be driven even close to extinction by global warming. In several instances, real-world data indicate warmer temperatures and higher atmospheric CO_2 concentrations will be highly beneficial, favoring a proliferation of species. IPCC continues to ignore in its reports such positive externalities of rising temperature and atmospheric CO_2.

References

IPCC-II. 2007. *Climate Change 2007: Impacts, Adaptation and Vulnerability.* Contribution of Working Group II to the Fourth Assessment Report of the Intergovernmental Panel on Climate Change. Parry, M.L., Canziani, O.F., Palutikof, J.P., van der Linden, P.J., and Hanson, C.D. (Eds.) Cambridge University Press, Cambridge, UK.

IPCC. 2014. Summary for Policymakers. In *Climate Change 2014: Impacts, Adaptation, and Vulnerability*. Contribution of Working Group II to the Fifth Assessment Report of the Intergovernmental Panel on Climate Change. Draft dated October 28, 2013.

Idso, C.D., Carter, R.M., and Singer, S.F. 2013a. (Eds.) *Climate Change Reconsidered II: Physical Science*. Chicago, IL: The Heartland Institute.

Idso, C.D., Carter, R.M., Singer, S.F., and Soon, W. 2013b. Scientific critique of IPCC's 2013 "Summary for Policymakers," *Policy Brief*. Nongovernmental International Panel on Climate Change (NIPCC), October.

5.1 The Extinction Hypothesis

- IPCC's view of future species extinction relies on a narrow view of the literature that is highly selective and based almost entirely on model projections as opposed to real-world observations. The latter often contradict the former.

5.1.1 Model Shortcomings

The species extinction hypothesis began to appear in the discussion of potential impacts of CO_2-induced global warming in the late twentieth and early twenty-first centuries. Thomas *et al.* (2004), for example, developed projections of future habitat distributions for more than a thousand plant and animal species. Using those projections, they produced estimates of extinction probabilities associated with climate change scenarios for the year 2050 promoted by IPCC (IPCC, 2007). Their ominous projections (the extinction of more than a million species if anthropogenic CO_2 emissions were not quickly and dramatically reduced) were widely disseminated to the popular media even before the research was published. The projections were typically portrayed as well-founded scientific predictions of what was bound to occur.

The 19 authors first determined the "climate envelopes" of 1,103 species, each envelope representing the current climatic conditions under which a given species was found in nature. Then, after selecting those species where the habitat area would be expected to decrease in response to an increase in temperature, they used an empirical power-law relationship that relates species number to habitat area size to determine extinction probability calculations.

At first blush, their procedure seems reasonable enough, all else being equal. But all else is rarely equal when something changes in the real world. Stockwell (2004) provided an entirely different analysis of the available data, noting most climate change effects research accentuates the "losers" while deprecating the "winners." Stockwell notes Thomas *et al.*'s approach to the issue "ignores species that are currently threatened with extinction by non-climatic factors, and which could therefore benefit from an expanded potential habitat and so escape extinction in the new CO_2/climate regime." As Stockwell describes it, "a CO_2- or climate-driven range expansion would clearly help species that are threatened with extinction due to increasing habitat loss attributable to expanding urbanization and agricultural activities; while it may help other species that are threatened with extinction by habitat fragmentation to cross geographical barriers that were previously insurmountable obstacles to them." Consequently, he continues, "by neglecting the many species that fall into these and other like categories, no decrease in extinctions is possible under Thomas *et al.*'s approach to the problem, even under [a] free dispersal scenario, with the result that a massive increase in extinctions is a foregone conclusion."

Stockwell further notes, "the no dispersal scenario also forces an unrealistic decrease in range with any climatic change that shifts habitat area without reducing it; while 'overfitting' reduces ranges even more, producing systematic errors on the order of 10–20%, particularly with smaller data sets, deficiencies in data sampling and modeling methods, and the inclusion of irrelevant variables (Stockwell and Peterson 2002a; 2002b; 2003)."

With respect to Bakkenes *et al.* (2002), one of the studies relied on by Thomas *et al.*, for example, Stockwell writes, "two independent climate variables adequately explain 93% of the variation in their dependent variable; while the use of more climate variables ends up incorporating more random variation than it does actual signal, leading to a contraction of the climate envelope and a systematic bias towards smaller predicted ranges." It should come as no surprise, therefore, as Stockwell continues, "that in this study and that of Peterson *et al.* (2002)—which comprise two of the six major studies on which the analysis of Thomas *et al.* is based—the use of only two climate variables by the two studies yields extinction percentages of 7% and 9%, while the four additional studies upon which Thomas *et al.* rely (which use from 3 to 36 independent variables) yield extinction percentages ranging from 20% to 34%, consistent with what would be expected from errors associated with statistical over-fitting."

Because these ecological models are so unreliable, the common-sense response should be to attempt to verify model-based projections with independent data. However, Stockwell notes, "their single attempt to do so with a real-world extinction supposedly caused by global warming (Pounds *et al.*, 1999) has been satisfactorily explained by changes in local weather patterns due to upwind deforestation of adjacent lowlands (Lawton *et al.*, 2001)." Stockwell concludes, "Thomas *et al.* have a dearth of pertinent hard data to support their contentions; and while the absence of evidence does not necessarily disprove a claim, the lack of any real extinction data to support the results of their analysis certainly suggests that the models they are using are not 'tried and true'."

Stockwell concludes, "Thomas *et al.* (2004) seek to create the impression of impending ecological disaster due to CO_2-induced global warming, claiming their results justify mandating reductions of greenhouse gas emissions," but their findings "are forced by the calculations, confounded with statistical bias, lack supporting real-world evidence, and are perforated with speculation." Stockwell concludes "their doctrine of 'massive extinction' is actually a case of 'massive extinction *bias*'."

It may be argued Thomas *et al.* provide a service to conservation by raising awareness of the potential for species extinction due to climate change, but promoting biased methods that are poorly developed and unsupported by evidence is not scientifically responsible. The discrepancy between the forecasts of future impacts that include large-scale range reduction has yet to be reconciled with the relatively few extinctions from quite large and rapid climate changes in the past (Moritz and Agudo, 2013).

Botkin *et al.* (2007) are highly critical of the application of such methods, particularly when the results are at variance with the evidence provided by the fossil record. And in another critique of the Thomas *et al.* paper, Dormann (2007) found it important to "review the main shortcomings of species distribution models and species distribution projections" such as those employed and derived by Thomas *et al.* He carefully analyzed three aspects of what he described as "problems associated with species distribution models."

The first of these aspects is general species distribution model issues, under which Dormann listed four major problems. The second is extrapolation issues, where he found five major problems; and the third is statistical issues, where he listed six major problems. The methods employed and findings claimed by studies such as Thomas *et al.*, Dormann writes, "have been challenged for conceptual and statistical reasons" by many other researchers, including Buckley and Roughgarden (2004), Harte *et al.* (2004), Thuiller *et al.* (2004), Lewis (2006), and Botkin *et al.* (2007). Dormann thus concludes, "projections of species distributions are not merely generating hypotheses to be tested by later data" but instead are being presented as "predictions of tomorrow's diversity, and policy makers and the public will interpret them as forecasts, similar to forecasts about tomorrow's weather," which he clearly believes is unwarranted and unwise.

Detailed intercomparative studies have borne out these concerns about the quality of species' distribution models. Forecasts of the future geographic distribution of six species of Falco from northern Europe ranged from a contraction in 80% of the species to no net loss in any species, seriously hampering their efficacy in conservation practices (Rodriguez-Castaneda *et al.* 2012).

The most effective criticism has been of the method used to estimate extinction rates by reversing the species-area accumulation curve, a species-area relationship (SAR) used to estimate extinction rates before they are actually observed, the so-called "extinction debt" owing to reduction in habitat and population size during a climate change. Researchers He and Hubbell (2011) show Thomas *et al.* (2005) overestimate the extinction debt from habitat loss largely due to a sampling artifact.

Pereira *et al.* (2012) responded by claiming He and Hubbell's SAR estimates are themselves biased. Thomas and Williamson (2012) report extinction is caused by many factors, not just habitat loss, and species already have responded to climate change in a manner consistent with high future extinction risks. In reply, He and Hubbell (2012) show the Pereira *et al.* (2012) claims are not substantiated and the SAR method of Thomas *et al.* (2005) is not appropriate for estimating extinction rates caused by habitat loss of any kind, concluding, "this so-called backward SAR method is a method for estimating endemic species, not 'extinction debt.' The backward SAR method has nothing to do with, and does not measure, extinction debt." Subsequent debate has clarified the proofs and results are general and explain the widely recognized overestimation of extinction by the backward SAR method, which should not be used to estimate species extinction in practice (He and Hubbell, 2013).

Despite the multitude of problems associated with

the Thomas *et al.* paper, the extinction hypothesis was revived by Parmesan (2006). In reviewing 866 papers addressing the subject of ecological and evolutionary responses to the global warming of the prior few decades, Parmesan raised new concerns about the ability of Earth's many species of plants and animals to maintain a viable foothold on the planet if temperatures continue to rise. But much of the evidence cited by Parmesan actually weighs *against* this concern.

Parmesan notes "most observations of climate-change responses have involved alterations of species' phenologies." She reports, for example, many species had exhibited "advancement of spring events," such that there was "a lengthening of vegetative growing season in the Northern Hemisphere," which is something most would consider a positive phenomenon. She also reports "summer photosynthetic activity increased from 1981–1991"—another positive response—and the growing season throughout the United States "was unusually long during the warm period of the 1940s," but "since 1996, growing season length has increased only in four of the coldest, most-northerly zones (42°–45° N latitude), not in the three warmest zones (32°–37° N latitude)."

The negativity Parmesan associates with these mostly positive warming-induced phenological changes arises from the possibility there may be "mismatches" across different trophic levels in natural ecosystems, such as between the time each year's new crop of herbivores appears and the time of appearance of the plants they depend on for food. Eleven plant-animal associations were studied intensively in this regard, and in seven of them, Parmesan states, "they are more out of synchrony now than at the start of the studies."

Of course there always will be winners and losers (some big and some small) in such animal-plant matchups during periods of climate change, and probably many "draws." In addition, the paucity of pertinent data at the time of the Parmesan study precluded a valid determination of which of the three alternatives is the most likely to predominate. As one example of a "big loser" in the face of recent global warming, Parmesan reports, "field studies have documented that butterfly-host asynchrony has resulted directly in population crashes and extinctions." But population extinctions are not species extinctions, and she acknowledges the local extinctions to which she referred merely resulted in "shifting [the] mean location of extant populations northward [in the Northern Hemisphere] and

upward." Newer research conducted since the publication of Parmesan's study suggests there could be many more wins and draws than losses as species cope with and adapt to such trophic mismatches.

A second major biological response to global warming addressed by Parmesan is species migration, often said to lead to range restrictions that make it difficult for species to maintain the minimum viable population size required for their continued existence. For example, it is often claimed global warming will be so fast and furious that many species will not be able to migrate poleward in latitude or upward in altitude rapidly enough to avoid extinction, or if located on mountaintops they will run out of suitable new habitat to which they can flee when faced with rising temperatures. On this subject, Parmesan essentially rehashed the earlier findings of the meta-analyses of Root *et al.* (2003) and Parmesan and Yohe (2003), which predominantly portrayed species ranges as expanding in the face of rising temperatures, since warming provides an opportunity for species to expand their ranges at their cold-limited boundaries while often providing a much reduced impetus for them to retreat at the heat-limited boundaries of their ranges. An example of this phenomenon cited by Parmesan occurred in the Netherlands between 1979 and 2001, where she reports "77 new epiphytic lichens colonized from the south, nearly doubling the total number of species for that community."

Parmesan also reports "increasing numbers of researchers use analyses of current intraspecific genetic variation for climate tolerance to argue for a substantive role of evolution in mitigating negative impacts of future climate change," additionally noting the fossil record contains "a plethora of data indicating local adaptation to climate change at specific sites." In addition, she states, there is evidence many existing species during earlier periods of dramatic climate change "appeared to shift their geographical distributions as though tracking the changing climate." In both of these situations the outcomes were clearly positive.

The greatest push by Parmesan for a decisively negative consequence of global warming is her claim that "documented rapid loss of habitable climate space makes it no surprise that the first extinctions of entire species attributed to global warming are mountain-restricted species," "many cloud-forest-dependent amphibians have declined or gone extinct on a mountain in Costa Rica (Pounds *et al.*, 1999, 2005)," and "among harlequin frogs in Central and South American tropics, an astounding 67% have disappeared over the past 20–30 years," citing Pounds *et al.* (2006) regarding the latter. Such claims subsequently were shown by several researchers to be incorrect (see Amphibians, Section 5.2), as all the extinctions and disappearances of the amphibian species to which Parmesan referred had nothing at all to do with "rapid loss of habitable climate space" at the tops of mountains. As Pounds *et al.* (2006) note, the loss of these species "is largest at middle elevations, even though higher-elevation species generally have smaller ranges." In addition, as noted in an earlier review of the subject by Stuart *et al.* (2004), many of the amphibian species declines "took place in seemingly pristine habitats," which had not been lost to global warming nor even modestly altered. The extinctions and species disappearances appeared not to have been due to rising temperatures *per se*, but to the fungal disease chytridiomycosis, which is caused by *Batrachochytrium dendrobatidis*, as noted by both Stuart *et al.* (2004) and Pounds *et al.* (2006).

The fallacy of the montane range restriction assumption was shown by Tingley *et al.* (2012) in a study of breeding ranges of birds across three elevational transects in the Sierra Nevada Mountains (USA). While rising temperature over the past century pushed species upslope, they found increased precipitation pulled them downslope, resulting in range shifts that were heterogeneous within species and among regions. Thus despite increasing temperature in montane environments, the highly variable precipitation regimes create highly heterogeneous responses by species at range margins.

Other studies have poked further holes in the model-based animal extinction hypothesis, some for similar reasons, others for new ones.

Noting "climate envelopes (or the climatic niche concept) are the current methods of choice for prediction of species distributions under climate change," Beale *et al.* (2008) state, "climate envelope methods and assumptions have been criticized as ecologically and statistically naive (Pearson and Dawson, 2003; Hampe, 2004)," and "there are many reasons why species distributions may not match climate, including biotic interactions (Davis *et al.*, 1998), adaptive evolution (Thomas *et al.*, 2001), dispersal limitation (Svenning and Skov, 2007), and historical chance (Cotgreave and Harvey, 1994)."

Beale *et al.* evaluated the degree of matchup of species distributions to environment by generating synthetic distributions that retained the spatial structure of observed distributions but were randomly placed with respect to climate. They report, "using

data on the European distribution of 100 bird species, we generated 99 synthetic distribution patterns for each species," and "for each of the 100 species, we fitted climate envelope models to both the true distribution and the 99 simulated distributions by using standard climate variables." They determined the goodness-of-fit of the many distribution patterns, because, as they note, "there has been no attempt to quantify how often high goodness-of-fit scores, and hence ostensibly good matches between distribution and climate, can occur by chance alone."

The three U.K. researchers determined "species-climate associations found by climate envelope methods are no better than chance for 68 of 100 European bird species." And, they write, "because birds are perceived to be equally strongly associated with climate as other species groups and trophic levels (Huntley *et al.*, 2004)," their results "cast doubt on the predictions of climate envelope models for all taxa." They further state, "many, if not most, published climate envelopes may be no better than expected from chance associations alone, questioning the implications of many published studies." The researchers conclude, "scientific studies and climate change adaptation policies based on the indiscriminate use of climate envelope methods irrespective of species sensitivity to climate may be misleading and in need of revision."

These results are not so surprising in view of the well-known ecological principle that critical life-history events and interspecies relationships often can be the major factor limiting the spread of a species. Correspondingly, seasonal climate and ecosystem productivity variables have been found to be more statistically significant determinants of range than the broader annual climate variables typically used in ecological niche models (Stockwell, 2006).

Nogues-Bravo (2009) states climate envelope models "are sensitive to theoretical assumptions, to model classes and to projections in non-analogous climates, among other issues." He reviewed the pertinent scientific literature to determine how appropriate existing models were for determining whether a species will be driven to extinction by hypothesized planetary warming. He explains, "the studies reviewed: (1) rarely test the theoretical assumptions behind niche modeling such as the stability of species climatic niches through time and the equilibrium of species with climate; (2) they only use one model class (72% of the studies) and one paleoclimatic reconstruction (62.5%) to calibrate their models; (3) they do not check for the occurrence of non-analogous climates (97%); and (4) they do not use independent data to validate the models (72%)."

Nogues-Bravo notes, "ignoring the theoretical assumptions behind niche modeling and using inadequate methods for hindcasting" may produce "a cascade of errors and naïve ecological and evolutionary inferences." He concludes, "there are a wide variety of challenges that [climate envelope models] must overcome in order to improve the reliability of their predictions through time."

Randin et al. (2009) focused their attention on the quality of species distribution models (SDMs). They note, "the mean temperature interpolated from local stations at a 20-meter resolution contains more variability than expressed by the mean temperature within a 50-km x 50-km grid cell in which variation in elevation is poorly represented." Or, as they describe elsewhere in their paper, "climatic differences along elevation gradients, as apparent at 25-m x 25-m resolution, allow plant species to find suitable climatic conditions at higher elevation under climate change," whereas "models at a 10' x 10' resolution [10 minutes of latitude x 10 minutes of longitude, which correspond to 16-km x 16-km cells in the Swiss Alps, where they carried out their analyses] reflect the mean climatic conditions within the cell, and thus provide imprecise values of the probability of occurrence of species along a thermal gradient."

In testing this "local high-elevation habitat persistence hypothesis," Randin et al. assessed "whether climate change-induced habitat losses predicted at the European scale (10 x 10' grid cells) are also predicted from local-scale data and modeling (25-m x 25-m grid cells)." For 78 mountain species modeled at both European and local scales, they found the "local-scale models predict persistence of suitable habitats in up to 100% of species that were predicted by a European-scale model to lose all their suitable habitats in the area."

Randin et al. suggest the vastly different results they obtained when using fine and coarse grid scales might help explain what they call the Quaternary Conundrum: "why fewer species than expected went extinct during glacial periods when models predict so many extinctions with similar amplitude of climate change (Botkin et al., 2007)." In addition, they note, "coarse-resolution predictions based on SDMs are commonly used in the preparation of reports by the Intergovernmental Panel on Climate Change," which are then used by "conservation planners, managers, and other decision makers to anticipate biodiversity losses in alpine and other systems across local, regional, and larger scales."

Willis and Bhagwat (2009) discuss other problems that arise from coarse model scales. In a "perspective" published in Science the two raised a warning flag, stating, "coarse spatial scales fail to capture topography or 'microclimatic buffering' and they often do not consider the full acclimation capacity of plants and animals," citing Botkin et al. (2007).

As an example of this model-based deficiency, Willis and Bhagwat cite Randin et al. (2009), noting for alpine plant species growing in the Swiss Alps, "a coarse European-scale model (with 16 km by 16 km grid cells) predicted a loss of all suitable habitats during the 21st century, whereas a model run using local-scale data (25 m by 25 m grid cells) predicted persistence of suitable habitats for up to 100% of plant species." The two Europeans note Luoto and Heikkinen (2008) "reached a similar conclusion in their study of the predictive accuracy of bioclimatic envelope models on the future distribution of 100 European butterfly species," finding "a model that included climate and topographical heterogeneity (such as elevational range) predicted only half of the species losses in mountainous areas for the period from 2051 to 2080 in comparison to a climate-only model."

Another problem was the models' failure to consider the capacity of plants and animals to acclimatize to warmer temperatures. Willis and Bhagwat note "many studies have indicated that increased atmospheric CO_2 affects photosynthesis rates and enhances net primary productivity—more so in tropical than in temperate regions—yet previous climate-vegetation simulations did not take this into account." They cite Lapola et al. (2009), who developed a new vegetation model for tropical South America, the results of which indicate "when the CO_2 fertilization effects are considered, they overwhelm the impacts arising from temperature," so "rather than the large-scale die-back predicted previously, tropical rainforest biomes remain the same or [are] substituted by wetter and more productive biomes."

"Another complexity," note Willis and Bhagwat, is the fact that "over 75% of the Earth's terrestrial biomes now show evidence of alteration as a result of human residence and land use," which has resulted in "a highly fragmented landscape" that has been hypothesized to make it especially difficult for the preservation of species. Nevertheless, they report Prugh et al. (2008) have "compiled and analyzed raw data from previous research on the occurrence of 785 animal species in >12,000 discrete habitat fragments on six continents," and "in many cases, fragment size and isolation were poor predictors of occupancy." They further note "this ability of species to persist in what would appear to be a highly undesirable and fragmented landscape has also been recently demonstrated in West Africa," where "in a census on the presence of 972 forest butterflies over the past 16 years, Larsen [2008] found that despite an 87% reduction in forest cover, 97% of all species ever recorded in the area are still present."

Suggitt *et al.* (2011) note "most multi-cellular terrestrial organisms experience climate at scales of millimeters to meters," yet "most species-climate associations are analyzed at resolutions of kilometers or more," in what is "commonly known as the 'bioclimate approach' or 'climate envelope' modeling." They write, "because individuals experience heterogeneous microclimates in the landscape, species sometimes survive where the average background climate appears unsuitable," which the vast majority of bioclimate studies do not consider in their analyses.

Suggitt *et al.* recorded temperatures in numerous microsites at two locations where the vegetation was relatively homogenous (the Lake Vyrnwy Royal Society for the Protection of Birds reserve in Wales, and High Peak in the Peak District National Park in England) in September 2007 and January 2008, and in numerous microsites within three habitat types (woodland, heathland, and grassland) in Skipwith Common in North Yorkshire, UK, in September 2008 and January 2009. The seven scientists report, "thermal differences between habitats, and slope and aspects, were of the same order of magnitude as projected increases in global average surface temperatures," and in some cases, microclimate temperature variations exceeded estimates of warming under all of IPCC's emissions scenarios, "which range from 1.1 to a 6.4°C rise in global mean temperatures (IPCC, 2007)."

Suggitt *et al.* add, "these large temperature differences provide opportunities for individual organisms that are able to move short distances to escape unfavorable microclimates," and, hence, "populations may shift microhabitats (slopes, aspects and vegetation density) in response to inter-annual variation in the climate." They state their results indicate "the incorporation of habitat and topographical information is essential for species that (a) have some level of flexibility in their habitat associations, and (b) are at least partially limited by temperature extremes." In the real world of nature, the "bioclimate approach" and "climate envelope" modeling are not adequate for describing how species will respond to future changes in climate.

Sears *et al.* (2011) analyzed how spatial heterogeneity can impact biological responses to thermal landscapes at scales more relevant to organisms than the (much larger) scales typically employed by standard climate envelopes. They examined the effects of topographic relief on the range of operative temperatures available for behavioral thermoregulation of animals within various parts of an area described by a given climate envelope. Their results indicated "empirical studies alone suggest that the operative temperatures of many organisms vary by as much as 10–20°C on a local scale, depending on vegetation, geology, and topography," and even this variation in abiotic factors "ignores thermoregulatory behaviors that many animals use to balance heat loads." Through a set of simulations of these phenomena, they "demonstrate how variability in elevational topography can attenuate the effects of warming climates." They found "identical climates can produce very different microclimates at the spatial scales experienced by organisms"; "greater topographic relief should decrease selective pressure on thermal physiology for organisms that use behavior to avoid thermal extremes in heterogeneous environments," citing Huey *et al.* (2003); and "topographic diversity should buffer the impacts of climate change by facilitating behavioral thermoregulation."

Sears *et al.* say well-known relationships in biophysical ecology show "no two organisms experience the same climate in the same way," and "changing climates do not always impact organisms negatively." They conclude, "when coupled with thermoregulatory behavior, variation in topographic features can mask the acute effect of climate change in many cases," rendering the climate envelope approach to assessing species responses to climate change rather useless if not downright deceptive.

Dobrowski (2011) writes, "the response of biota to climate change of the past is pertinent to understanding present day biotic response to anthropogenic warming," and "one such adaptive response garnering increased attention is the purported utilization of climatic refugia by biota." Historically, these refugia were "typically thought of as large regions in which organisms took refuge during glacial advances and retreats during the Pleistocene, which then acted as sources for colonization during more favorable climatic periods." But "in addition to these large-scale refugia," he writes, "there is compelling evidence that climatic refugia occurred at local scales during the Last Glacial Maximum and were also utilized during interglacial warm periods, including the current interglacial (Willis and Van Andel, 2004; Birks and Willis, 2008)."

Dobrowski notes, "modeling using global climate models (GCMs) and regional climate models (RCMs) is done at scales of tens to hundreds of kilometers, whereas research suggests that temperature varies at scales of < 1 km in areas of complex terrain (Urban *et al.*, 2000; Fridley, 2009)." He reports, "Hijmans *et al.* (2005) showed that there can be temperature variation of up to 33°C within one 18-km raster cell." In addition, "GCMs and RCMs can simulate free-air conditions but fail to accurately estimate surface climate due to terrain features that decouple upper atmospheric conditions from boundary layer effects (Grotch and Maccracken, 1991; Pepin and Seidel, 2005)."

Dobrowski points out many researchers "have recently commented on the potential of topographically driven meso- or micro-climatic variation in mountain environments for providing refugia habitats for populations of species threatened by climate warming," citing Luoto and Heikkinen (2008), Randin *et al.* (2009), and Seo *et al.* (2009). And he notes these researchers "point to lower rates of predicted habitat loss and lower predicted extinction probabilities from species distribution models when using finely resolved climate data as compared with coarse scaled data," stating, "they suggest that this is evidence of 'local scale refugia' (Randin *et al.*, 2009) or 'reserves to shelter species' (Seo *et al.*, 2009)."

Dobrowski concludes, "microrefugia are likely to be found in terrain positions that promote the consistent decoupling of the boundary layer from the free-atmosphere," and "these terrain positions are likely to have climate states and trends that are decoupled from regional averages," which is "a requisite for microrefugia to persist through time." Thus, he concludes, "convergent environments (local depressions, valley bottoms, sinks, and basins) are primary candidates for microrefugia based on these criteria," which bodes well for the once-considered-impossible survival of many species of plants and animals in a possible further warming of the planet.

Lande (2009) writes, "the primary mechanisms of phenotypic adaptation are Darwinian evolution by natural selection on genetic variation, and phenotypic plasticity through environmental influence on individual development," further stating, "rapid phenotypic adaptation may be necessary to prevent [the] extinction of modern species subject to anthropogenic global warming, especially those

[species] with long generations such as large-bodied vertebrates and perennial plants." Against this backdrop and while noting "genetic variance in plasticity within and/or among populations has commonly been observed (Scheiner, 1993, 2002)," Lande employed "quantitative genetic models of phenotypic plasticity to analyze the dynamics of phenotypic adaptation to a sudden extreme environmental change" that is "beyond the usual range of background environmental fluctuations."

Lande's model suggests, "during the first generation in the new environment the mean fitness suddenly drops and the mean phenotype jumps towards the new optimum phenotype by plasticity," after which "adaptation occurs in two phases." First, "rapid evolution of increased plasticity allows the mean phenotype to closely approach the new optimum," after which the new phenotype "undergoes slow genetic assimilation, with reduction in plasticity compensated by genetic evolution of reaction norm elevation in the original environment." Such findings suggest there is a sound observational and mechanistic basis for concluding Earth's flora and fauna are genetically capable of coping with the type of rapid CO_2-induced global warming IPCC contends will drive innumerable plant and animal species to extinction.

5.1.2 Paleoecological Records

- As in past species extinctions, future species losses are unlikely to be directly attributable to climate changes that act over long terms and to which species are well adapted. Species losses in the future are more likely to be attributable to the novel, relatively rapid twentieth and twenty-first century anthropogenic processes of habitat loss and the transportation-mediated dispersal of pathogens and predators (including man) into previously isolated populations.

Most of the world's major species "body types" were laid down during the Cambrian period 600 million years ago (Levinton, 1992). These species have dealt successfully through the ages with new pest enemies, new diseases, ice ages, and global temperature swings greater than that predicted to result from CO_2-induced global warming.

During the Paleocene-Eocene Thermal Maximum (PETM), some 56 million years ago, it is believed, large amounts of carbon were released to the ocean-atmosphere system and global temperatures may have risen by 5–8°C, although more recent climate modelling indicates changes in cloud properties and an increase in shortwave radiation played a much greater role in the warm PETM period than previously believed (Kiehl and Shields, 2013).

McInerney and Wing (2011) reviewed much of the scientific literature on the insights being sought by biologists concerned about potential species extinctions due to CO_2-induced global warming, and they give their assessment of the current status of the grand enterprise in which many scientists have been involved since the early 1990s, when the PETM and its significance first began to be recognized (Kennett and Stott, 1991; Koch et al., 1992).

Although there was a major extinction of benthic foraminifera in the world's oceans, the two researchers write, "most groups of organisms did not suffer mass extinction." In fact, they say, "it is surprising that cool-adapted species already living at higher latitudes before the onset of the PETM are not known to have experienced major extinctions," and "this absence of significant extinction in most groups is particularly interesting in light of the predictions of substantial future extinction with anthropogenic global warming." In addition, "low levels of extinction in the face of rapid environmental change during the Quaternary pose a similar challenge to modeled extinctions under future greenhouse warming," citing Botkin et al. (2007). Finally, they observe, "rapid morphological change occurred in both marine and terrestrial lineages, suggesting that organisms adjusted to climate change through evolution as well as dispersal."

McInerney and Wing conclude by noting "research on the PETM and other intervals of rapid global change has been driven by the idea that they provide geological parallels to future anthropogenic warming." The many research results they review seem to suggest Earth's plants and animals, both on land and in the sea, may be much better equipped to deal with the environmental changes that may occur in response to anthropogenic CO_2 emissions than what many students of the subject have long believed.

Hof et al. (2011) present evidence demonstrating "recent geophysical studies challenge the view that the speed of current and projected climate change is unprecedented." In one such study, for example, they report Steffensen et al. (2008) showed temperatures in Greenland warmed by up to 4°C/year near the end of the last glacial period. They state this change and other rapid climate changes during the Quaternary (the last 2.5 million years) did not cause a noticeable level of broad-scale, continent-wide extinctions of species. Instead, these rapid changes appeared to "primarily affect a few specific groups, mainly large mammals (Koch and Barnosky, 2006) and European trees (Svenning, 2003)," so "few taxa became extinct during the Quaternary (Botkin et al., 2007)."

How were the bulk of Earth's species able to survive a climatic change that many today believe is unsurvivable? Hof et al. suggest "species may have used strategies other than shifting their geographical distributions or changing their genetic make-up." They note, for example, "intraspecific variation in physiological, phenological, behavioral or morphological traits may have allowed species to cope with rapid climatic changes within their ranges (Davis and Shaw, 2001; Nussey et al., 2005; Skelly et al., 2007)," based on "preexisting genetic variation within and among different populations, which is an important prerequisite for adaptive responses," noting "both intraspecific phenotypic variability and individual phenotypic plasticity may allow for rapid adaptation without actual microevolutionary changes." Hof et al. conclude, "species are probably more resilient to climatic changes than anticipated in most model assessments of the effect of contemporary climate change."

Indeed, as shown in the subsections below, model-based projections of animal extinctions in response to rising temperature and atmospheric CO_2 suffer a major loss of credibility when tested against real-world data. Although there likely will be some changes in species population dynamics, few if any species will be driven to extinction. In contrast, a number of studies indicate many animal species will benefit from a warming climate and rising atmospheric CO_2 concentrations, resulting in a proliferation, as opposed to extinction, of species.

Vegas-Vilarrubia et al. (2011) contend "current extinction estimates for the near-future should be revised in light of palaeoecological information, which shows that spatial reorganizations and persistence in suitable microrefugia have been more common than extinction during the Quaternary." As a result, they say, "an interesting consequence is the possibility of new unknown species combinations with no modern analogues."

The two phenomena that come into play in these ecosystem transformations are acclimation and adaptation, "with the first relying on phenotypic plasticity and the second involving genetic changes of potential evolutionary significance." Vegas-Vilarrubia et al. note "some authors propose that spatial reorganizations without extinction will be the dominant biotic response to the near-future global changes." But "it is also possible that ecosystems never attain equilibrium," they write, and "transient states perpetuate because of the recurrent action of environmental change." They note "one of the main lessons from this is that ecosystems may express their resilience when confronted with environmental shifts by attaining several possible equilibrium states, as manifested in changes in biodiversity and/or composition, without losing their ecological functions."

Vegas-Vilarrubia *et al.* cite the global warming that occurred at the end of the Younger Dryas (~13,000 to 11,500 years ago), which serves as one of the more powerful analogs of projected global warming "because both magnitude and rates of change parallel those predicted for the present century." This prior real-world transformation "seems to have consisted of ecological reorganizations and changes in community composition because of differential species migration patterns and rates," but they note, "so far, it has not been possible to associate large-scale extinctions to the Younger Dryas climatic reversal."

Mergeay and Santamaria (2012) continue that line of thinking in an editorial introducing nine papers in a special issue of *Evolutionary Applications*. The two special-issue editors note Shine (2012) opens the issue by "showing how evolution can rapidly modify ecologically relevant traits in invading as well as native species." Bijlsma and Loeschcke (2012) then "tackle the interaction of drift, inbreeding and environmental stress," and Angeloni *et al.* (2012) "provide a conceptual tool-box for genomic research in conservation biology and highlight some of its possibilities for the mechanistic study of functional variation, adaptation and inbreeding."

Van Dyck (2012) shows "an organism's perception of its environment is subject to selection, a mechanism that could reduce the initial impact of environmental degradation or alleviate it over the longer run." Urban *et al.* (2012) argue "certain consequences of global change can only be accounted for by interactions between ecological and evolutionary processes." And Lemaire *et al.* (2012) highlight "the important role of evolution in predator-prey interactions."

Focusing on eco-evolutionary interactions, Palkovacs *et al.* (2012) "review studies on phenotypic change in response to human activities" and "show that phenotypic change can sometimes cascade across populations, communities and even entire ecosystems." Bonduriansky *et al.* (2012) examine "non-genetic inheritance and its role in adaptation,"

dissecting "the diversity of epigenetic and other transgenerational effects." Finally, Santamaria and Mendez (2012) "build on the information reviewed in all previous papers to identify recent advances in evolutionary knowledge of particular importance to improve or complement current biodiversity policy."

"Overall," Mergeay and Santamaria (2012) conclude, "these nine papers offer compelling evidence for the role of evolutionary processes in the maintenance of biodiversity and the adaptation to global change."

Meylan *et al.* (2012) focused on "the role of hormonally mediated maternal effects in inducing phenotypic plasticity as a response to rising temperatures and extreme climatic events," citing Marquis *et al.* (2008) on lizards. The three researchers describe how the discovery of maternal androgens and glucocorticoids in egg yolks, together with the intra-clutch variation of these hormones (Groothuis and Schwabl, 2008), make it possible for the offspring phenotype to be "manipulated in response to environmental conditions experienced by the female (Weaver *et al.*, 2004)." This maternal effect can be considered a form of "intergenerational phenotypic (developmental) plasticity," which could prove crucial "in coping with unpredictable environments." They suggest "hormones are a critical link between the environment and the genome" because they "may mediate the expression of phenotypic variation, generate trait integration, shape multivariate trade-offs (Sinervo *et al.*, 2008) and either directly or indirectly shape phenotypic plasticity during ontogeny and later into adulthood (Lessells, 2008)."

Meylan *et al.* further state, "the hormonal cascades involved in organizational effects during development may be modulated by environmental stressors and the maternal response as given by the duration and magnitude of elevated glucocorticoids." They discuss "the phenotypic and population dynamic consequences of prenatal exposure to steroid hormones resulting in context-dependent expression of traits by the offspring," ultimately describing "how hormone-mediated maternal effects may enhance rapid adaptation to changing environmental conditions." Finally, the three ecologists write, "females exposed to abiotic stressors during reproduction may alter the phenotypes by manipulation of hormones to the embryos," and they conclude, "hormone-mediated maternal effects, which generate phenotypic plasticity, may be one avenue for coping with global change."

Clearly, Earth's life forms are well-endowed with complex change-management strategies, either through behavior or otherwise. More recent developments have sought to correct or augment the limitation of static, deterministic paradigms such as niche modeling and species area curves with more dynamic and stochastic paradigms—particularly exploring the consequences of "niche assembly" vs. "dispersal assembly" on extinction risk and biodiversity management (Stockwell, 2013). It is well-known that the composition of many communities is not ruled consistently by species' ecological niches or functional roles, and that they also incorporate stochastic processes (e.g. coastal fish metacommunities, see Mouillot, 2007). Recent work is beginning to redress the incomplete "niche-based" frameworks that have produced unrealistic and counterfactual estimates of extinction loss.

The most potent of the tools has been "unified neutral theory" (UNT, Hubbell, 2001), which provides a simple yet rigorous evaluation of the role of "dispersal assembly" in communities' richness and has provided deeper insights into extinction estimates than "niche assembly" alone might offer. It is clear the SAR-based extinction estimates pioneered by Thomas *et al.* (2005) exaggerate the extinction rates, due to the inherent bias of structural errors (He and Hubbell, 2012) and through disregarding the species that benefit from climate change (Stockwell, 2004). However, it is hypothesized that habitat reductions from any cause will increase the probability of extinction, as rarity usually precedes extinction, even if the effect is not immediately apparent. This is the basis for the notion of "extinction debt." This is a dilemma, for if every environmental change increases extinctions, why haven't all species gone extinct?

A recent application of the UNT simulations of habitat reductions has identified two distinctive species area curves: imminent extinctions from habitat loss and delayed total extinctions indicative of extinction debt. The lag times for relaxation of the community into a lower species richness following habitat loss are often very large, within the order of thousands of years (Halley and Sgardeli, 2014). This suggests much of the "extinction debt" from a specific climate disruption may be redeemed by environmental or physiological changes in the intervening period between when the extinction debt is incurred and when the population has dwindled to unsustainable levels.

Another UNT simulation of two types of colonizing dispersal events—the "volcanic island" and the "land bridge" (Rosindell and Harmon, 2013) shows the stark difference between the colonization of a virgin habitat that slowly builds up diversity, and

the drastic reduction of biodiversity from the sudden connection of unrelated communities via a transportation corridor. As in past species extinctions, future species losses are unlikely to be directly attributable to climate changes that act over long terms and to which species are well adapted. Species losses in the future are more likely to be attributable to the novel, relatively rapid twentieth and twenty-first century anthropogenic processes of habitat loss and the transportation-mediated dispersal of pathogens and predators (including man) into previously isolated populations.

It is clear niche-model-based projections of extinctions are riddled with assumptions and limitations that make them an unreliable guide to the impact of climate change on species. The vast majority of the predicted extinctions likely will not occur. A significant body of real-world evidence suggests most of Earth's plants and animals will be able to easily adapt, survive, and even thrive in the face of projected climate change, even under the worst-case scenarios of CO_2-induced global warming predicted by IPCC. As shown hereafter and in Chapter 4 (see Section 4.4 on Extinction), far from being a detriment to the biosphere, the air's rising CO_2 content is enhancing vegetative productivity and fostering a great proliferation of plant and animal species all around the world, helping to protect them from other anthropogenic forces that might otherwise drive them to extinction, independent of whatever the planet's climate may do.

References

Angeloni, F., Wagemaker, C.A.M., Vergeer, P., and Ouborg, N.J. 2012. Genomic toolboxes for conservation biologists. *Evolutionary Applications* 5: 130–143.

Bakkenes, M., Alkemade, J.R.M., Ihle, F., Leemans, R., and Latour, J.B. 2002. Assessing effects of forecasted climate change on the diversity and distribution of European higher plants for 2050. *Global Change Biology* 8: 390–407.

Beale, C.M., Lennon, J.J., and Gimona, A. 2008. Opening the climate envelope reveals no macroscale associations with climate in European birds. *Proceedings of the National Academy of Sciences USA* 105: 14,908–14,912.

Bijlsma, R. and Loeschcke, V. 2012. Genetic erosion impedes adaptive responses to stressful environments. *Evolutionary Applications* 5: 117–129.

Birks, H.J.B. and Willis, K.J. 2008. Alpine trees and refugia in Europe. *Plant Ecology and Diversity* 1: 147–160.

Bonduriansky, R., Crean, A.J., and Day, D.T. 2012. The implications of nongenetic inheritance for evolution in changing environments. *Evolutionary Applications* **5**: 192–201.

Botkin, D.B., Saxe, H., Araujo, M.B., Betts, R, Bradshaw, R.H.W., Cedhagen, T., Chesson, P., Dawson, T.P., Etterson, J.R., Faith, D.P., Ferrier, S., Guisan, A., Skjoldborg Hansen, A., Hilbert, D.W., Loehle, C., Margules, C., New, M., Sobel, M.J., and Stockwell, D.R.B. 2007. Forecasting the effects of global warming on biodiversity. *BioScience* **57**: 227–236.

Buckley, L.B. and Roughgarden, J. 2004. Biodiversity conservation: Effects of changes in climate and land use change. *Nature* **430**: 10.1038/nature02717.

Cotgreave, P. and Harvey, P.H. 1994. Associations among biogeography, phylogeny and bird species diversity. *Biodiversity Letters* **2**: 46–55.

Davis, A.J., Jenkinson, I.S., Lawton, J.H., Shorrocks, B., and Wood, S. 1998. Making mistakes when predicting shifts in species range in response to global warming. *Nature* **391**: 783–786.

Davis, M.B. and Shaw, R.G. 2001. Range shifts and adaptive responses to Quaternary climate change. *Science* **292**: 673–679.

Dobrowski, S.Z. 2011. A climatic basis for microrefugia: the influence of terrain on climate. *Global Change Biology* **17**: 1022–1035.

Dormann, C.F. 2007. Promising the future? Global change projections of species distributions. *Basic and Applied Ecology* **8**: 387–397.

Fridley, J.D. 2009. Downscaling climate over complex terrain: high finescale (< 1000 m) spatial variation of near-ground temperatures in a montane forested landscape (Great Smoky Mountains). *Journal of Applied Meteorology and Climatology* **48**: 1033–1049.

Grotch, S.L. and Maccracken, M.C. 1991. The use of general circulation models to predict climatic change. *Journal of Climate* **4**: 283–303.

Groothuis, T.G.G. and Schwabl, H. 2008. Hormone-mediated maternal effects in birds: mechanisms matter but what do we know of them? *Philosophical Transactions of the Royal Society B* **363**: 1647–1661.

Halley, J.M. and Sgardeli, V. 2014. Extinction debt and the species-area relationship: a neutral perspective. *Global Ecology and Biogeography* **23**: 113–123.

Hampe, A. 2004. Bioclimate envelope models: what they detect and what they hide. *Global Ecology and Biogeography* **13**: 469–471.

Harte, J., Ostling, A., Green, J.L., and Kinzig, A. 2004.

Biodiversity conservation: Climate change and extinction risk. *Nature* **430**: 10.1038/nature02718.

He, F. and Hubbell, S.P. 2011. Species-area relationships always overestimate extinction rates from habitat loss. *Nature* **473**: 368–371.

He, F. and Hubbell, S.P. 2012. He and Hubbell reply. *Nature*: **482**: E5-E6.

He, F. and Hubbell, S.P. 2013. Estimating extinction from species-area relationships: why the numbers do not add up. *Ecology* **94**: 1905–1912.

Hijmans, R.J., Cameron, S.E., Parra, J.L., Jones, P.G., and Jarvis, A. 2005. Very high resolution interpolated climate surfaces for global land areas. *International Journal of Climatology* **25**: 1965–1978.

Hof, C., Levinsky, I., Araujo, M.B., and Rahbek, C. 2011. Rethinking species' ability to cope with rapid climate change. *Global Change Biology* **17**: 2987–2990.

Hubbell, S.P. 2001. *The Unified Neutral Theory of Biodiversity and Biogeography*. Princeton University Press, 375pp.

Huey, R.B., Hertz, P.E., and Sinervo, B. 2003. Behavioral drive versus behavioral inertia in evolution: a null model approach. *American Naturalist* **161**: 357–366.

Huntley, B., Green, R.E., Collingham, Y.C., Hill, J.K., Willis, S.G., Bartlein, P.J., Cramer, W., Hagemeijer, W.J.M., and Thomas, C.J. 2004. The performance of models relating species geographical distributions to climate is independent of trophic level. *Ecology Letters* **7**: 417–426.

IPCC, 2007. *Climate Change 2007: Impacts, Adaptation and Vulnerability. Contribution of Working Group II to the Fourth Assessment Report of the Intergovernmental Panel on Climate Change*. Parry, M.L., *et al.* (Eds.) Cambridge, UK: Cambridge University Press.

IPCC. 2007. *Climate Change 2007: The Physical Science Basis. Contribution of Working Group I to the Fourth Assessment Report of the Intergovernmental Panel on Climate Change*. Cambridge University Press, Cambridge, United Kingdom.

Kennett, J.P. and Stott, L.D. 1991. Abrupt deep-sea warming, palaeoceanographic changes and benthic extinctions at the end of the Palaeocene. *Nature* **353**: 225–229.

Kiehl, J.T. and Shields, C.A. 2013. Sensitivity of the Palaeocene-Eocene Thermal Maximum climate to cloud properties. *Philosophical Transactions of the Royal Society A* **371**: 1471–2962.

Koch, P.L. and Barnosky, A.D. 2006. Late Quaternary extinctions: state of the debate. *Annual Review of Ecology, Evolution and Systematics* **37**: 215–250.

Koch, P.L., Zachos, J.C., and Gingerich, P.D. 1992. Correlation between isotope records in marine and continental carbon reservoirs near the Paleocene/Eocene boundary. *Nature* **358**: 319–322.

Lande, R. 2009. Adaptation to an extraordinary environment by evolution of phenotypic plasticity and genetic assimilation. *Journal of Evolutionary Biology* **22**: 1435–1446.

Lapola, D.M, Oyama, M.D., and Nobre, C.A. 2009. Exploring the range of climate biome projections for tropical South America: The role of CO_2 fertilization and seasonality. *Global Biogeochemical Cycles* **23**: 10.1029/2008GB003357.

Larsen, T.B. 2008. Forest butterflies in West Africa have resisted extinction ... so far (Lepidoptera: Papilionoidea and Hesperioidea). *Biodiversity and Conservation* **17**: 2833–2847.

Lawton, R.O., Nair, U.S., Pielke Sr., R.A., and Welch, R.M. 2001. Climatic impact of tropical lowland deforestation on nearby montane cloud forests. *Science* **294**: 584–587.

Lemaire, V., Bruscotti, S., Van Gremberghe, I., Vyverman, W., Vanoverbeke, J., and De Meester, L. 2012. Genotype x genotype interactions between the toxic cyanobacterium *Microcystis* and its grazer, the water flea *Daphnia*. *Evolutionary Applications* **5**: 168–182.

Lessells, C.M. 2008. Neuroendocrine control of life histories: what do we need to know to understand the evolution of phenotypic plasticity? *Philosophical Transactions of the Royal Society B* **363**: 1589–1598.

Levinton, J. 1992. The big bang of animal evolution. *Scientific American* **267**: 84–91.

Lewis, O.T. 2006. Climate change, species-area curves and the extinction crisis. *Philosophical Transactions of the Royal Society B* **361**: 163–171.

Luoto, M. and Heikkinen, R.K. 2008. Disregarding topographical heterogeneity biases species turnover assessments based on bioclimatic models. *Global Change Biology* **14**: 483–494.

Marquis, O., Massot, M., and Le Galliard, J.F. 2008. Intergenerational effects of climate generate cohort variation in lizard reproductive performance. *Ecology* **89**: 2575–2583.

McInerney, F.A. and Wing, S.L. 2011. The Paleocene-Eocene Thermal Maximum: A perturbation of carbon cycle, climate, and biosphere with implications for the future. *Annual Review of Earth and Planetary Sciences* **39**: 489–516.

Mergeay, J. and Santamaria, L. 2012. Evolution and biodiversity: the evolutionary basis of biodiversity and its potential for adaptation to global change. *Evolutionary Applications* **5**: 103–106.

Meylan, S., Miles, D.B., and Clobert, J. 2012. Hormonally mediated maternal effects, individual strategy and global change. *Philosophical Transactions of the Royal Society B* **367**: 1647–1664.

Moritz, C. and Agudo, R. 2013. The future of species under climate change: resilience or decline? *Science* **341**: 504–508.

Mouillot, D. 2007. Niche-assembly vs. dispersal-assembly rules in coastal fish metacommunities: implications for management of biodiversity in brackish lagoons. *Journal of Applied Ecology* **44**: 760–767.

Nogues-Bravo, D. 2009. Predicting the past distribution of species climatic niches. *Global Ecology and Biogeography* **18**: 521–531.

Nussey, D.H., Postma, E., Gienapp, P., and Visser, M.E. 2005. Selection on heritable phenotypic plasticity in a wild bird population. *Science* **310**: 304–306.

Palkovacs, E., Kinnison, M.T., Correa, C., Dalton, C.M., and Hendry, A. 2012. Ecological consequences of human-induced trait change: fates beyond traits. *Evolutionary Applications* **5**: 183–191.

Parmesan, C. 2006. Ecological and evolutionary responses to recent climate change. *Annual Review of Ecology, Evolution, and Systematics* **37**: 637–669.

Parmesan, C. and Yohe, G. 2003. A globally coherent fingerprint of climate change impacts across natural systems. *Nature* **421**: 37–42.

Pearson, R.G. and Dawson, T.P. 2003. Predicting the impacts of climate change on the distribution of species: Are bioclimate envelope models useful? *Global Ecology and Biogeography* **12**: 361–371.

Pepin, N.C. and Seidel, D.J. 2005. A global comparison of surface and free-air temperatures at high elevations. *Journal of Geophysical Research* **110**: 10.1029/2004JD005047.

Pereira, H.M., Borda-de-Água, L., and Santos Martins, I. 2012. Geometry and scale in species–area relationships. *Nature* **482**: E3–E4.

Peterson, A.T., Ortega-Huerta, M.A., Bartley, J., Sánchez-Cordero, V., Soberón, J., Buddemeier, R.H., and Stockwell, D.R.B. 2002. Future projections for Mexican faunas under global climate change scenarios. *Nature* **416**: 626–629.

Pounds, J.A., Bustamante, M.R., Coloma, L.A., Consuegra, J.A., Fogden, M.P.L., Foster, P.N., La Marca, E., Masters, K.L., Merino-Viteri, A., Puschendorf, R., Ron, S.R., Sanchez-Azofeifa, G.A., Still, C.J., and Young, B.E. 2006.

Widespread amphibian extinctions from epidemic disease driven by global warming. *Nature* **439**: 161–167.

Pounds, J.A., Fogden, M.P.L., and Campbell, J.H. 1999. Biological response to climate change on a tropical mountain. *Nature* **398**: 611–615.

Pounds, J.A., Fogden, M.P.L., and Masters, K.L. 2005. Responses of natural communities to climate change in a highland tropical forest. In: Lovejoy, T. and Hannah, L. (Eds.) *Climate Change and Biodiversity*, Yale University Press, New Haven, Connecticut, USA, pp. 70–74.

Prugh, L.R., Hodges, K.E., Sinclair, R.E., and Brashares, J.S. 2008. Effect of habitat area and isolation on fragmented animal populations. *Proceedings of the National Academy of Sciences USA* **105**: 20,770–20,775.

Randin, C.F., Engler, R., Normand, S., Zappa, M., Zimmermann, N.E., Pearman, P.B., Vittoz, P., Thuiller, W., and Guisan, A. 2009. Climate change and plant distribution: local models predict high-elevation persistence. *Global Change Biology* **15**: 1557–1569.

Rodriguez-Castaneda, G., Hof, A., Jansson, R., and Harding, L. 2012. Predicting the fate of biodiversity using species' distribution models: enhancing model compareability and repeatability. *PloS ONE.* **7**: 1–10.

Root, T.L., Price, J.T., Hall, K.R., Schneider, S.H., Rosenzweig, C., and Pounds, J.A. 2003. Fingerprints of global warming on wild animals and plants. *Nature* **421**: 57–60.

Rosindell, J.A. and Harmon L.J. 2013. A unified model of species immigration, extinction and abundance on islands. *Journal of Biogeography* **40**: 1107–1118.

Santamaria, L. and Mendez, P.F. 2012. Evolution in biodiversity policy—current gaps and future needs. *Evolutionary Applications* **5**: 202–218.

Scheiner, S.M. 1993. Genetics and evolution of phenotypic plasticity. *Annual Review of Ecology and Systematics* **24**: 35–68.

Scheiner, S.M. 2002. Selection experiments and the study of phenotypic plasticity. *Journal of Evolutionary Biology* **15**: 889–898.

Sears, M.W., Raskin, E., and Angilletta Jr., M.J. 2011. The world is not flat: Defining relevant thermal landscapes in the context of climate change. *Integrative and Comparative Biology* **51**: 666–675.

Seo, C., Thorne, J.H., Hannah, L., and Thuiller, W. 2009. Scale effects in species distribution models: implications for conservation planning under climate change. *Biology Letters* **5**: 39–43.

Sinervo, B., Clobert, J., Miles, D.B., McAdam, A.G., and Lancaster, L.T. 2008. The role of pleiotropy versus signaler-receiver gene epistasis in life history trade-offs: dissecting the genomic architecture of organismal design in social systems. *Heredity* **101**: 197–211.

Shine, R. 2012. Invasive species as drivers of evolutionary change: cane toads in tropical Australia. *Evolutionary Applications* **5**: 107–116.

Skelly, D.K., Joseph, L.N., Possingham, H.P., Freidenburg, L.K., Farrugia, T.J., Kinnison, M.T., and Hendry, A.P. 2007. Evolutionary responses to climate change. *Conservation Biology* **21**: 1353–1355.

Steffensen, J.P., Andersen, K.K., Bigler, M., Clausen, H.B., Dahl-Jensen, D., Fischer, H., Goto-Azuma, K., Hansson, M., Johnsen, S.F., Jouzel, J., Masson-Delmotte, V., Popp, T., Rasmussen, S.O., Rothlisberger, R., Ruth, U., Stauffer, B., Siggaard-Anderson, M.-L., Sveinbjornsdottir, A.E., Svensson, A., and White, J.W.C. 2008. High-resolution Greenland Ice Core data show abrupt climate change happens in few years. *Science* **321**: 680–684.

Stockwell, D.R.B. 2004. *Biased Towards Extinction*. Guest Editorial, *CO$_2$ Science* **7** (19): http://www.co2science.org/ articles/ V7/N19/EDIT.php.

Stockwell, D.R.B. 2006. Improving ecological niche models by data mining large environmental datasets for surrogate models. *Ecological Modelling* **192**: 188–196.

Stockwell, D.R.B. 2013. A theory ready for extinction. *Quadrant Online.* http://quadrant.org.au/opinion/doomed-planet/2013/12/theory-fit-extinction/.

Stockwell, D.R.B. and Peterson, A.T. 2002a. Controlling bias during predictive modeling with museum data. In *Predicting Species Occurrences: Issues of Scale and Accuracy.* Scott, J.M., *et al.* (Eds.) Covello, CA: Island Press.

Stockwell, D.R.B. and Peterson, A.T. 2002b. Effects of sample size on accuracy of species distribution models. *Ecological Modelling* **148**: 1–13.

Stockwell, D.R.B. and Peterson, A.T. 2003. Comparison of resolution of methods for mapping biodiversity patterns from point-occurrence data. *Ecological Indicators* **3**: 213–221.

Stuart, S.N., Chanson, J.S., Cox, N.A., Young, B.E., Rodrigues, A.S.L., Fischman, D.L., and Waller, R.W. 2004. Status and trends of amphibian declines and extinctions worldwide. *Science* **306**: 1783–1786.

Suggitt, A.J., Gillingham, P.K., Hill, J.K., Huntley, B., Kunin, W.E., Roy, D.B., and Thomas, C.D. 2011. Habitat microclimates drive fine-scale variation in extreme temperatures. *Oikos* **120**: 1–8.

Svenning, J.C. 2003. Deterministic Plio-Pleistocene extinctions in the European cool-temperate tree flora. *Ecology Letters* **6**: 646–653.

Svenning, J.C. and Skov, F. 2007. Could the tree diversity pattern in Europe be generated by postglacial dispersal limitation? *Ecology Letters* **10**: 453–460.

Thomas, C.D., Bodsworth, E.J., Wilson, R.J., Simmons, A.D., Davies, Z.G., Musche, M., and Conradt, L. 2001. Ecological and evolutionary processes at expanding range margins. *Nature* **411**: 577–581.

Thomas, C.D., Cameron, A., Green, R.E., Bakkenes, M., Beaumont, L.J., Collingham, Y.C., Erasmus, B.F.N., Ferreira de Siqueira, M., Grainger, A., Hannah, L., Hughes, L., Huntley, B., van Jaarsveld, A.S., Midgley, G.F., Miles, L., Ortega-Huerta, M.A., Peterson, A.T., Phillips, O.L., and Williams, S.E. 2004. Extinction risk from climate change. *Nature* **427**: 145–148.

Thomas, C.D. and Williamson, M. 2012. Extinction and climate change. *Nature* **482**: E4-E5.

Thuiller, W., Araújo, M.B., Pearson, R.G., Whittaker, R.J., Brotons, L., and Lavorel, S. 2004. Biodiversity conservation: Uncertainty in predictions of extinction risk. *Nature* **430**: 10.1038/nature02716.

Tingley, M.W., Koo, M.S., Moritz, C., Rush, A.C., and Beissinger, S.R. 2012. The push and pull of climate change causes heterogeneous changes in avial elevational ranges. *Global Change Biology* **18**: 3279–3290.

Urban, D.L., Miller, C., Halpin, P.N., and Sephenson, N.L. 2000. Forest gradient response in Sierran landscapes: the physical template. *Landscape Ecology* **15**: 603–620.

Urban, M.C., De Meester, L., Vellend, M., Stoks, R., and Vanoverbeke, J. 2012. A crucial step towards realism: responses to climate change from an evolving metacommunity perspective. *Evolutionary Applications* **5**: 154–167.

Van Dyck, H. 2012. Changing organisms in rapidly changing anthropogenic landscapes: the significance of the "Umwelt"-concept and functional habitat for animal conservation. *Evolutionary Applications* **5**: 144–153.

Vegas-Vilarrubia, T., Rull, V., Montoya, E., and Safont, E. 2011. Quaternary palaeoecoloogy and nature conservation: a general review with examples from the neotropics. *Quaternary Science Reviews* **30**: 2361–2388.

Weaver, I.C.G., Cervoni, N., Champagne, F.A., D'Alessio, A.C., Sharma, S., Seckl, J.R., Symov, S., Szyf, M., and Meaney, M.J. 2004. Epigenetic programming by maternal behavior. *Nature Neuroscience* **7**: 847–854.

Willis, K.J. and Bhagwat, S.A. 2009. Biodiversity and climate change. *Science* **326**: 806–807.

Willis, K.J. and Van Andel, T.H. 2004. Trees or no trees? The environments of central and eastern Europe during the last glaciation. *Quaternary Science Reviews* **23**: 2369–2387.

5.1.3 Other Studies

- The planet's animal species have inherent abilities enabling them to cope with climate changes over a period of a few generations, a single generation, or even in real time.

Results of other studies also suggest the model-based species extinction hypothesis is unlikely to occur. In a review paper published in *Current Biology*, for example, Erwin (2009) explored past epochs and the myriad nooks and crannies of Earth today, searching for the primary trigger of speciation. His conclusion? Warmth is the fire that fuels the process by which species originate, whereas cold tends to destroy what warmth produced.

Headquartered in the Department of Paleobiology at the National Museum of Natural History in Washington, DC (USA), Erwin writes, "some of the best evidence for a link between biodiversity and climate comes from latitudinal gradients in diversity, which provide an avenue to explore the more general relationship between climate and evolution." In reviewing that evidence, he notes, "among the wide range of biotic hypotheses, those with the greatest empirical support indicate that warmer climates [1] have provided the energetic foundation for increased biodiversity by fostering greater population size and thus increased extinction resistance, [2] have increased metabolic scope, [3] have allowed more species to exploit specialized niches as a result of greater available energy, and [4] have generated faster speciation and/or lower extinction rates." He states, "in combination with geologic evidence for carbon dioxide levels and changing areas of tropical seas, these observations provide the basis for a simple, first-order model of the relationship between climate through the Phanerozoic and evolutionary patterns and diversity," and "such a model suggests that we should expect greatest marine diversity during globally warm intervals," as is typically also found for terrestrial diversity.

Erwin notes "the three best-studied mass extinction events are associated with sharp changes in climate and support the contention that rapid shifts in climate can reduce global diversity," which sounds much like the mantra of IPCC regarding global warming. However, the climate shifts Erwin cites consist mostly of cooling, and it is not only the shift to cooling but stagnating in a cool state that bodes ill for biodiversity. As Erwin describes it, "the long interval of stagnant evolution during the Permo-Carboniferous glaciation is consistent with studies of modern-day latitudinal diversity that [indicate] rates of evolutionary innovation and diversification are higher in high-energy climates than in low-energy climates."

Further explaining this conceptual framework, Erwin notes "contemporary studies suggest a positive relationship between high-energy climates and [1] increased diversification rates, [2] increased number of niches because of increased metabolic scope, and [3] more specialized niches, and possibly because of [4] niche construction." He writes, "studies showing that the tropics are a cradle of diversity, pumping clade representatives into higher latitudes, as well as evidence of increased ordinal level originations in the tropics, and of the sudden appearance of several mammalian groups during the Paleocene-Eocene Thermal Maximum suggest an asymmetric pattern of innovations associated with high-energy climate regimes."

Erwin concludes, "there is an intriguing possibility that diversity does not track climate, but rather builds up during warm intervals but without falling by proportional amounts when climates turn cooler," with the result that "warmer climates may serve as an evolutionary diversification pump with higher diversity persisting [throughout following cooler periods], at least for a time."

Two generalizations clearly can be made: warmth typically begets speciation, and cold tends to lead to species extinctions.

Independent support for this thesis was provided in papers by Jaramillo *et al*. (2010) and Willis *et al*. (2010). Jaramillo *et al*. (2010) examined the Paleocene-Eocene Thermal Maximum (PETM), which occurred some 56.3 million years ago, at sites in Venezuela and Columbia. The PETM provides an interesting analog to the Current Warm Period, and it is postulated carbon dioxide rose rapidly in that era over a period of 10,000 to 20,000 years and global temperatures were elevated approximately 5 °C for 100,000 to 200,000 years.

The PETM was clearly identifiable in terms of temperature, where it was between 31 and 34 °C during the peak of global warmth. Using pollen and other organic materials, the authors were able to identify various plant species that existed during this period. In spite of the high temperatures and possibly less-moist conditions, the number of drought-tolerant plants did not increase, nor were moisture-requiring plants shown to decrease during the PETM. These facts lead the authors to speculate either rainfall or water use efficiency increased because of higher levels of atmospheric carbon dioxide, thereby compensating for the higher temperatures.

They also note the PETM brought a radical increase in diversity, measured in both absolute terms (number of species/taxa) and in evenness (relatively more even species percentages). This was achieved by addition of new taxa. The origination rate for new taxa during the PETM was two to six times higher than during the periods before and after, but extinction rates were not unusual. The species/taxa that originated, and the overall diversity, continued after the PETM. Thus the gains in plant species richness during the PETM were relatively persistent rather than transient.

It is believed tropical forests of today are currently growing in climates near the maximum temperature the plants can tolerate (~27.5 °C), and thus future global warming in tropical zones may stress plants and cause a reduction in forest growth, perhaps driving some species to extinction. However, Jaramillo *et al*. show temperatures of 31 to 34 °C seem not only to have been tolerated but to have caused a burst of speciation in the PETM, including major taxa that persist today. The high temperatures of the PETM were not detrimental to the tropical moist forests examined in this study.

Willis *et al*. (2010) identified past historical periods when climate was similar to that projected by global climate models for the next century or so, or in which the rate of temperature change was unusually rapid. These periods were examined for any climate-related extinctions.

The first period they examined was the Eocene Climatic Optimum (53–51 million years ago), when the atmosphere's CO_2 concentration exceeded 1,200 ppm and tropical temperatures were 5–10°C warmer than current values. Far from causing extinctions of the tropical flora (where the data are best), the four researchers report, "all the evidence from low-latitude records indicates that, at least in the plant fossil record, this was one of the most biodiverse intervals of time in the Neotropics." They also note "ancestors of many of our modern tropical and temperate plants evolved ... when global temperatures and CO_2 were much higher than present, ... indicating that they have much wider ecological tolerances than are predicted based on present-day climates alone."

The second period they examined consisted of two rapid-change climatic events in the Holocene—one at 14,700 years ago and one at 11,600 years ago—when temperatures increased in the mid- to high-latitudes of the Northern Hemisphere by up to 10°C over periods of less than 60 years. Many sites show evidence of rapid plant responses to rapid warming during these events. The authors note, "at no site yet studied, anywhere in the world, is there evidence in the fossil record for large-scale climate-driven extinction during these intervals of rapid warming." They report extinctions did occur due to the cold temperatures of the glacial epoch, when subtropical species in southern Europe were driven out of their ecological tolerance zone.

Willis et al. also make use of recent historical data, such as the 3°C rise in temperature at Yosemite Park over the past 100 years. Comparing surveys of mammal fauna conducted near the beginning and end of this period, they detected some changes but no local extinctions. Thus they determined for all the periods they studied, there were no detectable extinctions during very warm temperatures or very rapid warming.

D'Odorico et al. (2008) write, "recent climate change predictions indicate that, in addition to trends in the mean values of climate variables, an increase in interannual variability is expected to occur in the near future." Also noting "environmental fluctuations are usually believed to play a 'destructive role' in ecosystem dynamics," they explore the validity of this latter assumption in the context of current climate model predictions, asking, "Can environmental variability have only 'negative' effects on ecosystem dynamics?"

After lengthy mathematical analysis, D'Odorico et al. determined "opportunities for species existence/coexistence are found to increase with 'moderate' values of the variance of environmental fluctuations, while they decrease when these fluctuations are relatively strong." This outcome constitutes what has come to be known as the "intermediate disturbance hypothesis," which grew out of the work of Connell (1978), who, in the words of D'Odorico et al., suggested "coral reefs and rain forests maintain high levels of diversity only in a non-equilibrium state," and Huston (1979), who noted "most communities have relatively high levels of diversity because environmental variability maintains them in a non-equilibrium state."

Noting numerous real-world indications (Chapin et al., 1997; Steneck et al., 2002; Bengtsson et al., 2003; Elmqvist et al., 2003; Bellwood et al., 2004; Folke et al., 2004) that "biodiversity may enhance ecosystem resilience," the four researchers provide a theoretical basis for this phenomenon, demonstrating the validity of the ecological equivalent of the common dictum of physical exercise gurus: no pain, no gain. This evidence suggests what IPCC considers

unfavorable may in fact be just what is needed to increase the diversity and resilience of myriad terrestrial and aquatic ecosystems and propel them to higher levels of activity in the brave new world of our CO_2-enriched future.

In an overview of a symposium titled "Molecules to Migration: Pressures of Life," held in Africa on the Maasai Mara National Reserve of Kenya, Fuller et al. (2010) note the theoretical approach most commonly used to predict future species distributions in a CO_2-enriched and warmer world (the "climate envelope" approach) assumes "animals and plants can persist only in areas with an environment similar to the one they currently inhabit." This approach, they point out, "typically ignores the potential physiological capacity of animals to respond to climate change." They explain how "behavioral, autonomic, and morphological modifications such as nocturnal activity, selective brain cooling, and body color may potentially serve as buffers to the consequences of climate change."

The six scientists note all organisms "have the capacity to adapt to changing environmental conditions both by phenotypic plasticity within a life span and by microevolution over a few life spans." They note, "there is evidence that microevolution—that is, heritable shifts in allele frequencies in a population (without speciation)—has occurred in response to climate warming," citing Bradshaw and Holzapfel (2006, 2008). They also point out phenotypic plasticity "is likely to represent the first response of individual organisms." They report "adaptive changes in phenotype induced by climate change have been documented, for example, in the morphology and phenology of birds (Charmantier et al., 2008) and mammals (Reale et al., 2003; Linnen et al., 2009; Maloney et al., 2009; Ozgul et al., 2009)."

Fuller et al. cite Pincebourde et al. (2009), who "showed that intertidal sea stars can behaviorally regulate their thermal inertia by increasing their rate of water uptake during high tide on hot days," which is "a response that affords protection against extreme aerial temperatures during subsequent low tides." Next they note "exposure of humans to hot conditions on successive days induces an increase in sweat capacity (Nielsen et al., 1993)." They state, "other adaptations also ensue, including plasma volume expansion and decreased electrolyte content of sweat," and thus "a typical unacclimatized male, who can produce about 600 ml of sweat per hour, can double that output with heat acclimatization (Henane and Valatx, 1973)." This "phenotypic adaptation (in this case, heat acclimatization) can alter physiological tolerance (the risk of heat illness)," they note.

The Australian, South African, and U.S. scientists also cite several studies—Zervanos and Hadley (1973), Belovsky and Jordan (1978), Grenot (1992), Hayes and Krausman (1993), Berger *et al.* (1999), Dussault *et al.* (2004), Maloney *et al.* (2005), and Hetem *et al.* (2010)—of large herbivores that "increase nocturnal activity in the face of high diurnal heat loads." They state "another adaptation that may enhance plasticity in response to aridity that is available to oryx and other artiodactyls, as well as members of the cat family (Mitchell *et al.*, 1987), is selective brain cooling," in which cooling of the hypothalamus and the temperature sensors that drive evaporative heat loss "inhibits evaporative heat loss and conserves body water (Kuhnen, 1997; Fuller *et al.*, 2007)," which "is likely to be particularly valuable to animals under concurrent heat stress and dehydration." Finally, they suggest maintaining genetic diversity for a trait such as fur or feather color that adapts various organisms to different thermal environments "may provide important plasticity for future climate change," citing Millien *et al.* (2006), and "there is already evidence that, over the past 30 years as the climate has warmed, the proportion of dark-colored to light-colored Soay sheep has decreased on islands in the outer Hebrides," citing Maloney *et al.* (2009).

Clearly, the planet's animal species have inherent abilities enabling them to cope with climate changes over a period of a few generations, a single generation, or even in real time.

References

Bellwood, D.R., Houghes, T.P., Folke, C., and Nystrom, M. 2004. Confronting the coral reef crisis. *Nature* **429**: 827–833.

Belovsky, G.E. and Jordan, P.A. 1978. The time-energy budget of a moose. *Theoretical Population Biology* **14**: 76–104.

Bengtsson, J., Angelstam, P., Elmqvist, T., Emanuelsson, U., Folke, C., Ihse, M., Moberg, F., and Nystrom, M. 2003. Reserves, resilience and dynamic landscapes. *Ambio* **32**: 389–396.

Berger, A., Scheibe, K.-M., Eichhorn, K., Scheibe, A., and Streich, J. 1999. Diurnal and ultradian rhythms of behavior in a mare group of Przewalski horse (*Equus ferus przewalskii*), measured through one year under semi-reserve conditions. *Applied Animal Behavior Science* **64**: 1–17.

Bradshaw, W.E. and Holzapfel, C.M. 2006. Climate change: evolutionary response to rapid climate change. *Science* **312**: 1477–1478.

Bradshaw, W.E. and Holzapfel, C.M. 2008. Genetic response to rapid climate change: it's seasonal timing that matters. *Molecular Ecology* **17**: 157–166.

Chapin III, F.S., Walker, B.H., Hobbs, R.J., Hooper, D.U., Lawton, J.H., Sala, O.E., and Tilman, D. 1997. Biotic controls of the functioning of ecosystems. *Science* **277**: 500–504.

Charmantier, A., McCleery, R.H., Cole, L.R., Perrins, C., Kruuk, L.E.B., and Sheldon, B.C. 2008. Adaptive phenotypic plasticity in response to climate change in a wild bird population. *Science* **320**: 800–803.

Connell, J.H. 1978. Diversity in tropical rain forests and coral reefs: high diversity of trees and corals is maintained only in a non-equilibrium state. *Science* **199**: 1302–1310.

D'Odorico, P., Laio, F., Ridolfi, L., and Lerdau, M.T. 2008. Biodiversity enhancement induced by environmental noise. *Journal of Theoretical Biology* **255**: 332–337.

Dussault, C., Ouellet, J.P., Courtois, R., Huot, J., Breton, L., and Larochelle, J. 2004. Behavioral responses of moose to thermal conditions in the boreal forest. *Ecoscience* **11**: 321–328.

Elmqvist, T., Folke, C., Nystrom, M., Peterson, G., Bengtsson, L., Walker, B., and Norberg, J. 2003. Response diversity and ecosystem resilience. *Frontiers in Ecology and Environment* **1**: 488–494.

Erwin, D.H. 2009. Climate as a driver of evolutionary change. *Current Biology* **19**: R575–R583.

Folke, C., Carpenter, S., Walker, B., Scheffer, M., Elmqvist, T., Gunderson, L., and Holling, C.S. 2004. Regime shifts, resilience and biodiversity in ecosystem management. *Annual Review of Ecology and Evolution Systems* **35**: 557–581.

Fuller, A., Dawson, T., Helmuth, B., Hetem, R.S., Mitchell, D., and Maloney, S.K. 2010. Physiological mechanisms in coping with climate change. *Physiological and Biochemical Zoology* **83**: 713–720.

Fuller, A., Meyer, L.C.R., Mitchell, D., and Maloney, S.K. 2007. Dehydration increases the magnitude of selective brain cooling independently of core temperature in sheep. *American Journal of Physiology* **293**: R438–R446.

Grenot, C.J. 1992. Ecophysiological characteristics of large herbivorous mammals in arid Africa and the Middle East. *Journal of Arid Environments* **23**: 125–155.

Hayes, C.L. and Krausman, P.R. 1993. Nocturnal activity of female desert mule deer. *Journal of Wildlife Management* **57**: 897–904.

Henane, R. and Valatx, J.L. 1973. Thermoregulatory

changes induced during heat acclimatization by controlled hyperthermia in man. *Journal of Physiology* **230**: 255–271.

Hetem, R.S., Strauss, W.M., Fick, L.G., Maloney, S.K., Meyer, L.C., Shobrak, M., Fuller, A., and Mitchell, D. 2010. Variation in the daily rhythm of body temperature of free-living Arabian oryx (*Oryx leucoryx*): does water limitation drive heterothermy? *Journal of Comparative Physiology B* **180**: 10.1007/s00360–010–0480-z.

Huston, M. 1979. A general hypothesis of species diversity. *American Naturalist* **113**: 81–101.

Jaramillo, C., Ochoa, D., Contreras, L., Pagani, M., Carvajal-Ortiz, H., Pratt, L.M., Krishnan, S., Cardona, A., Romero, M., Quiroz, L., Rodriguez, G., Rueda, M.J., de la Parra, F., Morón, S., Green, W., Bayona, G., Montes, C., Quintero, O., Ramirez, R., Mora, G., Schouten, S., Bermudez, H., Navarrete, R., Parra, F., Alvarán, M., Osorno, J., Crowley, J.L., Valencia, V., and Vervoort, J. 2010. Effects of rapid global warming at the Paleocene-Eocene boundary on neotropical vegetation. *Science* **330**: 957–961.

Kuhnen, G. 1997. Selective brain cooling reduces respiratory water loss during heat stress. *Comparative Biochemistry and Physiology A* **118**: 891–895.

Linnen, C.R., Kingsley, E.P., Jensen, J.D., and Hoekstra, H.E. 2009. On the origin and spread of an adaptive allele in deer mice. *Science* **325**: 1095–1098.

Maloney, S.K., Fuller, A., and Mitchell, D. 2009. Climate change: is the dark Soay sheep endangered? *Biological Letters* **5**: 826–829.

Maloney, S.K., Moss, G., Cartmell, T., and Mitchell, D. 2005. Alteration in diel activity patterns as a thermo-regulatory strategy in black wildebeest (*Connochaetes gnou*). *Journal of Comparative Physiology A* **191**: 1055–1064.

Millien, V., Lyons, S.K., Olson, L., Smith, F.A., Wilson, A.B., and Yom-Tov, Y. 2006. Ecotypic variation in the context of global climate change: revisiting the rules. *Ecology Letters* **9**: 853–869.

Mitchell, D., Laburn, H.P., Nijland, M.J.M., and Zurovsky, Y. 1987. Selective brain cooling and survival. *South African Journal of Science* **83**: 598–604.

Nielsen, B., Hales, J.R.S., Strange, S., Christensen, N.J., Warberg, J., and Saltin, B. 1993. Human circulatory and thermoregulatory adaptations with heat acclimation and exercise in a hot, dry environment. *Journal of Physiology* **46**: 467–485.

Ozgul, A., Tuljapurkar, S., Benton, T.G., Pemberton, J.M., Clutton-Brock, T.H., and Coulson, T. 2009. The dynamics of phenotypic change and the shrinking sheep of St. Kilda. *Science* **325**: 464–467.

Pincebourde, S., Sanford, E., and Helmuth, B. 2009. An intertidal sea star adjusts thermal inertia to avoid extreme body temperatures. *American Naturalist* **174**: 890–897.

Reale, D., McAdam, A.G., Boutin, S., and Berteaux, D. 2003. Genetic and plastic responses of a northern mammal to climate change. *Proceedings of the Royal Society B* **270**: 591–596.

Steneck, R.S., Graham, M.H., Bourque, B.J., Corbett, D., Erlandson, J.M., Estes, J.A., and Tegner, M.J. 2002. Kelp forest ecosystems: biodiversity, stability, resilience and future. *Environmental Conservation* **29**: 436–459.

Willis, K.J., Bennett, K.D., Bhagwat, S.A., and Birks, H.J.B. 2010. Perspective: 4 deg C and beyond: what did this mean for biodiversity in the past? *Systematics and Biodiversity* **8**: 3–9.

Zervanos, S.M. and Hadley, N.F. 1973. Adaptational biology and energy relationships of the collared peccary (*Tayassu tajacu*). *Ecology* **54**: 759–774.

5.2 Amphibians

• Research suggests amphibian populations will suffer little, if any, harm from projected CO_2-induced global warming, and they may even benefit from it.

Still *et al.* (1999) and Pounds *et al.* (1999) published a pair of papers in *Nature* dealing with the cause of major decreases in frog and toad populations in the highland forests of Monteverde, Costa Rica. Those diebacks—in which 20 of 50 local species went extinct locally, or were extirpated—had occurred over the prior two decades, a period described by IPCC as having experienced unprecedented warming. Holmes (1999), in a popular science article describing the mystery's putative solution, wrote the authors of the two reports made "a convincing case blaming global climate change for these ecological events." Then came the study of Lawton *et al.* (2001), who challenged this hypothesis, presenting "an alternative mechanism [of] upwind deforestation of lowlands" as the cause of the amphibian decline.

Lawton *et al.* began their analysis by noting the trade winds that reach the Monteverde cloud-forest ecosystem flow across approximately 100 km of lowlands in the Rio San Juan basin, and that deforestation proceeded rapidly in the Costa Rican part of the basin over the past century. By 1992, only 18 percent of the original lowland forest remained. The four scientists noted this conversion of forest to pasture and farmland altered the properties of the air flowing across the landscape. The reduced evapotranspiration that followed deforestation, for example, decreased the moisture content of the air mass, and regional atmospheric model simulations suggested there should be reduced cloud formation and higher cloud bases over such deforested areas, which would cause there to be fewer and higher-based clouds than otherwise would have been the case when the surface-modified air moved into the higher Monteverde region.

Thus there were two competing theories from which to choose a candidate mechanism for the environmental changes that had altered the Monteverde cloud-forest ecosystem: one that was global in nature (CO_2-induced warming) and one that was local (upwind lowland deforestation). Lawton *et al.* resolved the matter. Noting the lowland forests north of the San Juan River in southeastern Nicaragua had remained largely intact—providing a striking contrast to the mostly deforested lands in neighboring Costa Rica—they used satellite imagery to show "deforested areas of Costa Rica's Caribbean lowlands remain relatively cloud-free when forested regions have well-developed dry season cumulus cloud fields," noting further the prominent zone of reduced cumulus cloudiness in Costa Rica "lies directly upwind of the Monteverde tropical montane cloud forest." Consequently, they demonstrated by direct observation the effects predicted by the theory they espoused did indeed occur in the real world, alongside a "control" area identical in all respects but for the deforestation that produced the cloud effects.

Two years later, Nair *et al.* (2003) demonstrated the reduced evapotranspiration that followed prior and ongoing deforestation upwind of the Monteverde cloud forest decreased the moisture contents of the air masses that ultimately reached the tropical preserve, and regional atmospheric model simulations they conducted indicated there also should have been reduced cloud formation and higher cloud bases over these areas than there were before the deforestation began. Three years later, Ray *et al.* (2006) extended the work of Lawton *et al.* and Nair *et al.* while exploring in more detail the impact of deforestation in Costa Rican lowland and premontane regions on orographic cloud formation during the dry season month of March.

Ray *et al.* used the mesoscale numerical model of Colorado State University's Regional Atmospheric Modeling System to derive high-spatial-resolution simulations "constrained by a variety of ground based and remotely sensed observations," in order to

"examine the sensitivity of orographic cloud formation in the Monteverde region to three different land use scenarios in the adjacent lowland and premontane regions," namely, "pristine forests, current conditions and future deforestation."

This observation-constrained modeling work revealed historic "deforestation has decreased the cloud forest area covered with fog in the montane regions by around 5–13% and raised the orographic cloud bases by about 25–75 meters in the afternoon." In addition, they write, their work suggests "further deforestation in the lowland and premontane regions would lead to around [a] 15% decrease in the cloud forest area covered with fog and also raise the orographic cloud base heights by up to 125 meters in the afternoon."

As additional cases of amphibian mass mortality were reported throughout the world, Parmesan (2006) and Pounds *et al.* (2006) pointed accusing fingers at atmospheric CO_2, this time claiming global warming was promoting the spread of *Batrachochytrium dendrobatidis* (*Bd*), a non-hyphal zoosporic fungus that was the immediate cause of the amphibian declines and triggering outbreaks of chytridiomycosis via what came to be known as the climate-linked epidemic hypothesis (CLEH).

Investigating this concept in the Penalara Natural Park in the Sierra de Guadarrama of Central Spain, Bosch *et al.* (2007) looked for relationships between 20 meteorological variables and the development of chytridiomycosis infection in the area's amphibian populations, focusing on "two time periods according to the lack (1976–1996) or presence (1997–2003) of observed chytrid-related mortalities." This work revealed "a significant association between change in local climatic variables and the occurrence of chytridiomycosis," leading them to conclude, "rising temperature is linked to the occurrence of chytrid-related disease."

Being careful not to be too adamant about what their data implied, however, Bosch *et al.* note "associations between climate and disease do not necessarily imply causation." They also state, "chytrid-related declines are probably the result of a complex web of interaction, and the effects of climate will be conditional on other factors such as host density, amphibian community composition, microbial competitors and zooplankton predators, to name but a few." To disentangle this network and break it down into its key components, they say it will be necessary "to collect seasonal data on amphibian densities, contemporary and historical measurements of the prevalence and intensity of infection, seasonal mortalities, and fine-scale meteorological conditions from a range of sites that represent altitudinal clines," and conduct "molecular epidemiological analyses."

Lips *et al.* (2008) evaluated data pertaining to population declines of frogs of the genus *Atelopus*, as well as similar data from other amphibian species, in Lower Central America and Andean South America, based on their own work and that of others recorded in the scientific literature. They sought to determine whether the documented population declines were more indicative of an emerging infectious disease or a climate-change-driven infectious disease, noting in this regard, "both field studies on amphibians (Briggs *et al.*, 2005; Lips *et al.*, 2006) and on fungal population genetics (Morehouse *et al.*, 2003; Morgan *et al.*, 2007) strongly suggest that *Bd* is a newly introduced invasive pathogen."

Lips *et al.* say their findings reveal "a classical pattern of disease spread across native populations, at odds with the CLEH proposed by Pounds *et al.* (2006)." Emphasizing the latter's "analyses and re-analyses of data related to the CLEH all fail to support that hypothesis," Lips *et al.* conclude their own analyses support "a hypothesis that *Bd* is an introduced pathogen that spreads from its point of origin in a pattern typical of many emerging infectious diseases," reemphasizing that "the available data simply do not support the hypothesis that climate change has driven the spread of *Bd* in our study area."

Although the four U.S. scientists make it clear disease dynamics are "affected by micro- and macro-climatic variables," and "such synergistic effects likely act on *Bd* and amphibians," their work clearly shows the simplistic scenario represented by the CLEH—which posits, in their words, that "outbreaks of chytridiomycosis are triggered by a shrinking thermal envelope"—paints an unrealistic picture of the role of global climate change in the much-more-complicated setting of real-world biology, where many additional factors may play even greater roles in determining amphibians' well-being.

Laurance (2008) tested the hypothesis, put forward by Pounds *et al.* (2006), that "the dramatic, fungal pathogen-linked extinctions of numerous harlequin frogs (*Atelopus* spp.) in upland rainforests of South America mostly occurred immediately following exceptionally warm years, implicating global warming as a likely trigger for these extinctions." He used "temperature data for eastern Australia, where at least 14 upland-rainforest frog species [had] also experienced extinctions or striking population declines attributed to the same fungal pathogen, and where temperatures [had] also risen significantly in recent decades." This work provided "little direct support for the warm-year hypothesis of Pounds *et al.*" Instead, Laurance "found stronger support for a modified version of the warm-year hypothesis," where frog declines were likely to occur only following three consecutive years of unusually warm weather; and these declines were observed "only at tropical latitudes, where rising minimum temperatures were greatest."

Laurance states many researchers "remain unconvinced that ongoing disease-linked amphibian declines are being widely instigated by rising global temperatures or associated climatic variables, as proposed by Pounds *et al.*" He notes, for example, "chytrid-linked amphibian declines have been documented on several continents and at varying times" and to date, "no single environmental stressor has been identified that can easily account for these numerous population crashes." He continues, "it stretches plausibility to argue that the chytrid pathogen is simply an opportunistic, endemic micro-parasite that has suddenly begun causing catastrophic species declines as a consequence of contemporary global warming."

Rohr *et al.* (2008) provided a rigorous test of the two competing hypotheses by evaluating "(1) whether cloud cover, temperature convergence, and predicted temperature-dependent *Bd* growth are significant positive predictors of amphibian extinctions in the genus *Atelopus* and (2) whether spatial structure in the timing of these extinctions can be detected without making assumptions about the location, timing, or number of *Bd* emergences." The five scientists report, "almost all of our findings are contrary to the predictions of the chytrid-thermal-optimum hypothesis," even noting "not all of the data presented by Pounds *et al.* (2006) are consistent with the chytrid-thermal-optimum hypothesis." They write, "there was no regional temperature convergence in the 1980s when extinctions were increasing, and that convergence only occurred in the 1990s when *Atelopus spp.* extinctions were decreasing, opposite to the conclusions of Pounds *et al.* (2006) and the chytrid-thermal-optimum hypothesis." On the other hand, they report, "there is a spatial structure to the timing of *Atelopus spp.* extinctions but that the cause of this structure remains equivocal, emphasizing the need for further molecular characterization of *Bd*."

Alford *et al.* (2009) quantified four movement characteristics of three groups of radio-tracked cane toads (*Bufo marinus*) at three places in Australia: a location where the toads had been established for some 50 years at the time of their sampling; a location where the first toads arrived about six months before sampling began in 1992 and 1993; and a location where sampling occurred for a period of 13 months, starting at the time of the toads' initial arrival in 2005. For all of the movement parameters they studied, "toads from the current invasion front differed dramatically from animals in the long-established population, while toads from the earlier invasion front were intermediate between these extremes."

The five researchers report "cane toads are now spreading through tropical Australia about 5-fold faster than in the early years of toad invasion." They state "the current invasion-front animals achieved these [high invasion speeds] by rarely reusing the same retreat site two days in succession, by travelling further each night when they did move, and by moving along straighter paths." Therefore, as they describe it, the toad invasion front "advances much more rapidly than would occur if the toads retained ancestral behaviors (less frequent relocation, with shorter movements, and fewer toads using straight paths)." And because "invasion-front toads in 1992 were more dispersive than origin-population toads in the same year, but … invasion-front toads have continued to evolve heightened dispersal ability and dispersed even more effectively in 2005 than they did in 1992," these observations suggest "as long as toads continue to invade suitable new habitat, dispersal ability will be selected upwards."

Alford et al. write the rapidity and magnitude of the shifts in cane toads "are truly remarkable," having been accomplished in only 50 generations (about 70 years), and they state "such a major shift over such a brief period testifies to the intense selective pressure exerted on frontal populations of range-shifting species." This development, in their words, "not only has implications for our understanding of the rates of invasion by non-native species, but also for the rate of range-shift in native taxa affected by climate change." The capacity for species to respond to changing environments may be underestimated when it is based on observations of individuals at the core of their range.

Further exploring this issue, Bustamante et al. (2010) exposed groups of Panamanian golden frogs (*Atelopus zeteki*) to varying dosages of zoospores of *Bd* and different temperatures and hydric environments to ascertain whether the frogs were susceptible to the pathogen and, if so, how environmental factors might affect the frogs' survival. These operations indicated "frogs exposed to a dosage of 100 *Bd* zoospores survived significantly longer than those

that had been exposed to 10^4 or 10^6 zoospores." They also found "exposed frogs housed at 23°C survived significantly longer than those that were housed at 17°C," and "exposed frogs held in dry conditions survived significantly longer than those in wet conditions."

Since their study was conducted in a laboratory, Bustamante et al. acknowledge their results "do not directly test hypotheses about the relation between climate change and the decline of the frogs in the field," but they note their data nevertheless "do not support the contention that rising global temperatures are necessary to cause the death of amphibians infected with this pathogen, because the pathogen was just as lethal at 17°C as at 23°C, and frogs at the warmer temperature lived significantly longer than those at the cooler one." This result is inconsistent with the climate-linked epidemic hypothesis of Pounds et al. (2006)—and Bustamante was a coauthor of that paper.

Anchukaitis and Evans (2010) state "widespread amphibian extinctions in the mountains of the American tropics have been blamed on the interaction of anthropogenic climate change and a lethal pathogen." However, they note, "limited meteorological records make it difficult to conclude whether current climate conditions at these sites are actually exceptional in the context of natural variability," casting doubt once again on the contention modern global warming was the primary culprit in the demise of the Monteverde golden toad (*Bufo periglenes*).

Anchukaitis and Evans developed annual proxy records of hydroclimatic variability over the past century within the Monteverde Cloud Forest of Costa Rica, based on measurements of the stable oxygen isotope ratio ($\delta^{18}O$) made on trees lacking annual rings, as described in the papers of Evans and Schrag (2004) and Anchukaitis et al. (2008). That work revealed, "contrary to interpretations of the short instrumental record (Pounds et al., 1999), no long-term trend in dry season hydroclimatology can be inferred from our $\delta^{18}O$ time series at Monteverde (1900–2002)." Instead, they found, "variability at the interannual scale dominates the isotope signal, particularly during the period of increased ENSO variance since the late 1960s," and they add, "there is no evidence of a trend associated with global warming." They emphasize "the extinction of the Monteverde golden toad appears to have coincided with an exceptionally dry interval caused by the 1986–1987 El Niño event," which they describe as "one of the longest driest periods in the last 100 years," based on their $\delta^{18}O$ chronology. In addition, they report, there is currently no consensus on how anthropogenic climate change might influence the El Niño Southern Oscillation, and "ENSO anomalies in the most recent decades are not beyond the range of natural variability during the instrumental period (Rajagopalan *et al.*, 1997)."

Anchukaitis and Evans conclude their analysis suggests "the cause of the specific and well-documented extinction of the Monteverde golden toad was the combination of the abnormally strong ENSO-forced dryness and the lethality of the introduced chytrid fungus, but was not directly mediated by anthropogenic temperature trends, a finding from paleoclimatology that is in agreement with statistical reanalysis (Rohr *et al.*, 2008; Lips *et al.*, 2008) of the 'climate-linked epidemic hypothesis'." The latter two analyses also had revealed the chytrid-thermal-optimum hypothesis, as it alternatively has been described, to be devoid of merit. Consequently, even in the case of struggling amphibians, there are no real-world data indicating global warming is, or ever will be, responsible for driving them to extinction.

Noting "phenotypic plasticity, the capacity of a genotype to produce distinct phenotypes under different environmental conditions, is a common and powerful method of adaptation in nature," Orizaola and Laurila (2009) investigated variations in temperature-induced plasticity in larval life-history traits among populations of an isolated "meta-population" of pool frogs (*Rana lessonae*) in Central Sweden. They exposed larvae from three closely located populations to two temperatures (20 and 25°C) in the laboratory and then documented their growth and development responses at the two different temperatures. According to the two Swedish researchers, the results indicated "in general, larvae exposed to warmer temperature experienced higher survival and metamorphosed faster." They also found "differences among the populations in both trait mean values and in the plastic responses," and "among-family variation within populations was found in growth rate and time to metamorphosis, as well as in plasticity, suggesting that these traits have a capacity to evolve."

Orizaola and Laurila also report finding "strong population differentiation at a microgeographic scale in life-history characteristics and temperature-induced plasticity in [the] isolated amphibian meta-population." They report, in spite of "the near absence of molecular genetic variation within [the] meta-population, our study detected strong variation in trait means and plastic responses both among and within populations, possibly suggesting that natural selection

is shaping life-history traits of the local populations." This phenomenon may be preparing pool frogs for still further temperature increases by providing them "ample phenotypic variation" to deal with a potentially warming environment.

Skelly *et al.* (2007) critique the use of the "climate-envelope approach" to predict extinctions, citing as their primary reason for doing so the fact that this approach "implicitly assumes that species cannot evolve in response to changing climate," when in numerous cases they can do so effectively. Noting "many examples of contemporary evolution in response to climate change exist," the group of seven scientists from the United States, Canada, and Australia report, "in less than 40 years, populations of the frog *Rana sylvatica* have undergone localized evolution in thermal tolerance (Skelly and Freidenburg, 2000), temperature-specific development rate (Skelly, 2004), and thermal preference (Freidenburg and Skelly, 2004)," and "laboratory studies of insects show that thermal tolerance can change markedly after as few as 10 generations (Good, 1993)." Since "studies of microevolution in plants show substantial trait evolution in response to climate manipulations (Bone and Farres, 2001)," they state, "collectively, these findings show that genetic variation for traits related to thermal performance is common and evolutionary response to changing climate has been the typical finding in experimental and observational studies (Hendry and Kinnison, 1999; Kinnison and Hendry, 2001)."

Although evolution obviously will be slower among long-lived trees and large mammals, where long generation times are the norm, Skelly *et al.* say the case for rapid evolutionary responses among many other species "has grown much stronger (e.g., Stockwell *et al.*, 2003; Berteaux *et al.*, 2004; Hariston *et al.*, 2005; Bradshaw and Holzapfel, 2006; Schwartz *et al.*, 2006; Urban *et al.*, 2007)." They write, "on the basis of the present knowledge of genetic variation in performance traits and species' capacity for evolutionary response, it can be concluded that evolutionary change will often occur concomitantly with changes in climate as well as [with] other environmental changes (e.g., Grant and Grant, 2002; Stockwell *et al.*, 2003; Balanya *et al.*, 2006; Jump *et al.*, 2006; Pelletier *et al.*, 2007)." Frogs, as noted above, are no exception to this general rule.

Catenazzi *et al.* (2010) write, "climate change has been proposed as a driver of amphibian declines," but they note this hypothesis has been largely displaced by a competing theory built around the observation that the pathogen *Bd* has been "associated with amphibian declines throughout the world (Berger *et al.*, 1998; Briggs *et al.*, 2005; Lips *et al.*, 2006)" in a manner indicating an introduced and subsequently spreading epidemic disease. They studied the recent collapse in anuran species richness and abundance in the Upper Manu National Park of Southeastern Peru.

Catenazzi *et al.* surveyed frogs in the Peruvian Andes in montane forests along a steep elevation gradient (1,200–3,700 m), using visual encounter surveys to sample stream-dwelling and arboreal species and leaf-litter plots to sample terrestrial-breeding species, in order to compare species richness and abundance among the wet seasons of 1999, 2008, and 2009. The U.S. and Peruvian researchers found there had been "a dramatic decline in species richness of amphibians"—a mean decline of 38% in the area of their study over the 10-year period—with stream-breeding species being "disproportionally represented among the missing taxa in 2008 and 2009." They state this result "is consistent with observations in other Neotropical (Lips, 1998) and Australian (Laurance *et al.*, 1996; Williams and Hero, 1998) sites where the species richness and abundance of frogs have declined or frogs have been extirpated," noting "declines in these other areas are unequivocally linked to the introduction of *Bd* to naïve amphibian populations (Berger *et al.*, 1998; Lips *et al.*, 2006)."

Their results show "the geographic and elevational distribution of *Bd* extends to southern Peru," noting this extent is consistent with Lips *et al.*'s (2008) hypothesis of *Bd* spreading southward in a wave from a *Bd* introduction site in southwestern Ecuador. Alternatively, they suggest the *Bd* introduction site could be Cusco, which "receives more visitors than any other tourist destination in Peru." And, noting "frogs originating from many streams, ponds and lakes of the Bolivian-Peruvian Altiplano are sold live in the city for human consumption," they suggest this frog trade "could facilitate the spread of *Bd* over large areas in southern Peru."

Given the above observations, plus the fact that "*Bd* occurs in a wide range of land-cover types and microclimates," Catenazzi *et al.* say "it is unclear how climate change would increase the rate of spread or the virulence of such an opportunistic pathogen in frog populations." They conclude it hasn't. Despite decades of research and a general belief that the link between *Bd* arrival and population decline is well-resolved in regions such as Australia, there is no evidence the arrival of *Bd* coincided with amphibian population decline, because the present data are not adequate to determine whether *Bd* was present prior to initial sampling (Phillips *et al.*, 2012). Phillips *et al.* (2012) conclude, "more generally, our discovery of a complete lack of evidence linking the arrival of *Bd* and the timing of population declines in northeastern Australia points to the alarming ease with which paradigms can become established even in the absence of critical tests of those paradigms." An alternative explanation for the upturn in recorded fungal infections is not global warming, but human-mediated intensification of fungal disease dispersal, caused by transportation and modification of natural environments (Fisher *et al.*, 2012).

In a nine-year study conducted in the Little Rock Creek Basin, located within the Selway-Bitterroot Wilderness just south of Hamilton, Montana (USA), McCaffery and Maxell (2010) "evaluated relationships among local climate variables, annual survival and fecundity, and population growth rates" in "a high-elevation population of a temperate pond-breeding frog species, the Columbia spotted frog (*Rana luteiventris*)." They monitored all life stages of the species and related the resulting demographic data to climate data collected at a nearby weather station. The two University of Montana biologists report "parameters that describe winter severity were negatively correlated with survival, transition, and breeding probabilities in this high-elevation *R. luteiventris* population," and there was "an increase in survival and breeding probability as severity of winter decreased."

"Contrary to much of what has been discussed in the literature," McCaffery and Maxell write, "these results suggest that under certain circumstances, a warming climate may be helpful to some amphibian populations, particularly those that live in harsh conditions at the edge of their thermal tolerances." As a case in point, they state their results "unambiguously demonstrate that earlier ending winters with lower snowpack in this system lead to higher survival rates, higher probabilities of breeding, and higher population viability." Thus, they conclude, "more generally, amphibians and other ectotherms inhabiting alpine or boreal habitats at or near their thermal ecological limits may benefit from the milder winters provided by a warming climate."

Additional studies show other real-world data that refute the contention global warming is driving amphibians to extinction. Berger *et al.* (2004), for example, found lower temperatures enhanced the development of chytridiomycosis in a study of eastern Australian frogs, and Seimon *et al.* (2007) determined glacial recession in the Peruvian Andes has been creating new amphibian habitats at recently deglaciated sites. Woodhams *et al.* (2010) note "amphibian skin peptides are one important defense against chytridiomycosis," and examining "the population-level variation in this innate immune defense [is important] to understand its relationship with disease dynamics." Briggs *et al.* (2010) note some amphibians with chytridiomycosis "develop only minor infections and suffer little or no negative effects." And Zukerman (2010) reports some of the most devastated populations of Australia's barred river frogs (*Mixophyes esiteratus*), tusked-frogs (*Adelotus sp.*), and several tree frog species (*Litoria sp.*), once thought to have been wiped out by the fungus, are now showing strong signs of recovery.

All in all, the above studies suggest amphibian populations will suffer little, if any, harm from projected CO_2-induced global warming, and they may even benefit from it.

References

Alford, R.A., Brown, G.P., Schwarzkopf, L, Phillips, B.L., and Shine, R. 2009. Comparisons through time and space suggest rapid evolution of dispersal behavior in an invasive species. *Wildlife Research* **36**: 23–28.

Anchukaitis, K.J. and Evans, M.N. 2010. Tropical cloud forest climate variability and the demise of the Monteverde golden toad. *Proceedings of the National Academy of Sciences, USA* **107**: 5036–5040.

Anchukaitis, K.J., Evans, M.N., Wheelwright, N.T., and Schrag, D.P. 2008. Stable isotope chronology and climate signal in neotropical montane cloud forest trees. *Journal of Geophysical Research* **113**: G03030.

Balanya, J., Oller, J.M., Huey, R.B., Gilchrist, G.W., and Serra, L. 2006. Global genetic change tracks global climate warming in *Drosophila subobscura*. *Science* **313**: 1773–1775.

Berger, L, Speare, R, Hines, H.B., Marantelli, G., Hyatt, A.D., McDonald, K.R., Skerratt, L.F., Olsen, V., Clarke, J.M., Gillespie, G., Mahony, M., Sheppard, N., Williams, C., and Tyler, M.J. 2004. Effect of season and temperature on mortality in amphibians due to chytridiomycosis. *Australian Veterinary Journal* **82**: 432–439.

Berger, L., Speare, R., Daszak, P., Green, D.E., Cunningham, A.A., Goggin, C.L., Slocombe, R., Ragan, M.A., Hyatt, A.D., McDonald, K.R., Hine, H.B., Lips, K.R., Marantelli, G., and Parkes, H. 1998. Chytridiomycosis causes amphibian mortality associated with population declines in the rainforests of Australia and Central America. *Proceedings of the National Academy of Sciences USA* **95**: 9031–9036.

Berteaux, D., Reale, D., McAdam, A.G., and Boutin, S.

2004. Keeping pace with fast climatic change: can arctic life count on evolution? *Integrative and Comparative Biology* **44**: 140–151.

Bone, E. and Farres, A. 2001. Trends and rates of microevolution in plants. *Genetica* **112–113**: 165–182.

Bosch, J., Carrascal, L.M., Duran, L., Walker, S., and Fisher, M.C. 2007. Climate change and outbreaks of amphibian chytridiomycosis in a montane area of Central Spain: Is there a link? *Proceedings of the Royal Society B* **274**: 253–260.

Bradshaw, W.E. and Holzapfel, C.M. 2006. Evolutionary response to rapid climate change. *Science* **312**: 1477–1478.

Briggs, C.J., Knapp, R.A., and Vredenburg, V.T. 2010. Enzootic and epizootic dynamics of the chytrid fungal pathogen of amphibians. *Proceedings of the National Academy of Sciences, USA* **107**: 9695–9700.

Briggs, C.J., Vredenburg, V., Knapp, R.A., and Rachowicz, L.J. 2005. Investigating the population-level effects of chytridiomycosis, an emerging infectious disease of amphibians. *Ecology* **86**: 3149–3159.

Bustamante, H.M., Livo, L.J., and Carey, C. 2010. Effects of temperature and hydric environment on survival of the Panamanian Golden Frog infected with a pathogenic chytrid fungus. *Integrative Zoology* **5**: 143–153.

Catenazzi, A., Lehr, E., Rodriguez, L.O., and Vredenburg, V.T. 2010. *Batrachochytrium dendrobatidis* and the collapse of anuran species richness and abundance in the Upper Manu National Park, southeastern Peru. *Conservation Biology* **25**: 382–391.

Evans, M.N. and Schrag, D.P. 2004. A stable isotope-based approach to tropical dendroclimatology. *Geochimica et Cosmochimica Acta* **68**: 3295–3305.

Fisher, M.C., Briggs, C.J., Brownstein, J.S., Madoff, L.C., McCraw, S.L., and Gurr, S.J. 2012. Emerging fungal threats to animal, plant and ecosystem health. *Nature* **484**: 186–194.

Freidenburg, L.K. and Skelly, D.K. 2004. Microgeographical variation in thermal preference by an amphibian. *Ecology Letters* **7**: 369–373.

Good, D.S. 1993. Evolution of behaviors in *Drosophila melanogaster* in high-temperatures: genetic and environmental effects. *Journal of Insect Physiology* **39**: 537–544.

Grant, P.R. and Grant, B.R. 2002 . Unpredictable evolution in a 30-year study of Darwin's finches. *Science* **296**: 707–711.

Hairston, N.G., Ellner, S.P., Geber, M.A., Yoshida, T., and Fox, J.A. 2005. Rapid evolution and the convergence of ecological and evolutionary time. *Ecology Letters* **8**: 1114–1127.

Hendry, A.P. and Kinnison, M.T. 1999. The pace of modern life: measuring rates of contemporary micro-evolution. *Evolution* **53**: 637–653.

Holmes, R. 1999. Heads in the clouds. *New Scientist* (8 May): 32–36.

Jump, A.S., Hunt, J.M., Martinez-Izquierdo, J.A., and Peñuelas, J. 2006. Natural selection and climate change: temperature-linked spatial and temporal trends in gene frequency in *Fagus sylvatica*. *Molecular Ecology* **15**: 3469–3480.

Kinnison, M.T. and Hendry, A.P. 2001. The pace of modern life II: from rates of contemporary microevolution to pattern and process. *Genetica* **112–113**: 145–164.

Laurance, W.F. 2008. Global warming and amphibian extinctions in eastern Australia. *Austral Ecology* **33**: 1–9.

Laurance, W.F., McDonald, K.R., and Speare, R. 1996. Epidemic disease and the catastrophic decline of Australian rain forest frogs. *Conservation Biology* **10**: 406–413.

Lawton, R.O., Nair, U.S., Pielke Sr., R.A., and Welch, R.M. 2001. Climatic impact of tropical lowland deforestation on nearby montane cloud forests. *Science* **294**: 584–587.

Lips, K.R. 1998. Decline of a tropical montane amphibian fauna. *Conservation Biology* **12**: 106–117.

Lips, K.R., Brem, F., Brenes, R., Reeve, J.D., Alford, R.A., Voyles, J., Carey, C., Livo, L., Pessier, A.P., and Collins, J.P. 2006. Emerging infectious disease and the loss of biodiversity in a Neotropical amphibian community. *Proceedings of the National Academy of Sciences USA* **103**: 3165–3170.

Lips, K.R., Diffendorfer, J., Mendelson III, J.R., and Sears, M.W. 2008. Riding the wave: reconciling the roles of disease and climate change in amphibian declines. *PLoS (Public Library of Science) Biology* **6**(3): e72. doi:10.1371/journal.pbio.0060072.

McCaffery, R.M. and Maxell, B.A. 2010. Decreased winter severity increases viability of a montane frog population. *Proceedings of the National Academy of Sciences, USA* **107**: 8644–8649.

Morehouse, E.A., James, T.Y., Ganley, A.R.D., Vilgalys, R., Berger, L., Murphy, P.J., and Longcore, J.E. 2003. Multilocus sequence typing suggests the chytrid pathogen of amphibians is a recently emerged clone. *Molecular Ecology* **12**: 395–403.

Morgan, J.A.T., Vredenburg, V., Rachowicz, L.J., Knapp, R.A., Stice, M.J., Tunstall, T., Bingham, R.E., Parker, J.M., Longcore, J.E., Moritz, C., Briggs, C.J., and Taylor, J.W. 2007. Enigmatic amphibian declines and emerging infectious disease: population genetics of the frog-killing fungus *Batrachochytrium dendrobatidis*. *Proceedings of*

the National Academy of Sciences USA **104**: 13,845–13,850.

Nair, U.S., Lawton, R.O., Welch, R.M., and Pielke Sr., R.A. 2003. Impact of land use on Costa Rican tropical montane cloud forests: sensitivity of cumulus cloud field characteristics to lowland deforestation. *Journal of Geophysical Research* **108**: 10.1029/2001JD001135.

Orizaola, G. and Laurila, A. 2009. Microgeographic variation in temperature-induced plasticity in an isolated amphibian metapopulation. *Evolutionary Ecology* **23**: 979–991.

Parmesan, C. 2006. Ecological and evolutionary responses to recent climate change. *Annual Review of Ecology, Evolution, and Systematics* **37**: 637–669.

Pelletier, F., Clutton-Brock, T., Pemberton, J., Tuljapurkar, S., and Coulson, T. 2007. The evolutionary demography of ecological change: linking trait variation and population growth. *Science* **315**: 1571–1574.

Phillips, B.L., Puschendorf, R., VanDerWal, J., and Alford, R.A. 2012. There is no evidence for a temporal link between pathogen arrival and frog extinctions in North-Eastern Australia. *PloS ONE* **7**: e52502.

Pounds, J.A., Bustamante, M.R., Coloma, L.A., Consuegra, J.A., Fogden, M.P.L., Foster, P.N., La Marca, E., Masters, K.L., Merino-Viteri, A., Puschendorf, R., Ron, S.R., Sanchez-Azofeifa, G.A., Still, C.J., and Young, B.E. 2006. Widespread amphibian extinctions from epidemic disease driven by global warming. *Nature* **439**: 161–167.

Pounds, J.A., Fogden, M.P.L., and Campbell, J.H. 1999. Biological response to climate change on a tropical mountain. *Nature* **398**: 611–615.

Rajagopalan, B., Lall, U., and Cane, M.A. 1997. Anomalous ENSO occurrences: An alternate view. *Journal of Climate* **10**: 2351–2357.

Ray, D.K., Nair, U.S., Lawton, R.O., Welch, R.M., and Pielke Sr., R.A. 2006. Impact of land use on Costa Rican tropical montane cloud forests: Sensitivity of orographic cloud formation to deforestation in the plains. *Journal of Geophysical Research* **111**: 10.1029/2005JD006096.

Rohr, J.R., Raffel, T.R., Romansic, J.M., McCallum, H., and Hudson, P.J. 2008. Evaluating the links between climate, disease spread, and amphibian declines. *Proceedings of the National Academy of Sciences USA* **105**: 17,436–17,441.

Schwartz, M.W., Iverson, L.R., Prasad, A.M., Matthews, S.N., and O'Connor, R.J. 2006. Predicting extinctions as a result of climate change. *Ecology* **87**: 1611–1615.

Seimon, T.A., Seimon, A., Daszak, P., Halloy, S.R.P., Schloegel, L.M., Aguilar, C.A., Sowell, P., Hyatt, A.D., Konecky, B., and Simmons, J.E. 2007. Upward range extension of Andean anurans and chytridiomycosis to extreme elevations in response to tropical deglaciation. *Global Change Biology* **13**: 288–299.

Skelly, D.K. 2004. Microgeographic countergradient variation in the wood frog, *Rana sylvatica*. *Evolution* **58**: 160–165.

Skelly, D.K. and Freidenburg, L.K. 2000. Effects of beaver on the thermal biology of an amphibian. *Ecology Letters* **3**: 483–486.

Skelly, D.K., Joseph, L.N., Possingham, H.P., Freidenburg, L.K., Farrugia, T.J., Kinnison, M.T., and Hendry, A.P. 2007. Evolutionary responses to climate change. *Conservation Biology* **21**: 1353–1355.

Still, C.J., Foster, P.N., and Schneider, S.H. 1999. Simulating the effects of climate change on tropical montane cloud forests. *Nature* **398**: 608–610.

Stockwell, C.A., Hendry, A.P., and Kinnison, M.T. 2003. Contemporary evolution meets conservation biology. *Trends in Ecology and Evolution* **18**: 94–101.

Urban, M.C., Philips, B., Skelly, D.K., and Shine, R. 2007. The cane toad's (*Chaunus* [*Bufo*] *marinus*) increasing ability to invade Australia is revealed by a dynamically updated range model. *Proceedings of the Royal Society of London B*: 10.1098/rspb.2007.0114.

Williams, S.E. and Hero, J.-M. 1998. Rainforest frogs of the Australian wet tropics: Guild classification and the ecological similarity of declining species. *Proceedings of the Royal Society of London B* **265**: 597–602.

Woodhams, D.C., Kenyon, N., Bell, S.C., Alford, R.A., Chen, S., Billheimer, D., Shyr, Y., and Rollins-Smith, L.A. 2010. Adaptations of skin peptide defenses and possible response to the amphibian chytrid fungus in populations of Australian green-eyed treefrogs, *Litoria genimaculata*. *Diversity and Distributions* **16**: 703–712.

Zukerman, W. 2010. Fungus out! The frog resistance is here. *New Scientist* **2790** (10 December) http://www.newscientist.com/article/mg20827903.500-fungus-out-the-frog-resistance-is-here.html.

5.3 Arthropods

- Enhanced plant productivity driven by elevated levels of atmospheric CO_2 tends to support greater abundance of soil microarthropods.

Arthropods are invertebrate animals composed of a segmented body, jointed appendages, and an exoskeleton. A handful of studies have examined how these animals may be affected by Earth's rising atmospheric CO_2 concentration. One of the early emerging hypotheses is that if the productivity of the plants at the base of a food chain is enhanced by the aerial fertilization effect of extra CO_2, they could be expected to support greater animal populations at the other end, including arthropods.

Siemann (1998) studied the effects of both short- and long-term nitrogen fertilization on plant productivity and arthropod communities in an upland grass ecosystem in Minnesota. In both situations, plant productivity was enhanced; arthropods responded by increasing both their numbers and the number of their species, suggesting if atmospheric CO_2 enrichment tends to enhance plant productivity, it also will increase arthropod numbers and ecosystem species richness.

Rillig *et al.* (1999) confirmed this conclusion. In serpentine and sandstone grasslands in California, they found an approximate doubling of the air's CO_2 content significantly enhanced the masses of fungi living in the soil, resulting in large increases in the numbers of fungal-feeding microarthropods (108 and 39% increases in the sandstone and serpentine grasslands, respectively). Likewise, in a study of poplar tree cuttings in Michigan, Lussenhop *et al.* (1998) observed the fine roots of the trees in their approximately doubled CO_2 treatment supported twice as many microarthropods as the fine roots of the trees growing in ambient air. And in a multiple-microcosm study of mini-terrestrial ecosystems conducted in the United Kingdom, Jones *et al.* (1998) found a 53% increase in atmospheric CO_2 concentration produced an enhanced soil fungal population that supported 52% more soil microarthropods.

Sanders *et al.* (2004) studied effects of atmospheric CO_2 enrichment on the plant and arthropod communities of the understory of a closed-canopy sweetgum plantation (which reduces the light available to the understory between 70 and 95% during the growing season) in a study where the air's CO_2 content was increased by approximately 48%. They report total arthropod abundance did not differ between ambient and elevated CO_2 plots, nor did the abundances of detritivores, omnivores, or parasitoids. They conclude, "changes in plant community composition did not translate into differences in arthropod communities."

Sticht *et al.* (2006) investigated how elevated atmospheric CO_2 concentration (550 ppm as opposed to the ambient concentration of about 380 ppm) delivered via free-air CO_2 enrichment (FACE) technology interacted with two levels of nitrogen (N) fertilization (normal N and half-normal N) to influence the abundance and diversity of collembolans in a field planted to winter wheat at the Federal Agricultural Research Centre in Braunschweig, Lower Saxony, Germany, where the 45% increase in the air's CO_2 content increased aboveground wheat biomass production by approximately 14%. Invertebrate communities in general, and collembolans in particular, play an important role in maintaining soil fertility, as the authors say they "participate in organic matter decomposition and can stimulate nutrient mobilization and plant nutrient uptake (e.g. Wardle *et al.*, 2004)."

The German researchers found "CO_2 enrichment enhanced the collembolan abundance by 58% under conventional N fertilization and by 100% under restricted N supply," and "under FACE conditions the collembolan diversity was higher (28 species) compared to ambient air conditions (23 species)." Sticht *et al.* conclude, "an increase in collembolan abundance and diversity can be expected as a result of enhanced quantity and changed quality of organic matter input into the soil associated with elevated atmospheric CO_2." And since this phenomenon "can stimulate nutrient mobilization and plant nutrient uptake," as they note, it is especially encouraging that its relative strength was greatest when nitrogen was most limiting in their experiment.

Enhanced plant productivity driven by elevated levels of atmospheric CO_2 tends to support greater abundance of soil microarthropods.

References

Jones, T.H., Thompson, L.J., Lawton, J.H., Bezemer, T.M., Bardgett, R.D., Blackburn, T.M., Bruce, K.D., Cannon, P.F., Hall, G.S., Hartley, S.E., Howson, G., Jones, C.G., Kampichler, C., Kandeler, E., and Ritchie, D.A. 1998. Impacts of rising atmospheric carbon dioxide on model terrestrial ecosystems. *Science* **280**: 441–443.

Lussenhop, J., Treonis, A., Curtis, P.S., Teeri, J.A., and Vogel, C.S. 1998. Response of soil biota to elevated atmospheric CO_2 in poplar model systems. *Oecologia* **113**: 247–251.

Rillig, M.C., Field, C.B., and Allen, M.F. 1999. Soil biota responses to long-term atmospheric CO_2 enrichment in two California annual grasslands. *Oecologia* **119**: 572–577.

Sanders, N.J., Belote, R.T., and Weltzin, J.F. 2004. Multitriphic effects of elevated atmospheric CO_2 on understory plant and arthropod communities. *Environmental Entomology* **33**: 1609–1616.

Siemann, E. 1998. Experimental tests of effects of plant productivity and diversity on grassland arthropod diversity. *Ecology* **79**: 2057–2070.

Sticht, C., Schrader, S., Giesemann, A., and Weigel, H.-J. 2006. Effects of elevated atmospheric CO_2 and N fertilization on abundance, diversity and C-isotopic signature of collembolan communities in arable soil. *Applied Soil Ecology* **34**: 219–229.

Wardle, D.A., Bardgett, R.D., Klironomos, J.N., Setala, H., van der Putten, W.H., and Wall, D.H. 2004. Ecological linkages between aboveground and belowground biota. *Science* **304**: 1629–1633.

5.4 Birds

- Although some changes in bird populations and their habitat areas have been documented in the literature, linking such changes to CO_2-induced global warming remains elusive. Also, when there have been changes, they often are positive, as many species have adapted and are thriving in response to rising temperatures of the modern era.

One of the great concerns associated with predictions of CO_2-induced global warming is the claim that the number of birds and their habitat areas will decline. Some estimates go so far as to suggest global warming could result in the extinction of several bird species. In the following subsections, such claims are examined through peer-reviewed studies conducted on birds in an effort to see how they have responded to what IPCC has called the unprecedented rise in atmospheric CO_2 and temperature of the late-twentieth and early twenty-first century.

Although some changes in bird populations and their habitat areas have been documented in the literature, linking such changes to CO_2-induced global warming remains elusive. Also, when there have been changes, they often are positive, as many species have adapted and are thriving in response to rising temperatures of the modern era.

5.4.1 Population Dynamics

How has modern warming impacted bird population dynamics? Several researchers have addressed this question for various bird species in many locations across the planet. This section summarizes what they have learned.

Schmidt *et al.* (2009) employed Bayesian hierarchical models to estimate the population size of trumpeter swans (*Cygnus buccinator*) based on aerial survey data collected by the U.S. Fish and Wildlife

Service throughout all known nesting habitats in the state of Alaska. These data collections were first made in 1968 and subsequently in 1975 and every five years thereafter through 2005. The results indicated "adult swan populations in Alaska increased at an average rate of 5.9% annually and cygnet production increased at 5.3% annually." The authors also found "cygnet production exhibited higher rates of increase at higher latitudes in later years," which they opine was "a response to warmer spring temperatures." The five researchers conclude, "trumpeter swan populations are increasing in Alaska, especially at northern latitudes," stating their study "represents one of the first to demonstrate a shift in breeding range of a bird possibly due to climate change." Hence, "for trumpeter swans, it appears that breeding range limits in Alaska have expanded" in response to the warming experienced there between 1968 and 2005.

White *et al.* (2011) analyzed how Great Cormorant numbers varied over the years in response to changes in sea surface temperature (SST) in the vicinity of Greenland's Disko Bay, using data obtained from the U.S. National Climate Data Center plus data for the number of breeding pairs of Great Cormorants in Disko Bay and adjacent areas they obtained from aerial and boat-based surveys described by Boertmann *et al.* (1996) and Boertmann (2006) for the period 1946–2005. According to the six scientists, population change rates of Great Cormorant colonies in the vicinity of Disko Bay "were significantly positively correlated with mean winter SST," adding, "populations increased during relatively warm years and decreased during relatively cold years," while also noting "the highest rates of population change correspond with periods of relatively high SST in recent years and during the 1960s." White *et al.* conclude, "taken together, the positive relationship between rates of population change in Cormorants and SST, the likely positive impact of Arctic warming on the preferred prey species of Cormorants, and the flexible food preferences and foraging strategies of Cormorants suggest that Cormorants are likely to benefit from a warming Arctic."

Grandgeorge *et al.* (2008) analyzed population sizes and phylogenetic and spatial structures of British and Irish seabirds based on "(1) presence or absence of the seabird species in the different counties of Britain and Ireland between 1875 to 1900 and 1968 to 1972, (2) seabird breeding censuses of Britain and Ireland from 1969 to 1970, 1985 to 1988 and 1998 to 2002, (3) at-sea abundance and distribution surveys of seabirds in the North Sea from 1980 to 1985 and 1990 to 1995, and (4) a bioenergetics model to estimate energy expenditures for 40 seabird species." With respect to population dynamics, their work revealed total seabird numbers "increased at an average rate of 1% per annum between 1969 and 2002, with a related increase of 115% in predicted total seabird predation." Also, "between 1875 and 1972 no seabird species was lost and there was an overall expansion in breeding range of the seabird population of Britain and Ireland, with the number of counties occupied increasing from 31 to 47."

The six scientists conclude, "the seabird community of Britain and Ireland has been remarkably resilient to environmental change in the 20th century." In fact, it "prospered during the 20th century" and "significantly raised ocean temperatures in the North Sea (Beaugrand, 2004)" may even have "created more favorable environmental conditions for some seabird species," citing Thompson (2006).

Lemoine *et al.* (2007) used data from the *Breeding Bird Atlas* of Lake Constance, which borders Germany, Switzerland, and Austria, to analyze the impact of land-use and climate changes on the region's abundance of Central European birds between the periods 1980–1981 and 1990–1992, and between 1990–1992 and 2000–2002. They found "the total number of [bird] species in the Lake Constance region increased from 141 species in 1980 to 146 species in 1990 and to 154 species in 2000," and "winter temperatures increased by 2.71°C and spring temperatures increased by 2.12°C over the 23 years from the first to the last census." These and other data led them to conclude, "increases in temperature appear to have allowed increases in abundance of species whose range centers were located in southern Europe and that may have been limited by low winter or spring temperature." In addition, they report "the impact of climate change on bird populations increased in importance between 1990 and 2000 and is now more significant than any other tested factor."

Seoane and Carrascal (2008) write, "it has been hypothesized that species preferring low environmental temperatures, which inhabit cooler habitats or areas, would be negatively affected by global warming as a consequence of the widely accepted increase of temperature during the last two decades." They note "this effect is assumed to be more intense at higher latitudes and altitudes because these areas seem to be changing more rapidly." They devised a study "to assess whether population changes agree with what could be expected under global warming (a decrease in species typical of cooler environments)," focusing on birds. Working in the Spanish portion of the Iberian Peninsula in the southwestern part of the Mediterranean Basin, the two researchers determined breeding population changes for 57 species of common passerine birds between 1996 and 2004 in areas without any apparent land-use changes. This work revealed, "one-half of the study species showed significant increasing recent trends despite the public concern that bird populations are generally decreasing," and "only one-tenth showed a significant decrease."

Seoane and Carrascal state, "the coherent pattern in population trends we found disagrees with the proposed detrimental effect of global warming on bird populations of western Europe." They are not the only ones to have reached this conclusion. They note, for example, "one-half of terrestrial passerine birds in the United Kingdom exhibited increasing recent trends in a very similar time period (1994–2004)," citing Raven et al. (2005), and they explain, "there is also a marked consistency between the observed increasing trends for forest and open woodland species in the Iberian Peninsula and at more northern European latitudes in the same recent years," citing Gregory et al. (2005). Likewise, they write, "Julliard et al. (2004a), working with 77 common bird species in France, found that species with large ecological breadth showed a tendency to increase their numbers throughout the analyzed period."

Seoane and Carrascal state, "bird species that inhabit dense wooded habitats show striking patterns of population increase throughout time." Noting "this is also the case with those bird species mainly distributed across central and northern Europe that reach their southern boundary limits in the north of the Iberian Peninsula," they theorize "these short- to medium-term population increases may be due to concomitant increases in productivity." In support of this notion they cite Julliard et al. (2004b) and the empirical observations of Myneni et al. (1997), Tucker et al. (2001), Zhou et al. (2001), Fang et al. (2003), and Slayback et al. (2003), whose work figured prominently in establishing the reality of the late twentieth-century warming- and CO_2-induced greening of the Earth phenomenon (see Section 4.2 on Biospheric Productivity), which has produced, in the words of the Spanish scientists, "an increase in plant growth or terrestrial net primary production in middle latitudes of the Northern Hemisphere since the 1980s, particularly in forest environments." It is clear the supposedly unprecedented warmth of the past two decades has not led to what Seoane and Carrascal call

"the proposed detrimental effect of global warming on bird populations of western Europe."

Qian et al. (2009) compiled a comprehensive dataset of bird species richness in China based on pertinent scientific literature published over the past three decades for 207 localities, the vast majority of which were national nature reserves with a mean area of 3270 km^2, which dataset they analyzed for their relationships to 13 environmental variables. The authors observe, "of all environmental variables examined, normalized difference vegetation index [NDVI], a measure of plant productivity, is the best variable to explain the variance in breeding bird richness." Four of the 13 variables they tested explained 45.3% of the total species richness variance, with 21.2% being accounted for by NDVI, 12.5% by elevation range, and 11.6% by annual potential evapotranspiration and mean annual temperature together. They note the two most important predictors of their study (NDVI and elevation range) "have been found to be major predictors for breeding bird richness in other regions and the whole of the globe, indicating that the finding of [their] study at a smaller scale is to a large degree consistent with those of previous studies of breeding birds at larger scales."

In a major review of plant-animal interactions in 51 terrestrial ecosystems conducted 20 years earlier, McNaughton et al. (1989) found the biomass of plant-eating animals is a strongly increasing function of aboveground primary production, and in a subsequent review of 22 aquatic ecosystems, Cyr and Pace (1993) found the herbivore biomass of watery habitats also increases in response to increases in vegetative productivity. Thus it is abundantly clear greater plant productivity—both terrestrial and aquatic—leads to greater populations of plants and the animals that feed upon them, which should lead to greater ecosystem biodiversity and a reduced risk of extinction. Atmospheric CO_2 enrichment increases plant productivity (see Chapter 1), which supports more animal life, which leads to greater animal biodiversity, which is good for the planet and good for mankind.

A warmer climate has benefited birds on Australia's Heard Island, some 4,000 kilometers southwest of Perth. Over the last five decades of the twentieth century, as this sub-Antarctic island experienced a local warming of approximately 1°C, there were rapid increases in flora and fauna. The population of the King penguin, for example, "exploded from only three breeding pairs in 1947 to 25,000," and the Heard Island cormorant, listed previously as "vulnerable," increased to 1,200 pairs. Recovering from near extinction, fur seals now number 28,000 adults and 1,000 pups (Pockely, 2001).

Penguins in Antarctica also have fared well in warmer times. In response to dramatic warming observed on the western Antarctic Peninsula over the past several decades, the penguin population has become more diverse as chinstrap and gentoo penguins have begun to take up residence among the long-inhabiting Adelie penguin population (Smith *et al.*, 1999). A study of penguin populations on the Ardley Peninsula of maritime Antarctica by Sun *et al.* (2000) found over the past 3,000 years the penguin population was lowest at 1,800–2,300 years BP, during a period of low temperature.

Huang *et al.* (2009) reported similar findings after evaluating paleo-evidence for penguin populations at Gardner Island in East Antarctica. According to the five researchers, penguins colonized the site shortly after it became ice-free 8,500 years ago. A pronounced population peak is evident in the data from about 4,700 to 2,400 BP, which corresponds closely to a substantially warmer period at this site. The authors document four other studies showing a penguin optimum roughly 3,000 to 4,000 years ago and coinciding with notably warm conditions. Together, these five studies encompass East Antarctica, the Ross Sea region, and the West Antarctic Peninsula. With all data currently available pointing to penguins having been most abundant during the warmest period of the Holocene several thousand years ago, it would seem reasonable to believe penguins will respond positively, not negatively, to any future warming.

Although global warming, regardless of its cause (natural or anthropogenic), appears to favor the population of many bird species, other human-related factors may offset such benefits and induce harm. For example, studies on the population dynamics of King penguins, *Aptenodytes patagonicus*, have been ongoing for many years. Recently, these fish-eating, top-of-the-food-chain predators have been used as indicator species for studies on the impacts of climate change in the southern hemisphere (Croxall *et al.*, 2002; Tynan 1998). In many respects, penguins have become "polar bear equivalents" of the Antarctic ecosystem. It appears something other than global warming has had a major influence on their population in recent years.

Saraux *et al.* (2011) note "in 2007, the Intergovernmental Panel on Climate Change highlighted an urgent need to assess the responses of marine ecosystems to climate change. Because they lie in a high-latitude region, the Southern Ocean ecosystems are expected to be strongly affected by global warming. Using top predators of this highly productive ocean (such as penguins) as integrative indicators may help us assess the impacts of climate change on marine ecosystems."

Following that charge from IPCC, several reports have used data collected from penguins marked with flipper bands (Barbraud and Weimerskirch 2001; Jenouvrier *et al.*, 2009) to predict impacts on the entire population from climate change scenarios modeled for the future. Flipper bands are metal markers attached to the upper part of the front flipper, where they are easily visible on land or in the water. Since penguins are birds that fly through the water, these "flippers" are actually wings and thus the sole source of a penguin's swimming power. Banding involves a single loop slipped over the upper, muscular section of one wing (equivalent to the human upper arm) and is meant to remain there for the life of the bird. These bands themselves, however, might have an influence on the data being collected on these penguins.

Research was conducted over a decade, in part to test the assumption that birds would adapt within a year at most to any negative effects of the metal flipper band (Barbraud and Weimerskirch 2001). Saraux *et al.* (2011) analyzed differences in reproduction and survival on 50 banded and 50 unbanded penguins over 10 years. The researchers evaluated annual and overall survival, arrival time at the breeding colony, laying dates, breeding success, success in chick rearing, duration of feeding trips ("foraging") and population growth.

They found the "banding of free-ranging king penguins (*Aptenodytes patagonicus*) impairs both survival and reproduction, ultimately affecting population growth rate." Over the 10-year period, banded birds were found to produce 39% fewer chicks and had a survival rate 16% lower than non-banded birds. Much of this effect appeared to be due to an increased time banded birds required to find sufficient food (both before and during the summer breeding season) and to their relatively late arrival at the breeding colony.

Saraux and colleagues write "one of our major findings is that responses of flipper-banded penguins to climate variability (that is, changes in sea surface temperature and in the Southern Oscillation index) differ from those of non-banded birds. We show that only long-term investigations may allow an evaluation of the impact of flipper bands and that every major life-history trait can be affected, calling into question the banding schemes still going on. In addition, our understanding of the effects of climate change on marine ecosystems based on flipper-band data should be reconsidered."

Another human-related activity with a significant impact on bird populations is the construction of wind farms. Pearce-Higgins *et al.* (2009) note "the displacement of birds away from turbines can result in individuals abandoning otherwise suitable habitat," and this "has been found to occur in a number of individual wind farm studies," citing Leddy *et al.* (1999), Larsen and Madsen (2000), Kowallik and Borbach-Jaene (2001), Hotker (2006), Hotker *et al.* (2006), and Larsen and Guillemette (2007). Pearce-Higgins *et al.* report, "some poorly sited wind farms have resulted in sufficient deaths to produce a population-level effect," citing Barrios and Rodriguez (2004, 2007), Everaert and Stienen (2006), Smallwood and Thelander (2007), Sterner *et al.* (2007), and Thelander and Smallwood (2007).

Pearce-Higgins *et al.* assessed the degree of occurrence of 12 widely distributed species of breeding birds within the vicinity of wind farm infrastructure (turbines, access tracks, and overhead transmission lines) on 12 wind farms located within unenclosed upland habitats (moorland, rough grassland, and blanket bog) in the United Kingdom, including most of the existing large upland wind farms in Scotland and northern England. The five UK scientists obtained "considerable evidence for localized reduction in breeding bird density on upland wind farms." After accounting for habitat variation, they report, "seven of the twelve species studied exhibited significantly lower frequencies of occurrence close to the turbines," and there was "equivocal evidence of turbine avoidance in a further two," and "no species were more likely to occur close to the turbines." Access tracks proved much less of a nuisance than turbines, and there was no evidence for consistent avoidance of overhead transmission lines. They conclude, "levels of turbine avoidance suggest breeding bird densities may be reduced within a 500-m buffer of the turbines by 15–52%, with buzzard (*Buteo buteo*), hen harrier (*Circus cyaneus*), golden plover (*Pluvialis apricaria*), snipe (*Gallinago gallinago*), curlew (*Numenius arquata*) and wheatear (*Oenanthe oenanthe*) most affected."

Pearce-Higgins *et al.* say their findings emphasize the need for a "strategic approach" to ensure wind farm development avoids areas with high densities of potentially vulnerable species, not only in the UK but also "across other similar windy semi-natural habitats in northwest Europe, southern South America, and central North America." Efforts should be made to "avoid high densities of potentially vulnerable open country species such as waders and raptors," they write. Their findings augment those of many others who have raised serious questions about the constructing of wind farms in inappropriate locations.

References

Barbraud, C. and Weimerskirch, H. 2001. Emperor penguins and climate change. *Nature* **411**: 183–186.

Barrios, L. and Rodriguez, A. 2004. Behavioral and environmental correlates of soaring bird mortality at on-shore wind turbines. *Journal of Applied Ecology* **41**: 72–81.

Barrios, L. and Rodriguez, A. 2007. Spatiotemporal patterns of bird mortality at two wind farms of Southern Spain. In: De Lucas, M., Janss, G.F.E. and Ferrer, M. (Eds.) *Birds and Wind Farms.* Quercus, Madrid, Spain, pp. 56–72.

Beaugrand, G. 2004. The North Sea regime shift: evidence, mechanisms and consequences. *Progress in Oceanography* **60**: 245–262.

Boertmann, D. 2006. Survey of Kittiwake colonies in Disko Bay and adjacent waters. Research Note, National Environmental Research Institute, Aarhus, Denmark.

Boertmann, D., Mosbech, A., Falk, K., and Kampp, K. 1996. Seabird colonies in western Greenland (60°–79°30'N. lat.). Research Note, National Environmental Research Institute, Aarhus, Denmark.

Croxall, J.P., Trathan, P.N., and Murphy, E.J. 2002. Environmental change and Antarctic seabird populations. *Science* **297**: 1510–1514.

Cyr, H. and Pace, M.L. 1993. Magnitude and patterns of herbivory in aquatic and terrestrial ecosystems. *Nature* **361**: 148–150.

Everaert, J. and Stienen, E.W.M. 2006. Impact of wind turbines on birds in Zeebrugge (Belgium). Significant effect on breeding tern colony due to collisions. *Biodiversity and Conservation* **16**: 3345–3359.

Fang, J., Piao, S., Field, C.B., Pan, Y., Guo, Q., Zhou, L., Peng, C., and Tao, S. 2003. Increasing net primary production in China from 1982 to 1999. *Frontiers in Ecology and the Environment* **1**: 293–297.

Grandgeorge, M., Wanless, S., Dunn, T.E., Maumy, M., Beaugrand, G., and Gremillet, D. 2008. Resilience of the British and Irish seabird community in the twentieth century. *Aquatic Biology* **4**: 187–199.

Gregory, R.D., van Strien, A.J., Vorisek, P., Gmelig Meyling, A.W., Noble, D.G., Foppen, R.P.B., and Gibbons, D.W. 2005. Developing indicators for European birds. *Philosophical Transactions of the Royal Society B: Biological Sciences* **360**: 269.

Hotker, H. 2006. *The Impact of Repowering of Wind Farms on Birds and Bats*. Michael-Otto-Institut im NABU, Bergenhusen.

Hotker, H., Thomsen, K.-M., and Jeromin, H. 2006. *Impacts on Biodiversity of Exploitation of Renewable Energy Sources: The Example of Birds and Bats—Facts, Gaps in Knowledge, Demands for Further Research and Ornithological Guidelines for the Development of Renewable Energy Exploitation*. Michael-Otto-Institut im NABU, Bergenhusen.

Huang, T., Sun, L, Wang, Y., Liu, X., and Zhu, R. 2009. Penguin population dynamics for the past 8500 years at Gardner Island, Vestfold Hills. *Antarctic Science* **21**:571–578.

Jenouvrier, S., Caswell, H., Barbraud, C., Holland, M, Stroeve, J., and Weimerskirch, H. 2009. Demographic models and IPCC climate projections predict the decline of an emperor penguin population. *Proceedings of the National Academy of Sciences USA* **106**: 1844–1847.

Julliard, R., Jiguet, F., and Couvet, D. 2004a. Common birds facing global changes: what makes a species at risk? *Global Change Biology* **10**: 148–154.

Julliard, R., Jiguet, F., and Couvet, D. 2004b. Evidence for the impact of global warming on the long-term population dynamics of common birds. *Proceedings of the Royal Society B: Biological Sciences* **271**: S490–S492.

Kowallik, C. and Borbach-Jaene, J. 2001. Impact of wind turbines on field utilization by geese in coastal areas in NW Germany. *Vogelkundliche Berichte aus Niedersachen* **33**: 97–102.

Larsen, J.K. and Guillemette, M. 2007. Effects of wind turbines on flight behavior of wintering common eiders: Implications for habitat use and collision risk. *Journal of Applied Ecology* **44**: 516–522.

Larsen, J.K. and Madsen, J. 2000. Effects of wind turbines and other physical elements on field utilization by pink-footed geese (*Anser brachyrhynchus*): a landscape perspective. *Landscape Ecology* **15**: 755–764.

Leddy, K.L., Higgins, K.F., and Naugle, D.E. 1999. Effects of wind turbines on upland nesting birds in conservation reserve program grasslands. *Wilson Bulletin* **111**: 100–104.

Lemoine, N., Bauer, H.-G., Peintinger, M., and Bohning-Gaese, K. 2007. Effects of climate and land-use change on species abundance in a central European bird community. *Conservation Biology* **21**: 495–503.

McNaughton, S.J., Oesterheld, M., Frank, D.A., and Williams, K.J. 1989. Ecosystem-level patterns of primary productivity and herbivory in terrestrial habitats. *Nature* **341**: 142–144.

Myneni, R.C., Keeling, C.D., Tucker, C.J., Asrar, G., and Nemani, R.R. 1997. Increased plant growth in the northern high latitudes from 1981 to 1991. *Nature* **386**: 698–702.

Pearce-Higgins, J.W., Stephen, L., Langston, R.H.W., Bainbridge, I.P., and Bullman, R. 2009. The distribution of breeding birds around upland wind farms. *Journal of Applied Ecology* **46**: 1323–1331.

Pockely, P. 2001. Climate change transforms island ecosystem. *Nature* **410**: 616.

Qian, H., Wang, S., Li, Y., and Wang, X. 2009. Breeding bird diversity in relation to environmental gradients in China. *Acta Oecologica* **35**: 819–823.

Raven, M.J., Noble, D.G., and Baillie, S.R. 2005. *The Breeding Bird Survey 2004*. Thetford, UK: British Trust for Ornithology.

Saraux, C., Le Bohec, C., Durant, J.M., Viblanc, V.A., Gauthier-Clerc, M., Beaune, D., Park, Y-H., Yoccoz, N.G., Stenseth, N.C., and Le Maho, Y. 2011. Reliability of flipper-banded penguins as indicators of climate change. *Nature* **469**: 203–206.

Schmidt, J.H., Lindberg, M.S., Johnson, D.S., Conant, B., and King, J. 2009. Evidence of Alaskan trumpeter swan population growth using Bayesian hierarchical models. *Journal of Wildlife Management* **73**: 720–727.

Seoane, J. and Carrascal, L.M. 2008. Interspecific differences in population trends of Spanish birds are related to habitat and climatic preferences. *Global Ecology and Biogeography* **17**: 111–121.

Slayback, D., Pinzon, J., and Tucker, C. 2003. Northern hemisphere photosynthetic trends 1982–1999. *Global Change Biology* **9**: 1–15.

Smallwood, K.S. and Thelander, C. 2007. Bird mortality in the Altamont pass wind resource area, California. *Journal of Wildlife Management* **72**: 215–223.

Smith, R.C., Ainley, D., Baker, K., Domack, E., Emslie, S., Fraser, B., Kennett, J., Leventer, A., Mosley-Thompson, E., Stammerjohn, S., and Vernet M. 1999. Marine ecosystem sensitivity to climate change. *BioScience* **49**: 393–404.

Sterner D., Orloff, S., and Spiegel, L. 2007. Wind turbine collision research in the United States. In: De Lucas, M., Janss, G.F.E., and Ferrer, M. (Eds.) *Birds and Wind Farms*. Quercus, Madrid, Spain, pp. 81–100.

Sun, L., Xie, Z., and Zhao, J. 2000. A 3,000-year record of penguin populations. *Nature* **407**: 858.

631

Thelander, C.G. and Smallwood, K.S. 2007. The Altamont pass wind resource area's effect on birds: a case history. In: De Lucas, M., Janss, G.F.E., and Ferrer, M. (Eds.) *Birds and Wind Farms*. Quercus, Madrid, Spain, pp. 25–46.

Thompson, P.M. 2006. Identifying drivers of change: did fisheries play a role in the spread of North Atlantic fulmars? In Boyd, I.A., Wanless, S., and Camphuysen, C.J. (Eds.) *Management of Marine Ecosystems: Monitoring Change in Upper Trophic Levels*. Cambridge, UK: Cambridge University Press.

Tucker, C.J., Slayback, D.A., Pinzon, J.E., Los, S.O., Myneni, R.B., and Taylor, M.G. 2001. Higher northern latitude NDVI and growing season trends from 1982 to 1999. *International Journal of Biometeorology* **45**: 184–190.

Tynan, C.T. 1998. Ecological importance of the southern boundary of the Antarctic Circumpolar current. *Nature* **392**: 708–710.

White, C.R., Boertmann, D., Gremillet, D., Butler, P.J., Green, J.A., and Martin, G.R. 2011. The relationship between sea surface temperature and population change of Great Cormorants *Phalacrocorax carbo* breeding near Disko Bay, Greenland. *Ibis: The International Journal of Avian Science* **153**: 170–174.

Zhou, L., Tucker, C.J., Kaufmann, R.K., Slayback, D., Shabanov, N.V., and Myneni, R.B. 2001. Variations in northern vegetation activity inferred from satellite data of vegetation index during 1981 to 1999. *Journal of Geophysical Research* **106**: 20.069–20,083.

5.4.2 Range Expansion

IPCC claims the increase in temperature predicted to result from the ongoing rise in the air's CO_2 content will be of such magnitude and speed that many species of plants and animals will not be able to migrate poleward in latitude or upward in elevation rapidly enough to avoid extinction as they are forced to seek cooler living conditions. There are many reasons for rejecting this contention, one of the most powerful being that increases in the air's CO_2 content generally enable plants to endure warmer weather, and as a result there is little or no need for them to shift the heat-limiting warm-temperature boundaries of their ranges as temperatures rise (see Section 3.13 and Section 4.2.3). At the cold-limiting cool-temperature boundaries of their ranges, warming provides opportunities for plants to push poleward and upward, resulting in expansions of their ranges and reductions in their risk of extinction.

This section reviews studies that suggest birds may respond in like manner, mimicking the respective shifts and non-shifts of the cold- and heat-limited boundaries of the ranges of the plants and associated herbivore life forms on which they depend for food.

Thomas and Lennon (1999) helped initiate extinction concerns about birds when they analyzed temporal trends in the spatial distributions of British birds over a 20-year period of global warming, looking for climate-induced changes in their breeding ranges. They found the northern margins of southerly species' breeding ranges shifted northward by an average of 19 km from 1970 to 1990, while the southern margins of northerly species' breeding ranges did not shift at all, in the mean. British birds thus expanded their ranges in the face of global warming, clearly a positive response that makes extinction less likely than it was before the warming.

Norment *et al.* (1999) analyzed bird surveys conducted along the Thelon River and its tributaries in the Canadian Northwest Territories from the 1920s through much of the 1990s, finding three bird species had expanded their breeding ranges southward, nine northward, and 16 were new to the area. The authors note the primarily northward range expansions may be explained by "a recent warming trend at the northern treeline during the 1970s and 1980s." Alternatively, they note the influx of new species may result from "increasing populations in more southerly areas." In either case, the birds appear to be faring quite well—even thriving—in the face of increasing temperatures in this forest-tundra landscape, which also appears to be the case in Norway (Saether *et al.*, 2000).

Research suggests seabirds of Greenland are also likely to benefit from global warming. According to Wagner and Melles (2001), a significant number of seabirds inhabited the area around Liverpool Land, on the east coast of Greenland, during the Medieval Warm Period (900–1300 AD), yet there was little or no (inferred) bird presence for a several-hundred-year period prior to this time (Dark Ages Cold Period) and another significant absence of birds thereafter during the Little Ice Age, which marked "the coldest period since the early Holocene in East Greenland." As temperatures have risen over the past 100 years, seabirds once again have expanded their range to inhabit the area.

Kinzelbach (2004) explored the range history of the serin, a bird that "was a topic of particular interest to ornithologists of the 19th and 20th century" due to "the rapid expansion of its range in historical times." The author reexamined "all the sources of records of the serin in 16th century Europe, ... both those already known and some that have been newly discovered." The data confirmed the findings of Mayr (1926), that "north of 48°N there were no free-living populations of *Serinus serinus* in the 16th century." During that period, the serin's range was constrained, Kinzelbach reports, as it "was halted by colder periods of the Little Ice Age after 1585, only resuming a rapid expansion at the beginning of the 19th century," after which it was "able to expand its range from the Mediterranean region throughout large areas of Central Europe within a mere 200 years."

Brommer (2004) categorized birds of Finland as either northerly (34 species) or southerly (116 species) and quantified changes in their range margins and distributions from two atlases of breeding birds, one covering the period 1974–1979 and one for 1986–1989, to determine how the two groups of species responded to what he called "the period of the Earth's most rapid climate warming in the last 10,000 years," citing McCarthy *et al.* (2001). Southern species experienced a mean poleward advancement of their northern range boundaries of 18.8 km over the 12-year period, while the southern-range boundaries of the northern species remained essentially unaltered. Noting similar results had been obtained for birds in the United Kingdom (Thomas and Lennon, 1999) and other animals (primarily butterflies) elsewhere (Parmesan, 1996; Parmesan *et al.*, 1999), Brommer concludes, "in general, for Northern Hemisphere species, southerly range margins of species are less responsive to climate change than the northerly margins." This demonstrates once again the ranges of birds (and possibly other animals) in a warming world likely will increase, as their northern range boundaries expand poleward and upward while their southern range boundaries remain largely unaltered, which should render them less subject to extinction than they are currently or have been in the past.

For the portion of the United States east of the Rocky Mountains, Hitch and Leberg (2007) used data from the North American Breeding Bird Survey to evaluate shifts in the northern range boundaries of 26 species of birds with southern distributions and the southern range boundaries of 29 species of birds with northern distributions between the periods 1967–1971 and 1998–2002. They found the northern margins of the southern group of birds showed significant northward shifts that averaged 2.35 km per year for all species studied, which they describe as being "consistent with the results of Thomas and Lennon (1999) from Great Britain." Also in agreement with the observations on British birds, they determined

"levels of warming do not appear to be so great [that] they are forcing birds to abandon the southernmost portions of their distributions."

Grandgeorge *et al.* (2008) analyzed population sizes and phylogenetic and spatial structures of British and Irish seabirds based on "(1) presence or absence of the seabird species in the different counties of Britain and Ireland between 1875 to 1900 and 1968 to 1972, (2) seabird breeding censuses of Britain and Ireland from 1969 to 1970, 1985 to 1988 and 1998 to 2002, (3) at-sea abundance and distribution surveys of seabirds in the North Sea from 1980 to 1985 and 1990 to 1995, and (4) a bioenergetics model to estimate energy expenditures for 40 seabird species." They found "a marked expansion in the breeding range of seabirds in Britain and Ireland between 1875 and 1972." In addition, they report total seabird numbers "increased at an average rate of 1% per annum between 1969 and 2002, with a related increase of 115% in predicted total seabird predation." Also, they state, "between 1875 and 1972 no seabird species was lost and there was an overall expansion in breeding range of the seabird population of Britain and Ireland, with the number of counties occupied increasing from 31 to 47."

The six scientists conclude, "the seabird community of Britain and Ireland has been remarkably resilient to environmental change in the 20th century." In fact, it "prospered during the 20th century," and "significantly raised ocean temperatures in the North Sea (Beaugrand, 2004)" may have "created more favorable environmental conditions for some seabird species," citing Thompson (2006).

Brommer (2008) notes a "population-level change expected under a climate-warming scenario is a poleward shift in the distribution of organisms," and he states many believe birds that "do not shift their range margin consist of species that are declining, and would therefore be of particular management concern." A few years earlier, Brommer (2004) had measured the range sizes and northern range margin locations of 116 bird species with a predominantly southern distribution in Finland, and of those species "the trend slope describing the change in their abundance for the period 1983–2005 was calculated for 53 species by Vaisanen (2006)." This, he notes, resulted in "the largest dataset available of the long-term trends in population numbers of Finnish birds that is comparable across species, because it has both been gathered and analyzed using the same procedures." Brommer (2008) determined the concomitant changes in the northern range margins of the 53 species.

The Finnish bird specialist found "species foraging in wet habitats had experienced strong range margin shifts as compared with other feeding ecologies." However, he found "no evidence that those feeding ecological groups that showed a relatively small shift in range margin had experienced low population growth or a population decline." Therefore, in discussing "the lack of correlation between the shift in range margin of the different feeding ecologies and the change in their mean abundance," Brommer states this real-world finding "is contrary to expected under a climate-change scenario, because, all else being equal, a clear range-margin shift should indicate a good capacity to track climatic change, which should result in a more positive trend in abundance if climate change is indeed the main driver of population-level change."

Maclean *et al.* (2008) analyzed counts of seven wading bird species—the Eurasian oystercatcher, grey plover, red knot, dunlin, bar-tailed godwit, Eurasian curlew, and common redshank—made at approximately 3,500 sites in Belgium, Denmark, France, Germany, Ireland, the Netherlands, and the United Kingdom on at least an annual basis since the late 1970s. They did this in order to determine what range adjustments the waders may have made in response to regional warming, calculating the weighted geographical centroids of the bird populations for all sites with complete coverage for every year between 1981 and 2000. They found "the weighted geographical centroid of the overwintering population of the majority of species has shifted in a northeasterly direction, perpendicular to winter isotherms," with overall 20-year shifts ranging from 30 to 119 km. In addition, they report, "when the dataset for each species was split into 10 parts, according to the mean temperature of the sites, responses are much stronger at the colder extremities of species ranges." They found, "at warmer sites, there was no palpable relationship between changes in bird numbers and changes in temperature." They conclude, "range expansions rather than shifts are occurring" as the planet warms.

Maclean *et al.* note the commonly used climate-envelope approach to predicting warming-induced species migrations "essentially assumes that as climate alters, changes at one margin of a species' range are mirrored by those at the other, such that approximately the same 'climate space' is occupied regardless of actual climate," whereas the evidence suggests "that this may not be the case: climate space can also change."

Maclean *et al.* further write, "it is actually not surprising that responses to temperature appear only to be occurring at the colder extremities of species ranges," for "it has long been known that it is common for species to be limited by environmental factors at one extremity, but by biological interactions at the other," citing Connell (1983) and Begon *et al.* (2005). They conclude it is likely "the warmer extremities of the species ranges examined in this study are controlled primarily by biotic interactions, whereas the colder margins are dependent on temperature."

In a model-based study, Jensen *et al.* (2008) state "global climate change is expected to shift species ranges polewards, with a risk of range contractions and population declines of especially high-Arctic species," citing the Arctic Climate Impact Assessment (ACIA, 2005). To evaluate this claim, they constructed species distribution models for the Svalbard-nesting pink-footed goose (*Anser brachyrhynchus*), in order to "relate their occurrence to environmental and climatic variables." They used the most parsimonious of the models to "predict their distribution under a warmer climate scenario," based on "mean May temperature, the number of frost-free months and the proportion of moist and wet moss-dominated vegetation in the area," the latter being "an indicator of suitable feeding conditions."

They found global warming "will have a positive effect on the suitability of Svalbard for nesting geese in terms of range expansion into the northern and eastern parts of Svalbard which are currently unsuitable." They also note this result does not even consider whether glaciers will decrease in size and expose still more potential nest sites. Thus they conclude by stating increased temperatures could help the population of pink-footed geese, as "elongation of the frost-free season in Svalbard may relax their dependence on the acquisition of body stores before arrival (so-called 'capital' breeding, *sensu* Drent and Daan, 1980), so that geese will have more time to acquire the necessary resources upon arrival and still breed successfully," noting "both factors are likely to have a positive effect on the population growth."

Zuckerberg *et al.* (2009) "used the New York State Breeding Birds Atlas, a statewide survey of 5,332 25-km^2 blocks surveyed in 1980–1985 and 2000–2005, to test several predictions that the birds of New York State are responding to climate change." They found "all bird species (n = 129) included in this analysis showed an average northward range shift in their mean latitude of 3.58 km." Citing a number of other studies, the researchers conclude, "the repeated pattern of a predicted northward shift in bird ranges in various geographic regions of the [Northern Hemisphere] provides compelling evidence that climate change is driving range shifts." This provides compelling evidence Earth's birds did precisely what they should have done, over the period of Zuckerberg *et al.*'s study, in order to maintain a strong presence on the planet in the face of the rising temperatures (natural or anthropogenic) of that period.

Hockey and Midgley (2009) write, "in the influential fourth assessment report of the Intergovernmental Panel on Climate Change, Rosenzweig *et al.* (2007) tested several thousand time-series data sets for changes in species behavior and geographic range consistent with climate change, reaching the conclusion that it is very likely that climate change is driving changes in natural biological systems." They note, "the use of such large data sets in meta-analyses may discourage the close inspection of observations and result in naively misattributing observed shifts to climate when other explanations may be more parsimonious."

To test this hypothesis, Hockey and Midgley "collated information about recent range changes in South African birds, specifically indigenous species that have colonized the Cape Peninsula, at the south-western tip of Africa in the Western Cape province, since the 1940s," where they state there have been "widespread anthropogenic changes of many kinds to the landscape, including urbanization, commercial afforestation and the introduction and spread of invasive alien trees, most of which occurred before climate change accelerated in the 1970s."

The two researchers found the colonization events "concur with a 'climate change' explanation, assuming extrapolation of Northern Hemisphere results and simplistic application of theory," but "on individual inspection, all but one may be more parsimoniously explained by direct anthropogenic changes to the landscape than by the indirect effects of climate change." Also, "no *a priori* predictions relating to climate change, such as colonizers being small and/or originating in nearby arid shrub-lands, were upheld."

The South African scientists state their work suggests "observed climate changes have not yet been sufficient to trigger extensive shifts in the ranges of indigenous birds in this region, or that *a priori* assumptions are incorrect." Either way, they continue, "this study highlights the danger of naive attribution of range changes to climate change, even if those range changes accord with the predictions of climate-change models," because "misattribution could

distract conservationists from addressing pressing issues involving other drivers of biodiversity change such as habitat transformation, and obscure important lessons that might be learned from the dynamics that pertain to such changes."

Tyrberg (2010) compared fossil avifaunas of the Last Interglacial (LIG), about 130,000 to 117,000 years ago from multiple sites around the world to the modern avifaunas found in those locations. During much of this time interval, the globe was about 2°C warmer than it is today, and it was up to 10°C warmer in much of the Arctic. For fossil faunas, only species that still exist were included in the comparisons, because during the cold period of the last glacial, which followed the LIG, many species went extinct due to the cold, and climate tolerance can be determined reliably only for living species.

Based on the areal distributions of fossil avifaunas in different parts of the world, regions were delineated in which many of the identified species coexisted. If it was found the same sets of species share the same common ranges today, it was concluded the avifauna, as a whole, did not respond to any significant degree to the warmer temperatures of the LIG.

For sites that were about 2°C warmer during the LIG—including four sites in Florida, one in Alaska, two in Germany, and one in New Zealand—species present during the LIG were found to be the same as those that inhabit those regions today. At a site in Wales, however, where LIG temperatures were a full 4°C warmer than today, the fossil avifauna was similar to the current avifauna of Spain and Portugal, indicating the fossil avifauna had located themselves further northward during the LIG in response to the much greater warmth of that period. And in another exception to the study's primary findings of similar faunal structures, the LIG avifauna at a site in North Africa (which is now desert, with no birds present) was similar to that of the area south of the desert today, indicating—in light of the fact that during the LIG the Sahara desert received much more rainfall than it does currently—precipitation was the overriding factor determining both the current and fossil avifauna choice of territories.

Tyrberg concludes, "as for the effect of the generally warmer climate during the LIG it seems clear that differences on the order of 2°C or less, both on land and in sea-surface temperatures, are barely, if at all, detectable in the avifaunas."

Popy *et al.* (2010) employed data from two bird atlas surveys performed on a 1 km by 1 km grid (the first in 1992–1994 and the second in 2003–2005) in an alpine valley in the Italian Piedmont in search of evidence for an upward shift in the ranges of 75 bird species (68 of which were detected in both surveys) over this period, during which time the region's mean air temperature rose by 1.0°C. They found "the number of species whose mean elevation increased (n = 42) was higher than the number whose mean elevation decreased (n = 19), but the overall upward shift [29 m] was not significantly different from zero." In addition, they state even the 29-m increase was "smaller than would be expected from 'climatic envelope' models," as the "1.0°C increase in temperature would be equivalent to *c.* 200 m in elevation, based on an average gradient of -0.5°C per 100 m." In addition, they write, "at the European scale, no overall expansion or contraction of the distributions of the studied species was detected." Popy *et al.* conclude, "until a better understanding of the underlying mechanisms is achieved, predictions based only on 'climate envelope' models should be either validated or considered cautiously."

Using the same sampling techniques employed by Terborgh and Weske (1975) in 1969, and working at five of the nine localities studied by those earlier investigators, Forero-Medina *et al.* (2011) resampled bird communities at five elevations (690, 1310, 1570, 1970, and 2220 meters) within the Reserva Comunal El Sira on the Cerros del Sira massif in Peru some 41 years later, in 2010. They sought to determine what changes might have occurred in the elevations of the several species encountered at the two sampling times. Of the 55 species encountered in both sampling periods, 36 had moved up in elevation, 12 had moved down, and seven had not moved in either direction, resulting in an average upward shift of 49 meters for the 55 bird species over the 41-year period. They describe this change in elevation as being "significantly smaller" than the 152-meter increase one would have expected from the amount of warming experienced throughout the region between the times of the two studies.

In an attempt to determine to what extent tropical and subtropical birds from lower latitudes may have been making their way northwards in response to regional warming since the mid–1970s, Rappole *et al.* (2011) conducted a three-year field study on ranch land of the Welder Wildlife Refuge along a 30-km stretch of the Aransas River in southeastern Texas, which they say is located "at the northern end of the New World subtropics." Their findings indicate "range change is occurring at a rapid rate for tropical, subtropical, and warm desert birds in Texas." They report, "comparisons between former (1974) and current avian distributions for the region show significant breeding range extension of 40–220 km to the north, northeast or east for at least 68 species, many of which cross major biogeographic boundaries." They conclude "change in key parameters of habitat, e.g. seasonal food availability, as affected by factors related to climate change, e.g. mean annual precipitation, temporal distribution of precipitation (monthly means), or monthly means for nighttime-low temperatures during the breeding season, provide the most likely explanations for observed range extensions."

As for the single overriding "environmental factor associated with avian range shift in South Texas," Rappole *et al.* identify "change in mean annual temperature," as documented by Norwine and John (2007). They report the movement of this "large segment of the subtropical avian community into temperate habitats has not been met with a corresponding shift of temperate species as had been predicted by a number of models." Quite to the contrary, they continue, "the communities now overlap, creating, in effect, novel communities." These new communities possess a greater biodiversity than the ones that existed there prior to the arrival of the many new tropical and subtropical bird species.

The findings cited in this section make it clear that where confirmed regional warming over the time periods has been investigated, the vast majority of studies of bird range adjustments have revealed opportunistic poleward expansions of their cold-limited boundaries with little or no change in the locations of their (supposedly) heat-limited boundaries. This behavior is not a matter of massive range reductions or of bird species rushing, or even inching, toward extinction, as is often projected in model-based studies. Instead, the species are fortifying themselves against the possibility of extinction, behaving as resilient evolutionary survivors and colonizing new habitat as it becomes available, strengthening their populations against the myriad challenges associated with environmental change.

References

ACIA. 2005. *Arctic Climate Impact Assessment*. New York, NY: Cambridge University Press.

Beaugrand, G. 2004. The North Sea regime shift: evidence, mechanisms and consequences. *Progress in Oceanography* **60**: 245–262.

Begon, M., Townsend, C., and Harper, J. 2005. *Ecology: From Individuals to Ecosystems*. Oxford, UK: Blackwell.

Brommer, J.E. 2004. The range margins of northern birds shift polewards. *Annales Zoologici Fennici* **41**: 391–397.

Brommer, J.E. 2008. Extent of recent polewards range margin shifts in Finnish birds depends on their body mass and feeding ecology. *Ornis Fennica* **85**: 109–117.

Connell, J.H. 1983. On the prevalence and relative importance of interspecific competition: evidence from field experiments. *The American Naturalist* **122**: 661–696.

Drent, R.H. and Daan, S. 1980. The prudent parent: energetic adjustment in avian breeding. *Ardea* **68**: 225–252.

Forero-Medina, G., Terborgh, J., Socolar, S.J., and Pimm, S.L. 2011. Elevational ranges of birds on a tropical montane gradient lag behind warming temperatures. *PLoS ONE* **6**: e28535.

Grandgeorge, M., Wanless, S., Dunn, T.E., Maumy, M., Beaugrand, G., and Gremillet, D. 2008. Resilience of the British and Irish seabird community in the twentieth century. *Aquatic Biology* **4**: 187–199.

Hitch, A.T. and Leberg, P.L. 2007. Breeding distributions of North American bird species moving north as a result of climate change. *Conservation Biology* **21**: 534–539.

Hockey, P.A.R. and Midgley, G.F. 2009. Avian range changes and climate change: a cautionary tale from the Cape Peninsula. *Ostrich* **80**: 29–34.

Jensen, R.A., Madsen, J., O'Connell, M., Wisz, M.S., Tommervik, H., and Mehlum, F. 2008. Prediction of the distribution of Arctic-nesting pink-footed geese under a warmer climate scenario. *Global Change Biology* **14**: 1–10.

Kinzelbach, R.K. 2004. The distribution of the serin (*Serinus serinus* L., 1766) in the 16th century. *Journal of Ornithology* **145**: 177–187.

Maclean, I.M.D., Austin, G.E., Rehfisch, M.M., Blew, J., Crowe, O., Delany, S., Devos, K., Deceuninck, B., Gunther, K., Laursen, K., van Roomen, M., and Wahl, J. 2008. Climate change causes rapid changes in the distribution and site abundance of birds in winter. *Global Change Biology* **14**: 2489–2500.

Mayr, E. 1926. Die Ausbreitung des Girlitz (*Serinus canaria serinus* L.). Ein BEitrag Zur Tiergeographie. *Journal of Ornithology* **74**: 571–671.

McCarthy, J.J., Canziani, O.F., Leary, N.A., Dokken, D.J., and White, K.S. (Eds.) 2001. *Climate Change 2001: Impacts, Adaptation, and Vulnerability.* Cambridge, UK: Cambridge University Press.

Norment, C.J., Hall, A., and Hendricks, P. 1999. Important bird and mammal records in the Thelon River Valley, Northwest Territories: Range expansions and possible causes. *The Canadian Field-Naturalist* **113**: 375–385.

Norwine, J. and John, K. 2007. Welcome to the Anthropocene: South Texas climate. In: Norwine, J. and John, K. (Eds.) *The Changing Climate of South Texas: 1900–2100.* Texas A & M University, Kingsville, Texas, USA, pp. 1–4.

Parmesan, C. 1996. Climate and species' range. *Nature* **382**: 765–766.

Parmesan, C., Ryrholm, N., Stefanescu, C., Hill, J.K., Thomas, C.D., Descimon, H., Huntley, B., Kaila, L., Kullberg, J., Tammaru, T., Tennent, W.J., Thomas, J.A., and Warren, M. 1999. Poleward shifts in geographical ranges of butterfly species associated with regional warming. *Nature* **399**: 579–583.

Popy, S., Bordignon, L., and Prodon, R. 2010. A weak upward elevational shift in the distributions of breeding birds in the Italian Alps. *Journal of Biogeography* **37**: 57–67.

Rappole, J.H., Glasscock, S., Goldberg, K., Song, D., and Faridani, S. 2011. Range change among new world tropical and subtropical birds. In: Schuchmann, K.-L. (Ed.) *Tropical Vertebrates in a Changing World.* Bonner Zoologische Monographien No. 57: 151–167.

Rosenzweig, C., Casassa, G., Karoly, D.J., Imeson, A., Liu, C., Menzel, A., Rawlins, S., Root, T.L., Seguin, B., and Tryjanowski, P. 2007. Assessment of observed changes and responses in natural and managed systems. In Parry, M., *et al.* (Eds.) *Climate Change 2007: Impacts, Adaptation and Vulnerability.* Working Group II Contribution to the 4th Assessment Report of the Intergovernmental Panel on Climate Change, pp. 79–131. Cambridge, UK: Cambridge University Press.

Saether, B.-E., Tufto, J., Engen, S., Jerstad, K., Rostad, O.W., and Skatan, J.E. 2000. Population dynamical consequences of climate change for a small temperate songbird. *Science* **287**: 854–856.

Terborgh, J. and Weske, J.S. 1975. The role of competition in the distribution of Andean birds. *Ecology* **56**: 562–576.

Thomas, C.D. and Lennon, J.J. 1999. Birds extend their ranges northwards. *Nature* **399**: 213.

Thompson, P.M. 2006. Identifying drivers of change: did fisheries play a role in the spread of North Atlantic fulmars? In Boyd, I.A., Wanless, S., and Camphuysen, C.J. (Eds.) *Management of Marine Ecosystems: Monitoring Change in Upper Trophic Levels.* Cambridge, UK: Cambridge University Press.

Tyrberg, T. 2010. Avifaunal responses to warm climate: the message from last interglacial faunas. *Records of the Australian Museum* **62**: 193–205.

Vaisanen, R.A. 2006. Maalinnuston kannanvaihtelut Etela-ja Pohjois-Suomessa 1983–2005. *Linnut-vuosikirja* **2005**: 83–98.

Wagner, B. and Melles, M. 2001. A Holocene seabird record from Raffles So sediments, East Greenland, in response to climatic and oceanic changes. *Boreas* **30**: 228–239.

Zuckerberg, B., Woods, A.M., and Porter, W.F. 2009. Poleward shifts in breeding bird distributions in New York State. *Global Change Biology* **15**: 1866–1883.

5.4.3 Adaptation, Evolution, and Phenotypic Responses

Amid concerns of species extinctions in response to rising temperatures, observational data indicate birds are effectively coping with and adapting to various challenges to their existence, real or perceived, arising from global warming. This section examines adaptive responses pertaining to reproductive success, timing of spring arrival, and trophic mismatches. In brief, the findings discussed here provide ample reason to conclude birds likely will benefit from future global warming.

5.4.3.1 Reproductive Success

Concerns have been expressed that global warming may upset certain reproductive traits in birds, leading to downward trends in the populations of many species. However, as discussed below, birds are well-equipped to respond to warming, often adapting their breeding habits so their reproductive success is frequently higher at warmer temperatures.

Brown *et al.* (1999) studied a population of individually recognizable, color-banded Mexican jays in the Chiricahua Mountains of Arizona (USA) over the period 1971–1998 for trends in egg-laying dates and monthly minimum air temperatures. Over this 29-year period, they determined the date of first nest construction occurred 10.8 days earlier, and the date of first clutch came 10.1 days earlier. These changes were associated with significant upward trends in monthly minimum temperature in the study area; in many bird species "breeding is timed so as to have young in the nest when the principal food of the nestlings is at its peak." With warmer minimum temperatures occurring earlier over their study period, they suggest this climatic trend could be producing an earlier abundance of such food, which would help explain the earlier egg-laying date.

The researchers also identified a second way in which earlier-occurring warmer night temperatures might lead to earlier breeding dates in birds: by alleviating thermal stresses on females on cold nights. Citing several studies that had revealed similar breeding trends in European birds, they suggest the "recognition of similar trends on both continents in very different environments is consistent with the interpretation that some avian populations are already responding to climate changes in the last 29 years or so." These widespread changes are positive in nature, for not only are bird ranges increasing in size as air temperatures rise, the temporal availability of food needed to sustain important life processes is advancing in synchrony with the timing of egg-laying.

Visser *et al.* (2003) examined laying dates for 24 populations of great and blue tits (*Parus major* and *Parus caeruleus*, respectively) in six European countries from 1979 to 1998, during which time several (but not all) of the locations studied exhibited increases in near-surface air temperature. Results indicated "the phenological response to large-scale changes in spring temperature varies across a species' range, even between populations situated close to each other." They also report "this variation cannot be fully explained by variation in the temperature change during the pre- and post-laying periods." Their results "show the value of replicating population studies across parts of a species' range, as the effects of climate change may differ, even within a single species, on a small geographical scale."

Halupka *et al.* (2008) documented various breeding parameters of reed warblers (long-lived passerine birds that winter in Africa but breed in the reed beds of marshlands in the Palaearctic) during 12 breeding seasons (1970–1973, 1980–1983, 1994, 2003, and 2005–2006) and compared trends in what they measured with concomitant trends in mean monthly temperatures. They found temperatures in the mean breeding season (April-August) increased significantly between 1970 and 2006, as did the mean temperature of each individual month of the breeding season, with the average temperature for the May-July period rising by 2°C. Egg-laying started three weeks earlier in 2005 and 2006 than in 1970 (as assessed by the first-egg date of the earliest pair of breeding birds), and the median first-egg date shifted forward by 18 days.

The end of egg-laying, however, did not change significantly in either direction, so there was a corresponding increase in the length of the egg-laying period, and with this longer laying period available to them, more birds were able to rear second broods. In the 1970s and 1980s, for example, the Polish researchers report, "only about 0–15% of individuals laid second clutches," but "between 1994 and 2006 up to 35% of birds reared second broods." In addition, they report, "during seasons with warm springs, early nests were better protected by being hidden in newly emerged reeds," and "as a result, these nests suffered fewer losses from predation." They conclude, "the studied population of reed warblers benefits from climate warming."

Based on bird-ringing records spanning 41 years (1964–2004), Husek and Adamik (2008) "documented shifts in the timing of breeding and brood size in a long-distance migrant, the red-backed shrike (*Lanius collurio*) from a central European population." They compared their results with the climatic history of the region over the same period. They determined temperatures in May increased significantly over the period of their study, and "in line with this increasing May temperature" there was "a 3- to 4-day shift towards earlier breeding." This pattern, they write, "is consistent with the results of similar studies on other long-distance migrating songbirds (e.g., Dunn, 2004)." In addition, they report, there was "an increase in brood size by approximately 0.3 nestlings since 1964." They state, "given that early broods are usually larger (Lack, 1968; this study) and that they have a higher nest success (Muller *et al.*, 2005), this may have a positive effect on future population increases as the temperature continues to rise."

After observing two second clutches in a newly established population of tree swallows in the Shenandoah Valley of Virginia (USA), Monroe *et al.* (2008) monitored all late nests in the following two breeding seasons to see what they could learn about the phenomenon. This revealed, "among all females nesting in the early breeding rounds of 2006 and 2007, 5% of birds with successful first clutches later laid second clutches." The mean productivity for double-brooded females for 2006–2007 was 4.4 ± 1.3 fledglings from first clutches and 3.4 ± 0.8 from second clutches, so "double-brooded females significantly increased their total annual productivity compared to birds nesting only in the early rounds of breeding." The productivity of the double-brooded females was approximately 75 percent greater than that of the single-brooded females. Monroe *et al.* conclude, "in general, late summer and fall nesting among North American birds is underappreciated and may be increasing due to global warming," citing Koenig and Stahl (2007).

Dyrcz and Halupka (2009) examined long-term responses in the breeding performance of Great Reed Warblers living on fish ponds near Milicz in southwest Poland during various years from 1970 to 2007 (1970–1974, 1981–1984, 1997, and 2004–2007), over which period mean temperatures during the egg-laying months of the species (May–July) rose by 2.2°C, from 15.3 to 17.5°C. The two researchers found a "significant advancement in both earliest and annual median first-egg-laying dates" that "correlated with temperature increases early in the season." Latest first-egg-laying dates remained unchanged, as did several other breeding statistics, including clutch size, nest losses, and number of young per nest. Consequently—and contrary to a Bavarian population of Great Reed Warblers that also advanced its latest first-egg-laying date—the Polish bird population expanded its breeding season in response to regional warming, whereas the Bavarian birds merely shifted theirs, as documented by Schaefer *et al.* (2006).

Dyrcz and Halupka conclude, "the studied population does not benefit from climate warming (as found in Bavaria), but apparently does not suffer," reiterating "the Great Reed Warbler has adapted well ... by shifting the timing of breeding." The results of their study, they state, "do not confirm the prediction of Bairlein and Winkel (2000) that long-distance migrants would suffer due to climate change." In addition, they write, a comparison of their data with that of the Bavarian population "provides evidence that different populations of the same species can adapt in different ways to climate change," noting "this was also previously found for woodland species," citing Visser *et al.* (2002) and Sanz (2003).

Wesolowski and Cholewa (2009) investigated evidence for climate warming in Bialowieza National Park of East Poland over the period 1975–2007 to determine "whether local populations of four sedentary birds (*Sitta europaea, Poecile palustris, Cyanistes caeruleus, Parus major*) advanced their breeding phenology during that time, and how breeding phenology was affected by temperature variation during the period preceding egg laying." According to the authors, "mean yearly temperatures varied strongly across years, with a significant warming (~1°C) trend," and "in all species the onset of breeding was vary variable across years (up to 30 days), as birds started breeding earlier in springs with higher temperatures in the pre-laying period." They note the spring of 1990—when February and March were extremely warm with "mean temperatures 15°C higher than these months' averages, equivalent to the 'worst' IPCC warming scenario"—served as a natural experiment, showing "what would happen when the late winter/early spring period got substantially warmer." They found "all four species were able to react to this challenge by advancing the onset of breeding to unusually early dates that are usually found only in the Mediterranean populations."

The two researchers write, "the ability to react even in these extreme conditions shows that the range of phenotypic plasticity in these birds is far greater than normally observed, and suggests that there is still unexpressed potential in lay date flexibility." They therefore conclude, "local birds are already prepared to cope with envisaged warming, suggesting that there is no need for new response mechanisms." In addition, they state this phenomenon is "clearly noticeable among different groups of organisms in Bialowieza National Park (e.g. timing of bud burst in trees, Wesolowski and Rowinski, 2006, 2008; development of herbs on the forest floor, Falinski 2001, Sparks *et al.*, 2009)," and they thus also conclude, "birds, trees and herbs in this primeval forest apparently 'read' environmental cues in a similar way and react to them in a comparable fashion," probably because "they have been exposed to the same vagaries of local climate over ages if not millennia, and there was plenty of time to match phenology of interacting species with one another."

Thomas *et al.* (2010) note "the timing of annual breeding is a crucial determinant of reproductive success, individual fitness, and population performance, particularly in insectivorous passerine birds," because "by synchronizing hatching with the narrow time window of maximal food abundance, parents can enhance their reproductive success through an increase in offspring growth rate and body condition, survival to fledging, and subsequent recruitment into the breeding population." They studied two populations of blue tits in northern Corsica (Muro and Pirio) to determine "how laying date is related to spring temperatures and vegetation phenology." These two factors were assumed to figure highly in determining the peak period of blue tit food abundance (caterpillars). They discovered "Blue Tits use a cue system that is context specific to fine-tune laying dates to match local conditions both on a spatial (habitat) scale and on a temporal (inter-annual) scale," and their "reliance on both temperature and phenology when breeding late in the season, as occurs in most populations where tits have been intensively studied north of the Mediterranean region, satisfactorily explains how these populations can advance breeding in response to rising spring temperatures while maintaining a relatively large variation in the onset of breeding on a local spatial scale."

Thomas *et al.* acknowledge, "if a single

environmental feature [such as temperature] were responsible for the timing of breeding, climate change could cause a severe decline in breeding success, with negative demographic consequences." However, they state they "have not detected any consistent mismatch between Blue Tit breeding dates and caterpillar peak [abundance] dates over the 14 and 21 years for which they have data for Muro and Pirio, respectively." Their findings, they conclude, "offer some hope that breeding populations will respond well to global warming."

Barnagaud *et al.* (2011) note "deciphering the effects of climatic conditions on population dynamics is of major importance in understanding how organisms are likely to be affected by climate changes." Toward that end, they "used broad scale annual censuses of adult and young Black Grouse in the French Alps between 1990 and 2007 to test whether the breeding success of the species is affected by inter-annual climatic variation and long-term climate change," based on "annual counts of Black Grouse hens and chicks carried out by the French Mountain Galliforms Observatory on 58 counting sites," where "counts were performed on the same sites and areas from one year to another, with the same operators."

They note "the Alps are currently undergoing a significant global change in climatic conditions, with warmer temperatures and drier conditions, especially in winter, that reflect particularly well such large scale processes as the NAO [North Atlantic Oscillation]," citing Beniston *et al.* (1997), Giorgi *et al.* (1997), and Beniston (2005, 2006). They determined "the [current] optimal weather conditions for the reproduction of the Black Grouse in the French Alps correspond to average winter NAO values for the last 30 years," which suggests, they write, "the species has adapted to more frequent positive NAO anomalies in the last decades, i.e., to a warmer and drier climate."

Noting "neither the numbers of hens nor the breeding indexes have declined during the last 18 years," they further state "this result is consistent with recent reports (Storch, 2007) suggesting that the alpine populations of Black Grouse which declined during most of the twentieth century (Magnani, 1987) have stabilized in the past two decades, despite the climate warming threat." They point out "this absence of decline agrees with community-level studies showing lower-than-expected effects of climate change on alpine birds (Archaux, 2004)." The seven scientists also say their results indicate "Black Grouse have until now been able to track climatic trends towards a warmer and drier climate," and they "appear to be more threatened by declines in the availability of suitable areas and changes in habitat structure than by direct effects of climate warming on [their] reproduction." Thus, they conclude, "even a highly specialized mountain species can track rapid climate changes without decreasing its productivity, at least within the limits of current climate changes."

Weimerskirch *et al.* (2012) write, "in marine systems, wind is a major component of the environment, and climate change-induced alterations in oceanic wind regimes and strength have already occurred and are predicted to increase." With respect to what has "already occurred," they note "over the past fifty years, Southern Hemisphere westerlies have shifted poleward and increased in intensity," which could affect "the movement or distribution of wind-dependent species, such as migratory land birds or pelagic seabirds." The latter, the authors note, "rely extensively on wind to move at low costs between breeding and foraging sites," citing Weimerskirch *et al.* (2000) and Wakefield *et al.* (2009).

Weimerskirch *et al.* analyzed the possible influence of wind conditions over the Southern Ocean on the foraging ecology and life-history traits of the wandering albatross (*Diomedea exulans*), one of the most wide-ranging pelagic seabirds, employing data on the duration of their foraging trips and breeding success collected over the period 1966–2010, and foraging performance and body mass collected over the period 1989–2010, focusing on breeding birds from the Crozet Islands, which are situated in the windiest area of the Southern Ocean.

Over the period of time characterized by IPCC as having experienced unprecedented global warming, the foraging range of wandering albatrosses shifted poleward, as the wind also "strongly increased and shifted poleward," the four researchers report. As a result of this change, albatross "rates of travel and flight speeds have increased," a trend they say also has been found to have occurred in the southwestern Indian Ocean over the past 30 years by Peron *et al.* (2010). One important consequence of this change was a 22% decrease in the duration of albatross foraging trips between 1970 and 2008 (a drop from 12.4 to 9.7 days). And as a consequence of this change, they write, "breeding success has improved, and birds have increased in mass by more than one kilogram," a 10–12% increase in body weight for males and females alike.

The above-described real-world wind changes of the past half-century, in the words of Weimerskirch *et al.* (2012), "have affected positively the foraging efficiency and foraging range of wandering albatrosses, ultimately improving breeding success and reducing mortality risks, respectively." As can be estimated from their graph of the pertinent data, albatross breeding success rose from approximately 65% to 77% over the period studied.

References

Archaux, F. 2004. Breeding upwards when climate is becoming warmer: no bird response in the French Alps. *Ibis* 146: 138–144.

Bairlein, F. and Winkel, W. 2000. Birds and climate change. In Lozan, J.L., Grassl, H., and Hupfer, P. (Eds.) *Climate of the 21st Century: Changes and Risks*. Hamburg, Germany: Wissenschaftliche Auswertungen, pp. 278–282.

Barnagaud, J.-Y., Crochet, P.A., Magnani, Y., Laurent, A.B., Menoni, E., Novoa, C., and Gimenez, O. 2011. Short-term response to the North Atlantic Oscillation but no long-term effects of climate change on the reproductive success of an alpine bird. *Journal of Ornithology* 152: 631–641.

Beniston, M. 2005. Mountain climates and climatic change: an overview of processes focusing on the European Alps. *Pure and Applied Geophysics* 162: 1587–1606.

Beniston, M. 2006. Mountain weather and climate: a general overview and a focus on climatic change in the Alps. *Hydrobiologia* 562: 3–16.

Beniston, M., Diaz, S., and Bradley, R.W. 1997. Climatic change at high elevation sites: an overview. *Climatic Change* 36: 233–251.

Brown, J.L, Shou-Hsien, L., and Bhagabati, N. 1999. Long-term trend toward earlier breeding in an American bird: a response to global warming? *Proceedings of the National Academy of Science, U.S.A.* 96: 5565–5569.

Dunn, P. 2004. Breeding dates and reproductive performance. *Advances in Ecological Research* 35: 69–87.

Dyrcz, A. and Halupka, L. 2009. The response of the Great Reed Warbler *Acrocephalus arundinaceus* to climate change. *Journal of Ornithology* 150: 39–44.

Falinski, J.B. 2001. Phytophenological atlas of the forest communities and species of Bialowieza National Park. *Phytocoenosis NS* 13: 1–176.

Giorgi, F., Hurrell, J.W., and Marinucci, M.R. 1997. Elevation dependency of the surface climate change signal: a model study. *Journal of Climate* 10: 288–296.

Halupka, L., Dyrcz, A., and Borowiec, M. 2008. Climate change affects breeding of reed warblers *Acrocephalus scirpaceus*. *Journal of Avian Biology* 39: 95–100.

Husek, J. and Adamik, P. 2008. Long-term trends in the timing of breeding and brood size in the Red-Backed Shrike *Lanius collurio* in the Czech Republic, 1964–2004. *Journal of Ornithology* **149**: 97–103.

Koenig, W.D. and Stahl, J.T. 2007. Late summer and fall nesting in the Acorn Woodpecker and other North American terrestrial birds. *The Condor* **109**: 334–350.

Lack, D. 1968. Ecological Adaptations for Breeding in Birds. London, UK: Methuen.

Magnani, Y. 1987. *Reflexions sur la dynamique d'une population de Tetras lyre Tetrao tetrix L. des Alpes francaises.* In: Institut d'analyse des systemes biologiques et socio-economiques. Laboratoire de biometrie, Universite Claude Bernard Lyon I, Lyon.

Monroe, A.P., Hallinger, K.K., Brasso, R.L., and Cristol, D.A. 2008. Occurrence and implications of double brooding in a southern population of tree swallows. *The Condor* **110**: 382–386.

Muller, M., Pasinelli, G., Schiegg, K., Spaar, R., and Jenni, L. 2005. Ecological and social effects on reproduction and local recruitment in the red-backed shrike. *Oecologia* **143**: 37–50.

Peron, C., Authier, M., Barbraud, C., Delord, K., Besson, D., and Weimerskirch, H. 2010. Interdecadal changes in at-sea distribution and abundance of sub-antarctic seabirds along a latitudinal gradient in the Southern Indian Ocean. *Global Change Biology* **16**: 1895–1909.

Sanz, J.J. 2003. Large-scale effect of climate change on breeding parameters of pied flycatchers in Western Europe. *Ecography* **26**: 45–50.

Schaefer, T., Lebedur, G., Beier, J., and Leisler, B. 2006. Reproductive responses of two related coexisting songbird species to environmental changes: global warming, competition, and population sizes. *Journal of Ornithology* **147**: 47–56.

Sparks, T., Jaroszewicz, B., Krawczyk, M., and Tryjanowski, P. 2009. Advancing phenology in Europe's last remaining primeval forest: Are we in danger of underestimating the response to increasing temperatures? *Climate Research* **39**: 221–226.

Storch, I. 2007. Grouse: Status Survey and Conservation Action Plan 2006–2010. IUCN, Gland, Switzerland.

Thomas, D.W., Bourgault, P., Shipley, B., Perret, P., and Blondel, J. 2010. Context-dependent changes in the weighting of environmental cues that initiate breeding in a temperate passerine, the Corsican Blue Tit (*Cyanistes caeruleus*). *The Auk* **127**: 129–139.

Visser, M.E., Adriaensen, F., van Balen, J.H., Blondel, J., Dhondt, A.A., van Dongen, S., du Feu, C., Ivankina, E.V., Kerimov, A.B. de Laet, J., Matthysen, E., McCleery, R.,

Orell, M., and Thomson, D.L. 2003. Variable responses to large-scale climate change in European Parus populations. *Proceedings of the Royal Society of London B* **270**: 367–372.

Visser, M.E., Silverin, B., Lambrechts, M.M., and Tinbergen, J.M. 2002. No evidence for tree phenology as a cue for the timing of reproduction in tits *Parus* spp. *Avian Science* **2**: 1–10.

Wakefield, E., Phillips, R.A., Matthiopoulos, J., Fukuda, A., Higuchi, H., Marshall, G.J., and Trathan, P.N. 2009. Wind field and sex constrain the flight speeds of central-place foraging albatrosses. *Ecological Monographs* **79**: 663–679.

Weimerskirch, H., Guionnet, T., Martin, J., Shaffer, S.A., and Costa, D.P. 2000. Fast and fuel efficient? Optimal use of wind by flying albatrosses. *Proceedings of the Royal Society B* **267**: 1869–1874.

Weimerskirch, H., Louzao, M. de Grissac, S., and Delord, K. 2012. Changes in wind pattern alter albatross distribution and life-history traits. *Science* **335**: 211–214.

Wesolowski, T. and Cholewa, M. 2009. Climate variation and bird breeding seasons in a primeval temperate forest. *Climate Research* **38**: 199–208.

Wesolowski, T. and Rowinski, P. 2006. Timing of bud burst and tree-leaf development in a multispecies temperate forest. *Forest Ecology and Management* **237**: 387–393.

Wesolowski, T. and Rowinski, P. 2008. Late leaf development in pedunculate oak *Quercus robur*: an antiherbivore defense? *Scandinavian Journal of Forest Research* **23**: 386–394.

5.4.3.2 Spring Arrival Dates

Changes in the date of spring migration arrival date of birds have been viewed by some as a fingerprint of climate change and possibly of species distress. Trends in this parameter should be evaluated with caution before making such a leap.

A case in point is the study of Mills (2005), who used data collected at Long Point Bird Observatory on the north shore of Lake Erie in Ontario, Canada over the period 1975–2000 to investigate whether there had been changes in the timing of spring and autumn migrations of 13 species of birds that might be viewed as ecological responses to global warming. He analyzed for trends in the day of first arrival in the spring, and in the days of first, second, and third quartile arrivals in the spring, as well as like departures in the autumn.

All 13 species exhibited earlier trends in the date

of first arrival in the spring. When subjected to stringent thresholds of statistical analysis, however, only one species was considered to exhibit a definite trend. Spring quartile analyses were not nearly as universal. Only nine of the 13 species trended toward an earlier arrival date, and four trended toward a later arrival date. Of the nine that trended toward an earlier arrival date, only two were statistically significant, leaving the author to conclude, "most individuals of most species cannot conclusively be said to have migrated in 2000 earlier than their 1975 ancestors." Analysis of the quartile means revealed no significant phenological change by bird sex. With respect to autumn trends, five species showed delayed migration, two showed advanced migration, and six exhibited no trend.

Mills writes, "caution should be exercised in drawing broad conclusions about changes in migration phenology" with respect to global warming. He notes, for example, using first arrival dates to characterize migration systems "can be problematic because they are data from one tail of a distribution, they comprise a mostly male population and they may not correlate well with the balance of the migration period." He also notes "changes do not appear to be universal in spring, and change in that season is (a) considerably less than that suggested by [first arrival date] analysis and (b) both less complex and less common than that exhibited during autumn migration."

For studies that show a more conclusive link between temperature and date of bird migration, rather than considering such observations to be a sign of species in distress, an alternative and perhaps more correct interpretation is that such changes are simply a manifestation of the ability of birds to adapt or evolve in response to an environmental perturbation. Model-based claims of species decline typically do not account for adaptative or evolutionary responses, but because birds are winged creatures, it would be expected that under the threat of global warming they might take flight and migrate to cooler regions of the globe as an adaptive measure. Several studies of bird migration dates suggest they may be doing so.

Gordo and Sanz (2006) analyzed a large database of about 44,000 records they assembled from observations at more than 1,300 sites throughout Spain during the period 1944–2004 in a study of the migratory behavior for five trans-Saharan bird species: *Ciconia ciconia* or white stork, *Cuculus canorus* or cuckoo, *Apus apus* or swift, *Hirundo rustica* or barn swallow, and *Luscinia megarhynchos* or nightingale. This phenomenon previously had been proposed by the country's Instituto Nacional de Meteorologia as "a potential bioindicator of the timing of seasons," the current study of which the two Spanish researchers describe as "the most complete and thorough analysis available for the Mediterranean region."

Gordo and Sanz report "spring arrival dates have tended to advance since the mid–1970s," and "individuals arrived earlier in warmer years," noting "the earlier arrivals related to higher temperatures should be due to the advancement of the spring course in the Iberian Peninsula and consequently the presence of ecological suitable conditions for an early colonization of first breeders." They found "current arrival dates are similar or even seem to be a bit later to those occurring at the beginning of the study period." According to Gordo and Sanz, "the advance in arrival date recorded over the last few decades should be better interpreted as a trend towards re-establishing the timing of migration after an anomalous period of delayed arrivals during the 1970s–1980s," which suggests birds have been adapting to temperature changes throughout the Mediterranean region, where temperatures were likely warmer in the mid–1940s than they were throughout the 1990s and during the first years of the twenty-first century.

Studying the skylark (*Alauda arvensis*), which is migratory in Eastern and Northern Europe but resident in areas with milder winters (such as the UK), Askeyev *et al.* (2009) analyzed the dates of their spring arrival in the Volga-Kama region of the Tatarstan Republic of Russia, using "one of the longest extant records of bird migration in the world," which runs from 1811 to 2008, with sporadic missing years in the first half of the record. They report March temperatures rose about 5.2°C over their study period, but 3.7°C (~70%) of that warming occurred over the final three decades of the nearly two-century-long interval. They also found a corresponding inflection point in the rate-of-advancement of skylark spring arrival-date that was approximately 15 times greater (0.368 day per year) than it was over the study period's first 17 decades (0.024 day per year).

Plotting arrival-date as a function of temperature, they found the inflection point occurred at a mean March temperature of –3.5°C, suggesting a mean rate of advancement of spring arrival-date of 0.5 day per °C for mean March temperature increases below a negative 3.5°C, and a mean rate of advancement of arrival-date of 3.4 days per °C for mean March temperature increases above –3.5°C. That represents close to a seven-fold increase in the rate of advancement of spring arrival-date upon exceeding this biological "tipping point" temperature.

Askeyev *et al.* conclude, "the nonlinear nature of the relationship between first arrival and temperature suggests that above a critical temperature threshold a much more rapid change in first arrival date will occur." This observation suggests regardless of whether "tipping points" occur in the realm of climatology, they do in fact occur, and in some cases already have occurred, to the benefit of certain of Earth's birds—the hotter it gets, the better they do what they need to do to deal with the evolving situation.

Van Buskirk *et al.* (2012) state, "phenological responses to climate change are well-documented in plants and animals," and "it is widely assumed that much of the shift in phenology is due to facultative changes in the activities or physiologies of individuals induced by environmental conditions, known as phenotypic plasticity." However, they write, "phenotypic plasticity is not the only mechanism that can produce population responses to climate change," noting "gradual or sudden shifts in the selection regime can be triggered by environmental change, and these in turn can alter the genetic composition of populations." They point out "rapid evolved responses to climate change are widely anticipated by evolutionary biologists (Bradshaw and Holzapfel, 2001; Davis *et al.*, 2005; Gienapp *et al.*, 2008; Hoffman and Willi, 2008; Hoffmann and Sgro, 2011), and already have been observed in a few cases (Umina *et al.*, 2005; Bradshaw and Holzapfel, 2008)."

Between June 1961 and August 2006, Van Buskirk *et al.* operated 35 mist nets for five to six days a week on a 10-ha study area on the Powdermill Nature Reserve in Pennsylvania (USA), in order to obtain the data needed to estimate the magnitude of temperature-induced phenotypic plasticity in spring arrival date of 27 species of birds in eastern North America, by recording the effects of annual variation in spring temperature on the behavior of thousands of individuals. They hypothesized that if phenotypic plasticity could not account for the totality of observed shifts in migration phenology over this period, what remained unaccounted for could be attributed, at least partly, to microevolutionary change.

The three researchers report "for 2441 individuals detected in multiple years, arrival occurred earlier during warm years, especially in species that migrate short distances," but the change in phenology predicted "under a model of pure phenotypic plasticity" fell far short of the change in arrival date

they observed, explaining only 13–25% of the climate-induced trend in phenology. Although they acknowledge their approach to the problem "probably underestimates the full scope of plasticity," Van Buskirk *et al.* say their data suggest "part of the response to environmental change [warming] has been caused by microevolution." They also conclude "the estimated evolutionary rates [0.016 haldanes] are plausible."

The three scientists write, "rapid genetic response to climate change is widely seen as a critical component of the kind of adaptation that will be required of many organisms," especially in a world that warms as suggested by the models employed by IPCC. In addition, "the contribution of plasticity will allow individuals to adjust their phenotype to short-term environmental fluctuations, which are projected to increase under most scenarios of climate change." That's good news for birds.

References

Askeyev, O.V., Sparks, T.H., and Askeyev, I.V. 2009. Earliest recorded Tatarstan skylark in 2008: non-linear response to temperature suggests advances in arrival dates may accelerate. *Climate Research* **38**: 189–192.

Bradshaw, W.E. and Holzapfel, C.M. 2001. Genetic shift in photoperiodic response correlated with global warming. *Proceedings of the National Academies of Science USA* **98**: 14,509–14,511.

Bradshaw, W.E. and Holzapfel, C.M. 2008. Genetic responses to rapid climate change: it's seasonal timing that matters. *Molecular Ecology* **17**: 156–166.

Davis, M.B., Shaw, R.G., and Etterson, J.R. 2005. Evolutionary responses to changing climate. *Ecology* **86**: 1704–1714.

Gienapp, P., Teplitsky, C., Alho, J.S., Mills, J.A., and Merila, J. 2008. Climate change and evolution: disentangling environmental and genetic responses. *Molecular Ecology* **17**: 167–178.

Gordo, O. and Sanz, J.J. 2006. Climate change and bird phenology: a long-term study in the Iberian Peninsula. *Global Change Biology* **12**: 1993–2004.

Hoffmann, A.A. and Sgro, C.M. 2011. Climate change and evolutionary adaptation. *Nature* **470**: 479–485.

Hoffmann, A.A. and Willi, Y. 2008. Detecting genetic responses to environmental change. *Nature Reviews Genetics* **9**: 421–432.

Mills, A.M. 2005. Changes in the timing of spring and autumn migration in North American migrant passerines during a period of global warming. *Ibis* **147**: 259–269.

Umina, P.A., Weeks, A.R., Kearney, M.R., McKechnie, S.W., and Hoffmann, A.A. 2005. Rapid shift in a classic clinal pattern in *Drosophila* reflecting climate change. *Science* **308**: 691–693.

Van Buskirk, J., Mulvihill, R.S., and Leberman, R.C. 2012. Phenotypic plasticity alone cannot explain climate-induced change in avian migration timing. *Ecology and Evolution* **2**: 2430–2437.

5.4.3.3 Trophic Mismatches

Another concern about the potential effects of global warming is that, as the world warms, mismatches may occur among various life cycle stages of plants, the insects that feed on them, and numerous species of animals, such as birds, that feed on insects and provide them as food for their young, a situation that could spell disaster for some species. This concept has been said by Visser and Both (2005) to constitute an "insufficient adjustment" to climate change. This section investigates the validity of such concerns, finding trophic mismatches are a non-problem in most instances.

Bauer *et al.* (2010) examined the effect of 47 years of warming (1961–2007) on the time of leafing-out of dominant English oak trees (*Quercus robur*) at four research sites in the Czech Republic located in full-grown, multi-aged floodplain forests that had been under no forestry management. The researchers also evaluated the time of appearance of the two most abundant species of caterpillars in the floodplain forests—the winter moth (*Operophtera brumata*) and the tortrix moth (*Tortrix viridana*)—and the first and mean laying dates of two of the ecosystem's most common birds: great tits (*Parus major*) and collared flycatchers (*Ficedula albicollis*).

According to the researchers, "mean annual temperature showed a significant increase of 0.27–0.33°C per decade, with approximately the same magnitude of change during spring at all sites." They also found, "on average (all four sites), the bud burst date for English Oak has advanced by 7.9 days and full foliage by 8.9 days, with approximately the same shifts being recorded for the peak of the beginning and end of frass for herbivorous caterpillars," the observational variable they used to characterize the caterpillars' presence. Last, they determined "the first laying date of Great Tits has advanced by between 6.2 to 8.0 days," and "the mean laying date has advanced by 6.4 to 8.0 days." Similarly, the "Collared Fly-catcher first laying date has advanced by 8.5 to 9.2 days over the past 47 years, and the mean laying date by 7.7 to 9.6 days."

Bauer *et al.* state "trends in the timing of reproduction processes of both bird species are coherent with the trends in development of English Oak and with peak herbivorous caterpillar activity." In this specific food chain, the common shifting of the different organisms' phenological stages toward the beginning of the year "does not appear to have led to mistiming in the trophic food chain."

Citing Visser *et al.* (1998, 2006) and Visser (2008), Matthysen *et al.* (2011) note "the increasing mismatch between great tit *Parus major* laying dates and their caterpillar food supply in the Netherlands has rapidly become a classic example of a lack of adaptation to climate change." However, they report, "other populations of the same bird species have subsequently been shown to advance their laying dates much more strongly" in order to match the earlier spring growth of vegetation that typically occurs during periods of extended warming, citing Cresswell and McCleery (2003) and Charmantier *et al.* (2008).

Matthysen *et al.* "studied the breeding cycle of two sympatric and closely related species, the blue tit *Cyanistes caeruleus* and the great tit *Parus major,* in a rich oak-beech forest," where they had collected data on the breeding biology of the birds from 1979 to 2007 in a 12-hectare plot provided with nest boxes inside the Peerdsbos forest near Antwerp, Belgium. Both bird species were shown to have "advanced their mean first-egg dates by 11–12 days over the last three decades," and "the time from first egg to fledging has shortened by 2–3 days, through a decrease in laying interruptions, incubation time and nestling development time." As a consequence, they write, "the average time of fledging has advanced by 15.4 and 18.6 days for blue and great tits, respectively, and variance in fledging dates has decreased by 70–75%." Most important, they note, "indirect estimates of the food peak suggest that both species have maintained synchronization with the food supply," and "analyses of within-individual variation show that most of the change can be explained by individual plasticity in laying date, fledging date and nest time." Matthysen *et al.* emphasize "synchronization of the nestling period with the food supply not only depends on first-egg dates but also on additional reproductive parameters including laying interruptions, incubation time and nestling growth rate." As a result of adjustments in these several related phenomena, they report, "both of our study species have been able to maintain synchrony with their food supply in the face of global warming."

Vatka *et al.* (2011) further investigated the possibility global warming may lead to trophic mismatches between the times when birds of temperate and boreal regions require an abundance of food to feed their new hatchlings and the times when that food is available in its greatest abundance, as in the cases of great tits, blue tits, and pied flycatchers in the Netherlands, which require a timely abundance of caterpillars to feed their young (Visser *et al.*, 1998; Visser *et al.*, 2006; Both *et al.*, 2009). Vatka *et al.* note, "the same has not happened with great tits in England (Cresswell and McCleery, 2003) nor with great tits and collared flycatchers in the Czech Republic (Bauer *et al.*, 2010)." They describe yet a third type of food supply-and-demand response to warming they recently observed and documented.

Working with data collected in northern Finland over the period 1975–2009 within coniferous, deciduous, and mixed forests of varying ages—including young stands, swamps, and clear cuttings—the three Finnish scientists studied "changes in the timing of breeding in the willow tit (*Poecile montanus*), and the timing of its caterpillar food resource in relation to warming springs," using "generalized linear mixed effect models to study the importance of synchrony between the timing of breeding in willow tits and the caterpillar food availability on the breeding success, measured as nestling survival rate and mean nestling weight." In contrast to prior no change results and poorer synchrony findings, Vatka *et al.* report they not only "found no signs of emerging asynchrony" but that synchrony actually improved during the study, and it had moderate positive effects on breeding success. The observed improvement in synchrony mirrors results from the coal tit in the Netherlands, the authors add, citing Both *et al.* (2009).

Reed *et al.* (2013) studied a wild population of great tits (*Parus major*) in the Netherlands in relation to the phenology of their food supply, noting "great tits rely on caterpillars to feed their chicks and strive to match their breeding time with the pronounced seasonal peak in caterpillar biomass, which enhances offspring survival." The researchers studied this by "using almost four decades of individual-level life-history data from a great tit population." They report warmer springs had indeed "generated a mismatch between the annual breeding time and the seasonal food peak, intensifying directional selection for earlier laying dates." However, they found inter-annual variation in population mismatch had not affected population growth, and they "demonstrated a mechanism contributing to this uncoupling, whereby

fitness losses associated with mismatch are counter-acted by fitness gains due to relaxed competition." The team of Dutch, French, Norwegian, and U.S. scientists states their findings imply "natural populations may be able to tolerate considerable maladaptation driven by shifting climatic conditions without undergoing immediate declines." They conclude, "our results imply that considerable directional selection might be demographically tolerable on decadal time scales without immediate population declines, effectively buying time for microevolution to restore adaptation."

Burthe *et al.* (2012) "compared phenological trends for species from four levels of a North Sea food web over 24 years [1983–2006] when sea surface temperature (SST) increased significantly," starting with primary producers (phytoplankton), primary consumers (zooplankton), and secondary consumers (sandeels), and finally focusing on five seabird predators—the common guillemot (*Uria aalge*), razor bill (*Alca torda*), European shag (*Phalacrocorax aristotelis*), black-legged kittiwake (*Rissa tridactyla*), and Atlantic puffin (*Fratercula arctica*)—all of which are seabirds that prey on current-year sandeels (*Ammodytes marinus*). The nine researchers say they found "little consistency in phenological trends between adjacent trophic levels, no significant relationships with SST, and no significant pairwise correlations between predator and prey phenologies," which they take as evidence "trophic mismatching is occurring." Yet in spite of the supposed trophic mismatches discovered over the course of their research, Burthe *et al.* report, "to date, there is no evidence that these changes are impacting on the breeding success of any of the seabird species."

Although much remains to be learned about this topic, it is clear trophic mismatches, thought to be initiated by global warming, need not produce negative responses from bird populations. Many bird species may not be affected at all, and others may even benefit from such a climate change.

References

Bauer, Z., Trnka, M., Bauerova, J., Mozny, M., Stepanek, P., Bartosova, L., and Zalud, Z. 2010. Changing climate and the phenological response of great tit and collared flycatcher populations in floodplain forest ecosystems in Central Europe. *International Journal of Biometeorology* **54**: 99–111.

Both, C., van Asch, M., Bijlsma, R.G., van den Burg, A.B., and Visser, M.E. 2009. Climate change and unequal phenological changes across four trophic levels: constraints or adaptations? *Journal of Animal Ecology* **78**: 73–83.

Burthe, S., Daunt, F., Butler, A., Elston, D.A., Frederiksen, M., Johns, D., Newell, M., Thackeray, S.J., and Wanless, S. 2012. Phenological trends and trophic mismatch across multiple levels of a North Sea pelagic food web. *Marine Ecology Progress Series* **454**: 119–133.

Charmantier, A., McCleery, R.H., Cole, L.R., Perrins, C., Kruuk, L.E.B., and Sheldon, B.C. 2008. Adaptive phenotypic plasticity in response to climate change in a wild bird population. *Science* **320**: 800–803.

Cresswell, W. and McCleery, R. 2003. How great tits maintain synchronization of their hatch date with food supply in response to long-term variability in temperature. *Journal of Animal Ecology* **72**: 356–366.

Matthysen, E., Adriaensen, F., and Dhondt, A.A. 2011. Multiple responses to increasing spring temperatures in the breeding cycle of blue and great tits (*Cyanistes caeruleus, Parus major*). *Global Change Biology* **17**: 1–16.

Reed, T.E., Grotan, V., Jenouvrier, S., Saether, B.-E., and Visser, M.E. 2013. Population growth in a wild bird is buffered against phonological mismatch. *Science* **340**: 488–491.

Vatka, E., Orell, M., and Rytkonen, S. 2011. Warming climate advances breeding and improves synchrony of food demand and food availability in a boreal passerine. *Global Change Biology* **17**: 3002–3009.

Visser, M.E. 2008. Keeping up with a warming world; assessing the rate of adaptation to climate change. *Proceedings of the Royal Society B-Biological Sciences* **275**: 649–659.

Visser, M.E. and Both, C. 2005. Shifts in phenology due to global climate change: the need for yardstick. *Proceedings of the Royal Society B* **272**: 2561–2569.

Visser, M.E., Holleman, L.J.M., and Gienapp, P. 2006. Shifts in caterpillar biomass phenology due to climate change and its impact on the breeding biology of an insectivorous bird. *Oecologia* **147**: 164–172.

Visser, M.E., van Noordwijk, A.J., Tinbergen, J.M., and Lessells, C.M. 1998. Warmer springs lead to mistimed reproduction in great tits (*Parus major*). *Proceedings of the Royal Society B-Biological Sciences* **265**: 1867–1870.

5.4.3.4 Other Responses

Additional adaptive or evolutionary responses to warming, not discussed in the prior subsections, have been identified in the literature for birds, each of which suggests birds are adequately suited to withstand any of the temperature changes predicted to accompany the future rise in atmospheric CO_2.

In regard to the challenges migratory animals may face due to potential changes in climate, Dias *et al.* (2011) write, "existing phenotypic plasticity *per se* may allow, within certain limits, the persistence of species and populations (even if in suboptimal circumstances), gaining time for selection to act, or for more favorable environmental conditions to be restored," noting "there is strong evidence that recent climate changes may have already impacted migratory behavior" as it pertains to birds, citing Fiedler (2003) and Newton (2008).

Dias *et al.* evaluated individual flexibility in the migration strategies of a highly pelagic seabird, the Cory's shearwater (*Calonectris diomedea*). They deployed leg-mounted geolocators weighing approximately 3.6 grams at the end of the breeding seasons of 2006, 2007, and 2008, recovering them in the early stages of the subsequent breeding seasons, to track the migration of 57 of the birds that spent the breeding season at Selvagem Grand Island (30°02' N, 15°52' W). The five researchers report 14 birds that were tracked for more than one non-breeding season "showed a remarkable capacity to change winter destinations between years," with some shifting all the way from the South Atlantic to the North Atlantic, and from the Atlantic Ocean to the Indian Ocean. They found individual birds "also showed flexibility in stopover behavior and migratory schedule." Dias *et al.* conclude Cory's shearwaters are in a good position "to face the consequences of a changing environment," adding, "whether Cory's shearwaters are unusual in this respect, or whether future analyses will reveal that flexibility in migration strategies is a more general trait of marine migratory fauna is something that repeated tracking of individuals in coming years should clarify."

According to Forero-Medina *et al.* (2011), "the tropics contain most of the world's species at risk of extinction (Pimm and Jenkins, 2010), yet few studies evaluate the response of tropical species to climate disruption other than through modeling (Jetz *et al.*, 2007; Marini *et al.*, 2009; La Sorte and Jetz, 2010)." Using the same sampling techniques employed by Terborgh and Weske (1975) in 1969, and working at five of the nine localities studied by those earlier investigators, Forero-Medina *et al.* (2011) resampled bird communities at five elevations (690, 1310, 1570, 1970, and 2220 meters) within the Reserva Comunal El Sira on the Cerros del Sira massif in Peru 41 years later in 2010, seeking to determine what changes might have occurred in the elevations of the several species encountered at the two sampling times. Of the 55 species encountered in both sampling years, the four researchers report 36 had moved up in elevation, 12 had moved down, and seven had not moved in either direction, resulting in an average upward shift of 49 meters for the 55 bird species over the 41-year period. They describe this change in elevation as "significantly smaller" than the 152-meter increase one would have expected from the amount of warming experienced throughout the region between the times of the two studies.

Forero-Medina *et al.* note more than one mountain had been involved in the initial study of Terborgh and Weske (1975), and "the same bird species exhibited different elevation ranges on different mountains, indicating considerable flexibility in the occupancy of habitat and independence of temperature (Diamond, 1970; Terborgh, 1985)." Therefore, they write, "the limited upward elevational shifts reported here are unlikely to be simple responses to increased temperature *per se*." Instead, they suggest, "birds are likely responding to gradual changes in the nature of the habitat or availability of food resources through their dependence on long-lived elements of the ecosystem (trees), and how the species' competitors respond." They note "the rate of migration of trees is less (45%) than that predicted from the temperature increase of the region," and "similar lags in the response of trees may be occurring at the Sira, accounting for the lag in response of birds."

Put another way, Forero-Medina *et al.* conclude, "instead of being directly dependent on temperature, birds may be responding to gradual changes in the nature of their habitat or availability of food resources, and presence of competitors," so "endothermy [the ability of certain animals to control their body temperature] may provide birds with some flexibility to temperature changes and allow them to move less than expected."

Van Buskirk *et al.* (2010) write, "recent climate change has caused comparatively rapid shifts in the phenology and geographic distributions of many plants and animals," but "there is debate over the degree to which populations can meet the challenges of climate change with evolutionary or phenotypic responses in life history and morphology," which for a warming climate includes a reduction in body size. They devised an experimental strategy to explore the issue further, studying the body sizes of birds captured in mist-nets and traps between June 1961 and November 2006 at the Powdermill Nature Reserve, a field station operated by the Carnegie

Museum of Natural History in Pennsylvania (USA) at a location broadly representative of bird communities in the Appalachian region of eastern North America. At this location, 35 mist nets were operated five to six days per week during spring and autumn migrations. A reduced number of nets was used during summer, and birds for winter banding were caught in wire traps when the temperature was below freezing.

The three researchers report migrating birds captured at the banding station "have steadily decreasing fat-free mass and wing chord since 1961, consistent with a response to a warmer climate" and confirming "phenotypic responses to climate change are currently underway in entire avian assemblages," where "size was negatively correlated with temperature in the previous year, and long-term trends were associated with the direction of natural selection acting on size over the winter." In addition, they note, "species undergoing the strongest selection favoring small wing chord showed the most rapid long-term declines in wing [size]," which suggests "phenotypic changes are therefore in line with the prevailing selection regime." Noting "in summer, 51 of 65 breeding species had negative slopes of mass against year, 20 of 26 wintering species had negative slopes, 60 of 83 spring migrants had negative slopes, and 66 of 75 autumn migrants had negative slopes," Van Buskirk *et al.* state their results "offer compelling evidence that climate change has already produced observable adaptive shifts in morphology, behavior, and phenology of a great many species," which suggests these birds have evolved a capacity for rapid phenotypic shifts to optimum body mass in response to climate fluctuations.

Additional support for this thesis comes from Carey (2009), who notes "organisms living today are descended from ancestors that experienced considerable climate change in the past," and thus suggests, "species that persist into future climates may be able to do so in part owing to the genetic heritage passed down from ancestors who survived climate changes in the past." She also states, "if climate change were the only new challenge facing birds, one might imagine that many species could become adapted to new conditions and survive with existing population variability and the genetic information that their ancestors used to survive past climate change."

Karell *et al.* (2011) theorize "global climate warming changes the environment of most organisms and is expected to lead to a change in selection pressures with micro-evolutionary consequences that allow the adaptation of organisms to the new environment and thereby long-term population persistence." They further note, "microevolution in response to climate change has been demonstrated in invertebrate populations (Umina *et al.*, 2005; Balanya *et al.*, 2006)," but "these studies lack information on the mechanisms and selective factors linking particular genotypes to climate."

Karell *et al.* explored "the links between climate change and alteration of the selective regime on a highly heritable phenotypic trait, plumage coloration in the tawny owl (*Strix aluco*), a common bird of prey throughout the temperate regions of Europe." They used data from 1981 to 2008 in a 250-km^2 study area in Southern Finland dominated by mixed forests, agricultural areas, and small freshwater courses, where "plumage coloration was scored using a semi-continuous ordinal scale (range from 4 (grey) to 14 reddish-brown)) on all breeding individuals on each encounter ($N = 1116$ records of 491 individuals) using a standardized and repeatable scoring that shows coloration is independent of age and sex." In addition, they scored museum skin specimens collected between 1915 and 1980; and they extracted the data on all records of adult ringed and recaptured tawny owls in Finland to which color morph (grey or brown) had been assigned during 1961–2008. Finally, they write, "measures of temperature and snow depth from the time window that correlated best with annual tawny owl survival were selected as covariates for further modeling."

The five Finnish researchers determined "brown individuals had lower survival than grey ones as snow cover became deeper" and there was a "lower survival for brown individuals compared with grey ones in cold temperatures," as cooler conditions would be expected to promote a deeper snow cover. Thus they report as snow depth decreased over time in response to warming, "there was a time trend in survival of the color morphs from 1981–2008, in which survival of the grey morph was fairly stable across years, whereas survival of brown individuals improved dramatically towards the end of the time series." They also report this phenotypic change was present on a larger nationwide scale—the increase of the brown morph occurred "all over Finland, involving thousands of individuals," such that "the survival propensities of the morphs have equalized in recent, mild winters."

Karell *et al.* remark the phenotypic change they documented "is unlikely to be caused by genetic drift, because drift is only a major force for changing allele frequencies in small populations." Therefore, "given the strong genetic underpinning of tawny owl morphs," they say they consider the observed pheno-

typic trend in the proportion of the brown morph as "indicative for a shift in gene frequencies." Hence, they conclude, to the best of their knowledge, the results of their study constitute "the first empirical evidence of climate-driven change in selection on a heritable trait," providing a whole new perspective on the potential of Earth's fauna to withstand the challenges of global warming.

Gremillet *et al.* (2012) state little auks (*Alle alle*) are the most numerous seabirds in the North Atlantic, with an estimated population of 40 to 80 million individuals, citing Stempniewicz (2001), and they consume up to 24% of local plankton production, citing Karnovsky and Hunt (2002). The researchers also note the "little auk field metabolic rate is 70% higher than predicted by body mass, and they have very limited capacity to store fat." Consequently, they say, little auks "are predicted to be particularly sensitive to altered feeding conditions," citing Harding *et al.* (2009). More specifically, they write, the recent work of Karnovsky *et al.* (2010) "showed a very strong link between summer SST [sea surface temperature] within the foraging areas of little auks, species composition of local zooplankton communities, and dietary preferences of the birds, whereby colder water contained more larger copepods, which were also preferentially fed upon by little auks," so "birds had to feed on smaller, less profitable copepod species in warmer water." As a result of these observations, they hypothesize "higher SSTs would modify little auk diet, foraging effort, provisioning rates, breeding success and adult survival," which they presume would significantly decline in response to warming.

In an integrative study of the behavior, physiology, and fitness of colonies of little auks at three sites of significantly different temperature—Kap Hoegh, East Greenland (70°43'N, 22°38'W), Hornsund, West Spitsbergen (77°00'N, 15°22'E), and Kongsfjorden, West Spitsbergen (79°01'N, 12°25'E)—Gremillet *et al.* evaluated the effects of ocean warming on little auks across the Greenland Sea over the period 2005–2007. They noted "comparing the ecophysiology of little auks from different colonies subject to contrasting SST regimes at one moment in time" would allow them to "simulate the effect that increasing water temperatures might have on this Arctic species across the 21st century."

"During the study period," the researchers write, "little auks maintained their fitness despite contrasting ocean surface temperatures and copepod availability across the Greenland Sea." Gremillet *et al.* write, "contrary to our hypothesis, the birds responded to a wide range of sea surface temperatures via plasticity of their foraging behavior, allowing them to maintain their fitness levels," indicating "they are successful at dealing with the influence of current climate change in the Arctic." In the concluding sentence of their abstract, the team of nine scientists from eight countries (Canada, Denmark, France, Ireland, Norway, Poland, South Africa, and the United States) writes, "predicted effects of climate change are significantly attenuated by such plasticity, confounding attempts to forecast future effects of climate change using envelope models."

According to Smit *et al.* (2013), "one of the main predictions of bioclimatic envelope models is that populations near the climatic extremes of species' distributions, where thermoregulatory costs are presumably high, are performing sub-optimally and are at greater risk of extinction," citing Thomas *et al.* (2004). However, Smit *et al.* suggest, "if populations are physiologically adapted (genetic variation across generations and/or plastic adjustments) to their respective climates, species may be capable of maintaining high levels of performance throughout their geographic ranges," citing Chown *et al.* (2010) and Glanville *et al.* (2012).

Smit *et al.* investigated the effects of air temperature (T_A) on body temperature (T_B) and the behavior of an arid-zone endotherm, the White-Browed Sparrow-Weaver (*Plocepasser mahali*) at two sites 100 km apart, in the southern Kalahari Desert of South Africa, over two consecutive summer seasons. The four researchers found a relatively large variation in T_B that occurred both within and between populations, suggesting "an arid-zone passerine responds differently to prevailing weather conditions in two locations over its range, and that it also responds to seasonal changes in weather conditions." This further suggests "a species' current range may not be an accurate representation of its climatic tolerance."

"Taken together with the data of Glanville *et al.* (2012)," Smit *et al.* explain, this result "suggests that the thermal physiology of endotherms is far more flexible than previously thought, and could potentially contribute to the adaptation of populations under changing climatic conditions," citing Boyles *et al.* (2011)." They conclude, "when predicting species' responses to climate change, their sensitivity (sensu Williams *et al.*, 2008) should be resolved at the population, rather than species, level."

References

Balanya, J., Oller, J.M., Huey, R.B., Gilchrist, G.W., and Serra, L. 2006. Global genetic change tracks global climate warming in *Drosophila subobscura. Science* **313**: 1773–1775.

Boyles, J.G., Seebacher, F., Smit, B., and McKechnie, A.E. 2011. Adaptive thermoregulation in endotherms may alter responses to climate change. *Integrative and Comparative Biology* **51**: 676–690.

Carey, C. 2009. The impacts of climate change on the annual cycles of birds. *Philosophical Transactions of the Royal Society B* **364**: 3321–3330.

Chown, S.L., Hoffmann, A.A., Kristensen, T.N., Angilletta, M.J., Stenseth, N.C., and Pertoldi, C. 2010. Adapting to climate change: a perspective from evolutionary physiology. *Climate Research* **43**: 3–15.

Diamond, J.M. 1970. Ecological consequences of island colonization by Southwest Pacific birds, I. Types of niche shifts. *Proceedings of the National Academy of Sciences USA* **67**: 529–536.

Dias, M.P., Granadeiro, J.P., Phillips, R.A., Alonso, H., and Catry, P. 2011. Breaking the routine: individual Cory's shearwaters shift winter destinations between hemispheres and across ocean basins. *Proceedings of the Royal Society B* **278**: 1786–1793.

Fiedler, W. 2003. Recent changes in migration behavior of birds: a compilation of field observations and ringing data. In: Berthold, P., Gwinner, E., and Sonnenschein, E. (Eds.) *Avian Migration.* Springer, Berlin, Germany, pp. 21–38.

Forero-Medina, G., Terborgh, J., Socolar, S.J., and Pimm, S.L. 2011. Elevational ranges of birds on a tropical montane gradient lag behind warming temperatures. *PLoS ONE* **6**: e28535.

Glanville, E.J., Murray, S.A., and Seebacher, F. 2012. Thermal adaptation in endotherms: climate and phylogeny interact to determine population-level responses in a wild rat. *Functional Ecology* **26**: 390–398.

Gremillet, D., Welcker, J., Karnovsky, N.J., Walkusz, W., Hall, M.E., Fort, J., Brown, Z.W., Speakman, J.R., and Harding, A.M.A. 2012. Little auks buffer the impact of current Arctic climate change. *Marine Ecology Progress Series* **454**: 197–206.

Harding, A.M.A., Egevang, C., Walkusz, W., Merkel, F., Blanc, S., and Gremillet, D. 2009. Estimating prey capture rates of a planktivorous seabird, the little auk (*Alle alle*), using diet, diving behavior, and energy consumption. *Polar Biology* **32**: 785–796.

Jetz, W., Wilcove, D.S., and Dobson, A.P. 2007. Projected impacts of climate and land-use change on the global diversity of birds. *PLoS Biology* **5**: 3157.

Karell, P., Ahola, K., Karstinen, T., Valkama, J., and Brommer, J.E. 2011. Climate change drives microevolution in a wild bird. *Nature Communications*: 10.1038/ncomms1213.

Karnovsky, N., Harding, A.M.A., Walkusz, V., Kwasniewski, S., Goszczko, I., Wiktor, J., Routti, H., Bailey, A., McFadden, L., Brown, Z., Beaugrand, G., and Gremillet, D. 2010. Foraging distributions of little auks (*Alle alle*) across the Greenland Sea: Implications of present and future climate change. *Marine Ecology Progress Series* **415**: 283–293.

Karnovsky, N.J. and Hunt Jr., G.L. 2002. Estimation of carbon flux to dovekies (*Alle alle*) in the North Water. *Deep Sea Research II* **49**: 5117–5130.

La Sorte, F.A. and Jetz, W. 2010. Projected range contractions of montane biodiversity under global warming. *Proceedings of the Royal Society B Biological Sciences* **277**: 3401–3410.

Marini, M.A., Barbet-Massin, M., Lopes, L.E., and Jiguet, F. 2009. Predicted climate-driven bird distribution changes and forecasted conservation conflicts in a neotropical savanna. *Conservation Biology* **23**: 1558–1567.

Newton, I. 2008. *The Migration Ecology of Birds*. Academic Press, London, United Kingdom.

Pimm, S.L. and Jenkins, G.L. 2010. Extinctions and the practice of preventing them. In: Sodhi, N.S. and Ehrlich, P.R. (Eds.) *Conservation Biology for All*. Oxford University Press, Oxford, United Kingdom, pp. 181–198.

Smit, B., Harding, C.T., Hockey, P.A.R., and McKechnie, A.E. 2013. Adaptive thermoregulation during summer in two populations of an arid-zone passerine. *Ecology* **94**: 1142–1154.

Stempniewicz, L. 2002. *Alle alle* little auk. *The Journal of the Birds of the Western Palearctic*. Oxford University Press, Oxford, United Kingdom. *BWP Update* **3**: 175–201.

Terborgh, J. 1985. The role of ecotones in the distribution of Andean birds. *Ecology* **66**: 1237–1246.

Terborgh, J. and Weske, J.S. 1975. The role of competition in the distribution of Andean birds. *Ecology* **56**: 562–576.

Thomas, C.D., Cameron, A., Green, R.E., Bakkenes, M., Beaumont, L.J., Collingham, Y.C., Barend, F., Erasmus, N., Ferreira de Siqueira, M., Grainger, A., Hannah, L., Hughes, L., Huntley, B., van Jaarsveld, A.S., Midgley, G.F., Miles, L., Ortega-Huerta, M.A., Peterson, A.T., Phillips, O.L., and Williams, S.E. 2004. Extinction risk from climate change. *Nature* **427**: 145–148.

Umina, P.A., Weeks, A.R., Kearney, M.R., McKechnie, S.W., and Hoffmann, A. 2005. A rapid shift in a classical clinal pattern in *Drosophila* reflecting climate change. *Science* **308**: 691–693.

Van Buskirk, J., Mulvihill, R.S., and Leberman, R.C. 2010. Declining body sizes in North American birds associated with climate change. *Oikos* **119**: 1047–1055.

Williams, S.E., Shoo, L.P., Isaac, J.L., Hoffman, A.A., and Langham, G. 2008. Towards an integrated framework for assessing the vulnerability of species to climate change. *PLoS Biology* **6**: 2621–2626.

5.5 Insects

- Published research indicates rising temperatures will not likely increase, and may decrease, plant damage from leaf-eating herbivores, as rising atmospheric CO_2 boosts the production of certain defensive compounds in plants that are detrimental to animal pests.

Included among the many animal-related concerns over global warming is the worry there will be an increase in the intensity of herbivore pressure on plants. This section reviews research that has been conducted on this topic, beginning with research regarding aphids and then moths, and then regarding specific kinds of vegetation (herbaceous plants, woody plants, and other plants.

5.5.1 Aphids

We begin our survey of the effects of rising temperature and CO_2 levels on aphids with Ma *et al*. (2004), who conducted detailed experiments on the impacts of high temperature, period of exposure, and developmental stage on the survival of the aphid *Metopolophium dirhodum*, which they say "is the most abundant of the three cereal aphid species in Germany and central European countries." This protocol revealed "temperatures over 29°C for 8 hours significantly reduced survival, which decreased generally as the temperature increased." The researchers also determined "exposing aphids to 32.5°C for 4 hours or longer significantly reduced survival," and "mature aphids had a lower tolerance of high temperatures than nymphs." Ma *et al*. conclude, "global warming may play a role in the long-term changes in the population abundance of *M. dirhodum*." Specifically, "an increase in TX [daily average temperature] of 1°C and MaxT [maximum daily temperature] of 1.3°C during the main period of the aphid population increase would result in a 33% reduction in peak population size," and "an increase in TX of 2°C and MaxT of 2.6°C would result in an early population collapse (74% reduction of population size)."

Adler *et al.* (2007) examined the effects of long-term experimental warming on an aphid-sagebrush (*Obtusicauda coweni-Artemisia tridentata*) interaction out-of-doors in the field at the Rocky Mountain Biological Laboratory, Colorado (USA), where five of ten 3-m x 10-m plots in an ungrazed montane meadow were warmed by overhead infrared heaters that provided a continuous heat flux of 22 W/m^2 to the plots ever since 1993. Working at this facility for three consecutive years (1996–1998), they determined how warming affected aphid density, and they used additional observations, manipulative experiments, and chemical analyses to explore some of the mechanisms that might mediate potential effects of warming on aphid density.

The four researchers report, "in no year did we find support for the prediction that warming increased aphid abundance or population growth." They found "warming decreased aphid density on sagebrush in one year, tended to decrease aphids in a second year, and had no effect in a third year." In the first of these years (1997), "there were over 3 times as many aphids per stalk in control compared to warmed plots," and "the proportion of stems infested was almost twice as high." Furthermore, "in enclosures that excluded predators, warming decreased aphid population growth by an amount consistent with observed field density differences," and in a separate snow-manipulation experiment in unheated plots, they found "the timing of snowmelt did not affect aphid density." Adler *et al.* conclude, "long-term studies within a natural community context may provide counterexamples to the prediction that warming will increase herbivore pressure on plants."

Much more research has been conducted on the direct and indirect response of aphids to rising atmospheric CO_2. Docherty *et al.* (1997), for example, grew beech and sycamore saplings in glasshouses maintained at atmospheric CO_2 concentrations of 350 and 600 ppm, while groups of three sap-feeding aphid species were allowed to feed on the saplings. Overall, the elevated CO_2 had few significant effects on aphid feeding and performance. There was, however, a non-significant tendency for elevated CO_2 to reduce the individual weights and population sizes of the aphids, suggesting future increases in the air's CO_2 content might reduce aphid feeding pressures on beech and sycamore saplings, and possibly other plants as well.

Whittaker (1999) reviewed the scientific literature on population responses of herbivorous insects to atmospheric CO_2 enrichment, concentrating on papers resulting from relatively long-term studies. The only herbivorous insects found to exhibit population increases in response to elevated CO_2 exposure were those classified as phloem feeders; specifically, aphids. Although this finding appeared to favor aphids over plants, additional studies came to different conclusions.

Newman *et al.* (1999) grew tall fescue plants for two weeks in open-top chambers maintained at atmospheric CO_2 concentrations of 350 and 700 ppm before inoculating them with aphids (*Rhopalosiphum padi*). After nine additional weeks of differential CO_2 exposure, the plants were harvested and their associated aphids counted. Although elevated CO_2 increased plant dry matter production by 37%, this did not result in similar increases in aphid colonization. The plants grown in air of elevated CO_2 concentration contained far fewer aphids than the plants grown in ambient air.

Percy *et al.* (2002) grew the most widely distributed tree species in all of North America—trembling aspen—in 12 30-m-diameter FACE rings in air maintained at ambient CO_2 and O_3 concentrations, ambient O_3 and elevated CO_2 (560 ppm during daylight hours), ambient CO_2 and elevated O_3 (46.4–55.5 ppb during daylight hours), and elevated CO_2 and O_3 over each growing season from 1998 through 2001. Throughout the experiment they assessed a number of the young trees' growth characteristics and the responses of the sap-feeding aphid *Chaitophorus stevensi*, which they say "infests aspen throughout its range." By itself, elevated CO_2 did not affect aphid abundance, but it increased the densities of natural enemies of the aphids, which over the long term would tend to reduce aphid numbers. Also, by itself, elevated O_3 did not affect aphid abundance, but it had a strong negative effect on natural enemies of aphids, which over the long term would tend to increase aphid numbers. When both trace gases were applied together, elevated CO_2 completely counteracted the reduction in the abundance of natural enemies of aphids caused by elevated O_3. Hence, elevated CO_2 tended to reduce the negative impact of aphids on trembling aspen in this study.

Holopainen (2002) reviewed the scientific literature addressing the joint effects of elevated concentrations of atmospheric O_3 and CO_2 on aphid-plant interactions. Compiling the results of 26 pertinent studies, Holopainen found atmospheric CO_2 enrichment increased aphid performance in six studies, decreased it in six studies, and had no significant impact on it in the remaining 14 studies. Similar results were found for aphid-plant interactions in the presence of elevated O_3 concentrations.

Newman (2003) reviewed the scientific literature on aphid responses to concurrent increases in atmospheric CO_2 and air temperature and also investigated the subject via the aphid population model of Newman *et al.* (2003). He concluded when the air's CO_2 concentration and temperature are both elevated, "aphid population dynamics will be more similar to current ambient conditions than expected from the results of experiments studying either factor alone." The only general conclusion that can be drawn, Newman states, is "insect responses to CO_2 are unlikely to all be in the same direction." Nevertheless, "the lack of a simple common phenomenon does not deny that there is some overriding generality in the responses by the system."

Awmack *et al.* (2004) conducted a two-year study at the Aspen FACE site near Rhinelander, Wisconsin (USA) of the individual and combined effects of elevated CO_2 (+200 ppm) and O_3 (1.5 x ambient) on the performance of *Cepegillettea betulaefoliae* aphids feeding on paper birch trees, in what they call "the first investigation of the long-term effects of elevated CO_2 and O_3 atmospheres on natural insect herbivore populations." At the individual scale, they report, "elevated CO_2 and O_3 did not significantly affect [aphid] growth rates, potential fecundity (embryo number) or offspring quality." At the population scale, "elevated O_3 had a strong positive effect," but "elevated CO_2 did not significantly affect aphid populations."

In comparing their results with those of prior related studies, the three scientists report "the responses of other aphid species to elevated CO_2 or O_3 are also complex." In particular, they note "tree-feeding aphids show few significant responses to elevated CO_2 (Docherty *et al.*, 1997), while crop-feeding species may respond positively (Awmack *et al.*, 1997; Bezemer *et al.*, 1998; Hughes and Bazzaz, 2001; Zhang *et al.*, 2001; Stacey and Fellowes, 2002), negatively (Newman *et al.*, 1999) or not at all (Hughes and Bazzaz, 2001), and the same species may show different responses on different host plant species (Awmack *et al.*, 1997; Bezemer *et al.*, 1999)." In summarizing their observations, they state "aphid individual performance did not predict population responses to CO_2 and O_3," and they conclude, "elevated CO_2 and O_3 atmospheres are unlikely to affect *C. betulaefoliae* populations in the presence of natural enemy communities."

In a study of a different aphid (*Chaitophorus stevensis*) conducted at the same FACE site, Mondor *et al.* (2004) focused on pheromones, which they note "are utilized by insects for several purposes, including alarm signaling," and which in the case of phloem-feeding aphids induces high-density groups of them on exposed leaves of trembling aspen trees to disperse and move to areas of lower predation risk. In this experiment the four treatments were: control (367 ppm CO_2, 38 ppb O_3), elevated CO_2 (537 ppm), elevated O_3 (51 ppb), and elevated CO_2 and O_3 (537 ppm CO_2, 51 ppb O_3). Within each treatment, several aspen leaves containing a single aphid colony of 25 ± 2 individuals were treated in one of two ways: (1) an aphid was prodded lightly on the thorax so as to not produce a visible pheromone droplet, or (2) an aphid was prodded more heavily on the thorax and induced to emit a visible pheromone droplet, after which, in the words of the scientists, "aphids exhibiting any dispersal reactions in response to pheromone emission as well as those exhibiting the most extreme dispersal response, walking down the petiole and off the leaf, were recorded over 5 min."

Mondor *et al.*'s observations were striking. They found the aphids they studied "have diminished escape responses in enriched carbon dioxide environments, while those in enriched ozone have augmented escape responses, to alarm pheromone." They report, "0% of adults dispersed from the leaf under elevated CO_2, while 100% dispersed under elevated O_3," indicating the effects of elevated CO_2 and elevated O_3 on aphid response to pheromone alarm signaling are diametrically opposed. Elevated O_3 (which is detrimental to vegetation) helped aphids escape predation and therefore live to do further harm to the leaves they infest, but elevated CO_2 (which is beneficial to vegetation) made it more difficult for aphids to escape predation and thereby provided an additional benefit to plant foliage. Mondor *et al.* state this phenomenon may be of broader scope than what is revealed by their specific study, noting other reports suggest "parasitoids and predators are more abundant and/or efficacious under elevated CO_2 levels (Stiling *et al.*, 1999; Percy *et al.*, 2002), but are negatively affected by elevated O_3 (Gate *et al.*, 1995; Percy *et al.*, 2002)."

Chen *et al.* (2004) grew spring wheat from seed to maturity in high-fertility well-watered pots out-of-doors in open-top chambers (OTCs) maintained at atmospheric CO_2 concentrations of 370, 550, and 750 ppm. Approximately two months after seeding, 20 apterous adult aphids (*Sitobion avenae*) from an adjacent field were placed on the wheat plants of each of 25 pots in each OTC, and 15 pots were left as controls. At subsequent five-day intervals, both apterous and alate aphids were counted. About one month later, 10 alate morph fourth instar nymphs were introduced onto the plants of each of nine control pots, and for the next two weeks the number of offspring laid on those plants were recorded and removed daily to measure reproductive activity. At the end of the study, the wheat plants were harvested and their various growth responses determined.

The scientists found the introduced aphid populations increased after infestation, peaked during the grain-filling stage, and declined a bit as the wheat matured. On the final day of measurement, aphids in the 550 ppm CO_2 treatment were 32% more numerous than those in ambient air, and aphids in the 750 ppm treatment were 50% more numerous. Alate aphids also produced more offspring on host plants grown in elevated CO_2: 13% more in the 550 ppm treatment, and 19% more in the 750 ppm treatment.

As for the wheat plants, Chen *et al.* report "elevated CO_2 generally enhanced plant height, aboveground biomass, ear length, and number of and dry weight of grains per ear, consistent with most other studies." With respect to aboveground biomass, for example, the 550 ppm treatment displayed an increase of 36%, and the 750 ppm treatment displayed an increase of 50%, in the case of both aphid-infested and non-infested plants.

Chen *et al.* comment, "aphid infestation caused negative effects on all the plant traits measured ... but the negative effects were smaller than the positive effects of elevated CO_2 on the plant traits." They conclude, "the increased productivity occurring in plants exposed to higher levels of CO_2 more than compensate for the increased capacity of the aphids to cause damage." In this experiment, therefore, both the plant and the insect that feeds on it were benefited by the applied increases in atmospheric CO_2 concentration.

Chen *et al.* (2005) grew transgenic cotton plants for 30 days in well-watered and fertilized sand/vermiculite mixtures in pots set in controlled-environment chambers maintained at atmospheric CO_2 concentrations of 370, 700, and 1,050 ppm. A subset of aphid-infected plants was additionally supplied with predatory ladybugs, and three generations of cotton aphids (*Aphis gossypii*) were subsequently allowed to feed on some of the plants. Based on measurements made throughout this complex set of operations, Chen *et al.* found "plant height, biomass, leaf area, and carbon:nitrogen ratios were significantly higher in plants exposed to elevated CO_2 levels," and "more dry matter and fat content and less soluble protein were found in *A. gossypii* in elevated CO_2*." They also found "cotton aphid fecundity significantly increased ... through successive generations reared on plants grown under elevated CO_2"; "significantly higher mean relative growth rates were observed in lady beetle larvae under elevated CO_2"; and "the larval and pupal durations of the lady beetle were significantly shorter and [their] consumption rates increased when fed *A. gossypii* from elevated CO_2 treatments." Chen *et al.* say their study "provides the first empirical evidence that changes in prey quality mediated by elevated CO_2 can alter the prey preference of their natural enemies," and in this particular case, they found this phenomenon could "enhance the biological control of aphids by lady beetle."

According to Auad *et al.* (2012), the yellow sugarcane aphid—first called *Chaitophorus flavus*, but later changed to *Sipha flava*—"has an extensive geographic range that includes all the Americas and Hawaii," and it "is not only a serious pest of sugarcane, but it infests corn, sorghum, wheat, and several other grasses." They note "plant injury caused by this aphid is often severe and is associated with the release of an unidentified toxin followed by leaf chlorosis (Breen and Teetes, 1986; Webster, 1990)." In Brazil, where Auad *et al.* reside, the four scientists report elephant grass (*Pennisetum purpureum*)—one of the most widely used grasses for dairy cattle forage—"is being compromised by *S. flava* attack." The four Brazilian researchers investigated the "effects of elevated CO_2 alone and in combination with elevated temperature on the interactions of *S. flava* and one of its hosts," *P. purpureum*.

Auad *et al.* discovered "the combination of elevated CO_2 and high temperature significantly decreased the duration of nymphal stadia" and "the longevity and reproductive success of *S. flava*," such that "adults produced fewer nymphs in an environment with elevated CO_2 and high temperature than an environment with elevated CO_2 and lower fluctuating temperatures."

The four researchers conclude "*S. flava* populations will significantly decrease under future climatic conditions when both the concentration of atmospheric CO_2 and temperature are projected to increase."

Klaiber *et al.* (2013) "used a model system comprised of Brussels sprout (*Brassica oleraceae* var. *gemmifera*) and a specialized herbivorous insect, the cabbage aphid (*Brevicoryne brassicae*) to test for the effects of various periods of exposure to an elevated (2 x ambient) CO_2 concentration on key plant functional traits and on host plant location behavior by the insect, assessed as plant colonization rates." With respect to plant/herbivore interactions, the four Swiss scientists say, "doubling the ambient CO_2 concentration had a marked effect on plant colonization by winged aphids particularly when plants were exposed to CO_2 for longer periods." After an exposure of only two weeks, for example, there was no difference in colonization rate, whereas after six and 10 weeks "elevated CO_2 led to a respective 15 and 26% reduction of colonization rates" by the cabbage aphid. The authors also note plant volatile emissions, which have been linked to attracting insects, were significantly reduced at the higher CO_2 concentration. Klaiber *et al.* conclude, "in agro-ecosystems, reduced crop plant colonization by an herbivorous pest insect under elevated CO_2 might be advantageous."

It appears the ongoing rise in the air's CO_2 content will likely not have a major impact on aphid-plant interactions, although the scales appear to be tipped in favor of plants over aphids. It is also possible both plants and aphids will benefit from atmospheric CO_2 enrichment, but with plants benefiting more.

References

Adler, L.S., De Valpine, P., Harte, J., and Call, J. 2007. Effects of long-term experimental warming on aphid density in the field. *Journal of the Kansas Entomological Society* **80**: 156–168.

Auad, A.M., Fonseca, M.G., Resende, T.T., and Maddalena, I.S.CP. 2012. Effect of climate change on longevity and reproduction of *Sipha flava* (Hemiptera: Aphididae). *Florida Entomologist* **95**: 433–444.

Awmack, C.S., Harrington, R., and Leather, S.R. 1997. Host plant effects on the performance of the aphid *Aulacorthum solani* (Homoptera: Aphididae) at ambient and elevated CO_2. *Global Change Biology* **3**: 545–549.

Awmack, C.S., Harrington, R., and Lindroth, R.L. 2004. Aphid individual performance may not predict population responses to elevated CO_2 or O_3. *Global Change Biology* **10**: 1414–1423.

Bezemer, T.M., Jones, T.H., and Knight, K.J. 1998. Long-term effects of elevated CO_2 and temperature on populations of the peach potato aphid *Myzus persicae* and its parasitoid *Aphidius matricariae*. *Oecologia* **116**: 128–135.

Bezemer, T.M., Knight, K.J., and Newington, J.E., *et al.* 1999. How general are aphid responses to elevated atmospheric CO_2? *Annals of the Entomological Society of America* **92**: 724–730.

Breen, J.P. and Teets, G.L. 1986. Relationships of the yellow sugarcane aphid (Homoptera: Aphididae) density to sorghum damage. *Journal of Economic Entomology* **79**: 1106–1110.

Chen, F., Ge, F., and Parajulee, M.N. 2005. Impact of elevated CO_2 on tri-trophic interaction of *Gossypium hirsutum*, *Aphis gossypii*, and *Leis axyridis*. *Environmental Entomology* **34**: 37–46.

Chen, F.J., Wu, G., and Ge, F. 2004. Impacts of elevated CO_2 on the population abundance and reproductive activity of aphid *Sitobion avenae* Fabricius feeding on spring wheat. *JEN* **128**: 723–730.

Docherty, M., Wade, F.A., Hurst, D.K., Whittaker, J.B., and Lea, P.J. 1997. Responses of tree sap-feeding herbivores to elevated CO_2. *Global Change Biology* **3**: 51–59.

Gate, I.M., McNeill, S., and Ashmore, M.R. 1995. Effects of air pollution on the searching behaviour of an insect parasitoid. *Water, Air and Soil Pollution* **85**: 1425–1430.

Holopainen, J.K. 2002. Aphid response to elevated ozone and CO_2. *Entomologia Experimentalis et Applicata* **104**: 137–142.

Hughes, L. and Bazzaz, F.A. 2001. Effects of elevated CO_2 on five plant-aphid interactions. *Entomologia Experimentalis et Applicata* **99**: 87–96.

Klaiber, J., Najar-Rodriguez, A.J., Piskorski, R., and Dorn, S. 2013. Plant acclimation to elevated CO_2 affects important plant functional traits, and concomitantly reduces plant colonization rates by an herbivorous insect. *Planta* **237**: 29–42.

Ma, C.S., Hau, B., and Poehling, M.-M. 2004. The effect of heat stress on the survival of the rose grain aphid, *Metopolophium dirhodum* (Hemiptera: Aphididae). *European Journal of Entomology* **101**: 327–331.

Mondor, E.B., Tremblay, M.N., Awmack, C.S., and Lindroth, R.L. 2004. Divergent pheromone-mediated insect behavior under global atmospheric change. *Global Change Biology* **10**: 1820–1824.

Newman, J.A. 2003. Climate change and cereal aphids: the relative effects of increasing CO_2 and temperature on aphid population dynamics. *Global Change Biology* **10**: 5–15.

Newman, J.A., Gibson, D.J., Hickam, E., Lorenz, M., Adams, E., Bybee, L., and Thompson, R. 1999. Elevated carbon dioxide results in smaller populations of the bird cherry-oat aphid *Rhopalosiphum padi*. *Ecological Entomology* **24**: 486–489.

Newman, J.A., Gibson, D.J., Parsons, A.J., and Thornley, J.H.M. 2003. How predictable are aphid population responses to elevated CO_2? *Journal of Animal Ecology* **72**: 556–566.

Percy, K.E., Awmack, C.S., Lindroth, R.L., Kubiske, M.E., Kopper, B.J., Isebrands, J.G., Pregitzer, K.S., Hendrey, G.R., Dickson, R.E., Zak, D.R., Oksanen, E., Sober, J., Harrington, R., and Karnosky, D.F. 2002. Altered performance of forest pests under atmospheres enriched by CO_2 and O_3. *Nature* **420**: 403–407.

Stacey, D. and Fellowes, M. 2002. Influence of elevated CO_2 on interspecific interactions at higher trophic levels. *Global Change Biology* **8**: 668–678.

Stilling, P., Rossi, A.M., and Hungate, B., *et al.* 1999. Decreased leaf-miner abundance in elevated CO_2: reduced leaf quality and increased parasitoid attack. *Ecological Applications* **9**: 240–244.

Webster, J.A. 1990. Yellow sugarcane aphid (Homoptera: Aphididae): detection and mechanisms of resistance among Ethiopian sorghum lines. *Journal of Economic Entomology* **83**: 1053–1057.

Whittaker, J.B. 1999. Impacts and responses at population level of herbivorous insects to elevated CO_2. *European Journal of Entomology* **96**: 149–156.

Zhang, J., Liu, J., and Wang, G., *et al.* 2001. Effect of elevated atmospheric CO_2 concentration on *Rhopalsiphum padi* population under different soil water levels. *Yingyong Shengtai Xuebao* **12**: 253–256.

5.5.2 Moths

Among the insects most responsible for herbivore pressure on plants is moths. This section reviews research on how moths are likely to fare in a warmer world with higher levels of CO_2 in the air.

Kerslake *et al.* (1998) collected five-year-old heather plants from a Scottish moor and grew them in open-top chambers maintained at atmospheric CO_2 concentrations of 350 and 600 ppm for 20 months, with and without soil nitrogen fertilization. Twice during the study, larvae of *Operophtera brumata*, a voracious winter moth whose outbreaks have caused extensive damage to heather moorland in recent years, were allowed to feed on current-year shoots for up to one month. The survivorship of larvae placed on CO_2-enriched foliage was not significantly different from that of larvae placed on foliage produced in ambient air, regardless of nitrogen treatment. In addition, feeding on CO_2-enriched foliage did not affect larval growth rate, development, or final pupal weight. Consequently, Kerslake *et al.* conclude their study "provides no evidence that increasing atmospheric CO_2 concentrations will affect the potential for outbreak of *Operophtera brumata* on this host."

Hattenschwiler and Schafellner (1999) grew seven-year-old spruce trees at atmospheric CO_2 concentrations of 280, 420, and 560 ppm in various nitrogen deposition treatments for three years, after which they performed needle quality assessments and allowed nun moth (*Lymantria monacha*) larvae to feed on current-year needles for 12 days. This moth is an especially voracious defoliator that resides in most parts of Europe and East Asia between 40 and 60° N latitude, and it is commonly regarded as the "coniferous counterpart" of its close relative the gypsy moth, which feeds primarily on deciduous trees.

The two scientists observed elevated CO_2 significantly enhanced needle starch, tannin, and phenolic concentrations, while significantly decreasing needle water and nitrogen contents. Thus, atmospheric CO_2 enrichment reduced overall needle quality from the perspective of this foliage-consuming moth, as nitrogen content is the primary factor associated with leaf quality. Increasing nitrogen deposition, on the other hand, tended to enhance needle quality, for it lowered starch, tannin, and phenolic concentrations while boosting needle nitrogen content. The positive influence of nitrogen deposition on needle quality was not large enough to completely offset the quality reduction caused by elevated CO_2.

Larvae placed on CO_2-enriched foliage consumed less needle biomass than larvae placed on low-CO_2-grown foliage, regardless of nitrogen treatment, and the larvae feeding on CO_2-enriched foliage exhibited reduced relative growth rates and attained an average biomass only two-thirds of that attained by larvae consuming foliage produced at 280 ppm CO_2. Hattenschwiler and Schafellner conclude, "altered needle quality in response to elevated CO_2 will impair the growth and development of *Lymantria monacha* larvae," which should lead to reductions in the degree of spruce tree destruction caused by this voracious defoliator.

Stiling *et al.* (2002) studied the effects of an approximate doubling of the air's CO_2 concentration on a number of characteristics of several insect herbivores feeding on plants native to a scrub-oak forest ecosystem at the Kennedy Space Center, Florida (USA) in eight ambient and eight CO_2-enriched open-top chambers. They found the "relative levels of damage by the two most common herbivore guilds, leaf-mining moths and leaf-chewers (primarily larval lepidopterans and grasshoppers), were significantly lower in elevated CO_2 than in ambient CO_2," and "the response to elevated CO_2 was the same across all plant species." Also, "more host-plant induced mortality was found for all miners on all plants in elevated CO_2 than in ambient CO_2." These effects were so powerful that in addition to the relative densities of insect herbivores being reduced in the CO_2-enriched chambers, and "even though there were more leaves of most plant species in the elevated CO_2 chambers," the total densities of leaf miners in the high-CO_2 chambers were also lower for all plant species. It would appear that in a higher CO_2 world of the future, Earth's natural ecosystems may be able to better withstand the onslaughts of various insect pests, including moths, that have plagued them in the past. Stiling et al. note, is "reductions in herbivore loads in elevated CO_2 could boost plant growth beyond what might be expected based on pure plant responses to elevated CO_2."

In a follow-up study to that of Stilling et al., conducted at the same facilities, Rossi et al. (2004), focused on the abundance of a guild of lepidopteran leafminers that attack the leaves of myrtle oak, as well as various leaf chewers. They periodically examined 100 marked leaves in each of 16 open-top chambers for nine months, after which "differences in mean percent of leaves with leafminers and chewed leaves on trees from ambient and elevated chambers were assessed using paired t-tests." This protocol revealed "both the abundance of the guild of leafmining lepidopterans and damage caused by leaf chewing insects attacking myrtle oak were depressed in elevated CO_2." Leafminer abundance was 44% lower ($P = 0.096$) in the CO_2-enriched chambers compared to the ambient-air chambers, and the amount of leaves suffering chewing damage was 37% lower ($P = 0.072$) in the CO_2-enriched air.

Williams et al. (2003) bagged first instar gypsy moth larvae on branches of red maple saplings entering their fourth year of growth within open-top chambers maintained at four sets of CO_2/temperature conditions: (1) ambient temperature, ambient CO_2, (2) ambient temperature, elevated CO_2 (ambient + 300 ppm), (3) elevated temperature (ambient + 3.5°C), ambient CO_2, and (4) elevated temperature, elevated CO_2. For these conditions they measured several parameters to test their hypothesis that a CO_2-enriched atmosphere would lead to reductions in foliar nitrogen concentrations and increases in defensive phenolics that would in turn lead to increases in insect mortality.

The results indicated "larvae feeding on CO_2-enriched foliage ate a comparably poorer food source than those feeding on ambient CO_2-grown plants, irrespective of temperature." Nevertheless, they determined "CO_2-induced reductions in foliage

quality were unrelated to insect mortality, development rate and pupal weight." They concluded, "phytochemical changes resulted in no negative effects on gypsy moth performance," but neither did they help them.

Noting increases in the atmosphere's CO_2 concentration typically lead to greater decreases in the concentrations of nitrogen in the foliage of C_3 as opposed to C_4 grasses, Barbehenn et al. (2004) note "it has been predicted that insect herbivores will increase their feeding damage on C_3 plants to a greater extent than on C_4 plants (Lincoln et al., 1984, 1986; Lambers, 1993)." To test this hypothesis, they grew Lolium multiflorum (Italian ryegrass, a common C_3 pasture grass) and Bouteloua curtipendula (sideoats gramma, a native C_4 rangeland grass) in chambers maintained at either the ambient atmospheric CO_2 concentration of 370 ppm or the doubled CO_2 concentration of 740 ppm for two months, after which newly molted sixth-instar larvae of Pseudaletia unipuncta (a grass-specialist noctuid) and Spodoptera frugiperda (a generalist noctuid) were allowed to feed on the two grasses.

As expected, Barbehenn et al. found foliage protein concentration decreased by 20% in the C_3 grass but by only 1% in the C_4 grass when they were grown in CO_2-enriched air. They write, "to the extent that protein is the most limiting of the macronutrients examined, these changes represent a decline in the nutritional quality of the C_3 grass." However, and "contrary to our expectations," they add, "neither caterpillar species significantly increased its consumption rate to compensate for the lower concentration of protein in [the] C_3 grass." They note "this result does not support the hypothesis that C_3 plants will be subject to greater rates of herbivory relative to C_4 plants in future [high-CO_2] atmospheric conditions (Lincoln et al., 1984)." In addition, and "despite significant changes in the nutritional quality of L. multiflorum under elevated CO_2," they note "no effect on the relative growth rate of either caterpillar species on either grass species resulted," and there were "no significant differences in insect performance between CO_2 levels." They suggest "post-ingestive mechanisms could provide a sufficient means of compensation for the lower nutritional quality of C_3 plants grown under elevated CO_2."

Barbehenn et al. suggest "there will not be a single pattern that characterizes all grass feeders" with respect to their feeding preferences and developmental responses in a world where certain C_3 plants may experience foliar protein concentrations lower than those they exhibit today, nor will the changes that may occur necessarily be detrimental to herbivore development or the health and vigor of their host plants. Nevertheless, subsequent studies continue to suggest moth species likely will be negatively impacted by the ongoing rise in the air's CO_2 content.

A case in point is the study of Chen *et al.* (2005), who grew well-watered and fertilized cotton plants of two varieties (one expressing *Bacillus thuringiensis* toxin genes and one a non-transgenic cultivar from the same recurrent parent) in pots placed within open-top chambers maintained at either 376 or 754 ppm CO_2 in Sanhe County, Hebei Province, China, from planting in mid-May to harvest in October. Immature bolls were periodically collected and analyzed for various chemical characteristics, and others were stored under refrigerated conditions for later feeding to larvae of the cotton bollworm. They found the elevated CO_2 treatment increased immature boll concentrations of condensed tannins by approximately 22% and 26% in transgenic and non-transgenetic cotton, respectively, and it slightly decreased the body biomass of the cotton bollworm and reduced moth fecundity. The Bt treatment was even more effective in this regard, and in the combined Bt-high-CO_2 treatment the negative cotton bollworm responses were expressed most strongly.

Bidart-Bouzat *et al.* (2005) grew three genotypes of mouse-ear cress (*Arabidopsis thaliana*) from seed in pots within controlled-environment chambers maintained at either ambient CO_2 (360 ppm) or elevated CO_2 (720 ppm). On each of half of the plants (the herbivory treatment) in each of these CO_2 treatments, they placed two second-instar larvae of the diamondback moth (*Plutella xylostella*) at bolting time and removed them at pupation, which resulted in an average of 20% of each plant's total leaf area in the herbivory treatment being removed. Then, each pupa was placed in a gelatin capsule until adult emergence and ultimate death, after which insect gender was determined and the pupa's weight recorded.

At the end of this herbivory trial, the leaves of the control and larvae-infested plants were analyzed for concentrations of individual glucosinolates—a group of plant-derived chemicals that can act as herbivore deterrents (Mauricio and Rausher, 1997)—and total glucosinolate production was determined by summation of the individual glucosinolate assays. Influences of elevated CO_2 on moth performance and its association with plant defense-related traits also were evaluated.

Overall, the researchers found herbivory by larvae of the diamondback moth did not induce any increase in the production of glucosinolates in the mouse-ear cress in the ambient CO_2 treatment. However, the three scientists report, "herbivory-induced increases in glucosinolate contents, ranging from 28% to 62% above basal levels, were found under elevated CO_2 in two out of the three genotypes studied." In addition, "elevated CO_2 decreased the overall performance of diamondback moths." And because "induced defenses can increase plant fitness by reducing subsequent herbivore attacks (Agrawal, 1999; Kessler and Baldwin, 2004)," Bidart-Bouzat *et al.* suggest "the pronounced increase in glucosinolate levels under CO_2 enrichment may pose a threat not only for insect generalists that are likely to be more influenced by rapid changes in the concentration of these chemicals, but also for other insect specialists more susceptible than diamondback moths to high glucosinolate levels (Stowe, 1998; Kliebenstein *et al.*, 2002)."

In a study of a major crop species, Wu *et al.* (2006) grew spring wheat (*Triticum aestivum* L.) from seed to maturity in pots placed in open-top chambers maintained at either 370 or 750 ppm CO_2 in Sanhe County, Hebei Province, China, after which they reared three generations of cotton bollworms (*Helicoverpa armigera* Hubner) on the milky grains of the wheat while monitoring a number of bollworm developmental characteristics. They report, "significantly lower pupal weights were observed in the first, second and third generations," and "the fecundity of *H. armigera* decreased by 10% in the first generation, 13% in the second generation and 21% in the third generation," resulting in a "potential population decrease in cotton bollworm by 9% in the second generation and 24% in the third generation." In addition, they observe, "population consumption was significantly reduced by 14% in the second generation and 24% in the third generation," and the efficiency of conversion of ingested food was reduced "by 18% in the first generation, 23% in the second generation and 30% in the third generation." They conclude, the "net damage of cotton bollworm on wheat will be less under elevated atmospheric CO_2," while "at the same time, gross wheat production is expected to increase by 63% under elevated CO_2."

Wu *et al.* (2007) write, "significant decreases in the protein, total amino acid, water and nitrogen content by 15.8%, 17.7%, 9.1% and 20.6% and increases in free fatty acid by 16.1% were observed in cotton bolls grown under elevated CO_2." When fed with these cotton bolls, the larval survival rate of *H. armigera* "decreased by 7.35% in the first generation, 9.52% in the second generation and 11.48% in the third generation under elevated CO_2 compared with ambient CO_2." In addition, "the fecundity of *H. armigera* decreased by 7.74% in the first generation, 14.23% in the second generation and 16.85% in the third generation." They conclude, "fecundity capacity is likely to be reduced even further in the next generation."

The synergistic effects of these several phenomena, note Wu *et al.*, "resulted in a potential population decrease in cotton bollworm by 18.1% in the second generation and 52.2% in the third generation under elevated CO_2," with the result that "the potential population consumption of cotton bollworm decreased by 18.0% in the second generation and 55.6% in the third generation ... under elevated CO_2 compared with ambient CO_2." They conclude, "the potential population dynamics and potential population consumption of cotton bollworm will alleviate the harm to [cotton] plants in the future rising-CO_2 atmosphere."

Esper *et al.* (2007) reconstructed an annually resolved history of population cycles of a foliage-feeding Lepidopteran commonly known as the larch budmoth (*Zeiraphera diniana* Gn.)—or LBM for short—in the European Alps in the southern part of Switzerland. As is typical of many such insect pests, they note, "during peak activity, populations may reach very high densities over large areas," resulting in "episodes of massive defoliation and/or tree mortality" that could be of great ecological and economic significance.

The team of Swiss and U.S. researchers first developed a history of LBM outbreaks over the 1,173-year period AD 832–2004, which they describe as "the longest continuous time period over which any population cycle has ever been documented." They did so using radiodensitometric techniques to characterize the tree-ring density profiles of 180 larch (*Larix deciduas* Mill.) samples, where "LBM outbreaks were identified based upon characteristic maximum latewood density (MXD) patterns in wood samples, and verified using more traditional techniques of comparison with tree-ring chronologies from non-host species," i.e., fir and spruce. Then they developed a matching temperature history for the area by combining "a tree-ring width-based reconstruction from AD 951 to 2002 integrating 1527 pine and larch samples (Buntgen *et al.*, 2005) and a MXD-based reconstruction from AD 755 to 2004 based upon the same 180 larch samples used in the current study for LBM signal detection (Buntgen *et al.*, 2006)."

From AD 832 to 1981, there were 123 LBM outbreaks with a mean reoccurrence time of 9.3 years,

and "there was never a gap that lasted longer than two decades." From 1981 to the end of their study in 2004, however, there were no LBM outbreaks, and since there had never before (within their record) been such a long outbreak hiatus, they conclude, "the absence of mass outbreaks since the 1980s is truly exceptional."

To what do Esper *et al.* attribute this unprecedented recent development? Noting "conditions during the late twentieth century represent the warmest period of the past millennium"—as per their temperature reconstruction for the region of the Swiss Alps in which they worked—they point to "the role of extraordinary climatic conditions as the cause of outbreak failure," and they discuss what they refer to as the "probable hypothesis" of Baltensweiler (1993), who described a scenario by which local warmth may lead to reduced LBM populations.

Warmth may indeed explain the lack of LBM outbreaks, but given the results of other studies examined in this section, it should be noted atmospheric CO_2 concentrations since 1980 also have been unprecedented over the 1,173-year period of Esper *et al.*'s study. The suppression of LBM outbreaks over the past quarter-century may have been the result of some synergistic consequence of the two factors (temperature and CO_2) acting in unison, and a third possibility may involve only the increase in the air's CO_2 content.

Esper *et al.* say their findings highlight the "vulnerability of an otherwise stable ecological system in a warming environment," in what would appear to be an attempt to attach an undesirable connotation to the observed outcome. This wording seems strange indeed, for it is clear the "recent disruption of a major disturbance regime," as Esper *et al.* refer to the suppression of LBM outbreaks elsewhere in their paper, would be considered by most people to be a positive outcome, indeed something to be welcomed.

Buntgen *et al.* (2009) analyzed raw measurements of 3,151 tree-ring width (TRW) series and 150 maximum latewood density (MXD) series from 70 larch host sites and 73 spruce non-host sites spread across the European Alps and Tatra Mountains that extended back in time approximately 300 years. Focusing on the European Alps—"because periodic growth depressions caused by LBM outbreaks were not found in the TRW and MXD chronologies from the Tatra Mountains"—Buntgen *et al.* discovered "a distinct periodicity at 8–9 years from sites at elevations between 1750 and 1900 meters above sea level." In the middle of the twentieth century, for example, they documented synchronized outbreak pulses at approximately 1936, 1945, 1954, 1963, 1972, and 1981. These outbreaks, the scientists write, "occurred independently of rising temperatures," all the way from the beginning-of-the-end of "the Little Ice Age until recent warmth." They report this long stretch of persistent and synchronized Alpine-wide defoliation—which Esper *et al.* (2007) had followed back to AD 832—finally "ceased during recent decades," when "unprecedented warming in all seasons characterized the post–1980 period."

Knepp *et al.* (2007) studied two species of oak tree—*Quercus alba* L. (white oak) and *Quercus velutina* Lam. (black oak)—and their susceptibility to *Antheraea polyphemus*, a leaf-chewing generalist lepidopteran herbivore that represents the most abundant feeding guild in the hardwood trees that grow beneath the canopy of the unmanaged loblolly pine plantation that hosts the Forest Atmosphere Carbon Transfer and Storage (FACTS–1) research site in the Piedmont region of North Carolina (USA), where the leaf-chewer can consume 2–15% of the forest's net primary production in any given year. The researchers examined host plant preference and larval performance of *A. polyphemus* when fed foliage of the two tree species that had been grown in either ambient or CO_2-enriched air (to 200 ppm above ambient) in this long-running FACE experiment. They determined "growth under elevated CO_2 reduced the food quality of oak leaves for caterpillars," and "consuming leaves of either oak species grown under elevated CO_2 slowed the rate of development of *A. polyphemus* larvae." In addition, they found feeding on foliage of *Q. velutina* that had been grown under elevated CO_2 led to reduced consumption by the larvae and greater mortality. They conclude, "reduced consumption, slower growth rates, and increased mortality of insect larvae may explain [the] lower total leaf damage observed previously in plots of this forest exposed to elevated CO_2," as documented by Hamilton *et al.* (2004) and Knepp *et al.* (2005).

Kampichler *et al.* (2008) also worked with oak trees. Noting, however, "systems studied so far have not included mature trees," they attempted to remedy this situation by determining "the abundance of dominant leaf-galls (spangle-galls induced by the cynipid wasps *Neuroterus quercusbaccarum* and *N. numismalis*) and leaf-mines (caused by the larvae of the moth *Tischeria ekebladella*) on freely colonized large oaks in a mixed forest in Switzerland, which received CO_2 enrichment [540 ppm vs. 375 ppm during daylight hours] from 2001 to 2004" via "the

Swiss Canopy Crane (SCC) and a new CO_2 enrichment technique (web-FACE)" in a forest that they say "is 80–120 years old with a canopy height of 32–38 m, consisting of seven deciduous and four coniferous species."

The German, Mexican, and Swiss researchers discovered that although elevated CO_2 reduced various leaf parameters (water content, proteins, non-structural carbohydrates, tannins, etc.) at the SCC site, "on the long term, their load with cynipid spangle-galls and leaf-mines of *T. ekebladella* was not distinguishable from that in oaks exposed to ambient CO_2 after 4 years of treatment." Consequently, although speculation has run rampant over the years about the long-term effects of atmospheric CO_2 enrichment on plant foliage and its subsequent effects on animals of various trophic levels, Kampichler *et al.* conclude in the situation they investigated, "CO_2 enrichment had no lasting effect in all three [animal] taxa, despite the substantial and consistent change in leaf chemistry of oak due to growth in elevated CO_2."

The results of the studies reviewed above indicate the ongoing rise in the air's CO_2 content will not cause greater damage to Earth's vegetation by the larvae of the many moths that inhabit the planet. If anything, it could reduce the damage they cause.

References

Agrawal, A.A. 1999. Induced-responses to herbivory in wild radish: effects on several herbivores and plant fitness. *Ecology* **80**: 1713–1723.

Baltensweiler, W. 1993. Why the larch bud moth cycle collapsed in the subalpine larch-cembran pine forests in the year 1990 for the first time since 1850. *Oecologia* **94**: 62–66.

Barbehenn, R.V., Karowe, D.N., and Spickard, A. 2004. Effects of elevated atmospheric CO_2 on the nutritional ecology of C_3 and C_4 grass-feeding caterpillars. *Oecologia* **140**: 86–95.

Bidart-Bouzat, M.G., Mithen, R., and Berenbaum, M.R. 2005. Elevated CO_2 influences herbivory-induced defense responses of *Arabidopsis thaliana*. *Oecologia* **145**: 415–424.

Buntgen, U., Esper, J., Frank, D.C., Nicolussi, K., and Schmidhalter, M. 2005. A 1052-year tree-ring proxy for alpine summer temperatures. *Climate Dynamics* **25**: 141–153.

Buntgen, U., Frank, D., Liebhold, A., Johnson, D., Carrer, M., Urbinati, C., Grabner, M., Nicolussi, K., Levanic, T., and Esper, J. 2009. Three centuries of insect outbreaks across the European Alps. *New Phytologist* **182**: 929–941.

Buntgen, U., Frank, D.C., Nievergelt, D., and Esper, J. 2006. Alpine summer temperature variations, AD 755–2004. *Journal of Climate* **19**: 5606–5623.

Chen, F., Wu, G., Ge, F., Parajulee, M.N., and Shrestha, R.B. 2005. Effects of elevated CO_2 and transgenic Bt cotton on plant chemistry, performance, and feeding of an insect herbivore, the cotton bollworm. *Entomologia Experimentalis et Applicata* **115**: 341–350.

Esper, J., Buntgen, U., Frank, D.C., Nievergelt, D., and Liebhold, A. 2007. 1200 years of regular outbreaks in alpine insects. *Proceedings of the Royal Society B* **274**: 671–679.

Hamilton, J.G., Zangerl, A.R., Berenbaum, M.R., Pippen, J.S., Aldea, M., and DeLucia, E.H. 2004. Insect herbivory in an intact forest understory under experimental CO_2 enrichment. *Oecologia* **138**: 566–573.

Hattenschwiler, S. and Schafellner, C. 1999. Opposing effects of elevated CO_2 and N deposition on *Lymantria monacha* larvae feeding on spruce trees. *Oecologia* **118**: 210–217.

Kampichler, C., Teschner, M., Klein, S., and Korner, C. 2008. Effects of 4 years of CO_2 enrichment on the abundance of leaf-galls and leaf-mines in mature oaks. *Acta Oecologica* **34**: 139–146.

Kerslake, J.E., Woodin, S.J., and Hartley, S.E. 1998. Effects of carbon dioxide and nitrogen enrichment on a plant-insect interaction: the quality of *Calluna vulgaris* as a host for *Operophtera brumata*. *New Phytologist* **140**: 43–53.

Kessler, A. and Baldwin, I.T. 2004. Herbivore-induced plant vaccination. Part I. The orchestration of plant defenses in nature and their fitness consequences in the wild tobacco, *Nicotiana attenuata*. *Plant Journal* **38**: 639–649.

Kliebenstein, D., Pedersen, D., Barker, B., and Mitchell-Olds, T. 2002. Comparative analysis of quantitative trait loci controlling glucosinolates, myrosinase and insect resistance in *Arabidopsis thaliana*. *Genetics* **161**: 325–332.

Knepp, R.G., Hamilton, J.G., Mohan, J.E., Zangerl, A.R., Berenbaum, M.R., and DeLucia, E.H. 2005. Elevated CO_2 reduces leaf damage by insect herbivores in a forest community. *New Phytologist* **167**: 207–218.

Knepp, R.G., Hamilton, J.G., Zangerl, A.R., Berenbaum, M.R., and DeLucia, E.H. 2007. Foliage of oaks grown under elevated CO_2 reduces performance of *Antheraea polyphemus* (Lepidoptera: Saturniidae). *Environmental Entomology* **36**: 609–617.

Lambers, H. 1993. Rising CO_2, secondary plant metabolism, plant-herbivore interactions and litter decomposition. Theoretical considerations. *Vegetatio* **104/105**: 263–271.

Lincoln, D.E., Couvet, D., and Sionit, N. 1986. Responses of an insect herbivore to host plants grown in carbon dioxide enriched atmospheres. *Oecologia* **69**: 556–560.

Lincoln, D.E., Sionit, N., and Strain, B.R. 1984. Growth and feeding response of *Pseudoplusia includens* (Lepidoptera: Noctuidae) to host plants grown in controlled carbon dioxide atmospheres. *Environmental Entomology* **13**: 1527–1530.

Mauricio, R. and Rausher, M.D. 1997. Experimental manipulation of putative selective agents provides evidence for the role of natural enemies in the evolution of plant defense. *Evolution* **51**: 1435–1444.

Rossi, A.M., Stiling, P., Moon, D.C., Cattell, M.V., and Drake, B.G. 2004. Induced defensive response of myrtle oak to foliar insect herbivory in ambient and elevated CO_2. *Journal of Chemical Ecology* **30**: 1143–1152.

Stiling, P., Moon, D.C., Hunter, M.D., Colson, J., Rossi, A.M., Hymus, G.J., and Drake, B.G. 2002. Elevated CO_2 lowers relative and absolute herbivore density across all species of a scrub-oak forest. *Oecologia* DOI 10.1007/s00442-002-1075-5.

Stowe, K.A. 1998. Realized defense of artificially selected lines of *Brassica rapa*: effects of quantitative genetic variation in foliar glucosinolate concentration. *Environmental Entomology* **27**: 1166–1174.

Williams, R.S., Lincoln, D.E., and Norby, R.J. 2003. Development of gypsy moth larvae feeding on red maple saplings at elevated CO_2 and temperature. *Oecologia* **137**: 114–122.

Wu, G., Chen, F.-J., and Ge, F. 2006. Response of multiple generations of cotton bollworm *Helicoverpa armigera* Hubner, feeding on spring wheat, to elevated CO_2. *Journal of Applied Entomology* **130**: 2–9.

Wu, G., Chen, F.-J., Sun, Y.-c., and Ge, F. 2007. Response of successive three generations of cotton bollworm, *Helicoverpa armigera* (Hubner), fed on cotton bolls under elevated CO_2. *Journal of Environmental Sciences* **19**: 1318–1325.

5.5.3 Other Herbivores

Besides aphids and moths, other herbivores consume vast amounts of foliage, roots, seeds, and other forms of vegetation. Because experiments involving temperatures and CO_2 content of the air often are conducted on specific types of plants, it is useful to sort the research results by the types of plants being studied. This section looks at research on herbaceous plants, woody plants, and finally other plants.

5.5.3.1 Herbaceous Plants

Insect pests have greatly vexed Earth's herbaceous plants in the past and likely will continue to do so in the future. It is possible, however, that the ongoing rise in the atmosphere's CO_2 content may impact this phenomenon, for better or for worse. Several studies have addressed this subject as it applies to herbaceous plant species, and these studies indicate such plants will be able to continue to cope with the periodic assaults of leaf-damaging herbivores as the air's CO_2 content continues to increase.

Kerslake *et al.* (1998) grew five-year-old heather (*Calluna vulgaris*) plants collected from a Scottish moor in open-top chambers maintained at atmospheric CO_2 concentrations of 350 and 600 ppm. Twice during the study, larvae of the destructive winter moth *Operophtera brumata*, outbreaks of which periodically cause extensive damage to heather moorland, were allowed to feed upon current-year shoots. Feeding on the high-CO_2-grown foliage did not affect larval growth rates, development, or final pupal weights, nor was moth survivorship significantly altered. The authors conclude their study "provides no evidence that increasing atmospheric CO_2 concentrations will affect the potential for outbreak of *Operophtera brumata* on this host."

Newman *et al.* (1999) inoculated tall fescue (*Festuca arundinacea*) plants growing in open-top chambers maintained at atmospheric CO_2 concentrations of 350 and 700 ppm with bird cherry-oat aphids (*Rhopalosiphum padi*). After nine weeks, the plants growing in the CO_2-enriched air had experienced a 37% increase in productivity and were covered with far fewer aphids than the plants growing in ambient air.

Goverde *et al.* (1999) collected four genotypes of *Lotus corniculatus* near Paris and grew them in controlled environment chambers kept at atmospheric CO_2 concentrations of 350 and 700 ppm. Larvae of the Common Blue Butterfly (*Polyommatus icarus*) that were allowed to feed on the foliage produced in the CO_2-enriched air ate more, grew larger, and experienced shorter development times than larvae feeding on the foliage produced in the ambient-air treatment, suggesting this butterfly species likely will become increasingly robust and plentiful as the air's CO_2 content continues to rise.

Brooks and Whittaker (1999) removed grassland monoliths containing eggs of the xylem-feeding spittlebug *Neophilaenus lineatus* from the UK's Great Dun Fell in Cumbria and placed them in glasshouses maintained at atmospheric CO_2 concentrations of 350 and 600 ppm for two years. Survival of the spittlebug's nymphal states was reduced by 24% in both of the generations produced in their experiment, suggesting this particular insect likely will cause less tissue damage to the plants of this species-poor grassland in a CO_2-enriched world of the future.

Joutei *et al.* (2000) grew bean (*Phaseolus vulgaris*) plants in controlled environments kept at atmospheric CO_2 concentrations of 350 and 700 ppm, to which they introduced the destructive agricultural mite *Tetranychus urticae*. Female mites produced 34% and 49% less offspring in the CO_2-enriched chambers in their first and second generations, respectively. This CO_2-induced reduction in the reproductive success of this invasive insect, which negatively affects more than 150 crop species worldwide, bodes well for mankind's ability to grow the food needed to feed the planet's growing population in the years ahead.

Peters *et al.* (2000) fed foliage derived from FACE plots of calcareous grasslands of Switzerland (maintained at 350 and 650 ppm CO_2) to terrestrial slugs, finding they exhibited no preference toward the CO_2 treatment from which the foliage was derived. Also, in a study that targeted no specific insect pest, Castells *et al.* (2002) found a doubling of the air's CO_2 content enhanced the total phenolic concentrations of two Mediterranean perennial grasses (*Dactylis glomerata* and *Bromus erectus*) by 15% and 87%, respectively; these compounds tend to enhance plant defensive and resistance mechanisms to attacks by both herbivores and pathogens (see Section 2.19).

Plants re-emit a substantial portion of their assimilated CO_2 back to the atmosphere as volatile organic compounds (VOCs). These substances affect both the chemical and physical properties of the air, where they generate large quantities of organic aerosols that can impact the planet's climate by forming cloud condensation nuclei that may lead to enhanced cooling during the day by reflecting a greater portion of the incoming solar radiation back to space. In addition, many VOCs protect numerous plants from a host of insect pests.

To see how these phenomena may be affected by the ongoing rise in the atmosphere's CO_2 concentration and by localized areas and time periods of high ozone (O_3) pollution, Himanen *et al.* (2009) exposed groups of both normal (non-transgenic) oilseed rape (*Brassica napus* ssp. *oleifera* L.) plants and transgenic plants, containing an introduced gene that produces *Bacillus thuringiensis* (Bt) crystal endotoxin (Cry) proteins that limit herbivorous insect attacks, to air of 360 and 720 ppm CO_2, as well as O_3-free air and air of 100 ppb O_3. These experiments were conducted in controlled-environment chambers where the plants were grown from seed for 17–18 days in 0.66-liter pots filled with a 2:1:1 mixture of fertilized compost, *Sphagnum* peat, and sand. The non-transgenic plants grown in CO_2-enriched air produced 27% more shoot biomass than those grown in ambient air, and the transgenic plants produced 25% more. In the O_3-enriched air, the non-transgenic plants produced 29% less shoot biomass than those grown in O_3-free air, and the transgenic plants produced 34% less. In addition, on a per-dry-weight basis, Himanen *et al.* say the "doubled CO_2 significantly increased terpenoid emissions from intact oilseed rape plants compared with those released from the corresponding plants grown in control CO_2," and they report there were no O_3-induced increases in VOC emissions. Thus, in addition to the fact that "production of *Bacillus thuringiensis* crystal endotoxin proteins in a crop plant limits specific herbivorous insect attack without the need for chemical treatments," the seven scientists conclude "elevated CO_2 conditions could modify herbivore-induced defenses [VOC emissions] at the vegetative stage, and enhance indirect defense in the future."

Although many studies have explored the direct effects of atmospheric CO_2 enrichment on plant growth and development, Klaiber *et al.* (2013) note the effects of elevated CO_2 on the behavioral responses of insect pests associated with major food crops have not been thoroughly investigated: "the potential effects of plant acclimation to CO_2 on host plant colonization by specialized herbivorous insects, which is a key step in the process of plant attack leading to potential yield losses, are largely unknown."

Klaiber *et al.* "used a model system comprised of Brussels sprout (*Brassica oleraceae* var. *gemmifera*) and a specialized herbivorous insect, the cabbage aphid (*Brevicoryne brassicae*) to test for the effects of various periods of exposure to an elevated (2 x ambient) CO_2 concentration on key plant functional traits and on host plant location behavior by the insect, assessed as plant colonization rates."

Plant height, leaf number, leaf area, fresh weight, and dry weight all increased in the elevated CO_2 treatments with respect to values obtained under ambient conditions, regardless of the length of CO_2 exposure. Leaf stomatal conductance also benefited at the higher CO_2 level, being reduced by nearly 50% by the end of the 10-week experiment. With respect to plant/herbivore interactions, the four Swiss scientists say "doubling the ambient CO_2 concentration had a marked effect on plant colonization by winged aphids particularly when plants were exposed to CO_2 for longer periods." After an exposure of only two weeks, for example, there was no difference in colonization rate, whereas after six and 10 weeks "elevated CO_2 led to a respective 15 and 26% reduction of colonization rates" by the cabbage aphid. The authors also note plant volatile emissions, which have been linked to attracting insects, were reduced significantly at the higher CO_2 concentration. Klaiber *et al.* conclude, "in agroecosystems, reduced crop plant colonization by an herbivorous pest insect under elevated CO_2 might be advantageous."

The majority of evidence to date suggests rising atmospheric CO_2 concentrations may reduce the frequency and severity of pest outbreaks detrimental to agriculture, without seriously impacting herbivorous organisms found in natural ecosystems that are normally viewed in a more favorable light.

References

Brooks, G.L. and Whittaker, J.B. 1999. Responses of three generations of a xylem-feeding insect, *Neophilaenus lineatus* (Homoptera), to elevated CO_2. *Global Change Biology* 5: 395–401.

Castells, E., Roumet, C., Peñuelas, J., and Roy, J. 2002. Intraspecific variability of phenolic concentrations and their responses to elevated CO_2 in two mediterranean perennial grasses. *Environmental and Experimental Botany* 47: 205–216.

Goverde, M., Bazin, A., Shykoff, J.A., and Erhardt, A. 1999. Influence of leaf chemistry of *Lotus corniculatus* (Fabaceae) on larval development of *Polyommatus icarus* (Lepidoptera, Lycaenidae): effects of elevated CO_2 and plant genotype. *Functional Ecology* 13: 801–810.

Himanen, S.J., Nerg, A.-M., Nissinen, A., Pinto, D.M., Stewart Jr., C.N., Poppy, G.M., and Holopainen, J.K. 2009. Effects of elevated carbon dioxide and ozone on volatile terpenoid emissions and multitrophic communication of transgenic insecticidal oilseed rape (*Brassica napus*). *New Phytologist* 181: 174–186.

Joutei, A.B., Roy, J., Van Impe, G., and Lebrun, P. 2000. Effect of elevated CO_2 on the demography of a leaf-sucking mite feeding on bean. *Oecologia* 123: 75–81.

Kerslake, J.E., Woodin, S.J., and Hartley, S.E. 1998. Effects of carbon dioxide and nitrogen enrichment on a plant-insect interaction: the quality of *Calluna vulgaris* as a host for *Operophtera brumata*. *New Phytologist* 140: 43–53.

Klaiber, J., Najar-Rodriguez, A.J., Piskorski, R., and Dorn,

S. 2013. Plant acclimation to elevated CO_2 affects important plant functional traits, and concomitantly reduces plant colonization rates by an herbivorous insect. *Planta* **237**: 29–42.

Newman, J.A., Gibson, D.J., Hickam, E., Lorenz, M., Adams, E., Bybee, L., and Thompson, R. 1999. Elevated carbon dioxide results in smaller populations of the bird cherry-oat aphid *Rhopalosiphum padi*. *Ecological Entomology* **24**: 486–489.

Peters, H.A., Baur, B., Bazzaz, F., and Korner, C. 2000. Consumption rates and food preferences of slugs in a calcareous grassland under current and future CO_2 conditions. *Oecologia* **125**: 72–81.

5.5.3.2 Woody Plants

Insect pests have vexed Earth's trees in the past and likely will continue to do so in the future. The ongoing rise in the atmosphere's CO_2 content may affect this phenomenon, for better or for worse. The sections that follow review the results of several studies that have addressed this subject as it applies to woody plant species. These studies suggest Earth's woody plants will fare much better in a CO_2-enriched future with respect to the periodic assaults of leaf-damaging herbivores.

5.5.3.2.1 Cotton

Bt toxins produced by *Bacillus thuringiensis* supplied to plants via foliar application have been used as a means of combating crop pests for more than 50 years. The effectiveness of this pest management technique depends primarily on the amount of Bt-produced toxins ingested by susceptible insects. Consequently, Coviella and Trumble (2000) wondered whether atmospheric CO_2 enrichment might enhance the effectiveness of the technique by inducing susceptible insects to eat more treated foliage and thus be more effectively eradicated. If soil nitrogen levels are low, foliar nitrogen concentrations in CO_2-enriched air are often reduced from what they are at the current atmospheric CO_2 concentration, and, it is supposed, insects thus must eat more foliage to get the amount of nitrogen they require for proper growth and development. In eating more foliage, the insects would ingest more Bt-produced toxins, and they would be more severely affected by them.

To test this hypothesis, Coviella and Trumble grew cotton plants in 20 three-liter pots in each of six Teflon-film chambers in a temperature-controlled greenhouse; three of the chambers were maintained at an atmospheric CO_2 concentration of 370 ppm, and three were maintained at 900 ppm CO_2. In addition, half of the plants in each chamber received high levels of nitrogen (N) fertilization, while half received low levels (30 as opposed to 130 mg N/kg soil/week). After 45 days, leaves were removed from the plants and dipped in a solution containing *Bacillus thuringiensis*, after which known amounts of treated leaf material were fed to *Spodoptera exigua* larvae and their responses measured and analyzed.

These protocols revealed plants grown in the elevated CO_2 chambers did indeed have significantly lower foliar nitrogen concentrations than plants grown in the ambient CO_2 chambers under the low N fertilization regime, but this was not the case under the high N regime. Also, older larvae fed with foliage grown in elevated CO_2 with low N fertilization consumed significantly more plant material than those fed with foliage grown in ambient CO_2, but again no differences were observed in the high N treatment. In addition, and "consistent with the effect of higher Bt toxin intake due to enhanced consumption," the researchers found "insects fed on low N plants had significantly higher mortality in elevated CO_2," but again, no such effect was evident in the high N treatment. Coviella and Trumble conclude, "increasing atmospheric CO_2 is making the foliar applications more efficacious," especially in the case of soils low in nitrogen.

In addition to applying Bt toxins to plants by spraying, the ability of plants to produce them internally has been achieved by means of genetic engineering. However, there is concern foreign genes from agricultural plants may be transferred into wild relatives of transgenic crop lines and thereby upset the "balance of nature." In one of the first studies to address this concern, Coviella *et al.* (2000) grew cotton plants in the same manner as Coviella and Trumble—in 12 Teflon-film chambers in a temperature-controlled greenhouse, where six of the chambers were maintained at an atmospheric CO_2 concentration of 370 ppm and six were maintained at 900 ppm. Half the plants in each chamber were of a transgenic line containing the Bt gene for the production of the Cry1Ac toxin that is mildly toxic to *Spodoptera exigua*, and the other half were of a near isogenic line without the Bt gene. In addition, half the plants in each chamber received high levels of nitrogen (N) fertilization, while half received low levels (30 as opposed to 130 mg N/kg soil/week). Between 40 and 45 days after emergence, leaves were removed from the plants and fed to the *S. exigua* larvae, after which a number of larval responses were measured and analyzed, along with various leaf properties.

The researchers found the low-N plants in the elevated CO_2 treatment had lower foliar N concentrations than the low-N plants in the ambient CO_2 treatment; the transgenic plants from the low-N, high CO_2 treatment produced lower levels of Bt toxin than did the transgenic plants from the low-N, ambient CO_2 treatment. The high level of N fertilization only partially compensated for this latter high-CO_2 effect. In the ambient CO_2 treatment there was also a significant increase in days to pupation for insects fed transgenic plants, but this difference was not evident in elevated CO_2. In addition, pupal weight in ambient CO_2 was significantly higher in nontransgenic plants, and, again this difference was not observed in elevated CO_2.

Coviella et al. say their results "support the hypothesis that the lower N content per unit of plant tissue caused by the elevated CO_2 will result in lower toxin production by transgenic plants when nitrogen supply to the plants is a limiting factor." They also note "elevated CO_2 appears to eliminate differences between transgenic and nontransgenic plants for some key insect developmental/fitness variables including length of the larval stage and pupal weight." These results, in turn, suggest that in the case of inadvertent Bt gene transference to wild relatives of transgenic crop lines, elevated levels of atmospheric CO_2 will tend to negate certain of the negative effects the wayward genes might otherwise inflict on the natural world.

Coviella et al.'s results suggest transgenic plants designed to produce Bt-type toxins may become less effective in carrying out the objective of their design as the air's CO_2 content continues to rise. Coupling this observation with the fact that the foliar application of Bacillus thuringiensis to crops should become even more effective in a higher-CO_2 world of the future, as per the findings of Coviella and Trumble, it could be argued the implantation of toxin-producing genes in plants is not the way to proceed in the face of the ongoing rise in the air's CO_2 content, which reduces the effectiveness of the genetic implantation technique at the same time it increases the effectiveness of foliar application. It is important to see what other researchers have learned about the subject.

Chen et al. (2005b) grew well-watered and fertilized cotton plants of two varieties (GK–12, expressing Cry1A (c) genes from Bacillus thuringiensis, and Simian–3, a non-transgenic cultivar

from the same recurrent parent) in pots in open-top chambers maintained at either 376 or 754 ppm CO_2 in Sanhe County, Hebei Province, China, from planting in mid-May to harvest in October. Throughout this period, several immature bolls were collected and analyzed for chemical characteristics. Others were stored under refrigerated conditions for later feeding to larvae of the cotton bollworm, when various parameters related to bollworm growth and development were monitored. The scientists found the elevated CO_2 treatment increased immature boll concentrations of condensed tannins by approximately 22% and 26% in transgenic and non-transgenetic cotton, respectively. In addition, Chen et al. report elevated CO_2 slightly decreased the body biomass of the cotton bollworm and reduced moth fecundity. The Bt treatment was even more effective in this regard, and in the combined Bt-high-CO_2 treatment the negative cotton bollworm responses were expressed most strongly.

In a parallel study, Chen et al. (2005a) grew transgenic Bacillus thuringiensis cotton (GK–12) plants from seed for a period of 30 days in well-watered and fertilized sand/vermiculite mixtures in pots located in controlled-environment chambers maintained at atmospheric CO_2 concentrations of 370, 700, and 1,050 ppm. Three generations of cotton aphids (Aphis gossypii) were subsequently allowed to feed on some of the plants, and a subset of the aphid-infected plants was supplied with predatory ladybugs. Chen et al. report "plant height, biomass, leaf area, and carbon:nitrogen ratios were significantly higher in plants exposed to elevated CO_2 levels," and "more dry matter and fat content and less soluble protein were found in A. gossypii in elevated CO_2." They report "cotton aphid fecundity significantly increased ... through successive generations reared on plants grown under elevated CO_2." They also report "significantly higher mean relative growth rates were observed in lady beetle larvae under elevated CO_2," and "the larval and pupal durations of the lady beetle were significantly shorter and [their] consumption rates increased when fed A. gossypii from elevated CO_2 treatments." Hence, they conclude, their study "provides the first empirical evidence that changes in prey quality mediated by elevated CO_2 can alter the prey preference of their natural enemies." They found this phenomenon could "enhance the biological control of aphids by lady beetle" while enhancing control by means of negative Bt-induced effects on the aphids.

Wu et al. (2011) state, "secondary metabolites present in plants provide protection against invaders because of their antimicrobial activity (Kamra *et al.*, 2006)," and "elevated CO_2 leads to plants allocating more carbohydrate resources to their secondary metabolism (Agrell *et al.*, 2004; Casteel *et al.*, 2008)," which may thus induce them to "generate higher concentrations of defensive compounds that are toxic [to] herbivorous insects (Coviella and Trumble, 1999)." Preeminent in this group of compounds are condensed tannins, naturally occurring secondary carbon compounds produced in the leaves of virtually all families of plants that comprise up to 50% of the dry weight of their leaves. Another such compound of note is gossypol, a natural toxin present in the cotton plant that helps to protect it from insect pests such as the cotton bollworm.

Wu *et al.* studied the allocation of the carbohydrate resources of two cotton (*Gossypium hirsutum* L.) cultivars—transgenic Bt cotton (cv. GK–12) and non-transgenic Bt cotton (cv. Simian–3)—to condensed tannins and gossypol both before and after injury inflicted on the plants by the cotton bollworm (*Helicoverpa armigera* Hubner) over periods of one, three, and 12 hours in controlled-environment chambers maintained at atmospheric CO_2 concentrations of either 370 or 750 ppm.

Before any bollworm injury to the plants, the extra CO_2 led to increases of 12 and 14% in the condensed tannin concentrations in the foliage of the Bt-transgenic and non-transgenic cotton plants, respectively; increases of 10 and 10% in the gossypol concentrations of the transgenic and non-transgenic plants, respectively; and a 4% decrease in Bt toxin in the transgenic plants. After bollworm injury for periods of one, three, and 12 hours, the non-transgenic plants experienced condensed tannin increases of 14, 9, and 9%, respectively, and transgenic plants experienced increases of 16, 9, and 9%, respectively. Corresponding results for gossypol were increases of 7, 10, and 6% for the non-transgenic cultivar and 7, 7, and 6% for the transgenic cultivar. The transgenic plants also exhibited Bt toxin decreases of 3, 3, and 5%, respectively.

In discussing the implications of their findings, the four Chinese scientists state prior studies have demonstrated increases in condensed tannins and gossypol typically occur "in response to an increasing CO_2 atmosphere, especially in combination with injury caused by herbivorous insects (Druy *et al.*, 1998; Roth and Lindroth, 1994)," and they suggest these increases "may compensate for the Bt toxin loss in the transgenic Bt cotton," which appears to be an outcome of their study as well. Thus we may expect cotton to become ever less susceptible to damage by the cotton bollworm as the air's CO_2 content continues to rise.

References

Agrell, J., Anderson, P., Oleszek, W., Stochmal, A., and Agrell, C. 2004. Combined effects of elevated CO_2 and herbivore damage on alfalfa and cotton. *Journal of Chemical Ecology* **30**: 2309–2324.

Casteel, C.L., O'Neill, B.F., Zavala, J.A., Bilgin, D.D., Berenbaum, M.R., and DeLucia, E.H. 2008. Transcriptional profiling reveals elevated CO_2 and elevated O_3 alter resistance of soybean (*Glycine max*) to Japanese beetles (*Popillia japonica*). *Plant, Cell and Environment* **31**: 419–434.

Chen, F., Ge, F., and Parajulee, M.N. 2005a. Impact of elevated CO_2 on tri-trophic interaction of *Gossypium hirsutum*, *Aphis gossypii*, and *Leis axyridis*. *Environmental Entomology* **34**: 37–46.

Chen, F., Wu, G., Ge, F., Parajulee, M.N., and Shrestha, R.B. 2005b. Effects of elevated CO_2 and transgenic Bt cotton on plant chemistry, performance, and feeding of an insect herbivore, the cotton bollworm. *Entomologia Experimentalis et Applicata* **115**: 341–350.

Coviella, C.E., Morgan, D.J.W., and Trumble, J.T. 2000. Interactions of elevated CO_2 and nitrogen fertilization: Effects on production of *Bacillus thuringiensis* toxins in transgenic plants. *Environmental Entomology* **29**: 781–787.

Coviella, C.E. and Trumble, J.T. 1999. Effects of elevated atmospheric carbon dioxide on insect-plant interactions. *Conservation Biology* **13**: 700–712.

Coviella, C.E. and Trumble, J.T. 2000. Effect of elevated atmospheric carbon dioxide on the use of foliar application of *Bacillus thuringiensis*. *BioControl* **45**: 325–336.

Drury, S.J., Good, J.E.G., Perrins, C.M., Buse, A., and Kaye, T. 1998. The effects of increasing CO_2 and temperature on oak leaf palatability and the implications for herbivorous insects. *Global Change Biology* **4**: 55–61.

Kamra, D.N., Agrawal, N., and Chaudhary, L.C. 2006. Inhibition of ruminal methanogenesis by tropical plants containing secondary compounds. *International Congress Series* **1293**: 156–163.

Roth, S.K. and Lindroth, R.L. 1994. Effects of CO_2-mediated changes in paper birch and white pine chemistry on gypsy moth performance. *Oecologia* **98**: 133–138.

Wu, G., Chen, F.J., Ge, F., and Xiao, N.-W. 2011. Impacts of elevated CO_2 on expression of plant defensive compounds in Bt-transgenic cotton in response to infestation by cotton bollworm. *Agricultural and Forest Entomology* **13**: 77–82.

5.5.3.2.2 Maple

Williams *et al.* (2003) studied *Acer rubrum* saplings beginning their fourth year of growth in open-top chambers maintained at four atmospheric CO_2/ temperature conditions: (1) ambient temperature, ambient CO_2, (2) ambient temperature, elevated CO_2 (ambient + 300 ppm), (3) elevated temperature (ambient + 3.5°C), ambient CO_2, and (4) elevated temperature, elevated CO_2. They bagged first instar gypsy moth larvae on various branches of the trees and observed their behavior.

They found "larvae feeding on CO_2-enriched foliage ate a comparably poorer food source than those feeding on ambient CO_2-grown plants, irrespective of temperature," and there was a minor reduction in leaf water content due to CO_2 enrichment. They report the "CO_2-induced reductions in foliage quality (e.g. nitrogen and water) were unrelated to insect mortality, development rate and pupal weight," and these and any other phytochemical changes that may have occurred "resulted in no negative effects on gypsy moth performance." They also found "irrespective of CO_2 concentration, on average, male larvae pupated 7.5 days earlier and female larvae 8 days earlier at elevated temperature." Noting anything that prolongs the various development stages of insects potentially exposes them to greater predation and parasitism risk, they conclude the observed temperature-induced hastening of the insects' development likely would expose them to less predation and parasitism risk, which would confer an advantage on this particular herbivore in this particular situation.

Hamilton *et al.* (2004) note many single-species investigations have suggested increases in atmospheric CO_2 will increase herbivory (Bezemer and Jones, 1998; Cannon, 1998; Coviella and Trumble, 1999; Hunter, 2001; Lincoln *et al.*, 1993; Whittaker, 1999). However, because there are so many feedbacks and complex interactions among the numerous components of real-world ecosystems, they warn against putting too much faith in these predictions until relevant real-world ecosystem-level experiments have been completed.

In one such study they conducted at the Duke Forest FACE facility near Chapel Hill, North Carolina (USA), Hamilton *et al.* "measured the amount of leaf tissue damaged by insects and other herbivorous arthropods during two growing seasons in a deciduous forest understory continuously exposed to ambient (360 ppm) and elevated (560 ppm) CO_2 conditions." This forest is dominated by loblolly pine trees that account for fully 92% of the ecosystem's total woody biomass. In addition, it contains 48 species of other woody plants (trees, shrubs, and vines) that have naturally established themselves in the forest's understory. Hamilton *et al.* quantify the loss of foliage due to herbivory experienced by three deciduous tree species, one of which was *Acer rubrum*.

The results indicate "elevated CO_2 led to a trend toward reduced herbivory in [the] deciduous understory in a situation that included the full complement of naturally occurring plant and insect species." In 1999, for example, "elevated CO_2 reduced overall herbivory by more than 40%," and in 2000 they observed "the same pattern and magnitude of reduction."

With respect to changes in foliage properties that might have been expected to lead to increases in herbivory, Hamilton *et al.* report they "found no evidence for significant changes in leaf nitrogen, C/N ratio, sugar, starch or total leaf phenolics in either year of [the] study," noting these findings agree with those of "another study performed at the Duke Forest FACE site that also found no effect of elevated CO_2 on the chemical composition of leaves of understory trees (Finzi and Schlesinger, 2002)."

Hamilton *et al.* thus conclude their landmark paper by emphasizing that "despite the large number of studies that predict increased herbivory, particularly from leaf chewers, under elevated CO_2, our study found a trend toward reduced herbivory two years in a row." In addition, they note their real-world results "agree with the only other large-scale field experiment that quantified herbivory for a community exposed to elevated CO_2 (Stilling *et al.*, 2003)."

Consequently, and contrary to the predictions of increased destruction of natural ecosystems by insects and other herbivorous arthropods in a CO_2-enriched world of the future, just the opposite appears to be the more likely outcome: greater plant productivity plus less foliage consumption by herbivores, "whether expressed on an absolute or a percent basis," as Hamilton *et al.* found in their study.

Knepp *et al.* (2005) quantified leaf damage by chewing insects on saplings of seven species (including *Acer rubrum*) in 2001, 2002, and 2003; five additional species (including *Acer barbatum*) were included in 2001 and 2003. They found "across the seven species that were measured in each of the three years, elevated CO_2 caused a reduction in the percentage of leaf area removed by chewing insects," such that "the percentage of leaf tissue damaged by insect herbivores was 3.8% per leaf under ambient

CO_2 and 3.3% per leaf under elevated CO_2." The greatest effects were observed in 2001, when "across 12 species the average damage per leaf under ambient CO_2 was 3.1% compared with 1.7% for plants under elevated CO_2," "indicative of a 46% decrease in the total area and total mass of leaf tissue damaged by chewing insects in the elevated CO_2 plots."

Knepp *et al.* write, "given the consistent reduction in herbivory under high CO_2 across species in 2001, it appears some universal feature of chemistry or structure that affected leaf suitability was altered by the treatment." Another possibility they discuss is "forest herbivory may decrease under elevated CO_2 because of a decline in the abundance of chewing insects," citing Stilling *et al.* (2002) to this effect and noting "slower rates of development under elevated CO_2 prolongs the time that insect herbivores are susceptible to natural enemies, which may be abundant in open-top chambers and FACE experiments but absent from greenhouse experiments." In addition, they suggest "decreased foliar quality and increased per capita consumption under elevated CO_2 may increase exposure to toxins and insect mortality," also noting "CO_2-induced changes in host plant quality directly decrease insect fecundity," citing Coviella and Trumble (1999) and Awmack and Leather (2002).

Knepp *et al.* conclude, "in contrast to the view that herbivore damage will increase under elevated CO_2 as a result of compensatory feeding on lower quality foliage, our results and those of Stiling *et al.* (2002) and Hamilton *et al.* (2004) in open experimental systems suggest that damage to trees may decrease."

But what if herbivore-induced damage increases, for whatever reason in some situations, in a future CO_2-enriched world?

The likely answer is provided by Kruger *et al.* (1998), who grew well-watered and fertilized one-year-old *Acer saccharum* saplings in glasshouses maintained at atmospheric CO_2 concentrations of either 356 or 645 ppm for 70 days, to determine the effects of elevated CO_2 on photosynthesis and growth. On the 49th day of differential CO_2 exposure, 50% of the saplings' leaf area was removed from half of the trees in order to study the impact of concomitant simulated herbivory. They found the 70-day CO_2 enrichment treatment increased the total dry weight of the non-defoliated seedlings by about 10%. When the trees were stressed by simulated herbivory, the CO_2-enriched maples produced 28% more dry weight over the final phase of the study than the maples in the ambient-air treatment.

Kruger *et al.* thus conclude, in a high-CO_2 world of the future "sugar maple might be more capable of tolerating severe defoliation events which in the past have been implicated in widespread maple declines."

References

Awmack, C.S. and Leather, S.R. 2002. Host plant quality and fecundity in herbivorous insects. *Annual Review of Entomology* **47**: 817–844.

Bezemer, T.M. and Jones, T.H. 1998. Plant-insect herbivore interactions in elevated atmospheric CO_2: quantitative analyses and guild effects. *Oikos* **82**: 212–222.

Cannon, R.J. 1998. The implications of predicted climate change for insect pests in the UK, with emphasis on non-indigenous species. *Global Change Biology* **4**: 785–796.

Coviella, C.E. and Trumble, J.T. 1999. Effects of elevated atmospheric carbon dioxide on insect-plant interactions. *Conservation Biology* **13**: 700–712.

Finzi, A.C. and Schlesinger, W.H. 2002. Species control variation in litter decomposition in a pine forest exposed to elevated CO_2. *Global Change Biology* **8**: 1217–1229.

Hamilton, J.G., Zangerl, A.R., Berenbaum, M.R., Pippen, J., Aldea, M., and DeLucia, E.H. 2004. Insect herbivory in an intact forest understory under experimental CO_2 enrichment. *Oecologia* **138**: 10.1007/s00442-003-1463-5.

Hunter, M.D. 2001. Effects of elevated atmospheric carbon dioxide on insect-plant interactions. *Agricultural and Forest Entomology* **3**: 153–159.

Knepp, R.G., Hamilton, J.G., Mohan, J.E., Zangerl, A.R., Berenbaum, M.R., and DeLucia, E.H. 2005. Elevated CO_2 reduces leaf damage by insect herbivores in a forest community. *New Phytologist* **167**: 207–218.

Kruger, E.L., Volin, J.C., and Lindroth, R.L. 1998. Influences of atmospheric CO_2 enrichment on the responses of sugar maple and trembling aspen to defoliation. *New Phytologist* **140**: 85–94.

Lincoln, D.E., Fajer, E.D., and Johnson, R.H. 1993. Plant-insect herbivore interactions in elevated CO_2 environments. *Trends in Ecology and Evolution* **8**: 64–68.

Stiling, P., Moon, D.C., Hunter, M.D., Colson, J., Rossi, A.M., Hymus, G.J., and Drake, B.G. 2003. Elevated CO_2 lowers relative and absolute herbivore density across all species of a scrub-oak forest. *Oecologia* **134**: 82–87.

Whittaker, J.B. 1999. Impacts and responses at population level of herbivorous insects to elevated CO_2. *European Journal of Entomology* **96**: 149–156.

Williams, R.S., Lincoln, D.E., and Norby, R.J. 2003. Development of gypsy moth larvae feeding on red maple saplings at elevated CO_2 and temperature. *Oecologia* **137**: 114–122.

5.5.3.2.3 Oak

Dury *et al.* (1998) grew four-year-old *Quercus robur* seedlings in pots in greenhouses maintained at ambient and twice-ambient atmospheric CO_2 concentrations in combination with ambient and elevated (ambient plus 3°C) air temperatures for approximately one year to study the interactive effects of elevated CO_2 and temperature on leaf nutritional quality. They found the elevated air temperature treatment significantly reduced leaf palatability, and leaf toughness increased as a consequence of temperature-induced increases in condensed tannin concentrations. In addition, the higher temperatures significantly reduced leaf nitrogen content, and elevated CO_2 caused a temporary increase in leaf phenolic concentrations and a decrease in leaf nitrogen content.

In one of the first attempts to move outside the laboratory and greenhouse and study the effects of atmospheric CO_2 enrichment on trophic food webs in a natural ecosystem, Stiling *et al.* (1999) enclosed portions of a native scrub-oak community in Florida (USA) within 3.6-m-diameter open-top chambers and fumigated them with air having CO_2 concentrations of either 350 or 700 ppm for approximately one year, to see whether elevated CO_2 would impact leaf miner densities, feeding rates, and mortality in this nutrient-poor ecosystem.

They found total leaf miner densities were 38% less on the foliage of trees growing in CO_2-enriched air than on the foliage of trees growing in ambient air. In addition, atmospheric CO_2 enrichment consistently reduced the absolute numbers of the study's six leaf miner species. However, the elevated CO_2 treatment increased the leaf area consumed by the less abundant herbivore miners by approximately 40% relative to the areas mined by the more abundant herbivores present on the foliage exposed to ambient air. In spite of this increase in feeding, the leaf miners in the CO_2-enriched chambers experienced significantly greater mortality than those in the ambient-air chambers. Although CO_2-induced reductions in leaf nitrogen content played a minor role in this phenomenon, the greatest factor contributing to increased herbivore mortality was a four-fold increase in parasitization by various wasps, which could more readily detect the more-exposed leaf miners on the CO_2-enriched foliage.

If extended to agricultural ecosystems, these findings suggest crops may experience less damage from such herbivores in a high-CO_2 world of the future, thus increasing potential harvest and economic gains. In addition, with reduced numbers of leaf miners in CO_2-enriched air, farmers could reduce their dependency on chemical pesticides to control them, thus reducing the negative impacts of these agricultural chemicals on the environment.

In another study conducted on five scrub-oak forest species at the same experimental facility, Stiling *et al.* (2002b) investigated the effects of an approximate doubling of the air's CO_2 concentration on a number of characteristics of several insect herbivores. As before, they found the "relative levels of damage by the two most common herbivore guilds, leaf-mining moths and leaf-chewers (primarily larval lepidopterans and grasshoppers), were significantly lower in elevated CO_2 than in ambient CO_2, for all five plant species," and they found "the response to elevated CO_2 was the same across all plant species." In addition, "more host-plant induced mortality was found for all miners on all plants in elevated CO_2 than in ambient CO_2." These effects were so powerful that in addition to the relative densities of insect herbivores being reduced in the CO_2-enriched chambers, and "even though there were more leaves of most plant species in the elevated CO_2 chambers," the total densities of leaf miners in the high-CO_2 chambers were lower for all plant species. In a high-CO_2 world of the future, many plants may be able to better withstand the onslaughts of various insect pests that have plagued them in the past. Another intriguing implication of this finding, as Stiling *et al.* note, is "reductions in herbivore loads in elevated CO_2 could boost plant growth beyond what might be expected based on pure plant responses to elevated CO_2."

Rossi *et al.* (2004) studied the same ecosystem, which is dominated by two species of scrub oak (*Quercus geminata* and *Q. myrtifolia*) that account for more than 90% of the ecosystem's biomass, focusing on the abundance of a guild of lepidopteran leaf-miners that attack the leaves of *Q. myrtifolia*, as well as various leaf chewers. They followed 100 marked leaves in each of 16 open-top chambers (half of them exposed to ambient air and half exposed to air containing an extra 350 ppm of CO_2) for nine months. "Differences in mean percent of leaves with leafminers and chewed leaves on trees from ambient and elevated chambers were assessed using paired *t*-tests."

The researchers report, "both the abundance of the guild of leafmining lepidopterans and damage caused by leaf chewing insects attacking myrtle oak were depressed in elevated CO_2." They found leafminer abundance was 44% lower ($P = 0.096$) in the CO_2-enriched chambers compared to the ambient-air chambers, and the abundance of leaves suffering chewing damage was 37% lower ($P = 0.072$) in the CO_2-enriched air.

Concentrating on the same ecosystem, where atmospheric enrichment with an extra 350 ppm of CO_2 was begun in May 1996, Hall *et al.* (2005b) studied the four species that dominate the community and are present in every experimental chamber: the three oaks (*Quercus myrtifolia*, *Q. chapmanii*, and *Q. geminata*) plus the nitrogen-fixing legume *Galactia elliottii*. At three-month intervals from May 2001 to May 2003, undamaged leaves were removed from each of these species in all chambers and analyzed for various chemical constituents, and 200 randomly selected leaves of each species in each chamber were scored for the presence of six types of herbivore damage.

The researchers found no significant differences between the CO_2-enriched and ambient-treatment leaves of any single species in terms of condensed tannins, hydrolyzable tannins, total phenolics, or lignin. However, in all four species together there were always greater concentrations of all four leaf constituents in the CO_2-enriched leaves, with across-species mean increases of 6.8% for condensed tannins, 6.1% for hydrolyzable tannins, 5.1% for total phenolics, and 4.3% for lignin. In addition, there were large and often significant CO_2-induced decreases in all leaf damage categories among all species: chewing (-48%, P < 0.001), mines (-37%, P = 0.001), eye spot gall (-45%, P < 0.001), leaf tier (-52%, P = 0.012), leaf mite (-23%, P = 0.477), and leaf gall (-16%, P = 0.480). Hall *et al.* conclude the changes they observed in leaf chemical constituents and herbivore damage "suggest that damage to plants may decline as atmospheric CO_2 levels continue to rise."

Hall *et al.* (2005a) studied the effects of an extra 350 ppm of CO_2 on litter quality, herbivore activity, and their interactions. Over the three years of this experiment (2000, 2001, 2002), they determined "changes in litter chemistry from year to year were far larger than effects of CO_2 or insect damage, suggesting that these may have only minor effects on litter decomposition." The one exception to this finding was "condensed tannin concentrations[, which] increased under elevated CO_2 regardless of species, herbivore damage, or growing season," rising by 11% in 2000, 18% in 2001, and 41% in 2002 as a result of atmospheric CO_2 enrichment, as best we can

determine from their bar graphs. The five researchers also report, "lepidopteran larvae can exhibit slower growth rates when feeding on elevated CO_2 plants (Fajer *et al.*, 1991) and become more susceptible to pathogens, parasitoids, and predators (Lindroth, 1996; Stiling *et al.*, 1999)," noting further that at their field site, "which hosts the longest continuous study of the effects of elevated CO_2 on insects, herbivore populations decline[d] markedly under elevated CO_2 (Stiling *et al.*, 1999, 2002a, 2003; Hall *et al.*, 2005)."

Focusing their attention on two species of oak tree—*Quercus alba* L. (white oak) and *Quercus velutina* Lam. (black oak)—Knepp *et al.* (2007) examined host plant preference and larval performance of *A. polyphemus* when fed foliage of the two tree species that had been grown in either ambient or CO_2-enriched air (to 200 ppm above ambient) in a long-running FACE experiment at the Forest Atmosphere Carbon Transfer and Storage (FACTS–1) research site in the Piedmont region of North Carolina (USA). They found "growth under elevated CO_2 reduced the food quality of oak leaves for caterpillars," and "consuming leaves of either oak species grown under elevated CO_2 slowed the rate of development of *A. polyphemus* larvae." In addition, they report feeding on foliage of *Q. velutina* grown under elevated CO_2 led to reduced consumption by the larvae and greater mortality. The researchers opine, "reduced consumption, slower growth rates, and increased mortality of insect larvae may explain [the] lower total leaf damage observed previously in plots of this forest exposed to elevated CO_2," as documented by Hamilton *et al.* (2004) and Knepp *et al.* (2005).

Stiling *et al.* (2010) note in a CO_2-enriched atmosphere, "plant quality for herbivores is reduced because of decreases in plant nitrogen concentrations and increases in secondary metabolites (Poorter *et al.*, 1997; Curtis and Wang, 1998; Peñuelas and Estiarte, 1998)," but "Stiling *et al.* (2009) recently showed that, over long time periods under continuously elevated CO_2, the increases in plant biomass under elevated CO_2 over compensate for reductions in foliage quality by providing a greater quantity of biomass for herbivores." Seeking to determine whether this might also be true for insectivores and detritivores, Stiling *et al.* employed pitfall trapping over the last three of 11 years of continuous CO_2 enrichment (to 350 ppm above ambient) in eight of 16 open-top chambers that enclosed portions of a scrub-oak ecosystem in Florida (USA) composed of a mix of three oak tree species (*Quercus myrtifolia, Q. geminate,* and *Q. chapmanii*) that accounted for approximately 90% of the total aboveground ecosystem biomass, and they employed sticky traps over another six months of the study.

The three researchers report 110,618 insects and other arthropods from 25 orders were recovered from the pitfall traps, and 39,305 insects and other arthropods from 14 orders were found on the sticky traps. These data, they write, "revealed increases of insect herbivore species such as Thysanoptera (thrips), Hemiptera, and Lepidoptera, but no effects on insectivores such as spiders, parasitic wasps, and ants, or on detritivores such as Diptera (flies), Psocoptera (book lice), Blattodea (cockroaches), Collembola (spring tails), Orthoptera (crickets) and Coleoptera (beetles)."

Stiling *et al.* conclude the "increase in the number of herbivores, including raspers, suckers, and chewers, under elevated CO_2" was "likely caused by an increase in plant biomass under elevated CO_2," which for the scrub-oak ecosystem they studied amounted to 67% (Seiler *et al.*, 2009). But they additionally conclude, "increases in plant biomass and herbivore abundance brought about by elevated CO_2 do not influence insect abundance at other trophic levels such as insectivores, parasitoids and predators, or decomposers." They note their results are similar to those of two other studies (Sanders *et al.*, 2004; Hillstrom and Lindroth, 2008) that also "failed to detect effects of elevated CO_2 on most guilds." Thus, the "bottom-up effect brought about by higher plant biomass as a result of many years of elevated CO_2" in this experiment appears to enhance abundance of herbivores only.

The evidence cited above suggests herbivore damage to oak trees by various insect pests will decline as the air's CO_2 concentration continues to climb.

References

Curtis, P.S. and Wang, X. 1998. A meta-analysis of elevated CO_2 effects on woody plant mass, form, and physiology. *Oecologia* **113**: 299–313.

Dury, S.J., Good, J.E.G., Perrins, C.M., Buse, A., and Kaye, T. 1998. The effects of increasing CO_2 and temperature on oak leaf palatability and the implications for herbivorous insects. *Global Change Biology* **4**: 55–61.

Fajer, E.D., Bowers, M.D., and Bazzaz, F.A. 1991. The effects of enriched CO_2 atmospheres on the buckeye butterfly, *Junonia coenia*. *Ecology* **72**: 751–754.

Hall, M.C., Stiling, P., Hungate, B.A., Drake, B.G., and Hunter, M.D. 2005a. Effects of elevated CO_2 and herbivore damage on litter quality in a scrub oak ecosystem. *Journal of Chemical Ecology* **31**: 2343–2356.

Hall, M.C., Stiling, P., Moon, D.C., Drake, B.G., and Hunter, M.D. 2005b. Effects of elevated CO_2 on foliar quality and herbivore damage in a scrub oak ecosystem. *Journal of Chemical Ecology* **31**: 267–285.

Hamilton, J.G., Zangerl, A.R., Berenbaum, M.R., Pippen, J.S., Aldea, M., and DeLucia, E.H. 2004. Insect herbivory in an intact forest understory under experimental CO_2 enrichment. *Oecologia* **138**: 566–573.

Hillstrom, M.L. and Lindroth, R.L. 2008. Elevated atmospheric carbon dioxide and ozone alter forest insect abundance and community composition. *Insect Conservation and Diversity* **1**: 233–241.

Knepp, R.G., Hamilton, J.G., Mohan, J.E., Zangerl, A.R., Berenbaum, M.R., and DeLucia, E.H. 2005. Elevated CO_2 reduces leaf damage by insect herbivores in a forest community. *New Phytologist* **167**: 207–218.

Knepp, R.G., Hamilton, J.G., Zangerl, A.R., Berenbaum, M.R., and DeLucia, E.H. 2007. Foliage of oaks grown under elevated CO_2 reduces performance of *Anthcraea polyphemus* (Lepidoptera: Saturniidae). *Environmental Entomology* **36**: 609–617.

Lindroth, R.L. 1996. CO_2-mediated changes in tree chemistry and tree-Lepidoptera interactions. In: Koch, G.W. and Mooney, H.A. (Eds.) *Carbon Dioxide and Terrestrial Ecosystems*. Academic Press, San Diego, California, USA, pp. 105–120.

Peñuelas, J. and Estiarte, M. 1998. Can elevated CO_2 affect secondary metabolism and ecosystem function? *Trends in Ecology and Evolution* **13**: 20–24.

Poorter, H., van Berkel, Y., Baxter, B., Den Hertog, J., Dijkstra, P., Gifford, R.M., Griffin, K.L., Roumet, C., Roy, J., and Wong, S.C. 1997. The effect of elevated CO_2 on the chemical composition and construction costs of leaves. *Plant, Cell and Environment* **10**: 472–482.

Rossi, A.M., Stiling, P., Moon, D.C., Cattell, M.V., and Drake, B.G. 2004. Induced defensive response of myrtle oak to foliar insect herbivory in ambient and elevated CO_2. *Journal of Chemical Ecology* **30**: 1143–1152.

Sanders, N.J., Belote, R.T., and Weltzen, J.F. 2004. Multitrophic effects of elevated atmospheric CO_2 on understory plant and arthropod communities. *Environmental Entomology* **33**: 1609–1616.

Seiler, T.J., Rasse, D.P., Li, J., Dijkstra, P., Anderson, H.P., Johnson, D.P., Powell, T.L., Hungate, B.A., Hinkle, C.R., and Drake, B.G. 2009. Disturbance, rainfall and contrasting species responses mediated aboveground biomass response to 11 years of CO_2 enrichment in a Florida scrub-oak ecosystem. *Global Change Biology* **15**: 356–367.

Stiling, P., Cattell, M., Moon, D.C., Rossi, A., Hungate, B.A., Hymus, G., and Drake, B.G. 2002a. Elevated atmospheric CO_2 lowers herbivore abundance, but increases leaf abscission rates. *Global Change Biology* **8**: 658–667.

Stiling, P., Forkner, R., and Drake, B. 2010. Long-term exposure to elevated CO_2 in a Florida scrub-oak forest increases herbivore densities but has no effect on other arthropod guilds. *Insect Conservation and Diversity* **3**: 152–156.

Stiling, P., Moon, D.C., Hunter, M.D., Colson, J., Rossi, A.M., Hymus, G.J., and Drake, B.G. 2002b. Elevated CO_2 lowers relative and absolute herbivore density across all species of a scrub-oak forest. *Oecologia* **134**: 82–87.

Stiling, P., Moon, D.C., Rossi, A.M., Hungate, B., and Drake, B. 2009. Seeing the forest for the trees: long term exposure to elevated CO_2 increases some herbivore densities. *Global Change Biology* **15**: 1895–1902.

Stiling, P., Rossi, A.M., Hungate, B., Dijkstra, P., Hinkle, C.R., Knot III, W.M., and Drake, B. 1999. Decreased leaf-miner abundance in elevated CO_2: Reduced leaf quality and increased parasitoid attack. *Ecological Applications* **9**: 240–244.

5.5.3.3 Other Plants

Gleadow *et al.* (1998) grew eucalyptus seedlings in glasshouses maintained at 400 and 800 ppm CO_2 for a period of six months, observing biomass increases of 98% and 134% in high and low nitrogen treatments, respectively. They also studied a sugar-based compound called prunasin, which produces cyanide in response to tissue damage caused by foraging herbivores. Although elevated CO_2 caused no significant change in leaf prunasin content, the proportion of nitrogen allocated to prunasin increased by approximately 20% in the CO_2-enriched saplings, suggestive of a potential for increased prunasin production had the saplings been under attack by herbivores.

In a study involving mechanical defoliation, Lovelock *et al.* (1999) grew seedlings of the tropical tree *Copaifera aromatica* for 50 days in pots placed within open-top chambers maintained at atmospheric CO_2 concentrations of 390 and 860 ppm. At the 14-day point of the experiment, half of the seedlings in each treatment had about 40% of their total leaf area removed. None of the defoliated trees of either CO_2 treatment fully recovered from this manipulation, but at the end of the experiment the total plant biomass of the defoliated trees in the CO_2-enriched treatment was 15% greater than that of the defoliated trees in the ambient-CO_2 treatment, attesting to the benefits of atmospheric CO_2 enrichment in helping trees deal with herbivory.

Docherty *et al.* (1997) grew beech and sycamore saplings in glasshouses maintained at atmospheric CO_2 concentrations of 350 and 600 ppm, and groups of three sap-feeding aphid species and two sap-feeding leafhopper species were allowed to feed on them. Overall, elevated CO_2 had few significant effects on the performance of the insects, although there was a non-significant tendency for elevated CO_2 to reduce the individual weights and populations of the aphids.

Hattenschwiler and Schafellner (1999) grew seven-year-old spruce (*Picea abies*) trees at atmospheric CO_2 concentrations of 280, 420, and 560 ppm and various nitrogen deposition treatments for three years, allowing nun moth larvae to feed on current-year needles for 12 days. Larvae placed on the CO_2-enriched foliage consumed less needle biomass than larvae placed on the ambiently grown foliage, regardless of nitrogen treatment. This effect was so pronounced that the larvae feeding on needles produced by the CO_2-enriched trees attained an average final biomass only two-thirds of that attained by the larvae that fed on needles produced at 280 ppm CO_2. Since the nun moth is a deadly defoliator that resides in most parts of Europe and East Asia between 40 and 60°N latitude and is commonly regarded as the coniferous counterpart of its close relative the gypsy moth, which feeds primarily on deciduous trees, the results of this study suggest the ongoing rise in the air's CO_2 content likely will lead to significant reductions in damage to spruce and other coniferous trees by this voracious insect pest.

Holton *et al.* (2003) reared parasitized and non-parasitized forest tent caterpillars (*Malacosoma disstria*) on two quaking aspen (*Populus tremuloides*) genotypes (216, which is O_3-tolerant, and 259, which is O_3-sensitive) alone and in combination at the Aspen FACE site in northern Wisconsin (USA), in plots exposed to ambient air, ambient air + 200 ppm extra CO_2, ambient air + 50% extra ozone, and ambient air + 200 ppm extra CO_2 and 50% extra O_3 during the daylight hours of one full growing season. They found "elevated CO_2 had little effect on both primary and secondary metabolites of aspen." Thus it was not surprising to learn "elevated CO_2 had few biologically significant effects on forest tent caterpillar performance." Elevated O_3, on the other hand, altered foliar composition much more than did elevated CO_2, and, as they discovered, it improved tent caterpillar performance under ambient CO_2 conditions, but not in CO_2-enriched air. In addition, elevated O_3 decreased the larval survivorship of the parasite of the caterpillar. Without an increase in the air's CO_2 content commensurate with that projected for O_3 over the coming half-century, therefore, quaking aspen—the most widely distributed tree in North America—would be in for a world of hurt.

Mattson et al. (2004) note "although there have been many studies on the effects of elevated CO_2 on the interaction between plants and their insect herbivores (see Bezemer and Jones, 1998; Hunter, 2001), comparable studies on mammalian herbivores are lacking altogether, even though mammals play important roles in dynamics of many ecosystems (McNaughton and Sabuni, 1988; Pastor and Naiman, 1992)." Mattson et al. grew one-year-old seedlings of silver birch (Betula pendula) in closed-top chambers for one summer and autumn in pots containing an unfertilized commercial peat maintained at three soil nitrogen (N) levels (low $-$ 0 kg N ha^{-1}, medium = 150 kg N ha^{-1}, high = 500 kg N ha^{-1}) and two temperature (T) levels (ambient and ambient + 3°C) in air of either 362 or 700 ppm CO_2 concentration. Feeding trials with caged Eurasian hares (Lepus timidus) were then carried out, and a number of chemical analyses were made of the tops of the seedlings and the basal parts of their stems.

In a second experiment, Mattson et al. grew paper birch (Betula papyrifera) from seed for two 140-day growing seasons in well-watered and fertilized pots placed within FACE rings maintained at atmospheric CO_2 concentrations of either 362 or 562 ppm, after which (in an unplanned aspect of the study) North American eastern cottontail rabbits (Sylvilagus floridanus) fed ad libitum, consuming bark tissue down to and scoring the wood, on the basal third of the seedlings, and these tissues were tested for the presence of various herbivore-deterring chemical constituents.

"As expected," they write, the results indicate "elevated CO_2 substantially increased the above-ground woody biomass growth of both paper birch (63%) and silver birch (21%)." In addition, noting "numerous studies have shown that elevated atmospheric CO_2 often, but not always, elicits increases in carbon partitioning to carbon-based secondary plant compounds," which often act as deterrents to herbivory, they say their findings "confirm this general pattern in silver and paper birch." Finally, they report high CO_2 reduced hare feeding on silver birch shoots by as much as 48% and reduced rabbit feeding on paper birch stems by about

51%, whereas neither temperature nor severe early-season defoliation (another experimental treatment) affected the trees' resistance against these mammalian herbivores.

Calling the anti-herbivory effect of elevated CO_2 "remarkably strong" and noting rabbits "overwhelmingly preferred ambient CO_2 plants," Mattson et al. say their data "clearly suggest that the defensive biochemistry of paper birch twigs as well as the main stem were [positively] altered as the result of elevated CO_2." As the air's CO_2 content continues to rise, at least these two species of birch trees apparently will have a significantly easier time of getting established and growing to maturity.

Sanders et al. (2004) studied effects of atmospheric CO_2 enrichment on the plant and arthropod communities of the understory of a closed-canopy sweetgum plantation (which reduces the light available to the understory between 70 and 95% during the growing season) in a FACE study where the air's CO_2 content was increased by approximately 48%. The authors report under such conditions there were large adjustments in the relative productivities of the five dominant species that account for more than 90% of the biomass and annual production of the understory vegetation. Overall, however, the total understory productivities of the two CO_2 treatments were not significantly different from each other. Also, Sanders et al. report, "C:N ratios for four of the five dominant plant taxa did not differ between ambient and elevated CO_2," and "there were no overall treatment or species x treatment effects" with respect to this parameter.

The three scientists further report they "found no effect of elevated CO_2 on herbivory," and "even for the one species that showed an effect of CO_2 on C:N ratio, herbivores did not compensate by foraging more." In addition, total arthropod abundance did not differ between ambient and elevated CO_2 plots, nor did the abundances of detritivores, omnivores, or parasitoids. They conclude, "changes in plant community composition did not translate into differences in arthropod communities." Sanders et al. state "idiosyncratic, species-specific responses to elevated CO_2 may buffer one another: the abundances of some species increase while others decrease," and, therefore, "to understand the potential effects of global [environmental] change on the complexity of multitrophic interactions that structure most communities, field experiments on entire communities are necessary."

Noting the "detrimental effects of ozone on plants are well known," and "carbon dioxide [CO_2]

generally affects trees in opposite ways to ozone [O_3]," Valkama *et al.* (2007) conducted a literature review they describe as "the first quantitative analysis of the interactive effects of elevated O_3 and elevated CO_2 on tree chemistry and herbivore performance," based on the results of "63 studies conducted on 22 tree species and 10 insect herbivore species and published between 1990 and 2005."

With respect to ways elevated O_3 may benefit insect herbivores that tend to damage trees, Valkama *et al.* determined "elevated O_3 significantly shortened development time of insect herbivores [when they are exposed and vulnerable to attack by various enemies] and increased their pupal mass in the overall dataset." In addition, the "relative growth rate of chewers was significantly increased by 3.5% under elevated O_3." However, "these effects were counteracted by elevated CO_2," such that "elevated O_3 in combination with CO_2 had no effect on herbivore performance," with the exception that when elevated CO_2 was added to the O_3-enriched air, it not only counteracted the O_3-induced increase in pupal biomass, but reduced it by 7% below what it was in ambient air. This analysis of the vast majority of pertinent experimental data obtained prior to 2006 suggests the ongoing rise in the air's CO_2 content likely plays an extremely important role in negating, and in some cases even more than negating, the damage otherwise capable of being done to Earth's forests by voracious insect pests.

In a study involving only changes in temperature, Andrew and Hughes (2007) "investigated how the relationship of herbivorous insects and their host plants may change under a warmer climate" by "transplanting a host plant species to locations subject to mean annual temperatures 1.2°C higher than at the species' current warmest boundary and 5.5°C higher than at its coolest edge." They "compared the structure and composition of the herbivorous insect community that colonized the transplants (i) to that of the host plant species within its natural range and (ii) to a congeneric plant species that grew naturally at the transplant latitude." In addition, they "investigated whether the herbivore community and rates of herbivory were affected by the latitudinal origin of the transplants."

According to the two Australian researchers, their study indicated "rates of herbivory did not significantly differ between the transplants and plants at sites within the natural range," and "there were no significant differences in herbivore species richness or overall rates of herbivory on the transplants originating from different latitudes." They state in the abstract of their paper, "if this result holds for other plant-herbivore systems, we might expect that under a warmer climate, broad patterns in insect community structure and rates of herbivory may remain similar to that at present, even though species composition may change substantially." Or as stated in their concluding paragraph, "if these results can be generalized to other plant hosts, we might predict that as climate zones shift poleward and mobile organisms like flying insects respond by migrating to stay within their current climatic envelope, plants will be colonized by new herbivore species within similar guilds to those currently supported," and "changes in the composition, but not necessarily the structure, of these new communities may, therefore, result."

Huttunen *et al.* (2007) grew silver birch (*Betula pendula* Roth) seedlings in pots filled with peat at three levels of nitrogen (N) fertility—no N, moderate N (130 kg N ha^{-1}), and high N (270 kg N ha^{-1})—within climate-controlled closed-top chambers from mid-June to October 2002 at the Mekrijarvi Research Station of the University of Joensuu, Finland. The chambers were maintained at atmospheric CO_2 concentrations of either 360 or 720 ppm and at either ambient air temperatures or elevated air temperatures 2°C above ambient from June to August and 4°C above ambient for the remainder of the growing season, while mimicking larval and adult leaf-feeding patterns exhibited during real-world defoliation by manually damaging the leaves of the seedlings by tearing off the apical halves of either 25% or 50% of all leaves greater than 1 cm in length on 1 July (mid-season) and again on 29 July (late-season). They then determined total plant shoot and root biomass once the plants went dormant in October.

As best as can be determined from the authors' bar graphs of their results, and averaged over all three defoliation treatments, the elevated CO_2 treatment increased the biomass of the seedlings in the moderate and high N fertility treatments much more than in the no N fertility treatment (29 and 30%, respectively, vs. 13%). The same was true of the combined elevated CO_2 and elevated temperature treatment, where the corresponding treatment-induced biomass increases were 34 and 36% vs. 20%. These results indicate the heightened temperatures tended to augment the beneficial effects of the elevated CO_2 treatment, with the greatest amplification being manifest in the no N fertility treatment (54% vs. 17 and 20% in the moderate and high N treatments, respectively). Averaged over all three N fertility treatments, the elevated CO_2 increased the plant biomass of the undefoliated seedlings by approximately 25%, that of the 25%-defoliated seedlings by

24%, and that of the 50%-defoliated seedlings by 22%. The elevated CO_2 and elevated temperature treatment increased the plant biomass of the same three categories of seedlings by approximately 31%, 30%, and 29%, respectively. The six Finnish scientists conclude "climatic change"—which they specifically define to mean elevated atmospheric temperature and CO_2—"will have a positive impact on the compensatory ability of defoliated silver birch seedlings."

One year later in a similar analysis, Huttunen *et al.* (2008) studied the leaf palatability of first-year silver birch (*Betula pendula*) seedlings to adult blue alder leaf beetles (*Agelastica alni*), periodically measuring a host of seedling parameters related to plant chemical and morphological defense properties. The seedlings were grown in climate-controlled closed-top chambers maintained at ambient and twice-ambient atmospheric CO_2 concentrations and at ambient and ambient plus 2°C air temperatures. The authors also examined the additional effects of three levels of added soil nitrogen (none, moderate, and high) plus two levels of manual defoliation (25% and 50%) on leaf palatability.

The researchers' findings were varied and complex, indicative of complicated interactions with the potential to cascade through several trophic levels and change the dynamics of forest ecosystems. "In the worst scenario," as they describe what could happen, "the consequences may include widespread damage to trees." However, they report, their study indicated the blue alder leaf beetle's "total leaf consumption was higher under the ambient climatic conditions than under elevated temperature, elevated CO_2, or the combination of elevated temperature and CO_2."

Hamilton *et al.* (2012) write, "the response of complex plant and animal communities to global change is highly variable (Tylianakis *et al.*, 2008)," but they note "recent studies have documented that loss of foliage to arthropod herbivores decreases under elevated CO_2 in woody communities (Hamilton *et al.*, 2004; Knepp *et al.*, 2005; Stiling and Cornelissen, 2007)." They also note the fitness and in some cases population size of herbivorous insects may decline in communities exposed to elevated CO_2 (Hillstrom and Lindroth, 2008; Hillstrom *et al.*, 2010)," although the "effects of elevated CO_2 on naturally occurring arthropod assemblages have not yet been widely characterized."

Working at the Duke Forest FACE facility in the Piedmont region of North Carolina (USA)—where three 30-meter-diameter plots of an expansive stand of loblolly pine had their atmospheric CO_2 concentrations boosted by approximately 200 ppm, and where three other such plots were maintained at the normal ambient CO_2 concentration—Hamilton *et al.* counted arthropods found in each of the six plots every two weeks throughout June and July 2005, in order to assign them to different feeding guilds. In addition, "stable isotope data for spiders collected in ambient and elevated CO_2 plots were analyzed to determine the extent to which herbivorous prey species moved into and out of the elevated CO_2 plots."

The seven U.S. scientists say their isotopic data "gave no indication that the treatment plots represented a 'boundary' to the movement of insects." In addition, there was no detectable effect of elevated CO_2 on the total number of individual arthropods in the two sets of treatment plots. However, "there was an increase in the numbers of individuals collected in primarily predaceous orders (Araneae and Hymenoptera; from 60% to more than 150%) under elevated CO_2 and a decrease in the numbers in primarily herbivorous orders (Lepidoptera and Coleoptera; from -30 to -45%)." Hamilton *et al.* conclude, "decreases in herbivorous arthropods and increases in predaceous arthropods may contribute to reduced herbivory under elevated CO_2 in forest systems."

Novick *et al.* (2012) write "warmer climates induced by elevated atmospheric CO_2 are expected to increase damaging bark beetle activity in pine forests," yet they say, "the effect of elevated CO_2 on resin production—the tree's primary defense against beetle attack—remains largely unknown." They note "resin physically ejects or entombs attacking beetles and, when volatile components of resin have evaporated, seals wounds in the bark," as revealed by the studies of Ruel *et al.* (1998) and Wilkens *et al.* (1998). Novick *et al.* assessed the effect of elevated CO_2 on resin production of dominant-and-unfertilized 27-year-old loblolly pine (*Pinus taeda* L.) trees growing under both ambient and elevated (ambient + 200 ppm) atmospheric CO_2 concentrations in the Duke Forest of North Carolina (USA) over the period March to October 2009.

The four researchers report the elevated CO_2 treatment increased resin flow by 140% in dominant trees growing in unfertilized subplots. This CO_2-induced resin flow enhancement "persisted throughout the growing season." Novick *et al.* conclude, "forests with low- to mid-range fertility"—which, in their words, "currently represent the majority of southern pine forests (Fox *et al.*, 2007)"—"may become increasingly protected from bark beetle attacks in an elevated CO_2 climate." They note, "previous studies have shown that even more modest increases in resin flow (i.e., enhancements less than or equal to 100%) significantly increase the survival probability of pine trees experiencing bark beetle attack," as demonstrated by Reeve *et al.* (1995) and Strom *et al.* (2002).

Working at the aspen free-air CO_2 enrichment (Aspen FACE) site in north-central Wisconsin (USA), Nabity *et al.* (2012) investigated how herbivore damage types (leaf-chewing, gall-forming, and leaf-folding) alter component processes of photosynthesis under both ambient and elevated (ambient + 200 ppm) atmospheric CO_2 concentrations in aspen (*Populus tremuloides*, genotype 216) trees, as well as how leaf-chewing insects impact photosynthesis in birch (*Betula papyrifera*) trees. They found "growth under elevated CO_2 reduced the distance that herbivore-induced reductions in photosynthesis propagated away from the point of damage in aspen and birch." Nabity *et al.* conclude their findings suggest "at least for these species," elevated CO_2 "may reduce the impact of herbivory on photosynthesis," a very positive development.

The balance of evidence suggests Earth's non-woody plants are adequately prepared to deal with the challenges of herbivorous insects as the air's CO_2 content continues to rise.

References

Andrew, N.R. and Hughes, L. 2007. Potential host colonization by insect herbivores in a warmer climate: a transplant experiment. *Global Change Biology* **13**: 1539–1549.

Bezemer, T.M. and Jones, T.H. 1998. Plant-insect herbivore interactions in elevated atmospheric CO_2: quantitative analyses and guild effects. *Oikos* **82**: 212–222.

Docherty, M., Wade, F.A., Hurst, D.K., Whittaker, J.B., and Lea, P.J. 1997. Responses of tree sap-feeding herbivores to elevated CO_2. *Global Change Biology* **3**: 51–59.

Fox, T.R., Jokela, E.J., and Allen, H.L. 2007. The development of pine plantation silviculture in the southern United States. *Journal of Forestry* **105**: 337–347.

Gleadow, R.M., Foley, W.J., and Woodrow, I.E. 1998. Enhanced CO_2 alters the relationship between photosynthesis and defense in cyanogenic *Eucalyptus cladocalyx* F. Muell. *Plant, Cell and Environment* **21**: 12–22.

Hamilton, J.G., Zangerl, A.R., Berenbaum, M.R., Pippen, J.S., Aldea, M., and DeLucia, E.H. 2004. Insect herbivory in an intact forest understory under experimental CO_2 enrichment. *Oecologia* **138**: 566–573.

Hamilton, J.G., Zangerl, A.R., Berenbaum, M.R., Sparks, J.P., Elich, L., Eisenstein, A., and DeLucia, E.H. 2012. Elevated atmospheric CO_2 alters the arthropod community in a forest understory. *Acta Oecologica* **43**: 80–85.

Hattenschwiler, S. and Schafellner, C. 1999. Opposing effects of elevated CO_2 and N deposition on *Lymantria monacha* larvae feeding on spruce trees. *Oecologia* **118**: 210–217.

Hillstrom, M.L. and Lindroth, R.L. 2008. Elevated atmospheric carbon dioxide and ozone alter forest insect abundance and community composition. *Insect Conservation and Diversity* **1**: 233–241.

Hillstrom, M.L., Vigue, L.M., Coyle, D.R., Raffa, K.F., and Lindroth, R.L. 2010. Performance of the invasive weevil *Polydrusus sericeus* is influenced by atmospheric CO_2 and host species. *Agricultural and Forest Entomology* **12**: 285–292.

Holton, M.K., Lindroth, R.L., and Nordheim, E.V. 2003. Foliar quality influences tree-herbivore-parasitoid inter-actions: effects of elevated CO_2, O_3, and plant genotype. *Oecologia* **137**: 233–244.

Hunter, M.D. 2001. Effects of elevated atmospheric carbon dioxide on insect-plant interactions. *Agricultural and Forest Entomology* **3**: 153–159.

Huttunen, L., Niemela, P., Julkunen-Titto, R., Heiska, S., Tegelberg, R., Rousi, M., and Kellomaki, S. 2008. Does defoliation induce chemical and morphological defenses in the leaves of silver birch seedlings under changing climate? *Chemoecology* **18**: 85–98.

Huttunen, L., Niemela, P., Peltola, H., Heiska, S., Rousi, M., and Kellomaki, S. 2007. Is a defoliated silver birch seedling able to overcompensate the growth under changing climate? *Environmental and Experimental Botany* **60**: 227–238.

Knepp, R.G., Hamilton, J.G., Mohan, J.E., Zangerl, A.R., Berenbaum, M.R., and DeLucia, E.H. 2005. Elevated CO_2 reduces leaf damage by insect herbivores in a forest community. *New Phytologist* **167**: 207–218.

Lovelock, C.E., Posada, J., and Winter, K. 1999. Effects of elevated CO_2 and defoliation on compensatory growth and photosynthesis of seedlings in a tropical tree, *Copaifera aromatica*. *Biotropica* **31**: 279–287.

Mattson, W.J., Kuokkanen, K., Niemela, P., Julkunen-Tiitto, R., Kellomaki, S., and Tahvanainen, J. 2004. Elevated CO_2 alters birch resistance to Lagomorpha herbivores. *Global Change Biology* **10**: 1402–1413.

McNaughton, S.J. and Sabuni G.A. 1988. Large African mammals as regulators of vegetation structure. In: Werger,

M.J.A., Van der Aart, P.J.M., During, H.J., and Verhoeven, J.T.A. (Eds.) *Plant Form and Vegetation Structure.* SPB Academic Publishing, The Hague, The Netherlands, pp. 339–354.

Nabity, P.D., Hillstrom, M.L., Lindroth, R.L., and DeLucia, E.H. 2012. Elevated CO_2 interacts with herbivory to alter chlorophyll fluorescence and leaf temperature in *Betula papyrifera* and *Populus tremuloides. Oecologia* **169**: 905–913.

Novick, K.A., Katul, G.G., McCarthy, H.R., and Oren, R. 2012. Increased resin flow in mature pine trees growing under elevated CO_2 and moderate soil fertility. *Tree Physiology* **32**: 752–763.

Pastor, J. and Naiman, R.J. 1992. Selective foraging and ecosystem processes in boreal forest. *American Naturalist* **139**: 690–705.

Reeve, J.D., Ayres, M.P., Lorio Jr., P.L. Cappuccino, N., and Price, P.W. 1995. Host suitability, predation, and bark beetle population dynamics. In: Cappuccino, N. and Price, P.W. (Eds.) *Population Dynamics: New Approaches and Synthesis.* Academic Press, San Diego, California, USA, pp. 339–357.

Ruel, J.J., Ayres, M.P., and Lorio, P.L. 1998. Loblolly pine responds to mechanical wounding with increased resin flow. *Canadian Journal of Forest Research* **28**: 596–602.

Sanders, N.J., Belote, R.T., and Weltzin, J.F. 2004. Multitriphic effects of elevated atmospheric CO_2 on understory plant and arthropod communities. *Environmental Entomology* **33**: 1609–1616.

Stiling, P. and Cornelissen, T. 2007. How does elevated carbon dioxide (CO_2) affect plant-herbivore interactions? A field experiment and meta-analysis of CO_2-mediated changes on plant chemistry and herbivore performance. *Global Change Biology* **13**: 1–20.

Strom, B.L., Goyer, R.A., Ingram Jr., L.L., Boyd, G.D.L., and Lott, L.H. 2002. Oleoresin characteristics of progeny of loblolly pines that escaped attack by the southern pine beetle. *Forest Ecology and Management* **157**: 169–178.

Tylianakis, J.M., Didham, R.K., Bascompte, J., and Wardle, D.A. 2008. Global change and species interactions in terrestrial ecosystems. *Ecology Letters* **11**: 1351–1363.

Valkama, E., Koricheva, J., and Oksanen, E. 2007. Effects of elevated O_3, alone and in combination with elevated CO_2, on tree leaf chemistry and insect herbivore performance: a meta-analysis. *Global Change Biology* **13**: 184–201.

Wilkens, R.T., Ayres, M.P., Lorio Jr., P.L., and Hodges, J.D. 1998. Environmental effects on pine tree carbon budgets and resistance to bark beetles. In: Mickler, R.A. and Fox, S. (Eds.) *The Productivity and Sustainability of Southern Forest Ecosystems in a Changing Environment.* Springer, New York, New York, USA, pp. 591–616.

5.5.4 Butterflies

- Global warming is creating opportunities for butterflies to expand their populations and ranges, just the opposite of alarmist projections of range contractions and butterfly species demise in response to a CO_2-induced warming of Earth.

IPCC claims butterflies are at risk of extinction due to global warming. This section reviews research studying how butterflies respond to rising air temperatures and CO_2 concentrations and comes to a very different conclusion.

5.5.4.1 Response to Temperature

Research on the impact on butterflies of temperature changes has found impacts on populations and ranges and also has revealed how butterflies adapt, evolve, and in other ways respond to changes in temperature. The following sections summarize that research.

5.5.4.1.1 Population Dynamics

In response to model-based projections in which global warming enhances the prospect for animal species demise, several researchers have conducted studies on butterflies to test the viability of this hypothesis. Fleishman *et al.* (2001), for example, used comprehensive data on butterfly distributions from six mountain ranges in the U.S. Great Basin to study how butterfly populations of that region may respond to IPCC-projected climate change. Their work revealed "few if any species of montane butterflies are likely to be extirpated from the entire Great Basin (i.e., lost from the region as a whole)." The three researchers note "during the Middle Holocene, approximately 8000–5000 years ago, temperatures in the Great Basin were several degrees warmer than today." They conclude, "we might expect that most of the montane species—including butterflies—that currently inhabit the Great Basin would be able to tolerate the magnitude of climatic warming forecast over the next several centuries."

Other scientists have focused on the response of butterflies to warming during the twentieth century, warming IPCC claims is unprecedented in the past one to two thousand years.

Davies *et al.* (2006) studied the silver-spotted skipper butterfly (*Hesperia comma*), noting during the twentieth century it "became increasingly rare in

Britain [as] a result of the widespread reduction of sparse, short-turfed calcareous grassland containing the species' sole larval host plant, sheep's fescue grass," while describing the "refuge" colonies of 1982 as but a "remnant" of what once had been. To examine whether global warming might drive the already-decimated species to extinction, the four researchers analyzed population density data and estimates of the percent of bare ground and the percent of sheep's fescue available to the butterflies, based on surveys conducted in Surrey in the chalk hills of the North Downs, south of London, in 1982 (Thomas *et al.*, 1986), 1991 (Thomas and Jones, 1993), 2000 (Thomas *et al.*, 2001; Davies *et al.*, 2005), and 2001 (R.J. Wilson, unpublished data). They also assessed egg-laying rates in different microhabitats, the effects of ambient and oviposition site temperatures on egg-laying, and the effects of sward composition on egg location. This multifaceted work revealed, "in 1982, 45 habitat patches were occupied by *H. comma*," but "in the subsequent 18-year period, the species expanded and, by 2000, a further 29 patches were colonized within the habitat network." In addition, they found "the mean egg-laying rate of *H. comma* females increased with rising ambient temperatures" and "a wider range of conditions have become available for egg-laying."

Davies *et al.* write, "climate warming has been an important driving force in the recovery of *H. comma* in Britain [as] the rise in ambient temperature experienced by the butterfly will have aided the metapopulation re-expansion in a number of ways." First, they note, "greater temperatures should increase the potential fecundity of *H. comma* females," and "if this results in larger populations, for which there is some evidence (e.g. 32 of the 45 habitat patches occupied in the Surrey network experienced site-level increases in population density between 1982 and 2000), they will be less prone to extinction," with "larger numbers of dispersing migrant individuals being available to colonize unoccupied habitat patches and establish new populations." Second, "the wider range of thermal and physical microhabitats used for egg-laying increased the potential resource density within each grassland habitat fragment," and "this may increase local population sizes." Third, "colonization rates are likely to be greater as a result of the broadening of the species realized niche, [because] as a larger proportion of the calcareous grassland within the species' distribution becomes thermally suitable, the relative size and connectivity of habitat patches within the landscape increases." Fourth, "higher temperatures may directly increase

flight (dispersal) capacity, and the greater fecundity of immigrants may improve the likelihood of successful population establishment." Davies *et al.* conclude, "the warmer summers predicted as a consequence of climate warming are likely to be beneficial to *H. comma* within Britain," and "warmer winter temperatures could also allow survival in a wider range of microhabitats."

Dennis and Sparks (2007) analyzed data on the general abundance of Lepidoptera in Britain over the period 1864–1952, based on information assembled by Beirne (1955) via his examination of "several thousand papers in entomological journals describing annual abundances of moths and butterflies." The two researchers report "abundances of British Lepidoptera were significantly positively correlated with Central England temperatures in the current year for each month from May to September and November," and "increased overall abundance in Lepidoptera coincided significantly with increased numbers of migrants," having derived the latter data from Williams (1965). In addition, they report Pollard (1988) subsequently found much the same thing for 31 butterfly species over the period 1976–1986, and Roy *et al.* (2001) extended the latter investigation to 1997 and found "strong associations between weather and population fluctuations and trends in 28 of 31 species which confirmed Pollard's (1988) findings." These observations indicate the warming-driven increase in Lepidopteran species and numbers in Britain has been an ongoing phenomenon since the end of the Little Ice Age.

Checa *et al.* (2009) studied the composition and structure of butterfly communities of the "rotting-carrion guild" of the Nymphalidae family over a period of 13 months (April 2002–April 2003) in areas surrounding the Yasuni Scientific Research Station in the Ecuadorian Amazon inside the Yasuni National Park. They obtained their data using traps baited with rotten shrimp that had been fermenting for 11–20 days. Checa *et al.* captured 9,236 individual Nymphalidae butterflies representing 208 species, including two species that had not previously been found in Ecuador, and two "new" species that had not previously been found anywhere. They discovered "a constant replacement of species throughout the year," and "these communities had the highest species richness and abundance during the months with high temperatures." They note the mean temperature of their study area "only varies over one degree during the whole year."

The four researchers comment on "temperature's central role in the biology and life history of butterflies," noting "several key processes for butterfly survival depend on regulation of internal temperature," including mimetism and fast flight (Chai and Srygley, 1990), and fecundity and longevity, which they say have been found to be "higher at higher temperatures (Karlsson and Wiklund, 2005)." Hence, they conclude, "the tight relationship between temperature and butterfly population levels," or abundance, as well as butterfly species richness, likely will be "of major importance" for tropical butterflies in surviving potential future global warming.

References

Beirne, B.P. 1955. Natural fluctuations in abundance of British Lepidoptera. *Entomologist's Gazette* **6**: 21–52.

Chai, P. and Srygley, B. 1990. Predation and the flight, morphology and temperature of neotropical rain-forest butterflies. *The American Naturalist* **135**: 748–765.

Checa, M.F., Barragan, A., Rodriguez, J., and Christman, M. 2009. Temporal abundance patterns of butterfly communities (Lepidoptera: Nymphalidae) in the Ecuadorian Amazonia and their relationship with climate. *Annales de la Société Entomologique de France (NS)* **45**: 470–486.

Davies, Z.G., Wilson, R.J., Brereton, T.M., and Thomas, C.D. 2005. The re-expansion and improving status of the silver-spotted skipper butterfly (*Hesperia comma*) in Britain: a metapopulation success story. *Biological Conservation* **124**: 189–198.

Davies, Z.G., Wilson, R.J., Coles, S., and Thomas, C.D. 2006. Changing habitat associations of a thermally constrained species, the silver-spotted skipper butterfly, in response to climate warming. *Journal of Animal Ecology* **75**: 247–256.

Dennis, R.L.H. and Sparks, T.H. 2007. Climate signals are reflected in an 89 year series of British Lepidoptera records. *European Journal of Entomology* **104**: 763–767.

Fleishman, E., Austin, G.T., and Murphy, D.D. 2001. Biogeography of Great Basin butterflies: revisiting patterns, paradigms, and climate change scenarios. *Biological Journal of the Linnean Society* **74**: 501–515.

Karlsson, B. and Wiklund, C. 2005. Butterfly life history and temperature adaptations: Dry open habitats select for increased fecundity and longevity. *The Journal of Animal Ecology* **74**: 99–104.

Pollard, E. 1988. Temperature, rainfall and butterfly numbers. *Journal of Applied Ecology* **25**: 819–828.

Roy, D.B., Rothery, P., Moss, D., Pollard, E., and Thomas,
J.A. 2001. Butterfly numbers and weather: predicting historical trends in abundance and the future effects of climate change. *Journal of Animal Ecology* **70**: 201–217.

Thomas, C.D., Bodsworth, E.J., Wilson, R.J., Simmons, A.D., Davies, Z.G., Musche, M., and Conradt, L. 2001. Ecological and evolutionary processes at expanding range margins. *Nature* **411**: 577–581.

Thomas, C.D. and Jones, T.M. 1993. Partial recovery of a skipper butterfly (*Hesperia comma*) from population refuges: lessons for conservation in a fragmented landscape. *Journal of Animal Ecology* **62**: 472–481.

Thomas, J.A., Thomas, C.D., Simcox, D.J., and Clarke, R.T. 1986. Ecology and declining status of the silver-spotted skipper butterfly (*Hesperia comma*) in Britain. *Journal of Applied Ecology* **23**: 365–380.

Williams, C.B. 1965. *Insect Migration*. London, UK: Collins.

5.5.4.1 2 Range Expansion

IPCC claims the increase in temperature predicted to result from the ongoing rise in the air's CO_2 content will be of such magnitude and speed that many species of plants and animals will not be able to migrate poleward in latitude or upward in elevation rapidly enough to avoid extinction, as they are forced to seek cooler living conditions. However, there are many reasons for rejecting this contention, one of the most powerful being increases in the air's CO_2 content generally enable plants to endure warmer weather, so there is little or no need for them to shift the heat-limiting warm-temperature boundaries of their ranges as temperatures rise (See Sections 3.13, 4.2.3, and 4.4, this volume). At the cold-limiting cool-temperature boundaries of their ranges, on the other hand, warming provides opportunities for plants to push poleward and upward, which results in expansions of their ranges and reductions in their risk of extinction.

This section reviews several studies examining butterfly range habitat, revealing butterflies may be mimicking the respective shifts and stability of the cold- and heat-limited boundaries of the ranges of the plants on which they depend for food.

Parmesan *et al.* (1999) examined the distributional changes of non-migratory butterfly species whose northern boundaries were in northern Europe and whose southern boundaries were in southern Europe or northern Africa, over the prior century of global warming. They found the northern range boundaries shifted northward for 65% of the 52 species examined, remained stable for 34%, and shifted southward for 2%. As to the southern boundaries, of the 40 species examined there, 22% shifted their southern range boundary northward, for 72% it remained stable, and for 5% it shifted southward. Because "nearly all northward shifts involved extensions at the northern boundary with the southern boundary remaining stable," as the 13 researchers explain, "most species effectively expanded the size of their range when shifting northwards."

Thomas *et al.* (2001) documented an unusually rapid expansion of the ranges of two butterfly species (the silver-spotted skipper and the brown argus) along with two cricket species (the long-winged cone-head and Roesel's bush cricket). They observed the warming-induced "increased habitat breadth and dispersal tendencies have resulted in about 3- to 15-fold increases in expansion rates." In commenting on these findings, Pimm (2001) remark the geographical ranges of these insects were "expanding faster than expected" and the synergies involved in the many intricacies of the range expansion processes were "unexpected."

Crozier (2004) notes "*Atalopedes campestris*, the sachem skipper butterfly, expanded its range from northern California into western Oregon in 1967, and into southwestern Washington in 1990," where she reports temperatures rose by 2–4°C over the prior half-century. In an attempt to assess the importance of this regional warming for the persistence of *A. campestris* in the recently colonized areas, Crozier "compared population dynamics at two locations (the butterfly's current range edge and just inside the range) that differ by 2–3°C." Then, to determine the role of over-winter larval survivorship, she "transplanted larvae over winter to both sites."

According to Crozier, "combined results from population and larval transplant analyses indicate that winter temperatures directly affect the persistence of *A. campestris* at its northern range edge, and that winter warming was a prerequisite for this butterfly's range expansion." Noting "populations are more likely to go extinct in colder climates," Crozier writes, "the good news about rapid climate change [of the warming type] is that new areas may be available for the introduction of endangered species." The species she studied responded to regional warming by extending its northern range boundary, thereby expanding its range.

Menendez *et al.* (2006) provided what they call "the first assessment, at a geographical scale, of how species richness has changed in response to climate change," concentrating on British butterflies. They tested "whether average species richness of resident British butterfly species has increased in recent decades, whether these changes are as great as would be expected given the amount of warming that has taken place, and whether the composition of butterfly communities is changing towards a dominance by generalist species." They determined "average species richness of the British butterfly fauna at 20 x 20 km grid resolution has increased since 1970–82, during a period when climate warming would lead us to expect increases." They also found, as expected, "southerly habitat generalists increased more than specialists," which require a specific type of habitat that is sometimes difficult for them to find, especially in the modern world where habitat destruction is commonplace. In addition, they determined observed species richness increases lagged behind those expected on the basis of climate change.

These results "confirm," according to the nine U.K. researchers, "that the average species richness of British butterflies has increased since 1970–82." Some of the range shifts responsible for the increase in species richness take more time to occur than those of other species, and the researchers state their results imply "it may be decades or centuries before the species richness and composition of biological communities adjusts to the current climate."

In another analysis from Britain, Gonzalez-Megias *et al.* (2008) investigated species turnover in 51 butterfly assemblages by examining regional extinction and colonization events that occurred between the two periods 1976–1982 and 1995–2002. The five researchers found regional colonizations exceeded extinctions: "over twice as many sites gained species as lost species," so "the average species richness of communities has increased." They also found species abundances following colonization likewise increased, because of "climate-related increases in the [land's] carrying capacity."

Comparing their results with a broader range of animal studies, Gonzalez-Megias *et al.* found "analyses of distribution changes for a wide range of other groups of animals in Britain suggest that southern representatives of most taxa are moving northwards at a rate similar to—and in some cases faster than—butterflies (Hickling *et al.*, 2006)," and they report, "as with butterflies, most of these taxonomic groups have fewer northern than southern representatives, so climate-driven colonisations are likely to exceed extinctions." They suggest "most of these taxa will also be experiencing slight community-level increases in species richness."

White and Kerr (2006) "report butterfly species' range shifts across Canada between 1900 and 1990 and develop spatially explicit tests of the degree to which observed shifts result from climate or human population density," describing the latter factor as "a reasonable proxy for land use change." In this category they included such elements as "habitat loss, pesticide use, and habitat fragmentation," all of which anthropogenic-driven factors have been tied to declines of various butterfly species. In addition, they state to their knowledge, "this is the broadest scale, longest term dataset yet assembled to quantify global change impacts on patterns of species richness." They found butterfly species richness "generally increased over the study period, a result of range expansion among the study species." They further found this increase "from the early to late part of the 20th century was positively correlated with temperature change," which had to have been the cause of the increase, for they also found species richness was "negatively correlated with human population density change."

Westwood and Blair (2010) measured the responses of 19 common butterfly species of the boreal forests of Manitoba (Canada) to temperature changes experienced there during 1971–2004, focusing on each species' date of first appearance, week of peak abundance, and length of flight period. Autumn temperatures were found to have warmed significantly, and the two Canadian researchers observed "13 of 19 species showed a significant increase in flight period extending longer into the autumn," when "flight period extensions increased by 31.5 ± 13.9 days over the study period." They also note "two species, *Junonia coenia* and *Euphydryas phaeton*, increased their northerly ranges by ~150 and 70 km, respectively."

Westwood and Blair state "warmer autumns and winters may be providing opportunities for range extensions of more southerly butterfly species held at bay by past climatic conditions." They cite other investigators who have obtained similar results, stating "northward expansions in butterfly species range correlating with northward shifts in isotherms have been documented in both Europe and North America (Karl *et al.*, 1996; Parmesan, 1996; Parmesan *et al.*, 1999; Hill *et al.*, 1999; Hickling *et al.*, 2006)," and "in Canada, the Gorgone checkerspot (*Chlosyne gorgone*, Hubner) and the Delaware skipper (*Anatryone logan*, W.H. Edwards) have recently expanded their northern ranges significantly (Kerr, 2001)."

Forister *et al.* (2010) analyzed 35 years of butterfly presence-absence data collected by a single observer at 10 sites approximately every two weeks along an elevation gradient stretching from sea level to an altitude of 2,775 meters in the Sierra Nevada Mountains of Northern California (USA). During the data-collection period both maximum and minimum temperatures rose, low-altitude habitat was negatively affected by encroaching land development, and there was no systematic variation in precipitation. The eight researchers found species richness over this period "declined at half of the sites, with the most severe reductions at the lowest elevations," where "habitat destruction [was] greatest." At intermediate elevations, they report, there were "clear upward shifts in the elevational ranges of species, consistent with the influence of global warming." And at the highest site, they found species richness increased, and "in addition to an increase in richness, abundance has also generally increased at the highest-elevation site."

Noting the Arctic is predicted to be especially susceptible to potential threats from climate change, citing Overpeck *et al.* (1996), Franzen and Ockinger (2012) studied temporal changes in the insect species richness and community composition of wild bees, butterflies, and moths over a period of 64 years at five sites in northern Sweden's Padjelanta National Park (one of the largest National Parks in Europe, located just north of the Arctic Circle, between 66°45' and 67°35'N, and 15°06' and 18°36'E). The insect data were collected during surveys conducted over the period 2006–2008 and were compared with similar data collected in 1998 and 1944, while corresponding climate data were obtained from a weather station located at 66.89°N, 18.02°E.

The two researchers determined there had been a significant increase in the daily mean temperature during the vegetation season (May–September) between 1944 and 2008, when the temperature rose at a rate of 0.015°C per year, yielding an increase of almost 1°C over the 64-year study period. With respect to insect responses, they found the total number of bumble bee, butterfly, and moth species increased from 52 in 1944 to 64 in 2008; for wild bees, which increased only from 15 to 16 species, the increase was not statistically significant. For butterflies and moths, the combined species number increase (from 37 to 48) was statistically significant. Franzen and Ockinger state, "high alpine insect species are apparently still performing relatively well," noting "both southern species, such as *Erebia ligea* and *Polyommatus icarus*, and high alpine species, such as *Boloria chariclea* and *Lasionycta staudingeri*, seem to have colonized the area," and "ranges and species richness are even increasing in our study region, due to retreating glaciers and plant colonizations." In light of these real-world observations, they say "it is possible that warming will simply improve the performance and abundance of species in cold areas, as their mobility increases and new habitats become available," citing Ashton *et al.* (2009), Bale and Hayward (2010), and Kullman (2010).

According to Oliver *et al.* (2012), "climate warming threatens the survival of species at their warm, trailing-edge range boundaries but also provides opportunities for the ecological release of populations at the cool, leading edges of their distributions," so "as the climate warms," they continue, "leading-edge populations are expected to utilize an increased range of habitat types, leading to larger population sizes and range expansion." Oliver *et al.* tested "the hypothesis that the habitat associations of British butterflies have expanded over three decades of climate warming." They characterized "the habitat breadth of 27 southerly distributed species from 77 monitoring transects between 1977 and 2007 by considering changes in densities of butterflies across 11 habitat types."

In response to the overall climate warming that occurred between 1977 and 2007, but "contrary to expectation," as the five UK researchers report, 20 of the 27 species of butterflies they studied "showed long-term contractions in their habitat associations, despite some short-term expansions in habitat breadth in warmer-than-usual years," when the butterflies they studied spread out from their primary habitat to occupy other sites. They say these findings suggest some non-climatic driver must be responsible for most of the habitat contractions of British butterflies over the past three decades, for they note, "butterfly population declines in the past century have been primarily driven by habitat destruction and degradation, particularly in relation to agricultural intensification and abandonment," citing Asher *et al.* (2001) and Warren *et al.* (2001). They lament the likelihood these other anthropogenic-induced constraints "appear to be out-weighing the positive effects of a warming climate on habitat breadth." In the final sentence of their paper, they suggest, "only if other non-climatic drivers can be reduced or reversed will species be able to fully exploit any emerging opportunities provided by climate warming."

It appears the real world of nature is behaving just the opposite of alarmist projections of range contractions and butterfly species demise in response to a CO_2-induced warming of Earth.

References

Asher, J., Warren, M., Fox, R., Harding, P., Jeffcoate, G., and Jeffcoate, S. 2001. *The Millennium Atlas of Butterflies in Britain and Ireland.* Oxford University Press, Oxford, United Kingdom.

Ashton, S., Gutierrez, D., and Wilson, R.J. 2009. Effects of temperature and elevation on habitat use by a rare mountain butterfly: implications for species responses to climate change. *Ecological Entomology* **34**: 437–446.

Bale, J.S. and Hayward, S.A.L. 2010. Insect overwintering in a changing climate. *Journal of Experimental Biology* **213**: 980–994.

Crozier, L. 2004. Warmer winters drive butterfly range expansion by increasing survivorship. *Ecology* **85**: 231–241.

Forister, M.L., McCall, A.C., Sanders, N.J., Fordyce, J.A., Thorne, J.H., O'Brien, J., Waetjen, D.P., and Shapiro, A.M. 2010. Compounded effects of climate change and habitat alteration shift patterns of butterfly diversity. *Proceedings of the National Academy of Sciences USA* **107**: 2088–2092.

Franzen, M. and Ockinger, E. 2012. Climate-driven changes in pollinator assemblages during the last 60 years in an Arctic mountain region in Northern Scandinavia. *Journal of Insect Conservation* **16**: 227–238.

Gonzalez-Megias, A., Menendez, R., Roy, D., Brereton, T., and Thomas, C.D. 2008. Changes in the composition of British butterfly assemblages over two decades. *Global Change Biology* **14**: 1464–1474.

Hickling, R., Roy, D.B., Hill, J.K., Fox, R., and Thomas, C.D. 2006. The distributions of a wide range of taxonomic groups are expanding polewards. *Global Change Biology* **12**: 450–455.

Hill, J.K., Thomas, C.D., and Huntley, B. 1999. Climate and habitat availability determine 20th century changes in a butterfly's range margin. *Proceedings of the Royal Society of London, Series B* **266**: 1197–1206.

Karl, T.R., Knight, R.W., Easterling, D.R., and Quayle, R.G. 1996. Indices of climate change for the United States. *Bulletin of the American Meteorological Society* **77**: 279–292.

Kerr, J.K. 2001. Butterfly species richness patterns in Canada: energy, heterogeneity, and the potential consequences of climate change. *Conservation Ecology* **5**: 10.

Kullman, L. 2010. Alpine flora dynamics: a critical review of responses to climate change in the Swedish Scandes since the early 1950s. *Nordic Journal of Botany* **28**: 398–408.

Menendez, R., Gonzalez-Megias, A., Hill, J.K., Braschler,

B., Willis, S.G., Collingham, Y., Fox, R., Roy, D.B., and Thomas, C.D. 2006. Species richness changes lag behind climate change. *Proceedings of the Royal Society B* **273**: 1465–1470.

Oliver, T.H., Thomas, C.D., Hill, J.K., Brereton, T., and Roy, D.B. 2012. Habitat associations of thermophilous butterflies are reduced despite climatic warming. *Global Change Biology* **18**: 2720–2729.

Overpeck, J., Rind, D., Lacis, A., and Healy, R. 1996. Possible role of dust-induced regional warming in abrupt climate change during the last glacial period. *Nature* **384**: 447–449.

Parmesan, C. 1996. Climate and species' range. *Nature* **382**: 765–766.

Parmesan, C., Ryrholm, N., Stefanescu, C., Hill, J.K., Thomas, C.D., Descimon, H., Huntley, B., Kaila, L., Kullberg, J., Tammaru, T., Tennent, W.J., Thomas, J.A., and Warren, M. 1999. Poleward shifts in geographical ranges of butterfly species associated with regional warming. *Nature* **399**: 579–583.

Pimm, S.L. 2001. Entrepreneurial insects. *Nature* **411**: 531–532.

Thomas, C.D., Bodsworth, E.J., Wilson, R.J., Simmons, A.D., Davies, Z.G., Musche, M., and Conradt, L. 2001. Ecological and evolutionary processes at expanding range margins. *Nature* **411**: 577–581.

Warren, M.S., Hill, J.K., Thomas, J.A., Asher, J., Fox, R., Huntley, B., Roy, D.B., Telfer, M.G., Jeffcoate, S., Harding, P., Jeffcoate, G., Willis, S.G., Greatorex-Davies, J.N., Moss, D., and Thomas, C.D. 2001. Rapid responses of British butterflies to opposing forces of climate and habitat change. *Nature* **414**: 65–69.

Westwood, A.B. and Blair, D. 2010. Effect of regional climate warming on the phenology of butterflies in boreal forests in Manitoba, Canada. *Environmental Entomology* **39**: 1122–1133.

White, P. and Kerr, J.T. 2006. Contrasting spatial and temporal global change impacts on butterfly species richness during the 20th century. *Ecography* **29**: 908–918.

5.5.4.1.3 Adaptation, Evolution, and Phenotypic Responses

Few studies have investigated adaptive or evolutionary responses of butterflies to increased temperature. But those that have done so suggest butterflies are well-equipped to manage any of the temperature changes projected by IPCC for the future.

Hughes *et al.* (2007) examined evolutionary changes in adult flight morphology in six populations of the speckled wood butterfly—*Pararge aegeria*—along a transect from its distribution core to its warming-induced northward-expanding range margin. The results were compared with the output of an individual-based spatially explicit model developed "to investigate impacts of habitat availability on the evolution of dispersal in expanding populations." The empirical data the researchers gathered in Britain "were in agreement with model output" and "showed increased dispersal ability with increasing distance from the distribution core." This included favorable changes in thorax shape, abdomen mass, and wing aspect ratio for both males and females, as well as thorax mass and wing loading for females. The researchers state, "increased dispersal ability was evident in populations from areas colonized >30 years previously."

Hughes *et al.* suggest "evolutionary increases in dispersal ability in expanding populations may help species track future climate changes and counteract impacts of habitat fragmentation by promoting colonization." However, they report, in the specific situation they investigated, "at the highest levels of habitat loss, increased dispersal was less evident during expansion and reduced dispersal was observed at equilibrium, indicating that for many species, continued habitat fragmentation is likely to outweigh any benefits from dispersal."

Another means by which butterflies can cope with higher temperatures is through the production of heat-shock proteins (HSPs). According to Karl *et al.* (2008), HSPs "are thought to play an important ecological and evolutionary role in thermal adaptation," where "the up-regulation of stress-inducible HSPs may help organisms to cope with stress thus enhancing survival (Sorensen *et al.*, 2003; Dahlhoff, 2004; Dahlhoff and Rank, 2007)." Working with *Lycaena tityrus*, a widespread temperate-zone butterfly that ranges from western Europe to central Asia, Karl *et al.* tested this hypothesis by comparing expression patterns of stress-inducible HSPs across replicated populations originating from different altitudes and across different ambient temperatures. Their observations revealed "a significant interaction between altitude and rearing temperature [that] indicates that low-altitude animals showed a strongly increased HSP70 expression at the higher compared with at the lower rearing temperature." This is exactly where one would expect to see such a response in light of its obvious utility in warmer conditions.

Karl *et al.* observe "HSP70 expression increased substantially at the higher rearing temperature in low-altitude butterflies ... [which] might represent an adaptation to occasionally occurring heat spells," suggesting this response should serve these organisms well if the dramatic warming predicted by IPCC should come to pass.

Pateman *et al.* (2012) note there are many situations in nature where one species has a close-to-exclusive relationship with another species, such as a predator-prey relationship in the animal kingdom, an animal-plant symbiotic relationship such as that between corals and the zooxanthellae they host, or the relationship between a butterfly and the plant species that acts as a host for the larval stage of the butterfly. Such interactions, according to Pateman *et al.*, are most commonly regarded as additional constraints, "because they may limit species to a narrower set of physical conditions (and, hence, narrower geographic ranges) than their fundamental climatic niches might otherwise allow." Thus if the world warms to a substantial degree, there may be a mismatch between the climatic needs of the two species, resulting in one or both of them suffering from the change in climate.

Pateman *et al.* studied the brown argus butterfly (*Aricia agestis*), which "has spread northward in Great Britain by ~79 km in 20 years, which is 2.3 times faster than the average expansion rate documented for species globally (Chen *et al.*, 2011)," endeavoring to discover what accelerated the butterfly's dramatic rate of range expansion. They analyzed the effect of climate on brown argus butterfly populations associated with different larval host plants, based on count data developed by volunteers who monitored more than 200 fixed transects in Britain, as described by Pollard and Yates (1993). Results revealed warmer summers typically result in higher brown argus larval population densities on both rockrose and Geraniaceae plants, but under cooler conditions the rockrose host plant was more favorable than Geraniaceae plants. Over the past two decades, as the frequency of warm summers increased, the five UK researchers found the brown argus butterfly adapted by expanding its larval presence onto Geraniaceae plants they had largely avoided under cooler conditions. That led to a significant expansion in the size of their range, as they had an additional plant species on which to lay their eggs and have their larvae develop successfully.

The five researchers state in the concluding sentence of the abstract of their paper, "interactions among species are often seen as constraints on species' responses to climate change, but we show that temperature-dependent changes to interspecific interactions can also facilitate change." Or as they state in the concluding sentence of the body of their paper, "we suggest that altered interactions among species do not necessarily constrain distribution changes but can facilitate expansions," thereby providing another real-world example of a previously unappreciated means by which an animal species can benefit from global warming and expand its range of territorial occupancy. And contrary to the view that generalist species will more rapidly exploit new regions made available by climate change, field assays of butterflies in recently colonized areas are composed of more specialized species, such as the UK brown argus butterfly, because of their aggressive colonization of their widely dispersed host plant (Bridle *et al.*, 2014).

References

Bridle, J.R., Buckley, J., Bodsworth, E.J., and Thomas, C.D. 2014. Evolution on the move: specialization on widespread resources associated with rapid range expansion in response to climate change. *Proceedings of the Royal Society B* **281**: 20131800, doi:10.1098/rspb.2013.1800.

Chen, I.C., Hill, J.K., Ohlemülle, R., Roy, D.B., and Thomas, C.D. 2011. Rapid range shifts of species associated with high levels of climate warming. *Science* **333**: 1024–1026.

Dahlhoff, E.P. 2004. Biochemical indicators of stress and metabolism: applications for marine ecological studies. *Annual Review of Physiology* **66**: 183–207.

Dahlhoff, E.P. and Rank, N.E. 2007. The role of stress proteins in responses of a montane willow leaf beetle to environmental temperature variation. *Journal of Biosciences* **32**: 477–488.

Hughes, C.L., Dytham, C., and Hill, J.K. 2007. Modelling and analyzing evolution of dispersal in populations at expanding range boundaries. *Ecological Entomology* **32**: 437–445.

Karl, I., Sorensen, J.G., Loeschcke, V., and Fischer, K. 2008. HSP70 expression in the Copper butterfly *Lycaena tityrus* across altitudes and temperatures. *Journal of Evolutionary Biology* **22**: 172–178.

Pateman, R.M., Hill, J.K., Roy, D.B., Fox, R., and Thomas, C.D. 2012. Temperature-dependent alterations in host use drive rapid range expansion in a butterfly. *Science* **336**: 1028–1030.

Pollard, E. and Yates, T.J. 1993. *Monitoring Butterflies for Ecology and Conservation*. Chapman & Hall, London, United Kingdom.

Sorensen, J.G., Kristensen, T.N., and Loeschcke, V. 2003. The evolutionary and ecological role of heat shock proteins. *Ecology Letters* **6**: 1025–1037.

5.5.4.2 Response to Elevated CO$_2$

Few studies have been conducted on the response of butterflies to increased levels of atmospheric CO$_2$, but those that have been done suggest rising CO$_2$ will confer a net benefit on their growth and survival.

Early work on the subject was provided by Groverde *et al.* (1999). Birdfoot Deer Vetch (*Lotus corniculatus*) is a cyanogenic plant that produces foliar cyanoglycosides to deter against herbivory by insects. The Common Blue Butterfly (*Polyommatus icarus*), however, regularly feeds on this plant—it possesses an enzyme that detoxifies these cyanide-containing defensive compounds. To study the effects of elevated CO$_2$ and genotype on the leaf quality of Birdfoot Deer Vetch and the larval development of the Common Blue Butterfly, Groverde *et al.* grew four genotypes of *Lotus corniculatus*, differing in cyanoglycoside and tannin concentrations, in controlled environmental chambers receiving atmospheric CO$_2$ concentrations of either 350 or 700 ppm.

Elevated CO$_2$ significantly increased leaf tannin and starch contents in a genotypically dependent and independent manner, respectively, while decreasing leaf cyanoglycoside contents, regardless of genotype. Atmospheric CO$_2$ enrichment did not significantly affect leaf water, sugar, protein, or nitrogen content. Thus, these CO$_2$-induced changes in leaf chemistry (higher starch and tannin and lower cyanoglycoside concentrations) increased its palatability, as indicated by greater leaf dry weight consumption of CO$_2$-enriched leaves by butterfly larvae. In addition, increased leaf consumption of CO$_2$-enriched leaves led to greater larval biomass and shorter larval developmental times, indicating atmospheric CO$_2$ enrichment affected leaf quality to positively influence larvae of the Common Blue Butterfly. Moreover, larval mortality was lower when feeding on CO$_2$-enriched, rather than ambiently grown, leaves. Thus, as the CO$_2$ content of the air rises, it is likely Birdfoot Deer Vetch plants will increase their photosynthetic rates and differentially invest their additional carbon gains in storage, structural, and defensive compounds. Atmospheric CO$_2$ enrichment likely will increase leaf starch and tannin contents and decrease cyanoglycoside contents, without affecting sugar, protein, water, and nitrogen contents. Col-

lectively, these chemical changes would improve the palatability of Birdfoot Deer Vetch leaves to the Common Blue Butterfly larvae.

In a follow-up study four years later, Groverde *et al.* (2004), abandoned the controlled environment chamber design of Groverde *et al.* (1999) and grew Birdfoot Deer Vetch plants from seed for three months in tubes recessed into the ground under natural conditions in a nutrient-poor calcareous grassland where an extra 232 ppm of CO$_2$ was supplied to them via a screen-aided CO$_2$ control (SACC) system (Leadley *et al.*, 1997; 1999) and insect larvae were allowed to feed on the plants (half of which received extra phosphorus fertilizer) for the final month of the experiment.

The 63% increase in atmospheric CO$_2$ concentration enhanced the total dry weight of plants growing on the unfertilized soil by 21.5% and that of the plants growing on the phosphorus-enriched soil by 36.3%. The elevated CO$_2$ treatment had no effect on pupal and adult insect mass. Goverde *et al.* report there were "genotype-specific responses in the development time of *P. icarus* to elevated CO$_2$ conditions," with larvae originating from different mothers developing better under either elevated CO$_2$ or ambient CO$_2$, and for still others the CO$_2$ concentration had no effect on development. Condensed tannins in the foliage of plants growing on the nutrient-poor calcareous soil were increased by 23.7% in the CO$_2$-enriched air.

The results of this study and its predecessor suggest the ongoing rise in the air's CO$_2$ content likely will be positive for *L. corniculatus* plants, while ranging from positive to nil for the insect herbivore *P. icarus* that feeds on them. In addition, the authors suggest rising levels of CO$_2$ might be "a selective factor, affecting both plant and herbivore populations and their interaction," and, therefore, "genotype-specific responses must be considered because this will affect the outcome of elevated CO$_2$ for plant-herbivore interactions." It is currently unclear what the range of those potential outcomes might be. Finally, since the presence of condensed tannins in foliage eaten by ruminants tends to decrease their emissions of methane, it might be expected the CO$_2$-induced increases in the concentrations of these substances in the leaves of *L. corniculatus* may help reduce the atmospheric concentration of this powerful greenhouse gas in a CO$_2$-enriched world of the future.

Groverde *et al.* (2002) raised larvae of the satyrid butterfly (*Coenonympha pamphilus*) in seminatural, undisturbed calcareous grassland plots exposed to atmospheric CO_2 concentrations of 370 and 600 ppm for five growing seasons. Elevated atmospheric CO_2 concentration was shown to increase foliar concentrations of total nonstructural carbohydrates and condensed tannins in the grassland plants. In what is often considered a negative impact, however, it decreased foliar nitrogen concentrations. Nevertheless, this phenomenon had no discernible negative impact on butterfly growth and performance characteristics. Larval developmental time, for example, was not affected by elevated CO_2, nor was adult dry mass. The elevated CO_2 increased lipid concentrations in adult male butterflies by nearly 14%, and marginally increased the number of eggs in female butterflies.

As atmospheric CO_2 concentrations increase, larvae of the satyrid butterfly likely will not be negatively affected by feeding on grassland plants that may exhibit reduced foliar nitrogen concentrations. Increases in the air's CO_2 concentration may increase the fitness of this butterfly species. Adult males exposed to elevated CO_2, for example, exhibited greater body concentrations of lipids, compounds used as energy resources in these and other butterflies. In addition, elevated CO_2 increased egg numbers in females, which also suggests an increase in fitness. Thus, this species—and perhaps others—likely will respond positively to future increases in the air's CO_2 concentration.

References

Goverde, M., Bazin, A., Shykoff, J.A., and Erhardt, A. 1999. Influence of leaf chemistry of *Lotus corniculatus* (Fabaceae) on larval development of *Polyommatus icarus* (Lepidoptera, Lycaenidae): effects of elevated CO_2 and plant genotype. *Functional Ecology* **13**: 801–810.

Goverde, M., Erhardt, A., and Niklaus, P.A. 2002. In situ development of a satyrid butterfly on calcareous grassland exposed to elevated carbon dioxide. *Ecology* **83**: 1399–1411.

Goverde, M., Erhardt, A., and Stocklin, J. 2004. Genotype-specific response of a lycaenid herbivore to elevated carbon dioxide and phosphorus availability in calcareous grassland. *Oecologia* **139**: 383–391.

Leadley, P.W., Niklaus, P., Stocker, R., and Korner, C. 1997. Screen-aided CO_2 control (SACC): a middle-ground between FACE and open-top chamber. *Acta Oecologia* **18**: 207–219.

Leadley, P.W., Niklaus, P.A., Stocker, R., and Korner, C. 1999. A field study of the effects of elevated CO_2 on plant biomass and community structure in a calcareous grassland. *Oecologia* **118**: 39–49.

5.5.5 Other Insects

5.5.5.1 Response to Temperature

It is important to determine what effect global warming might have on the delicate balance between various plants and the insects that feed on them. Several researchers have done just that for several insect species. This section examines what has been reported for other types of insects not previously discussed in this chapter.

In some cases, researchers have found higher temperatures do indeed inhibit insect growth and survival. For some insect species, humankind might consider this a good thing.

Zhang *et al.* (2009), for example, note "the Oriental migratory locust (*Locusta migratoria manilensis*) has been one of the most damaging agricultural pests throughout Chinese history." Based on the decadal locust abundance data of Ma (1958) for the AD 950s–1950s, the decadal Yangtze Delta flood and drought frequency data of Jiang *et al.* (2005) for the AD 1000s–1950s, and the decadal mean temperature records of Yang *et al.* (2002) for the AD 950s–1950s, Zhang *et al.* employed wavelet analysis "to shed new light on the causal relationships between locust abundance, floods, droughts and temperature in ancient China."

The international team of Chinese, French, German, and Norwegian researchers say coolings of 160- to 170-year intervals dominated climatic variability in China over the past millennium, and these cooling periods promoted locust plagues by enhancing temperature-associated drought/flood events. The six scientists say their results suggest "global warming might not only imply reduced locust plague[s], but also reduced risk of droughts and floods for entire China." They note these findings "challenge the popular view that global warming necessarily accelerates natural and biological disasters such as drought/flood events and outbreaks of pest insects," the view long championed by the assessment reports of the Intergovernmental Panel on Climate Change. In direct contrast to that view, Zhang *et al.* say their results are an example of "benign effects of global warming on the regional risk of natural disasters."

Reineke and Hauck (2012) note "the grape leafhopper *Empoasca vitis* is regarded as a major insect pest in many European grapevine growing areas, with an increasing importance realized in recent years, maybe as a result of climatic change."

Reineke and Hauck studied in the laboratory the

development of larval instars of two leafhopper species, *E. vitis* and *E. rosae,* on grapevine leaves under different temperature regimes. The two German researchers report the shortest larval developmental time they observed occurred at night temperatures of 13–15°C and day temperatures of 23–25°C, which they say "was in agreement with predicted optimal temperatures for both species." In addition, "at the temperature regime of 20°C night and 30°C day temperature, either no egg hatch was observed or early development of first-instar larvae was not successful for both species." Reineke and Hauck conclude, "these results suggest that warm (18°C) nights and moderately warm (28°C) days are representing the upper thermal threshold for development of both *E. vitis* and *E. rosae* embryonic stages on grapevine leaves, questioning current assumptions of an increasing importance of *E. vitis* as a grapevine pest under future climate change."

Bertelsmeier *et al.* (2013) write, "climate change and invasive species are two of the most serious threats of biodiversity," noting "a general concern is that these threats interact, and that a globally warming climate could favor invasive species," with the result that "many native species are displaced, leading to local extinctions of fauna and flora." They note "several studies suggest that climate change could exacerbate the threat posed by invasive species, especially poikilotherms [animals having a body temperature that varies with the temperature of their surroundings], by removing thermal barriers and allowing them to establish at higher latitudes."

The three French researchers focused their attention on ants, because "ants are among the worst invasive species (Rabitsch 2011; Holway *et al.* 2002; Lach and Hooper-Bui 2010)," and "they are small, numerous and colonial" and can therefore "rapidly colonize a new habitat." They studied the big-headed ant, *Pheidole megacephala*, considered one of the world's 100 worst invasive species. They used ecological niche models to estimate the species' potential suitable habitat in 2020, 2050, and 2080 with an ensemble forecast obtained from five modeling techniques, including three global circulation models and two CO_2 emission scenarios, by means of which they generated world maps with suitable climatic conditions and assessed changes, both qualitatively and quantitatively.

"Surprisingly," Bertelsmeier *et al.* write, their results suggest "the invasion of big-headed ants is not only unlikely to benefit from climate change, but may even suffer from it," as their projections showed "a global decrease in the invasive potential of big-headed ants as early as 2020 and becoming even stronger by 2080, reaching a global loss of 19.4% of area with favorable climate." They note this finding is just the opposite of classical views of global climate change, wherein the ranges of many invading species are believed to increase in response to warming, especially those that are currently limited by climate. *P. megacephala* "will experience very little shifts in potential habitat," the French scientists conclude, as their niche envelope, presenting favorable climatic conditions, "will mostly shrink."

The analysis of Bertelsmeier *et al.* suggests, as they clearly state, "the worst invasive species of today may not be the worst invasive species of tomorrow," if Earth begins to warm again. After the planet's nearly two-decade climate-change hiatus, it's anyone's guess as to when that might happen.

Other insect species have benefited from a little global warming, as illustrated by recent temperature-induced expansions of their ranges.

Hickling *et al.* (2005), for example, analyzed changes in the northern and southern range boundaries of 37 non-migratory British Odonata (dragonfly and damselfly) species—four of which have northern ranges, 24 of which have southern ranges, and nine of which are ubiquitous—between the two ten-year periods 1960–1970 and 1985–1995. Their work revealed all but two of the 37 species increased their ranges between the two ten-year periods. They report their "findings that species are shifting northwards faster at their northern range margin than at their southern range margin, are consistent with the results of Parmesan *et al.* (1999)," adding, "this could suggest that species at their southern range margins are less constrained by climate than by other factors."

Poniatowski and Fartmann (2011) state the majority of central European orthopterans (an order of insects that includes grasshoppers, crickets, and locusts) "are flightless and have low dispersal ability," citing Reinhardt *et al.* (2005). However, they note, "since the 1980s—the beginning of the strong global temperature increase—some short-winged (brachypterous) species have been able to expand their ranges rapidly," as reported by Thomas *et al.* (2001), Simmons and Thomas (2004), Gardiner (2009), and Wissmann *et al.* (2009). In those cases, the scientists write, "long-winged (macropterous) individuals of the predominantly short-winged (flightless) species are assumed to have been responsible for the range shifts," citing the findings and conclusions of Simmons and Thomas (2004), Gardiner (2009), and Hochkirch and Damerau (2009).

Poniatowski and Fartmann studied the migration behavior of *Metrioptera roeselii*, a medium-sized bush-cricket, 13–26 mm in total length, which is currently expanding its range northwards in large parts of Europe (Kleukers *et al.*, 2004; Gardiner, 2009; Wissmann *et al.*, 2009)." This species is wing-dimorphic, but they note "the short-winged (brachypterous) morph dominates."

Based on their analyses of the relationships between bush-cricket densities and several meso-climate/weather parameters, the two German researchers found cricket abundances were positively correlated with warm and dry weather conditions during the hatching times of the nymphs, leading them to conclude, "the development of long-winged individuals is determined by density stress (crowding), as has been shown for locusts (Uvarov, 1966)." They further note, "similar results have also been reported for other bush-crickets," citing Ando and Hartley (1982), Sanger (1984), and Higaki and Ando (2003). Poniatowski and Fartmann conclude, "the rapid northward range expansion of *M. roeselii* is indirectly driven by climate change," explaining, "favorable (warm/dry) weather conditions lead to high densities at high latitudes (cf. Bale *et al.*, 2002) and in turn result in many macropters," the "potential dispersers" that get the species where it needs to go in order to survive in a world of evolving warmth.

Instead of experiencing range expansions in response to rising temperatures, other insect species have invoked adapted mechanisms allowing them to maintain their populations and habitat area.

Sparks *et al.* (2010) note "honeybees are an essential component of modern agriculture," and "large acreages of pollinator-dependent crops, such as apples, almonds, blueberries and cranberries, require managed pollinators, mainly the honeybee, to ensure maximized production." They report several modern studies suggest synchronization of pollinator activity and flowering may be changed by rapid global warming, leading to deficient pollination when it is most needed and resulting in reduced crop productivity. Noting little work has focused on this imagined problem, the six Polish scientists decided to investigate the dates of honeybees' first cleansing flights, which occur in the early spring of each year after overwintering and "are undertaken by worker bees excreting faeces accumulated in their recta while restricted in the hive for the winter during cold weather."

Sparks *et al.* analyzed annual records of the first observed cleansing flights of honeybees from 80–130 hives for each of the 25 years of the 1985–2009 period in the vicinity of Poznan, Poland. They found a significant relationship between the date of the first cleansing flight and the January to March mean temperature, as well as the previous June to September mean temperature. In the two-variable model of this phenomenon they developed, "the regression coefficients suggested a 1°C increase in previous June to September mean temperature was associated with a 9.11 ± 2.36 day advance, and a 1°C increase in January to March temperature was associated with a 3.41 ± 1.00 day advance, in first cleansing flight date."

Thus they discovered "first cleansing flight dates in [their] study advanced by over 1 month during the 25 years that observations were kept," and this advancement was "similar to changes reported in first appearance dates of other insects (e.g. Roy and Sparks, 2000; Sparks *et al.*, 2005; Harrington *et al.*, 2007), including other hymenopterans like wasps (Tryjanowski *et al.*, 2010)." This demonstrates, as has been observed by still others, "cleansing behavior is related to late winter/spring temperature (e.g. Kronenberg and Heller, 1982; Seeley, 1985)," and provides more evidence of honeybees "continued synchrony with the plant species that rely heavily on this major pollinator," as the plants' flowering dates fluctuate with the ups and downs of spring temperatures and their longer-term trends.

Bartomeus *et al.* (2011) preface their analysis by noting "the phenology of many ecological processes is modulated by temperature, making them potentially sensitive to climate change," and because of this fact, "mutualistic interactions may be especially vulnerable because of the potential for phenological mismatching if the species involved do not respond similarly to changes in temperature." Bartomeus *et al.* explored this situation with real-world data by presenting "an analysis of climate-associated shifts in the phenology of wild bees, the most important pollinators world-wide, and [comparing] these shifts to published studies of bee-pollinated plants over the same time period." They "used long-term data to compare phenological shifts for 10 bee species to shifts in 106 native plant species that are visited by these same bee species," which typically "have annual cycles that include an obligatory larval or adult diapause before spring emergence." The plant data for this comparison were provided by Primack *et al.* (2004) and Miller-Rushing *et al.* (2006) for Massachusetts (AD 1885–2003), by Bradley *et al.* (1999) for Wisconsin (1936–1999), by Cook *et al.* (2008) for New York (1931–2008), and by Abu-Asab *et al.* (2001) for Washington, DC (1970–1999, a time interval bracketing the period of greatest temperature increase), and the bee data were developed by Bartomeus *et al.*

The results indicate "over the past 130 years, the phenology of 10 bee species from northeastern North America has advanced by a mean of 10.4 ± 1.3 days," and "most of this advance has taken place since 1970, paralleling global temperature increases." The scientists note "when the best available data are used to estimate analogous rates of advance for plants, these rates are not distinguishable from those of the bees." Bartomeus *et al.* conclude, among the generalist bee species they studied, "bee emergence is keeping pace with shifts in host-plant flowering." This finding suggests historical global warming—which IPCC contends has been unprecedented over the past millennium or two—has not detrimentally interfered with the longstanding mutually beneficial relationship between the emergence of adult wild bees and the flowering of the plants they visit.

Balanya *et al.* (2006) determined the magnitude and direction of shifts over time [13 to 46 years, mean = 24.1 years] in chromosome inversion frequencies and in ambient temperature for 26 populations of the cosmopolitan fly species *Drosophila subobscura* on three continents, to determine whether "ambient temperatures have warmed at these sites and also whether genotypes characteristic of low latitudes have increased in frequency." The authors report warming occurred at 22 of the 26 sites they investigated, and "chromosome frequencies shifted toward a more low-latitude pattern in 21 of the 22 sites that warmed over the sample interval," indicating "inversion frequencies have changed in step with climate on three continents." As a result, "genotype frequencies and climate at a given site have become more equatorial over the sample intervals," with the observed shifts being "equivalent to moving the historical sample site ~1° of latitude closer to the equator."

The authors describe the genetic shift they uncovered as "exceptionally rapid," being "detectable even for samples separated by fewer than two decades." In addition, they say, "the ability of *D. subobscura* (Rodriguez-Trelles *et al.*, 1998; Orengo and Prevosti, 1996; Sole *et al.*, 2002)—and probably other species with short generation times (Bradshaw and Holzapfel, 2001; Umina *et al.*, 2005; Levitan and Etges, 2005; Kinnison and Hendry, 2001)—to respond genetically and rapidly to imposed environmental shifts may partially buffer their persistence in a globally warming world (Bradshaw and Holzapfel, 2006)."

Zivanovic and Mestres (2011) collected *Drosophila subobscura* flies from a swampy area on the bank of the Danube river near the town of Apatin, approximately 200 km northwest of Belgrade, Serbia, and analyzed inversion polymorphisms in them, comparing their results (from 2008 and 2009) with results obtained from flies collected at the same site in June 1994, because, as they put it, "genes located within inversions are associated with a variety of traits including those involved in climate adaptation," citing Hoffmann and Rieseberg (2008). The scientists found a significant increase in the frequency of certain chromosomal arrangements characteristic of southern latitudes, which they describe as "warm adapted," and a significant decrease in the frequency of such arrangements characteristic of northern latitudes, which they describe as "cold adapted."

The two researchers say their observations suggest they have detected "the effect of selection on chromosomal polymorphism composition," and, therefore, "some form of natural selection appears to be acting as a reaction to the increase in temperature associated with [the] many heat waves that have markedly affected the Balkan Peninsula," especially over the past decade and a half. They also note their results "agree with those from southwestern and central European populations (Rodriguez-Trelles and Rodriguez, 1998; Sole *et al.*, 2002; Balanya *et al.*, 2004, 2006, 2009)." In addition, they note similar things have been observed in *D. melanogaster* in Australia, citing Anderson *et al.* (2005) and Umina *et al.* (2005), and in *D. robusta* in North America, citing Levitan and Etges (2005). They report, "the climate change of recent decades has led to heritable genetic changes in animal species as diverse as birds, squirrels and mosquitoes (Bradshaw and Holzapfel, 2006)," revealing many forms of animal life may be well equipped to evolve with sufficient rapidity to survive the challenges of rapid global warming.

Nyamukondiwa and Terblanche (2010) write, "acclimation, acclimatization or hardening responses all describe different forms of phenotypic plasticity (i.e. the ability of an organism to respond to environmental stimuli with a change in phenotype)," as described by West-Eberhard (2003) and Whitman (2009). In addition, they state, "phenotypic plasticity may alter the performance of an organism through compensatory modifications of physiological function and tolerance as a result of changes in environmental conditions," suggesting this multifaceted phenomenon likely will play a major role in determining future geographic distributions of insects in a warming world.

The two South African scientists explored the phenomenon as it operates in two species of fruit fly (*Ceratitis rosa* and *C. capitata*). Using a full-factorial design, as they describe it, they investigated one-week-long acclimation responses of each species' critical minimum and maximum temperature (CT_{min} and CT_{max}) to exposure to temperatures of 20, 25, and 30°C, as well as their interactions with short-term sub-lethal temperature exposures to the same conditions as arrived at via different rates of warming. They report, "generally, increasing the acclimation temperature significantly increased CT_{max}, whereas decreasing the acclimation temperature significantly lowered CT_{min}." In addition, "slower ramping rates significantly increase CT_{max} in both *C. rosa* and *C. capitata*." This suggests "more time during heating (i.e. a slower heating rate) provides the flies with an opportunity to develop some heat protection, and therefore suggests that *C. capitata*, and possibly also *C. rosa*, might have short-term phenotypic plasticity of high temperature tolerance." They describe this as being "similar to the rapid heat hardening or the heat shock responses in *Drosophila* (Loeschcke and Hoffmann, 2006; Johnson *et al.*, 2009) and other insect species (Huang *et al.*, 2007)."

Nyamukondiwa and Terblanche conclude fruit flies "are capable of adjusting their thermal tolerance within a single generation at both weekly and hourly time scales," noting "high temperature acclimation improves high temperature tolerance, in keeping with much of the literature on thermal acclimation (Whitman, 2009)." They also state "both *C. rosa* and *C. capitata* have the capacity to adjust their thermal tolerance over short timescales in the wild," further stating this phenomenon will "probably allow both species to track changes in ambient temperature and survive sudden extremes of temperature that might otherwise be potentially lethal," citing Chown and Nicolson (2004).

This phenomenon is not restricted to flies. The two researchers indicate, for example, in several insect species "survival of lethal temperatures or critical thermal limits to activity can be significantly improved by prior exposure to sub-lethal temperatures," citing Lee *et al.* (1987), Kelty and Lee (2001), Shreve *et al.* (2004), and Powell and Bale (2006). This phenomenon is a major mechanism used by insects to cope with temperature variation at both daily (Kelty and Lee, 2001; Kelty, 2007; Overgaard and Sorensen, 2008) and seasonal (Powell and Bale, 2006; Hoffmann *et al.*, 2005; Terblanche *et al.*, 2006) time scales.

Harada *et al.* (2011) write "in temperate areas, insects are adapted physiologically or behaviourally to either [1] tolerate seasonally fluctuating changes in temperature through diapause or to [2] avoid adverse conditions through migration," with the most predictable time cue for seasonal adaptation by insects being photoperiod (Tauber *et al.*, 1986). Thus, "it is assumed that the critical photoperiod of insects is becoming gradually shortened as a result of global warming," and if populations are adapting to the consequent longer growing seasons and later onsets of winter, it would be expected that the number of yearly broods produced "should increase, that photoperiodic responses of diapause induction and wing-form determination will continue to diminish ... and that overwintering adults will cease to migrate between water courses and overwintering land sites far from water, and will begin overwintering nearer summer habitats."

In an effort to determine whether such adjustments have been occurring in the life cycle of nymphs of the water strider *Aquarius paludum* in the Kochi prefecture of Japan over the past two decades, Harada *et al.* measured a number of pertinent parameters that had been assessed by Harada and Numata (1993) two decades earlier, over the period 1989–1991. They found *A. paludum* nymphs were trivoltine (i.e., produced three broods yearly) in 1991, but more recently the generation number appears to have increased to four or more. They also found overwintering adults of both sexes had no mature flight muscles in October and November 2008, which "contrasts with previous observations," and "the 2008 population also shows a low flight propensity in response to shorter day lengths."

The Japanese scientists from Kochi University thus opine, "the absence of mature flight muscles in the autumn, and the lower flight propensity under shorter days, may comprise evidence of a cessation of dispersal between the freshwater summer habitats and overwintering sites on land far from the bodies of water." And they observe, "the increase in daily-minimum temperature during the winter in the Kochi-Nankoku area over the last 15 years may allow adults of *A. paludum* to overwinter without dispersal nearer to their summer habitat," which could lead to the proportion of adults overwintering close to the water bodies increasing from the current estimate of 60 to 70% to between 90 and 100% within ten years. Thus, they conclude, *A. paludum* populations in the Kochi-Nankoku region "are continuing to show adaptive change, apparently in relation to global warming."

Brakefield and de Jong (2011) note "a variety of processes can enable organisms, including insects, to respond successfully to climate change (Stenseth *et al.*, 2002; Bradshaw and Holzapfel, 2006; Parmesan, 2006)," including "habitat tracking, phenotypic plasticity and genetic adaptation." Evidence for the first of these mechanisms, in their words, "is becoming commonplace," as is the case with many species of butterflies that are "clearly responding with northern extensions in their range limits (Parmesan and Yohe, 2003; Hickling *et al.*, 2006)," as well as with moths and other insects that "are moving up altitudinal gradients (Chen *et al.*, 2009)." On the other hand, they write, "the extent to which changes in phenotypic plasticity are (or will be) involved in the numerous reports of changes in phenology (Brakefield, 1987; Roy and Sparks, 2000; Amano *et al.*, 2010) is not clear." And they remark, "there are as yet few reports of genetic changes within populations linked to climate change," although "the pitcher plant mosquito, *Wyeomyia smithii*, showed a genetic response to climate change, which involved changes in sensitivity to photoperiod (Bradshaw *et al.*, 2006)," which "could be detected over a period as short as five years."

Hoping to contribute to the search for genetic responses to climate change, Brakefield and de Jong report on the most recent data describing changes in a cline in the frequency of melanism morphs of the two-spot ladybird beetle, *Adalia bipunctata* L., along a transect that extends inland from the seacoast in the Netherlands.

At the time of the beetle's first survey in 1980, the two researchers report, "the frequency of melanics increased over some 40 km from 10% near the coast to nearly 60% inland." Additional surveys in 1991 and 1995 "demonstrated some progressive change in cline shape," and new samples from 1998 and 2004 confirmed these dynamics, so "over a period of about fifty generations of the beetle, the cline had decayed rapidly to yield rather uniform frequencies of melanic morphs at around 20% along the whole transect by 2004." They remark, "climate data and evidence for thermal melanism in this species support our contention that these dynamics reflect a dramatic example of a rapid genetic response within populations to climate change and local selection." Brakefield and de Jong conclude by stating their study "adds to potential examples of how some organisms are likely to be responding to climate change through direct genetic responses within populations."

It appears rising temperatures will be beneficial for some insect species, but perhaps not for others. Nevertheless, it does not appear there will be a widespread extinction of insect species, as most will adapt as they likely have done as temperatures have waxed and waned in the past.

References

Abu-Asab, M.S., Peterson, P.M., Shetler, S.G., and Orli, S.S. 2001. Earlier plant flowering in spring as a response to global warming in the Washington, DC, area. *Biodiversity and Conservation* **10**: 597–612.

Amano, T., Smithers, R.J., Sparks, T.H., and Sutherland, W.J. 2010. A 250-year index of first flowering dates and its response to temperature changes. *Proceedings of the Royal Society of London B* **277**: 2451–2457.

Anderson, A.R., Hoffmann, A.A., McKechnie, S.W., Umina, P.A., and Weeks, A.R. 2005. The latitudinal cline in the *In(3R) Payne* inversion polymorphism has shifted in the last 20 years in Australian *Drosophila melanogaster* populations. *Molecular Ecology* **14**: 851–858.

Ando, Y. and Hartley, J.C. 1982. Occurrence and biology of a long-winged form of conocephalus discolor. *Entomologia Experimentalis Applicata* **32**: 238–241.

Balanya, J., Huey, R.B., Gilchrist, G.W., and Serra, L. 2009. The chromosomal polymorphism of *Drosophila subobscura*: A micro evolutionary weapon to monitor global change. *Heredity* **103**: 364–367.

Balanya, J., Oller, J.M., Huey, R.B., Gilchrist, G.W., and Serra, L. 2006. Global genetic change tracks global climate warming in *Drosophila subobscura*. *Science* **313**: 1773–1775.

Balanya, J., Sole, E., Oller, J.M., Sperlich, D., and Serra, L. 2004. Long-term changes in the chromosomal inversion polymorphism of *Drosophila subobscura*. II. European populations. *Journal of Zoological Systematics and Evolutionary Research* **42**: 191–201.

Bale, J.S., Masters, G.J., Hodkinson, I.D., Awmack, C., Bezemer, T.M., Brown, V.K., Butterfield, J., Buse, A., Coulson, J.C., Farrar, J., Good, J.E.G., Harrington, R., Hartleuy, S., Jones, T.H., Lindroth, R.L., Press, M.C., Symrnioudis, I., Watt, A.D., and Whittaker, J.B. 2002. Herbivory in global climate change research: direct effects of rising temperature on insect herbivores. *Global Change Biology* **8**: 1–16.

Bartomeus, I., Ascher, J.S., Wagner, D, Danforth, B.N., Colla, S., Kornbluth, S., and Winfree, R. 2011. Climate-associated phenological advances in bee pollinators and bee-pollinated plants. *Proceedings of the National Academy of Sciences, USA* **108**: 20,645–20,649.

Bertelsmeier, C., Luque, G.M., and Courchamp, F. 2013. Global warming may freeze the invasion of big-headed ants. *Biological Invasions* **15**: 1561–1572.

Bradley, N.L., Leopold, A.C., Ross, J., and Huffaker, W. 1999. Phenological changes reflect climate change in Wisconsin. *Proceedings of the National Academy of Sciences, USA* **96**: 9701–9704.

Bradshaw, W.E. and Holzapfel, C.M. 2001. From the Cover: Genetic shift in photoperiodic response correlated with global warming. *Proceedings of the National Academy of Sciences USA* **98**: 14,509–14,511.

Bradshaw, W.E. and Holzapfel, C.M. 2006. Evolutionary response to rapid climate change. *Science* **312**: 1477–1478.

Bradshaw, W.E., Holzapfel, C.M., and Mathias, D. 2006. Circadian rhythmicity and photoperiodism in the pitcher-plant mosquito: Can the seasonal timer evolve independently of the circadian clock? *American Naturalist* **167**: 601–605.

Brakefield, P.M. 1987. Geographical variability in, and temperature effects on, the phenology of *Maniola jurtina* and *Pyronia tithonus* in England and Wales. *Ecological Entomology* **12**: 139–148.

Brakefield, P.M. and de Jong, P.W. 2011. A steep cline in ladybird melanism has decayed over 25 years: a genetic response to climate change? *Heredity* **107**: 574–578.

Chen, I.-C., Shiu, H.-J., Benedick, S., Holloway, J.D., Chey, V.K., Barlow, H.S., Hill, J.K., and Thomas, C.D. 2009. Elevation increases in moth assemblages over 42 years on a tropical mountain. *Proceedings of the National Academy of Sciences USA* **106**: 1479–1483.

Chown, S.L. and Nicolson, S.W. 2004. *Insect Physiological Ecology: Mechanisms and Patterns*. Oxford, UK: Oxford University Press.

Cook, B.I., Cook, E.R., Huth, P.C., Thompson, J.E., and Smiley, D. 2008. A cross-taxa phenological dataset from Mohonk Lake, NY and its relationship to climate. *International Journal of Climatology* **28**: 1369–1383.

Gardiner, T. 2009. Macropterism of Roesel's bushcricket *Metrioptera roeselii* in relation to climate change and landscape structure in Eastern England. *Journal of Orthoptera Research* **12**: 95–102.

Harada, T. and Numata, H. 1993. Two critical daylengths for the determination of wing forms and the induction of adult diapause in the water strider, *Aquarius paludum*. *Die Naturwissenschaften* **80**: 430–432.

Harada, T., Takenaka, S., Maihara, S., Ito, K., and Tamura, T. 2011. Changes in life-history traits of the water strider *Aquarious paludum* in accordance with global warming. *Physiological Entomology* **36**: 309–316.

Harrington, R., Clark, S.J., Welham, S.J., Verrier, P.J., Denholm, C.H., Hulle, M., Maurice, D., Rounsevell, M.D., and Cocu, N. 2007. Environmental change and the phenology of European aphids. *Global Change Biology* **13**: 1550–1564.

Hickling, R., Roy, D.B., Hill, J.K., Fox, R., and Thomas, C.D. 2006. The distributions of a wide range of taxonomic groups are expanding polewards. *Global Change Biology* **12**: 1–6.

Hickling, R., Roy, D.B., Hill, J.K., and Thomas, C.D. 2005. A northward shift of range margins in British Odonata. *Global Change Biology* **11**: 502–506.

Higaki, M. and Ando, Y. 2003. Effects of crowding and photoperiod on wing morph and egg production in *Eobiana engelhardti subtropica* (Orthoptera: Tettigoniiade). *Applied Entomology and Zoology* **38**: 321–325.

Hochkirch, A. and Damerau, M. 2009. Rapid range expansion of a wing-dimorphic bush-cricket after the 2003 climatic anomaly. *Biological Journal of the Linnean Society* **97**: 118–127.

Hoffmann, A.A. and Rieseberg, L.H. 2008. Revisiting the impact of inversions in evolution: From population genetic markers to drivers of adaptive shifts and speciation? *Annual Review of Ecology, Evolution, and Systematics* **39**: 21–42.

Hoffmann, A.A., Shirriffs, J., and Scott, M. 2005. Relative importance of plastic versus genetic factors in adaptive differentiation: geographic variation for stress resistance in *Drosophila melanogaster* from eastern Australia. *Functional Ecology* **19**: 222–227.

Holway, D., Lach, L., Suarez, A.V., Tsutsui, N.D., and Case, T.J. 2002. The causes and consequences of ant invasions. *Annual Review of Ecology and Systematics* **33**: 181–233.

Huang, L.H., Chen, B., and Kang, L. 2007. Impacts of mild temperature hardening on thermo tolerance, fecundity and Hsp gene expression in *Liriomyza huidobrensis*. *Journal of Insect Physiology* **53**: 1199–1205.

Jiang, T., Zhang, Q., Blender, R., and Fraedrich, K. 2005. Yangtze delta floods and droughts of the last millennium: abrupt changes and long-term memory. *Theoretical and Applied Climatology* **82**: 131–141.

Johnson, T.K., Cockerell, F.E., Carrington, L.B., Rako, L., Hoffmann, A.A., and McKechnie, S.W. 2009. The capacity of *Drosophila* to heat harden associates with low rates of heat-shocked protein synthesis. *Journal of Thermal Biology* **34**: 327–331.

Kelty, J.D. 2007. Rapid cold-hardening of *Drosophila melanogaster* in a field setting. *Physiological Entomology* **32**: 343–350.

Kelty, J.D. and Lee Jr., R.E. 2001. Rapid cold-hardening of *Drosophila melanogaster* (Diptera: Drosophilidae) during ecologically based thermoperiodic cycles. *Journal of Experimental Biology* **204**: 1659–1666.

Kinnison, M.T. and Hendry, A.P. 2001. The pace of

modern life II: from rates of contemporary microevolution to pattern and process. *Genetica* **112–113**: 145–164.

Kleukers, R.M.J.C., van Nieukerken, E.J., Ode, B., Willemse, L.P.M., and van Wingerden, W.K.R.E. 2004. De sprinkhanen en krekels van Nederland (Orthoptera). In: *Nederlandse Fauna 1, 2nd Edition,* National Natuurhistorisch Museum, KNNV Uitgeverij & EIS-Nederland, Leiden, The Netherlands.

Kronenberg, F. and Heller, C. 1982. Colonial thermoregulation in honey bees (*Apis mellifera*). *Journal of Comparative Physiology* **148**: 65–76.

Lach, L. and Hooper-Bui, L.M. 2010. Consequences of ant invasions. In: Lach, L., Parr, C.L., and Abbott, K.L. (Eds.) *Ant Ecology.* Oxford University Press, New York, New York, USA, pp. 261–286.

Lee, R.E., Chen, C.P., and Denlinger, D.L. 1987. A rapid cold-hardening process in insects. *Science* **238**: 1415–1417.

Levitan, M. and Etges, W.J. 2005. Climate change and recent genetic flux in populations of *Drosophila robusta*. *BMC Evolutionary Biology* **5**: 10.1186/1471-2148-5-4.

Loeschcke, V. and Hoffmann, A.A. 2006. Consequences of heat hardening on a field fitness component in *Drosophila* depend on environmental temperature. *American Naturalist* **169**: 175–183.

Ma, S. 1958. The population dynamics of the oriental migratory locust (*Locusta migratoria manilensis* Meyen) in China. *Acta Entomologica Sinica* **8**: 1–40.

Miller-Rushing, A.J., Primack, R.B., Primack, D., and Mukunda, S. 2006. Photographs and herbarium specimens as tools to document phenological changes in response to global warming. *American Journal of Botany* **93**: 1667–1674.

Nyamukondiwa, C. and Terblanche, J.S. 2010. Within-generation variation of critical thermal limits in adult Mediterranean and Natal fruit flies *Ceratitis capitata* and *Ceratitis rosa*: thermal history affects short-term responses to temperature. *Physiological Entomology* **35**: 255–264.

Orengo, D.J. and Prevosti, A. 1996. Evolution. *International Journal of Organic Evolution* **50**: 1346.

Overgaard, J. and Sorensen, J.G. 2008. Rapid thermal adaptation during field temperature variations in *Drosophila melanogaster*. *Cryobiology* **56**: 159–162.

Parmesan, C. 2006. Ecological and evolutionary responses to recent climate change. *Annual Review of Ecology, Evolution and Systematics* **37**: 637–669.

Parmesan, C., Ryrholm, N., Stefanescu, C., Hill, J.K., Thomas, C.D., Descimon, H., Huntley, B., Kaila, L., Kullberg, J., Tammaru, T., Tennent, W.J., Thomas, J.A., and Warren, M. 1999. Poleward shifts in geographical ranges of butterfly species associated with regional warming. *Nature* **399**: 579–583.

Parmesan, C. and Yohe, G. 2003. A globally coherent fingerprint of climate change impacts across natural systems. *Nature* **421**: 37–42.

Poniatowski, D. and Fartmann, T. 2011. Weather-driven changes in population density determine wing dimorphism in a bush-cricket species. *Agriculture, Ecosystems and Environment* **145**: 5–9.

Powell, S.J. and Bale, J.S. 2006. Effect of long-term and rapid cold hardening on the cold torpor temperature of an aphid. *Physiological Entomology* **31**: 348–352.

Primack, D., Imbres, C., Primack, R.B., Miller-Rushing, A.J., and Del Tredici, P. 2004. Herbarium specimens demonstrate earlier flowering times in response to warming in Boston. *American Journal of Botany* **91**: 1260–1264.

Rabitsch, W. 2011. The hitchhiker's guide to alien ant invasions. *BioControl* **56**: 551–572.

Reineke, A. and Hauck, M. 2012. Larval development of *Empoasca vitis* and *Edwardsiana rosae* (Homoptera: Cicadellidae) at different temperatures on grapevine leaves. *Journal of Applied Entomology* **136**: 656–664.

Reinhardt, K., Kohler, G., Maas, S., and Detzel, P. 2005. Low dispersal ability and habitat specificity promote extinctions in rare but not in widespread species: the Orthoptera of Germany. *Ecography* **28**: 593–602.

Rodriguez-Trelles, F. and Rodriguez, M.A. 1998. Rapid microevolution and loss of chromosomal diversity in *Drosophila* in response to climate warming. *Evolutionary Ecology* **12**: 829–838.

Rodriguez-Trelles, F., Rodriguez, M.A., and Scheiner, S.M. 1998. Tracking the genetic effects of global warming: *Drosophila* and other model systems. *Conservation Ecology* **2**: 2.

Roy, D.B. and Sparks, T.H. 2000. Phenology of British butterflies and climate change. *Global Change Biology* **6**: 407–416.

Sanger, K. 1984. Die Populationsdichte als Ursache makropterer Okomorphosen von Tessellana vittata (Charp.) (Orthoptera, Tettigoniidae). *Zoologischer Anzeiger* **213**: 68–76.

Seeley, T.D. 1985. *Honeybee Ecology.* Princeton University Press, Princeton, New Jersey, USA.

Shreve, S.M., Kelty, J.D., and Lee, R.E. 2004. Preservation of reproductive behaviors during modest cooling: rapid cold-hardening fine-tunes organismal response. *Journal of Experimental Biology* **207**: 1797–1802.

Simmons, A.D. and Thomas, C.D. 2004. Changes in dispersal during species' range expansions. *American Naturalist* **164**: 378–395.

Sole, E., Balanya, J., Sperlich, D., and Serra, L. 2002. Long-term changes in the chromosomal inversion polymorphism of *Drosophila subobscura*. I. Mediterranean populations from southwestern Europe. *Evolution: International Journal of Organic Evolution* **56**: 830–835.

Sparks, T.H., Croxton, P.J., Collinson, N., and Taylor, P.W. 2005. Examples of phenological change, past and present, in UK farming. *Annals of Applied Biology* **146**: 531–537.

Sparks, T.H., Langowska, A., Glazaczow, A., Wilkaniec, Z., Bienkowska, M., and Tryjanowski, P. 2010. Advances in the timing of spring cleaning by the honeybee *Apis mellifera* in Poland. *Ecological Entomology* **35**: 788–791.

Stenseth, N.C., Mysterud, A., Ottersen, G., Hurrell, J.W., Chan, K.S., and Lima, M. 2002. Ecological effects of climate fluctuations. *Science* **297**: 1292–1296.

Tauber, M.J., Tauber, C.A., and Masaki, S. 1986. *Seasonal Adaptations of Insects*. Oxford University Press, New York, New York, USA.

Terblanche, J.S., Klok, C.J., Krafsur, E.S., and Chown, S.L. 2006. Phenotypic plasticity and geographic variations in thermal tolerance and water loss of tsetse *Glossina pallidipes* (Diptera: Glossinidae): implications for distribution modeling. *American Journal of Tropical Medicine and Hygiene* **74**: 786–794.

Thomas, C.D., Bodsworth, E.J., Wilson, R.J., Simmons, A.D., Davies, Z.G. Musche, M., and Conradt, L. 2001. Ecological and evolutionary processes at expanding range margins. *Nature* **411**: 577–581.

Tryjanowski, P., Pawlikowski, T., Pawlikowski, K., Banaszak-Cibicka, W., and Sparts, T.H. 2010. Does climate influence phenological trends in social wasps (Hymenoptera: Vespinae) in Poland? *European Journal of Entomology* **107**: 203–208.

Umina, P.A., Weeks, A.R., Kearney, M.R., McKechnie, S.W., and Hoffmann, A.A. 2005. A rapid shift in a classic clinical pattern in *Drosophila* reflecting climate change. *Science* **308**: 691–693

Uvarov, B.P. 1966. *Grasshoppers and Locusts: A Handbook of General Acridology, Volume 1*. Cambridge University Press, Cambridge, United Kingdom.

West-Eberhard, M.J. 2003. *Developmental Plasticity and Evolution*. New York, NY: Oxford University Press.

Whitman, D.W. 2009. Acclimation. In Whitman, D.W. and Ananthakrishnan, T.N. (Eds.) *Phenotypic Plasticity of Insects. Mechanisms and Consequences*. Enfield, NH: Science Publishers, pp. 675–739.

Wissmann, J., Schielzeth, H., and Fartmann, T. 2009. Landscape-scale expansion of Roesel's bush-cricket *Metrioptera roeselii* (Orthoptera: Tettigoniidae) at the north-western range limit in Central Europe. *Entomologia Generalis*. **31**: 317–326.

Yang, B., Brauning, A., Johnson, K.R., and Yafeng, S. 2002. Temperature variation in China during the last two millennia. *Geophysical Research Letters* **29**: 10.1029/2001GL014485.

Zhang, Z., Cazelles, B., Tian, H., Stige, L.C., Brauning, A., and Stenseth, N.C. 2009. Periodic temperature-associated drought/flood drives locust plagues in China. *Proceedings of the Royal Society B* **276**: 823–831.

Zivanovic, G. and Mestres, F. 2011. Changes in chromosomal polymorphism and global warming: The case of *Drosophila subobscura* from Apatin (Serbia). *Genetics and Molecular Biology* **34**: 489–495.

5.5.5.2 Response to Elevated CO_2

As the air's CO_2 content continues to rise, it is important to determine what effect this might have on the delicate balance between various plants and the insects that feed on them. This section reviews the results of studies that have reported on insects not previously discussed at any length, where it is seen the ongoing rise in the air's CO_2 content likely plays an important role in negating the damage being done to Earth's vegetation by voracious insect pests.

Docherty *et al.* (1997), in addition to studying aphids, studied two sap-feeding leafhopper species that were allowed to feed on saplings of beech and sycamore grown in glasshouses maintained at atmospheric CO_2 concentrations of 350 and 600 ppm. As far as they could determine, there were no significant effects of the extra CO_2 on either the feeding or performance characteristics of either leafhopper species.

In a literature review of more than 30 studies published two years later, Whittaker (1999) found chewing insects (leaf chewers and leaf miners) showed either no change or reductions in abundance in response to atmospheric CO_2 enrichment. They note, however, population reductions in this feeding guild often were accompanied by increased herbivory in response to CO_2-induced reductions in leaf nitrogen content.

Contemporaneously, Brooks and Whittaker (1999) removed grassland monoliths from the Great Dun Fell of Cumbria, UK—which contained eggs of a destructive xylem-feeding spittlebug (*Neophilaenus lineatus*)—and grew them in glasshouses maintained for two years at atmospheric CO_2 concentrations of 350 and 600 ppm. During the course of their experiment, two generations of the xylem-feeding insect were produced; in each case, elevated CO_2 reduced the survival of nymphal stages by an average of 24%. Brooks and Whittaker suggest this reduction in survival rate may have been caused by CO_2-induced reductions in stomatal conductance and transpirational water loss, which may have reduced xylem nutrient-water availability.

Stiling *et al.* (1999) report the results of what may have been the first attempt to study the effects of elevated CO_2 on trophic webs in a natural ecosystem; specifically, a nutrient-poor scrub-oak community in Florida (USA), where 16 open-top chambers of 3.6-m diameter were fumigated with air of either 350 or 700 ppm CO_2 for approximately one year. At the end of this period, total leaf miner densities were 38% less on the CO_2-enriched foliage than on the foliage of the ambiently grown plants. Moreover, atmospheric CO_2 enrichment consistently reduced the numbers of all six species of leaf miners studied. In a compensatory development, exposure to elevated CO_2 increased the amount of leaf area consumed by the less-abundant leaf miners by approximately 40%. Nevertheless, leaf miners in the CO_2-enriched chambers experienced significantly greater mortality than those in the control chambers. Although CO_2-induced reductions in leaf nitrogen content were determined to have played a minor role in the mortality increase, the greatest factor contributing to this phenomenon was a fourfold increase in parasitization by various wasps that could more readily detect the more-exposed leaf miners on the CO_2-enriched foliage.

Three years later, Stiling *et al.* (2002) reported even more dramatic effects of elevated CO_2 on leaf chewers. The relative levels of damage by these insects (primarily larval lepidopterans and grasshoppers) were significantly lower in the elevated CO_2 chambers than in the ambient CO_2 chambers for all five of the plant species that accounted for more than 98% of the total plant biomass of the ecosystem. In addition, the response to elevated CO_2 was the same across all plant species. Also, they report more host-plant-induced mortality was found for all miners on all plants in elevated CO_2 than in ambient CO_2. These effects were so powerful that in addition to the relative densities of insect herbivores being reduced in the CO_2-enriched chambers, and even though there were more leaves on most plant species in the elevated CO_2 chambers, the total densities of leaf miners in the high-CO_2 chambers were also lower for all plant species. Stiling *et al.* note, "reductions in herbivore loads in elevated CO_2 could boost plant growth beyond what might be expected based on pure plant responses to elevated CO_2," a beneficial effect.

In a natural ecosystem in Wisconsin (USA) comprised predominantly of trembling aspen (*Populus tremuloides* Michx.), Percy *et al.* (2002) studied the effects of increases in CO_2 alone (to 560 ppm during daylight hours), O_3 alone (to 46.4–55.5 ppb during daylight hours), and CO_2 and O_3 together on the forest tent caterpillar (*Malacosoma disstria*), a common leaf-chewing lepidopteran found in North American hardwood forests. By itself, elevated CO_2 reduced caterpillar performance by reducing female pupal mass, and elevated O_3 alone improved caterpillar performance by increasing female pupal mass. When both gases were applied together, the elevated CO_2 completely counteracted the enhancement of female pupal mass caused by elevated O_3. Hence, either alone or in combination with undesirable increases in the air's O_3 concentration, elevated CO_2 tended to reduce the performance of the forest tent caterpillar. This finding is particularly satisfying because, in the words of Percy *et al.*, "historically, the forest tent caterpillar has defoliated more deciduous forest than any other insect in North America" and because "outbreaks can reduce timber yield up to 90% in one year, and increase tree vulnerability to disease and environmental stress."

Also working at the Aspen FACE site in northern Wisconsin, USA, Kopper and Lindroth (2003) studied the effects of elevated CO_2 (560 ppm) and elevated O_3 (1.5 x ambient) on trembling aspen (*Populus tremuloides* Michaux) trees, while the aspen blotch leafminer (*Phyllonorycter tremuloidiella* Braun) was allowed to naturally colonize the trees. Although there were some minor alterations in foliar chemistry in the CO_2- and O_3-enriched treatments, they produced "little to no change in larval performance," although both elevated CO_2 and O_3 "reduced colonization rates by nearly half."

Holton *et al.* (2003) reared both parasitized and non-parasitized forest tent caterpillars (*Malacosoma disstria*) on two quaking aspen (*Populus tremuloides*) genotypes (216, which is O_3-tolerant, and 259, which is O_3-sensitive) alone and in combination, also at the Aspen FACE site in northern Wisconsin, where trees were exposed to ambient air, ambient air + 200 ppm extra CO_2, ambient air + 50% extra ozone, and ambient air + 200 ppm extra CO_2 and 50% extra O_3 during the daylight hours of one full growing season. They found "elevated CO_2 had little effect on both primary and secondary metabolites of aspen." Thus, "elevated CO_2 had few biologically significant effects on forest tent caterpillar performance." Elevated O_3, on the other hand, altered foliar composition much more than did elevated CO_2; and, as they discovered, it improved tent caterpillar performance under ambient CO_2 conditions, but not in CO_2-enriched air. In addition, elevated O_3 decreased the larval survivorship of the parasite of the caterpillar.

These findings suggest the ongoing rise in the air's CO_2 content likely will be very important to the future well-being of quaking aspen trees, especially when atmospheric O_3 concentrations are increasing concurrently. Elevated levels of atmospheric CO_2 are known to significantly increase the productivity of aspen trees, making them more robust (Percy *et al.* (2002). Moreover, the extra CO_2 of this study totally thwarted the positive impact of the extra O_3 on caterpillar performance, thus eliminating a major negative consequence for the trees. As the authors note, "aspen growth is significantly increased under high CO_2, but decreased under high O_3," and "that difference is likely to be exacerbated by the impacts of CO_2 and O_3 on herbivorous insects and parasitoids as documented in this study." Without an increase in the air's CO_2 content commensurate with that projected for O_3 over the coming half-century, therefore, quaking aspen—the most widely distributed tree in North America—would suffer.

Johns *et al.* (2003) performed, in their words, "a factorial experiment to examine the effects of elevated CO_2 and increased temperature on both the leaf-chewing adults and leaf-mining larvae of two closely related beetle species, *Octotoma championi* Baly and *Octotoma scabripennis* Guerin-Meneville (Coleoptera: Chrysomelidae), feeding on the host plant *Lantana camara* L. (Verbenaceae)." The study was conducted in environment-controlled growth chambers maintained at atmospheric CO_2 concentrations of 360 or 700 ppm and at low (22°C/18°C) or high (25°C/21°C) day/night temperatures, where well-watered and fertilized plants were grown from cuttings for just over 13 months. Under the high temperature treatment, plants grown at ambient CO_2 suffered wilting and premature leaf loss, despite daily watering, but this effect was ameliorated at elevated CO_2. They also report "the wilting of plants in the ambient CO_2/high temperature treatment reduced the emergence success of the beetles," and "consumption rates of free-living beetles were not affected by either CO_2 or temperature," whereas "in short-term trials using excised foliage, beetles given no choice between ambient and elevated CO_2-grown foliage consumed more from ambient plants."

The authors state "this study indicates that under future conditions of higher temperatures, amelioration of water stress in host plants growing in elevated CO_2

may benefit some endophagous insects by reducing premature leaf loss," and they note "under some circumstances, this benefit may outweigh the deleterious effects of lower leaf nitrogen," which is typically described as posing a major problem for insects in a high-CO_2 world of the future. In addition, Johns *et al.* say their results indicate "foliage consumption under elevated CO_2 by mobile, adult insects on whole plants may not be significantly increased, as was previously indicated by short-term experiments using excised foliage."

According to Heagle (2003), the Western flower thrip (*Frankliniella occidentalis*) "is one of the most important and difficult to control plant pests," as "it feeds on numerous plant species and spreads the tomato spotted wilt virus, which also affects numerous plant species." In an effort to learn how this pest might respond to increasing concentrations of atmospheric CO_2, Heagle grew well-watered and fertilized white clover (*Trifolium repens*) plants from virus-free stolons in 1-liter pots filled with Metro Mix 220 and placed between two rows of thrip-invested plants growing in 15-liter pots, after which they were grown for either 27 or 35 additional days in continuous-stirred tank reactor chambers (CSTRs) maintained at either ambient or elevated atmospheric CO_2 concentrations (396 or 745 ppm) and located within a non-filtered-air greenhouse. The USDA researcher reports, "at elevated CO_2, clover shoot weight and laminae weight were ~50% greater, and laminar area was ~20% greater than at ambient CO_2." In addition, he notes the "thrips population size was not significantly affected by CO_2, but laminar area scarred by thrips feeding was ~90% greater at elevated than at ambient CO_2." Nevertheless, because of the CO_2-induced increase in clover growth, "undamaged leaf area was approximately 15% greater at elevated than at ambient CO_2."

Barbehenn *et al.* (2004a) note "it has been hypothesized that herbivores will disproportionately increase their feeding damage on C_3 plants to compensate for the larger changes in C_3 plants in elevated CO_2 (Lincoln *et al.*, 1984, 1986; Lambers, 1993)." This is assumed because increases in the air's CO_2 content typically lead to greater decreases in the concentrations of nitrogen and, therefore, protein in the foliage of C_3 as compared to C_4 grasses (Wand *et al.*, 1999). In a test of this hypothesis, Barbehenn *et al.* grew *Lolium multiflorum* Lam. (Italian ryegrass, a common C_3 pasture grass) and *Bouteloua curti-pendula* (Michx.) Torr. (sideoats gramma, a native C_4 rangeland grass) in chambers maintained at either the ambient atmospheric CO_2 concentration of 370 ppm or the doubled CO_2 concentration of 740 ppm for two months, after which grasshopper (*Melanoplus sanguinipes*) nymphs that had been reared to the fourth instar stage were allowed to feed on the grasses' foliage.

As expected, foliage protein concentration decreased much more in the C_3 grass than in the C_4 grass (22% vs. 7%) when the grasses were grown in CO_2-enriched air. However, and "contrary to the hypothesis that insect herbivores will increase their feeding rates disproportionately in C_3 plants under elevated atmospheric CO_2," Barbehenn *et al.* report "*M. sanguinipes* did not significantly increase its consumption rate when feeding on the C_3 grass grown under elevated CO_2," suggesting this observation implies "post-ingestive mechanisms enable these grasshoppers to compensate for variable nutritional quality in their host plants" and noting some of these post-ingestive responses may include "changes in gut size, food residence time, digestive enzyme levels, and nutrient metabolism (Simpson and Simpson, 1990; Bernays and Simpson, 1990; Hinks *et al.*, 1991; Zanotto *et al.*, 1993; Yang and Joern, 1994a,b)." Their data indicate, if anything, *M. sanguinipes* growth rates were increased, perhaps by as much as 12%, when they fed on the C_3 foliage that had been produced in the CO_2-enriched, as compared to the ambient-treatment, air.

As was also found by Barbehenn *et al.* (2004b), the CO_2-induced decrease in leaf protein concentration observed in this study did not induce an increase in foliage consumption in the C_3 plant studied, nor did it reduce the growth rate of the herbivore studied. The authors state "although compensatory feeding was commonly observed in early studies [of this subject], the absence of compensatory feeding on C_3 plants grown under elevated CO_2 has since been observed frequently among herbivorous insects (Bezemer and Jones, 1998)."

Noting the "detrimental effects of ozone on plants are well known," and "carbon dioxide [CO_2] generally affects trees in opposite ways to ozone [O_3]," Valkama *et al.* (2007) conducted a literature review they describe as "the first quantitative analysis of the interactive effects of elevated O_3 and elevated CO_2 on tree chemistry and herbivore performance," based on the results of "63 studies conducted on 22 tree species and 10 insect herbivore species and published between 1990 and 2005." With respect to ways by which elevated O_3 may benefit insect herbivores that tend to damage trees, Valkama *et al.* determined "elevated O_3 significantly shortened development time of insect herbivores [when they are exposed and vulnerable to attack by various enemies] and increased their pupal mass in the overall dataset." In addition, they found the "relative growth rate of chewers was significantly increased by 3.5% under elevated O_3." However, they discovered "these effects were counteracted by elevated CO_2," such that "elevated O_3 in combination with CO_2 had no effect on herbivore performance." When elevated CO_2 was added to the O_3-enriched air, it not only counteracted the O_3-induced increase in pupal biomass, but reduced it by 7% below what it was in ambient air.

Stiling and Cornelissen (2007) "report the results of the longest-known field study (9 years) to examine the effects of elevated carbon dioxide on leaf miner densities in a scrub-oak community at Kennedy Space Center, Florida [USA]." They then describe the results of various meta-analyses they employed to determine "the effects of elevated CO_2 on both plants (n = 59 studies) and herbivores (n = 75 studies)," where ambient CO_2 concentrations ranged between 350 and 420 ppm and elevated concentrations ranged between 550 and 1,000 ppm. With respect to the first subject of their review, Stiling and Cornelissen report "the densities of all leaf miner species (6) on all host species (3) were lower in every year in elevated CO_2 than they were in ambient CO_2." With respect to the second subject, they write, "elevated CO_2 significantly decreased herbivore abundance (-21.6%), increased relative consumption rates (+16.5%), development time (+3.87%) and total consumption (+9.2%), and significantly decreased relative growth rate (-8.3%), conversion efficiency (-19.9%) and pupal weight (-5.03%)." They also note "host plants growing under enriched CO_2 environments exhibited significantly larger biomass (+38.4%), increased C/N ratio (+26.57%), and decreased nitrogen concentration (-16.4%), as well as increased concentrations of tannins (+29.9%)." Thus with plant biomass increasing and herbivorous pest abundance decreasing (by +38.4% and -21.6%, respectively, in response to an approximate doubling of the atmosphere's CO_2 concentration), it appears plants will fare increasingly well as the air's CO_2 content continues to climb.

Kampichler *et al.* (2008) write, "since CO_2 enrichment alters the composition of live plant tissues, the ongoing global increase of atmospheric CO_2 concentration is expected to affect plant-animal interactions," but "systems studied so far have not included mature trees." They set out to determine "the abundance of dominant leaf-galls (spangle-galls induced by the cynipid wasps *Neuroterus quercusbaccarum* and *N. numismalis*) and leaf-mines (caused by the larvae of the moth *Tischeria ekebladella*) on freely colonized large oaks in a mixed forest in Switzerland, which received CO_2 enrichment [540 ppm vs. 375 ppm during daylight hours] from 2001 to 2004" by means of "the Swiss Canopy Crane (SCC) and a new CO_2 enrichment technique (web-FACE)" in a forest they describe as "80–120 years old with a canopy height of 32–38 m, consisting of seven deciduous and four coniferous species."

The German, Mexican and Swiss researchers report elevated CO_2 reduced various leaf parameters (water content, proteins, non-structural carbohydrates, tannins, etc.) at the SCC site, but "on the long term, their load with cynipid spangle-galls and leaf-mines of *T. ekebladella* was not distinguishable from that in oaks exposed to ambient CO_2 after 4 years of treatment." Kampichler *et al.* conclude, "CO_2 enrichment had no lasting effect in all three [animal] taxa, despite the substantial and consistent change in leaf chemistry of oak due to growth in elevated CO_2."

Rao *et al.* (2009) determined what foliage-mediated effects atmospheric CO_2 enrichment might have on another pernicious insect pest. They explain castor "is an important non-edible oilseed crop grown in many parts of the arid and semi-arid regions of India," and the castor semilooper (*Achaea janata*) and tobacco caterpillar (*Spodoptera litura*) "occur during early and late stages of growth of castor, respectively," when castor oil yields can be reduced "by 30–50% by the semilooper alone" and the tobacco caterpillar "can cause yield losses of 25–40%."

Rao *et al.* allowed larvae of both species to feed on castor foliage grown in present-day air (presumed to contain 350 ppm CO_2) and in air enriched with CO_2 to concentrations of 550 and 700 ppm. Their results indicate, "compared to the larvae fed on ambient CO_2 foliage, the larvae fed on 700 and 550 ppm CO_2 foliage exhibited greater consumption." However, the efficiency of conversion of both ingested and digested food into larval biomass "decreased in the case of larvae grown on 700 and 550 ppm CO_2 foliage," so they "grew slower and took longer time (two days more than ambient) to pupation," which would allow significantly more time (~13 percent) for them to be preyed upon by higher orders of creatures, many of which are considered to be much less of a threat to crop production than are insect larvae.

In the case of castor beans, then, it would appear in addition to the productivity enhancement likely to be provided by the stimulation of photosynthesis driven by atmospheric CO_2 enrichment—an approximate 34 percent increase in response to a 300 ppm increase in the air's CO_2 content (Grimmer and Komor, 1999; Grimmer *et al.*, 1999)—a substantial increase in atmospheric CO_2 likely also would curtail yield losses currently caused by the castor semilooper and tobacco caterpillar.

Hillstrom *et al.* (2010) write, "natural forest systems constitute a major portion of the world's land area, and are subject to the potentially negative effects of both global climate change and invasion by exotic insects." They report, "a suite of invasive weevils has become established in the northern hardwood forests of North America," noting it is "unknown" how these insects will respond to continued increases in the air's CO_2 content.

Hillstrom *et al.* collected 200 mating pairs of *Polydrusus sericeus* weevils—which they describe as "the second most abundant invasive weevil species in northern hardwood forests"—from birch trees growing on the perimeter of the Aspen Face facility in Oneida County, Wisconsin (USA). They fed them leaves taken from the birch, aspen, and maple trees growing within either the facility's ambient-air rings or its CO_2-enriched rings (maintained at a target concentration of 560 ppm) under controlled laboratory conditions throughout the summer of 2007, while closely monitoring parameters affecting weevil longevity and fecundity.

According to the five researchers, all from the University of Wisconsin's Department of Entomology, the results indicate feeding the weevils with foliage produced on trees in the CO_2-enriched plots had no effect on male longevity, but it reduced female longevity by 19 percent. They also note, "*Polydrusus sericeus* egg production rate declined by 23% and total egg production declined by 29% for females fed foliage produced under elevated CO_2 compared with ambient CO_2."

Hillstrom *et al.* conclude, "concentrations of elevated CO_2 above 500 ppm have the potential to decrease *P. sericeus* populations by reducing female longevity and fecundity," which should be particularly beneficial for the northern hardwood forests of North America that are currently growing under atmospheric CO_2 concentrations of 390 ppm and rising.

The vast majority of pertinent experimental data suggest in the neverending battle between insect herbivores and the plants on whose foliage they feast, the ongoing rise in the air's CO_2 content likely plays an extremely important role in negating, and in some cases even more than negating, the damage otherwise capable of being done to Earth's vegetation by voracious insect pests.

References

Barbehenn, R.V., Karowe, D.N., and Chen, Z. 2004a. Performance of a generalist grasshopper on a C_3 and a C_4 grass: compensation for the effects of elevated CO_2 on plant nutritional quality. *Oecologia* **140**: 96–103.

Barbehenn, R.V., Karowe, D.N., and Spickard, A. 2004b. Effects of elevated atmospheric CO_2 on the nutritional ecology of C_3 and C_4 grass-feeding caterpillars. *Oecologia* **140**: 86–95.

Bernays, E.A. and Simpson, S.J. 1990. Nutrition. In: Chapman, R.F. and Joern, A. (Eds.) *Biology of Grasshoppers*. Wiley, New York, NY, pp. 105–127.

Bezemer, T.M. and Jones, T.H. 1998. Plant-insect herbivore interactions in elevated atmospheric CO_2: quantitative analyses and guild effects. *Oikos* **82**: 212–222.

Brooks, G.L. and Whittaker, J.B. 1999. Responses of three generations of a xylem-feeding insect, *Neophilaenus lineatus* (Homoptera), to elevated CO_2. *Global Change Biology* **5**: 395–401.

Docherty, M., Wade, F.A., Hurst, D.K., Whittaker, J.B., and Lea, P.J. 1997. Responses of tree sap-feeding herbivores to elevated CO_2. *Global Change Biology* **3**: 51–59.

Grimmer, C. and Komor, E. 1999. Assimilate export by leaves of *Ricinus communis* L. growing under normal and elevated carbon dioxide concentrations: the same rate during the day, a different rate at night. *Planta* **209**: 275–281.

Grimmer, C., Bachfischer, T., and Komor, E. 1999. Carbohydrate partitioning into starch in leaves of *Ricinus communis* L. grown under elevated CO_2 is controlled by sucrose. *Plant, Cell and Environment* **22**: 1275–1280.

Heagle, A.S. 2003. Influence of elevated carbon dioxide on interactions between *Frankliniella occidentalis* and *Trifolium repens*. *Environmental Entomology* **32**: 421–424.

Hillstrom, M.L., Vigue, L.M., Coyle, D.R., Raffa, K.F., and Lindroth, R.L. 2010. Performance of the invasive weevil *Polydrusus sericeus* is influenced by atmospheric CO_2 and host species. *Agricultural and Forest Entomology* **12**: 285–292.

Hinks, C.R., Cheeseman, M.T., Erlandson, M.A., Olfert, O., and Westcott, N.D. 1991. The effects of kochia, wheat and oats on digestive proteinases and the protein economy of adult grasshoppers, *Malanoplus sanguinipes*. *Journal of Insect Physiology* **37**: 417–430.

Holton, M.K., Lindroth, R.L., and Nordheim, E.V. 2003. Foliar quality influences tree-herbivore-parasitoid interactions: effects of elevated CO_2, O_3, and plant genotype. *Oecologia* **137**: 233–244.

Johns, C.V., Beaumont, L.J., and Hughes, L. 2003. Effects of elevated CO_2 and temperature on development and consumption rates of *Octotoma championi* and *O. scabripennis* feeding on *Lantana camara*. *Entomologia Experimentalis et Applicata* **108**: 169–178.

Kampichler, C., Teschner, M., Klein, S., and Korner, C. 2008. Effects of 4 years of CO_2 enrichment on the abundance of leaf-galls and leaf-mines in mature oaks. *Acta Oecologica* **34**: 139–146.

Kopper, B.J. and Lindroth, R.L. 2003. Responses of trembling aspen (*Populus tremuloides*) phytochemistry and aspen blotch leafminer (*Phyllonorycter tremuloidiella*) performance to elevated levels of atmospheric CO_2 and O_3. *Agricultural and Forest Entomology* **5**: 17–26.

Lambers, H. 1993. Rising CO_2, secondary plant metabolism, plant-herbivore interactions and litter decomposition. Theoretical considerations. *Vegetatio* **104/105**: 263–271.

Lincoln, D.E., Sionit, N., and Strain, B.R. 1984. Growth and feeding response of *Pseudoplusia includens* (Lepidoptera: Noctuidae) to host plants grown in controlled carbon dioxide atmospheres. *Environmental Entomology* **13**: 1527–1530.

Lincoln, D.E., Couvet, D., and Sionit, N. 1986. Responses of an insect herbivore to host plants grown in carbon dioxide enriched atmospheres. *Oecologia* **69**: 556–560.

Percy, K.E., Awmack, C.S., Lindroth, R.L., Kubiske, M.E., Kopper, B.J., Isebrands, J.G., Pregitzer, K.S., Hendrey, G.R., Dickson, R.E., Zak, D.R., Oksanen, E., Sober, J., Harrington, R., and Karnosky, D.F. 2002. Altered performance of forest pests under atmospheres enriched by CO_2 and O_3. *Nature* **420**: 403–407.

Rao, M.S., Srinivas, K., Vanaja, M., Rao, G.G.S.N., Venkateswarlu, B., and Ramakrishna, Y.S. 2009. Host plant (*Ricinus communis* Linn.) mediated effects of elevated CO_2 on growth performance of two insect folivores. *Current Science* **97**: 1047–1054.

Simpson, S.J. and Simpson, C.L. 1990. The mechanisms of nutritional compensation by phytophagous insects. In: Bernays, E.A. (Ed.) *Insect-Plant Interactions*, Vol. 2. CRC Press, Boca Raton, FL, pp. 111–160.

Stiling, P. and Cornelissen, T. 2007. How does elevated carbon dioxide (CO_2) affect plant-herbivore interactions? A field experiment and meta-analysis of CO_2-mediated changes on plant chemistry and herbivore performance. *Global Change Biology* **13**: 1–20.

Stiling, P., Moon, D.C., Hunter, M.D., Colson, J., Rossi, A.M., Hymus, G.J., and Drake, B.G. 2002. Elevated CO_2 lowers relative and absolute herbivore density across all species of a scrub-oak forest. *Oecologia* DOI 10.1007/s00442-002-1075-5.

Stiling, P., Rossi, A.M., Hungate, B., Dijkstra, P., Hinkle, C.R., Knot III, W.M., and Drake, B. 1999. Decreased leaf-miner abundance in elevated CO_2: Reduced leaf quality and increased parasitoid attack. *Ecological Applications* **9**: 240–244.

Valkama, E., Koricheva, J., and Oksanen, E. 2007. Effects of elevated O_3, alone and in combination with elevated CO_2, on tree leaf chemistry and insect herbivore performance: a meta-analysis. *Global Change Biology* **13**: 184–201.

Wand, S.J.E., Midgley, G.F., Jones, M.H., and Curtis, P.S. 1999. Responses of wild C_4 and C_3 grass (Poaceae) species to elevated atmospheric CO_2 concentration: a meta-analytic test of current theories and perceptions. *Global Change Biology* **5**: 723–741.

Whittaker, J.B. 1999. Impacts and responses at population level of herbivorous insects to elevated CO_2. *European Journal of Entomology* **96**: 149–156.

Yang, Y. and Joern, A. 1994a. Gut size changes in relation to variable food quality and body size in grasshoppers. *Functional Ecology* **8**: 36–45.

Yang, Y. and Joern, A. 1994b. Influence of diet quality, developmental stage, and temperature on food residence time in the grasshopper *Melanoplus differentialis*. *Physiological Zoology* **67**: 598–616.

Zanotto, F.P., Simpson, S.J., and Raubenheimer, D. 1993. The regulation of growth by locusts through post-ingestive compensation for variation in the levels of dietary protein and carbohydrate. *Physiological Entomology* **18**: 425–434.

5.6 Mammals

- The warming-induced extinctions of mammals that have been predicted to occur are highly unlikely to be realized in nature, and warming in fact opens new territories for mammal range expansions. In addition, rising atmospheric CO_2 concentrations may produce changes in the palatability of the trunk and branch tissues of certain trees that may protect them from being killed by hares and rabbits.

It has been projected global warming will lead to a mass demise, if not extinction, of species across Earth because they will not be able to migrate rapidly enough to keep up with the shifting climatic zones to which they are currently accustomed, or they will literally "run out of places to run," as in the case of mountain-top dwellers. As logical as that hypothesis might sound, more complex studies, such as the ones reviewed here, indicate it is wrong. Earth's plants and animals are not the simpletons the models often characterize them to be; they possess a wide array of strategies for coping with environmental change and re-colonizing former territories after having once been forced out of them.

Norment *et al.* (1999) summarized and compared the results of many surveys of mammal populations observed along the Thelon River and its tributaries in the Canadian Northwest Territories from the 1920s through much of the 1990s. Red squirrel, moose, porcupine, river otter, and beaver were found to have established themselves in the studied area in recent years, significantly increasing its biodiversity. Norment *et al.* suggest the primarily northward range expansions that produced these results may be explained by "a recent warming trend at the northern treeline during the 1970s and 1980s." Alternatively, they note the influx of new species also may be due to "increasing populations in more southerly areas." In either case, these several mammal species appear to be faring quite well, and perhaps thriving, in the face of increasing temperatures in this forest-tundra landscape.

Pockely (2001) report the results of a survey of the plants and animals on Australia's Heard Island, located some 4,000 kilometers southwest of Perth. Over the past 50 years this sub-Antarctic island has experienced a local warming of approximately 1°C that has resulted in a modest retreat of its glaciers; for the first time in a decade, scientists are documenting what this warming and melting has done to the ecology of the island. Pockley reports on the "rapid increases in flora and fauna" that have accompanied the warming, quoting Dana Bergstrom, an ecologist at the University of Queensland in Brisbane, as saying areas that previously were poorly vegetated are now "lush with large expanses of plants." He also notes populations of fur seals have expanded rapidly. He cites Eric Woehler of Australia's environment department as informing him fur seals have emerged from "near extinction" to a population of 28,000 adults and 1,000 pups.

Between these far-flung chilly regions (where warming would be expected to enhance the abilities of land mammals to survive and reproduce), Lawler (1998) examined biogeographic relationships of mammals typically found on mountaintops in the Great Basin of western North America, with the objective of determining their future well-being in the face of predicted climate-driven changes in their environment. Contrary to the conclusions of earlier, more simplistic studies that predicted dramatic global warming-induced reductions in the numbers of mammals in this region, Lawlor concludes "virtually no extinctions can be expected from a projected 3°C rise in temperature." The results of this study, as well as those of Grayson (2000) and Grayson and Madson (2000), stand in stark contrast to model-based extinction predictions.

Working with the entire population of about 325 red squirrels (*Tamiasciurus hudsonicus*) near Kluane Lake, Yukon (Canada), Reale *et al.* (2003) ear-tagged and monitored the reproductive activity of all females each year from 1989 to 2001, while identifying and similarly dealing with most of their young from birth to adulthood, and weather data were collected at a monitoring station located 50 km from their study site. In addition, noting "spruce cones stored in the autumn of a given year are an important source of food for reproductive females in the spring of the following year," they counted the number of cones on the top three meters of about 300 trees every August.

The four Canadian researchers report spring temperature rose by nearly 2°C over the course of their study, but there was "no particular trend for precipitation." They found the mean number of spruce cones available over a female's lifetime rose more than 35% over the 10 years of their observations, "a large increase in the abundance of food experienced by female squirrels." They also report the squirrels responded to these environmental changes by advancing breeding by 18 days over the 10-year study period, representing an advancement of six days per squirrel generation. Quoting Reale *et al.*, "this dramatic advancement in breeding comprised a plastic response to increased food abundance as well as a microevolutionary response to selection." Or as they write in the concluding sentence of their paper, "the combination of phenotypic changes within generations and microevolutionary changes among generations resulted in large phenotypic responses to rapid changes in environmental conditions experienced by this population of squirrels over the past ten years."

Mattson *et al.* (2004) grew one-year-old seedlings of silver birch trees in closed-top chambers for one summer and autumn in pots containing an unfertilized commercial peat maintained at three soil nitrogen levels and two temperature regimes in air of either 362 or 700 ppm CO_2. Feeding trials with caged Eurasian hares were carried out and a number of chemical analyses made of the tops of the seedlings and the basal parts of their stems. In a second experiment, they grew paper birch trees from seed for two 140-day growing seasons in well-watered and fertilized pots placed within FACE rings maintained at atmospheric CO_2 concentrations of either 362 or 562 ppm, after which (in an unplanned aspect of the study) North American eastern cottontail rabbits fed *ad libitum*, consuming bark tissue down to and scoring the wood, on the basal third of the seedlings, and these tissues were tested for the presence of various herbivore-deterring chemical constituents.

"As expected," the authors state, "elevated CO_2 substantially increased the above-ground woody biomass growth of both paper birch (63%) and silver birch (21%)." In addition, noting "numerous studies have shown that elevated atmospheric CO_2 often, but not always, elicits increases in carbon partitioning to carbon-based secondary plant compounds," which tend to act as deterrents to herbivory, they say their findings "confirm this general pattern in silver and paper birch." Finally, they report high CO_2 reduced hare feeding on silver birch shoots by as much as 48%, and it reduced rabbit feeding on paper birch stems by about 51%, while neither temperature nor severe early-season defoliation (another experimental treatment) affected tree resistance against these mammalian herbivores.

Calling the anti-herbivory effect of elevated CO_2 "remarkably strong," and noting rabbits "overwhelmingly preferred ambient CO_2 plants," Mattson *et al.* say their data "clearly suggest that the defensive biochemistry of paper birch twigs as well as the main stem were [positively] altered as the result of elevated CO_2."

Millar and Westfall (2010) studied American pikas, small generalist herbivores that are relatives of rabbits and hares, inhabit patchily distributed rocky slopes of western North American mountains, and are good at tolerating cold. Pikas are widely believed to have a physiological sensitivity to warming, which when "coupled with the geometry of decreasing area at increasing elevation on mountain peaks," in the words of the two scientists, "has raised concern for the future persistence of pikas in the face of climate change." They note the species "has been petitioned under California [USA] state and federal laws for endangered species listing."

In a study designed to investigate the validity of the basis for that classification, Millar and Westfall developed a rapid assessment method for determining pika occurrence and used it "to assess geomorphic affinities of pika habitat, analyze climatic relationships of sites, and evaluate refugium environments for pikas under warming climates." The researchers gathered data over two field seasons in the Sierra Nevada Mountains of California, the southwestern Great Basin of California and Nevada, and the central Great Basin of Nevada, as well as a small area in the central Oregon Cascades.

The two U.S. Forest Service researchers report, "whereas concern exists for diminishing range of pikas relative to early surveys, the distribution and extent in our study, pertinent to four subspecies and the Pacific southwest lineage of pikas, resemble the diversity range conditions described in early 20th-century pika records (e.g., Grinnell and Storer, 1924)." The lowest site at which they detected the current presence of pikas, at an elevation of 1,827 meters, "is below the historic lowest elevation of 2350 m recorded for the subspecies by Grinnell and Storer (1924) in Yosemite National Park; below the low elevation range limit for the White Mountains populations given by Howell (1924) at 2440 m; and below the lowest elevation described for the southern Sierra Nevada populations of 2134 m (Sumner and Dixon, 1953)." In addition, they write, "a similar situation occurred for another lagomorph of concern, pygmy rabbit (*Brachylagus idahoensis*), where a rapid assessment method revealed much wider distribution than had been implied from historic population databases or resurvey efforts (Himes and Drohan, 2007)."

Millar and Westfall thus conclude "pika populations in the Sierra Nevada and southwestern Great Basin are thriving, persist in a wide range of thermal environments, and show little evidence of extirpation or decline." Moreover, the documentation of a similar phenomenon operating among pygmy rabbits suggests still other animals also may be better able to cope with various aspects of climate change than we have been led to believe.

In a study of moose, Lowe *et al.* (2010) write, "intuitively, we would expect that a large northern ungulate with low tolerance for high temperatures would gradually be pushed out of the southern reaches of its range as the climate continues to warm and temperature conditions become increasingly unfavorable," because "persistent temperatures above the upper critical limit will suppress foraging time and consequently cause mass loss during the summer, and that this reduced condition could affect overwinter survival and productivity," citing Schwartz and Renecker (1998).

The authors "tested the hypothesis that climate limits the southern distribution of moose (*Alces alces*) by documenting space use and behavior of 36 females at the margin of the species' range in Ontario, Canada." They did this in 2006, 2007, and 2008 through the use of "global positioning system (GPS) telemetry to study their habitat use and movement," in an attempt "to document behavioral mechanisms indicative of adaptive responses to warm temperatures." This work was conducted during periods of the year when ambient temperatures frequently exceeded known critical thresholds (-5°C in winter and 14°C in summer) that had been demonstrated by Dussault *et al.* (2004) to induce heat stress in moose.

Lowe *et al.* "detected no differences in habitat use relative to thermoregulation thresholds," which they deemed to be particularly important during the summer, when they report the temperatures of all habitat classes greatly exceeded—by an average of 6°C, and by as much as 19°C in the first week of August 2006—the 14°C threshold for a large extent of the day and partially during the night. As a result, the three Canadian researchers conclude "moose in their southern range either ameliorate heat stress at a finer resolution than we measured or are more resilient to temperature than previously thought."

In a contemporaneous study, Garroway *et al.* (2010) write, "many species have responded to contemporary climate change through shifts in their geographic ranges," and "this could lead to increased sympatry [i.e., partially overlapping ranges] between recently diverged species, likely increasing the potential for hybridization." They further note this phenomenon "can be positive if it increases genetic variability and creates new gene combinations that increase the potential to adapt."

To test this hypothesis, between 2002 and 2004 Garroway *et al.* conducted more than 1,600 successful live-trappings of southern (*Glaucomys volans*) and northern (*Glaucomys sabrinus*) flying squirrels throughout portions of Ontario (Canada) and Pennsylvania (USA). From the hairs of these squirrels they extracted nuclear and mitochondrial DNA.

It already had been determined by Bowman *et al.* (2005) that *G. volans* had expanded its range from the south beginning in the mid–1990s in concert with a series of warm winters; the nine Canadian and U.S. researchers' new findings indicate "the expansion of *G. volans* north into the *G. sabrinus* range in Ontario has resulted in the formation of a new hybrid zone." In addition, their analyses suggest "the hybridization was recent, coinciding with the recent increase in sympatry." They state, to their knowledge "this is the first report of hybrid zone formation following a range expansion induced by contemporary climate change." These findings indicate yet another way in which living organisms can both physically (by shifting their ranges) and genetically (by hybridization) successfully confront the challenges global warming may present.

Coulson *et al.* (2011) write "environmental change has been observed to generate simultaneous responses in population dynamics, life history, gene frequencies, and morphology in a number of species." But they wonder, "how common are such eco-evolutionary responses to environmental change likely to be?" asking, "are they inevitable [and] do they require a specific type of change?"

The team of six researchers used theory and data obtained from a study of wolves in Yellowstone Park, which is located mostly in the U.S. state of Wyoming but also reaches into smaller parts of Montana and Idaho. They "used survival and reproductive success data, body weights, and genotype at the K locus (*CBD103*, a β-defensin gene that has two alleles and determines coat color), which were collected from 280 radio-collared wolves living in the park between 1998 and 2009." They note "body weight and genotype at the K locus vary across U.S. wolf populations" and both traits influence fitness, citing the studies of Schmitz and Kolenosky (1985), Anderson *et al.* (2009), and MacNulty *et al.* (2009).

The four researchers say their results "do reveal that, for Yellowstone wolves, (i) environmental change will inevitably generate eco-evolutionary responses; (ii) change in the mean environment will have more profound population consequences than changes in the environmental variance; and (iii) environmental change affecting different functions can generate contrasting eco-evolutionary dynamics," which suggests "accurate prediction of the consequences of environmental change will probably prove elusive."

The general principles Coulson *et al.* found to apply to Yellowstone wolves should clearly apply to all other animals as well, suggesting the "climate envelope" approach used to predict shifts in the ranges of Earth's many animal species—and sometimes their extinction—in response to IPCC-predicted global warming fails to accurately describe the way real animals respond to climate change in the real world.

Hof *et al.* (2012) note "it is supposed that the large expected climate change at high northern latitudes ... makes species in (sub)arctic regions particularly susceptible (Virkkala *et al.*, 2008; Sala *et al.*, 2000; Jetz *et al.*, 2007), especially the European part of the (sub)arctic, since this region is the most geographically complex with the most infrastructure and great cultural, social, and political heterogeneity (Nilsson *et al.*, 2010)." Hof *et al.* "assessed potential changes in the geographic distribution of all terrestrial mammal species currently present in (sub)arctic Europe," along with additional species that might possibly colonize the region from the south. They used "species distribution modeling, incorporating projections of future climate and vegetation, in order to provide a better insight into the magnitude of the risk mammal species are facing, and the potential community level changes they have to endure due to climate change."

"Contrary to expectation," the three Swedish researchers report their modeling of species distributions suggests "predicted climate change up to 2080 will favor most mammals presently inhabiting (sub)arctic Europe," and "no species is predicted to go extinct." Hof *et al.* conclude, "for most (sub)arctic mammals it is not climate change per se that will threaten them, but possible constraints on their dispersal ability and changes in community composition."

Canale *et al.* (2012) say, "understanding whether, and to what extent, females can flexibly adjust their energetic investment to reproduction according to unpredicted food shortages is essential to predict whether organisms could compensate climate changes by plastic phenotype adjustments," citing Bronson (2009), Moreno and Moller (2011), and Wingfield *et al.* (2011). The three researchers "experimentally tested the consequences of chronic-moderate and short-acute food shortages on the reproductive output of a small seasonally breeding primate, the grey mouse lemur (*Microcebus murinus*) under thermo-neutral conditions," where "two food treatments were respectively designed to simulate the energetic constraints imposed by a lean year (40% caloric restriction over eight months) or by a sudden, severe climatic event occurring shortly before reproduction (80% caloric restriction over a month)." During this time they "assessed the resilience of the early stages of reproduction (mating success, fertility, and gestation to these contrasted food treatments, and on the later stages (lactation and offspring growth) in response to the chronic food shortage only."

They found "food deprived mouse lemurs managed to maintain constant ... reproductive parameters, including oestrus timing, estrogenization level at oestrus, mating success, litter size, and litter mass as well as their overall number of surviving offspring at weaning," although "offspring growth was delayed in food restricted mothers." The three researchers say their results suggest "heterothermic, fattening-prone mammals display important reproductive resilience to energetic bottlenecks," and "more generally, species living in variable and unpredictable habitats may have evolved a flexible reproductive physiology that helps buffer environmental fluctuations."

Tveraa *et al.* (2013) write, "for caribou in Greenland earlier springs have been suggested to result in a lower reproductive success," based on the assumption "*Rangifer* (caribou/reindeer) might be unable to adjust their timing of reproduction to the earlier surge of high quality food," and this potential failure could "cause a mismatch between optimal forage conditions and the timing of reproduction." Therefore, they state, "concerns have been raised regarding the future viability of *Rangifer* in Arctic and sub-Arctic tundra ecosystems."

Tveraa *et al.* "analyzed a 10-year dataset of satellite derived measures of vegetation green-up, population densities, calf body masses and female reproductive success in 19 reindeer (*Rangifer tarandus*) populations in Northern Norway." The four Norwegian researchers report "an early onset of spring and high peak plant productivity had positive effects on calf autumn body masses and female reproductive success," and "the quantity of food available, as determined by the onset of vegetation green-up and plant productivity over the summer, were the main drivers of body mass growth and reproductive success." Hence, they found no evidence for a negative effect of the speed of spring green-up, nor did they detect "a negative mismatch between early springs and subsequent recruitment." Tveraa *et al.* conclude the "effects of global warming on plant productivity and onset of spring are likely to positively affect sub-Arctic reindeer."

The studies presented above show the warming-induced extinctions of mammals that have been predicted to occur are highly unlikely to be realized in nature, and warming in fact opens new territories for mammal range expansions. In addition, rising atmospheric CO_2 concentrations may produce changes in the palatability of the trunk and branch tissues of certain trees that may protect them from being killed by hares and rabbits.

References

Anderson, T.M., vonHoldt, B.M., Candille, S.I., Musiani, M., Greco, C., Stahler, D.R., Smith, D.W., Padhukasahasram, B., Randi, E., Leonard, J.A., Bustamante, C.D., Ostrander, E.A., Tang, H., Wayne, R.K, and Barsh, G.S. 2009. Molecular and evolutionary history of melanism in North American gray wolves. *Science* **323**: 1339–1343.

Bowman, J., Holloway, G.L., Malcolm, J.R., Middel, K.R.,

and Wilson, P.J. 2005. Northern range boundary dynamics of southern flying squirrels: evidence of an energetic bottleneck. *Canadian Journal of Zoology* **83**: 1486–1494.

Bronson, F.H. 2009. Climate change and seasonal reproduction in mammals. *Philosophical Transactions of the Royal Society B-Biological Sciences* **364**: 3331–3340.

Canale, C.I., Huchard, E., Perret, M., and Henry, P.-Y. 2012. Reproductive resilience to food shortage in a small heterothermic primate. *PLoS ONE* **7**: 10.1371/journal.pone.0041477.

Coulson T., MacNulty, D.R., Stahler, D.R., vonHoldt, B., Wayne, R.K., and Smith, D.W. 2011. Modeling effects of environmental change on wolf population dynamics, trait evolution, and life history. *Science* **334**: 1275–1278.

Dussault, C., Ouellet, J.-P., Courtois, R., Huot, J., Breton L., and Larochelle, J. 2004. Behavioural responses of moose to thermal conditions in the boreal forest. *Ecoscience* **11**: 321–328.

Garroway, C.J., Bowman, J., Cascaden, T.J., Holloway, G.L., Mahan, C.G., Malcolm, J.R., Steele, M.A., Turner, G., and Wilson, P.J. 2010. Climate change induced hybridization in flying squirrels. *Global Change Biology* **16**: 113–121.

Grayson, D.K. 2000. Mammalian responses to Middle Holocene climatic change in the Great Basin of the western United States. *Journal of Biogeography* **27**: 181–192.

Grayson, D.K. and Madson, D.B. 2000. Biogeographic implications of recent low-elevation recolonization by *Neotoma cinerea* in the Great Basin. *Journal of Mammalogy* **81**: 1100–1105.

Grinnell, J. and Storer, T.I. 1924. *Animal Life in the Yosemite*. Berkeley, CA: University of California Press.

Himes, J.G. and Drohan, P.J. 2007. Distribution and habitat selection of the pygmy rabbit, *Brachylagus idahoensis*, in Nevada (USA). *Journal of Arid Environments* **68**: 371–382.

Hof, A.R., Jansson, R., and Nilsson, C. 2012. Future climate change will favor non-specialist mammals in the (Sub)Arctics. *PLOS ONE*: 10.1371/journal.pone.0052574.

Howell, A.H. 1924. *Revision of the American Pikas*. North American Fauna No. 47. Washington, DC: USDA Bureau of Biological Survey.

Jetz, W., Wilcove, D., and Dobson, A. 2007. Projected impacts of climate and land-use change on the global diversity of birds. *PLoS Biology* **5**: 1211–1219.

Lawlor, T.E. 1998. Biogeography of great mammals: Paradigm lost? *Journal of Mammalogy* **79**: 111–1130.

Lowe, S.J., Patterson, B.R., and Schaefer, J.A. 2010. Lack of behavioral responses of moose (*Alces alces*) to high ambient temperatures near the southern Periphery of their range. *Canadian Journal of Zoology* **88**: 1032–1041.

MacNulty, D.R., Smith, D.W., Mech, L.D., and Eberly, L.E. 2009. Body size and predatory performance in wolves: is bigger better? *Journal of Animal Ecology* **78**: 532–539.

Mattson, W.J., Kuokkanen, K., Niemela, P., Julkunen-Tiitto, R., Kellomaki, S., and Tahvanainen, J. 2004. Elevated CO_2 alters birch resistance to Lagomorpha herbivores. *Global Change Biology* **10**: 1402–1413.

Millar, C.I. and Westfall, R.D. 2010. Distribution and climatic relationships of the American Pika (*Ochotona princeps*) in the Sierra Nevada and Western Great Basin, U.S.A.: periglacial landforms as refugia in warming climates. *Arctic, Antarctic, and Alpine Research* **42**: 76–88.

Moreno, J. and Moller, A.P. 2011. Extreme climatic events in relation to global change and their impact on life histories. *Current Zoology* **57**: 375–389.

Nilsson, C., Jansson, R., Keskitalo, E.C.H., Vlassova, T., Sutinen, M.L., Moen, J., and Chapin III, F.S. 2010. Challenges to adaptation in northernmost Europe as a result of global climate change. *AMBIO* **39**: 81–84.

Norment, C.J., Hall, A., and Hendricks, P. 1999. Important bird and mammal records in the Thelon River Valley, Northwest Territories: Range expansions and possible causes. *The Canadian Field-Naturalist* **113**: 375–385.

Pockely, P. 2001. Climate change transforms island ecosystem. *Nature* **410**: 616.

Reale, D., McAdam, A.G., Boutin, S., and Berteaux, D. 2003. Genetic and plastic responses of a northern mammal to climate change. *Proceedings of the Royal Society B* **270**: 591–596.

Sala, O.E., Chapin III, F.S., Armesto, J.J., Berlow, E., Bloomfield, J., Dirzo, R., Huber-Sanwald, E., Huenneke, L.F., Jackson, R.B., Kinzig, A., Leemans, R., Lodge, D., Mooney, H.A., Oesterheld, M., Poff, N.L., Sykes, M.T., Walker, B.H., Walker, M., and Wall, D.H. 2000. Global biodiversity scenarios for the year 2100. *Science* **287**: 1770–1774.

Schmitz, O.J. and Kolenosky, G.B. 1985. Wolves and coyotes in Ontario: morphological relationships and origins. *Canadian Journal of Zoology* **63**: 1130–1137.

Schwartz, C.C. and Renecker, L.A. 1998. Nutrition and energetics. In Franzmann, A.W. and Schwartz, C.C. (Eds.) *Ecology and Management of the North American Moose.* Washington, DC: Smithsonian Institution, pp. 441–478.

Sumner, L. and Dixon, J.S. 1953. *Birds and Mammals of the Sierra Nevada.* Berkeley, Ca: University of California Press.

Tveraa, T., Stien, A., Bardsen, B.-J., and Fauchald, P. 2013. Population densities, vegetation green-up, and plant productivity: Impacts on reproductive success and juvenile body mass in reindeer. *PLoS ONE* **8**: 10.1371/journal.pone.0056450.

Virkkala, R., Heikkinen, R.K., Leikola, N., and Luoto, M. 2008. Projected large-scale range reductions of northern-boreal land bird species due to climate change. *Biological Conservation* **141**: 1343–1353.

Wingfield, J.C., Kelley, J.P., and Angelier, F. 2011. What are extreme environmental conditions and how do organisms cope with them? *Current Zoology* **57**: 363–374.

5.7 Parasites and Other Diseases

One of the perceived great tragedies of CO_2-induced global warming is that rising temperatures will increase the development, transmission, and survival rates of parasites and other diseases in general, leading to biological interactions that will raise the prevalence of disease among animals in the future. This section examines that claim.

In a provocative paper analyzing the intricacies of this complex issue, Hall *et al.* (2006) begin by asking, "Will an increasingly warmer world necessarily become a sicker world?" They pose this question because "increased temperatures can accelerate the fitness of parasites, reduce recruitment bottlenecks for parasites during winter, and weaken hosts," and "warmer temperatures may allow vectors of parasites to expand their range," which would enable them to "introduce diseases to novel habitats," which is frequently claimed about mosquitoes and malaria (see Section 7.2, this volume). They continue, "these doom-and-gloom scenarios do not necessarily apply to all taxa or all situations," and "warming does not necessarily increase the fitness of all parasites."

The four biologists and their statistician coauthor note the "virulence of parasites may not change, may decrease, or may respond unimodally to increasing temperatures (Stacey *et al.*, 2003; Thomas and Blanford, 2003)." They also observe, "vital rates increase with temperature until some optimum is reached," and "once temperature exceeds this optimum, vital rates decline gradually with increasing temperature for some taxa, but rapidly for others," such that "in some host-parasite systems, a parasite's optimum occurs at cooler temperatures than the optimum of its host," citing Carruthers *et al.* (1992), Blanford and Thomas (1999), and Blanford *et al.* (2003) on fungus-grasshopper associations. In such cases, "a host can use warmer temperatures to help defeat its parasites through behavioral modification of its thermal environment."

The situation sometimes can be even more complex than this: "warmer temperatures can also lead to shifts in temperature optima (Huey and Hertz, 1984; Huey and Kingsolver, 1989, 1993)," and "the exact evolutionary trajectory of host-parasite systems in a warmer world may depend sensitively upon underlying genetic correlation structures and interactions between host genotypes, parasite genotypes, and the environment (Blanford *et al.*, 2003; Thomas and Blanford, 2003; Stacey *et al.*, 2003; Mitchell *et al.*, 2004)." Consequently, they conclude, "longer-term response of the physiology of host-parasite systems to global warming becomes difficult to predict."

The researchers also note "other species can profoundly shape the outcome of parasitism in host populations," and "predators provide an important example" because predators "can actually inhibit epidemics by selectively culling sick hosts and/or by maintaining host densities below levels required for parasites to persist (Hudson *et al.*, 1992; Packer *et al.*, 2003, Lafferty, 2004; Ostfeld and Holt, 2004; Duffey *et al.*, 2005; Hall *et al.*, 2005)." Therefore, Hall *et al.* conclude, "global warming does not necessarily mean that disease prevalence will increase in all systems."

Morgan and Wall (2009) echo many of the salient points raised in the Hall *et al.* paper and further elucidate the complex nature of this topic. With respect to the relationship between temperature and parasitic development, the two authors note, "just as development rates of many parasites of veterinary importance increase with temperature, so [too] do their mortality rates [increase]." They reiterate, "temperature will also affect mortality indirectly through the action of predators, parasitoids, pathogens and competitors, whose development and abundance are also potentially temperature sensitive," so "the net effect of climate change could be complex and far from easily predicted."

The two UK researchers suggest "several biological mechanisms (including increased parasite mortality and more rapid acquisition of immunity), in tandem with changes in husbandry practices (including reproduction, housing, nutrition, breed selection, grazing patterns and other management interventions), might act to mitigate increased parasite development rates, preventing dramatic rises in overall levels of diseases." Because "optimum mitigation strategies will be highly system specific and depend on detailed understanding of interactions between climate, parasite abundance, host availability

and the cues for and economics of farmer intervention," they conclude "there is a need for research that considers likely effects of climate change and mitigation strategies in terms of the whole host-parasite system, including anthropogenic responses, and not just in terms of parasite population dynamics." One year later, two such papers were published, both attempting to account for the response of human behavior on parasite abundance and disease incidence.

Focusing on cutaneous myiasis (blowfly strike) in sheep, Wall and Ellse (2011) employed a stochastic simulation model "to examine the changes in the seasonal incidence of ovine cutaneous myiasis on farms in the United Kingdom and the likely effects of changes in husbandry and control strategies" in the face of projected changes in climate. The authors note "the ability of this model to successfully account for observed patterns of strike has been confirmed previously by comparison of predicted with observed strike incidence patterns observed on 370 farms in England and Wales," citing Wall *et al.* (2002).

The two UK researchers report, "the simulations show that the range of elevated temperatures predicted by current climate change scenarios result in an elongated blowfly season with earlier spring emergence and a higher cumulative incidence of strike," and "overall, higher temperatures increased strike incidence disproportionately in ewes in early summer, but had relatively less direct effect on the pattern of lamb strike incidence," noting "a 3°C increase in average temperature approximately doubles the cumulative incidence of strike in lambs but results in four times more strikes in ewes." However, as the researchers conclude in the abstract of their paper, "the simulations suggest that integrated changes in husbandry practices are likely to be able to manage expected increases in strike, given the range of climate changes currently predicted." They explain in the body of the paper, "modest changes in husbandry practices should be able to manage expected increases in strike, under the range of climate changes currently predicted," demonstrating "consideration of the likely impact of climate change must take into account animal management practices as well as parasite biology (Morgan and Wall, 2009)."

Working with two additional co-authors on the same host and parasite, Wall *et al.* (2011) came to a similar conclusion, reporting, "the models suggest that simple changes in some husbandry practices, such as shearing or trap use, could have an important effect in reducing early season ewe strike incidences," and "practical measures exist which, with modest changes in husbandry practices, should be able to manage expected increases in strike." The key message of this latter work is the authors' conclusion that "simple extrapolations of the known effects of temperature on ectoparasite development," in an attempt to "predict changes in disease incidence in a warmer climate," is simply "too simplistic." They emphasize "attempts to predict the likely impact of climate change on disease incidence must take into account changes in farmer behavior and animal management practices as well as parasite biology."

Baffoe *et al.* (2012) write, "with the prospect of warmer temperatures as a consequence of ongoing climate change, it is important to investigate how such increases will affect parasitoids and their top-down suppression of herbivory in agroecosystems." They studied a parasitoid that afflicts a common beetle that feeds on several short-rotation species of commercially coppiced willow trees in northern and central Europe, a trophic cascade described in more detail by Peacock *et al.* (1999), Bjorkman *et al.* (2003), and Dalin (2011). Baffoe *et al.* conducted laboratory experiments in which they "studied how the performance and biocontrol efficiency of the willow 'bodyguard' *Perilitus brevicollis* Haliday (Hymenoptera: Braconidae) were affected at different constant temperatures (10, 15, 20, 25°C) when parasitizing a pest insect, the blue willow beetle (*Phratora vulgatissima* L., Coleoptera: Chrysomelidae)." They did this by focusing on "the parasitoid's thermal threshold for development, development rate, adult body size, survival rate and the herbivore's consumption rate."

The four Swedish scientists report parasitism had no impact on herbivory at 10°C, but "parasitoid performance (survival and development rate) generally increased with increasing temperature up to 20°C." In addition, "the feeding capacity of the studied parasitized herbivores is reduced more at high than low temperatures." Thus, "these data suggest that *P. brevicollis* should become a better biocontrol agent if temperatures increase," a transformation that should have substantial positive consequences for willow trees in northern and central Europe, as well as for the enterprise of their commercial harvesting.

Bentley and Burgner (2011) examined the host/ parasite relationship between juvenile sockeye salmon (*Oncorhynchus nerka*) and the tapeworm *Triaenophorus crassus* in an Alaskan watershed that had experienced a 1.9°C increase in summer water temperature over the prior 46 years. At the beginning of their experiment, Bentley and Burgner hypothesized the warming of the region "would have

resulted in a corresponding increase in fish metabolism, and thus potential consumption rates, that would increase infestation rates of the tapeworm *Triaenophorus crassus*." To test their hypothesis, they compared infestation rate data for *T. crassus* collected between 1948 and 1960 with similar data obtained in 2008 and 2009 from the Wood River system of Bristol Bay, Alaska.

The two U.S. researchers from the University of Washington's School of Aquatic and Fishery Sciences report, "comparing the average summer air temperature to the parasite prevalence of juvenile sockeye salmon, we found no significant relationship over the fifteen years of collected data." Moreover, "evaluating the influence of average summer air temperature on the parasite infestation rates of juvenile sockeye salmon, we again found no significant relationship for either parasite abundance or parasite intensity." They note, "when we compared the 13 years of historic parasite prevalence to equivalent data collected in 2008 and 2009, we did not find a statistically significant positive long-term trend in the data," and "the parasite abundance of examined sockeye salmon smolts also did not exhibit a statistically significant long-term trend using the eight years of historic data and the two years of contemporary data." Finally, "evaluating the relationship between time and parasite intensity produced similar results as the other five comparisons, with there not being a statistically significant positive relationship."

Bentley and Burgner conclude their data demonstrate "the complex effects of warming have not summed to generate a measurable change in the infestation rates of juvenile sockeye salmon in the Wood River system." Given the many factors involved in host/parasite interrelationships, together with their great complexities, it is quite possible global warming will never significantly impact parasite infestation rates in the animals they attack.

Shifting from parasites to infectious diseases, Kampen and Werner (2010) write, "with few exceptions, vector-borne diseases have long been considered of minor importance in central and northern Europe." However, they note, "since the advent of bluetongue disease (BTD) in 2006, and the 2007 chikungunya fever outbreak in Italy, this attitude has changed." Focusing on BTD, a non-contagious insect-borne viral disease of ruminants (mainly sheep, but also affecting antelope, buffalo, cattle, deer, dromedaries, and goats) caused by the bluetongue virus (BTV), Kampen and Werner describe what is known about the outbreak of this serious animal disease in central Europe.

The two German researchers report "BTD was the first 'exotic' disease to arrive," but "it did not slowly spread northwards but jumped in through a still unknown entry point." It all started, as they describe it, "with about 2000 affected ruminant farming facilities in 2006 in the central western part of Europe," where the BTV–8 virus—which they say "had never been observed in Europe before," and for which DNA sequencing data suggested sub-Saharan Africa as its most likely point of origin—"managed to overwinter and spread in all directions in 2007, producing almost 60,000 outbreaks (farms affected) in ten European countries up to early 2008." And now, they say, the BTV–1 virus strain "appears to be approaching from the south, with some 4900 outbreaks in France in 2008," reiterating, "nobody had expected a novel and independent virus introduction into central Europe together with indigenous biting midges able to transmit BTV."

As for possible routes of introduction of the virus, they mention BTV-positive ruminants imported either legally or illegally, virus-carrying midges transported by wind over hundreds of kilometers, accidental importation by ship or aircraft, contaminated vaccines, and trade with the products of infected animals.

Kampen and Werner conclude, "it is due to continuing globalization rather than to climate change that even central and northern Europe are at risk of new pathogens as well as vectors of disease entering and establishing."

Conte *et al.* (2009) note, "the midge *Culicoides imicola* is the principal vector of bluetongue virus (BTV) that causes an infectious disease of domestic and wild ruminants," and "over the last ten years, BTV has invaded Mediterranean countries and much of Northern Europe," inducing several scientists to contend the BTV vector had expanded its range northward "because of rising temperatures," as suggested by Mellor (2004), Purse *et al.* (2005), and Mellor *et al.* (2008). However, Goffredo *et al.* (2003) made a careful examination of *Culicoides* population data in Italy prior to 2000 and determined "trapping conditions of previous collections would have had very little chance of catching *C. imicola*" or detecting its presence, suggesting there was insufficient evidence for a warming-induced northward expansion of the BTV vector because it already may already been present there but undetected.

In response to even earlier fears of a potential BTV invasion, a national surveillance program for *C. imicola* had been established in Italy in 2000, where 70,000 light-trap collections were made at about 3,800 sites. Using the first year of data obtained from this program, Conte *et al.* defined the spatial distributions of three *C. imicola* infection zones: zone I (endemicity), zone II (transition), and zone III (absence). Using data from 2002–2007, they quantified how *C. imicola* populations evolved through time in these three zones, working under the logical assumption that "a species that is undergoing geographical range expansion should have a population that remains stable over time in zone I and increases in zones II and III."

The three researchers say their results indicate there was "no detectable range expansion of *C. imicola* population in Italy over the past six years." They report "a weak, but significant reduction was observed in the transition zone." Conte *et al.* therefore conclude their data "support the hypothesis that the spread of BTV in Italy is not because of the geographical expansion of its main vector, but to a modification of the interaction between the virus, the vector and the environment, as may also have been the case in northern Europe." They say their results show "precautions should be taken when inferring range progression for species requiring highly targeted forms of sampling and for which a constant probability of detection over time should be established." This research demonstrates it is easy to blame global warming for the poleward expansion of a vector-spread disease, but quite another thing to prove that claim.

References

Baffoe, K., Dalin, P., Nordlander, G., and Stenberg, J.A. 2012. Importance of temperature for the performance and biocontrol efficiency of the parasitoid *Perilitus brevicollis* (Hymenoptera: Braconidae) on *Salix. BioControl* **57**: 611–618.

Bentley, K.T. and Burgner, R.L. 2011. An assessment of parasite infestation rates of juvenile sockeye salmon after 50 years of climate warming in southwest Alaska. *Environmental Biology of Fishes* **92**: 267–273.

Bjorkman, C., Dalin, P., and Eklund, K. 2003. Generalist natural enemies of a willow leaf beetle (*Phratora vulgatissima*): abundance and feeding habits. *Journal of Insect Behavior* **16**: 747–764.

Blanford, S. and Thomas, M.B. 1999. Host thermal biology: the key to understanding host-pathogen interactions and microbial pest control? *Agricultural and Forest Entomology* **1**: 195–202.

Blanford, S., Thomas, M.B., Pugh, C., and Pell, J.K. 2003.

Temperature checks the Red Queen: Resistance and virulence in a fluctuating environment. *Ecology Letters* 6: 2–5.

Carruthers, R.I., Larkin, T.S., Firstencel, H., and Feng, Z. 1992. Influences of thermal ecology on the mycosis of a rangeland grasshopper. *Ecology* 73: 190–204.

Conte, A., Gilbert, M., and Goffredo, M. 2009. Eight years of entomological surveillance in Italy show no evidence of *Culicoides imicola* geographical range expansion. *Journal of Applied Ecology* 46: 1332–1339.

Dalin, P. 2011. Diapause induction and termination in a commonly univoltine leaf beetle (*Phratora vulgatissima*). *Insect Science* 18: 443–450.

Duffy, M.A., Hall, S.R., Tessier, A.J., and Huebner, M. 2005. Selective predators and their parasitized prey: top-down control of epidemics. *Limnology and Oceanography* 50: 412–420.

Goffredo, M., Conte, A., Cocciolito, R., and Meiswinkel, R. 2003. Distribution and abundance of *Culicoides imicola* in Italy. *Veterinaria Italiana* 47: 22–32.

Hall, S.R., Duffy, M.A., and Caceres, C.E. 2005. Selective predation and productivity jointly drive complex behavior in host-parasite systems. *American Naturalist* 180: 70–81.

Hall, S.R., Tessier, A.J., Duffy, M.G., Huebner, M., and Caceres, C.E. 2006. Warmer does not have to mean sicker: temperature and predators can jointly drive timing of epidemics. *Ecology* 87: 1684–1695.

Hudson, P.J., Dobson, A.P., and Newborn, D. 1992. Do parasites make prey vulnerable to predation? Red Grouse and parasites. *Journal of Animal Ecology* 61: 681–692.

Huey, R.B. and Hertz, P.E. 1984. Is a jack-of-all-temperatures a master of none? *Evolution* 38: 441–444.

Huey, R.B. and Kingsolver, J.G. 1989. Evolution of thermal sensitivity of ectotherm performance. *Trends in Ecology and Evolution* 4: 131–135.

Huey, R.B. and Kingsolver, J.G. 1993. Evolution of resistance to high temperature in ectotherms. *American Naturalist* 142: S21-S46.

Kampen, H. and Werner, D. 2010. Three years of bluetongue disease in central Europe with special reference to Germany: what lessons can be learned? *Wiener Klinische Wochenschrift* 122 (Suppl. 3): 31–39.

Lafferty, K.D. 2004. Fishing for lobsters indirectly increases epidemics in sea urchins. *Ecological Applications* 14: 1566–1573.

Mellor, P.S. 2004. Infection of the vectors and bluetongue epidemiology in Europe. *Veterinaria Italiana* 40: 167–174.

Mellor, P.S., Carpenter, S., Harrup, L, Baylis, M., and

Mertens, P.P.C. 2008. Bluetongue in Europe and the Mediterranean Basin: History of occurrence prior to 2006. *Preventive Veterinary Medicine* 87: 4–20.

Mitchell, S.E., Halves, J., and Lampert, W. 2004. Coexistence of similar genotypes of *Daphnia magna* in intermittent populations: response to thermal stress. *Oikos* 106: 469–478.

Morgan, E.R. and Wall, R. 2009. Climate change and parasitic disease: farmer mitigation? *Trends in Parasitology* 25: 308–313.

Ostfeld, R.S. and Holt, R.D. 2004. Are predators good for your health? Evaluating evidence for top-down regulation of zoonotic disease reservoirs. *Frontiers in Ecology and the Environment* 2: 13–20.

Packer, C., Holt, R.D., Hudson, P.J., Lafferty, K.D., and Dobson, A.P. 2003. Keeping the herds healthy and alert: implications of predator control for infectious disease. *Ecology Letters* 6: 797–802.

Peacock, L., Herrick, S., and Brain, P. 1999. Spatio-temporal dynamics of willow beetle (*Phratora vulgatissima*) in short-rotation coppice willows grown as monocultures or a genetically diverse mixture. *Agricultural and Forest Entomology* 1: 287–296.

Purse, B.V., Mellor, P.S., Rogers, D.J., Samuel, A.R., Mertens, P.P.C., and Baylis, M. 2005. Climate change and the recent emergence of bluetongue in Europe. *Nature Reviews Microbiology* 3: 171–181.

Stacey, D.A., Thomas, M.B., Blanford, S., Pell, J.K., Pugh, C., and Fellowes, M.D. 2003. Genotype and temperature influence pea aphid resistance to a fungal entomopathogen. *Physiological Entomology* 28: 75–81.

Thomas, M.B. and Blanford, S. 2003. Thermal biology in insect-parasite interactions. *Trends in Ecology and Evolution* 18: 344–350.

Wall, R., Cruickshank, I., Smith, K.E., French, N.P., and Holme, A.S. 2002. Development and validation of a simulation model for sheep blowfly strike. *Medical and Veterinary Entomology* 16: 335–346.

Wall, R. and Ellse, L.S. 2011. Climate change and livestock parasites: integrated management of sheep blowfly strike in a warmer environment. *Global Change Biology* 17: 1770–1777.

Wall, R., Rose, H, Ellse, L., and Morgan, E. 2011. Livestock ectoparasites: Integrated management in a changing climate. *Veterinary Parasitology* 180: 82–89.

5.8 Polar Bears

- Polar bears have survived historic changes in climate that have exceeded those of the twentieth century or are forecast by computer models to occur in the future. In addition, some populations of polar bears appear to be stable despite rising temperatures and summer sea ice declines. The biggest threat they face is not from global warming, but commercial hunting by humans, which has historically taken a huge toll on polar bear populations.

In its contribution to IPCC's *Fourth Assessment Report*, Working Group II claimed global warming is "inducing declining survival rates, smaller size, and cannibalism among polar bears" (IPCC, 2007-II). It predicted a bleak future for the species if atmospheric CO_2 concentrations continue to rise. However, polar bears have survived historic changes in climate that have exceeded those of the twentieth century or are forecast by computer models to occur in the future. In addition, some populations of polar bears appear to be stable despite rising temperatures and summer sea ice declines. The biggest threat they face is not from global warming, but commercial hunting by humans, which has historically taken a huge toll on polar bear populations.

Polar bears evolved from brown bears (*Ursus arctos*). While it was formerly thought this speciation event occurred sometime in the past 400,000 years and probably no more than 200,000 years ago (Arnason *et al.*, 1995; Davis *et al.*, 2008; Harington, 2008), that picture has now changed. The oldest polar bear fossil ever found (dated to 110,000–130,000 years old) was reported in 2008 (Ingolfsson *et al.*, 2008) and a complete mitochondrial DNA (mtDNA) sequence of it was generated two years later (Lindqvist *et al.*, 2010). This discovery spawned a suite of papers on polar bear genetics that fail to agree when polar bears arose as a distinct species: Edwards *et al.* (2011) suggest a possible range of 400,000 to two million years ago; Hailer *et al.* (2012), suggest a date of about 600,000 years ago; and Miller *et al.* (2012), suggest this event occurred four to five million years ago.

Although there is some disagreement about the onset of this species, it is clear that because the oldest polar bear fossil is at least 110,000–130,000 years old, polar bears have survived at least one glacial-interglacial cycle and perhaps as many as 10 or more.. Focusing on the last major interglacial (MIS 5e, the Eemian, which lasted from ca. 130,000–115,000

years ago), there not only appears to have been less winter Arctic ice than today (including no ice in the Bering Sea), but late summer ice was reduced to a remnant off northern Greenland and Ellesmere Island (Polyak *et al.*, 2010). During the current interglacial, or Holocene, there were at least two warm periods (the Early Holocene Climatic Optimum and the Medieval Warm Period) when sea ice was less extensive than it is now (Atkinson, 2009; Dyke and England, 2003; Dyke *et al.*, 1996; Kaufman *et al.*, 2004; Polyak *et al.*, 2010; Steffensen *et al.*, 2008).

Polar bears obviously survived large-scale and often sudden climate changes in the historic past, such as those described above. This does not mean their populations remained constant throughout this period; their numbers likely rose in some periods and declined in others. But past changes in climate have not led to their extinction, which leads to the question: Why would temperature changes predicted to be of the same scale or less than those that occurred in the past be projected to cause a near-future extinction of polar bears?

In order to ascertain whether there are indeed risks to polar bears from model-predicted increases in global temperature and associated sea ice decline, researchers have examined various aspects of polar bear population dynamics and life history traits as they relate to temperature changes that have taken place over the past 30 years. Several of their findings are presented in the subsections below, where it is seen that polar bears are well-equipped to adapt with the challenges they may face as a result of any CO_2-induced global warming.

References

Arnason, U., Bodin, K., Gullberg, A., Ledje, C., and Mouchaty, S. 1995. A molecular view of pinniped relationships with particular emphasis on the true seals. *Journal of Molecular Evolution* **40**: 78–85.

Atkinson, N. 2009. A 10400-year-old bowhead whale (*Balaena mysticetus*) skull from Ellef Ringnes Island, Nunavut: implications for sea-ice conditions in high Arctic Canada at the end of the last glaciation. *Arctic* **62**: 38–44.

Davis, C.S., Stirling, I., Strobeck, C., and Coltman, D.W. 2008. Population structure of ice-breeding seals. *Molecular Ecology* **17**: 3078–3094.

Dyke, A.S. and England, J.H. 2003. Canada's most northerly postglacial bowhead whales (*Balaena mysticetus*): Holocene sea-ice conditions and polynya development. *Arctic* **56**:14–20.

Dyke, A.S., Hooper, J., and Savelle, J. M. 1996. A history of sea ice in the Canadian Arctic Archipelago based on postglacial remains of bowhead whale (*Balaena mysticetus*). *Arctic* **49**: 235–255.

Edwards, C.J., Suchard, M.A., Lemey, P., Welch, J.J., Barnes, I., Fulton, T.L., Barnett, R., O'Connell, T.C., Coxon, P., Monoghan, N., Valdiosera, C.E., Lorenzen, E.D., Willerslev, E., Baryshnikov, G.F., Rambaut, A., Thomas, M.G., Bradley, D.G., and Shapiro, B. 2011. Ancient hybridization and an Irish origin for the modern polar bear matriline. *Current Biology* **21**: 1251–1258.

Hailer, F., Kutschera, V.E., Hallstrom, B.M., Klassert, D., Fain, S.R., Leonard, J.A., Arnason, U., and Janke, A. 2012. Nuclear genomic sequences reveal that polar bears are an old and distinct bear lineage. *Science* **336**: 344–347.

Harington, C.R. 2008. The evolution of Arctic marine mammals. *Ecological Applications* **18** : S23-S40.

Ingolfsson, Ó. and Wiig, Ø. 2008 Late Pleistocene fossil find in Svalbard: the oldest remains of a polar bear (*Ursus maritiumus* Phipps, 1744) ever discovered. *Polar Research* **28**:455–462.

IPCC. 2007-II. *Climate Change 2007: Impacts, Adaptation and Vulnerability*. Contribution of Working Group II to the Fourth Assessment Report of the Intergovernmental Panel on Climate Change. Parry, M.L., Canziani, O.F., Palutikof, J.P., van der Linden, P.J., and Hanson, C.E. (Eds.) Cambridge University Press, Cambridge, UK.

Kaufman, D.S., Ager, T.A., Anderson, N.J., Anderson, P.M., Andrews, J.T., Bartlein, P.J., Brubaker, L.B., Coats, L.L., Cwynar, L.C., Duvall, M.L., Dyke, A.S., Edwards, M.E, Eisner, W.R., Gajewski, K., Geirsdóttir, A., Hu, F.S., Jennings, A.E., Kaplan, M.R., Kerwin, M.W., Lozhkin, A.V., MacDonald, G.M., Miller, G.H., Mock, C.J., Oswald, W.W., Otto-Bliesner, B.L., Porinchu, D.F., Rühland, K., Smol, J.P., Steig, E.J., and Wolfe, B.B. 2004. Holocene thermal maximum in the western Arctic (0–180°W). *Quaternary Science Reviews* **23**: 529–560.

Lindqvist, C., Schuster, S.C., Sun, Y., Talbot, S.L., Qi, J., Ratan, A., Tomsho, L., Kasson, L., Zeyl, E., Aars, J., Miller, W., Ingólfsson, Ó., Bachmann, L., and Wiig, Ø. 2010. Complete mitochondrial genome of a Pleistocene jawbone unveils the origin of polar bear. *Proceedings of the National Academy of Sciences USA* **107**: 5053–5057.

Miller, W., Schuster, S.C., Welch, A.J., Ratan, A., Bedoya-Reina, O.C., Zhao, F., Kim, H.L., Burhans, R.C., Drautz, D.I., Wittekindt, N.E., Tomsho, L.P., Ibarra-Laclette, E., Herrera-Estrella, L., Peacock, E., Farley, S., Sage, G.K., Rode, K., Obbard, M., Montiel, R., Bachmann, L., Ingolfsson, Ó., Aars, J., Mailund, T., Wiig, Ø., Talbot, S.L., and Lindqvist, C. 2012. Polar and brown bear genomes reveal ancient admixture and demographic footprints of past climate change. *Proceedings of the National Academy of Sciences* **109**: 14295–14296.

Polyak, L., Alley, R.B., Andrews, J.T., Brigham-Grette, J., Cronin, T.M., Darby, D.A., Dyke, A.S., Fitzpatrick, J.J., Funder, S., Holland, M., Jennings, A.E., Miller, G.H., O'Regan, M., Savelle, J., Serreze, M., St. John, K., White, J.W.C., and Wolff, E. 2010. History of sea ice in the Arctic. *Quaternary Science Reviews* **29**: 1757–1778.

Steffensen, J.P., Andersen, K.K., Bigler, M., Clausen, H., Dahl-Jensen, D., Fischer, H., Goto-Azuma, K., Hansson, M., Johnsen, S.J., Jouzei, J., Masson-Delmotte, V., Popp, T., Rasmussen, S.O., Röthlisberger, R., Ruth, U., Stauffer, B., Siggaard-Andersen, M.-L., Sveinbjörnsdóttir, Á.E., Svensson, A., and White, J.W.C. 2008. High-resolution Greenland ice core data show abrupt climate change happens in few years. *Science* **321**: 680–684.

5.8.1 Population

The world's polar bear populations live in the wild only in the Northern Hemisphere on land and sea ice in the area surrounding the North Pole. Polar bears tend to stay in, or return to, local areas (Taylor and Lee, 1995; Bethke *et al.,* 1996; Taylor *et al.,* 2001), although some migration is known to occur (Messier *et al.,* 2001; Amstrup *et al.,* 2004). Their range expands and contracts with the accretion and contraction of sea ice with the seasons, with bears moving south during the winter as sea ice advances (Amstrup *et al.,* 2000). In some areas (e.g., Hudson Bay, Foxe Basin, Baffin Bay, and James Bay) polar bears move from sea ice to land for several months during the summer open-water season (Ferguson *et al.,* 1997; Lunn *et al.,* 1997; Taylor *et al.,* 2001, 2005).

The total polar bear population is unknown, since its numbers in the Arctic Basin, East Greenland, Chukchi Sea, and the Kara Sea have never been counted (Aars *et al.,* 2006; Obbard *et al.,* 2010). The official estimate has been given as 20,000–25,000 since 2005 (Aars *et al.,* 2006; Obbard *et al.,* 2010), despite claims of declining numbers. The total has remained stable despite the fact that the former estimate for the Chukchi Sea was reduced from 2,000 to zero between 2005 and 2009.

There is even less certainty regarding the number of polar bears in the 1950s and 1960s, with most estimates around 5,000 to 10,000. Virtually all scientists agree polar bear populations have grown since the 1970s. For example, Derocher (2009) has stated, "after the signing of the International Agreement on Polar Bears in the 1970s, harvests were controlled and the numbers increased. There is no argument from anyone on this point." Ramsay and

Stirling (1988) wrote, "if a population was reduced in the past and the causal agent was no longer in effect, then the population would be expected to recover to its approximate pre-decline level."

Even though polar bear populations grew during the second half of the twentieth century, a time when IPCC claims there was a rapid increase in global temperatures and loss of sea ice, Derocher and others say this population growth is evidence of the effects of hunting bans and quotas and does not contradict their claim that warming temperatures and melting sea ice have hurt polar bear populations. They point, with apparent merit, to negative demographic impacts on polar bear populations identified in the Southern Beaufort Sea and in Western Hudson Bay, and possible adverse nutritional impacts in the Northern Beaufort Sea and Southern Hudson Bay, due to changes in local sea ice conditions.

But this observation falls short of providing evidence global warming threatens polar bears with extinction. If anthropogenic global warming were a real threat to polar bears, its effects should be observable throughout the Current Warm Period, not just the last few years, and the warming would have to affect more than only a small number of sub-populations, as appears to have been the case (see discussion below). The modified argument—that global warming only in recent years is negatively affecting only some subpopulations of polar bears but not others—is not what is being reported in daily newspapers or even what IPCC claims. The real-world long-term trends in polar bear populations contradict what would be expected if the theory of anthropogenic global warming were true.

The polar bear population is divided into 19 subpopulations for management purposes (see Figure 5.8.1.1). In 2005, according to the IUCN Polar Bear Specialist Group, five subpopulations were declining, five were stable, two were increasing, and on seven there was insufficient data on which to base a decision (Aars *et al.*, 2006). Significantly, four of the five subpopulations listed as declining were at risk due to hunting, not reduced sea ice (Aars *et al.,* 2006). This is hardly a picture of a species in steep decline, or even in decline at all. It certainly does not provide an empirical basis for predictions of imminent extinction.

More recently, this view has changed somewhat (Obbard *et al.,* 2010). Seven subpopulations are now considered data-deficient (no trend given, including one that was rated as increasing in 2005), seven are listed as declining (including one subpopulation considered to have 'data deficient' status and

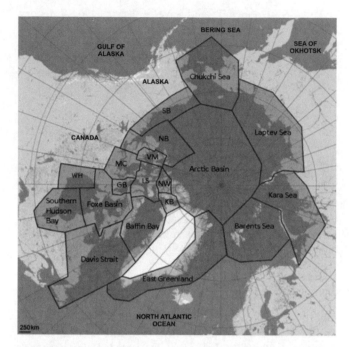

Figure 5.8.1.1. Polar bear subpopulations, as defined by the IUCN Polar Bear Specialist Group. Modified from map provided by the PBSG (2009). GB, Gulf of Boothia; KB, Kane Basin; LS, Lancaster Sound; MC, M'Clintock Channel; NB, Norwegian Bay; VM, Viscount Melville; NB, Northern Beaufort; SB, Southern Beaufort; WHB, Western Hudson Bay.

another—the Chukchi—that has never been surveyed but is determined to have a "reduced" status and declining trend based on sea ice reductions and suspected poaching), three are considered stable, and one is considered to be increasing. Suspected overhunting and/or poaching are considered the primary reason five of the seven declining populations are at risk, based on modeled projections over the next 10 years. For another, declines in body condition, modeled over the next 10 years, are the basis for it being given a "declining" trend (Southern Beaufort).

Only one of the seven declining populations (Western Hudson Bay) has documented a statistically significant decline in population numbers. Obbard *et al.* state, "our status report currently indicates that two subpopulations (WH [Western Hudson Bay] and SB [Southern Beaufort]) have likely declined due to climate change. It is thought that there may also be some impacts of climate change in other populations (CS [Chukchi Sea], SH [Southern Hudson Bay]), however data are not conclusive or available." New research in the Chukchi by Rode *et al.* (2014) suggests bears there are in good condition and reproducing very well, indicating projected negative effects due to declining summer sea ice have not materialized.

In addition, whereas the decline in Western Hudson Bay polar bear numbers (about 22%) is stated to have occurred between 1987 and 2004 (Regehr *et al.*, 2007a), Obbard *et al.* (2010) acknowledge this population had been stable prior to 1998 (Stirling *et al.*, 1999). This means the statistically significant decline really occurred between 1998 and 2004 (seven years), during which there was no apparent trend in sea ice breakup dates (Regehr *et al.*, 2007a), although both 1998 and 2003 were relatively early breakup years (occurring about June 14 both years, according to the new method used by Cherry *et al.*, 2013). If the population was still on a declining trend after 2004, there should be fewer polar bears in Western Hudson Bay now than in 2004.

No data have yet been made available from mark-recapture studies undertaken between 2005 and 2011, but an aerial survey, similar to those conducted in the Barents Sea and Baffin Bay, was conducted by the Nunavut Government in 2011 (Stapleton *et al.*, 2012a). Stapleton and colleagues' estimate of the current population number is about 1,000 (95% confidence interval, range of 715–1398). Although the two methods (mark-recapture and aerial survey) cannot be directly compared, the authors say the aerial survey was "consistent with the 2004 capture-based estimate but inconsistent with projections suggesting continued decreases in abundance." So while Obbard *et al.* (2010) say "data from this subpopulation [WHB] provide the best indications of how polar bears respond to the negative effects of climate warming," it appears the population has not continued to decline as predicted.

Similar aerial surveys have been done to the north, in Foxe Basin by Stapleton *et al.* (2012b). In that study, the authors undertook a helicopter survey throughout the territory of Foxe Basin polar bears in the summers of 2009 and 2010, concluding "our abundance estimates were highly consistent between years and survey methods, (~2,580 bears (95% CI: about 2,100–3,200), and were comparable to an estimate from the early 1990s. Our results suggest that Nunavut's management regime has enabled polar bear abundance in FB to remain relatively stable."

Hunting historically has been the greatest threat to polar bear populations. The arrival of snowmobiles, helicopters, and high-powered rifles led to "harvest" levels that were not sustainable (Taylor *et al.*, 2002; Taylor *et al.*, 2006; Taylor *et al.*, 2008). Hunting was largely unregulated until passage of the 1974 International Agreement for the Conservation of Polar

Bears and Their Habitat. Greenland didn't institute a quota for polar bear hunting until 2006 (Polar Bear Technical Committee, 2006). Annual kills for most populations now have been substantially reduced, but it will take at least 20 years for populations to recover.

The range of polar bears is affected by changes in climate but not in a linear fashion with temperature or the extent or thickness of sea ice. Sea ice extent and thickness are only indirectly related to polar bear populations. Only two subpopulations—the Western Hudson Bay (WH) and Southern Beaufort Sea (SB) populations—may have declined (Ferguson *et al.*, 2005; Regehr *et al.*, 2006, 2007a,b; Rode *et al.*, 2007; Hunter *et al.*, 2007); one of these (WH) is disputed (Dyck *et al.*, 2007), and the other (SB) is not a statistically significant decline.

Taylor and Dowsley (2008) summarized recent population surveys as follows: Of six polar bear populations recently evaluated during the climate warming period, two populations appear to have been reduced (WH, SB), two populations appear to have remained constant (SH, NB), one population appears to have increased (DS), and one was abundant but the information was not sufficient to estimate a trend (BS). Seven other populations (VM, LS, NW, BB, KB, MC, GB) surveyed during the period of climate warming had vital rates sufficient to sustain substantial rates of harvest (*i.e.*, hunting) at the time they were studied. Information from a Foxe Basin (FB) population survey was sufficient to document the population had remained abundant although it had been harvested at a relatively high rate and the survival and recruitment estimates necessary to determine trend were not available. The biological information on the remaining four populations (CS, LS, KS, EG) and the few bears that may inhabit the Arctic Basin is insufficient to suggest anything about current numbers or trend.

Taylor and Dowsley say "the increase to current high numbers of polar bears in the Davis Strait has occurred during the current warming period, and has occurred with declining sea ice conditions that are sometimes less than 40% coverage at winter maximum (Stirling and Parkinson, 2006). Clearly the DS bears do manage to hunt successfully in unconsolidated pack ice." They comment, as do Dyck *et al.* (2007), that polar bears have been observed to successfully hunt seals in tidal flats along shores during ice-free periods. "Considered together," Taylor and Dowsley conclude, "these demographic data do not suggest that polar bears as a species are headed for extinction in the next three generations (45 years) or the foreseeable future. The demographic data do support increased monitoring, and augmenting periodic population surveys with ecological and behavioral studies." They also observe, "to date, no population has been expatriated due to climate change effects, so the effect of decreased densities, alternative food sources, or behavioral adaptation to less ice on population persistence is not known."

Stirling and Derocher (2012) contend "polar bears will largely disappear from the southern portions of their range by mid-century." Western Hudson Bay is clearly included in this subset of all polar bear territory, as it lies below the Arctic Circle. But what other portions of the range lie below this point? Southern Hudson Bay, the Bering Sea, most of the Chukchi Sea, and most of Davis Strait also lie below the Arctic Circle; their population status already has been discussed. However, Southern Hudson Bay (SH), which extends to about 52°N, should presumably show more pronounced effects from global warming than even Western Hudson Bay to the north.

Obbard *et al.* (2010) say in their summary, "recent analysis of coastal survey data (Stirling *et al.* 2004) suggests polar bear numbers in SH have remained unchanged in recent years" and they consider this population to be one of three "stable" polar bear subpopulations. In a more comprehensive study of Southern Hudson Bay bears, Obbard *et al.* (2007) state, "reductions in survival of juvenile, subadult and senescent polar bears were demonstrated for the WH population (Regehr *et al.*, 2007), but were only weakly supported by our data." Obbard *et al.* (2007) also note, "abundance in the Southern Hudson Bay population was unchanged between two intensive capture-recapture periods, which were separated by almost 20 years (1984–86 *vs.* 2003–05. This was so despite the evidence for a decline of 22% in abundance for the neighboring Western Hudson Bay population over roughly the same period (*i.e.*, 1987–2004; Regehr *et al.*, 2007)." They conclude, "it appears that changes in environmental factors such as sea ice distribution and duration … have not yet resulted in unambiguous changes in survival or to a consequent reduction in population size in the SH population to this date." This is in spite of the fact that Obbard *et al.* (2006), in a dedicated study of Southern Hudson Bay polar bears, found body condition (fatness) was "significantly poorer for bears captured from 2000 to 2005 than for bears captured from 1984 to 1986," and concluded, "the significance of a trend toward poorer body condition over time is unknown." Nonetheless, in 2009 the province of

Ontario listed Southern Hudson Bay polar bears as a "threatened" species (Obbard *et al.,* 2010).

The deep water over the Arctic Basin is often assumed to be of such low productivity (e.g., Amstrup *et al.*, 2007; Fischbach *et al.*, 2007; Obbard *et al.*, 2010) that it is largely unsuitable for polar bears except as a transit corridor. This assumption is contradicted by measurements of significant amounts of phytoplankton and ice algae (e.g., Gosselin *et al.*, 1997; Stirling, 1997) as well as reports at the North Pole of "small fish" (estimated as 5–8cm, presumably young polar cod, *Boreogadus saida*) thrown up by icebreakers, and algal growth visible on the underside of broken ice chunks (Todd *et al.*, 1992). Polar cod and their prey are the food of ringed seals and are known to live under ice of all types, including multiyear and first-year drifting sea ice regardless of the ocean depth (Lønne and Gulliksen, 1989). The cracks ("leads") that continuously develop in moving multiyear ice allow thinner first-year ice to form, creating habitat for seals and thus potential food for polar bears (Stirling, 1997). Although the Arctic Basin is undoubtedly less productive than continental shelf areas, it may be more productive than has been assumed.

Ovsyanikov (2010) summarizes preliminary results of two distinct pieces of polar bear research conducted by Russian biologists from 2005–2008: on Wrangel Island in the Chukchi Sea and in the central Arctic Basin. Although the Wrangel Island work was a continuation of population monitoring that has been ongoing since 1990, the Arctic Basin surveys conducted in 2005 and 2007 were the first of this kind.

The late-summer Arctic Basin surveys were split between two years, each taking a different route: the 2005 expedition surveyed northward from Wrangel Island (in the far eastern Russian Arctic), on both sides of the 180° meridian up to 79°15' N, and the 2007 trip surveyed north from Franz Joseph Land (in the far western Russian Arctic, at about 81°N, 60°E), to the North Pole and back. Observations were taken 24 hours/day from the ship bridge for the duration of the trips, and sightings of both bears and ringed seals were recorded.

In 2005, 18 bears were seen north of Wrangel, 12 of these above 75°N, which marks the edge of the continental shelf at this location. Ten of the bears seen were in four family groups, and three of these families were observed north of the continental shelf. All were in good physical condition. A female and her single cub-of-the-year were observed feeding on a ringed seal at 78°50.20' N, 177°27.40' W, where water depth under the ice was 1,500 m. In addition, seven tracks of lone bears were recorded north of the continental shelf. A total of 48 ringed seals were observed from Wrangel Island to 79°15' N, more than half of these between 78°–79° N.

In 2007, the survey ship worked the other side of the Arctic Basin, north of Franz Joseph Land, where the continental shelf ends at around 82°–83° N (Weber, 1983). Seven polar bears were sighted beyond 81° N, all of them in good condition and all recorded on fields of substantial ice. One female was observed and photographed at the North Pole on 1–2 August 2007. A total of 61 tracks of single bears were also recorded, with a concentration around 82° N. Eleven ringed seals also were observed, five between 82° and 83° N, three between 83° and 87° N, and three between 89° and 90° N (including one at the North Pole). A lower proportion of the observations of seals and bears were noted beyond the continental shelf north of Franz Joseph Land than were sighted north of Wrangel Island but a few seals and at least one bear were recorded close to, or at, the North Pole.

Ovsyanikov suggests ringed seals living at the periphery of the Arctic Ocean move into the central Arctic Basin as the pack ice recedes in late summer and polar bears that choose to stay on the pack ice (rather than moving onto land) move along with the seals and the ice into the central Arctic beyond the continental shelves. Previous reports also have documented the presence of both ringed seals (Todd *et al.*, 1992) and polar bears in the central Arctic Basin (Van Meurs and Splettstoesser, 2003), and in 1992–1993, a female tracked via satellite by Durner and Amstrup (1995) migrated from Prudhoe Bay in the southern Beaufort to northern Greenland via the central Arctic Basin (going as far north as 88°).

Ovsyanikov's Arctic Basin survey confirms ringed seals and polar bears do not require ice that is positioned over shallow, continental shelf waters, although higher densities of both species undoubtedly exist in such areas (e.g., Derocher *et al.*, 2004). Ovsyanikov's study, although limited, is the first systematic look at polar bears and ringed seal abundance within the Arctic Basin. Further surveys may reveal the Arctic Basin is a more important habitat for polar bears than has been assumed, especially given the new finds of significant blooms of phytoplankton under thick annual ice (Arrigo *et al.*, 2011), discussed previously.

Years prior to the discovery reported by Arrigo and colleagues in 2011, Amstrup (2003) said, "Despite apparent preferences for the more productive waters near shorelines and polynyas (areas of persistent open water), polar bears occur throughout the polar basin including latitudes >88°N (Stefansson 1921; Papanin 1939; Durner and Amstrup 1995)." Amstrup also notes "the frequency of recent observations deep in the polar basin, however, mandates recognition that a separate stock could occur there." Although polar bear research in the remote and formidable Arctic Basin has so far been marginal, evidence to date suggests a significant population of polar bears live their entire lives in the Arctic Basin, although their official contribution to the global population estimate is still zero (Obbard *et al.*, 2010).

Polar bears are adapted to extremes of both warming and cooling that can and do occur. Under hostile climate conditions, polar bears will move out of affected areas and return when conditions improve and when the sea ice is neither too thick nor too ephemeral. If local sea ice changes continue for whatever reason, some subpopulations may be expatriated or decline to low numbers. However, polar bears as a species are not in danger of extinction and have not reached worrying levels of population decline.

References

Aars J., Lunn N.J., and Derocher, A.E. (Eds) 2006. Polar Bears: Proceedings of the 14th Working Meeting of the IUCN/SSC Polar Bear Specialist Group, 20–24 June 2005, Seattle, Washington, USA. *Occasional Paper of the IUCN Species Survival Commission*. Gland (Switzerland) and Cambridge (UK).

Amstrup, S.C. 2003. Polar bear (*Ursus maritimus*). In: Feldhamer, G.A., Thompson, B.C., and Chapman, J.A. (Eds.) *Wild Mammals of North America*. Baltimore, MD: Johns Hopkins University Press, pp. 587–610.

Amstrup, S.C., Durner, G., Stirling, I., Lunn, N.J., and Messier, F. 2000. Movements and distribution of polar bears in the Beaufort Sea. *Canadian Journal of Zoology* **78**: 948–966.

Amstrup, S.C., McDonald, T.L., and Durner, G.M. 2004. Using satellite radio telemetry data to delineate and manage wildlife populations. *Wildlife Society Bulletin* **32**: 661–679.

Amstrup, S.C., Marcot, B.G., and Douglas, D.C. 2007. *Forecasting the rangewide status of polar bears at selected times in the 21st century*. Administrative Report, U.S. Department of the Interior-U.S. Geological Survey, Reston, VA.

Arrigo, K.R., Perovich, D.K., Pickart, R.S., Brown, Z.W., van Dijken, G.L., Lowry, K.E., Mills, M.M., Palmer, M.A., Balch, W.M., Bahr, F., Bates, N.R., Benitez-Nelson, C.,

Bowler, B., Brownlee, E., Ehn, J.K., Frey, K.E., Garley, R., Laney, S.R., Lubelczyk, L., Mathis, J., Matsuoka, A., Mitchell, B.G., Moore, G.W.K., Ortega-Retuerta, E., Pal, S., Polashenski, C.M., Reynolds, R.A., Schieber, B., Sosik, H.M., Stephens, M., and Swift, J.H. 2012 Massive phytoplankton blooms under Arctic Sea ice. *Science* **336**: 1408.

Bethke, R., Taylor, M.K., Amstrup, S., and Messier, F. 1996. Population delineation of polar bears using satellite collar data. *Ecological Applications* **6**: 311–317.

Cherry, S.G., Derocher, A.E., Thiemann, G.W., and Lunn, N.J. 2013. Migration phenology and seasonal fidelity of an Arctic marine predator in relation to sea ice dynamics. *Journal of Animal Ecology* **82**: 912–921.

Derocher, A. 2009. Ask the experts: Are polar bear populations increasing? Polar Bears International. Web site, last accessed April 30, 2009. http://www.polarbears international.org/ask-the-experts/ population/

Derocher, A.E., Lunn, N.J., and Stirling, I. 2004. Polar bears in a warming climate. *Integrative and Comparative Biology* **44**: 163–176.

Durner, G.M. and Amstrup, S.C. 1995. Movements of a polar bear from northern Alaska to northern Greenland. *Arctic* **48**: 338–341.

Dyck, M.G., Soon, W., Baydack, R.K., Legates, D.R., Baliunas, S., Ball, T.F., and Hancock, L.O. 2007. Polar bears of western Hudson Bay and climate change: Are warming spring air temperatures the 'ultimate' survival control factor? *Ecological Complexity* **4**: 73–84.

Ferguson, S.H., Taylor, M.K., and Messier, F. 1997. Space use by polar bears in and around Auyuittuq National Park, Northwest Territories, during the ice-free period. *Canadian Journal of Zoology* **75**: 1585–1594.

Ferguson, S.H., Stirling, I., and McLoughlin, P. 2005. Climate change and ringed seal (Phoca hispida) recruitment in western Hudson Bay. *Marine Mammal Science* **21**: 121–135.

Fischbach, A.S., Amstrup, S.C., and Douglas, D.C. 2007. Landward and eastward shift of Alaskan polar bear denning associated with recent sea ice changes. *Polar Biology* **30**: 1395–1405.

Gosselin, M., Levasseur, M., Wheeler, P.A., Horner, R.A., and Booth, B.C. 1997. New measurements of phytoplankton and ice algae production in the Arctic Ocean. *Deep-Sea Research II* **44**: 1623–1644.

Hunter, C.M., Caswell, H., Runge, M.C., Amstrup, S.C., Regehr, E.V., and Stirling, I. 2007. Polar bears in the southern Beaufort Sea II: Demography and population growth in relation to sea ice conditions. USGS Alaska Science Center, Anchorage, Administrative Report.

Lønne, O.J. and Gulliksen, B. 1989. Size, age and diet of polar cod, Boreogadus saida (Lepechin 1773), in ice covered waters. *Polar Biology* **9**: 187–191.

Lunn, N.J., Stirling, I., and Nowicki, S.N. 1997. Distribution and abundance of ringed (Phoca hispida) and bearded seals (Erignathus barbatus) in western Hudson Bay. *Canadian Journal of Fisheries and Aquatic Sciences* **54**: 914–921.

Messier, F., Taylor, M.K., Plante, A., and Romito, T. 2001. Atlas of polar bear movements in Nunavut, Northwest Territories, and neighboring areas. Nunavut Wildlife Service and University of Saskatchewan, Saskatoon, SK.

Obbard, M.E., Cattet, M.R.L., Moody, T., Walton, L.R., Potter, D., Inglis, J., and Chenier, C. 2006. Temporal trends in the body condition of southern Hudson Bay polar bears. Ontario Ministry of Natural Resources, Applied Research and Development Branch, Sault Ste, Marie, Canada. Climate Change Research Information Note 3. Available from http://sit.mnr.gov.on.ca.

Obbard, M.E., McDonald, T.L., Howe, E.J., Regehr, E.V., and Richardson, E.S. 2007. Polar bear population status in southern Hudson Bay, Canada. Administrative Report, U.S. Department of the Interior- U.S. Geological Survey, Reston, VA.

Obbard, M.E., Theimann, G.W., Peacock, E., and DeBryn, T.D. (Eds.) 2010. *Polar Bears: Proceedings of the 15th meeting of the Polar Bear Specialists Group IUCN/SSC, 29 June–3 July, 2009*, Copenhagen, Denmark. Gland, Switzerland and Cambridge UK, IUCN.

Ovsyanikov, N. 2010. Polar bear research on Wrangel Island and in the central Arctic Basin. In: Obbard, M.E., Theimann, G.W., Peacock, E., and DeBryn, T.D. (Eds.) *Proceedings of the 15th meeting of the Polar Bear Specialists Group IUCN/SSC, 29 June–3 July, 2009*. Gland, Switzerland and Cambridge UK, IUCN, pp. 171–178.

Papanin, I. 1939. *Life on an Ice-floe*. Hutchinson, London.

Polar Bear Technical Committee. 2006. Minutes of the 2006 Federal/Provincial/Territorial Polar Bear Technical Committee Meeting, St. John's, Newfoundland and Labrador, 6–8 February 2006. Canadian Wildlife Service, Edmonton, AB.

Ramsay, M.A. and Stirling, I. 1988. Reproductive biology and ecology of female polar bears (*Ursus maritimus*). *Journal of Zoology London* **214**: 601–624.

Regehr, E.V., Amstrup, S.C., and Stirling, I. 2006. Polar bear population status in the Southern Beaufort Sea. U.S. Geological Survey Open-File Report 2006–1337.

Regehr, E.V., Lunn, N.J., Amstrup, S.C., and Stirling, I. 2007a. Survival and population size of polar bears in western Hudson Bay in relation to earlier sea ice breakup. *Journal of Wildlife Management* **71**: 2673–2683.

Regehr, E.V., Hunter, C.M., Caswell, H., Amstrup, S.C., and Stirling, I. 2007b. Polar bears in the southern Beaufort Sea I: survival and breeding in relation to sea ice conditions, 2001–2006. Administrative Report, U.S. Department of the Interior-U.S. Geological Survey, Reston, VA.

Rode, K.D., Amstrup, S.C., and Regehr, E.V. 2007. Polar bears in the southern Beaufort Sea III: stature, mass, and cub recruitment in relationship to time and sea ice extent between 1982 and 2006. Administrative Report, U.S. Department of the Interior-U.S. Geological Survey, Reston, VA.

Rode, K.D., Regehr, E.V., Douglas, D., Durner, G., Derocher, A.E., Thiemann, G.W., and Budge, S. 2014. Variation in the response of an Arctic top predator experiencing habitat loss: feeding and reproductive ecology of two polar bear populations. *Global Change Biology* **20**: 76–88.

Stapleton, S., Atkinson, S., Hedman, D., and Garshelis, D. 2012a. Western Hudson Bay polar bear aerial survey, 2011. Final report, May 14, 2012, prepared for the Government of Nunavut, Igloolik.

Stapleton, S., Peacock, E., and Garshelis, D. 2012b. Foxe Basin polar bear aerial survey. Nunavut Wildlife Research Trust, Government of Nunavut, Igloolik.

Stefansson, V. 1921. *The Friendly Arctic.* Macmillan, New York.

Stirling, I. 1997. The importance of polynyas, ice edges, and leads to marine mammals and birds. *Journal of Marine Systems* **10**: 9–21.

Stirling, I., Lunn, N.J., and Iacozza, J. 1999. Long-term trends in the population ecology of polar bears in Western Hudson Bay in relation to climate change. *Arctic* **52**: 294–306.

Stirling, I. and Parkinson, C.L. 2006. Possible effects of climate warming on selected populations of polar bears (*Ursus maritimus*) in the Canadian Arctic. *Arctic* **59**: 261–275.

Taylor, M. and Dowsley, M. 2008. Demographic and ecological perspectives on the status of polar bears. Science & Public Policy Institute, Washington D.C.

Todd, F.S., Headland, R.K., and Lasca, N. 1992. Animals at the North Pole. *Polar Record* **28**: 321–322.

Taylor, M.K. and Lee, L.J. 1995. Distribution and abundance of Canadian polar bear populations: a management perspective. *Arctic* **48**: 147–154.

Taylor, M.K., Akeeagok, S., Andriashek, D., Barbour, W., Born, E.W., Calvert, W., Cluff, H.D., Ferguson, S., Laake, J., Rosing-Asvid, A., Stirling, I., and Messier, F. 2001. Delineating Canadian and Greenland polar bear (*Ursus*

maritimus) populations by cluster analysis of movements. *Canadian Journal of Zoology* **79**: 690–709.

Taylor, M.K., Laake, J., Cluff, H.D., Ramsay, M., and Messier, F. 2002. Managing the risk of harvest for the Viscount Melville Sound polar bear population. *Ursus* **13**: 185–202.

Taylor, M.K., Laake, J., McLoughlin, P.D., Born, E.W., Cluff, H.D., Ferguson, S.H., Rosing-Asvid, A., Schweinsburg, R., and Messier, F. 2005. Demography and viability of a hunted population of polar bear. *Arctic* **58**: 203–214.

Taylor, M.K., Laake, J.L., McLoughlin, P.D., Cluff, H.D., and Messier, F. 2006. Demographic parameters and harvest-explicit population viability analysis for polar bears in M'Clintock Channel, Nunavut. *Journal of Wildlife Management* **70**: 1667–1673.

Taylor, M.K., Laake, J., McLoughlin, P.D., Cluff, H.D., Born, E.W., Rosing-Asvid, A., and Messier, F. 2008. Population parameters and harvest risks for polar bears (*Ursus maritimus*) in Kane Basin, Nunavut and Greenland. *Polar Biology* **31**: 491–499.

Todd, F.S., Headland, R.K., and Lasca, N. 1992. Animals at the North Pole. *Polar Record* **28**: 321–322.

Van Meurs, R. and Splettstoesser, J.F. 2003. Farthest north polar bear. *Arctic* **56**: 309.

Weber, J.R. 1983. Maps of the Arctic Basin sea floor: A history of bathymetry and its interpretation. *Arctic* **36**: 121–142.

5.8.2 Life History

5.8.2.1 Choice of Den Location by Females

In the fall, pregnant polar bear females make maternity dens in drifted snow, either on land or drifting pack ice, where they hibernate over the winter (Mauritzen *et al.*, 2001). The tiny cubs are born during hibernation (from mid-November to January) and are nursed within the den for at least two months. Mothers and cubs emerge around March-April. Individual females appear to have preferences for den location: females that den on land and those that den on ice are known in most subpopulations studied, except western Hudson Bay and around Svalbard in the Barents Sea, where all females appear to den on land (Mauritzen *et al.*, 2001; Ferguson *et al.*, 2000; Fischbach *et al.*, 2007; Lentfer, 1975; Zeyl *et al.*, 2010). According to Amstrup (2003), although it was once believed there were several high-density "core" areas for denning, "over much of their range, we now know, polar bears den in a more diffuse pattern where individual dens are scattered over broad reaches of habitat at low density." And as Zeyl *et al.* (2010) have stated, "long-term fidelity of denning areas and faithfulness to denning substrate (*i.e.*, land vs. ice) has been observed."

Do females switch their den locations from one year to the next? If so, what is the level of loyalty ("fidelity") to either the area (the particular place on land) or the substrate (land vs. ice)? As all Svalbard-area females appear to den on land, the issue addressed in the paper by Zeyl *et al.* was whether mothers switched from one denning area to another within the Svalbard region, and whether related individuals (especially mothers and daughters) tended to den in the same area.

The authors used data collected from a technique called "mark-recapture," along with results from analysis of mitochondrial DNA (mtDNA, the kind inherited from mothers) to investigate the amount of loyalty individual female polar bears had to five denning areas around Svalbard. They also used these data to address whether any loyalty to a specific area was transmitted from mothers to daughters to such an extent that it would result in genetic clustering of mtDNA haplotypes in different den areas.

The results of the study indicate female polar bears have a moderate degree of loyalty to their chosen den areas (3/13 females switched areas from one year to the next) and daughters had a tendency to den in the same areas as their mothers (only 2/8 did not). There was not, however, the kind of genetic clustering expected if such loyalty had been ongoing over a long period of time. Although the distances between successive mark-recapture locations for Svalbard females were similar to distances reported for land-denning females in western Hudson Bay (23.7 km vs. 34 km, respectively), these were much lower than documented for females in the Beaufort Seas (308 km), where a significant proportion of bears den on sea ice (Amstrup and Gardner, 1994), the authors note. Zeyl and colleagues also note the level of denning site loyalty demonstrated by female polar bears on Svalbard is markedly lower than recorded for brown bears, their closest living relatives (who of course always den on land).

Zeyl and colleagues suggest female polar bears may switch the precise location of their dens from one year to the next depending on prevailing snow or sea ice conditions. In a similar study, Fischbach *et al.* (2007) documented some females who switched between pack ice dens and land dens (*i.e.*, a switch of substrate type). Zeyl *et al.* suggest there is more flexibility than previously assumed in den site choice among polar bear females.

The demonstrated willingness of polar bear females to switch den locations from one year to the next, despite a general tendency towards den site loyalty, almost certainly gives them the flexibility they need as a species to persist in the face of sea ice conditions that vary from year to year. The ability of polar bear females to shift from one den site location to another or one substrate to another is just one aspect of the kind of plasticity needed to survive in this habitat.

Amstrup and Gardner (1994) stated, "contrary to previous hypotheses (Stirling and Andriashek, 1992), substantial polar bear denning occurs in the Beaufort Sea region of northern Alaska and adjacent Canada. Bears that den on pack ice are subject to risks not encountered by bears that den on land. Unstable, moving ice caused early abandonment of dens and, apparently, loss of cubs. However, the persistence of pack-ice denning indicated that those risks are not overwhelming."

As one Russian polar bear researcher commented years ago regarding bears in the eastern Russian Arctic (Kochnev, 2006), "our investigations on Wrangel Island have shown the polar bear is a very plastic animal: it can rapidly change its way of life, spatial distribution and behavior according to new ecological conditions." Zeyl and colleagues (2010) seem to agree, stating, "females are likely able to change denning locations if unsuitable ice conditions prevent them from reaching their preferred denning areas. We consider this plasticity an important attribute of polar bears when facing climate change."

Working in the same Southern Beaufort region as Fischbach *et al.* (2007), Schliebe *et al.* (2008) found in 2000–2005 an average of 3.7% of polar bears spent time on land between mid-September and the end of October; the rest were on the pack ice. They state, "across all years and survey dates between mid-September and the end of October, an average of 4 ± 2 bears/100 km (57 ± 28 bears total) were observed. Thus, a maximum of 8.0% and an average of 3.7% of the estimated 1,526 bears in the SBS population (Regehr *et al.*, 2006) were observed on land." This means there were, on average, only 56 bears on land in the fall each year (out of 1,526 bears), suggesting most pregnant females in the Southern Beaufort made their dens in the pack ice and never came to land in fall. Schliebe *et al.* conclude, "overall, we did not detect an increasing trend in polar bear densities along the Beaufort Sea coast of Alaska during the six years of this study," indicating bears were not being forced on land due to declining summer ice coverage.

These studies make it apparent an unknown number of polar bear females den in the offshore pack ice and many Southern Beaufort bears never set foot on land. Amstrup (2003), in his discussion of pack-ice denning in the Beaufort Sea, says this about offshore denning: "despite the absence of conclusive reports, sea-ice denning probably occurs at some level in other areas." Amstrup suggests these areas include the Arctic Basin, given "the recent recognition of a possible polar basin stock of polar bears." In addition, he suggests the "linear coastline of central Arctic Russia may be more similar to the Beaufort Sea than other areas, and hence may be another area where sea-ice denning is common."

Given the known and predicted use of offshore ice for denning, it is rather astonishing that the report supplied in support of the listing of the polar bear as a threatened species in the United States (Bergen *et al.*, 2007) modeled only future changes to terrestrial denning habitat. Since those models did not address offshore sea ice denning habitat at all, it means those studies ignored a huge amount of polar bear habitat that is likely critical to their resilience to changing sea ice conditions.

References

Amstrup, S.C. 2003. Polar bear (*Ursus maritimus*). In: Feldhamer, G.A., Thompson, B.C., and Chapman, J.A. (Eds.) *Wild Mammals of North America*. Baltimore, MD: Johns Hopkins University Press, pp. 587–610.

Amstrup, S.C. and Gardner, C. 1994. Polar bear maternity denning in the Beaufort Sea. *The Journal of Wildlife Management* **58**: 1–10.

Bergen, S., Durner, G.M., Douglas, D.C., and Amstrup, S.C. 2007. Predicting movements of female polar bears between summer sea ice foraging habitats and terrestrial denning habitats of Alaska in the 21st century: Proposed methodology and pilot assessment. Administrative Report, USGS Alaska Science Center, Anchorage, AK.

Ferguson, S.H., Taylor, M.K., and Messier, F. 2000. Influence of sea ice dynamics on habitat selection by polar bears. *Ecology* **81**: 761–772.

Fischbach, A.S., Amstrup, S.C., and Douglas, D.C. 2007. Landward and eastward shift of Alaskan polar bear denning associated with recent sea ice changes. *Polar Biology* **30**: 1395–1405.

Kochnev, A.A. 2006. Research on polar bear autumn aggregations on Chukotka, 1989–2004. In: Aars, J., Lunn, N.J., and Derocher, A.E. (Eds.) Polar Bears: Proceedings of the 14th Working Meeting of the IUCN/SSC Polar Bear Specialist Group, 20–24 June 2005, Seattle, Washington, USA. *Occasional Paper of the IUCN Species Survival Commission 32*. Gland, Switzerland, and Cambridge, UK: IUCN, pp. 157–165.

Lentfer, J.W. 1975. Polar bear denning on drifting sea ice. *Journal of Mammalogy* **56**: 716–718.

Mauritzen, M., Derocher, A.E., and Wiig, Ø. 2001. Space-use strategies of female polar bears in a dynamic sea ice habitat. *Canadian Journal of Zoology* **79**: 1704–1713.

Regehr, E.V., Amstrup, S.C., and Stirling, I. 2006. Polar bear population status in the Southern Beaufort Sea. U.S. Geological Survey Open-File Report 2006–1337.

Schliebe, S., Rode, K.D., Gleason, J.S., Wilder, J., Proffitt, K., Evans, T.J., and Miller, S. 2008. Effects of sea ice extent and food availability on spatial and temporal distribution of polar bears during the fall open-water period in the southern Beaufort Sea. *Polar Biology* **31**: 999–1010.

Stirling, I. and Andriashek, D. 1992. Terrestrial maternity denning of polar bears in the eastern Beaufort Sea area. *Arctic* **45**: 363–366.

Zeyl, E., Ehrich, D., Aars, J., Bachmann, L., and Wiig, Ø. 2010. Denning-area fidelity and mitochondrial DNA diversity of female polar bears (*Ursus maritimus*) in the Barents Sea. *Canadian Journal of Zoology* **88**: 1139–1148.

5.8.2.2 Mortality Due to Den Collapse

In a list of suggested risks to polar bears in a warmer world, Derocher *et al.* (2004) state, "An additional concern specific to female polar bears in dens with altricial cubs is the possibility that rain might become more frequent in late winter and cause the snow cover over dens to collapse and suffocate the occupants." Stirling and Derocher (2012) provide more up-to-date and detailed information on this concern. Their paper summarizes all of the known anecdotal reports of rain on snow events that led to the collapse of polar bear maternity dens and/or ringed seal birthing lairs. They state "such rain on snow events are predicted to increase as the climate warms in the Arctic."

Stirling and Derocher describe four incidents: one case of a maternity den collapse (involving a six-year-old, probably first-time mother and two cubs three to four weeks old) in the southern Beaufort in 1989, apparently caused by warm weather followed by heavy snow in late January, reported originally by Clarkson and Irish (1991); a rain event in early March 1990 in western Hudson Bay that was not associated with den collapses and which led to "no evidence of dead bears the following summer"; rain and warm weather in early April 1979 in southeastern Baffin Island that resulted in "increased predation mortality of ringed seal pups" by polar bears and Arctic foxes; a warm period, also in southeastern Baffin Island, in late April 1990, that was reported to have generated a tripling of polar bear predation success on newborn ringed seal pups because ringed seal birthing lairs were easier to break or had melted and collapsed.

These details indicate each of the den collapse incidents occurred in 1990 or before, not in more recent years as might be expected if such events were associated with warmer temperatures. It appears there has not been a single documented event of this kind since 1990, despite increasing temperatures and "progressive unidirectional changes to sea ice distribution" (Stirling and Derocher, 2012). Instead, it appears warm spells in winter and rain in the spring occur rarely in the Arctic, even in a warming world, and do not pose a significant risk to polar bears or their ringed seal prey. Anecdotal reports such as these are not evidence and do not contribute to our understanding of how polar bears respond to unidirectional climate change.

References

Clarkson, P.L. and Irish, D. 1991. Den collapse kills female polar bear and two newborn cubs. *Arctic* **44:** 83–84.

Derocher, A.E., Lunn, N.J., and Stirling, I. 2004. Polar bears in a warming climate. *Integrative and Comparative Biology* **44:** 163–176.

Stirling, I. and Derocher, A.E. 2012. Effects of climate warming on polar bears: a review of the evidence. *Global Change Biology* **18:** 2694–2706

5.8.3 Nutrition and Reproductive Success

Researchers have expressed concern over the relationships between temperature and sea ice breakup and the nutrition and physical condition of polar bears and reproductive success. Closer scrutiny of these claims suggests they lack empirical bases.

5.8.3.1 Nutritional Stress and Declines in Body Condition

According to Stirling and Derocher (2012), "the most comprehensive long-term research on polar bear demography, body condition, subpopulation size, abundance, and reproductive success has been conducted on the Western Hudson Bay subpopulation." For bears in this subpopulation, they found "statistically significant relationships have been documented between progressively earlier dates of sea ice breakup (which shortens the feeding time for polar bears at the most important time of the year just before coming ashore, and lengthens the fasting period)," and declines in the following parameters: mean body condition during the fall ice-free period; mean weights of suspected pregnant females prior to denning in fall; and survival of juvenile, subadult, and old (senescent) adult bears.

These claimed correlations between these life history parameters and "progressively earlier dates of sea ice breakup" in Western Hudson are based on published sea ice data only up to 1998. As their figure caption notes, data after that time (1999 to 2007) is attributed to "N.J. Lunn and I. Stirling, unpublished data." In contrast, the figure they include showing global sea ice declines, based on Stroeve *et al.* (2007), is updated to 2011 with publicly available data provided by the U.S. National Snow and Ice Data Center. Moreover, although Stirling and Derocher say "the mean mass of adult females declined (by about 20%) between 1980 and 2007" (mass being a "proxy" for body condition, which they say is tied closely to litter size, age at weaning, and cub survival), the data used to reach this conclusion are for 1980 to 2004 only: the data from 2006 to 2007 are not available in the peer-reviewed literature. This means the data on which these claims are made are strikingly out of date and/or unavailable, and the conclusions may no longer be valid.

Stirling and Derocher's claim of "progressive unidirectional changes to sea ice distribution" may be accurate for global sea ice coverage but not for ice on Hudson Bay. In a recent paper on breakup in Western Hudson Bay, Cherry *et al.* (2013) show between 1991 and 2009, there was considerable variability in breakup dates. Polar bears left the ice later in 2009 than in 1992, indicating breakup dates have not been progressively earlier since 1992. Only nine of 19 breakup dates in this period fell in June (with none falling in the first half of the month), suggesting there was little or no impact on the critical November–June feeding period. And although some bears apparently chose a favorite location to come ashore even if there was enough ice to spend more time hunting, many bears were flexible enough in their choice of where and when they left the ice to adapt to yearly variability in conditions. Overall, it appears variability may be the most prominent feature of sea ice breakup dates for Western Hudson Bay and most polar bear females can and do take these variations in stride.

Polar bears in the Southern Beaufort region have also been reasonably well-studied. This subpopulation is shared between the United States and Canada and comprises most of the north coast of Alaska and about an equal length of the western Canadian Arctic coastline. It is characterized by a dynamic mix of annual and multiyear sea ice. Bears in the Southern Beaufort routinely den on the sea ice rather than on land and reach their maximum weights in the fall, rather than in summer, as do bears in Western Hudson Bay—probably because they spend little, if any, time on land during the summer.

Durner and Amstrup (1996) note, "polar bears in western Hudson Bay differ from other populations because the sea ice substrate required for hunting melts completely by late summer (Ramsay and Stirling, 1988), and all members of the population fast or consume only low-energy food (Derocher *et al.*, 1992). On the other hand, polar bears inhabiting certain areas of the Canadian Arctic archipelago (e.g., Viscount Melville Sound) may be food deprived because of stable sea ice conditions during winter and low seal densities (Messier *et al.*, 1994). Because polar bears in Alaska [*i.e.*, the Southern Beaufort] follow seasonal changes in dynamic pack ice (Amstrup and DeMaster, 1988), they may not face the food scarcity that characterizes the Hudson Bay population during summer and the northern Canadian population during the winter."

In other words, even before there were declines in sea ice coverage purportedly caused by global warming, polar bear biologists saw marked differences among subpopulations in patterns of body condition changes from season to season. In light of that understanding, do reports that blame global warming for declines in polar bear size and body condition (and associated declines in cub production and/or survival) stand up to scrutiny?

Rode *et al.* (2010) studied polar bears in the Southern Beaufort between 1982 and 2006. They used a subjective definition of sea ice conditions, called "optimal ice habitat," which is not a quality measured by satellites but "resource selection function (RSF) models" that use data from satellite-collared polar bears (1985–1995) to show where the bears that researchers captured on land or near shore moved throughout the year. Using this method, a decline in area (km^2-months) of "optimal ice habitat" (ice neither too thin nor too thick) could mean sea ice got thicker, got thinner, or disappeared—it is not possible to tell which. Rode *et al.* (2010) conclude,

"the decline over time in the availability of sea ice corresponded with declining trends in most measures of bear sizes and condition." But because their "decline over time in availability" is not a straightforward decline in sea ice extent or timing of the ice-free period, but a decline in "optimal ice habitat," it is unlikely this parameter is really useful in addressing whether reduced levels of summer sea ice in the Southern Beaufort are the proximate cause of negative impacts on polar bears.

In direct contraction of a statement made by Obbard *et al.* (2010), discussed in more detail near the end of this section, Rode *et al.* (2010) say, "declines in the size of bears in this population have occurred during a time period when the number of bears in the region also appears to be lower than previously thought (Regehr *et al.*, 2006), and the trend in numbers appears to be downward (Regehr *et al.*, 2010). Though the mechanism associated with population-level change is not clear, nutritional limitations in the population are apparent as a result of the observed declines in bear skull sizes and body lengths. ... Thus, nutritional factors may also have played a role in the observed population-level changes." Although nutritional stress has indeed been documented for this area, there has not been a statistically significant decline in the population, a point reiterated by Regehr *et al.* (2007): "changes in the sea ice have not yet been associated with changes in the size of the SB polar bear population (Regehr *et al.*, 2006)." Obbard *et al.* (2010) concur.

Even more surprising is recent research on polar bears in the neighboring Chukchi Sea subpopulation (shared between the United States and Russia), which has shown either no negative effects or marked improvement despite at least twice as much summer sea ice loss as in the Southern Beaufort. Rode *et al.* (2014) captured, measured, and released polar bears on the sea ice between mid-March and early May, 2008–2011; others did similar work in 1986–1994. Rode *et al.* compared data collected on body condition, litter size, and juvenile survival ("reproductive indices") in the Chukchi Sea between the two periods (1986–1994 and 2008–2011). They also compared body condition and reproduction in the Chukchi and neighboring Southern Beaufort for the period 2008–2011. They evaluated these metrics in relation to sea ice loss and prey availability; for Chukchi bears in 2008–2011 only, they also determined diet composition from analysis of fat samples ("fatty acid signatures") and fasting behavior from analysis of blood samples ("levels of blood urea nitrogen and creatinine").

The authors found "in 2008–2011, CS [Chukchi] bears were either larger and in better condition, or similar in size and condition, to CS bears in 1986–1994." They also found "no difference in the number of yearlings per female, yearling litter size, or the annual percentage of females with yearlings between periods in the CS. ... Overall, CS bears in 2008–2011 were larger and in better condition than SB [Southern Beaufort] bears during the same period." The number of yearlings per female in spring was also higher in the Chukchi Sea than in the Southern Beaufort.

Most surprisingly, Chukchi bears were larger and heavier than virtually all other subpopulations studied. Rode *et al.* (2014) found "spring COY litter sizes are among the highest reported for 18 of 19 polar bear populations. ... [S]pring litter sizes of CS yearlings from the study were also higher than other populations." The authors note, "the larger body mass of adult females in the CS corresponded not only with larger litter sizes, but also with heavier yearlings (Fig.5 [in original document]) which have a greater chance of survival." Rode *et al.* state, "body size, condition, and reproductive indices of CS polar bears did not decline over time between 1986–1994 and 2008–2011 despite a 44-day increase in the number of reduced-ice days. Furthermore, CS bears were larger, in better condition, and appeared to have higher recruitment compared to the adjacent SB population during 2008–2011. These differences were biologically significant."

In the Chukchi subpopulation, the authors conclude, "body condition was maintained or improved when sea ice declined" and "continued high biological productivity in the Chukchi and northern Bering seas may be allowing polar bears and their prey to prosper despite habitat loss." Regarding Southern Beaufort bears, they state, "Our evaluation of nutritional ecology for polar bears is consistent with lower prey availability in the SB compared to the CS."

These results were unexpected because the Southern Beaufort and Chukchi Seas are considered similar ice ecoregions and polar bears were predicted to respond similarly to summer sea ice loss. Both have been classified as "divergent" ice ecoregions by researchers attempting to predict how polar bear habitat might fare over the next 25 to 95 years based on computer-projected sea ice declines (Amstrup, 2011; Amstrup *et al.,* 2008, 2010; Durner *et al.,* 2009). Durner and colleagues, for example, state, "within the Divergent ecoregion, rates of decline are projected to be greatest in the Southern Beaufort, Chukchi, and Barents Sea subpopulations." Two

conclusions can be drawn from this study: Declines in summer sea ice extent can markedly benefit polar bear survival, and extent of sea ice loss in summer is not the paramount determiner of polar bear health and population status, at least over the short term.

In the eastern Arctic, there also has been recent work done on Davis Strait polar bears, the most southerly polar bear subpopulation. Whereas the southernmost portion of the Southern Hudson Bay region (James Bay) lies at about 52°N and the southernmost portion of Western Hudson Bay lies at about 55°N, bears in the Davis Strait polar bear subpopulation occur regularly to at least 50°N, with some moving as far south in spring as 47°N.

Based on mark-recapture studies undertaken from 1974 to 1979 and from 2005 to 2007, Peacock *et al.* (2013) state, "the overall amount of sea ice declined and breakup has become progressively earlier" since the 1970s. Nonetheless, they "estimated the abundance of the Davis Strait polar bear subpopulation to 2,158, which results in a relatively high population density of polar bears of approximately 5.1 bears/1,000 km^2 of sea ice habitat (Taylor and Lee, 1995). This density is greater than polar bear densities in other seasonal-ice subpopulations, which are approximately 3.5 bears/1,000 km^2." So despite declining sea ice since the 1970s, the density of bears in this region has reached a higher level than any other subpopulation known that loses ice completely in summer. The authors conclude, "survival and reproduction of bears in southern Davis Strait was greater than in the north and tied to a concurrent dramatic increase in breeding harp seals (*Pagophilus groenlandicus*) in Labrador."

They suggest the Davis Strait polar bear subpopulation is characterized by "low recruitment rates, average adult survival rates, and high population density." The high density of bears in this region may be affecting recruitment (*i.e.,* reproduction), the authors conclude, "low reproductive rates may reflect negative effects of greater densities or worsening ice conditions." In other words, polar bear populations with a high density of animals may show changes to life history parameters similar to those expected in populations affected by declines in sea ice. However, effects of high density and less time spent feeding due to reduced sea ice appear to be viable explanations for the observed conditions in Davis Strait, and these factors are not necessarily mutually exclusive. Nevertheless, polar bears in Davis Strait appear to be increasing in number, not declining as reported by the IUCN/SSC Polar Bear Specialist Group (Obbard *et al.,* 2010) and others, despite the declines in sea ice.

In a similar study that compared Davis Strait polar bears to those in Baffin Bay to the North, Rode *et al.* (2012) "examined trends in body condition metrics of captured bears and relationships with summertime ice concentration between 1977 and 2010 for the Baffin Bay (BB) and Davis Strait (DS) polar bear populations." Both of these regions are dominated by annual (first year) ice. They conclude, "we suggest that declining body condition in BB may be a result of recent declines in sea ice habitat. In DS, high population density and/or sea ice loss may be responsible for the declines in body condition. ... Though a decline in body condition was observed for DS between 1978 and 1994, there was no relationship between body condition and sea ice concentrations at that time." In other words, the decline in condition of polar bears in Davis Strait may be evidence the population has reached "carrying capacity" despite the declining trend in annual sea ice extent. This result suggests declines in body condition may not necessarily be the harbinger of doom for polar bears some researchers have proposed but instead a signal more bears exist than the local habitat can support.

One of the presumed repercussions of polar bears that end up in poor condition due to nutritional stress, especially if they get to the point of starving, is an increase in propensity for infanticide and cannibalism. These phenomena are well-known in all bears (Taylor *et al.,* 1985), but there have been no long-term, carefully designed scientific studies on infanticide or cannibalism among polar bears, so no baseline data exist with which to compare recent anecdotal reports. This has not stopped some polar bear researchers and conservation advocates from using these anecdotal observations as a kind of "supporting evidence" for contending polar bears are already being negatively impacted by global warming.

Stirling and Derocher (2012) state, "There have been several well-publicized observations that are consistent with predictions of the effects of climate warming on polar bears, but cannot be statistically linked. For example, intraspecific aggression and cannibalism were predicted to increase in polar bears with climate warming (Derocher *et al.*, 2004, Table 1). Observations of infanticide and cannibalism by thin adult males on land during the open water period have been documented (e.g., Lunn and Stenhouse, 1985; Derocher and Wiig, 1999; Amstrup *et al.*, 2006; Stone and Derocher, 2007)."

However, of the references cited, only Lunn and Stenhouse (1985) report a confirmed instance of a thin (*i.e.,* starving) adult male killing and consuming another adult bear during the open water period, and

that event occurred in 1984. Amstrup *et al.* (2006), who report three incidents of cannibalism in the Southern Beaufort, did not know the condition of the bears that killed and partially consumed other bears, as no one witnessed these attacks. In addition, contrary to the notion that cannibalism is associated with starvation, in the most recent case published (one not mentioned by Stirling and Derocher), Stirling and Ross (2011) report three cases of cannibalism on the sea ice around Svalbard, all of which involved males in good or very good condition killing other young bears. They say "the three observations we describe are different from most other reports of infanticide and cannibalism in polar bears because they took place between midsummer and early autumn. ... All three adult males appeared to be in good physical condition (*i.e.*, not obviously thin), and one was both very large and very fat."

Stirling *et al.* (2008), in a follow-up to the report of Amstrup *et al.* (2006), state, "these observations, along with cannibalized and starved polar bears found on the sea ice in the same general area in the springs of 2004 through 2006, suggest that during those years, polar bears in the southern Beaufort Sea were nutritionally stressed." They point out several severe winter storms piled up thick ridges of sea ice in the landfast ice zone, which made seal hunting difficult for polar bears. They acknowledge the nutritional stress was caused by heavy ice conditions in 2004 and 2005 (confirmed by Harwood *et al.,* 2012 and Melling *et al.,* 2005) but suggest the heavy ice may have been caused by open water many months prior in the Chukchi Sea far to the west. However, there have been heavy ice years in this region every decade since the 1960s (long before there was increased open water in the fall) and starving bears in spring were documented in most of those heavy ice years (Stirling, 2002; Stirling and Lunn, 1997; Stirling *et al.,* 2008), suggesting the cause of heavy spring ice is something other than increased open water in the summer.

The impact of the most recent heavy ice years on ringed seals is documented by Harwood *et al.* (2012), for the Amundson Gulf, which lies in the south half of the Northern Beaufort polar bear subpopulation (and immediately east of the Southern Beaufort areas discussed above). They examined "the relationship between ringed seal body condition and reproduction and spring sea ice conditions in prime ringed seal habitat" in the western Canadian Arctic between 1992 and 2011. They found "failure to ovulate was obvious in 2005, the most extreme late ice clearance year in our series, when only 30.0% of the mature adult females sampled ovulated." The authors conclude, "Seals sampled in years of late ice clearing had, on average, lower body condition than those sampled in years of earlier ice clearing, particularly in the case of subadults" and for mature females, "marked declines were seen in 1974 (Smith, 1987), in 1987 (Kingsley and Byers, 1998), and in 2005 (this study), all times when seals were in significantly poorer body condition. ... Signals were detected in the most extreme ice years (e.g., when fast ice breakup occurred 3–8 weeks later than the average since 1970) and were linked to the degree of severity of winters, as indicated by the annual ice regime." They note, "In the Beaufort/Amundsen regions, for example, observations over the last 40 years have revealed large fluctuations in ice presence and thickness over intervals of years to decades, with so far only small trends towards earlier ice clearance and longer open water seasons (Melling and Riedel, 2004; Melling et al., 2005)."

Pilfold et al. (2012) corroborate the declines in ringed seal pup production documented by Harwood et al. (2012) in their study of the age composition of ringed seals killed by polar bears in the eastern Beaufort from 1971 to 2006. They show, in their Figure 3, a higher proportion of pups were killed during the low or average spring ice years of 1971–1973 (when about 45% of seals killed were pups) and 2007–2011 (about 80% pups) than in the heavy spring ice years of 1974 to 1975 (none killed were pups), 1985 to 1987 (about 10% pups), or in 2003 to 2006 (about 40% pups). In other words, since the early 1970s, polar bears killed fewer seal pups in springs with heavy sea ice conditions, suggesting fewer seal pups were available.

Another perspective on these events is provided by Cherry et al. (2009), who compared the fasting physiology of eastern Beaufort Sea polar bears during two known heavy spring ice periods: 1985–1986 and 2005–2006. In their analysis of the proportion of urea vs. creatinine (considered an indicator of fasting) from blood samples drawn in the eastern Beaufort Sea (which include the southern portion of the Northern Beaufort subpopulation) in April-May 1985–1986 and 2005–2006, they found "the proportions of polar bears fasting were 9.6% in 1985, 10.5% in 1986, 21.4% in 2005, and 29.3% in 2006. ... The increased number of polar bears in a physiological fasting state from all sex, age, and reproductive classes in 2005 and 2006 corresponded with broad scale changes in Arctic sea ice composition, which may have affected prey availability." They write, "none of the bears displayed physical or behavioral traits indicative of an animal in the advanced stages of starvation." This seems to corroborate the finding by Amstrup et al. (2006), who found in the spring of 2004, the year before Cherry et al. took their samples, "70 of 148 (47%) of bears captured as independent animals (i.e., not including cubs captured with their mothers) were in the lean condition classes 1 and 2." This is perhaps not very surprising, as polar bears are generally at their leanest in March, and if they are slow to put on weight for any reason over the spring months, by April or May they would not yet be in optimum condition (although they might be so a few months later).

Cherry et al.'s discussion of the "changes in Arctic sea ice" in their introduction attempts to imply the changes over time in the percentage of fasting bears was caused by reduced ice and more open water. They say, for example, "the Arctic ice-ocean system has been warming faster than global averages since the 1960s." They conclude, "Beaufort Sea bears reach their lightest weights in late March and rely on a 2–3 month spring feeding period, when fat and naïve ringed seal pups are available, to gain the fat reserves necessary for survival and reproduction (Stirling and Øritsland, 1995; Stirling, 2002). ... [T]he recent increase in bears fasting during April and May suggests that there has been a decrease in prey availability at that time of year. ... [T]he precise means through which prey have apparently become less available to polar bears in the Beaufort Sea remains unknown." But as discussed above, "the precise means" have been documented—evidence from this region suggests heavy sea ice in the spring during 2004–2006, which resulted in precipitous declines in ringed seal pup production, was almost certainly the cause of more bears fasting (Harwood et al., 2012; Melling et al., 2005; Stirling, 2002; Stirling et al., 2008).

Regehr et al. (2010) provide another attempt to shift attention from heavy ice conditions in spring to low sea ice conditions in late summer. These researchers "evaluated the effects of sea ice conditions on vital rates (survival and breeding probabilities) for polar bears in the southern Beaufort Sea" with models, based on data collected from 2001 to 2006 on polar bears and the number of ice-free days each year. They conclude, "in the most supported models, polar bear survival declined with an increasing number of days per year that waters over the continental shelf were ice free. In 2001–2003, the ice-free period was relatively short (mean 101 days) and adult female survival was high (0·96–0·99, depending on reproductive state). In 2004 and

2005, the ice-free period was longer (mean 135 days) and adult female survival was low (0·73–0·79, depending on reproductive state). Breeding rates and cub litter survival also declined with increasing duration of the ice-free period. Confidence intervals on vital rate estimates were wide."

Regehr *et al.* did not include possible effects of heavy sea ice conditions in spring in their models, which, as shown above, tends to have a direct negative impact on polar bear life history parameters in the eastern Beaufort (Harwood *et al.,* 2012; Melling *et al.,* 2005; Stirling, 2002; Stirling and Lunn, 1997). Regehr *et al.*'s models considered only number of ice-free days in summer as a possible association. As a consequence their results and conclusions add little to our understanding of changes in polar bear survival or body condition in the Southern Beaufort.

It should be noted that despite the repeated bouts of less-than-optimum conditions every decade or so, polar bear numbers in the Southern Beaufort appear to have remained remarkably stable. Obbard *et al.* (2010) note,

> through the 1980s and early 1990s, observations suggested that the SB subpopulation was increasing. Amstrup *et al.* (2001) found the SB subpopulation may have reached as many as 2,500 polar bears in the late 1990s. However, that estimate was not considered reliable due to methodological difficulties, and management decisions continued to be based on a population size of 1,800. Results from an intensive mark-recapture study conducted from 2001–2006 in both the USA and Canada indicated that the SB subpopulation included 1,526 (95% CI = 1,211–1,841) polar bears in 2006 (Regehr *et al.,* 2006). This suggests that the size of the SB subpopulation declined between the late 1990s and 2006, although low precision in the previous estimate of 1,800 precluded a statistical determination."

In other words, although there is evidence of nutritional stress in 2004–2006, it did not result in a statistically significant decline in numbers of polar bears in the Southern Beaufort region.

In addition, polar bears that live in the region around Banks Island and the Amundsen Gulf in the past were often included in studies of the "eastern Beaufort," but they now are considered part of the Northern Beaufort subpopulation, one of the few subpopulations some researchers consider as having a stable population trend (Obbard *et al.,* 2010; Stirling *et al.,* 2011).

Surprisingly, one question seldom addressed in studies on nutritional stress and associated behaviors such as cannibalism is this: Do polar bears ever starve under conditions that cannot be blamed on sea ice changes? Indeed, they do. Amstrup (2003) notes

> starvation of independent young as well as very old animals must account for much of the natural mortality among polar bears. ... Also, age structure data show that subadults aged 2–5 years survive at lower rates than adults (Amstrup, 1995), probably because they are still learning hunting and survival skills. ... I once observed a 3-year-old subadult that weighed only 70 kg in November. This was near the end of the autumn period in which Beaufort Sea bears reach their peak weights (Durner and Amstrup, 1996), and his cohorts at that time weighed in excess of 200 kg. This young animal apparently had not learned the skills needed to survive and was starving to death.

It appears the anecdotal reports of cannibalism, infanticide, and den collapses due to spring rain are being included for their emotional appeal to the public but are not associated with recent declines in local or global sea ice or with recent increases in temperature. Data supporting claims of declines in body condition for Western Hudson Bay polar bears are seriously out of date and/or unpublished, and in the Southern Beaufort, declines in body condition due to heavy ice conditions in spring have been documented every decade since the 1960s. Despite attempts to blame these phenomena on global warming, peer-reviewed research suggest otherwise.

References

Amstrup, S.C. 2003. Polar bear (*Ursus maritimus*). In: Feldhamer, G.A., Thompson, B.C., and Chapman, J.A. (Eds.) *Wild Mammals of North America.* Baltimore, MD: Johns Hopkins University Press, pp. 587–610.

Amstrup, S.C. 1995. Movements, distribution, and population dynamics of polar bears in the Beaufort Sea. Ph.D. dissertation, University of Alaska Fairbanks, Fairbanks.

Amstrup, S.C. 2011. Polar bears and climate change: certainties, uncertainties, and hope in a warming world. In: Watson, R.T., Cade, T.J., Fuller, M., Hunt, G., and Potapov, E. (Eds.) *Gyrfalcons and Ptarmigan in a Changing World, Volume 1.* Boise, ID: The Peregrine Fund, pp. 11–20.

Amstrup, S.C. and DeMaster, D.P. 1988. Polar Bear. In: Lentfer, J.W. (Ed.) *Selected Marine Mammals of Alaska: Species Accounts with Research and Management*

Recommendations. Washington, DC: Marine Mammal Commission, pp. 39–56.

Amstrup, S.C., DeWeaver, E.T., Douglas, D.C., Marcot, B.G., Durner, G.M., Bitz, C.M., and Bailey, D.A. 2010. Greenhouse gas mitigation can reduce sea-ice loss and increase polar bear persistence. *Nature* **468:** 955–958.

Amstrup, S.C., Marcot, B.G., and Douglas, D.C. 2008. A Bayesian network modeling approach to forecasting the 21st century worldwide status of polar bears. In: DeWeaver, E.T., Bitz, C.M., and Tremblay, L.B. (Eds.) *Arctic Sea Ice Decline: Observations, Projections, Mechanisms, and Implications,* Geophysical Monograph 180. Washington, DC: American Geophysical Union, pp. 213–268.

Amstrup, S.C., McDonald, T.L., and Stirling, I. 2001. Polar bears in the Beaufort Sea: A 30-year mark-recapture case history. *Journal of Agricultural, Biological, and Environmental Statistics* **6:** 221–234.

Amstrup, S.C., Stirling, I., Smith, T.S., Perham, C., and Thiemann, B.W. 2006. Recent observations of intraspecific predation and cannibalism among polar bears in the Southern Beaufort Sea. *Polar Biology* **29**: 997–1002.

Cherry, S.G., Derocher, A.E., Stirling, I., and Richardson, E.S. 2009. Fasting physiology of polar bears in relation to environmental change and breeding behavior in the Beaufort Sea. *Polar Biology* **32:** 383–391.

Cherry, S.G., Derocher, A.E., Thiemann, G.W., and Lunn, N.J. 2013. Migration phenology and seasonal fidelity of an Arctic marine predator in relation to sea ice dynamics. *Journal of Animal Ecology* **82:** 912–921.

Derocher, A.E., Lunn, N.J., and Stirling, I. 2004. Polar bears in a warming climate. *Integrative and Comparative Biology* **44**: 163–176.

Derocher, A.E., Stirling, I., and Andriashek, D. 1992. Pregnancy rates and progesterone levels of polar bears in western Hudson Bay. *Canadian Journal of Zoology* **70:** 561–566.

Derocher, A.E. and Wiig, Ø. 1999. Infanticide and cannibalism of juvenile polar bears (*Ursus maritimus*) in Svalbard. *Arctic* **52:** 307–310.

Durner, G.M. and Amstrup, S.C. 1996. Mass and body-dimension relationships of polar bears in northern Alaska. *Wildlife Society Bulletin* **24:** 480–484.

Durner, G.M., Douglas, D.C., Nielson, R.M., Amstrup, S.C., McDonald, T.L., Stirling, I., Mauritzen, M., Born, E.W., Wiig, Ø., DeWeaver, E., Serreze, M.C., Belikov, S.E., Holland, M.M., Maslanik, J., Aars, J., Bailey, D.A., and Derocher, A.E. 2009. Predicting 21st-century polar bear habitat distribution from global climate models. *Ecological Monographs* **79:** 25–58.

Harwood, L.A., Smith, T.G., Melling, H., Alikamik, J., and

Kingsley, M.C.S. 2012. Ringed seals and sea ice in Canada's western Arctic: harvest-based monitoring 1992-2011. *Arctic* **65:** 377–390.

Kingsley, M.C.S. and Byers, T.J. 1998. Failure of reproduction in ringed seals (*Phoca hispida*) in Amundsen Gulf, Northwest Territories in 1984–1987. In: Heide-Jørgensen, M.P. and Lydersen, C. (Eds.) *Ringed Seals in the North Atlantic.* NAMMCO Scientific Publication 1. Tromsø: The North Atlantic Marine Mammal Commission, pp. 197–210.

Lunn, N.J. and Stenhouse, G.B. 1985. An observation of possible cannibalism by polar bears (*Ursus maritimus*). *Canadian Journal of Zoology* **63:** 1516–1517.

Melling, H. and Riedel, D.A. 2004. Draft and movement of pack ice in the Beaufort Sea: A time-series presentation April 1990–August 1999. *Canadian Technical Report of Hydrography and Ocean Sciences* **238.**

Melling, H., Riedel, D.A., and Gedalof, Z. 2005. Trends in the draft and extent of seasonal pack ice, Canadian Beaufort Sea. *Geophysical Research Letters* **32:** L24501.

Messier, F., Taylor, M.K., and Ramsay, M.A. 1994. Denning ecology of polar bears in the Canadian High Arctic. *Journal of Mammalogy* **75:** 420–430.

Obbard, M.E., Theimann, G.W., Peacock, E., and DeBryn, T.D. (Eds.) 2010. *Polar Bears: Proceedings of the 15th meeting of the Polar Bear Specialists Group IUCN/SSC, 29 June-3 July, 2009.* Copenhagen, Denmark. Gland, Switzerland and Cambridge UK, IUCN.

Peacock, E., Taylor, M.K., Laake, J., and Stirling, I. 2013. Population ecology of polar bears in Davis Strait, Canada and Greenland. *Journal of Wildlife Management* **77:** 463–476.

Pilfold, N.W., Derocher, A.E., Stirling, I., Richardson, E., and Andriashek, D. 2012. Age and sex composition of seals killed by polar bears in the eastern Beaufort Sea. *PLoS ONE* **7:** e41429.

Ramsay, M.A. and Stirling, I. 1988. Reproductive biology and ecology of female polar bears (*Ursus maritimus*). *Journal of Zoology London* **214:** 601–624.

Regehr, E.V., Amstrup, S.C., and Stirling, I. 2006. *Polar bear population status in the southern Beaufort Sea.* U.S. Geological Survey Open-File Report 2006-1337.

Regehr, E.V., Hunter, C.M., Caswell, H., Amstrup, S.C., and Stirling, I. 2010. Survival and breeding of polar bears in the southern Beaufort Sea in relation to sea ice. *Journal of Animal Ecology* **79:** 117–127.

Regehr, E.V., Hunter, C.M., Caswell, H., Amstrup, S.C., and Stirling, I. 2007. Polar bears in the southern Beaufort Sea I: survival and breeding in relation to sea ice conditions, 2001–2006. Administrative Report, U.S. Department of the Interior- U.S. Geological Survey, Reston, VA.

Rode, K.D., Amstrup, S.C., and Regehr, E.V. 2010. Reduced body size and cub recruitment in polar bears associated with sea ice decline. *Ecological Applications* **20**: 768–782.

Rode, K.D., Peacock, E., Taylor, M., Stirling, I., Born, E.W., Laidre, K.L., and Wiig, Ø. 2012. A tale of two polar bear populations: ice habitat, harvest, and body condition. *Population Ecology* **54**: 3–18.

Rode, K.D., Regehr, E.V., Douglas, D., Durner, G., Derocher, A.E., Thiemann, G.W., and Budge, S. 2014. Variation in the response of an Arctic top predator experiencing habitat loss: feeding and reproductive ecology of two polar bear populations. *Global Change Biology* **20**: 76–88.

Smith, T.G. 1987. The ringed seal, *Phoca hispida,* of the Canadian western Arctic. *Canadian Bulletin of Fisheries and Aquatic Sciences* **216**.

Stirling, I. 2002. Polar bears and seals in the eastern Beaufort Sea and Amundsen Gulf: a synthesis of population trends and ecological relationships over three decades. *Arctic* **55** (Suppl. 1): 59–76.

Stirling, I. and Derocher, A.F. 2012. Effects of climate warming on polar bears: a review of the evidence. *Global Change Biology* **18**: 2694–2706

Stirling, I. and Lunn, N.J. 1997. Environmental fluctuations in arctic marine ecosystems as reflected by variability in reproduction of polar bears and ringed seals. In: Woodin, S.J. and Marquiss, M. (Eds.) *Ecology of Arctic Environments.* Blackwell Science, UK, pp. 167–181.

Stirling, I., McDonald, T.L., Richardson, E.S., Regehr, E.V., and Amstrup, S.C. 2011. Polar bear population status in the northern Beaufort Sea, Canada, 1971–2006. *Ecological Applications* **21**: 859–876.

Stirling, I. and Øritsland, N.A. 1995. Relationships between estimates of ringed seal (*Phoca hispida*) and polar bear (*Ursus maritimus*) populations in the Canadian Arctic. *Canadian Journal of Fisheries and Aquatic Sciences* **52**: 2594–2612.

Stirling, I., Richardson, E., Thiemann, G.W., and Derocher, A.E. 2008. Unusual predation attempts of polar bears on ringed seals in the southern Beaufort Sea: possible significance of changing spring ice conditions. *Arctic* **61**: 14–22.

Stirling, I. and Ross, J.E. 2011. Observations of cannibalism by polar bears (*Ursus maritimus*) on summer and autumn sea ice at Svalbard, Norway. *Arctic* **64**: 478–482.

Stone, I.R. and Derocher, A.E. 2007. An incident of polar bear infanticide and cannibalism on Phippsøya, Svalbard. *Polar Record* **43**: 171–173.

Stroeve, J., Holland, M.M., Scambos, T., and Serreze, M. 2007. Arctic sea ice decline: faster than forecast. *Geophysical Research Letters* **34**: L09501, doi: 10.1029/2007/GL029703.

Taylor, M., Larsen, T., and Schweinsburg, R.E. 1985. Observations of intraspecific aggression and cannibalism in polar bears (*Ursus maritimus*). *Arctic* **38**: 303–309.

Taylor, M., and Lee, J. 1995. Distribution and abundance of Canadian polar bear populations: a management perspective. *Arctic* **48**: 147–154.

5.8.3.2 Changes in Reproductive Success

A warmer Arctic portending dramatic declines in sea ice is predicted to have significant effects on the reproductive success of polar bears, based on changes already documented in some subpopulations. Stirling and Derocher (2012) have this to say about reproductive success in the western Hudson Bay subpopulation: "the proportion of independent yearlings fell from over 81% before 1980 to a mean of 34% in 1980–1992 (Derocher and Stirling, 1995). By the late 1990s, the proportion of independent yearlings dropped to <10% (Stirling *et al.*, 1999) and by the early 2000s was almost nonexistent (I. Stirling, unpublished data)."

In the 1999 paper the authors cite, Stirling *et al.* say this: "The proportion of yearlings that were independent in the annual capture samples fluctuated widely at 3–4 year intervals, but overall the maximum proportions have declined from about 60% in 1982 to 15–20% since 1991 (Fig. 6). There was no statistically significant relationship between the proportion of lone yearlings and the time of [sea ice] breakup in the same year (r =- 0.205, n = 14, p = 0.46)." More importantly, Stirling *et al* (1999) also point out, "for about the last 12 years [ending 1998], estimates of population size have remained relatively constant (Lunn *et al.*, 1997; this study), indicating that the declines in condition and natality have not led to a decline in population." In other words, the well-documented change from weaning at 2.5 years rather than 1.5 years had no immediate negative impact on the population up to 1992, and any additional data collected on this phenomenon are not available in the peer-reviewed literature.

Derocher and Stirling (1995) state: "the results of our analyses suggest that the unique reproductive characteristics of polar bears in western Hudson Bay in the 1960s and 1970s were either a function of a population increasing from a depleted state and feeding on a relatively abundant prey base, or density-independent fluctuations in prey population size, or availability due to sea ice variation." Therefore, declining sea ice is not the only reason reproductive parameters, such as age at weaning, might change. And since the assertion that the proportion of independent yearlings was "almost nonexistent" by the early 2000s is based on unpublished data, we cannot be sure the claimed further decline in proportion of independent yearlings has had any significant impact on population size, since previous changes did not.

In addition, it should be noted the proportion of independent yearlings being approximately zero is the norm for virtually all other polar bear subpopulations studied (Ramsay and Stirling, 1988; Van de Velde *et al.,* 2003). Western Hudson Bay always has been anomalous in this feature. In that respect, in weaning their cubs at 2.5 years rather than 1.5 years, Western Hudson Bay polar bears may simply be returning to normal.

Stirling and Lunn (1997) perhaps put it best:

In the early to mid-1980s, the natality [cub production] of female polar bears in western Hudson Bay was the highest recorded anywhere in polar bear range, and nowhere else did females successfully wean cubs at 1.5 years of age instead of at the normal age of 2.5 years. Subsequently, a long-term decline in condition of adult female polar bears and survival of their cubs was documented from the 1970s through the late 1980s (Derocher and Stirling, 1992), as reflected by a significant decline in condition indices. This decline did not constitute a threat to the population because even when natality was at its lowest in the late 1980s, the rates were still higher than the upper range of values for bears elsewhere in the Arctic (e.g., Stirling *et al.*, 1976, 1980). ... The more important (but unanswered) question is probably not why natality declined from the early 1980s but how could natality have been sustained at a level so much higher than other polar bear populations in the first place, what facilitated the successful weaning of yearlings there but nowhere else in their range, and how could females manage these physiological feats in a habitat where pregnant females must also fast for 8 months or more?"

They did not answer their question.

Rode *et al.* (2014), in their recent study of Chukchi Sea polar bears, found "spring COY litter sizes are among the highest reported for 18 of 19 polar bear populations. ... [S]pring litter sizes of CS yearlings from the study were also higher than other populations." The authors note, "the larger body mass of adult females in the CS corresponded not only with larger litter sizes, but also with heavier yearlings (Fig.5) which have a greater chance of survival" and "body size, condition, and reproductive indices of CS polar bears did not decline over time between 1986–1994 and 2008–2011 despite a 44-day increase in the number of reduced-ice days." In other words, contrary to predictions, reproductive parameters of Chukchi Sea polar bears did not decline, despite marked declines in summer sea ice.

References

Derocher, A.E. and Stirling, I. 1992. The population dynamics of polar bears in western Hudson Bay. In: McCullogh, D. R. and Barrett, R.H. (Eds.) *Wildlife 2001: Populations.* London: Elsevier Applied Science, pp. 1150–1159.

Derocher, A.E. and Stirling, I. 1995. Temporal variation in reproduction and body mass of polar bears in western Hudson Bay. *Canadian Journal of Zoology* **73:** 1657–1665.

Lunn, N.J., Stirling, I., Andriashek, D., and Kolenosky, G.B. 1997. Re-estimating the size of the polar bear population in western Hudson Bay. *Arctic* **50:** 234–240.

Ramsay, M.A. and Stirling, I. 1988. Reproductive biology and ecology of female polar bears (*Ursus maritimus*). *Journal of Zoology London* **214:** 601–624.

Stirling, I., Calvert, W., and Andriashek, D. 1980. Population ecology studies of the polar bear in the area of southeastern Baffin Island. *Canadian Wildlife Service Occasional Papers* **44.**

Stirling, I. and Derocher, A.E. 2012. Effects of climate warming on polar bears: a review of the evidence. *Global Change Biology* **18:** 2694–2706.

Stirling, I. and Lunn, N.J. 1997. Environmental fluctuations in arctic marine ecosystems as reflected by variability in reproduction of polar bears and ringed seals. In: Woodin, S.J. and Marquiss, M. (Eds.) *Ecology of Arctic Environments.* UK: Blackwell Science, pp. 167–181.

Stirling, I., Lunn, N.J., and Iacozza, J. 1999. Long-term trends in the population ecology of polar bears in Western Hudson Bay in relation to climate change. *Arctic* **52:** 294–306.

Stirling, I., Pearson, A.M., and Bunnell, F.L. 1976. Population ecology studies of polar and grizzly bears in northern Canada. *Transactions of the North American Wildlife and Natural Resources Conference* **41:** 421–429.

Van de Velde, F., Stirling, I., and Richardson, E. 2003. Polar bear (*Ursus maritimus*) denning in the area of the Simpson Peninsula, Nunavut. *Arctic* **56:** 191–197.

5.8.4 Effects of more open water

Polar bears use sea ice as a platform for hunting, traveling, and denning. They are known to be excellent swimmers, capable of swimming long distances between ice flows. But what happens during the late summer, when the edge of the pack ice is many kilometers offshore for months at a time? Although some polar bears spend this "open water" period on land, is it because they are incapable of swimming to the ice edge once it gets beyond a certain point? Or are polar bears, particularly females with cubs, able to swim hundreds of kilometers from land to the ice edge during the "open water" season if they choose to do so?

Working from three points along the coast of the Beaufort and Chukchi Seas, Alaska (Barrow, Prudhoe Bay, Kaktovik) between 2004 and 2009, Pagano et al. (2012) attached radio collars during March through May (but also in August 2008) to 62 female polar bears, some of which had cubs with them. The number of bears successfully monitored for this study varied each year; as only two collars were deployed in 2007 and one of these failed, data from 2007 were excluded. The authors analyzed global positioning system (GPS) data from the 52 radio collars that successfully transmitted signals between 1 June and 31 October each year and compared these to the position of the sea ice edge determined from satellite imagery. Some additional data from bears collared between 1985 and 2009 were used to assess whether an early cessation of signal transmission during the open water period (July through September), from bears that had been at sea and were not later re-sighted, could be assumed to indicate the bears had drowned while swimming.

The authors found 50 "long-distance" swimming events (>50 km) were made by 20 of the bears monitored (38% of the total), and 12 of the 20 bears that swam long distances did so multiple times in the same year. The researchers found the majority of the long-distance swims were from unconsolidated sea ice (ice concentration <50%) to the main pack ice (mean distance 155.9 km, range 114.5–197.4 km, 25 swims). Relatively few bears swam from land to another area of land (mean distance 106.2 km, range 53.7–288.3 km, 7 swims) or from unconsolidated sea ice to land (mean distance 169.1 km, range 69.9–302.6 km, 6 swims). Only three swims involved bears moving from land to unconsolidated sea ice (mean distance 102.3 km, range 68.3–113.7 km), and only two were bears moving from land to the main pack ice (mean distance 402.5 km, range 117.9–687.1 km).

There were no long-distance swimming data prior to 2004 with which to compare this study's data, and sampling differences among years precluded the researchers from determining any trend in their results.

They also found there was no significant difference in the rate of cub mortality between females with cubs that undertook long-distance swims and those that did not. It also appeared premature cessation of radio collar signal transmission did not necessarily indicate a bear had drowned; some bears whose signals stopped prematurely probably drowned, but drowning was not the only explanation for signal failure.

Pagano et al. calculated the mean distance between the mainland coast and the sea ice edge at the end of September for each year of the study period. This distance varied from a low of about 200 km (achieved in 2005, 2006, and 2009) and a high of about 430 km (achieved in 2008). Mean distance from the shore to the ice in 2004 was about 300 km, and in 2007 it was about 380 km. Each of these measurements varied somewhat depending on the configuration of the shoreline, but in 2008 the ice edge was definitely farther away than in any other year since 1979. However, the largest number of long-distance swimming events took place in 2009, when the ice edge in this region was about the same distance offshore as in 2005 and 2006. The longest swim was recorded in late August/early September of 2008 at a point where the sea ice was >500 km offshore: a female with a year-old cub swam 687.1 km in just over nine days, as described in detail by Durner et al. (2011). This bear was one of only two individuals in the Pagano et al. study that swam from land to the main pack ice edge; after a few weeks meandering around at the edge of the pack ice, this bear then walked back to shore on the rapid-forming ice, arriving on land at the end of October. The second-longest swim (366.0 km) was recorded in 2005, when the pack ice edge was about the same distance offshore as in 2009.

Pagano et al. state, "we show that both adult female polar bears and their dependent young possess an ability to swim long distances." They also observe, "most of the long-distance swimming events that we identified involved bears swimming from unconsolidated sea ice to the main pack ice or to land." In other words, few swims recorded were from land to sea ice, indicating that during the open water season most southern Beaufort and Chukchi Sea polar bears are on the sea ice, not on land—a point also made by Durner et al. (2011). In addition, the results of this study suggest that despite there being little or nothing for female polar bears and their cubs to eat on shore during the late summer months in the southern Beaufort Sea, the few bears that remain on shore are apparently not hungry enough to undertake long-distance swims to the pack ice to relieve their fast, although they appear able to do so. Despite an overall decline in September sea ice levels between 1979 and 2010, this study found no significant correlation between increased long-distance swims and increased amounts of open water in this region over time.

Although polar bears are clearly accomplished swimmers, an anecdotal account of polar bears that apparently drowned in open water, purported to be evidence of global warming and declining sea ice effects, has garnered remarkable media attention. Monnett and Gleason (2006) report what appeared at the time to be four dead polar bears that drowned in open water in 2004. The bodies were observed from aircraft while surveying for bowhead whales (*Balaena mysticetus*) after a September storm. However, like the anecdotal accounts of cannibalism and den collapses attributed to global warming by Stirling and Derocher (2012) discussed previously, no baseline scientific studies have quantified the number of swimming polar bears that have drowned under any conditions vs. those that have not. So while these isolated events continue to be touted as probable effects of global warming, there is no scientific evidence they are anything of the sort. Scientists do controlled, well-designed studies precisely because anecdotes cannot be trusted to give an unbiased picture of events. The inclusion of anecdotal events as supporting evidence of global warming is an appeal to emotions, rather than scientific reasoning.

References

Durner, G.M., Whiteman, J.P., Harlow, H.J., Amstrup, S.C., Regehr, E.V., and Ben-David, M. 2011. Consequences of long-distance swimming and travel over deep-water pack ice for a female polar bear during a year of extreme sea ice retreat. *Polar Biology* **34**: 975–984.

Monnett, C. and Gleason, J.S. 2006. Observations of mortality associated with extended open-water swimming by polar bears in the Alaskan Beaufort Sea. *Polar Biology* **29**: 681–687.

Pagano, A.M., Durner, G.M., Amstrup, S.C., Simac, K.S., and York, G.S. 2012. Long-distance swimming by polar bears (Ursus maritimus) of the southern Beaufort Sea during years of extensive open water. *Canadian Journal of Zoology* **90**: 663–676.

Stirling, I. and Derocher, A.E. 2012. Effects of climate warming on polar bears: a review of the evidence. *Global Change Biology* **18**: 2694–2706.

5.9 Reptiles

- Studies of the effects of rising temperatures on reptiles find they often are able to tolerate a greater range of environmental conditions than they have been exposed to in the recent past, demonstrate abilities to thermo-regulate to achieve body temperatures close to their preferred temperatures, and often benefit from warmer temperatures.

Many are the predictions of species decline and possible extinction arising from warming-induced changes in the characteristics of regions to which the species are endemic. Concerns over the fate of reptiles are no exception, yet the results of several research studies conducted on this topic suggest these animals are in no such danger.

Chamaille-Jammes *et al.* (2006) studied four discontinuous subpopulations of the common lizard (*Lacerta vivipara*), a small live-bearing lacertid that lives in peat bogs and heath lands across Europe and Asia, concentrating on a small region near the top of Mont Lozere in southeast France, at the southern limit of the species' range. From 1984 to 2001 they monitored several life-history traits of the sub-populations, including body size, reproduction characteristics, and survival rates, while local air temperatures rose by approximately 2.2°C. They found individual body size increased dramatically in all four lizard populations over the 18-year study period, with snout-vent length expanding by roughly 28 percent. This increase in body size occurred in all age classes and, as they describe it, "appeared related to a concomitant increase in temperature experienced during the first month of life (August)." As a result, they found "adult female body size increased markedly, and, as fecundity is strongly dependent on female body size, clutch size and total reproductive output also increased." In addition, for a population where capture-recapture data were available, they learned "adult survival was positively related to May temperature."

Since all fitness components investigated responded positively to the increase in temperature, the French researchers state, "it might be concluded that the common lizard has been advantaged by the shift in temperature." This finding, they write, stands in stark contrast to the "habitat-based prediction that these populations located close to mountain tops on the southern margin of the species range should be unable to cope with the alteration of their habitat." They conclude, "to achieve a better prediction of a species persistence, one will probably need to combine both habitat and individual-based approaches." Furthermore, they note individual responses, such as those documented in their study (which were all positive), represent "the ultimate driver of a species response to climate change."

Noting tropical species long have been thought to be "especially sensitive to climatic fluctuations because their narrow thermal tolerances and elevational ranges can restrict their ability to persist in, or disperse across, alternate habitats," Bell *et al.* (2010) compared "responses to historical climate fluctuation in a montane specialist skink, *Lampropholis robertsi*, and its more broadly distributed congener, *L. coggeri*, both endemic to rainforests of northeast Australia." They combined "spatial modeling of potential distributions under representative palaeoclimates, multi-locus phylogeography and analyses of phenotypic variation." The seven scientists write, "both species exhibit pronounced phylogeographic structuring for mitochondrial and nuclear genes, attesting to low dispersal and high persistence across multiple isolated regions." Referring specifically to *L. robertsi*, the researchers state their evidence demonstrates "persistence and isolation" of most populations of the montane species "throughout the strong climate oscillations of the late Pleistocene, and likely extending back to the Pliocene."

Noting many of the isolated refugia they studied "are particularly rich in narrowly endemic species," Bell *et al.* state this characteristic has been attributed to "their relative stability during recent episodes of climate change (Williams and Pearson, 1997; Yeates *et al.*, 2002; Graham *et al.*, 2006; VanDerWal *et al.*, 2009)." Furthermore, they say these observations "support the general hypothesis that isolated tropical montane regions harbor high levels of narrow-range taxa because of their resilience to past climate change," citing Fjeldsa and Lovett (1997) and Jetz *et al.* (2004). Thus, "at first sight, species such as *L. robertsi* would seem especially prone to local extinction and loss of considerable genetic diversity with any further warming; yet, these populations and those of other high-montane endemic species (*Cophixalus* frogs; Hoskin, 2004) have evidently persisted through past warming events."

Rodder *et al.* (2010) state, "if the climate changes, island endemics may be restricted in their ability to conduct range shifts depending on the topographic variability and the size of the island," and "species that inhabit islands characterized by low altitudinal variation may be the ones most strongly affected by climate change due to the lack of possibilities for horizontal or upward range shifts." However, they note only a small part of the fundamental niche of a species may currently be available to it, and the species may possess a hitherto-unknown ability to tolerate a much greater range of environmental conditions than that to which it may have been exposed in the recent past. Therefore, in determining what climatic conditions a species may be able to tolerate in the future, they state "a comparison between conditions tolerated in the present and in the past may be helpful."

Focusing on *Phelsuma parkeri*, an endemic gecko species native to the relatively flat (0 to < 100 m elevation) island of Pemba, Tanzania, Rodder *et al.* observed the species and provided information on its current spatial distribution in terms of both physical and environmental space, as well as its adaptability to habitat modification by humans. With respect to past climatic conditions, they employed simulations of the Last Glacial Maximum provided by the Community Climate System Model and the Model for Interdisciplinary Research on Climate, while with respect to the future, they employed climate change predictions based on three other models and the emission scenarios reported in the *Special Report on Emissions Scenarios* by the Intergovernmental Panel on Climate Change.

The three researchers report a comparison of current climatic conditions with those derived from model simulations for 21,000 years ago revealed "no climate conditions analogous to those of today existed during the Last Glacial Maximum," noting there were "decreases of between 1.4 and 2.8°C in the minimum temperature of the coldest month and of between 2.1 and 3.4°C in the maximum temperature of the warmest month throughout the island" compared to the corresponding temperatures of today. As for the future, the climate models they used suggested "the minimum temperature of the coldest month may increase about 1.2 to 3.8°C and the maximum temperature of the warmest month by about 2.0 to 3.7°C." Rodder *et al.* say their results suggest "*P. parkeri* is distributed over the largest part of the island, that it is well adapted to current land use, and that it is most likely not threatened by climate change."

Moreno-Rueda *et al.* (2011) "used data on the distributions of reptiles in Spain during the 20th century to analyze whether the distributions of these reptiles have changed as climate has changed." They compared "the distributions of reptile species before 1975"—the year, they say, according to IPCC (2007), the current period of warming began—"with distributions during 1991–2005." The authors report, "after controlling for sampling effort, geographic bias in sampling, phylogeny, and spatial autocorrelation, the northern limits of the distribution of reptiles in Spain shifted northward between 1940–1975 and 1991–2005," but "there was no similar shift southward in the southern limits of species' ranges." In addition, the mean latitude of the ranges of the species they examined "shifted northward by an equivalent of 0.5 km/year, which is similar to the magnitude of range shifts in other taxonomic groups (Parmesan and Yohe, 2003)."

Noting they were "the first to show there is a correlation between changes in latitudinal distribution and increases in temperature for a wide variety of species of reptiles in Spain," the four researchers say their "finding that reptiles are expanding their northern ranges, potentially in response to climate change, could mean the probability of extinction associated with increases in temperature may be lower than expected."

According to Amiel and Shine (2012), a hatchling reptile's sex, body size, and shape, as well as its locomotor performance, "can be influenced not only by its genes, but also by the temperature that it experiences during incubation." At the time of their study little was known about whether incubation temperature can also affect a hatchling's cognitive skills. Amiel and Shine examined "whether incubation temperature affects lizards' ability to learn the location of a safe retreat site during a predatory attack," because mastering this cognitive task "is directly relevant to individual survival and therefore fitness," citing Paulissen (2008).

The pair of Australian researchers worked with the scincid lizard *Bassiana duperreyi*, by first "randomly dividing eggs from each clutch between two incubation treatments ('hot' = diel cycle of 22 ± 7.5°C; 'cold' = diel cycle of 16 ± 7.5°C)," treatments that "mimic thermal regimes typical of natural nests at low (hot) versus high (cold) elevations." They then conducted a specific test designed to evaluate the young lizards' cognitive skills and their abilities to act appropriately to escape the perceived danger. Amiel and Shine report finding "hot-incubated lizards achieved higher learning scores than did cold-incubated lizards," and "the number of errors they made decreased more from the first to the second half

of the trials than was the case for cold-incubated lizards." They speculate, based on Ahmad and Zamenhof (1978), Rissman *et al.* (2002), Valenzuela and Lance (2004), and Radder *et al.* (2008), "thermal effects on hormone levels during incubation may induce structural variation in parts of the brain that control behaviors such as learning." Amiel and Shine conclude, "climate change may simultaneously generate novel challenges for post-hatching organisms, while also modifying their ability to respond flexibly to such challenges." They specifically opine, "in *B. duperreyi*, hotter natural nests over recent decades (due to climate change) probably have produced hatchling lizards with enhanced learning abilities."

Clarke and Zani (2012) note observed real-world temperature increases typically have been "asymmetrically distributed over diurnal time frames, with daily minima increasing at a faster rate than daily maxima," citing Karl *et al.* (1991, 1993), Easterling *et al.* (1997, 2000), and DeGaetano and Allen (2002), whereas most previous studies of the effects of global warming on biological systems have boosted temperatures by the same amount during all hours of the day and night. Clarke and Zani conducted their study of the potential impact of global warming on the common side-blotched lizard (*Uta stansburiana*)—which they collected about 20 km south of Burns, Oregon (USA) at the northern edge of the Great Basin Desert—employing the latter, more-realistic imposed mode of asymmetric nighttime-only warming.

Working at their field laboratory, Clarke and Zani simulated observed trends in the asymmetric alteration of the local diurnal temperature range by increasing the nighttime temperatures in the incubators into which they transferred the female lizards (from their daytime cages) during their ovarian cycle. They treated the eggs the female lizards produced in a similar manner during their incubation period, carefully documenting the differences they detected throughout the entire reproductive process between the female parent and progeny lizards of the warmed and control treatments.

The two U.S. researchers discovered higher night-time temperatures during the female lizards' ovarian cycles "increased the probability of reproductive success and decreased the duration of the reproductive cycle." They found the higher temperatures had neither positive nor negative effects on "embryo stage or size at oviposition, clutch size, egg mass or relative clutch mass." They also report "higher incubation temperatures increased hatchling size and decreased incubation period," noting "subsequent hatchlings were more likely to survive winter if they hatched earlier."

Clarke and Zani state, "as our findings confirm that climate warming is likely to increase the rate of development as well as advance reproductive phenology, we predict that warmer nights during the breeding season will increase reproductive output as well as subsequent survival in many temperate ectotherms, both of which should have positive fitness effects." Thus, they conclude, "these effects are primarily beneficial for this population of northern lizards," and they predict "future changes will continue to benefit the reproduction, growth and survival of individuals at this site."

Leal and Gunderson (2012) write, "the general view is that climate change will have a major impact on biodiversity by increasing the extinction risk of many species or changing their distributions," based on "the implicit assumption that species are relatively fixed entities, unable to respond to rapid changes in ecological conditions, including climatic variables, over an ecological timescale." They state "evidence that some organisms are able to respond to climatic changes over short timescales has begun to emerge (e.g., Grant and Grant, 2002; Walther *et al.*, 2002; Bradshaw and Holzapfel, 2006)."

Nearly 40 years ago, the tropical Caribbean lizard *Anolis cristatellus*, native to an area of xeric forest in northeastern Puerto Rico, was found in Miami, Florida, by Schwartz and Thomas (1975) in a location where minimum temperatures in winter can average 10°C cooler than in Puerto Rico, but where maximum temperatures in summer are much more similar. Taking advantage of this situation, Leal and Gunderson set about to determine whether the cold tolerance or critical thermal minimum temperature (CT_{min}) of the introduced populations had diverged from that of the source populations of *A. cristatellus* since their physical separation in 1975. As a check on their experimental procedures, they also conducted studies to see whether the critical thermal maximum temperature (CT_{max}) of the two groups of lizards remained about the same.

They found "the introduced population tolerates significantly colder temperatures (by ~3°C) than does the Puerto Rican source population," while the maximum temperatures tolerated "did not differ." These observations "demonstrate that changes in thermal tolerance occurred relatively rapidly (~35 generations), which strongly suggests that the thermal physiology of tropical lizards is more labile than previously proposed." They conclude, "regardless of

the mechanism, the adaptive lability of thermal tolerance in *A. cristatellus* over an ecological timescale" provides "a glimpse of hope for tropical lizards under the current conditions of rapid climate change."

Valdecantos *et al.* (2013) note "temperature has a great impact on ectotherms, affecting physiological, behavioral and life history traits such as reproductive timing (Zug *et al.*, 2001; Labra and Bozinovic, 2002), reproductive mode (Shine, 2004), growth rate, survivorship (Huey, 1982), locomotion (Hertz *et al.*, 1983; Angilleta *et al.*, 2002) and diet (Espinoza *et al.*, 2004)." They note late twentieth century global warming "has been suggested as a potential threat for lizards at a global scale," citing Sinervo *et al.* (2010).

The researchers studied four related species— *Liolaemus irregularis*, *L. albiceps*, *L. multicolor*, and *L. yanalcu*—that inhabit high-elevation desert areas in Northwestern Argentina, Northern Chile, and Southwestern Bolivia, working both in the laboratory and at four sites near San Antonio de los Cobres in Salta, Argentina, where they measured body temperatures (Tb), air temperatures (Ta), soil temperatures (Ts), operative temperatures in the field (Te), and preferred body temperatures (Tpref) for all four species.

The four Argentine researchers report their study revealed all four species, "despite living at high elevation and harsh climatic conditions," were able to "behaviorally or physiologically thermo-regulate to achieve body temperatures close to their preferred temperatures." They conclude, "as proposed by Labra *et al.* (2009)," "many species are conservative in some aspects (e.g. Tpref), yet labile in others (e.g. Tb)," thus "allowing them to inhabit a wide range of environments."

Moritz *et al.* (2012) note it is often assumed large central populations of a species have higher genetic diversity and, therefore, greater potential for adaptive response to environmental change. But they state "this is not always the case," and "lineages that have persisted as isolates in peripheral areas through past climate change might well have genotypes that will confer greater resistance to future warming and which could be exploited for genetic translocation," citing Chown *et al.* (2010).

Moritz *et al.* (2012) tested this hypothesis through comparative assays of minimum and maximum critical thermal limits (CT_{min} and CT_{max}), as well as optimal performance parameters, including CT_{opt}, across central and peripheral lineages of three species of ground-dwelling skinks (scincid lizards) endemic to the rainforests of northeast Australia:

Gnypetoscincus queenslandiae, Carlia rubrigularis, and *Saproscincus basiliscus.*

Results of the analysis indicate "peripheral lineages show significantly increased optimal performance temperatures (T_{opt}) relative to central populations, as well as elevated CT_{min}." Moritz *et al.* conclude the peripheral lineages they examined "appear to have evolved higher thermal optima relative to centrally located lineages," noting this finding "contrasts with the usual assumption that local adaptation of peripheral populations will be overwhelmed by gene flow from the center of the species range or, in the absence of immigration, will experience higher extinction rates." Thus the authors state, "long-isolated populations in peripheral rainforests harbor genotypes that confer resilience to future warming."

Sea turtles, like many other reptiles, have what is called "temperature-dependent sex determination" (TSD), which means the temperature experienced by each developing embryo (within its individual eggshell casing, laid within a nest built by the mother on a terrestrial beach) determines its sex (Janzen, 1994). In turtles, males require somewhat cooler embryonic conditions than females: a temperature of 29°C generates a sex ratio among hatchlings of about 50:50, whereas at higher temperatures, more females are produced (Hawkes *et al.*, 2009). (Strangely enough, in the tuatara, another TSD reptile, the opposite is true: more males are produced at higher temperatures.) As a result, strongly skewed offspring sex ratios are common in TSD reptiles.

The amount of global warming predicted for the next century by some climate scientists is considered a threat to TSD-species because it is feared the higher temperatures will generate such extreme sex ratio biases (e.g. 100% females) that extinction will be inevitable (e.g. Fuentes *et al.*, 2010; Janzen, 1994; Witt *et al.*, 2010). As a highly female-skewed hatchling sex ratio already occurs in marine turtles (Hawkes *et al.* 2009), "predicted increases in global temperatures are expected to exacerbate this trend," say Wright *et al.*, 2012.

Although living sea turtle species have survived substantial temperature fluctuations in the recent past (Janzen and Paukstis, 1988), Wright *et al.* (2012) investigated whether they will be able to adapt to future warming. Wright *et al.* examined the mating behavior of green sea turtles (*Chelonia mydas*) to see if it was compensating for the extreme female-skewed sex ratios of hatchlings currently produced in the Mediterranean (86–96% female). They undertook genetic typing of tissue samples taken in 2008 from 20 nesting females and 809 of their offspring (from 37 clutches of eggs), from a single rookery beach in northern Cyprus. Paternity analysis of the hatchlings allowed the researchers to determine how many males had mated with the females they sampled. They also put a satellite transmitter on a single male to map his movements during the breeding season.

Sea surface temperatures at the study site rose by, on average, less than 1°C over the past 50 years, and the female bias that exists today in adult green sea turtles is probably the result of a similar extent of female bias among hatchlings produced approximately 30 years ago (due to the late age at sexual maturity in this species)—that is, the authors assumed many more breeding-aged adult turtles in the population were female than were male.

They found, "despite an offspring sex ratio of 95 per cent females, there were at least 1.4 reproductive males to every breeding female"—28 males breeding with 20 females tested. The authors suggest males may breed more often than females (females breed every 2–4 years). In addition, the male they tracked visited a number of rookeries in the region, suggesting males may mate with females on a number of different beaches. Together, the authors suggest, these mating behaviors partially compensate for the lower abundance of males within the population, so "male mating patterns have the potential to buffer the disruptive effects of climate change on marine turtle populations, many of which are already seriously threatened." Furthermore, Wright *et al.* conclude, "current mating patterns will help to preserve genetic variation that may be critical if marine turtles are to adapt behaviorally or physiologically to a warming climate and have, no doubt, contributed to their persistence through historical climatic upheaval."

Citing Lavergne *et al.* (2010), Refsnider and Janzen (2012) also studied turtles, writing, "adaptation to climate change may be impossible even when high genetic variation is present if the rate of environmental change is too rapid and the population demography is insufficiently dynamic," adding, "species with temperature-dependent sex determination may be particularly threatened by climate change, because altered temperatures could skew sex ratios." Refsnider and Janzen experimentally tested nest-site choice in the long-lived turtle *Chrysemys picta*, to see whether nesting behavior "could compensate for potential skews in sex ratios caused by rapid climate change." They collected females from five populations spread across the species' range, housed them in a semi-natural common garden, and waited to see what would happen.

The two researchers report "females from transplanted populations showed similar choice of shade cover over nests to local females," which suggests, in their words, "behavioral phenotypic plasticity in female choice of shade cover over the nest site may comprise an immediate mechanism by which long-lived reptiles with temperature-dependent sex determination can avoid skews in sex ratio potentially caused by rapid climate change."

References

Ahmad, G. and Zamenhof, S. 1978. Serotonin as a growth factor for chick embryo brain. *Life Sciences* **22**: 963–970.

Amiel, J.J. and Shine, R. 2012. Hotter nests produce smarter young lizards. *Biology Letters* **8**: 372–374.

Angilleta Jr., M.J., Niewiarowski, P.H., and Navas, C.A. 2002. The evolutions of thermal physiology in ectotherms. *Journal of Thermal Biology* **27**: 249–268.

Bell, R.C., Parra, J.L., Tonione, M., Hoskin, C.J., Mackenzie, J.B., Williams, S.E., and Moritz, C. 2010. Patterns of persistence and isolation indicate resilience to climate change in montane rainforest lizards. *Molecular Ecology* **19**: 2531–2544.

Bradshaw, W.E. and Holzapfel, C.M. 2006. Evolutionary responses to rapid climate change. *Science* **312**: 1477–1478.

Chamaille-Jammes, S., Massot, M., Aragon, P., and Clobert, J. 2006. Global warming and positive fitness response in mountain populations of common lizards *Lacerta vivipara*. *Global Change Biology* **12**: 392–402.

Chown, S., Hoffmann, A.A., Kristensen, T.N., Angilletta Jr., M.J., Stenseth, N.C., and Pertoldi, C. 2010. Adapting to climate change: a perspective from evolutionary physiology. *Climate Research* **43**: 3–15.

Clarke, D.N. and Zani, P.A. 2012. Effects of night-time warming on temperate ectotherm reproduction: potential fitness benefits of climate change for side-blotched lizards. *The Journal of Experimental Biology* **215**: 1117–1127.

DeGaetano, A.T. and Allen, R.J. 2002. Trends in twentieth-century temperature extremes across the United States. *Journal of Climate* **15**: 3188–3205.

Easterling, D.R., Horton, B., Jones, P.D., Peterson, T.C., Karl, T.R., Parker, D.E., Salinger, M.J., Razuvayev, V., Plummer, N., Jamason, P., and Folland, C.K. 1997. Maximum and minimum temperature trends for the globe. *Science* **277**: 364–367.

Easterling, D.R., Karl, T.R., Gallo, K.P., Robinson, D.A., Trenberth, K.E., and Dai, A. 2000. Observed climate variability and change of relevance to the biosphere. *Journal of Geophysical Research* **105**: 20,101–20,114.

Espinoza, R.R., Wiens, J.J., and Tracy, C.R. 2004. Recurrent evolution of herbivory in small, cold-climate lizards: breaking the ecophysiological rules of reptilian herbivory. *Proceedings of the National Academy of Sciences USA* **101**: 16,819–16,824.

Fjeldsa, J. and Lovett, J.C. 1997. Biodiversity and environmental stability. *Biodiversity and Conservation* **6**: 315–323.

Fuentes, M.M.P.B., Hamann, M., and Limpus, C.J. 2010. Past, current and future thermal profiles of green turtle nesting grounds:implications from climate change. *Journal of Experimental Marine Biology and Ecology* **383**: 56–64.

Graham, C.H., Moritz, C., and Williams, S.E. 2006. Habitat history improves prediction of biodiversity in rainforest fauna. *Proceedings of the National Academy of Sciences, USA* **103**: 632–636.

Grant, P.R. and Grant, R.B. 2002. Unpredictable evolution in 30-year study of Darwin's finches. *Science* **296**: 707–711.

Hawkes, L.A., Broderick, A.C., Godfrey, M.H., and Godley, B.J. 2009. Climate change and marine turtles. *Endangered Species Research* **7**: 137–154.

Hertz, P.E., Huey, R., and Nevo, E. 1983. Homage to Santa Rita: thermal sensitivity of sprint speed in agamid lizards. *Evolution* **37**: 1075–1084.

Hoskin, C.J. 2004. Australian microhylid frogs (*Cophixalus* and *Austrochaperina*): phylogeny, taxonomy, calls, distributions and breeding biology. *Australian Journal of Zoology* **52**: 237–269.

Huey, R.B. 1982. Temperature, physiology, and the ecology of the reptiles. In: Gans, C. (Ed.) *Biology of the Reptilia*, Vol. 12. Wiley, New York, New York, USA, pp. 25–91.

Janzen, F.J. 1994. Climate change and temperature-dependent sex determination in reptiles. *Proceedings of the National Academy of Science USA* **91**: 7487–7490.

Janzen, F.J. and Paukstis, G.L. 1988. Environmental sex determination in reptiles. *Nature* **332**: 790.

Jetz, W., Rahbek, C., and Colwell, R.K. 2004. The coincidence of rarity and richness and the potential signature of history in centers of endemism. *Ecology Letters* **7**: 1180–1191.

Karl, T.R., Kukla, G., Razuvayev, V.N., Changery, M.J., Quayle, R.G., Helm Jr., R.R., Easterling, D.R., and Fu, C.B. 1991. Global warming: evidence for asymmetric diurnal temperature change. *Geophysical Research Letters* **18**: 2253–2256.

Karl, T.R., Jones, P.D., Knight, R.W., Kukla, G., Plummer, N., Razuvayev, V., Gallo, K.P., Lindseay, J., Charlson, P.J., and Peterson, T.D. 1993. Asymmetric trends of daily maximum and minimum temperature. *Bulletin of the American Meteorology Society* **74**: 1007–1023.

Labra, A. and Bozinovic, F. 2002. Interplay between pregnancy and physiological thermoregulation in *Liolaemus* lizards. *Ecoscience* **9**: 421–426.

Labra, A., Pienar, J., and Hansen, T.F. 2009. Evolution of thermal physiology in Liolaemus lizards: adaptation, phylogenetic inertia, and niche tracking. *American Naturalist* **174**: 204–220.

Lavergne, S., Mouquet, N., Thuiller, W., and Ronce, O. 2010. Biodiversity and climate change: integrating evolutionary and ecological responses of species and communities. *Annual Review of Ecology, Evolution and Systematics* **41**: 321–350.

Leal, M. and Gunderson, A.R. 2012. Rapid change in the thermal tolerance of a tropical lizard. *The American Naturalist* **180**: 815–822.

Moreno-Rueda, G., Pleguezuelos, J.M., Pizarro, M., and Montori, A. 2011. Northward shifts of the distributions of Spanish reptiles in association with climate change. *Conservation Biology* **26**: 278–283.

Moritz, C., Langham, G., Kearney, M., Krockenberger, A., VanDerWal, J., and Williams, S. 2012. Integrating phylogeography and physiology reveals divergence of thermal traits between central and peripheral lineages of tropical rainforest lizards. *Philosophical Transactions of the Royal Society B* **367**: 1680–1687.

Parmesan, C. and Yohe, G. 2003. A globally coherent fingerprint of climate change impacts across natural systems. *Nature* **421**: 37–42.

Paulissen, M.A. 2008. Spatial learning in the little brown skink, *Scincella lateralis*: the importance of experience. *Animal Behavior* **76**: 135–141.

Radder, R., Quinn, A.E., Georges, A., Sarre, S.D., and Shine, R. 2008. Genetic evidence for co-occurrence of chromosomal and thermal sex-determining systems in a lizard. *Biology Letters* **4**: 176–178.

Refsnider, J.M. and Janzen, F.J. 2012. Behavioural plasticity may compensate for climate change in a long-lived reptile with temperature-dependent sex determination. *Biological Conservation* **152**: 90–95.

Rissman, E.F., Heck, A.L., Leonard, J.E., Shupnik, M.A., and Gustafsson, J. 2002. Disruption of estrogen receptor ß gene impairs spatial learning in female mice. *Proceedings of the National Academy of Sciences USA* **99**: 3996–4001.

Rodder, D., Hawlitschek, O., and Glaw, F. 2010. Environmental niche plasticity of the endemic gecko

Phelsuma parkeri Loveridge 1941 from Pemba Island, Tanzania: a case study of extinction risk on flat islands by climate change. *Tropical Zoology* **23**: 35–49.

Schwartz, A. and Thomas, R. 1975. *A Check-List of West Indian Amphibians and Reptiles*. Carnegie Museum of Natural History Special Publication 1. Carnegie Museum of Natural History, Pittsburgh, Pennsylvania, USA.

Shine, R. 2004. Does viviparity evolve in cold climate reptiles because pregnant females maintain stable (not high) body temperature? *Evolution* **58**: 1809–1818.

Sinervo, B., Mendez-de-la-Cruz, F., Miles, D.B., Heulin, B., Bastiaans, E., Villagran-Santa Cruz, M., Lara-Resendiz, R., Martinez-Mendez, N., Calderon-Espinosa, M.L., Meza-Lazaro, R.N., Gadsden, H., Avila, L.J., Morando, M., De la Riva, I.J., Sepulveda, P.V., Rocha, C.F.D., Ibarguengoytia, N., Puntriano, C.A., Massot, M., Lepetz, V., Oksanen, T.A., Chapple, D.G., Bauer, A.M., Branch, W.R., Clobert, J., and Sites, J.W. 2010. Erosion of lizard diversity by climate change and altered thermal niches. *Science* **328**: 894–899.

Valdecantos, S., Martinez, V., Lobo, F., and Cruz, F.B. 2013. Thermal biology of Liolaemus lizards from the high Andes: Being efficient despite adversity. *Journal of Thermal Biology* **38**: 126–134.

Valenzuela, N. and Lance, V. (Eds.) 2004. *Temperature-Dependent Sex Determination in Vertebrates*. Smithsonian Institution, Washington, DC, USA.

VanDerWal, J., Shoo, L.P., and Williams, S.E. 2009. New approaches to understanding late Quaternary climate fluctuations and refugial dynamics in Australian wet tropical rain forests. *Journal of Biogeography* **36**: 291–301.

Walther, G.-R., Post, E., Convey, P., Menzel, A., Parmesan, C., Beebee, T.J.C., Fromentin, J.-M., Hoegh-Guldberg, O., and Bairlein, F. 2002. Ecological responses to recent climate change. *Nature* **416**: 389–395.

Williams, S.E. and Pearson, R.G. 1997. Historical rainforest contractions, localized extinctions and patterns of vertebrate endemism in the rainforests of Australia's wet tropics. *Proceedings of the Royal Society of London Series B—Biological Sciences* **264**: 709–716.

Witt, M.J., Hawkes, L.A., Godfrey, M.H., Godley, B.J., and Broderick, A.C. 2010. Predicting the impacts of climate change on a globally distributed species: the case of the loggerhead turtle. *Journal of Experimental Biology* **213**: 901–911.

Wright, L.I., Stokes, K.L., Fuller, W.J., Godley, B.J., McGowan, A., Snape, R., Tregenza, T., and Broderick, A.C. 2012. Turtle mating patterns buffer against disruptive effects of climate change. *Proceedings of the Royal Society B: Biological Sciences* Published online before print January 25, 2012 doi: 10.1098/rspb.2011.2285.

Yeates, D.K., Bouchard, P., and Monteith, G.B. 2002. Patterns and levels of endemism in the Australian wet tropics rainforest: evidence from flightless insects. *Invertebrate Systematics* **16**: 605–661.

Zug, G.R., Vitt, L.J., and Caldwell, J.P. 2001. *Herpetology. An Introductory Biology of Amphibians and Reptiles.* Second Edition. Academic Press, San Diego, California, USA. 630 pp.

5.10 Worms

- It appears earthworms and soil nematodes respond to increases in the air's CO_2 content, via a number of plant-mediated phenomena, in ways that further enhance the positive effects of atmospheric CO_2 enrichment on plant growth and development, while helping to sequester more carbon more securely in the soil and thereby reducing the potential for CO_2-induced global warming.

"Earthworms," writes Edwards (1988), "play a major role in improving and maintaining the fertility, structure, aeration and drainage of agricultural soils." As noted by Sharpley *et al.* (1988), for example, "by ingestion and digestion of plant residue and subsequent egestion of cast material, earthworms can redistribute nutrients in a soil and enhance enzyme activity, thereby increasing plant availability of both soil and plant residue nutrients," as others also have demonstrated (Bertsch *et al.*, 1988; McCabe *et al.*, 1988; Zachmann and Molina, 1988). Kemper (1988) describes how "burrows opened to the surface by surface-feeding worms provide drainage for water accumulating on the surface during intense rainfall," noting "the highly compacted soil surrounding the expanded burrows has low permeability to water which often allows water to flow through these holes for a meter or so before it is absorbed into the surrounding soil."

Hall and Dudas (1988) report the presence of earthworms appears to mitigate the deleterious effects of certain soil toxins. Logsdon and Lindon (1988) describe a number of other beneficial effects of earthworms, including enhancement of soil aeration, since under wet conditions earthworm channels do not swell shut as many soil cracks do; enhancement of soil water uptake, since roots can explore deeper soil layers by following earthworm channels; and enhancement of nutrient uptake, since earthworm casts and channel walls have a more neutral pH and higher available nutrient level than bulk soil.

In light of these observations, there is great interest about what may happen to earthworms as the air's CO_2 content and temperature rise.

With respect to how rising atmospheric CO_2 concentrations might impact earthworms, Edwards (1988) writes, "the most important factor in maintaining good earthworm populations in agricultural soils is that there be adequate availability of organic matter." Hendrix *et al.* (1988) and Kladivko (1988) report greater levels of plant productivity promote greater levels of earthworm activity. Consequently, since the most ubiquitous and powerful effect of atmospheric CO_2 enrichment is its stimulation of plant productivity (see Chapter 1, this volume), which leads to enhanced delivery of organic matter to soils, it logically follows this aerial fertilization effect of the ongoing rise in the air's CO_2 content should increase earthworm populations and amplify the many beneficial services they provide for plants.

Then there's the second most significant and common impact of atmospheric CO_2 enrichment on plants: its antitranspirant effect, whereby elevated levels of atmospheric CO_2 reduce leaf stomatal apertures and slow the rate of evaporative water loss from the vast bulk of Earth's vegetation. Growth chamber studies and field experiments that have studied this phenomenon provide voluminous evidence it often leads to increased soil water content in many terrestrial ecosystems (see Section 2.33, this volume), which is something earthworms favor.

Zaller and Arnone (1997) fumigated open-top and -bottom chambers they established in a calcareous grassland near Basal, Switzerland with air of either 350 or 600 ppm CO_2 for an entire growing season. They found the mean annual soil moisture content in the CO_2-enriched chambers was 10% greater than that observed in the ambient-air chambers. They note cumulative surface earthworm cast production after only one year was 35% greater in the CO_2-enriched chambers than in the control chambers. In addition, because earthworm casts are rich in organic carbon and nitrogen, the cumulative amount of these important nutrients on a per-land-area basis was found to be 28% greater in the CO_2-enriched chambers than in the ambient-air chambers. In a subsequent study of the same grassland, Zaller and Arnone (1999) report plants growing in close proximity to the earthworm casts produced more biomass than similar plants growing further away from them. They also found the CO_2-induced growth stimulation experienced by the various grasses was greater for those plants growing nearer the earthworm casts.

These observations show atmospheric CO_2 enrichment sets in motion a self-enhancing cycle of positive biological phenomena whereby increases in the air's CO_2 content stimulate plant productivity and reduce plant evaporative water loss, which results in more organic matter entering the soil and a longer soil moisture retention time and/or greater soil water contents. All of this leads to the development of larger and more active earthworm populations, which enhance many important soil properties, including fertility, structure, aeration, and drainage. These improved properties further enhance the growth of the plants.

There are additional reasons for optimism regarding this process. As Jongmans *et al.* (2003) point out, "the rate of organic matter decomposition can be decreased in worm casts compared to bulk soil aggregates (Martin, 1991; Haynes and Fraser, 1998)." They conducted a micro-morphological investigation of structural development and organic matter distribution in two calcareous marine loam soils on which pear trees had been grown for 45 years. One of the soils exhibited little or no earthworm activity and the other exhibited high earthworm activity, due to different levels of heavy metal contamination of the soils as a consequence of the prior use of different amounts of fungicides. Based on their results and other studies they cite, they conclude, "earthworms play an important role in the intimate mixing of organic residues and fine mineral soil particles and the formation of organic matter-rich micro-aggregates and can, therefore, contribute to physical protection of organic matter, thereby slowing down organic matter turnover and increasing the soil's potential for carbon sequestration." That is, atmospheric CO_2 enrichment that stimulates the activity of earthworms also leads to more—and more secure—sequestration of carbon in Earth's soils, thereby reducing the potential for CO_2-induced global warming.

Cole *et al.* (2002) report, "in the peatlands of northern England, which are classified as blanket peat, it has been suggested that the potential effects of global warming on carbon and nutrient dynamics will be related to the activities of dominant soil fauna, and especially enchytraeid worms." Cole *et al.* say they hypothesized warming would lead to increased enchytraeid worm activity, which would lead to higher grazing pressure on microbes in the soil, and since enchytraeid grazing has been observed to enhance microbial activity (Cole *et al.*, 2000), they further hypothesized more carbon would be liberated in dissolved organic form, "supporting the view that global warming will increase carbon loss from blanket peat ecosystems."

The scientists constructed small microcosms from soil and litter they collected near the summit of Great Dun Fell, Cumbria, England. Subsequent to "defaunating" this material by reducing its temperature to -80°C for 24 hours, they thawed and inoculated it with native soil microbes. Half of the microcosms were incubated in the dark at 12°C and half at 18°C, the former temperature being approximately equal to mean August soil temperature at a depth of 10 cm at the site of soil collection, and the latter being "close to model predictions for soil warming that might result from a doubling of CO_2 in blanket peat environments."

Ten seedlings of an indigenous grass of blanket peat were then transplanted into each of the microcosms, while 100 enchytraeid worms were added to each of half of the mini-ecosystems. These procedures resulted in the creation of four experimental treatments: ambient temperature, ambient temperature + enchytraeid worms, elevated temperature, and elevated temperature + enchytraeid worms. The resulting 48 microcosms—sufficient to destructively harvest three replicates of each treatment four times throughout the course of the 64-day experiment—were arranged in a fully randomized design and maintained at either 12 or 18°C with alternating 12-hour light and dark periods. In addition, throughout the course of the study the microcosms were given distilled water every two days to maintain their original weights.

Contrary to their hypothesis, the scientists found elevated temperature reduced the ability of the enchytraeid worms to enhance the loss of carbon from the microcosms. At the normal ambient temperature, for example, the presence of the worms enhanced dissolved organic carbon (DOC) loss by 16%, and at the elevated temperature expected for a doubling of the air's CO_2 content, the worms had no effect at all on DOC. In addition, Cole *et al.* note, "warming may cause drying at the soil surface, forcing enchytraeids to burrow to deeper subsurface horizons." Hence, since the worms are known to have little influence on soil carbon dynamics below a depth of 4 cm (Cole *et al.*, 2000), the scientists conclude this additional consequence of warming would further reduce the ability of enchytraeids to enhance carbon loss from blanket peatlands.

Summarizing their findings, Cole *et al.* say, "the soil biotic response to warming in this study was negative." That is, it resulted in a reduced loss of carbon to the atmosphere, which would tend to slow the rate of rise of the air's CO_2 content, as was suggested by the study of Jongmans *et al.*

Maraldo *et al.* (2010) also studied enchytraeids, recognizing their important contribution "to the decomposition processes and nutrient mineralization." Such activities have been shown to lead to increased nutrient availability and uptake by plants (Laakso and Setala, 1999; Cragg and Bardgett, 2001). Enchytraeids provide these benefits directly, as Maraldo *et al.* describe it, "by consuming large amounts of organic matter," and indirectly "by their feeding activity and modifications of soil structure." They note, "the presence of enchytraeids is especially important in nutrient poor ecosystems" such as "temperate heathland and northern coniferous forests, where their biomass dominates the soil faunal community," citing Cragg (1961) and Swift *et al.* (1998).

Working on a hilly, nutrient-poor, sandy soil with a dry heath/grassland cover at Brandbjerg, Denmark, Maraldo *et al.* conducted an experiment beginning October 2005 and extending through 2007. The seven scientists studied the individual and combined effects of soil warming, drought, and atmospheric CO_2 enrichment.

They warmed the soil so as to achieve a mean daily temperature increase of 0.3°C in winter and 0.7°C in summer at a depth of 5 cm, using a scaffolding that carried a curtain, which reflected the outgoing infrared radiation from the soil/plant surface back toward the ground, that was automatically pulled over the vegetation at sunset and retracted at sunrise. They achieved drought conditions by reducing peak soil water content by 11 percent and 13 percent compared to control plots in 2006 and 2007, using waterproof curtains that were automatically pulled over the vegetation during rain events. And they used a free-air CO_2 enrichment (FACE) system to increase the air's CO_2 concentration from 382 to 481 ppm.

Maraldo *et al.* report their experimentally imposed warming had no significant impact on enchytraeid biomass production, but their drought treatment decreased it by 40 percent. The extra 99 ppm of CO_2 stimulated enchytraeid biomass by 40 percent. At certain times this latter phenomenon was "especially positive," as in the summer of 2007, when "the total enchytraeid biomass in the CO_2 plots was increased by 108% compared to ambient plots." They found no interactions among the three factors, so "the positive effect of increased CO_2 [+40%] and the negative effect of drought [-40%] were cancelled out when applied in combination."

Bossuyt *et al.* (2005) note "earthworms ingest large quantities of organic materials that are mixed and excreted as casts (Parmelee *et al.*, 1990; Martin and Marinissen, 1993; Jegou *et al.*, 1998) and improve stable macroaggregation (Guggenberger *et al.*, 1996; Marinissen and Hillenaar, 1996; Scullion and Malik, 2000)," as also has been found by van Rhee (1977), De Vleesschauwer and Lal (1981), and McKenzie and Dexter (1987). In addition, they remark, "the retention of organic C in soil is becoming more important since the rise in atmospheric CO_2 and global warming are recent concerns," and "earthworms are known to play a role in aggregate formation and soil organic matter (SOM) protection." However, they say, "it is still unclear at what scale and how quickly earthworms manage to protect SOM." They conducted a pair of experiments to address that question.

In the first experiment, Bossuyt *et al.* measured soil aggregate size distribution and total C and ^{13}C in three treatments—control soil, soil + ^{13}C-labeled sorghum leaf residue, and soil + ^{13}C-labeled residue + earthworms—after 20 days of incubation, where earthworms were added after the eighth day. In the second experiment, they determined the protected C and ^{13}C pools inside the newly formed casts and macro- and micro-soil-aggregates. They found the proportion of large water-stable macroaggregates was on average 3.6 times greater in the soil-residue samples that contained earthworms than in those that lacked earthworms, and the macroaggregates in the earthworm treatment contained approximately three times more sequestered carbon.

Bossuyt *et al.* state, "earthworms were found to form a significant pool of protected C in microaggregates within large macroaggregates after 12 days of incubation," thereby demonstrating the rapidity with which earthworms perform their vital function of sequestering carbon in soils when plant residues become available to them.

Don *et al.* (2008) studied the effects of anecic earthworms—which generally inhabit a single vertical burrow throughout their entire lives that can be as much as five meters in depth but is generally in the range of one to two meters—on soil carbon stocks and turnover at two extensively managed grassland sites in Thuringia, Germany. Analyzing enzyme activity, stable isotopes, nuclear magnetic resonance spectroscopy, and the ^{14}C age of the earthworm burrow linings, the seven German scientists found "the carbon distribution in soils is changed by anecic earthworms' activity with more carbon stored in the subsoil where earthworms slightly increase the carbon stocks." They also state "the translocation of carbon from [the] organic layer to the subsoil will decrease the carbon vulnerability to mineralization," because "carbon in the organic layer and the surface soil is much more prone to disturbances with rapid carbon loss than subsoil carbon."

Don *et al.* note "earthworms are present in almost all ecosystems around the globe with particularly high abundances in grasslands, where they increase productivity (Partsch *et al.*, 2006)" and where "100–800 burrows per square meter have been reported by Lavelle (1988)." The presence and activity of earthworms play important roles in helping Earth's soils store and preserve carbon—and thereby mitigate the rate of rise of the atmosphere's CO_2 concentration.

Yeates *et al.* (2003) report a number of results they obtained from a season-long FACE study of a 30-year-old New Zealand pasture, where three experimental plots were maintained at the ambient atmospheric CO_2 concentration of 360 ppm and three others at a concentration of 475 ppm (a CO_2 enhancement of only 32%) for a period of four to five years. The pasture contained about 20 species of plants, including C_3 and C_4 grasses, legumes, and forbs, but the scientists' attention was focused more on what happened to the microfauna inhabiting the soil in which the plants grew.

Nematode populations increased significantly in response to the 32% increase in the air's CO_2 concentration. Of the various feeding groups studied, Yeates *et al.* report the relative increase "was lowest in bacterial-feeders (27%), slightly higher in plant (root) feeders (32%), while those with delicate stylets (or narrow lumens; plant-associated, fungal-feeding) increased more (52% and 57%, respectively)." The greatest nematode increases were recorded among omnivores (97%) and predators (105%). Most dramatic, root-feeding populations of the *Longidorus* nematode taxon rose by 330%. Also increasing in abundance were earthworms: *Aporrectodea caliginosa* by 25% and *Lumbricus rubellus* by 58%. Enchytraeids decreased in abundance, by approximately 30%.

Yeates *et al.* note the introduction of lumbricids has been demonstrated to improve soil conditions in New Zealand pastures (Stockdill, 1982), which helps pasture plants grow. Hence, the CO_2-induced increase in earthworm numbers observed in Yeates *et al.*'s study would be expected to do more of the same, and the reduced abundance of enchytraeids they documented in the CO_2-enriched pasture would lead to less carbon being released to the air from the soil, as per the known ability of enchytraeids to promote

carbon loss from British peat lands under current temperatures.

Larsen and Clarke (2002) fed diets with and without coenzyme Q to wild-type nematodes (*Caenorhabditis elegans*) and several mutants during the adult phases of their lives, recording the lengths of time they survived. They found "withdrawal of coenzyme Q (Q) from the diet of wild-type nematodes extends adult life-span by ~60%." They also report the lifespans of the four mutants they studied were extended by a Q-less diet. More detailed analyses of their results led them to conclude the lifespan extensions were due to reduced generation and increased scavenging of reactive oxygen species.

The results and conclusions of this study are similar to those of Melov *et al.* (2000), who also studied *C. elegans*, testing the theory reactive oxygen species cause aging by examining the effects of two superoxide dismutase-/catalase-like mimetics (EUK–8 and EUK–134) on the lifespans of normal and mutant *C. elegans* worms that ingested various amounts of the mimetics. In every experiment, treatment of normal worms with the antioxidant mimetics significantly increased both mean and maximum lifespan. Treatment of normal worms with but 0.05 mM EUK–134, for example, increased their mean lifespan by fully 54%; in mutant worms whose normal lifespan was genetically shortened by 37%, treatment with 0.5 mM EUK–134 restored their lifespan to normal by increasing their mutation-reduced lifespan by 67%. They also determined these effects were not caused by a reduction in worm metabolism, which could have reduced the production of oxygen radicals, but "by augmenting natural antioxidant defenses without having any overt effects on other traits."

Melov *et al.* say their results "suggest that endogenous oxidative stress is a major determinant of the rate of aging." The significance of this statement resides in the fact that antioxidants tend to reduce such stresses in animals, and in the observation atmospheric CO_2 enrichment has been shown to significantly enhance the concentrations of many of these plant constituents (see Antioxidants, Section 7.3.1) as well as the concentrations of several substances that have been proven effective in fighting cancers, viral infections, and other animal maladies (see Health Effects of CO_2, Section 7.3).

It appears earthworms and soil nematodes respond to increases in the air's CO_2 content, via a number of plant-mediated phenomena, in ways that further enhance the positive effects of atmospheric CO_2 enrichment on plant growth and development, while helping to sequester more carbon more securely in the soil and thereby reducing the potential for CO_2-induced global warming.

References

Bertsch, P.M., Peters, R.A., Luce, H.D., and Claude, D. 1988. Comparison of earthworm activity in long-term no-tillage and conventionally tilled corn systems. *Agronomy Abstracts* **80**: 271.

Bossuyt, H., Six, J., and Hendrix, P.F. 2005. Protection of soil carbon by microaggregates within earthworm casts. *Soil Biology & Biochemistry* **37**: 251–258.

Cole, L., Bardgett, R.D., and Ineson, P. 2000. Enchytraeid worms (Oligochaeta) enhance mineralization of carbon in organic upland soils. *European Journal of Soil Science* **51**: 185–192.

Cole, L., Bardgett, R.D., Ineson, P., and Hobbs, P.J. 2002. Enchytraeid worm (Oligochaeta) influences on microbial community structure, nutrient dynamics and plant growth in blanket peat subjected to warming. *Soil Biology & Biochemistry* **34**: 83–92.

Cragg, J.B. 1961. Some aspects of the ecology of moorland animals. *Journal of Ecology* **49**: 477.

Cragg, R.G. and Bardgett, R.D. 2001. How changes in soil faunal diversity and composition within a trophic group influence decomposition processes. *Soil Biology and Biochemistry* **33**: 2073–2081.

De Vleesschauwer, D. and Lal, R. 1981. Properties of worm casts under secondary tropical forest regrowth. *Soil Science* **132**: 175–181.

Don, A., Steinberg, B., Schoning, I., Pritsch, K., Joschko, M., Gleixner, G., and Schulze, E.-D. 2008. Organic carbon sequestration in earthworm burrows. *Soil Biology & Biochemistry* **40**: 1803–1812.

Edwards, C.A. 1988. Earthworms and agriculture. *Agronomy Abstracts* **80**: 274.

Guggenberger, G., Thomas, R.J., and Zech, W. 1996. Soil organic matter within earthworm casts of an anecic-endogeic tropical pasture community, Columbia. *Applied Soil Ecology* **3**: 263–274.

Hall, R.B. and Dudas, M.J. 1988. Effects of chromium loading on earthworms in an amended soil. *Agronomy Abstracts* **80**: 275.

Haynes, R.J. and Fraser, P.M. 1998. A comparison of aggregate stability and biological activity in earthworm casts and uningested soil as affected by amendment with wheat and lucerne straw. *European Journal of Soil Science* **49**: 629–636.

Hendrix, P.F., Mueller, B.R., van Vliet, P., Bruce, R.R., and Langdale, G.W. 1988. Earthworm abundance and distribution in agricultural landscapes of the Georgia piedmont. *Agronomy Abstracts* **80**: 276.

Jegou, D., Cluzeau, D., Balesdent, J., and Trehen, P. 1998. Effects of four ecological categories of earthworms on carbon transfer in soil. *Applied Soil Ecology* **9**: 249–255.

Jongmans, A.G., Pulleman, M.M., Balabane, M., van Oort, F., and Marinissen, J.C.Y. 2003. Soil structure and characteristics of organic matter in two orchards differing in earthworm activity. *Applied Soil Ecology* **24**: 219–232.

Kemper, W.D. 1988. Earthworm burrowing and effects on soil structure and transmissivity. *Agronomy Abstracts* **80**: 278.

Kladivko, E.J. 1988. Soil management effects on earthworm populations and activity. *Agronomy Abstracts* **80**: 278.

Laakso, J. and Setala, H. 1999. Sensitivity of primary production to changes in the architecture of belowground food webs. *Oikos* **87**: 58–64.

Larsen, P.L. and Clarke C.F. 2002. Extension of life-span in *Caenorhabditis elegans* by a diet lacking coenzyme Q. *Science* **295**: 120–123.

Lavelle, P. 1988. Earthworm activities and the soil system. *Biology and Fertility of Soils* **6**: 237–251.

Logsdon, S.D. and Linden, D.L. 1988. Earthworm effects on root growth and function, and on crop growth. *Agronomy Abstracts* **80**: 280.

Maraldo, K., Krogh, P.H., van der Linden, L., Christensen, B., Mikkelsen, T.N., Beier, C., and Holmstrup, M. 2010. The counteracting effects of atmospheric CO_2 concentrations and drought episodes: studies of enchytraeid communities in a dry heathland. *Soil Biology & Biochemistry* **42**: 1958–1966.

Marinissen, J.C.Y. and Hillenaar, S.I. 1996. Earthworm induced distribution of organic matter in macro-aggregates from differently managed arable fields. *Soil Biology & Biochemistry* **29**: 391–395.

Martin, A. 1991. Short- and long-term effects of the endogenic earthworm *Millsonia anomala* (Omodeo) (Megascolecidae, Oligochaeta) of tropical savannas on soil organic matter. *Biology and Fertility of Soils* **11**: 234–238.

Martin, A. and Marinissen, J.C.Y. 1993. Biological and physico-chemical processes in excrements of soil animals. *Geoderma* **56**: 331–347.

McCabe, D., Protz, R., and Tomlin, A.D. 1988. Earthworm influence on soil quality in native sites of southern Ontario. *Agronomy Abstracts* **80**: 281.

McKenzie, B.M. and Dexter, A.R. 1987. Physical

properties of casts of the earthworm *Aporrectodea rosea*. *Biology and Fertility of Soils* **5**: 328–332.

Melov, S., Ravenscroft, J., Malik, S., Gill, M.S., Walker, D.W., Clayton, P.E., Wallace, D.C., Malfroy, B., Doctrow, S.R., and Lithgow, G.J. 2000. Extension of life-span with superoxide dismutase/catalase mimetics. *Science* **289**: 1567–1569.

Parmelee, R., Beare, M.H., Cheng, W., Hendrix, P.F., Rider, S.J., Crossley, D.A., and Coleman, D.C. 1990. Earthworms and enchytraeids in conventional and no-tillage agroecosystems. A biocide approach to assess their role in organic matter breakdown. *Biology and Fertility of Soils* **10**: 1–10.

Partsch, S., Milcu, A., and Scheu, S. 2006. Decomposers (Lumbricadae, Collembola) affect plant performance in model grasslands of different diversity. *Ecology* **87**: 2548–2558.

Scullion, J. and Malik, A. 2000. Earthworm activity affecting organic matter, aggregation and microbial activity in soils restored after open cast mining for coal. *Soil Biology & Biochemistry* **32**: 119–126.

Sharpley, A.N., Syers, J.K., and Springett, J. 1988. Earthworm effects on the cycling of organic matter and nutrients. *Agronomy Abstracts* **80**: 285.

Stockdill, S.M.J. 1982. Effects of introduced earthworms on the productivity of New Zealand pastures. *Pedobiologia* **24**: 29–35.

Swift, M.J., Andren, O., Brussaard, L., Briones, M., Couteaux, M.M., Ekschmitt, K., Kjoller, A., Loiseau, P., and Smith, P. 1998. Global change, soil biodiversity, and nitrogen cycling in terrestrial ecosystems—three case studies. *Global Change Biology* **4**: 729–743.

van Rhee, J.A. 1977. A study of the effect of earthworms on orchard productivity. *Pedobiologia* **17**: 107–114.

Yeates, G.W., Newton, P.C.D., and Ross, D.J. 2003. Significant changes in soil microfauna in grazed pasture under elevated carbon dioxide. *Biology and Fertility of Soils* **38**: 319–326.

Zachmann, J.E. and Molina, J.A. 1988. Earthworm-microbe interactions in soil. *Agronomy Abstracts* **80**: 289.

Zaller, J.G. and Arnone III, J.A. 1997. Activity of surface-casting earthworms in a calcareous grassland under elevated atmospheric CO_2. *Oecologia* **111**: 249–254.

Zaller, J.G. and Arnone III, J.A. 1999. Interactions between plant species and earthworm casts in a calcareous grassland under elevated CO_2. *Ecology* **80**: 873–881.

6

Aquatic Life

Key Findings

Introduction

6.1 Ocean Warming

6.2 Freshwater Warming

6.3 Ocean "Acidification"

6.4 Freshwater "Acidification"

6.5 Simultaneous Ocean Warming and "Acidification"

Key Findings

The key findings of this chapter, which challenge the alarming and negative projections of United Nations' Intergovernmental Panel on Climate Change (IPCC), are presented in the bullet points below.

- Multiple studies from multiple ocean regions confirm ocean productivity tends to increase with temperature. Subjects of this research include phytoplankton and macroalgae, corals, crustaceans, and fish.

- Rising seawater temperature is conducive to enhanced coral calcification, leading some experts to forecast coral calcification will increase by about 35% beyond pre-industrial levels by 2100, and no extinction of coral reefs will occur in the future.

- Many aquatic species demonstrate the capability to adjust their individual critical thermal maximum (the upper temperature at which the onset of behavioral incapacitation occurs) upwards in response to temperature increases of the amount forecast by IPCC.

- Aquatic life has survived decadal, centennial, and millennial-scale climate oscillations that have persisted for millions of years. Evidence indicates they are well-equipped to adapt to forecasted increases in temperature, if necessary.

- Caution should be applied when interpreting results from laboratory-based studies of lower seawater pH levels. Such studies often are incapable, or fall far short, of mimicking conditions in the real world, and thus they frequently yield results quite different than what is observed in nature.

- Rising atmospheric CO_2 levels do not pose a significant threat to aquatic life. Many aquatic species have shown considerable tolerance to declining pH values predicted for the next few centuries, and many have demonstrated a likelihood of positive responses in empirical studies.

- The projected decline in ocean pH levels in the year 2100 (as compared to preindustrial times) may be significantly overstated, amounting to only half of the 0.4 value IPCC predicts.

- The natural variability of oceanic pH is often much greater than the change in pH levels forecast by IPCC.

- Natural fluctuations in pH may have a large impact on the development of resilience in marine populations, as heterogeneity in the environment with regard to pH and pCO_2 exposure may result in populations that are acclimatized to variable pH or extremes in pH.

- For those aquatic species showing negative responses to pH declines in experimental studies, there are adequate reasons to conclude such responses will be largely mitigated through phenotypic adaptation or evolution during the many decades to centuries the pH concentration is projected to fall.

Introduction

Some observers have suggested rising atmospheric carbon dioxide (CO_2) concentrations may harm aquatic life via global warming, in which the temperatures of the world's water bodies rise, and through the absorption of additional CO_2 from the air into water, thereby lowering the pH of the waters to which aquatic life is accustomed. IPCC projects marine and freshwater species will be negatively affected by these processes and will experience future declines, in some instances so severe as to cause species extinctions.

In contrast, the material presented in this chapter, representing the findings of hundreds of peer-reviewed research analyses, suggests a much better future is in store for Earth's aquatic life. Many laboratory and field studies have demonstrated growth and developmental improvements in response to higher temperatures and reduced water pH levels. Other research has illustrated the capability of marine and freshwater species to tolerate and adapt to rising temperature and pH decline of the planet's water bodies. When such observations are considered, the pessimistic projections of IPCC give way to considerable optimism with respect to the future of the planet's marine life.

This chapter begins by summarizing research on the impact of rising ocean temperatures on phytoplankton and macroalgae, corals, crustaceans, fish, and other marine species. Researchers have found repeatedly that many species benefit rather than suffer from rising temperatures, including temperature increases forecast by IPCC. Section 6.2 examines research on the effects of warmer temperatures on freshwater species. Much less research has been conducted in this area, but it too highlights beneficial effects of warming on phytoplankton, several species of fish, and freshwater mussels.

Section 6.3 addresses the threat of so-called "ocean acidification." The phrase is an improper choice because natural seawater is basic (alkaline), with an average pH level typically around 8.1, and the oceans will never become acidic (below 7.0) due to IPCC's worst-case scenarios of future anthropogenic CO_2 emissions. The prospect of oceans and lakes becoming "acidic" is frightening to the general public, and rightly so. While many scientists conducting research in this area use the term, perhaps to attract public attention to their work, more accurate and less judgmental phrases are "lower oceanic pH," "lower seawater pH levels," and "ocean pH reduction." The research summarized in this section makes it clear that rising atmospheric CO_2 levels do not pose as significant a threat to aquatic life as claimed by IPCC. Many aquatic species have shown considerable tolerance to declining pH values predicted for the next few centuries, and many have demonstrated a likelihood of positive responses in empirical studies.

Section 6.4 summarizes research on freshwater

"acidification." The number of studies examining this topic is dramatically smaller than the number concerning oceans, but those highlighted here reveal findings typically more positive than negative.

Section 6.5 investigates research on the combined effects of rising temperatures and falling pH levels on marine plants and animals. Research in this area is not as plentiful, but what exists is generally reassuring: Many studies show the combination of higher temperatures and falling pH levels to be beneficial, not harmful, to marine life.

6.1 Ocean Warming

According to IPCC, global warming will warm the planet's oceans, resulting in catastrophic effects on marine plants and animals. In a draft of the Summary for Policymakers of its contribution to IPCC's Fifth Assessment Report, Working Group II claims "Open-ocean net primary production is projected to redistribute and to fall globally by 2100 under RCP8.5. Climate change adds to threats of over-fishing and other non-climatic stressors, thus complicating marine management regimes (*high confidence*)" (IPCC 2014-II, p. 9). More warnings along these lines appear in Working Group II's draft full report, as shown by excerpts presented at the beginning of Section 6.1.2 below.

IPCC's frequent description of the modern rise in global temperature as "unprecedented" suggests there already should be signs of negative impacts on oceanic productivity and marine life, but a review of the scholarly literature on this subject reveals just the opposite: Productivity is rising and species are flourishing, except in cases where human activities such as over-fishing, pollution, generation of silt, and other damaging practices are to blame. The studies highlighted in this section yield little evidence to support IPCC's point of view.

6.1.1 Phytoplankton and Macroalgae

This section examines research on the impacts of ocean warming on marine phytoplankton and macroalgae. The key findings are presented in the bullet points below, followed by an expanded discussion of those findings.

- Multiple studies from multiple ocean regions confirm ocean productivity tends to increase with temperature.

- Several observation-based analyses reveal phytoplankton productivity has increased over the past several decades in response to the instrumental-era rise in temperature.

- Evidence suggests marine plants are well-equipped to adapt and evolve to forecasted increases in future temperature, as they have done so in responding to decadal, centennial, and millennial-scale climate oscillations that have persisted for millions of years.

Sarmiento *et al.* (2004) conducted a massive computational study employing six coupled climate model simulations to determine the biological response of the global ocean to climate warming they simulated from the beginning of the Industrial Revolution to the year 2050. Based on vertical velocity, maximum winter mixed-layer depth, and sea-ice cover, they defined six biomes and calculated how their surface geographies would change in response to their calculated changes in global climate. Next, they used satellite ocean color and climatological observations to develop an empirical model for predicting surface chlorophyll concentrations from the final physical properties of the world's oceans as derived from their global warming simulations. They then used three primary production algorithms to estimate the response of oceanic primary production to climate warming based on their calculated chlorophyll concentrations. The 13 scientists from Australia, France, Germany, Russia, the United Kingdom, and the United States arrived at a global warming-induced increase in global ocean primary production ranging from 0.7 to 8.1%.

In addition to Sarmiento *et al.*'s model-based study, a number of real-world observations also suggest IPCC's concerns about future declines in ocean productivity in response to rising temperatures are unfounded. Goes *et al.* (2005) analyzed seven years (1997–2004) of satellite-derived ocean surface phytoplankton productivity data, as well as associated sea surface temperatures (SSTs) and winds in the Arabian Sea. They report for the region located between 52 to 57°E and 5 to 10°N, "the most conspicuous observation was the consistent year-by-year increase in phytoplankton biomass over the 7-year period." This change was so significant that by the summer of 2003, they write, "chlorophyll *a* concentrations were >350% higher than those observed in the summer of 1997." They also report the increase in chlorophyll *a* was "accompanied by an intensification of sea surface winds, in particular of the zonal (east-to-west) component," noting these "summer monsoon winds are a coupled atmosphere-land-ocean phenomenon, whose strength is significantly correlated with tropical SSTs and Eurasian snow cover anomalies on a year-to-year basis." They write, "reduced snow cover over Eurasia strengthens the spring and summer land-sea thermal contrast and is considered to be responsible for the stronger southwest monsoon winds." They note "the influence of southwest monsoon winds on phytoplankton in the Arabian Sea is not through their impact on coastal upwelling alone but also via the ability of zonal winds to laterally advect newly upwelled nutrient-rich waters to regions away from the upwelling zone." They conclude, "escalation in the intensity of summer monsoon winds, accompanied by enhanced upwelling and an increase of more than 350% in average summertime phytoplankton biomass along the coast and over 300% offshore, raises the possibility that the current warming trend of the Eurasian landmass is making the Arabian Sea more productive."

Drinkwater (2006) examined marine ecosystems of the North Atlantic, determining "in the 1920s and 1930s, there was a dramatic warming of the air and ocean temperatures in the northern North Atlantic and the high Arctic, with the largest changes occurring north of 60°N." This warming "led to reduced ice cover in the Arctic and subarctic regions and higher sea temperatures," as well as northward shifts of multiple marine ecosystems. This early twentieth century warming "contributed to higher primary and secondary production," Drinkwater writes, and "with the reduced extent of ice-covered waters, more open water allow[ed] for higher production than in the colder periods."

McGregor et al. (2007) state, "coastal upwelling occurs along the eastern margins of major ocean basins and develops when predominantly along-shore winds force offshore Ekman transport of surface waters, which leads to the ascending (or upwelling) of cooler, nutrient-rich water." They note these regions of coastal upwelling account for about 20% of the global fish catch while constituting less than 1% of the area covered by the world's oceans. To better understand this productivity-enhancing phenomenon of great practical and economic significance, they studied its long-term history along the northwest coast of Africa—in the heart of the Cape Ghir upwelling system off the coast of Morocco—by analyzing two sediment cores having decadal-or-better resolution that extend from the late Holocene to the end of the twentieth century—from 520 BC to AD 1998.

The four researchers found an anomalous cooling of sea surface temperatures during the twentieth century, which they say "is consistent with increased upwelling." They note, the "upwelling-driven sea surface temperatures also vary out of phase with millennial-scale changes in Northern Hemisphere temperature anomalies and show relatively warm conditions during the Little Ice Age and relatively cool conditions during the Medieval Warm Period."

McGregor et al. offer an explanation for how this happens, posing a scenario that starts with an impetus for warming that leads to near-surface air temperatures over land becoming warmer than those over the ocean. The greater warming over the land "deepens the thermal low-pressure cell over land while a higher-pressure center develops over the slower-warming ocean waters." As this occurs, "winds blow clockwise around the high and anticlockwise around the continental low." With the coast representing the boundary between the two centers, the resulting wind is "oriented alongshore and southward (equator-ward), which thus drives the upwelling and negative sea surface temperature anomalies."

McGregor et al. say similar anti-phased thermal behavior—the cooling of coastal waters that leads to enhanced coastal upwelling during periods of hemispheric or global warming—has been observed in the Arabian Sea and along the Iberian margin, as well as in parts of the California Current and the Peru-Chile Current. This suggests as global warming enhances the upwelling of cooler nutrient-rich waters along the eastern margins of major ocean basins, it helps to significantly enhance global-ocean primary productivity, which leads to an increase in global-ocean secondary productivity, as represented by the global fish catch.

Boyd et al. (2007) reported somewhat analogous findings in their review of iron enrichment experiments conducted between 1993 and 2005. These experiments conclusively demonstrate, they write, "phytoplankton grow faster in warmer open-ocean waters, as predicted by algal physiological relationships." These findings indicate total ocean productivity should have benefited immensely from twentieth century global warming and likely will continue to benefit from continued global warming.

Marasovic et al. (2005) analyzed monthly observations of basic hydrographic, chemical, and biological parameters, including primary production, made since the 1960s at two oceanographic stations, one near the coast of Croatia (Kastela Bay) and one in the middle Adriatic Sea. They found mean annual primary production in Kastela Bay averaged about 430 mg C m^{-2} d^{-1} over the period 1962–1972, exceeded 600 mg C m^{-2} d^{-1} in 1972–1982, and rose to more than 700 mg C m^{-2} d^{-1} in 1982–1996, accompanied by a similar upward trend in percent oxygen saturation of the surface water. The initial value of primary production in the open sea was much less (approximately 150 mg C m^{-2} d^{-1}), but it began to follow the upward trend of the Kastela Bay data after about one decade. Marasovic *et al.* conclude, "even though all the relevant data indicate that the changes in Kastela Bay are closely related to an increase of anthropogenic nutrient loading, similar changes in the open sea suggest that primary production in the Bay might, at least partly, be due to global climatic changes," which are "occurring in the Mediterranean and Adriatic Sea open waters" and may be directly related to "global warming of air and ocean" because "higher temperature positively affects photosynthetic processes."

Raitsos *et al.* (2005) investigated the relationship between Sea-viewing Wide Field-of-view Sensor (SeaWiFS) chlorophyll *a* measurements in the Central Northeast Atlantic and North Sea (1997–2002) and simultaneous measurements of the Phytoplankton Color Index (PCI) collected by the Continuous Plankton Recorder survey, an upper-layer plankton monitoring program that has operated in the North Sea and North Atlantic Ocean since 1931. By developing a relationship between the two databases over their five years of overlap, the scientists were able to produce a Chl-*a* history for the Central Northeast Atlantic and North Sea for the period 1948–2002. Of this record they say "an increasing trend is apparent in mean Chl-*a* for the area of study over the period 1948–2002." They report "there is clear evidence for a stepwise increase after the mid–1980s, with a minimum of 1.3mg m^{-3} in 1950 and a peak annual mean of 2.1 mg m^{-3} in 1989 (62% increase)." Alternatively, the data may represent a steadier long-term upward trend upon which is superimposed a decadal-scale oscillation. In a final comment on their findings, they note, "changes through time in the PCI are significantly correlated with both sea surface temperature and Northern Hemisphere temperature," citing Beaugrand and Reid (2003).

Antoine *et al.* (2005) applied revised data-processing algorithms to two ocean-sensing satellites, the Coastal Zone Color Scanner (CZCS) and SeaWiFS, over the periods 1979–1986 and 1998–2002, respectively, to provide an analysis of the decadal changes in global oceanic phytoplankton biomass. The results showed "an overall increase of the world ocean average chlorophyll concentration by about 22%" over the two decades under study.

Hirawake *et al.* (2005) analyzed chlorophyll *a* data obtained from Japanese Antarctic Research Expedition cruises made on the Southern Ocean by the Fuji and Shirase icebreakers between Tokyo and Antarctica from 15 November to 28 December of nearly every year between 1965 and 2002 in a study of interannual variations of phytoplankton biomass, calculating results for the equatorial region between 10°N and 10°S, the Subtropical Front (STF) region between 35°S and 45°S, and the Polar Front (PF) region between 45°S and 55°S. They found an increase in chl *a* "in the waters around the STF and the PF, especially after 1980 around the PF in particular," and "in the period between 1994 and 1998, the chl *a* in the three regions exhibited rapid gain simultaneously." They also found "significant correlations between chl *a* and year through all of the period of observation around the STF and PF, and the rates of increase are 0.005 and 0.012 mg chl *a* m^{-3} y^{-1}, respectively." They report the satellite data of Gregg and Conkright (2002) "almost coincide with our results." The Japanese scientists note, "simply considering the significant increase in the chl *a* in the Southern Ocean, a rise in the primary production as a result of the phytoplankton increase in this area is also expected."

Sepulveda *et al.* (2005) presented "the first reconstruction of changes in surface primary production during the last century from the Puyuhuapi fjord in southern Chile, using a variety of parameters (diatoms, biogenic silica, total organic carbon, chlorins, and proteins) as productivity proxies." Noting the fjord is located in "a still-pristine area," they state it is "suitable to study changes in past export production originating from changes in both the paleo-Patagonian ice caps and the globally important Southern Ocean."

They found the productivity of the Puyuhuapi fjord "was characterized by a constant increase from the late 19th century to the early 1980s, then decreased until the late 1990s, and then rose again to present-day values." For the first of these periods (1890–1980), they report "all proxies were highly correlated (r > 0.8, p < 0.05)" and "all proxies reveal an increase in accumulation rates." From 1980 to the present, the pattern differed among the various proxies. The researchers state, "considering that the top 5 cm of the sediment column (~10 years) are diagenetically active, and that bioturbation by benthic organisms may have modified and mixed the sedimentary signal, paleo-interpretation of the period 1980–2001 must be taken with caution." Their work provides substantial solid evidence that, for the first 90 years of the 111-year record, surface primary production in the Puyuhuapi fjord rose dramatically, and with lesser confidence it appears to have leveled out over the past two decades.

While IPCC worries recent "unprecedented" increases in mean global air temperature and CO_2 concentration have been bad for the biosphere, Sepulveda *et al.* present yet another case of an ecosystem apparently thriving in such conditions. Nevertheless, claims of impending ocean productivity declines have not ceased, and the study of Behrenfeld *et al.* (2006) is often cited as support of such claims. Working with NASA's Sea-viewing Wide Field-of-view Sensor (SeaWiFS), the team of 10 U.S. scientists calculated monthly changes in net primary production (NPP) from similar changes in upper-ocean chlorophyll concentrations detected from space over the past decade. They report this period was dominated by an initial NPP increase of 1,930 teragrams of carbon per year (Tg C yr^{-1}), which they attributed to the significant cooling of "the 1997 to 1999 El Niño to La Niña transition," and they note this increase was "followed by a prolonged decrease averaging 190 Tg C yr^{-1}," which they attributed to subsequent warming.

The researchers' explanation for the means by which changing temperatures drove the two trends in NPP is based on their presumption a warming climate increases the density contrast between warmer surface waters and cooler underlying nutrient-rich waters. The enhanced stratification that occurs with warming, they say, "suppresses nutrient exchange through vertical mixing," which decreases NPP by reducing the supply of nutrients to the surface waters where photosynthesizing phytoplankton predominantly live. The scientists suggest "surface cooling favors elevated vertical exchange," by contrast, which increases NPP by enhancing the supply of nutrients to the ocean's surface waters, which have a greater concentration of phytoplankton than the underlying waters do because of light requirements for photosynthesis.

Real-world observations raise questions about that explanation. From approximately the middle of 2001 to the end of the data series in early 2006 (which accounts for more than half the data record), there has been, if anything, a slight increase in global NPP. Does this observation mean there has been little or no net global warming since mid-2001? Or does it mean the global ocean's mean surface temperature declined over that five-year period? Neither alternative accords

with the model-based projections of CO_2-induced climate warming.

The relationship between global warming and oceanic productivity may not be nearly as strong as what Behrenfeld *et al.* suggest. They leave themselves significant wiggle room in this regard, stating, "modeling studies suggest that shifts in ecosystem structure from climate variations may be as [important as] or more important than the alterations in bulk integrated properties reported here," noting some "susceptible ecosystem characteristics" that might shift include "taxonomic composition, physiological status, and light absorption by colored dissolved organic material." Given enough time, then, the phenomena Behrenfeld *et al.* describe could result in important "shifts in ecosystem structure" that could compensate, or even overcompensate, for what might initially appear to be negative warming-induced consequences.

Another reason for not concluding too much from the Behrenfeld *et al.* oceanic NPP dataset is that it may be of too short a duration to reveal what might be occurring on a longer timescale throughout the world's oceans, or its position in time may prevent the detection of greater short-term changes of the opposite sign that may have occurred a few years earlier or might occur in the near future. The central regions of the world's major oceans were long thought to be essentially vast biological deserts (Ryther, 1969), but several studies of primary photosynthetic production conducted in those regions in the 1980s (Shulenberger and Reid, 1981; Jenkins, 1982; Jenkins and Goldman, 1985; Reid and Shulenberger, 1986; Marra and Heinemann, 1987; Laws *et al.*, 1987; Venrick *et al.*, 1987; Packard *et al.*, 1988) yielded results that suggest marine productivity at that time was at least twice as great as it likely was for a long time before 1969, causing many scientists of that day to speculate "the ocean's deserts are blooming" (Kerr, 1986).

Of even greater interest, perhaps, the 1970–1988 dataset of Jones *et al.* (1999) indicates Earth underwent a linear-regression-derived global warming of 0.333°C; the database of the Global Historical Climatology Network indicates the planet experienced a similarly calculated global warming of 0.397°C. The mean of these two values (0.365°C) is nearly twice as great as the warming that occurred over the post-1999 period studied by Behrenfeld *et al.*, yet this earlier much larger warming—which Behrenfeld *et al.*'s work suggests should have produced a major decline in ocean productivity—was accompanied by a huge increase in ocean productivity. It would appear Behrenfeld *et al.* got the cause-and-effect relationship between global warming and ocean productivity exactly backwards.

Since publication of the Behrenfeld *et al.* study, other researchers have found no cause for alarm with respect to ocean productivity and rising global temperatures. Arrigo *et al.* (2008) write, "between the late 1970s and the early part of the 21st century, the extent of Arctic Ocean sea ice cover has declined during all months of the year, with the largest declines reported in the boreal summer months, particularly in September ($8.6 \pm 2.9\%$ per decade)," citing Serreze *et al.* (2007). To "quantify the change in marine primary productivity in Arctic waters resulting from recent losses of sea ice cover," the authors "implemented a primary productivity algorithm that accounts for variability in sea ice extent, sea surface temperature, sea level winds, downwelling spectral irradiance, and surface chlorophyll *a* concentrations," and "was parameterized and validated specifically for use in the Arctic (Pabi *et al.*, 2008) and utilizes forcing variables derived either from satellite data or NCEP reanalysis fields."

Arrigo *et al.* determined "annual primary production in the Arctic increased yearly by an average of 27.5 Tg C per year since 2003 and by 35 Tg C per year between 2006 and 2007." Thirty percent of the increase was attributable to decreased minimum summer ice extent, and 70% was due to a longer phytoplankton growing season. Arrigo *et al.* conclude if the trends they discovered continue, "additional loss of ice during Arctic spring could boost productivity >3-fold above 1998–2002 levels." If the 26% increase in annual net CO_2 fixation in the Arctic Ocean between 2003 and 2007 continues, they state, "this would represent a weak negative feedback on climate change."

Smith and Comiso (2008) employed phytoplankton pigment assessments, surface temperature estimates, modeled irradiance, and observed sea ice concentrations—all derived from satellite data—and incorporated them into a vertically integrated production model to estimate primary productivity trends according to the technique of Behrenfeld *et al.* (2002). The two authors state "the resultant assessment of Southern Ocean productivity is the most exhaustive ever compiled and provides an improvement in the quantitative role of carbon fixation in Antarctic waters."

Over the nine years (1997–2006) analyzed in the study, "productivity in the entire Southern Ocean showed a substantial and significant increase," and this increase can be calculated from the graphical representation of their results as ~17% per decade. The two researchers note "the highly significant increase in the productivity of the entire Southern Ocean over the past decade implies that long-term changes in Antarctic food webs and biogeochemical cycles are presently occurring," and these changes are positive.

Peck *et al.* (2010) note the loss of glaciers and ice shelves at the Antarctic Peninsula is often thought of as something that "will predominantly increase warming of the Earth because of changes in albedo and heat uptake by newly uncovered ground and ocean." They state an important opposing effect of this phenomenon "is the opening up of new areas for biological productivity."

Working with the database of Cook *et al.* (2005), which contains a detailed centennial history of changes in all coastal ice fronts associated with the Antarctic Peninsula compiled from historical accounts, aerial photographs, and satellite imagery, Peck *et al.* developed a time series of changes in the surface ice/water boundary surrounding the Antarctic Peninsula since the early twentieth century. Complementing this information with a 10-year time series of chlorophyll depth profiles (1997–2007) from a near-shore site in northern Marguerite Bay developed by Clarke *et al.* (2008), Peck *et al.* reconstructed the magnitude of new oceanic production that developed around the Antarctic Peninsula as sea ice progressively gave way to open water.

The five researchers with the British Antarctic Survey report as the ice cover along the Antarctic Peninsula has retreated over the past 50 years, "more than 0.5 Mtonnes of carbon has been incorporated into biological standing stock that was not there previously, 3.5 Mtonnes is fixed by phytoplankton blooms and 0.7 Mtonnes deposited to the seabed." They state if only 15% of the remaining ice-covered areas act in the same way, "over 50 Mtonnes of new carbon would be fixed annually and around 10 Mtonnes of this deposited to the seabed in coastal or adjacent areas," and "over 9 Mtonnes of carbon would be locked up in biological communities in the water column or on the sea bed." They suggest over a period of tens, hundreds, or thousands of years, "this process may act as a climate control mechanism."

Brown *et al.* (2011) investigated the widespread assumption the Bering Sea is "rapidly warming and losing sea ice" by employing "satellite-derived sea ice concentration, sea surface temperature, and ocean color data as input to a primary productivity algorithm to take stock of environmental change and primary production" in this region. As the three U.S. researchers report, "rather than declining," they found mean annual sea ice extent in the Bering Sea "has exhibited no significant change over the satellite sea ice record (1979–2009)," because significant warming during the satellite sea surface temperature record (1982–2009) "is mainly limited to the summer months." In addition, and despite certain hotspots of primary production and a strong pulse in the spring, they also determined "the rate of annual area-normalized primary production in the Bering Sea (124 g C per m^2 per year) is below the global mean (140 g C per m^2 per year)." By "comparing warm, low-ice years (2001–2005) with cold, high-ice years (1998–2000 and 2006–2007)," they conclude "Bering Sea primary productivity is likely to rise under conditions of future warming and sea ice loss." That rise could be substantial, as they report, "basin-wide annual primary production ranged from 233 to 331 Tg C per year under the influence of highly variable sea ice and temperature conditions."

Chavez et al. (2011) reviewed the concepts and methods used to estimate ocean primary production (PP), after which they used the modern global instrumental record of sea surface temperature (SST) to analyze the principal modes of interannual to multidecadal climate and ocean variability. They then compared spatiotemporal patterns derived from in situ and satellite time-series of PP with the known time-series of climate and ocean variability, to identify the processes responsible for the observed patterns in PP. They introduced paleoclimate studies into their work to broaden the temporal context and "lead into speculation regarding century-scale variability."

Based on the first part of their analysis, the three researchers from the Monterey Bay Aquarium Research Institute of Moss Landing, California (USA) write, "general conclusions from the satellite and in situ time-series presented here are that PP is increasing globally," and they note global marine PP appears to have risen over the past several decades in association with multidecadal variations in climate. They report data from Continuous Plankton Recorder surveys conducted in the north Atlantic depict "increases in chlorophyll from the 1950s to the present," citing McQuatters-Gollop et al. (2007).

In the second part of their analysis, Chavez et al. report ocean sediment cores containing an "undisturbed history of the past" have been analyzed for variations in PP over timescales that include the Little Ice Age (LIA, ~1400–1800; Gutierrez et al., 2009). Based on reconstructed flux rates of total organic carbon (Sifeddine et al., 2008); diatoms, silica, and

fish scales; bones; and vertebrae, they determined during the LIA the ocean off Peru had "low PP, diatoms and fish," but "at the end of the LIA, this condition changed abruptly to the low subsurface oxygen, eutrophic upwelling ecosystem that today produces more fish than any region of the world's oceans (Chavez et al., 2008)." The researchers conclude, "in coastal environments, PP, diatoms and fish and their associated predators are predicted to decrease and the microbial food web to increase under global warming scenarios," citing Ito et al. (2010). However, they write, "present-day trends and the sedimentary record seem to indicate that the opposite might occur."

Tremblay et al. (2011) note the Canadian Beaufort Shelf and adjacent bays make up a small part of the Arctic Ocean but are of "prime social, economical and cultural importance" for coastal communities because they are "hotspots of marine productivity and staging" and "feeding areas for large aggregations of resident and migrant marine birds and mammals," citing Carmack and MacDonald (2002). Wondering what would happen to the productivity of this important coastal region if it were to warm further, Tremblay et al. set out to compare time series of ice cover, wind forcing, and satellite-based assessments of photosynthetic carbon production for the years 2002–2008 with corresponding in situ measurements of salinity, nutrients, new production, biological stocks, and biogenic fluxes obtained during overwintering surveys in 2003–2004 and 2007–2008.

In 2007–2008, the 15 researchers report, in areas where ice was no longer present due to enhanced seasonal warming, there was significant wind-induced upwelling of growth-promoting nitrates, which were brought up from deep and dark waters into the euphotic zone, where photosynthesis occurs. As a result of this fertilization effect, the herbivorous copepod Calanus glacialis—which they say is "the key link between diatom production and apex consumers on Arctic shelves," citing Soreide et al. (2010)—experienced a total abundance "3 to 33 times higher than in 2003 during mid-fall and 1.6 to 13 fold higher than in 2004 during early summer."

On the region's central shelf, they observed "sedimentary chlorophyll a was over 20-fold higher than at any station not influenced by upwelling," and "benthic carbon demand was among the highest ever observed in the Arctic ocean," citing Clough et al. (2005). The end result of these related phenomena was the "repeated instances of ice ablation and upwelling during fall 2007 and summer 2008 multiplied the production of ice algae, phytoplankton, zooplankton and benthos by 2 to 6 fold."

Tremblay *et al.* conclude the phenomena they observed are "likely to prevail with the increasingly deep and frequent seaward retreat of the central ice pack and the greater incidence of upwelling-favorable winds," as described in detail by Yang (2009), and "new production is also bound to rise as winds gain in intensity and upwelling draws deeper into the nutrient-rich, upper Pacific halocline."

McMinn and Martin (2013) note "most algae regularly experience periods of darkness ranging from a few hours to a few days," during which time "they are unable to photosynthesize, and so must consume stored energy products." The scientists note "some organisms such as polar algae and some microalgal cysts and spores are exposed to darkness for months to years, and these must use alternative strategies to survive." McMinn and Martin—who work at the University of Tasmania's Institute for Marine and Antarctic Studies—reviewed the scientific literature on this subject and found "some taxa, such as dinoflagellates, form cysts and become dormant," while "others use physiological methods or adopt mixotrophy," and "the longest documented survival of more than a century was for dinoflagellates buried in sediments in a Norwegian fjord." In the future, they opine, polar microalgae will have to survive "the same period of seasonal darkness but at higher temperatures, and this will require a greater drawdown of stored energy." McMinn and Martin report "recent experimental work has shown that both Arctic [Martin *et al.*, 2012] and Antarctic [Reeves *et al.*, 2011] phytoplankton are able to survive increases of up to 6°C in the dark." Because such a temperature increase is "unlikely to be experienced in a few centuries as a result of climate change," polar microalgae should be safe for a long, long time to come.

According to Aberle *et al.* (2012), in places such as the Baltic Sea a "temporal match of zooplankton peaks with the spring phytoplankton bloom is required to provide an efficient energy transfer up the food web at the start of the growing season," but some scientists have predicted "warming will affect the different trophic levels unequally" and result in a counterproductive "temporal mismatch between predators and their prey." Aberle *et al.* conducted a set of indoor mesocosm experiments "to analyze time-lags between phytoplankton and micro-zooplankton during the spring succession of Baltic Sea plankton in relation to changing temperature [0 and 6°C above the decadal mean] and light conditions," along with "model simulations using a modified Rosenzweig and MacArthur (1963) predator-prey model incorporating temperature-dependent growth, grazing and mortality rates of autotrophic and heterotrophic components."

The five German scientists say "during the experiments, we observed reduced time-lags between the peaks of phytoplankton and protozoan biomass in response to warming," adding "warming induced a shift in micro-zooplankton phenology leading to a faster species turnover." The models they employed also "predicted reduced time-lags between the biomass peaks of phytoplankton and its predators (both micro-zooplankton and copepods) with warming." Aberle *et al.* conclude their study shows "instead of a mismatch, warming might lead to a stronger match between protist grazers and their prey."

Renaudie *et al.* (2010) conducted a quantitative micropalaeontological analysis of siliceous phytoplankton remains found in a sediment core extracted from the seabed at an ocean depth of 2,549 meters at ODP Site 1260 (~9.2°N, 54.65°W) on the Demerara Rise, a continental shelf located off the coast of Surinam, focusing on a 200,000-year period of warmth during the Eocene between approximately 40.0 and 40.2 million years ago. The five French scientists found "the pre-warming flora, dominated by cosmopolitan species of the diatom genus *Triceratium*, was replaced during the warming interval by a new and more diverse assemblage, dominated by *Paralia sulcata* (an indicator of high productivity) and two endemic tropical species of the genus *Hemiaulus*." They found "the critical warming interval was characterized by a steady increase in tropical species of the genus *Hemiaulus*." They also state, "the microflora preserved above the critical interval was once again of low diversity and dominated by various species of the diatom genus *Hemiaulus*." Renaudie *et al.*'s findings establish warmer is better, a maxim exemplified in the current case by the greater productivity of the tropical ocean during the warmer period and the ocean's continuous upward trend in the diversity of phytoplanktonic species throughout the period of warming.

Cermeño (2011) states "micro-organisms dominate terrestrial, aquatic and aerial ecosystems and largely rule our planet's life by playing pivotal roles in global biogeochemical cycles," citing Staley and Fuhrman (2002) and Falkowski *et al.* (2008). He declares these facts indicate "life on Earth is microbe dependent." Cermeño used records of climatic variability and microfossil data from the world's oceans covering the past 65 million years to "explore the linkage between the rate of climate change and the probability of extinction, origination and net diversification of marine planktonic diatoms and calcareous nannoplankton," analyzing the evolutionary dynamics of the two phytoplankton groups throughout the 65-million-year period of study and comparing the results with the climate change record.

Cermeño states his findings demonstrate "the probability of extinction of microbial plankton species did not increase during periods of enhanced climatic instability over the past 65 million years." He says his results show "exceptional climatic contingencies, such as those occurring across the Late Palaeocene-Eocene and the Eocene-Oligocene boundary transitions, caused substantial morphological diversification." Cermeño concludes, "to the extent that contemporaneous trends in climate change have analogies with the climates of the geological period analyzed here, my results suggest that these microbial plankton groups will persist in the future ocean, perhaps even expanding their ranges of morphological diversity."

Cannariato *et al.* (1999) provide additional evidence marine biota are well-equipped to adapt to rising temperatures. They investigated the character, magnitude, and speed of responses of benthic foraminifera to millennial-scale climate oscillations manifest in data obtained from an ocean sediment core in the Santa Barbara Basin of the Northeast Pacific that covered the most recent 60,000 years. Although a number of rapid climatic switches were noted throughout the record, representing periods of "extreme environmental variability," the scientists found no extinctions, and the benthic ecosystems "appear to be both resilient and robust in response to rapid and often extreme environmental conditions." Although faunal turnovers occurred within decades, they did so "without extinction or speciation."

Ladah *et al.* (1999) examined the density and population structure of giant kelp "forests" located near Bahia Tortugas, Baja California, Mexico, before, during, and after the 1998 El Niño. At the height of the extreme warming event, sea surface temperatures (SSTs) were 3°C higher than the previous 10-year average for this region, and they led to the complete disappearance of the giant kelp that historically had inhabited the area. However, when the SST anomalies subsided, the giant kelp were once again found to be growing there, and from evidence derived from population structure data and the rapidity with which the plants reestablished themselves, Ladah *et al.* deduced "a microscopic stage that was not visible during dive surveys survived the stressful conditions

of ENSO and caused the recruitment event, supporting the hypothesis that a bank of microscopic forms can survive conditions stressful to macroscopic algae." They note there was independent evidence to suggest "microscopic stages may subsist in nature under low light intensities in a semi-dormant state until conditions become favorable."

In a follow-up study published several years later, Ladah and Zertuche-Gonzalez (2004) found a second and more likely predominant means by which the return of the giant kelp was made possible. Although all giant kelp growing at 15 m depth or shallower died during the peak warmth of the El Niño, the pair of researchers discovered there were numerous large fertile adults located between 25 and 40 m depth unaffected by the high surface water temperatures. Although the upper 15 meters of these plants died and sloughed off, regenerated fronds reached the surface of the sea by the fall of 1998.

The two scientists write, "survival in deep water during this extreme El Niño may have been due to local hydrography, such as internal waves bringing cool nitrate-rich water into the deeper regions of the shelf from below the thermocline, providing a refugium against the warm temperatures, low nutrients, and heavy wave action associated with warming events." They also note "the increased light that often occurs after canopy removal apparently resulted in ... recruitment events ... from newly produced spores from nearby fertile individuals surviving in deeper waters." They conclude "deep-water populations may regularly survive El Niño warming in this region due to internal wave activity, and go undetected due to the depth at which they occur and the sloughing of the shallow (<15 m) biomass."

Zheng *et al.* (2012) state dinoflagellates "are generally believed to prefer warm temperatures and presumably may do better in the face of temperature increases," noting *Prorocentrum donghaiense* was able to grow at temperatures ranging from 10 to 27°C and achieved its maximum specific growth rate at the latter temperature (Xu *et al.*, 2010). For *P. minimum*, they note, "growth rates increased from 0.25/day at 4°C to 0.98/day at 20°C," citing Lomas and Gilbert (1999a,b). They report the composition of phytoplankton exposed to a temperature rise in the vicinity of a nuclear power plant's thermal effluent "tipped toward dinoflagellates both in terms of species number and cell abundance (Li *et al.*, 2011)," probably because "some dinoflagellates were found to produce heat-shock proteins to stabilize protein secondary structure in response to thermal stress

(Alexandrov, 1994)." They further note, "heat shock protein 70 was induced in *Alexandrium tamarense* when subjected to a 10°C jump from its acclimated temperature of 20°C (Kobiyama *et al.*, 2010)."

Zheng *et al.* studied the effects of temperature shock on the growth of the dinoflagellate *Polarella glacialis*, "by monitoring its physiological and biochemical responses to temperature rises from 4°C to 10 and 15°C" while examining the growth rate and expression of two important genes for this alga. The three researchers state, "it is noteworthy that in the present study the cultures were directly transferred from 4°C to 10 and 15°C without progressive intermediate steps," and in response to these sudden temperature shifts, "the cultures first experienced a period of declination, then cell density tended to become stable, a sign that a part of the cell population survived." Zheng *et al.* conclude, "if the species can survive such heat shock in the long term, there is good opportunity that it can be transported from polar regions to temperate or even warmer waters," which perhaps explains why "taxa closely related to this species occur in temperate aquatic environments (Lin *et al.*, 2009, 2010)." If *P. glacialis* and related species can do that, they should have no problem coping with projected global warming.

Clark *et al.* (2013) used "a quantitative genetic breeding design to establish whether there is a heritable variation in thermal sensitivity in two populations of a habitat-forming intertidal macroalga, *Hormosira banksii* (Turner) Descaisne," in which "gametes from multiple parents were mixed and growth and photosynthetic performance were measured in the resulting embryos, which were incubated under control and elevated temperatures (20°C and 28°C)." The four researchers report "significant interactions between male genotype and temperature in one population indicated the presence of genetic variation in thermal sensitivity," such that "selection for more tolerant genotypes thus has the ability to result in the evolution of increased thermal tolerance." They found "genetic correlations between embryos grown in the two temperatures were positive, indicating that those genotypes that performed well in elevated temperature also performed well in control temperature." Clark *et al.* conclude their "finding of genetic variation in thermal tolerance of *H. banksii* embryos suggests resilience to thermal stresses."

References

Aberle, N., Bauer, B., Lewandowska, A., Gaedke, U., and Sommer, U. 2012. Warming induces shifts in microzooplankton phenology and reduces time-lags between phytoplankton and protozoan production. *Marine Biology* **159**: 2441–2453.

Alexandrov, V.Y. 1994. *Functional Aspects of Cell Response to Heat Shock*. Academic Press, San Diego, California, USA.

Antoine, D., Morel, A., Gordon, H.R., Banzon, V.J., and Evans, R.H. 2005. Bridging ocean color observations of the 1980s and 2000s in search of long-term trends. *Journal of Geophysical Research* **110**: 10.1029/2004JC002620.

Arrigo, K.R., van Dijken, G., and Pabi, S. 2008. Impact of a shrinking Arctic ice cover on marine primary production. *Geophysical Research Letters* **35**: 10.1029/2008GL035028.

Beaugrand, G. and Reid, P.C. 2003. Long-term changes in phytoplankton, zooplankton and salmon related to climate. *Global Change Biology* **9**: 801–817.

Behrenfeld, M, Maranon, E., Siegel, D.A., and Hooker, S.B. 2002. Photo-acclimation and nutrient-based model of light-saturated photosynthesis for quantifying ocean primary production. *Marine Ecology Progress Series* **228**: 103–117.

Behrenfeld, M.J., O'Malley, R.T., Siegel, D.A., McClain, C.R., Sarmiento, J.L., Feldman, G.C., Milligan, A.J., Falkowski, P.G., Letelier, R.M., and Boss, E.S. 2006. Climate-driven trends in contemporary ocean productivity. *Nature* **444**: 752–755.

Boyd, P.W., Jickells, T., Law, C.S., Blain, S., Boyle, E.A., Buesseler, K.O., Coale, K.H., Cullen, J.J., de Baar, H.J.W., Follows, M., Harvey, M., Lancelot, C., Levasseur, M., Owens, N.P.J., Pollard, R., Rivkin, R.B., Sarmiento, J., Schoemann, V., Smetacek, V., Takeda, S., Tsuda, A., Turner, S., and Watson, A.J. 2007. Mesoscale iron enrichment experiments 1993–2005: Synthesis and future directions. *Science* **315**: 612–617.

Brown, Z.W., van Dijken, G.L., and Arrigo, K.R. 2011. A reassessment of primary production and environmental change in the Bering Sea. *Journal of Geophysical Research* **116**: 10.1029/2010JC006766.

Cannariato, K.G., Kennett, J.P., and Behl, R.J. 1999. Biotic response to late Quaternary rapid climate switches in Santa Barbara Basin: Ecological and evolutionary implications. *Geology* **27**: 63–66.

Carmack, E. and MacDonald, R.W. 2002. Oceanography of the Canadian Shelf of the Beaufort Sea: A setting for marine life. *Arctic* **55**: 29–45.

Cermeño, P. 2011. Marine planktonic microbes survived

climatic instabilities in the past. *Proceedings of the Royal Society B* **279**: 474–479.

Chavez, F.P., Bertrand, A., Guevara, R., Soler, P., and Csirke, J. 2008. The northern Humboldt Current System: brief history, present status and a view towards the future. *Progress in Oceanography* **79**: 95–105.

Chavez, F.P., Messie, M., and Pennington, J.T. 2011. Marine primary production in relation to climate variability and change. *Annual Review of Marine Science* **3**: 227–260.

Clark, J.S., Poore, A.G.B., Ralph, P.J., and Doblin, M.A. 2013. Potential for adaptation in response to thermal stress in an intertidal macroalga. *Journal of Phycology* **49**: 630–639.

Clarke, A., Meredith, M.P., Wallace, M.I., Brandon, M.A., and Thomas, D.N. 2008. Seasonal and interannual variability in temperature, chlorophyll and macronutrients in northern Maguerite Bay, Antarctica. *Deep Sea Research Part II* **55**: 1988–2006.

Clough, L.M., Renaud, P.E., and Ambrose, W.G. 2005. Impacts of water depth, sediment pigment concentration, and benthic macrofaunal biomass on sediment oxygen demand in the western Arctic Ocean. *Canadian Journal of Fisheries and Aquatic Sciences* **62**: 1756–1765.

Cook, A.J., Fox, A.J., Vaughan, D.G., and Ferrigno, J.G. 2005. Retreating glacier fronts on the Antarctic Peninsula over the past half-century. *Science* **308**: 541–544.

Drinkwater, K.F. 2006. The regime shift of the 1920s and 1930s in the North Atlantic. *Progress in Oceanography* **68**: 134–151.

Falkowski, P.G., Fenchel, T., and DeLong, E.F. 2008. The microbial engines that drive Earth's biogeochemical cycles. *Science* **320**: 1034–1039.

Goes, J.I., Thoppil, P.G., Gomes, H. do R., and Fasullo, J.T. 2005. Warming of the Eurasian landmass is making the Arabian Sea more productive. *Science* **308**: 545–547.

Gregg, W.W. and Conkright, M.E. 2002. Decadal changes in global ocean chlorophyll. *Geophysical Research Letters* **29**: 10.1029/2002GL014689.

Gutierrez, D., Sifeddine, A., Field, D.B., Ortlieb, L., Vargas, G., Chavez, F.P., Velazcol, F., Ferreira, V., Tapia, P., Salvatteci, R., Boucher, H., Morales, M.C., Valdes, J., Reyss, J.-L., Campusano, A., Boussafir, M., Mandeng-Yogo, M., Garcia, M., and Baumgartner, T. 2009. Rapid reorganization in ocean biogeochemistry off Peru towards the end of the Little Ice Age. *Biogeosciences* **6**: 835–848.

Hirawake, T., Odate, T., and Fukuchi, M. 2005. Long-term variation of surface phytoplankton chlorophyll a in the Southern Ocean during 1965–2002. *Geophysical Research Letters* **32**: 10.1029/2004GL021394.

Ito, S., Rose, K.A., Miller, A.J., Drinkwater, K., Brander, K., Overland, J.E., Sundby, S., Churchitser, E., Hurrell, J.W., and Yamanaka, Y. 2010. Ocean ecosystem responses to future global change scenarios: a way forward. In: Marange, M., Werner, R., Field, J., and Hofmann, E. (Eds.) *Marine Ecosystems and Global Change.* Oxford University Press, New York, New York, USA, pp. 287–322.

Jenkins, W.J. 1982. Oxygen utilization rates in North Atlantic subtropical gyre and primary production in oligotrophic systems. *Nature* **300**: 246–248.

Jenkins, W.J. and Goldman, J.C. 1985. Seasonal oxygen cycling and primary production in the Sargasso Sea. *Journal of Marine Research* **43**: 465–491.

Jones, P.D., Parker, D.E., Osborn, T.J., and Briffa, K.R. 1999. Global and hemispheric temperature anomalies—land and marine instrument records. In *Trends: A Compendium of Data on Global Change.* Carbon Dioxide Information Analysis Center, Oak Ridge National Laboratory, U.S. Department of Energy, Oak Ridge, TN, USA.

Kerr, R.A. 1986. The ocean's deserts are blooming. *Science* **232**: 1345.

Kobiyama, A., Tanaka, S., Kaneko, Y., Lim, P.-T., and Ogata, T. 2010. Temperature tolerance and expression of heat shock protein 70 in the toxic dinoflagellate *Alexandrium tamarense* (Dinophyceae). *Harmful Algae* **9**: 180–185.

Ladah, L.B. and Zertuche-Gonzalez, J.A. 2004. Giant kelp (*Macrocystis pyrifera*) survival in deep water (25–40 m) during El Niño of 1997–1998 in Baja California, Mexico. *Botanica Marina* **47**: 367–372.

Ladah, L.B., Zertuche-Gonzalez, J.A., and Hernandez-Carmona, G. 1999. Giant kelp (*Macrocystis pyrifera*, Phaeophyceae) recruitment near its southern limit in Baja California after mass disappearance during ENSO 1997–1998. *Journal of Phycology* **35**: 1106–1112.

Laws, E.A., Di Tullio, G.R., and Redalje, D.G. 1987. High phytoplankton growth and production rates in the North Pacific subtropical gyre. *Limnology and Oceanography* **32**: 905–918.

Li, T., Liu, S., Huang, L, Huang, H., Lian, J., Yan, Y., and Lin, S. 2011. Diatom to dinoflagellate shift in the summer phytoplankton community in a bay impacted by nuclear power plant thermal effluent. *Marine Ecology Progress Series* **424**: 75–85.

Lin, S., Zhang, H., Hou, Y., Zhuang, Y., and Miranda, L. 2009. High-level diversity of dinoflagellates in the natural environment, revealed by assessment of mitochondrial cox 1 and cob genes for dinoflagellate DNA barcoding. *Applied and Environmental Microbiology* **75**: 1279–1290.

Lin, S., Zhang, H., Zhuang, Y., Tran, B., and Gill, J. 2010. Spliced leader-based metatranscriptomic analyses lead to recognition of hidden genomic features in dinoflagellates. *Proceedings of the National Academy of Sciences USA* **107**: 20,033–20,038.

Lomas, M.W. and Gilbert, P.M. 1999a. Temperature regulation of nitrate uptake: a novel hypothesis about nitrate uptake and reduction in cool-water diatoms. *Limnology and Oceanography* **44**: 556–572.

Lomas, M.W. and Gilbert, P.M. 1999b. Interactions between NO^{3-} and NH^{4+} uptake and assimilation: comparison of diatoms and dinoflagellates at several growth temperatures. *Marine Biology* **133**: 541–551.

Marasovic, I., Nincevic, Z., Kuspilic, G., Marinovic, S., and Marinov, S. 2005. Long-term changes of basic biological and chemical parameters at two stations in the middle Adriatic. *Journal of Sea Research* **54**: 3–14.

Marra, J. and Heinemann, K.R. 1987. Primary production in the North Pacific central gyre: Some new measurements based on ^{14}C. *Deep-Sea Research* **34**: 1821–1829.

Martin, A., McMinn, A., Heath, M., Hegseth, E.N., and Ryan, K.G. 2012. The physiological response to increased temperature in over-wintering sea-ice algae and phytoplankton in McMurdo Sound, Antarctica and Tromso, Norway. *Journal of Experimental Marine Biology and Ecology* **428**: 57–66.

McGregor, H.V., Dima, M., Fischer, H.W., and Mulitza, S. 2007. Rapid 20th-century increase in coastal upwelling off northwest Africa. *Science* **315**: 637–639.

McMinn, A. and Martin, A. 2013. Dark survival in a warming world. *Proceedings of the Royal Society B* **280**: 10.1098/rspb.2012.2909.

McQuatters-Gollop, A., Raitsos, D.E., Edwards, M., Pradhan, Y., Mee, L.D., Lavender, S.J., and Attrill, M.J. 2007. A long-term chlorophyll data set reveals regime shift in North Sea phytoplankton biomass unconnected to nutrient trends. *Limnology and Oceanography* **52**: 635–648.

Pabi, S., van Dijken, G.S., and Arrigo, K.R. 2008. Primary production in the Arctic Ocean, 1998–2006. *Journal of Geophysical Research* **113**: 10.1029/2007JC004578.

Packard, T.T., Denis, M., Rodier, M., and Garfield, P. 1988. Deep-ocean metabolic CO_2 production: Calculations from ETS activity. *Deep-Sea Research* **35**: 371–382.

Peck, L.S., Barnes, D.K.A., Cook, A.J., Fleming, A.H., and Clarke, A. 2010. Negative feedback in the cold: ice retreat produces new carbon sinks in Antarctica. *Global Change Biology* **16**: 2614–2623.

Raitsos, D., Reid, P.C., Lavender, S.J., Edwards, M., and Richardson, A.J. 2005. Extending the SeaWiFS chlorophyll data set back 50 years in the northeast Atlantic. *Geophysical Research Letters* **32**: 10.1029/2005GL022484.

Reeves, S., McMinn, A., and Martin, A. 2011. The effect of prolonged darkness on the growth, recovery and survival of Antarctic sea ice diatoms. *Polar Biology* **34**: 1019–1032.

Reid, J.L. and Shulenberger, E. 1986. Oxygen saturation and carbon uptake near 28°N, 155°W. *Deep-Sea Research* **33**: 267–271.

Renaudie, J., Danelian, T. Saint Martin, S., Le Callonnec, L., and Tribovillard, N. 2010. Siliceous phytoplankton response to a Middle Eocene warming event recorded in the tropical Atlantic (Demerara Rise, ODP Site 1260A). *Palaeogeography, Palaeoclimatology, Palaeoecology* **286**: 121–134.

Rosenzweig, M.L. and MacArthur, R.H. 1963. Graphical representation and stability conditions of predator-prey interactions. *American Naturalist* **97**: 209–223.

Ryther, J.H. 1969. Photosynthesis and fish production in the sea. *Science* **166**: 72–76.

Sarmiento, J.L., Slater, R., Barber, R., Bopp, L., Doney, S.C., Hirst, A.C., Kleypas, J., Matear, R., Mikolajewicz, U., Monfray, P., Soldatov, V., Spall, S.A., and Stouffer, R. 2004. Response of ocean ecosystems to climate warming. *Global Biogeochemical Cycles* **18**: 10.1029/2003GB002134.

Sepulveda, J., Pantoja, S., Hughen, K., Lange, C., Gonzalez, F., Munoz, P., Rebolledo, L., Castro, R., Contreras, S., Avila, A., Rossel, P., Lorca, G., Salamanca, M., and Silva, N. 2005. Fluctuations in export productivity over the last century from sediments of a southern Chilean fjord (44°S). *Estuarine, Coastal and Shelf Science* **65**: 587–600.

Serreze, M.C., Holland, M.M., and Stroeve, J. 2007. Perspectives on the Arctic's shrinking sea-ice cover. *Science* **315**: 1533–1536.

Shulenberger, E. and Reid, L. 1981. The Pacific shallow oxygen maximum, deep chlorophyll maximum, and primary production, reconsidered. *Deep-Sea Research* **28**: 901–919.

Sifeddine, A., Gutierrez, D., Ortlieb, L., Boucher, H., Velazco, F., Field, D.B., Vargas, G., Boussafir, M., Salvatteci, R., Ferreira, V., García, M., Valdes, J., Caquineau, S., Mandeng-Yogo, M., Cetin, F., Solis, J., Soler, P., and Baumgartner, T. 2008. Changes in terrestrial runoff, water mass oxygenation and upwelling productivity recorded in laminated sediments off the Central Peruvian Coast spanning the last centuries. *Progress in Oceanography* **79**: 190–197.

Smith Jr., W.O. and Comiso, J.C. 2008. Influence of sea ice on primary production in the Southern Ocean: A satellite perspective. *Journal of Geophysical Research* **113**: 10.1029/2007JC004251.

Soreide, J.E., Leu, E., Graeve, M., and Falk-Petersen, S. 2010. Timing of blooms, algal food quality and Calanus glacialis reproduction and growth in a changing Arctic. *Global Change Biology* **16**: 3154–3163.

Staley, J.T. and Fuhrman, J.A. 2002. Microbial diversity. In: Mooney, H. and Canadell, J.G. (Eds.) *Encyclopedia of Global Environmental Change.* Wiley & Sons, Chichester, United Kingdom, pp. 421–425.

Tremblay, J.-E., Belanger, S., Barber, D.G., Asplin, M., Martin, J., Darnis, G., Fortier, L., Gratton, Y., Link, H., Archambault, P., Sallon, A., Michel, C., Williams, W.J., Philippe, B., and Gosselin, M. 2011. Climate forcing multiplies biological productivity in the coastal Arctic Ocean. *Geophysical Research Letters* **38**: 10.1029/2011GL048825.

Venrick, E.L., McGowan, J.A., Cayan, D.R., and Hayward, T.L. 1987. Climate and chlorophyll a: Long-term trends in the central North Pacific Ocean. *Science* **238**: 70–72.

Xu, N., Duan, S., Li, A., Zhang, C., Cai, Z., and Hu, Z. 2010. Effects of temperature, salinity and irradiance on the growth of the harmful dinoflagellate *Prorocentrum donghaiense* Lu. *Harmful Algae* **9**: 13–17.

Yang, J.Y. 2009. Seasonal and interannual variability of downwelling in the Beaufort Sea. *Journal of Geophysical Research* **114**: 10.1029/2008JC005084.

Zheng, S., Wang, G., and Lin, S. 2012. Heat shock effects and population survival in the polar dinoflagellate *Polarella glacialis. Journal of Experimental Marine Biology and Ecology* **438**: 100–108.

6.1.2 Corals

Perhaps no other species of marine life is projected by IPCC to experience as much hardship and degradation in response to rising temperatures as corals. Several statements from a draft of Working Group II's contribution to IPCC's *Fifth Assessment Report* illustrate these concerns:

> The frequency and magnitude of coral bleaching and mortality will increase in the next few decades (*very high confidence*).

> Under the A1B CO_2 emission scenario, 99% of the grid cells experience at least one severe bleaching event over 2090–2099.

> Half of the coral reefs may avoid high frequency bleaching through 2100 assuming hypothetical

acclimation and/or adaptation (*limited evidence, low agreement*).

> — Chapter 5, Coastal Systems and Low-Lying Areas, Working Group II, IPCC *Fifth Assessment Report*, draft dated March 28, 2013, p. 19.

> It is *very likely* that coral reef ecosystems will not survive changes in sea temperature beyond an additional increase of 1°C.

> Combining the known sensitivity of coral reefs within the Caribbean and Coral Triangle sub-regions, with the exposure to higher temperatures that are projected under medium (RCP4.5) to high (RCP8.5) scenarios, reveals that both coral reef rich regions are *virtually certain* to experience levels of thermal stress that cause coral bleaching every 1–2 years by the mid to late part of this century (*robust evidence, high levels of agreement, very high confidence*).

> The frequency of mass mortality events (DHM > 5; Figure 30–11 A,C) climbs towards events that occur every 1–2 years by mid to late of this century under low to high climate change scenarios (*robust evidence, high levels of agreement, very high confidence*).

> Mass mortality events that impact coral reefs will result in changes to community composition in the short term (2010–2039) and a continuing downward trend in reef building coral stocks in the longer term.

> — Chapter 30, The Ocean, Working Group II, IPCC *Fifth Assessment Report*, draft dated March 28, 2013, p. 35.

> There is *robust evidence* and *high agreement* that coral reefs are one of the most vulnerable marine ecosystems.

> Even under optimistic assumptions regarding corals being able to rapidly adapt to thermal stress, one-third (9–60%, 68% uncertainty range) of the world's coral reefs are projected to be subject to long-term degradation under the RCP3-PD scenario. Under the RCP4.5 scenario, this fraction increases to two-thirds (30–88%, 68% uncertainty range).

> If present day corals have residual capacity to acclimatize and/or adapt, half of the coral reefs may avoid high frequency bleaching through 2100 (*limited evidence, limited agreement*). Evidence of

corals adapting rapidly, however, to climate change is missing or equivocal.

— Technical Summary, Working Group II, IPCC *Fifth Assessment Report*, draft dated March 28, 2013, pp. 67–68.

This section examines the future of Earth's corals in response to possible global warming, beginning with a review of the literature on the many suspected causes of coral bleaching, almost all of which have been attributed (often implausibly) to CO_2-induced global warming. Thereafter, the discussion turns to the possibility corals can adapt to the various environmental threats they face, followed by an examination of whether the widespread bleaching events seen in recent decades are indeed caused by global warming. The discussion concludes with a brief examination of an indirect temperature-related threat to corals—rising sea levels—which IPCC predicts will occur to a significant degree over the twenty-first century and beyond as global warming melts large portions of the ice presently stored in the world's glaciers and ice sheets.

This survey offers a much different perspective on the future of Earth's corals than that predicted by IPCC. Though rising temperatures have challenged and may continue to challenge Earth's corals, a large body of evidence indicates many corals can adapt to and even overcome the temperature-related challenges they are projected to face in response to CO_2-induced global warming. In reaching its overly pessimistic conclusions about corals, IPCC has clearly and improperly ignored the weight of the many research findings summarized here.

6.1.2.1 Causes of Coral Bleaching

This section reviews studies examining the causes of coral bleaching. The key findings are as follows:

- Many studies attribute high sea water temperatures as the primary cause of coral bleaching. However, the crucial link between temperature and coral reef bleaching may not reside in the absolute temperature of the water surrounding the corals but in the rapidity with which the temperature either rises above or falls below the temperature regime to which the corals are normally adapted.

- A number of studies have provided evidence inconsistent with the global-warming-induced coral

bleaching hypothesis, pointing to other important factors and causes of coral bleaching, including solar irradiance, a solar radiation-temperature stress synergism, changes in salinity, bacterial infections, increased sedimentation, and exposure to toxicants.

- Many sources of coral stress and survival have little or nothing to do with rising CO_2 concentrations or temperatures.

Coral bleaching ranks among the more frequently cited negative consequences projected to result from CO_2-induced global warming. A loss of color in certain reef-building corals occurs when algal symbionts, or zooxanthellae, living within the host corals are subjected to various stresses and expelled from them, resulting in a loss of photosynthetic pigments from the coral colony. If the stress is mild, or short in duration, the affected corals often recover and regain their normal complement of zooxanthellae. If the stress is prolonged, or extreme, the corals eventually die, being deprived of their primary food source.

One of the most frequently cited causes of coral bleaching is anomalously high water temperature (Linden, 1998). The origin of this attribution can be traced to the strong El Niño event of 1982–1983, in which widespread bleaching was reported in corals exposed to unusually high surface water temperatures (Glynn, 1988). Since then, a number of other such observations have been made (Cook *et al.*, 1990; Glynn 1991; Montgomery and Strong, 1994; Brown *et al.*, 1996), and several laboratory studies have demonstrated elevated seawater temperatures can indeed induce bleaching in corals (Hoegh-Guldberg and Smith, 1989; Jokiel and Coles, 1990; Glynn and D'Croz, 1990).

Anomalously *low* seawater temperatures also have been identified with coral bleaching (Walker *et al.*, 1982; Coles and Fadlallah, 1990; Muscatine *et al.*, 1991; Gates *et al.*, 1992; Saxby *et al.*, 2003; Hoegh-Guldberg and Fine 2004; Yu *et al.*, 2004; Kemp *et al.*, 2011). These observations suggest the crucial link between temperature and coral reef bleaching may not be in the absolute temperature of the water surrounding the corals, but in the rapidity with which the temperature varies from the temperature regime to which the corals are normally adapted.

Winter *et al.* (1998), for example, studied relationships between coral bleaching and nine temperature indices, concluding, although "prolonged heat stress may be an important precondition for bleaching to occur," sharp temperature changes act as the "immediate trigger." Jones (1997) reported coral bleaching on a portion of Australia's Great Barrier Reef just after average daily sea water temperature rose by 2.5°C over a brief period of eight days. Kobluk and Lysenko (1994) observed severe coral bleaching after an 18-hour *decline* of 3°C in seawater temperature. Because the corals studied by the latter researchers had experienced massive bleaching two years earlier as a result of an anomalous 4°C *increase* in water temperature, the authors conclude coral bleaching is more a function the rapidity of a temperature change than of the absolute magnitude or sign of the change, of heating or cooling.

Podesta and Glynn (1997) provided further evidence seawater temperatures *per se* are not the critical factors in coral bleaching. They examined a number of temperature-related indices of surface waters near Panama over the period 1970–1994. Their analysis revealed for the two years of highest maximum monthly sea surface temperature, 1972 and 1983, coral bleaching was reported only in 1983; 1972 produced no bleaching whatsoever, even though water temperatures that year were just as high as they were in 1983.

Another prominent cause of coral bleaching is solar radiation, a link dating back more than a century to when MacMunn (1903) postulated ultraviolet radiation could damage corals. It wasn't until half-a-century later that scientists began to confirm this suspicion (Catala-Stucki, 1959; Siebeck, 1988; Gleason and Wellington, 1995).

Many investigators of the solar irradiance-coral reef bleaching link have studied the phenomenon by transplanting reef corals from deep to shallow waters. Gleason and Wellington (1993), for example, transplanted samples of the reef-building coral *Montastrea annularis* from a depth of 24 meters to depths of 18 and 12 meters. Using sheets of acrylic plastic to block out ultraviolet radiation on some of the coral samples, they found the shielded corals experienced less bleaching than the unshielded corals, and the unshielded corals at the 12-meter depth had significantly lower amounts of zooxanthellae and chlorophyll per square centimeter than all other treatment and control groups. Similarly, Hoegh-Guldberg and Smith (1989) reported bleaching in the corals *Stylophora pistillata* and *Seriatopora hystrix* when they were moved from a depth of 6 meters to 1.2 meters. Vareschi and Fricke (1986) obtained similar results when moving *Plerogyra sinuosa* from a depth of 25 meters to 5 meters. As in the case of temperature stress, Glynn (1996) notes artificially

reduced light levels also have been observed to cause coral bleaching.

A number of laboratory studies have provided additional evidence for a link between intense solar irradiance and coral reef bleaching, but identifying a specific wavelength or range of wavelengths as the cause of the phenomenon has proven difficult. Fitt and Warner (1995), for example, reported the most significant decline in symbiont photosynthesis in the coral *Montastrea annularis* occurred when it was exposed to ultraviolet and blue light, but other studies have reported coral bleaching to be most severe at shorter ultraviolet wavelengths (Droller *et al.*, 1994; Gleason and Wellington, 1995). Still others have found it to be most strongly expressed at longer photosynthetically active wavelengths (Lesser and Shick, 1989; Lesser *et al.*, 1990; Brown *et al.*, 1994).

As additional studies provided evidence for a solar-induced mechanism of coral reef bleaching (Brown *et al.*, 1994; Williams *et al.*, 1997; Lyons *et al.*, 1998), some also provided evidence for a synergism of solar radiation and temperature stress (Gleason and Wellington, 1993; Rowan *et al.*, 1997; Jones *et al.*, 1998). Researchers have found a number of situations, for example, in which corals underwent bleaching when changes in both of these parameters combined to produce particularly stressful conditions (Lesser *et al.*, 1990; Glynn *et al.*, 1992; Brown *et al.*, 1995), such as during periods of low wind velocity and calm seas, which favor the intense heating of shallow waters and concurrent strong penetration of solar radiation.

This two-parameter interaction has much to recommend it as a primary cause of coral bleaching. It is the mechanism favored by Hoegh-Guldberg (1999), who claimed, in one of the strongest attempts made to that point in time to portray global warming as the cause of bleaching in corals, "coral bleaching occurs when the photosynthetic symbionts of corals (zooxanthellae) become increasingly vulnerable to damage by light at higher than normal temperatures."

The story is considerably more complicated than that. In a review paper on coral bleaching, Brown (1997) listed several potential causes, including elevated seawater temperature, decreased seawater temperature, intense solar radiation, the combination of intense solar radiation and elevated temperature, reduced salinity, and bacterial infections. In a similar review, Meehan and Ostrander (1997) added increased sedimentation and exposure to toxicants.

With respect to seawater salinity, Meehan and Ostrander (1997) note, as with temperature, both high and low values have been observed to cause coral bleaching. Low values typically occur as a result of seawater dilution caused by high precipitation or storm runoff; high values are much rarer, typically occurring only near desalinization plants.

A number of studies also have described the role of bacterial infections in causing coral reef bleaching (Ritchie and Smith, 1998). This phenomenon, too, may have a connection to high seawater temperatures. In a study of the coral *Oculina patagonica* and the bacterial agent *Vibrio* AK–1, for example, Kushmaro *et al.* (1996, 1997) conclude bleaching of colonies of this coral along the Mediterranean coast has its origin in bacterial infection, and that warmer temperatures may lower the resistance of the coral to infection and/or increase the virulence of the bacterium. In subsequent studies of the same coral and bacterium, Toren *et al.* (1998) and Kushmaro *et al.* (1998) further demonstrated this high temperature effect may operate by enhancing the ability of the bacterium to adhere to the coral.

Kushmaro *et al.* (1998) comment on the "speculation that increased seawater temperature, resulting from global warming or El Niño events, is the direct cause of coral bleaching." Against this presumption, they cite several studies of coral bleaching events not associated with any major sea surface temperature anomalies, and they explicitly state, "it is not yet possible to determine conclusively that bleaching episodes and the consequent damage to reefs is due to global climate change." Likewise, Toren *et al.* (1998) note the extensive bleaching that occurred on the Great Barrier Reef during the summer of 1982 was not associated with any major sea surface temperature increase, and "several authors have reported on the patchy spatial distribution and spreading nature of coral bleaching." They note this observation conflicts with the global-warming-induced coral bleaching hypothesis. Instead, they write, "the progression of observable changes that take place during coral bleaching is reminiscent of that of developing microbial biofilms," a point that will later be seen to be of great significance.

High rates of sedimentation have been demonstrated to lead to coral bleaching (Wesseling *et al.*, 1999), and most historical increases in sedimentation rates are clearly human-induced. Umar *et al.* (1998), for example, listed such contributing anthropogenic activities as deforestation, agricultural practices, coastal development, construction, mining, drilling, dredging, and tourism. Nowlis *et al.* (1997) discussed "how land development can increase the risk of severe damage to coral reefs by sediment runoff during storms." However, it has been difficult to determine just how much these phenomena have varied over the past few centuries.

McCulloch *et al.* (2003) recreated a 250-year record of sediment transfer to Havannah Reef—a site on the inner Great Barrier Reef of northern Queensland, Australia—by flood plumes from the Burdekin River. They found sediments suspended in the Burdekin River contain barium (Ba), which is desorbed from the particles that carry it as they enter the ocean, where growing corals incorporate it into their skeletons along with calcium (Ca). When more sediment is carried to the sea by periodic flooding and more gradual longer-term changes in land use that exacerbate soil erosion, the resultant increases in sediment load are recorded in the Ba/Ca ratio of coral skeleton material. McCulloch *et al.* measured Ba/Ca ratios in a 5.3-meter-long coral core from Havannah Reef that covered the period from about 1750 to 1985, as well as in some shorter cores from Havannah Reef and nearby Pandora Reef that extended the proxy sediment record to 1998.

The results revealed before the time of European settlement, which began in the Burdekin catchment in 1862, there was "surprisingly little evidence for flood-plume related activity from the coral Ba/Ca ratios." Soon after, land clearance and domestic grazing intensified, and the soil became more vulnerable to monsoon-rain-induced erosion. By 1870, baseline Ba/Ca ratios had risen by 30%, and "within one to two decades after the arrival of European settlers in northern Queensland, there were already massive impacts on the river catchments that were being transmitted to the waters of the inner Great Barrier Reef." During subsequent periods of flooding, the transport of suspended sediment to the reef increased by five- to ten-fold over what had been characteristic of pre-European settlement times.

In a companion article, Cole (2003) report corals from East Africa "tell a similar tale of erosion exacerbated by the imposition of colonial agricultural practices in the early decades of the twentieth century." There, similar coral data from Malindi Reef, Kenya, indicate "a low and stable level of barium before about 1910 which rises dramatically by 1920, with a simultaneous increase in variance," which was also evident in the Australian data.

Cole concludes "human activity, in the form of changing land use, has added sedimentation to the list of stresses experienced by reefs." As land-use intensification is a widespread phenomenon, she notes, "many reefs close to continents or large islands are likely to have experienced increased delivery of sediment over the past century," which suggests the stress levels produced by this phenomenon are likely to have increased over the past century as well. Cole concludes as coastal populations continue to rise, "this phenomenon is likely to expand."

A number of poisonous substances are known to induce coral bleaching. Some—such as herbicides, pesticides, and even excess nutrients that make their way from farmlands to the sea (Simkiss, 1964; Pittock, 1999)—are of human origin. Other poisons originate in the sea itself, many the result of metabolic waste products of other creatures (Crossland and Barnes, 1974) and some a by-product of the coral host itself (Yonge, 1968). Each of these toxicants presents the coral community with its own distinct challenge.

Taken together, these findings identify a number of sources of stress on coral survival and growth that have little or nothing to do with rising CO_2 concentrations or temperatures. They also clearly indicate human population growth and economic development have predisposed coral reefs to incidences of bleaching and subsequent mortality via a gradual intensification of near-coastal riverine sediment transport rates.

References

Brown, B.E. 1997. Coral bleaching: Causes and consequences. *Coral Reefs* 16: S129-S138.

Cole, J. 2003. Dishing the dirt on coral reefs. *Nature* 421: 705–706.

Brown, B.E., Dunne, R.P., and Chansang, H. 1996. Coral bleaching relative to elevated seawater temperature in the Andaman Sea (Indian Ocean) over the last 50 years. *Coral Reefs* 15: 151–152.

Brown, B.E., Dunne, R.P., Scoffin, T.P., and Le Tissier, M.D.A. 1994. Solar damage in intertidal corals. *Marine Ecology Progress Series* 105: 219–230.

Brown, B.E., Le Tissier, M.D.A., and Bythell, J.C. 1995. Mechanisms of bleaching deduced from histological studies of reef corals sampled during a natural bleaching event. *Marine Biology* 122: 655–663.

Brown, B.E., Le Tissier, M.D.A., and Dunne, R.P. 1994. Tissue retraction in the scleractinian coral *Coeloseris mayeri*, its effect upon coral pigmentation, and preliminary implications for heat balance. *Marine Ecology Progress Series* 105: 209–218.

Catala-Stucki, R. 1959. Fluorescence effects from corals irradiated with ultra-violet rays. *Nature* 183: 949.

Coles, S.L. and Fadlallah, Y.H. 1990. Reef coral survival and mortality at low temperatures in the Arabian Gulf: New species-specific lower temperature limits. *Coral Reefs* 9: 231–237.

Cook, C.B., Logan, A., Ward, J., Luckhurst, B., and Berg Jr., C.J. 1990. Elevated temperatures and bleaching on a high latitude coral reef: The 1988 Bermuda event. *Coral Reefs* 9: 45–49.

Crossland, C.J. and Barnes, D.J. 1974. The role of metabolic nitrogen in coral calcification. *Marine Biology* 28: 325–332.

Droller, J.H., Faucon, M., Maritorena, S., and Martin, P.M.V. 1994. A survey of environmental physico-chemical parameters during a minor coral mass bleaching event in Tahiti in 1993. *Australian Journal of Marine and Freshwater Research* 45: 1149–1156.

Fitt, W.K. and Warner, M.E. 1995. Bleaching patterns of four species of Caribbean reef corals. *Biological Bulletin* 189: 298–307.

Gates, R.D., Baghdasarian, G., and Muscatine, L. 1992. Temperature stress causes host cell detachment in symbiotic cnidarians: Implication for coral bleaching. *Biological Bulletin* 182: 324–332.

Gleason, D.F. and Wellington, G.M. 1993. Ultraviolet radiation and coral bleaching. *Nature* 365: 836–838.

Gleason, D.F. and Wellington, G.M. 1995. Variation in UVB sensitivity of planula larvae of the coral *Agaricia agaricites* along a depth gradient. *Marine Biology* 123: 693–703.

Glynn, P.W. 1988. El Niño-Southern Oscillation 1982–83: Nearshore population, community, and ecosystem responses. *Annual Review of Ecology and Systematics* 19: 309–345.

Glynn, P.W. 1991. Coral bleaching in the 1980s and possible connections with global warming trends. *Ecology and Evolution* 6: 175–179.

Glynn, P.W. 1996. Coral reef bleaching: facts, hypotheses and implications. *Global Change Biology* 2: 495–509.

Glynn, P.W. and D'Croz, L. 1990. Experimental evidence for high temperature stress as the cause of El-Niño-coincident coral mortality. *Coral Reefs* 8: 181–190.

Glynn, P.W., Imai, R., Sakai, K., Nakano, Y., and Yamazato, K. 1992. Experimental responses of Okinawan (Ryukyu Islands, Japan) reef corals to high sea temperature and UV radiation. *Proceedings of the 7th International Coral Reef Symposium* 1: 27–37.

Hoegh-Guldberg, O. 1999. Climate change, coral bleaching and the future of the world's coral reefs. *Marine and Freshwater Research* 50: 839–866.

Hoegh-Guldberg, O. and Fine, M. 2004. Low temperatures cause coral bleaching. *Coral Reefs* **23**: 444.

Hoegh-Guldberg, O. and Smith, G.J. 1989. The effect of sudden changes in temperature, light and salinity on the population density and export of zooxanthellae from the reef corals *Stylophora pistillata* Esper. and *Seriatopora hystrix* Dana. *Journal of Experimental Marine Biology and Ecology* **129**: 279–303.

IPCC 2007. *Climate Change 2007: The Physical Science Basis.* Contribution of Working Group I to the Fourth Assessment Report of the Intergovernmental Panel on Climate Change. Cambridge University Press.

Jokiel, P.L. and Coles, S.L. 1990. Response of Hawaiian and other Indo-Pacific reef corals to elevated sea temperatures. *Coral Reefs* **8**:155–162.

Jones, R.J. 1997. Changes in zooxanthellae densities and chlorophyll concentrations in corals during and after a bleaching event. *Marine Ecology Progress Series* **158**: 51–59.

Jones, R.J., Hoegh-Guldberg, O., Larkum, A.W.D., and Schreiber, U. 1998. Temperature-induced bleaching of corals begins with impairment of the CO_2 fixation mechanism in zooxanthellae. *Plant, Cell and Environment* **21**: 1219–1230.

Kemp, D.W., Oakley, C.A., Thornhill, D.J., Newcomb, L.A., Schmidt, G.W., and Fitt, W.K. 2011. Catastrophic mortality on inshore coral reefs of the Florida Keys due to severe low-temperature stress. *Global Change Biology* **17**: 3468–3477.

Kobluk, D.R. and Lysenko, M.A. 1994. "Ring" bleaching in Southern Caribbean *Agaricia agaricites* during rapid water cooling. *Bulletin of Marine Science* **54**: 142–150.

Kushmaro, A., Rosenberg, E., Fine, M., and Loya, Y. 1997. Bleaching of the coral *Oculina patagonica* by *Vibrio* AK–1. *Marine Ecology Progress Series* **147**: 159–165.

Kushmaro, A., Loya, Y., Fine, M., and Rosenberg, E. 1996. Bacterial infection and coral bleaching. *Nature* **380**: 396.

Kushmaro, A., Rosenberg, E., Fine, M., Ben Haim, Y., and Loya, Y. 1998. Effect of temperature on bleaching of the coral *Oculina patagonica* by *Vibrio* AK–1. *Marine Ecology Progress Series* **171**: 131–137.

Lesser, M.P. and Shick, J.M. 1989. Effects of irradiance and ultraviolet radiation on photoadaptation in the zooxanthellae of *Aiptasia pallida*: Primary production, photoinhibition, and enzymatic defense against oxygen toxicity. *Marine Biology* **102**: 243–255.

Lesser, M.P., Stochaj, W.R., Tapley, D.W., and Shick, J.M. 1990. Bleaching in coral reef anthozoans: Effects of irradiance, ultraviolet radiation, and temperature on the activities of protective enzymes against active oxygen. *Coral Reefs* **8**: 225–232.

Linden, O. 1998. Coral mortality in the tropics: Massive causes and effects. *Ambio* **27**: 588.

Lyons, M.M., Aas, P., Pakulski, J.D., Van Waasbergen, L., Miller, R.V., Mitchell, D.L., and Jeffrey, W.H. 1998. DNA damage induced by ultraviolet radiation in coral-reef microbial communities. *Marine Biology* **130**: 537–543.

MacMunn, C.A. 1903. On the pigments of certain corals, with a note on the pigment of an asteroid. Gardiner, J.S. (Ed.) *The fauna and geography of the Maldive and Laccadive Archipelagoes.* Cambridge, UK: Cambridge University Press. Vol. 1, pp. 184–190.

McCulloch, M., Fallon, S., Wyndham, T., Hendy, E., Lough, J., and Barnes, D. 2003. Coral record of increased sediment flux to the inner Great Barrier Reef since European settlement. *Nature* **421**: 727–730.

Meehan, W.J. and Ostrander, G.K. 1997. Coral bleaching: A potential biomarker of environmental stress. *Journal of Toxicology and Environmental Health* **50**: 529–552.

Montgomery, R.S. and Strong, A.E. 1994. Coral bleaching threatens oceans life. *EOS* **75**: 145 147.

Muscatine, L., Grossman, D., and Doino, J. 1991. Release of symbiotic algae by tropical sea anemones and corals after cold shock. *Marine Ecology Progress Series* **77**: 233–243.

Nowlis, J.S., Roberts, C.M., Smith, A.H., and Siirila, E. 1997. Human-enhanced impacts of a tropical storm on nearshore coral reefs. *Ambio* **26**: 515–521.

Pittock, A.B. 1999. Coral reefs and environmental change: Adaptation to what? *American Zoologist* **39**: 10–29.

Podesta, G.P. and Glynn, P.W. 1997. Sea surface temperature variability in Panama and Galapagos: Extreme temperatures causing coral bleaching. *Journal of Geophysical Research* **102**: 15,749–15,759.

Ritchie, K.B. and Smith, G.W. 1998. Type II white-band disease. *Revista De Biologia Tropical* **46**: 199–203.

Rowan, R., Knowlton, N., Baker, A., and Jara, J. 1997. Landscape ecology of algal symbionts creates variation in episodes of coral bleaching. *Nature* **388**: 265–269.

Saxby, T., Dennison, W.C., and Hoegh-Guldberg, O. 2003. Photosynthetic responses of the coral *Montipora digitata* to cold temperature stress. *Marine Ecology Progress Series* **248**: 85–97.

Siebek, O. 1988. Experimental investigation of UV tolerance in hermatypic corals (Scleractinian). *Marine Ecology Progress Series* **43**: 95–103.

Simkiss, K. 1964. Phosphates as crystal poisons of calcification. *Biological Review* **39**: 487–505.

Toren, A., Landau, L., Kushmaro, A., Loya, Y., and

761

Rosenberg, E. 1998. Effect of temperature on adhesion of *Vibrio* strain AK–1 to *Oculina patagonica* and on coral bleaching. *Applied and Environmental Microbiology* **64**: 1379–1384.

Umar, M.J., McCook, L.J., and Price, I.R. 1998. Effects of sediment deposition on the seaweed Sargassum on a fringing coral reef. *Coral Reefs* **17**: 169–177.

Vareschi, E. and Fricke, H. 1986. Light responses of a scleractinian coral (*Plerogyra sinuosa*). *Marine Biology* **90**: 395–402.

Walker, N.D., Roberts, H.H., Rouse Jr., L.J., and Huh, O.K. 1982. Thermal history of reef-associated environments during a record cold-air outbreak event. *Coral Reefs* **1**: 83–87.

Wesseling, I., Uychiaoco, A.J., Alino, P.M., Aurin, T., and Vermaat, J.E. 1999. Damage and recovery of four Philippine corals from short-term sediment burial. *Marine Ecology Progress Series* **176**: 11–15.

Williams, D.E., Hallock, P., Talge, H.K., Harney, J.N., and McRae, G. 1997. Responses of *Amphistegina gibbosa* populations in the Florida Keys (U.S.A.) to a multi-year stress event (1991–1996). *Journal of Foraminiferal Research* **27**: 264–269.

Winter, A., Appeldoorn, R.S., Bruckner, A., Williams Jr., E.H., and Goenaga, C. 1998. Sea surface temperatures and coral reef bleaching off La Parguera, Puerto Rico (northeast Caribbean Sea). *Coral Reefs* **17**: 377–382.

Yonge, C.M. 1968. Living corals. *Proceedings of the Royal Society of London B* **169**: 329–344.

Yu, K.-F., Zhao, J.-X., Liu, T.-S., Wei, G.-J., Wang, P.X., and Collerson, K.D. 2004. High-frequency winter cooling and reef coral mortality during the Holocene climatic optimum. *Earth and Planetary Science Letters* **224**: 143–155.

6.1.2.2 Responses to Temperature-Related Stresses

Considering the many threats to the health of corals outlined in the previous section, many have questioned how these repositories of underwater biodiversity could possibly escape irreversible bleaching and death. In response to such concerns, Glynn (1996) noted, "numerous reef-building coral species have endured three periods of global warming, from the Pliocene optimum (4.3–3.3 million years ago) through the Eemian interglacial (125 thousand years ago) and the mid-Holocene (6000–5000 years ago), when atmospheric CO_2 concentrations and sea tem-

peratures often exceeded those of today." Glynn observed "an increase in sea warming of less than 2°C would result in a greatly increased diversity of corals in certain high latitude locations."

Living organisms are resilient. Various life forms can tolerate temperatures from below freezing to the boiling point of water; others inhabit niches where light intensity varies from complete darkness to full sunlight. Given time to adapt, nearly all living organisms can learn to survive in conditions well outside their normal zones of environmental tolerance. As Gates and Edmunds (1999) note, numerous studies indicate "corals routinely occupy a physically heterogeneous environment," which "suggests they should possess a high degree of biological flexibility." Their successful responses to the different threats that cause coral bleaching prove that flexibility and are examined in the subsections below.

References

Gates, R.D. and Edmunds, P.J. 1999. The physiological mechanisms of acclimatization in tropical reef corals. *American Zoologist* **39**: 30–43.

Glynn, P.W. 1996. Coral reef bleaching: facts, hypotheses and implications. *Global Change Biology* **2**: 495–509.

6.1.2.2.1 Thermal Adaptation

The studies reviewed in this section examine the concept of thermal adaptation, which refers to the ability of corals to adapt to temperature stresses in the future of similar or even greater magnitude than what they have experienced in the past. The key findings are presented in the bullet points below followed by an expanded discussion of those findings. (Citations for passages in quotation marks in the bullet points are included in the main body of the section.)

- As living entities, corals are not only affected by the various elements of their environment, they also react or respond to them. When changes in environmental factors pose a challenge to their continued existence, they sometimes take major defensive or adaptive actions, including thermal adaptation, to ensure their survival.

- Multiple studies demonstrate corals are thermally adapting to rising sea water temperatures. Bleaching at many reefs is either reduced or no longer occurs at temperatures that previously caused it.

- Cold water coral species also have been shown to display resilience in adapting to temperature increases as large as 5°C.

- Coral genera most susceptible to thermal stress sometimes display the greatest increase in thermal tolerance.

- Genotypic analyses suggest "the physiological plasticity of the host and/or symbiotic components" plays an important role in thermal adaptation.

- There is "a growing body of evidence to support the notion that corals inhabiting more thermally unstable habitats outperform conspecifics from reefs characterized by more stable temperatures when exposed to elevated temperatures."

- "Previous exposure to an environmentally variable microhabitat adds substantially to coral-algal thermal tolerance, beyond that provided by heat-resistant symbionts alone." Similarly, the thermal adaptive capacity of some corals "is likely facilitated by a combination of short-term acclimation in individuals during acute environmental conditions (e.g., recurrent bleaching events) and long-term adaptation among coral populations to chronic environmental conditions (e.g., extreme temperatures)."

- "It is premature to suggest that widespread reef collapse is a certain consequence of ongoing bleaching, or that this will inevitably lead to fisheries collapses."

Fang *et al.* (1997) experimented with samples of *Acropora grandis* taken from the hot water outlet of a nuclear power plant near Nanwan Bay, Taiwan. In 1988, the year the power plant began full operation, the coral samples were completely bleached within two days of exposure to a temperature of 33°C. Two years later, however, "samples taken from the same area did not even start bleaching until six days after exposure to 33°C temperatures," illustrating their ability to thermally adapt.

Middlebrook *et al.* (2008) reported similar findings. They collected multiple upward-growing branch tips of the reef-building coral *Acropora aspera* from three large colonies at the southern end of Australia's Great Barrier Reef and placed them on racks immersed in running seawater within four 750-liter tanks maintained at the mean local ambient tem-perature (27°C) and exposed to natural reef-flat summer daily light levels. Two weeks before a simulated bleaching event—where water temperature was raised to a value of 34°C for six days—they boosted the water temperature in one of the tanks to 31°C for 48 hours, and in another tank they boosted it to 31°C for 48 hours one week before the simulated bleaching event. In the third tank they had no pre-heating treatment, and in the fourth tank they used no pre-heating nor any simulated bleaching event. At different points throughout the study, they measured photosystem II efficiency, xanthophyll and chloro-phyll *a* concentrations, and *Symbiodinium* densities.

Middlebrook *et al.* found the symbionts of the corals exposed to the 48-hour pre-bleaching thermal stress "were found to have more effective photo-protective mechanisms," including "changes in non-photochemical quenching and xanthophyll cycling." They determined "these differences in photo-protection were correlated with decreased loss of symbionts, with those corals that were not pre-stressed performing significantly worse, losing over 40% of their symbionts and having a greater reduction in photosynthetic efficiency," whereas "pre-stressed coral symbiont densities were unchanged at the end of the bleaching." Middlebrook *et al.* say their study "conclusively demonstrates that thermal stress events two weeks and one week prior to a bleaching event provide significantly increased thermal tolerance to the coral holobiont, suggesting that short time-scale thermal adaptation can have profound effects on coral bleaching."

In another laboratory-based study, Bellantuono *et al.* (2012) "tested the response of *Acropora millepora* to thermal preconditioning by exposing coral nubbins to 28°C (3°C below bleaching threshold) for 10 days, prior to challenging them with water temperatures of 31°C for 8 days," while "in another treatment (non-preconditioned), corals were exposed to 31°C without prior exposure to the 28°C treatment." They conducted these procedures in a set of "transparent tanks plumbed into flowing sea water, with four replicate tanks for each treatment."

The three researchers discovered short-term preconditioning to higher-than-ambient temperatures (but still 3°C below the experimentally determined bleaching threshold) for 10 days provided thermal tolerance for the scleractinian coral and its symbionts. Based on various genotypic analyses they conducted, they determined "the acclimatization of this coral species to thermal stress does not come down to simple changes in *Symbiodinium* symbiont shuffling and/or the bacterial communities that associate with reef-building corals bacterial shuffling." These findings, Bellantuono *et al.* write, suggest "the physiological plasticity of the host and/or symbiotic components appears to play an important role in responding to ocean warming." They describe real-world examples of this phenomenon possibly playing a crucial role in preserving corals exposed to extreme warm temperatures in the past (Fang *et al.*, 1997; Middlebrook *et al.*, 2008; Maynard *et al.*, 2008b).

South of Malta in the Mediterranean Sea, Naumann *et al.* (2013) collected live specimens of two scleractinian cold-water coral (CWCs) species, *Dendrophyllia cornigera* and *D. dianthus*. They transferred the specimens into two identically equipped and darkened 100-L flow-through aquaria through which Mediterranean subsurface seawater was continuously pumped from a 50-meter depth and supplied to the tanks at a rate of about one liter per minute. They maintained this water at a temperature of 12.5 ± 0.1°C for approximately 30 months before initiating the primary phase of their experiment, which was to increase the temperature of one of the aquariums by 0.5°C per day up to 17.5 ± 0.1°C, thereafter maintaining it for a further 87 days, while conducting "daily visual assessments of coral health (i.e. tentacle protrusion, suspension feeding and mortality/survival) and monthly growth measurements by the buoyant weight technique (Davies, 1989)," ultimately translating the latter into coral dry weight data.

The three researchers write, "over the entire experimental period, both CWC species showed neither differences in tentacle protrusion and suspension feeding nor mortality at ambient (12.5°C) or elevated (17.5°C) seawater temperatures." They state, "*D. cornigera* specimens developed a non-quantified number of new polyps at both temperatures suggesting efficient thermal acclimatization." They report "*D. dianthus* exhibited growth rates for ambient and elevated temperatures of 0.23 ± 0.08% per day and 0.19 ± 0.06% per day, whereas *D. cornigera* grew at 0.05 ± 0.01% per day under ambient and 0.14% ± 0.07% per day under elevated temperature conditions." Their findings "suggest that *D. dianthus* and *D. cornigera* may be capable of surviving in warmer environments than previously reported, and thus challenge temperature as the paramount limiting environmental factor for the occurrence of some CWC species."

Multiple researchers have confirmed the phenomenon of thermal adaptation in corals in response to real-world temperature-related stresses. Brown *et al.* (2002) conducted a 17-year study of coral reef flats at Ko Phuket, Thailand, assessing reef changes in response to elevated sea temperatures in 1991, 1995, 1997, and 1998. Although the authors state many corals bleached "during elevated sea temperatures in May 1991 and 1995," they report "no bleaching was recorded in 1997." In addition, they write, "in May 1998 very limited bleaching occurred although sea temperatures were higher than previous events in 1991 and 1995 (Dunne and Brown, 2001)." When bleaching did take place, they note, "it led only to partial mortality in coral colonies, with most corals recovering their color within 3–5 months of initial paling."

Riegl (2003) reviewed what was known at the time about the responses of coral reefs to high-temperature-induced bleaching, focusing primarily on the Arabian Gulf, which they note "has recently experienced high-frequency recurrences of temperature-related bleaching (1996, 1998, 2002)." Riegl reports in each of the three high-temperature years, sea surface temperature (SST) anomalies of 2 to 2.5°C above average *in situ* measured summer maximum SSTs persisted from April to September, and local maxima of *in situ* measured SSTs were 35.5°C in 1996 and 37°C in 2002. In response to these high-temperature events, *Acropora*, which during the 1996 and 1998 events always bleached first and suffered heaviest mortality, bleached less than all other corals in 2002 at Sir Abu Nuair (an offshore island of the United Arab Emirates) and recovered along the coast of Dubai between Jebel Ali and Ras Hasyan. Riegl states, "the unexpected resistance of Sir Abu Nuair *Acropora* to bleaching in 2002 might indicate support for the hypothesis of Baker (2001) and Baker *et al.* (2002) that the symbiont communities on recovering reefs of the future might indeed be more resistant to subsequent bleaching," and "the Arabian Gulf perhaps provides us with some aspects which might be described as a 'glimpse into the future,' with ... hopes for at least some level of coral/zooxanthellae adaptation."

Jimenez and Cortes (2003a) documented coral cover variability in the Pacific between 1992 and 2001, when the El Niño warming events of 1991–1992 (weak) and 1997–1998 ("the strongest in recorded history") affected coral communities along the Costa Rican central Pacific coast, after which they reported their observations and those of other scientists pertaining to these and earlier warming events caused by the El Niños of 1982–1983 (very strong) and 1986–1987 (moderate). The authors report there was a "paucity of bleaching and mortality in the study area in 1987 despite sea temperature anomalies similar to or higher than in other years in which bleaching and mortality occurred," and this situation "may have been the result of the higher cloud cover and runoff which, in combination, decreased solar radiation stress." They suggest "similar atmospheric conditions during 1998 may explain the considerably small number of corals that bleached that year in the upwelling area of [Costa Rica's] Golfo de Papagayo," where they report "few corals bleached, even though sea temperature anomalies were higher than in autumn 1997."

As to the 1997–1998 El Niño, considered to be "the strongest event on record (McPhaden, 1999; Enfield, 2001)," the authors report "mortality of entire colonies associated with this event was remarkably low in Costa Rica, less than 6% (Jimenez *et al.*, 2001)," and "only one coral species, *Psammocora stellata*, disappeared at one locality (Cambutal) after the 1997–1998 warming event." This disappearance "did not have an effect on the percent of total cover, which was not significantly dissimilar to previous years." They report "this species was not affected in Mexico by the 1997–1998 warming episode (Carriquiry *et al.*, 2001)."

Jimenez and Cortes note conspecific corals "have shown differences in susceptibility to bleach, mortality rates and recovery capabilities (Brown, 1997; Hoegh-Guldberg, 1999; Marshall and Baird, 2000; Fitt *et al.*, 2001; Glynn *et al.*, 2001)," which may "reflect corals' adaptation to local conditions, different warming intensities at each locality, thermal acclimation, and presence of several clades of symbionts." They state moderate warming events "may positively affect coral reef communities," noting "increases in growth rates, reproductive activity and recruitment pulses have been observed after some El Niño episodes (Glynn *et al.*, 1991, 1994; Feingold, 1995; Guzman and Cortes, 2001; Vargas-Angel *et al.*, 2001; Jimenez and Cortes, 2003b)."

Guzman and Cortes (2007) note coral reefs of the eastern Pacific Ocean "suffered unprecedented mass mortality at a regional scale as a consequence of the anomalous sea warming during the 1982–1983 El Niño." At Cocos Island (5°32'N, 87°04'W), in particular, where they conducted a survey of three representative reefs in 1987, they found remaining live coral cover was only 3% of what it had been before the great El Niño four years earlier (Guzman and Cortes, 1992). Based on this finding and the similar observations of other scientists at other reefs, they predicted "the recovery of the reefs' framework would take centuries, and recovery of live coral

cover, decades." In 2002, nearly 20 years after the disastrous coral-killing warming, they returned to see how correct they were after their initial assessment of the El Niño damage, quantifying "the live coral cover and species composition of five reefs, including the three previously assessed in 1987."

Regarding thermal tolerance, the most interesting aspect of their study was the occurrence of a second major El Niño between the two assessment periods. Guzman and Cortes state "the 1997–1998 warming event around Cocos Island was more intense than all previous El Niño events," noting temperature anomalies "above 2°C lasted 4 months in 1997–1998 compared to 1 month in 1982–83." Nevertheless, they report, "the coral communities suffered a lower and more selective mortality in 1997–1998, as was also observed in other areas of the eastern Pacific (Glynn *et al.*, 2001; Cortes and Jimenez, 2003; Zapata and Vargas-Angel, 2003)," indicating some type of thermal adaptation occurred after the 1982–1983 El Niño.

Maynard *et al.* (2008a) question the wisdom of "popularizing predictions based on essentially untested assumptions," among which they list IPCC-held claims, "all corals live close to their thermal limits" and "corals cannot adapt/acclimatize to rapid rates of change."

In discussing the first of these "untested assumptions," the three Australian researchers say "predictions that reefs will disappear as a result of global warming are based, at least in part, on the assumption corals are living close to their maximum thermal limits." However, they note, "the severity of bleaching responses varies dramatically within and among taxa," citing McClanahan *et al.* (2009), and "such variable bleaching susceptibility implies that there is a considerable variation in the extent to which coral species are adapted to local environmental conditions."

The three scientists report little is known about the sensitivity of coral population response to climate-induced changes in growth, mortality, and fecundity, but they state a large body of evidence "supports temperature tolerance varying among species, populations, communities, and reef regions (Marshall and Baird, 2000; Coles and Brown, 2003)." They conclude, "even in the absence of an adaptive response, a change in the relative abundance of species is a far more likely outcome of climate change than the disappearance of reef corals," citing Loya *et al.* (2001), McClanahan (2002), and Hughes *et al.* (2003).

The three researchers clearly accept there is "an

adaptive response," in contradiction of the second untested assumption Maynard *et al.* (2008a) discuss, stating "a number of studies suggest that bleaching mortality rates have declined and thermal tolerance has increased in some regions." They report, for example, "mortality rates in the Eastern Pacific were significantly lower in 1998 when compared with 1982 and 1983 (Glynn *et al.*, 2001)," and "Maynard *et al.* (2008b) found thermal tolerance of three common coral genera on the Great Barrier Reef to be greater in 2002 than that expected from the relationship between temperature stress and bleaching severity observed in 1998."

The Australian scientists say there is "circumstantial evidence for ongoing evolution of temperature tolerance between both species and reefs," citing Coles and Brown (2003). In addition, they suggest "symbiont shuffling from less to more stress-resistant clades is another mechanism by which corals may increase the thermal tolerance of the holobiont." And they declare "there is growing evidence that such shuffling can increase thermal tolerance, at least in the short term (Berkelmans and van Oppen, 2006)." Thus Maynard *et al.* (2008a) conclude, "it is premature to suggest that widespread reef collapse is a certain consequence of ongoing bleaching, or that this will inevitably lead to fisheries collapses."

Adjeroud *et al.* (2009) observed coral reefs of the Tiahura outer reef sector at the western end of the north shore of Moorea, French Polynesia, a region they say is "largely free of direct anthropogenic disturbances." They describe the results of detailed observations made there periodically since the early 1970s and annually since 1991. This history, they write, "constitutes one of the longest records of coral reef dynamics." Concentrating on the period of detailed annual observations (1991 onward), the 10 researchers report a significant decline in coral cover followed the two disturbances of 1991 (a major bleaching event and a cyclone), when "coral cover (pooled among genera) declined from 51.0 ± 9.5% in early 1991 to 24.2 ± 14.4% in 1992, and 22.5 ± 9.3% in 1993." This decline, they write, was "among the most rapid of this magnitude recorded following natural disturbances." In contrast, they found "the bleaching events of 1994, 2002 and 2003 had no detectable effects on coral cover, even though the thermal anomalies causing these events and their short-term impacts in terms of bleaching prevalence were similar to the 1991 bleaching event."

Adjeroud *et al.* say their results reveal "corals can recover rapidly following a dramatic decline," noting

similar recoveries of coral cover have been documented at several other locations, citing Connell (1997), Halford *et al.* (2004), Emslie *et al.* (2008), and Sheppard *et al.* (2008). They state their work "supports the hypothesis that some reefs will undergo gradual changes in structure of their coral communities in response to major stress rather than collapse abruptly," citing Loya *et al.* (2001), Hughes *et al.* (2003), and Wakeford *et al.* (2008).

Maynard *et al.* (2008b) analyzed the bleaching severity of three genera of corals (*Acropora, Pocillopora,* and *Porites*) along five sites in the central section of Australia's Great Barrier Reef in late February and March of 1998 and 2002. Regarding the influence of temperature, the four researchers report "the amount of accumulated thermal stress (as degree heating days) in 2002 was more than double that in 1998 at four of the five sites," and "average surface irradiance during the 2002 thermal anomaly was 15.6–18.9% higher than during the 1998 anomaly." They found "in 2002, bleaching severity was 30–100% lower than predicted from the relationship between severity and thermal stress in 1998, despite higher solar irradiances during the 2002 thermal event." In addition, "coral genera most susceptible to thermal stress (*Pocillopora* and *Acropora*) showed the greatest increase in tolerance."

Maynard *et al.* state their findings are "consistent with previous studies documenting an increase in thermal tolerance between bleaching events (1982–1983 vs. 1997–1998) in the Galapagos Islands (Podesta and Glynn, 2001), the Gulf of Chiriqi, the Gulf of Panama (Glynn *et al.*, 2001), and on Costa Rican reefs (Jimenez *et al.*, 2001)." They also note "Dunne and Brown (2001) found similar results ... in the Andaman Sea, in that bleaching severity was far reduced in 1998 compared to 1995 despite sea-temperature and light conditions being more conducive to widespread bleaching in 1998."

The Australian scientists say "the range in bleaching tolerances among corals inhabiting different thermal realms suggests that at least some coral symbioses have the ability to adapt to much higher temperatures than they currently experience in the central Great Barrier Reef," citing Coles and Brown (2003) and Riegl (1999, 2002). They note, "even within reefs there is a significant variability in bleaching susceptibility for many species (Edmunds, 1994; Marshall and Baird, 2000), suggesting some potential for a shift in thermal tolerance based on selective mortality (Glynn *et al.*, 2001; Jimenez *et al.*, 2001) and local population growth alone." Their results suggest "a capacity for acclimatization or adaptation." Maynard *et al.* (2008b) conclude "there is emerging evidence of high genetic structure within coral species (Ayre and Hughes, 2004)," suggesting "the capacity for adaptation could be greater than is currently recognized." As Skelly *et al.* (2007) state, "on the basis of the present knowledge of genetic variation in performance traits and species' capacity for evolutionary response, it can be concluded that evolutionary change will often occur concomitantly with changes in climate as well as other environmental changes."

Focusing more on such evolutionary possibilities, Meyer *et al.* (2009) "performed controlled crosses between three genetically distinct colonies of the branching coral *Acropora millepora*," and then "compared the families of larvae (which in this species naturally lack symbionts) for several physiological traits." They conducted this work at two water temperatures—the standard culturing temperature of 28°C and an elevated temperature of 32°C—as well as an even higher temperature of 34°C maintained for two full days.

Results of the U.S., Canadian, and Australian researchers' analysis confirmed the existence of phenotypic variance for several pertinent thermal and dispersive factors among the families of coral they studied. This finding, they write, "suggests the existence of considerable heritable variation in natural coral populations," and this in turn supports "the possibility of effective adaptive responses to climate change." In addition, they report other analyses of the species they studied have found "high levels of genetic diversity both within and between reefs (Smith-Keune and van Oppen, 2006)," and "studies in other coral species have also uncovered substantial genetic diversity within populations (Ayre and Hughes, 2000; Underwood, 2009; Wang *et al.*, 2009)." Myer *et al.* conclude "additive genetic variance exists within coral populations for several traits that might reasonably be expected to have fitness consequences during global climate change," which "supports the possibility of effective adaptive responses to climate change."

Grimsditch *et al.* (2010) say "it has been shown that it is possible for colonies to acclimatize to increased temperatures and high irradiance levels so that they are able to resist bleaching events when they occur." They note "threshold temperatures that induce coral bleaching-related mortality vary worldwide— from 27°C in Easter Island (Wellington *et al.*, 2001) to 36°C in the Arabian Gulf (Riegl, 1999)—according to the maximum water temperatures that are normal in the area, implying a capacity of corals and/or zooxanthellae to acclimatize to high temperatures depending on their environment."

Grimsditch *et al.* examined "bleaching responses of corals at four sites (Nyali, Mombasa Marine Park, Kanamai and Vipingo) representing two distinct lagoon habitats on the Kenyan coast (deeper and shallower lagoons)." This was done for the coral community as a whole, and zooxanthellae densities and chlorophyll levels were monitored for three target species (*Pocillopora damicornis*, *Porites lutea,* and *Porites cylindrica*) during a non-bleaching year (2006) and a mild bleaching year (2007). They found "during the 2007 bleaching season, corals in the shallow lagoons of Kanamai and Vipingo were more resistant to bleaching stress than corals in the deeper lagoons of Mombasa Marine Park and Nyali." This result suggests, they write, "corals in the shallower lagoons have acclimatized and/or adapted to the fluctuating environmental conditions they endure on a daily basis and have become more resistant to bleaching stress."

Osborne *et al.* (2011) note "coral decline is frequently described as ongoing with the integrity and persistence of the reef system threatened by a number of different stressors," citing Bellwood *et al.* (2004), and "climate change is widely regarded as the single greatest threat to coral reef ecosystems." They also note "the scale and extent of bleaching on the GBR [Great Barrier Reef] since 1998 is unprecedented (Oliver *et al.*, 2009)," "coral disease is an emerging stressor that was first recorded on the GBR in the early 1990s (Willis *et al.*, 2004; Lough, 2007)," and various harmful environmental disturbances "appear to be increasing in frequency and severity."

To quantify the trend in live coral cover of the Great Barrier Reef between 1995 and 2009, which IPCC contends was the warmest decade-and-a-half experienced by the planet in the past millennium, the scientists surveyed coral communities annually on 47 reefs in six latitudinal sectors across 1300 km of the GBR, surveying between two and five reefs in each sub-region. They did so at three sites on the northeast flank of each reef, with each site consisting of five 50-m transects marked by steel rods at depths between six and nine meters. They note "percent cover of live hard coral was estimated from a randomly selected sequence of images taken along the transects using a point-sampling technique in a quincunx pattern (Adbo *et al.*, 2004)."

They found "coral cover increased in six sub-regions and decreased in seven sub-regions," with some of the changes "being very dynamic and others changing little." With respect to the entire reef system, they report "overall regional coral cover was stable (averaging 29% and ranging from 23% to 33% across years) with no net decline between 1995 and 2009." They state they found "no evidence of consistent, system-wide decline in coral cover since 1995." In spite of the purportedly unprecedented negative influences arrayed against them over the past decade-and-a-half, GBR corals appear to have held their own, adapting to the purported onslaught of stresses and maintaining a stable presence.

According to Oliver and Palumbi (2011), "the vast majority of studies that investigate the effects of fluctuating thermal regimes on thermal tolerance have examined daily thermal cycles in which the hottest temperatures lasted on the timescale of hours," and in eight of 10 such studies—performed on taxa as diverse as corals, crustaceans, fish, and amphibians— "organisms that were acclimated to a daily fluctuating thermal regime showed thermal tolerance or tolerance-relevant gene expression (e.g., heat shock proteins) that was equal to, or greater than, that of organisms acclimated to a thermal regime held constant at the maximum temperature of the fluctuating regime," citing Hutchison and Ferrance (1970), Otto (1974), Sastry (1979), Thorp and Wineriter (1981), Threader and Houston (1983), Podrabsky and Somero (2004), Schaefer and Ryan (2006), and Putnam *et al.* (2010).

Studying back-reef pools in American Samoa that differ in diurnal thermal variation, Oliver and Palumbi experimentally heat-stressed *Acropora hyacinthus* corals from a thermally moderate lagoon pool and a more thermally variable pool that naturally experienced two- to three-hour high temperature events during summer low tides. They compared coral mortality and photosystem II photochemical efficiency of colony fragments collected from each of these lagoons that they exposed to either ambient (28.0°C) or elevated (31.5°C) water temperatures. The two researchers report in the heated treatment, "moderate pool corals showed nearly 50% mortality whether they hosted heat-sensitive or heat-resistant symbionts," whereas "variable pool corals, all of which hosted heat-resistant symbionts, survived well, showing low mortalities statistically indistinguishable from controls held at ambient temperatures." Also in the heated treatment, they state, "moderate pool corals hosting heat-sensitive algae showed rapid rates of decline in algal photosystem II photochemical efficiency," whereas those "hosting heat-resistant algae showed intermediate levels of decline." They found "variable pool corals hosting heat-resistant algae showed the least decline."

Oliver and Palumbi say their results suggest "previous exposure to an environmentally variable microhabitat adds substantially to coral-algal thermal tolerance, beyond that provided by heat-resistant symbionts alone," indicating a latent potential of Earth's corals to adapt to warmer temperatures than scientists believed possible in the past, should they gradually begin to experience recurring daily episodes of greater warmth in a gradually warming world.

In a study designed to investigate how coral assemblages in the Persian Gulf might cope with global warming via reproductive biology, Bauman *et al.* (2011) examined six locally common coral species on two shallow reef sites in Dubai, United Arab Emirates, in 2008 and 2009, to investigate their patterns of reproduction, focusing primarily on the timing and synchrony of spawning. They found the reproductive biology of the six coral species in the southern Persian Gulf "appears to be well adapted to extreme annual environmental fluctuations" and is "remarkably similar to conspecifics elsewhere in the Indo-Pacific (Baird *et al.*, 2009a,b)." They also found "the adaptive capacity of corals in the Persian Gulf is likely facilitated by a combination of short-term acclimation in individuals during acute environmental conditions (e.g., recurrent bleaching events) and long-term adaptation among coral populations to chronic environmental conditions (e.g., extreme temperatures)."

Bauman *et al.* state their work "confirms that corals are capable of reproductive activities under extreme environmental conditions," as Coles and Fadlallah (1991) and Coles and Brown (2003) also found. They conclude "coral populations can survive and proliferate in extreme conditions that are projected to occur in many other regions of the world by the end of this century," noting, "the recovery of these coral assemblages following mortality induced by a number of recent temperature-related bleaching events (1996, 1998 and 2002) suggests these assemblages are also resilient to extreme fluctuations in water temperature," citing Riegl (1999, 2003) and Burt *et al.* (2008).

Serrano *et al.* (2013) investigated the adaptation of corals to temperature-related stresses through range expansion or migration. The team of researchers state, "despite the evidence that some coral species appear to be responding to climatic warming by expanding their distributions toward the poles (Wooddroffe, 2011), it has been argued that latitudinal migration is unlikely to occur rapidly enough to respond to the current projected temperature change (3–6°C over the next 100 years (IPCC, 2007)) due to the significant distance involved (i.e., the latitudinal temperature gradient is ~1.5°C/1000 km), the effects of temperature on reproduction, and the decrease in carbonate ion concentrations at high latitudes." Serrano *et al.* analyzed a long-term, large-scale observational dataset to characterize the dynamics of a hermatypic coral (*Oculina patagonica*) in regard to its "recent northward range shift along the coast of Catalonia," while examining "the main factors that could have influenced this spread," which they did "by monitoring 223 locations including natural and artificial habitats along >400 km of coastline over the last 19 years (1992–2010)."

The six Spanish scientists report *Oculina patagonica* "increased from being present in one location in 1992 to occur on 19% of the locations in 2010, and exhibited an acceleration of its spreading over time driven by the joint action of neighborhood and long-distance dispersal." They further note the "northward expansion has occurred at the fastest rate (22 km per year) reported for a coral species thus far." Serrano *et al.* write, "a coral species with particular biological characteristics that allow it to withstand the temperature challenge that accompanies northward migration as well as the natural and anthropogenic side effects that this type of migration involves (i.e., competition with macroalgae, high sediment loads, turbidity, water chemistry) has accomplished a successful northward expansion and may be able to keep pace with the global warming prediction of ~3°C over the next 100 years."

Yamano *et al.* (2011) report "although most studies of climate change effects on corals have focused on temperature-induced coral bleaching in tropical areas, poleward range shifts and/or expansions may also occur in temperate areas, as suggested by geological records and present-day eyewitnesses in several localities," citing Greenstein and Pandolfi (2008) and Precht and Aronson (2004). Yamano *et al.* collected records of coral species occurrence from eight temperate regions of Japan along a latitudinal gradient, where they obtained what they describe as "the first large-scale evidence of the poleward range expansion of modern corals, based on 80 years of national records ... where century-long measurements of *in situ* sea-surface temperatures have shown statistically significant rises."

They found "four major coral species categories, including two key species for reef formation in tropical areas, showed poleward range expansions since the 1930s, whereas no species demonstrated southward range shrinkage or local extinction," adding "the speed of these expansions reached up to

14 km per year," which they say "is far greater than that for other species." They note, "in regions with poleward current flows (east coast of the United States [Precht and Aronson, 2004], east coast of South America, east coast of Africa and east coast of Australia [Figueira and Booth, 2010]) the speed would be much greater."

The Japanese scientists conclude their results, "in combination with recent findings suggesting range expansions of tropical coral-reef associated organisms, strongly suggest that rapid, fundamental modifications of temperate coastal ecosystems could be in progress." They suggest "temperate areas may serve as refugia for tropical corals in an era of global warming."

Van Woesik *et al.* (2012) examined the response of more than 30,000 coral colonies at 80 sites in Palau during a regional thermal-stress event in 2010, to determine "whether any habitats were comparatively resistant to thermal stress." The six scientists discovered "bleaching was most severe in the northwestern lagoon, in accordance with satellite-derived maximum temperatures and anomalous temperatures above the long-term averages," noting corals there "suffered the most extensive bleaching and the highest mortality." But "in the bays where temperatures were higher than elsewhere, bleaching and mortality were low." They suggest "constant exposure to high temperatures, and high vertical attenuation of light caused by naturally high suspended particulate matter buffered the corals in bays from the 2010 regional thermal-stress event." Van Woesik *et al.* conclude their study shows "reefs around bays were more resistant to regional thermal stress than patch and outer reefs," and "nearshore reefs in the bays are therefore valuable refuges to buffer coral-reef ecosystems against climate change-induced disturbances." Those bays "should be given high conservation status because they provide refugia for coral populations as the oceans continue to warm."

Carilli *et al.* (2012) note "observations indicating that mass bleaching events have recently become more common, combined with projected increases in heat stress, have prompted dire predictions for the future of coral reefs under unabated greenhouse gas emissions scenarios," citing Hoegh-Guldberg (1999) and Donner *et al.* (2005). They point out, "there is evidence that corals may adapt to better withstand heat stress via a number of mechanisms," as "corals might acquire more thermally-resistant symbionts (Buddemeier and Fautin, 1993; Rowan, 2004), or might increase their own physiological mechanisms to reduce bleaching susceptibility by producing oxidative enzymes (Coles and Brown, 2003) or photoprotective compounds (Salih *et al.*, 2000)." They emphasize there is evidence suggesting the susceptibility of a given coral or reef to bleaching depends on the thermal history of that coral or reef (Thompson and Van Woesik, 2009; Donner, 2011; Brown *et al.*, 2002).

Carilli *et al.* "collected cores from massive *Porites sp.* corals in the Gilbert Islands of Kiribati to determine how corals along a natural gradient in temperature variability responded to recent heat stress events" and "examined changes in coral skeletal growth rates and partial mortality scars (Carilli *et al.*, 2010) to investigate the impact of the bleaching event in 2004 (Donner, 2011) on corals from different temperature variability regimes."

The three researchers—from Australia, Canada, and the United States—discovered the spatial patterns in skeletal growth rates and partial mortality scars found in corals from the central and northern islands suggest "corals subject to larger year-to-year fluctuations in maximum ocean temperature were more resistant to a 2004 warm-water event," and "a subsequent 2009 warm event had a disproportionately larger impact on those corals from the island with lower historical heat stress." Carilli *et al.* conclude, "coral reefs in locations with more frequent warm events may be more resilient to future warming."

Penin *et al.* (2013) "compared variations in spatial and taxonomic patterns between two bleaching events at the scale of an island (Moorea Island, French Polynesia)," where "nine stations involving three locations (Haapiti, Tiahura, and Viapahu) and three depths (6, 12, and 18 m) have been routinely surveyed for various scientific purposes since 2001," as described by Penin *et al.* (2007a, 2010). They measured bleaching intensity "two weeks following the first signs of bleaching (Penin *et al.*, 2007b)" for six coral genera (*Acropora, Montipora, Montastrea, Pavona, Pocillopora,* and *Porites*) at each of the nine stations in 2002 and 2007. The six coral genera accounted for 88% of the total coral assemblage.

Their measurements showed the "thermal stress was similar between the two years studied," but "the bleaching intensity was lower in 2007 (25–49%) than in 2002 (39–72%)" and "the response to elevated temperature was delayed in the latter year." They note "the outer slopes at Moorea Island are located in an oligotrophic oceanic environment and are not under terrestrial influence, which makes it unlikely that there was any effect of nutrients on the response of the corals, as has been proposed for other reef eco-

systems (Wooldridge and Done, 2009)." The three researchers conclude "it is likely that the observed decrease in stress response was the result of acclimatization of the coral/algal holobionts (Berkelmans *et al.*, 2004; Maynard *et al.*, 2008) or an influx of thermo-tolerant colonies between 2002 and 2007." They note several "similar decreases in susceptibility to thermal stress have been documented between successive bleaching events, including between 1991 and 1994 at Moorea Island (Adjeroud *et al.*, 2002), between 1998 and 2002 on the Great Barrier Reef in Australia (Maynard *et al.*, 2008b), and between 1982–83 and 1997–98 in Panama (Glynn *et al.*, 2001), Costa Rica (Jimenez *et al.*, 2001), and at the Galapagos Islands (Podesta and Glynn, 2001)."

Mayfield *et al.* (2013) write, "recent work has found that pocilloporid corals from regions characterized by unstable temperatures, such as those exposed to periodic upwelling, display a remarkable degree of phenotypic plasticity," and "some recent works have shown that not all corals bleach, or even manifest signs of stress, at elevated temperatures predicted to characterize reefs in the coming decades (Barshis *et al.*, 2013)." They also note "corals from highly variable temperature environments of both American Samoa (Oliver and Palumbi, 2011) and southern Taiwan (Mayfield *et al.*, 2011, 2013) have previously been shown to withstand exposure to temperatures (e.g., 30–31°C) that induce bleaching or even mortality in conspecifics from other regions (Jokiel and Coles, 1990; Brown, 1997)."

To "uncover the long-term impacts of elevated temperature exposure to corals from reefs that experience episodic upwelling," Mayfield *et al.* conducted a mesocosm-based experiment in which *P. damicornis* specimens collected from an upwelling coral reef on Houbihu (a small embayment within Nanwan Bay, southern Taiwan) were exposed for nine months to nearly 30°C, a temperature that the corals normally encounter *in situ* for just a few hours per year (Mayfield *et al.*, 2012). The three researchers write, "upon nine months of exposure to nearly 30°C, all colony (mortality and surface area), polyp (*Symbiodinium* density and chlorophyll *a* content), tissue (total thickness), and molecular (gene expression and molecular composition)-level parameters were documented at similar levels between experimental corals and controls incubated at 26.5°C, suggesting that this species can readily acclimate to elevated temperatures that cause significant degrees of stress, or even bleaching and mortality, in conspecifics of other regions of the Indo-Pacific."

Mayfield *et al.* state, "there is now a growing

body of evidence to support the notion that corals inhabiting more thermally unstable habitats outperform conspecifics from reefs characterized by more stable temperatures when exposed to elevated temperatures," citing Coles (1975), Castillo and Helmuth (2005), and Oliver and Palumbi (2011). They also report, "in other systems, provocative gene expression changes, such as the constitutive up-regulation of genes involved in thermotolerance (e.g., *hsps*; Heath *et al.*, 1993; Feder, 1996), underlie the capacity for organisms to inhabit high and/or variable temperature environments," as Barshis *et al.* (2013) also documented in corals.

References

Adbo, D., Burgess, S., Coleman, G., and Osborne, K. 2004. *Surveys of Benthic Reef Communities using Underwater Video*. Australian Institute of Marine Science, Townsville, Australia.

Adjeroud, M., Michonneau, F., Edmunds, P.J., Chancerelle, Y., Lison de Loma, T., Penin, L., Thibaut, L., Vidal-Dupiol, J., Salvat, B., and Galzin, R. 2009. Recurrent disturbances, recovery trajectories, and resilience of coral assemblages on a South Central Pacific reef. *Coral Reefs* **28**: 775–780.

Ayre, D.J. and Hughes, T.P. 2000. Genotypic diversity and gene flow in brooding and spawning corals along the Great Barrier Reef, Australia. *Evolution* **54**: 1590–1605.

Ayre, D.J. and Hughes, T.P. 2004. Climate change, genotypic diversity and gene flow in reef-building corals. *Ecology Letters* **7**: 273–278.

Baird, A.H., Guest, J.R., and Willis, B.L. 2009a. Systematic and biogeographical patterns in the reproductive biology of scleractinian corals. *Annual Review of Ecology, Evolution, and Systematics* **40**: 531–571.

Baird, A.H., Birrell, C.L., Hughes, T.P., McDonald, A., Nojima, S., Page, C. Pratchett, M.S., and Yamasaki, H. 2009b. Latitudinal variation in reproductive synchrony in *Acropora* assemblages: Japan vs. Australia. *Galaxea* **11**: 101–108.

Baker, A.C. 2001. Reef corals bleach to survive change. *Nature* **411**: 765–766.

Baker, A.C., Starger, C.J., McClanahan, T.R., and Glynn, P.W. 2002. Symbiont communities in reef corals following the 1997–98 El Niño—will recovering reefs be more resistant to a subsequent bleaching event? *Proceedings of the International Society of Reef Studies* (Abstract Volume 10: European Meeting, Cambridge, UK, September).

Barshis, D.J., Ladner, J.T., Oliver, T.A., Seneca, F.O.,

Traylor-Knowles, N., and Palumbi, S.R. 2013. Genomic basis for coral resilience to climate change. *Proceedings of the National Academy of Sciences USA* **110**: 1387–1392.

Brown, B.E. 1997. Coral bleaching: causes and consequences. *Coral Reefs* **16S**: 129–138.

Bauman, A.G., Baird, A.H., and Cavalcante, G.H. 2011. Coral reproduction in the world's warmest reefs: southern Persian Gulf (Dubai, United Arab Emirates). *Coral Reefs* **30**: 405–413.

Bellantuono, A.J., Hoegh-Guldberg, O., and Rodriguez-Lanetty, M. 2012. Resistance to thermal stress in corals without changes in symbiont composition. *Proceedings of the Royal Society B* **279**: 1100–1107.

Bellwood, D.R., Hughes, T.P., Folke, C., and Nystrom, M. 2004. Confronting the coral reef crisis. *Nature* **429**: 827–833.

Berkelmans, R., De'ath, G., Kininmonth, S., and Skirving, W.J. 2004. A comparison of the 1998 and 2002 coral bleaching events on the Great Barrier Reef: spatial correlation, patterns and predictions. *Coral Reefs* **23**: 74–83.

Berkelmans, R. and van Oppen, M. 2006. The role of zooxanthellae in the thermal tolerance of corals: a 'nugget of hope' for coral reefs in an era of climate change. *Proceedings of the Royal Society of London B* **273**: 2305–2312.

Brown, B. 1997. Coral bleaching: causes and consequences. *Coral Reefs* **16**: S129-S138.

Brown, B.E., Clarke, K.R., and Warwick, R.M. 2002. Serial patterns of biodiversity change in corals across shallow reef flats in Ko Phuket, Thailand, due to the effects of local (sedimentation) and regional (climatic) perturbations. *Marine Biology* **141**: 24–29.

Brown, N., Dunne, R., Goodson, M., and Douglas, A. 2002. Experience shapes the susceptibility of a reef coral to bleaching. *Coral Reefs* **21**: 119–126.

Buddemeier, R.W. and Fautin, D.G. 1993. Coral bleaching as an adaptive mechanism. *BioScience* **43**: 320–326.

Burt, J., Bartholomew, A., and Usseglio, P. 2008. Recovery of corals a decade after bleaching event in Dubai, United Arab Emirates. *Marine Biology* **154**: 27–36.

Carilli, J., Donner, S.D., and Hartmann, A.C. 2012. Historical temperature variability affects coral response to heat stress. *PLoS ONE* **7**: e34418.

Carilli, J., Norris, R.D., Black, B., Walsh, S.W., and McField, M. 2010. Century-scale records of coral growth rates indicate that local stressors reduce coral thermal tolerance threshold. *Global Change Biology* **16**: 1247–1257.

Carriquiry, J., Cupul-Magaña, A., Rodriguez-Zaragoza, F., and Medina-Rosas, P. 2001. Coral bleaching and mortality in the Mexican Pacific during the 1997–1998 El Niño and prediction from a remote sensing approach. *Bulletin of the Marine Sciences* **69**: 237–249.

Castillo, K.D. and Helmuth, B.S.T. 2005. Influence of thermal history on the response of *Montastraea annularis* to short-term temperature exposure. *Marine Biology* **148**: 261–270.

Coles, S. 1975. A comparison of effects of elevated temperature versus temperature fluctuations on reef corals at Kahe Point, Oahu. *Pacific Science* **29**: 15–18.

Coles, S.L. and Brown, B.E. 2003. Coral bleaching—capacity for acclimatization and adaptation. *Advances in Marine Biology* **46**: 183–223.

Coles, S.L. and Fadlallah, Y.H. 1991. Reef coral survival and mortality at low temperatures in the Arabian Gulf—new species-lower temperature limits. *Coral Reefs* **9**: 231–237.

Connell, J.H. 1997. Disturbance and recovery of coral assemblages. *Coral Reefs* **16**: S101-S113.

Cortes, J. and Jimenez, C. 2003. Corals and coral reefs of the Pacific of Costa Rica: history, research and status. In: Cortes, J. (Ed.) *Latin American Coral Reefs*. Elsevier, Amsterdam, The Netherlands, pp. 361–385.

Davies, P.S. 1989. Short-term growth measurements of corals using an accurate buoyant weighing technique. *Marine Biology* **101**: 389–395.

Donner, S.D. 2011. An evaluation of the effect of recent temperature variability on the prediction of coral bleaching events. *Ecological Applications* **21**: 1718–1730.

Donner, S.D., Skirving, W.J., Little, C.M., Oppenheimer, M., and Hoegh-Guldberg, O. 2005. Global assessment of coral bleaching and required rates of adaptation under climate change. *Global Change Biology* **11**: 2251–2265.

Dunne, R.P. and Brown, B.E. 2001. The influence of solar radiation on bleaching of shallow water reef corals in the Andaman Sea, 1993–98. *Coral Reefs* **20**: 201–210.

Edmunds, P.J. 1994. Evidence that reef-wide patterns of coral bleaching may be the result of the distribution of bleaching susceptible clones. *Marine Biology (Berlin)* **121**: 137–142.

Emslie, M.J., Cheal, A.J., Sweatman, H., and Delean, S. 2008. Recovery from disturbance of coral and reef fish communities on the Great Barrier Reef, Australia. *Marine Ecology Progress Series* **371**: 177–190.

Enfield, D. 2001. Evolution and historical perspective of the 1997–1998 El Niño-Southern Oscillation event. *Bulletin of the Marine Sciences* **69**: 7–25.

Fang, L.-S., Huang, S.-P., and Lin, K.-L. 1997. High temperature induces the synthesis of heat-shock proteins and the elevation of intracellular calcium in the coral *Acropora grandis*. *Coral Reefs* **16**: 127–131.

Feder, M. 1996. Ecological and evolutionary physiology of stress proteins and the stress response: the *Drosophila melanogaster* model. In: Johnston, I.A. and Bennett, A.F. (Eds.) *Animals and Temperature: Phenotypic and Evolutionary Adaptation*. Cambridge University Press, Cambridge, United Kingdom, pp. 79–102.

Feingold, J. 1995. Effects of Elevated Water Temperature on Coral Bleaching and Survival During El Niño Disturbance Events. Ph.D. Dissertation. University of Miami, Coral Gables, Florida.

Figueira, W.F. and Booth, D.J. 2010. Increasing ocean temperatures allow tropical fishes to survive overwinter in temperate waters. *Global Change Biology* **16**: 506–516.

Fitt, W., Brown, B., Warner, M., and Dunne, R. 2001. Coral bleaching: interpretation of thermal tolerance limits and thermal thresholds in tropical corals. *Coral Reefs* **20**: 51–65.

Gates, R.D. and Edmunds, P.J. 1999. The physiological mechanisms of acclimatization in tropical reef corals. *American Zoologist* **39**: 30–43.

Glynn, P.W., Colley, S., Eakin, C., Smith, D., Cortes, J., Gassman, N. Guzman, H., Del Rossario, J., and Feingold, J. 1994. Reef coral reproduction in the eastern Pacific: Costa Rica, Panama, and Galapagos Islands (Ecuador)—II. Poritidae. *Marine Biology* **118**: 191–208.

Glynn, P.W., Gassman, N., Eakin, M., Cortes, J., Smith, D., and Guzman, H. 1991. Reef coral reproduction in the eastern Pacific: Costa Rica, Panama, and Galapagos Islands (Ecuador)—I. Pocilloporidae. *Marine Biology* **109**: 355–368.

Glynn, P.W., Mate, J.L., Baker, A.C., and Calderon, M.O. 2001. Coral bleaching and mortality in Panama and Ecuador during the 1997–1998 El Niño-Southern Oscillation event: Spatial/temporal patterns and comparisons with the 1982–1983 event. *Bulletin of Marine Science* **69**: 79–109.

Greenstein, B.J. and Pandolfi, J.M. 2008. Escaping the heat: Range shifts of reef coral taxa in coastal Western Australia. *Global Change Biology* **14**: 10.1111/j.1365-2486.2007.01506.x.

Grimsditch, G., Mwaura, J.M., Kilonzo, J., and Amiyo, N. 2010. The effects of habitat on coral bleaching responses in Kenya. *Ambio* **39**: 295–304.

Guzman, H.M. and Cortes, J. 1992. Cocos Island (Pacific of Costa Rica) coral reefs after the 1982–83 El Niño disturbance. *Revista de Biologia Tropical* **40**: 309–324.

Guzman, H.M. and Cortes, J. 2001. Changes in reef community structure after fifteen years of natural disturbances in the eastern Pacific (Costa Rica). *Bulletin of the Marine Sciences* **69**: 133–149.

Guzman, H.M. and Cortes, J. 2007. Reef recovery 20 years after the 1982–1983 El Niño massive mortality. *Marine Biology* **151**: 401–411.

Halford, A., Cheal, A.J., Ryan, D., and Williams, D.McB. 2004. Resilience to large-scale disturbance in coral and fish assemblages on the Great Barrier Reef. *Ecology* **85**: 1892–1905.

Heath, A.G., Turner, B.J., and Davis, W.P. 1993. Temperature preferences and tolerances of three fish species inhabiting hyper-thermal ponds on mangrove islands. *Hydrobiologia* **259**: 47–55.

Hoegh-Guldberg, O. 1999. Climate change, coral bleaching and the future of the world's coral reefs. *Marine and Freshwater Research* **50**: 839–866.

Hughes, T.P., Baird, A.H., Bellwood, D.R., Card, M., Connolly, S.R., Folke, C., Grosberg, R., Hoegh-Guldberg, O., Jackson, J.B.C., Kleypas, J., Lough, J.M., Marshall, P., Nystrom, M., Palumbi, S.R., Pandolfi, J.M., Rosen, B., and Roughgarden, J. 2003. Climate change, human impacts, and the resilience of coral reefs. *Science* **301**: 929–933.

Hutchison, V.H. and Ferrance, M.R. 1970. Thermal tolerances of *Rana pipiens* acclimated to daily temperature cycles. *Herpetologica* **26**: 1–8.

IPCC. 2007. *Climate Change 2007: The Physical Science Basis*. Contribution of Working Group I to the Fourth Assessment Report of the Intergovernmental Panel on Climate Change. Solomon, S.D., Qin, M., Manning, Z., Marquis, M., Averyt, K., Tignor, M.B., Miller Jr., H.L., and Chen, Z. (Eds.) Cambridge University Press, Cambridge, United Kingdom.

Jimenez, C. and Cortes, J. 2003b. Growth of seven species of scleractinian corals in an upwelling environment of the eastern Pacific (Golfo de Papagayo, Costa Rica). *Bulletin of the Marine Sciences* **72**: 187–198.

Jimenez, C.E. and Cortes, J. 2003a. Coral cover change associated to El Niño, eastern Pacific, Costa Rica, 1992–2001. *Marine Ecology* **24**: 179–192.

Jimenez, C., Cortes, J., Leon, A., and Ruiz, E. 2001. Coral bleaching and mortality associated with the 1997–98 El Niño in an upwelling environment in the eastern Pacific (Gulf of Papagayo, Costa Rica). *Bulletin of the Marine Sciences* **68**: 151–169.

Jokiel, P.L. and Coles, S.L. 1990. Response of Hawaiian and other Indo Pacific reef corals to elevated temperatures. *Coral Reefs* **8**: 155–162.

Lough, J. 2007. Climate and climate change on the Great Barrier Reef. In: Johnson, J.E. and Marshall, P.A. (Eds.) *Climate Change and the Great Barrier Reef: A Vulnerability Assessment.* Great Barrier Reef Marine Park Authority and the Australian Greenhouse Office, Department of the Environment and Water Resources, Townsville, Australia, pp. 15–50.

Loya, Y., Sakai, K., Yamazato, K., Nakano, Y., Sambali, H., and van Woesik, R. 2001. Coral bleaching: the winners and the losers. *Ecology Letters* **4**: 122–131.

Marshall, P.A. and Baird, A.H. 2000. Bleaching of corals on the Great Barrier Reef: differential susceptibilities among taxa. *Coral Reefs* **19**: 155–163.

Mayfield, A.B., Chan, P.H., Putnam, H.P., Chen, C.S., and Fan, T.Y. 2012. The effects of a variable temperature regime on the physiology of the reef-building coral *Seriatopora hystrix*: results from a laboratory-based reciprocal transplant. *Journal of Experimental Biology* **215**: 4183–4195.

Mayfield, A.B., Chen, M., Meng, P.J., Lin, H.J., Chen, C.S., and Liu, P.J. 2013. The physiological response of the reef coral *Pocillopora damicornis* to elevated temperature: results from coral reef mesocosm experiments in southern Taiwan. *Marine Environmental Research* **86**: 1–11.

Mayfield, A.B., Fan, T.-Y., and Chen, C.-S. 2013. Physiological acclimation to elevated temperature in a reef-building coral from an upwelling environment. *Coral Reefs* **32**: 909–921.

Mayfield, A.B., Wang, L.H., Tang, P.C., Hsiao, Y.Y., Fan, T.Y., Tsai, C.L., and Chen, C.S. 2011. Assessing the impacts of experimentally elevated temperature on the biological composition and molecular chaperone gene expression of a reef coral. *PLOS ONE* **6**: e26529.

Maynard, J.A., Anthony, K.R.N., Marshall, P.A., and Masiri, I. 2008b. Major bleaching events can lead to increased thermal tolerance in corals. *Marine Biology* **155**: 173–182.

Maynard, J.A., Baird, A.H., and Pratchett, M.S. 2008a. Revisiting the Cassandra syndrome; the changing climate of coral reef research. *Coral Reefs* **27**: 745–749.

McClanahan, T., Maina, J., and Pet-Soede, L. 2002. Effects of the 1998 coral mortality event on Kenyan coral reefs and fisheries. *Ambio* **31**: 543–550.

McClanahan, T., Weil, E., Cortes, J., Baird, A.H., and Ateweberhan, M. 2009. Consequences of coral bleaching for sessile reef organisms. In: van Oppen, M.J.H. and Lough, J.M. (Eds.) *Ecological Studies: Coral Bleaching: Patterns, Processes, Causes and Consequences*. Springer-Verlag, Berlin, Germany.

McPhaden, M. 1999. Genesis and evolution of the 1997–98 El Niño. *Science* **283**: 950–954.

Meyer, E., Davies, S., Wang, S., Willis, B.L., Abrego, D., Juenger, T.E., and Matz, M.V. 2009. Genetic variation in responses to a settlement cue and elevated temperature in the reef-building coral *Acropora millepora*. *Marine Ecology Progress Series* **392**: 81–92.

Middlebrook, R., Hoegh-Guldberg, O., and Leggat, W. 2008. The effect of thermal history on the susceptibility of reef-building corals to thermal stress. *The Journal of Experimental Biology* **211**: 1050–1056.

Naumann, M.S., Orejas, C., and Ferrier-Pages, C. 2013. High thermal tolerance of two Mediterranean cold-water coral species maintained in aquaria. *Coral Reefs* **32**: 749–754.

Oliver, J.K., Berkelmans, R., and Eakin, C.M. 2009. Coral bleaching in space and time. In: van Oppen, M.J.H. and Lough, J.M. (Eds.) *Coral Bleaching: Patterns, Processes, Causes and Consequences*. Springer, New York, New York, USA, pp. 21–39.

Oliver, T.A. and Palumbi, S.R. 2011. Do fluctuating temperature environments elevate coral thermal tolerance? *Coral Reefs* **30**: 429–440.

Osborne, K., Dolman, A.M., Burgess, S.C., and Johns, K.A. 2011. Disturbance and the dynamics of coral cover on the Great Barrier Reef (1995–2009). *PLoS ONE* **6**: 10.1371/journal.pone.0017516.

Otto, R. 1974. The effects of acclimation to cyclic thermal regimes on heat tolerance of the western mosquitofish. *Transactions of the American Fisheries Society* **103**: 331–335.

Penin, L., Adjeroud, M., Pratchet, M.S., and Hughes, T.P. 2007a. Spatial distribution of juvenile and adult corals around Moorea (French Polynesia): implications for population regulation. *Bulletin of Marine Science* **80**: 379–389.

Penin, L., Adjeroud, M., Schrimm, M., and Lenihan, H. 2007b. High spatial variability in coral bleaching around Moorea (French Polynesia): patterns across locations and water depths. *Comptes Rendus Biologies* **330**: 171–181.

Penin, L., Michonneau, F., Baird, A.H., Connolly, S.R., Pratchett, M.S., Kayal, M., and Adjeroud, M. 2010. Early post-settlement mortality and the structure of coral assemblages. *Marine Ecology Progress Series* **408**: 55–64.

Penin, L., Vidal-Dupiol, J., and Adjeroud, M. 2013. Response of coral assemblages to thermal stress: are bleaching intensity and spatial patterns consistent between events. *Environmental Monitoring and Assessment* **185**: 5031–5042.

Podesta, G.P. and Glynn, P.W. 2001. The 1997–98 El Niño event in Panama and Galapagos: an update of thermal stress indices relative to coral bleaching. *Bulletin of Marine Science* **69**: 43–59.

Podrabsky, J. and Somero, G. 2004. Changes in gene expression associated with acclimation to constant temperatures and fluctuating daily temperatures in an annual killifish *Austrofundulus limnaeus*. *Journal of Experimental Biology* **207**: 2237–2254.

Precht, W.F. and Aronson, R.B. 2004. Climate flickers and range shifts of reef corals. *Frontiers in Ecology and the Environment* **2**: 307–314.

Putnam, H., Edmunds, P., and Fan, T. 2010. Effect of a fluctuating thermal regime on adult and larval reef corals. *Invertebrate Biology* **129**: 199–209.

Riegl, B. 1999. Corals in a non-reef setting in the southern Arabian Gulf (Dubai, UAE): fauna and community structure in response to recurring mass mortality. *Coral Reefs* **18**: 63–73.

Riegl, B. 2002. Effects of the 1996 and 1998 positive sea-surface temperature anomalies on corals, coral diseases and fish in the Arabian Gulf (Dubai, UAE). *Marine Biology (Berlin)* **140**: 29–40.

Riegl, B. 2003. Climate change and coral reefs: different effects in two high-latitude areas (Arabian Gulf, South Africa). *Coral Reefs* **22**: 433–446.

Rowan, R. 2004. Coral bleaching: Thermal adaptation in reef coral symbionts. *Nature* **430**: 742.

Salih, A., Larkum, A., Cox, G., Kuhl, M., and Hoegh-Guldberg, O. 2000. Fluorescent pigments in corals are photoprotective. *Nature* **408**: 850–853.

Sastry, A. 1979. Metabolic adaptation of *Cancer irroratus* developmental stages to cyclic temperatures. *Marine Biology* **51**: 243–250.

Schaefer, J. and Ryan, A. 2006. Developmental plasticity in the thermal tolerance of zebrafish *Danio rerio*. *Journal of Fish Biology* **69**: 722–734.

Serrano, E., Coma, R., Ribes, M., Weitzmann, B., Garcia, M., and Ballesteros, E. 2013. Rapid northward spread of a zooxanthellate coral enhanced by artificial structures and sea warming in the Western Mediterranean. *PLOS ONE* **8**: e52739.

Sheppard, C.R.C., Harris, A., and Sheppard, A.L.S. 2008. Archipelago-wide coral recovery patterns since 1998 in the Chagos Archipelago, central Indian Ocean. *Marine Ecology Progress Series* **362**: 109–117.

Skelly, D.K., Joseph, L.N., Possingham, H.P., Freidenburg, L.K., Farrugia, T.J., Kinnison, M.T., and Hendry, A.P. 2007. Evolutionary responses to climate change. *Conservation Biology* **21**: 1353–1355.

Smith-Keune, C. and van Oppen, M. 2006. Genetic structure of a reef-building coral from thermally distinct environments on the Great Barrier Reef. *Coral Reefs* **25**: 493–502.

Thompson, D.M. and Van Woesik, R. 2009. Corals escape bleaching in regions that recently and historically experienced frequent thermal stress. *Proceedings of the Royal Society B* **276**: 2893.

Thorp, J.W. and Wineriter, S.A. 1981. Stress and growth response of juvenile crayfish to rhythmic and arrhythmic temperature fluctuations. *Archives of Environmental Contamination and Toxicology* **10**: 69–77.

Threader, R. and Houston, A.H. 1983. Heat tolerance and resistance in juvenile rainbow trout acclimated to diurnally cycling temperatures. *Comparative Biochemistry and Physiology Part A: Physiology* **75**: 153–155.

Underwood, J.N. 2009. Genetic diversity and divergence among coastal and offshore reefs in a hard coral depend on geographic discontinuity and oceanic currents. *Evolutionary Applications* **2**: 222–233.

van Woesik, R., Houk, P., Isechal, A.L., Idechong, J.W., Victor, S., and Golbuu, Y. 2012. Climate-change refugia in the sheltered bays of Palau: analogs of future reefs. *Ecology and Evolution* **2**: 2474–2484.

Vargas-Angel, B., Zapata, F., Hernandez, H., and Jimenez, J. 2001. Coral and coral reef responses to the 1997–1998 El Niño event on the Pacific coast of Colombia. *Bulletin of the Marine Sciences* **69**: 111–132.

Wakeford, M., Done, T.J., and Johnson, C.R. 2008. Decadal trends in a coral community and evidence of changed disturbance regime. *Coral Reefs* **27**: 1–13.

Wang, S., Zhang, L., and Matz, M. 2009. Microsatellite characterization and marker development from public EST and WGS databases in the reef-building coral *Acropora millepora* (Cnidaria, Anthozoa, Scleractinia). *Journal of Heredity* **100**: 329–337.

Wellington, G.M., Glynn, P.W., Strong, A.E., Nauarrete, S.A., Wieters, E., and Hubbard, D. 2001. Crisis on coral reefs linked to climate change. *EOS, Transactions, American Geophysical Union* **82**: 1,7.

Willis, B.L., Page, C.A., and Dinsdale, E.A. 2004. Coral disease on the Great Barrier Reef. In: Rosenberg, E. and Loya, Y. (Eds.) *Coral Health and Disease*. Springer-Verlag, Berlin, Germany, pp. 69–104.

Wooddroffe, C.D. 2011. Poleward extension of reefs. In: Hopley, D. (Ed.) *Encyclopedia of Modern Coral Reefs: Structure, Form and Process*. Springer-Verlag, Berlin, Germany, pp. 813–815.

Wooldridge, S.A. and Done, T.J. 2009. Improved water quality can ameliorate effects of climate change on corals. *Ecological Applications* **19**: 1492–1499.

Yamano, H., Sugihara, K., and Nomura, K. 2011. Rapid poleward range expansion of tropical reef corals in response to rising sea surface temperatures. *Geophysical Research Letters* **38**: 10.1029/2010GL046474.

Zapata, F.A. and Vargas-Angel, B. 2003. Corals and coral reefs of the Pacific coast of Columbia. In: Cortes, J. (Ed.) *Latin American Coral Reefs*. Elsevier, Amsterdam, The Netherlands, pp. 419–447.

6.1.2.2.2 Symbiont Shuffling

The studies reviewed in this section examine symbiont shuffling, the ability of corals to replace the zooxanthellae expelled during a stress-induced bleaching episode with one or more varieties of zooxanthellae more tolerant of that particular stress. The key findings are presented in the bullet points below, followed by an expanded discussion of those findings.

- Zooxanthellae that reside within the cells of host corals are highly diverse, comprising perhaps hundreds of species, of which several are typically found in each species of coral.

- Many corals respond to stress by replacing the zooxanthellae expelled during a stress-induced bleaching episode with one or more varieties of zooxanthellae more tolerant of that stress.

- Coral bleaching is an adaptive strategy for "shuffling" symbiont genotypes to create associations better adapted to new environmental conditions, as opposed to "a breakdown of a stable relationship that serves as a symptom of degenerating environmental conditions."

- Multiple studies confirm the strategy of symbiont shuffling is occurring in nature.

- Symbiont shuffling "represents a mechanism for rapid acclimatization of the holobiont to environmental change."

Although once considered to be members of the single species *Symbiodinium microoadriacticum*, the zooxanthellae that reside within membrane-bound vacuoles in the cells of host corals are highly diverse, comprising perhaps hundreds of species, with each species of coral typically possessing several of these species (Trench, 1979; Rowan and Powers, 1991; Rowan *et al.*, 1997). One way corals respond to stress is to replace the zooxanthellae expelled by the coral host during a stress-induced bleaching episode with one or more varieties of zooxanthellae more tolerant of that particular stress.

Rowan *et al.* (1997) suggest this phenomenon

occurs in many of the most successful Caribbean corals that act as hosts to dynamic multispecies communities of symbionts, and "coral communities may adjust to climate change by recombining their existing host and symbiont genetic diversities," thereby reducing the amount of damage that might be expected from another occurrence of anomalously high temperatures. Buddemeier and Fautin (1993) propose coral bleaching is an adaptive strategy for "shuffling" symbiont genotypes to create associations better adapted to new environmental conditions. Kinzie (1999) suggests coral bleaching "might not be simply a breakdown of a stable relationship that serves as a symptom of degenerating environmental conditions," but also "may be part of a mutualistic relationship on a larger temporal scale, wherein the identity of algal symbionts changes in response to a changing environment."

The findings of Rowan and Knowlton (1995) and Gates and Edmunds (1999) provide additional evidence of this process of replacing less-stress-tolerant symbionts with more-stress-tolerant ones. The process seems to be successful, for as Glynn (1996) observed, "despite recent incidences of severe coral reef bleaching and mortality, no species extinctions have yet been documented."

These observations accord well with the experimental findings of Fagoonee *et al.* (1999), who suggest coral bleaching events "may be frequent and part of the expected cycle." Gates and Edmunds (1999) report "several of the prerequisites required to support this hypothesis have now been met"; after describing them in some detail, they conclude "there is no doubt that the existence of multiple *Symbiodinium* clades, each potentially exhibiting a different physiological optima, provide corals with the opportunity to attain an expanded range of physiological flexibility which will ultimately be reflected in their response to environmental challenge." This phenomenon may explain the paradox posed by Pandolfi (1999): "a large percentage of living coral reefs have been degraded, yet there are no known extinctions of any modern coral reef species." This result is exactly what would be expected if periods of stress lead to the acquisition of more-stress-resistant zooxanthellae by coral hosts.

Hoegh-Guldberg (1999) challenged the symbiont shuffling hypothesis by noting the stress-induced replacement of less-stress-tolerant varieties of zooxanthellae by more-stress-tolerant varieties "has never been observed." Although that was true at the time it was written, subsequent studies have produced the long-sought proof that transforms the hypothesis into fact.

Baker (2001) transplanted corals of different combinations of host and algal symbiont from shallow (2–4 m) to deep (20–23 m) water and vice versa. After eight weeks, nearly half of the corals transplanted from deep to shallow water had experienced partial or severe bleaching, whereas none of the corals transplanted from shallow to deep water bleached. After one year, and despite even more bleaching at shallow depths, upward transplants showed no mortality, but nearly 20% of downward transplants had died.

The symbiont shuffling hypothesis explains Baker's results as follows. The corals transplanted upwards were presumed to have adjusted their algal symbiont distributions, via bleaching, to favor more-tolerant species, whereas the corals transplanted downward were assumed to have not done so, since they did not bleach. Baker suggests these findings "support the view that coral bleaching can promote rapid response to environmental change by facilitating compensatory change in algal symbiont communities." Without bleaching, he continues, "suboptimal host-symbiont combinations persist, leading eventually to significant host mortality." Baker proposed coral bleaching may "ultimately help reef corals to survive." It may also explain why reefs, though depicted by IPCC as environmentally fragile, have survived the large environmental changes experienced throughout geologic time.

Adjeroud *et al.* (2002) provided additional evidence for the veracity of the symbiont shuffling hypothesis through their study of the interannual variability of coral cover on the outer slope of the Tiahura sector of Moorea Island, French Polynesia, between 1991 and 1997, which focused on the impacts of bleaching events caused by thermal stress when sea surface temperatures rose above 29.2°C. Soon after the start of their study, they observed a severe decline in coral cover following a bleaching event that began in March 1991, which was followed by another bleaching event in March 1994. They report the latter bleaching event "did not have an important impact on coral cover," even though "the proportion of bleached colonies ... and the order of susceptibility of coral genera were similar in 1991 and 1994 (Gleason, 1993; Hoegh-Guldberg and Salvat, 1995)." Between 1991 and 1992 total coral cover dropped from 51.0 to 24.2%, but "coral cover did not decrease between 1994 and 1995."

Adjeroud *et al.* note a "possible explanation of the low mortality following the bleaching event in 1994 is that most of the colonies in place in 1994 were those that survived the 1991 event or were young recruits derived from those colonies," and "one may assume that these coral colonies and/or their endosymbiotic zooxanthellae were phenotypically and possibly genotypically resistant to bleaching events," exactly what the symbiont shuffling hypothesis would predict. They say "this result demonstrates the importance of understanding the ecological history of reefs (i.e., the chronology of disturbances) in interpreting the specific impacts of a particular disturbance."

Brown *et al.* (2002) published the results of a 17-year study of coral reef flats at Ko Phuket, Thailand, in which they assessed coral reef changes in response to elevated water temperatures in 1991, 1995, 1997, and 1998. They write, "many corals bleached during elevated sea temperatures in May 1991 and 1995, but no bleaching was recorded in 1997." They report, "in May 1998 very limited bleaching occurred although sea temperatures were higher than previous events in 1991 and 1995 (Dunne and Brown, 2001)"; when bleaching did take place, "it led only to partial mortality in coral colonies, with most corals recovering their color within 3–5 months of initial paling.

Riegl (2003) reviewed what is known about the responses of real-world coral reefs to high-temperature-induced bleaching, focusing primarily on the Arabian Gulf, which experienced high-frequency recurrences of temperature-related bleaching in 1996, 1998, and 2002. *Acropora*, which during the 1996 and 1998 events always bleached first and suffered heaviest mortality, bleached less than all other corals in 2002 at Sir Abu Nuair (an offshore island of the United Arab Emirates) and recovered along the coast of Dubai between Jebel Ali and Ras Hasyan. Riegl writes, "the unexpected resistance of Sir Abu Nuair *Acropora* to bleaching in 2002 might indicate support for the hypothesis of Baker (2001) and Baker *et al.* (2002) that the symbiont communities on recovering reefs of the future might indeed be more resistant to subsequent bleaching," and "the Arabian Gulf perhaps provides us with some aspects which might be described as a 'glimpse into the future,' with ... hopes for at least some level of coral/zooxanthellae adaptation."

Kumaraguru *et al.* (2003) assessed the damage inflicted on a number of coral reefs within Palk Bay (located on the southeast coast of India just north of the Gulf of Mannar) by a major warming event that produced monthly mean sea surface temperatures of 29.8 to 32.1°C from April through June 2002, after which they studied the degree of recovery of the reefs. They determined "a minimum of at least 50% and a maximum of 60% bleaching were noticed among the six different sites monitored." They continue, "the corals started to recover quickly in August 2002 and as much as 52% recovery could be noticed." By comparison, they note, "recovery of corals after the 1998 bleaching phenomenon in the Gulf of Mannar was very slow, taking as much as one year to achieve similar recovery." The Indian scientists state, "the process of natural selection is in operation, with the growth of new coral colonies, and any disturbance in the system is only temporary." They conclude, "the corals will resurge under the sea."

Rowan (2004) described how he measured the photosynthetic responses of two zooxanthellae genotypes or clades—*Symbiodinium C* and *Symbiodinium D*—to increasing water temperature and found the photosynthetic prowess of the former decreased at higher temperatures whereas that of the latter increased. He notes "adaptation to higher temperature in *Symbiodinium D* can explain why *Pocillopora* spp. hosting them resist warm-water bleaching whereas corals hosting *Symbiodinium C* do not," and "it can also explain why *Pocillopora* spp. living in frequently warm habitats host only *Symbiodinium D*, and, perhaps, why those living in cooler habitats predominantly host *Symbiodinium C*." These observations, he concludes, "indicate that symbiosis recombination may be one mechanism by which corals adapt, in part, to global warming."

Baker *et al.* (2004) "undertook molecular surveys of *Symbiodinium* in shallow scleractinian corals from five locations in the Indo-Pacific that had been differently affected by the 1997–98 El Niño-Southern Oscillation (ENSO) bleaching event." Along the coasts of Panama, they surveyed ecologically dominant corals in the genus *Pocillopora* before, during, and after ENSO bleaching, finding "colonies containing *Symbiodinium* in clade D were already common (43%) in 1995 and were unaffected by bleaching in 1997, while colonies containing clade C bleached severely." They found "by 2001, colonies containing clade D had become dominant (63%) on these reefs."

After describing similar observations in the Persian (Arabian) Gulf and the western Indian Ocean along the coast of Kenya, Baker *et al.* summarize say their results indicate "corals containing thermally tolerant *Symbiodinium* in clade D are more abundant on reefs after episodes of severe bleaching and mortality, and that surviving coral symbioses on these reefs more closely resemble those found in high-temperature environments," where clade D predominates. They conclude by noting the symbiont changes they observed "are a common feature of severe bleaching and mortality events," and they predict "these adaptive shifts will increase the resistance of these recovering reefs to future bleaching."

Lewis and Coffroth (2004) described a controlled experiment in which they induced bleaching in a Caribbean octocoral (*Briareum* sp.) and then exposed it to exogenous *Symbiodinium* sp. containing rare variants of the chloroplast 23S ribosomal DNA (rDNA) domain V region (cp23S-genotype), after which they documented the symbionts' repopulation of the coral, whose symbiont density had been reduced to less than 1% of its original level by the bleaching. In an analogous study, Little *et al.* (2004) investigated the acquisition of symbionts by juvenile *Acropora tenuis* corals growing on tiles they attached to different portions of reef at Nelly Bay, Magnetic Island (an inshore reef in the central section of Australia's Great Barrier Reef).

Lewis and Coffroth state their results show "the repopulation of the symbiont community involved residual populations within *Briareum* sp., as well as symbionts from the surrounding water," noting "recovery of coral-algal symbioses after a bleaching event is not solely dependent on the *Symbiodinium* complement initially acquired early in the host's ontogeny," but "these symbioses also have the flexibility to establish new associations with symbionts from an environmental pool." Similarly, Little *et al.* report, "initial uptake of zooxanthellae by juvenile corals during natural infection is nonspecific (a potentially adaptive trait)," and "the association is flexible and characterized by a change in (dominant) zooxanthella strains over time."

Lewis and Coffroth conclude "the ability of octocorals to reestablish symbiont populations from multiple sources provides a mechanism for resilience in the face of environmental change." Little *et al.* conclude the "symbiont shuffling" observed by both groups "represents a mechanism for rapid acclimatization of the holobiont to environmental change."

Chen *et al.* (2005) reported on their study of the seasonal dynamics of *Symbiodinium* algal phylotypes via bimonthly sampling over an 18-month period of *Acropora palifera* coral on a reef flat at Tantzel Bay, Kenting National Park, southern Taiwan, in an attempt to detect real-world symbiont shuffling. They found two levels of symbiont shuffling in host corals: between *Symbiodinium* phylotypes C and D, and among different variants within each phylotype. The most significant changes in symbiont composition occurred at times of significant increases in seawater temperature during late spring and early summer, perhaps as a consequence of enhanced stress experienced at that time, leading Chen *et al.* to state their work revealed "the first evidence that the symbiont community within coral colonies is dynamic ... involving changes in *Symbiodinium* phylotypes."

Van Oppen *et al.* (2005) sampled zooxanthellae from three common species of scleractinian corals at 17 sites along a latitudinal and cross-shelf gradient in the central and southern sections of the Great Barrier Reef four to five months after the major bleaching event of 2002, recording the health status of each colony at the time of its collection and identifying its zooxanthella genotypes, of which there are eight distinct clades (A-H) with clade D being the most heat-tolerant. They found "there were no simple correlations between symbiont types and either the level of bleaching of individual colonies or indicators of heat stress at individual sites." They write, "there was a very high post-bleaching abundance of the heat tolerant symbiont type D in one coral population at the most heat-stressed site."

The Australian researchers say they suspect the post-bleaching abundance of clade D zooxanthellae at the high heat-stress site was due to "a proliferation in the absolute abundance of clade D within existing colonies that were previously dominated by clade C zooxanthellae." In the four to five months before sampling them, the writers note, "mixed C-D colonies that had bleached but survived may have shifted (shuffling) from C-dominance to D-dominance, and/or C-dominated colonies may have suffered higher mortality during the 2002 bleaching event" and subsequently been repopulated by a predominance of clade D genotypes.

Berkelmans and van Oppen (2006) investigated the thermal acclimatization potential of *Acropora millepora* corals at Australia's Great Barrier Reef to rising temperatures through transplantation and experimental manipulation. They found the adult corals "are capable of acquiring increased thermal tolerance and that the increased tolerance is a direct result of a change in the symbiont type dominating their tissues from *Symbiodinium* type C to D." Two years later, working with an expanded group of authors (Jones *et al.*, 2008), the two researchers reported similar findings following the occurrence of a natural bleaching event.

Before that bleaching event, Jones *et al.* report, "*A. millepora* at Miall reef associated predominantly with *Symbiodinium* type C2 (93.5%) and to a much lesser extent with *Symbiodinium* clade D (3.5%) or mixtures of C2 and D (3.0%)." During the bleaching event, they report, "the relative difference in bleaching susceptibility between corals predominated by C2 and D was clearly evident, with the former bleaching white and the latter normally pigmented," whereas corals harboring a mix of *Symbiodinium* C2 and D were "mostly pale in appearance." Three months after the bleaching event, they observed "a major shift to thermally tolerant type D and C1 symbiont communities ... in the surviving colonies"; the latter types had not been detected in any of the corals before bleaching. They report, "this shift resulted partly from a change of symbionts within coral colonies that survived the bleaching event (42%) and partly from selective mortality of the more bleaching-sensitive C2-predominant colonies (37%)." All of the colonies that harbored low levels of D-type symbionts before the bleaching event survived and changed from clade C2 to D predominance.

Jones *et al.* write, "as a direct result of the shift in symbiont community, the Miall Island *A. millepora* population is likely to have become more thermo-tolerant," as they note "a shift from bleaching-sensitive type C2 to clade D increased the thermal tolerance of this species by 1–1.5°C." They say their results "strongly support the reinterpreted adaptive bleaching hypothesis of Buddemeier *et al.* (2004), which postulates that a continuum of changing environmental states stimulates the loss of bleaching-sensitive symbionts in favor of symbionts that make the new holobiont more thermally tolerant." They state their observations "provide the first extensive colony-specific documentation and quantification of temporal symbiont community change in the field in response to temperature stress, suggesting a population-wide acclimatization to increased water temperature."

Lien *et al.* (2007) examined the symbiont diversity in a scleractinian coral, *Oulastrea crispata*, throughout its entire latitudinal distribution range in the West Pacific, from tropical peninsular Thailand (<10°N) to high-latitudinal outlying coral communities in Japan (>35°N). Those results convincingly demonstrate, the six scientists write, "that phylotype D is the dominant *Symbiodinium* in scleractinian corals throughout tropical reefs and marginal outlying non-reefal coral communities." They learned this particular symbiont clade "favors 'marginal habitats' where other symbionts are poorly suited to the stresses, such as irradiance, temperature fluctuations, sedimentation, etc." As a major component of the symbiont repertoire of most scleractinian corals in most places, the apparent near-universal presence of *Symbiodinium* phylotype D thus provides, Lien *et al.*

write, "a flexible means for corals to routinely cope with environmental heterogeneities and survive the consequences (e.g., recover from coral bleaching)."

Also in 2007, Mieog *et al.* (2007) utilized a newly developed real-time polymerase chain reaction assay, which they say "is able to detect Symbiodinium clades C and D with >100-fold higher sensitivity compared to conventional techniques," to test 82 colonies of four common scleractinian corals (*Acropora millepora*, *Acropora tenuis*, *Stylophora pistillata*, and *Turbinaria reniformis*) from 11 locations on Australia's Great Barrier Reef for evidence of the presence of background *Symbiodinium* clades. They found "ninety-three percent of the colonies tested were dominated by clade C and 76% of these had a D background." The latter symbionts, they write, "are amongst the most thermo-tolerant types known to date," being found "on reefs that chronically experience unusually high temperatures or that have recently been impacted by bleaching events, suggesting that temperature stress can favor clade D." Mieog *et al.* conclude the clade D symbiont backgrounds detected in their study may act as a safety net, "allowing corals to become more thermo-tolerant through symbiont shuffling as seawater temperatures rise due to global warming." They suggest symbiont shuffling is likely to play a role in the way "corals cope with global warming conditions," leading to new competitive hierarchies and, ultimately, "the coral community assemblages of the future."

Despite the hope symbiont shuffling provides—that corals will be able to cope with any future global warming, whether anthropogenic or natural—some researchers have claimed few coral symbioses host more than one type of symbiont, which has led some commentators to argue symbiont shuffling is not an option for most coral species to survive the coming thermal onslaught of global warming. That claim has been shown to be incorrect.

Working with samples of the widely distributed massive corals *Porites lobata* and *Porites lutea*—collected from Kaneohe Bay, Hawaii—Apprill and Gates (2007) compared the identity and diversity of *Symbiodinium* symbiont types obtained using cloning and sequencing of internal transcribed spacer region 2 (ITS2) with those obtained using the more commonly applied downstream analytical techniques of denaturing gradient gel electrophoresis (DGGE). The results revealed "a total of 11 ITS2 types in *Porites lobata* and 17 in *Porites lutea* with individual colonies hosting from one to six and three to eight ITS2 types for *P. lobata* and *P. lutea*, respectively." The two authors report, "of the clones examined, 93% of the *P. lobata* and 83% of the *P. lutea* sequences are not listed in GenBank," noting they resolved "sixfold to eightfold greater diversity per coral species than previously reported."

In a "perspective" that accompanied Apprill and Gates' paper, van Oppen (2007) wrote, "the current perception of coral-inhabiting symbiont diversity at nuclear ribosomal DNA is shown [by Apprill and Gates] to be a significant underestimate of the wide diversity that in fact exists." These findings, in her words, "have potentially far-reaching consequences in terms of our understanding of *Symbiodinium* diversity, host-symbiont specificity and the potential of corals to acclimatize to environmental perturbations through changes in the composition of their algal endosymbiont community."

Baird *et al.* (2007) also discount the argument symbiont shuffling is not an option for most coral species, because it is the sub-clade that must be considered within this context, citing studies that indicate "there are both heat tolerant and heat susceptible sub-clades within both clades C and D *Symbiodinium*." Hence, the more relevant question becomes: How many coral species can host more than one sub-clade? The answer is that most, if not all, likely do. As Baird *et al.* note, "biogeographical data suggest that when species need to respond to novel environments, they have the flexibility to do so."

Although most prior research into how and when such sub-clade changes might occur has been on adult colonies switching symbionts in response to warming-induced bleaching episodes, Baird *et al.* suggest "change is more likely to occur between generations," because initial coral infection typically occurs in larvae or early juveniles, which are much more flexible than adults. They note, "juveniles of *Acropora tenuis* regularly harbor mixed assemblages of symbionts, whereas adults of the species almost invariably host a single clade," and larvae of *Fungia scutaria* ingest symbionts from multiple hosts, although they generally harbor but one symbiont as adults.

The Australian researchers say there is no need for an acute disturbance, such as bleaching, to induce clade or sub-clade change. Instead, if ocean temperatures rise in the future, they foresee juveniles naturally hosting more heat-tolerant sub-clades and maintaining them into adulthood.

In a further assessment of the size of the symbiont diversity reservoir, especially among juvenile coral species, Pochon *et al.* (2007) collected more than 1,000 soritid specimens over a depth of 40 meters on a single reef at Gun Beach on the island of Guam, Micronesia, throughout an entire year. They studied the specimens by means of molecular techniques to identify unique internal transcribed spacer–2 (ITS–2) types of ribosomal DNA (rDNA), in a project self-described as "the most targeted and exhaustive sampling effort ever undertaken for any group of *Symbiodinium*-bearing hosts."

Pochon *et al.* identified 61 unique symbiont types in only three soritid host genera, making the Guam *Symbiodinium* assemblage the most diverse derived to date from a single reef. They report, "the majority of mixed genotypes observed during this survey were usually harbored by the smallest hosts." The authors speculate "juvenile foraminifera may be better able to switch or shuffle heterogeneous symbiont communities than adults," so as juveniles grow, "their symbiont communities become 'optimized' for the prevailing environmental conditions," suggesting this phenomenon "may be a key element in the continued evolutionary success of these protests in coral reef ecosystems worldwide."

The work of Mumby (1999), who analyzed the population dynamics of juvenile corals in Belize both before and after a massive coral bleaching event in 1998, supports that statement. Although 70 to 90% of adult coral colonies were severely bleached during the event, only 25% of coral recruits exhibited signs of bleaching. One month after the event, they concluded "net bleaching-induced mortality of coral recruits ... was insignificant," demonstrating the ability of juvenile corals to successfully weather such bleaching events.

Fitt *et al.* (2009) note the various *Symbiodinium* clades that comprise the algal symbiont found in their coral host have been thought "to exert a major influence on the ability of reef-building corals to survive high-temperature stress." They add that if the host itself plays a role in this process, "the hypothesis that corals simply shuffle or swap their *Symbiodinium* for clades that are more thermally tolerant does not tell the whole story." In fact, it suggests corals may be even more adept at coping with rising temperatures than scientists previously believed.

Fitt *et al.* studied a number of coral host and *Symbiodinium* properties and processes in two ubiquitous Indo-Pacific reef corals known to be either very susceptible (*Stylophora pistillata*) or resistant (*Porites cylindrica*) to heat stress, exposing them to seawater temperatures of either 28°C (normal ambient) or 32°C (elevated) for five days before returning them to the normal ambient temperature. The 16 scientists report finding "both physiological and biochemical differences of both symbiont and host origin in the response to high-temperature stress." They say "hypotheses that talk only in terms of the thermal characteristics of the symbiont may miss critical information concerning questions surrounding the thermal tolerance of corals in the coming century." They note "there are dynamic photoprotective mechanisms in both the host and zooxanthellae that include ultraviolet radiation absorbing mycosporine-like amino acids (Shick and Dunlap, 2002; Lesser, 2004), excess excitation energy dissipation in photosystem II via the xanthophyll cycle (Brown et al. 1999; Gorbunov et al., 2001), the expression of heat-shock proteins and other stress markers (Black et al., 1995; Downs et al., 2000; Lesser and Farrell, 2004), the up-regulation of antioxidant enzymes (Lesser, 1996; Lesser and Farrell, 2004; Lesser, 2006), host energy reserve utilization (Porter et al., 1989; Grottoli et al., 2004, 2006), and heterotrophic plasticity (Grotolli et al., 2006)." All of these phenomena, they write, "presumably have underlying influences on any response to thermal stress, and hence, contribute to the overall differences within and between species in regard to their bleaching sensitivity." This diverse group of phenomena that can help both the coral host and its algal symbionts adjust to rising temperatures indicate Earth's corals are well-equipped to deal with whatever further warming may come their way.

Silverstein et al. (2012) state many reef-building corals "have been shown to respond to environmental change by shifting the composition of their algal symbiont (genus Symbiodinium) communities," and "these shifts have been proposed as a potential mechanism by which corals might survive climate stressors, such as increased temperatures." They say "conventional molecular methods suggest this adaptive capacity may not be widespread because few (~25%) coral species have been found to associate with multiple Symbiodinium clades." They hasten to add, "these methods can fail to detect low abundance symbionts (typically less than 10–20% of the total algal symbiont community)."

To determine whether additional Symbiodinium clades might be present but undetected in various corals using conventional discovery and identification techniques, Silverstein et al. "applied a high-resolution, real-time PCR [polymerase chain reaction] assay to survey Symbiodinium (in clades A-D) from 39 species of phylogenetically and geographically diverse scleractinian corals." This survey, they write, "included 26 coral species thought to be restricted to hosting a single Symbiodinium clade," referring to the latter corals as symbiotic specialists.

The three U.S. scientists say they "detected at least two Symbiodinium clades (C and D) in at least one sample of all 39 coral species tested," and "all four Symbiodinium clades were detected in over half (54%) of the 26 symbiotic specialist coral species." They report, "on average, 68% of all sampled colonies within a given coral species hosted two or more symbiont clades." Silverstein et al. conclude, "the ability to associate with multiple symbiont clades is common in scleractinian (stony) corals," and in regard to coral-algal symbiosis, "specificity is rarely absolute." They conclude "the potential for reef corals to adapt or acclimatize to environmental change via symbiont community shifts may therefore be more phylogenetically widespread than has previously been assumed."

Cumbo et al. (2013) note "coral reefs thrive in part because of the symbiotic partnership between corals and Symbiodinium," but "the point at which symbiosis is established (i.e., larva vs. juvenile) remains uncertain, as does the source of free-living Symbiodinium in the environment." They investigated "the types of symbionts taken up by Acropora larvae exposed to sediments collected from three different locations on the Great Barrier Reef, and compared this to the Symbiodinium types within adult cnidarians for each location." In addition, they "tested whether the Symbiodinium types changed during ontogeny by comparing types within the larvae, juvenile and adults of the same species at each location."

The three researchers report, "Symbiodinium clearly reside in the sediments of shallow reef communities and are capable of initiating symbiosis with aposymbiotic coral larvae," and "the larvae of many species of corals are promiscuous, associating with multiple Symbiodinium types independent of coral species or location." Cumbo et al. say their findings suggest "as sea surface temperatures rise, the promiscuity of larvae could benefit corals by allowing them to acquire symbionts with the greatest heat tolerance in each new generation (LaJeunesse et al., 2004; Baird et al., 2007)." In addition, although "this mechanism of acclimatization will most likely be restricted to species that show horizontal transmission of symbionts," they note such species account for approximately 85% of all species.

References

Adjeroud, M., Augustin, D., Galzin, R., and Salvat, B. 2002. Natural disturbances and interannual variability of coral reef communities on the outer slope of Tiahura (Moorea, French Polynesia): 1991 to 1997. *Marine Ecology Progress Series* **237**: 121–131.

Apprill, A.M. and Gates, R.D. 2007. Recognizing diversity in coral symbiotic dinoflagellate communities. *Molecular Ecology* **16**: 1127–1134.

Baird, A.H., Cumbo, V.R., Leggat, W., and Rodriguez-Lanetty, M. 2007. Fidelity and flexibility in coral symbioses. *Marine Ecology Progress Series* **347**: 307–309.

Baker, A.C. 2001. Reef corals bleach to survive change. *Nature* **411**: 765–766.

Baker, A.C., Starger, C.J., McClanahan, T.R., and Glynn, P.W. 2002. Symbiont communities in reef corals following the 1997–98 El Niño—will recovering reefs be more resistant to a subsequent bleaching event? *Proceedings of the International Society of Reef Studies* (Abstract Volume 10: European Meeting, Cambridge, UK, September).

Baker, A.C., Starger, C.J., McClanahan, T.R., and Glynn, P.W. 2004. Corals' adaptive response to climate change. *Nature* **430**: 741.

Berkelmans, R. and van Oppen, M.J.H. 2006. The role of zooxanthellae in the thermal tolerance of corals: a "nugget of hope" for coral reefs in an era of climate change. *Proceedings of the Royal Society B* **273**: 2305–2312.

Black, N.A., Voellmy, R., and Szmant, A.M. 1995. Heat shock protein induction in *Montastraea faveolata* and *Aiptasia pallida* to elevated temperatures. *Biological Bulletin* **188**: 234–240.

Brown, B.E., Ambarsari, I., Warner, M.E., Fitt, W.K., Dunne, R.P., and Gibb, S.W. 1999. Cummings DG Diurnal changes in photochemical efficiency and xanthophyll concentrations in shallow water reef corals: evidence for photoinhibition and photoprotection. *Coral Reefs* **18**: 99–105.

Brown, B.E., Clarke, K.R., and Warwick, R.M. 2002. Serial patterns of biodiversity change in corals across shallow reef flats in Ko Phuket, Thailand, due to the effects of local (sedimentation) and regional (climatic) perturbations. *Marine Biology* **141**: 24–29.

Buddemeier, R.W., Baker, A.C., Fautin, D.G., and Jacobs, J.R. 2004. The adaptive hypothesis of bleaching. In Rosenberg, E. and Loya, Y. (Eds.) *Coral Health and Disease*, Springer, Berlin, Germany, p. 427–444.

Buddemeier, R.W. and Fautin, D.G. 1993. Coral bleaching as an adaptive mechanism. *BioScience* **43**: 320–326.

Chen, C.A., Wang, J.-T., Fang, L.-S., and Yang, Y.W. 2005. Fluctuating algal symbiont communities in *Acropora palifera* (Schleractinia: Acroporidae) from Taiwan. *Marine Ecology Progress Series* **295**: 113–121.

Cumbo, V.R., Baird, A.J., and van Oppen, M.J.H. 2013.

The promiscuous larvae: flexibility in the establishment of symbiosis in corals. *Coral Reefs* **32**: 111–120.

Downs, C.A., Mueller, E., Phillips, S., Fauth, J.E., and Woodley, C.M. 2000. A molecular biomarker system for assessing the health of coral (*Montastraea faveolata*) during heat stress. *Marine Biotechnology* **2**: 533–544.

Dunne, R.P. and Brown, B.E. 2001. The influence of solar radiation on bleaching of shallow water reef corals in the Andaman Sea, 1993–98. *Coral Reefs* **20**: 201–210.

Fagoonee, I., Wilson, H.B., Hassell, M.P., and Turner, J.R. 1999. The dynamics of zooxanthellae populations: A long-term study in the field. *Science* **283**: 843–845.

Fitt, W.K., Gates, R.D., Hoegh-Guldberg, O., Bythell, J.C., Jatkar, A., Grottoli, A.G., Gomez, M., Fisher, P., Lajuenesse, T.C., Pantos, O., Iglesias-Prieto, R., Franklin, D.J., Rodrigues, L.J., Torregiani, J.M., van Woesik, R., and Lesser, M.P. 2009. Response of two species of Indo-Pacific corals, *Porites cylindrica* and *Stylophora pistillata*, to short-term thermal stress: The host does matter in determining the tolerance of corals to bleaching. *Journal of Experimental Marine Biology and Ecology* **373**: 102–110.

Gates, R.D. and Edmunds, P.J. 1999. The physiological mechanisms of acclimatization in tropical reef corals. *American Zoologist* **39**: 30–43.

Gleason, M.G. 1993. Effects of disturbance on coral communities: bleaching in Moorea, French Polynesia. *Coral Reefs* **12**: 193–201.

Glynn, P.W. 1996. Coral reef bleaching: facts, hypotheses and implications. *Global Change Biology* **2**: 495–509.

Grottoli, A.G., Rodrigues, I.J., and Juarez, C. 2004. Lipids and stable carbon isotopes in two species of Hawaiian corals, *Porites compressa* and *Montipora verrucosa*, following a bleaching event. *Marine Biology* **145**: 621–631.

Grotolli, A.G., Rodriguez, I.J., and Palardy, J.E. 2006. Heterotrophic plasticity and resilience in bleached corals. *Nature* **440**: 1186–1189.

Gorbunov, M.Y., Kolber, Z.S., Lesser, M.P., and Falkowski, P.G. 2001. Photosynthesis and photoprotection in symbiotic corals. *Limnology and Oceanography* **46**: 75–85.

Hoegh-Guldberg, O. 1999. Climate change, coral bleaching and the future of the world's coral reefs. *Marine and Freshwater Research* **50**: 839–866.

Hoegh-Guldberg, O. and Salvat, B. 1995. Periodic mass-bleaching and elevated sea temperatures: bleaching of outer reef slope communities in Moorea, French Polynesia. *Marine Ecology Progress Series* **121**: 181–190.

Jones, A.M., Berkelmans, R., van Oppen, M.J.H., Mieog,

J.C., and Sinclair, W. 2008. A community change in the algal endosymbionts of a scleractinian coral following a natural bleaching event: field evidence of acclimatization. *Proceedings of the Royal Society B* **275**: 1359–1365.

Kinzie III, R.A. 1999. Sex, symbiosis and coral reef communities. *American Zoologist* **39**: 80–91.

Kumaraguru, A.K., Jayakumar, K., and Ramakritinan, C.M. 2003. Coral bleaching 2002 in the Palk Bay, southeast coast of India. *Current Science* **85**: 1787–1793.

LaJeunesse, T.C., Bhagooli, R., Hidaka, M., DeVantier, L., Done, T., Schmidt, G.W., Fitt, W.K., and Hoegh-Guldberg, O. 2004. Closely related *Symbiodinium* spp. differ in relative dominance in coral reef host communities across environmental, latitudinal and biogeographic gradients. *Marine Ecology Progress Series* **284**: 147–161.

Lien, Y.-T., Nakano, Y., Plathong, S., Fukami, H., Wang, J.-T., and Chen, C.A. 2007. Occurrence of the putatively heat-tolerant *Symbiodinium* phylotype D in high-latitudinal outlying coral communities. *Coral Reefs* **26**: 35–44.

Lesser, M.P. 1996. Exposure of symbiotic dinoflagellates to elevated temperatures and ultraviolet radiation causes oxidative stress and inhibits photosynthesis. *Limnology and Oceanography* **41**: 271–283.

Lesser, M.P. 2004. Experimental coral reef biology. *Journal of Experimental Marine Biology and Ecology* **300**: 227–252.

Lesser, M.P. 2006. Oxidative stress in marine environments: biochemistry and physiological ecology. *Annual Review of Physiology* **68**: 253–278.

Lesser, M.P. and Farrell, J.H. 2004. Solar radiation increases the damage to both host tissues and algal symbionts of corals exposed to thermal stress. *Coral Reefs* **23**: 367–377.

Lewis, C.L. and Coffroth, M.A. 2004. The acquisition of exogenous algal symbionts by an octocoral after bleaching. *Science* **304**: 1490–1492.

Little, A.F., van Oppen, M.J.H., and Willis, B.L. 2004. Flexibility in algal endosymbioses shapes growth in reef corals. *Science* **304**: 1492–1494.

Mieog, J.C., van Oppen, M.J.H., Cantin, N.E., Stam, W.T., and Olsen, J.L. 2007. Real-time PCR reveals a high incidence of *Symbiodinium* clade D at low levels in four scleractinian corals across the Great Barrier Reef: implications for symbiont shuffling. *Coral Reefs* **26**: 449–457.

Mumby, P.J. 1999. Bleaching and hurricane disturbances to populations of coral recruits in Belize. *Marine Ecology Progress Series* **190**: 27–35.

Pandolfi, J.M. 1999. Response of Pleistocene coral reefs to environmental change over long temporal scales. *American Zoologist* **39**: 113–130.

Pochon, X., Garcia-Cuetos, L., Baker, A.C., Castella, E., and Pawlowski, J. 2007. One-year survey of a single Micronesian reef reveals extraordinarily rich diversity of *Symbiodinium* types in soritid foraminifera. *Coral Reefs* **26**: 867–882.

Porter, J.W., Fitt, W.K., Spero, J.H., Rogers, C.S., and White, M.W. 1989. Bleaching in reef corals: physiological and stable isotopic responses. *Proceedings of the National Academy of Sciences USA* **86**: 9342–9346.

Riegl, B. 2003. Climate change and coral reefs: different effects in two high-latitude areas (Arabian Gulf, South Africa). *Coral Reefs* **22**: 433–446.

Rowan, R. 2004. Thermal adaptation in reef coral symbionts. *Nature* **430**: 742.

Rowan, R. and Knowlton, N. 1995. Intraspecific diversity and ecological zonation in coral-algal symbiosis. *Proceeding of the National Academy of Sciences, U.S.A.* **92**: 2850–2853.

Rowan, R., Knowlton, N., Baker, A., and Jara, J. 1997. Landscape ecology of algal symbionts creates variation in episodes of coral bleaching. *Nature* **388**: 265–269.

Rowan, R. and Powers, D. 1991. Molecular genetic identification of symbiotic dinoflagellates (zooxanthellae). *Marine Ecology Progress Series* **71**: 65–73.

Shick, J.M. and Dunlap, W.C. 2002. Mycosporine-like amino acids and related gadusols: biosynthesis, accumulation, and UV-protective functions in aquatic organisms. *Annual Review of Physiology* **64**: 223–262.

Silverstein, R.N., Correa, A.M.S., and Baker, A.C. 2012. Specificity is rarely absolute in coral-algal symbiosis: implications for coral response to climate change. *Proceedings of the Royal Society B* **279**: 2609–2618.

Trench, R.K. 1979. The cell biology of plant-animal symbiosis. *Annual Review of Plant Physiology* **30**: 485–531.

Van Oppen, M.J.H. 2007. Perspective. *Molecular Ecology* **16**: 1125–1126.

Van Oppen, M.J.H., Mahiny, A.J., and Done, T.J. 2005. Geographic distribution of zooxanthella types in three coral species on the Great Barrier Reef sampled after the 2002 bleaching event. *Coral Reefs* **24**: 482–487.

6.1.2.2.3 Other Stress Response Strategies

The studies reviewed in this section examine other stress response strategies known to operate in corals under stressful conditions. The key findings are presented in the bullet points below, followed by an expanded discussion of those findings.

- Some corals increase their expression of heat shock proteins that help repair heat-damaged constituents of their bodies as another strategy to cope with heat stress.

- The coral probiotic hypothesis, or bacterial shuffling, posits that many corals rearrange their bacterial populations in a manner akin to symbiont shuffling as another response to environmental stress.

- Corals employ other strategies of coping with and adapting to environmental stresses, further suggesting they will be able to continue to cope with the many environmental threats they face now and may face in the future.

In addition to thermal acclimation and symbiont shuffling, corals have other means to cope with and adapt to environmental stresses. One such mechanism is the production of heat shock proteins that help repair heat-damaged constituents of their bodies (Black *et al.*, 1995; Hayes and King, 1995; Fang *et al.*, 1997). Sharp *et al.* (1997), for example, demonstrated sub-tidal specimens of *Goniopora djiboutiensis* typically have much lower constitutive levels of a 70-kD heat shock protein than do their intertidal conspecifics, and they have shown corals transplanted from subtidal to intertidal locations (where temperature extremes are greater and more common) typically increase their expression of this heat shock protein.

Roberts *et al.* (1997) reported similar results in field work with *Mytilus californianus*. Gates and Edmunds (1999) observed an increase in the 70-kD heat shock protein after six hours of exposure of *Montastraea franksi* to a 2–3°C increase in temperature, followed by another heat shock protein increase at the 48-hour point of exposure to elevated water temperature. They state the first of these protein increases "provides strong evidence that changes in protein turnover during the initial exposure to elevated temperature provides this coral with the biological flexibility to acclimatize to the elevation in sea water temperature," and the second increase "indicates another shift in protein turnover perhaps associated with an attempt to acclimatize to the more chronic level of temperature stress."

Reshef *et al.* (2006) discussed another adaptive bleaching mechanism, developing a case for what they call the coral probiotic hypothesis, which might also be referred to as bacterial shuffling. This concept, they write, "posits that a dynamic relationship exists between symbiotic microorganisms and environmental conditions which brings about the selection of the most advantageous coral holobiont." It is analogous to the adaptive bleaching hypothesis of Buddemeier and Fautin (1993), or what was referred to in the preceding section as symbiont shuffling, in which corals exposed to some type of stress—such as that induced by exposure to unusually high water temperatures or solar irradiance—first lose their dinoflagellate symbionts (bleach) and then regain a new mixture of zooxanthellae better suited to the stress conditions. The two phenomena work in precisely the same way, in one case by the corals rearranging their zooxanthellae populations (symbiont shuffling) and in the other by the corals rearranging their bacterial populations (bacterial shuffling).

The team of Israeli researchers looked for examples of corals developing resistance to emerging diseases. Corals lack an adaptive immune system—they possess no antibodies (Nair *et al.*, 2005)—and therefore can protect themselves against specific diseases in no other way than to adjust the relative sizes of the diverse bacterial populations associated with their mucus and tissues so as to promote the growth of those types of bacteria that tend to mitigate most effectively against the specific disease that happens to be troubling them.

Reshef *et al.* described the discovery that bleaching of *Oculina patagonica* corals in the Mediterranean Sea was caused by the bacterium *Vibrio shiloi*, together with the finding that bleaching of *Pocillopora damicornis* corals in the Indian Ocean and Red Sea was the result of an infection with *Vibrio coralliilyticus*. They report "during the last two years *O. patagonica* has developed resistance to the infection by *V. shiloi*," "*V. shiloi* can no longer be found on the corals," and "*V. shiloi* that previously infected corals are unable to infect the existing corals." They write, "by some unknown mechanism, the coral is now able to lyse the intracellular *V. shiloi* and avoid the disease." Because corals lack the ability to produce antibodies and have no adaptive immune system, the only logical conclusion to be drawn from these observations is that bacterial shuffling must be at work.

The Israeli scientists note "Hoegh-Guldberg (1999, 2004) has predicted that coral reefs will have only remnant populations of reef-building corals by the middle of this century," based on "the assumption that corals cannot adapt rapidly enough to the predicted temperatures in order to survive." They report considerable evidence has been collected in support of the adaptive bleaching hypothesis, and they emphasize the hundreds of different bacterial species associated with corals "give the coral holobiont an enormous genetic potential to adapt rapidly to changing environmental conditions." They state, "it is not unreasonable to predict that under appropriate selection conditions, the change could take place in days or weeks, rather than decades required for classical Darwinian mutation and selection," and "these rapid changes may allow the coral holobiont to use nutrients more efficiently, prevent colonization by specific pathogens and avoid death during bleaching by providing carbon and energy from photosynthetic prokaryotes," of which they say there is "a metabolically active, diverse pool" in most corals.

Another example of adaptation to stress comes from studies of corals that exhibit a "zonation" of their symbiont taxa with depth, where symbiont algae that are less tolerant of intense solar radiation grow on corals at greater depths below the ocean surface (Rowan and Knowlton, 1995; Rowan et al., 1997). Researchers also have demonstrated zooxanthellae in corals possess a number of light-quenching mechanisms that can be employed to reduce the negative impacts of excess light (Hoegh-Guldberg and Jones, 1999; Ralph et al., 1999). Both the coral host and its symbionts also have the capacity to produce amino acids that act as natural "sunscreens" (Hoegh-Guldberg, 1999); and they can regulate their enzyme activities to enhance internal scavenging systems that remove noxious oxygen radicals produced in coral tissues as a result of high light intensities (Dykens and Shick, 1984; Lesser et al., 1990; Matta and Trench, 1991; Shick et al., 1996).

Another means corals can use to lessen the stress of solar irradiance is coral tissue retraction. Brown et al. (1994) studied the phenomenon in the scleractinian coral Coeloseris mayeri at coral reefs in Phuket, Thailand by examining the retraction and recovery of coral tissues over a tidal cycle. They found extreme tissue retraction occurred approximately 85 minutes after initial sub-aerial coral exposure. Tissue retraction did not involve any reduction in chlorophyll concentration or algae symbiont abundance; the tissues expanded over the coral skeletons to pre-retraction conditions following the return of the tide. The adaptive benefits of tissue retraction, the authors write, "include increased albedo, leading to a reduction in absorbed solar energy of 10%, ... and possible avoidance of photochemical damage or photoinhibition at high solar irradiance."

Nakamura and van Woesik (2001) evaluated the bleaching of large and small coral colonies along the western coast of Okinawa, Japan during the summers of 1998 and 2001, arguing small coral colonies should survive thermal and light stress more readily than large coral colonies based on mass transfer theory, which suggests rates of passive diffusion are more rapid for small colonies than for large colonies. Bena and van Woesik (2004) offer still another reason why large coral colonies may suffer more than small colonies during environmental conditions conducive to bleaching: Small Acropora recruits "contain high concentrations of fluorescent proteins (Papina et al., 2002), which have photoprotective properties (Salih et al., 2000)," and "a high concentration of photoprotective pigments in early life, when planulae are near the surface and as newly settled recruits, may facilitate survival during this phase as well as during stress events involving both high irradiance and thermal anomalies (van Woesik, 2000)."

In addition to the adaptive phenomena described above, Earth appears to possess a natural "heat vent" over the tropics that suppresses the intensity of temperature and/or solar radiation to which corals are exposed whenever dangerously high water temperatures are approached. According to Hoegh-Guldberg (1999), 29.2°C is the threshold water temperature above which significant bleaching can be expected to occur in many tropical corals. As Sud et al. (1999) have demonstrated, deep atmospheric convection is typically initiated whenever sea surface temperatures (SSTs) reach a value of about 28°C, so that an upper SST on the order of 30°C is rarely exceeded. As SSTs reach 28–29°C, the cloud-base air mass is charged with sufficient moist static energy for the clouds to reach the upper troposphere. At this point, the billowing cloud cover reduces the amount of solar radiation received at the surface of the sea, while cool and dry downdrafts produced by the moist convection tend to promote ocean surface cooling by increasing sensible and latent heat fluxes at the air-sea interface that cause temperatures there to decline. This "thermostat-like control," as Sud et al. describe it, tends "to ventilate the tropical ocean efficiently and help contain the SST between 28–30°C," which is essentially a fluctuating temperature band of ±1°C centered on the bleaching threshold temperature of 29.2°C identified by Hoegh-Guldberg.

Other intriguing observations indicate a natural phenomenon of this nature. Satheesh and Ramanathan (2000), for example, determined polluted air from south and southeast Asia absorbs enough solar radiation over the northern Indian Ocean during the dry monsoon season to heat the atmosphere there by 1–3°C per day at solar noon, thereby greatly reducing the intensity of solar radiation received at the surface of the sea. Ackerman *et al.* (2000), however, calculated this atmospheric heating would decrease cloud-layer relative humidity and reduce boundary-layer mixing, thereby leading to a 25 to 50% drop in daytime cloud cover relative to that of an aerosol-free atmosphere, which could negate the surface cooling effect suggested by Satheesh and Ramanathan. In a test of this hypothesis based on data obtained from the Extended Edited Cloud Report Archive, Norris (2001) determined daytime low-level ocean cloud cover (which tends to cool the water surface) not only did not decrease from the 1950s to 1990s, it increased, in both the Northern and Southern Hemispheres and at essentially all hours of the day.

Norris remarks, "the observed all-hours increase in low-level cloud cover over the time period when soot aerosol has presumably greatly increased argues against a dominant effect of soot solar absorption contributing to cloud 'burn-off.'" He says "other processes must be compensating," one of which could be the phenomenon Sud *et al* described.

Another process is the "adaptive infrared iris" phenomenon Lindzen *et al.* (2001) described. Working with upper-level cloudiness data from the Japanese Geostationary Meteorological Satellite and SST data from the National Centers for Environmental Prediction, the atmospheric scientists found a strong inverse relationship between upper-level cloud area and the mean SST of cloudy regions, such that the area of cirrus cloud coverage (which tends to warm the planet) normalized by a measure of the area of cumulus coverage (which tends to cool the planet) decreased about 22 percent for each 1°C increase in the SST of the cloudy regions.

"Essentially," the scientists write, "the cloudy-moist region appears to act as an infrared adaptive iris that opens up and closes down the regions free of upper-level clouds, which more effectively permit infrared cooling, in such a manner as to resist changes in tropical surface temperatures." So powerful is this phenomenon, Lindzen *et al.* say they are confident it could "more than cancel all the positive feedbacks in the more sensitive current climate models" routinely used to predict the climatic consequences of projected increases in atmospheric CO_2 concentration.

Is there any real-world evidence the natural thermostat discovered by Sud *et al.* and Lindzen *et al.* has been instrumental in preventing coral bleaching? Mumby *et al.* (2001) examined long-term meteorological records from the vicinity of the Society Islands, which provide what they call "the first empirical evidence that local patterns of cloud cover may influence the susceptibility of reefs to mass bleaching and subsequent coral mortality during periods of anomalously high SST." Regarding the great El Niño of 1998, Mumby and his colleagues determined SSTs in the Society Islands sector of French Polynesia were above the 29.2°C bleaching threshold for a longer period of time (two months) than in all prior bleaching years of the historical record. Mass coral bleaching, which was extensive in certain other areas, was found to be "extremely mild in the Society Islands" and "patchy at a scale of 100s of km."

What provided the coral relief from extreme sun and heat? As Mumby and his associates write, "exceptionally high cloud cover significantly reduced the number of sun hours during the summer of 1998," much as one would have expected Earth's natural thermostat to have done in the face of such anomalously high SSTs. The marine scientists also note extensive spotty patterns of cloud cover, besides saving most of the coral they studied, "may partly account for spatial patchiness in bleaching intensity and/or bleaching-induced mortality in other areas."

Although the natural thermostat cannot protect all of Earth's corals from life-threatening bleaching during all periods of anomalously high SSTs, it apparently protects enough of them enough of the time to ensure sufficiently large numbers of corals survive and grow, since living reefs have persisted over the eons in spite of the continuing recurrence of ever-present environmental threats. That may be how it has always been, although a host of unprecedented anthropogenic forces of site-specific origin might be weakening the abilities of some species to tolerate the thermal and solar stresses they have successfully weathered in the past.

Smith *et al.* (2005) note "photoinhibition of photosynthesis and photodamage to photosystem II of the zooxanthellae, with the consequent increase in the production of damaging reactive oxygen species (ROS), have been implicated as the cause of thermal bleaching (Brown, 1997; Fitt *et al.*, 2001; Lesser, 2004; Tchernov *et al.*, 2004)." They also report the "thermal bleaching of many corals is ultimately the result of the destruction of photosynthetic pigments by ROS," and the production by the zooxanthellae of one particular ROS, hydrogen peroxide, "may be a signal that triggers a response in the host cell to eject the zooxanthellae or shed the host cell from the coral."

These facts resonate with other findings presented in this volume (see Section 7.3, Health Effects of CO_2) and suggest the ongoing rise in the air's CO_2

content may ultimately provide the solution to the worldwide problem of heat-induced coral bleaching. This concept originates from research conducted in the terrestrial realm, which reveals, Ren et al. (2001) write, "elevated CO_2 can enhance the capacity of plants to resist stress-induced oxidative damage."

In the case of ozone pollution, the primary problems occur in the leaf mesophyll, where ozone dissolves into the wet surfaces of exposed cell walls. There, reactions of ozone with water and solutes in the apoplasm lead to the formation of several ROS, including hydrogen peroxide (H_2O_2), hydroperoxide, superoxide, hydroxyl radicals, and singlet oxygen (Foyer et al., 1994; Kangasjarvi et al., 1994; Wohlgemuth et al., 2002), all of which promote oxygen toxicity (Podila et al., 2001).

In a free-air CO_2 enrichment (FACE) study of this phenomenon in aspen and paper birch seedlings exposed to ambient air, ozone-enriched air, CO_2-enriched air, or air enriched with both ozone and CO_2, Oksanen et al. (2003) found H_2O_2 accumulation occurred only "in ozone-exposed leaves and not in the presence of elevated CO_2," adding "CO_2 enrichment appears to alleviate chloroplastic oxidative stress." Similarly, in a study of mature holm and white oak trees that had been growing near natural CO_2 springs in central Italy for 30 to 50 years, Schwanz and Polle (1998) found they exhibited significant reductions in their amounts of lipid peroxidation.

Yu et al. (2004) sought to ascertain whether the ROS-fighting properties of elevated CO_2 might also operate in the aquatic realm. They grew the marine microalgae Platymonas subcordiformis in the laboratory at ambient levels of atmospheric CO_2 and UV-B radiation flux density, and at elevated levels of 5,000 ppm CO_2 and/or UV-B radiation characteristic of what would result from a 25% stratospheric ozone depletion under clear sky conditions in summer. They found the elevated UV-B treatment significantly decreased microalgal dry weight and photosynthetic rate, whereas the elevated CO_2 treatment enhanced dry weight and photosynthetic rate. They also report elevated UV-B significantly increased the production of the toxic superoxide anion and hydrogen peroxide, as well as malonyldialdehyde, which is an end product of lipid peroxidation, whereas elevated CO_2 did just the opposite. In the treatment consisting of both elevated UV-B and elevated CO_2, the concentrations of these three substances were lower than those observed in the elevated UV-B and ambient CO_2 treatment.

Yu et al. say their results suggest "CO_2 enrichment could reduce oxidative stress of reactive oxygen species to P. subcordiformis, and reduce the lipid peroxidation damage of UV-B to P. subcordiformis." They note, "CO_2 enrichment showed a protective effect against the oxidative damage of UV-B-induced stress," and, therefore, elevated CO_2 can enhance "the capacity of stress resistance." They conclude, "algae grown under high CO_2 would better overcome the adverse impact of environmental stress factors that act via generation of activated oxygen species."

Smith et al. (2005) write, "thermal bleaching of many corals is ultimately the result of the destruction of photosynthetic pigments by ROS," and as Oksanen et al. (2003) observe, "CO_2 enrichment appears to alleviate chloroplastic oxidative stress." It is thus clear some as-yet-undefined level of atmospheric CO_2 enrichment could completely counter coral thermal bleaching. In addition, since the presence of hydrogen peroxide, as Smith et al. (2005) write, "may be a signal that triggers a response in the host cell to eject the zooxanthellae or shed the host cell from the coral," and as Yu et al. (2004) write, "CO_2 enrichment could reduce ... lipid peroxidation damage," it readily follows some degree of atmospheric CO_2 enrichment should cause host cells not to eject their zooxanthellae.

References

Ackerman, A.S., Toon, O.B., Stevens, D.E., Heymsfield, A.J., Ramanathan, V., and Welton, E.J. 2000. Reduction of tropical cloudiness by soot. Science 288: 1042–1047.

Bena, C. and van Woesik, R. 2004. The impact of two bleaching events on the survival of small coral colonies (Okinawa, Japan). Bulletin of Marine Science 75: 115–125.

Black, N.A., Voellmy, R., and Szmant, A.M. 1995. Heat shock protein induction in Montastrea faveoluta and Aiptasia pallida exposed to elevated temperature. Biological Bulletin 188: 234–240.

Brown, B.E. 1997. Coral bleaching: causes and consequences. Coral Reefs 16: S129-S138.

Brown, B.E., Le Tissier, M.D.A., and Dunne, R.P. 1994. Tissue retraction in the scleractinian coral Coeloseris mayeri, its effect upon coral pigmentation, and preliminary implications for heat balance. Marine Ecology Progress Series 105: 209–218.

Buddemeier, R.W. and Fautin, D.G. 1993. Coral bleaching as an adaptive mechanism. BioScience 43: 320–326.

Dykens, J.A. and Shick, J.M. 1984. Photobiology of the symbiotic sea anemone Anthopleura elegantissima:

Defense against photo-dynamic effects, and seasonal photoacclimatization. *Biological Bulletin* **167**: 693–697.

Fang, L.-S., Huang, S.-P., and Lin, K.-L. 1997. High temperature induces the synthesis of heat-shock proteins and the elevation of intracellular calcium in the coral *Acropora grandis*. *Coral Reefs* **16**: 127–131.

Fitt, W.K., Brown, B.E., and Warner, M.E., *et al.* 2001. Coral bleaching: interpretation of thermal tolerance limits and thermal thresholds in tropical corals. *Coral Reefs* **20**: 51–65.

Foyer, C., Lelandais, M., and Kunert, K. 1994. Photo-oxidative stress in plants. *Physiologia Plantarum* **92**: 224–230.

Gates, R.D. and Edmunds, P.J. 1999. The physiological mechanisms of acclimatization in tropical reef corals. *American Zoologist* **39**: 30–43.

Hayes, R.L. and King, C.M. 1995. Induction of 70-kD heat shock protein in scleractinian corals by elevated temperature: Significance for coral bleaching. *Molecular Marine Biology and Biotechnology* **4**: 36–42.

Hoegh-Guldberg, O. 1999. Climate change, coral bleaching and the future of the world's coral reefs. *Marine and Freshwater Research* **50**: 839–866.

Hoegh-Guldberg, O. 2004. Coral reefs in a century of rapid environmental change. *Symbiosis* **37**: 1–31.

Hoegh-Guldberg, O. and Jones, R. 1999. Photoinhibition and photoprotection in symbiotic dinoflagellates from reef-building corals. *Marine Ecology Progress Series* **183**: 73–86.

Kangasjarvi, J., Talvinen, J., Utriainen, M., and Karjalainen, R. 1994. Plant defense systems induced by ozone. *Plant, Cell and Environment* **17**: 783–794.

Lesser, M.P. 2004. Experimental biology of coral reef systems. *Journal of Experimental Marine Biology and Ecology* **300**: 217–252.

Lesser, M.P., Stochaj, W.R., Tapley, D.W., and Shick, J.M. 1990. Bleaching in coral reef anthozoans: Effects of irradiance, ultraviolet radiation, and temperature on the activities of protective enzymes against active oxygen. *Coral Reefs* **8**: 225–232.

Lindzen, R.S., Chou, M.-D., and Hou, A.Y. 2001. Does the Earth have an adaptive infrared iris? *Bulletin of the American Meteorological Society* **82**: 417–432.

Matta, J.L. and Trench, R.K. 1991. The enzymatic response of the symbiotic dinoflagellate *Symbiodinium micro-adriaticum* (Freudenthal) to growth under varied oxygen tensions. *Symbiosis* **11**: 31–45.

Mumby, P.J., Chisholm, J.R.M., Edwards, A.J.,

Andrefouet, S., and Jaubert, J. 2001. *Marine Ecology Progress Series* **222**: 209–216.

Nair, S.V., Del Valle, H., Gross, P.S., Terwilliger, D.P., and Smith, L.C. 2005. Macroarray analysis of coelomocyte gene expression in response to LPS in the sea urchin. Identification of unexpected immune diversity in an invertebrate. *Physiological Genomics* **22**: 33–47.

Nakamura, T. and van Woesik, R. 2001. Differential survival of corals during the 1998 bleaching event is partially explained by water-flow rates and passive diffusion. *Marine Ecology Progress Series* **212**: 301–304.

Norris, J.R. 2001. Has northern Indian Ocean cloud cover changed due to increasing anthropogenic aerosol? *Geophysical Research Letters* **28**: 3271–3274.

Oksanen, E., Haikio, E., Sober, J., and Karnosky, D.F. 2003. Ozone-induced H_2O_2 accumulation in field-grown aspen and birch is linked to foliar ultrastructure and peroxisomal activity. *New Phytologist* **161**: 791–799.

Papina, M., Sakihama, Y., Bena, C., van Woesik, R., and Yamasaki, H. 2002. Separation of highly fluorescent proteins by SDS-PAGE in Acroporidae corals. *Comp. Biochem. Phys.* **131**: 767–774.

Podila, G.K., Paolacci, A.R., and Badiani, M. 2001. The impact of greenhouse gases on antioxidants and foliar defense compounds. In: Karnosky, D.F., Ceulemans, R., Scarascia-Mugnozza, G.E., and Innes, J.L. (Eds.) *The Impact of Carbon Dioxide and Other Greenhouse Gases on Forest Ecosystems*. CABI Publishing, Vienna, Austria, pp. 57–125.

Ralph, P.J., Gaddemann, R., Larkum, A.W.E., and Schreiber, U. 1999. In situ underwater measurements of photosynthetic activity of coral-reef dwelling endo-symbionts. *Marine Ecology Progress Series* **180**: 139–147.

Ren, H.X., Chen, X., and Wu, D.X. 2001. Effects of elevated CO_2 on photosynthesis and antioxidative ability of broad bean plants grown under drought condition. *Acta Agronomica Sinica* **27**: 729–736.

Reshef, L., Koren, O., Loya, Y., Zilber-Rosenberg, I., and Rosenberg, E. 2006. The coral probiotic hypothesis. *Environmental Microbiology* **8**: 2068–2073.

Roberts, D.A., Hofman, G.E., and Somero, G.N. 1997. Heat-shock protein expression in *Mytilus californianus*: Acclimatization (seasonal and tidal height comparisons) and acclimation effects. *Biological Bulletin* **192**: 309–320.

Rowan, R. and Knowlton, N. 1995. Intraspecific diversity and ecological zonation in coral-algal symbiosis. *Proceeding of the National Academy of Sciences, U.S.A.* **92**: 2850–2853.

Rowan, R., Knowlton, N., Baker, A., and Jara, J. 1997. Landscape ecology of algal symbionts creates variation in episodes of coral bleaching. *Nature* **388**: 265–269.

Salih, A., Larkum, A., Cox, G., Kuhl, M., and Hoegh-Guldberg, O. 2000. Fluorescent pigments in corals are photoprotective. *Nature* **408**: 850–853.

Satheesh, S.K. and Ramanathan, V. 2000. Large differences in tropical aerosol forcing at the top of the atmosphere and Earth's surface. *Nature* **405**: 60–63.

Schwanz, P. and Polle, A. 1998. Antioxidative systems, pigment and protein contents in leaves of adult mediterranean oak species (*Quercus pubescens* and *Q. ilex*) with lifetime exposure to elevated CO_2. *New Phytologist* **140**: 411–423.

Sharp, V.A., Brown, B.E., and Miller, D. 1997. Heat shock protein (hsp 70) expression in the tropical reef coral *Goniopora djiboutiensis*. *Journal of Thermal Biology* **22**: 11–19.

Shick, J.M., Lesser, M.P., and Jokiel, P.L. 1996. Ultraviolet radiation and coral stress. *Global Change Biology* **2**: 527–545.

Smith, D.J., Suggett, D.J., and Baker, N.R. 2005. Is photoinhibition of zooxanthellae photosynthesis the primary cause of thermal bleaching in corals? *Global Change Biology* **11**: 1–11.

Sud, Y.C., Walker, G.K., and Lau, K.-M. 1999. Mechanisms regulating sea-surface temperatures and deep convection in the tropics. *Geophysical Research Letters* **26**: 1019–1022.

Tchernov, D., Gorbunov, M.Y., and de Vargas, C., *et al.* 2004. Membrane lipids of symbiotic algae are diagnostic of sensitivity to thermal bleaching in corals. *Proceedings of the National Academy of Sciences USA* **101**: 13,531–13,535.

van Woesik, R. 2000. Modelling processes that generate and maintain coral community diversity. *Biodiversity and Conservation* **9**: 1219–1233.

Wohlgemuth, H., Mittelstrass, K., Kschieschan, S., Bender, J., Weigel, H.-J., Overmyer, K., Kangasjarvi, J., Sandermann, H., and Langebartels, C. 2002. Activation of an oxidative burst is a general feature of sensitive plants exposed to the air pollutant ozone. *Plant, Cell and Environment* **25**: 717–726.

Yu, J., Tang, X-X., Zhang, P-Y., Tian, J-Y., and Cai, H-J. 2004. Effects of CO_2 enrichment on photosynthesis, lipid peroxidation and activities of antioxidative enzymes of *Platymonas subcordiformis* subjected to UV-B radiation stress. *Acta Botanica Sinica* **46**: 682–690.

6.1.2.3 Resilience of Corals

The studies reviewed in this section examine observational evidence for the resilience of corals in responding to stress events that routinely occur in nature. The key findings are presented in the bullet points below, followed by an expanded discussion of those findings.

- Corals have been around for a very long time, experiencing climatic conditions that have changed dramatically, from conditions both warmer and colder than the present.

- Many researchers have documented rapid recoveries of corals following recent mass bleaching/mortality events, and such recoveries have occurred on time scales previously assumed to be nearly impossible.

- A growing body of research indicates coral resilience is the rule, not the exception, and these findings are at odds with IPCC's projections of future coral demise.

As illustrated in the preceding section (6.1.2.2 Responses to Temperature-Related Stresses), numerous studies attest to the ability of corals to adapt and evolve in response to temperature-related stresses. Nevertheless, there have been many recorded instances where the severity of coral bleaching from temperature-related stresses was great enough to cause mass mortality of corals, and these occurrences have led IPCC to conclude corals are among the most vulnerable species of marine life, saying it "is *very likely* that coral reef ecosystems will not survive changes in sea temperature beyond an additional increase of 1°C." (p. 35 of Chapter 30. The Ocean, Working Group II, IPCC *Fifth Assessment Report*, dated March 28, 2013).

Corals, however, have been around for a very long time, experiencing climatic conditions that have changed dramatically, from conditions both warmer and colder than the present, suggesting they are much more resilient than IPCC claims.

The earliest coral reefs date to the Palaeozoic Era, more than 450 million years ago (Hill, 1956). The scleractinian corals, the major builders of the reefs of today (Achituv and Dubinsky, 1990), appeared in the mid-Triassic some 240 million years later (Hill, 1956), when Earth was considerably warmer than it is today (Chadwick-Furman, 1996). Although reef-building ceased for a time after the extinctions at the end of the Triassic, the Scleractinia came back during the Jurassic (Newell, 1971; Veron, 1995) and continued to exhibit great robustness throughout the Cretaceous, even when temperatures were as much as 8–15°C higher (Chadwick-Furman, 1996; Veizer *et al.*, 1999), and atmospheric CO_2 concentrations two to seven times higher (Berner and Kothavala, 2001), than they are today.

At the end of the Cretaceous, 70% of the genera and one-third of the families of scleractinian corals disappeared (Veron, 1995) in the greatest biospheric extinction event in geological history, which may have been caused by a large asteroid impact (Alvarez *et al.*, 1980; 1984). They developed again, however, throughout the Cenozoic, particularly during the Oligocene and Miocene (Chadwick-Furman, 1996). Throughout the past two million years of the Pleistocene, they survived at least 17 glacial-interglacial cycles of dramatic climate change and sea-level fluctuation, successfully adapting, over and over again, to these enormous environmental challenges (Pandolfi, 1999). According to Benzie (1999), this evidence suggests "coral reef communities are relatively resilient, have survived previous global climate change, and appear likely to survive future changes."

Such resilience helps explain why many researchers have documented rapid recoveries of corals following recent mass bleaching/mortality events, on time scales previously assumed to be nearly impossible. As more research is conducted on this topic, it appears coral resilience is the rule, not the exception. These findings are vastly at odds with IPCC's projections of future coral demise.

An early example of such resilience was observed after the widespread bleaching of corals in the Indian and Pacific Oceans during the peak warmth of the 1998 El Niño, the deadly effects of which were described at the time as the most extensive ever seen. Many of the devastated corals were not expected to recover (Normile, 2000). But barely a year later many of the reefs were in fact recovering, with large amounts of new coral found in what had been made to look like "graveyards" by the prior year's marine heat wave. Normile quotes Terry Done of the Institute of Marine Science in Cape Ferguson as saying these real-world observations forced many people to admit coral reefs are indeed "more resilient than we had thought." Since that admission, many more studies have illustrated similar recoveries as scientists have investigated and tracked coral recoveries.

Kayanne *et al.* (2002) assessed coral cover within the reef flat of Shiraho Reef, Ishigaki Island (situated at the southernmost end of the Ryukyus Islands of Japan) just before, during, and six times after an unprecedented bleaching event that began in early July 1998 and ended in early October of that year. They note "massive *Porites* were susceptible to bleaching, but regained their algae after the bleaching and sustained their coverage." Branching *Porites*, *Montipora,* and *Acropora* corals experienced significant mortality of 41.1%, 55.4%, and 82.4%, respectively, and approximately two-thirds of the surviving corals were completely or partly bleached. Nevertheless, coverage of large patches of the branching *Montipora* coral, initially reduced by 66%, recovered to pre-bleaching levels after two years.

Kayanne *et al.* note "the recovery of corals to their pre-bleaching levels has been inferred to take from 10 to 30 years for damaged coral populations and from 5 to 10 years for bleached corals that do not die (Hoegh-Guldberg, 1999; Wilkinson *et al.*, 1999)." Shiraho Reef, they report, "is recovering at an unexpectedly fast rate." The authors conclude, "even susceptible species have a high potential to regain zooxanthellae after bleaching or to recover after mortality."

Adjeroud *et al.* (2005) initiated a monitoring program on 13 islands (eight atolls and five high volcanic islands) in four of the five archipelagoes of French Polynesia, to document the effects of natural perturbations on coral assemblages. For the period covered by their report (1992–2002), these reefs were subjected to three major coral bleaching events (1994, 1998, 2002) and three cyclones (1997), and before this period the sites had experienced an additional seven bleaching events and 15 cyclones as well as several *Acanthaster planci* outbreaks.

They found the impacts of the bleaching events varied among the different study locations. They observed three temporal trends: "(1) ten sites where coral cover decreased in relation to the occurrence of major disturbances; (2) nine sites where coral cover increased, despite the occurrence of disturbances affecting seven of them; and (3) a site where no significant variation in coral cover was found." They report, "an interannual survey of reef communities at Tiahura, Moorea, showed that the mortality of coral colonies following a bleaching event was decreasing with successive events, even if the latter have the same intensity (Adjeroud *et al.*, 2002)."

The seven French scientists say the "spatial and temporal variability of the impacts observed at several scales during the present and previous surveys may reflect an acclimation and/or adaptation of local populations," and "coral colonies and/or their endosymbiotic zooxanthellae may be phenotypically (acclimation) and possibly genotypically (adaptation) resistant to bleaching events," citing Rowan *et al.* (1997), Hoegh-Guldberg (1999), Kinzie *et al.* (2001), and Coles and Brown (2003) in support of this conclusion.

Pratchett *et al.* (2013) developed a history of variations in coral bleaching among four key genera of reef-building corals (*Acropora, Montipora, Pocillopora,* and *Porites*) in Moorea, focusing on four mass-bleaching events that occurred there in 1991, 1994, 2002, and 2007. They documented the history of the bleaching susceptibility of each of the four coral genera in each of the four events, finding "*Acropora* and *Montipora* consistently bleached in far greater proportions than *Pocillopora* and *Porites*." They also found "an apparent and sustained decline in the proportion of colonies that bleached during successive bleaching events, especially for *Acropora* and Montipora." In 2007, for example, only 77% of *Acropora* colonies bleached compared with 98% in 1991. They acknowledge "temporal variation in the proportion of coral colonies bleached may be attributable to differences in environmental conditions among years" but also state, "alternately, the sustained declines in bleaching incidence among highly susceptible corals may be indicative of acclimation or adaptation." Pratchett *et al.* suggest it may be "that gradual removal of highly susceptible genotypes (through selective mortality of individuals, populations, and/or species) is producing a coral assemblage that is more resistant to sustained and ongoing ocean warming," which further suggests "there is some capacity for adaptation, which will delay devastating effects of global climate change."

Golbuu *et al.* (2007) examined recovery rates of coral communities on the Palauan reef complex of Micronesia (7°30'N, 134°30'E) at two depths (3 and 10 m) at several sites (nine outer-reef wave-exposed sites, four on the east coast and five on the west coast; two patch reef sites; and two sheltered-bay sites) three, four, and seven years after the 1998 El Niño-Southern Oscillation (ENSO)-induced bleaching event. The nine researchers report, "coral populations recovered rapidly on the reefs of Palau," but "recovery trajectories changed over time and were habitat and depth-dependent," noting "seven years after the bleaching event, some reefs supported >30% coral cover, and some habitats supported >40% coral cover." They observe "recovery within the bays at 3 m was mostly a consequence of growth of remnant (surviving) coral colonies, while recovery on the exposed slopes was mostly likely a consequence of

both remnant regrowth and sexual recruitment events at 10 m, and more a consequence of recruitment at 3 m."

Guzman and Cortes (2007) studied coral reefs of the eastern Pacific Ocean that "suffered unprecedented mass mortality at a regional scale as a consequence of the anomalous sea warming during the 1982–1983 El Niño." At Cocos Island (5°32'N, 87°04'W), they found in a survey of three representative reefs, which they conducted in 1987, the remaining live coral cover was only 3% what it had been before the great El Niño four years earlier (Guzman and Cortes, 1992). Based on this finding and the similar observations of other scientists at other reefs, they predicted "the recovery of the reefs' framework would take centuries, and recovery of live coral cover, decades."

In 2002, nearly 20 years after the disastrous coral-killing warming, they returned to see how accurate their prediction had been, quantifying "the live coral cover and species composition of five reefs, including the three previously assessed in 1987." The two researchers report overall mean live coral cover increased nearly fivefold, from 2.99% in 1987 to 14.87% in 2002, at the three sites studied during both periods, and the mean live coral cover of all five sites studied in 2002 was 22.7%. They found "most new recruits and adults belonged to the main reef building species from pre–1982 ENSO, *Porites lobata*, suggesting that a disturbance as outstanding as El Niño was not sufficient to change the role or composition of the dominant species."

The 1998 El Niño-induced bleaching episode severely affected most Indian Ocean reefs, with the Maldives suffering 90% coral mortality in their central atolls. Before this mass mortality, Lasagna *et al.* (2008) write, "hard coral cover was generally between 30 and 60%, often reaching 100% in shallow water." One year later, they report, "coral cover had decreased to less than 8%, and reefs were dominated by algae."

In April 2006, Lasagna *et al.* "re-examined the status of the Maldivian reefs, focusing on their benthic composition to evaluate the possible change in dominance from hard corals to non-constructional organisms such as soft corals, algae or sponges," which have been predicted to replace hard corals after major bleaching episodes. The seven Italian scientists report, "eight years after the 1998 coral mass mortality, hard coral cover varied from 12% to 37%," and "cover of soft corals, algae and sponges was comparatively low (approximately 7% on average)." They say "a recent inventory of coral species showed that their number is larger than that known before 1998 (Pichon and Benzoni, 2007)."

McClanahan *et al.* (2009) conducted surveys of coral reefs in northern Tanzania "in 2004/5 with the aim of comparing them over an ~8-year period during a time of increased efforts at fisheries management and the 1998 El Niño Southern Oscillation (ENSO) and Indian Ocean Dipole coral mortality event that caused 45% mortality in northern Tanzania and much of the Indian Ocean." The Kenyan, Swedish, Tanzanian, and U.S. researchers report their repeated surveys "indicate general stability of these reefs over time," and "in the context of the high bleaching and mortality of western Indian Ocean reefs after 1998 (Goreau *et al.*, 2000; McClanahan *et al.*, 2007), the general stability and improvement of these reefs six to seven years after the largest ENSO in recent history (McPhaden, 1999) indicates reefs with considerable resilience to climate change."

Because "all reefs exhibited some resilience and ecological stability and even improvements during this time of climate and management change," McClanahan *et al.* conclude this observation "creates considerably more optimism for poor countries, such as Tanzania, to effectively manage their reefs in an environment of climate change." They conclude, "Tanzanian and possibly many other reefs that exhibit similar environmental conditions have the ability to recover from large-scale climatic and human disturbances."

Scopelitis *et al.* (2009) sought to determine the responses of corals of Saint-Leu Reef on la Reunion (a mountainous volcanic island of the Mascarene Archipelago in the Southwest Indian Ocean) to major devastating events that occurred there over the prior 35 years (between 1973 and 2007), including a category 5 cyclone (Firinga, of 29 January 1989). These events "caused 99% coral cover loss (Naim *et al.*, 1997)." A severe coral bleaching event in March 2002 followed on the heels of cyclone Dina of January 2002, and other bleaching episodes occurred in 1983, March–April 1987, and February 2003.

Scopelitis *et al.* studied vertical images of the reef provided by five aerial photographs taken in 1973, 1978, 1989, 1997, and 2003, along with two Quickbird satellite images taken in 2002 and 2006, as well as periodic quantitative *in situ* observations of parts of the reef-top that could be used to document ecological and substratum characteristics that produce the color and texture observable in the photos and satellite images. From these observations they constructed a history of changes in the reef's coral community over a period of 35 years (1973–2007).

"Despite the multiple disturbance events," the six scientists write, "the coral community distribution and composition in 2006 on Saint-Leu Reef did not display major differences compared to 1973." This pattern of recurrent recovery is truly remarkable, especially since "in the wake of cyclone Firinga, Saint-Leu Reef phase-shifted and became algae-dominated for a period of five years," and even more impressive given that no corals had survived an unnamed cyclone of 27 January 1948. Such findings, the Australian and French researchers write, indicate "a high degree of coral resilience at the site, led by rapid recovery of compact branching corals."

According to Crabbe (2009), "coral reefs throughout the world are under severe challenges from a variety of environmental factors including overfishing, destructive fishing practices, coral bleaching, ocean acidification, sea-level rise, algal blooms, agricultural run-off, coastal and resort development, marine pollution, increasing coral diseases, invasive species, and hurricane/cyclone damage."

Crabbe employed a number of tools to analyze the resilience of the fringing reefs around Discovery Bay, Jamaica, documenting the responses of their populations "to a number of environmental stressors, in particular hurricanes and the mass bleaching event of 2005," which he describes as "by far the major acute influence on the reef sites." The UK researcher reports "there was a reduction in numbers of colonies in the smallest size class for all the species at all the sites in 2006, after the mass bleaching of 2005, with subsequent increases for all species at all sites in 2007 and 2008." At Dairy Bull Reef, he notes, "live coral cover increased from 13 ± 5% in 2006 to 20 ± 9% in 2007 and 31 ± 7% in 2008," and "live *Acropora* species increased from 2 ± 2% in 2006 to 10 ± 4% in 2007 and 22 ± 7% in 2008."

The UK researcher concludes his results "indicate good levels of coral resilience on the fringing reefs around Discovery Bay in Jamaica," even after having "suffered from long term human-induced chronic stressors, such as overfishing and land development," along with "die-off of the long-spined sea urchin" and "coral disease." Crabbe states he and a colleague "found a variety of clades of zooxanthellae, including clade C, in corals at Dairy Bull Reef (Crabbe and Carlin, 2007)," and "the potential for symbiont shuffling, as we have found in 111 colonies of *Acropora* species from the Ningaloo Reef, Australia (Crabbe and Carlin, 2009), may be a factor in their recovery," citing Stat *et al.* (2008).

In early 2006, mass bleaching of corals on

inshore reefs of the Keppel Islands in the southern Great Barrier Reef (GBR) caused high coral mortality, with severe bleaching affecting 77–95% of coral colonies (Weeks *et al.*, 2008; Jones *et al.*, 2008). This event, Diaz-Pulido *et al.* (2009) write, was followed by "an extraordinary bloom of the brown seaweed *Lobophora variegata*," which was "unprecedented in magnitude on the GBR" and "exacerbated coral mortality by overgrowing stressed coral tissue." After the natural seasonal decline in *L. variegata*, which in some places had increased its cover by 200–300% by August 2006, "the cover of branching *Acropora* corals at most sites showed an extremely rapid recovery," the Australian researchers write, "reaching pre-bleaching levels by December 2006–April 2007 ca 12–14 months after the onset of bleaching."

"Unexpectedly," as they describe it, "this rapid reversal did not involve reestablishment of corals by recruitment of coral larvae, as often assumed, but depended on several ecological mechanisms previously underestimated." Most interesting in this regard was "the 'phoenix effect' in which apparently dead coral branches regenerate live tissue (Krupp *et al.*, 1993; Jokiel *et al.*, 1993; Riegl and Piller, 2001)." This "remnant surviving coral tissue," Diaz-Pulido *et al.* continue, "rapidly expanded upwards along the dead coral branches and actively overgrew *L. variegata*, as well as a range of other algal types, including filamentous algal turfs, fleshy seaweeds and crustose coralline algae," resulting in "a 'seaweed sandwich' with algae engulfed between new and old layers of [coral] skeleton."

Noting reefs of the Keppel Islands "have shown rapid recovery of coral dominance, despite repeated coral bleaching events (1998, 2002, and 2006), severe flood plumes (e.g. 1991, 2008), and dense algal overgrowth," Diaz-Pulido *et al.* conclude these and other reefs that are "able to rapidly recover abundant corals may serve as key refugia, or sources of larvae for reef recovery at broader scales," and the phenomena they document in their research "may well be critical to the overall resilience and persistence of coral reef ecosystems globally."

Bruno *et al.* (2009) recognized additional resilience of corals against algal growth that often ensues after a bleaching event, noting one of the great concerns of marine scientists is "coral reefs are moving toward or are locked into a seaweed-dominated state." Bruno *et al.* "analyzed 3,581 quantitative surveys of 1,851 reefs performed between 1996 and 2006 to determine the frequency, geographical extent, and degree of macroalgal dominance of coral reefs and of coral to macroalgal phase shifts around the world."

The five marine researchers found "the replacement of corals by macroalgae as the dominant benthic functional group is less common and less geographically extensive than assumed," noting "only 4% of reefs were dominated by macroalgae (i.e., >50% cover)." Across the Indo-Pacific, where regional averages of macroalgal cover were 9–12%, they found "macroalgae only dominated 1% of the surveyed reefs." In addition, "between 1996 and 2006, phase shift severity decreased in the Caribbean, did not change in the Florida Keys and Indo-Pacific, and increased slightly on the Great Barrier Reef."

Bruno *et al.* state "coral reef ecosystems appear to be more resistant to macroalgal blooms than assumed," and "the mismatch between descriptions of reef degradation in the literature and patterns in nature was caused by the generalization of a relatively small number of examples." They conclude their analysis suggests "the macroalgae problem has been exaggerated," and "overall," there has been "no general recent trend (i.e., post–1995) toward macroalgal dominance." They write, "macroalgal cover may currently be close to the historical baseline across most of the world."

Zapata *et al.* (2010) developed an extended history from data they obtained over the period 1998–2004 from 20 permanent transects at two sites on one of the largest and best developed coral reefs in the Colombian Pacific (La Azufrada reef on Gorgona Island), plus data obtained there even earlier by others. The four Colombian researchers report comparisons with previous studies showed the reef at La Azufrada returned to "pre-disturbance (1979) levels of coral cover within a 10-year period after the 1982–83 El Niño, which caused 85% mortality," and subsequently, "the effects of the 1997–98 El Niño, indicated by the difference in overall live coral cover between 1998 and 1999, were minor (<6% reduction)." They report "despite recurrent natural disturbances, live coral cover in 2004 was as high as that existing before 1982 at La Azufrada." Zapata *et al.* conclude "the recent history of La Azufrada reef since coral reef studies began at Gorgona Island three decades ago (Prahl *et al.*, 1979; Glynn *et al.*, 1982) suggests a remarkable ability of this reef to recover from past perturbations," which are of the type (extreme El Niño-driven temperature increases leading to coral bleaching) IPCC claims should be especially deadly and from which coral recovery should not be expected.

According to van Woesik *et al.* (2011), "over the

past three decades, thermal stress events have damaged corals globally," but few studies "have tracked the recovery process or assessed whether winners in the short term are also winners in the long term." They repeatedly evaluated (1997, 1999, 2000, 2001, 2004, 2007, 2010) a coral assemblage on the southeastern reef of Sesoko Island at the Tropical Biosphere Research Center of the University of the Ryukyus, Okinawa, Japan (26°38'N, 127°52'E), which experienced significant thermal stress events in 1998 and 2001.

The four researchers report, "by 2007, species richness had recovered to ~13 species per m², which was similar to species richness in 1997," and "hard coral cover increased from 3% in 2001 to 47% in 2010." They also found "species composition had undergone change," as "some species were thermally tolerant and increased in relative abundance through time," some "increased in relative abundance through the thermal stress and remained constant thereafter," and some "were neither winners nor losers through time."

Van Woesik *et al.* conclude the ecosystem they studied was "able to absorb the thermal stressors without undergoing change to a less desirable state," citing the similar findings of Holling (1973) and Scheffer and Carpenter (2003). They note "*Acropora* populations had fully recovered seven years after an extreme thermal-stress event in Palau (Golbuu *et al.*, 2007)," and in the Arabian Gulf, "Riegl and Purkis (2009) showed that *Acropora* assemblages could recover from thermal-stress cycles occurring every fifteen years."

Marimuthu *et al.* (2013) investigated the recovery of the corals in the Andaman and Nicobar Islands in the eastern part of the Bay of Bengal following a significant warming event in summer 2010. At the time, sea surface temperatures (SSTs) rose to about 34°C, resulting in the bleaching of 74 to 77% of the corals surrounding Havelock Island and Port Blair Bay, respectively. Marimuthu *et al.* utilized pre-bleaching population data obtained by the line intercept transect (LIT) method of English *et al.* (1997) in July 2010, along with post-bleaching data they collected in January 2011 for the most severely affected corals, which included *Acropora cerealis, A. humilis, Montipora* sp., *Favia pallida, Diploastrea* sp., *Goniopora* sp., *Fungia concinna, Gardinero-series* sp., *Porites* sp., *Favites abdita,* and *Lobophyllia robusta*. They found "the observed post bleaching recovery [January 2011] of coral cover was 21.1% at Port Blair Bay and 13.29% at Havelock Island," and "once the sea water temperature resumed

back to the normal condition, most of the corals where found recovered."

Gilmour *et al.* (2013) note, "coral reef recovery from major disturbance is hypothesized to depend on the arrival of propagules from nearby undisturbed reefs," and, therefore, "reefs isolated by distance or current patterns are thought to be highly vulnerable to catastrophic disturbance." In a test of this hypothesis, Gilmour *et al.* set out to "document the recovery of coral assemblages at Australia's largest oceanic reef system, where changes in assemblage structure and key demographic parameters were quantified for 16 years, through a regime of disturbances beginning with a catastrophic mass bleaching event in 1998." The authors focused on "the Scott system of reefs, which is surrounded by oceanic waters on the edge of Western Australia's continental shelf" and is "more than 250 km from the mainland and other reefs in the region, and more than 1000 km from a major center of urbanization."

The five Australian researchers report finding "for 6 years, recruitment rates were <6% of those prior to the disturbance," and "on the basis of these rates of change," they say "recovery was projected to take decades." Within just 12 years, "coral cover, recruitment, generic diversity, and community structure were again similar to the pre-bleaching years." The coral recovery "may have been even faster if not for a series of more moderate disturbances, including two cyclones, an outbreak of disease, and a second bleaching."

Gilmour *et al.* say their results demonstrate "even corals with a negligible supply of larvae from outside can recover relatively quickly from disturbances in the absence of chronic human pressures." They suggest "addressing local pressures, such as pollution and overfishing, is as important to the recovery of coral reefs as the establishment of networks of marine protected areas." They conclude, "managing local pressures to promote resilience will be critical to preventing the global degradation of coral reefs," which is true of several other damaging phenomena, many of which have particular application to Australia's Great Barrier Reef. These include rising nutrient levels caused by runoff from agricultural activity on land; outbreaks of the coral-devouring crown-of-thorns starfish; the barbed hooks and scything nets used in fishing; tourists and the developers who build resorts and marinas for them; increased sediment levels; the nets of prawn trawlers stirring up the growing load of sediments; the 6–10 tons of "bycatch" for each ton of prawns netted that are caught and die, which dramatically changes the composition of reef life; sea life depleted to the point of exhaustion by over-fishing; huge catamarans and dive boats that take thousands of visitors to the Barrier Reef each day and dump their sewage in the sea on the way home; the live reef-fish trade; fishermen using dynamite and cyanide; coral diseases; and pollution.

Mondal *et al.* (2013) studied the fringing reefs off Little Andaman Island at the juncture of the Bay of Bengal and the Andaman Sea. A number of such reefs were essentially destroyed when a 2004 tsunami swept across them with devastating consequences. Five years later in 2009, however, 34 species of scleractinian corals had reappeared (Sawall *et al.*, 2010). But the next year brought a massive bleaching event caused by a dramatic increase in sea surface temperatures above their normal average ranges (Mondal and Raghunathan, 2011), after which Mondal *et al.* (2013) found "the bleached corals were transformed mostly into dead ones."

In February 2012 the three Indian researchers dove to depths of up to 35 meters to identify and record what species of scleractinian corals they encountered at three locations around Little Andaman Island. They employed the line intercept transect method (Bradbury *et al.*, 1886) with a series of 20-meter transects randomly placed at intervals of 10 meters, with three replicates of the procedure carried out at depths of 5, 10, 15, 20, 25, 30, and 35 meters. They discovered 124 species of youthful scleractinian corals, 90 more than the 34 species detected by Sawall *et al.* in 2009. Mondal *et al.* report the minimum value of the Shannon-Weaver Diversity Index was 5.09, which they state "is above the optimum hypothetical value," whereas the minimum value of Simpson's Density Index was 0.94, which they report "is very near to the maximum value which is most advantageous."

In light of these observations and because "bleaching was the only physiological process which happened in between 2009 and 2012," Mondal *et al.* conclude "bleaching is a prime regulator for the settlement of new recruitment of scleractinian corals which leads to diversified reef area," further noting "the adaptive features of bleaching can be seen as a mechanism that enables the exchange of symbionts in a better fit of the holobiont to a changed environment," citing Graham *et al.* (2011).

According to Miranda *et al.* (2013), sub-lethal bleaching effects "occur when corals do not experience mortality after bleaching, but rather undergo a temporary loss of zooxanthellae and/or of their photosynthetic pigments, with later recovery." This implies, they write, "corals have an adaptive capacity or resistance to seasonal changes in environmental conditions," as suggested by Buddemeir and Fautin (1993), Hennige *et al.* (2010), and Hughes *et al.* (2011).

The three Brazilian researchers note "thermal anomalies on the Brazilian coast have been monitored by NOAA satellite imaging since 1998." They also observe, "there have been many reports of bleaching events occurring in association with ocean warming events," but "only Dutra *et al.* (2000) reported observations of the reefs after the occurrence of the beaching phenomenon." They studied the effects of bleaching in the corals of Caramuanas reef—comprised of three main flat reef banks (13°07'S, 38°43'W; 13°07'S, 38°44'W; 13°08'S, 38°44'W)—by comparing them during and immediately after the thermal anomalies related to the ENSO event of 2010 in terms of "frequency and severity of bleaching, live coral cover, number of colonies, class size, disease occurrence and mortality rate," based on samples taken at 12 fixed transects in three reef locations.

Miranda *et al.* found, "after this bleaching event, neither the rate of mortality nor the number of colonies with disease increased; the size class structure of the most abundant species did not vary; and the number of live colonies and live coral cover also remained the same." They report, "the reef showed certain resilience to the perturbations caused by the 2010 ENSO event." In further support of their findings, they write, "the sub-lethal effects of bleaching in Brazilian corals have been observed previously," noting, "in 1998, the northern littoral of Bahia experienced a bleaching event that affected up to 60% of the coral community, which after one year have completely recovered," as reported by Dutra *et al.* (2000).

Miranda *et al.* point out, "the Brazilian zooxanthellate coral fauna is characterized by endemic species, with some reminiscent of a Tertiary coral fauna that may be adapted to these inhospitable environment conditions," citing Leao *et al.* (2003). They cite as some examples various species of the genus *Mussismilia*, as these species had "the lowest percent of bleached colonies," adding, "those that bleached completely recovered during this investigation." With respect to potential policy implications of their findings, the Brazilian biologists suggest "eliminating or reducing anthropogenic effects on this reef may increase its resistance and resilience to bleaching, allowing its maintenance," so "the Caramuanas reef could then act as a reserve of species and genes for this geographic region."

Earth's corals likely will be able to cope with any further increases in water temperatures, anthropogenic or natural. Corals have survived such warmth and worse many times in the past, including the Medieval Warm Period, Roman Warm Period, and Holocene Optimum, as well as numerous times during prior interglacial periods. There is no reason to think they cannot do so again if the need arises.

References

Achituv, Y. and Dubinsky, Z. 1990. Evolution and zoogeography of coral reefs. Dubinsky, Z. (Ed.) *Ecosystems of the world: Coral reefs*. Elsevier, New York, NY.

Adjeroud, M., Augustin, D., Galzin, R., and Salvat, B. 2002. Natural disturbances and interannual variability of coral reef communities on the outer slope of Tiahura (Moorea, French Polynesia): 1991 to 1997. *Marine Ecology Progress Series* **237**: 121–131.

Adjeroud, M., Chancerelle, Y., Schrimm, M., Perez, T., Lecchini, D., Galzin, R., and Salvat, B. 2005. Detecting the effects of natural disturbances on coral assemblages in French Polynesia: A decade survey at multiple scales. *Aquatic Living Resources* **18**: 111–123.

Alvarez, L.W., Alvarez, W., Asaro, F., and Michel, H.V. 1980. Extraterrestrial cause for the Cretaceous-Tertiary extinction. *Science* **208**: 1095–1108.

Alvarez, W., Alvarez, L.W., Asaro, F., and Michel, H.V. 1984. The end of the Cretaceous: Sharp boundary or gradual transition? *Science* **223**: 1183–1186.

Benzie, J.A.H. 1999. Genetic structure of coral reef organisms: Ghosts of dispersal past. *American Zoologist* **39**: 131–145.

Berner, R.A. and Kothavala, Z. 2001. GEOCARB III: A revised model of atmospheric CO_2 over phanerozoic time. *American Journal of Science* **301**: 182–204.

Bradbury, R.H., Reichelt, R.E., Meyer, D.L., and Birtles, R.A. 1886. Patterns in the distribution of crinoid community at Davies Reef on the central Great Barrier Reef. *Coral Reefs* **5**: 189–196.

Bruno, J.F., Sweatman, H., Precht, W.F., Selig, E.R., and Schutte, V.G.W. 2009. Assessing evidence of phase shifts from coral to macroalgal dominance on coral reefs. *Ecology* **90**: 1478–1484.

Buddemeier, R.W. and Fautin, D.G. 1993. Coral bleaching as an adaptive mechanism. *Bioscience* **43**: 320–326.

Chadwick-Furman, N.E. 1996. Reef coral diversity and global change. *Global Change Biology* **2**: 559–568.

Coles, S.L. and Brown, B.E. 2003. Coral bleaching-capacity for acclimatization and adaptation. *Advances in Marine Biology* **46**: 183–223.

Crabbe, M.J.C. 2009. Scleractinian coral population size structures and growth rates indicate coral resilience on the fringing reefs of North Jamaica. *Marine Environmental Research* **67**: 189–198.

Crabbe, M.J.C. and Carlin, J.P. 2007. Industrial sedimentation lowers coral growth rates in a turbid lagoon environment, Discovery Bay, Jamaica. *International Journal of Integrative Biology* **1**: 37–40.

Crabbe, M.J.C. and Carlin, J.P. 2009. Multiple Symbiodinium clades in *Acropora* species scleractinian corals from the Ninagloo reef, Australia. *International Journal of Integrative Biology* **5**: 72–74.

Diaz-Pulido, G., McCook, L.J., Dove, S., Berkelmans, R., Roff, G., Kline, D.I., Weeks, S., Evans, R.D., Williamson, D.H., and Hoegh-Guldberg, O. 2009. Doom and boom on a resilient reef: Climate change, algal overgrowth and coral recovery. *PLoS ONE* **4**: e5239.

Dutra, L.X.C., Kikuchi, R.K.P., and Leao, Z.M.A.N. 2000. Thirteen months monitoring coral bleaching on Bahia's north coast, Brazil. *Proceedings of the International Coral Reef Symposium*. Indonesian Institute of Sciences, Bali, p. 373.

English, S., Wilkinson, C., and Baker, V. 1997. *Survey Manual for Tropical Marine Resources*. Australian Institute of Marine Sciences, Townsville, Australia.

Gilmour, J.P., Smith, L.D., Heyward, A.J., Baird, A.H., and Pratchett, M.S. 2013. Recovery of an isolated coral reef system following severe disturbance. *Science* **340**: 69–71.

Glynn, P.W., von Prahl, H., and Gunl, F. 1982. Coral reef of Gorgona island, Colombia, with special reference to corallivores and the influence on community structural reef development. *Anales del Instituto de Investigaciones Marinas de Punta Betín* **12**: 185–214.

Golbuu, Y., Victor, S., Penland, L., Idip Jr., D., Emaurois, C., Okaji, K., Yukihira, H., Iwase, A., and van Woesik, R. 2007. Palau's coral reefs show differential habitat recovery following the 1998-bleachng event. *Coral Reefs* **26**: 319–332.

Goreau, T., McClanahan, T., Hayes, R., and Strong, A. 2000. Conservation of coral reefs after the 1998 global bleaching event. *Conservation Biology* **14**: 5–15.

Graham, N.A.J., Nash, K.L., and Kool, J.T. 2011. Coral reef recovery dynamics in a changing world. *Coral Reefs* **30**: 283–294.

Guzman, H.M. and Cortes, J. 1992. Cocos Island (Pacific of Costa Rica) coral reefs after the 1982–83 El Niño disturbance. *Revista de Biologia Tropical* **40**: 309–324.

Guzman, H.M. and Cortes, J. 2007. Reef recovery 20 years after the 1982–1983 El Niño massive mortality. *Marine Biology* **151**: 401–411.

Hennige, S.J., Smith, D.J., Walsh, S., Mcginley, M.P., Warner, M.E., and Suggett, D.J. 2010. Acclimation and adaptation of scleractinian coral communities along environmental gradients within an Indonesian reef system. *Journal of Experimental Marine Biology and Ecology* **391**: 143–152.

Hill, D. Rugosa and Moore, R.D. (Eds.) 1956. *Treatise on invertebrate paleontology*, Volume F, Coelenterata. Lawrence, KS: Geological Society of America/University of Kansas Press, pp. 233–323.

Hoegh-Guldberg, O. 1999. Climate change, coral bleaching and the future of the world's coral reefs. *Marine and Freshwater Research* **50**: 839–866.

Holling, C.S. 1973. Resilience and stability of ecological systems. *Annual Review of Ecology and Systematics* **4**: 1–23.

Hughes, T.P., Baird, A.H., Bellwood, M., Card, S.R., Connolly, C., Folke, R., Grosberg, O., Hoegh-Guldberg, J., Jackson, B.C., Kleypas, J., Lough, J.M., Marshall, P., Nystrom, M., Palumbi, S.R., Pandolfi, J.M., Rosen, B., and Roughgarden, J. 2011. Climate change, human impacts, and the resilience of coral reefs. *Science* **301**: 929–933.

Jokiel, P.I., Hunter, C.I., Taguchi, S., and Watarai, I. 1993. Ecological impact of a freshwater "reef kill" in Kaneohe Bay, Oahu, Hawaii. *Coral Reefs* **12**: 177–184.

Jones, A.M., Berkelmans, R., van Oppen, M.J.H., Mieog, J.C., and Sinclair, W. 2008. A community shift in the symbionts of a scleractinian coral following a natural bleaching event: field evidence of acclimatization. *Proceedings of the Royal Society of London, Series B* **275**: 1359–1365.

Kayanne, H., Harii, S., Ide, Y., and Akimoto, F. 2002. Recovery of coral populations after the 1998 bleaching on Shiraho Reef, in the southern Ryukyus, NW Pacific. *Marine Ecology Progress Series* **239**: 93–103.

Kinzie III, R.A., Takayama, M., Santos, S.C., and Coffroth, M.A. 2001. The adaptive bleaching hypothesis: Experimental tests of critical assumptions. *Biological Bulletin* **200**: 51–58.

Krupp, D.A., Jokiel, P.I., and Chartrand, T.S. 1993. Asexual reproduction by the solitary scleractinian coral *Fungia scutaria* on dead parent corolla in Kaneohe Bay, Oahu, Hawaiian Islands. *Proceedings of the Seventh International Coral Reef Symposium* **1**: 527–534.

Lasagna, R., Albertelli, G., Giovannetti, E., Grondona, M., Milani, A., Morri, C., and Bianchi, C.N. 2008. Status of Maldivian reefs eight years after the 1998 coral mass mortality. *Chemistry and Ecology* **24**: 67–72.

Leao, Z.M.A.N., Kikuchi, R.K.P., and Testa, V. 2003. Corals and coral reefs of Brazil. In: Cortes, J. (Ed.) *Latin America Coral Reefs*. Elsevier, Amsterdam, The Netherlands, pp. 9–52.

Marimuthu, N., Wilson, J.J., Vinithkumar, N.V., and Kirubagaran, R. 2013. Coral reef recovery in South Andaman Islands after the bleaching event 2010. *Journal of Ocean University of China (Oceanic and Coastal Sea Research)* **12**: 91–96.

McClanahan, T.R., Ateweberhan, M., Sebastian, C.R., Graham, N.A.J., Wilson, S.K., Bruggemann, H., and Guillaume, M. 2007. Western Indian Ocean coral communities, bleaching responses, and susceptibility to extinction. *Marine Ecology Progress Series* **337**: 1–13.

McClanahan, T.R., Muthiga, N.A., Maina, J., Kamukuru, A.T., and Yahya, S.A.S. 2009. Changes in northern Tanzania coral reefs during a period of increased fisheries management and climatic disturbance. *Aquatic Conservation: Marine and Freshwater Ecosystems* **19**: 758–771.

McPhaden, M.J. 1999. Genesis and evolution of the 1997–98 El Niño. *Science* **283**: 950–954.

Miranda, R.J., Cruz, I.C.S., and Leao, Z.M.A.N. 2013. Coral bleaching in the Caramuanas reef (Todos os Santos Bay, Brazil) during the 2010 El Niño event. *Latin American Journal of Aquatic Research* **41**: 351–360.

Mondal, T. and Raghunathan, C. 2011. An observation on the coral bleaching in Andaman Islands. *International Journal of Environmental Science* **1**: 37–51.

Mondal, T., Raghunathan, C., and Venkataraman, K. 2013. Bleaching: The driving force of scleractinian new recruitment at Little Andaman Island, Andaman and Nicobar Islands. *Proceedings of the National Academy of Sciences, India, Section B Biological Sciences* **83**: 585–592.

Naim, O., Cuet, P., and Letourneur, Y. 1997. Experimental shift in benthic community structure. In: *Final Proceedings of the 8th International Coral Reef Symposium*. Panama, pp. 1873–1878.

Newell, N.D. 1971. An outline history of tropical organic reefs. *Novitates* **2465**: 1–37.

Normile, D. 2000. Global Warming: Some coral bouncing back from El Niño. *Science* **288**: 941–942.

Pandolfi, J.M. 1999. Response of Pleistocene coral reefs to environmental change over long temporal scales. *American Zoologist* **39**: 113–130.

Pichon, M. and Benzoni, F. 2007. Taxonomic re-appraisal of zooxanthellate scleractinian corals in the Maldive Archipelago. *Zootaxa* **1441**: 21–33.

Prahl, H., von Guhl, F., and Grogl, M. 1979. *Gorgona.* Futura, Bogota, Colombia.

Pratchett, M.S., McCowan, D., Maynard, J.A., and Heron, S.F. 2013. Changes in bleaching susceptibility among corals subject to ocean warming and recurrent bleaching in Moorea, French Polynesia. *PLOS ONE* **8**: e70443.

Riegl, B. and Piller, W.E. 2001. "Cryptic" tissues inside *Acropora* frameworks (Indonesia): a mechanism to enhance tissue survival in hard times while also increasing framework density. *Coral Reefs* **20**: 67–68.

Riegl, B. and Purkois, S. 2009. Model of coral population response to accelerated bleaching and mass mortality in a changing climate. *Ecological Modelling* **220**: 192–208.

Rowan, R., Knowlton, N., Baker, A., and Jara, J. 1997. Landscape ecology of algal symbionts creates variation in episodes of coral bleaching. *Nature* **388**: 265–269.

Sawall, Y., Phongsuwan, N., and Richter, C. 2010. Coral recruitment and recovery after the 2004 tsunami around the Phi Phi Islands (Krabi Province) and Phuket, Andaman Sea, Thailand. *Helgoland Marine Research* **64**: 357–365.

Scheffer, M. and Carpenter, S.R. 2003. Catastrophe regime shifts in ecosystems: linking theory to observation. *Trends in Ecology and Evolution* **18**: 648–656.

Scopelitis, J., Andrefouet, S., Phinn, S., Chabanet, P., Naim, O., Tourrand, C., and Done, T. 2009. Changes of coral communities over 35 years: Integrating in situ and remote-sensing data on Saint-Leu Reef (la Reunion, Indian Ocean). *Estuarine, Coastal and Shelf Science* **84**: 342–352.

Stat, M., Morris, E., and Gates, R.D. 2008. Functional diversity in coral-dinoflagellate symbiosis. *Proceedings of the National Academy of Sciences USA* **105**: 9256–9261.

van Woesik, R., Sakai, K., Ganase, A., and Loya, Y. 2011. Revisiting the winners and the losers a decade after coral bleaching. *Marine Ecology Progress Series* **434**: 67–76.

Weeks, S.J., Anthony, K.R.N., Bakun, A., Feldman, G.C., and Hoegh-Guldberg, O. 2008. Improved predictions of coral bleaching using seasonal baselines and higher spatial resolution. *Limnology and Oceanography* **53**: 1369–1375.

Veizer, J., Ala, D., Azmy, K., Bruckschen, P., Buhl, D., Bruhn, F., Carden, G.A.F., Diener, A., Ebneth, S., Godderis, Y., Jasper, T., Korte, C., Pawellek, F., Podlaha, O., and Strauss, H. 1999. $^{87}Sr/^{86}Sr$, $\delta^{13}C$ and $\delta^{18}O$ evolution of Phanerozoic seawater. *Chemical Geology* **161**, 59–88.

Veron, J.E.N. 1995. *Corals in space and time.* Comstock/Cornell, Ithaca, NY.

Wilkinson, C., Linden, O., Cesar, H., Hodgson, G., Rubens, J., and Strong, A.E. 1999. Ecological and socioeconomic impacts of 1998 coral mortality in the Indian Ocean: an ENSO impact and a warning of future change? *Ambio* **28**: 188–196.

Zapata, F.A., Rodriguez-Ramirez, A., Caro-Zambrano, C., and Garzon-Ferreira, J. 2010. Mid-term coral-algal dynamics and conservation status of a Gorgona Island (Tropical Eastern Pacific) coral reef. *International Journal of Tropical Biology and Conservation* **58** (Suppl. 1): 81–94.

6.1.2.4 Sea-level Rise

The studies reviewed in this section examine the threat potentially large increases in sea level may pose to corals. The key findings are presented in the bullet points below, followed by an expanded discussion of those findings. (Citations for passages in quotation marks in the bullet points are included in the main body of the section.)

- The warming-induced sea-level rise predicted for the coming century—which could be greatly exaggerated if predictions of CO_2-induced global warming are wrong—falls well within the range of typical coral vertical extension rates and can be less than half the rate of certain branching corals.

- Most coral reefs are known to have responded successfully to the sea-level rises that occurred between 14,000 and 6,000 years ago, which were more than twice as rapid as what is being predicted for the coming century.

- Earth's oceans have undergone, and their coral reefs survived, at least 17 major cycles of sea-level rise and fall during the Pleistocene, the most recent low phase of which ended 18,000 years ago with a global sea level some 120–135 meters below where it is today.

- Even if reef vertical growth rates could not keep up with rising sea levels, that would not spell their doom, as "propagules of the species could keep pace and settle at suitable depths each generation."

- Rising sea levels likely would benefit many coral reefs. Over the past 6,000 years, relatively stable sea levels have limited upward reef growth, resulting in the development of extensive reef flats. Rising sea levels likely would release them from this vertical constraint.

Some researchers claim CO_2-induced global warming will melt large portions of planetary ice, thereby raising sea levels at a rate faster than corals can adjust to, while reducing the amount of life-sustaining light that reaches coral algal symbionts. Such concerns are overblown and unlikely to occur, as discussed in the studies reviewed below.

The approximate 30- to 60-cm warming-induced sea-level rise that is predicted for the coming century—which could turn out to be greatly exaggerated if predictions of CO_2-induced global warming are wrong—falls well within the range (2 to 6 mm per year) of typical coral vertical extension rates, which exhibited a modal value of 7 to 8 mm per year during the Holocene and can be more than double that value in certain branching corals (Hopley and Kinsey, 1988; Done, 1999). Moreover, most coral reefs are known to have responded successfully to the sea-level rises that occurred between 14,000 and 6,000 years ago, which were accompanied by large changes in "CO_2 concentrations, ... rainfall, cloud cover, storms and currents" (Wilkinson, 1996), and which were more than twice as rapid as what is being predicted for the coming century (Digerfeldt and Hendry, 1987).

Earth's oceans have undergone, and their coral reefs have survived (Chadwick-Furman, 1996), at least 17 major cycles of sea-level rise and fall during the Pleistocene, the most recent low phase of which ended 18,000 years ago with a global sea level some 120–135 meters below where it is now (Grigg and Epp, 1989). And most coral reefs handle increases in sea level, even rapid increases, much better than decreases (White *et al.*, 1998).

Even if reef vertical growth rates could not keep up with rising sea levels, that would not spell their doom. One of the important characteristics of essentially all reef cnidarians is their ability to produce free-swimming planulae, spores, or dispersive larval stages. Kinzie (1999) notes, "no matter how quickly sea level might rise, propagules of the species could keep pace and settle at suitable depths each generation," thereby creating what he calls jump-up reefs that "might well contain most of the species present in the original community." Done (1999) notes "coral communities have a history of tracking their preferred environmental niche which may suggest that as an entity, they will be predisposed to 'adapt' to prospective changes in environment over the next century," citing precedents that clearly demonstrate "coral communities have historically had a good capacity to track their re-distributed preferred physical niches."

As Kinzie and Buddemeier (1996) recount, coral reefs have survived many periods of "massive environmental changes" throughout the geologic record. Reefs are survivors, they state, "because they do not simply tolerate environmental changes" but "exhibit an impressive array of acclimations" that allow them to deal with a variety of challenges to their continued existence in any given area. It is highly unlikely anticipated increases in sea level would spell the doom of Earth's corals.

Rising sea levels may actually have a *positive* effect on coral reefs (Roberts, 1993). Over the past 6,000 years, relatively stable sea levels have limited upward reef growth, resulting in the development of extensive reef flats. As Buddemeier and Smith (1988) and Wilkinson (1996) have noted, the sea-level rises predicted to result from CO_2-induced global warming should be beneficial, permitting increased growth in these growth-restricted areas. As Chadwick-Furman (1996) noted, "many coral reefs have already reached their upward limit of growth at present sea level (Buddemeier, 1992), and may be released from this vertical constraint by a rise in sea level." She also notes rising sea levels may allow more water to circulate between segregated lagoons and outer reef slopes, which could "increase the exchange of coral propagules between reef habitats and lead to higher coral diversity in inner reef areas." She, too, concludes "coral reefs are likely to survive predicted rates of global change."

References

Buddemeier, R.W. 1992. Corals, climate and conservation. *Proceedings of the Seventh International Coral Reef Symposium* 1: 3–10.

Buddemeier, R.W. and Smith, S.V. 1988. Coral-reef growth in an era of rapidly rising sea-level—predictions and suggestions for long-term research. *Coral Reefs* 7: 51–56.

Chadwick-Furman, N.E. 1996. Reef coral diversity and global change. *Global Change Biology* 2: 559–568.

Digerfeldt, G. and Hendry, M.D. 1987. An 8000 year Holocene sea-level record from Jamaica: Implications for interpretation of Caribbean reef and coastal history. *Coral Reefs* 5: 165–170.

Done, T.J. 1999. Coral community adaptability to environmental change at the scales of regions, reefs and reef zones. *American Zoologist* 39: 66–79.

Grigg, R.W. and Epp, D. 1989. Critical depth for the survival of coral islands: Effects on the Hawaiian Archipelago. *Science* 243: 638–641.

Hopley, D. and Kinsey, D.W. 1988. The effects of a rapid short-term sea-level rise on the Great Barrier Reef.

Pearman, G.I. (Ed.) *Greenhouse: Planning for climate change*. CSIRO Publishing, East Melbourne, Australia, pp. 189–201.

IPCC, 2007-II. *Climate Change 2007: Impacts, Adaptation and Vulnerability*. Contribution of Working Group II to the Fourth Assessment Report of the Intergovernmental Panel on Climate Change. Parry, M.L., Canziani, O.F., Palutikof, J.P., van der Linden, P.J., and Hanson, C.E. (Eds.) Cambridge University Press, Cambridge, UK.

Kinzie III, R.A. 1999. Sex, symbiosis and coral reef communities. *American Zoologist* **39**: 80–91.

Kinzie III, R.A. and Buddemeier, R.W. 1996. Reefs happen. *Global Change Biology* **2**: 479–494.

Roberts, C.M. 1993. Coral reefs: Health, hazards and history. *Trends in Ecology and Evolution* **8**: 425–427.

White, B., Curran, H.A., and Wilson, M.A. 1998. Bahamian coral reefs yield evidence of a brief sea-level lowstand during the last interglacial. *Carbonates & Evaporites* **13**: 10–22.

Wilkinson, C.R. 1996. Global change and coral reefs: Impacts on reefs, economies and human cultures. *Global Change Biology* **2**: 547–558.

6.1.3 Crustaceans

The studies reviewed in this section examine the impact of rising temperatures on crustacean species. The key findings, which challenge the alarming and negative projections of IPCC, are presented in the bullet points below, followed by an expanded discussion of those findings. (Citations for passages in quotation marks in the bullet points are included in the main body of the section.)

- The larval form of the kelp crab is capable of adapting to both higher and lower temperatures than those at which it may have lived for long periods in the past.

- At higher temperatures, red king crab (*Paralithodes camtschaticus*) experienced "accelerated growth" and a "positive, indirect effect on survival," as "larger size associated with high temperature could provide for earlier refuge in size from the typical fish and invertebrate predators."

- A modest warming would prove advantageous to hymenosomatid crabs, increasing larval growth and survival rates, as well as fecundity.

- European green crabs (*Carcinus maenas*) on the west coast of North America have demonstrated phenotypic thermal tolerance and adaptation.

- *Palaemonetes varians*, a shallow-water brackish shrimp, "shows genuine acclimation capacities" due to the plasticity inherent in the organism's critical thermal limit and heat shock response to temperature.

- Some Branchiopod crustaceans display "substantial physiological plasticity or important adaptive variation," which enables them "to better cope with environmental change."

- "Copepod diversity, especially in extra-tropical regions, is likely to increase with climate change as their large-scale distributions respond to climate warming," because of a "strong positive correlation between diversity and temperature."

Storch *et al.* (2009) note, "temperature is often invoked as the main determinant of distribution ranges and boundaries for marine and terrestrial species," and the larval stages of many marine species "are more vulnerable to thermal and osmotic stresses than adults." They explored the rigidity of this temperature determinant of livable range for the Chilean kelp crab (*Taliepus dentatus*) in its most temperature-sensitive larval state. They studied stage zoea I larvae of two populations of the crab—one from Southern Chile (SC, 43°54'S) and one from Central Chile (CC, 33°29'S)—measuring "temperature-dependent activity, oxygen consumption, cardiac performance, body mass and the carbon and nitrogen composition in order to (1) examine thermal effects from organismal to cellular levels, and (2) compare the thermal tolerance of larvae from two environmental temperature regimes."

The six researchers report, "the thermal tolerance window of zoea from SC was found to be shifted to lower temperatures when compared with those from CC"; that is, the thermal tolerance window of zoea from CC was found to be shifted to higher temperatures when compared with those from SC. The Chilean and German scientists conclude "the small but clear shift between thermal tolerance windows between populations suggests an optimization of reaction norms and local adaptation in larvae of *T. dentatus*," noting "this differentiation allows the species to cover a wider range of distribution than when restricted to one and the same thermal window for all populations," which suggests the larval form of the kelp crab is capable of adapting to both higher and lower temperatures than those at which it may have lived for long periods in the past.

Stoner *et al.* (2010) write, "temperature is a dominant environmental factor that mediates the behavior, physiology, growth, survival, distribution, and recruitment of ectothermic animals living in temperate and high latitudes." They investigated how the growth and survival of the red king crab (RKC: *Paralithodes camtschaticus*) "may be affected by warming trends expected in Alaska," since the RKC was once that state's "most economically valuable crustacean fishery." The authors reared RKC in "four temperature treatments ranging from 1.5 to 12°C for a period of 60 days, both individually and in low-density populations," measuring various physiological processes and properties throughout this period.

The three researchers report "temperature had no significant effect on survival of RKC," and "there was no consistent difference in survival between individually cultured crabs and those in populations." Growth, they found, "was very slow at 1.5°C, and increased rapidly with temperature with both a contracted inter-molt period and small increase in growth increment." In addition, "20% of the crabs held at 1.5°C never molted, while more than 90% of the crabs in 12°C reached juvenile state 4 or higher." Overall, "growth increased as an exponential function of temperature, with slightly higher growth rates observed in populations than for isolated individuals." They found "no evidence that culturing RKC juveniles at elevated temperatures led to a decrease in condition or nutritional status."

Stoner *et al.* conclude the "accelerated growth" they observed in the RKC raised at the highest temperature might have a "positive, indirect effect on survival," as "larger size associated with high temperature could provide for earlier refuge in size from the typical fish and invertebrate predators on RKC."

Van den Brink *et al.* (2012) note "hymenosomatid crabs of the genus *Halicarcinus* have a reproductive strategy involving a terminal, pubertal moult where reproduction begins only when growth has ceased." This strategy, they explain, "allows females to maximize their reproductive output during a comparatively short (approximately six month) adult life span by producing broods continuously and successively, without the need for the female to suspend reproduction for moulting," citing Van den Brink and McLay (2009, 2010). Van den Brink *et al.* investigated the effect of temperature on brood development for "three intertidal hymenosomatid crabs: *Halicarcinus cookii*, *H. varius* and *H. innominatus*," which they collected from intertidal habitats around the Kaikoura Peninsula of New Zealand.

The results yielded three main findings. First, "if temperatures rise 2°C as predicted, each of the three species could produce one extra brood per female lifetime," which the authors say "would result in the production of over 1000 extra larvae per female resulting in a 10–15% increase in fecundity" that could "result in a single female producing 10–50 extra surviving offspring per lifetime." Second, "an increase in temperature is also likely to increase larval growth rates ... resulting in shorter development times," which "may also increase survival rates to final instars and eventually adults, thus potentially increasing the size of the population." Third, "the current six month peak breeding season in the three *Halicarcinus* species may increase as temperatures rise," which "may allow the three *Halicarcinus* crabs more time to carry eggs and therefore produce even more offspring per lifetime." These findings indicate a modest warming would prove extremely beneficial to hymenosomatid crabs.

Kelley *et al.* (2011) note, "measuring variation in physiological traits over broad spatial and temporal scales in an effort to investigate the ecological impacts of these traits (Chown *et al.*, 2004)" can "aid in predicting how species or communities will respond to climate change," citing Baker *et al.* (2004), Harley *et al.* (2006), Hassol (2004), Helmuth *et al.* (2002, 2005), Kennedy *et al.* (2002), Parmesan (2006), Parmesan and Yohe (2003), Portner *et al.* (2001), and Stillman (2003). Employing this approach in their study of the European green crab (*Carcinus maenas*), Kelley *et al.* measured the upper lethal thermal thresholds of two populations of the invasive species living at the southern and northern limits of its current range on the west coast of North America—Sea Drift Lagoon, Stinson Beach California (CA; 37°54'27.82"N), and Pipestem Inlet, Vancouver Island, British Columbia (BC; 49°02.3'N). The two sites are separated by 1,200 km of coastline—where "ambient sea surface temperature in the northern part of the North American west coast range is 5 to 10°C lower, depending on the time of year, than near the southern range limit." The species' expansion from its initial introduction at the south end of its range to its current northern end occurred over a period of about 20 years.

The three U.S. scientists determined the warm-adapted southern CA group of crabs had the highest level of organismal thermotolerance and the greatest degree of heat shock protein 70 (Hsp70) production. They also found carapace widths of male and female

C. maenas individuals from CA were significantly smaller than those in BC. Kelley *et al.* say these findings "provide evidence that the northeastern Pacific population of *C. maenas* has incurred a shift in thermal tolerance compared to its southern counterpart," and "thermal adaptation at the level of the phenotype is a likely cause due to the short timescale of the invasion and the genetic connectivity of the two populations."

The authors state that over just two decades "it is possible that a large, northern cold-water phenotype may have already arisen," which further suggests the reverse of this phenomenon also could have occurred over the same length of time if the driving force for phenotypic change had arisen due to the crabs migrating from a cooler to a warmer environment, or, by further inference, that it could have occurred during a period of equivalent climatic warming in the same physical setting without any relocation. This is yet another example of a species demonstrating a capacity to cope with projected global warming, without the need to migrate.

Ravaux *et al.* (2012) point out "all organisms possess some capacity to modify their behavioral, physiological or morphological characteristics in response to changes in environmental temperature" via a phenomenon they characterize as thermal acclimation, citing Angilletta (2009). This special case of phenotypic plasticity would be of great significance to all organisms in a warming world. Ravaux *et al.* studied *Palaemonetes varians*, a shallow-water brackish shrimp native to Western Europe, assessing both cold- and warm-acclimated specimens collected from the Bay of Mont Saint-Michel (France), the plasticity of a common index of thermal tolerance, the critical thermal maximum (CT_{max}), and the plasticity of a widespread and conserved molecular response to stress, known simply as heat shock response (HSR).

The seven scientists determined *P. varians* "shows genuine acclimation capacities" due to the plasticity inherent in the organism's thermal limit (CT_{max}) and its heat shock response (*hsp*70 induction temperature). Ravaux *et al.* conclude *P. varians* "is readily able to expand its thermal range since it can shift its thermal maximum to higher temperatures and also mobilize the HSR over a wide range of temperatures above those experienced in nature." They state the shrimp "is potentially capable of expanding its upper thermal range," which suggests it may not have to migrate toward cooler regions in a potentially warming world of the future.

Pinceel *et al.* (2013) studied the ability of large branchiopod crustaceans to phenotypically adapt, constructing "a molecular phylogeny based on a data set which includes about 85% of the *Branchinella* species currently known to science, as well as a number of recently discovered lineages." They discovered "substantial physiological plasticity or important adaptive variation present in some species, potentially enabling them to better cope with environmental change."

Letessier *et al.* (2011) modeled the influence of a suite of physical, chemical, and biological variables on euphausiid species abundance. Euphausiids are small, pelagic, shrimplike crustaceans of the order Euphausiacea; the authors say they constitute "an important component of the pelagic realm," where they "graze directly on phytoplankton and provide a food source for a range of predators including birds, seals, baleen whales and many commercially important fish species," citing Verity *et al.* (2002). The authors used a generalized additive model running environmental changes based on IPCC A1B climate scenario to make predictions of future species abundance changes in the Pacific and Atlantic Oceans, which they sub-divided into cells having east-to-west lengths of 300 km and north-to-south lengths of 200 km.

Letessier *et al.* found "the main drivers of species abundance, in order of decreasing importance, were sea surface temperature (SST, explaining 29.53% of species variability), salinity (20.29%), longitude (-15.01%, species abundance decreased from West to East), distance to coast (10.99%) and dissolved silicate concentration (9.03%)." The three UK researchers say their results suggest "the present broad patterns apparent in species abundance (low in high latitudes, high in intermediate latitudes and intermediate in the tropics) will become less pronounced in a warming ocean," and eventually, "species abundance will be enhanced within intermediate-to-high latitudes (30°N to 60°N and 30°S to 60°S) and diminished in the tropics (20°N to 20°S)." These changes, they write, are "consistent with changes already observed to be occurring in terrestrial systems in Europe and America," citing Rosenzweig *et al.* (2008), and with "already-observed changes in zooplankton assemblages in the North Atlantic (i.e., communities shifting north)," as reported by Beaugrand *et al.* (2002), Beaugrand and Ibanez (2004), and Richardson and Schoeman (2004). Considered in their entirety, such shifts in euphausiid species abundance may be viewed as positive developments, especially in light of the three scientists' finding that both the Atlantic and Pacific

Oceans "will on average see an increase in species abundance per cell."

Rombouts *et al.* (2009) studied marine copepods—small ocean crustaceans that form a key trophic link between phytoplankton and fish. Some are planktonic and drift in sea water, but more are benthic and live on the ocean floor. Rombouts *et al.* developed the first global description of geographical variation in the diversity of marine copepods in relation to 10 environmental variables.

They found "ocean temperature was the most important explanatory factor among all environmental variables tested, accounting for 54 percent of the variation in diversity." They report "diversity peaked at subtropical latitudes in the Northern Hemisphere and showed a plateau in the Southern Hemisphere where diversity remained high from the Equator to the beginning of the temperate regions." This pattern, they write, "is consistent with latitudinal variations found for some other marine taxa, e.g. foraminifera (Rutherford *et al.*, 1999), tintinnids (Dolan *et al.*, 2006) and fish (Worm *et al.*, 2005; Boyce *et al.*, 2008), and also in the terrestrial environment, e.g. aphids, sawflies and birds (Gaston and Blackburn, 2000)."

"Given the strong positive correlation between diversity and temperature," the six scientists conclude, "local copepod diversity, especially in extra-tropical regions, is likely to increase with climate change as their large-scale distributions respond to climate warming." This state of affairs has typically been found on land for birds, butterflies, and several other terrestrial lifeforms, as their ranges expand and overlap in response to global warming. With more territory thus available to them, their foothold on the planet becomes increasingly strong, fortifying them against forces (many of them human-induced) that might otherwise lead to their extinction.

Tremblay *et al.* (2011) compared time series of ice cover, wind forcing, and satellite-based assessments of photosynthetic carbon production in the Canadian Beaufort Shelf for the years 2002–2008 with corresponding *in situ* measurements of salinity, nutrients, new production, biological stocks, and biogenic fluxes obtained during overwintering surveys of copepods in 2003–2004 and 2007–2008. The 15 researchers report that in 2007–2008, in areas where ice was no longer present, due to enhanced seasonal warming, there was significant wind-induced upwelling of growth-promoting nitrates, which were brought up from deep and dark waters into the euphotic zone, where photosynthesis occurs. As a result of this fertilization effect, the herbivorous copepod *Calanus glacialis*—which they say is "the key link between diatom production and apex consumers on Arctic shelves," citing Soreide *et al.* (2010)—experienced a total abundance "3 to 33 times higher than in 2003 during mid-fall and 1.6 to 13 fold higher than in 2004 during early summer." On the region's central shelf, the scientists observed "sedimentary chlorophyll *a* was over 20-fold higher than at any station not influenced by upwelling," and "benthic carbon demand was among the highest ever observed in the Arctic ocean," citing Clough *et al.* (2005). They report the "repeated instances of ice ablation and upwelling during fall 2007 and summer 2008 multiplied the production of ice algae, phyto-plankton, zooplankton and benthos by 2 to 6 fold."

Tremblay *et al.* conclude the phenomena they observed are "likely to prevail with the increasingly deep and frequent seaward retreat of the central ice pack and the greater incidence of upwelling-favorable winds," as described in detail by Yang (2009), and "new production is also bound to rise as winds gain in intensity and upwelling draws deeper into the nutrient-rich, upper Pacific halocline."

References

Angilletta, M.J. 2009. *Thermal Adaptation*. Oxford University Press, Oxford, United Kingdom.

Baker, A.C., Starger, C.J., McClanahan, T.R., and Glynn, P.W. 2004. Corals' adaptive response to climate change. *Nature* **430**: 741.

Beaugrand, G. and Ibanez, F. 2004. Monitoring marine plankton ecosystems. II: long-term changes in North Sea calanoid copepods in relation to hydro-climatic variability. *Marine Ecology Progress Series* **284**: 35–47.

Beaugrand, G., Reid, P.C., Ibanex, F., Lindley, J.A., and Edwards, M. 2002. Reorganization of North Atlantic marine copepod biodiversity and climate. *Science* **296**: 1692–1694.

Boyce, D.G., Tittensor, D.P., and Worm, B. 2008. Effects of temperature on global patterns of tuna and billfish richness. *Marine Ecology Progress Series* **355**: 267–276.

Carmack, E. and MacDonald, R.W. 2002. Oceanography of the Canadian Shelf of the Beaufort Sea: A setting for marine life. *Arctic* **55**: 29–45.

Chown, S.L., Gaston, K.J., and Robinson, D. 2004. Macrophysiology: large-scale patterns in physiological traits and their ecological implications. *Functional Ecology* **18**: 159–167.

Clough, L.M., Renaud, P.E., and Ambrose, W.G. 2005.

Impacts of water depth, sediment pigment concentration, and benthic macrofaunal biomass on sediment oxygen demand in the western Arctic Ocean. *Canadian Journal of Fisheries and Aquatic Sciences* **62**: 1756–1765.

Dolan, J.R., Lemee, R., Gasparini, S., Mousseau, L., and Heyndrickx, C. 2006. Probing diversity in the plankton: using patterns in Tintinnids (planktonic marine ciliates) to identify mechanisms. *Hydrobiologia* **555**: 143–157.

Gaston, J.K. and Blackburn, T.M. 2000. *Pattern and Process in Macroecology.* Blackwell Science Ltd., Oxford, United Kingdom.

Harley, C.D.G., Hughes, A.R., Hultgren, K.M., Miner, B.G., Sorte, C.J.B., Thornber, C.S., Rodriguez, L.F., Tomanek, L., and Williams, S.L. 2006. The impacts of climate change in coastal marine systems. *Ecological Letters* **9**: 228–241.

Hassol, S.J. 2004. *Impacts of a Warming Arctic.* Arctic Climate Impact Assessment. Cambridge University Press, New York, New York, USA.

Helmuth, B., Harley, C.D.G., Halpin, P.M., O'Donnell, M., Hofmann, G.E., and Blanchette, C.A. 2002. Climate change and latitudinal patterns of intertidal thermal stress. *Science* **298**: 1015–1017.

Helmuth, B., Kingsolver, J.G., and Carrington, E. 2005. Biophysics, physiological ecology, and climate change: does mechanism matter? *Annual Review of Physiology* **67**: 177–201.

Kelley, A.L., de Rivera, C.E., and Buckley, B.A. 2011. Intraspecific variation in thermotolerance and morphology of the invasive European green crab, *Carcinus maenas*, on the west coast of North America. *Journal of Experimental Marine Biology and Ecology* **409**: 70–78.

Kennedy, V.S., Twilley, R.R., Kleypas, J.A., Cowan, J.H., and Steven, S.R. 2002. *Coastal and Marine Ecosystems and Climate Change. Potential Effects on U.S. Resources.* Pew Center on Global Climate Change. Arlington, Virginia, USA.

Letessier, T.B., Cox, M.J., and Brierley, A.S. 2011. Drivers of variability in Euphausiid species abundance throughout the Pacific Ocean. *Journal of Plankton Research* **33**: 1342–1357.

Parmesan, C. 2006. Ecological and evolutionary responses to recent climate change. *Annual Review of Ecology, Evolution and Systematics* **37**: 637–669.

Pinceel, T., Vanschoenwinkel, B., Waterkeyn, A., Vanhove, M.P.M., Pinder, A., Timms, B.V., and Brendonck, L. 2013. Fairy shrimps in distress: a molecular taxonomic review of the diverse fairy shrimp genus *Branchinella* (Anostraca: Thamnocephalidae) in Australia in the light of ongoing environmental change. *Hydrobiologia* **700**: 313–327.

Portner, H.O., Berdal, B., Blust, R., Brix, O., Colosimo, A., De Wachter, B., Giuliani, A., Johansen, T., Fischer, T., and Knust, R. 2001. Climate induced temperature effects on growth performance, fecundity and recruitment in marine fish: developing a hypothesis for cause and effect relationships in Atlantic cod (*Gadus morhua*) and common ellpout (*Zoarces viviparous*). *Continental Shelf Research* **21**: 1975–1997.

Ravaux, J., Leger, N., Rabet, N., Morini, M., Zbinden, M., Thatje, S., and Shillito, B. 2012. Adaptation to thermally variable environments: capacity for acclimation of thermal limit and heat shock response in the shrimp *Palaemonetes varians*. *Journal of Comparative Physiology B* **182**: 899–907.

Richardson, A.J. and Schoeman, D.S. 2004. Climate impact on plankton ecosystems in the Northeast Atlantic. *Science* **305**: 1609–1612.

Rombouts, I., Beaugrand, G., Ibanez, F., Gasparini, S., Chiba, S., and Legendre, L. 2009. Global latitudinal variations in marine copepod diversity and environmental factors. *Proceedings of the Royal Society B* **276**: 3053–3062.

Rosenzweig, C., Karoly, D., Vicarelli, M., Neofotis, P., Wu, Q., Casassa, G., Menzel, A., Root, T.L., Estrella, N., Seguin, B., Tryjanowski, P., Liu, C., Rawlins, S., and Imeson, A. 2008. Attributing physical and biological impacts to anthropogenic climate change. *Nature* **453**: 353–357.

Rutherford, S., D'Hondt, S., and Prell, W. 1999. Environmental controls on the geographic distribution of zooplankton diversity. *Nature* **400**: 749–753.

Soreide, J.E., Leu, E., Graeve, M., and Falk-Petersen, S. 2010. Timing of blooms, algal food quality and Calanus glacialis reproduction and growth in a changing Arctic. *Global Change Biology* **16**: 3154–3163.

Stillman, J.H. 2003. Acclimation capacity underlies susceptibility to climate change. *Science* **301**: 65.

Stoner, A.W., Ottmar, M.L., and Copeman, L.A. 2010. Temperature effects on the molting, growth, and lipid composition of newly-settled red king crab. *Journal of Experimental Marine Biology and Ecology* **393**: 138–147.

Storch, D., Santelices, P., Barria, J., Cabeza, K., Portner, H.-O., and Fernandez, M. 2009. Thermal tolerance of crustacean larvae (zoea I) in two different populations of the kelp crab *Taliepus dentatus* (Milne-Edwards). *The Journal of Experimental Biology* **212**: 1371–1376.

Tremblay, J.-E., Belanger, S., Barber, D.G., Asplin, M., Martin, J., Darnis, G., Fortier, L., Gratton, Y., Link, H., Archambault, P., Sallon, A., Michel, C., Williams, W.J., Philippe, B., and Gosselin, M. 2011. Climate forcing multiplies biological productivity in the coastal Arctic

Ocean. *Geophysical Research Letters* **38**: 10.1029/2011GL048825.

Van den Brink, A.M. and McLay, C.L. 2009. The reproductive ecology and biology of the pillbox crab: *Halicarcinus cookii* (Brachyura: Hymenosomatidae) Filhol, 1885. MSc Thesis. University of Canterbury, Canterbury, New Zealand.

Van den Brink, A.M. and McLay, C.L. 2010. Competing for last place: mating behavior in a pill box crab. *Halicarcinus cookii* (Brachyura: Hymenosomatidae). *Zoologischer Anzeiger* **249**: 21–32.

Van den Brink, A.M., McLay, C.L., Hosie, A.M., and Dunnington, M.J. 2012. The effect of temperature on brood duration in three *Halicarcinus* species (Crustacea: Brachyura: Hymenosomatidae). *Journal of the Marine Biological Association of the United Kingdom* **92**: 515–520.

Verity, P.G., Smetacek, V., and Smayda, T.J. 2002. Status, trends and the future of the marine pelagic ecosystem. *Environmental Conservation* **29**: 207–237.

Worm, B., Oschlies, A., Lotze, H.K., and Myers, R.A. 2005. Global patterns of predator diversity in the open oceans. *Science* **309**: 1365–1369.

Yang, J.Y. 2009. Seasonal and interannual variability of downwelling in the Beaufort Sea. *Journal of Geophysical Research* **114**: 10.1029/2008JC005084.

6.1.4 Fish

The studies reviewed in this section examine the impact of rising temperatures on marine fish species. The key findings, which challenge the alarming and negative projections of IPCC, are presented in the bullet points below, followed by an expanded discussion of those findings. (Citations for passages in quotation marks in the bullet points are included in the main body of the section.)

- Primary production increases expected to result from future greenhouse gas emissions and their IPCC-projected impacts on climate "will provide opportunities to recover overfished fisheries, increase profitability of fisheries and conserve threatened biodiversity" around Australia.

- The population of one-year-old chum salmon in the Okhotsk Sea "was less during the period from the 1940s to the mid–1970s compared to the period from the mid–1980s to the present." This result "was directly affected by warmer sea surface temperatures associated with global warming."

- There has been a "rapid microevolution for earlier migration timing in" pink salmon in Alaska, which has allowed both the odd- and even-year groups of salmon "to remain resilient to environmental change."

- Despite having low critical thermal maximum temperatures, a geographically diverse group of 11 species of Antarctic fishes "maintained the capacity to increase their heat tolerance through warm acclimation."

- "Adult seahorses show great resilience to heat stress and are not expected to go through any physiological impairment and behavioral change with the projected near-future warming."

- "Tropical marine fishes inhabiting fringing nursery environments may have the upper thermal tolerance necessary to endure substantial increases in sea temperatures."

- Developmental plasticity in fish "may allow adaptation to changing environmental conditions to have delayed effects," and "this may attenuate some of the more severe predictions about organisms' responses to global warming and eutrophication."

Brown *et al.* (2010) noted "effects of climate-driven production change on marine ecosystems and fisheries can be explored using food web models that incorporate ecological interactions such as predation and competition," citing Cury *et al.* (2008). They used the output of an ocean general circulation model driven by a "plausible" greenhouse gas emissions scenario (IPCC 2007 scenario A2) to calculate changes in climate over a 50-year time horizon. They fed those results into a suite of models for calculating primary production of lower trophic levels (phytoplankton, macroalgae, seagrass, and benthic microalgae), and they used the results of those calculations as input to "twelve existing Ecopath with Ecosim (EwE) dynamic marine food web models to describe different Australian marine ecosystems." This protocol ultimately predicted "changes in fishery catch, fishery value, biomass of animals of conservation interest, and indicators of community composition."

The 17 scientists state under IPCC's "plausible

climate change scenario, primary production will increase around Australia" with "overall positive linear responses of functional groups to primary production change," and "generally this benefits fisheries catch and value and leads to increased biomass of threatened marine animals such as turtles and sharks." They note the calculated responses "are robust to the ecosystem type and the complexity of the model used." Brown *et al.* conclude the primary production increases suggested by their work to result from IPCC-envisioned greenhouse gas emissions and their calculated impacts on climate "will provide opportunities to recover overfished fisheries, increase profitability of fisheries and conserve threatened biodiversity."

Drinkwater (2006) reviewed the status of marine ecosystems of the northern North Atlantic in the early twentieth century during a regime shift, which he defined as "a persistent radical shift in typical levels of abundance or productivity of multiple important components of the marine biological community structure, occurring at multiple trophic levels and on a geographical scale that is at least regional in extent." Drinkwater reports, "in the 1920s and 1930s, there was a dramatic warming of the air and ocean temperatures in the northern North Atlantic and the high Arctic, with the largest changes occurring north of 60°N," and this warming "led to reduced ice cover in the Arctic and subarctic regions and higher sea temperatures," as well as northward shifts of multiple marine ecosystems.

The early twentieth century warming of North Atlantic waters "contributed to higher primary and secondary production," Drinkwater notes, and "with the reduced extent of ice-covered waters, more open water allow[ed] for higher production than in the colder periods." As a result, cod "spread approximately 1200 km northward along West Greenland," and "migration of 'warmer water' species also changed with earlier arrivals and later departures." Drinkwater notes, "new spawning sites were observed farther north for several species or stocks while for others the relative contribution from northern spawning sites increased." Also, "some southern species of fish that were unknown in northern areas prior to the warming event became occasional, and in some cases, frequent visitors."

Seo *et al.* (2011) note, "Pacific salmon (*Oncorhynchus* spp.) play an important role as both keystone species in North Pacific ecosystems and as an ecosystem service that provides human food resources for countries of the North Pacific rim," citing Kaeriyama (2008), and they observe the Hokkaido chum salmon (*O. keta*) experiences a period of critical mortality "characterized by size-dependent mortality and size-selective predation, immediately after seaward migration," citing Healey (1982), Kaeriyama (1986), Kaeriyama and Ueda (1998), and Kaeriyama *et al.* (2007). To determine the effect of global warming on this critical mortality period in the life of Hokkaido chum salmon, Seo *et al.* used multiple regression and path analysis to examine the effects of regional and larger spatial scales of climatic/oceanic conditions on the growth, survival, and population dynamics of the species.

The three researchers from the Faculty of Fisheries Sciences at Japan's Hokkaido University determined growth of one-year-old chum salmon in the Okhotsk Sea "was less during the period from the 1940s to the mid–1970s compared to the period from the mid–1980s to the present," and this result "was directly affected by warmer sea surface temperatures associated with global warming." They add, "the increased growth at age one led directly to higher survival rates and indirectly to larger population sizes."

Bentley and Burgner (2011) studied juvenile sockeye salmon (*Oncorhynchus nerka*) in an Alaskan watershed that had experienced a 1.9°C increase in summer water temperature over the prior 46 years. They hypothesized the warming of the region "would have resulted in a corresponding increase in fish metabolism, and thus potential consumption rates, that would increase infestation rates of the tapeworm *Triaenophorus crassus*." They tested their hypothesis by comparing infestation rate data for *T. crassus* collected between 1948 and 1960 with similar data obtained in 2008 and 2009 from the Wood River system of Bristol Bay, Alaska.

The two U.S. researchers from the University of Washington's School of Aquatic and Fishery Sciences say in "comparing the average summer air temperature to the parasite prevalence of juvenile sockeye salmon, we found no significant relationship over the fifteen years of collected data." They also report in "evaluating the influence of average summer air temperature on the parasite infestation rates of juvenile sockeye salmon, we again found no significant relationship for either parasite abundance or parasite intensity," and "when we compared the 13 years of historic parasite prevalence to equivalent data collected in 2008 and 2009, we did not find a statistically significant positive long-term trend in the data." Bentley and Burgner write, "the parasite abundance of examined sockeye salmon smolts also did not exhibit a statistically significant long-term trend using the eight years of historic data and the two years of contemporary data." They report, "evaluating the relationship between time and parasite intensity produced similar results as the other five comparisons, with there not being a statistically significant positive relationship." Bentley and Burgner conclude their data demonstrate "the complex effects of warming have not summed to generate a measurable change in the infestation rates of juvenile sockeye salmon in the Wood River system."

Kovach et al. (2012) studied salmon in Auke Creek, a small lake-outlet stream near Juneau, Alaska, where there have been complete daily counts of all adult pink salmon migrating into the creek since 1971. They used "phenotypic data on migration timing, archived genetic samples and data from a marker locus, the allele frequencies of which were experimentally altered more than 30 years ago, to determine whether change in migration timing in a population of pink salmon has a genetic basis (i.e., microevolution)." The three researchers determined both even- and odd-year adult pink salmon that spawn in the warming Alaskan stream are migrating into fresh water nearly two weeks earlier than their predecessors did 40 years ago. They also found experimental data "support the hypothesis that there has been directional selection for earlier migration timing, resulting in a substantial decrease in the late-migrating phenotype (from more than 30% to less than 10% of the total abundance)." They also report, "from 1983 to 2011, there was a significant decrease—over threefold—in the frequency of a genetic marker for late-migration timing, but there were minimal changes in allele frequencies at other natural loci."

Kovach et al. say "these results demonstrate that there has been rapid microevolution for earlier migration timing in this population," and this has allowed both the odd- and even-year groups of salmon "to remain resilient to environmental change," as also was demonstrated by Kinnison and Hairston (2007). They note, "population abundance in 2011 was the second highest on record," further indicating the salmon of Auke Creek are "persisting through rapid temperature warming."

Aurelio et al. (2013) examined "the effect of environmental warming on the metabolic and behavioral ecology of a temperate seahorse, *Hippocampus guttulatus*." They compared routine metabolic rates, thermal sensitivity, ventilation rates, food intake, and behavioral patterns at the average spring temperature (18°C), the average summer temperature (26°C), the temperature that seahorses often experience during summer heat wave events (28°C), and the temperature of a near-future warming (+2°C) scenario (= 30°C) in Portugal's Sado estuary.

The 10 scientists state "both newborn juveniles and adults showed significant increases in metabolic rates with rising temperatures," with newborn juveniles being "more impacted by future warming via metabolic depression." In addition, "in adult stages, ventilation rates also increased significantly with environmental warming, but food intake remained unchanged." They report, "the frequency of swimming, foraging, swinging, and inactivity did not significantly change between the different thermal scenarios." Aurelio et al. conclude "adult seahorses show great resilience to heat stress and are not expected to go through any physiological impairment and behavioral change with the projected near-future warming," but juveniles in their early life stages "display greater thermal sensitivity and may face greater metabolic challenges."

Bilyk and DeVries (2011) note "most animals do not have a static heat tolerance; rather it changes in response to their recent thermal history through acclimation." They continue, "given the long residence of Antarctic fishes in constant freezing seawater, this plasticity had long been thought either lost or marginal (Brett, 1970)." They say "understanding the heat tolerance of Antarctic fishes and its plasticity is critical for understanding the threat to this cold adapted fauna," especially "given the future predicted increases in water temperatures in the southern Ocean from global climate change."

Bilyk and DeVries employed the critical thermal maximum (CTMax) methodology—the temperature at which an animal loses the ability to escape from constant rapid warming (Paladino et al. 1980)—"to survey heat tolerance in a geographically diverse group of eleven species of Antarctic fishes acclimatized to the cold water temperatures of their natural habitats." They also used this methodology on eight of the species "following warm acclimation to 4°C, which when compared to their environmental CTMaxs provided a measure of the plasticity of their heat tolerance," as these fish "had been caught or held at temperatures below -0.9°C."

The researchers found "when acclimatized to their natural freezing water temperatures, environmental CTMaxs ranged from 11.95 to 16.17°C," and when the eight further-studied species were warm-acclimated to 4°C, "all showed a significant increase over their environmental CTMaxs, with several showing plasticity comparable in magnitude to some far more eurythermal fishes." Bilyk and DeVries write, "despite their low CTMaxs, all the Antarctic species maintained the capacity to increase their heat tolerance through warm acclimation," and when this capacity was quantified, it showed "a surprising level of thermal plasticity at low temperatures," which they say was surprising "given the presumed loss of selection for thermal flexibility that has long been assumed in this fauna."

Eme *et al.* (2011) write, "temperate fishes have been considered especially vulnerable to changing climate conditions," and "increasing water temperatures may also threaten shallow-water marine fishes inhabiting nursery environments, like tropical mangroves and seagrass beds." To evaluate these hypotheses, the authors "used critical thermal methodology to quantify critical thermal maxima (CTmaxima) of juvenile squaretail mullet (*Liza vaigiensis*) and juvenile crescent terapon (*Terapon jarbua*) captured from shallow seagrass nursery areas around Hoga Island, southeast Sulawesi, Indonesia."

The three U.S. researchers report groups of mullet acclimated to a constant temperature of 37°C, as well as temperature cycles of 35–39°C or 37–41°C, all displayed statistically similar mean CTmaxima of 44.7, 44.4, and 44.8°C, respectively. They found terapon acclimated to a constant temperature of 37°C or a temperature cycle of 37–40°C both displayed mean CTmaxima of 43.8°C. Eme *et al.* conclude "terapon and mullet demonstrate exceptional tolerance to high temperatures," and "it seems likely that shallow-water sea surface temperatures would have to be much higher to adversely affect these and other shallow water marine fishes (Eme and Bennett, 2009)," as these "exceptionally high CTmaxima afford mullet and terapon a significant measure of protection against changing habitat conditions." The scientists write, "despite diverse independent origins across taxa, fishes may share a common suite of physiological adaptations allowing them to survive periodic exposure to high environmental temperature (Hochachka and Somero, 2002; Somero, 2010)," and "exceptional thermal tolerance may be common throughout the biodiverse shallow waters of the Indo-Pacific." They conclude, "tropical marine fishes inhabiting fringing nursery environments may have the upper thermal tolerance necessary to endure substantial increases in sea temperatures."

In a controlled laboratory experiment, Donelson *et al.* (2012) reared the offspring from eight wild-caught damselfish (*Ancanthochromis polyacanthus*) for two generations, "in present day (+0.0°C) and predicted future increased water temperatures (+1.5°C and +3.0°C) to test their capacity for metabolic acclimation to ocean warming." After three months, the authors assessed the responses in resting metabolic rate (RMR) relative to maximum metabolic rate (MMR) for each individual. They used this "metabolic performance" measure to characterize changes in the ability of each fish to perform aerobic activities (which would include functions such as behavior, growth, and reproduction) at its summer average water temperature (+0.0°C) and above (+1.5°C and +3.0°C).

The experiment revealed second-generation offspring had superior metabolic performance at all temperatures when their parents had been reared to maturity at a temperature of +1.5°C or +3.0°C. In addition, one pair of damselfish (i.e., one particular genetic lineage) contributed many more second-generation offspring that did well at +3.0°C than did the other wild parents: 75% of all fish that reproduced at +3.0°C were the offspring of wild pair #41. In contrast, wild pair #41 contributed 57% of offspring reproducing at +1.5°C and only 44% of those reproducing at +0.0°C. Thus, in addition to acclimation occurring within two generations, there was rapid selection of genotypes (and associated phenotypes) tolerant of higher temperatures. Donelson *et al.* conclude "this study provides evidence that, contrary to some expectations, a tropical marine species has the capacity for acclimation and adaptation to temperature increases over timescales much shorter than the rate of anthropogenic climate change," and "the discovery that advantageous offspring phenotypes are produced within two generations could indicate that some tropical marine species are more capable of coping with global warming than has been suggested."

Grenchik *et al.* (2013) note "tropical ectotherms are predicted to be especially sensitive to global warming because they may possess a narrow thermal tolerance range as a result of having evolved in a relatively stable thermal environment." They say having a narrow thermal tolerance range would mean "tropical species tend to live close to their thermal optimum," so "even relatively small increases in temperature could lead to declines in individual performance," because "as water temperature increases, so does the cost of maintaining basic cell function (resting metabolic rate, RMR; Bret, 1971)."

Grenchik *et al.* reared newly settled juveniles of the tropical damselfish *Pomacentrus moluccensis* for four months in four temperature treatments: current-day summer average (28.5°C) and up to 3°C above the average (29.5, 30.5, and 31.5°C). The three Australian researchers found the RMRs of fish reared at 29.5 and 31.5°C were "significantly higher than the control group reared at 28.5°C," and "fish that developed in 30.5 and 31.5°C exhibited an enhanced ability to deal with acute temperature increases." They conclude, "this study shows that there is capacity for thermal acclimation during development, with individuals reared from an early age at some temperatures able to modify their physiology to maintain RMRs at near present-day levels," and this developmental thermal acclimation "may assist coral reef fish to cope with increases in water temperature without a substantial loss to performance."

Simpson *et al.* (2011) write, "marine ecosystems in the northeast Atlantic have warmed particularly rapidly, with mean sea temperatures in the North Sea and Celtic-Biscay Shelf regions increasing between 1982 and 2006 by 1.31°C and 0.72°C, respectively," four times faster than the global average. They considered these regions and timeframe to be ideal for determining how real-world fish respond to real-world warming. The researchers "assessed the full impacts of warming on the commercially important European continental shelf fish assemblage using a data-driven Eulerian (grid-based) approach that accommodates spatial heterogeneity in ecological and environmental conditions."

They analyzed "local associations of species abundance and community diversity with climatic variables, assessing trends in 172 cells from records of >100 million individuals sampled over 1.2 million km^2 from 1980–2008." They contrasted this work with the climate envelope approach, which relies on macro-ecological analyses of the effects of climate change on marine fish assemblages that do not account for "constraints on distributional shifts due to population dependence on essential habitat, such as favored substrates, appropriate predator and prey fields, and close proximity to nursery grounds, all of which are often unknown and difficult to quantify."

The seven scientists say they discovered "responses to warming in 72% of common species, with three times more species increasing in abundance than declining." These trends were "reflected in international commercial landings," where landings of nine species identified as declining in warm conditions fell by half during the period of their study, whereas landings of 27 species identified as increasing in warm conditions rose by 2.5 times. They write, this "profound reorganization of the relative abundance of species in local communities occurred despite decadal stability in the presence-absence of species," such as would have been suggested by the climate envelope approach on a larger spatial scale.

Simpson *et al.* conclude their "finding of stability in presence-absence of species over decadal periods, but significant temperature-driven responses in local species abundance and assemblage composition, suggests that climate envelope models based on species presence-absence alone will not predict the most ecologically and economically significant effects of climate change."

Lloyd *et al.* (2012) write, "at a broad geographical scale, species richness and diversity decrease as latitude increases both north and south of the equator," and in marine systems this distribution pattern "has been linked most consistently to variation in sea temperature," primarily via studies conducted in north-temperate seas, such as those of Fisher *et al.* (2008) and Hiddink and Hofstede (2008). Noting there is a paucity of such studies from the Southern Hemisphere, Lloyd *et al.* analyzed measurements of sea surface temperature and spear-fishing records pertaining to 84 species of marine fish personally harvested by one of their team. This analysis was performed for each day of diving over the years 1989–2007, during which time interval there was a 0.47°C increase in mean sea surface temperature, which rose from an average of 23.36°C for the period 1989–1996 to an average of 23.83°C for 2002–2007.

The five Australian researchers report over the specified time interval, "the proportion of the catch made up by temperate species, in terms of both the number and mass of fish, consistently decreased, whereas the proportion of the catch made up by tropical species consistently increased between the two time periods," and "the contribution of broadly distributed species to the overall catch remained approximately the same." In addition, "average species richness and diversity increased 33 and 15%, respectively, between the two time periods." These findings, the authors write, "are broadly consistent with a predicted poleward shift in species ranges and a predicted increase in species richness and diversity with increasing sea temperature," confirming "large-scale climate change causing a widening of the tropical belt and subsequent ocean warming is having a profound impact on marine species abundance patterns and community composition at a local scale in the sub-tropics."

Capelin (*Mallotus villosus*) are small, short-lived forage fish that are the primary prey of many top predators in northern marine ecosystems. They typically spawn in one of two specific habitats with divergent temperature regimes: beach (warm, variable) and deep water (demersal: cool, stable). In recent years there has been some concern about how capelin may respond to projected global warming.

In 2009 and 2010, Davoren (2012) investigated "the influence of temperature on spawning habitat selection in coastal Newfoundland by quantifying habitat-specific temperature, population-level habitat use, and individual-level movements of male capelin via acoustic telemetry." The Canadian researcher reports "capelin spawned only at beaches in 2009, when temperatures were significantly colder and frequently fell below suitable ranges at demersal sites, whereas demersal sites were predominantly used under opposing conditions in 2010." She remarks "males detected in both habitats primarily dispersed from the initial habitat when temperatures routinely fell outside of suitable ranges," noting "this movement often involved traveling long distances (11.0–32.7 km) against currents, suggesting energetic costs."

Davoren writes, "overall, temperature appeared to be an important environmental cue for habitat selection by capelin," and she concludes, "the flexible use of spawning habitats under divergent temperature conditions suggests that capelin have a high capacity to respond to and possibly tolerate predicted ocean-climate change."

Zambonino-Infante *et al.* (2013) note rising temperatures typically cause "a monotonic decrease in dissolved oxygen concentration in numerous coastal and estuarine ecosystems around the world, resulting in the increased frequency, intensity and length of hypoxia episodes in shallow areas," with a primary consequence of these phenomena being the progressive widening of the gap between the availability of dissolved oxygen in the coastal water and the metabolic demand of various marine animals. Zambonino-Infante *et al.* studied the common sole (*Solea solea*), which inhabits shallow marine areas highly exposed to environmental changes, to see "whether temperature and trophic conditions experienced during the larval stage had delayed effects on life-history traits and resistance to hypoxia at the juvenile state," thereby examining "the combined effect of global warming and hypoxia in coastal waters, which are potential stressors to many estuarine and coastal marine fishes."

Their analysis showed "warmer larval temperature had a delayed positive effect on body mass and resistance to hypoxia at the juvenile stage," which "suggests a lower oxygen demand of individuals that had experienced elevated temperatures during larval stages." Zambonino-Infante *et al.* say "this study clearly demonstrates that environmental conditions experienced during early developmental stages are important in controlling environmental adaptation performance at later life stages." They state "sole that had experienced elevated temperatures during their early-life exhibited higher body masses and tolerance to hypoxia, probably through long-term programming of metabolic pathways," noting "such a cohort effect on growth performance and hypoxia tolerance could have major implications for population dynamics." They conclude, "developmental plasticity in animals may allow adaptation to changing environmental conditions to have delayed effects," and "this may attenuate some of the more severe predictions about organisms' responses to global warming and eutrophication."

References

Aurelio, M., Faleiro, F., Lopes, V.M., Pires, V., Lopes, A.R., Pimentel, M.S., Repolho, T., Baptista, M., Narciso, L., and Rosa, R. 2013. Physiological and behavioral responses of temperate seahorses (*Hippocampus guttulatus*) to environmental warming. *Marine Biology* **160**: 2663–2670.

Bentley, K.T. and Burgner, R.L. 2011. An assessment of parasite infestation rates of juvenile sockeye salmon after 50 years of climate warming in southwest Alaska. *Environmental Biology of Fishes* **92**: 267–273.

Bilyk, K.T. and DeVries, A.L. 2011. Heat tolerance and its plasticity in Antarctic fishes. *Comparative Biochemistry and Physiology, Part A* **158**: 382–390.

Brett, J.R. 1970. Temperature. *Marine Ecology* **1**: 515–560.

Brett, J.R. 1971. Energetic responses of salmon to temperature. A study in some thermal relations in the physiological and freshwater ecology of sockeye salmon (*Oncohynchus nerka*). *American Zoologist* **11**: 99–113.

Brown, C.J., Fulton, E.A., Hobday, A.J., Matear, R.J., Possingham, H.P., Bulman, C., Christensen, V., Forrest, R.E., Gehrke, P.C., Gribble, N.A., Griffiths, S.P., Lozano-Montes, H., Martin, J.M., Metcalf, S., Okey, T.A., Watson, R., and Richardson, A.J. 2010. Effects of climate-driven primary production change on marine food webs: implications for fisheries and conservation. *Global Change Biology* **16**: 1194–1212.

Cury, P.M., Shin, Y.J., Planque, B., Durant, J.M., Fromentin, J.-M., Kramer-Schadt, S., Stenseth, N.C., Travers, M., and Grimm, V. 2008. Ecosystem oceanography for global change in fisheries. *Trends in Ecology and Evolution* **23**: 338–346.

Davoren, G.K. 2012. Divergent use of spawning habitat by male capelin (*Mallotus villosus*) in a warm and cold year. *Behavioral Ecology*: 10.1093/beheco/ars147.

Donelson, J.M., Munday, P.L., McCormick, M.I., and Pitcher, C.R. 2012. Rapid transgenerational acclimation of a tropical reef fish to climate change. *Nature Climate Change* 2: 30–32.

Drinkwater, K.F. 2006. The regime shift of the 1920s and 1930s in the North Atlantic. *Progress in Oceanography* 68: 134–151.

Eme, J. and Bennett, W.A. 2009. Critical thermal tolerance polygons of tropical marine fish from Sulawesi, Indonesia. *Journal of Thermal Biology* 34: 220–225.

Eme, J., Dabruzzi, T.F., and Bennett, W.A. 2011. Thermal responses of juvenile squaretail mullet (*Liza vaigiensis*) and juvenile crescent terapon (*Terapon jarbua*) acclimated at near-lethal temperatures, and the implications for climate change. *Journal of Experimental Marine Biology and Ecology* 399: 35–38.

Fisher, J.A.D., Frank, K.T., Petrie, B., Leggett, W.C., and Shackell, N.L. 2008. Temporal dynamics within a contemporary latitudinal diversity gradient. *Ecology Letters* 11: 883–897.

Grenchik, M.K., Donelson, J.M., and Munday, P.L. 2013. Evidence for developmental thermal acclimation in the damsel fish, *Pomacentrus moluccensis*. *Coral Reefs* 32: 85–90.

Healey, M.C. 1982. Timing and relative intensity of size-selective mortality of juvenile chum salmon (*Oncorhynchus keta*) during early sea life. *Canadian Journal of Fisheries and Aquatic Sciences* 39: 952–957.

Hiddink, J.G. and Hofstede, R.T. 2008. Climate induced increases in species richness of marine fishes. *Global Change Biology* 14: 453–460.

Hochachka, P.W. and Somero, G.N. 2002. *Biochemical Adaption: Mechanism and Process in Physiological Evolution.* Oxford University Press, Oxford, United Kingdom.

Kaeriyama, M. 1986. Ecological study on early life of the chum salmon, *Oncorhynchus keta* (Walbaum). *Scientific Reports of the Hokkaido Salmon Hatchery* 40: 31–92.

Kaeriyama, M. 2008. Ecosystem-based sustainable conservation and management of Pacific salmon. In: Tsukamoto, K., Kawamura, T., Takeuchi, T., Beard Jr., T.D., and Kaiser, M.J. (Eds.) *Fisheries for Global Welfare and Environment.* TERRA-PUB, Tokyo, Japan, pp. 371–380.

Kaeriyama, M. and Ueda, H. 1998. Life history strategy and migration pattern of juvenile sockeye (*Oncorhynchus nerka*) and chum salmon (*O. keta*) in Japan: a review. *North Pacific Anadromous Fish Commission Bulletin* 1: 163–171.

Kaeriyama, M., Yatsu, A., Noto, M., and Saitoh, S. 2007. Spatial and temporal changes in the growth patterns and survival of Hokkaido chum salmon populations in 1970–2001. *North Pacific Anadromous Fish Commission Bulletin* 4: 251–256.

Kinnison, M.T. and Hairston Jr., N.G. 2007. Eco-evolutionary conservation biology: contemporary evolution and the dynamics of persistence. *Functional Ecology* 21: 444–454.

Kovach, R.P., Gharrett, A.J., and Tallmon, D.A. 2012. Genetic change for earlier migration timing in a pink salmon population. *Proceedings of the Royal Society B* 279: 3870–3878.

Lloyd, P., Plaganyi, E.E., Weeks, S.J., Magno-Canto, M., and Plaganyi, G. 2012. Ocean warming alters species abundance patterns and increases species diversity in an African sub-tropical reef-fish community. *Fisheries Oceanography* 21: 78–94.

Paladino, F.V., Spotila, J.R., Schubauer, J.P., and Kowalski, K.T. 1980. The critical thermal maximum—a technique used to elucidate physiological stress and adaptation in fishes. *Reviews of Canadian Biology* 39: 115–122.

Seo H., Kudo, H., and Kaeriyama, M. 2011. Long-term climate-related changes in somatic growth and population dynamics of Hokkaido chum salmon. *Environmental Biology of Fishes* 90: 131–142.

Simpson, S.D., Jennings, S., Johnson, M.P., Blanchard, J.L., Schon, P.-J., Sims, D.W., and Genner, M.J. 2011. Continental shelf-wide response of a fish assemblage to rapid warming of the sea. *Current Biology* 21: 1565–1570.

Somero, G.N. 2010. The physiology of climate change: how potential for acclimatization and genetic adaptation will determine 'winners' and 'losers.' *Journal of Experimental Biology* 213: 912–920.

Zambonino-Infante, J.L., Claireaux, G., Ernande, B., Jolivet, A., Quazuguel, P., Severe, A., Huelvan, C., and Mazurais, D. 2013. Hypoxia tolerance of common sole juveniles depends on dietary regime and temperature at the larval stage: evidence for environmental conditioning. *Proceedings of the Royal Society B* 280: 10.1098/rspb.2012.3022.

6.1.5 Other Marine Species

In studying the impact of rising temperature on other marine species, researchers have made some important findings that challenge the projections of IPCC on this matter. As listed in the bullet points below and discussed further in the body of this section, such findings include:

- Single environmental metrics, such as air temperature, are not sufficient for making projections of the impacts of climate change.

- Caution should be applied when interpreting results from laboratory-based studies, which are often incapable of mimicking conditions in the real world and often yield results quite different from those observed in nature.

- Warmer temperatures capable of reducing sea ice density and cover reduce the risk of narwhal mortality.

- Intertidal marine species along Australia's east coast have easily withstood a significant climatic warming of ~1.5°C over the past 60 years without having to migrate poleward.

- Thermal heterogeneity within marine habitats must be fully understood in order to properly interpret and ascribe patterns of biogeographic response to climate change.

- Offspring of female turtles grew larger and survived better at hotter incubation. The increased heat tolerance appears to be genetically based.

Helmuth *et al.* (2011) note "virtually every physiological process is affected by the temperature of an organism's body, and ... with the advent of new molecular and biochemical techniques for studying organismal responses to thermal stress ... there has been a renewed interest in the effects of temperature extremes on the ecology and physiology of organisms given the observed and forecasted impacts of global climate change." Using a simple heat budget model that was ground-truthed with approximately five years of *in situ* temperature data obtained by biomimetic sensors, Helmuth *et al.* (2011) "explored the sensitivity of aerial (low tide) mussel body temperature at three tidal elevations to changes in air temperature, solar radiation, wind speed, wave height, and the timing of low tide at a site in central California USA (Bodega Bay)."

The six U.S. scientists found "while increases in air temperature and solar radiation can significantly alter the risk of exposure to stressful conditions, especially at upper intertidal elevations, patterns of risk can be substantially reduced by convective cooling such that even moderate increases in mean wind speed (~1 m/sec) can theoretically counteract the effects of substantial (2.5°C) increases in air

temperature." They also found "shifts in the timing of low tide (+1 hour), such as occur [when] moving to different locations along the coast of California, can have very large impacts on sensitivity to increases in air temperature," noting, "depending on the timing of low tide, at some sites increases in air temperature will primarily affect animals in the upper intertidal zone, while at other sites animals will be affected across all tidal elevations." In addition, "body temperatures are not always elevated even when low tide air temperatures are extreme," due to "the combined effects of convective cooling and wave splash."

Helmuth *et al.* say their findings suggest the timing and magnitude of organismal warming "will be highly variable at coastal sites, and can be driven to a large extent by local oceanographic and meteorological processes." They "strongly caution against the use of single environmental metrics such as air temperature" for "making projections of the impacts of climate change." Moreover, caution should be applied in interpreting the findings of laboratory-based studies, which often do not mimic conditions in the real world and therefore can yield results and implications quite different from those observed in the real world.

Byrne *et al.* (2011) studied the thermotolerance of the planktonic life phase of sea urchin *Heliocidaris erythrogramma* along the southeast coast of Australia, where sea surface temperatures (SSTs) have risen by 2.3°C over the past 60 years. They employed experimental treatments ranging from 18 to 26°C, with the latter value representing a 3 to 4°C increase above recent ambient SSTs. They found "development success across all stages (gastrula, 24 h; larva, 72 h; juvenile, 120 h) decreased with increasing temperature," and they acknowledge "significant deleterious effects were evident at +3 to 4°C." They also report, "larvae that developed through the early bottleneck of normal development at 26°C metamorphosed successfully," and there was a 25% decrease in planktonic larval duration (PLD) of the larvae in the highest of the temperature treatments. In parallel studies of progeny derived from the northern and southern parts of the coastline, they found "northern embryos had significantly higher thermotolerance."

The five researchers say ocean warming may be advantageous to *H. erythrogramma* larvae "through early settlement and reduction of the vulnerable planktonic period." They also state the higher thermotolerance of the species' northern embryos "provides the possibility that *H. erythrogramma* populations might keep up with a warming world through poleward migration of thermotolerant propagules, facilitated by the strong southward flow of the East Australian Current." They conclude "due to its extensive latitudinal distribution, its potential developmental thermotolerance and independence of its lecithotrophic larvae from exogenous food and the need to make a functional skeleton, *H. erythrogramma* may be particularly robust to ocean change."

Laidre and Heide-Jorgensen (2005) used a combination of long-term satellite tracking data, climate data, and remotely sensed sea ice concentrations to detect localized habitat trends of the narwhal (*Monodon monoceros*) in Baffin Bay between Greenland and Canada—which is home to the largest numbers of the world's narwhals—to study the species' vulnerability to ongoing and projected climate change. The two researchers write, "since 1970, the climate in West Greenland has cooled, reflected in both oceanographic and biological conditions (Hanna and Cappelen, 2003)," with the result "Baffin Bay and Davis Strait display strong significant increasing trends in ice concentrations and extent, as high as 7.5% per decade between 1979 and 1996, with comparable increases detected back to 1953 (Parkinson *et al.*, 1999; Deser *et al.*, 2000; Parkinson, 2000a,b; Parkinson and Cavalieri, 2002; Stern and Heide-Jorgensen, 2003)."

Laidre and Heide-Jorgensen report, "cetacean occurrence is generally negatively correlated with dense or complete ice cover due to the need to breathe at the surface," and "lacking the ability to break holes in the ice," narwhals are vulnerable to reductions in open water availability, as has been demonstrated by ice entrapment events "where hundreds of narwhals died during rapid sea ice formation caused by sudden cold periods (Siegstad and Heide-Jorgensen, 1994; Heide-Jorgensen *et al.*, 2002)." These events are becoming more likely as temperatures continue to decline and sea ice cover and variability increase; the researchers found the latter two trends to be "highly significant at or above the 95% confidence level." They conclude, "with the evidence of changes in sea ice conditions that could impact foraging, prey availability, and of utmost importance, access to the surface to breathe, it is unclear how narwhal subpopulations will fare in light of changes in the high Arctic." Clearly, warmer temperatures capable of reducing sea ice cover would benefit narwhals, making them less vulnerable to death from the cold.

Poloczanska *et al.* (2011) resurveyed a historical census of rocky-shore marine fauna that had been conducted in the 1940s and 1950s, to ascertain whether there had been subsequent latitudinal changes in the distribution and abundance of intertidal marine species consistent with global climate change along Australia's east coast, which, as they demonstrate, "has undergone rapid warming, with increases in temperature of ~1.5°C over the past 60 years." Their survey was conducted at 22 rocky-shore sites located between 23 and 35°S latitude, stretching across 1,500 km of coastline.

Of the 37 species the authors encountered that had distributional data available from both time periods, "only six species showed poleward shifts consistent with predictions of global climate change." Four others moved in the opposite direction "inconsistent with expectations under climate change," and the rest "showed no significant changes in range edges." The seven scientists state a combination of wave exposure, local currents, and the presence of large sand islands—"not temperature"—"is the primary factor influencing biogeographic distributions along the subtropical east coast of Australia."

The contemporaneous study of Seabra *et al.* (2011) supports this conclusion, describing how intertidal marine species can easily withstand significant climatic warming without having to migrate poleward. They examined the relative magnitudes of local-scale versus large-scale latitudinal patterns of the intertidal body temperatures of robolimpets (Lima and Wethey, 2009): autonomous temperature sensor/loggers mimicking the visual aspect and temperature trajectories of real limpets. These temperatures were measured at 30-minute intervals for recurring periods of 170 days at 13 exposed or moderately exposed rocky shores along 1,500 km of the Atlantic coast of the Iberian Peninsula, where they were attached to steep rocky surfaces—both north-facing (typically shaded) and south-facing (sun-exposed)—at three tidal heights covering the entire vertical range inhabited by real-life limpets.

The "most relevant finding" of the study, the four researchers write, was "sunny versus shaded differences were consistently larger than the variability associated with [a] the seasons, [b] shore-specific characteristics (topography, orientation, wave exposure, etc.) and [c] shore level." Seabra *et al.* say these findings emphasize the importance of analyzing temperature variability at scales relevant to the organisms being studied, "since the usage of sea surface temperature (SST) derived from remotely sensed data to model the distribution of intertidal species may be missing key environmental features," especially since their results "clearly show that other factors than SST play a much stronger role in determining the body temperatures of these organisms." They also suggest "the observed temperature variability may explain the weak correlations found in many studies modeling the distribution of intertidal species using SST data (e.g. Lima *et al.*, 2007b), which negatively impacts attempts of forecasting distributional changes in response to predicted climate warming."

Seabra *et al.* further state "habitat heterogeneity as determined by surface orientation and, to a lesser extent, height on the shore may provide thermal refugia allowing species to occupy habitats apparently inhospitable when considering only average temperatures," and "this may be important for understanding range shifts contrary to global warming predictions (e.g. Lima *et al.*, 2007a, 2009; Hilbish *et al.*, 2010)." Thus, they emphasize again "thermal heterogeneity within habitats must be fully understood in order to interpret patterns of biogeographic response to climate change."

Webster *et al.* (2011) note sponges comprise a major component of coral reef macrofauna and play key ecological roles, including providing habitat for other invertebrates and complex microbial symbioses, citing Bell (2008). Concerned that projected increases in air and sea surface temperatures of up to 4°C by 2100, as suggested in IPCC (2007) report, will have a direct and significant impact on sponges and their holobionts, Webster *et al.* "assessed the effect of elevated seawater temperature on bacterial communities in larvae of the Great Barrier Reef sponge, *Rhopaloeides odorabile*," in a series of laboratory experiments to "compare the thermal thresholds for the different life history phases of this model sponge species."

Although *R. odorabile* adults were previously observed to experience significant negative repercussions above 32°C, the four researchers found their larvae exhibited "a markedly higher thermal tolerance," with no adverse effects detected at temperatures up to 36°C, and their microbial communities "were conserved at temperatures up to 34°C." The Australian scientists state, "we demonstrated that sponge larvae maintain highly stable symbioses at seawater temperatures exceeding those that are predicted under current climate change scenarios." Given the likelihood both the sponge and its holobionts would experience considerable adaptive evolution between now and the end of the twenty-first century, it is safe to say predicted global warming would have little or no impact on their survival and normal functioning.

Weber *et al.* (2012) note, "temperature has a profound effect on hatching success, embryonic development and sex in marine turtles," and these effects have logically led to "growing concerns regarding the impacts of climate warming on their reproductive success." Weber *et al.* tested for "local adaptation in an island-nesting population of green turtles (*Chelonia mydas*) where incubation temperatures vary dramatically among closely adjacent nesting beaches," one with pale sand (Long Beach, LB) and one with dark sand (Northeast Bay, NEB) that was consistently 2–3°C warmer than the pale sand beach only 6 km away. They employed "a combination of *in situ* and common-garden approaches to compare survival (as a measure of fitness), developmental rates and size at hatching for offspring of LB and NEB females at different incubation temperatures, while simultaneously accounting for egg-mediated maternal effects."

The six scientists report the offspring of female turtles nesting on the naturally hot (black sand) beach "survived better and grew larger at hot incubation temperatures" compared with the offspring of females nesting on the cooler (pale sand) beach. These differences, they write, were caused by "shallower thermal reaction norms in the hot beach population, rather than shifts in thermal optima, and could not be explained by egg-mediated maternal effects." They conclude "the results of the common-garden experiment suggest that the increased heat-tolerance of NEB turtles has a genetic basis."

Weber *et al.* also say their results suggest "marine turtle nesting behavior can drive adaptive differentiation at remarkably fine spatial scales," and "previous studies may have underestimated the extent of adaptive structuring in marine turtle populations that may significantly affect their capacity to respond to environmental change." They conclude, whereas "global warming is predicted to have multiple deleterious effects on the reproductive success of marine turtles, including the loss of nesting beaches to rising sea levels, increasingly feminized populations and reduced hatching success," their results suggest "in at least one of these respects, marine turtles have the capacity to adapt to warmer temperatures."

Doonan *et al.* (2012) write, "*Katharina tunicata*, commonly known as the Black Katy Chiton, is an abundant intertidal grazer with a limited pelagic larval stage of approximately six days (Paine, 1992)," which is distributed along the Pacific coast of North America from Alaska's Aleutian Islands to southern California, where it is "an important regulator of intertidal ecosystems." They say the species "has recently suffered declines in localized parts of its range as a result of exploitation by humans and sea otters." Noting it is also "under threat from the effects of climate change," they sought to determine "whether local-scale barriers to gene flow could potentially compromise the dispersal capacity of the species in the face of climate change." They "used nuclear single-nucleotide polymorphisms and mitochrondrial DNA sequencing to elucidate fine-scale patterns of genetic variation between populations of the Black Katy Chiton separated by 15–150 km in southwest Vancouver Island."

The four UK researchers from Queen's University in Belfast report, "both the nuclear and mitochondrial data sets revealed no genetic differentiation between the populations studied," and "an isolation-with-migration analysis indicated extensive local-scale gene flow, suggesting an absence of barriers to dispersal." They write, "population demographic analysis also revealed long-term population stability through previous periods of climate change associated with the Pleistocene glaciations," and at the Pleistocene-Holocene transition of approximately ten thousand years ago, as discussed by Fields *et al.* (1993). Doonan *et al.* conclude, "taken together, the current evidence of high dispersal and a lack of biogeographic barriers to gene flow, coupled with the signature of long-term population stability through previous periods of climate change, suggest that this dispersal potential may act as a lifeline for *K. tunicata* as their southerly habitats rapidly warm, and a poleward migration is required for survival," citing Graham *et al.* (2010).

In an ecosystem-level study, Stuart-Smith *et al.* (2010) state, "despite increasing scientific and public concerns [about] the potential impacts of global ocean warming on marine biodiversity, very few empirical data on community-level responses to rising water temperatures are available." They undertook "a study of sub-tidal reef communities over a decadal time scale, comparing data on fishes, macroinvertebrates and macroalgae collected at 136 sites, spanning hundreds of kilometers around the island of Tasmania (southeastern Australia) in the early to mid 1990s, with data from the same sites in 2006/2007."

This region, they write, "has experienced relatively rapid warming during the last century as a consequence of a strengthening of the warm East Australian Current (Ridgway, 2007)," which manifested "an increase in sea surface temperature of 2.28 ± 0.35°C per century for the period 1944–2002 (Ridgway, 2007), which is considerably more rapid than the global mean of 0.6 ± 0.2°C per century estimated by Smith and Reynolds (2003), and a mean increase in surface air temperature of 0.6–0.8°C (Salinger, 2005; Hansen *et al.*, 2006)." The warming around this part of Tasmania has been more than three times greater than the global mean, making this region a prime location to examine the impacts of rising temperature on marine species in the real world.

Contrary to their expectations, the four researchers discovered "Tasmanian shallow rocky reef communities have been relative stable over the past decade," despite the "substantial rise in sea surface temperature over this period" and the "continuation of a considerable warming trend in oceanographic conditions over the last 50 years." They report, "the northeast and southeast bioregions, which are most influenced by the East Australian Current and hence have experienced the greatest warming over the last century, appeared to have actually changed very little," adding, "not only were Tasmanian reef communities remarkably similar between 1994 and 2006 in a multivariate sense, but univariate community characteristics such as species richness and total fish abundance were also consistent."

Poloczanska *et al.* (2013) "investigated the peer-reviewed literature that addresses the question of whether or not climate change impacts marine ecological phenomena, and found 208 studies of 857 species and assemblages." From these reports they extracted "1,735 observations of the following types of response: distribution, phenology, abundance, community change, calcification and demography," for which "either regional or global climate change was considered as a driver."

The 20 researchers report, "from this database, 81–83% of all observations for distribution, phenology, community composition, abundance, demography and calcification across taxa and ocean basins were consistent with the expected impacts of climate change." They add, "of the species responding to climate change, rates of distribution shifts were, on average, consistent with those required to track ocean surface temperature changes." The findings of this massive review of the relevant scientific literature indicate Earth's marine life is well-equipped to deal with predicted changes in the global ocean environment and are, in fact, already doing so.

Linares *et al.* (2013) note, "several studies have provided evidence that thermal stress affects the growth, survival and physiology of tropical and temperate macro-invertebrate species," but "few studies have focused on sub-tidal temperate species and the potential differential thermal tolerances of populations dwelling under contrasting temperature conditions." Linares *et al.* assessed "the role that environmental history plays in the response of the temperate gorgonian *Eunicella singularis* to thermal stress," comparing populations dwelling in the coldest and warmest areas of the NW Mediterranean Sea.

The four researchers report, "*E. singularis* populations from both areas exhibited a high resistance to thermal stress," but "populations from warmer areas had an increased tolerance to thermal stress," such that "the upper thermal limits found for cold and warm populations were 28 and 29°C, respectively." Linares *et al.* conclude by noting their results "agree with results for other Mediterranean anthozoans (Rodolfo-Metalpa *et al.* 2006; Torrents *et al.*, 2008) and tropical corals (Middlebrook *et al.*, 2008), demonstrating thereby that shallow populations (acclimated to warm temperature conditions) have a higher tolerance to thermal stress than deep populations."

References

Bell, J.J. 2008. The functional roles of marine sponges. *Estuarine, Coastal and Shelf Science* **79**: 341–353.

Byrne, M., Selvakumaraswamy, P., Ho, M.A., Woolsey, E., and Nguyen, H.D. 2011. Sea urchin development in a global change hotspot, potential for southerly migration of thermotolerant propagules. *Deep-Sea Research II* **58**: 712–719.

Deser, C., Walsh, J.E., and Timlin, M.S. 2000. Arctic sea ice variability in the context of recent atmospheric circulation trends. *Journal of Climatology* **13**: 617–633.

Doonan, J., Beatty, G.E., Sigwart, J.D., and Provan, J. 2012. Extensive local-scale gene flow and long-term population stability in the intertidal mollusk *Katharina tunicata* (Mollusca: Polyplacophora). *Biological Journal of the Linnean Society* **106**: 589–597.

Fields, P.A., Graham, J.B., Rosenblatt, R.H., and Somero, G.N. 1993. Effects of expected global climate change on marine faunas. *Trends in Ecology and Evolution* **8**: 361–367.

Graham, C.H., VanDerWal, J., Philips, S.J., Moritz, C., and Williams, S.E. 2010. Dynamic refugia and species persistence: tracking spatial shifts in habitat through time. *Ecography* **33**: 1062–1069.

Hanna, E. and Cappelen, J. 2003. Recent cooling in coastal southern Greenland and relation with the North Atlantic Oscillation. *Geophysical Research Letters* **30**: 321–323.

Hansen, J., Sato, M., Ruedy, R., Lo, K., Lea, D.W., and

Medina-Elizade, M. 2006. Global temperature change. *Proceedings of the National Academy of Sciences USA* **103**: 14,288–14,293.

Heide-Jorgensen, M.P., Richard, P., Ramsay, M., and Akeeagok, S. 2002. *Three recent Ice Entrapments of Arctic Cetaceans in West Greenland and the Eastern Canadian High Arctic.* Volume 4, NAMMCO Scientific Publications, pp. 143–148.

Helmuth, B., Yamane, L., Lalwani, S., Matzelle, A., Tockstein, A., and Gao, N. 2011. Hidden signals of climate change in intertidal ecosystems: What (not) to expect when you are expecting. *Journal of Experimental Marine Biology and Ecology* **400**: 191–199.

Hilbish, T.J., Brannock, P.M., Jones, K.R., Smith, A.B., Bullock, N.B., and Wethey, D.S. 2010. Historical changes in the distributions of invasive and endemic marine invertebrates are contrary to global warming predictions: the effects of decadal climate oscillations. *Journal of Biogeography* **37**: 423–431.

IPCC. 2007. *Climate Change 2007: The Physical Basis.* Contribution of Working Group I to the Fourth Assessment Report of the Intergovernmental Panel on Climate Change. IPCC, Geneva, Switzerland.

Laidre, K.L. and Heide-Jorgensen, M.P. 2005. Arctic sea ice trends and narwhal vulnerability. *Biological Conservation* **121**: 509–517.

Lima, F.P., Queiroz, N., Ribeiro, P.A., Xavier, R., Hawkins, S.J., and Santos, A.M. 2009. First record of *Halidrys siliquosa* (Linnaeus) Lyngbye in the Portuguese coast: counter-intuitive range expansion? *Marine Biodiversity Records* **2**: 10.1017/S1755267208000018.

Lima, F.P., Ribeiro, P.A., Queiroz, N., Hawkins, S.J., and Santos, A.M. 2007a. Do distributional shifts of northern and southern species of algae match the warming pattern? *Global Change Biology* **13**: 2592–2604.

Lima, F.P., Ribeiro, P.A., Queiroz, N., Xavier, R., Tarroso, P., Hawkins, S.J., and Santos, A.M. 2007b. Modeling past and present geographical distribution of the marine gastropod *Patella rustica* as a tool for exploring responses to environmental change. *Global Change Biology* **13**: 2065–2077.

Lima, F.P. and Wethey, D.S. 2009. Robolimpets: measuring intertidal body temperatures using biomimetic loggers. *Limnology and Oceanography: Methods* **7**: 347–353.

Linares, C., Cebrian, E., Kipson, S., and Garrabou, J. 2013. Does thermal history influence the tolerance of temperate gorgonians to future warming? *Marine Environmental Research* **89**: 45–52.

Middlebrook, R., Hoegh-Guldberg, O., and Leggat, W.

2008. The effect of thermal history on the susceptibility of reef-building corals to thermal stress. *Journal of Experimental Biology* **211**: 1050–1056.

Paine, R.T. 1992. Food-web analysis through field measurement of per capita interaction strength. *Nature* **355**: 73–75.

Parkinson, C.L. 2000a. Variability of Arctic sea ice: the view from space, and 18-year record. *Arctic* **53**: 341–358.

Parkinson, C.L. 2000b. Recent trend reversals in Arctic Sea ice extents: possible connections to the North Atlantic oscillation. *Polar Geography* **24**: 1–12.

Parkinson, C.L. and Cavalieri, D.J. 2002. A 21-year record of Arctic sea-ice extents and their regional, seasonal and monthly variability and trends. *Annals of Glaciology* **34**: 441–446.

Parkinson, C., Cavalieri, D., Gloersen, D., Zwally, J., and Comiso, J. 1999. Arctic sea ice extents, areas, and trends, 1978–1996. *Journal of Geophysical Research* **104**: 20,837 20,856.

Poloczanska, E.S., Brown, C.J., Syderman, W.J., Kiessling, W., Schoeman, D.S., Moore, P.J., Brander, K., Bruno, J.F., Buckley, L.B., Burrows, M.T., Duarte, C.M., Halpern, B.S., Holding, J., Kappel, C.V., O'Connor, M.I., Pandolfi, J.M., Parmesan, C., Schwing, F., Thompson, S.A., and Richardson, A.J. 2013. Global imprint of climate change on marine life. *Nature Climate Change* **3**: 919–925.

Poloczanska, E.S., Smith, S., Fauconnet, L., Healy, J., Tibbetts, I.R., Burrows, M.T., and Richardson, A.J. 2011. Little change in the distribution of rocky shore faunal communities on the Australian east coast after 50 years of rapid warming. *Journal of Experimental Marine Biology and Ecology* **400**: 145–154.

Ridgway, K.R. 2007. Long-term trend and decadal variability of the southward penetration of the East Australian current. *Geophysical Research Letters* **34**: 10.1029/2007GL030393.

Rodolfo-Metalpa, R., Richard, C., Allemand, D., and Ferrier-Pages, C. 2006. Growth and photosynthesis of two Mediterranean corals, *Cladocora caespitosa* and *Oculina patagonica*, under normal and elevated temperatures. *Journal of Experimental Biology* **2009**: 4546–4556.

Salinger, M. 2005. Climate variability and change: past, present and future—an overview. *Climatic Change* **70**: 9–29.

Seabra, R., Wethey, D.S., Santos, A.M., and Lima, F.P. 2011. Side matters: Microhabitat influence on intertidal heat stress over a large geographical scale. *Journal of Experimental Marine Biology and Ecology* **400**: 200–208.

Siegstad, H. and Heide-Jorgensen, M.P. 1994. Ice entrapments of narwhals (*Monodon monoceros*) and white whales (*Delphinapterus leucas*) in Greenland. *Meddeleser om Gronland Bioscience* **39**: 151–160.

Smith, T.M. and Reynolds, R.W. 2003. Extended reconstruction of global sea surface temperatures based on COADS data (1854–1997). *Journal of Climate* **16**: 1495–1510.

Stern, H.L. and Heide-Jorgensen, M.P. 2003. Trends and variability of sea ice in Baffin Bay and Davis Strait, 1953–2001. *Polar Research* **22**: 11–18.

Stuart-Smith, R.D., Barrett, N.S., Stevenson, D.G., and Edgar, G.J. 2010. Stability in temperate reef communities over a decadal time scale despite concurrent ocean warming. *Global Change Biology* **16**: 122–134.

Torrents, O., Tambutte, E., Caminiti, N,. and Garrabou, J. 2008. Upper thermal thresholds of shallow vs. deep populations of the precious Mediterranean red coral *Corallium rubrum* (L.): assessing the potential effects of warming in the NW Mediterrancan. *Journal of Experimental Marine Biology and Ecology* **357**: 7–19.

Weber, S.B., Broderick, A.C., Groothuis, T.G.G., Ellick, J., Godley, B.J., and Blount, J.D. 2012. Fine-scale thermal adaptation in a green turtle nesting population. *Proceedings of the Royal Society B* **279**: 1077–1084.

Webster, N.S., Botte, E.S., Soo, R.M., and Whalan, S. 2011. The larval sponge holobiont exhibits high thermal tolerance. *Environmental Microbiology Reports* **3**: 756–762.

6.2 Freshwater Warming

The vast majority of studies examining the potential effects of CO_2-induced global warming on aquatic life are focused on marine life, but some scientists have conducted research on the impacts of elevated temperature on freshwater species. The following bulleted key findings indicate the cautious optimism this research suggests, and the findings are discussed in greater detail thereafter.

- Increases in water temperature at Lake Zurich from 1977 to 2008 have resulted in an increase in the number of phytoplankton species and phytoplankton families.

- Annual bass growth is positively and significantly correlated with annual temperature metrics, revealing above-average growth during the warmest and driest years.

- Golden perch growth rates likely will increase in

southerly Australian populations due to warmer temperatures and a lengthening of the growing season.

- Over the past two decades, when IPCC claims Earth warmed at a rate and to a degree unprecedented over the past millennium, the majority of French fish—plus some newcomers to the country's streams and rivers—thrived under warmer water conditions, increasing in both species numbers (diversity) and population size.

- Many predictions of the impact of climate change on aquatic life assume a species-specific response to changing environments, yet substantial differences in thermal plasticity have been observed between populations within species, enabling some populations to cope effectively with changes in the environment that other populations cannot tolerate. The probability of climate-induced species extinctions is much lower than what is often projected.

- Three species of freshwater mussels can adjust their individual critical thermal maximum (the upper temperature at which the onset of behavioral incapacitation occurs) upwards in response to periodic heat waves or significantly warmer years.

In contrast to IPCC-based projections, modest warming has been shown to be highly beneficial to some freshwater species.

Pomati *et al.* (2012) explain that among human impacts on aquatic biodiversity, eutrophication has caused a number of undesirable environmental effects worldwide, including "a general reduction in species richness (Smith and Schindler, 2009) and a loss of ecosystem resilience against further degradation (Folke *et al.*, 2004)." They indicate "lake restoration programs in many regions started at the peak of the eutrophication period (late 1970s, early 1980s)," but the resulting reduction in nutrient loading "coincided with rising temperature from climate warming," citing Van Donk *et al.* (2003) and Jeppesen *et al.* (2005), so we currently have "limited understanding of how combined climate change and reduction in nutrients affect species richness, ecosystem functioning or resilience."

Pomati *et al.* analyzed physical and biological parameters in Lake Zurich on the Swiss Plateau just north of the Swiss Alps at depths of 0, 1, 2.5, 5, 7.5, 10, 12.5, 15, 20, 30, 40, 80, 120, and 135 meters that had been collected monthly over a number of decades

by the Zurich Water Supply Company, focusing on data from 1977 to 2008. The five scientists discovered increases in water temperature ($0.24°C$/decade at the lake surface; $0.13°C$/decade near the lake bottom) and spatial (depth) heterogeneity were the best predictors of phytoplankton richness, as the number of phytoplankton species increased from about 40 to 100 and the number of phytoplankton families increased from approximately 25 to 45. They note phytoplankton richness and spatial heterogeneity had the strongest effects on zooplankton richness.

The researchers write, "our analysis highlights that climate warming and re-oligotrophication may favor an increase in spatial (depth) heterogeneity in the water column of deep lakes, enhancing the potential for phytoplankton species co-existence and an increase in plankton richness." They conclude, "although our study focuses on a single lake, the responses we have documented may be common at least throughout lakes within the European peri-alpine climatic region," citing Buergi and Stadelmann (2002), Buergi *et al.* (2003), and Anneville *et al.* (2005).

Morrongiello *et al.* (2011) analyzed the yearly growth increments laid down in the otoliths—aragonite ($CaCO_3$) structures in fish that are used for acoustic perception and balance, also known as earstones—of populations of a native fish species (the golden perch) living in two artificial impoundments (Lakes Mokoan and Eppalock) near their southerly distribution limits in central Victoria, Australia. Over a 15-year period that both predated and encompassed a significant supra-seasonal drought, the authors determined "fish growth declined as water levels in the lakes dropped during the drought," but "this effect was offset by increased growth in warmer years." It was in fact more than offset; based on the relationships they found in their data, future projections of mean annual growth of two-year-old golden perch in Lakes Mokoan and Eppalock in the year 2070, respectively, increase by 14.9% and 17.2% under low CO_2 emission and 56.5% and 58.6% under high CO_2 emission scenarios compared with 1990 CO_2 levels. The Australian scientists conclude, "despite climatic models predicting significant declines in future water availability, fish growth may increase due to a disproportionate lengthening of the growing season." They forecast "golden perch growth rates in southerly [Australian] populations may increase as warmer conditions associated with climate change will lengthen the growing season and make these high [southern] latitude habitats more favorable."

Rypel (2009) applied tree-ring techniques to the

otoliths of 397 largemouth bass (*Micropterus salmoides* Lacepede) to explore potential relationships between annual bass growth and various climate metrics in the southeastern USA, as manifest in six rivers and seven reservoirs in Georgia, Alabama, and Mississippi sampled during the summers and autumns of 2005–2008. Rypel reports, "results from multiple regressions suggested that on average roughly 50% of the annual variability in largemouth bass growth was attributable to climatic variations," with annual growth indices typically being found to be "above-average during the warmest, driest years, and below-average during the coldest, wettest years," because "annual bass growth was significantly negatively correlated with annual precipitation metrics, and significantly positively correlated with annual temperature metrics."

These findings indicate the warming and drying that are predicted by models to occur in many places will benefit largemouth bass because an increase in temperature generally "stimulates metabolism, and enhances growth rates of fishes," Rypel writes, citing Beitinger and Fitzpatrick (1979) and Brander (1995).

Poulet *et al.* (2011) write, "over the past 200 years, owing to the industrial and agricultural revolutions, various new and intense pressures have been applied to freshwater ecosystems resulting in the decline of many species both in range and number (Maitland, 1995)." Of these additional threats, they highlight five: overexploitation, water pollution, flow modification, destruction or degradation of habitat, and invasion by exotic species, citing Dudgeon *et al.* (2006). Poulet *et al.* used the extensive electrofishing database of the French National Agency for Water and Aquatic Environment to evaluate time trends of 48 freshwater fish taxa at 590 sites across France over the period 1990–2009, to assess the recent and ongoing net impact of these modern threats to the fish of France.

The three French researchers found "species richness increased steadily from the beginning of the monitoring period," and "the number of species displaying a significant increase in spatial distribution or abundance was greater than those showing a significant decrease." They write, "these results are in agreement with recent findings which describe an increase in the number of species and density of fish communities in large French rivers over the past 25 years," citing Daufresne and Boet (2007). They add, "predictions about the future distribution of 30 common fish species in French streams in 2008, suggested increases in local species richness and in occurrences of the majority of species (Buisson *et al.*,

2008)," and they note "both studies described population growth of warm and cool water species in response to global warming."

Over the past two decades, when IPCC claims Earth warmed at a rate and to a degree unprecedented over the past millennium or two, the majority of French fish, plus some newcomers to the country's streams and rivers, thrived under warmer water conditions, increasing in both species numbers (diversity) and population size.

While not all aquatic species may respond in such a positive manner, there is little reason to accept IPCC's model-based projections of widespread future species decline (and possible extinctions) in response to CO_2-induced global warming. A growing body of evidence demonstrates the ability of aquatic life to adapt and evolve to overcome challenges imposed by rising water temperatures.

Seebacher *et al.* (2012) note "within-individual plasticity (acclimation) counteracts potentially negative physiological effects resulting from environmental changes and thereby maintains fitness across a broad range of environments." They write, "the capacity for the acclimation of individuals may therefore determine the persistence of populations in variable environments."

They "determined phylogenetic relationships by Amplified Fragment Length Polymorphism (AFLP) analysis of six populations of mosquitofish (*Gambusia holbrooki*) from coastal and mountain environments and compared their capacity for thermal acclimation." The six scientists demonstrated mosquitofish populations "are divided into distinct genetic lineages and that populations within lineages have distinct genetic identities." They report, "there were significant differences in the capacity for acclimation between traits (swimming performance, citrate synthase and lactate dehydrogenase activities), between lineages, and between populations within lineages," demonstrating "there can be substantial variation in thermal plasticity between populations within species." They conclude "similar responses are likely to be found in other species that comprise structured populations."

Noting "many predictions of the impact of climate change on biodiversity assume a species-specific response to changing environments," Seebacher *et al.* argue, "this resolution can be too coarse and ... analysis of the impacts of climate change and other environmental variability should be resolved to a population level," because their findings suggest some populations of a species may be able to cope with a change of climate with which others cannot, thereby preventing the otherwise-inevitable climate-induced extinction of the species.

Gailbraith *et al.* (2012) studied thermal adaptation of three species of freshwater mussels (*Alasmidonta varicosa*, *Elliptio complanata*, and *Strophitus undulatus*) that had been acclimatized to a water temperature of either 15 or 25°C. The temperature of the water in which the mussels were immersed was gradually raised at a rate of 0.35°C per minute, until the researchers observed the onset of extreme gaping, a periodic valve movement resulting in the rapid opening and closing of the mussels' shells that indicates their impending demise. The authors thus studied the mussels' critical thermal maximum (CTM), defined as the upper (warm) temperature at which the onset of behavioral incapacitation (usually loss of equilibrium) occurs—in the words of Gailbraith *et al.* quoting Hutchison (1961)—"the animal loses its ability to escape from conditions that will promptly lead to its death." Although it sounds like a fixed, immutable value for a given species, the CTM has been proven to be a function of temperature itself.

The three U.S. researchers report, "responses varied by species, but mussels acclimated to 25°C generally had a higher CTM than mussels acclimated to 15°C." For one of the three species (*E. complanata*), they observed the effects of acclimation and another variable (aeration) were interactive, leading them to conclude "combinations of environmental stressors may influence thermal tolerance" and "such responses vary among species." They note results similar to theirs "are well documented for other freshwater organisms, particularly for fish (Becker and Genoway, 1979; Elliott, 1981) but also for the zebra mussel, *Dreissena polymorpha* (McMahon and Ussery, 1995; Lutterschmidt and Hutchison, 1997)."

Although multiple factors may thus come into play in determining an animal's current CTM, it is evident from the results of Galbraith *et al.* that some degree of warming above that species-specific value can at times lead to a longer-term increase in the species' CTM. In the case of global warming, the evidence suggests species may adjust their individual CTMs upward in response to periodic heat waves or significantly warmer years.

Crozier *et al.* (2011) note "environmental change can shift the phenotype of an organism through either evolutionary or non-genetic processes," but "despite abundant evidence of phenotypic change in response to recent climate change, we typically lack sufficient genetic data to identify the role of evolution." They studied the potential role of rapid evolution by investigating the drivers of a long-term trend toward earlier upstream migration date in adult sockeye salmon (*Oncorhynchus nerka* Walbaum) that currently migrate up the Columbia River 10.3 days earlier than they did in the 1940s. Noting water temperature records in the lower river showed a rise of 2.6°C in mean July temperature since 1949, the researchers "developed a functional model relating survival during upstream migration to temperature on the basis of the results of recent studies that tracked individual fish through the migration," after which they "hindcast this function over the historical record to estimate the putative selection differential over the time series." Thereafter, they "assembled a set of possible environmental drivers of interannual variation in migration timing from the literature" and used "a state-space modeling framework to combine selection and these environmental variables as covariates to explain mean population migration date in a formal time-series analysis," employing "model-selection techniques to determine which factors best predicted annual migration timing."

The three researchers from the Northwest Fisheries Science Center in Seattle, Washington (USA) determined "an evolutionary response to thermal selection was capable of explaining up to two-thirds of the phenotypic trend" they observed, and "adaptive plastic responses to June river flow explain most of the remainder." Crozier *et al.* note the amount of evolutionary change they calculated to have taken place "is typical of numerous studies of contemporary evolution," citing Hendry and Kinnison (1999) and Kingsolver *et al.* (2001). They suggest evolutionary change "will play an important role in protecting species from extinction during ongoing climate change, as demonstrated in recent simulations of evolution in Fraser River sockeye salmon," citing Reed *et al.* (2011). They conclude, "directional environmental changes are very likely to induce more rapid evolution in the future."

References

Anneville, O., Gammeter, S., and Straile, D. 2005. Phosphorus decrease and climate variability: mediators of synchrony in phytoplankton changes among European perialpine lakes. *Freshwater Biology* **50**: 1731–1746.

Becker, C.D. and Genoway, R.G. 1979. Evaluation of the critical thermal maximum for determining thermal tolerance of freshwater fish. *Environmental Biology of Fishes* **4**: 245–256.

Beitinger, T.L. and Fitzpatrick, L.C. 1979. Physiological

and ecological correlates of preferred temperature in fish. *Integrative and Comparative Biology* **19**: 319–329.

Brander, K. 1995. The effect of temperature on growth of Atlantic cod (*Gadus morhua* L.). *ICES Journal of Marine Science* **52**: 1–10.

Buergi, H.R. and Stadelmann, P. 2002. Change of phytoplankton composition and biodiversity in Lake Sempach before and during restoration. *Hydrobiologia* **469**: 33–48.

Buergi, H.R., Bührer, H., and Keller B. 2003. Long-term changes in functional properties and biodiversity of plankton in Lake Greifensee (Switzerland) in response to phosphorus reduction. *Aquatic Ecosystem Health and Management* **6**: 147–158.

Buisson, L., Thuillier, W., Lek, S., Lim, P., and Grenouillet, G. 2008. Climate change hastens turnover of stream fish assemblages. *Global Change Biology* **14**: 1–17.

Crozier, L.G., Scheuerell, M.D., and Zabel, R.W. 2011. Using time series analysis to characterize evolutionary and plastic responses to environmental change: A case study of a shift toward earlier migration date in sockeye salmon. *The American Naturalist* **178**: 755–773.

Daufresne, M. and Boet, P. 2007. Climate change impacts on structure and diversity of fish communities in rivers. *Global Change Biology* **13**: 2467–2478.

Dudgeon, D., Arthington, A.H., Gessner, M.O., Kawabata, Z.I., Knowler, D.J., Leveque, C., Naiman, R.J., Prieur-Richard, A.H., Soto, D., Stiassny, M.L.J., and Sullivan, C.A. 2006. Freshwater biodiversity: importance, threats, status and conservation challenges. *Biological Reviews* **81**: 163–182.

Elliott, J.M. 1981. Thermal stress on freshwater teleosts. In: Pickering, A.D. (Ed.) *Stress and Fish*. Academic Press, New York, New York, USA, pp. 207–245.

Folke, C., Carpenter, S., Walker, B., Scheffer, M., Elmqvist, T., Gunderson, L., and Holling, C.S. 2004. Regime shifts, resilience and biodiversity in ecosystem management. *Annual Review of Ecology, Evolution and Systematics* **35**: 557–581.

Galbraith, H.S., Blakeslee, C.J., and Lellis, W.A. 2012. Recent thermal history influences thermal tolerance in freshwater mussel species (Bivalvia: Unionoida). *Freshwater Science* **31**: 83–92.

Hendry, A.P. and Kinnison, M.T. 1999. Perspective: the pace of modern life: measuring rates of contemporary microevolution. *Evolution* **53**: 1637–1653.

Hutchison, V.H. 1961. Critical thermal maxima in salamanders. *Physiological Zoology* **34**: 92–125.

Jeppesen, E., Sondergaard, M., Jensen, J.P., Havens, K.E., Anneville, O., Carvalho, L., Coveney, M.F., Deneke, R., Dokulil, M.T., Foy, B., Gerdeaux, D., Hampton, S.E., Hilt, S., Kangur, K., Kohler, J., Lammens, E.H., Lauridsen, T.L., Manca, M., Miracle, M.R., Moss, B., Noges, P., Persson, G., Phillips, G., Portielje, R., Romo, S., Schelske, C.L., Straile, D., Tatrai, I., Willen, E., and Winder, M. 2005. Lake responses to reduced nutrient loading—an analysis of contemporary long-term data from 35 case studies. *Freshwater Biology* **50**: 1747–1771.

Kingsolver, J.G., Hoekstra, H.E., Hoekstra, J.M., Berrigan, D., Vignieri, S.N., Hill, C.E., Hoang, A., Gibert, P., and Beerli, P. 2001. The strength of phenotypic selection in natural populations. *American Naturalist* **157**: 245–261.

Lutterschmidt, W.I. and Hutchison, V.H. 1997. The critical thermal maximum: history and critique. *Canadian Journal of Zoology* **75**: 1561–1574.

Maitland, P.S. 1995. The conservation of freshwater fish: past and present experience. *Biological Conservation* **72**: 259–270.

McMahon, R.F. and Ussery, T.A. 1995. Thermal Tolerance of Zebra Mussels (Dreissena polymorpha) Relative to Rate of Temperature Increase and Acclimation Temperature. U.S. Army Corps of Engineers, Washington, D.C.

Morrongiello, J.R., Crook, D.A., King, A.J., Ramsey, D.S., and Brown, P. 2011. Impacts of drought and predicted effects of climate change on fish growth in temperate Australian lakes. *Global Change Biology* **17**: 745–755.

Pomati, F., Matthews, B., Jokela, J., Schildknecht, A., and Ibelings, B.W. 2012. Effects of re-oligotrophication and climate warming on plankton richness and community stability in a deep mesotrophic lake. *Oikos* **121**: 1317–1327.

Poulet, N., Beaulaton, L., and Dembski, S. 2011. Time trends in fish populations in metropolitan France: insights from national monitoring data. *Journal of Fish Biology* **79**: 1436–1452.

Reed, T.E., Schindler, D., Hague, M., Paterson, D., Meir, E., Waples, R.S., and Hinch, S. 2011. Time to evolve? Potential evolutionary responses of Fraser River sockeye salmon to climate change and effects on persistence. *PLoS ONE* **6**: e20380.

Rypel, A.L. 2009. Climate-growth relationships for largemouth bass (*Micropterus salmoides*) across three southeastern USA states. *Ecology of Freshwater Fish* **18**: 620–628.

Seebacher, F., Holmes, S., Roosen, N.J., Nouvian, M., Wilson, R.S., and Ward, A.J.W. 2012. Capacity for thermal acclimation differs between populations and phylogenetic lineages within a species. *Functional Ecology* **26**: 1418–1428.

Smith, V.H. and Schindler, D.W. 2009. Eutrophication science: where do we go from here? *Trends in Ecology and Evolution* **24**: 201–207.

Van Donk, E., Santamaria, L., and Mooij, W.M. 2003. Climate warming causes regime shifts in lake food webs: a reassessment. *Limnology and Oceanography* **48**: 1350–1353.

6.3 Ocean "Acidification"

6.3.1 Introduction

As the air's CO_2 content rises in response to increasing anthropogenic CO_2 emissions, more CO_2 dissolves in the surface waters of the world's oceans. Theoretical reasoning, some of it reviewed in Section 6.3.1.2 below, suggests the pH values—a negative or inverse measure of the acidity of water—of the planet's oceanic waters should be gradually decreasing.

By some estimates, the globe's seawater has declined by about 0.1 pH unit relative to what it was in preindustrial times, and model calculations imply there could be an additional drop somewhere in the neighborhood of 0.3 to 0.7 pH by the year 2300. IPCC and others refer to this small potential change in oceanic pH and its presumed impacts on aquatic life as "ocean acidification." That term, however, is misleading and deceptive. The world's oceans are currently basic (or alkaline), with an average pH of around 8.1, and there is no chance future anthropogenic CO_2 emissions will ever cause the oceans to become acidic (pH less than 7). The general public, not scientifically trained, naturally interprets the phrase literally and assumes rising atmospheric CO_2 is turning the world's oceans, lakes, and streams into a dangerous acid that is harming (or will harm) marine life.

IPCC characterizes the projected pH reduction as a cause for great concern, because it has been postulated to harm calcifying marine life such as corals, not only by reducing the calcifying rates of marine organisms but also by impeding the responses of other growth and developmental parameters of these organisms. The ocean chemistry aspect of this ocean acidification hypothesis is rather straightforward, but it is not as solid as model projections make it out to be. Some researchers, including Pieter

Tans, senior scientist at the National Oceanic and Atmospheric Administration (NOAA) Earth System Research Laboratory in Boulder, Colorado (USA), have published papers suggesting the drop in oceanic pH will not be nearly as great as IPCC and others predict. Figures 6.3.1.1 and 6.3.1.2 illustrate Tans' analysis.

The first of the two figures depicts much of the past and projected history of fossil-fuel carbon utilization, together with historical and projected atmospheric CO_2 concentrations to the year 2500, as calculated by Tans (2009). As the figure shows, the air's CO_2 concentration is expected to peak well before 2100 and at only 500 ppm, as compared to the 800 ppm predicted in one of IPCC's scenarios. It is

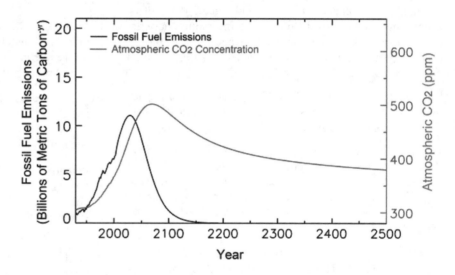

Figure 6.3.1.1. Past and projected trends of fossil-fuel carbon utilization and the atmosphere's CO_2 concentration. Adapted from Tans (2009).

also worth noting that by the year 2500, the air's CO_2 concentration should actually drop back to about what it is today.

When these emission estimates are calculated for their expected reductions of oceanic pH, as shown in Figure 6.3.1.2, the projected pH change at 2100 is far below what IPCC estimates. The pH projections from Tans' data also suggest a recovery to values near those of today by the year 2500, a striking contradiction of IPCC's estimates. (Tans' research is described in more detail in the next section.)

The increase of CO_2 in the air should lead to additional weathering of terrestrial carbonates and dissolution of marine carbonates, which would increase delivery of Ca^{2+} and CO_3^{2-} to the oceans and largely compensate for the CO_2-induced decrease in

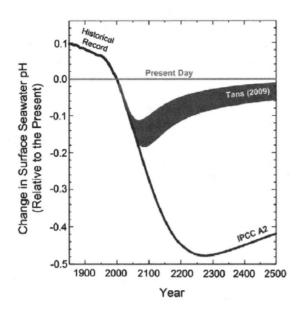

Figure 6.3.1.2. Past and projected trends of oceanic pH based on fossil-fuel carbon utilization estimates from Tans (2009) and IPCC's A2 scenario.

oceanic calcium carbonate saturation, further suggesting IPCC's projections of ocean acidification may be exaggerated. In addition, as with all phenomena involving living organisms, the introduction of life into the ocean acidification picture greatly complicates things, as several interrelated biological phenomena must be considered; when they are, it becomes much more difficult to draw such sweeping negative conclusions as IPCC does.

As the research reviewed in the subsections below demonstrates, the rising CO_2 content of Earth's atmosphere may be a beneficial phenomenon with many positive consequences for the oceans as well as other aspects of the environment (Idso, 2009).

Before proceeding into those specifics, however, we provide a brief discussion of changes in oceanic pH, followed by some additional considerations of ocean chemistry.

References

Caldeira, K. and Wickett, M.E. 2003. Anthropogenic carbon and ocean pH. *Nature* **425**: 365.

Caldeira, K. and Wickett, M.E. 2005. Ocean model predictions of chemistry changes from carbon dioxide emissions to the atmosphere and ocean. *Journal of Geophysical Research* **110**: 10.1029/2004JC002671.

Idso, C.D. 2009. *CO₂, Global Warming and Coral Reefs.*

Vales Lake Publishing, LLC, Pueblo West, Colorado, USA.

Tans, P. 2009. An accounting of the observed increase in oceanic and atmospheric CO_2 and an outlook for the future. *Oceanography* **22**: 26–35.

6.3.1.1 Assessing and Projecting Changes in Oceanic pH

Based on four theoretical constructs—a geochemical model, an ocean general-circulation model, an IPCC CO_2 emissions scenario for the twenty-first century, and a projected logistic function for the burning of Earth's post-twenty-first century fossil-fuel reserves —Caldeira and Wickett (2003) calculated the atmospheric CO_2 concentration could approach 2,000 ppm around the year 2300, leading to a surface seawater pH reduction of 0.7 unit, a change they describe as being much more rapid and considerably greater "than any experienced in the past 300 million years." This long time interval makes the phenomenon sound truly catastrophic, especially as IPCC claims this "ocean acidification" phenomenon will impede the process of calcification in corals and other marine life. In judging the plausibility of this scenario, it is important first to know whether the acidification phenomenon is really severe and unprecedented.

In a special issue of *Oceanography* published in December 2009, Feely *et al.* (2009) review what is known about the current pH status of the world's oceans and what can likely be expected by the end of the current century. The three researchers write, "estimates based on the Intergovernmental Panel on Climate Change business-as-usual emission scenarios suggest that atmospheric CO_2 levels could approach 800 ppm near the end of the century," and "corresponding biogeochemical models for the ocean indicate that surface water pH will drop from a pre-industrial value of about 8.2 to about 7.8 in IPCC A2 scenario by the end of this century." They warn, as a result, "the skeletal growth rates of calcium-secreting organisms will be reduced" and conclude, "if anthropogenic CO_2 emissions are not dramatically reduced in the coming decades, there is the potential for direct and profound impacts on our living marine ecosystems."

In the same issue of *Oceanography*, Tans (2009) presents a much different take on the subject. He begins by noting the anthropogenic component of the air's CO_2 concentration "depends primarily on the total amount emitted, not on the rate of emissions," and "unfortunately, IPCC reports have not helped public understanding of this fact by choosing, somewhat arbitrarily, a rather short time horizon (100 years is most commonly used) for climate forcing by CO_2."

"Instead of adopting the common economic point of view, which, through its emphasis on perpetual growth, implicitly assumes infinite Earth resources," Tans notes the cumulative extraction of fossil-fuel carbon currently stands at about 345 gigatons of carbon (GtC), and there appears to be another 640 or so GtC of proven reserves, yielding a total original reserve of about 1,000 GtC, from which he proceeds with his analysis.

The past and projected history of fossil-fuel carbon utilization, together with historical and projected atmospheric CO_2 concentrations out to the year 2500, as calculated by Tans, is presented in Figure 6.3.1.1 above. According to the data presented there, Tans shows the air's CO_2 concentration peaking well before 2100 at only 500 ppm, as compared to the 800 ppm Feely et al. take from IPCC. By the year 2500, the air's CO_2 concentration drops back to about what it is today, according to Tans' analysis.

Based on his more modest projections of future atmospheric CO_2 concentrations, Tans finds the projected pH reduction of ocean waters in the year 2100 to be only one-half of the 0.4 value calculated by Feely et al., with a recovery to a reduction of slightly more than 0.1 pH unit by 2500, which is less than the range of pH values typical of today's oceans (8.231 in the Arctic Ocean minus 8.068 in the North Indian Ocean equals 0.163, according to Feely et al.). Graphical data presented by Pelejero et al. (2010) depict interannual pH variations in the North Atlantic Ocean near Bermuda ranging from a high of approximately 8.18 to a low of about 8.03 at various times over the years 1984 to 2007 (Bates, 2007), further demonstrating large pH variations are occurring in some ocean basins as a result of seasonal seawater variability.

Even greater natural pH variability is evident on both shorter and longer time scales in still other of Pelejero et al.'s graphs. Over a mere two days in July 2001 on a Molokai (Hawaii) Reef flat, for example, seawater pH ranged from a high of 8.29 to a low of 7.79 (Yates and Halley, 2006). Over a period of about a decade in the mid-twentieth century, the pH at Arlington Reef in Australia's Great Barrier Reef system ranged from a high of approximately 8.25 to a low of about 7.71 (Wei et al., 2009). These natural and recurring pH declines (0.50 and 0.54) are greater than the 0.3 to 0.4 decline IPCC expects to occur between now and the end of the century, and much

greater than Tans' estimate of about 0.2.

Hofmann et al. (2011) state "natural variability in pH is seldom considered when effects of ocean acidification are considered," and they suggest this omission is disturbing because "natural variability may occur at rates much higher than the rate at which carbon dioxide is decreasing ocean pH," which is about 0.0017 pH unit per year, according to Dore et al. (2009) and Byrne et al. (2010). They contend "ambient fluctuation in pH may have a large impact on the development of resilience in marine populations," noting "heterogeneity in the environment with regard to pH and pCO_2 exposure may result in populations that are acclimatized to variable pH or extremes in pH."

Hofmann et al. recorded continuous high-resolution time series of upper-ocean patterns of pH variability with autonomous sensors deployed at 15 locations from 40.7303°N to 77.8000°S latitude and from 0 to 166.6712°E longitude and 0 to 162.1218°W longitude, over a variety of ecosystems ranging from polar to tropical, open ocean to coastal, and kelp forest to coral reef. The 18 researchers report their measurements revealed "a continuum of month-long pH variability with standard deviations from 0.004 to 0.277 and ranges spanning 0.024 to 1.430 pH units." This variability was "highly site-dependent, with characteristic diel, semi-diurnal, and stochastic patterns of varying amplitudes."

Hofmann et al. write, "these biome-specific pH signatures disclose current levels of exposure to both high and low dissolved CO_2, often demonstrating that resident organisms are already experiencing pH regimes that are not predicted until 2100." These facts suggest the current real-world heterogeneity of the world's oceans with regard to pH and pCO_2 exposure may already have "result[ed] in populations that are acclimatized to variable pH or extremes in pH," such as those that have been predicted to be the new norm in 2100. Lower ocean pH levels may therefore not mature in the way projected by IPCC, a conclusion Loaiciga (2006) shares, having written years earlier, "on a global scale and over the time scales considered (hundreds of years), there would not be accentuated changes in either seawater salinity or acidity from the rising concentration of atmospheric CO_2."

Marine photosynthesis may also reduce CO_2-induced lowering of ocean pH levels lower ocean pH levels, as it tends to increase surface seawater pH, countering the tendency for pH to decline as the air's CO_2 content rises, as demonstrated by Lindholm and Nummelin (1999). This phenomenon has been found to dramatically increase the pH of marine bays, lagoons, and tidal pools (Gnaiger *et al.*, 1978; Santhanam, 1994; Macedo *et al.*, 2001; Hansen, 2002) and significantly enhance the surface water pH of areas as large as the North Sea (Brussaard *et al.*, 1996).

Middelboe and Hansen (2007) studied a wave-exposed boulder reef in Aalsgaarde on the northern coast of Zealand, Denmark, plus a sheltered shallow-water area in Kildebakkerne in the Roskilde Fjord, Denmark. As one would expect if photosynthesis tends to increase surface-water pH, the two researchers found "daytime pH was significantly higher in spring, summer and autumn than in winter at both study sites," often reaching values of 9 or more during peak summer growth periods vs. 8 or less in winter. They also found "diurnal measurements at the most exposed site showed significantly higher pH during the day than during the night," sometimes reaching values greater than 9 during daylight hours but typically dipping below 8 at night, and "diurnal variations were largest in the shallow water and decreased with increasing water depth."

In addition to their own findings, Middelboe and Hansen cite Pearson *et al.* (1998), who found pH averaged about 9 during the summer in populations of *Fucus vesiculosus* in the Baltic Sea; Menendez *et al.* (2001), who found maximum pH was 9 to 9.5 in dense floating macroalgae in a brackish coastal lagoon in the Ebro River Delta; and Bjork *et al.* (2004), who found pH values as high as 9.8 to 10.1 in isolated rock pools in Sweden. Noting "pH in the sea is usually considered to be stable at around 8 to 8.2," the two Danish researchers conclude "pH is higher in natural shallow-water habitats than previously thought."

Liu *et al.* (2009) note, "the history of ocean pH variation during the current interglacial (Holocene) remains largely unknown," and it "would provide critical insights on the possible impact of acidification on marine ecosystems." Working with 18 samples of fossil and modern *Porites* corals recovered from the South China Sea, the nine researchers employed ^{14}C dating using the liquid scintillation counting method, along with positive thermal ionization mass spectrometry to generate high-precision δ^{11}B (boron) data, from which they reconstructed the paleo-pH record of the past 7,000 years, as depicted in Figure 6.3.1.1.2.

As the figure illustrates, there is nothing unusual, unnatural, or unprecedented about the two most recent pH values. They are not the lowest of the record, nor is the rate of decline that led to them the greatest of the record. This strongly indicates these recent values have little to do with the nearly 40%

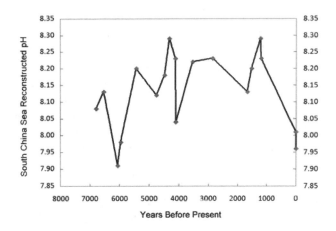

Figure 6.3.1.1.2. Reconstructed pH history of the South China Sea. Created from Table 1 of Liu *et al.* (2009).

increase in the air's CO_2 concentration that occurred over the course of the Industrial Revolution. As for the prior portion of the record, Liu *et al.* note there is also "no correlation between the atmospheric CO_2 concentration record from Antarctica ice cores and δ^{11}B-reconstructed paleo-pH over the mid-late Holocene up to the Industrial Revolution."

Further insight comes from the earlier work of Pelejero *et al.* (2005), who developed a more refined history of seawater pH spanning the period 1708–1988 (depicted in Figure 6.3.1.1.3), based on δ^{11}B data obtained from a massive *Porites* coral from Flinders Reef in the western Coral Sea of the southwestern Pacific. These researchers also found "no notable trend toward lower δ^{11}B values." They discovered "the dominant feature of the coral δ^{11}B record is a clear interdecadal oscillation of pH, with δ^{11}B values ranging between 23 and 25 per mil (7.9 and 8.2 pH units)," which they say "is synchronous with the Interdecadal Pacific Oscillation."

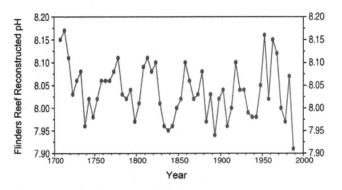

Figure 6.3.1.1.3. Reconstructed pH history of Flinders Reef of the Western Coral Sea of the Southwestern Pacific. Adapted from Pelejero *et al.* (2005).

Pelejero *et al.* also compared their results with coral extension and calcification rates obtained by Lough and Barnes (1997) over the same 1708–1988 time period. As best as can be determined from their graphical representations of these two coral growth parameters, extension rates over the last 50 years of this period were about 12% greater than they were over the first 50 years, and calcification rates were approximately 13% greater over the last 50 years.

Wei *et al.* (2009) derived the pH history of Arlington Reef (off the north-east coast of Australia). Their data show a 10-year pH minimum centered at about 1935 (which obviously was not CO_2-induced) and a shorter, more variable minimum at the end of the record (which also was not CO_2-induced). Apart from these two non-CO_2-related exceptions, the majority of the data once again fall within a band that exhibits no long-term trend.

Numerous scientific studies have demonstrated atmospheric CO_2 enrichment stimulates pH-boosting photosynthesis in marine micro- and macro-algae (see Sections 6.3.2 and 6.5.1). This phenomenon suggests anything else that enhances marine photosynthesis—such as nutrient delivery to the waters of the world's coastal zones (i.e., eutrophication)—may do so as well, as Borges and Gypens (2010) have found.

Employing an idealized biogeochemical model of a river system (Billen *et al.*, 2001) and a complex biogeochemical model describing carbon and nutrient cycles in the marine domain (Gypens *et al.*, 2004), the two researchers investigated "the decadal changes of seawater carbonate chemistry variables related to the increase of atmospheric CO_2 and of nutrient delivery in the highly eutrophied Belgian coastal zone over the period 1951–1998." They write, "the increase of primary production due to eutrophication could counter the effects of ocean acidification on surface water carbonate chemistry in coastal environments," and "changes in river nutrient delivery due to management regulation policies can lead to stronger changes in carbonate chemistry than ocean acidification," as well as changes "faster than those related solely to ocean acidification." They add, "the response of carbonate chemistry to changes of nutrient delivery to the coastal zone is stronger than ocean acidification."

Given its failure to account for the full spectrum of important phenomena that affect ocean acidification, IPCC's current assessment of potential impacts on aquatic life should be considered far more uncertain and much less extreme than IPCC claims it to be.

References

Bates, N.R. 2007. Interannual variability of the oceanic CO_2 sink in the subtropical gyre of the North Atlantic Ocean over the last 2 decades. *Journal of Geophysical Research* **112**: 10.1029/2006JC003759.

Billen, G., Garnier, J., Ficht, A., and Cun, C. 2001. Modeling the response of water quality in the Seine river estuary to human activity in its watershed over the last 50 years. *Estuaries* **24**: 977–993.

Bjork, M., Axelsson, L., and Beer, S. 2004. Why is *Ulva intestinalis* the only macroalga inhabiting isolated rockpools along the Swedish Atlantic coast? *Marine Ecology Progress Series* **284**: 109–116.

Borges, A.V. and Gypens, N. 2010. Carbonate chemistry in the coastal zone responds more strongly to eutrophication than to ocean acidification. *Limnology and Oceanography* **55**: 346–353.

Brussaard, C.P.D., Gast, G.J., van Duyl, F.C., and Riegman, R. 1996. Impact of phytoplankton bloom magnitude on a pelagic microbial food web. *Marine Ecology Progress Series* **144**: 211–221.

Byrne, R.H., Mecking, S., Feely, R.A., and Liu, X. 2010. Direct observations of basin-wide acidification of the North Pacific Ocean. *Geophysical Research Letters* **37**: 10.1029/2009GL040999.

Caldeira, K. and Wickett, M.E. 2003. Anthropogenic carbon and ocean pH. *Nature* **425**: 365.

Dore, J.E., Lukas, R., Sadler, D.W., Church, M.J., and Karl, D.M. 2009. Physical and biogeochemical modulation of ocean acidification in the central North Pacific. *Proceedings of the National Academy of Sciences USA* **106**: 12,235–12,240.

Feely, R.A., Doney, S.C., and Cooley, S.R. 2009. Ocean acidification: Present conditions and future changes in a high-CO_2 world. *Oceanography* **22**: 36–47.

Gnaiger, E., Gluth, G., and Weiser, W. 1978. pH fluctuations in an intertidal beach in Bermuda. *Limnology and Oceanography* **23**: 851–857.

Gypens, N., Lancelot, C., and Borges, A.V. 2004. Carbon dynamics and CO_2 air-sea exchanges in the eutrophied costal waters of the Southern Bight of the North Sea: A modelling study. *Biogeosciences* **1**: 147–157.

Hansen, P.J. 2002. The effect of high pH on the growth and survival of marine phytoplankton: implications for species succession. *Aquatic Microbiology and Ecology* **28**: 279–288.

Hofmann, G.E., Smith, J.E., Johnson, K.S., Send, U., Levin, L.A., Micheli, F., Paytan, A., Price, N.N., Peterson, B., Takeshita, Y., Matson, P.G., Crook, E.D., Kroeker,

K.J., Gambi, M.C., Rivest, E.B., Frieder, C.A., Yu, P.C., and Martz, T.R. 2011. High-frequency dynamics of ocean pH: A multi-ecosystem comparison. *PLoS ONE* **6**: e28983.

Lindholm, T. and Nummelin, C. 1999. Red tide of the dinoflagellate *Heterocapsa triquetra* (Dinophyta) in a ferry-mixed coastal inlet. *Hydrobiologia* **393**: 245–251.

Liu, Y., Liu, W., Peng, Z., Xiao, Y., Wei, G., Sun, W., He, J., Liu, G., and Chou, C.-L. 2009. Instability of seawater pH in the South China Sea during the mid-late Holocene: Evidence from boron isotopic composition of corals. *Geochimica et Cosmochimica Acta* **73**: 1264–1272.

Loaiciga, H.A. 2006. Modern-age buildup of CO_2 and its effects on seawater acidity and salinity. *Geophysical Research Letters* **33**: 10.1029/2006GL026305.

Lough, J.M. and Barnes, D.J. 1997. Several centuries of variation in skeletal extension, density and calcification in massive *Porites* colonies from the Great Barrier Reef: A proxy for seawater temperature and a background of variability against which to identify unnatural change. *Journal of Experimental and Marine Biology and Ecology* **211**: 29–67.

Macedo, M.F., Duarte, P., Mendes, P., and Ferreira, G. 2001. Annual variation of environmental variables, phytoplankton species composition and photosynthetic parameters in a coastal lagoon. *Journal of Plankton Research* **23**: 719–732.

Menendez, M., Martinez, M., and Comin, F.A. 2001. A comparative study of the effect of pH and inorganic carbon resources on the photosynthesis of three floating macro-algae species of a Mediterranean coastal lagoon. *Journal of Experimental Marine Biology and Ecology* **256**: 123–136.

Middelboe, A.L. and Hansen, P.J. 2007. High pH in shallow-water macroalgal habitats. *Marine Ecology Progress Series* **338**: 107–117.

Pearson, G.A., Serrao, E.A., and Brawley, S.H. 1998. Control of gamete release in fucoid algae: sensing hydrodynamic conditions via carbon acquisition. *Ecology* **79**: 1725–1739.

Pelejero, C., Calvo, E., and Hoegh-Guldberg, O. 2010. Paleo-perspectives on ocean acidification. *Trends in Ecology and Evolution* **25**: 332–344.

Pelejero, C., Calvo, E., McCulloch, M.T., Marshall, J.F., Gagan, M.K., Lough, J.M., and Opdyke, B.N. 2005. Preindustrial to modern interdecadal variability in coral reef pH. *Science* **309**: 2204–2207.

Santhanam, R., Srinivasan, A., Ramadhas, V., and Devaraj, M. 1994. Impact of *Trichodesmium* bloom on the plankton and productivity in the Tuticorin bay, southeast coast of India. *Indian Journal of Marine Science* **23**: 27–30.

Tans, P. 2009. An accounting of the observed increase in oceanic and atmospheric CO_2 and an outlook for the future. *Oceanography* **22**: 26–35.

Wei, G., McCulloch, M.T., Mortimer, G., Deng, W., and Xie, L. 2009. Evidence for ocean acidification in the Great Barrier Reef of Australia. *Geochimica et Cosmochimica Acta* **73**: 2332–2346.

Yates, K.K. and Halley, R.B. 2006. CO_3^2 concentration and pCO_2 thresholds for calcification and dissolution on the Molokai reef flat, Hawaii. *Biogeosciences* **3**: 357–369.

6.3.1.2 Some Thoughts on Ocean Chemistry

Contributed by Tom V. Segalstad
Associate Professor of Geochemistry
(Resource- and Environmental Geology)
University of Oslo, Norway

The "acidification" of the ocean—or rather its potential progression toward less alkaline conditions—is postulated to result in serious consequences to marine life, including the dissolution of lime shells of various marine organisms. However, the foundation of the ocean acidification scare is disputed and challenged in the scientific literature as indicated in the multiple peer-reviewed studies referenced throughout Sections 6.3–6.5. The present section approaches and critiques the hypothesis from a geochemical perspective.

Water (H_2O) in the ocean is about one pH unit alkaline. Water protolyses as:

$$H_2O \leftrightarrow H^+ + OH^- \quad [1]$$

The ordinary hydrogen atom (H) has one proton and one electron. When the hydrogen's electron is lost to the hydoxyl (OH^-), the remaining H^+ is just a proton. This dissociation of water is called protolysis: the formation of a proton from water.

The concentration of such protons in water determines its acidity or alkalinity. A high concentration is typical of acids, while a dominance of hydroxyl is typical of alkalies. Water is considered neutral (neither alkaline or acidic) when concentrations of H^+ and OH^- are equal. In thermodynamics the concentration is commonly expressed as activity—a thermodynamic concentration, denoted "a".

pH ("power of hydrogen") is a measure of the acidity of water, defined as the negative logarithm to the activity of H^+ (a_{H+}):

pH ≡ - log a_{H+} [2]

The protolysis constant for the chemical reaction for water protolysis, equation [1], has a value of $\sim 10^{-14}$ at 25°C. At this temperature, the pH has a range up to 14 units, with a value of 14 representing the most alkaline waters, a value of 7 indicating neutral water, and values below 7 for acidic waters. The protolysis constant varies with temperature (and somewhat by pressure), so the value for neutral water changes with changing temperatures. Dissolved gases and solids also can change the pH of water.

6.3.1.2.1 The Assertion of Ocean Acidification

Oceanic pH varies naturally with latitude and ocean depth across Earth. Hence, no single value exists to define oceanic pH. For instance, the pH of surface waters in the western Pacific Ocean varies from around 7.8 to 8.5 between 60°N and 60°S. Although significant pH variations can occur both above and below this range, ocean water is generally characterized as alkaline. And because pH units of measure fall on a logarithmic scale (each pH unit change requires an order of magnitude change in the activity of H^+), large additions of gases and/or dissolved solids into water are needed to induce significant changes in pH.

Some researchers assert ocean waters have become less alkaline (by about 0.1 pH unit) since preindustrial times (e.g., Caldeira and Wickett, 2003). Ocean waters are projected to experience a further pH decline of 0.1–0.2 unit during the next decennia, and a reduction of 0.5–0.7 by the year 2100, caused by anthropogenic CO_2 (NIVA, 2008).

In its first assessment report, published in 1990, IPCC claimed anthropogenic CO_2 has a long lifetime in the atmosphere, of between 50 and 200 years. This long lifetime, according to IPCC, accounts for the modern rise in atmospheric CO_2, which they assert is caused by anthropogenic CO_2 emissions accumulating in the air year after year. Solomon et al. (2009) suggest an even longer residence time for anthropogenic CO_2 in the atmosphere, estimating it may be more than 1,000 years, where the CO_2 content flattens out asymptotically towards infinity in their model. Other researchers have provided contrasting findings. Many scientific papers, for example, contend the atmospheric CO_2 lifetime (halflife) is much shorter, at around five years (Bolin and Eriksson, 1959), that a similar lifetime is found for oceanic CO_2, and that natural processes play a far more significant role

influencing the atmospheric content of CO_2 than previously thought (e.g., Segalstad, 1992; 1996; 1998; 2008; 2009; Starr, 1993; Rohde, 2000).

It is important to note the dissolution of CO_2 in water is governed by Henry's Law, evidenced by the fact there is approximately 50 times more CO_2 dissolved in the ocean than in the atmosphere at present. It is this vast mass of dissolved CO_2 in the ocean that holds the regulating power—not the relatively small amount of CO_2 contained in the air. Furthermore, the chemical reaction speeds involved in the dissolution of CO_2 are high, as is the ocean circulation speed in the upper parts of the ocean.

The ocean acidification hypothesis also ignores the presence of vast amounts of dissolved calcium in the ocean: the upper 200 m of ocean water contains enough dissolved calcium to bind all anthropogenic CO_2 as precipitated calcium carbonate (in the ocean) without affecting the ocean's pH (Jaworowski et al., 1992a; Segalstad, 1996; 1998). The ocean acidification hypothesis also ignores or downplays other oceanic buffers (pH stabilizing reactions), the thermodynamic stability of solid calcium carbonate in ocean water, and photosynthesis by marine biological systems. Many assertions of ocean acidification are based on a methodology that has been called into serious question. For example, the Norwegian Institute for Water Research (NIVA, 2008) built its assertions of ocean acidification on a paper by Haugan and Drange (1996), who derived their claims from the work of Spivack et al. (1993). This latter group of authors presented a proxy history of the ocean's pH over the past 21 million years that used boron isotopes in foraminifera from only five dated boron isotope analyses. This methodology was challenged by Lemarchand et al. (2000), who found the boron isotopes in foraminifera represent changes in the marine boron isotope budget rather than changes in the ocean's pH. Claims that the oceans are presently "acidifying," if based on boron isotope measurements, are highly questionable, if not altogether invalid.

6.3.1.2.2 The Geochemistry of CO_2

Depending on physical conditions, CO_2 can both rapidly dissolve and de-gas in water. This is succinctly demonstrated in the making of carbonated sodas canned by breweries and the degassing of the dissolved CO_2 to the air with time upon opening the soda container.

The dissolved CO_2 first hydrolyzes with the water

into carbonic acid, H_2CO_3. Next, the carbonic acid protolyzes in two steps, first producing H^+ and dissolved bicarbonate HCO_3^-, and next producing H^+ and dissolved carbonate CO_3^{2-}. With the presence of vast amounts of dissolved calcium Ca^{2+} in the ocean, calcium combines with dissolved carbonate or bicarbonate (the dominating dissolved carbon species in the ocean) to form solid calcium carbonate. In simple terms, this process explains how and why some marine organisms form solid calcium carbonate shells. And it further explains how and why the chemical sedimentation of precipitated calcium carbonate can occur to make limestone (or dolomite) on the ocean floor.

Budyko *et al.* (1987) has pointed out periods of maximum carbonate precipitation (as limestone and dolomite) tend to occur at times of intense volcanism (releasing vast amounts of CO_2 from Earth's interior). These periods also tend to correspond with periods of higher atmospheric CO_2, highlighting a geochemical path of CO_2 that initiates from Earth's interior, degasses from volcanoes to the atmosphere, dissolves into the oceans, and precipitates solid marine carbonate rocks on the ocean floor. The chemical reactions for these processes are illustrated below, where (g) = gas, (aq) = aqueous (dissolved in water), and (s) = solid. The protolysis of the water must be added to the system because the ocean water is alkaline, dominated by hydroxyl OH^-. By adding all the partial reactions in this system, the total net reaction for the marine precipitation of solid calcium carbonate from the air's CO_2 and dissolved calcium in ocean water can be obtained:

CO_2 (g) $\leftrightarrow$ CO_2 (aq)	dissolution [3]
CO_2 (aq) + H_2O $\leftrightarrow$ H_2CO_3 (aq)	hydrolysis [4]
H_2CO_3 (aq) $\leftrightarrow$ H^+ + HCO_3^- (aq)	1st protolysis [5]
HCO_3^- (aq) $\leftrightarrow$ H^+ + CO_3^{2-} (aq)	2nd protolysis [6]
Ca^{2+} (aq) + CO_3^{2-} (aq) $\leftrightarrow$ $CaCO_3$ (s)	precipitation [7]
$2 H^+ + 2 OH^- \leftrightarrow 2 H_2O$	protolysis [1]
CO_2 (g) + Ca^{2+} (aq) + $2 OH^- \leftrightarrow CaCO_3$ (s) + H_2O	total net reaction [8]

The Law of Mass Action ensures when all these chemical reactions have been accounted for in the total net reaction (and when increasing the amount of a gas, CO_2, in the air), calcium carbonate (solid) will be stabilized in the ocean, because the chemical reaction will be forced in the direction from left to right. This result is the opposite of what is commonly asserted (that solid calcium carbonate would be dissolved by the increasing amount of CO_2 in the air).

A simple example of this equation is seen in the oft-demonstrated school chemistry experiment of blowing one's exhaled breath (CO_2 gas) through a straw into a reaction tube with dissolved calcium hydroxide $Ca(OH)_2$ in water. Solid calcium carbonate precipitates out into the solution within seconds, providing a good visual of what happens in the ocean when gaseous CO_2 dissolves in the ocean, where there is an ample supply of dissolved calcium and hydroxyl.

6.3.1.2.3 pH Stabilizing Reactions in the Ocean

A "buffer" can be defined as a reaction system that modifies or controls the magnitude of an intensive (mass independent) thermodynamic variable, such as pressure, temperature, concentration, pH (acidity), etc. The ocean's carbonate system acts as a pH buffer through the presence of a weak acid (H_2CO_3 and its protolysis products) and a salt of the acid ($CaCO_3$). The pH of the water can be calculated as:

$$pH \approx [\log K + a(CO_2, g) + a(Ca^{2+}, aq)] / -2 \qquad [9]$$

where K is the chemical equilibrium constant, and a the activity (thermodynamic concentration). At the ocean surface the $a(Ca^{2+}, aq)$ is much larger than the $a(CO_2, g)$. Therefore the alkalinity is the determining factor for the pH, and not the activity (or the fugacity or the partial pressure) of atmospheric CO_2 (Charlson and Emerson, 2000).

In his book on geochemical thermodynamic calculations, Bethke (1996) shows that in a system with only water and CO_2, without mineral buffers present, more than a doubling of the amount of CO_2 in the air above the water surface will lead to a pH decrease of less than 0.4 pH unit. He further demonstrates this is within the natural variation, and thus nothing to worry about.

The ocean is not chemically uniform. Colder water will have a naturally lower pH, because the protolysis constant for water changes with temperature. An upwelling ocean current with colder water, or movement of water from higher latitudes, may lead to a somewhat lower pH within the natural variation—without an anthropogenic influence.

It is also important to note when solid calcium carbonate is brought into the system, a change in the amount of CO_2 gas alone cannot change the pH, because of the buffer action of the calcium carbonate. Thermodynamic calculations on an ocean water composition in equilibrium with calcium carbonate at 25°C show the pH would have to be lowered by 2 units in order to dissolve the calcium carbonate at this temperature. This means the H^+ concentration would have to be increased by 2

$$CaAl_2Si_2O_8 \text{ (s)} + 2H^+ + H_2O \leftrightarrow Al_2Si_2O_5(OH)_4 \text{ (s)} + Ca^{2+} \text{ (aq)} \qquad [10]$$

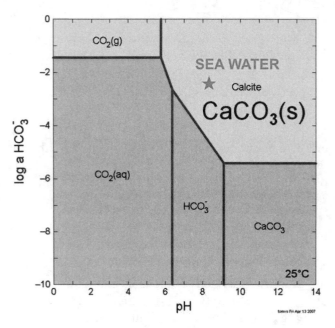

Figure 6.3.1.2.1. A phase diagram for the system CO_2—H_2O—$CaCO_3$ at 25°C and water composition of average sea water. The blue stability fields show the stability of different aqueous species for given pH and log activity of bicarbonate. The green star indicates the sea water position, within the $CaCO_3$ stability field. The diagram was constructed using the program package "The Geochemist's Workbench," by Craig Bethke.

logarithm units, i.e. 100 times (see Figure 6.3.1.2.1).

When adding more CO_2 (g), more bicarbonate will be produced. Yet as the phase diagram illustrates (Figure 6.3.1.2.1), such a CO_2 addition will only stabilize $CaCO_3$ even more—the star in the figure (denoting the sea water composition) would move upward. Furthermore, the star would have to be moved out of the $CaCO_3$ (s) stability field in order for calcium carbonate (calcite) to be dissolved. This is impossible to do by adding CO_2 (g) when calcium carbonate is present (Segalstad, 2008). Hence, the pH of ocean water appears to be well buffered with respect to adding more CO_2 to the atmosphere. At 0°C the pH would have to be lowered 1.5 pH units for solid calcium carbonate (calcite) to be dissolved.

The carbonate buffer is not the only pH buffer

acting in the ocean. The ocean has a set of other mineral-buffer-reactions, such as the buffer:

This anorthite feldspar $\leftrightarrow$ kaolinite buffer has a buffering capacity 1,000 times larger than the ocean's carbonate buffer (Stumm and Morgan, 1970). There are also clay mineral buffers, plus a calcium silicate $\leftrightarrow$ calcium carbonate CO_2 buffer (MacIntyre, 1970; Krauskopf, 1979) [for simplicity]:

$$CaSiO_3 \text{ (s)} + CO_2 \text{ (g)} \leftrightarrow CaCO_3 \text{ (s)} + SiO_2 \text{ (s)} \qquad [11]$$

All these buffers act as a "security net" under the CO_2 (g) $\leftrightarrow$ $CaCO_3$ (s) buffer. Together they constitute an almost infinite buffer capacity (Stumm and Morgan, 1970; Segalstad and Jaworowski, 1991).

The last two buffers mentioned are slower than the CO_2 (g) $\leftrightarrow$ $CaCO_3$ (s) buffer at low temperatures. But their reactions are fast at the hot mid-ocean ridges, where temperatures can reach several hundred degrees C. There is no shortage of dissolved calcium in the ocean water, because this element is constantly being added from weathered surface rocks to the ocean by rivers, and by water-rock interactions at hot mid-ocean ridges.

Rainwater has a pH of about 5.7 (Krauskopf, 1979), because of the acidity caused by dissolution and protolysis of atmospheric CO_2. All the acidic rain supplied to the ocean water through the millennia have not changed the ocean's pH of near 8, which also supports the notion of strong pH buffering in ocean water (Pytkowicz, 1972).

6.3.1.2.4 Carbon Isotopes and Mass Balance Calculations

Stable $^{13}C/^{12}C$ isotope ratios, expressed as $\delta^{13}C$ vs. PDB, provide the only way to determine unequivocally the fraction of anthropogenic CO_2 in the atmosphere. The natural atmospheric CO_2 reservoir has $\delta^{13}C \approx$ -7‰ when in isotopic equilibrium with marine HCO_3^- (aq) and $CaCO_3$ (s). CO_2 gas from burning of fossil-fuel and biogenic materials has $\delta^{13}C \approx$ -26‰ (Ohmoto and Rye, 1979; Deines, 1980).

IPCC identifies 280 ppmv (ppm by volume) as the preindustrial CO_2 value, but that may be arbitrarily influenced by the selection of low-value

CO_2 data from ice cores (where measured values up to 7,400 ppmv were omitted), as well as from the mismatching of contemporary measurements with different ages (Jaworowski et al., 1992a; 1992b). IPCC claims the rise in CO_2 to 353 ppmv in 1990, and 379 ppmv in 2005, is due only to anthropogenic CO_2 (IPCC, 1990; 2007).

The $\delta^{13}C$ value reported for atmospheric CO_2 was -7.489‰ in December 1978, decreasing 10 years later to -7.807‰ in December 1988 (Keeling et al., 1989). If the resultant decrease were solely the product of mixing natural CO_2 with CO_2 produced from the burning of fossil fuels or plants (~79% / ~21% CO_2 mix; lifetime 50–200 years; IPCC, 1990), the current atmospheric CO_2 $\delta^{13}C$ value should be -11, much lower than reported (Segalstad, 1992; 2008).

The December 1988 atmospheric CO_2 composition has been computed for its 748 Gt C (Gt = 10^{15} g) total mass and $\delta^{13}C$ value of -7.807‰ for three components: (1) natural fraction remaining from the preindustrial atmosphere, (2) cumulative fraction remaining from all annual fossil-fuel CO_2 emissions, and (3) carbon isotope mass-balanced natural fraction. The masses of component (1) and (2) were computed for different atmospheric lifetimes of CO_2 (Segalstad, 1992).

The result fits a lifetime of about five years, in agreement with ^{14}C studies (see Sundquist, 1985; Segalstad, 1998; 2009; for further references). The mass of all past fossil-fuel and biogenic emissions remaining in the current atmosphere was -30 Gt C or less; i.e. a maximum of around 4% of the total, corresponding to an atmospheric concentration of approximately 14 ppmv. The implication of the five-year lifetime is that approximately 135 Gt C (18%) of the atmospheric CO_2 is dynamically exchanged each year (Segalstad, 1992; 1996; 1998; 2008).

The above calculations also demonstrate that over this 10-year period (1978–1988), at least 96% of the atmospheric CO_2 is attributed to non-fossil-fuel sources, and this percentage has not likely varied much in the years since. Hence, it is clear marine degassing and juvenile degassing from sources such as volcanoes must be much more important for the atmospheric CO_2 budget than the burning of fossil-fuels and biogenic materials. IPCC has failed to recognize this conclusion.

6.3.1.2.5 Can Anthropogenic Carbon Double the Atmospheric CO₂ Content?

Many models suggest there is enough fossil carbon on Earth that, if burned, would raise the atmospheric CO_2 concentration to two or more times its preindustrial value. There are reasons to conclude such an increase may never occur.

The equilibrium partition coefficient for the CO_2 distribution between the atmosphere and ocean is approximately 1:50 (Revelle and Suess, 1957; Skirrow, 1975), given by Henry's Law and the Henry's Law Constant. This partition coefficient can be used to set an upper limit for how much the CO_2 concentration will rise in the atmosphere if all available fossil carbon fuel (coal, petroleum, gas) were burned.

To permanently double the current level of CO_2 in the atmosphere under chemical equilibrium conditions, the atmosphere would have to be supplied with approximately *51 times* the present amount of CO_2 if equilibrium should be attained, in order to keep the partition coefficient (air:sea = 1:50) constant according to Henry's Law. At the double amount of CO_2 in the air, the new ratio would have to be 2:100. In other words, an increase of one unit CO_2 in air leads to an increase of 50 units CO_2 in the sea; thus a total of 51 units has to be supplied. All available fossil fuel carbon amounts to 11 times the amount of carbon in today's atmospheric CO_2 (Jaworowski et al., 1992a). Therefore, mankind does not have enough fossil fuel to double the current level of atmospheric CO_2 under equilibrium conditions, all other factors held constant.

If the total fossil fuel reservoir of 7,200 Gt C were burned during the next 300 years, only the dissolved organics (carbon pool of about 1,000 Gt C) would consume all manmade CO_2 by their photosynthesis, because this period covers 6 to 15 turnovers of the upper-ocean pool of dissolved organic carbon, based on radiocarbon (^{14}C) studies. However, the vast oceanic dissolved inorganic carbon reservoir of 38,000 Gt C indicates the sea is a much more powerful sink for atmospheric CO_2. Hence, it is unlikely a permanent doubling of the amount of atmospheric CO_2 is attainable by human activities. See Jaworowski et al. (1992a) for further details and references.

6.3.1.2.6 Conclusion

Brian Mason (1966) wrote in his textbook, *Geochemistry* (3rd edition), "The ocean may thereby act as a self-balancing mechanism in which most of the elements have reached an equilibrium concentration."

That statement remains valid, as seen through a considerable constancy of sedimentation and pH over many past hundreds of millions of years. The circulation of CO_2 among the atmosphere, ocean, and biosphere is a fast exchange, with an average measured lifetime (half-life) for one atmospheric CO_2 molecule of about five years (Bolin and Eriksson, 1959; Segalstad, 1992; 1996; 1998; 2008; 2009; Starr, 1993; Rohde, 2000).

According to Mason, "it is apparent that the oceans, by controlling the amount of atmospheric CO_2, play a vital part in maintaining stable conditions suitable for organic life on the Earth." As the material above demonstrates, physical chemistry and thermodynamics provide strong reasons for questioning the validity of the so-called ocean "acidification" hypothesis, especially when considering the vast buffering capacity of the ocean's many buffering mechanisms.

References

Bethke, C.M. 1996. *Geochemical reaction modeling. Concepts and applications.* Oxford University Press, Oxford, United Kingdom, 397 pp.

Bolin, B. and Eriksson, E. 1959. Changes in the carbon dioxide content of the atmosphere and sea due to fossil fuel combustion. In: Bolin, B. (Ed.) *The Atmosphere and the Sea in Motion. Scientific Contributions to the Rossby Memorial Volume.* The Rockefeller Institute Press, New York, pp. 130–142.

Budyko, M.I., Ronov, A.B., and Yanshin, A.L. 1987. *History of the Earth's Atmosphere.* Springer-Verlag, Berlin, Germany, 139 pp.

Caldeira, K. and Wickett, M.E. 2003. Anthropogenic carbon and ocean pH. *Nature* **425**: 365.

Charlson, R.J. and Emerson, S. 2000. The acid-base and oxidation-reduction balances of the Earth. In: Jacobson, M.C., Charlson, R.J., Rohde, H.M. and Orians, G.H. (Eds.) *Earth System Science. From Biogeochemical Cycles to Global Change.* Elsevier International Geophysical Series 72, pp. 421–438.

Deines, P. 1980. The isotopic composition of reduced organic carbon. In: Fritz, P. and Fontes, J.C. (Eds.) *Handbook of Environmental Isotope Geochemistry, Vol. 1.* Elsevier, Amsterdam, The Netherlands, pp. 329–406.

Haugan, P.M. and Drange, H. 1996. Effects of CO_2 on the ocean environment. *Energy Convers. Mgmt.* **37**: 1019–1022.

IPCC. 1990. *Climate Change: IPCC Scientific Assessment.* Contribution of Working Group I to the First Assessment Report of the Intergovernmental Panel on Climate Change. Houghton, J.T., Jenkins, G.J., and Ephraums, J.J. (Eds.) Cambridge University Press, Cambridge, 365 pp.

IPCC. 2007. *Climate Change 2007: The Physical Science Basis.* Contribution of Working Group 1 to the Fourth Assessment Report of the Intergovernmental Panel on Climate Change. Solomon, S., Qin, D., Mannning, M., Chen, Z., Marquis, M., Averyl, K.B., Tignor, M., and Miller, H.L. (Eds.) Cambridge University Press, Cambridge, 431 pp.

Jaworowski, Z., Segalstad, T.V., and Hisdal, V. 1992a. *Atmospheric CO_2 and Global Warming: A Critical Review*; 2nd revised edition. Norsk Polarinstitutt, Meddelelser [Norwegian Polar Institute, Memoirs] 119, 76 pp.

Jaworowski, Z., Segalstad, T.V., and Ono, N. 1992b. Do glaciers tell a true atmospheric CO_2 story? *Science of the Total Environment* **114**: 227–284.

Keeling, C.D., Bacastow, R.B., Carter, A.F., Piper, S.C., Whorf, T.P., Heimann, M., Mook, W.G., and Roeloffzen, H. 1989. A three-dimensional model of atmospheric CO_2 transport based on observed winds: 1. Analysis of observational data. In: Peterson, D.H. (Ed.) *Aspects of Climate Variability in the Pacific and the Western Americas.* American Geophysical Union, Geophysical Monograph 55, pp. 165–236.

Krauskopf, K.B. 1979. *Introduction to Geochemistry, 2nd ed.* McGraw-Hill, Inc., New York, New York, 617 pp.

Lemarchand, D., Gaillardet, J., Lewin, É., and Allègre, C.J. 2000. The influence of rivers on marine boron isotopes and implications for reconstructing past ocean pH. *Nature* **408**: 951–954.

MacIntyre, R. 1970. Why the sea is salt. *Scientific American* **223**: 104–115.

Mason, B. 1966. *Principles of Geochemistry, 3rd. ed.* John Wiley & Sons, Inc., New York, New York, 329 pp.

NIVA. 2008. *Acidification of the Ocean.* [Part of Management Plan for the Norwegian Sea]. Norwegian Institute for Water Research [NIVA], Report No. 5526–2008, 72 pp. [In Norwegian].

Ohmoto, H. and Rye, R.O. 1979. Isotopes of sulfur and carbon. In: Barnes, H.L. (Ed.) *Geochemistry of Hydrothermal Ore Deposits, 2nd. ed.* John Wiley & Sons, New York, New York, pp. 509–567.

Pytkowicz, R.M. 1972. The chemical stability of the oceans and the CO_2 system. In: Dyrssen, D. and Jagner, D. (Eds.) *The Changing Chemistry of the Oceans.* Almquist & Wiksell, Stockholm / Wiley Interscience, New York, New York, pp. 147–152.

Revelle, R. and Suess, H.E. 1957. Carbon dioxide exchange between atmosphere and ocean and the question of an increase of atmospheric CO_2 during the past decades. *Tellus* **9**: 18–27.

Rohde, H. 2000. Modeling biogeochemical cycles. In: Jacobson, M.C., Charlson, R.J., Rohde, H., and Orians, G.H. (Eds.) *Earth System Science. From Biogeochemical Cycles to Global Change*. Elsevier International Geophysical Series 72, pp. 62–84.

Segalstad, T.V. 1992. The amount of non-fossil-fuel CO_2 in the atmosphere. AGU Chapman Conference on Climate, Volcanism, and Global Change. 23–27 March, Hilo, Hawaii. Abstracts, p. 25. Oral presentation + poster. Available at: http://www.CO2web.info/hawaii.pdf.

Segalstad, T.V. 1996. The distribution of CO_2 between atmosphere, hydrosphere, and lithosphere; minimal influence from anthropogenic CO_2 on the global "Greenhouse Effect." In: Emsley, J. (Ed.) *The Global Warming Debate. The Report of the European Science and Environment Forum*. Bourne Press Ltd., Bournemouth, Dorset, U.K., pp. 41–50.

Segalstad, T.V. 1998. Carbon cycle modelling and the residence time of natural and anthropogenic atmospheric CO_2: on the construction of the "Greenhouse Effect Global Warming" dogma. In: Bate, R. (Ed.) *Global Warming: The Continuing Debate*. ESEF, Cambridge, U.K. (ISBN 0952773422), pp. 184–219.

Segalstad, T.V. 2008. Carbon isotope mass balance modelling of atmospheric vs. oceanic CO_2. 33rd International Geological Congress, Oslo. 9 August. Oral presentation + poster. Available at: http://www.cprm.gov.br/33IGC/1345952.html.

Segalstad, T.V. 2009. Correct timing is everything—also for CO_2 in the air. *CO_2 Science* **12**: (5 August). Available at: http://www.co2science.org/articles/V12/N31/EDIT.php.

Segalstad, T.V. and Jaworowski, Z. 1991. CO_2 og globalt klima. *Kjemi* **51**: 13–15.

Skirrow, G. 1975. The dissolved gases—carbon dioxide. In: Riley, J.P. and Skirrow, G. (Eds.) *Chemical Oceanography, Vol. 2, 2nd ed.* Academic Press, Waltham, Massachusetts, pp. 1–192.

Solomon, S., Plattner, G.-K., Knutti, R., and Friedlingstein, P. 2009. Irreversible climate change due to carbon dioxide emissions. *Proceedings of The National Academy of Sciences of the USA* **106**: 1704–1709.

Spivack, A.J., You, C.-F., and Smith, H.-J. 1993. Foraminiferal boron isotope ratios as a proxy for surface ocean pH over the past 21 Myr. *Nature* **363**: 149–151.

Starr, C. 1993. Atmospheric residence time and the carbon cycle. *Energy* **18**: 1297–1310.

Stumm, W. and Morgan, J.J. 1970. *Aquatic Chemistry. An Introduction Emphasizing Chemical Equilibria in Natural Waters*. John Wiley & Sons, Inc., New York, New York, 583 pp.

Sundquist, E.T. 1985. Geological perspectives on carbon dioxide and the carbon cycle. In Sundquist, E.T and Broecker, W.S. (Eds.) *The Carbon Cycle and Atmospheric CO_2: Natural Variations Archean to Present*. American Geophysical Union, Geophysical Monograph **32**: 5–59.

6.3.2 Effects on Marine Plants

6.3.2.1 Phytoplankton

6.3.2.1.1 Coccolithophores

Coccolithophores are single-celled algae and protists found throughout the surface euphotic zones of the world's oceans. They contain chlorophyll, conduct photosynthesis, and possess special plates or scales known as coccoliths, which they create through calcification. This section reviews the results of studies that address how they may be affected by a possible decline in ocean pH levels in a CO_2-enriched world of the future. Several of the findings challenge the alarming negative projections of IPCC, as noted in the bullet points below and further discussed in the main portion of the section.

- Shifts in dominance among species of coccolithophores or clones within a species have been found to occur as the air's CO_2 content rises, which may enable the species to function much as they do today—if not better—in a high-CO_2 world of the future.

- Contemporary evolution likely will help to maintain the functionality of microbial processes at the base of marine food webs in the face of projected lower pH levels.

- Various coccolithophore species appear able to track the environmental value of ocean pH in real time.

- There is evidence the coccolithophore *Calcidiscus leptoporus* has adjusted successfully to the 80 ppm CO_2 difference between preindustrial and the present, as well as the 180 ppm CO_2 difference between glacial times and the present.

Riebesell (2004) notes a doubling of present-day atmospheric CO_2 concentrations "is predicted to cause a 20–40% reduction in biogenic calcification of the predominant calcifying organisms, the corals, coccolithophorids, and foraminifera." But he also notes "a moderate increase in CO_2 facilitates photosynthetic carbon fixation of some phytoplankton groups," including "the coccolithophorids *Emiliania huxleyi* and *Gephyrocapsa oceanica*." In what constitutes a major challenge to the model-based claim atmospheric CO_2 enrichment will harm such marine organisms, Riebesell suggests "CO_2-sensitive taxa, such as the calcifying coccolithophorids, should therefore benefit more from the present increase in atmospheric CO_2 compared to the non-calcifying diatoms."

Leonardos and Geider (2005) grew a non-calcifying strain (PML 92A) of the marine coccolithophorid *Emiliania huxleyi* (Lohmann) Hay & Mohler in chemostats-cyclostats aerated with air of either 360 or 2,000 ppm CO_2 under both high- and low-light conditions in seawater either replete with or deficient in nitrogen and/or phosphorus, while measuring a suite of physical and biochemical properties of the coccolithophorid populations and the media in which they lived. They found "increased atmospheric CO_2 concentration enhances CO_2 fixation into organic matter," but "only under certain conditions, namely high light [HL] and nutrient limitation." Under N-limited conditions, for example, they found particulate organic carbon (POC) "was greatest under HL and elevated CO_2 (by up to 46% relative to HL and ambient CO_2)." Their work also revealed "the increase in POC was a consequence of both an increase in cell density and an increase in the cell organic carbon content."

The two UK researchers state "enhanced CO_2 uptake by phytoplankton such as *E. huxleyi*, in response to elevated atmospheric CO_2, could increase carbon storage in the nitrogen-limited regions of the oceans and thus act as a negative feedback on rising atmospheric CO_2 levels." According to their calculations, if the results obtained for *E. huxleyi* are indicative of the effects of CO_2 on primary production in other N-limited phytoplankton, changes of the magnitude they measured in *E. huxleyi* due to increased CO_2 could increase export production of the oligotrophic ocean by an amount equivalent to the estimated postindustrial increase in the terrestrial carbon sink.

Leonardos and Geider state their findings are "consistent with the response of primary productivity to manipulation of aqueous phase CO_2 in the oligotrophic North Atlantic (Hein and Sand-Jensen, 1996)," where increases in primary productivity "of

up to 100% were observed, although the average increase was 15% to 19%." They note "stimulation of carbon fixation by elevated CO_2 had already been documented for nutrient-limited lake phytoplankton (Urabe *et al.*, 2003)."

Working with two previously untested coccolithophores—*Calcidiscus leptoporus* and *Coccolithus pelagicus*—which they describe as two of the most productive marine calcifying species, Langer *et al.* (2006) conducted batch-culture experiments in which they observed a deterioration of coccolith production above as well as below present-day CO_2 concentrations in *C. leptoporus*, and a lack of a CO_2 sensitivity of calcification in *C. pelagicus* over an atmospheric CO_2 concentration range of 98–915 ppm. Both observations, they write, "refute the notion of a linear relationship of calcification with the carbonate ion concentration and carbonate saturation state," as various scientists proposed early on.

With respect to *C. leptoporus*, Langer *et al.* observed that at both higher and lower CO_2 concentrations than those of today, the proportion of coccoliths showing incomplete growth and malformation notably increased. To determine whether this takes place in the real world, the seven scientists studied coccolith morphologies in six sediment cores extracted along a range of latitudes in the Atlantic Ocean. They report changes in coccolith morphology similar to those "occurring in response to the abrupt CO_2 perturbations applied in our experimental treatments are not mirrored in the sedimentary record." This finding indicates, as they suggest, "in the natural environment *C. leptoporus* has adjusted to the 80 ppm CO_2 and 180 ppm CO_2 difference between present, preindustrial and glacial times, respectively."

The team of researchers from Germany and the United Kingdom write, "it is reasonable to assume that *C. leptoporus* has adapted its calcification mechanism to the change in carbonate chemistry having occurred since the last glacial maximum," suggesting as a possible explanation for this phenomenon "the population is genetically diverse, containing strains with diverse physiological and genetic traits, as already demonstrated for *E. huxleyi* (Brand, 1981, 1982, 1984; Conte *et al.*, 1998; Medlin *et al.*, 1996; Paasche, 2002; Stolte *et al.*, 2000)." They also state this adaptive ability "is not likely to be confined to *C. leptoporus* but can be assumed to play a role in other coccolithophore species as well." Langer *et al.* conclude such populations "may be able to evolve so that the optimal CO_2 level for calcification of the species tracks the environmental value." The authors conclude "genetic diversity, both between and within species, may allow calcifying organisms to prevail in a high CO_2 ocean."

Working with the same sediment core, Halloran et al. (2008) analyzed the size distribution of $CaCO_3$ particles in the less-than–10-μm sediment fraction over the past quarter-century. They found a history of "changing particle volume since the late 20th century consistent with an increase in the mass of coccoliths produced by the larger coccolithophore species," leading them to conclude "in the real ocean the larger coccolithophore species increase their calcification in response to anthropogenic CO_2 release." The four researchers state this positive calcification response "could be attributed to an alleviation of CO_2 limitation in species that partly rely on the diffusive supply of dissolved carbon dioxide for photosynthesis, as demonstrated by a rise in photosynthetic efficiency with increasing carbon dioxide in cultures of E. huxleyi (Rost et al., 2003)."

Stoll (2009) addressed the speculative claims of scientists promoting the view "ocean acidification in response to excess carbon dioxide in the atmosphere could become a problem for marine organisms, especially those that make skeletons or shells out of calcium carbonate," including the coccolithophorids that are, by volume, the most important shell producers. She had a much more optimistic view of the subject, thanks in large part to the research findings of Langer et al. (2009).

The latter scientists—from France, Germany, Spain, and the Netherlands—grew four strains of the coccolithophore Emiliania huxleyi in dilute batch cultures of seawater with carbonate chemistries characteristic of those expected to prevail beneath an atmosphere with CO_2 concentrations ranging from approximately 200 to 1,200 ppm, while they measured particulate organic carbon content, particulate inorganic carbon content, and organic and inorganic carbon production. They found the four strains "did not show a uniform response to carbonate chemistry changes in any of the analyzed parameters and none of the four strains displayed a response pattern previously described for this species." In light of these findings, other aspects of their earlier studies (Langer et al. 2006, 2007), and the diverse findings of others who had used different strains of the species, the five scientists conclude "the sensitivity of different strains of E. huxleyi to acidification differs substantially" and "likely has a genetic basis."

Stoll agrees with that assessment. She notes the work of those who foresaw disastrous consequences typically "precludes the kind of natural selection and

adaptation that might occur over decades and centuries in the ocean." Langer et al. (2009) state "shifts in dominance between species and/or between clones within a species might therefore be expected," as the air's CO_2 content continues to rise; but they note far too often "the possibility of adaptation is not taken into account."

Stoll notes the great genetic diversity that exists in the real world, both among and within species, "is good insurance in a changing ocean." It can be interpreted as evidence coccolithophorids are well prepared for whatever the future may bring, for as Langer et al. (2006) state, "genetic diversity, both between and within species, may allow calcifying organisms to prevail in a high CO_2 ocean." That appears to be the consensus of most studies that have moved on from theoretical speculation to the intermediate crucible of laboratory experimentation and the final test of real-world observation.

Beaufort et al. (2011) note "culture experiments investigating the physiological response of coccolithophore calcification to increased CO_2 have yielded contradictory results between and even within species," citing Riebesell et al. (2000), Langer et al. (2006), Iglesias-Rodriguez et al. (2008), and Langer et al. (2009). They investigated 180 surface-water and 555 sediment-core samples encompassing a wide spectrum of present and past oceanic conditions, some stretching back in time as much as 40,000 years.

The 13 researchers report, "significant overall correlations of coccolith mass with pH and pCO_2 were recorded, but with notable regional variations, indicating that these parameters are not solely responsible for the observed trend." They also report some cultured strains of coccolithophores "are capable of maintaining calcification (degree and/or rate) over certain carbonate-chemistry ranges, a phenomenon that could contribute to localized within-sample deviations from the broad trend linking coccolith mass to carbonate chemistry." The results indicated changes in the relative abundance of taxa were "predominantly responsible for the decrease in coccolith mass with ocean acidification that was seen in modern samples."

Beaufort et al. also note, "in Patagonian-shelf and Chilean upwelling waters with low CO_3^{2-}, in which the overall trend would predict low coccolith mass," they detected "an unexpectedly highly calcified Emiliania huxleyi morphotype," and "the relative abundance of this morphotype increased with decreasing pH along the Pacific transect towards Chile." Noting "coccolith morphotype is thought to be subject to genetic regulation (Langer et al., 2009)," they state "this highly calcified *E. huxleyi* morphotype may be a genetic entity with an adaptation enabling it to calcify heavily in the relatively acidic upwelling waters."

The scientists conclude "the presence of highly calcified *E. huxleyi* in CO_2-rich modern waters demonstrates that prediction of future responses is unlikely to be straightforward," and "such complexity could account for the lack of an obvious overall direction in the response of coccolithophore calcification over a potentially analogous ocean acidification event about 55 million years ago at the Palaeocene-Eocene Thermal Maximum," citing Gibbs *et al.* (2006).

Fiorini *et al.* (2011) measured the growth rates of three coccolithophores (*Emiliania huxleyi, Calcidiscus leptoporus,* and *Syracosphaera pulchra*) in laboratory batch cultures in their haploid and diploid life stages, while they were growing in filtered seawater maintained in equilibrium with air containing either 400 or 760 ppm CO_2. For all three species, "the growth rate was consistently higher at elevated pCO_2," but "the response of other processes varied among species." Calcification rates of *C. leptoporus* and *S. pulchra*, for example, did not change at elevated pCO_2, whereas this important process was increased in the case of *E. huxleyi*. They also found these CO_2-induced impacts were most pronounced in the haploid stage.

Fiorini *et al.* state these effects "must be taken into account when predicting the fate of coccolithophores in the future ocean." The European scientists write, "the phenotypic and physiological differences of the two life stages allow each species to use two different niches to exploit a wider range of ecological conditions (Cros *et al.*, 2000), to limit the competition in the utilization of resources (food, light) inside the species and to rapidly escape negative selection pressures exerted on one stage such as grazing, parasitic attack, viral infections (Frada *et al.*, 2008), or abrupt environmental changes (Noel *et al.*, 2004)." In this way, they continue, "the survival of a species is ensured by one life stage when the environmental conditions do not favor the development of the other life stage (Houdan *et al.*, 2005)."

Lohbeck *et al.* (2012) note the present understanding of the sensitivity of marine life to lower ocean pH levels has been based primarily on short-term experiments that often depict negative effects. Suggesting phytoplanktonic species with short generation times "may be able to respond to environmental alterations through adaptive evolution," they studied "the ability of the world's single most important calcifying organism, the coccolithophore *Emiliania huxleyi*, to evolve in response to ocean acidification in two 500-generation selection experiments."

The three German researchers grew freshly isolated coccolithophore genotypes from Bergen, Norway, in batch cultures for more than 500 asexual generations at three different atmospheric CO_2 concentrations—ambient (400 ppm), medium (1,100 ppm), and high (2,200 ppm)—where the medium CO_2 treatment was chosen to represent the atmospheric CO_2 level projected for the beginning of the next century. They conducted a multi-clone experiment designed to provide existing genetic variation that "would be readily available to genotypic selection," plus a single-clone experiment initiated with one "haphazardly chosen genotype," where evolutionary adaptation would require new mutations.

Compared with populations kept at ambient CO_2 partial pressure, Lohbeck *et al.* found those selected at increased CO_2 levels "exhibited higher growth rates, in both the single- and multi-clone experiment, when tested under ocean acidification conditions." Calcification rates were somewhat lower under CO_2-enriched conditions in all cultures, but the research team state they were "up to 50% higher in adapted [medium and high CO_2] compared with non-adapted cultures." They conclude "contemporary evolution could help to maintain the functionality of microbial processes at the base of marine food webs in the face of global change."

The marine biologists say the swift adaptation processes they observed may "have the potential to affect food-web dynamics and biogeochemical cycles on timescales of a few years, thus surpassing predicted rates of ongoing global change including ocean acidification." They also note "a recent study reports surprisingly high coccolith mass in an *E. huxleyi* population off Chile in high-CO_2 waters (Beaufort *et al.*, 2011)." This observation, they write, indicates "across-population variation in calcification, in line with findings of rapid microevolution identified here."

Lohbeck *et al.* suggest "contemporary evolution could help to maintain the functionality of microbial processes at the base of marine food webs in the face of global change." Writing about this development in a *News & Views* item in the same issue of *Nature Geoscience*, Collins (2012) notes, "marine microbes, with their large population sizes and fast division rates, are certainly going to evolve over a timeframe of decades," and "we can expect that future coccolithophore populations will be shaped by a combination of species succession and adaptive evolution."

McCarthy *et al.* (2012) note diatoms are a type of algae, most of which are unicellular, that serve as primary producers in various marine food chains. They investigated how diatoms might respond to continued increases in the air's CO_2 content, since they are responsible for about 40% of current marine primary productivity (Field *et al.*, 1998). The team of four Canadian researchers grew the coccolithophore *Emiliania huxleyi* and two strains of the diatom *Thalassiosira pseudonana* under low light in turbidostat photobioreactors bubbled with air containing either 390 ppm or 750 ppm CO_2, finding "increased CO_2 led to increased growth rates in all three strains" and "CO_2 thus had a fertilization effect on all species, enhancing growth rates 20%–40%." They observe, "total cellular protein did not change between ambient and 750 ppm CO_2 treatments," but "cellular RUBISCO content showed a 2- to 3-fold increase with [elevated] CO_2 in both *E. huxleyi* and in the coastal diatom strain."

McCarthy *et al.* note the CO_2 fertilization effect on the growth rates of *T. pseudonana* and *E. huxleyi* provides these species with increased competitive ability. They conclude their results suggest "there could be a net increase in capacity for primary productivity at 750 ppm CO_2, at least with regard to small diatoms and coccolithophores in coastal environments," where the two types of phytoplankton provide the bulk of current marine primary productivity.

Smith *et al.* (2012) write, "laboratory studies are unrealistic in many respects and, because of their typically short timescales, preclude the possibility of evolutionary adaptation to the imposed change, a key uncertainty in OA [ocean acidification] research," citing Gattuso and Buddemeier (2000), Langer *et al.* (2006), and Ridgwell *et al.* (2009). They decided "to complement laboratory experiments with observational studies of coccolithophores living in the natural habitats to which they are evolutionarily adapted."

Focusing on two morphotypes (over-calcified and normal) of the world's most abundant coccolithophore species (*Emiliania huxleyi*), Smith *et al.* assessed their numbers, along with seawater carbonate chemistry and other environmental variables, at monthly intervals between September 2008 and August 2009 along a 1,000 km route, including over deep oceanic waters in the Bay of Biscay. They found a pronounced seasonality in the morphotypes of *E. huxleyi*. "Surprisingly," they write, "the over-calcified morphotype was found to dominate the *E. huxleyi* population in winter," even though seawater pH and $CaCO_3$ saturation were lowest in winter. The heavily calcified form of *E. huxleyi* dominated dramatically, shifting from less than 10% of the total *E. huxleyi* population in summer to more than 90% of the population in winter.

Smith *et al.* acknowledge their findings "do not suggest that the changing carbonate chemistry was necessarily responsible for this shift in morphotypes." But "if it was not, then the alternative is that carbonate chemistry is not the sole and overriding control over coccolithophore calcification." This, they write, should "seriously call into question" the contention "ocean acidification will lead to a replacement of heavily-calcified coccolithophores by lightly-calcified ones."

Jin *et al.* (2013) note, "as a key group of oceanic primary producers, coccolithophores play a crucial role in the global carbon cycle, not only in terms of photosynthesis but also by producing calcium carbonate in the form of extracellular plates." They note coccolithophores are "important in the sulfur cycle in terms of dimethyl-sulphide (DMS) production (Malin and Erst, 1997)," which leads to enhanced cloud formation and the reflectance back to space of increased amounts of incoming solar radiation, which tends to cool the planet.

The three researchers also note the particulate inorganic carbon (PIC) produced by coccolithophores in the surface ocean sinks to deep in the sea; this phenomenon, known as the carbonate pump, "is a critical part of the global carbon cycle and has a major feedback effect on global climate (Hutchins, 2011)." Jin *et al.* grew in a laboratory environment the coccolithophore *Gephyrocapsa oceanica* for approximately 670 generations in water in equilibrium with both ambient and CO_2-enriched (1,000 ppm) air, with the latter treatment reducing the water's pH to a value of 7.8.

Jin *et al.* found "high CO_2-selected cells showed increases in photosynthetic carbon fixation, growth rate, cellular particulate organic carbon (POC) or nitrogen (PON) production, and a decrease in the C:N elemental ratio, indicating a greater up-regulation of PON than of POC production under ocean acidification." They note these findings are "in good agreement with a recent study in which *E. huxleyi* positively adapted to increased CO_2 levels," citing Lohbeck *et al.* (2012). Jin *et al.* conclude their data indicate "the coccolithophorid could adapt to ocean acidification with enhanced assimilations of carbon and nitrogen."

The experimental findings and real-world observations discussed above suggest coccolithophores are well-equipped to deal with whatever decline in ocean pH levels may be on the way.

References

Beaufort, L., Probert, I., de Garidel-Thoron, T., Bendif, E.M., Ruiz-Pino, D., Metzl, N., Goyet, C., Buchet, N., Coupel, P., Grelaud, M., Rost, B., Rickaby, R.E.M., and de Vargas, C. 2011. Sensitivity of coccolithophores to carbonate chemistry and ocean acidification. *Nature* **476**: 80–83.

Brand, L.E. 1981. Genetic variability in reproduction rates in marine phytoplankton populations. *Evolution* **38**: 1117–1127.

Brand, L.E. 1982. Genetic variability and spatial patterns of genetic differentiation in the reproductive rates of the marine coccolithophores *Emiliania huxleyi* and *Gephyrocapsa oceanica*. *Limnology and Oceanography* **27**: 236–245.

Brand, L.E. 1984. The salinity tolerance of forty-six marine phytoplankton isolates. *Estuarine and Coastal Shelf Science* **18**: 543–556.

Collins, S. 2012. Evolution on acid. *Nature Geoscience* **5**: 310–311.

Conte, M., Thompson, A., Lesley, D., and Harris, R.P. 1998. Genetic and physiological influences on the alkenone/alkenonate versus growth temperature relationship in *Emiliania huxleyi* and *Gephyrocapsa oceanica*. *Geochimica et Cosmochimica Acta* **62**: 51–68.

Cros, L., Kleijne, A., Zeltner, A., Billard, C., and Young, J.R. 2000. New examples of holococcolith-heterococcolith combination coccospheres and their implications for coccolithophorid biology. *Marine Micropaleontology* **39**: 1–34.

Field, C.B., Behrenfeld, M.J., Randerson, J.T., and Falkowski, P. 1998. Primary production of the biosphere: integrating terrestrial and oceanic components. *Science* **281**: 137–140.

Fiorini, S., Middelburg, J.J., and Gattuso, J.-P. 2011. Testing the effects of elevated pCO$_2$ on coccolithophores (Prymnesiophyceae): Comparison between haploid and diploid life stages. *Journal of Phycology* **47**: 1281–1291.

Frada, M., Probert, I., Allen, M.J., Wilson, W.H., and de Vargas, C. 2008. The "Cheshire Cat" escape strategy of the coccolithophore *Emiliania huxleyi* in response to viral infection. *Proceedings of the National Academy of Sciences USA* **105**: 15,944–15,949.

Gattuso, J.P. and Buddemeier, R.W. 2000. Ocean biogeochemistry: Calcification and CO$_2$. *Nature* **407**: 311–313.

Gibbs, S.J., Brown, P.R., Sessa, J.A., Bralower, T.J., and Wilson, P.A. 2006. Nannoplankton extinction and origination across the Paleocene-Eocene Thermal Maximum. *Science* **314**: 1770–1773.

Halloran, P.R., Hall, I.R., Colmenero-Hidalgo, E., and Rickaby, R.E.M. 2008. Evidence for a multi-species coccolith volume change over the past two centuries: understanding a potential ocean acidification response. *Biogeosciences* **5**: 1651–1655.

Hein, M. and Sand-Jensen, K. 1997. CO$_2$ increases oceanic primary production. *Nature* **388**: 526–527.

Houdan, A., Probert, I., Van Lenning, K., and Lefebvre, S. 2005. Comparison of photosynthetic responses in diploid and haploid life-cycle phases of *Emiliania huxleyi* (Prymnesiophyceae). *Marine Ecology Progress Series* **292**: 139–146.

Hutchins, D.A. 2011. Oceanography: forecasting the rain ratio. *Nature* **476**: 41–42.

Iglesias-Rodriguez, M.D., Halloran, P.R., Rickaby, R.E.M., Hall, I.R., Colmenero-Hidalgo, E., Gittins, J.R., Green, D.R.H., Tyrrell, T., Gibbs, S.J., von Dassow, P., Rehm, E., Armbrust, E.V., and Boessenkool, K.P. 2008. Phytoplankton calcification in a high-CO$_2$ world. *Science* **320**: 336–340.

Jin, P., Gao, K., and Beardall, J. 2013. Evolutionary responses of a coccolithophorid *Gephyrocapsa oceanica* to ocean acidification. *Evolution* **67**: 1869–1878.

Langer, G., Geisen, M., Baumann, K.-H., Klas, J., Riebesell, U., Thoms, S., and Young, J.R. 2006. Species-specific responses of calcifying algae to changing seawater carbonate chemistry. *Geochemistry, Geophysics, Geosystems* **7**: 10.1029/2005GC001227.

Langer, G., Gussone, N., Nehrke, G., Riebesell, U., Eisenhauer, A., and Thoms, S. 2007. Calcium isotope fractionation during coccolith formation in *Emiliania huxleyi*: Independence of growth and calcification rate. *Geochemistry, Geophysics, Geosystems* **8**: 10.1029/2006GC001422.

Langer, G., Nehrke, G., Probert, I., Ly, J., and Ziveri, P. 2009. Strain-specific responses of *Emiliania huxleyi* to changing seawater carbonate chemistry. *Biogeosciences Discussions* **6**: 4361–4383.

Leonardos, N. and Geider, R.J. 2005. Elevated atmospheric carbon dioxide increases organic carbon fixation by *Emiliania huxleyi* (Haptophyta), under nutrient-limited high-light conditions. *Journal of Phycology* **41**: 1196–1203.

Lohbeck, K.T., Riebesell, U., and Reusch, T.B.H. 2012.

Adaptive evolution of a key phytoplankton species to ocean acidification. *Nature Geoscience* **5**: 346–351.

Malin, G. and Erst, G.O. 1997. Algal production of dimethyl sulfide and its atmospheric role. *Journal of Phycology* **33**: 889–896.

McCarthy, A., Rogers, S.P., Duffy, S.J., and Campbell, D.A. 2012. Elevated carbon dioxide differentially alters the photophysiology of *Thalassiosira pseudonana* (Bacillariophyceae) and *Emiliania huxleyi* (Haptophyta). *Journal of Phycology* **48**: 635–646.

Medlin, L.K., Barker, G.L.A., Green, J.C., Hayes, D.E., Marie, D., Wreiden, S., and Vaulot, D. 1996. Genetic characterization of *Emiliania huxleyi* (Haptophyta). *Journal of Marine Systems* **9**: 13–32.

Noel, M.-H., Kawachi, K., and Inouye, I. 2004. Induced dimorphic life cycle of a coccolithophorid, *Calyptrosphaera sphaeroidea* (Prymnesiophyceae, Haptophyta). *Journal of Phycology* **40**: 112–129.

Paasche, E. 2002. A review of the coccolithophorid *Emiliania huxleyi* (Prymnesiophyceae), with particular reference to growth, coccolith formation, and calcification-photosynthesis interactions. *Phycologia* **40**: 503–529.

Ridgwell, A., Schmidt, D.N., Turley, C., Brownlee, C., Maldonado, M.T., Tortell, P., and Young, J.R. 2009. From laboratory manipulations to Earth system models: Scaling calcification impacts of ocean acidification. *Biogeosciences* **6**: 2611–2623.

Riebesell, U. 2004. Effects of CO_2 enrichment on marine phytoplankton. *Journal of Oceanography* **60**: 719–729.

Riebesell, U., Zondervan, I., Rost, B., Tortell, P.D., Zeebe, R.E., and Morel, F.M.M. 2000. Reduced calcification of marine plankton in response to increased atmospheric CO_2. *Nature* **407**: 364–367.

Rost, B., Riebesell, U., Burkhart, S., and Sultemeyer, D. 2003. Carbon acquisition of bloom-forming marine phytoplankton. *Limnology and Oceanography* **48**: 55–67.

Smith, H.E.K., Tyrrell, T., Charalampopoulou, A., Dumousseaud, C., Legge, O.J., Birchenough, S., Pettit, L.R., Garley, R., Hartman, S.E., Hartman, M.C., Sagoo, N., Daniels, C.J., Achterberg, E.P., and Hydes, D.J. 2012. Predominance of heavily calcified coccolithophores at low $CaCO_3$ saturation during winter in the Bay of Biscay. *Proceedings of the National Academy of Sciences USA* **109**: 8845–8849.

Stoll, H. 2009. A biogeochemist sees the value of diversity in a changing ocean. *Nature* **460**: 935.

Stolte, W., Kraay, G.W., Noordeloos, A.A.M., and Riegman, R. 2000. Genetic and physiological variation in pigment composition of *Emiliania huxleyi* (Prymnesiophyceae) and the potential use of its pigment ratios as a quantitative physiological marker. *Journal of Phycology* **96**: 529–589.

Urabe, J., Togari, J., and Elser, J. 2003. Stoichiometric impacts of increased carbon dioxide on a planktonic herbivore. *Global Change Biology* **9**: 818–825.

6.3.2.1.2 Cyanobacteria

Cyanobacteria—also known as blue-green algae, blue-green bacteria, or Cyanophyta (the smallest of which, less than two micrometers in diameter, are typically referred to as picocyanobacteria)—obtain their energy through photosynthesis and are thus important primary producers in many areas of the world's oceans, as well as significant components of the marine nitrogen cycle. This section briefly reviews studies that address how they may be affected by lower ocean pH levels in a CO_2-enriched world of the future, as noted in the bullet points below and further discussed in the main body of the section.

- Ocean acidification enhances the productivity of one of the world's most important diazotrophic (N-fixing) cyanobacteria (*Trichodesmium erythraeum*) in N-limited oligotrophic regions of the world's oceans, providing more essential nitrogen to support greater amounts of higher-order marine animal life.

- The same is true of the unicellular diazotrophic cyanobacterium *Crocosphaera*, recognized as being perhaps equally as important as *Trichodesmium* to the global ocean's nitrogen cycle.

- Acidification-induced increases in photosynthesis and N_2 fixation by both types of cyanobacteria may stimulate productivity in N-limited oligotrophic regions and thus provide a negative feedback on rising atmospheric CO_2 levels.

- The potentially toxic cyanobacterium *Cylindrospermopsis raciborskii* becomes less profuse as atmospheric CO_2 concentrations rise.

Arguing cyanobacteria "should be one of the focus points regarding biological responses to the rise in atmospheric CO_2 concentration," Lu *et al.* (2006) studied physiological changes in phycocyanin (PC)-rich and phycoerythrin (PE)-rich *Synechococcus* strains of picocyanobacteria under atmospheric CO_2 concentrations of 350, 600, and 800 ppm in batch cultures maintained in one-liter glass flasks under a

12-hour:12-hour light:dark regime for periods of 12 days, measuring physiological parameters related to the growth and well-being of the picocyanobacteria. They found the growth of the PE strain was unaffected by atmospheric CO_2 enrichment, but the PC strain grown at 800 ppm CO_2 experienced a 36.7% increase in growth compared to when it was grown at 350 ppm CO_2.

The PC strain showed no significant change in carbohydrate content over the CO_2 range investigated, but the PE strain exhibited a CO_2-induced increase of 37.4% at 800 ppm CO_2. The PC strain exhibited a 36.4% increase in its RNA/DNA ratio between 350 and 800 ppm CO_2, and this ratio, Lu *et al.* write, "provides a good estimate of metabolic activities and has been used extensively as a biochemical indicator of growth rate in a variety of marine organisms." In both *Synechococcus* strains, cellular pigment contents were generally greater in the CO_2-enriched treatments than in the ambient-air controls. At day 12 in the PE strain, for example, they averaged more than 70% greater at 800 ppm CO_2 than at 350 ppm CO_2.

These results clearly indicate both strains of the *Synechococcus* picocyanobacteria benefited greatly from the extra CO_2, albeit in different ways. In comparing the different responses of the two strains, Lu *et al.* conclude, "the PC strain would probably benefit more than the PE strain from future increases in atmospheric CO_2 concentration," but "differences in photosynthetic characteristics may allow the coexistence of the two picocyanobacterial strains through a subtle form of niche differentiation," citing Ernst *et al.* (2003) and Stomp *et al.* (2004). Consequently, there is reason to believe the continuing rise in atmospheric CO_2 content will lead to a significant increase in primary production and nutrient cycling throughout the world's oceans, driven by the positive impacts of "acidification" on these very tiny organisms.

Levitan *et al.* (2007) note, "among the principal players contributing to global aquatic primary production, the nitrogen (N)-fixing organisms (diazotrophs) are important providers of new N to the oligotrophic areas of the oceans." They cite several studies demonstrating "cyanobacterial (phototrophic) diazotrophs in particular fuel primary production and phytoplankton blooms which sustain oceanic food-webs and major economies and impact global carbon (C) and N cycling." They examined how the ongoing rise in the air's CO_2 content might impact these relationships, exploring the response of the cyanobacterial diazotroph *Trichodesmium* to changes in the atmosphere's CO_2 concentration. They studied this particular diazotroph because it contributes more than 50% of total marine N fixation.

The eight Israeli and Czech researchers grew *Trichodesmium* IMS101 stock cultures in a YBCII medium (Chen *et al.*, 1996) at 25°C and a 12-hour:12-hour light/dark cycle (with the light portion of the cycle in the range of 80–100 μmol photons $m^{-2} s^{-1}$) in equilibrium with air of three CO_2 concentrations (250, 400, and 900 ppm, representing low, ambient, and high concentrations, respectively). They continuously bubbled air of the three CO_2 concentrations through the appropriate culture vessels throughout various experimental runs, each lasting a little over three weeks, while they periodically monitored a number of diazotrophic physiological processes and properties. They found *Trichodesmium* in the high CO_2 treatment "displayed enhanced N fixation, longer trichomes, higher growth rates and biomass yields." In the high CO_2 treatment there was "a three- to four-fold increase in N fixation and a doubling of growth rates and biomass," and the cultures in the low CO_2 treatment reached a stationary growth phase after only five days, "while both ambient and high CO_2 cultures exhibited exponential growth until day 15 before declining."

The researchers suggest "enhanced N fixation and growth in the high CO_2 cultures occurs due to reallocation of energy and resources from carbon concentrating mechanisms required under low and ambient CO_2." They conclude, "in oceanic regions, where light and nutrients such as P and Fe are not limiting, we expect the projected concentrations of CO_2 to increase N fixation and growth of *Trichodesmium*," and "other diazotrophs may be similarly affected, thereby enhancing inputs of new N and increasing primary productivity in the oceans." They state in the final sentence of their paper, "*Trichodesmium*'s dramatic response to elevated CO_2 may consolidate its dominance in subtropical and tropical regions and its role in C and N cycling, fueling subsequent primary production, phytoplankton blooms, and sustaining oceanic food-webs."

Fu *et al.* (2008) examined "the physiological responses of steady-state iron (Fe)-replete and Fe-limited cultures of the biogeochemically critical marine unicellular diazotrophic cyanobacterium *Crocosphaera* [*watsonii*] at glacial (190 ppm), current (380 ppm), and projected year 2100 (750 ppm) CO_2 levels." They employed semi-continuous culturing methods that used filtered, microwave-sterilized surface Sargasso seawater enriched with phosphate and trace nutrients. When the seawater was replete with iron, daily primary production at 750 ppm CO_2 was 21% greater than it was at 380 ppm, whereas at 190 ppm CO_2 it was 38% lower than at 380 ppm. When the seawater was iron-limited, daily primary production at 750 ppm CO_2 was 150% greater than it was at 380 ppm, and at 190 ppm CO_2 it was 22% lower than at 380 ppm. N_2 fixation rates varied little among the three CO_2 treatments when the seawater was iron-limited; but when the seawater was replete with iron, N_2 fixation at 750 ppm CO_2 was 60% greater than it was at 380 ppm, and at 190 ppm CO_2 it was 33% lower than at 380 ppm.

Fu *et al.* write, "several studies examining the marine diazotrophic cyanobacterium *Trichodesmium* have shown significant increases in N_2 fixation and photosynthesis in response to elevated CO_2 concentration (Hutchins *et al.*, 2007; Levitan *et al.*, 2007; Ramos *et al.*, 2007)," and their data "extend these findings to encompass the marine unicellular N_2-fixing cyanobacterium *Crocosphaera*." This group, they add, "is now recognized as being perhaps equally as important as *Trichodesmium* to the ocean nitrogen cycle (Montoya *et al.*, 2004)." They conclude, "anthropogenic CO_2 enrichment could substantially increase global oceanic N_2 and CO_2 fixation."

Kranz *et al.* (2009) write, "marine phytoplankton contribute up to 50% of global primary production (Falkowski *et al.*, 1998) and influence Earth's climate by altering various biogeochemical cycles (Schlesinger, 2005)." They also note, among diazotrophic cyanobacteria (dinitrogen-fixers), *Trichodesmium* species contribute "about half of all marine N_2 fixation (Mahaffey *et al.*, 2005)," supporting "a large fraction of biological productivity in tropical and subtropical areas and exerting, over long timescales, a significant influence on global carbon cycles by providing a major source of reactive N to the water column (Falkowski and Raven, 1997)."

Kranz *et al.* grew *Trichodesmium erythraeum* IMS101 in semi-continuous batch cultures through which they bubbled air with CO_2 concentrations of either 370 or 1,000 ppm. After the cultures were acclimated to their respective CO_2 concentrations for at least 14 days (covering more than five generations), the scientists measured the rates of particulate organic carbon (POC) and particulate organic nitrogen (PON) fixation, discovering "a strong increase in photosynthesis and N_2 fixation under elevated CO_2 levels," such that POC and PON production rates rose "by almost 40%."

The German scientists note other scientists have worked with the same *Trichodesmium* species:

"Barcelos e Ramos *et al.* (2007) and Levitan *et al.* (2007) observed stimulation in N_2 fixation by approximately 40% and even up to 400%, while Hutchins *et al.* (2007) obtained stimulation by up to 35%." Kranz *et al.* write, "the observed increase in photosynthesis and N_2 fixation could have potential biogeochemical implications, as it may stimulate productivity in N-limited oligotrophic regions and thus provide a negative feedback on rising atmospheric CO_2 levels."

Kranz *et al.* (2011) wrote, "marine phytoplankton are responsible for almost half of all photosynthetic carbon fixation on Earth and play a vital role in altering the CO_2 exchange between ocean and atmosphere," citing Maier-Reimer *et al.* (1996) and Gruber (2004). They point out a lack of nitrates often limits phytoplanktonic growth, and diazotrophic cyanobacteria that fix nitrogen, such as *Trichodesmium* species, thus play "a crucial role in many marine ecosystems by providing a new source of biologically available nitrogen." The scientists describe how atmospheric CO_2 enrichment helps enhance both parts of this important phenomenon.

The three researchers from the Alfred Wegener Institute for Polar and Marine Research in Bremerhaven, Germany report, "four recent studies tested the effect of different CO_2 concentrations on the growth, biomass production and elemental composition of *Trichodesmium* (Barcelos e Ramos *et al.*, 2007; Hutchins *et al.*, 2007; Kranz *et al.*, 2009; Levitan *et al.*, 2007)," and these studies "concordantly demonstrated higher growth and/or production rates under elevated pCO_2, with a magnitude exceeding those CO_2 effects previously seen in other marine phytoplankton."

Focusing on particulate organic nitrogen (PON) production, they note *Trichodesmium* species are particularly effective in this regard: "the stimulation in N_2 fixation and/or PON production between present-day pCO_2 values (370–400 ppm) and those predicted for the year 2100 (750–1000 ppm) ranged between 35 and 240%." They state "data on CO_2 dependency of N_2 fixation rates from recent publications suggest that N_2 fixation by *Trichodesmium* species might increase by more than 20 Tg N per year to about 100 Tg N per year until the end of this century," citing Hutchins *et al.* (2009).

These findings indicate the oceans are primed to do their part in preserving and protecting the biosphere, as they ramp up their productivity to sustain a greater population of aquatic organisms that may be tapped to supply additional food for the planet's burgeoning human population, and remove from the atmosphere and sequester in their sediments increasing amounts of carbon as anthropogenic CO_2 emissions continue to rise.

Garcia *et al.* (2011) emphasize N_2 fixation by marine diazotrophic cyanobacteria (such as various species of *Trichodesmium*) "contributes substantial new nitrogen to marine environments, including the North Atlantic, Pacific, and Indian Oceans (Carpenter *et al.*, 1993; Capone *et al.*, 1997, 2005; Karl *et al.*, 2002)." They further note phosphorus and iron have been identified as key factors that control N_2 fixation in those environments. They report other studies suggest the current low partial pressure of CO_2 in the atmosphere "may be another possible limiting factor for N_2 fixation and CO_2 fixation by *Trichodesmium*," citing Barcelos e Ramos *et al.* (2007), Hutchins *et al.* (2007), Levitan *et al.* (2007, 2010), and Kranz *et al.* (2009).

In a laboratory study designed to explore the limiting potential of low partial pressure of CO_2, Garcia *et al.* examined the effects of near-present-day (~380 ppm) and elevated (~750 ppm) atmospheric CO_2 concentrations on CO_2 and N_2 fixation by *T. erythraeum* isolates from the Pacific and Atlantic Oceans under a range of irradiance conditions. According to the seven scientists, "the positive effect of elevated CO_2 on gross N_2 fixation was large (~50% increase) under mid and/or low irradiances compared with that at high light (~20% increase)," noting data from Kranz *et al.* (2010) and Levitan *et al.* (2010) corroborated their findings. In the Kranz *et al.* study, they report, "under low light, gross N_2-fixation rates were 200% higher in a high-CO_2 treatment (900 ppm) compared with a low-CO_2 treatment (150 ppm), whereas under high light, gross N_2-fixation rates were only 112% higher under elevated CO_2." In the case of CO_2 fixation, they found CO_2-fixation rates increased significantly "in response to high CO_2 under mid- and high irradiances only."

As the atmosphere's CO_2 concentration continues to rise, therefore, this phenomenon should boost the growth rates of marine diazotrophic cyanobacteria and enable them to make more nitrogen available to themselves and co-occurring species, which should significantly increase both the quantity and quality of the worldwide phytoplanktonic food base that ultimately supports all marine animal life.

Holland *et al.* (2012) studied the potentially toxic cyanobacterium *Cylindrospermopsis raciborskii*, originally described as a tropical-subtropical species but increasingly found in temperate regions. Noting "climate change is hypothesized to be a factor in this expansion," the five researchers state, "identifying

future risk from this, and other nuisance cyanobacteria, is paramount." Working with a strain of the cyanobacterium that was originally isolated from a lake near Brisbane (Australia), Holland *et al.* "used continuous (turbidostats) and batch cultures grown under two different light regimes, and adjusted the alkalinity of the media (with an associated change in pH, HCO_3^- and CO_2) to assess the effect of these parameters on the specific growth rate, inorganic carbon acquisition and photosynthetic parameters of *C. raciborskii*."

Although there were insufficient data to confirm results obtained from the low-light experiments, the Australian researchers discovered "there was a positive linear relationship in the 'high' light turbidostats between the growth rate and pH," as the potentially toxic *C. raciborskii* grew more profusely when atmospheric CO_2 concentrations were low and water pH was high, leading Holland *et al.* to conclude high-CO_2/low-pH conditions may change the composition of marine communities "to favor species that are better adapted to these new growth conditions, such as Chrysophytes," which are known to produce "more than half of the food consumed by aquatic animals," citing Maberly *et al.* (2009).

Teira *et al.* (2012) "tested the direct effect of an elevated CO_2 concentration (1,000 ppm) on the biomass and metabolic rates (leucine incorporation, CO_2 fixation and respiration) of two isolates belonging to two relevant marine bacterial families, Rhodobacteraceae (strain MED165) and Flavobacteriaceae (strain MED217)," referring to the former as simply *Roseobacter* and the latter as *Cytophaga*. "Contrary to some expectations," they found "lowering pH did not negatively affect bacterial growth." Doing so in fact increased the growth efficiency of *Cytophaga*. The scientists note, "in both cases, the bacterial activity under high CO_2 would increase the buffering capacity of seawater," concluding the responses of the two marine bacterial families "would tend to increase the pH of seawater, acting as a negative feedback between elevated atmospheric CO_2 concentrations and ocean acidification."

Lomas *et al.* (2012) note, "marine cyanobacteria, both unicellular *Prochlorococcus* and *Synechococcus* and colonial *Trichodesmium* spp., play important roles in the ocean carbon cycle and the biological carbon pump, particularly in the subtropical and tropical gyres (e.g. Partensky *et al.*, 1999; Capone *et al.*, 2005)," adding, *Trichodesmium* "is thought to account for about half of the total N_2-fixation in the oceans," citing Barcelos e Ramos *et al.* (2007),

Hutchins *et al.* (2007), Levitan *et al.* (2007), and Kranz *et al.* (2009, 2010).

Working on board the RV Atlantic Explorer between July 2009 and April 2010 at the Bermuda Atlantic Time-series Study (BATS) site in the subtropical North Atlantic Ocean about 86 km southeast of Bermuda, Lomas *et al.* examined the C-fixation responses of natural assemblages of cyanobacteria dominated by *Synechococcus* and *Prochlorococcus* and the N_2- and C-fixation responses of isolated *Trichodesmium* colonies to changes in pH/pCO_2 conditions between the time of the last glacial minimum (8.4/150 ppm) and projected year 2100 values (7.8/800 ppm). They found "whole community assemblages dominated by *Prochloro-coccus* and *Synechococcus*, whether nutrient-replete or P-limited, did not show a clear response of C-fixation rates to changes in pH/pCO_2." They observed "Fe- and P-replete colonies of *Trichodesmium* increased N_2-fixation rates at pH 7.8 by 54% over ambient pH/pCO_2 conditions, while N_2-fixation at pH 8.4 was 21% lower than at ambient pH/pCO_2." They found C-fixation rates of *Trichodesmium* "were on average 13% greater at low pH than at ambient pH and 37% greater than at high pH." They note "these results for natural populations of all three cyanobacteria concur with previous research and suggest that one important response to changes in ocean pH and pCO_2 might be an increase in N_2 and C fixation by *Trichodesmium* under nutrient-replete conditions."

Lomas *et al.* say their results for *Trichodesmium*, along with similar findings by several other marine scientists, suggest "ocean acidification would likely result in a positive feedback on the growth and physiology of natural populations, resulting in a positive change in their role in ocean carbon and nitrogen cycles."

References

Barcelos e Ramos, J., Biswas, H., Schulz, K.G., La Roche, J., and Riebesell, U. 2007. Effect of rising atmospheric carbon dioxide on the marine nitrogen fixer *Trichodesmium. Global Biogeochemical Cycles* **21**: 10.1029/2006GB002898.

Capone, D.G., Burns, J.A., Montoya, J.P., Subramaniam, A., Mahaffey, C., Gunderson, T., Michaels, A.F., and Carpenter, E.J. 2005. Nitrogen fixation by *Trichodesmium* spp.: An important source of new nitrogen to the tropical and subtropical North Atlantic Ocean. *Global Bio-geochemical Cycles* **19**: 10.1029/2004GB002331.

Capone, D.G., Zehr, J.P., Paerl, W.H., Bergman, B., and Carpenter, E.J. 1997. *Trichodesmium*, a globally significant marine cyanobacterium. *Science* **276**: 1221–1229.

Carpenter, E.J., O'Neil, J.M., Dawson, R., Capone, D.G., Siddiqui, P.J.A., Roenneberg, G.T., and Bergman, B. 1993. The tropical diazotrophic phytoplankter *Trichodesmium*: biological characteristics of two common species. *Marine Ecology Progress Series* **95**: 295–304.

Chen, Y.B., Zehr, J.P., and Mellon, M. 1996. Growth and nitrogen fixation of the diazotrophic filamentous non-heterocystous cyanobacterium *Trichodesmium* sp IMS101 in defined media: evidence for a circadian rhythm. *Journal of Phycology* **32**: 916–923.

Ernst, A., Becker, S., Wollenzien, U.I.A., and Postius, C. 2003. Ecosystem-dependent adaptive radiations of picocyanobacteria inferred from 16S rRNA and ITS–1 sequence analysis. *Microbiology* **149**: 217–228.

Falkowski, P.G., Barber, R., and Smetacek, V. 1998. Biogeochemical controls and feedbacks on ocean primary production. *Science* **281**: 200–206.

Falkowski, P.G. and Raven, J.A. 1997. *Aquatic Photosynthesis*. Blackwell Science, Massachusetts, USA.

Fu, F.-X., Mulholland, M.R., Garcia, N.S., Beck, A., Bernhardt, P.W., Warner, M.E., Sanudo-Wilhelmy, S.A., and Hutchins, D.A. 2008. Interactions between changing pCO_2, N_2 fixation, and Fe limitation in the marine unicellular cyanobacterium *Crocosphaera. Limnology and Oceanography* **53**: 2472–2484.

Galloway, J.N., Dentener, F.J., Capone, D.G., Boyer, E.W., Howarth, R.W., Seitzinger, S.P., Asner, G.P., Cleveland, C.C., Green, P.A., Holland, E.A., Karl, D.M., Michaels, A.F., Porter, J.H., Townsend, A.R., and Vöosmarty, C.J. 2004. Nitrogen cycles: past, present, and future. *Biogeochemistry* **70**: 153–226.

Garcia, N.S., Fu, F.-X., Breene, C.L., Bernhardt, P.W., Mulholland, M.R., Sohm, J.A., and Hutchins, D.A. 2011. Interactive effects of irradiance and CO_2 on CO_2 fixation and N_2 fixation in the diazotroph *Trichodesmium erythraeum* (Cyanobacteria). *Journal of Phycology* **47**: 1292–1303.

Gruber, N. 2004. The dynamics of the marine nitrogen cycle and its influence on atmospheric CO_2. In: Follows, M. and Oguz, T. (Eds.) *The Ocean Carbon Cycle and Climate*. Kluwer, Dordrecht, Germany, pp. 97–148.

Holland, D.P., Pantorno, A., Orr, P.T., Stojkovic, S., and Beardall, J. 2012. The impacts of a high CO_2 environment on a bicarbonate user: The cyanobacterium *Cylindro-spermopsis raciborskii. Water Research* **46**: 1430–1437.

Hutchins, D.A., Fu, F.-X., Zhang, Y., Warner, M.E., Feng, Y., Portune, K., Bernhardt, P.W., and Mulholland, M.R. 2007. CO_2 control of *Trichodesmium* N_2 fixation, photosynthesis, growth rates, and elemental ratios: Implications for past, present, and future ocean biogeochemistry. *Limnology and Oceanography* **52**: 1293–1304.

Hutchins, D.A., Mulholland, M.R., and Fu, F. 2009. Nutrient cycles and marine microbes in a CO_2-enriched ocean. *Oceanography* **22**: 128–145.

Karl, D., Michaels, A., Bergman, B., Capone, D., Carpenter, E., Letelier, R., Lipschultz, F., Paerl, H., Sigman, D., and Stal, L. 2002. Dinitrogen fixation in the world's oceans. *Biogeochemistry* **57/58**: 47–98.

Kranz, S.A., Eichner, M., and Rost, B. 2011. Interactions between CCM and N_2 fixation in *Trichodesmium*. *Photosynthesis Research* **109**: 73–84.

Kranz, S.A., Levitan, O., Richter, K.-U., Prasil, O., Berman-Frank, I., and Rost B. 2010. Combined effects of CO_2 and light on the N_2-fixing cyanobacterium *Trichodesmium* IMS101: physiological responses. *Plant Physiology* **154**: 334–345.

Kranz, S.A., Sultemeyer, D., Richter, K.-U., and Rost, B. 2009. Carbon acquisition by *Trichodesmium*: The effect of pCO_2 and diurnal changes. *Limnology and Oceanography* **54**: 548–559.

Levitan, O., Kranz, S.A., Spungin, D., Prasil, O., Rost, B., and Berman-Frank, I. 2010. Combined effects of CO_2 and light on the N_2-fixing cyanobacterium *Trichodesmium* IMS101: a mechanistic view. *Plant Physiology* **154**: 346–356.

Levitan, O., Rosenberg, G., Setlik, I., Setlikova, E., Grigel, J., Klepetar, J., Prasil, O., and Berman-Frank, I. 2007. Elevated CO_2 enhances nitrogen fixation and growth in the marine cyanobacterium *Trichodesmium*. *Global Change Biology* **13**: 531–538.

Lomas, M.W., Hopkinson, B.M., Losh, J.L., Ryan, D.E., Shi, D.L., Xu, Y., and Morel, F.M.M. 2012. Effect of ocean acidification on cyanobacteria in the subtropical North Atlantic. *Aquatic Microbial Ecology* **66**: 211–222.

Lu, Z., Jiao, N., and Zhang, H. 2006. Physiological changes in marine picocyanobacterial *Synechococcus* strains exposed to elevated CO_2 partial pressure. *Marine Biology Research* **2**: 424–430.

Maberly, S.C., Ball, L.A., Raven, J.A., and Sultemeyer, D. 2009. Inorganic carbon acquisition by Chrysophytes. *Journal of Phycology* **45**: 1052–1061.

Mahaffey, C., Michaels, A.F., and Capone, D.G. 2005. The conundrum of marine N_2 fixation. *American Journal of Science* **305**: 546–595.

Maier-Reimer, E., Mikolajewicz, U., and Winguth, A. 1996. Future ocean uptake of CO_2: interaction between ocean circulation and biology. *Climate Dynamics* **12**: 711–722.

Montoya, J.P., Holl, C.M., Zehr, J.P., Hansen, A., Villareal, T.A., and Capone, D.G. 2004. High rates of N_2 fixation by unicellular diazotrophs in the oligotrophic Pacific Ocean. *Nature* **430**: 1027–1031.

Partensky, F., Hess, W.R., and Vaulot, D. 1999. *Prochlorococcus*, a marine photosynthetic prokaryote of global significance. *Microbiology and Molecular Biology Reviews* **63**: 106–127.

Ramos, J.B.E., Biswas, H., Schulz, K.G., Laroche, J., and Riebesell, U. 2007. Effect of rising atmospheric carbon dioxide on the marine nitrogen fixer *Trichodesmium*. *Global Biogeochemical Cycles* **21**: 10.1029/2006GB002898.

Schlesinger, W.H. 2005. *Biogeochemistry*. Elsevier, Amsterdam, The Netherlands.

Stomp, M., Huisman, J., de Jongh, F., Veraart, A.J., Gerla, D., Rijkeboer, M., Ibelings, B.W., Wollenzien, U.I.A., and Stal, L.J. 2004. Adaptive divergence in pigment composition promotes phytoplankton biodiversity. *Nature* **432**: 104–107.

Teira, E., Fernandez, A., Alvarez-Salgado, X.A., Garcia-Martin, E.E., Serret, P., and Sobrino, C. 2012. Response of two marine bacterial isolates to high CO_2 concentration. *Marine Ecology Progress Series* **453**: 27–36.

6.3.2.1.3 Diatoms

Diatoms are a type of algae, most of which are unicellular, although they also form colonies that take the shape of filaments or ribbons. A unique feature of diatom cells is that they are encased within a special cell wall made of silica that is called a frustule, which can assume a wide variety of forms but usually consists of two asymmetrical sides with a split between them. Functionally, diatoms serve as primary producers in various marine food chains, and thus it is important to know how they may respond to continued increases in the air's CO_2 content. This section reviews much of what scientists have learned about the subject over the past several years, as summarized in the following bullet points.

- The light-saturated photosynthetic rate of the widely distributed *Skeletonema costatum* diatom is increased by elevated CO_2's stimulating of cell numbers, chlorophyll *a* content, the photosynthetic chemistry of photosystem II, and the efficiency of its light reaction.

- The growth-promoting effect of elevated atmospheric CO_2 on diatoms and coccolithophores probably has been responsible for limiting the rise in atmospheric CO_2 since the dawn of the Industrial Revolution to approximately 90% of what it otherwise would have been.

- Because diatoms are responsible for about half of the world's primary marine production, their enhanced growth due to atmospheric CO_2 enrichment should provide a significant brake on the rate of rise of the air's CO_2 content and reduce its ability to cause global warming.

- As diatoms serve as primary producers in numerous marine food chains, the several trophic levels above them should benefit from lower ocean pH levels as the atmosphere's CO_2 content continues to rise.

Chen and Gao (2004) grew a strain (2042) of *Skeletonema costatum*—a unicellular marine diatom, widely distributed in coastal waters throughout the world, that constitutes a major component of natural assemblages of most marine phytoplankton—in filtered nutrient-enriched seawater maintained at 20°C under a 12-hour/12-hour light/dark cycle at a light intensity of 200 μmol m^{-2} s^{-1}, while continuously aerating both cultures with air of either 350 or 1,000 ppm CO_2 as they measured physiological parameters of the diatom's photosynthetic activity.

The scientists report cell numbers of the diatom "increased steadily throughout the light period, and they were 1.6 and 2.1 times higher after the 12-hour light period for the alga grown at 350 and 1000 ppm CO_2, respectively." They also found chlorophyll *a* concentrations in the bulk of the two CO_2 cultures "increased 4.4- and 5.4-fold during the middle 8 hours of the light period for the alga grown at 350 and 1000 ppm CO_2, respectively," and "the contents of cellular chlorophyll *a* were higher for the alga grown at 1000 ppm CO_2 than that at 350 ppm CO_2." The initial slope of the light saturation curve of photosynthesis and the photochemical efficiency of photosystem II "increased with increasing CO_2, indicating that the efficiency of light-harvesting and energy conversion in photosynthesis were increased." The two scientists report "the light-saturated photosynthesis rate based on cell number, the chlorophyll *a* content, the photosynthetic chemistry of photosystem II and the efficiency of the light reaction all increased to various degrees with elevated CO_2."

Three years later, in a study conducted between 15 May and 9 June of 2005 at the Espegrend Marine Biological Station of the University of Bergen, on a fjord in southern Norway, Riebesell *et al.* (2007) maintained nine cylindrical mesocosms—which extended from the water surface to a depth of 9–10 meters—in equilibrium with air of either ambient CO_2 concentration (350 ppm), doubled CO_2 (700 ppm) or tripled CO_2 (1,050 ppm), while measuring several phytoplanktonic physiological parameters. They found "net community carbon consumption under increased CO_2 exceeded present rates by 27% (2 x CO_2) and 39% (3 x CO_2)," and continuous oxygen measurements in the mesocosms identified "enhanced net photosynthesis to be the source of the observed CO_2 effect."

Noting "the phytoplankton groups dominating in the mesocosm studies—diatoms and coccolithophores—are also the main primary producers in high productivity areas and are the principal drivers of biologically induced carbon export to the deep sea," the 11 scientists say their findings "underscore the importance of biologically driven feedbacks in the ocean to global change." Noting "increased CO_2 has been shown to enhance fixation of free nitrogen, thereby relaxing nutrient limitation by nitrogen availability and increasing CO_2 uptake (Barcelos e Ramos *et al.*, 2007)," Arrigo (2007) states in a *News & Views* discussion of Riebesell *et al.*'s paper "neither these, nor other possible non-steady-state biological feedbacks, are currently accounted for in models of global climate—a potentially serious omission, given that the biological pump is responsible for much of the vertical CO_2 gradient in the ocean." Arrigo reports the diatom and coccolithophore growth-promoting effect of CO_2 measured and described by Riebesell *et al.* probably has been responsible for limiting the rise in atmospheric CO_2 since the dawn of the Industrial Revolution to approximately 90% of what it otherwise would have been.

Sobrino *et al.* (2008) grew cultures of *Thalassiosira pseudonana*, "a widely distributed diatom," exposing them to either photosynthetically active radiation (PAR: 400–700 nm) or PAR plus ultraviolet radiation (UVR: 280–400 nm) in 500-mL Teflon bottles maintained at 20°C, using a semi-continuous approach that employed daily dilutions with fresh growth medium (filtered seawater from the Gulf Stream that was enriched with f/2 nutrients) through which air of one of two atmospheric CO_2 concentrations (380 or 1,000 ppm) was continuously bubbled. They discovered exposure of the seawater medium to CO_2-enriched air increased the photosynthetic rate of the marine diatoms by approximately 45% in the presence of PAR and by about 60% in the presence of both PAR and UVR, and it increased their growth rate by approximately 20% in both of the radiation environments. They note, "among the phytoplankton species inhabiting the [ocean's] surface layer, diatoms are responsible for almost 40% of the ocean primary productivity (Nelson *et al.*, 1995)."

Tortell *et al.* (2008) measured CO_2 uptake of *in situ* phytoplankton assemblages collected at 35 stations in the Ross Sea polynya during austral spring and summer, together with ^{14}C uptake for a subset of 11 station samples, while they conducted CO_2 manipulation experiments with phytoplankton collected at three Ross Sea locations in the Southern Ocean via shipboard incubations using a semi-continuous batch-culture technique. The researchers report, "for the *Phaeocystis*-dominated springtime phytoplankton assemblages, there was a statistically significant increase in ^{14}C fixation between 100 and 380 ppm CO_2, but no further effects observed at 800 ppm CO_2." In the case of the diatom-dominated summertime phytoplankton assemblages, the CO_2-induced increase in both relative growth rate and primary productivity continued through 800 ppm, and it promoted "a shift towards larger chain-forming species." Noting the larger chain-forming species of diatoms "are prolific bloom formers with a very high capacity for organic carbon export to the sediments (Stickley *et al.*, 2005)," Tortell *et al.* conclude "potential CO_2-dependent productivity increases and algal species shifts could thus act to increase the efficiency of the biological pump, enhancing Southern Ocean CO_2 uptake and contributing to a negative feedback on increased atmospheric CO_2."

Wu *et al.* (2010) suggest increased CO_2 availability may benefit marine phytoplankton, because "the low affinity of their carboxylating enzyme (Rubisco) for CO_2 (Badger *et al.*, 1998) ... could lead to enhanced phytoplankton growth and photosynthetic carbon fixation" in a high-CO_2 world of the future, as had been suggested by the work of Riebesell *et al.* (1993) and Hein and Sand-Jensen (1997).

Wu *et al.* cultured the diatom *Phaeodactylum tricornutum*, which had been isolated from the South China Sea, for at least 20 generations in artificial seawater equilibrated with air of either 388 or 1,000 ppm CO_2, which resulted in water pH values of either 8.15 or 7.80, respectively, while they measured the diatom's photosynthetic carbon fixation, dark respiration, and growth rates. The three researchers found photosynthetic carbon fixation was enhanced by 12% under the high CO_2 and low pH conditions. Since dark respiration also was enhanced, the daily

net photosynthetic production was stimulated by a lesser 5.8%, and this value "closely agreed with the observed increase in growth," which they had independently determined to have been enhanced by 5.2% under the high CO_2 and low pH conditions.

Wu *et al.* write, if "the roughly 5% increase in the growth of diatoms were taken into account based on the values obtained in this study, this would allow diatoms to rapidly accumulate more biomass (by about 34% in 6 days) and draw down available nitrogen and other nutrients, leading to a greater biological carbon flux to the deep sea." And because diatoms contribute "about half of the marine primary production," this phenomenon would provide a significant brake on the rate of rise of the atmosphere's CO_2 concentration and its ability to cause global warming.

Boelen *et al.* (2011) assessed the photophysiology of the Antarctic diatom *Chaetoceros brevis* in seawater equilibrated with ambient CO_2 air (380 ppm) and air of approximately twice-ambient CO_2 (750 ppm) and half-ambient CO_2 (190 ppm), under four irradiance regimes: two simulating deep and shallow vertical mixing, and two that mimicked limiting and saturating stable water column conditions.

The six scientists found no significant differences between the enhanced and reduced CO_2 levels with respect to "growth, pigment content and composition, photosynthesis, photoprotection and Rubisco activity." They conclude, "within the range tested, CO_2 does not significantly affect the photo-physiological performance of *C. brevis*." Their results "agree with other studies on marine diatoms showing little or no effect of elevated CO_2 on growth (Burkhardt *et al.*, 1999) or maximum rates of photosynthesis (Rost *et al.*, 2003; Trimborn *et al.*, 2009)," although they note in other studies "elevated CO_2 concentrations enhanced growth rates (e.g., Riebesell *et al.*, 1993; Clark and Flynn, 2000)," and "a recent field study in the Southern Ocean (Tortell *et al.*, 2008) showed an increase in phytoplankton productivity and the promotion of large chain-forming *Chaetoceros* species under elevated CO_2."

Boelen *et al.* state, "under saturating and limiting, as well as under dynamic and constant irradiance conditions, the marine Antarctic diatom *C. brevis* has the ability to adjust its cellular physiology in response to changing CO_2 levels with minimal effects on growth and photosynthesis." Although this maintenance of the status quo could be considered a neutral response to elevated CO_2, it also could be regarded as a positive finding, given that many people contend atmospheric CO_2 enrichment will be bad for almost all forms of oceanic life.

Crawfurd *et al.* (2011) note diatoms are very important for the productivity of the world's oceans, as they contribute about 45% of global marine primary production, citing Mann (1999); therefore it is essential to understand how diatoms and other marine phytoplankton will respond to the higher aqueous CO_2 and lower pH conditions that will prevail in ocean surface waters in the near future, as a result of the dissolution of anthropogenic CO_2 in them. They grew more than 100 generations of the diatom *Thalassiosira pseudonana* in seawater maintained in equilibrium with air of either current (ambient) CO_2 concentration or expected end-of-the-century (twice-ambient) CO_2 concentration (380 or 760 ppm)—which produced pH values of 8.1 and 7.8, respectively—for three months, after which they evaluated a number of the species' physical and physiological characteristics. The five UK researchers found "very few effects on *T. pseudonana* of long-term culture at different pCO_2 and pH." They report, "growth rates were identical in cultures supplied with 780 or 360 ppm CO_2," and "similar results have been reported for other diatom species," citing Tortell *et al.* (1997), Tortell (2000), Kim *et al.* (2006), and Shi *et al.* (2009). Crawfurd *et al.* conclude, "if all diatoms respond in a similar fashion to *T. pseudonana*, acidification of this magnitude in the future ocean may have little effect on diatom productivity."

McCarthy *et al.* (2012) grew two strains of the diatom *Thalassiosira pseudonana* under low light in turbidostat photobioreactors bubbled with air containing either 390 or 750 ppm CO_2. They found the increased concentration of CO_2 led to increased growth rates in both strains of 20%–40%. They also report total cellular protein did not change between the ambient and 750 ppm CO_2 treatments, but cellular rubisco content showed a two- to three-fold increase with elevated CO_2. McCarthy *et al.* state the CO_2 fertilization effect on the growth rate of *T. pseudonana* observed at low light and nutrient repletion imparts this species with increased competitive ability, concluding "there could be a net increase in capacity for primary productivity at 750 ppm CO_2, at least with regard to small diatoms in coastal environments."

Li *et al.* (2012) investigated the diatom *Phaeodactylum tricornutum* as a model organism, culturing its cells in both low CO_2 (390 ppm) and high CO_2 (1,000 ppm), as well as at low nitrogen (10 μmol/L) and high nitrogen (110 μmol/L) concentrations. They report, "no direct effects on growth rate were found between the CO_2 treatments" and "no direct effects on pigmentation were found between the CO_2 treatments." They also note "no significant change in the [quantum] yield was found between the low and high CO_2 levels" and "increased dissolved CO_2 concentration did not affect the mean cell size and cell volume of *Phaeodactylum tricornutum*." Moreover, "under the nitrogen replete treatment the CO_2 concentration did not affect the C:N ratio, even though the cells at the high CO_2 level significantly increased their nitrogen content by 13%."

Real-world data suggest diatoms will continue to operate much as they have over prior millennia as the air's CO_2 content continues to rise, or they will be significantly stimulated to do everything they did before, only much better and on a larger scale. Given that diatoms serve as the primary producers in numerous marine food chains, the several trophic levels above them also should be at worst unharmed, and probably benefited by, lower ocean pH levels.

References

Arrigo, K.R. 2007. Marine manipulations. *Nature* **450**: 491–492.

Badger, M.R., Andrews, T.J., Whitney, S.M., Ludwig, M., Yellowlees, D.C., Leggat, W., and Price, G.D. 1998. The diversity and coevolution of Rubisco, plastids, pyrenoids, and chloroplast-based CO_2-concentrating mechanisms in algae. *Canadian Journal of Botany* **76**: 1052–1071.

Barcelos e Ramos, J., Biswas, H., Schulz, K.G., LaRoche, J., and Riebesell, U. 2007. Effect of rising atmospheric carbon dioxide on the marine nitrogen fixer *Trichodesmium*. *Global Biogeochemical Cycles* **21**: 10.1029/2006GB002898.

Boelen, P., van de Poll, W.H., van der Strate, H.J., Neven, I.A., Beardall, J., and Buma, A.G.J. 2011. Neither elevated nor reduced CO_2 affects the photophysiological performance of the marine Antarctic diatom *Chaetoceros brevis*. *Journal of Experimental Marine Biology and Ecology* **406**: 38–45.

Burkhardt, S., Riebesell, U., and Zondervan, I. 1999. Effects of growth rate, CO_2 concentration, and cell size on the stable carbon isotope fractionation in marine phytoplankton. *Geochimica et Cosmochimica Acta* **63**: 3729–3741.

Chen, X. and Gao, K. 2004. Characterization of diurnal photosynthetic rhythms in the marine diatom *Skeletonema costatum* grown in synchronous culture under ambient and elevated CO_2. *Functional Plant Biology* **31**: 399–404.

Clark, D.R. and Flynn, K.J. 2000. The relationship between the dissolved inorganic carbon concentration and growth rate in marine phytoplankton. *Proceedings of the Royal Society of London Series B* **267**: 953–959.

Crawfurd, K.J., Raven, J.A., Wheeler, G.L., Baxgter, E.J., and Joint, I. 2011. The response of *Thalassiosira pseudonana* to long-term exposure to increased CO_2 and decreased pH. *PLoS ONE* **6**: e26695.

Hein, M. and Sand-Jensen, K. 1997. CO_2 increases oceanic primary production. *Nature* **388**: 526–527.

Kim, J.-M., Lee, K., Shin, K., Kang, J.-H., Lee, H.-W., Kim, M., Jang, P.-G., and Jang, M.-C. 2006. The effect of seawater CO_2 concentration on growth of a natural phytoplankton assemblage in a controlled mesocosm experiment. *Limnology and Oceanography* **51**: 1629–1636.

Li, W., Gao, K., and Beardall, J. 2012. Interactive effects of ocean acidification and nitrogen-limitation on the diatom *Phaeodactylum tricornutum*. *PLOS ONE* **7**: e51590.

Mann, D.G. 1999. The species concept in diatoms. *Phycologia* **38**: 437–495.

McCarthy, A., Rogers, S.P., Duffy, S.J., and Campbell, D.A. 2012. Elevated carbon dioxide differentially alters the photophysiology of *Thalassiosira pseudonana* (Bacillariophyceae) and *Emiliania huxleyi* (Haptophyta). *Journal of Phycology* **48**: 635–646.

Nelson, D.M., Treguer, P., Brzezinski, M.A., Leynaert, A., and Queguiner, B. 1995. Production and dissolution of biogenic silica in the ocean: Revised global estimates, comparison with regional data and relationship to biogenic sedimentation. *Global Biogeochemical Cycles* **9**: 359–372.

Riebesell, U., Schulz, K.G., Bellerby, R.G.J., Botros, M., Fritsche, P., Meyerhofer, M., Neill, C., Nondal, G., Oschlies, A., Wohlers, J., and Zollner, E. 2007. Enhanced biological carbon consumption in a high CO_2 ocean. *Nature* **450**: 545–548.

Riebesell, U., Wolf-Gladrow, D.A., and Smetacek, V.S. 1993. Carbon dioxide limitation of marine phytoplankton growth rates. *Nature* **361**: 249–251.

Rost, B., Riebesell, U., Burkhardt, S., and Suitemeyer, D. 2003. Carbon acquisition of bloom-forming marine phytoplankton. *Limnology and Oceanography* **48**: 55–67.

Shi, D., Xu, Y., and Morel, F.M.M. 2009. Effects of the pH/pCO_2 control method on medium chemistry and phytoplankton growth. *Biogeosciences* **6**: 1199–1207.

Sobrino, C., Ward, M.L., and Neale, P.J. 2008. Acclimation to elevated carbon dioxide and ultraviolet radiation in the diatom *Thalassiosira pseudonana*: Effects on growth, photosynthesis, and spectral sensitivity of photoinhibition. *Limnology and Oceanography* **53**: 494–505.

Stickley, C.E., Pike, J., Leventer, A., Dunbar, R., Domack,

E.W., Brachfeld, S., Manley, P., and McClennan, C. 2005. Deglacial ocean and climate seasonality in laminated diatom sediments, Mac Robertson Shelf, Antarctica. *Palaeogeography, Palaeoclimatology, Palaeoecology* **227**: 290–310.

Tortell, P.D. 2000. Evolutionary and ecological perspectives on inorganic carbon acquisition in phytoplankton. *Limnology and Oceanography* **45**: 744–750.

Tortell, P.D., Payne, C.D., Li, Y., Trimborn, S., Rost, B., Smith, W.O., Riesselman, C., Dunbar, R.B., Sedwick, P., and DiTullio, G.R. 2008. CO_2 sensitivity of Southern Ocean phytoplankton. *Geophysical Research Letters* **35**: 10.1029/2007GL032583.

Tortell, P.D., Reinfelder, J.R., and Morel, F.M.M. 1997. Active uptake of bicarbonate by diatoms. *Nature* **390**: 243–244.

Trimborn, S., Wolf-Gladrow, D., Richter, K.U., and Rost, B. 2009. The effect of pCO_2 on carbon acquisition and intracellular assimilation in four marine diatoms. *Journal of Experimental Marine Biology and Ecology* **376**: 26–36.

Wu, Y., Gao, K., and Riebesell, U. 2010. CO_2-induced seawater acidification affects physiological performance of the marine diatom *Phaeodactylum tricornutum*. *Biogeosciences* **7**: 2915–2923.

6.3.2.1.4 Foraminifera

Foraminifera are amoeboid protists with reticulating pseudopods—fine strands of cytoplasm that subdivide into branches that merge to form a dynamic network. They are typically less than one mm in size (but can be much larger), and they produce an elaborate calcium carbonate shell called a test, which may have one or more chambers. According to Schiebel (2002), these widespread calcifying protozoa are responsible for 32–80% of the global deep-ocean flux of calcite. Therefore, it is important to determine how various forams, as they are often called, may be affected by likely future declines in ocean pH levels. This section describes some of what scientists have learned about this subject over the past several years, briefly summarized in the following bullet points.

- Some foraminiferal species will tolerate CO_2 values one to two orders of magnitude higher than those predicted for the next few centuries.

- Other forams will tolerate CO_2 values one to two orders of magnitude greater than those predicted to occur for the extreme case of burning all the fossil fuels in Earth's crust.

- Some forams not only survive but successfully reproduce in seawater maintained in equilibrium with air containing as much as 200,000 ppm of CO_2.

Lombard *et al.* (2010) cultured specimens of *Orbulina universa* collected by scuba divers off the coast of Catalina Island, California (USA) and *Globigerinoides sacculifer* obtained near Puerto Rico (USA) under high and low irradiances (335 and 35 μmol photons m^{-2} s^{-1}, respectively) in filtered seawater that had its pH and carbonate ion concentration (CO_3^{2-}) manipulated by adding NaOH or HCl to it. They measured the forams' initial and final size, survival time (days from collection to gametogenesis), and final shell weight for individuals that underwent gametogenesis and grew at least one chamber. They determined under the IS92a "business as usual" scenario as defined by IPCC and projected for the year 2100, the calcification rates of *G. sacculifer* and *O. universa* "could decline by 6–13% compared to recent rates." That is not a large decline, and the four researchers note, "the future increase in temperature [predicted by IPCC] could increase the production of calcite by foraminifera, counter-acting the negative impact of ocean acidification."

Kuroyanagi *et al.* (2009) cultured asexually produced individuals of *Marginopora kudakajimensis*—a large calcifying microorganism that contributes to organic and inorganic carbon production in coral reefs—under laboratory conditions for 71 days in glass jars containing approximately 110 ml of filtered natural seawater (control pH of about 8.2) and two less-basic pH conditions of about 7.9 and 7.7, with the lower values being created by addition of 0.1 N HCl. In declining from the control pH of 8.2 to a pH of 7.9, the mean maximum shell diameter of the large foraminifer rose by 8.6%; its mean shell weight rose by a much smaller and insignificant 0.7%. As the seawater's pH declined to 7.7, the organism's mean maximum shell diameter fell by 12.1% and its mean shell weight fell by 49.3%. Kuroyanagi *et al.* conclude if oceanic pH remains within the range of 8.2 to 7.9, "large foraminifers should be able to maintain present calcification rates."

Bernhard *et al.* (2009) grew the marine foraminiferal protist *Allogromia laticollaris*—which they described as "a ubiquitous protistan constituent of marine microbial systems" and "an important link in the marine food web"—in a mixture of 32% seawater and Alga-Gro seawater medium in 20-ml glass culture tubes, examining its response to several

super-high atmospheric CO_2 concentrations to which the tubes were exposed: 15,000, 30,000, 60,000, 90,000 and 200,000 ppm, values compared to the study's atmospheric control concentration of 375 ppm CO_2. The protist was "able to survive 10–14-day exposure to elevated CO_2 as high as 200,000 ppm." They write, "both ATP [adenosine triphosphate, an indicator of cellular energy] data and microscopic examination demonstrated that considerable populations of *A. laticollaris* survived exposure to all experimental treatments of elevated CO_2, even both replicates of the 200,000-ppm CO_2 experiments." They also found "at least three specimens reproduced during exposure to either 90,000 ppm or 200,000 ppm CO_2," whereas "such reproduction was observed only once in an atmospheric [375-ppm CO_2] treatment."

The four researchers state "*A. laticollaris* is an appropriate species to predict the response of shallow-water thecate foraminifera to predicted increases in atmospheric CO_2, given its isolation [i.e., acquisition] from a shallow-water semi-tropical setting." They say their results indicate "at least some foraminiferal species will tolerate CO_2 values that are one to two orders of magnitude higher than those predicted for the next few centuries." Indeed, their results indicate *A. laticollaris* will tolerate CO_2 values one to two orders of magnitude greater than those predicted to occur for the "extreme case" of burning all fossil fuels in Earth's crust.

But aren't *all* forams amazingly resilient creatures? In a study broaching this question, Cannariato *et al.* (1999) investigated the character, magnitude, and speed of biotic responses of benthic foraminifera to millennial-scale climatic oscillations, using data from an ocean sediment core in the Northeast Pacific that extended back in time some 60,000 years. A number of rapid climatic switches over the 60,000-year record were noted, representing periods of what the three researchers call "extreme environmental variability." They found no evidence of extinctions, and the benthic ecosystems appeared to be "both resilient and robust in response to rapid and often extreme environmental conditions." The scientists note faunal turnovers occurred within decades throughout the record "without extinction or speciation." They conclude, "broad segments of the biosphere are well adapted to rapid climate change," which suggests broad segments of the biosphere may be equally well adapted to lower ocean pH levels.

Hikami *et al.* (2011) measured foram net calcification rates of two algal symbiont-bearing, reef-dwelling forams (*Amphisorus kudakajimensis* and *Calcarina gaudichaudii*) in seawater maintained at five pCO_2 concentrations (245, 375, 588, 763, and 907 ppm). They also conducted a second culture experiment in seawater in which bicarbonate ion concentrations were varied, while keeping carbonate ion concentration constant.

In the first experiment, Hikami *et al.* found "net calcification of *A. kudakajimensis* was reduced under higher pCO_2, whereas calcification of *C. gaudichaudii* generally increased with increased pCO_2." In the second experiment, they found "calcification was not significantly different between treatments in *Amphisorus hemprichii*, a species closely related to *A. kudakajimensis*, or in *C. gaudichaudii*."

Explaining the results of their first experiment, the nine researchers note the upward calcification trend of *Calcarina* with rising pCO_2 "can probably be attributed to the increase in CO_2, possibly through enhancement of symbiont photosynthesis, a phenomenon known as the CO_2-fertilizing effect (e.g., Ries *et al.*, 2009)." They note *Calcarina* harbor diatoms, and "both a single-species culture experiment (Wu *et al.*, 2010) and a mesocosm bloom experiment (Engel *et al.*, 2008) have shown that high-CO_2 seawater is favorable to diatom growth," which in turn stimulates calcification. They also note Rost *et al.* (2006) report dinoflagellates, which are harbored by *Amphisorus*, "use HCO_3^- as their carbon source, so their rate of carbon fixation may remain unaffected by fluctuating CO_2 levels."

As for the second experiment, the seawater pH varied but little between the different bicarbonate ion concentration treatments, resulting in little variation in the calcification rates of both species. Hikami *et al.* conclude the different influences of sea-water chemistry they observed in the two forams may have been attributable to the different types of symbiotic algae they hosted.

Vogel and Uthicke (2012) note, "several studies highlight the importance of large benthic foraminifera (LBF) as biological indicators for water quality and ecosystem health," citing Hallock *et al.* (2003), Uthicke and Nobes (2008), and Uthicke *et al.* (2010), but "impacts of ocean acidification on LBF physiology are not well studied." They investigated "the influence of increased CO_2 on calcification and photobiology of LBF hosting different types of photosynthetic endosymbionts." The two researchers collected samples of the foraminifers *Amphistegina radiata*, *Heterostegina depressa*, and *Marginopora vertebralis* from two locations on Australia's Great Barrier Reef on several field trips between October 2010 and April 2011. They exposed the samples in a laboratory over a period of six weeks to four seawater conditions (467, 784, 1,169, and 1,662 ppm CO_2), periodically measuring a number of physiological parameters and processes.

The researchers found no negative effects of elevated CO_2 on the calcification of any of the LBF species investigated compared to control conditions. The growth rate of *M. vertebralis* increased with elevated CO_2, with mean calcification rates at the two highest CO_2 treatments (1,169 and 1,662 ppm) being 63% greater than those at the two lowest treatments (467 and 784 ppm). Increased CO_2 had no effect on chlorophyll *a* content in either *A. radiata* or *H. depressa*, but "chlorophyll *a* content approximately doubled in *M. vertebralis* from initial to final measurements." In addition, "the maximum quantum yield of *A. radiata*, *H. depressa* and *M. vertebralis* did not vary significantly between different CO_2 treatments." Nor did they find significant negative impacts on photosynthetic production and respiration in the three LBF species.

Vogel and Uthicke say their study "illustrated that the species investigated were still able to build up their calcite skeletons in CO_2 conditions predicted for the year 2100 and beyond," and "contrary to expectations, *M. vertebralis* showed significantly increased growth rates in elevated CO_2."

References

Bernhard, J.M., Mollo-Christensen, E., Eisenkolb, N., and Starczak, V.R. 2009. Tolerance of allogromiid Foraminifera to severely elevated carbon dioxide concentrations: Implications to future ecosystem functioning and paleoceanographic interpretations. *Global and Planetary Change* **65**: 107–114.

Cannariato, K.G., Kennett, J.P., and Behl, R.J. 1999. Biotic response to late Quaternary rapid climate switches in Santa Barbara Basin: Ecological and evolutionary implications. *Geology* **27**: 63–66.

Engel, A., Schulz, K.G., Riebesell, U., Bellerby, R., Delille, B., and Schartau, M. 2008. Effects of CO_2 on particle size distribution and phytoplankton abundance during a mesocosm bloom experiment (PeECE II). *Biogeosciences* **5**: 509–521.

Hallock, P., Lidz, B.H., Cockey-Burkhard, E.M., and Donnelly, K.B. 2003. Foraminifera as bioindicators in coral reef assessment and monitoring: the FORAM Index. *Environmental Monitoring and Assessment* **81**: 221–238.

Hikami, M., Ushie, H., Irie, T., Fujita, K., Kuroyanagi, A., Sakai, K., Nojiri, Y., Suzuki, A., and Kawahata, H. 2011. Contrasting calcification responses to ocean acidification between two reef foraminifers harboring different algal symbionts. *Geophysical Research Letters* **38**: 10.1029/2011GL048501.

Kuroyanagi, A., Kawahata, H., Suzuki, A., Fujita, K., and Irie, T. 2009. Impacts of ocean acidification on large benthic foraminifers: Results from laboratory experiments. *Marine Micropaleontology* **73**: 190–195.

Lombard, F., da Rocha, R.E., Bijma, J., and Gattuso, J.-P. 2010. Effect of carbonate ion concentration and irradiance on calcification in planktonic foraminifera. *Biogeosciences* **7**: 247–255.

Ries, J.B., Cohen, A.L., and McCorkle, D.C. 2009. Marine calcifiers exhibit mixed responses to CO_2-induced ocean acidification. *Geology* **37**: 1131–1134.

Rost, B., Richter, K.-U., Riebesell, U., and Hansen, P.J. 2006. Inorganic carbon acquisition in red-tide dino-flagellates. *Plant, Cell, and Environment* **29**: 810–822.

Schiebel, R. 2002. Planktic foraminiferal sedimentation and the marine calcite budget. *Global Biogeochemical Cycles* **16**: 1010.1029/2001GB001459.

Uthicke, S. and Nobes, K. 2008. Benthic Foraminifera as ecological indicators for water quality on the Great Barrier Reef. *Estuarine, Coastal and Shelf Science* **78**: 763–773.

Uthicke, S., Thompson, A., and Schaffelke, B. 2010. Effectiveness of benthic foraminiferal and coral assemblages as water quality indicators on inshore reefs of the Great Barrier Reef, Australia. *Coral Reefs* **29**: 209–225.

Vogel, N. and Uthicke, S. 2012. Calcification and photobiology in symbiont-bearing benthic foraminifera and responses to a high CO_2 environment. *Journal of Experimental Marine Biology and Ecology* **424–425**: 15–24.

Wu, Y., Gao, K., and Riebesell, U. 2010. CO_2-induced seawater acidification affects physiological performance of the marine diatom *Phaeodactylum tricornutum*. *Biogeosciences* **7**: 2915–2923.

6.3.2.1.5 Other Individual Types

Scientists also have studied phytoplankton other than coccolithophores, cyanobacteria, diatoms, and foraminifera, and this brief section reviews the findings of studies where the responses of these species to lower ocean pH levels have been either experimentally or observationally determined, as described in the bullet points below and in the text that follows them.

- Atmospheric CO_2 enrichment induced "a protective effect against the oxidative damage of UV-B-induced stress" in *Platymonas subcordiformis*, suggesting elevated CO_2 should be able to "enhance the capacity of [UV-B] stress resistance."

- A study of *Stichococcus cylindricus* and *Stichococcus minor* revealed the two marine microalgae "were able to tolerate a broad range of pH from pH 5.0 to 9.5," as well as a broad range of salinities.

- A 2.63-fold increase in the air's CO_2 content led to increases in photosynthetic rates among the 16 ecotypes of a unicellular species of marine green alga (*Ostreococcus tauri*) that ranged from 1.02- to 2.18-fold greater than the current mean, while CO_2-induced size differences among ecotypes were found to range from 1.3- to 1.9-fold greater than the current mean. Differences in plastic responses for C/N ratios, which partly determine the food quality of phytoplankton, were found to range from 1.06- to 1.56-fold greater than the current mean.

Gordillo *et al.* (2003) studied the CO_2-induced growth response of the microalgal chlorophyte *Dunaliella viridis*, which possesses a carbon-concentrating mechanism and has been used as a model species for the study of inorganic carbon uptake. They batch-cultured the chlorophyte, one of the most ubiquitous eukaryotic organisms found in hypersaline environments, in 250-ml Perspex cylinders under laboratory conditions at high (5 mM) and low (0.5 mM) nitrate concentrations, while continuously aerating the cultures with air of either 350 or 10,000 ppm CO_2.

They found atmospheric CO_2 enrichment had little effect on dark respiration in both N treatments, and it had little effect on photosynthesis in the low-N treatment. In the high-N treatment, the extra CO_2 increased photosynthesis by 114%. In the case of biomass production, the results were even more divergent: in the low-N treatment elevated CO_2 had no effect, but in the high-N treatment it nearly tripled the cell density of the culture solution. Gordillo *et al.* note "it has long been debated whether phytoplankton species are growth-limited by current levels of CO_2 in aquatic systems, i.e. whether an increase in atmospheric CO_2 could stimulate growth (Riebesell *et al.*, 1993)." Their results clearly indicate it can, if sufficient nitrogen is available.

Gordillo *et al.* also learned that in the high-N treatment, where elevated CO_2 greatly stimulated photosynthesis and biomass production, once the logarithmic growth phase had run its course and equilibrium growth was attained, approximately 70% of the carbon assimilated by the chlorophyte was released to the water, whereas in the low- CO_2 treatment only 35% was released. Gordillo *et al.* write, "the release of organic carbon to the external medium has been proposed as a mechanism for maintaining the metabolic integrity of the cell (Ormerod, 1983)," and "according to Wood and Van Valen (1990), organic carbon release would be a sink mechanism protecting the photosynthetic apparatus from an overload of products that cannot be invested in growth or stored." They also note stores of photosynthetic products "are reduced to avoid over-load and produce a high demand for photosynthates." Under these conditions, they conclude the process would "divert assimilated C to either the production of new biomass, or the release to the external medium once the culture conditions do not allow further exponential growth."

A second consequence of CO_2-enhanced organic carbon release is that the internal C:N balance of the phytoplankton is maintained within a rather tight range. This phenomenon has been observed in the green seaweed *Ulva rigida* (Gordillo *et al.*, 2001) and the cyanobacterium *Spirulina platensis* (Gordillo *et al.*, 1999). What the study of Gordillo *et al.* (2003) reveals about the response of *Dunaliella viridis* to atmospheric CO_2 enrichment may be applicable to many, if not most, aquatic plants.

Yu *et al.* (2004) grew the marine microalgae *Platymonas subcordiformis* (Wille) Hazen at ambient levels of atmospheric CO_2 concentration and UV-B radiation flux density as well as at elevated levels of 5,000 ppm CO_2 and UV-B radiation characteristic of that anticipated to result from a 25% stratospheric ozone depletion under clear sky conditions in summer. By itself, they report, the elevated UV-B treatment "significantly decreased [microalgal] dry weight, photosynthetic rate, chlorophyll *a* and carotenoid contents," and the elevated CO_2 treatment by itself "enhanced dry weight and photosynthetic rate, but chlorophyll *a* content and carotenoid content had no major difference compared with those of ambient UV-B and ambient CO_2." They also report elevated UV-B by itself significantly increased the production of the toxic superoxide anion and hydrogen peroxide, as well as malonyldialdehyde, which is an end-product of lipid peroxidation, whereas elevated CO_2 by itself did just the opposite. In the treatment consisting of both elevated UV-B and elevated CO_2, the concentrations of these three malevolent substances were lower than those observed in the elevated UV-B and ambient CO_2

treatment. Finally, they note elevated CO_2 decreased the levels of several antioxidant enzymes found in the microalgae, reflecting their reduced need for detoxification of reactive oxygen species in the elevated CO_2 treatment.

Yu *et al.* conclude atmospheric CO_2 enrichment "could reduce the oxidative stress of reactive oxygen species to *P. subcordiformis*, and reduce the lipid peroxidation damage of UV-B to *P. subcordiformis*." They also state, "CO_2 enrichment showed a protective effect against the oxidative damage of UV-B-induced stress," and, therefore, elevated CO_2 should be able to "enhance the capacity of stress resistance." They conclude microalgae grown under high CO_2 "would better overcome the adverse impact of environmental stress factor[s] that act via generation of activated oxygen species."

Moazami-Goudarzi and Colman (2012) measured the growth rates of two marine microalgae (*Stichococcus cylindricus* and *Stichococcus minor*) in artificial seawater, as per Berges *et al.* (2001), within 125-ml Erlenmeyer flasks at pH values of 5.0, 6.0, 7.0, 8.2, 9.0, and 9.5, as well as at a variety of salinity levels (25, 50, 100, 200, and 470 mM). The two Canadian researchers discovered both species had similar growth rates and grew over the range of pH 5.0 to 9.5, with "cells grown at pH 5.0, 6.0 and 7.0 showing no significant difference in growth rates." They also report "both species were found to have similar growth rates and to grow over a range of salinies at sodium chloride concentrations of 25, 50, 100, 200 and 470 mM." Moazami-Goudarzi and Colman found *S. minor* and *S. cylindricus* "were able to tolerate a broad range of pH from pH 5.0 to 9.5," as well as the broad range of salinities they investigated.

Schaum *et al.* (2013) write, "marine phytoplankton are the foundation of ocean eco-systems," noting "these small but mighty microbes are responsible for roughly half of global carbon fixation" and they "form a fundamental part of the biological carbon pump that exports fixed carbon to the deep ocean." They state "empirical studies so far predict changes [in response to rising atmospheric CO_2 concentrations] in phytoplankton communities using single or a few genotypes to represent functional groups," whereas the real-world variation in responses within functional groups "has not been quantified." The four researchers used "16 ecotypes of *Ostreococcus tauri* [a unicellular species of marine green alga] from nine habitat types," which "were obtained from the Roscoff Culture Collection and the Plymouth Marine Laboratory, grown in Keller medium and made clonal by dilution, so that each culture originated from single cells." Those samples were "acclimated for 5–7 asexual generations to 380 ppm CO_2 or 1,000 ppm CO_2 in a closed-system and grown in semi-continuous batch cultures at low densities," allowing the researchers to "quantify variations in plastic responses to elevated CO_2 for ecologically relevant traits such as photosynthesis" while also characterizing "changes in traits affecting food quality for five of these ecotypes."

Schaum *et al.* note they were able to "link plasticity in photosynthesis rates to changes in the relative fitness of ecotypes during asexual growth," and they were further able to "use this link to predict which ecotypes are likely to rise in frequency in a high-CO_2 environment." They found the 2.63-fold increase in the air's CO_2 content of their experiment led to increases in photosynthetic rates among the 16 ecotypes they studied, ranging from 1.02- to 2.18-fold greater than the current mean, and CO_2-induced size differences among ecotypes were found to range from 1.3- to 1.9-fold greater than the current mean. Differences in plastic responses for C/N ratios, which partly determine the food quality of phytoplankton, were found to range from 1.06- to 1.56-fold greater than the current mean. The four scientists conclude, "as CO_2 levels increase, *O. tauri* will grow and photosynthesize faster, and have larger cells with a higher C/N ratio than contemporary cells," with the result "*Ostreococcus*, along with other green algae and cyanobacteria, are likely to increase in abundance in high-CO_2 conditions" with concomitant benefits for the biosphere.

References

Berges, J.A., Franklin, D.J., and Harrison, P.J. 2001. Evolution of an artificial seawater medium: improvements in enriched seawater, artificial water over the last two decades. *Journal of Phycology* 37: 1138–1145.

Gordillo, F.J.L, Jimenez, C., Figueroa, F.L., and Niell, F.X. 1999. Effects of increased atmospheric CO_2 and N supply on photosynthesis, growth and cell composition of the cyanobacterium *Spirulina platensis* (Arthrospira). *Journal of Applied Phycology* 10: 461–469.

Gordillo, F.J.L, Jimenez, C., Figueroa, F.L., and Niell, F.X. 2003. Influence of elevated CO_2 and nitrogen supply on the carbon assimilation performance and cell composition of the unicellular alga *Dunaliella viridis*. *Physiologia Plantarum* 119: 513–518.

Gordillo, F.J.L., Niell, F.X., and Figueroa, F.L. 2001. Non-photosynthetic enhancement of growth by high CO_2 level

in the nitrophilic seaweed *Ulva rigida* C. Agardh (Chlorophyta). *Planta* 213: 64–70.

Moazami-Goudarzi, M. and Colman, B. 2012. Changes in carbon uptake mechanisms in two green marine algae by reduced seawater pH. *Journal of Experimental Marine Biology and Ecology* 413: 94–99.

Ormerod, J.G. 1983. The carbon cycle in aquatic ecosystems. In: Slater, J.H., Whittenbury, R., and Wimpeny, J.W.T. (Eds.) *Microbes in Their Natural Environment*. Cambridge University Press, Cambridge, UK, pp. 463–482.

Riebesell, U., Wolf-Gladrow, D.A., and Smetacek, V. 1993. Carbon dioxide limitation of marine phytoplankton growth rates. *Nature* 361: 249–251.

Schaum, E., Rost, B., Millar, A.J., and Collins, S. 2013. Variation in plastic responses of a globally distributed picoplankton species to ocean acidification. *Nature Climate Change* 3: 298–302.

Wood, A.M. and Van Valen, L.M. 1990. Paradox lost? On the release of energy rich compounds by phytoplankton. *Marine Microbial Food Webs* 4: 103–116.

Yu, J., Tang, X-X., Zhang, P-Y., Tian, J-Y., and Cai, H-J. 2004. Effects of CO_2 enrichment on photosynthesis, lipid peroxidation and activities of antioxidative enzymes of *Platymonas subcordiformis* subjected to UV-B radiation stress. *Acta Botanica Sinica* 46: 682–690.

6.3.2.1.6 Mixtures of All Types

The studies reviewed in this section examine what scientists have learned about potential impacts of lower ocean pH levels on mixtures of various types of marine phytoplankton. The key findings, which challenge the alarming and negative projections of IPCC, are presented in the bullet points below, followed by an expanded discussion of those findings. (Citations for passages in quotation marks in the bullet points are included in the main body of the section.)

- Ultra-high CO_2 enrichment (5,000 ppm) promoted the growth of six species of marine microalgae.

- The effects of atmospheric CO_2 enrichment on various marine phytoplankton in a fjord adjacent to the Large-Scale Facilities of the Biological Station of the University of Bergen in Espegrend, Norway revealed no significant species shifts between treatments, and "the ecosystem composition, bacterial and phytoplankton abundances and productivity, grazing rates and total grazer abundance and reproduction were not significantly affected by CO_2 induced effects."

- "Changes in iron speciation and the resulting potential negative feedback mechanism of phytoplankton productivity on atmospheric CO_2"—i.e., the drawdown of atmospheric CO_2 due to enhanced phytoplanktonic growth and transferral of the carbon thus removed from the atmosphere to the ocean depths—"need to be considered when assessing the ecological effects of ocean acidification."

- The "broad level of pH-tolerance" observed in coastal environments likely results from the adaptation of organisms living there to the large pH fluctuations that routinely occur "as a result of respiratory and photosynthetic processes," as well as "hydrographical events," that alter the "seasonal, and even diurnal, fluctuations in coastal seawater pH" over a large range.

- "Nitrifying organisms in coastal systems tolerate a wide range of pH values," suggesting "the current hypothesis of the negative impacts of ocean acidification on nitrification, at least for the coastal ocean, might need reevaluation."

- Atmospheric CO_2 enrichment is not likely to lead to a degradation of planktonic food quality in Arctic waters.

Wolf-Gladrow et al. (1999) examined the direct effects of atmospheric CO_2 enrichment on marine phytoplankton, including the consequences of these phenomena for the world's oceanic carbon pump, finding the ongoing rise in the air's CO_2 content may also benefit the planet's marine biota, producing significant increases in phytoplanktonic growth rates that may "serve as negative feedbacks to anthropogenic CO_2 increase."

More than a decade later, Joint et al. (2011) note "the pH of the surface ocean is changing as a result of increases in atmospheric carbon dioxide," and "there are concerns about potential impacts of lower pH and associated alterations in seawater carbonate chemistry on the biogeochemical processes in the ocean." They note "it is important to place these changes within the context of pH in the present-day ocean."

According to the three researchers, "marine and freshwater assemblages have always experienced variable pH conditions." For example, "phytoplankton blooms can rapidly reduce pCO_2, with a concomitant increase in pH," which subsequently declines as the blooms die out, demonstrating "pH is naturally variable and that marine organisms—particularly microbes—must already be capable of adapting to rapid and sometimes large changes in pH." They also note, "oceanic pH can change by up to 0.06 pH unit during the year even in the oligotrophic Central Pacific, which does not experience the dramatic phytoplankton blooms of temperate oceans." Regarding freshwater ecosystems, Joint et al. report, "Maberly (1996) showed that diel variations in a lake can be as much as 2–3 pH units," and "Talling (2006) showed that in some English lakes, pH could change by >2.5 pH units over a depth of only 14 m," noting "phytoplankton, bacteria, archaea and metazoans are all present in lakes, and appear to be able to accommodate large daily and seasonal changes in pH."

The three researchers conclude, "perhaps the most appropriate null hypothesis to test is that marine microbes possess the flexibility to accommodate pH change and there will be no catastrophic changes in marine biogeochemical processes that are driven by phytoplankton, bacteria and archaea." Many researchers have done just that.

Yu et al. (2006) grew monocultures of six species of marine microalgae (Chlorella sp., Dunaliella salina, Isochrysis galbana Parke 8701, Nitzschia closterium, Platymanas subcordiformis, and Platymanas sp.) in Erlenmeyer flasks under 14:10 dark:light 24-hour cycles through which air of either 360 or 5,000 ppm CO_2 was continuously bubbled for five days. They measured algal cell densities at one-day intervals in order to calculate and compare algal specific growth rates. All six species responded positively to the ultra-high CO_2 enrichment of the air, with the ratios of their specific growth rates in the CO_2-enriched compared to ambient-air treatments being 1.15 for Chlorella sp., 1.35 for Dunaliella salina, 1.35 for Isochrysis galbana, 1.40 for Nitzschia closterium, 1.47 for Platymanas subcordiformis, and 1.60 for Platymanas sp.

Yu et al. conclude, a "high concentration of CO_2 promotes the growth of microalgae," citing not only their results but also the findings of other researchers, including Lin (1991), Nobutaka et al. (1992), Riebesell et al. (1993), Hein and Sand-Jensen (1997), Liang and Yonemoto (1999), Hu and Gao (2001), and Xia and Gao (2001, 2002). They note, "possibly, the CO_2 enrichment made the chloroplast[s] more developed," so "both the photosynthesis and cell division rate were increased," and, therefore, "the algal cell density was enhanced."

Vogt *et al.* (2008) studied the effects of atmospheric CO_2 enrichment on various marine microorganisms in nine marine mesocosms maintained within two-meter-diameter polyethylene bags submerged to a depth of 10 meters in a fjord adjacent to the Large-Scale Facilities of the Biological Station of the University of Bergen in Espegrend, Norway. They maintained three of the mesocosms at ambient levels of CO_2 (~375 ppm), three at levels expected to prevail at the end of the current century (760 ppm or 2x CO_2), and three at levels predicted for the middle of the next century (1,150 ppm or 3x CO_2), taking measurements of numerous ecosystem parameters over a period of 24 days.

Vogt *et al.* detected no significant phytoplankton species shifts between treatments, and "the ecosystem composition, bacterial and phytoplankton abundances and productivity, grazing rates and total grazer abundance and reproduction were not significantly affected by CO_2 induced effects," citing the work of Riebesell *et al.* (2007), Riebesell *et al.* (2008), Egge *et al.* (2007), Paulino *et al.* (2007), Larsen *et al.* (2007), Suffrian *et al.* (2008), and Carotenuto *et al.* (2007). The eight researchers say their observations suggest "the system under study was surprisingly resilient to abrupt and large pH changes."

Three oceanic CO_2-enrichment experiments (I, II, and III) were carried out in 2001, 2003, and 2005 at the Marine Biological Station of the University of Bergen at Espegrend, Norway, where researchers maintained nine marine ecosystems in two-meter-diameter polyethylene bags submerged to a depth of 10 meters in an adjacent fjord, keeping three of the mesocosms at ambient levels of CO_2 (1xCO_2), three others at 2xCO_2 and three more at 3xCO_2 (via aeration of the water column and the overlying atmosphere with CO_2-enriched air). They performed this work in the context of the Pelagic Ecosystem CO_2 Enrichment (PeECE) program, enabling the PeECE I, PeECE II, and PeECE III experiments.

After a one-time addition of nutrients intended to initiate a phytoplankton bloom on the day before the start of their 24-day study, Egge *et al.* (2009) measured primary production in the nine mesocosms at two-day intervals during the PeECE III experiment, along with oxygen production and consumption, the presence of transparent exopolymer particles, and the composition of the phytoplanktonic community. The seven scientists report, "in the second half of the experiment there was a tendency of higher production at elevated CO_2 levels," which was "visible from ca. day 10 in the cumulative production, with a significant difference between 3x and 1x CO_2 from day 20 onward," as shown in Figure 6.3.2.1.6.1.

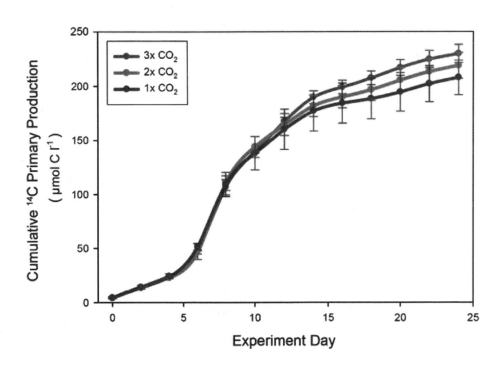

Figure 6.3.2.1.6.1. Cumulative primary production from the start of the PeECE III experiment of Egge *et al.* (2009), adapted from the authors' paper.

Egge *et al.* state their results "demonstrate a small, but statistically significant effect of elevated CO_2 on daily primary production" that is "consistent with the over-consumption of dissolved inorganic carbon at elevated CO_2 reported by Riebesell *et al.* (2007) and Bellerby *et al.* (2008)." These observations once again suggest the planet's rising atmospheric CO_2 concentration may stimulate oceanic primary production and thereby enable the sustaining of a greater population of higher-trophic-level marine organisms.

Breitbarth *et al.* (2010) write, "studies of artificial and natural iron input have demonstrated iron control of phytoplankton productivity and CO_2 drawdown over vast oceanic regions (Boyd *et al.*, 2007; Blain *et al.*, 2007; Pollard *et al.*, 2009) and in coastal upwelling regions (Bruland *et al.*, 2001; Hutchins and Bruland, 1998)," and "temporal control of iron on phytoplankton productivity was also observed in a Norwegian fjord system (Ozturk *et al.*, 2002)." Breitbarth *et al.* measured dissolved iron (dFe) concentrations as well as levels and oxidation rates of Fe(II)—a necessary trace element (the ferrous species of iron) used by almost all living organisms—over the course of natural phytoplanktonic blooms to determine whether lower ocean pH levels may affect iron speciation in seawater. The researchers made measurements in mesocosms consisting of two-meter-diameter polyethylene bags submerged to a depth of 10 meters and maintained in equilibrium with air possessing CO_2 concentrations of either 350, 700, or 1,050 ppm via aeration of the water column and the overlying atmosphere with air of the three CO_2 concentrations (Schulz *et al.*, 2008).

The eight researchers report CO_2 perturbation and phytoplanktonic bloom development resulted in pH value ranges of 8.13–8.26, 7.82–8.08, and 7.67–7.97 at 3570, 700, and 1050ppm CO_2, respectively. They say their measurements revealed significantly higher dFe concentrations in the high CO_2 treatment compared to the mid and low CO_2 treatments, and the high-CO_2 mesocosms showed higher values of FE(II) compared to the lower CO_2 treatments.

Breitbarth *et al.* conclude "ocean acidification may lead to enhanced Fe-bioavailability due to an increased fraction of dFe and elevated Fe(II) concentrations in coastal systems ... due to pH induced changes in organic iron complexation and Fe(II) oxidation rates," noting these phenomena "will result in increased turnover of Fe in surface seawater, potentially maintaining iron bioavailability given a sufficient supply of total Fe, since equilibrium partitioning eventually restores the biolabile Fe pools that have been depleted by biological uptake." They write, "these processes may further fuel increased phytoplankton carbon acquisition and export at future atmospheric CO_2 levels," citing Riebesell *et al.* (2007). They conclude, "changes in iron speciation and the resulting potential negative feedback mechanism of phytoplankton productivity on atmospheric CO_2"—the drawdown of atmospheric CO_2 due to enhanced phytoplanktonic growth and transferral of the carbon thus removed from the atmosphere to the ocean depths—"need to be considered when assessing the ecological effects of ocean acidification."

According to Wyatt *et al.* (2010), "the assimilation of inorganic nutrients fuels phytoplankton growth," and therefore, "any alteration in the bioavailability of these nutrients is likely to impact productivity and, by extension, climate regulation through the uptake of CO_2 by marine algae." The authors note, "the reduction of surface ocean pH anticipated for the next century will alter the equilibrium coefficient between dissolved ammonia (NH_3(aq)) and ammonium (NH_4^+) shifting the equilibrium towards NH_4^+ (Zeebe and Wolf-Gladrow, 2001; Bell *et al.*, 2007, 2008)." As a result, the future decease in ocean pH due to the ongoing rise in the air's CO_2 content could result in the transfer of more gaseous NH_3 from the overlying atmosphere to the ocean, as has been noted by Jacobson (2005).

Wyatt *et al.* collected surface seawater samples from a coastal monitoring site in the Western English Channel (WEC) from 17 March to 21 July 2008, a period of time that included two distinct phases of the annual spring phytoplankton bloom (a pre-bloom period of five weeks and the bloom proper of 11 weeks). They measured ambient pH for carbonate system estimates and dissolved inorganic nutrients, and they equilibrated the samples with CO_2-in-air mixtures that resulted in CO_2 concentrations of 380, 500, 760, and 1,000 ppm that led to pH values of 8.05, 8.01, 7.87, and 7.76, respectively, to be compared with the mean ambient value of 8.18.

The six scientists report the phytoplankton community "was predominantly limited by the availability of inorganic nitrogen," and "during early and mid-summer, NH_X became the primary source of inorganic nitrogen." They also found "an overall increase in NH_X concentrations by 20% was observed between the present day CO_2 treatment (380 ppm) and 1000 ppm." Wyatt *et al.* write, "as excess CO_2 dissociates in the oceans, the increased hydrogen ion concentration ionizes NH_3(aq) and decreases the ratio of NH_3(aq):NH_4^+," and this reduction in NH_3(aq) "would lead to an imbalance in the equilibrium between NH_3(aq) in the surface water and gaseous NH_3 in the overlying atmosphere resulting in the drawdown of atmospheric NH_3 to the surface ocean." Whereas the surface waters of the WEC "are a net source of 150 μmol/m^2/year of NH_3 to the atmosphere at present (2009)," they say it is likely "the WEC will become a net sink of 300 μmol/m^2/year for atmospheric NH_3 as atmospheric CO_2 rises to 717 ppm and the surface pH decreases to 7.83," due to the increase in phytoplanktonic productivity driven by the increased transfer of gaseous NH_3 from the air to the surface waters of the WEC. This phenomenon would boost the productivity of higher oceanic trophic levels, help sequester more carbon at the bottom of the sea, and thereby reduce the rate of increase in radiative forcing that is speculated to fuel global warming.

Nielsen *et al.* (2012) set out to test "whether reduced pH would affect plankton communities over an incubation period of 14 days." They conducted their experiment "in a laboratory microcosm setup using a natural plankton community from the Derwent River estuary, Australia," in which "two treatments with reduced pH (8.0 and 7.7) were compared to an unaltered control of pH 8.3," and "measured parameters included community photosynthesis, nutrient uptake and biomass build-up, as well as enumeration of 25 protist taxa and quantitative HPLC of phytoplankton pigments." They found nutrient uptake and photosynthetic parameters "were all unaffected by pH treatments 8.3–7.7," treatments they say "match the predicted 21st century changes in CO_2 and pH." They note "cellular carbon and total particulate organic carbon were both completely unaffected by pH treatment within this range," and "the same was true for the succession of all 25 enumerated protist species." They report "phytoplankton pigment analysis did not show effects of pH either," and "the investigated plankton community was thus, in all ways, resilient to pH changes between 8.3 and 7.7," noting once again these changes are equivalent to the changes predicted for the next century.

Nielsen *et al.* write, "others have also found no or very limited changes in phytoplankton communities in response to 21st century predicted changes in pH and CO_2," citing Kim *et al.* (2006), Riebesell *et al.* (2007), and Suffrian *et al.* (2008). They also note, "many coastal plankton communities are impervious to such changes," citing Nielson *et al.* (2010). One potential reason for this "broad level of pH-tolerance," as they describe it, is "pH in coastal waters often fluctuates as a result of respiratory and photosynthetic processes" and "hydrographical events," with the result "seasonal, and even diurnal, fluctuations in coastal seawater pH have been shown to encompass 7.5 to 9.6 (Macedo *et al.*, 2001; Hansen, 2002)." They conclude "it is unlikely that the investigated plankton community would be significantly affected by a pH and CO_2 change as predicted for the 21st century."

Regarding the effects of lower ocean pH levels on the marine nitrogen cycle, Fulweiler *et al.* (2011)

write, "the current hypothesis, based on the manipulation of water column pH in laboratory studies, states decreasing pH will impact the nitrogen cycle by decreasing nitrification," and this decrease in the microbial conversion of ammonium to nitrate would likely negatively impact both marine phytoplankton composition and production.

Fulweiler *et al.* "compiled an existing unique data set of concurrent water column nitrification rates and water column pH values from a temperate New England estuary (Narragansett Bay, Rhode Island, USA)," which had been obtained and reported previously by Berounsky (1990) and Berounsky and Nixon (1985a,b, 1990, 1993). Fulweiler *et al.* say they "found the exact opposite trend to the current hypothesis: water column nitrification rates were highest at low pH and decreased significantly as pH increased," and "these results are in direct contradiction to some of the more recently published studies examining the impact of ocean acidification on marine nitrification (Huesemann *et al.*, 2002; Beman *et al.*, 2011)." They note their findings "are consistent with previous studies from three decades ago," citing Anthonisen *et al.* (1976) and Focht and Verstraete (1977).

Fulweiler *et al.* emphasize their results "highlight that nitrifying organisms in coastal systems tolerate a wide range of pH values," and "the degree of negative correlation with pH may depend on site-specific environmental conditions." They conclude their findings indicate "the current hypothesis of the negative impacts of ocean acidification on nitrification, at least for the coastal ocean, might need reevaluation."

Leu *et al.* (2013) write, "ocean acidification occurs as a consequence of increasing atmospheric CO_2 concentrations, and is thought to represent a major threat for some groups of marine organisms" because polyunsaturated fatty acids or PUFAs— essential metabolites that are synthesized only by algae and therefore have to be acquired via their ingestion by all other organisms—may not be as prominent in Arctic plankton in a high-CO_2 world as they are today, leading to a degradation of planktonic food quality. The five researchers studied the effect of lower ocean pH levels on a natural plankton community in the Arctic in a large-scale mesocosm experiment carried out in Kongsfjorden (Svalbard, Norway at 79°N), where nine mesocosms of ~50 m^3 each were exposed to eight CO_2 levels (from natural background conditions to ~1,420 ppm, yielding pH values ranging from ~8.3 to 7.5).

Leu *et al.* report, "no indications were found for a

generally detrimental effect of ocean acidification on the planktonic food quality in terms of essential fatty acids." They write, "it is remarkable that the overall community response with respect to the relative amount of PUFAs to increased CO_2 concentrations was rather positive." They conclude "findings about detrimental effects of ocean acidification on single species in laboratory studies (as, for instance, Riebesell et al. (2000) or Tsuzuki et al. (1990)), and even their consequences for grazers (Rossoll et al., 2012) are probably less relevant in a natural situation where other, more CO_2-tolerant species take over."

Leu et al. write, "the overall availability of essential PUFAs for higher trophic levels seems not to be affected negatively, although the specific fatty acid composition may change." They note "the overall amount of essential PUFAs available to the entire community (or at least within a certain size class) is the important measure for the algal food quality," which "also holds true for the implications for trophic transfer efficiency and consequences for phytoplankton-zooplankton ratios," as discussed by Brett and Muller-Navarra (1997).

Aberle et al. (2013) also set out to "test whether Arctic coastal plankton communities will be in any way affected by high pCO_2/low pH and thus susceptible to ocean acidification [(OA)]." They conducted a mesocosm experiment on a natural Arctic plankton community in Kongsfjorden, Svalbard. Over a period of about one month, they deployed and moored nine polyethylene mesocosms and injected CO_2-enriched seawater into them to achieve three degrees of CO_2 equilibrium concentrations—low (175–250 ppm), intermediate (340–600 ppm), and high (675–1,085 ppm). They added nutrients to all three mesocosm treatments 13 days later "to ensure a sufficient nutrient supply for bloom development."

Aberle et al. report they "found almost no direct effects of OA on microzooplankton composition and diversity," and "both the relative shares of ciliates and heterotrophic dinoflagellates as well as the taxonomic composition of microzooplankton remained unaffected by changes in pCO_2/pH." Aberle et al. conclude they must reject their hypothesis that a high CO_2 concentration would alter microzooplankton community structure, carrying capacity, or phenology, on the basis of their mesocosm experiment, noting the findings of their study point to "a relatively high robustness of microzooplankton towards elevated CO_2 in coastal waters."

Johnson et al. (2013) write, "in response to low ambient CO_2 concentrations, most marine microalgae have evolved a carbon concentrating mechanism (CCM) to elevate concentrations at the site of carbon fixation (Beardall and Giordano, 2002; Raven and Beardall, 2003; Raven et al., 2011)." They note, since "increases in dissolved CO_2 are predicted to cause down-regulation of microalgal CCM capacity (Giordano et al., 2005; Hopkinson et al., 2011)," which should reduce the energetic costs of CCMs (Raven, 1991), this phenomenon "will potentially allow more energy for other growth processes." They write, "as the carbon acquisition mechanisms and efficiencies of CCMs differ between algae, it is thought that rising CO_2 will benefit different species to varying degrees (Hein and Sand-Jensen, 1997; Tortell et al., 2000; Rost et al., 2003; Beardall and Raven, 2004; Riebesell, 2004; Fu et al., 2008) and may result in dramatic community shifts with profound consequences for marine biogeochemistry (Hutchins et al., 2009)."

Johnson et al. compared periphyton assemblages on artificial substrata installed along a coastal CO_2 gradient, ranging from a median value of 419 to 592 to 1,611 ppm, at a shallow-water cold-vent system off the island of Vulcano, NE Sicily, with the aim of testing the hypothesis that periphyton assemblages respond to CO_2 gradients and characterizing any changes in diatom and cyanobacteria populations to better understand the ecological effects of real-world lower ocean pH levels .

The six scientists report periphyton communities were indeed "altered significantly as CO_2 concentrations increased," and "CO_2 enrichment caused significant increases in chlorophyll a concentrations and in diatom abundance." Furthermore, "by using chl a as an index of the photosynthetic standing crop (Underwood, 1984)," they say "periphyton biomass was found to increase substantially (fivefold) at the CO_2-enriched stations," indicating "elevations in CO_2 stimulate primary productivity in these benthic assemblages." Johnson et al. conclude lower ocean pH levels are "likely to have wide-ranging consequences from local-scale influences on the structure of overlying benthic communities to effects on food web structure and larger-scale biogeochemical cycles."

References

Aberle, N., Schulz, K.G., Stuhr, A., Malzahn, A.M., Ludwig, A., and Riebesell, U. 2013. High tolerance of microzooplankton to ocean acidification in an Arctic coastal plankton community. *Biogeosciences* **10**: 1471–1481.

Anthonisen, A.C., Loehr, R.C., Prakasam, T.B., and Srinath, E.G. 1976. Inhibition of nitrification by ammonia and nitrous acid. *Journal of Water Pollution Control Federation* **48**: 835–852.

Beardall, J. and Giordano, M. 2002. Ecological implications of microalgal and cyanobacterial CO_2 concentrating mechanisms and their regulation. *Functional Plant Biology* **29**: 335–347.

Beardall, J. and Raven, J.A. 2004. The potential effects of global climate change in microalgal photosynthesis, growth and ecology. *Phycologia* **43**: 31–45.

Bell, T.G., Johnson, M.T., Jickells, T.D., and Liss, P.S. 2007. Ammonia/ammonium dissociation coefficient in seawater: a significant numerical correction. *Environmental Chemistry* **4**: 183–186.

Bell, T.G., Johnson, M.T., Jickells, T.D., and Liss, P.S. 2008. Ammonia/ammonium dissociation coefficient in seawater: a significant numerical correction (vol. 4 pg 183, 2007). *Environmental Chemistry* **5**: 258 U8.

Bellerby, R.G.J., Schulz, K.G., Riebesell, U., Neil, C., Nondal, G., Johannessen, T., and Brown, K.R. 2008. Marine ecosystem community carbon and nutrient uptake stoichiometry under varying ocean acidification during the PeECE III experiment. *Biogeosciences* **5**: 1517–1527.

Beman, J.M., Chow, C.-E., King, A.L., Feng, Y., Fuhrman, J.A., Andersson, A., Bates, N.R., Popp, B.N., and Hutchins, D.A. 2011. Global declines in ocean nitrification rates as a consequence of ocean acidification. *Proceedings of the National Academy of Sciences USA* **108**: 208–213.

Berounsky, V.M. 1990. *Rates of Nitrification and Their Importance to the Nitrogen Cycle of Narragansett Bay.* University of Rhode Island, Rhode Island, USA.

Berounsky, V.M. and Nixon, S.W. 1985a. Eutrophication and the rate of net nitrification in a coastal marine ecosystem. *Estuarine, Coastal and Shelf Science* **20**: 773–781.

Berounsky, V.M. and Nixon, S.W. 1985b. The role of nitrification in contributing to low oxygen conditions in the Providence River Estuary (RI). *Estuaries* **8**: A102.

Berounsky, V.M. and Nixon, S.W. 1990. Temperature and the annual cycle of nitrification in waters of Narragansett Bay. *Limnology and Oceanography* **35**: 1610–1617.

Berounsky, V.M. and Nixon, S.W. 1993. Rates of nitrification along an estuarine gradient in Narragansett Bay. *Estuaries* **16**: 718–730.

Blain, S., Queguiner, B., Armand, L., Belviso, S., Bombled, B., Bopp, L., Bowie, A., Brunet, C., Brussaard, C., Carlotti, F., Christaki, U., Corbiere, A., Durand, I., Ebersbach, F., Fuda, J.-L., Garcia, N., Gerringa, L., Griffiths, B., Guigue, C., Guillerm, C., Jacquet, S., Jeandel, C., Laan, P., Lefevere, D., Lo Monaco, C., Malits, A.,

Mosseri, J., Obermosterer, I., Park, Y.-H., Picheral, M., Pondaven, P., Remenyi, T., Sandroni, V., Sarthou, G., Savoye, N., Scouarnec, L., Souhaut, M., Thuiller, D., Timmermans, K., Trull, T., Uitz, J., van Beek, P., Veldhuis, M., Vincent, D., Viollier, E., Vong, L., and Wagener, T. 2007. Effect of natural iron fertilization on carbon sequestration in the Southern Ocean. *Nature* **446**: 1070–1074.

Boyd, P.W., Jickells, T., Law, C.S., Blain, S., Boyle, E.A., Buesseler, K.O., Coale, K.H., Cullen, J.J., de Baar, H.J.W., Follows, M., Harvey, M., Lancelot, C., Levasseur, M., Owens, N.P.J., Pollard, R., Rivkin, R.B., Sarmiento, J., Schoemann, V., Smetacek, V., Takeda, S., Tsuda, A., Turner, S., and Watson, A.J. 2007. Mesoscale iron enrichment experiments 1993–2005: Synthesis and future directions. *Science* **315**: 612–617.

Breitbarth, E., Bellerby, R.J., Neill, C.C., Ardelan, M.V., Meyerhofer, M., Zollner, E., Croot, P.L., and Riebesell, U. 2010. Ocean acidification affects iron speciation during a coastal seawater mesocosm experiment. *Biogeosciences* **7**: 1065–1073.

Brett, M.T. and Muller-Navarra, D.C. 1997. The role of highly unsaturated fatty acids in aquatic food web processes. *Freshwater Biology* **38**: 483–499.

Bruland, K.W., Rue, E.L., and Smith, G.J. 2001. Iron and macronutrients in California coastal upwelling regimes: Implications for diatom blooms. *Limnology and Oceanography* **46**: 1661–1674.

Carotenuto, Y., Putzeys, S., Simonelli, P., Paulino, A., Meyerhofer, M., Suffrian, K., Antia, A., and Nejstgaard, J.C. 2007. Copepod feeding and reproduction in relation to phytoplankton development during the PeECE III mesocosm experiment. *Biogeosciences Discussions* **4**: 3913–3936.

Egge, J., Thingstad, F., Engel, A., Bellerby, R.G.J., and Riebesell, U. 2007. Primary production at elevated nutrient and pCO_2 levels. *Biogeosciences Discussions* **4**: 4385–4410.

Egge, J.K, Thingstad, T.F., Larsen, A., Engel, A., Wohlers, J., Bellerby, R.G.J., and Riebesell, U. 2009. Primary production during nutrient-induced blooms at elevated CO_2 concentrations. *Biogeosciences* **6**: 877–885.

Focht, D.D. and Verstraete, W. 1977. Biochemical ecology of nitrification and denitrification. *Advances in Microbial Ecology* **1**: 135–214.

Fu, F.-X., Zhang, Y., Warner, M.E., Feng, Y., Sun, J., and Hutchins, D.A. 2008. A comparison of future increased CO_2 and temperature effects on sympatric *Heterosigma akashiwo* and *Prorocentrum minimum*. *Harmful Algae* **7**: 76–90.

Fulweiler, R.W., Emery, H.E., Heiss, E.M., and

Berounsky, V.M. 2011. Assessing the role of pH in determining water column nitrification rates in a coastal system. *Estuaries and Coasts* **34**: 1095–1102.

Giordano, M., Beardall, J., and Raven, J.A. 2005. CO_2 concentrating mechanisms in algae: mechanism, environmental modulation, and evolution. *Annual Review of Plant Biology* **56**: 99–131.

Hansen, P.J. 2002. Effect of high pH on the growth and survival of marine phytoplankton: implications for species succession. *Aquatic Microbial Ecology* **28**: 279–288.

Hein, M. and Sand-Jensen, K. 1997. CO_2 increases oceanic primary production. *Nature* **388**: 526–527.

Hopkinson, B.M., Dupont, C.L., Allen, A.E., and Morel, F.M.M. 2011. Efficiency of the CO_2-concentrating mechanism of diatoms. *Proceedings of the National Academy of Sciences USA* **108**: 3830–3837.

Hu, H. and Gao, K. 2001. Effects of doubled atmospheric CO_2 on the growth and photosynthesis of *Chaetoceros muelleri*. *Acta Hydrobiologica Sinica* **25**: 636–638.

Huesemann, M.H., Skillman, A.D., and Crecelius, E.A. 2002. The inhibition of marine nitrification by ocean disposal of carbon dioxide. *Marine Pollution Bulletin* **44**: 142–148.

Hutchins, D.A. and Bruland, K.W. 1998. Iron-limited diatom growth and Si:N uptake ratios in a coastal upwelling regime. *Nature* **393**: 561–564.

Hutchins, D.A., Mulholland, M.R., and Fu, F.-X. 2009. Nutrient cycles and marine microbes in a CO_2-enriched ocean. *Oceanography* **22**: 128–145.

Jacobson, M.Z. 2005. Studying ocean acidification with conservative, stable numerical schemes for non-equilibrium air-ocean exchange and ocean equilibrium chemistry. *Journal of Geophysical Research* **110**: 10.1029/2004JD005220.

Johnson, V.R., Brownlee, C., Rickaby, R.E.M., Graziano, M., Milazzo, M., and Hall-Spencer, J.M. 2013. Responses of marine benthic microalgae to elevated CO_2. *Marine Biology* **160**: 1813–1824.

Joint, I., Doney, S.C., and Karl, D.M. 2011. Will ocean acidification affect marine microbes? *The ISME Journal* **5**: 1–7.

Kim, J.M., Lee, K., Shin, K., Kang, J.H., Lee, H.-W., Kim, M., Jang, P.-G., and Jang M.-C. 2006. The effect of seawater CO_2 concentration on growth of a natural phytoplankton assemblage in a controlled mesocosm experiment. *Limnology and Oceanography* **51**: 1629–1636.

Larsen, J.B., Larsen, A., Thyrhaug, R., Bratbak, G., and Sandaa, R.-A. 2007. Marine viral populations detected during a nutrient induced phytoplankton bloom at elevated pCO_2 levels. *Biogeosciences Discussions* **4**: 3961–3985.

Leu, E., Daase, M., Schulz, K.G., Stuhr, A., and Riebesell, U. 2013. Effect of ocean acidification on the fatty acid composition of a natural plankton community. *Biogeosciences* **10**: 1143–1153.

Liang, W. and Yonemoto, T. 1999. The culture of Gonidium (*Chlorella Ellipsoidea*) using light and the study of its growth. *Journal of Wuhan Yejin University of Science & Technology* **22**: 248–251.

Lin, H. 1991. Comparison of *Spirulina subsalsa* with other *Spirulina* species. *Acta Hydrobiologica Sinica* **15**: 27–34.

Maberly, S.C. 1996. Diel, episodic and seasonal changes in pH and concentrations of inorganic carbon in a productive lake. *Freshwater Biology* **35**: 579–598.

Macedo, M.F., Duarte, P., Mendes, P., and Ferreira, J.G. 2001. Annual variation of environmental variables, phytoplankton species composition and photosynthetic parameters in a coastal lagoon. *Journal of Plankton Research* **23**: 719–732.

Nielsen, L.T., Hallegraeff, G.M., Wright, S.W., and Hansen, P.J. 2012. Effects of experimental seawater acidification on an estuarine plankton community. *Aquatic Microbial Ecology* **65**: 271–285.

Nielsen, L.T., Jakobsen, H.H., and Hansen, P.J. 2010. High resilience of two coastal plankton communities to twenty-first century seawater acidification: evidence from micro-cosm studies. *Marine Biology Research* **6**: 542–555.

Nobutaka, H., Toshifumi, T., and Yoshiharu F., *et al.* 1992. Tolerance of microalgae to high CO_2 and high temperature. *Phytochemistry* **31**: 3345–3348.

Ozturk, M., Steinnes, E., and Sakshaug, E. 2002. Iron speciation in the Trondheim Fjord from the perspective of iron limitation for phytoplankton. *Estuarine, Coastal and Shelf Science* **55**: 197–212.

Paulino, A.I., Egge, J.K., and Larsen, A. 2007. Effects of increased atmospheric CO_2 on small and intermediate sized osmotrophs during a nutrient induced phytoplankton bloom. *Biogeosciences Discussions* **4**: 4173–4195.

Pollard, R.T., Salter, I., Sanders, R.J., Lucas, M.I., Moore, C.M., Mills, R.A., Statham, P.J., Allen, J.T., Baker, A.R., Bakker, D.C.E., Charette, M.A., Fielding, S., Fones, G.R., French, M., Hickman, A.E., Holland, R.J., Hughes, J.A., Jickells, T.D., Lampitt, R.S., Morris, P.J., Nedelec, F.H., Nielsdottir, M., Planquette, H., Popova, E.E., Poulton, A.J., Read, J.F., Seeyave, S., Smith, T., Stinchcombe, M., Taylor, S., Thomalla, S., Venables, H.J., Williamson, R., and Zubkov, M.V. 2009. Southern Ocean deep-water carbon export enhanced by natural iron fertilization. *Nature* **457**: 577–580.

Raven, J.A. 1991. Physiology of inorganic C acquisition and implications for resource use efficiency by marine phytoplankton: Relation to increased CO_2 and temperature. *Plant, Cell and Environment* **14**: 779–794.

Raven, J.A. and Beardall, J. 2003. CO_2 acquisition mechanisms in algae: carbon dioxide diffusion and carbon dioxide concentrating mechanisms. In: Larkum, A.W.W., Raven, J.A., and Douglas, S. (Eds.) *Advances in Photosynthesis and Respiration*. Springer, New York, New York.

Raven, J.A., Giordano, M., Beardall, J., and Maberly, S. 2011. Algal and aquatic plant carbon concentrating mechanisms in relation to environmental change. *Photosynthesis Research* **109**: 281–296.

Riebesell, U. 2004. Effects of CO_2 enrichment on marine phytoplankton. *Journal of Oceanography* **60**: 719–729.

Riebesell, U., Bellerby, R.G.J., Grossart, H.-P., and Thingstad, F. 2008. Mesocosm CO_2 perturbation studies: from organism to community level. *Biogeosciences Discussions* **5**: 641–659.

Riebesell, U., Revill, A.T., Holdsworth, D.G., and Volkman, J.K. 2000. The effects of varying CO_2 concentration on lipid composition and carbon isotope fractionation in *Emiliania huxleyi*. *Geochimica Cosmochimica Acta* **64**: 4179–4192.

Riebesell, U., Schulz, K., Bellerby, R., Botros, M., Fritsche, P., Meyerhofer, M., Neill, C., Nondal, G., Oschlies, A., Wohlers, J., and Zollner, E. 2007. Enhanced biological carbon consumption in a high CO_2 ocean. *Nature* **450**: 545–548.

Riebesell, U., Wolf-Gladrow, D.A., and Smetacek, V. 1993. Carbon dioxide limitation of marine phytoplankton growth rates. *Nature* **361**: 249–251.

Rossoll, D., Bermudez, R., Hauss, H., Schulz, K.G., Riebesell, U., Sommer, U., and Winder, M. 2012. Ocean acidification-induced food quality deterioration constrains trophic transfer. *PLoS ONE* **7**: e34737.

Rost, B., Riebesell, U., and Burkhardt, S. 2003. Carbon acquisition of bloom-forming marine phytoplankton. *Limnology and Oceanography* **48**: 55–67.

Schulz, K.G., Riebesell, U., Bellerby, R.G.J., Biswas, H., Meyerhofer, M., Muller, M.N., Egge, J.K., Nejstgaard, J.C., Neill, C., Wohlers, J., and Zollner, E. 2008. Build-up and decline of organic matter during PeECE III. *Biogeosciences* **5**: 707–718.

Suffrian, K., Simonelli, P., Nejstgaard, J.C., Putzeys, S., Carotenuto, Y., and Antia, A. N. 2008. Microzooplankton grazing and phytoplankton growth in marine mesocosms with increased CO_2 levels. *Biosciences* **5**: 1145–1156.

Talling, J.F. 2006. Interrelated seasonal shifts in acid-base and oxidation-reduction systems that determine chemical stratification in three dissimilar English lake basins. *Hydrobiologia* **568**: 275–286.

Tortell, P.D., Rau, G.H., and Morel, F.M.M. 2000. Inorganic carbon acquisition in coastal Pacific phytoplankton communities. *Limnology and Oceanography* **45**: 1485–1500.

Tsuzuki, M., Ohnuma, E., Sato, N., Takaku, T., and Kawaguchi, A. 1990. Effects of CO_2 concentration during growth on fatty acid composition in microalgae. *Plant Physiology* **93**: 851–856.

Underwood, A.J. 1984. The vertical distribution and seasonal abundance of intertidal microalgae on a rocky shore in New South Wales. *Journal of Experimental and Marine Biology and Ecology* **78**: 199–220.

Vogt, M., Steinke, M., Turner, S., Paulino, A., Meyerhofer, M., Riebesell, U., LeQuere, C., and Liss, P. 2008. Dynamics of dimethylsulphoniopropionate and dimethyl-sulphide under different CO_2 concentrations during a mesocosm experiment. *Biogeosciences* **5**: 407–419.

Wolf-Gladrow, D.A., Riebesell, U., Burkhardt, S., and Bijma, J. 1999. Direct effects of CO_2 concentration on growth and isotopic composition of marine plankton. *Tellus* **51B**: 461–476.

Wyatt, N.J., Kitidis, V., Woodward, E.M.S., Rees, A.P., Widdicombe, S., and Lohan, M. 2010. Effects of high CO_2 on the fixed nitrogen inventory of the Western English Channel. *Journal of Plankton Research* **32**: 631–641.

Xia, J. and Gao, K. 2001. Effects of high CO_2 concentration on growth and photosynthesis of *Spirulina maxima*. *Acta Hydrobiologica Sinica* **25**: 474–480.

Xia, J. and Gao, K. 2002. Effects of CO_2 enrichment on microstructure and ultrastructure of two species of fresh water green algae. *Acta Botanica Sinica* **44**: 527–531.

Yu, J., Tang, X., Tian, J., Zhang, P., and Dong, S. 2006. Effects of elevated CO_2 on sensitivity of six species of algae and interspecific competition of three species of algae. *Journal of Environmental Science* **18**: 353–358.

Zeebe, R.E. and Wolf-Gladrow, D.A. 2001. *CO_2 in Seawater: Equilibrium, Kinetics, Isotopes*. Elsevier Oceanographic Book Series, Amsterdam, The Netherlands, 346 pp.

6.3.2.2 Macroalgae

The studies reviewed in this section examine what scientists have learned about potential impacts of lower ocean pH levels on macroalgae. The key findings, which challenge the alarming and negative projections of IPCC, are presented in the bullet points below, followed by an expanded discussion of those findings. (Citations for passages in quotation marks in the bullet points are included in the main body of the section.)

- Cultures of two red macroalga grown in seawater treatments of + 650-ppm and +1,250-ppm CO_2 were enhanced by 20% and 60%, respectively, for *Gracilaria chilensis*, and by 130% and 190%, respectively, for *Gracilaria sp.*

- The ongoing rise in the air's CO_2 content likely will not "hasten the transformation of reef community structure from coral to algal dominance."

- "Elevated levels of CO_2 in seawater increase the growth rate of many seaweed species despite the variety of ways in which carbon is utilized in these algae."

- At twice the current ambient CO_2 concentration, daily net carbon gain and total wet biomass production rates of a red seaweed common to the Northeast Atlantic intertidal zone were 52 and 314% greater than under ambient CO_2 conditions.

- Slightly less than a doubling of the air's CO_2 concentration increased the mean relative growth rate of a brown seaweed from along the coast of Nanao Island, Shantou, China by about 50%, as well as its mean rate of nitrate uptake during the study's 12-hour light periods by some 200%, and its nitrate reductase activity by approximately 20% over a wide range of substrate nitrate concentrations.

- Elevated CO_2 experiments on eelgrass "led to significantly higher reproductive output, below-ground biomass and vegetative proliferation of new shoots in light-replete treatments."

- "Ocean acidification will stimulate seagrass biomass and productivity, leading to more favorable habitat and conditions for associated invertebrate and fish species."

- The global increase of CO_2 "may enhance seagrass survival in eutrophic coastal waters, where populations have been devastated by algal proliferation and reduced column light transparency."

- High pH values created by seagrass photosynthesis can help increase calcification rates of nearby marine organisms.

Gao *et al.* (1993) grew cultures of the red alga *Gracilaria sp.* and *G. chilensis* in vessels enriched with nitrogen and phosphorus continuously aerated with normal air of 350 ppm CO_2, air enriched with an extra 650 ppm CO_2, or air enriched with an extra 1,250 ppm CO_2 for 19 days. Compared to the control treatment, the relative growth enhancements in the +650-ppm and +1,250-ppm CO_2 treatments were 20% and 60%, respectively, for *G. chilensis*, and 130% and 190%, respectively, for *Gracilaria sp.* Gao *et al.* say these results suggest, "in their natural habitats or cultivation sites, photosynthesis and growth of *Gracilaria* species are likely to be CO_2-limited, especially when the population density is high and water movement is slow." As the air's CO_2 content continues to rise, these marine marcoalgae should be able to grow increasingly well. That also may be true of many other macroalgae, for Gao *et al.* note "photosynthesis by most macroalgae is probably limited by inorganic carbon sources in natural seawater," citing Surif and Raven (1989), Maberly (1990), Gao *et al.* (1991), and Levavasseur *et al.* (1991).

This finding might be construed to imply corals in a CO_2-enriched world may be out-competed by marine macroalgae, which, to quote Langdon *et al.* (2003), "are not conspicuous on healthy reefs, but due to various anthropogenic pressures … are becoming increasingly abundant." In an experiment they conducted at the Biosphere–2 facility near Oracle, Arizona (USA), where they studied gross primary production and calcification in a macrophyte-dominated ecosystem that had a coral cover of 3%, Langdon *et al.* found the ongoing rise in the air's CO_2 content will not "hasten the transformation of reef community structure from coral to algal dominance."

Xu *et al.* (2010) write, "*Gracilaria lemaneiformis* (Bory) Weber-van Bosse is an economically important red seaweed that is cultivated on a large scale in China due to the quantity and quality of agar in its cell walls." They note, "much attention has been paid to the biofiltration capacity of the species (Yang *et al.*, 2005, 2006; Zhou *et al.*, 2006)," and some researchers have suggested it to be "an excellent species for alleviating coastal eutrophication in China (Fei, 2004)." Xu *et al.* examined how this seaweed might respond to elevated CO_2. They grew plants from thalli collected at 0.5 m depth from a farm located in Shen'ao Bay, Nanao Island, Shantou (China) for 16 days in 3-L flasks of natural seawater maintained at either natural (0.5 μM) or high (30 μM) dissolved inorganic phosphorus (Pi) concentrations in contact with air of either 370 or 720 ppm CO_2, measuring their photosynthetic rates, biomass production, and uptake of nitrate and phosphate.

As best as can be determined from Xu *et al.*'s graphical representations of their results, the 95% increase in the air's CO_2 concentration increased algal photosynthetic rates by only 5% in the natural Pi treatment but approximately 41% in the high Pi treatment. With respect to biomass production, the elevated CO_2 elicited a 48% increase in the natural Pi treatment but no increase in biomass in the high Pi treatment. The extra 29.5 µM Pi in the high Pi treatment itself had boosted biomass production of the low-CO_2 natural-Pi treatment by approximately 83%, and additional CO_2 did not increase growth rates beyond that point.

The three Chinese researchers write, "elevated levels of CO_2 in seawater increase the growth rate of many seaweed species despite the variety of ways in which carbon is utilized in these algae." They note "some species, such as *Porphyra yezoensis* Ueda (Gao *et al.*, 1991) and *Hizikia fusiforme* (Harv.) Okamura (Zou, 2005) are capable of using HCO_3^-, but are limited by the current ambient carbon concentration in seawater," and "enrichment of CO_2 relieves this limitation and enhances growth." Regarding the results they obtained with *Gracilaria lemaneiformis*—which they say "efficiently uses HCO_3^- and whose photosynthesis is saturated at the current inorganic carbon concentration of natural seawater (Zou *et al.*, 2004)"—they write, "the enhancement of growth could be due to the increased nitrogen uptake rates at elevated CO_2 levels," which in their experiment were 40% in the natural Pi treatment, because "high CO_2 may enhance the activity of nitrate reductase (Mercado *et al.*, 1999; Gordillo *et al.*, 2001; Zou, 2005) and stimulate the accumulation of nitrogen, which could contribute to growth."

Kubler *et al.* (1999) grew a red seaweed common to the Northeast Atlantic intertidal zone, *Lomentaria articulata*, for three weeks in hydroponic cultures subjected to various atmospheric CO_2 and O_2 concentrations to determine the effects of these gases on growth. They report oxygen concentrations ranging between 10 and 200% of ambient had no significant effects on daily net carbon gain or total wet biomass production rates in this seaweed. In contrast, CO_2 concentrations ranging between 67 and 500% of ambient had highly significant effects. At twice the current ambient CO_2 concentration, for example, daily net carbon gain and total wet biomass production rates were 52 and 314% greater than under ambient CO_2 conditions. Although this seaweed was likely carbon-saturated, when grown at five times the ambient CO_2 concentration it still exhibited daily net carbon gain and wet biomass production rates 23 and 50%, respectively, greater than those of control plants.

Zou (2005) collected specimens of a brown seaweed (*Hizikia fusiforme* (Harv.) Okamura) from intertidal rocks along the coast of Nanao Island, Shantou, China, and maintained them in glass aquariums in filtered natural seawater enriched with 60 µM $NaNO_3$ and 6.0 µM NaH_2PO_4, where they were continuously aerated with ambient air of 360 ppm CO_2 or enriched air of 700 ppm CO_2. He measured the specimens' relative growth and nitrogen assimilation rates and their nitrate reductase activities. The CO_2 enrichment increased the seaweed's mean relative growth rate by about 50%, its mean rate of nitrate uptake during the study's 12-hour light periods by 200%, and its nitrate reductase activity by approximately 20% over a wide range of substrate nitrate concentrations.

Zou notes "the extract of *H. fusiforme* has an immunomodulating activity on humans and this ability might be used for clinical application to treat several diseases such as tumors (Suetsuna, 1998; Shan *et al.*, 1999)." He also reports the alga "has been used as a food delicacy and an herbal ingredient in China, Japan and Korea." He says it "is now becoming one of the most important species for seaweed mariculture in China, owing to its high commercial value and increasing market demand." In addition, Zou notes "the intensive cultivation of *H. fusiforme* would remove nutrients more efficiently with the future elevation of CO_2 levels in seawater, which could be a possible solution to the problem of ongoing coastal eutrophication."

Palacios and Zimmerman (2007) conducted an experiment on eelgrass (*Zostera marina*) at the Duke Energy-North America Power Plant at Moss Landing, California (USA), where flue gas generated by the power plant furnace was piped approximately 1 km to a site where it was bubbled through outdoor flow-through seawater aquaria at rates that produced four aqueous CO_2 treatments characteristic of: "(1) the present day atmosphere, with approximately 16 µM $CO_2(aq)$, (2) CO_2 projected for 2100 that increases the $CO_2(aq)$ concentration of seawater to approximately 36 µM $CO_2(aq)$, (3) CO_2 projected for 2200 that increases the $CO_2(aq)$ concentration of seawater to 85 µM $CO_2(aq)$, and (4) a dissolved aqueous CO_2 concentration of 1123 µM $CO_2(aq)$, which triples the light-saturated photosynthesis rate of eelgrass (Zimmerman *et al.*, 1997)."

The researchers found elevated CO_2 "led to significantly higher reproductive output, below-ground biomass and vegetative proliferation of new shoots in light-replete treatments," those receiving light at 33% of the surface irradiance level. They write, "shoots growing at 36 μM $CO_2(aq)$ were 25% larger than those in the unenriched treatment [16 μM $CO_2(aq)$]," and "at 85 μM $CO_2(aq)$ shoots were 50% larger than those in the unenriched treatment and at 1123 μM $CO_2(aq)$ shoots were almost twice as large as those in the unenriched treatment." They found at 1123 μM $CO_2(aq)$ "22% of the shoots differentiated into flowers, more than twice the flowering output of the other treatments at this light level."

Noting "increased $CO_2(aq)$ is capable of increasing eelgrass reproductive output via flowering, and area-specific productivity via vegetative shoot proliferation under naturally replete light regimes," Palacios and Zimmerman state "the resulting increases in eelgrass meadow density may initiate a positive feedback loop that facilitates the trapping of sediments and prevents their resuspension, thereby reducing turbidity and increasing light penetration in coastal habitats," such that the resulting increased light penetration "may allow seagrass colonization depths to increase even further."

The two researchers also suggest the CO_2-induced increase in the productivity of eelgrass may "enhance fish and invertebrate stocks as well." They suggest the "deliberate injection of CO_2 to seawater may facilitate restoration efforts by improving the survival rates of recently transplanted eelgrass shoots," noting "it can buffer the negative effects of transplant shock by increasing rhizome reserve capacity and promoting shoot proliferation in light-replete environments." In addition, they say it "may also facilitate eelgrass survival in environments where conditions are periodically limiting, such as long dark winters or unusually warm summers that produce unfavorable productivity to respiration ratios," and "CO_2 injection may also promote flowering and seed production necessary for expansion and maintenance of healthy eelgrass meadows." Finally, they suggest "rising concentrations of $CO_2(aq)$ may increase vegetative propagation and seed production of other seagrass populations besides eelgrass."

According to Suarez-Alvarez et al. (2012), "the increase of coastal activities which produce important amounts of wastes, including inorganic nutrients (Troell et al., 2003), makes micro- and macroalgae interesting organisms to predict possible impacts, responses, and remediation processes by considering biomass production through cultivation techniques,"

citing Gao et al. (1991, 1993), Gao and McKinley (1994), Keffer and Kleinheinz (2002), Doucha et al. (2005), and Israel et al. (2005). They note, "macroalgae, in particular, have been the object of additional interest for CO_2 remediation (Gao and McKinley, 1994) because of their solar energy conversion capacity, high productivity values (higher than most productive terrestrial crops) and the possibility of being, in many cases, intensively cultivated."

Suarez-Alvarez et al. cultivated 8-gram fragments of the macroalga Hypnea spinella in 1-L flasks containing filtered seawater enriched with 140 μM NH_4Cl and 14 μM KH_2PO_4 for seven days of acclimation. They then culled the plants to their initial density and grew them for nine more days at ambient (360 ppm), 750, or 1,600 ppm atmospheric CO_2, measuring various plant physiological properties and processes. The authors report light-saturated net photosynthesis rates in the 750 ppm and 1,600 ppm CO_2 treatments were 41.5% and 50.5% greater, respectively, than in the 360 ppm treatment. Relative growth enhancements were 85.6% and 63.2% greater, respectively, and maximum ammonium uptake rates were enhanced by 24.2% and 19.9%, respectively. "From a practical point of view," Suarez-Alvarez et al. write, "these results suggest that intensive culture of H. spinella operated in biofilters might be enhanced by CO_2 supply to generate higher biomass productivities and better nitrogen biofiltration efficiencies," and "the use of flue gases for this purpose would also improve the ability of bioremediation of these biofilters, as has already been tested for Gracilaria cornea," citing Israel et al. (2005).

Jiang et al. (2010) note "seagrasses are flowering plants that thrive in shallow oceanic and estuarine waters around the world, and are ranked as one of the most ecologically and economically valuable biological systems on Earth," citing Beer et al. (2006). They also observe Thalassia hemprichii "is among the most widely-distributed seagrass species in an Indo-Pacific flora, dominating in many mixed meadows," citing Short et al. (2007). They collected intact vegetative plants of T. hemprichii from Xincun Bay of Hainan Island, Southern China, which they transported to the laboratory and cultured in flow-through seawater aquaria bubbled with four concentrations of CO_2 representative of the present global ocean, with a pH of 8.10; the projected ocean for 2100, with a pH of 7.75; the projected ocean for 2200, with a pH of 7.50; and the ocean characteristic of "an extreme beyond the current predictions" (a 100-fold increase in free CO_2, with a pH of 6.2).

The three researchers found the "leaf growth rate of CO_2-enriched plants was significantly higher than that in the unenriched treatment," "nonstructural carbohydrates (NSC) of *T. hemprichii*, especially in belowground tissues, increased strongly with elevated CO_2," and "belowground tissues showed a similar response with NSC." The Chinese scientists list several implications of their finding that "CO_2 enrichment enhances photosynthetic rate, growth rate and NSC concentrations of *T. hemprichii*." With higher atmospheric CO_2 concentrations, they write, "colonization beyond current seagrass depth limits is possible," the extra stored NSC "can be used to meet the carbon demands of plants during periods of low photosynthetic carbon fixation caused by severe environmental disturbance such as underwater light reduction," it can enhance "rhizome growth, flowering shoot production and vegetative proliferation," and it "may buffer the negative effects of transplant shock by increasing rhizome reserve capacity." They also write, "the globally increasing CO_2 may enhance seagrass survival in eutrophic coastal waters, where populations have been devastated by algal proliferation and reduced column light transparency." They conclude "ocean acidification will stimulate seagrass biomass and productivity, leading to more favorable habitat and conditions for associated invertebrate and fish species."

Wu *et al.* (2008) listed several known effects of a CO_2-enriched atmosphere on micro- and macro-algae living in the world's oceans. According to the authors, "enriched CO_2 up to several times the present atmospheric level has been shown to enhance photosynthesis and growth of both phytoplanktonic and macro-species that have less capacity of CCMs [CO_2-concentrating mechanisms]," and "even for species that operate active CCMs and those whose photosynthesis is not limited by CO_2 in seawater, increased CO_2 levels can down-regulate their CCMs and therefore enhance their growth under light-limiting conditions," because "at higher CO_2 levels, less light energy is required to drive CCM." They report enhanced CO_2 levels have been found to enhance the activity of nitrogen reductase in several marine plants, and this phenomenon "would support enhanced growth rate by providing adequate nitrogen required for the metabolism under the high CO_2 level." They write, "altered physiological performances under high-CO_2 conditions may cause genetic alteration in view of adaptation over long time scales," and "marine algae may adapt to a high CO_2 oceanic environment so that evolved communities in [the] future are likely to be genetically different from contemporary communities."

Semesi *et al.* (2009) investigated whether diel variations in seawater pH caused by the photosynthetic activity of seagrass meadows within Chwaka Bay (Zanzibar, Tanzania) could affect the calcification and photosynthesis rates of calcareous red algae (*Hydrolithon* sp. and *Mesophyllum* sp.) and green algae (*Halimeda renschii*) growing within the marine meadows. They measured rates of calcification and relative photosynthetic electron transport (rETR) of the algae *in situ* in open-bottom incubation cylinders either in the natural presence of the rooted seagrasses or after their leaves had been removed.

Semesi *et al.* report "seagrass photosynthesis increased the seawater pH within the cylinders from 8.3–8.4 to 8.6–8.9 after 2.5 hours (largely in conformity with that of the surrounding seawater), which, in turn, enhanced the rates of calcification 5.8-fold for *Hydrolithon* sp. and 1.6-fold for the other 2 species." They also found "the rETRs of all algae largely followed the irradiance throughout the day and were (in *Mesophyllum* sp.) significantly higher in the presence of seagrasses." The three researchers conclude "algal calcification within seagrass meadows such as those of Chwaka Bay is considerably enhanced by the photosynthetic activity of the seagrasses, which in turn increases the seawater pH."

They state the high pH values created by seagrass photosynthesis are what caused the elevated calcification rates of the macroalgae, and this observation has further implications. It suggests, for example, the lowering of seawater pH caused by higher atmospheric CO_2 concentrations—which results in a lowering of the calcium carbonate saturation state of seawater, and which has been predicted to lead to reductions in coral calcification rates—may be counteracted by CO_2-induced increases in the photosynthetic activity of the symbiotic zooxanthellae of Earth's corals, which may boost the pH of seawater in intimate contact with the coral host, allowing the host to *increase* its calcification rate in CO_2-enriched seawater, or at least not suffer a major reduction in calcification.

Smith *et al.* (2013) provide additional support for this thesis. They state, "benthic marine primary producers affect the chemistry of their surrounding environment through metabolic processes." They note, "photosynthesis and respiration will elevate or depress the concentration of oxygen in the diffusive boundary layer," and "acid-base regulation and biomineralization/dissolution for calcifying species can alter the relative concentration of inorganic carbon species and thus pH."

To compare species-specific rates of change in pH and oxygen concentrations over a diel cycle for several species of common benthic coral reef organisms—including corals, turf algae, and fleshy and calcifying macroalgae—Smith *et al.* assessed the generality of results across divergent types of reefs in the Caribbean and Pacific. They found "more productive fleshy taxa have the potential to raise both oxygen and pH during the day to a greater extent than calcified species." This discovery, as well as similar observations reported by Anthony *et al.* (2011) and Kleypas *et al.* (2011), suggest "non-calcifying primary producers, especially those driving large amplitudes in diurnal pH fluctuations, may be important 'buffer organisms' against potential ocean acidification on coral reefs." They write, "while particular species of macroalgae can negatively affect corals in a variety of ways," some fleshy algae "may provide a buffering capacity to future ocean acidification scenarios."

Johnson *et al.* (2012) note, "CO_2 gradients in natural settings, where whole ecosystems have been exposed to elevated levels of CO_2, allow us to investigate changes in the interactions, competition, predation and/or herbivory that involve long-lived metazoan species in benthic marine ecosystems." They observe, "volcanic CO_2 gradients are beginning to reveal the ecological shifts that can be expected to occur with globally increasing atmospheric CO_2 in both temperate (Hall-Spencer *et al.*, 2008) and tropical ecosystems (Fabricius *et al.*, 2011)." Johnson *et al.* assessed the abundance of herbivores (sea urchins) and the response of brown macroalgae (*Padina* spp.) to increasing levels of CO_2 in two natural settings. One of the sites was a set of shallow, volcanic CO_2 seeps on the island of Vulcano, NE Sicily, where *P. pavonica* was studied. The other site, where they studied *P. australis*, was a comparable set of seeps in the D'Entrecasteaux Island group, Papua New Guinea.

The five scientists found "a reduction in sea urchin abundances alongside a proliferation of *Padina* spp., as CO_2 levels increased" along both temperate and tropical rocky shores. The predator sea urchins were absent from locations that had the highest CO_2 levels (lowest pH), while "even in the lowest pH conditions, *P. pavonica* and *P. australis* were still able to calcify, seemingly from the enhancement of photosynthesis under high levels of CO_2."

Johnson *et al.* suggest the absence of sea urchins in the CO_2-enriched areas "may be one explanation for the proliferation of *Padina* spp., as it becomes released from the top-down control by these keystone grazers," noting "this effect of sea urchin removal has been observed in other *Padina* sp. populations (Sammarco *et al.*, 1974) and across other Phaeophyte assemblages (Leinaas and Christie, 1996; Ling *et al.*, 2010)." They note "increased photosynthetic activity at high CO_2 has also been observed in other calcified macroalgae (Reiskind *et al.*, 1988; Semesi *et al.*, 2009)," and in "non-calcified macroalgae (Kubler *et al.*, 1999; Connell and Russell, 2010; Russell *et al.*, 2011)."

References

Anthony, K.R.N., Kleypas, J.A., and Gattuso, J.P. 2011. Coral reefs modify their seawater carbon chemistry—implications for impacts of ocean acidification. *Global Change Biology* **17**: 3655–3666.

Beer, S., Mtolera, M., Lyimo, T., and Bjork, M. 2006. The photosynthetic performance of the tropical seagrass *Halophila ovalis* in the upper intertidal. *Aquatic Botany* **84**: 367–371.

Connell, S.D. and Russell, B.D. 2010. The direct effects of increasing CO_2 and temperature on non-calcifying organisms: increasing the potential for phase shifts in kelp forests. *Proceedings of the Royal Society of London B* **277**: 1409–1415.

Doucha, J., Straka, F., and Livansky, K. 2005. Utilization of flue gas for cultivation of microalgae (*Chlorella* sp.) in an outdoor open thin-layer photobioreactor. *Journal of Applied Phycology* **17**: 403–412.

Fabricius, K.E., Langdon, C., Uthicke, S., Humphrey, C., Noonan, S., De'ath, G., Okazaki, R., Muehllehner, N., Glas, M.S., and Lough, J.M. 2011. Losers and winners in coral reefs acclimatized to elevated carbon dioxide concentrations. *Nature Climate Change* **1**: 165–169.

Fei, X.G. 2004. Solving the coastal eutrophication problem by large scale seaweed cultivation. *Hydrobiologia* **512**: 145–151.

Gao, K., Aruga, Y., Asada, K., Ishihara, T., Akano, T., and Kiyohara, M. 1991. Enhanced growth of the red alga *Porphyra yezoensis* Ueda in high CO_2 concentrations. *Journal of Applied Phycology* **3**: 355–362.

Gao, K., Aruga, Y., Asada, K., and Kiyohara, M. 1993. Influence of enhanced CO_2 on growth and photosynthesis of the red algae *Gracilaria* sp. and *Gracilaria chilensis*. *Journal of Applied Phycology* **5**: 563–571.

Gao, K. and McKinleuy, K.R. 1994. Use of macroalgae for

marine biomass production and CO_2 remediation: a review. *Journal of Applied Phycology* **6**: 45–60.

Gordillo, F.J.L., Niell, F.X., and Figueroa, F.L. 2001. Non-photosynthetic enhancement of growth by high CO_2 level in the nitrophilic seaweed *Ulva rigida* C. Agardh (Chlorophyta). *Planta* **213**: 64–70.

Hall-Spencer, J.M., Rodolfo-Metalpa, R., Martin, S., Ransome, E., Fine, M., Turner, S.M., Rowley, S.J., Tedesco, D., and Buia, M.-C. 2008. Volcanic carbon dioxide vents show ecosystem effects of ocean acidification. *Nature* **454**: 96–99.

Israel, A., Gavrieli, J., Glazer, A., and Friedlander, M. 2005. Utilization of flue gas from a power plant for tank cultivation of the red seaweed *Gracilaria cornea*. *Aquaculture* **249**: 311–316.

Jiang, Z.J., Huang, X.-P., and Zhang, J.-P. 2010. Effects of CO_2 enrichment on photosynthesis, growth, and biochemical composition of seagrass *Thalassia hemprichii* (Ehrenb.) Aschers. *Journal of Integrative Plant Biology* **52**: 904–913.

Johnson, V.R., Russell, B.D., Fabricius, K.A.E., Brownlee, C., and Hall-Spencer, J.M. 2012. Temperate and tropical brown macroalgae thrive, despite decalcification, along natural CO_2 gradients. *Global Change Biology* **18**: 2792–2803.

Keffer, J.E. and Kleinheinz, G.T. 2002. Use of *Chlorella vulgaris* for CO_2 mitigation in a photobioreactor. *Journal of Industrial Microbiology and Biotechnology* **29**: 275–280.

Kleypas, J.A., Anthony, K.R.N., and Gattuso, J.P. 2011. Coral reefs modify their seawater carbon chemistry—case study from a barrier reef (Moorea, French Polynesia). *Global Change Biology* **17**: 3667–3678.

Kubler, J.E., Johnston, A.M., and Raven, J.A. 1999. The effects of reduced and elevated CO_2 and O_2 on the seaweed *Lomentaria articulata*. *Plant, Cell and Environment* **22**: 1303–1310.

Langdon, C., Broecker, W.S., Hammond, D.E., Glenn, E., Fitzsimmons, K., Nelson, S.G., Peng, T.-S., Hajdas, I., and Bonani, G. 2003. Effect of elevated CO_2 on the community metabolism of an experimental coral reef. *Global Biogeochemical Cycles* **17**: 10.1029/2002GB001941.

Leinaas, H.P. and Christie, H. 1996. Effects of removing sea urchins (*Strongylocentrotus droebachiensis*): stability of the barren state and succession of kelp forest recovery in the east Atlantic. *Oecologia* **105**: 524–536.

Levavasseur, G., Edwards, G.E., Osmond, C.B. and Ramus, J. 1991. Inorganic carbon limitation of photosynthesis in *Ulva rotundata* (Chlorophyta). *Journal of Phycology* **27**: 667–672.

Ling, S.D., Ibbott, S., and Sanderson, J.C. 2010. Recovery of canopy-forming macroalgae following removal of the enigmatic grazing sea urchin *Heliocidaris erythrogramma*. *Journal of Experimental Marine Biology and Ecology* **395**: 135–146.

Maberly, S.C. 1990. Exogenous sources of inorganic carbon for photosynthesis by marine macroalgae. *Journal of Phycology* **26**: 439–449.

Mercado, J.M., Javier, F., Gordillo, L., Niell, F.X., and Figueroa, F.L. 1999. Effects of different levels of CO_2 on photosynthesis and cell components of the red alga *Porphyra leucosticia*. *Journal of Applied Phycology* **11**: 455–461.

Palacios, S.L. and Zimmerman, R.C. 2007. Response of eelgrass *Zostera marina* to CO_2 enrichment: possible impacts of climate change and potential for remediation of coastal habitats. *Marine Ecology Progress Series* **344**: 1–13.

Reiskind, J.B., Seamon, P.T., and Bowes, G. 1988. Alternative methods of photosynthetic carbon assimilation in marine macroalgae. *Plant Physiology* **87**: 686–692.

Russell, B.D., Passarelli, C.A., and Connell, S.D. 2011. Forecasted CO_2 modifies the influence of light in shaping subtidal habitat. *Journal of Phycology* **47**: 744–752.

Sammarco, P.W., Levington, J.S., and Ogden, J.C. 1974. Grazing and control of coral reef community structure by *Diadema antillarum* Philippi (Echinodermata: Echinoidea): a preliminary study. *Journal of Marine Research* **32**: 47–53.

Semesi, I.S., Beer, S., and Bjork, M. 2009. Seagrass photosynthesis controls rates of calcification and photosynthesis of calcareous macroalgae in a tropical seagrass meadow. *Marine Ecology Progress Series* **382**: 41–47.

Semesi, I.S., Kangwe, J., and Bjork, M. 2009. Alterations in seawater pH and CO_2 affect calcification and photosynthesis in the tropical coralline alga, *Hydrolithon* sp. (Rhodophyta). *Estuarine and Coastal Shelf Science* **84**: 337–341.

Shan, B.E., Yoshida, Y., Kuroda, E., and Yamashita, U. 1999. Immunomodulating activity of seaweed extract on human lymphocytes *in vitro*. *International Journal of Immunopharmacology* **21**: 59–70.

Short, F.T., Carruthers, T.J., Dennison, W.C., and Waycott, M. 2007. Global seagrass distribution and diversity: A bioregional model. *Journal of Experimental Marine Biology and Ecology* **350**: 3–20.

Smith, J.E., Price, N.N., Nelson, C.E., and Haas, A.F. 2013. Coupled changes in oxygen concentration and pH caused by metabolism of benthic coral reef organisms. *Marine Biology* **160**: 2437–2447.

Suarez-Alvarez, S., Gomez-Pinchetti, J.L., and Garcia-Reina, G. 2012. Effects of increased CO_2 levels on growth, photosynthesis, ammonium uptake and cell composition in the macroalga *Hypnea spinella* (Gigartinales, Rhodophyta). *Journal of Applied Phycology* **24**: 815–823.

Suetsuna, K. 1998. Separation and identification of angiotensin I-converting enzyme inhibitory peptides from peptic digest of *Hizikia fusiformis* protein. *Nippon Suisan Gakkaishi* **64**: 862–866.

Surif, M.B. and Raven, J.A. 1989. Exogenous inorganic carbon sources for photosynthesis in seawater by members of the Fucales and the Laminariales (Phaeophyta): ecological and taxonomic implications. *Oecologia* **78**: 97–103.

Troell, M., Halling, C., Neori, A., Chopin, T., Buschmann, A.H., Kautsky, N., and Yarish, C. 2003. Integrated mariculture: asking the right questions. *Aquaculture* **26**: 69–90.

Wu, H.-Y., Zou, D.-H., and Gao, K.-S. 2008. Impacts of increased atmospheric CO_2 concentration on photosynthesis and growth of micro- and macro-algae. *Science in China Series C: Life Sciences* **51**: 1144–1150.

Xu, Z., Zou, D., and Gao, K. 2010. Effects of elevated CO_2 and phosphorus supply on growth, photosynthesis and nutrient uptake in the marine macroalga *Gracilaria lemaneiformis* (Rhodophyta). *Botanica Marina* **53**: 123–129.

Yang, H., Zhou, Y., Mao, Y., Li, X., Liu, Y., and Zhang, F. 2005. Growth characters and photosynthetic capacity of *Gracilaria lemaneiformis* as a biofilter in a shellfish farming area in Sanggou Bay, China. *Journal of Applied Phycology* **17**: 199–206.

Yang, Y.F., Fei, X.G., Song, J.M., Hu, H.Y., Wang, G.C., and Chung, I.K. 2006. Growth of *Gracilaria lemaneiformis* under different cultivation conditions and its effects on nutrient removal in Chinese coastal waters. *Aquaculture* **254**: 248–255.

Zhou, Y., Yang, H., Hu, H., Liu, Y., Mao, Y., Zhou, H., Xu, X., and Zhang, F. 2006. Bioremediation potential of the macroalga *Gracilaria lemaneiformis* (Rhodophyta) integrated into fed fish culture in coastal waters of north China. *Aquaculture* **252**: 264–276.

Zimmerman, R.C., Kohrs, D.G., Steller, D.L., and Alberte, R.S. 1997. Impacts of CO_2-enrichment on productivity and light requirements of eelgrass. *Plant Physiology* **115**: 599–607.

Zou, D. 2005. Effects of elevated atmospheric CO_2 on growth, photosynthesis and nitrogen metabolism in the economic brown seaweed, *Hizikia fusiforme* (Sargassaceae, Phaeophyta). *Aquaculture* **250**: 726–735.

Zou, D., Xia, J., and Yang, Y. 2004. Photosynthetic use of exogenous inorganic carbon in the agarophyte *Gracilaria lemaneiformis* (Rhodophyta). *Aquaculture* **237**: 421–431.

6.3.3 Effects on Marine Animals

6.3.3.1 Bivalves

The studies reviewed in this section examine what scientists have learned about potential impacts of lower ocean pH levels on marine bivalves. The key findings, which challenge the alarming and negative projections of IPCC, are presented in the bullet points below, followed by an expanded discussion of those findings. (Citations for passages in quotation marks in the bullet points are included in the main body of the section.)

- Juvenile king scallops display a tolerance to lower ocean pH levels at pCO₂ levels below 1,600 ppm.

- Mussel larvae (*Mytilus edulis*) reared in a laboratory setting mimicking a cold-water environment revealed "no marked effect on fertilization success, development time, or abnormality to the D-shell stage, or on feeding of mussel larvae" from lower ocean pH levels , and under such conditions (pH 7.6) the larvae "were still able to develop a shell in seawater undersaturated with respect to aragonite."

- A laboratory experiment examining "the combined effects of elevated pCO₂ and food availability on juvenile *M. edulis* growth and calcification" showed "only minor impacts of pCO₂ up to 3350 µatm."

- At a naturally CO_2-enriched ocean site, growth and calcification rates of *M. edulis* were "seven times higher" at an "inner fjord field station (mean pCO₂ ca. 1000 µatm) in comparison to a low pCO₂ outer fjord station (ca. 600 µatm)," demonstrating "a high inherent resilience of calcifying benthic communities in an estuarine, eutrophic habitat to elevated seawater pCO₂," where "food supply, and not pCO₂, appears to be the primary factor driving biomass and biogenic $CaCO_3$ production, as well as community structure."

- "Selective breeding may be a solution to 'climate-proof' [the Sydney rock oyster] from the impacts of ocean acidification."

- Larvae spawned from adult Sydney rock oysters (*Saccostrea glomerata*) growing in elevated CO_2 (reduced pH) seawater "were larger and developed faster" than those spawned from adults growing under ambient conditions, suggesting "previous studies that have investigated the effects of elevated CO_2 on the larvae of molluscs and other marine organisms [whose predecessors had not been exposed to elevated CO_2] may overestimate the severity of their responses" to lower ocean pH levels.

- Sperm swimming speeds and fertilization success of the Pacific oyster (*Crassostrea gigas*) are slightly increased under lower ocean pH levels.

- Effects of lower ocean pH levels on *Crassostrea gigas* larvae "during the first three days of development are not significant as long as CO_3^{2-} concentrations remain above aragonite saturated conditions."

- The "pre-adapted ability to resist a wide range of decreased pH may provide *C. gigas* with the necessary tolerance to withstand rapid pH changes over the coming century."

- The discovery of four-decades-old mussels living "in natural conditions of pH values between 5.36 and 7.29" attest to "the extent to which long-term adaptation can develop tolerance to extreme conditions."

Sanders *et al.* (2013) "investigated the effects on oxygen consumption, clearance rates and cellular turnover in juvenile [king scallop] *Pecten maximus* following three months' laboratory exposure to four pCO_2 treatments (290, 380, 750, and 1140 ppm)." The four researchers state "none of the exposure levels were found to have significant effects on the clearance rates, respiration rates, condition index or cellular turnover (RNA:DNA) of individuals." These findings are compatible with those of Anderson *et al.* (2013), who also studied the growth, development, and survival of the initial larval stages of *P. maximus* and found them to be susceptible to the deleterious effects of lower ocean pH levels only at pCO_2 levels of 1,600 ppm and above. Sanders *et al.* conclude their results suggest "where food is in abundance, bivalves like juvenile *P. maximus* may display a tolerance to limited changes in seawater chemistry."

Berge *et al.* (2006) collected blue mussels (*Mytilus edulis* L.) from the outer part of the Oslofjord outside the Marine Research Station Solbergstrand in Norway and placed them in five 5-L aquariums continuously supplied with low-food-supply seawater extracted from the top meter of the Oslofjord outside the Marine Research Station Solbergstrand in Norway, continuously adding CO_2 to the waters of the aquaria so as to maintain them at five pH values (means of 8.1, 7.6, 7.4, 7.1, and 6.7) for 44 days. Shell lengths at either the time of death or at the end of the study were determined and compared to lengths measured at the start of the study.

According to the authors, "the increased concentration of CO_2 in the water and the correspondingly reduced pH had no acute effects on the mussels." The Norwegian researchers report, "mean increments of shell length were much lower for the two largest CO_2 additions compared to the values in the controls, while for the two smallest doses the growth [was] about the same as in the control, or in one case even higher," such that there were "no significant differences between the three aquaria within the pH range 7.4–8.1."

Berge *et al.* conclude their results "indicate that future reductions in pH caused by increased concentrations of anthropogenic CO_2 in the sea may have an impact on blue mussels," but "comparison of estimates of future pH reduction in the sea (Caldeira and Wickett, 2003) and the observed threshold for negative effects on growth of blue mussels [which they determined to lie somewhere between a pH of 7.4 and 7.1] do however indicate that this will probably not happen in this century." Caldeira and Wickett's calculation of the maximum level to which the air's CO_2 concentration might rise yields a value that approaches 2,000 ppm around the year 2300, representing a surface oceanic pH reduction of 0.7 units, which drops the pH only to 7.4, the upper limit of the "threshold for negative effects on growth of blue mussels" found by Berge *et al.*

Noting "there is a particular need to study effects of OA [lower ocean pH levels] on organisms living in cold-water environments due to the higher solubility of CO_2 at lower temperatures," Bechmann *et al.* (2011) maintained mussel (*Mytilus edulis*) larvae in a laboratory setting under the OA scenario predicted for the year 2100 (pH 7.6) and compared them against batches of larvae held under the current oceanic pH of 8.1 (the control treatment), keeping water temperature at a constant 10°C. They found "no marked effect on fertilization success, development time, or abnormality to the D-shell stage, or on feeding of mussel larvae in the low-pH treatment," and the *M. edulis* larvae "were still able to develop a shell in seawater under-saturated with respect to aragonite (a mineral form of $CaCO_3$)." They also found after two months of exposure the mussels were 28% smaller in the pH 7.6 treatment than in the control treatment. They write, "if only the larger larvae settle and survive in the field, the effects of OA on the mussel population may not be dramatic."

Thomsen *et al.* (2010) note, "as most laboratory experiments cannot account for species genetic adaptation potential, they are limited in their predictive power." Thus studies investigating "naturally CO_2-enriched habitats" have "recently gained attention, as they could more accurately serve as analogues for future, more acidic ecosystems." Thomsen *et al.* studied the macrobenthic community in Kiel Fjord, a naturally CO_2-enriched site in the Western Baltic Sea dominated by calcifying marine invertebrates. They determined in 34%, 23%, and 9% of the 42 weeks they were there, the partial pressure (*p*) of CO_2 in the water exceeded preindustrial pCO_2 (280 ppm) by a factor of three (>840 ppm), four (>1,120 ppm), and five (>1,400 ppm), respectively.

The German scientists report juvenile blue mussel (*Mytilus edulis*) recruitment "peaks during the summer months, when high water pCO_2 values of ~1000 ppm prevail." Their short-term laboratory research indicates "blue mussels from Kiel Fjord can maintain control rates of somatic and shell growth at a pCO_2 of 1400 ppm." At 4,000 ppm pCO_2, however, both shell mass and extension rates were significantly reduced; but "regardless of the decreased rates of shell growth at higher [1,400] pCO_2, all mussels increased their shell mass at least by 150% during the 8-week trial, even at Ωarg (Ωcalc) as low as 0.17 (0.28)," where Ω is the calcium carbonate saturate state of either aragonite (arg) or calcite (calc).

Thomsen *et al.* conclude it is likely "long-term acclimation to elevated pCO_2 increases the ability to calcify in *Mytilus* spp.," citing Michaelidis *et al.* (2005) and Ries *et al.* (2009) in addition to their own study. They say they could find "no causal relation-ship between the acid-base status and metabolic depression in this species at levels of ocean acidification that can be expected in the next few hundred years (IPCC, 2007)," after discovering in the waters of Kiel Fjord (and demonstrating in the laboratory) "communities dominated by calcifying invertebrates can thrive in CO_2-enriched coastal areas."

Working at the same location three years later with a different set of coauthors in a similarly coupled laboratory and field study, Thomsen *et al.* (2013) examined "the annual pCO_2 variability in [the Kiel Fjord] habitat and the combined effects of elevated pCO_2 and food availability on juvenile *M. edulis* growth and calcification." In the laboratory experiment, "mussel growth and calcification were found to chiefly depend on food supply, with only minor impacts of pCO_2 up to 3,350 µatm." In the field location (Kiel Fjord), where maximum pCO_2 values experienced during the summer were about 2,500 µatm at the surface of the fjord and more than 3,000 µatm at its bottom, they observed "seven times higher growth and calcification rates of *M. edulis* at a high pCO_2 inner fjord field station (mean pCO_2 ca. 1,000 µatm) in comparison to a low pCO_2 outer fjord station (ca. 600 µatm)." They note this high inner fjord productivity "was enabled by higher particulate organic carbon concentrations," as a result of the fjord's "being "highly impacted by eutrophication, which causes bottom water hypoxia and consequently high seawater pCO_2." Thomsen *et al.* conclude their study demonstrates "a high inherent resilience of calcifying benthic communities in an estuarine, eutrophic habitat to elevated seawater pCO_2," where "food supply, and not pCO_2, appears to be the primary factor driving biomass and biogenic $CaCO_3$ production, as well as community structure."

Range *et al.* (2011) conducted a 75-day controlled CO_2 perturbation experiment designed to test the effects of increased pCO_2 and reduced pH of seawater on the calcification, growth, and mortality of juvenile *Ruditapes decussatus* clams. They manipulated the carbonate chemistry of seawater by diffusing pure CO_2 into natural seawater to attain two reduced pH levels (by -0.4 and -0.7 pH unit compared to un-manipulated seawater). The authors hypothesized the juvenile clams would exhibit reduced net calcification, reduced growth of the shell and soft tissue, and increased mortality in the lower-pH conditions. At the conclusion of their experiment, however, the eight researchers found "no differences among pH treatments in terms of net calcification, size or weight of the clams," disproving the first two of their three hypotheses. Their third hypothesis also proved to be wrong—doubly wrong, in fact—for not only was juvenile clam mortality not increased in the low-pH seawater, mortality was significantly reduced in the acidified treatments, which they describe as an "unexpected result."

The Portuguese scientists conclude by noting life is intriguingly complex and "the generalized and intuitively attractive perception that calcification will be the critical process impacted by ocean acidification is being increasingly challenged," citing Widdicombe and Spicer (2008) and Findlay *et al.* (2009).

To provide a better understanding of the potential for the Sydney rock oyster (*Saccostrea glomerata*) to adapt to the threat of lower ocean pH levels , Parker *et al.* (2011) measured the within- and between-population variability in the species' growth response to elevated pCO$_2$, working with oysters (denoted as *wild*) they collected from intertidal and shallow subtidal habitats along the southeast coast of Australia, as well as two lines (QB and LKB) of the same species that had been selectively bred to support the country's oyster aquaculture industry. The authors report the wild oysters experienced a 64% reduction in growth after four days in an elevated pCO$_2$ environment of 1,000 ppm (with a water pH of 7.84) compared to wild oysters reared in the ambient pCO$_2$ environment of 375 ppm (with a water pH of 8.20). The growth reduction experienced by QB oysters growing in the same two environments was 45%, and that experienced by LKB oysters was 25%. They report the LKB oysters reared at elevated pCO$_2$ "grew slightly better than the wild oysters reared at ambient pCO$_2$." Such observations, Parker *et al.* write, provide "preliminary evidence that selective breeding may be a solution to 'climate-proof' important aquaculture industries from the impacts of ocean acidification."

Parker *et al.* (2012) introduce their follow-up study by noting analyses of the impact of lower ocean pH levels on marine organisms conducted to date "have only considered the impacts on 'adults' or 'larvae,' ignoring the potential link between the two life-history stages and the possible carry-over effects that may be passed from adult to offspring," citing Dupont *et al.* (2010), Hendriks *et al.* (2010), and Kroeker *et al.* (2010). Parker *et al.* placed adults of wild-collected and selectively bred populations of the Sydney rock oyster (*Saccostrea glomerata*), obtained at the beginning of reproductive conditioning, in seawater equilibrated with air of either 380 ppm CO$_2$ or 856 ppm CO$_2$ which produced seawater pH values of 8.2 and 7.9, respectively, after which they measured the development, growth, and survival responses of the two sets of larvae.

The six scientists found "larvae spawned from adults exposed to elevated PCO$_2$ were larger and developed faster." In addition, "selectively bred larvae of *S. glomerata* were more resilient to elevated CO$_2$ than wild larvae," as "measurement of the standard metabolic rate (SMR) of adult *S. glomerata* showed that at ambient CO$_2$, SMR is increased in selectively bred compared with wild oysters," and it is further increased "during exposure to elevated CO$_2$." These findings suggest "previous studies that have investigated the effects of elevated CO$_2$ on the larvae of molluscs and other marine organisms [whose predecessors had not been exposed to elevated CO$_2$] may overestimate the severity of their responses." They conclude "marine organisms may have the capacity to acclimate or adapt to elevated CO$_2$ over the next century."

Miller *et al.* (2009) grew larvae of two oyster species—the Eastern oyster (*Crassostrea virginica*) and the Suminoe oyster (*Crassostrea ariakensis*)—for up to 28 days in estuarine water in equilibrium with air of four CO$_2$ concentrations (280, 380, 560, and 800 ppm) chosen to represent atmospheric conditions in the preindustrial era, the present day, and the years 2050 and 2100, respectively, as projected by the IS92a business-as-usual scenario of IPCC. They maintained these levels by periodically aerating the aquaria with air containing 1% CO$_2$, assessing larval growth via image analysis and determining calcification by means of chemical analyses of calcium in the shells of the oyster larvae.

When the larvae of both species were cultured continuously from 96 hours post fertilization for 26 to 28 days while exposed to elevated CO$_2$ concentrations, they "appeared to grow, calcify and develop normally with no obvious morphological deformities, despite conditions of significant aragonite undersaturation." The scientists state these findings "run counter to expectations that aragonite shelled larvae should be especially prone to dissolution at high pCO$_2$." They note, "both oyster species generated larval shells that were of similar mean thickness, regardless of pCO$_2$, Ω$arag$ [aragonite compensation point] or shell area," remarking they "interpret the pattern of similar shell thickness as further evidence of normal larval shell development."

Working with another oyster species (*Crassostrea gigas*), Havenhand and Schlegel (2009) observed and measured sperm swimming behavior and fertilization kinetics in response to lower ocean pH levels . The oysters, collected from a mixed mussel/oyster bed on the coast of western Sweden, were kept in flow-through tanks of filtered sea water the scientists maintained at either the normal ambient pH level or a level reduced by about 0.35 units they created by bubbling CO$_2$ through the water. In water of pH 8.15, mean sperm swimming speeds were 92.1 ± 4.8μm/s, whereas in water of pH 7.8 they were slightly higher, at 94.3 ± 5.5μm/s, although the difference was not statistically significant. Mean fertilization success in water of pH 8.15 was 63.4%, whereas in water of pH 7.8 it was also slightly higher, at 64.1%; this difference, too, was not statistically significant.

The Swedish scientists state "the absence of significant overall effects of pH on sperm swimming behavior and fertilization success is remarkable," emphasizing power analyses they conducted "showed clearly that these results were not due to inadequate statistical power," and "the absence of significant effect is likely a true reflection of the responses of *Crassostrea gigas* gametes and zygotes from the Swedish west coast to levels of CO_2-induced acidification expected by the end of this century."

Gazeau *et al.* (2011) assessed "the impact of several carbonate-system perturbations on the growth of Pacific oyster (*Crassostrea gigas*) larvae during the first three days of development (until shelled D-veliger larvae)." They used filtered seawater obtained from the Oosterschelde (a nearby tidal inlet) with five chemistries obtained "by separately manipulating pH, total alkalinity and aragonite saturation state." The seven scientists report "developmental success and growth rates were not directly affected by changes in pH or aragonite saturation state but were highly correlated with the availability of carbonate ions ... as long as carbonate ion concentrations were above aragonite saturation levels." When carbonate ion concentrations dropped below aragonite saturation levels, they found growth and development "strongly decreased."

Gazeau *et al.* conclude, "the effects of ocean acidification on larvae of *Crassostrea gigas* from the Oosterschelde estuary during the first three days of development are not significant as long as CO_3^{2-} concentrations remain above aragonite saturated conditions." They add, "due to relatively high levels of total alkalinity in this area, it is not expected that seawater will become corrosive for aragonite following a decrease of 0.3 to 0.4 pH unit."

The French, English, and Dutch researchers also write, "most calcifying species, including mollusks, are able to concentrate Ca^{2+} and CO_3^{2-} ions at the site of calcification (McConnaughey and Gillikin, 2008)," and the bivalves they studied "should therefore be able to regulate calcification rates under suboptimal concentrations of Ca^{2+} and CO_3^{2-}." They note, "Thomsen *et al.* (2010) have shown that blue mussels are actively growing in a bay of the Western Baltic Sea naturally enriched with high CO_2 water," and "juvenile recruitment occurs in summer time coinciding with low pH levels and aragonite under-saturated conditions." Thus the evidence indicates lower ocean pH levels will not seriously affect mollusks.

Ginger *et al.* (2013) note, "our knowledge of the effect of reduced pH on *C. gigas* larvae presently relies presumptively on four short-term (< 4 days) survival and growth studies." They studied "the effects of long-term (40 days) exposure to pH 8.1, 7.7 and 7.4 on larval shell growth, metamorphosis, respiration and filtration rates at the time of metamorphosis," as well as the juvenile shell growth and structure of *C. gigas*. The seven scientists discovered "mean survival and growth rates were not affected by pH"; "the metabolic, feeding and metamorphosis rates of pediveliger larvae were similar, between pH 8.1 and 7.7"; "the pediveligers at pH 7.4 showed reduced weight-specific metabolic and filtration rates, yet were able to sustain a more rapid post-settlement growth rate"; and "no evidence suggested that low pH treatments resulted in alterations to the shell ultra-structures or elemental compositions (i.e., Mg/Ca and Sr/Ca ratios)." Ginger *et al.* conclude "larval and post-larval forms of the *C. gigas* in the Yellow Sea are probably resistant to elevated CO_2 and decreased near-future pH scenarios." They note "the pre-adapted ability to resist a wide range of decreased pH may provide *C. gigas* with the necessary tolerance to withstand rapid pH changes over the coming century."

Working with juvenile *Mytilus galloprovincialis* specimens obtained from a mussel raft in the Ria de Ares-Betanzos of Northwest Spain and reared in an experimental bivalve hatchery in Tavira, Portugal, Fernandez-Reiriz *et al.* (2012) tested the effects of three levels of seawater acidification caused by increasing concentrations of atmospheric CO_2: a natural control level plus two lesser levels of pH, one reduced by 0.3 pH unit and another reduced by 0.6 pH unit. They measured several responses of the mussels after 78 days of exposure to the three sets of pH conditions, focusing on clearance and ingestion rate, absorption efficiency, oxygen consumption, ammonia excretion, oxygen to nitrogen ratio, and scope for growth. The five researchers found no significant differences for clearance, ingestion, and respiration rates. The absorption efficiency and ammonium excretion rate of the juvenile mussels were inversely related to the 0.6 pH reduction, while the maximal scope for growth and tissue dry weight also were observed in the mussels exposed to the pH reduction of 0.6 unit. Fernandez-Reiriz *et al.* conclude their results suggest *M. galloprovincialis* "could be a tolerant ecophysiotype to CO_2 acidification, at least in highly alkaline coastal waters," noting, "mytilids are also able to dominate habitats with low alkalinity and high pCO_2," citing Thomsen *et al.* (2010).

Working with the same species of mussels obtained from the same location off the coast of

Northwest Spain under an identical pH regime, Range *et al.* (2012) tested the effects of seawater acidification on growth, calcification, and mortality of six-month-old juveniles. The eight researchers found the growth of the mussels, measured as relative increases in shell size and body weight during the 84 days of the experiment, "did not differ among treatments." A tendency for faster shell growth under elevated CO_2 was apparent, "at least during the first 60 days of exposure." They note calcification was reduced under elevated CO_2, but by only up to 9%. They state, "given that growth was unaffected, the mussels clearly maintained the ability to lay down $CaCO_3$, which suggests post-deposition dissolution as the main cause for the observed loss of shell mass." They also write, "mortality of the juvenile mussels during the 84 days was small (less than 10%) and was unaffected by the experimental treatments." The Portuguese scientists conclude "there is no evidence of CO_2-related mortalities of juvenile or adult bivalves in natural habitats, even under conditions that far exceed the worst-case scenarios for future ocean acidification (Tunnicliffe *et al.*, 2009)."

Tunnicliffe *et al.* (2009) studied *Bathymodiolus brevior*, "a vent-obligate species that relies partly on symbiotic sulphide-oxidizing bacteria for nutrition (von Cosel and Metivier, 1994)" and is found "at many sites in the western Pacific Ocean, where it occupies habitats of low hydrothermal fluid flux." Using remotely operated vehicles to collect mussel specimens, water samples, and imagery, Tunnicliffe *et al.* examined dense clusters of the vent mussel "in natural conditions of pH values between 5.36 and 7.29 on the northwest Eifuku volcano, Mariana arc, where liquid carbon dioxide and hydrogen sulfide emerge in a hydrothermal setting." They studied the vent mussels clusters along with mussels from "two sites in the southwestern Pacific: Hine Hina in the Lau backarc basin and Monowai volcano on the Kermadec arc," where "the same mussel species nestles in cracks and rubble where weak fluid flow emerges."

Based on the pH values they observed, the authors calculated saturation ratios for calcite (Ω_{calc}) ranging from 0.01 to 0.61, with an average value of only 0.18. They discovered "a dense mussel population, along with many other associated species (Limen and Juniper, 2006), on NW Eifuku, where chemosynthetic symbiosis provides an energetic benefit to living in a corrosive, low-pH environment." Tunnicliffe *et al.* say these findings attest to "the extent to which long-term adaptation can develop tolerance to extreme conditions." They report

discovering four-decades-old mussels living at the sites they visited, stating "the mussels' ability to precipitate shells in such low-pH conditions is remarkable."

In another study using extreme environmental conditions, Hammer *et al.* (2011) exposed specimens of the deep-sea bivalve *Acesta excavata* collected from cold-water reefs to water maintained in equilibrium with an atmospheric CO_2 concentration of approximately 33,000 ppm, which resulted in a pH value of 6.35—corresponding to conditions reported for water in close proximity to natural CO_2 seeps on the ocean floor—for periods of 0.5, 1, 4, 12, 24, or 96 hours, after which they retuned the bivalves to normal CO_2/pH conditions for 1, 4, 12, 24, or 96 hours. The three researchers report the exposure of *A. excavata* to water in equilibrium with the super-high CO_2 concentration "induced extra- and intra-cellular acidosis that remained uncompensated during exposure," and "oxygen consumption dropped significantly during the initial phase." They found it "approached control values at the end of exposure" and "no mortality was observed in exposed animals."

These observations, the researchers write, show "*A. excavata* displays higher tolerance to severe environmental hypercapnia [a condition where there is too much CO_2 in the blood] than what may be expected for deep-sea animals." They note Tunnicliffe *et al.* (2009) "found evidence that permanent exposure to similar conditions causes reduced growth rates and shell thickness in mussels adapted to live at deep-sea vents," and they speculate "such long-term effects may also develop in *A. excavata*." They note previous studies on other species that mostly involved exposure of fish to moderate hypercapnia (P_{CO2} = 10,000 ppm or less) frequently observed complete compensation of extracellular acidosis, citing Heisler (1984, 1986), and "marine invertebrates are often able to partially counteract acidosis through accumulation of bicarbonate ions," citing Lindinger *et al.* (1984), Portner *et al.* (1988), Michaelidis *et al.* (2005), Miles *et al.* (2007), Pane and Barry (2007), and Gutowska *et al.* (2010).

References

Andersen, S., Grefsrud, E.S., and Harboe, T. 2013. Effect of increased *p*CO$_2$ on early shell development in great scallop (*Pecten maximus* Lamark) larvae. *Biogeosciences Discussions* 10: 3281–3310.

Bechmann, R.K., Taban, I.C., Westerlund, S., Godal, B.F.,

Arnberg, M., Vingen, S., Ingvarsdottir, A., and Baussant, T. 2011. Effects of ocean acidification on early life stages of shrimp (*Pandalus borealis*) and mussel (*Mytilus edulis*). *Journal of Toxicology and Environmental Health, Part A* **74**: 424–438.

Berge, J.A., Bjerkeng, B., Pettersen, O., Schaanning, M.T., and Oxnevad, S. 2006. Effects of increased sea water concentrations of CO_2 on growth of the bivalve *Mytilus edulis* L. *Chemosphere* **62**: 681–687.

Caldeira, K. and Wickett, M.E. 2003. Anthropogenic carbon and ocean pH. *Nature* **425**: 365.

Dupont, S., Dorey, N., and Thorndyke, M. 2010. What meta-analysis can tell us about vulnerability of marine biodiversity to ocean acidification. *Estuarine, Coastal and Shelf Science* **89**: 182–185.

Fernandez-Reiriz, M.J., Range, P., Alvarez-Saldago, X.A., Espinosa, J., and Labarta, U. 2012. Tolerance of juvenile *Mytilus galloprovincialis* to experimental seawater acidification. *Marine Ecology Progress Series* **454**: 65–74.

Findlay, H.S., Wood, H.L., Kendall, M.A., Spicer, J.I., Twitchett, R.J., and Widdicombe, S. 2009. Calcification, a physiological process to be considered in the context of the whole organism. *Biogeosciences Discussions* **6**: 2267–2284.

Gazeau, F., Gattuso, J.-P., Greaves, M., Elderfield, H., Peene, J., Heip, C.H.R., and Middelburg, J.J. 2011. Effect of carbonate chemistry alteration on the early embryonic development of the Pacific oyster (*Crassostrea gigas*). *PLoS ONE* **6**: e23010.

Ginger, K.W.K., Vera, C.B.S., Dineshram, R., Dennis, C.K.S., Adela, L.J., Yu, Z., and Thiyagarajan, V. 2013. Larval and post-larval stages of Pacific oyster (*Crassostrea gigas*) are resistant to elevated CO_2. *PLoS ONE* **8**: e64147.

Gutowska, M., Melzner, F., Langenbuch, M., Bock, C., Claireaux, G., and Portner, H. 2010. Acid-base regulatory ability of the cephalopod (*Sepia officinalis*) in response to environmental hypercapnia. *Journal of Comparative Physiology B: Biochemical, Systemic, and Environmental Physiology* **180**: 323–334.

Hammer, K.M., Kristiansen, E., and Zachariassen, K.E. 2011. Physiological effects of hypercapnia in the deep-sea bivalve *Acesta excavata* (Fabricius, 1779) (Bivalvia; Limidae). *Marine Environmental Research* **72**: 135–142.

Havenhand, J.N. and Schlegel, P. 2009. Near-future levels of ocean acidification do not affect sperm motility and fertilization kinetics in the oyster *Crassostrea gigas*. *Biogeosciences* **6**: 3009–3015.

Heisler, N. 1984. Acid-base regulation in fishes. In: Hoar, W.S. and Randall, D.J. (Eds.) *Fish Physiology.* Academic Press, New York, New York, USA, pp. 315–401.

Heisler, N. 1986. Buffering and transmembrane ion transfer processes. In: Heisler, N. (Ed.) *Acid-Base Regulation in Animals.* Elsevier Science Publishers BV. Amsterdam, The Netherlands, pp. 3–47.

Hendriks, I.E., Duarte, C.M., and Alvarez, M. 2010. Vulnerability of marine biodiversity to ocean acidification: a meta-analysis. *Estuarine, Coastal and Shelf Sciences* **86**: 157–164.

IPCC. 2007. *The Physical Science Basis.* Contribution of Working Group I to the Fourth Assessment Report of the Intergovernmental Panel on Climate Change. Cambridge University, Cambridge, United Kingdom.

Kroeker, K.J., Kordas, R.L., Crim, R.N., and Singh, G.G. 2010. Meta-analysis reveals negative yet variable effects of ocean acidification on marine organisms. *Ecology Letters* **13**: 1419–1434.

Limen, H. and Juniper, S.K. 2006. Habitat controls on vent food webs at NW Eifuku Volcano, Mariana Arc. *Cahiers de Biologie Marine* **47**: 449–455.

Lindinger, M.I., Lauren, D.J., and McDonald, G. 1984. Acid-base balance in the sea mussel *Mytilus edulis*. III. Effects of environmental hypercapnia on intra- and extra-cellular acid-base balance. *Marine Biology Letters* **5**: 371–381.

McConnaughey, T.A. and Gillikin, D.P. 2008. Carbon isotopes in mollusk shell carbonates. *Geo-Marine Letters* **28**: 287–299.

Michaelidis, B., Ouzounis, C., Paleras, A., and Portner, H.O. 2005. Effects of long-term moderate hypercapnia on acid-base balance and growth rate in marine mussels *Mytilus galloprovincialis*. *Marine Ecology Progress Series* **293**: 109–118.

Miles, H., Widdicombe, S., Spicer, J.I., and Hall-Spencer, J. 2007. Effects of anthropogenic seawater acidification on acid-base balance in the sea urchin *Psammechinus miliaris*. *Marine Pollution Bulletin* **54**: 89–96.

Miller, A.W., Reynolds, A.C., Sobrino, C., and Riedel, G.F. 2009. Shellfish face uncertain future in high CO_2 world: Influence of acidification on oyster larvae calcification and growth in estuaries. *PLoS ONE* **4**: 10.1371/journal.pone.0005661.

Pane, E.F. and Barry, J.P. 2007. Extracellular acid-base regulation during short-term hypercapnia is effective in a shallow-water crab, but ineffective in a deep-sea crab. *Marine Ecology Progress Series* **334**: 1–9.

Parker, L.M., Ross, P.M., and O'Connor, W.A. 2011. Populations of the Sydney rock oyster, *Saccostrea glomerata*, vary in response to ocean acidification. *Marine Biology* **158**: 689–697.

Parker, L.M., Ross, P.M., O'Connor, W.A., Borysko, L,

Raftos, D.A., and Portner, H.-O. 2012. Adult exposure influences offspring response to ocean acidification in oysters. *Global Change Biology* **18**: 82–92.

Portner, H.O., Reipschlager, A., and Heisler, N. 1998. Acid-base regulation, metabolism and energetics in *Sipunculus nudus* as a function of ambient carbon dioxide level. *Journal of Experimental Biology* **201**: 43–55.

Range, P., Chicharo, M.A., Ben-Hamadou, R., Pilo, D., Matias, D., Joaquim, S., Oliveira, A.P., and Chicharo, L. 2011. Calcification, growth and mortality of juvenile clams *Ruditapes decussatus* under increased pCO_2 and reduced pH: Variable responses to ocean acidification at local scales? *Journal of Experimental Marine Biology and Ecology* **396**: 177–184.

Range, P., Pilo, D., Ben-Hamadou, R., Chicharo, M.A., Matias, D., Joaquim, S., Oliveira, A.P., and Chicharo, L. 2012. Seawater acidification by CO_2 in a coastal lagoon environment: Effects on life history traits of juvenile mussels *Mytilus galloprovincialis*. *Journal of Experimental Marine Biology and Ecology* **424–425**: 89–98.

Ries, J.B., Cohen, A.L., and McCorkle, D.C. 2009. Marine calcifiers exhibit mixed responses to CO_2-induced ocean acidification. *Geology* **37**: 1131–1134.

Sanders, M.B., Bean, T.P., Hutchinson, T.H., and Le Quesne, W.J.F. 2013. Juvenile king scallop, *Pecten maximus*, is potentially tolerant to low levels of ocean acidification when food is unrestricted. *PLOS ONE* **8**: e74118.

Thomsen, J., Casties, I., Pansch, C., Kortzinger, A., and Melzner, F. 2013. Food availability outweighs ocean acidification effects in juvenile *Mytilus edulis*: laboratory and field experiments. *Global Change Biology* **19**: 1017–1027.

Thomsen, J., Gutowska, M.A., Saphorster, J., Heinemann, A., Trubenbach, K., Fietzke, J., Hiebenthal, C., Eisenhauer, A., Kortzinger, A., Wahl, M., and Melzner, F. 2010. Calcifying invertebrates succeed in a naturally CO_2-rich coastal habitat but are threatened by high levels of future acidification. *Biogeosciences* **7**: 3879–3891.

Tunnicliffe, V., Davies, K.T.A., Butterfield, D.A., Embley, R.W., Rose, J.M., and Chadwick Jr., W.W. 2009. Survival of mussels in extremely acidic waters on a submarine volcano. *Nature Geoscience* **2**: 344–348.

von Cosel, R. and Metivier, B. 1994. Three new species of *Bathymodiolus* (Bivalvia: Mytilidae) from hydrothermal vents in the Lau Basin and the North Fiji Basin, Western Pacific, and the Snake Pit area, Mid-Atlantic Ridge. *The Veliger* **37**: 374–392.

Widdicombe, S. and Spicer, J.I. 2008. Predicting the impact of ocean acidification on benthic biodiversity: what can animal physiology tell us? *Journal of Experimental Marine Biology and Ecology* **366**: 187–197.

6.3.3.2 Corals

Some scientists predict the ongoing rise in the air's CO_2 content will play havoc with Earth's coral reefs in two ways: by stimulating global warming, which has been predicted to dramatically enhance coral bleaching, and by lower ocean pH levels , which is projected to lower the calcium carbonate saturation state of seawater and thereby reduce coral calcification rates. The first of these predictions was examined in Section 6.1.2 of this chapter. The topic of lower ocean pH levels is addressed here.

Several researchers have postulated many of Earth's corals are destined to die, with some species even facing extinction, because of the hypothesized connection between the ongoing rise in the air's CO_2 content and reduced rates of coral calcification (Buddemeier, 1994; Buddemeier and Fautin, 1996a,b; Gattuso *et al.*, 1998; Buddemeier, 2001). Kleypas *et al.* (1999), for example, calculated calcification rates of tropical corals already should have declined by 6 to 11% or more since 1880, as a result of the increase in atmospheric CO_2 concentration, and they predict the reductions could reach 17 to 35% by 2100 as a result of expected increases in the air's CO_2 content in the coming decades. Langdon *et al.* (2000) calculated a decrease in coral calcification rate of up to 40% between 1880 and 2065.

IPCC claimed in its most recent assessment report:

> Elevated temperature along with ocean acidification reduces the calcification rate of corals (*high confidence*), and may tip the calcium carbonate balance of reef frameworks towards dissolution (*medium evidence and agreement*).
>
> — p. 67 of the *Technical Summary*, Working Group II, IPCC Fifth Assessment Report, dated March 28, 2013

> Ocean acidification will cause a decrease of calcification of corals, which will cause not only a reduction in the coral's ability to grow its skeleton, but also in its contribution to reef building (*high confidence*).
>
> — p. 73 of the *Technical Summary*, Working Group II, IPCC Fifth Assessment Report, dated March 28, 2013)

> Ocean warming and acidification expected under RCP 8.5 will reduce calcification, elevate coral mortality and enhance sediment dissolution (*high confidence*; Manzello *et al.*, 2008). Coral reefs may stop growing and start dissolving when

atmospheric CO_2 reaches 560 ppm due to the combined effects of both drivers (*medium evidence*).

— p. 19 of *Chapter 5. Coastal Systems and Low-Lying Areas*, Working Group II, IPCC Fifth Assessment Report, dated March 28, 2013

The research summarized below reveals the dire assessment of IPCC is tenuous at best and more likely wholly incorrect. As Idso *et al.* (2000) have noted, coral calcification is more than a physical-chemical process described by a set of well-defined equations. It is a biologically driven physical-chemical process that may not be amenable to explicit mathematical description. They state, for example, "photosynthetic activity of zooxanthellae is the chief source of energy for the energetically-expensive process of calcification," and much evidence suggests "long-term reef calcification rates generally rise in direct proportion to increases in rates of reef primary production." They also note "the calcium carbonate saturation state of seawater actually rises with an increase in temperature, significantly countering the direct adverse oceanic chemistry consequences of an increase in atmospheric and/or hydrospheric CO_2 concentration." They conclude "the negative predictions of today could well be replaced by positive predictions tomorrow."

As revealed below, numerous scientific studies point toward a much more optimistic view of the future for the planet's corals.

References

Buddemeier, R.W. 1994. Symbiosis, calcification, and environmental interactions. *Bulletin Institut Oceanographique, Monaco* **13**: 119–131.

Buddemeier, R.W. 2001. Is it time to give up? *Bulletin of Marine Science* **69**: 317–326.

Buddemeier, R.W. and Fautin, D.G. 1996a. Saturation state and the evolution and biogeography of symbiotic calcification. *Bulletin Institut Oceanographique, Monaco* **14**: 23–32.

Buddemeier, R.W. and Fautin, D.G. 1996b. Global CO_2 and evolution among the *Scleractinia. Bulletin Institut Oceanographique, Monaco* **14**: 33–38.

Gattuso, J.-P., Frankignoulle, M., Bourge, I., Romaine, S., and Buddemeier, R.W. 1998. Effect of calcium carbonate saturation of seawater on coral calcification. *Global and Planetary Change* **18**: 37–46.

Idso, S.B., Idso, C.D., and Idso, K.E. 2000. CO_2, global warming and coral reefs: Prospects for the future. *Technology* **7S**: 71–94.

Kleypas, J.A., Buddemeier, R.W., Archer, D., Gattuso, J-P., Langdon, C., and Opdyke, B.N. 1999. Geochemical consequences of increased atmospheric carbon dioxide on coral reefs. *Science* **284**: 118–120.

Langdon, C., Takahashi, T., Sweeney, C., Chipman, D., Goddard, J., Marubini, F., Aceves, H., Barnett, H., and Atkinson, M.J. 2000. Effect of calcium carbonate saturation state on the calcification rate of an experimental coral reef. *Global Biogeochemical Cycles* **14**: 639–654.

6.3.3.2.1 Laboratory Studies

Researchers have predicted rates of coral calcification, and the photosynthetic rates of their symbiotic algae, will dramatically decline in response to what is typically referred to as an "acidification" of the world's oceans, as the atmosphere's CO_2 concentration continues to rise. This section examines evidence to the contrary obtained from laboratory-based studies. The key findings, which challenge the alarming and negative projections of IPCC, are presented in the bullet points below, followed by an expanded discussion of those findings. (Citations for passages in quotation marks in the bullet points are included in the main body of the section.)

- Larvae from *Acropora* coral species (A. *digitifera* and A. *tenuis*) "may be able to tolerate ambient pH decreases of at least 0.7 pH units."

- "Scleractinian coral species will be able to acclimate to a high CO_2 ocean even if changes in seawater pH are faster and more dramatic than predicted."

- Though short-term exposure to lower ocean pH levels resulted in a decline of calcification and net dissolution of calcium carbonate in *Lophelia pertusa*, longer-term (six months) exposure revealed *L. pertusa* was able to acclimate and experience slightly enhanced rates of calcification, maintaining net growth in waters sub-saturated with aragonite.

- Using "carbonate concentration or aragonite saturation state as the sole predictor of the effects of ocean acidification on coral calcification" is unreliable.

- "Other physiological mechanisms, such as a direct effect of reduced pH on calcium or bicarbonate ion transport and/or variable ability to regulate internal pH, are responsible for the variability in reported experimental effects of acidification on calcification."

- A "firmer grasp of the biological component of biomineralization is paramount" in determining the response of corals to lower ocean pH levels .

- The future increase in oceanic bicarbonate ions may "stimulate photosynthesis and calcification in a wide variety of hermatypic corals," reducing and potentially overcoming theoretical effects of lower ocean pH levels .

- Reef corals may mitigate the effects of seawater acidification by regulating pH in the fluid at the tissue-skeleton interface, and this mechanism "may explain how several coral species continue to calcify even in low pH seawater, which is undersaturated with respect to aragonite."

- The fleshy tissues in octocorals may act as a protective barrier against rising levels of pCO_2, helping to maintain a stable internal environment that avoids the adverse effects of lower ocean pH levels .

- Based "purely on thermodynamic grounds, the predicted change in surface ocean pH in the next decades would appear to have minimal effect on the capacity of [important] acid-rich proteins to precipitate carbonates," which suggests "these proteins will continue to catalyze calcification reactions at ocean pH values projected in the coming century."

Suwa *et al.* (2010) employed controlled infusions of pure CO_2 to create mean pH values of 8.03, 7.64, and 7.31 in filtered seawater that flowed continuously through three sets of multiple tanks into which they had introduced the gametes of two *Acropora* coral species (A. *digitifera* and A. *tenuis*) collected during a natural spawning event. Seven days later they determined their survival percentage, and after 10 more days they documented the size of the developing polyps. After 14 days they documented the percentage of polyps that had acquired zooxanthellae the researchers had collected from the giant clam *T. crocea* and released into the several treatment tanks.

They found "A. *digitifera* larval survival rate did not differ significantly among pH treatments," and the graphs of their data reveal survivorship in A. *tenuis* was about 18.5% greater in the lowest pH (highest CO_2) treatment than in the ambient seawater treatment. At the end of the subsequent 10-day study, polyp size was reduced in the lowest pH treatment, by about 14%, which is not too bad for an atmospheric CO_2 concentration reported by the authors to be in the range of 2,115–3,585 ppm. In the A. *tenuis* coral, this reduction in individual size was more than compensated by the greater percentage increase in survivorship. In addition, after only four days of exposure to the zooxanthellae derived from giant clams, all polyps in all treatments had acquired a full complement of the symbiotic zooxanthella.

The seven scientists say "the survival of coral larvae may not be strongly affected by pH change," or "in other words," as they continue, "coral larvae may be able to tolerate ambient pH decreases of at least 0.7 pH units." A pH decrease of that magnitude is likely never to occur, as it implies atmospheric CO_2 concentrations in the range of 2,115 to 3,585 ppm. If such high concentrations ever were to occur, they would be a long, long time in coming, giving corals far more than sufficient time to acclimate—and even evolve (Idso and Idso, 2009)—to cope with the slowly developing situation.

Takahashi and Kurihara (2013) measured the rates of calcification, respiration, and photosynthesis of the tropical coral *Acropora digitifera*, along with the coral's zooxanthellae density, under near-natural summertime temperature and sunlight conditions for five weeks. Their analysis revealed these "key physiological parameters" were not affected by either predicted mid-range CO_2 concentrations (pCO_2 = 744 ppm, pH = 7.97, Ω_{arag} = 2.6) or by high CO_2 concentrations (pCO_2 = 2,142 ppm, pH = 7.56, Ω_{arag} = 1.1) over the 35-day period of their experiment. They found "no significant correlation between calcification rate and seawater aragonite saturation (Ω_{arag})" and "no evidence of CO_2 impact on bleaching."

Kreif *et al.* (2010) collected two colonies of massive *Porites* corals (which form large multi-century-old colonies and calcify relatively slowly) and four colonies of the branching *Stylophora pistillata* coral (which is short-lived and deposits its skeleton rather rapidly) from a reef adjacent to the Interuniversity Institute for Marine Science in Eilat (Israel) at the northern tip of the Red Sea. They grew fragments of these corals in 1,000-liter tanks through which they pumped Gulf of Eilat seawater adjusted to be in equilibrium with air of three CO_2 concentrations

(385, 1,904, and 3,970 ppm), which led to corresponding pH values of 8.09, 7.49, and 7.19 and corresponding aragonite saturation state (Ω_{arag}) values of 3.99, 1.25, and 0.65. After an incubation period of six months for *S. pistillata* and seven months for the *Porites* corals, the researchers sampled several fragments and analyzed them for a number of properties. Fourteen months from the start of the experiment, they analyzed fragments of each coral species from each CO_2 treatment for zooxanthellae cell density, chlorophyll *a* concentration, and host protein concentration.

They report, "following 14 months incubation under reduced pH conditions, all coral fragments survived and added new skeletal calcium carbonate, despite Ω_{arag} values as low as 1.25 and 0.65." This occurred at a reduced rate of calcification compared to fragments growing in the normal pH treatment with a Ω_{arag} value of 3.99. Yet in spite of this reduction in skeletal growth, the scientists report, "tissue biomass (measured by protein concentration) was found to be higher in both species after 14 months of growth under increased CO_2." They further note Fine and Tchernov (2007) observed the same phenomenon, having "reported a dramatic increase (orders of magnitude larger than the present study) in protein concentration following incubation of scleractinian Mediterranean corals (*Oculina patagonica* and *Madracis pharencis*) under reduced pH," stating "these findings imply tissue thickening in response to exposure to high CO_2." Krief *et al.* also report "a decrease in zooxanthellae cell density with decreasing pH was recorded in both species," but "this trend was accompanied by an increase in chlorophyll concentration per cell at the highest CO_2 level."

The Israeli, French, and UK researchers say "the inverse response of skeleton deposition and tissue biomass to changing CO_2 conditions is consistent with the hypothesis that calcification stimulates zooxanthellae photosynthesis by enhancing CO_2 concentration within the coelenteron (McConnaughey and Whelan, 1997)," and "since calcification is an energy-consuming process ... a coral polyp that spends less energy on skeletal growth can instead allocate the energy to tissue biomass," citing Anthony *et al.* (2002) and Houlbreque *et al.* (2004). They suggest, "while reduced calcification rates have traditionally been investigated as a proxy of coral response to environmental stresses, tissue thickness and protein concentrations are a more sensitive indicator of the health of a colony," citing Houlbreque *et al.* (2004).

Krief *et al.* conclude "the long acclimation time of this study allowed the coral colonies to reach a steady state in terms of their physiological responses to elevated CO_2," and "the deposition of skeleton in seawater with $\Omega_{arag} < 1$ demonstrates the ability of both species to calcify by modifying internal pH toward more alkaline conditions." They further state "the physiological response to higher CO_2/lower pH conditions was significant, but less extreme than reported in previous experiments," suggesting "scleractinian coral species will be able to acclimate to a high CO_2 ocean even if changes in seawater pH are faster and more dramatic than predicted."

Form and Riebesell (2012) studied branches of *Lophelia pertusa*, collected from reefs off the coast of Norway, which they describe as "the most common reef framework-forming and ecosystem engineering cold-water coral with a cosmopolitan distribution (Zibrowius, 1980; Cairns, 1994; Freiwald *et al.*, 2004)." They conducted a short-term (eight-day) experiment and a long-term (178-day) experiment, in which they employed different atmospheric CO_2 treatments to create a range of water pH treatments from 8.029 to 7.768 in the eight-day study and from 7.944 to 7.755 in the 178-day study, measuring the corals' growth rates over these intervals. They report "short-term (1-week) high CO_2 exposure resulted in a decline of calcification by 26–29% for a pH decrease of 0.1 unit and net dissolution of calcium carbonate." In contrast, "*L. pertusa* was capable to acclimate to acidified conditions in long-term (6 months) incubations, leading to even slightly enhanced rates of calcification." In the long-term low-pH treatment, "net growth is sustained even in waters sub-saturated with respect to aragonite."

Crook *et al.* (2013) note "almost all tropical corals have algal symbionts (zooxanthellae)," while "most deep and cold-water corals lack zooxanthellae." Because the latter corals have no symbionts and rely solely on heterotrophy for energy, they "provide a simplified system for exploring the roles of nutrition (and energy) in coral calcification." Studying *Balanophyllia elegans*, a solitary azooxanthellate scleractinian coral common in shallow coastal waters around Monterey Bay, California (USA), where it is exposed seasonally to low-pH, high-pCO_2 upwelling waters, the five researchers conducted an eight-month factorial laboratory experiment in which they "measured the effects of three pCO_2 treatments (410, 770, and 1,220 µatm) and two feeding frequencies (3-day and 21-day intervals) on 'planulation' (larval release) by adult *B. elegans*, and on the survival, skeletal growth and calcification of newly settled juveniles."

Crook *et al.* report "pCO_2 had no effect on the numbers of brooded planulae larvae released," "higher food levels increased the number of larvae released by 50–200%," and "excess food enables corals to counteract partially some of the negative impacts of lower [aragonite] saturation states under higher pCO_2 conditions." They found "after 8 months of growth, high-food skeletons were up to 7 times larger (by volume) than low-food skeletons at every pCO_2 level," and "in every pCO_2 treatment, higher food led to both greater linear extension and greater calcification (skeletal weight) over the 8-month experiment." They also found "calcification by high-pCO_2, high-food corals was 4 times greater than in low-food corals at ambient pCO_2," and "even feeding on planktonic crustaceans only once every 21 days was still sufficient to maintain positive growth at high pCO_2, albeit very slowly." The five U.S. researchers conclude, "as long as food availability remains high, *B. elegans* may be able to largely compensate for the extra energy required for calcification at low saturations, even if calcification occurs at slightly lower rates than at modern pCO_2." They reinforce this conclusion in the last sentence of their paper's abstract, writing, "we conclude that food abundance is critical for azooxanthellate coral calcification, and that *B. elegans* may be partially protected from adverse consequences of ocean acidification in habitats with abundant heterotrophic food."

Nash *et al.* (2012) write, "coral reef ecosystems develop best in high-flow environments," but "their fragile frameworks are also vulnerable to high wave energy." They say the wave-resistant algal rims, which surround many shallow coral reefs and are predominantly made of crustose coralline algae (CCA), are critical structural elements for the survival of such coral reefs. The scientists note "concerns have been growing about the susceptibility of CCA to ocean acidification, because CCA Mg-calcite skeletons are more susceptible to dissolution under low pH conditions than are coral aragonite skeletons." They further note the recent discovery by Nash *et al.* (2011) of the stable carbonate known as dolomite in the CCA *Porolithon onkodes* necessitates a re-appraisal of the impacts of lower ocean pH levels on it and other CCAs, such as *P. pachydermum*.

The 11 researchers "carried out dissolution experiments on fragments of CCA collected fresh, but then dried, from the Heron Island reef front (Great Barrier Reef, Australia)," after which the fragments were exposed to ambient sea water as a control and an enriched CO_2 treatment, where "pH ranged from 7.85 to 8.55 (control) and 7.69–8.44 (treatment), tracking natural diurnal changes measured in the lagoon water." Nash *et al.* (2012) determined "dried dolomite-rich CCA have 6–10 times lower rates of dissolution than predominantly Mg-calcite CCA in both high-CO_2 (~700 ppm) and control (~380 ppm) environments." They found this stabilizing mechanism resulted from "a combination of reduced porosity due to dolomite infilling and selective dissolution of other carbonate minerals." Noting "the prevailing theories that Mg-calcites with higher Mg content will undergo greatest dissolution," they write, "we were surprised to find a trend in the opposite direction." As dolomite-rich CCA frameworks are common in shallow coral reefs globally, Nash *et al.* conclude "it is likely that they will continue to provide protection and stability for coral reef frameworks as CO_2 rises."

Egilsdottir *et al.* (2013) note "it has been suggested that organisms presently surviving in highly variable environments are likely to be more robust to ocean acidification," citing Moulin *et al.* (2011) and Raven (2011), and they hypothesize "the ability of organisms to tolerate significant pH/pCO_2 fluctuations may be a result of adaptation (a genetic trait shared by the population) and/or acclimation (owing to phenotypic plasticity of the individual)." The authors investigated the effect of elevated pCO_2 "in the articulated coralline red alga *Corallina elongata* from an intertidal rock pool on the north coast of Brittany (France), where pCO_2 naturally varied daily between 70 and 1,000 µatm." They grew the algae at four pCO_2 values (380, 550, 750, and 1,000 µatm) in laboratory mesocosms and measured several physiological responses of the coral.

The French and Icelandic researchers report "algae grown under elevated pCO_2 formed fewer new structures and produced calcite with a lower mMg/Ca ratio relative to those grown under 380 µatm." They also observe "respiration, gross primary production and calcification in light and dark were not significantly affected by increased pCO_2." Egilsdottir *et al.* conclude their study "supports the assumption that *C. elongata* from a tidal pool, where pCO_2 fluctuates over diel and seasonal cycles, [are] relatively robust to elevated pCO_2." They also state these observations portend "a greater resilience" of such organisms to the projected "highly variable pH/pCO_2 environments of future ocean acidification."

Ragazzola *et al.* (2013) note coralline algae have been shown to be a major contributor to the formation and stabilization of coral reefs and in enhancing coral larvae settlement, citing Chisholm (2000). Given "their crucial role in shallow water ecosystems and their worldwide distribution," the scientists write, "understanding the impact of ocean acidification on calcifying algae is fundamental," especially because "their high-Mg calcite skeleton is the most soluble polymorph of $CaCO_3$ (50% more soluble than calcite and 20% more soluble than aragonite)." Coralline algae are, therefore, "likely to be particularly sensitive to a reduction in Ω," which is the calcium carbonate saturation state of seawater, citing Ries (2011), Burdett *et al.* (2012), and Martin *et al.* (2013).

Because "species with wide geographic ranges, such as coralline algae, are in general very plastic and able to acclimatize to a variety of habitats through morphological and functional responses (Brody, 2004)," Ragazzola *et al.* cultured *Lithothamnion glaciale*, one of the main maerl-forming species in the northern latitudes, under different elevated CO_2 levels (410, 560, 840, and 1,120 ppm = 8.02, 7.92, 7.80, and 7.72 pH, respectively) for 10 months, with initial analyses of the various parameters they measured conducted at the three-month point of the study, as reported by Ragazzola *et al.* (2012). The six scientists report the growth rates of the plants in the three CO_2-enriched treatments after the first three months of their study were not significantly different from either each other or those of the ambient-treatment plants. At the end of the 10-month experiment, however, the CO_2-enriched plants' growth rates were approximately 60% lower than that of the ambient-treatment plants. However, the individual cell wall thicknesses of both inter and intra filaments at the three-month point of the study were significantly thinner than those of the control plants, while at the end of the 10-month study they were equivalent to those of the control plants.

Ragazzola *et al.* (2013) note a possible explanation of their findings is "a shift from what could be termed a 'passive' phase during the first three months to an 'active' phase by the end of ten months," whereby "during the 'passive' phase, the increased energy requirement for calcification due to higher CO_2 results in a reduction in the amount of calcite deposited in each cell well," but during the "active phase," *L. glaciale* reduces its growth rate so the cell wall structure can be better maintained. Because maintaining skeletal integrity is one of the main priorities of marine organisms living in high CO_2 environments, the German and UK researchers say "the results of this study indicate that seawater chemistry can drive phenotypic plasticity in coralline algae," and "the ability to change the energy allocation between cell growth and structural support is a clear adaptive response of the organism," which

"is likely to increase its ability to survive in a high CO_2 world."

Ries *et al.* (2010) "investigated the impact of CO_2-induced ocean acidification on the temperate scleractinian coral *Oculina arbuscula* by rearing colonies for 60 days in experimental seawaters bubbled with air-CO_2 gas mixtures of 409, 606, 903, and 2,856 ppm CO_2, yielding average aragonite saturation states (Ω_A) of 2.6, 2.3, 1.6 and 0.8." The authors observed "following the initial acclimation phase, survivorship in each experimental treatment was 100%," and in regard to the corals' rates of calcification and linear extension, "no significant difference was detected relative to the control treatment ($\Omega_A = 2.6$) for corals reared under Ω_A of 2.3 and 1.6," with the latter values corresponding to pH reductions from current conditions of 0.08 and 0.26, respectively. Ries *et al.* "propose that the apparent insensitivity of calcification and linear extension within *O. arbuscula* to reductions in Ω_A from 2.6 to 1.6 reflects the corals' ability to manipulate the carbonate chemistry at their site of calcification."

Herfort *et al.* (2008) note an increase in atmospheric CO_2 will cause an increase in the abundance of HCO_3^- (bicarbonate) ions and dissolved CO_2, and they also report several studies on marine plants have observed "increased photosynthesis with higher than ambient DIC [dissolved inorganic carbon] concentrations," citing Gao *et al.* (1993), Weis (1993), Beer and Rehnberg (1997), Marubini and Thake (1998), Mercado *et al.* (2001, 2003), Herfort *et al.* (2002), and Zou *et al.* (2003). The three researchers employed a wide range of bicarbonate concentrations "to monitor the kinetics of bicarbonate use in both photosynthesis and calcification in two reef-building corals, *Porites porites* and *Acropora* sp." Additions of HCO_3^- to synthetic seawater continued to increase the calcification rate of *Porites porites* until the bicarbonate concentration exceeded three times that of seawater, and photosynthetic rates of the coral's symbiotic algae were stimulated by HCO_3^- addition until they became saturated at twice the normal HCO_3^- concentration of seawater.

Similar experiments conducted on Indo-Pacific *Acropora* sp. showed calcification and photosynthetic rates in these corals were enhanced to an even greater extent, with calcification continuing to increase above a quadrupling of the HCO_3^- concentration and photosynthesis saturating at triple the concentration of seawater. The scientists monitored calcification rates of the *Acropora* sp. in the dark, writing, "although these were lower than in the light for a given HCO_3^- concentration, they still increased dramatically with

HCO_3^- addition, showing that calcification in this coral is light stimulated but not light dependent."

Herfort *et al.* suggest "hermatypic corals incubated in the light achieve high rates of calcification by the synergistic action of photosynthesis," which, as they have shown, is enhanced by elevated concentrations of HCO_3^- ions caused by the rise in the air's CO_2 content. The three researchers note over the next century the predicted increase in atmospheric CO_2 concentration "will result in about a 15% increase in oceanic HCO_3^-," and this development "could stimulate photosynthesis and calcification in a wide variety of hermatypic corals."

Jury *et al.* (2010) explain why some corals show positive responses to lower ocean pH levels in laboratory studies whereas others do not. They note, "physiological data and models of coral calcification indicate that corals utilize a combination of seawater bicarbonate and (mainly) respiratory CO_2 for calcification, not seawater carbonate," but "a number of investigators are attributing observed negative effects of experimental seawater acidification by CO_2 or hydrochloric acid additions to a reduction in seawater carbonate ion concentration and thus aragonite saturation state." They identify "a discrepancy between the physiological and geochemical views of coral biomineralization" and report, "not all calcifying organisms respond negatively to decreased pH or saturation state." They note, "together, these discrepancies suggest that other physiological mechanisms, such as a direct effect of reduced pH on calcium or bicarbonate ion transport and/or variable ability to regulate internal pH, are responsible for the variability in reported experimental effects of acidification on calcification."

Jury *et al.* performed incubations with the coral *Madracis auretenra* (= *Madracis mirabilis sensu* Wells, 1973) in modified seawater chemistries, where, as they describe it, "carbonate parameters were manipulated to isolate the effects of each parameter more effectively than in previous studies, with a total of six different chemistries." Among-treatment differences "were highly significant," and "the corals responded strongly to variation in bicarbonate concentration, but not consistently to carbonate concentration, aragonite saturation state or pH." They found, for example, "corals calcified at normal or elevated rates under low pH (7.6–7.8) when the sea water bicarbonate concentrations were above 1800 μM," and, conversely, "corals incubated at normal pH had low calcification rates if the bicarbonate concentration was lowered."

Jury *et al.* conclude "coral responses to ocean acidification are more diverse than currently thought," and they question "the reliability of using carbonate concentration or aragonite saturation state as the sole predictor of the effects of ocean acidification on coral calcification," stating "if we truly wish to decipher the response of coral calcification to ocean acidification, a firmer grasp of the biological component of biomineralization is paramount."

Venn *et al.* (2013) also focused on how lower ocean pH levels impact the physiological mechanisms that drive calcification, to provide knowledge helpful in predicting how corals and other marine calcifiers will respond and potentially acclimate to lower ocean pH levels . In corals, the authors note, the capacity to regulate pH in the fluid at the tissue-skeleton interface [subcalicoblastic medium (SCM)] and in the calcifying cells [calicoblastic epithelium (CE)] "has been widely proposed to be important in shaping calcification responses to ocean acidification." They studied the impact of seawater acidification on pH_{SCM} and pH_{CE} in the coral *Stylophora pistillata*, "using *in vivo* imaging of pH in corals exposed to reduced seawater pH and elevated pCO_2 in the laboratory for [both] long and short durations." This work included "exposures to levels of acidification and elevated pCO_2 many times greater than those predicted to occur at the end of this century."

Venn *et al.* say they "observed calcification (measured by growth of skeletal crystals and whole colonies) in all our treatments, including treatment pH 7.2, where aragonite was undersaturated." They continue, "this finding agrees with previous work with *S. pistillata* conducted elsewhere, where net calcification was also observed over a similar range of pH and pCO_2 (Krief *et al.*, 2010)." Such findings suggest, they write, "*S. pistillata* may have a high tolerance to decreases in seawater pH and changes in seawater chemistry," leading them to conclude "maintenance of elevated pH_{SCM} relative to the surrounding seawater may explain how several coral species continue to calcify even in low pH seawater, which is undersaturated with respect to aragonite (this study and Rodolfo-Metalpa *et al.* (2011) and Cohen *et al.*, (2009))." Venn *et al.* report, "reductions in calcification rate, both at the level of crystals and whole colonies, were only observed in our lowest pH treatment [pH 7.2] when pH was significantly depressed in the calcifying cells in addition to the SCM." "Overall," they say their findings suggest "reef corals may mitigate the effects of seawater acidification by regulating pH in the SCM."

Gabay *et al.* (2013) note octocorals possess "an internal calcium carbonate skeleton comprised of microscopic sclerites embedded in their tissue," citing Fabricius and Alderslade (2001), Jeng *et al.* (2011), and Tentori and Ofwegen (2011). They also note octocorals are "the second most important faunistic component in many reefs, often occupying 50% or more of the available substrate." They say "it is important to predict their response to a scenario of increased pCO_2."

Gabay *et al.* studied three species of octocorals from two families found in the Gulf of Aqaba at Eilat—the zooxanthellate *Ovabunda macrospiculata* and *Heteroxenia fuscens* (family Xeniidae) and *Sarcophyton* sp. (family Alcyoniidae)—which they maintained for five months under normal (8.2) and reduced (7.6 and 7.3) pH conditions, assessing their pulsation rate, protein concentration, polyp weight, density of zooxanthellae, and chlorophyll concentration per cell.

The three Israeli scientists found "no statistically significant difference between the octocorals exposed to reduced pH values compared to the control." They say "these findings indicate that octocorals may possess certain protective mechanisms against rising levels of pCO_2," and they suggest "their fleshy tissues act as a barrier, maintaining a stable internal environment and avoiding the adverse effects of the ambient elevated pCO_2." That notion accords with the observations of Rodolfo-Metalpa *et al.* (2011), and Gabay *et al.* note "this suggestion is further supported by our finding that the ultrastructural features of *O. macroscipulata* sclerites are not affected by increased ambient seawater acidity." They conclude, "octocorals might be able to acclimate and withstand rising levels of ocean acidification, even under conditions that are far beyond what is expected to occur by the end of the present century (pH 7.9)."

Mass *et al.* (2013) write, "despite the broad interest in coral calcification and the potential for climate-driven adverse effects, the molecules and biophysical mechanism responsible for the precipitation of carbonates are poorly understood." They note, "to date, we lack both a characterization of molecules involved in calcification and a mechanistic understanding of processes that lead to and control calcification," and this "lack of knowledge limits our ability to predict the response of corals to increasing atmospheric CO_2." The seven scientists "for the first time," identified, cloned, determined the amino acid sequence of, and characterized four highly acidic proteins they derived from the expression of genes obtained from the common stony coral *Stylophora pistillata*. Each of these proteins can spontaneously catalyze the precipitation of calcium carbonate in vitro.

They found "coral acid-rich proteins (CARPs) not only bind Ca^{2+} stoichiometrically but also precipitate aragonite in vitro in seawater at pH 8.2 and 7.6 via an electrostatic interaction with protons on bicarbonate anions." The seven U.S. researchers conclude, "based purely on thermodynamic grounds, the predicted change in surface ocean pH in the next decades would appear to have minimal effect on the capacity of these acid-rich proteins to precipitate carbonates." They note their findings "strongly suggest that these proteins will continue to catalyze calcification reactions at ocean pH values projected in the coming century."

Maier *et al.* (2013) note "previous experiments examining the effect of ocean acidification on the cold-water corals *L. pertusa* and *M. oculata* have indicated that their rates of calcification remain positive even in waters where Ω_a is < 1 (Maier *et al.*, 2009; Thresher *et al.*, 2011; Form and Riebesell, 2012)." They add that Form and Riebesell (2012) and Maier *et al.* (2012, 2013) found "calcification rates of these species remained positive at a partial pressure of CO_2 (pCO_2) of 1000 µatm, a value that is at the high end of projected changes by 2100." Maier *et al.* measured respiration rates "for both short and long periods of time at pCO_2 levels ranging from ambient (350 µatm) to elevated (1100 µatm) levels," using "the same experimental setup as a previous study demonstrating that elevated pCO_2 had no effect on the rate of calcification in these two species (Maier *et al.*, 2013)."

The six scientists report, "in the range of pCO_2 studied so far, up to 1215 µatm, no significant change in respiration was found as a function of increasing pCO_2." As for what "this means," Maier *et al.* write, "for the maintenance of high calcification rates over a large range of pCO_2 of up to 1,000 ppm, there is no evidence for a direct energy allocation from food uptake to calcification in order to compensate for higher energy required to maintain calcification constant despite a decrease in pH."

References

Anthony, K.R., Connolly, S.R., and Willis, B.L. 2002. Comparative analysis of energy allocation to tissue and skeletal growth in corals. *Limnology and Oceanography* **47**: 1417–1429.

Beer, S. and Rehnberg, J. 1997. The acquisition of inorganic carbon by the sea grass *Zostera marina*. *Aquatic Botany* **56**: 277–283.

Brody, H.M. 2004. *Phenotypic Plasticity: Functional and Conceptual Approaches*. Oxford University Press, Oxford, United Kingdom, p. 247.

Burdett, H.L., Aloisio, E., Calosi, P., Findlay, H.S., Widdicombe, S., Hatton, A.D., and Kamenos, N.A. 2012. The effect of chronic and acute low pH on the intracellular DMSP production and epithelial cell morphology of red coralline algae. *Marine Biology Research* 8: 756–763.

Cairns, S.D. 1994. Scleractinia of the temperate north Pacific. *Smithsonian Contributions to Zoology* 557: 1–150.

Chisholm, J.R.M. 2000. Calcification by crustose coralline algae on the northern Great Barrier Reef, Australia. *Limnology and Oceanography* 45: 1476–1484.

Cohen, A.L., McCorkle, D.C., De Putron, S., Gaetani, G.A., and Rose, K.A. 2009. Morphological and compositional changes in the skeletons of new coral recruits reared in acidified seawater: Insights into the biomineralization response to ocean acidification. *Geochemistry, Geophysics, Geosystems* 10: 1–12.

Crook, E.D., Cooper, H., Potts, D.C., Lambert, T., and Paytan, A. 2013. Impacts of food availability and pCO_2 on planulation, juvenile survival, and calcification of the azooxanthellate scleractinian coral *Balanophyllia elegans*. *Biogeosciences* 10: 7599–7608.

Egilsdottir, H., Noisette, F., Noel, L.M.-L.J., Olafson, J., and Martin, S. 2013. Effects of pCO_2 on physiology and skeletal mineralogy in a tidal pool coralline alga *Corallina elongata*. *Marine Biology* 160: 2103–2112.

Fabricius, K.E. and Alderslade, P. 2001. *Soft Corals and Sea Fans: A Comprehensive Guide to the Tropical Shallow Water Genera of the Central-West Pacific, the Indian Ocean and the Red Sea*. Australian Institute of Marine Science, Townsville, Australia, and New Litho, Melbourne, Australia.

Fine, M. and Tchernov, D. 2007. Scleractinian coral species survive and recover from decalcification. *Science* 315: 10.1126/science.1137094.

Form, A.U. and Riebesell, U. 2012. Acclimation to ocean acidification during long-term CO_2 exposure in the cold-water coral *Lophelia pertusa*. *Global Change Biology* 18: 843–853.

Freiwald, A., Fossa, J.H., Grehan, A., Koslow, T., and Roberts, J.M. 2004. *Cold-Water Coral Reefs*. UNEP-WCMC, Cambridge, United Kingdom.

Gabay, Y., Benayahu, Y., and Fine, M. 2013. Does elevated pCO_2 affect reef octocorals? *Ecology and Evolution* 3: 465–473.

Gao, K., Aruga, Y., Asada, K., Ishihara, T., Akano, T., and Kiyohara, M. 1993. Calcification in the articulated coralline alga *Corallina pilulifera*, with special reference to the effect of elevated CO_2 concentration. *Marine Biology* 117: 129–132.

Herfort, L., Thake, B., and Roberts, J. 2002. Acquisition and use of bicarbonate by *Emiliania huxleyi*. *New Phytologist* 156: 427–36.

Herfort, L., Thake, B., and Taubner, I. 2008. Bicarbonate stimulation of calcification and photosynthesis in two hermatypic corals. *Journal of Phycology* 44: 91–98.

Houlbreque, F., Tambutte, E., Allemand, D., and Ferrier-Pages, C. 2004. Interactions between zooplankton feeding, photosynthesis and skeletal growth in the scleractinian coral *Stylophora pistillata*. *Journal of Experimental Biology* 207: 1461–1469.

Idso, C.D. and Idso, S.B. 2009. *CO_2, Global Warming and Species Extinctions: Prospects for the Future*. Vales Lake Publishing, LLC, Pueblo West, Colorado, USA, 132 pp.

Jeng, M.S., Huang, H.D., Dai, C.F., Hsiao, Y.C., and Benayahu, Y. 2011. Sclerite calcification and reef-building in the fleshy octocoral genus *Sinularia* (Octocorallia: Alcyonacea). *Coral Reefs* 30: 925–933.

Jury, C.P., Whitehead, R.F., and Szmant, A.M. 2010. Effects of variations in carbonate chemistry on the calcification rates of *Madracis auretenra* (= *Madracis mirabilis sensu* Wells, 1973): bicarbonate concentrations best predict calcification rates. *Global Change Biology* 16: 1632–1644.

Krief, S., Hendy, E.J., Fine, M., Yam, R., Meibom, A., Foster, G.L., and Shemesh, A. 2010. Physiological and isotopic responses of scleractinian corals to ocean acidification. *Geochimica et Cosmochimica Acta* 74: 4988–5001.

Maier, C., Bils, F., Weinbauer, M.G., Watremez, P., Peck, M.A., and Gattuso, J.-P. 2013. Respiration of Mediterranean cold-water corals is not affected by ocean acidification as projected for the end of the century. *Biogeosciences* 10: 5671–5680.

Maier, C., Hegeman, J., Weinbauer, M.G., and Gattuso, J.-P. 2009. Calcification of the cold-water coral *Lophelia pertusa*, under ambient and reduced pH. *Biogeosciences* 6: 1671–1680.

Maier, C., Schubert, A., Berzunza Sanchez, M.M., Weinbauer, M.G., Watremez, P., and Gattuso, J.-P. 2013. End of the century pCO_2 levels do not impact calcification in Mediterranean cold-water corals. *PLOS ONE* 8: 10.1371/journal.pone.0062655.

Maier, C., Watremez, P., Taviani, M., Weinbauer, M.G., and Gattuso, J.-P. 2012. Calcification rates and the effect of ocean acidification on Mediterranean cold-water corals. *Proceedings of the Royal Society of London, Series B, Biological* 279: 1713–1723.

Martin, S., Cohu, S., Vignot, C., Zimmerman, G., and Gattuso, J. 2013. One-year experiment on the physiological response of the Mediterranean crustose coralline algae *Lithothamnion cabiochae*, to elevated pCO$_2$ and temperature. *Ecology and Evolution* 3: 676–693.

Marubini, F. and Thake, B. 1998. Coral calcification and photosynthesis: evidence for carbon limitation. In: *International Society for Reef Studies (ISRS), European Meeting*, Perpignan, France, 1–4 September, p. 119.

Mass, T., Drake, J.L., Haramaty, L., Kim, J.D., Zelzion. E., Bhattacharya, D., and Falkowski, P.G. 2013. Cloning and characterization of four novel coral acid-rich proteins that precipitate carbonates in vitro. *Current Biology* 23: 1126–1131.

McConnaughey, T. and Whelan, J.F. 1997. Calcification generates protons for nutrient and bicarbonate uptake. *Earth Science Reviews* 42: 95–117.

Mercado, J.M., Niell, F.X., and Gil-Rodriguez, M.C. 2001. Photosynthesis might be limited by light, not inorganic carbon availability, in three intertidal Gelidiales species. *New Phytologist* 149: 431–439.

Mercado, J.M., Niell, F.X., Silva, J., and Santos, R. 2003. Use of light and inorganic carbon acquisition by two morphotypes of *Zostera noltii* Hornem. *Journal of Experimental Marine Biology and Ecology* 297: 71–84.

Moulin, L., Catarino, A.I., Claessens, T., and Dubois, P. 2011. Effects of seawater acidification on early development of the intertidal sea urchin *Paracentrotus lividus* (Lamarck 1816). *Marine Pollution Bulletin* 62: 48–54.

Nash, M.C., Opdyke, B.N., Troitzsch, U., Russell, B.D., Adey, W.H., Kato, A., Diaz-Pulido, G., Brent, C., Gardner, M., Prichard, J., and Kline, D.I. 2012. Dolomite-rich coralline algae in reefs resist dissolution in acidified conditions. *Nature Climate Change* 3: 268–272.

Nash, M.C., Troitzsch, U., Opdyke, B.N., Trafford, J.M., Russell, B.D., and Kline, D.I. 2011. First discovery of dolomite and magnesite in living coralline algae and its geobiological implications. *Biogeosciences* 8: 3331–3340.

Ragazzola, F., Foster, L.C., Form, A.U., Buscher, J., Hansteen, T.H., and Fietzke, J. 2012. Ocean acidification weakens the structural integrity of coralline algae. *Global Change Biology* 18: 2804–2812.

Ragazzola, F., Foster, L.C., Form, A.U., Buscher, J., Hansteen, T.H., and Fietzke, J. 2013. Phenotypic plasticity of a coralline algae in a high CO$_2$ world. *Ecology and Evolution* 3: 3436–3446.

Raven, J.A. 2011. Effects on marine algae of changed seawater chemistry with increasing atmospheric CO$_2$. *Biology and Environment Proceedings of the Royal Irish Academy* 111B: 1–17.

Ries, J.B. 2011. Skeletal mineralogy in a high-CO$_2$ world. *Journal of Experimental Marine Biology and Ecology* 403: 54–64.

Ries, J.B., Cohen, A.L., and McCorkle, D.C. 2010. A nonlinear calcification response to CO$_2$-induced ocean acidification by the coral *Oculina arbuscula*. *Coral Reefs* 29: 661–674.

Rodolfo-Metalpa, R., Houlbreque, F., Tambutte, E., Boisson, F., Baggini, C., Patti, F.P., Jeffree, R., Fine, M., Foggo, A., Gattuso, J.P., and Hall-Spencer, J.M. 2011. Coral and mollusk resistance to ocean acidification adversely affected by warming. *Nature Climate Change* 1: 308–312.

Suwa, R., Nakamura, M., Morita, M., Shimada, K., Iguchi, A., Sakai, K., and Suzuki, A. 2010. Effects of acidified seawater on early life stages of scleractinian corals (Genus *Acropora*). *Fisheries Science* 76: 93–99.

Takahashi, A. and Kurihara, H. 2013. Ocean acidification does not affect the physiology of the tropical coral *Acropora digitifera* during a 5-week experiment. *Coral Reefs* 32: 305–314.

Tentori, E. and van Ofwegen, L.P. 2011. Patterns of distribution of calcite crystals in soft corals sclerites. *Journal of Morphology* 272: 614–628.

Thresher, R.E., Tilbrook, B., Fallon, S., Wilson, N.C., and Adkins, J. 2011. Effects of chronic low carbonate saturation levels on the distribution, growth and skeletal chemistry of deep-sea corals and other seamount megabenthos. *Marine Ecology Progress Series* 442: 87–99.

Venn, A.A., Tambutte, E., Holcomb, M., Laurent, J., Allemand, D., and Tambutte, S. 2013. Impact of seawater acidification on pH at the tissue-skeleton interface and calcification in reef corals. *Proceedings of the National Academy of Sciences USA* 110: 1634–1639.

Weis, V.M. 1993. Effect of dissolved inorganic carbon concentration on the photosynthesis of the symbiotic sea anemone *Aiptasia pulchella* Carlgren: role of carbonic anhydrase. *Journal of Experimental Marine Biology and Ecology* 174: 209–225.

Zibrowius, H. 1980. Les Scleractiniaires de la Mediterranee et de l'Atlantique nord-oriental. *Memoires de l'Institut Oceanographique.* Monaco 11: 1–284.

Zou, D.H., Gao, K.S., and Xia, J.R. 2003. Photosynthetic utilization of inorganic carbon in the economic brown alga, *Hizikia fusiforme* (Sargassaceae) from the South China Sea. *Journal of Phycology* 39: 1095–1100.

6.3.3.2.2 Field Studies

Some scientists have predicted rates of coral calcification and the photosynthetic rates of their symbiotic algae will decline dramatically in response to lower ocean pH levels as the atmosphere's CO_2 concentration continues to rise. As research evidence accumulates, however, the true story appears to be just the opposite. This section examines such evidence obtained from field-based studies conducted in the natural ocean. The key findings, which challenge the alarming and negative projections of IPCC, are presented in the bullet points below, followed by an expanded discussion of those findings. (Citations for passages in quotation marks in the bullet points are included in the main body of the section.)

- Theoretical calculations suggest rising atmospheric CO_2 over the past century should have led to a 6–14% decline in coral calcification via lower ocean pH levels , yet several studies show coral calcification rates have remained stable or increased.

- In contrast to model-based assumptions, the process of calcification in many corals is not correlated with aragonite saturation state or pH.

- Increases in calcification observed over the past century in many ocean regions have been shown to correlate strongly with increases in water temperature.

- Changes in pH did not affect the composition of associated microbial communities in two Mediterranean coral species.

- Cold-water corals are "likely to be much more resilient to decreasing seawater pH from ocean acidification than previously realized," because of their ability "to ameliorate or buffer external changes in seawater pH by up-regulating their internal (extracellular) pH at the site of calcification."

- The distribution and composition of deep-sea corals "are not constrained by carbonate levels below saturation."

- "The drawdown of total dissolved inorganic carbon due to photosynthesis and calcification of reef communities can exceed the drawdown of total alkalinity due to calcification of corals and calcifying algae, leading to a net increase in aragonite saturation state." Although "carbon fluxes of benthic reef communities cannot significantly counter changes in carbon chemistry at the scale of oceans, they provide a significant mechanism of buffering ocean acidification impacts at the scale of habitat to reef."

Field studies hold an advantage over laboratory-based studies in more aptly representing conditions in the real world, as many of those conditions are impossible or impractical to recreate in a laboratory setting. The findings produced in field studies tend to hold more weight and establish greater clarity on a scientific topic or question under investigation than findings produced in a laboratory setting. Such is the case with lower ocean pH levels . Whereas positive, negative, and neutral effects from this phenomenon have been observed on corals in laboratories, field-based studies in the ocean reveal the situation is much less dire than IPCC predicts. Many studies suggest a modest decline in oceanic pH may actually favor coral calcification and growth.

Pelejero *et al.* (2005), for example, developed a reconstruction of seawater pH spanning the period 1708–1988, based on the boron isotopic composition ($\delta^{11}B$) of a long-lived massive coral (*Porites*) from Flinders Reef in the western Coral Sea of the southwestern Pacific. They found "no notable trend toward lower $\delta^{11}B$ values" over the 300-year period investigated. They write, "the dominant feature of the coral $\delta^{11}B$ record is a clear interdecadal oscillation of pH, with $\delta^{11}B$ values ranging between 23 and 25 per mil (7.9 and 8.2 pH units)," which "is synchronous with the Interdecadal Pacific Oscillation." They also calculated changes in aragonite saturation state from the Flinders pH record that varied between ~3 and 4.5, and these values encompass "the lower and upper limits of aragonite saturation state within which corals can survive." They report, "skeletal extension and calcification rates for the Flinders Reef coral fall within the normal range for *Porites* and are not correlated with aragonite saturation state or pH." Thus, contrary to claims of great sensitivity of coral calcification to changes in pH and aragonite saturation, they found large cyclical changes in these parameters had essentially no detectable effect on either coral calcification or skeletal extension rates.

In a study of historical calcification rates determined from coral cores retrieved from 35 sites on the Great Barrier Reef, Lough and Barnes (1997) observed a statistically significant correlation between coral calcification rate and local water temperature. They found a 1°C increase in mean annual water temperature increased mean annual coral calcification rate by about 3.5 percent, but they also report there were "declines in calcification in *Porites* on the Great Barrier Reef over recent decades." They point out their data depict several extended periods of time when coral growth rates were either above or below the long-term mean, cautioning, "it would be unwise to rely on short-term values (say averages over less than 30 years) to assess mean conditions."

They report, "a decline in calcification equivalent to the recent decline occurred earlier this century and much greater declines occurred in the 18th and 19th centuries," long before anthropogenic CO_2 emissions had much of an impact on the air's CO_2 concentration. Over their entire dataset, Lough and Barnes write, "the 20th century has witnessed the second highest period of above average calcification in the past 237 years," not exactly to be expected in light of how dangerous high water temperatures are often said to be for corals, the claim that Earth is currently warmer than it has been at any other time during the entire past millennium, and the air's CO_2 content is currently much higher than it has been for more than a thousand years.

Bessat and Buigues (2001) reported similar findings after deriving a history of coral calcification rates, covering the period 1801–1990, from a core extracted from a massive *Porites* coral head on the French Polynesian island of Moorea. They note "recent coral-growth models highlight the enhanced greenhouse effect on the decrease of calcification rate," but instead of relying on theoretical calculations, they wanted to work with real-world data because the records preserved in ancient corals "may provide information about long-term variability in the performance of coral reefs, allowing unnatural changes to be distinguished from natural variability."

Bessat and Buigues found a 1°C increase in water temperature increased coral calcification rates at the site they studied by 4.5 percent. Then they found, "instead of a 6–14% decline in calcification over the past 100 years computed by the Kleypas group, the calcification has increased, in accordance with [the results of] Australian scientists Lough and Barnes." They also observed patterns of "jumps or stages" in the record, characterized by an increase in the annual rate of calcification, particularly at the beginning of the past century "and in a more marked way around 1940, 1960 and 1976," stating once again their results "do not confirm those predicted by the Kleypas *et al.* (1999) model."

Lough and Barnes (2000) delivered another major blow to the Kleypas *et al.* model when they assembled and analyzed the calcification characteristics of 245 similar-sized massive colonies of *Porites* corals obtained from 29 reef sites located along the length, and across the breadth, of Australia's Great Barrier Reef (GBR). The data spanned a latitudinal range of approximately 9° and an annual average sea surface temperature (SST) range of 25–27°C. To these data they added other published data from the Hawaiian Archipelago (Grigg, 1981, 1997) and Phuket, Thailand (Scoffin *et al.*, 1992), thus extending the latitudinal range of the expanded dataset to 20° and the annual average SST range to 23–29°C.

Lough and Barnes found the GBR calcification data were linearly related to the average annual SST data, as "a 1°C rise in average annual SST increased average annual calcification by 0.39 g cm^{-2} year^{-1}." Results were much the same for the extended dataset. They report, "the regression equation [calcification = 0.33(SST) - 7.07] explained 83.6% of the variance in average annual calcification (F = 213.59, p less than 0.00)," and "this equation provides for a change in calcification rate of 0.33 g cm^{-2} year^{-1} for each 1°C change in average annual SST."

Lough and Barnes say their findings "allow assessment of possible impacts of global climate change on coral reef ecosystems," and between the two 50-year periods 1880–1929 and 1930–1979, they calculate a calcification increase of 0.06 g cm^{-2} year^{-1}, noting "this increase of ~4% in calcification rate conflicts with the estimated decrease in coral calcification rate of 6–14% over the same time period suggested by Kleypas *et al.* (1999) as a response to changes in ocean chemistry." Even more stunning is their observation that between the two 20-year periods 1903–1922 and 1979–1998, "the SST-associated increase in calcification is estimated to be less than 5% in the northern GBR, ~12% in the central GBR, ~20% in the southern GBR and to increase dramatically (up to ~50%) to the south of the GBR." Lough and Barnes conclude coral calcification rates "may have already significantly increased along the GBR in response to global climate change."

Carricart-Ganivet (2004) developed relationships between coral calcification rate and annual average SST based on data collected from colonies of the reef-building coral *Montastraea annularis* at 12 locations in the Gulf of Mexico and Caribbean Sea. He found the calcification rate in the Gulf of Mexico increased 0.55 g cm^{-2} year^{-1} for each 1°C increase, and in the Caribbean Sea it increased 0.58 g cm^{-2} year^{-1} for each

1°C increase. Pooling these data with data regarding *M. annularis* and *M. faveolata* growing to a depth of 10 m at Carrie Bow Cay, Belize, data from reefs at St. Croix in the U.S. Virgin Islands, and data of *M. faveolata* growing to a depth of 10 m at Curacao, Antilles, Carricart-Ganivet reports a mean increase in calcification rate of ~0.5 g cm^{-2} year^{-1} for each 1°C increase in annual average SST, even greater than what Lough and Barnes found for *Porites* corals.

Working at two reef sites on the northwest coast of Cuba—one in the Guanahacabibes Gulf just off the Pinar del Rio Province and the other north of Havana Bay—Carricart-Ganivet and Gonzalez-Diaz (2009) measured yearly coral extension rates and densities of the dominant Caribbean reef-building coral *Montastraea annularis* for the period 1991 to 2003, from which data they calculated annual coral calcification rates. They plotted their results against mean annual sea surface temperature (SST, obtained from the UK's Hadley Centre) and compared their results with the earlier study of Carricart-Ganivet (2004). The results of these two investigations are illustrated in Figure 6.3.3.2.2.1, where it can be seen they are completely compatible with each other.

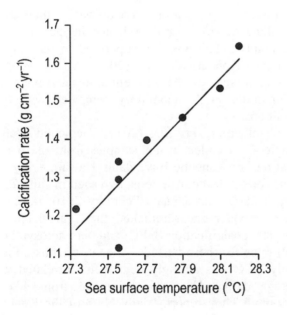

Figure 6.3.3.2.2.1. Mean yearly calcification rate of *Montastraea annularis* vs. mean annual sea surface temperature for the several sites studied by Carricart-Ganivet (2004) (blue circles) and the two sites studied by the authors (red circles). The line that has been fit to the data is defined by Calcification Rate = 0.51 SST - 12.85 (r^2 = 0.82, p < 0.002). Adapted from Carricart-Ganivet and Gonzalez-Diaz (2009).

Crabbe *et al.* (2006) determined the original growth rates of long-dead Quaternary corals found in limestone deposits on islands in the Wakatobi Marine National Park of Indonesia, which they compared to the growth rates of present-day corals of the same genera living in the same area. They found the Quaternary corals grew "in a comparable environment to modern reefs"—except, of course, for the air's CO_2 concentration, which is currently higher than it has been at any other time throughout the Quaternary, which spans the past 1.8 million years. Their measurements indicated the radial growth rates of the modern corals were 31 percent greater than those of their ancient predecessors in the case of *Porites* species, and 34 percent greater in the case of *Favites* species.

Cohen and Holcomb (2009) highlight several facts about the process of calcification in zooxanthellate corals. First, they report what is perhaps the most fundamental fact: "calcification is an active, physiological process that requires significant amounts of energy to drive it." Second, they note "increased photosynthesis [of coral symbiotic zooxanthellae] means increased photosynthate and more energy for calcification." Third, they report Atkinson *et al.* (1995) have shown "nutritionally replete zooxanthellate corals in naturally low [aragonite] saturation-state seawaters are capable of accreting skeletons at rates comparable to those achieved by conspecifics in high-saturation-state seawaters." Fourth, the two researchers write, "today, several reefs, including Galapagos, areas of Pacific Panama, and Jarvis (southern Line Islands), experience levels of aragonite saturation equivalent to that predicted for the open ocean under two times and three times pre-industrial CO_2 levels (Manzello *et al.*, 2008; Kathryn Shamberger [PMEL/NOAA] and colleagues, *pers. comm.*, August 2009)," and "available data on coral colony growth rates on these reefs, albeit limited, suggest that they are equivalent to and sometimes even rival those of conspecifics in areas where aragonite saturation states are naturally high, such as the western Pacific warm pool."

Probably the most important deduction from these observations, Cohen and Holcomb write, is "naturally elevated levels of inorganic nutrients and, consequently, high levels of primary and secondary production, may already be facilitating high coral calcification rates in regions with naturally high dissolved CO_2 levels." This further suggests Earth's corals, with their genetically diverse symbiotic zooxanthellae, are likely well-equipped to deal successfully with future increases in the air's CO_2

content.

The same phenomenon that powers the twin processes of coral calcification and phytoplanktonic growth (photosynthesis) tends to increase the pH of marine waters (Gnaiger *et al.*, 1978; Santhanam *et al.*, 1994; Brussaard *et al.*, 1996; Lindholm and Nummelin, 1999; Macedo *et al.*, 2001; Hansen, 2002). This phenomenon has been shown to have the ability to dramatically increase the pH of marine bays, lagoons, and tidal pools (Gnaiger *et al.*, 1978; Macedo *et al.*, 2001; Hansen, 2002) and significantly enhance the surface water pH of areas as large as the North Sea (Brussaard *et al.*, 1996).

In an example of this phenomenon, Middelboe and Hansen (2007) studied the pH of a wave-exposed boulder reef in Aalsgaarde on the northern coast of Zealand, Denmark, and a sheltered shallow-water area in Kildebakkerne in the estuary Roskilde Fjord, Denmark. They report, in line with what would be expected if photosynthesis tends to increase surface-water pH, "daytime pH was significantly higher in spring, summer and autumn than in winter at both study sites," often reaching values of 9 or more during peak summer growth periods vs. 8 or less in winter. They also found "diurnal measurements at the most exposed site showed significantly higher pH during the day than during the night," sometimes reaching values above 9 during daylight hours but typically dipping below 8 at night, and "diurnal variations were largest in the shallow water and decreased with increasing water depth."

Middelboe and Hansen cite the work of Pearson *et al.* (1998), who found pH averaged about 9 during the summer in populations of *Fucus vesiculosus* in the Baltic Sea; Menendez *et al.* (2001), who found maximum pH was 9 to 9.5 in dense floating macroalgae in a brackish coastal lagoon in the Ebro River Delta; and Bjork *et al.* (2004), who found pH values as high as 9.8 to 10.1 in isolated rock pools in Sweden. Noting "pH in the sea is usually considered to be stable at around 8 to 8.2," the two Danish researchers conclude "pH is higher in natural shallow-water habitats than previously thought."

Meron *et al.* (2012) state ocean acidification "has the potential to cause significant perturbations to the physiology of ocean organisms, particularly those such as corals that build their skeletons/shells from calcium carbonate," and this phenomenon "could also have an impact on the coral microbial community, and thus may affect coral physiology and health." They note most studies of declining pH effects on corals and/or their associated microbiota typically have been done under "controlled laboratory conditions." This approach clearly ignores any impacts declining pH values may have on the coral holobiont, some of which may be negative and some positive, which in the latter case is referred to as the probiotic hypothesis, as per Reshef *et al.* (2006).

The six scientists took advantage of a natural pH gradient off the coast of Ischia (Gulf of Naples, Italy) created by an underwater CO_2 flux from volcanic vents (Hall-Spencer *et al.*, 2008). They examined the potential impacts of a range of pH conditions (7.3 to 8.1) on coral microbial communities living under real-world conditions, focusing on two Mediterranean coral species: *Balanophyllia europaea* and *Cladocora caespitosa*.

The research team reports "pH did not have a significant impact on the composition of associated microbial communities in both coral species." They note "corals present at the lower pH sites exhibited only minor physiological changes" and "no microbial pathogens were detected." They conclude "at least for these two coral species, reduced pH does not seem to significantly reduce coral health," which suggests some of the contrary results obtained in laboratory studies could be due to the fact "laboratory environments cannot mimic the dynamism and microbial diversity present in nature," and the possibility "aquarium conditions themselves contribute to stress or disturbance in the microbial community." This view is supported in part by the finding of Kooperman *et al.* (2007), who noted, "the same coral species has different associated microbial communities in the laboratory compared with field conditions."

Shamberger *et al.* (2011) deployed "auto-samplers" to collect water samples from the barrier coral reef of Kaneohe Bay, Oahu, Hawaii, every two hours for six 48-hour periods, two each in June 2008, August 2009, and January/February 2010. Based on these seawater measurements, they calculated net ecosystem calcification (NEC) and net photosynthesis (NP) rates for these periods. The six scientists found "daily NEC was strongly negatively correlated with average daily pCO_2, which ranged from 421 to 622 ppm." They report, "daily NEC of the Kaneohe Bay barrier reef is similar to or higher than daily NEC measured on other coral reefs, even though Ω_{arag} levels (mean $\Omega_{arag} = 2.85$) are some of the lowest measured in coral reef ecosystems." Shamberger *et al.* conclude "it appears that while calcification rate and Ω_{arag} are correlated within a single coral reef ecosystem," as in the case of the barrier reef of Kaneohe Bay, "this relationship does not necessarily hold between different coral reef systems," and it can thus be expected "ocean acidification will not affect coral reefs uniformly and that some may be more sensitive to increasing pCO_2 levels than others." That implies (taking a more positive view of the subject) some coral reefs may be less sensitive to increasing pCO_2 than others.

McCulloch *et al.* (2012) state "for cold-water corals, which are already living at low levels of carbonate saturation, the shoaling of the saturation horizon as carbonate saturation states decrease [in response, for example, to rising atmospheric CO_2 concentrations] has the potential to cause dramatic declines in rates of calcification, or the dissolution of the carbonate skeletons of those living at or close to the saturation horizon." Since these corals are indeed living there, they speculate "they may have evolved adaptive strategies to counter the effects of low carbonate saturation states," one of which is to up-regulate their internal pH to a value that allows calcification to occur.

McCulloch *et al.* extended the novel approach of Trotter *et al.* (2011), based on boron isotopic systematics, to determine the relationship between seawater pH and the internal (extracellular) pH_{cf} at the site of calcification for several azooxanthellate cold-water scleractinian corals, collected from a large range of depths and geographically disparate sites, including southeast Australia, Chile's Comau Fjord, the Marmara Sea, a number of sites in the Mediterranean Sea, the northeast Atlantic Ocean, and the northwestern Hawaiian Islands.

The suite of "aragonitic cold-water coral species," as the 11 researchers describe them, "collectively show an overall trend of higher ΔpH [= pH_{cf} - seawater pH] values that is anti-correlated with seawater pH, with systematics generally consistent with biologically controlled pH up-regulation." This result indicates, "like symbiont-bearing tropical corals (Trotter *et al.*, 2011), they have the ability to ameliorate or buffer external changes in seawater pH by up-regulating their pH_{cf} at the site of calcification."

McCulloch *et al.* conclude "cold-water corals are likely to be much more resilient to decreasing seawater pH from ocean acidification than previously realized," because, as they see it, "decreasing seawater pH alone will only marginally affect calcification rates since this process would be largely countered by pH_{cf} up-regulation in cold-water corals, together with enhanced calcification rates from warming of the deep oceans."

Jantzen *et al.* (2013) write ocean acidification "is thought to negatively affect most marine-calcifying organisms, notably cold-water corals (CWC)," which might be expected to be especially sensitive due to the deep and cold waters in which they are typically found. They measured water profiles with a CTD (conductivity, temperature, depth) multi-probe profiler along the Comau fjord, extending down to 50–60 meters in 2010 and down to 225 meters in 2011, which allowed them to detect and describe the spatial distribution of the cold-water coral *Desmophyllum dianthus*.

The seven scientists determined *D. dianthus* grows along the fjord over its entire pH range, where "it occurs in shallow depths (below 12 m, pH 8.1) as part of a deep-water emergence community, but also in [water of] 225 m depth at a pH of 7.4." They report the cold-water coral thrives close to the aragonite saturation horizon and even below it, where they found "flourishing coral banks."

Jantzen *et al.* note other studies "question reduced calcification rates of corals in environments with lowered aragonite saturation state (Ω_{arg})," citing Marubini *et al.* (2008) and Jury *et al.* (2010), but they note "very recent studies hint at a higher acclimatization potential of cold-water corals to ocean acidification," citing Rodolfo-Metalpa *et al.* (2010), Trotter *et al.* (2011), Form and Riebesel (2012), and McCulloch *et al.* (2012a,b).

Thresher *et al.* (2011) state concerns about the effects of lower ocean pH levels on marine ecosystems "are based primarily on modeling studies and short-term laboratory exposure to low-carbonate conditions," citing Riegl *et al.* (2009), Veron *et al.* (2009), and Ries *et al.* (2010). They say "their relevance to long-term exposure in the field and the potential for ecological or evolutionary adjustment are uncertain," citing Maynard *et al.* (2008). In an effort "to determine the sensitivity of corals and allied taxa to long-term exposure to very low carbonate concentrations," Thresher *et al.* examined "the depth distribution and life-history characteristics of corals and other shell-forming megabenthos along the slopes of deep-sea seamounts and associated structure in the SW Pacific," where the gradient of water chemistry ranged from super-saturated in the case of aragonite and high-magnesium calcite (HMC) to under-saturated with calcite.

The five researchers "found little evidence that carbonate under-saturation to at least -30% affected the distribution, skeletal composition, or growth rates of corals and other megabenthos on Tasmanian seamounts." They found "both solitary scleractinian corals and colonial gorgonians were abundant at depths well below their respective saturation horizons and appeared healthy," and HMC echinoderms were common as deep as they sampled (4,011 m), in water approximately 45% under-saturated. They also report, "for both anthozoan and non-anthozoan taxa, there was no obvious difference in species' maximum observed depths as a function of skeletal mineralogy." In other words, the community "was not obviously shifted towards taxa with either less soluble or no skeletal structure at increasing depth." They conclude, "it is not obvious from our data that carbonate saturation state and skeletal mineralogy have any effect on species' depth distributions to the maximum depth sampled," and they saw "little evidence of an effect of carbonate under-saturation on growth rates and skeletal features."

Thresher et al. write, "the observation that the distributions of deep-sea corals are not constrained by carbonate levels below saturation is broadly supported by the literature," noting "solitary scleractinians have been reported as deep as 6 km (Fautin et al., 2009) and isidid gorgonians as deep as 4 km (Roark et al., 2005)." They say their own data also "provide no indication that conditions below saturation per se dictate any overall shifts in community composition."

Explaining these results, the researchers note one or more cell membranes may envelop the organisms' skeletons, largely isolating the calcification process and its associated chemistry from the bulk seawater, citing McConnaughey (1989), Adkins et al. (2003), and Cohen and McConnaughey (2003), and this phenomenon could presumably protect "the skeleton itself from the threat of low carbonate dissolution." In addition, Thresher et al. note, "calcification is energetically expensive, consuming up to 30% of the coral's available resources, and … normal calcification rates can be sustained in relatively low-carbonate environments under elevated feeding or nutrient regimes," as described in detail by Cohen and Holcomb (2009). Thresher et al. conclude, "Although saturation levels in those studies are considerably higher than those experienced by the deep-sea taxa we observed, the principle that elevated food availability could compensate for the higher costs of calcification in heterotrophic deepsea species appears plausible."

Thresher et al. say their data clearly suggest, whatever the cause, "a change in carbonate saturation horizons per se as a result of ocean acidification is likely to have only a slight effect on most of the live deep-sea biogenic calcifiers."

Anthony et al. (2011) used "a carbon flux model for photosynthesis, respiration, calcification and dissolution coupled with Lagrangian transport to examine how key groups of calcifiers (zooxanthellate corals) and primary producers (macroalgae) on coral reefs contribute to changes in the seawater carbonate system as a function of water residence time." The examination showed "the carbon fluxes of corals and macroalgae drive Ω_a in opposing directions," and "areas dominated by corals elevate pCO_2 and reduce Ω_a, thereby compounding ocean acidification effects in downstream habitats, whereas algal beds draw CO_2 down and elevate Ω_a, potentially offsetting ocean acidification impacts at the local scale." They also report simulations for two significantly elevated CO_2 scenarios (600 and 900 ppm CO_2) suggest "a shift in reef community composition from coral to algal dominance in upstream areas under ocean acidification will potentially improve conditions for calcification in downstream areas."

Kleypas et al. (2011) provided field validation of the simulations of Anthony et al. by examining the roles of three key members of benthic reef communities—corals, macroalgae, and sand—in modifying the chemistry of open-ocean source water. They found "the drawdown of total dissolved inorganic carbon due to photosynthesis and calcification of reef communities can exceed the drawdown of total alkalinity due to calcification of corals and calcifying algae, leading to a net increase in aragonite saturation state." They note there were no seagrasses on the reef flat they studied, and "research suggests that seagrasses may have an additional impact on reef seawater chemistry because they enhance the alkalinity flux from sediments (Burdige and Zimmerman, 2002), and they respond to CO_2 fertilization (Palacios and Zimmerman, 2007)."

These observations suggest reef communities gradually could alter their spatial compositions in a CO_2-acreting world to the point where seagrasses and other macroalgae take up residence in upstream regions, while corals and other calcifying organisms lay claim to downstream regions. Anthony et al. (2011) conclude, "although the carbon fluxes of benthic reef communities cannot significantly counter changes in carbon chemistry at the scale of oceans, they provide a significant mechanism of buffering ocean acidification impacts at the scale of habitat to reef."

Manzello et al. (2012) note although many people expect future ocean acidification (OA) resulting from rising atmospheric CO_2 concentrations to reduce the calcification rates of marine organisms, we have little understanding of how OA will manifest in dynamic, real-world systems, because "natural CO_2, alkalinity, and salinity gradients can significantly alter local carbonate chemistry, and thereby create a range of susceptibility for different ecosystems to OA." "To determine if photosynthetic CO_2 uptake associated with seagrass beds has the potential to create OA refugia," Manzello *et al.* repeatedly measured carbonate chemistry across an inshore-to-offshore gradient in the upper, middle, and lower Florida Reef Tract over a two-year period.

During times of heightened oceanic vegetative productivity, the five U.S. researchers found, "there is a net uptake of total CO_2 which increases aragonite saturation state (Ω_{arag}) values on inshore patch reefs of the upper Florida Reef Tract," and "these waters can exhibit greater Ω_{arag} than what has been modeled for the tropical surface ocean during preindustrial times, with mean Ω_{arag} values in spring equaling 4.69 ± 0.10." They report Ω_{arag} values on offshore reefs "generally represent oceanic carbonate chemistries consistent with present day tropical surface ocean conditions."

Manzello *et al.* hypothesize the pattern described above "is caused by the photosynthetic uptake of total CO_2 mainly by seagrasses and, to a lesser extent, macroalgae in the inshore waters of the Florida Reef Tract." They conclude these inshore reef habitats are "potential acidification refugia that are defined not only in a spatial sense, but also in time, coinciding with seasonal productivity dynamics," which further implies "coral reefs located within or immediately downstream of seagrass beds may find refuge from ocean acidification." They cite Palacios and Zimmerman (2007), whose work they describe as indicating "seagrasses exposed to high-CO_2 conditions for one year had increased reproduction, rhizome biomass, and vegetative growth of new shoots, which could represent a potential positive feedback to their ability to serve as ocean acidification refugia."

Noonan *et al.* (2013) write, "ocean acidification (OA) is expected to negatively affect coral reefs," but "little is known about how OA will change the coral-algal symbiosis on which reefs ultimately depend." They state, "to date it remains unknown if corals are able to respond to rising CO_2 concentrations by changing to better adapted dominant *Symbiodinium* types after long-term exposure to elevated pCO_2 in the field," the field being the ocean, in this case. Noonan *et al.* investigated "the dominant types of *Symbiodinium* associating with six species of scleractinian coral that were exposed to elevated partial pressures of carbon dioxide (pCO_2) *in situ* from settlement and throughout their lives." They did so "at three naturally occurring volcanic CO_2 seeps

(pCO_2 ~500 to 900 ppm, pH_{Total} 7.8–7.9) and adjacent control areas (pCO_2 ~390 ppm, pH_{Total} ~8.0–8.05) in Papua New Guinea," and "*Symbiodinium* associated with corals living in an extreme seep site (pCO_2 >1000 ppm) were also examined."

In five of the six species studied, the researchers report, "85–95% of samples exhibited the same *Symbiodinium* type across all sites, with remaining rare types having no patterns attributable to CO_2 exposure." The sixth species of coral did display "site specific differences in *Symbiodinium* types," but these were "unrelated to CO_2 exposure." The scientists write, "*Symbiodinium* types from the coral inhabiting the extreme CO_2 seep site were found commonly throughout the moderate seeps and control areas." These findings suggest the six species of coral Noonan *et al.* studied, plus the various *Symbiodinium* types they encountered, were able not only to survive but to function well throughout the full range of CO_2-induced pH values to which they had been exposed.

Wall and Edmunds (2013) note laboratory studies "typically are performed under conditions that do not replicate the natural environment perfectly, notably by providing light at a constant low intensity throughout the day, and with a spectral composition differing from ambient sunlight," citing Kinzie *et al.* (1984) and Schlacher *et al.* (2007). "Also of great importance," they write, "is the hydrodynamic regime of reef environments (Monismith, 2007), which is difficult to recreate in tanks and yet is critical for multiple aspects of coral physiology (Dennison and Barnes, 1988; Patterson *et al.*, 1991)."

Wall and Edmunds collected juvenile *Porites* spp. from 2–3 m depths on the back reef of Moorea, attached them to plastic bases with epoxy, and after allowing them to recover in a 1,000-L flow-through tank placed them in nine 150-L reservoirs consisting of three replicates each of filtered seawater maintained at three conditions: Treatment 1 (unmanipulated seawater), Treatment 2 (seawater equilibrated with pCO_2 at 98.9 Pa), and Treatment 3 (same as Treatment 2 but augmented with baking soda to increase [HCO_3^-] to 2730 µmol kg^{-1} at a pH_T of 7.69). They conducted three experiments on 4, 6, and 8 February 2012, where in each case the custom-cast, UV-transparent acrylic chambers they created remained on the reef for 28 hours.

They found no differences between the behaviors of the juvenile massive *Porites* corals in Treatments 1 and 2, but calcification was enhanced by fully 81% in Treatment 3 relative to Treatments 1 and 2. The two U.S. researchers conclude, "these findings indicate that juvenile massive *Porites* spp. are resistant to short exposures to OA *in situ*," and "they can increase calcification at low pH and low Ω_{arg} if $[HCO_3^-]$ is elevated." The latter finding leads them also to suggest calcification of juvenile *Porites* spp. may "be limited by dissolved inorganic carbon under ambient pCO_2 condition."

References

Adkins, J.F., Boyle, E.A., Curry, W.B., and Lutringer, A. 2003. Stable isotopes in deep-sea corals and a new mechanism for 'vital effects'. *Geochimica et Cosmochimica Acta* **67**: 1129–1143.

Anthony, K.R.N., Kleypas, J.A., and Gattuso, J.-P. 2011. Coral reefs modify their seawater carbon chemistry—implications for impacts of ocean acidification. *Global Change Biology* 10.1111/j.1365–2486.2011.02510.x.

Atkinson, M.J., Carlson, B., and Crowe, J.B. 1995. Coral growth in high-nutrient, low pH seawater: A case study in coral growth at the Waikiki aquarium. *Coral Reefs* **14**: 215–233.

Bessat, F. and Buigues, D. 2001. Two centuries of variation in coral growth in a massive *Porites* colony from Moorea (French Polynesia): a response of ocean-atmosphere variability from south central Pacific. *Palaeogeography, Palaeoclimatology, Palaeoecology* **175**: 381–392.

Bjork, M., Axelsson, L., and Beer, S. 2004. Why is Ulva intestinalis the only macroalga inhabiting isolated rockpools along the Swedish Atlantic coast? *Marine Ecology Progress Series* **284**: 109–116.

Brussaard, C.P.D., Gast, G.J., van Duyl, F.C., and Riegman, R. 1996. Impact of phytoplankton bloom magnitude on a pelagic microbial food web. *Marine Ecology Progress Series* **144**: 211–221.

Burdige, D.J. and Zimmerman, R.C. 2002. Impact of sea grass density on carbonate dissolution in Bahamian sediments. *Limnology and Oceanography* **47**: 1751–1763.

Carricart-Ganivet, J.P. 2004. Sea surface temperature and the growth of the West Atlantic reef-building coral *Montastraea annularis*. *Journal of Experimental Marine Biology and Ecology* **302**: 249–260.

Carricart-Ganivet, J.P. and Gonzalez-Diaz, P. 2009. Growth characteristics of skeletons of *Montastraea annularis* (Cnidaria: Scleractinia) from the northwest coast of Cuba. *Ciencias Marinas* **35**: 237–243.

Cohen, A.L. and Holcomb, M. 2009. Why corals care about ocean acidification: Uncovering the mechanism. *Oceanography* **22**: 118–127.

Cohen, A.L. and McConnaughey, T.A. 2003. Geochemical perspectives on coral mineralization. In: Dove, P.M., Weiner, S., and de Yoreo, J.J. (Eds.) *Reviews in Mineralogy and Geochemistry*, Volume 54. Mineralogical Society of America, New York, New York, USA, pp. 151–187.

Crabbe, M.J.C., Wilson, M.E.J., and Smith, D.J. 2006. Quaternary corals from reefs in the Wakatobi Marine National Park, SE Sulawesi, Indonesia, show similar growth rates to modern corals from the same area. *Journal of Quaternary Science* **21**: 803–809.

Dennison, W.C. and Barnes, D.J. 1988. Effect of water motion on coral photosynthesis and calcification. *Journal of Experimental Marine Biology and Ecology* **115**: 67–77.

Fautin, D.G., Guinotte, J.M., and Orr, J.C. 2009. Comparative depth distribution of corallimorpharians and scleractinians (Cnidaria; Anthozoa). *Marine Ecology Progress Series* **397**: 63–70.

Form, A. and Riebesel, U. 2012. Acclimation to ocean acidification during long-term CO_2 exposure in the cold-water coral *Lophelia pertusa*. *Global Change Biology* **18**: 843–853.

Gnaiger, E., Gluth, G., and Weiser, W. 1978. pH fluctuations in an intertidal beach in Bermuda. *Limnology and Oceanography* **23**: 851–857.

Grigg, R.W. 1981. Coral reef development at high latitudes in Hawaii. In: *Proceedings of the Fourth International Coral Reef Symposium*, Manila, Philippines, Vol. 1: 687–693.

Grigg, R.W. 1997. Paleoceanography of coral reefs in the Hawaiian-Emperor Chain—revisited. *Coral Reefs* **16**: S33-S38.

Hall-Spencer, J.M., Rodolfo-Metalpa, R., Martin, S., Ransome, E., Fine, M., Turner, S.M., Rowley, S.J., Tedesco, D., and Buia, M.-C. 2008. Volcanic carbon dioxide vents show ecosystem effects of ocean acidification. *Nature* **454**: 96–99.

Hansen, P.J. 2002. The effect of high pH on the growth and survival of marine phytoplankton: implications for species succession. *Aquatic Microbiology and Ecology* **28**: 279–288.

Jantzen, C., Haussermann, V., Forsterra, G., Laudien, J., Ardelan, M., Maier, S., and Richter, C. 2013. *Marine Biology* **160**: 2597–2607.

Jury, C., Whitehead, R.F., and Szmant, A. 2010. Effects of variations in carbonate chemistry on the calcification rates of *Madracis auretenra* (= *Madracis mirabilis* sensu Wells, 1973): bicarbonate concentrations best predict calcification rates. *Global Change Biology* **16**: 1632–1644.

Kinzie, R.A., Jokiel, P.L., and York, R. 1984. Effects of light of altered spectral composition on coral zooxanthellae associations and on zooxanthellae in vitro. *Marine Biology* **78**: 239–248.

Kleypas, J.A., Anthony, K.R.N., and Gattuso, J.-P. 2011. Coral reefs modify their seawater carbon chemistry—case study from a barrier reef (Moorea, French Polynesia). *Global Change Biology* 10.1111/j.1365–2486.2011.02530.x.

Kleypas, J.A., Buddemeier, R.W., Archer, D., Gattuso, J-P., Langdon, C., and Opdyke, B.N. 1999. Geochemical consequences of increased atmospheric carbon dioxide on coral reefs. *Science* **284**: 118–120.

Kooperman, N., Ben-Dov, E., Kramarsky-Winter, E., Barak, Z., and Kushmaro, A. 2007. Coral mucus-associated bacterial communities from natural and aquarium environments. *FEMS Microbiology Letters* **276**: 106–113.

Lindholm, T. and Nummelin, C. 1999. Red tide of the dinoflagellate *Heterocapsa triquetra* (Dinophyta) in a ferry-mixed coastal inlet. *Hydrobiologia* **393**: 245–251.

Lough, J.M. and Barnes, D.J. 1997. Several centuries of variation in skeletal extension, density and calcification in massive *Porites* colonies from the Great Barrier Reef: A proxy for seawater temperature and a background of variability against which to identify unnatural change. *Journal of Experimental and Marine Biology and Ecology* **211**: 29–67.

Lough, J.M. and Barnes, D.J. 2000. Environmental controls on growth of the massive coral *Porites*. *Journal of Experimental Marine Biology and Ecology* **245**: 225–243.

Macedo, M.F., Duarte, P., Mendes, P., and Ferreira, G. 2001. Annual variation of environmental variables, phytoplankton species composition and photosynthetic parameters in a coastal lagoon. *Journal of Plankton Research* **23**: 719–732.

Manzello, D.P., Enochs, I.C., Melo, N., Gledhill, D.K., and Johns, E.M. 2012. Ocean acidification refugia of the Florida Reef Tract. *PLoS ONE* **7**: e41715.

Manzello, D.P., Kleypas, J.A., Budd, D., Eakin, C.M., Glynn, P.W., and Langdon, C. 2008. Poorly cemented coral reefs of the eastern Tropical Pacific: Possible insights into reef development in a high-CO_2 world. *Proceedings of the National Academy of Sciences USA* **105**: 10.1073/pnas.0712167105.

Marubini, F., Ferrier-Pages, C., Furla, P., and Allemande, D. 2008. Coral calcification responds to seawater acidification, a working hypothesis towards a physiological mechanism. *Coral Reefs* **27**: 491–499.

Maynard, J.A., Baird, A.H., and Pratchett, M.S. 2008. Revisiting the Cassandra syndrome: the changing climate of coral reef research. *Coral Reefs* **27**: 745–749.

McConnaughey, T. 1989. ^{13}C and ^{18}O isotopic dis-

equilibrium in biological carbonates: 1. Patterns. *Geochimica et Cosmochimica Acta* **53**: 151–162.

McCulloch, M., Falter, J., Trotter, J., and Montagna, P. 2012a. Coral resilience to ocean acidification and global warming through pH up-regulation. *Nature Climate Change* **2**: 1–5.

McCulloch, M., Trotter, J., Montagna, P., Falter, J., Dunbar, R., Freiwald, A., Forsterra, G., Correa, M.L., Maier, C., Ruggeberg, A., and Taviana, M. 2012. Resilience of cold-water scleractinian corals to ocean acidification: Boron isotopic systematics of pH and saturation state up-regulation. *Geochimica et Cosmochimica Acta* **87**: 21–34.

Menendez, M., Martinez, M., and Comin, F.A. 2001. A comparative study of the effect of pH and inorganic carbon resources on the photosynthesis of three floating macro-algae species of a Mediterranean coastal lagoon. *Journal of Experimental Marine Biology and Ecology* **256**: 123–136.

Meron, D., Rodolfo-Metalpa, R., Cunning, R., Baker, A.C., Fine, M., and Banin, E. 2012. Changes in coral microbial communities in response to a natural pH gradient. *ISME Journal* **6**: 1775–1785.

Middelboe, A.L. and Hansen, P.J. 2007. High pH in shallow-water macroalgal habitats. *Marine Ecology Progress Series* **338**: 107–117.

Monismith, S.G. 2007. Hydrodynamics of coral reefs. *Annual Review of Fluid Mechanics* **39**: 37–55.

Moy, A.D., Howard, W.R., Bray, S.G., and Trull, T.W. 2009. Reduced calcification in modern Southern Ocean planktonic foraminifera. *Nature Geoscience* **2**: 276–280.

Noonan, S.H.C., Fabricius, K.E., and Humphrey, C. 2013. Symbiodinium community composition in Scleractinian corals is not affected by life-long exposure to elevated carbon dioxide. *PLOS ONE* **8**: e63985.

Orr, J.C., Fabry, V.J., Aumont, O., Bopp, L., Doney, S.C., Feely, R.A., Gnanadesikan, A., Gruber, N., Ishida, A., Joos, F., Key, R.M., Lindsay, K., Maier-Reimer, E., Matear, R., Monfray, P., Mouchet, A., Najjar, R.G., Plattner, G.-K., Rodgers, K.B., Sabine, C.L., Sarmiento, J.L., Schlitzer, R., Slater, R.D., Totterdell, I.J., Weirig, M.-F., Yamanaka, Y., and Yool, A. 2005. Anthropogenic ocean acidification over the twenty-first century and its impact on calcifying organisms. *Nature* **437**: 681–686.

Palacios, S. and Zimmerman, R.C. 2007. Response of eelgrass (*Zostera marina* L.) to CO_2 enrichment: Possible impacts of climate change and potential for remediation of coastal habitats. *Marine Ecology Progress Series* **344**: 1–13.

Patterson, M.R., Sebens, K.P., and Olson, R.R. 1991. *In situ* measurements of flow effects on primary production and dark respiration in reef corals. *Limnology and Oceanography* **36**: 936–948.

Pearson, G.A., Serrao, E.A., and Brawley, S.H. 1998. Control of gamete release in fucoid algae: sensing hydrodynamic conditions via carbon acquisition. *Ecology* **79**: 1725–1739.

Pelejero, C., Calvo, E., McCulloch, M.T., Marshall, J.F., Gagan, M.K., Lough, J.M., and Opdyke, B.N. 2005. Preindustrial to modern interdecadal variability in coral reef pH. *Science* **309**: 2204–2207.

Reshef, L, Koren, O., Loya, Y., Zilber-Rosenberg, I., and Rosenberg, E. 2006. The coral probiotic hypothesis. *Applied Environmental Microbiology* **8**: 2067–2073.

Riegl, B., Bruckner, A., Coles, S.L., Renaud, P., and Dodge, R.E. 2009. Coral reefs: threats and conservation in an era of global change. *Annals of the New York Academy of Sciences* **1162**: 136–186.

Ries, J.B., Cohen, A.L., and McCorkle, D.C. 2010. A nonlinear calcification response to CO_2-induced ocean acidification by the coral *Oculina arbuscula*. *Coral Reefs* **29**: 661–674.

Roark, E.B., Guilderson, T.P, Flood-Page, S., Dunbar, R.B., Ingram, B.L., Fallon, S.J., and McCulloch, M. 2005. Radiocarbon-based ages and growth rates of bamboo corals from the Gulf of Alaska. *Geophysical Research Letters* **32**: 10.1029/2004GL021919.

Rodolfo-Metalpa, R., Martin, S., Ferrier-Pages, C., and Gattuso, J.P. 2010. Response of the temperate coral Cladocora caespitosa to mid- and long-term exposure to pCO_2 and temperature levels projected for the year 2100 AD. *Biogeosciences* **7**: 289–300.

Santhanam, R., Srinivasan, A., Ramadhas, V., and Devaraj, M. 1994. Impact of *Trichodesmium* bloom on the plankton and productivity in the Tuticorin bay, southeast coast of India. *Indian Journal of Marine Science* **23**: 27–30.

Schlacher, T.A., Stark, J., and Fischer, A.B.P. 2007. Evaluation of artificial light regimes and substrate types for aquaria propagation of the staghorn coral *Acropora solitarvensis*. *Aquaculture* **269**: 278–289.

Scoffin, T.P., Tudhope, A.W., Brown, B.E., Chansang, H., and Cheeney, R.F. 1992. Patterns and possible environmental controls of skeletogenesis of *Porites lutea*, South Thailand. *Coral Reefs* **11**: 1–11.

Shamberger, K.E.F., Feely, R.A., Sabine, C.L., Atkinson, M.J., DeCarlo, E.H., and Mackenzie, F.T. 2011. Calcification and organic production on a Hawaiian coral reef. *Marine Chemistry* **127**: 64–75.

Thresher, R.E., Tilbrook, B., Fallon, S., Wilson, N.C., and Adkins, J. 2011. Effects of chronic low carbonate saturation levels on the distribution, growth and skeletal chemistry of deep-sea corals and other seamount megabenthos. *Marine Ecology Progress Series* **442**: 87–99.

Trotter, J.A., Montagna, P., McCulloch, M.T., Silenzi, S., Reynaud, S., Mortimer, G., Martin, S., Ferrier-Pages, C., Gattuso, J.-P., and Rodolfo-Metalpa, R. 2011. Quantifying the pH 'vital effect' in the temperate zooxanthellate coral Cladocora caespitosa: validation of the boron seawater pH proxy. *Earth and Planetary Science Letters* **303**: 163–173.

Veron, J.E.N., Hoegh-Guldberg, O., Lenton, T.M., Lough, J.M., Obura, D.O., Pearce-Kelly, P., Sheppard, C.R.C., Spalding, M., Stafford-Smith, M.G., and Rogers, A.D. 2009. The coral reef crisis: The critical importance of <350 ppm CO_2. *Marine Pollution Bulletin* **58**: 1428–1436.

Wall, C.B. and Edmunds, P.J. 2013. *In situ* effects of low pH and elevated HCO_3^- on juvenile massive *Porites* spp. in Moorea, French Polynesia. *Biological Bulletin* **225**: 92–101.

6.3.3.3 Crustaceans

The studies reviewed in this section examine what scientists have learned about potential impacts of lower ocean pH levels on marine crustaceans. The key findings, which challenge the alarming and negative projections of IPCC, are presented in the bullet points below, followed by an expanded discussion of those findings. (Citations for passages in quotation marks in the bullet points are included in the main body of the section.)

- Survival of shrimp larvae was not reduced by lower ocean pH levels .

- At reduced seawater pH the velvet swimming crab was able to "buffer changes to extra-cellular pH over 30 days exposure" and do so "with no evidence of net shell dissolution." In addition, "tolerance to heat, carapace mineralization, and aspects of immune response were not affected by hypercapnic conditions."

- The early life larval stages of the bay barnacle "are generally tolerant to near-future levels of ocean acidification," and this observation "is in line with findings for other barnacle species." In addition, its "substantial genetic variability in response to low pH may confer adaptive benefits under future ocean acidification."

- Vertically migrating adult Arctic copepods daily cross a pCO_2 range of less than 140 µatm and show "only minor responses to manipulated high CO_2," suggesting "the natural range of pCO_2 experienced by an organism determines its sensitivity to future OA."

Noting "there is a particular need to study effects of OA [ocean acidification] on organisms living in cold-water environments due to the higher solubility of CO_2 at lower temperatures," Bechmann et al. (2011) maintained shrimp (Pandalus borealis) larvae, from day 1 through day 36 post-hatching, under the OA scenario predicted for the year 2100 (pH 7.6) and compared them against batches of larvae held under the current oceanic pH of 8.1 (the control treatment), while water temperature was kept at a constant 5°C. Bechmann et al. report survival of the larvae was not reduced at any time during the experiment, but there was "a significant delay in zoeal progression (development time)," which "may increase the chance of loss by predation." They note "a multi-generation experiment with the copepod Acartia tonsa showed that effects of OA observed in the first generation were no longer present in the second and third generation (Dupont and Thorndyke, 2009)," implying that could also prove true in the situation they investigated. The eight Norwegian researchers conclude, "there are different opinions about how to extrapolate the effects of OA from a single species examined in relatively short-term experiments to the population and ecosystem level," noting "all agree that more data from relevant long-term experiments are needed to better predict effects at higher levels of biological organization," citing Dupont et al. (2010a,b), Hendriks and Duarte (2010), and Hendricks et al. (2010).

Small et al. (2010) investigated the potential effects of lower ocean pH levels on the velvet swimming or "devil" crab (Necora puber). Working with adult individuals collected from the lower intertidal zone of Mount Batten Beach, Plymouth, UK, the authors tested the effect of 30 days' exposure of the crabs to seawater maintained in 4-L aquaria at pH values of 8.0 (control), 7.3, and 6.7. They found "Necora puber was able to buffer changes to extra-cellular pH over 30 days exposure," and to do so "with no evidence of net shell dissolution." They report, "tolerance to heat, carapace mineralization, and aspects of immune response were not affected by hypercapnic conditions"— i.e., conditions that lead to more than the normal level of carbon dioxide in an organism's blood. About the only negative finding was a decline in whole-animal oxygen consumption, which they described as being "marginal" between

the control and medium hypercapnic conditions, but "significant" at the unrealistic future pH value of 6.7. Small et al. conclude their results "confirm that most physiological functions in N. puber are resistant to low pH/hypercapnia over a longer period than previously investigated."

In two experiments conducted over two successive years, Pansch et al. (2013) first assessed larval survival and development of the bay barnacle Amphibalanus improvisus while rearing nauplius larvae in six-well plates over 10 days in response to three pH treatments (8.02, 7.80, and 7.59). In the second experiment they assessed larval stage and size by rearing nauplius larvae in 5-L glass bottles over six days with two pH treatments (8.09 and 7.80). The three scientists report the "larval development of the barnacle was not significantly affected by the level of reduced pH that has been projected for the next 150 years," noting, "after 3 and 6 days of incubation, we found no consistent effects of reduced pH on developmental speed or larval size at pH 7.8 compared with the control pH of 8.1." They write, "after 10 days of incubation, there were no net changes in survival or overall development of larvae raised at pH 7.8 or 7.6 compared with the control pH of 8.0." In their many individual trials, they determined "there was significant variation in responses between replicate batches (parental genotypes) of some larvae," with some batches responding positively to reduced pH.

Pansch et al. say their results suggest "the non-calcifying larval stages of A. improvisus are generally tolerant to near-future levels of ocean acidification," and "this result is in line with findings for other barnacle species and suggests that barnacles do not show the greater sensitivity to ocean acidification in early life history reported for other invertebrate species." They also state the barnacle's "substantial genetic variability in response to low pH may confer adaptive benefits under future ocean acidification."

According to Lewis et al. (2013), "copepods comprise the dominant Arctic zooplankton; hence, their responses to OA [ocean acidification] have important implications for Arctic ecosystems, yet there is little data on their current under-ice winter ecology on which to base future monitoring or make predictions about climate-induced change." Lewis et al. examined "the natural distributions of the dominant Arctic copepods found under winter sea ice in relation to the current seawater carbonate chemistry conditions and compared these with their short-term responses to future high CO_2 conditions." They conducted this work "at the temporary Catlin Arctic

895

Survey Ice Base (CIB) during late winter to early spring in 2011," where "the zooplankton were dominated by adult calanoid copepods, comprising mainly the Arctic endemics *Calanus glacialis* and *Calanus hyperboreus* but also the smaller, globally occurring *Oithona similis*, together with the nauplii of various copepod species." They conducted a series of OA experiments "using these copepod species and life history stages to compare their response to future high CO_2 conditions with natural under-ice pCO_2 exposures."

The five researchers' data revealed "species and life stage sensitivities to manipulated conditions were correlated with their vertical migration behavior and with their natural exposures to different pCO_2 ranges," and "vertically migrating adult *Calanus* spp. crossed a pCO_2 range of >140 µatm daily and showed only minor responses to manipulated high CO_2," whereas "*Oithona similis*, which remained in the surface waters and experienced a pCO_2 range of <75 µatm, showed significantly reduced adult and nauplii survival in high CO_2 experiments."

Lewis *et al.* conclude, "the natural range of pCO_2 experienced by an organism determines its sensitivity to future OA," adding, "certainly, ubiquitous species in their adult form, living across a range of physicochemical conditions, are likely capable of surviving change." They also note the "larvae of many marine organisms are released at very specific times to coincide with favorable environmental or food conditions," and it seems logical to conclude the same would hold true in the future, making it easier for copepod larvae to survive future OA conditions as well.

Pedersen *et al.* (2013) investigated "the impact of medium-term exposure to CO_2 acidified seawater on survival, growth and development ... in the North Atlantic copepod *Calanus finmarchicus*." Using a custom-developed experimental system, "fertilized eggs and subsequent development stages were exposed to normal seawater (390 ppm CO_2) or one of three different levels of CO_2-induced acidification (3,300, 7,300, 9,700 ppm CO_2)." The four Norwegian researchers report, "following the 28-day exposure period, survival was found to be unaffected by exposure to 3,300 ppm CO_2, but significantly reduced at 7,300 and 9,700 ppm CO_2," values far beyond any atmospheric concentration predicted under even the most extreme of circumstances. Pedersen *et al.* conclude, "the absence of any apparent reduction in the overall survival during the present medium-term exposure to 3,300 ppm CO_2, indicates that survival of *Calanus* eggs and nauplii may be robust against the direct effects of the worst-case CO_2 scenario predicted for year 2300."

References

Bechmann, R.K., Taban, I.C., Westerlund, S., Godal, B.F., Arnberg, M., Vingen, S., Ingvarsdottir, A., and Baussant, T. 2011. Effects of ocean acidification on early life stages of Shrimp (*Pandalus borealis*) and mussel (*Mytilus edulis*). *Journal of Toxicology and Environmental Health, Part A* **74**: 424–438.

Dupont, S. and Thorndyke, M.C. 2009. Impact of CO_2-driven ocean acidification on invertebrates early life-history—What we know, what we need to know, and what we can do. *Biogeoscience Discussions* **6**: 3109–3131.

Dupont, S., Dorey, N., and Thorndyke, M. 2010a. What meta-analysis can tell us about vulnerability of marine biodiversity to ocean acidification? *Estuarine, Coastal and Shelf Science* **89**: 182–185.

Dupont, S., Ortega-Martinez, O., and Thorndyke, M. 2010b. Impact of near-future ocean acidification on echinoderms. *Ecotoxicology* **19**: 449–462.

Hendriks, I.E. and Duarte, C.M. 2010. Ocean acidification: Separating evidence from judgment—A reply to Dupont *et al.* Discussion. Estuarine, Coastal and Shelf Science **86**: 186–190.

Hendriks, I.E., Duarte, C.M., and Alvarez, M. 2010. Vulnerability of marine biodiversity to ocean acidification: A meta-analysis. *Estuarine, Coastal and Shelf Science* **86**: 157–164.

Lewis, C.N., Brown, K.A., Edwards, L.A., Cooper, G., and Findlay, H.S. 2013. Sensitivity to ocean acidification parallels natural pCO_2 gradients experienced by Arctic copepods under winter sea ice. *Proceedings of the National Academy of Sciences USA* **110**: 10.1073/pnas.131516210.

Pansch, C., Schlegel, P., and Havenhand, J. 2013. Larval development of the barnacle *Amphibalanus improvisus* responds variably but robustly to near-future ocean acidification. *ICES Journal of Marine Science* **70**: 805–811.

Pedersen, S.A., Hansen, B.H., Altin, D., and Olsen, A.J. 2013. Medium-term exposure of the North Atlantic copepod *Calanus finmarchicus* (Gunnerus, 1770) to CO_2-acidified seawater: effects on survival and development. *Biogeosciences* **10**: 7481–7491.

Small, D., Calosi, P., White, D., Spicer, J.I., and Widdicombe, S. 2010. Impact of medium-term exposure to CO_2 enriched seawater on the physiological functions of the velvet swimming crab *Necora puber*. *Aquatic Biology* **10**: 11–21.

6.3.3.4 Echinoderms

The studies reviewed in this section examine what scientists have learned about potential impacts of lower ocean pH levels on marine echinoderms. The key findings, which challenge the alarming and negative projections of IPCC, are presented in the bullet points below, followed by an expanded discussion of those findings. (Citations for passages in quotation marks in the bullet points are included in the main body of the section.)

- The common sea star *C. papposus* is "positively impacted by ocean acidification," as "larvae and juveniles raised at low pH grow and develop faster, with no negative effect on survival or skeletogenesis."

- Adults of the sea star *Luidia clathrata* exposed to end-of-century pH conditions "are relatively unimpaired in their regenerative capacity," which "encompasses not only their ability to re-grow their arms, but their ability to allocate materials and energy to regenerated somatic body components."

- "*Paracentrotus lividus* appears to be extremely resistant to low pH, with no effect on fertilization success or larval survival."

- "Polar and sub-polar sea urchin larvae can show a certain degree of resilience to acidification" and do not appear to be more susceptible to lower seawater pH than their temperate and tropical counterparts.

- Gametes from *Sterechinus neumayeri* are "relatively robust to pH change, especially to changes within the range predicted for the near future (i.e. a decrease of 0.3–0.5 pH units)."

- "Sea urchins inhabiting stressful intertidal environments produce offspring that may better resist future ocean acidification."

- In studies designed to reveal the effects of atmospheric CO_2 enrichment upon marine life, treatment comparisons should be made at equivalent development stages of the organism being studied. At such points along the life cycle, studies have shown there to be no significant physical differences between individuals raised under control or CO_2-enriched conditions.

- Lower ocean pH levels induced a developmental delay in *P. lividus*, yet "at a given developmental state (or size), larvae present the same calcium incorporation rate regardless of pH."

- *Strongylocentrotus purpuratus* sea urchins "demonstrate the capacity for rapid evolution in the face of ocean acidification and show that standing genetic variation could be a reservoir of resilience to climate change in [a] coastal upwelling ecosystem."

According to Dupont *et al.* (2010), "echinoderms are among the most abundant and ecologically successful groups of marine animals (Micael *et al.*, 2009), and are one of the key marine groups most likely to be impacted by predicted climate change events," presumably because "the larvae and/or adults of many species from this phylum form skeletal rods, plates, test, teeth, and spines from an amorphous calcite crystal precursor, magnesium calcite, which is 30 times more soluble than normal calcite (Politi *et al.*, 2004)." This fact normally would be thought to make it much more difficult for echinoderms (relative to most other calcifying organisms) to produce calcification-dependent body parts.

Dupont *et al.* studied naturally fertilized eggs of the common sea star *Crossaster papposus*, which they collected and transferred to five-liter culture aquariums filled with filtered seawater (a third of which was replaced every four days). They regulated the pH of the tanks to values of either 8.1 or 7.7 by adjusting environmental CO_2 levels to either 372 ppm or 930 ppm, documenting settlement success as the percentage of initially free-swimming larvae that affixed themselves to the aquarium walls, larval length at various time intervals, and degree of calcification. The three researchers report results the opposite of what is often predicted: The echinoderm larvae and juveniles were "positively impacted by ocean acidification." They found "larvae and juveniles raised at low pH grow and develop faster, with no negative effect on survival or skeletogenesis within the time frame of the experiment (38 days)." They report the sea stars' growth rates were "two times higher" in the low pH seawater, and "*C. papposus* seem to be not only more than simply resistant to ocean acidification, but are also performing better."

The Swedish scientists conclude, "in the future ocean, the direct impact of ocean acidification on growth and development potentially will produce an increase in *C. papposus* reproductive success," and "a decrease in developmental time will be associated with a shorter pelagic period with a higher proportion of eggs reaching settlement," leading the sea stars to become "better competitors in an unpredictable environment."

Schram et al. (2011) investigated the effects of lower ocean pH levels on another sea star, Luidia clathrata. The write, "two groups of sea stars, each with two arms excised, were maintained on a formulated diet in seawater bubbled with air alone (pH 8.2, approximating a pCO_2 of 380 ppm) or with a controlled mixture of air/CO_2 (pH 7.8, approximating a pCO_2 of 780 ppm)," and "arm length, total body wet weight, and righting responses were measured weekly." After 97 days, "a period of time sufficient for 80% arm regeneration," they state "protein, carbohydrate, lipid and ash levels were determined for body wall and pyloric caecal tissues of intact and regenerating arms of individuals held in both seawater pH treatments."

The four U.S. researchers report, "adults of the common soft bottom predatory sea star Luidia clathrata exposed to end-of-century conditions of ocean acidification (pH 7.8) are relatively unimpaired in their regenerative capacity," which "encompasses not only their ability to re-grow their arms, but their ability to allocate materials and energy to regenerated somatic body components." They found "no discernable pattern arising from exposure to a reduced seawater pH of 7.8 for 97 days on righting behavior," which they say is "an integrative measure of stress." Schram et al. conclude, "the demonstration of an organism's ability to sustain normal functions under these conditions is as equally important to document as those that are negatively impacted," because "this information will be critical to future assessments of prospective impacts of ocean acidification at the community level."

Schlegel et al. (2012) note "environmental factors directly affect populations by selecting resilient individuals," and "selection at the gametic level, or during early life, has strong and immediate effects at the population level, carrying over into subsequent life stages," as "heritability of this resilience leads to cascading adaptive effects in subsequent generations." As an example of this process, they report, "in free-spawning marine organisms, sperm selection during fertilization plays a key role by determining the nature and diversity of genotypes in the subsequent generation (Levitan, 1996; 2008) and thus their resilience to environmental change."

Schlegel et al. investigated "the effects of CO_2-induced ocean acidification on the early life history

stages in the Australasian sea urchin Heliocidaris erythrogramma, focusing on intra-specific variation in responses, which can be highly variable for this species (Evans and Marshall, 2005)." They followed "the A1FI-scenario from IPCC's 4th assessment report" and "compared the effects of present day conditions for southeast Australia with the end-of-century scenario (pCO_2=970 ppm; pH=0.3 unit reduction) and a high-CO_2 scenario (pCO_2=1600 ppm; pH=0.5 unit reduction)." The write, "observed effects on sperm swimming behavior were applied within an established fertilization kinetics modeling framework (Vogel et al., 1982; Styan et al., 2008) to predict fertilization outcomes of single urchin pairs at each pCO_2 level." These results "were then compared to observed results from fertilization experiments conducted in the laboratory."

Schlegel et al. found "acidification significantly decreased the proportion of motile sperm but had no effect on sperm swimming speed," and the four researchers state the subsequent fertilization experiments "showed strong inter-individual variation in responses to ocean acidification, ranging from a 44% decrease to a 14% increase in fertilization success." They say their results indicate "some individuals will exhibit enhanced fertilization success in acidified oceans, supporting the concept of 'winners' and 'losers' of climate change at an individual level." If these differences are heritable, they say, it is likely "ocean acidification will lead to selection against susceptible phenotypes as well as to rapid fixation of alleles that allow reproduction under more acidic conditions," and these phenomena "may ameliorate the biotic effects of climate change if taxa have sufficient extant genetic variation upon which selection can act."

Moulin et al. (2011) supplied real-world data indicating phenotypic adaptation to seawater of lower pH by conducting a field experiment on the sea urchin Paracentrotus lividus in an attempt "to compare the effect of pH on the progeny of individuals collected from the same shore, i.e., same population, but from distinct tide pools: one where night pH was significantly reduced and the other where this decline was not so important." The four Belgian researchers report the pH of coastal seawater at the site they studied (Aber, Crozon peninsula, southern Brittany, France) was 8.14, but they say at the end of the night low tides, tide pools 1 (subtidal) and 2 (intertidal) had pH values of, respectively, 7.8 and 7.4. Under these conditions, they detected "no significant difference in gonad maturity between individuals from the two tide pools," and "the offspring of sea urchins from the tide pool with higher pH decrease (tide pool 2) showed a better resistance to acidification at pH 7.4 than that of sea urchins from the tide pool with low pH decrease (tide pool 1) in terms of fertilization, viz. a reduction of over 30% [for tide pool 1] compared to about 20% for tide pool 2."

Moulin *et al.* conclude "sea urchins inhabiting stressful intertidal environments produce offspring that may better resist future ocean acidification." They also note "the fertilization rate of gametes whose progenitors came from the tide pool with higher pH decrease was significantly higher," suggesting "a possible acclimation or adaptation of gametes to pH stress."

Martin *et al.* (2011) write, "ocean acidification is predicted to have significant effects on benthic calcifying invertebrates, in particular on their early developmental states," and "echinoderm larvae could be particularly vulnerable to decreased pH, with major consequences for adult populations." The authors explored the effect of a gradient of decreasing pH from 8.1 to 7.0—corresponding to atmospheric CO_2 concentrations of ~400 ppm to ~6,630 ppm—on the larvae of the sea urchin *Paracentrotus lividus*, a common, economically and ecologically important species widely distributed throughout the Mediterranean Sea and the northeast Atlantic from Ireland to southern Morocco. The scientists used "multiple methods to identify the response of *P. lividus* to CO_2-driven ocean acidification at both physiological (fertilization, growth, survival and calcification) and molecular (expression of genes involved in calcification and development) levels."

They found "*Paracentrotus lividus* appears to be extremely resistant to low pH, with no effect on fertilization success or larval survival." They reported "larval growth was slowed when exposed to low pH," as larvae of *P. lividus* "collected at pH 7.5 at 46 hours post-fertilization (real age) were smaller than in the control treatment [pH 8.1] and corresponded to a virtual age of 36 hours (a delay in development of 10 hours)." They further report, "down to a pH of 7.25, the larvae at Day 3 have a normal morphology but are delayed in development," so the apparent decrease in calcification at that point in time is, as they put it, "simply an indirect consequence of the impact of low pH on developmental rate." They continue, "at a given developmental state (or size), larvae present the same calcium incorporation rate regardless of pH." The scientists also report "genes involved in development and biomineralization were upregulated by factors of up to 26 at low pH," which suggests "plasticity at the gene expression level" in *P. lividus*

"allows a normal, but delayed, development under low pH conditions."

Ericson *et al.* (2010) note in polar latitudes "the effects of changing pCO_2 and pH on gametes may be influenced by the carbonate chemistry of cold water, such as the already higher pCO_2 and lower seawater pH," and "it has also been predicted that ocean acidification effects on organisms may be more apparent and appear earliest in polar waters." Ericson *et al.* "investigated the effects of present-day pH 8.0, predicted ocean surface pH for the years 2100 and 2300 (pH 7.7 and pH 7.3, respectively) and an extreme pH (pH 7.0) on fertilization and embryogenesis in the Antarctic nemertean worm *Parborlasia corrugatus* and sea urchin *Sterechinus neumayeri*."

The four researchers found "fertilization success was not affected by pH in *P. corrugatus* across a range of sperm concentrations," and "fertilization success in *S. neumayeri* declined significantly in pH 7.0 and 7.3 seawater, but only at low sperm concentration." They observe, "seawater pH had no effect on the rate of egg cleavage in *S. neumayeri*, or the proportion of abnormal embryos 1-day post-fertilization," and "*P. corrugatus* embryogenesis was also relatively robust to pH changes, with a significant effect detected only when the seawater pH was decreased to 7.0." Ericson *et al.* conclude, "as in a number of other studies (see reviews by Byrne *et al.*, 2010; Dupont *et al.*, 2010), that gametes appeared relatively robust to pH change, especially to changes within the range predicted for the near future (i.e. a decrease of 0.3–0.5 pH units)," and they say their initial findings "do not support a view that polar species are more affected by lowered pH compared with temperate and tropical counterparts (as has also been shown for the later developmental stages of *S. neumayeri* (Clark *et al.*, 2009))."

Yu *et al.* (2013) tested the effects of high CO_2/low pH on early development and larval growth by exposing *Sterechinus neumayeri* to environmental levels of CO_2 in McMurdo Sound (control: 410 ppm) and mildly elevated CO_2 levels, both near the level of the aragonite saturation horizon (510 ppm), and to under-saturating conditions (730 ppm). Over the course of development from egg to late four-arm pluteus, they found, "(1) early embryological development was normal with the exception of the hatching process, which was slightly delayed, (2) the onset of calcification as determined by the appearance of $CaCO_3$ spicule nuclei was on schedule, (3) the lengths of the spicule elements, and the elongation of the spicule nuclei into the larval skeleton, were significantly shorter in the highest CO_2 treatment four days after the initial appearance of the spicule nuclei, and (4) finally, without evidence of true developmental delay, larvae were smaller overall under high CO_2 treatments; and arm length, the most plastic morphological aspect of the echinopluteus, exhibited the greatest response to high CO_2/low pH/low carbonate conditions." Yu *et al.* conclude, "effects of elevated CO_2 representative of near future climate scenarios are proportionally minor on these early development stages."

Yu *et al.* (2011) raised larvae of the purple sea urchin (*Strongylocentrotus purpuratus*) in seawater maintained at pCO_2 levels ranging from ambient to 1,000 and 1,450 ppm CO_2 (pH 7.7 and 7.5, respectively) while measuring, after three and six days of development, "total larval length (from the spicule tip of the postoral arm to the spicule tip of the aboral point) along the spicules, to assess effects of low pH upwelling water on morphology." They found "even at the highest pCO_2 treatments, larval development was normal in terms of timing and morphological appearance," although at both days 3 and 6 larvae in the 1,450 ppm CO_2 treatment were 7–13% smaller than control larvae. Yu *et al.* also report "the observed developmental progression and survival of cultures was within the norm typically observed for this species at this temperature range." They note, "a lack of developmental deformities at early stages for pCO_2 ~1000 ppm has been previously reported for this species (Todgham and Hofmann, 2009), and another local species, *Lytechinus pictus*, with a similar overlapping portion of its range in southern California (O'Donnell *et al.*, 2010)." They also remark, "there are even reports survival is increased in this species and its congener *S. droebachiensis* under some low pH conditions (Dupont and Thorndyke, 2008)."

Yu *et al.* conclude, "the effects of small magnitude in these urchin larvae are indicative of a potential resilience to near-future levels of ocean acidification."

Stumpp *et al.* (2011a) evaluated the impacts of elevated seawater pCO_2 (1,264 ppm vs. 375 ppm) on the early development of, and the larval metabolic and feeding rates of, *Strongylocentrotus purpuratus*. The researchers assessed growth and development daily, for three weeks, in terms of total body length, body rod length, postoral rod length, and posterolateral rod length, as well as mortality and feeding and metabolic rates. They found daily mortality rate (DMR) was higher under control conditions (DMR = 2.7% per day) than under high seawater pCO_2 (DMR = 2.2% per day). They also observed, in the elevated CO_2 treatment, larval development was about 8% slower, such that it took slightly longer for the organisms to reach equivalent development stages in the high CO_2 treatment.

As a result of the slower development of the larvae in the high CO_2 treatment, at any given time the individuals in this treatment were smaller and less well-developed than those in the control treatment, and if that were the only comparison made in this study, the effects of elevated CO_2 would seem to be negative. However, the researchers also made comparisons on the basis of development stage, and they found there were no long-term physical differences between the larvae living in the high and low CO_2 treatments.

Thus in studies designed to reveal the effects of atmospheric CO_2 enrichment on various species of marine life, treatment comparisons should be made at equivalent development stages of the organism being studied. At such points along the life cycle of the purple sea urchin, there were no significant physical differences between individuals raised in the control and CO_2-enriched conditions. Stumpp *et al.* conclude, "we suggest that body length is a useful scale of reference for studies in sea urchin larvae where a morphological delay in development occurs," and "using time post-fertilization as a reference may lead to misinterpretation of data"—by wrongfully assuming a negative result when in fact there may be no deleterious effect of lower ocean pH levels . Stumpp *et al.* (2011b) reached essentially the same conclusion in a companion paper, writing, "in studies in which a stressor induces an alteration in the speed of development, it is crucial to employ experimental designs with a high time resolution in order to correct for developmental artifacts," as this protocol "helps prevent misinterpretation of stressor effects on organism physiology."

Pespeni *et al.* (2013) note "little is known about the adaptive capacity of species to respond to an acidified ocean," and, as a result, "predictions regarding future ecosystem responses remain incomplete." They demonstrated lower ocean pH levels generate striking patterns of genome-wide selection in purple sea urchins (*Strongylocentrotus purpuratus*) cultured under CO_2 levels of 400 and 900 ppm. Working with seven populations collected along a 1,200 km mosaic of coastal upwelling-driven acidification of the California Current System, Pespeni *et al.* combined sequencing across the transcriptome of the purple sea urchin, growth measurements under experimental acidification, and tests of frequency shifts in 19,493 polymorphisms during development, detecting in the process "the widespread occurrence of genetic variation to tolerate ocean acidification."

Although larval development and morphology showed little response to elevated CO_2, the 11 researchers found "substantial allelic change in 40 functional classes of proteins involving hundreds of loci." They state "pronounced genetic changes, including excess amino acid replacements, were detected in all populations and occurred in genes for biomineralization, lipid metabolism, and ion homeostasis—gene classes that build skeletons and interact in pH regulation." They note "such genetic change represents a neglected and important impact of ocean acidification that may influence populations that show few outward signs of response to acidification." The researchers conclude "our results demonstrate the capacity for rapid evolution in the face of ocean acidification and show that standing genetic variation could be a reservoir of resilience to climate change in this coastal upwelling ecosystem."

Catarino et al. (2012) studied the development of larvae produced by adults of the Arbacia dufresnei urchin, which they collected from a sub-Antarctic population in the Straits of Magellan near Punta Arenas, Chile, immersed in high (8.0), medium (7.7), and low (7.4) pH seawater. The five scientists found "the proportion of abnormal larvae did not differ according to [pH] treatment." Although "lower pH induced a delay in development," which also was noted by Dupont et al. (2010), it "did not increase abnormality." Catarino et al. report, "even at calcium carbonate saturation states <1, skeleton deposition occurred," and they note specimens of Heliocidaris erythrogramma also "seem not to be affected by a pH decrease (until 7.6)," citing Byrne et al. (2009a,b). They note the Antarctic Sterechinus neumayeri is thought to be "more robust to ocean acidification than tropical and temperate sub-tidal species," citing Clark et al. (2009) and Ericson et al. (2010). The findings of Catarino et al., and those of the other researchers they cite, indicate "polar and sub-polar sea urchin larvae can show a certain degree of resilience to acidification." They conclude A. dufresnei has the potential to "migrate and further colonize southern regions."

Sunday et al. (2011) note the presumed acidification of Earth's oceans is predicted to impact marine biodiversity via "physiological effects impacting growth, survival, reproduction and immunology, leading to changes in species abundances and global distributions." They point out "the degree to which these changes will play out

critically depends on the evolutionary rate at which populations will respond to natural selection imposed by ocean acidification," and this phenomenon "remains largely unquantified," citing Stockwell et al. (2003) and Gienapp et al. (2008). Sunday et al. measured the potential for an evolutionary response to lower ocean pH levels in the larval development rate of the two coastal invertebrates, a sea urchin (Strongylocentrotus franciscanus) and a mussel species (Mytilus trossulus).

The four researchers report their experiment revealed "the sea urchin species Stronglyocentrotus franciscanus has vastly greater levels of phenotypic and genetic variation for larval size in future CO_2 conditions compared to the mussel species Mytilus trossulus." They demonstrate "S. franciscanus may have faster evolutionary responses within 50 years of the onset of predicted year-2100 CO_2 conditions despite having lower population turnover rates." Sunday et al. conclude their comparisons suggest "information on genetic variation, phenotypic variation, and key demographic parameters, may lend valuable insight into relative evolutionary potentials across a large number of species," thereby also indicating simplistic climate envelope models of species redistributions in a future CO_2-enriched and possibly warmer world are not up to the task of providing an accurate picture of future biological reality. They note "a genetic basis for variation in CO_2 responses has been found in the three previous studies in which it has been sought (Langer et al., 2009; Parker et al., 2011; Pistevos et al., 2011), supporting the notion that genetic variation exists at some level for almost all quantitative characters (Roff, 1997)."

References

Anderson, A.J., Mackenzie, F.T., and Bates, N.R. 2008. Life on the margin: implications of ocean acidification on Mg-calcite, high latitude and cold-water marine calcifiers. *Marine Ecology Progress Series* **373**: 265–273.

Byrne, M., Ho, M., Selvakumaraswamy, P., Nguyen, H.D., Dworjanyn, S.A., and Davis, A.R. 2009a. Temperature, but not pH, compromises sea urchin fertilization and early development under near-future climate change scenarios. *Proceedings of the Royal Society B* **276**: 1883–1888.

Byrne, M., Soars, N., Ho, M.A., Wong, E., McElroy, D., Selvakumaraswamy, P., Dworjanyn, S.A., and Davis, A.R. 2010. Fertilization in a suite of coastal marine invertebrates from SE Australia is robust to near-future ocean warming and acidification. *Marine Biology* **157**: 2061–2069.

Byrne, M., Soars, N., Selvakumaraswamy, P., Dworjanyn, S.A., and Davis, A.R. 2009b. Sea urchin fertilization in a warm, acidified and high pCO$_2$ ocean across a range of sperm densities. *Marine Environmental Research* **69**: 234–239.

Catarino, A.I., De Ridder, C., Gonzalez, M., Gallardo, P., and Dubois, P. 2012. Sea urchin *Arbacia dufresnei* (Blainville 1825) larvae response to ocean acidification. *Polar Biology* **35**: 455–461.

Clark, D., Lamare, M., and Barker, M. 2009. Response of sea urchin pluteus larvae (*Echinodermata: Echinoidea*) to reduced seawater pH: a comparison among a tropical, temperate, and a polar species. *Marine Biology* **156**: 1125–1137.

Dupont, S., Lundve, B., and Thorndyke, M. 2010. Near future ocean acidification increases growth rate of the lecithotrophic larvae and juveniles of the sea star *Crossaster papposus*. *Journal of Experimental Zoology (Molecular and Developmental Evolution)* **314B**: 382–389.

Dupont, S., Ortega-Martinez, O., and Thorndyke, M. 2010. Impact of near-future ocean acidification on echinoderms. *Ecotoxicology* **19**: 449–462.

Dupont, S. and Thorndyke, M.C. 2008. Ocean acidification and its impacts on the early life-history stages of marine animals. In: CIESM (Ed.) *Impacts of Acidification on Biological, Chemical and Physical Systems in the Mediterranean and Black Seas*. Number 36 in Briand, F. (Ed.) CIESM Workshop Monographs, Monaco.

Ericson, J.A., Lamare, M.D., Morley, S.A., and Barker, M.F. 2010. The response of two ecologically important Antarctic invertebrates (*Sterechinus neumayeri* and *Parborlasia corrugatus*) to reduced seawater pH: effects on fertilization and embryonic development. *Marine Biology* **157**: 2689–2702.

Evans, J.P. and Marshall, D.J. 2005. Male-by-female interactions influence fertilization success and mediate the benefits of polyandry in the sea urchin *Heliocidaris erythrogramma*. *Evolution* **59**: 106–112.

Gayathri, S., Lakshminarayanan, R., Weaver, J.C., Morse, D.E., Kini, R.M., and Valiyaveettil, S. 2007. In vitro study of magnesium-calcite biomineralization in the skeletal materials of the seastar *Pisaster giganteus*. *Chemistry—A European Journal* **13**: 3262–3268.

Gienapp, P., Teplitsky, C., Alho, J.S., Mills, J.A., and Merila, J. 2008. Climate change and evolution: disentangling environmental and genetic responses. *Molecular Ecology* **17**: 167–178.

Johnson, V.R., Russell, B.D., Fabricius, K.A.E., Brownlee, C., and Hall-Spencer, J.M. 2012. Temperate and tropical brown macroalgae thrive, despite decalcification, along natural CO$_2$ gradients. *Global Change Biology* **18**: 2792–2803.

Langer, G., Nehrke, G., Probert, I., Ly, J., and Ziveri, P. 2009. Strain-specific responses of *Emiliania huxleyi* to changing seawater carbonate chemistry. *Biogeosciences* **6**: 2637–2646.

Levitan, D.R. 1996. Effects of gamete traits on fertilization in the sea and the evolution of sexual dimorphism. *Nature* **382**: 153–155.

Levitan, D.R. 2008. Gamete traits influence the variance in reproductive success, the intensity of sexual selection, and the outcome of sexual conflict among congeneric sea urchins. *Evolution* **62**: 1305–1316.

Martin, S., Richier, S., Pedrotti, M.-L., Dupont, S., Castejon, C., Gerakis, Y., Kerros, M.-E., Oberhansli, F., Teyssie, J.-L., Jeffree, R., and Gattuso, J.-P. 2011. Early development and molecular plasticity in the Mediterranean sea urchin *Paracentrotus lividus* exposed to CO$_2$-driven acidification. *The Journal of Experimental Biology* **214**: 1357–1368.

Micael, J., Alves, M.J., Costa, A.C., and Jones, M.B. 2009. Exploitation and conservation of echinoderms. *Oceanography and Marine Biology* **47**: 191–208.

Moulin, L., Catarino, A.I., Claessens, T., and Dubois, P. 2011. Effects of seawater acidification on early development of the intertidal sea urchin *Paracentrotus lividus* (Lamarck 1816). *Marine Pollution Bulletin* **62**: 48–54.

O'Donnell, M.J., Todgham, A.E., Sewell, M.A., Hammond, L.M., Ruggiero, K., Fangue, N.A., Zippay, M.L., and Hofmann, G.E. 2010. Ocean acidification alters skeletogenesis and gene expression in larval sea urchins. *Marine Ecology Progress Series* **398**: 157–171.

Parker, L.M., Ross, P.M., and O'Connor, W.A. 2011. Populations of the Sydney rock oyster, *Saccostrea glomerata*, vary in response to ocean acidification. *Marine Biology* **158**: 689–697.

Pespeni, M.H., Sanford, E., Gaylord, B., Hill, T.M., Hosfelt, J.D., Jaris, H.K., LaVigne, M., Lenz, E.A., Russell, A.D., Young, M.K., and Palumbi, S.R. 2013. Evolutionary change during experimental ocean acidification. *Proceedings of the National Academy of Sciences USA* **110**: 6937–6942.

Pistevos, J.C.A., Calosi, P., Widdicombe, S., and Bishop, J.D.D. 2011. Will variation among genetic individuals influence species responses to global climate change? *Oikos* **120**: 675–689.

Politi, Y., Arod, T., Klein, E., Weiner, S., and Addadi, L. 2004. Sea urchin spine calcite forms via a transient amorphous calcite carbonate phase. *Science* **306**: 1161–1164.

Roff, D.A. 1997. *Evolutionary Quantitative Genetics*. Chapman and Hall, New York, New York, USA.

Schlegel, P., Havenhand, J.N, Gillings, M.R., and Williamson, J.E. 2012. Individual variability in reproductive success determines winners and losers under ocean acidification: A case study with sea urchins. *PLOS ONE* 7: e53118.

Schram, J.B., McClintock, J.B., Angus, R.A., and Lawrence, J.M. 2011. Regenerative capacity and biochemical composition of the sea star *Luidia clathrata* (Say) (Echinodermata: Asteroidea) under conditions of near-future ocean acidification. *Journal of Experimental Marine Biology and Ecology* 407: 266–274.

Stockwell, C.A., Hendry, A.P., and Kinnison, M.T. 2003. Contemporary evolution meets conservation biology. *Trends in Ecology and Evolution* 18: 94–101.

Stumpp, M., Dupont, S., Thorndyke, M.C., and Melzner, F. 2011b. CO_2 induced seawater acidification impacts sea urchin larval development II: Gene expression patterns in pluteus larvae. *Comparative Biochemistry and Physiology, Part A* 160: 320–330.

Stumpp, M., Wren, J., Melzner, F., Thorndyke, M.C., and Dupont, S.T. 2011a. CO_2 induced seawater acidification impacts sea urchin larval development I: Elevated metabolic rates decrease scope for growth and induce developmental delay. *Comparative Biochemistry and Physiology, Part A* 160: 331–340.

Styan, C.A., Kupriyanova, E., and Havenhand, J.N. 2008. Barriers to cross-fertilization between populations of a widely dispersed polychaete species are unlikely to have arisen through gametic compatibility arms-races. *Evolution* 62: 3041–3055.

Sunday, J.M., Crim, R.N., Harley, C.D.G., and Hart, M.W. 2011. Quantifying rates of evolutionary adaptation in response to ocean acidification. *PLoS ONE* 6: e22881.

Todgham, A.E. and Hofmann, G.E. 2009. Transcriptomic response of sea urchin larvae, Strongylocentrotus purpuratus, to CO_2-driven seawater acidification. *Journal of Experimental Biology* 212: 2579–2594.

Vogel, H., Czihak, G., Chang, P., and Wolf, W. 1982. Fertilization kinetics of sea urchin eggs. *Mathematical Biosciences* 58: 189–216.

Yu, P.C., Matson, P.G., Martz, T.R., and Hofmann, G.E. 2011. The ocean acidification seascape and its relationship to the performance of calcifying marine invertebrates: Laboratory experiments on the development of urchin larvae framed by environmentally-relevant pCO_2/pH. *Journal of Experimental Marine Biology and Ecology* 400: 288–295.

Yu, P.C., Sewell, M.A., Matson, P.G., Rivest, E.B., Kapsenberg, L., and Hofmann, G.E. 2013. Growth attenuation with developmental schedule progression in embryos and early larvae of *Sterechinus neumayeri* raised under elevated CO_2. *PLOS ONE* 8: e52448.

6.3.3.5 Fish

The studies reviewed in this section examine what scientists have learned about potential impacts of lower ocean pH levels on marine fish. The key findings, which challenge the alarming and negative projections of IPCC, are presented in the bullet points below, followed by an expanded discussion of those findings. (Citations for passages in quotation marks in the bullet points are included in the main body of the section.)

- Negative effects of lower ocean pH levels on fish are generally not manifested until the water reaches pH concentrations associated with atmospheric CO_2 levels several times the present value.

- Otoliths of fish grown in seawater of lower pH and aragonite saturation associated with higher CO_2 conditions are usually significantly larger than those of fish grown under present-day conditions.

- "CO_2-induced acidification up to the maximum values likely to be experienced over the next 100 years had no noticeable effect on embryonic duration, egg survivorship and size at hatching for *A. percula*, and tended to have a positive effect on the length and weight of larvae."

- "Most shallow-water fish tested to date appear to compensate fully their acid-base balance within several days of exposure to mild hypercapnia."

- "Future ocean acidification will probably not pose a problem for sperm behavior, and hence fertilization success, of Baltic cod."

- Lower ocean pH levels "neither affected the embryogenesis nor the hatch rate" of Atlantic herring. It also "showed no linear relationship between CO_2 and total length, dry weight, yolk sac area and otolith area of the newly hatched larvae."

- "Cobia exhibited resistance to treatment effects on growth, development, swimming ability, and swimming activity at 800 and 2100 µatm pCO_2," whereas "these scenarios resulted in a significant increase in otolith size (up to 25% larger area)."

- The larval clown fish "is robust to levels of ocean chemistry change that may occur over the next 50–100 years."

- Lower ocean pH levels significantly increased the size, density, and relative mass of larval cobia otoliths, which changes "could affect auditory sensitivity including a ~50% increase in hearing range at 2100 ppm CO_2."

- Lower ocean pH levels "did not appear to negatively affect size or condition of early larval walleye pollock." It induced "a trend toward larger body sizes among fish reared at elevated CO_2 levels."

Ishimatsu et al. (2005) note fish "constitute a major protein source in many countries," and the "potential reduction of fish resources by high-CO_2 conditions due to the diffusion of atmospheric CO_2 into the surface waters ... can be considered as another potential threat to the future world population." They conducted a survey of the scientific literature regarding the potential negative consequences for the health of marine fish of atmospheric CO_2 enrichment that could arise from continued anthropogenic CO_2 emissions.

Focusing on the possible threat of hypercapnia—a condition characterized by an excessive amount of CO_2 in the blood that typically results in acidosis, a serious and sometimes fatal condition—they say their survey revealed "hypercapnia acutely affects vital physiological functions such as respiration, circulation, and metabolism, and changes in these functions are likely to reduce growth rate and population size through reproduction failure." Although this potential threat sounds dire, it represents an egregious flight of the imagination away from what could realistically be expected to happen to fish in the future.

Ishimatsu et al. report "predicted future CO_2 concentrations in the atmosphere are lower than the known lethal concentrations for fish," noting "the expected peak value is about 1.4 torr [just under 1,850 ppm CO_2] around the year 2300 according to Caldeira and Wickett (2003)." As to just how far below the lethal CO_2 concentration for fish 1.4 torr is, in the case of short-term exposures on the order of a few days, Ishimatsu et al. cite a number of studies that yield median lethal concentrations ranging from 37 to 50 torr, values 26 and 36 times greater than the maximum CO_2 concentration expected some 300 years from now.

Regarding long-term exposures, the results are even more comforting. Ishimatsu et al. report Fivelstad et al. (1999) observed only 5 and 8% mortality at the end of 62 days of exposure to CO_2 concentrations of 5 and 9 torr, respectively, for freshwater Atlantic salmon smolts, and mere 1 and 5% mortalities for seawater postsmolts of the same species at 12 and 20 torr after 43 days (Fivelstad et al., 1998). Ishimatsu et al. note Smart et al. (1979) found little difference in mortality for freshwater rainbow trout reared for 275 days at 4 to 17 torr, and no mortality occurred by the tenth week of exposure of juvenile spotted wolf fish to 20 torr (Foss et al., 2003).

Fish embryos and larvae are often more vulnerable to environmental stresses than are adult fish. Yet even here, Ishimatsu et al. report the 24-hour median lethal concentration of CO_2 for eggs and larvae of several marine fish studied by Kikkawa et al. (2003) "ranged widely from 10 torr to 70 torr among species," with the smaller of these two values being more than seven times greater than the CO_2 concentration expected 300 years from now.

Ishimatsu et al.'s review reveals growth reductions of 24 to 48%, but again the CO_2 concentrations that induced those growth reductions ranged from 17 to 20 torr, or 12 to 14 times more than the CO_2 concentration expected 300 years from now. Consequently, Ishimatsu et al.'s scientific literature review suggests both freshwater and marine fish will most likely never experience any ill effects from elevated atmospheric CO_2 concentrations.

Melzner et al. (2009) state several of Earth's 30,000 species of teleost fish, which include virtually all the important sport and commercial fishes, have been shown able to "fully compensate extra cellular fluid pH" and "maintain oxygen consumption rates and growth performance under ocean acidification conditions (e.g. Larsen et al., 1997; Foss et al., 2003; Fivelstad et al., 1998, 2003; Deigweiher et al., 2008)." Noting no studies of these phenomena have lasted for more than a few days, they maintained a group of Atlantic Cod (Gadus morhua) for four months in a recirculating aquaculture system of 15 cubic meters at an atmospheric CO_2 partial pressure of 0.3 kPa (~3,000 ppm) and another group for 12 months at a CO_2 partial pressure of 0.6 kPa (~6,000 ppm). They then investigated the fishes' swimming metabolism in a swim-tunnel respirometer and took tissue samples of their gills for various chemical analyses, including gill Na^+/K^+-ATPase capacity, which serves as a general indicator for ion regulatory effort.

The six German scientists report, "motor activity in adult Atlantic Cod is not compromised by long-term exposure to water pCO_2 levels of 0.3–0.6 kPa," which are "scenarios exceeding the 0.2 kPa value predicted for surface ocean waters around the year 2300 (Caldeira and Wickett, 2003)." Melzner *et al.* conclude "adults of active fish species with a high ion regulatory capacity [which is employed to eliminate metabolic CO_2] are well equipped to cope with projected scenarios of global climate change."

Checkley *et al.* (2009) report on their work with fish otoliths—bony structures consisting of aragonite-protein bilayers which fish use to sense orientation and acceleration. Noting atmospheric CO_2 enrichment had been calculated to decrease the saturation state of carbonate minerals such as aragonite in the world's oceans, the six scientists "hypothesized that otoliths in eggs and larvae reared in seawater with elevated CO_2 would grow more slowly than they do in seawater with normal CO_2." To test this hypothesis, they "grew eggs and pre-feeding larvae of white sea bass (*Atractoscion nobilis*) under a range of CO_2 concentrations [380, 993 and 2,558 ppm] and measured the size of their sagittal otoliths."

"Contrary to expectations," Checkley *et al.* write, "the otoliths of fish grown in seawater with high CO_2, and hence lower pH and aragonite saturation, were significantly larger than those of fish grown under simulations of present-day conditions." They found "for 7- to 8-day-old fish grown under 993 and 2558 ppm CO_2, the areas of the otoliths were 7 to 9% and 15 to17% larger, respectively, than those of control fish grown under 380 ppm CO_2." The marine researchers note young fish are "able to control the concentration of ions (H^+ and Ca^{2+}) ... in the endolymph surrounding the otolith," where "with constant pH, elevated CO_2 increases CO_3^{2-} concentration and thus the aragonite saturation state, accelerating formation of otolith aragonite."

Munday *et al.* (2009) note "there is concern that continued increases in atmospheric CO_2 over the next century could have significant impacts on a wide range of marine species, not just those with calcified skeletons." In the case of fish, which "control their tissue pH by bicarbonate buffering and the exchange of ions, mostly across the gills," they write, "small changes in internal or external pH can readily be compensated (Heisler, 1989; Claiborne *et al.*, 2002)." Fish embryos and young larvae are possibly "more sensitive to pH changes than are juveniles and adults," and "significant effects of ocean acidification are most likely to be detected in these early life stages."

Munday *et al.* grew wild-caught pairs of the orange clownfish (*Amphiprion percula*) in a 70,000-liter recirculating seawater system at James Cook University's experimental marine aquarium facility.

They filled 70-liter tanks with seawater simulating a range of ocean acidification scenarios for the next 50–100 years—390 (current day), 550, 750, and 1,030 ppm atmospheric CO_2—while documenting egg, embryo, and larval development. The four researchers from the School of Marine and Tropical Biology of Australia's James Cook University determined "CO_2 acidification had no detectable effect on embryonic duration, egg survival and size at hatching," and it "tended to increase the growth rate of larvae." They observed, for example, 11 days after hatching, "larvae from some parental pairs were 15 to 18 per cent longer and 47 to 52 per cent heavier in acidified water compared to controls." There was a "positive relationship between length and swimming speed," and, they note, "large size is usually considered to be advantageous for larvae and newly settled juveniles."

Munday *et al.* note "the most common prediction is that ocean acidification could [negatively] affect individual performance (e.g. development, growth, survival, swimming ability)," especially during the early life history of the fish. However, they write, "contrary to expectations," their findings indicate "CO_2-induced acidification up to the maximum values likely to be experienced over the next 100 years had no noticeable effect on embryonic duration, egg survivorship and size at hatching for *A. percula*, and tended to have a positive effect on the length and weight of larvae." As for adult fish, they state "most shallow-water fish tested to date appear to compensate fully their acid-base balance within several days of exposure to mild hypercapnia," citing Michaelidis *et al.* (2007) and Ishimatsu *et al.* (2008).

Frommel *et al.* (2010) state, "elevated CO_2 concentrations can disturb the acid-base regulation, blood circulation, and respiration, as well as the nervous system of marine organisms, leading to long term effects such as reduced growth rates and reproduction," especially in fish, because most "are external fertilizers, and sperm are activated by seawater as they are expelled into the open ocean during a spawning event," citing Westin and Nissling (1991). Frommel *et al.* collected sperm from ripe adult male cod fish (*Gadus morhua*) caught during an August cruise through their spawning grounds in the Baltic Sea's Bornholm Basin. They exposed the fish to seawater that had been brought into equilibrium (by bubbling) with air of either 380 or 1,400 ppm CO_2 (leading to seawater pH values of 8.080 and 7.558, respectively), and they recorded sperm swimming behavior during the exposure period using a digital camera.

The scientists "found no significant effect of decreased pH on sperm speed, rate of change of direction or percent motility for the population of cod analyzed." Frommel *et al.* conclude "future ocean acidification will probably not pose a problem for sperm behavior, and hence fertilization success, of Baltic cod."

Franke and Clemmesen (2011) conducted a study in which eggs of Atlantic herring (*Clupea harengus* L.) were fertilized and incubated in artificially acidified seawater corresponding to atmospheric CO_2 concentrations of 1,260, 1,859, 2,626, 2,903, and 4,635 ppm and compared to a control treatment of 480 ppm CO_2 until the main hatch of the herring larvae occurred. "The development of the embryos was monitored daily and newly hatched larvae were sampled to analyze their morphometrics." The scientists report elevated CO_2 "neither affected the embryogenesis nor the hatch rate," and "the results showed no linear relationship between CO_2 and total length, dry weight, yolk sac area and otolith area of the newly hatched larvae." Franke and Clemmesen conclude "herring eggs can cope at current temperature conditions with an increase in CO_2," even one "exceeding future predictions of CO_2-driven ocean acidification."

Bignami *et al.* (2013a) state "there is a critical need to understand the effects of acidification on the vulnerable larval stages of marine fishes, as there is a potential for large ecological and economic impacts on fish populations and the human economies that rely on them." They studied "the larvae of *Rachycentron canadum* (cobia), a large, highly mobile, pelagic-spawning, widely distributed species with a life history and fishery value contrasting other species studied to date." Bignami *et al.* raised larval cobia through the first three weeks of ontogeny under conditions of predicted future ocean pH levels to determine effects on somatic growth, development, swimming ability, swimming activity, and the formation of otoliths.

The three U.S. researchers report "cobia exhibited resistance to treatment effects on growth, development, swimming ability, and swimming activity at 800 and 2100 μatm pCO_2," and "these scenarios resulted in a significant increase in otolith size (up to 25% larger area)." Bignami *et al.* conclude, "this study demonstrates that cobia is unlikely to experience a strong negative impact from CO_2-induced acidification predicted to occur within the next several centuries," which they speculate "may be due to the naturally variable environmental conditions this species currently encounters throughout ontogeny

in coastal environments," and "may lead to an increased acclimatization ability even during long-term exposure to stressors."

Munday *et al.* (2011a) state "in general, marine fish appear to be relatively tolerant to mild increases in ambient CO_2, presumably because well-developed mechanisms for acid-base regulation allow them to compensate for cellular acidosis caused by exposure to elevated pCO_2 (Portner *et al.*, 2005; Ishimatsu *et al.*, 2008; Melzner *et al.*, 2009)." However, because "fish otoliths (earbones) are composed of aragonite," there is a concern they "could be susceptible to the declining carbonate ion concentrations associated with ocean acidification." Such an effect could be quite serious because "fish ears detect sound, body orientation and acceleration from the position of the otoliths in the inner ear and movement of the otoliths over sensory hair cells (Helfman *et al.*, 1997; Popper and Lu, 2000)."

Munday *et al.* reared larvae of the marine clown fish *Amphiprion percula* throughout their larval phase at three pH levels—ambient or control conditions ($CO_2 \sim 390$ ppm, pH ~ 8.15) and higher CO_2/lower pH conditions ($CO_2 \sim 1,050$ ppm, pH ~ 7.8; $CO_2 \sim 1,721$ ppm, pH ~ 7.6) representative of conditions predicted to prevail in AD 2100 and AD 2200–2300, respectively—to ascertain whether the elevated CO_2/reduced pH conditions would alter otolith size, shape, symmetry (between left and right otoliths), or chemistry compared to current conditions. The four researchers report "there was no effect of the intermediate treatment on otolith size, shape, symmetry between left and right otoliths, or otolith elemental chemistry, compared with controls." In the more extreme treatment, otolith area and maximum length were slightly larger than for the controls, and "no other traits were significantly affected." Munday *et al.* state the larval clown fish appears "capable of regulating endolymphic fluid chemistry even in waters with pH values significantly lower than open ocean values," and they conclude "the larval clown fish is robust to levels of ocean chemistry change that may occur over the next 50–100 years." This conclusion is similar to that reached by Munday *et al.* (2011b), who "detected no effects of ~ 850 ppm CO_2 on size, shape or symmetry of otoliths on juvenile spiny damselfish, a species without a larval phase."

Miller *et al.* (2013) assessed the impact of lower ocean pH levels on the breeding success of cinnamon anemone fish. They employed three 8,000-L recirculating aquarium systems, each set to a different CO_2 and corresponding pH level. The treatments consisted of a current-day Control CO_2 (430 μatm), a mid-century Moderate CO_2 (584 µatm), and an end-of-century High CO_2 (1,032 µatm). They placed 18 pairs of cinnamon anemone fish (*Amphiprion melanopus*) collected from Australia's Great Barrier Reef into each of these three aquariums after all individuals had been weighed and measured for length. At the start of the experiment, they placed pairs of fish in individual 45-L tubs with continuous water flow at winter non-breeding temperatures and ambient pCO_2 values, which the scientists gradually adjusted over a two-week period to the desired levels. Then, they increased temperature by 0.5°C per week, until the average summer breeding temperature was reached, after which they kept the pairs of fish in these conditions for a nine-month period that included the summer breeding season, and the researchers recorded various assessments of breeding success.

The four Australian researchers report, "unexpectedly, increased CO_2 dramatically stimulated breeding activity." More than twice as many pairs of the fish bred in the Moderate and High CO_2 treatments (67% and 55%) compared to the Control treatment (27%). In addition, "pairs in the High CO_2 group produced double the number of clutches per pair and 67% more eggs per clutch compared to the Moderate and Control groups." The researchers determined "reproductive output in the High group was 82% higher than that in the Control group and 50% higher than that in the Moderate group." They note, "despite the increase in reproductive activity, there was no difference in adult body condition among the three treatment groups," and "there was no significant difference in hatchling length between the treatment groups." Miller *et al.* conclude "this study provides the first evidence of the potential effects of ocean acidification on key reproductive attributes of marine fishes and, contrary to expectations, demonstrates an initially stimulatory effect in response to increased pCO_2."

Bignami *et al.* (2013b) write, "the days- to month-long pelagic larval period is an ecologically vital ontogenetic phase in marine fishes because it constitutes the primary mode of dispersal in many species (Cowen and Sponaugle, 2009) and represents the life stage most susceptible to mortality (Houde, 1997)." They say, "during this phase, the sensory abilities of larval fishes are important determinants of survival (Montgomery *et al.*, 2006) and ultimately influence the persistence of viable populations." The five researchers "used new 3D microcomputed tomography to conduct *in situ* analysis of the impact of ocean acidification on otolith (ear stone) size and density of larval cobia (*Rachycentron canadum*), a large, economically important pantropical fish species that shares many life history traits with a diversity of high-value, tropical pelagic fishes."

According to the researchers, at an atmospheric partial pressure of 2,100 ppm CO_2 there was a significant increase in otolith size (up to 49% greater volume and 58% greater relative mass) and a 6% increase in otolith density, and the estimated relative mass of larval cobia otoliths in an end-of-century 800 ppm CO_2 treatment was 14% greater. Bignami *et al.* demonstrate "these changes could affect auditory sensitivity including a ~50% increase in hearing range at 2100 ppm CO_2." They say "this is a potentially optimistic result, indicating some resistance to acidification and suggesting that under near-future scenarios these impacts may be most relevant in habitats already experiencing high pCO$_2$ levels."

Hurst *et al.* (2013) examined the direct effects of projected ocean pH levels on the eggs and larvae of walleye pollock in a series of laboratory experiments to determine the effects of elevated CO_2 levels on size-at-hatch and early larval growth rates. They selected treatments to reflect ambient conditions and conditions predicted to occur in high latitude seas in the next century (a 400–600 ppm increase), as well as a significantly higher CO_2 treatment (~1,200 ppm). The three U.S. researchers report, "ocean acidification did not appear to negatively affect size or condition of early larval walleye pollock." They found "a trend toward larger body sizes among fish reared at elevated CO_2 levels," and they note this trend also has been observed in experiments with orange clownfish (Munday *et al.*, 2009) and in a study of juvenile walleye pollock conducted by Hurst *et al.* (2012). Such findings, the authors write, suggest "the growth dynamics of early life stages of walleye pollock are resilient to projected levels of ocean acidification."

References

Bignami, S., Enochs, I.C., Manzello, D.P., Sponaugle, S., and Cowen, R.K. 2013b. Ocean acidification alters the otoliths of a pantropical fish species with implications for sensory function. *Proceedings of the National Academy of Sciences USA* **110**: 7366–7370.

Bignami, S., Sponaugle, S., and Cowen, R.K. 2013a. Response to ocean acidification in larvae of a large tropical marine fish, *Rachycentron canadum*. *Global Change Biology* **19**: 996–1006.

Caldeira, K. and Wickett, M.E. 2003. Anthropogenic carbon and ocean pH. *Nature* **425**: 365.

Checkley Jr., D.M., Dickson, A.G., Takahashi, M., Radich,

J.A., Eisenkolb, N., and Asch, R. 2009. Elevated CO_2 enhances otolith growth in young fish. *Science* **324**: 1683.

Claiborne, J.B., Edwards, S.L., and Morrison-Shetlar, A.I. 2002. Acid-base regulation in fishes: cellular and molecular mechanisms. *Journal of Experimental Zoology* **293**: 302–319.

Cowen, R. and Sponaugle, S. 2009. Larval dispersal and marine population connectivity. *Annual Review of Marine Science* **1**: 433–466.

Deigweiher, K., Koschnick, N., Portner, H.O., and Lucassen, M. 2008. Acclimation of ion regulatory capacities in gills of marine fish under environmental hypercapnia. *American Journal of Physiology-Regulatory Integrative and Comparative Physiology* **295**: R1660-R1670.

Fivelstad, S., Haavik, H., Lovik, G., and Olsen, A.B. 1998. Sublethal effects and safe levels of carbon dioxide in seawater for Atlantic salmon postsmolts (*Salmo salar* L.): Ion regulation and growth. *Aquaculture* **160**: 305–316.

Fivelstad, S., Olsen, A.B., Asgard, T., Baeverfjord, G., Rasmussen, T., Vindhelm, T., and Stefansson, S. 2003. Long-term sublethal effects of carbon dioxide on Atlantic salmon smolts (*Salmo salar* L.): ion regulation, haematology, element composition, nephrocalcinosis and growth parameters. *Aquaculture* **215**: 301–319.

Fivelstad, S., Olsen, A.B., Kloften, H., Ski, H., and Stefansson, S. 1999. Effects of carbon dioxide on Atlantic salmon (*Salmo salar* L.) smolts at constant pH in bicarbonate rich freshwater. *Aquaculture* **178**: 171–187.

Foss, A., Rosnes, B.A., and Oiestad, V. 2003. Graded environmental hypercapnia in juvenile spotted wolfish (*Anarhichas minor* Olafsen): Effects on growth, food conversion efficiency and nephrocalcinosis. *Aquaculture* **220**: 607–617.

Franke, A. and Clemmesen, C. 2011. Effect of ocean acidification on early life stages of Atlantic herring (*Clupea harengus* L.). *Biogeosciences* **8**: 3697–3707.

Frommel, A.Y., Stiebens, V., Clemmesen, C., and Havenhand, J. 2010. Effect of ocean acidification on marine fish sperm (Baltic cod: *Gadus morhua*). *Biogeosciences* **7**: 3915–3919.

Heisler, N. 1989. Acid-base regulation in fishes. I. Mechanisms. In: Morris, R., Taylor, E.W., Brown, D.J.A., and Brown, J.A. (Eds.) *Acid Toxicity and Aquatic Animals*. Cambridge University Press, Cambridge, United Kingdom, pp. 85–96.

Helfman, G.S., Collette, B.B., and Facey, D.E. 1997. *The Diversity of Fishes*. Blackwell Science, Malden.

Houde, E. 1997. Patterns and trends in larval-stage growth and mortality of teleost fish. *Journal of Fish Biology* **51** (Supplement A): 52–83.

Hurst, T.P., Fernandez, E.R., and Mathis, J.T. 2013. Effects of ocean acidification on hatch size and larval growth of walleye pollock (*Theragra chalcogramma*). *ICES Journal of Marine Science* **70**: 812–822.

Hurst, T.P., Fernandez, E.R., Mathis, J.T., Miller, J.A., Stinson, C.S., and Ahgeak, E.F. 2012. Resiliency of juvenile walleye pollock to projected levels of ocean acidification. *Aquatic Biology* **17**: 247–259.

Ishimatsu, A., Hayashi, M., and Kikkawa, T. 2008. Fishes in high CO_2, acidified oceans. *Marine Ecology Progress Series* **373**: 295–302.

Ishimatsu, A., Hayashi, M., Lee, K.-S., Kikkawa, T., and Kita, J. 2005. Physiological effects of fishes in a high-CO_2 world. *Journal of Geophysical Research* **110**: 10.1029/2004JC002564.

Kikkawa, T., Ishimatsu, A., and Kita, J. 2003. Acute CO_2 tolerance during the early developmental stages of four marine teleosts. *Environmental Toxicology* **18**: 375–382.

Larsen, B.K., Portner, H.O., and Jensen, F.B. 1997. Extra- and intracellular acid-base balance and ionic regulation in cod (*Gadus morhua*) during combined and isolated exposures to hypercapnia and copper. *Marine Biology* **128**: 337–346.

Melzner, F., Gobel, S., Langenbuch, M., Gutowska, M.A., Portner, H.-O., and Lucassen, M. 2009. Swimming performance in Atlantic Cod (*Gadus morhua*) following long-term (4–12 months) acclimation to elevated seawater PCO_2. *Aquatic Toxicology* **92**: 30–37.

Melzner, F., Gutowska, M.A., Langenbuch, M., Dupont, S., Lucassen, M., Thorndyke, M.C., Bleich, M., and Portner, H.-O. 2009. Physiological basis for high CO_2 tolerance in marine ectothermic animals: pre-adaptation through lifestyle and ontogeny? *Biogeosciences* **6**: 2313–2331.

Michaelidis, B., Spring, A., and Portner, H.-O. 2007. Effects of long-term acclimation to environmental hypercapnia on extracellular acid-base status and metabolic capacity in Mediterranean fish *Sparus aurata*. *Marine Biology* **150**: 1417–1429.

Miller, G.M., Watson, S.-A., McCormick, M.I., and Munday, P.L. 2013. Increased CO_2 stimulates reproduction in a coral reef fish. *Global Change Biology* **19**: 3037–3045.

Montgomery, J.C., Jeffs, A., Simpson, S.D., Meekan, M., and Tindle, C. 2006. Sound as an orientation cue for the pelagic larvae of reef fishes and decapod crustaceans. *Advances in Marine Biology* **51**: 143–196.

Munday, P.L., Donelson, J.M., Dixson, D.L., and Endo, G.G.K. 2009. Effects of ocean acidification on the early life history of a tropical marine fish. *Proceedings of the Royal Society B* **276**: 3275–3283.

Munday, P.L., Gagliano, M., Donelson, J.M., Dixson, D.L., and Thorrold, S.R. 2011b. Ocean acidification does not affect the early life history development of a tropical marine fish. *Marine Ecology Progress Series* **423**: 211–221.

Munday, P.L., Hernaman, V., Dixson, D.L., and Thorrold, S.R. 2011a. Effect of ocean acidification on otolith development in larvae of a tropical marine fish. *Biogeosciences* **8**: 1631–1641.

Popper, A.N. and Lu, Z. 2000. Structure-function relationships in fish otolith organs. *Fisheries Research* **46**: 16–25.

Portner, H.-O., Langenbuch, M., and Michaelidis, B. 2005. Synergistic effects of temperature extremes, hypoxia, and increases in CO$_2$ on marine animals: From Earth history to global change. *Journal of Geophysical Research* **110**: 10.1029/2004jc002561.

Smart, G.R., Knox, D., Harrison, J.G., Ralph, J.A., Richards, R.H., and Cowey, C.B. 1979. Nephrocalcinosis in rainbow trout *Salmo gairdneri* Richardson: The effect of exposure to elevated CO$_2$ concentrations. *Journal of Fish Diseases* **2**: 279–289.

Westin, L. and Nissling, A. 1991. Effects of salinity on spermatozoa motility, percentage of fertilized-eggs and egg development of Baltic cod (*Gadus morhua*), and implications for cod stock fluctuations in the Baltic. *Marine Biology* **108**: 5–9.

6.3.3.6 Miscellaneous Animal Studies

The studies reviewed in this section examine what scientists have learned about potential impacts of lower ocean pH levels on other marine animals not discussed in prior subsections. The key findings, which challenge the alarming and negative projections of IPCC, are presented in the bullet points below, followed by an expanded discussion of those findings. (Citations for passages in quotation marks in the bullet points are included in the main body of the section.)

- For the common cuttlefish (*Sepia officinalis*), a decrease in pH to 7.85 "should lead to some possibly beneficial effects, such as a larger egg and presumably hatchling size and a better incorporation of the essential element[s] such as Zn in the embryonic tissue," and these phenomena "may improve the survival [of] the newly hatched juveniles."

- Adults of the branched calcitic bryozoan *Myriapora truncata* "are able to up-regulate their

calcification rates and survive in areas with higher levels of *p*CO$_2$ than are predicted to occur due to anthropogenic ocean acidification."

- The gastropod *Concholepas concholepas* demonstrates "the ability to maintain calcification even at *p*CO$_2$ levels of 1036 µatm." In addition, exposure to elevated *p*CO$_2$ during their early ontogeny "may actually increase the likelihood of *C. concholepas* surviving after being overturned by an exogenous cause."

- Juveniles of the Arctic pteropod *Limacina helicina* are able to extend their shells at an aragonite saturation state as low as 0.6, which may result from "the presence of a thin periostracal layer covering the calcareous surface" that might act to protect the shell in seawater of reduced pH.

- "Copepods, as a group, may be well equipped to deal with the chemical changes associated with ocean acidification."

- Sea anemone abundance along a natural seawater pH gradient of 8.2–7.6 was observed to be higher at the lowest pH.

- Lower ocean pH levels will have no impact on the oceans' "transparency to sound."

Lacoue-Labarthe *et al.* (2009) placed fertilized eggs of the common cuttlefish (*Sepia officinalis*) in five-liter plastic bottles filled with filtered and UV-sterilized Mediterranean seawater pumped from a depth of 30 meters at a site adjacent to Monaco Bay, after which the eggs were maintained throughout their full development time at controlled conditions of temperature (16 or 19°C) and pH (8.1, 7.85 or 7.6), with the latter values maintained within ± 0.05 of a pH unit by periodically bubbling pure CO$_2$ into the bottles (which were continuously aerated with CO$_2$-free air), resulting in mean CO$_2$ concentrations of the air in contact with the surface of the water of 400, 900, or 1,400 ppm.

According to the authors, "decreasing pH resulted in higher egg weight at the end of development at both temperatures ($p < 0.05$), with maximal values at pH 7.85 (1.60 ± 0.21 g and 1.83 ± 0.12 g at 16°C and 19°C, respectively)." They found "hatchlings were smaller when they developed at 16°C than at 19°C ($p < 0.05$)." They also observed zinc (Zn) accumulation "was higher at pH 7.85 during the full developmental period," when "high embryonic requirements for Zn are not fully covered by the maternal pool," so the higher accumulation of Zn "was associated with a greater rate of growth of both egg and embryo." Concurrently, there was a greater accumulation of potentially detrimental silver in the tissues of the hatchlings, but any deleterious effects of the extra silver apparently were overcome by the positive effects of lowered pH on beneficial zinc accumulation. Toxic cadmium accumulation was reduced in the lower pH (higher CO_2) treatments.

The seven scientists conclude, "decreasing pH until 7.85," as could be expected to occur in air enriched with carbon dioxide to a concentration of 900 ppm, "should lead to some possibly beneficial effects, such as a larger egg and presumably hatchling size and a better incorporation of the essential element[s] such as Zn in the embryonic tissue." These phenomena, they write, "may improve the survival [of] the newly hatched juveniles." They note Gutowska et al. (2008) demonstrated "calcification was enhanced in sub-adult cuttlefish reared at 6,000 ppm CO_2."

Gutowska et al. found, over a six-week test period, "juvenile S. officinalis maintained calcification under ~4000 and ~6000 ppm CO_2, and grew at the same rate with the same gross growth efficiency as did control animals," gaining approximately 4% body mass daily and increasing the mass of their calcified cuttlebone by more than 500%. Gutowska et al. conclude "active cephalopods possess a certain level of pre-adaptation to long-term increments in carbon dioxide levels," and they suggest our "understanding of the mechanistic processes that limit calcification must improve before we can begin to predict what effects future ocean acidification will have on calcifying marine invertebrates."

Rodolfo-Metalpa et al. (2010) conducted "the first coastal transplant experiment designed to investigate the effects of naturally acidified seawater on the rates of net calcification and dissolution of the branched calcitic bryozoan Myriapora truncata." Bryozoans or "moss animals" are a geologically important group of small animals that resemble corals; they are major calcifiers found on rocky shores in cool-water areas of the planet, where they comprise a significant component of the carbonate sediments in shallow sublittoral habitats, and where they form long-lived three-dimensional structures that provide attachment sites for numerous epifauna and trap sediment and food for a variety of infauna.

Rodolfo-Metalpa et al. transplanted colonies of the species to normal (pH 8.1), high (pH 7.66), and extremely high (pH 7.43) CO_2 conditions at gas vents located just off Italy's Ischia Island in the Tyrrhenian Sea. They calculated the net calcification rates of live colonies and the dissolution rates of dead colonies by weighing them before and after 45 days of in situ residence in May–June (when seawater temperatures ranged from 19 to 24°C) and after 128 days of in situ residence in July–October (when seawater temperatures ranged from 25–28°C). They found throughout the first and cooler observation period, "dead M. truncata colonies dissolved at high CO_2 levels (pH 7.66), whereas live specimens maintained the same net calcification rate as those growing at normal pH." At the extremely high CO_2 level, the net calcification rate of the live specimens was reduced to only about 20% of what it was at normal pH, though the moss animals survived. Throughout the second and warmer observation period, by contrast, calcification ceased in both the normal and the high CO_2 treatments, and in the extremely high CO_2 treatment the transplants died.

The five scientists conclude, "at moderate temperatures," such as those to which they are currently adapted, "adult M. truncata are able to up-regulate their calcification rates and survive in areas with higher levels of pCO_2 than are predicted to occur due to anthropogenic ocean acidification, although this ability broke down below mean pH 7.4." That level is far below what even IPCC predicts will occur in response to continued burning of fossil fuels.

According to Manriquez et al. (2013), in Chile "the gastropod Concholepas concholepas is both an economically and ecologically important species inhabiting subtidal and intertidal marine habitats." In these rocky environments, "the gastropods are often exposed to highly turbulent conditions," during which times they adhere tightly to the rock surface with their foot. The scientists note, "when feeding and handling prey items the foot of C. concholepas is often removed from the rock leaving it vulnerable to being dislodged." Thus it is in the gastropod's best interests to right itself as quickly as possible whenever this occurs.

To explore the impact of lower ocean pH levels on this self-preservation response, as well as the more basic phenomena of growth and calcification, Manriquez et al. collected small individuals of C. concholepas from a rocky intertidal area in northern Chile, transported them to a laboratory, and reared them in natural seawater for one month, after which 10 individuals were randomly assigned to one of three pCO_2 concentrations: 388 µatm (current), 716 µatm (medium), or 1,036 µatm (high). There they remained, under well-fed conditions, for 83 days, while the researchers made various measurements on days 0, 11, 45, 52, 62, 73, and 83 after the beginning of treatments.

At the end of the study period, the 11 researchers report, there were no significant among-treatment differences in peristomal length, wet weight, or buoyant weight, nor the shell weight of empty shells. They also determined, "on average, self-righting time was three times faster in individuals reared under increased pCO_2 levels than under normal seawater conditions." Manriquez *et al.* conclude "*C. concholepas* have the ability to maintain calcification even at pCO_2 levels of 1036 µatm ... in agreement with similar results reported in the literature for other invertebrates (Ries *et al.*, 2009; Manzello, 2010; Rodolfo-Metalpa *et al.*, 2011)." And they state, "during their early ontogeny, exposure to elevated pCO_2 may actually increase the likelihood of *C. concholepas* surviving after being overturned by an exogenous cause."

Citing Hunt *et al.* (2008), authors Comeau *et al.* (2012) write, "pteropods are pelagic mollusks that play an important role in the food web of extensive oceanic regions, particularly at high latitudes, where they are a major dietary component for zooplankton and higher predators, such as herring, salmon, whales and birds." Comeau *et al.* investigated the effect of lower ocean pH levels "using juveniles of the Arctic pteropod *Limacina helicina* from the Canada Basin of the Arctic Ocean," where they caught and extracted overwintering individuals from depths of 100 to 200 meters through a hole in the ice, thereafter maintaining the mollusks at three pH levels (8.05, 7.90, and 7.75) for eight days, after which they assessed them for mortality and shell growth.

Comeau *et al.* found pH did not impact the mortality of the pteropods, but the degree of linear extension of their shells decreased as pH declined. Nevertheless, the pteropods were able to extend their shells at an aragonite saturation state as low as 0.6, suggesting "the presence of a thin periostracal layer covering the calcareous surface, as shown on the Antarctic pteropod *Limacina helicina antarctica* (Sato-Okoshi *et al.*, 2010), might, among other mechanisms, protect the shell from a corrosive environment." Although much remains to be known about pteropod responses to a potential decline in seawater pH, these findings indicate pteropods possess a certain degree of adaptability to low pH levels, and the results of similar studies of other calcifying sea creatures suggest pteropods may be able to evolve in their ability to cope with declining seawater pH.

Weydmann *et al.* (2012) note the Arctic copepod *Calanus glacialis* "can comprise up to 70–80% of the zooplankton biomass in Arctic shelf seas (Blachowiak-Samolyk *et al.*, 2008; Conover, 1988; Hirche and Mumm, 1992), and is a key herbivore (Mumm *et al.*, 1998; Soreide *et al.*, 2008; Tande, 1991) as well as an important prey item for other zooplankton species (Falk-Petersen *et al.*, 2002, 2004), fish (Fortier *et al.*, 2001), and seabirds (Karnovsky *et al.*, 2003; Weslawski *et al.*, 1999; Wojczulanis *et al.*, 2006)." Noting "testing the potential impacts of ocean acidification on *C. glacialis* reproduction is vital," they investigated "how the reduction of sea surface pH from present day levels (pH 8.2) to a realistic model-based level of pH 7.6, and to an extreme level of pH 6.9, would affect the egg production and hatching success of *C. glacialis* under controlled laboratory conditions," where "reduced pH seawater was prepared by bubbling compressed CO_2 through filtered seawater, until the appropriate level of pH was reached."

The four researchers report, "CO_2-induced seawater acidification had no significant effect on *C. glacialis* egg production," and a reduction in pH to 6.9 only delayed hatching at what they called this "extreme level of pH." They also state there was no significant effect "on the survival of adult females"; this observation, they write, "is in agreement with previous studies on other copepod species," citing Mayor *et al.* (2007) and Kurihara and Ishimatsu (2008). Weydmann *et al.* conclude their results are "in agreement with previous studies on other copepod species and would indicate that copepods, as a group, may be well equipped to deal with the chemical changes associated with ocean acidification."

Suggett *et al.* (2012) state "non-calcifying anthozoans such as soft corals and anemones, play important ecological and biogeochemical roles in reef environments (e.g. Fitt *et al.*, 1982; Bak and Borsboom, 1984; Muller-Parker and Davy, 2001)." They collected pertinent data from 11–26 May 2011 on a sea anemone (*Anemonia viridis*) along a natural seawater pH gradient of 8.2–7.6—which would be expected to prevail across an atmospheric CO_2 gradient of 365–1,425 ppm—produced by a shallow cold vent system (Johnson *et al.*, 2011; 2012) that released CO_2 to coastal waters near Vulcano, Italy, about 25 km northeast of Sicily. The nine researchers found an increase in gross maximum photosynthesis, respiration rates, and dinoflagellate endosymbiont abundance (but unchanged diversity) with increasing CO_2. Sea anemone abundance increased with CO_2 and "dominated the invertebrate community at high CO_2 conditions." The enhanced productivity in the sea anemones they studied, Suggett *et al.* write, implies "an increase in fitness that may enable non-calcifying anthozoans to thrive in future environments, i.e. higher seawater CO_2." As they declare in the title of their paper, "Sea anemones may thrive in a high CO_2 world."

Meron *et al.* (2013) studied the physiology of *Anemonia viridis* growing naturally along a CO_2-vent-induced pH gradient near Ischia, Italy, also studying the nature of the associated microbial community (bacteria and endosymbiotic *Symbiodinium*), focusing on two specific locations that could be characterized as ambient (pCO_2 330 ppm, pH 8.1) and very CO_2-enriched (pCO_2 9,341 ppm, pH 7.0). Although the four researchers found reduction in pH had an impact on the composition and diversity of the anemones' associated microbial communities, "no significant changes were observed in *A. viridis* physiology, and no microbial stress indicators (i.e., pathogens, antibacterial activity, etc.) were detected." Meron *et al.* conclude, "it appears that elevated CO_2 does not have a negative influence on *A. viridis* that live naturally in the [very CO_2-enriched] site." They say "this suggests that natural long-term exposure and dynamic diverse microbial communities may contribute to the acclimation process of the host in a changing pH environment."

Mukherjee *et al.* (2013) "investigated the proteomic response of metamorphosing larvae of the tubeworm *Hydroides elegans*, challenged with two climate change stressors, ocean acidification (pH 7.6) and hypoxia (2.8 mg O_2 per liter)," as well as with both of the stressors combined. The seven scientists found concomitant exposure to the two climate change stressors "caused several proteins involved in energy metabolism, calcification and stress tolerance to be differentially expressed." This phenomenon "seemed to allow the tubeworm larvae to successfully metamorphose and carry out calcification." Mukherjee *et al.* conclude "the aragonite tube-forming tubeworm larvae have a high tolerance to hypoxia and may possess the capacity to acclimate over time, even in the face of ocean acidification."

Some researchers have recently looked at the possible effects of lower ocean pH levels on the oceans' "transparency to sound." Reeder and Chiu (2010) state "it has been reported that, given a 0.3 reduction in pH, from 8.1 to 7.8, a reduction in the acoustic absorption at low frequencies could result, suggesting a significant increase in ocean noise," and more recently "it has been suggested that low-frequency

sound will travel farther due to the ocean pH reduction expected by 2050," and most recently, researchers have suggested "in an ocean more transparent to sound, the resultant changes in propagation range will be noticeable in the operation of scientific, commercial and naval applications that are based on ocean acoustics."

Reeder and Chiu reviewed "the fundamental principles of acoustic transmission loss in the ocean and how the multiple transmission loss mechanisms impact ocean noise levels within the context of changing ocean pH." They conducted "an analytical analysis involving physical and empirical models of all relevant transmission loss mechanisms," focusing on "three ocean acoustic environments ... to elucidate the expected change in ocean noise level from sources at the surface as a function of frequency: shallow water, the acoustic surface duct and the deep ocean."

The two researchers in the Department of Oceanography of the Naval Postgraduate School in Monterey California (USA) report for even a large reduction in ocean pH from 8.1 to 7.4, there was "no observable change in ocean noise in the shallow water and surface duct environments for all frequencies—two environments which host a large portion of the marine mammal population." They also found "a negligible change in ocean noise level in the deep water environment for all frequencies ... which also provides an upper bound to the maximum expected increase in ocean noise level due to the fact that it does not fully account for the range-dependent water column sound speed, bottom topography and distributed sources."

Putting their results in the context of average background ocean noise levels as represented by Wenz (1962) curves, they found "a statistically insignificant change compared to the inherent variability of ocean noise associated with shipping and surface-generated mechanisms." Thus, "after 250 years," they write, "there would still be no significant modifications to the Wenz curves," which suggests lower ocean pH levels will have no negative impact on ocean noise.

References

Bak, R.P.M. and Borsboom, J.L.A. 1984. Allelopathic interaction between a reef coelenterate and benthic algae. *Oecologia* 63: 194–198.

Blachowiak-Samolyk, K., Soreide, J.E., Kwasniewski, S., Sundfjord, A., Hop, H., Falk-Petersen, S., and Hegseth, E.N. 2008. Hydrodynamic control of mesozooplankton abundance and biomass in northern Svalbard waters (79–81 degrees N). *Deep Sea Research Part 2, Topical Studies in Oceanography* **55**: 2210–2224.

Comeau, S., Alliouane, S., and Gattuso, J.-P. 2012. Effects of ocean acidification on overwintering juvenile Arctic pteropods *Limacina helicina*. *Marine Ecology Progress Series* **456**: 279–284.

Conover, R.J. 1988. Comparative life histories in the genera *Calanus* and *Neocalanus* in high latitudes of the northern hemisphere. *Hydrobiologia* **167/168**: 127–142.

Falk-Petersen, S., Dahl, T.M., Scott, C.L., Sargent, J.R., Gulliksen, B., Kwasniewski, S., Hop, H., and Millar, R.M. 2002. Lipid biomarkers and trophic linkages between ctenophores and copepods in Svalbard waters. *Marine Ecology Progress Series* **227**: 187–194.

Falk-Petersen, S., Haug, T., Nilssen, K.T., Wold, A., and Dahl, T.M. 2004. Lipids and trophic linkages in harp seal (*Phoca groenlandica*) from the Eastern Barents Sea. *Polar Research* **23**: 43–50.

Fitt, W.K., Pardy, R.L., and Littler, M.M. 1982. Photosynthesis, respiration, and contribution to community productivity of the asymbiotic sea anemone *Anthopleura elegantissima*. *Journal of Experimental Marine Biology and Ecology* **61**: 213–232.

Fortier, M., Fortier, L., Hattori, H., Saito, H., and Legendre, L. 2001. Visual predators and the diel vertical migration of copepods under Arctic sea ice during the midnight sun. *Journal of Plankton Research* **23**: 1263–1278.

Gutowska, M.A., Portner, H.-O., and Melzner, F. 2008. Growth and calcification in the cephalopod *Sepia officinalis* under elevated seawater pCO_2. *Marine Ecology Progress Series* **373**: 303–309.

Hirche, H.J. and Mumm, N. 1992. Distribution of dominant copepods in the Nansen Basin, Arctic Ocean, in summer. *Deep Sea Research* **39**: 485–505.

Hunt, B., Pakhomov, E., Hosie, G., Siegel, V., Ward, P., and Bernard, K. 2008. Pteropods in Southern Ocean ecosystems. *Progress in Oceanography* **78**: 193–221.

Johnson, V.R., Brownlee, C., Rickaby, R.E.M., Graziano, M., Milazzo, M., and Hall-Spencer, J.M. 2011. Responses of marine benthic microalgae to elevated CO_2. *Marine Biology* **158**: 2389–2404.

Johnson, V.R., Russell, B.D., Fabricius, K.E., Brownlee, C., and Hall-Spencer, J.M. 2012. Temperate and tropical brown macroalgae thrive, despite decalcification, along natural CO_2 gradients. *Global Change Biology* **18**: 2792–2803.

Karnovsky, N.J., Weslawski, J.M., Kwasniewski, S., Walkusz, W., and Beszczynska-Moeller, A. 2003. Foraging behavior of little auks in heterogeneous environment. *Marine Ecology Progress Series* **253**: 289–303.

Kurihara, H. and Ishimatsu, A. 2008. Effects of high CO_2 seawater on the copepod *Acartic tsuensis*. *Marine Pollution Bulletin* **56**: 1086–1090.

Lacoue-Labarthe, T., Martin, S., Oberhansli, F., Teyssie, J.-L., Markich, S., Ross, J., and Bustamante, P. 2009. Effects of increased pCO_2 and temperature on trace element (Ag, Cd and Zn) bioaccumulation in the eggs of the common cuttlefish, *Sepia officinalis*. *Biogeosciences* **6**: 2561–2573.

Manriquez, P.H., Jara, M.E., Mardones, M.L., Navarro, J.M., Torres, R., Lardies, M.A., Vargas, C.A., Duarte, C., Widdicombe, S., Salisbury, J., and Lagos, N.A. 2013. Ocean acidification disrupts prey responses to predator cues but not net prey shell growth in *Concholepas concholepas* (loco). *PLOS ONE* **8**: e68643.

Manzello, D.P. 2010. Ocean acidification hot spots: Spatiotemporal dynamics of the seawater CO_2 system of eastern Pacific coral reefs. *Limnology and Oceanography* **55**: 239–248.

Mayor, D.J., Matthews, C., Cook, K., Zuur, A.F., and Hay, S. 2007. CO_2-induced acidification affects hatching success in *Calanus finmarchicus*. *Marine Ecology Progress Series* **350**: 91–97.

Meron, D., Buia, M.-C., Fine, M., and Banin, E. 2013. Changes in microbial communities associated with the sea anemone *Anemonia viridis* in a natural pH gradient. *Microbial Ecology* **65**: 269–276.

Mukherjee, J., Wong, K.K.W., Chandramouli, K.H., Qian, P.-Y., Leung, P.T.Y., Wu, R.S.S., and Thiyagarajan, V. 2013. Proteomic response of marine invertebrate larvae to ocean acidification and hypoxia during metamorphosis and calcification. *The Journal of Experimental Biology* **216**: 4580–4589.

Muller-Parker, M. and Davy, S.K. 2001. Temperate and tropical algal-sea anemone symbioses. *Invertebrate Biology* **120**: 104–123.

Mumm, N., Auel, H., Hanssen, H., Hagen, W., Richter, C., and Hirche, H.J. 1998. Breaking the ice: large-scale distribution of mesozooplankton after a decade of Arctic and trans-polar cruises. *Polar Biology* **20**: 189–197.

Reeder, D.B. and Chiu, C.-S. 2010. Ocean acidification and its impact on ocean noise: Phenomenology and analysis. *Journal of the Acoustical Society of America* **128**: 10.1121/1.3431091.

Ries, J.B., Cohen, A.L., and McCorkle, D.C. 2009. Marine calcifiers exhibit mixed responses to CO_2-induced ocean acidification. *Geology* **37**: 1131–1134.

Rodolfo-Metalpa, R., Houlbreque, F., Tambutte, E., Boisson, F., Baggini, C., Patti, F.P., Jeffree, R., Fine, M., Foggo, A., Gattuso, J.P., and Hall-Spencer, J.M. 2011. Coral and mollusk resistance to ocean acidification

913

adversely affected by warming. *Nature Climate Change* **1**: 308–312.

Rodolfo-Metalpa, R., Lombardi, C., Cocito, S., Hall-Spencer, J.M., and Gambi, M.C. 2010. Effects of ocean acidification and high temperatures on the bryozoan *Myriapora truncata* at natural CO_2 vents. *Marine Ecology* **31**: 447–456.

Sato-Okoshi, W., Okoshi, K., Sasaki, H., and Akiha, F. 2010. Shell structure characteristics of pelagic and benthic molluscs from Antarctic waters. *Polar Science* **4**: 257–261.

Soreide, J., Falk-Petersen, S., Nost, H.E., Hop, H., Carroll, M.L., Hobson, K., and Blachowiak-Samolyk, K. 2008. Seasonal feeding strategies of *Calanus* in the high-Arctic Svalbard region. *Deep Sea Research Part II* **55**: 2225–2244.

Suggett, D.J., Hall-Spencer, J.M., Rodolfo-Metalpa, R., Boatman, T.G., Payton, R., Pettay, D.T., Johnson, V.R., Warner, M.E., and Lawson, T. 2012. Sea anemones may thrive in a high CO_2 world. *Global Change Biology* **18**: 3015–3025.

Tande, K.S. 1991. Calanus in North Norwegian fjords and in the Barents Sea. *Polar Research* **10**: 389–407.

Wenz, G.M. 1962. Acoustic ambient noise in the ocean: Spectra and sources. *Journal of the Acoustical Society of America* **34**: 1936–1956.

Weslawski, J.M., Koszteyn, J., Kwasniewski, S., Stempniewicz, L., and Malinga, M. 1999. Summer food resources of the little auk, *Alle alle* (L.) in the European Arctic seas. *Polish Polar Research* **20**: 387–403.

Weydmann, A., Soreide, J.E., Kwasniewski, S., and Widdicombe, S. 2012. Influence of CO_2-induced acidification on the reproduction of a key Arctic copepod *Calanus glacialis*. *Journal of Experimental Marine Biology and Ecology* **428**: 39–42.

Wojczulanis, K., Jakubas, D., Walkusz, W., and Wennerberg, L. 2006. Differences in food delivered to chicks by males and females of Little Auks (*Alle alle*) on south Spitsbergen. *Journal of Ornithology* **147**: 543–548.

6.3.3.7 Multiple Animal Studies

The studies reviewed in this section examine what scientists have learned about potential impacts of lower ocean pH levels on animals as obtained from studies in which multiple species are discussed. The key findings, which challenge the alarming and negative projections of IPCC, are presented in the bullet points below, followed by an expanded discussion of those findings. (Citations for passages in quotation marks in the bullet points are included in the main body of the section.)

- The impact of elevated atmospheric CO_2 on marine calcification "is more varied than previously thought."

- Different stress effects on interacting species resulting from lower ocean pH levels "may not only enhance but also buffer community level effects."

- "Biological processes can provide homeostasis against changes in pH in bulk waters of the range predicted during the 21st century."

- The world's marine biota are "more resistant to ocean acidification than suggested by pessimistic predictions identifying ocean acidification as a major threat to marine biodiversity" and "may not be the widespread problem conjured into the 21st century."

Ries *et al.* (2009) "reared 18 calcifying species for 60 days in isothermal (25°C) experimental seawaters equilibrated with average [atmospheric] CO_2 values of 409, 606, 903 and 2856 ppm, corresponding to modern CO_2, and ~2, 3 and 10 times pre-industrial levels (~280 ppm), respectively, and yielding average seawater saturation states of 2.5, 2.0, 1.5 and 0.7 with respect to aragonite," after which "the organisms' net rates of calcification (total calcification minus total dissolution) under the various CO_2 treatments were estimated from changes in their buoyant weight and verified with dry weight measurements after harvesting." The three Woods Hole Oceanographic Institution (USA) researchers report, "in ten of the 18 species (temperate corals, pencil urchins, hard clams, conchs, serpulid worms, periwinkles, bay scallops, oysters, whelks, soft clams), net calcification decreased with increasing CO_2," and "in six of the ten negatively impacted species (pencil urchins, hard clams, conchs, periwinkles, whelks, soft clams) [they] observed net dissolution of the shell in the highest CO_2 treatment."

They continue, "in four of the 18 species (limpets, purple urchins, coralline red algae, calcareous green algae), net calcification increased relative to the control under intermediate CO_2 levels (605 and 903 ppm), and then declined at the highest CO_2 level (2856 ppm)." Finally, they write, "in three species (crabs, lobsters, and shrimps), net calcification was greatest under the highest level of CO_2 (2856 ppm)," and "one species, the blue mussel, exhibited no response to elevated CO_2."

Ries et al. conclude "the impact of elevated atmospheric CO_2 on marine calcification is more varied than previously thought," with responses ranging from negative to neutral to positive.

Kurihara et al. (2007) extracted sedimentary mud from the seafloor of Tanabe Bay on the Kii Peninsula of Japan and incubated it in marine microcosms continuously aerated for 56 days with air of either 360 or 2,360 ppm CO_2 while they periodically measured the abundance and biomass of different members of the meiobenthic community contained in the sediments. Meiofauna are small benthic invertebrates larger than microfauna but smaller than macrofauna; they are metazoan animals that can pass through a 0.5–1 mm mesh but are retained by a 30–45 μm mesh. In marine environments, they typically are found between grains of damp sand on the seashore or in muddy sediments at the bottoms of water bodies.

The authors "observed no significant differences in the abundance of total meiofauna, nematodes, harpacticoid copepods (including adults and copepodites) and nauplii by the end of the experiment." They say there "may have been successful recruitments under elevated CO_2 conditions" and "elevated CO_2 had not impacted the reproduction of nematodes and harpacticoid copepods." These observations, the three researchers write, "suggest that the projected atmospheric CO_2 concentration in the year 2300 does not have acute effects on the meiofauna."

Appelhans et al. (2012) note "the impact of seawater acidification on calcifying organisms varies at the species level," and "if the impact differs between predator and prey in strength and/or sign, trophic interactions may be altered." This consequence, if true, could play havoc with many marine ecosystems as currently constituted. In a study designed to explore the potential for such interactions in the brackish western Baltic Sea, Appelhans et al. investigated the impacts of three seawater pCO_2 levels (650, 1,250 and 3,500 ppm) on the growth of two predatory species (the common sea star Asterias rubens and the shore crab Carcinus maenas), also determining whether the conditions affected the quantity or size of prey consumed (the blue mussel Mytilus edulis). The five German scientists found "growth of Mytilus edulis was generally very low and not significantly affected by acidification." They write, "a trend toward a lower shell mass with increasing seawater pCO_2 was observed," and "the mean maximum breaking resistance of mussel shells was significantly lowered by ~20% at the highest level of 3500 ppm."

As for the predators, they report, "acidification did not provoke a measurable shift in prey size preferred by either predator." They also found intermediate acidification levels (corresponding to 1,250 ppm CO_2) "had no significant effect on growth or consumption in either predator species," but the highest acidification level (corresponding to 3,500 ppm CO_2) "reduced feeding and growth rates in sea stars by 56%, while in crabs a 41% decrease in consumption rates of mussels could be demonstrated." "Interestingly," Appelhans et al. conclude, "the enhanced vulnerability of mussels seems to be neutralized by the decreased consumption of the predators under high acidification." They write, "these results illustrate that different stress effects on interacting species may not only enhance but also buffer community level effects," noting, "when stress effects are similar (and weak) on interacting species, biotic interactions may remain unaffected."

Hurd et al. (2011) observe, "most ocean acidification studies so far have been simplistic" because they have not "jointly considered physical, chemical and biological interactions." They note "the emerging discipline of marine ecomechanics (Denny and Helmuth, 2009; Denny and Gaylord, 2010) provides a valuable framework in which such inter-disciplinary research can be conducted." The old experimental approach, they write, "overlooks the existence of a discrete micro-layer (i.e., diffusion boundary layer, DBL) at the surface of many aquatic organisms that buffers them from the surrounding mainstream seawater (Vogel, 1996)." This is achieved by metabolic processes that alter the water chemistry within the DBL, with photosynthesis increasing pH, and calcification and respiration reducing pH (Hurd et al., 2009). They continue, "the chemical environment within the DBL differs from that in the mainstream seawater just micrometers away, with implications for both the dissolution of, and formation of, calcium carbonate (Borowitzka and Larkum, 1976; Ries et al., 2009)."

In a study employing the still-evolving ecomechanic approach, Hurd et al. used pH micro-electrodes and oxygen micro-optodes to measure the DBL thickness at the surface of the coralline seaweed Sporolithon durum, the sea urchin Evechinus chloroticus, and the abalone Haliotis iris, at a range of seawater velocities (0–10 cm/sec) that reflected those found within a temperate reef in Southern New Zealand (45.38°S) that may be vulnerable to ocean acidification (OA). For S. durum, they also determined whether DBL thickness would be affected when mainstream seawater pH was reduced to 7.5, the projected worst-case scenario for the year 2215 as calculated by Caldeira and Wickett (2003). In addition, they measured pH fluctuations at the surface of *S. durum* on a timescale of hours at ambient seawater pH and pH 7.5 at two different flows (1.5 and 6.3 cm/sec), and for the invertebrates they measured surface pH fluctuations at ambient pH and a flow of 1.5 cm/sec.

The seven scientists determined coralline seaweeds encounter a wide range of pH values over each daily cycle, but they are able to increase their pH substantially due to photosynthesis and to withstand periods of very low pH (relative to the present day and comparable to values predicted for coming centuries) under low flows. As to sea urchins, the scientists found they are currently subjected to—and readily survive—very low pH values (7.5) at their surfaces in slow seawater flows, values equivalent to those predicted to occur in the future. And abalone, the researchers write, "have a very thin DBL and hence their outer surface is subjected to the pH in the mainstream seawater, in all flow conditions," yet they too persist, probably because they are "internal calcifiers" and "the reduced pH predicted for future oceans may not directly alter their rates of calcification."

Hurd *et al.* conclude their findings "support the view that although the role of chemistry on OA is well understood, the biological responses to OA will be complex," citing their own work and that of Fabry *et al.* (2008). They also note, "both the site of calcification and the ecomechanics of the biota, i.e., the interactions between their morphology, physiology and the surrounding hydrodynamic environment, must be considered." Their work suggests marine calcifiers are much more robust to OA than originally thought.

Findlay *et al.* (2011) provide further evidence of the importance of biology in controlling calcification. They note, "calcifying marine organisms such as molluscs and foraminifera, crustaceans, echinoderms, corals and coccolithophores are predicted to be most vulnerable to decreasing oceanic pH (ocean acidification)." They point out there is a possibility for "increased or maintained calcification under high carbon dioxide conditions," and their experiment demonstrates the reality of this phenomenon in different types of calcifying marine animals. Working with five calcifying organisms—two gastropods (the limpet *Patella vulgata* and the periwinkle *Littorina littorea*), a bivalve mussel (*Mytilus edulis*), one crustacean (the cirripede *Semibalanus balanoides*), and one echinoderm (the brittlestar *Amphiura filiformis*)—Findlay *et al.* "measured either the calcium (Ca^{2+}) concentration in the calcified structures or shell morphological parameters as a proxy for a net change in calcium carbonate in live individuals exposed to lowered pH," where the lower pH of the seawater employed was created by the bubbling of CO_2 into header tanks.

"Contrary to popular predictions," they write, the results indicated "the deposition of calcium carbonate can be maintained or even increased in acidified seawater." In fact, four of the five species they studied actually exhibited increased levels of calcium in low pH conditions. In the case of *Littorina littorea*, for example, all morphological shell parameters—width, height, thickness, area, perimeter, aperture area, and aperture perimeter—"increased in low pH treatments compared to the control," and "there was ~67% more growth in shell height, ~30% more growth in shell width and ~40% more growth in shell thickness under low pH conditions compared to the control." They also observed a large amount of dissolution taking place on isolated shells and arms of the creatures they studied, but they found "the presence of a live animal within its calcium carbonate structure offset this dissolution."

Findlay *et al.* say their findings demonstrate "there is a great degree of biological control on calcification with complex links to other physiological processes," and "increasing evidence in the literature agrees with the results of [our] study," noting, "McDonald *et al.* (2009) showed calcification in another barnacle species (*Amphibalaus amphitrite*) to continue, and possibly even increase, under low pH conditions (pH 7.4); Arnold *et al.* (2009) demonstrated larval lobsters (*Homarus gammarus*) were able to lay down calcium carbonate structure in pH conditions 0.3 units below the control levels; Checkley *et al.* (2009) showed young fish have enhanced aragonite otolith growth when grown under elevated CO_2; Maier *et al.* (2009) showed that, although there was a decrease in calcification in cold-water corals, overall they showed a positive net calcification at aragonite saturation states below 1, and longer-term experiments suggest these corals may actually maintain or even increase calcification over longer timescales at low pH (Schubert *et al.*, 2010)."

In what was at the time the most comprehensive analysis ever conducted of experimental studies that have explored the effects of rising atmospheric CO_2 concentrations on marine biota, Hendriks *et al.* (2010) assembled a database of 372 experimentally evaluated responses of 44 marine species to lower ocean pH levels induced by equilibrating seawater with CO_2-enriched air. They note, "warnings that ocean acidification is a major threat to marine biodiversity are largely based on the analysis of predicted changes in ocean chemical fields," which are derived from theoretical models that do not account for numerous biological phenomena and have only "limited experimental support."

Of the published reports they scrutinized, only 154 assessed the significance of responses relative to controls. Of those reports, 47 reported no significant response, so "only a minority of studies" demonstrated "significant responses to acidification." When the results of that minority group of studies were pooled, there was no significant mean effect. Nevertheless, the three researchers found some types of organisms and certain functional processes did exhibit significant responses to lower seawater pH levels.

Since their analyses to this point had included some extremely high acidification treatments, they repeated their analyses for only those pH levels induced by atmospheric CO_2 concentrations of 2,000 ppm or less, as that concentration had been predicted to occur around the year 2300 by Caldeira and Wickett (2003). In this second analysis, Hendriks et al. once again found the overall response, including all biological processes and functional groups, was not significantly different from that of the various control treatments, although calcification was reduced by 33 ± 4.5% and fertility by 11 ± 3.5% across groups, whereas survival and growth showed no significant overall responses. When the upper limiting CO_2 concentrations were in the range of 731–759 ppm, just below the value predicted by IPCC (2007) for the end of the twenty-first century (790 ppm)—calcification rate reductions of only 25% were observed.

The three researchers say this decline "is likely to be an upper limit, considering that all experiments involve the abrupt exposure of organisms to elevated pCO_2 values, while the gradual increase in pCO_2 that is occurring in nature may allow adaptive and selective processes to operate," citing Widdicombe et al. (2008) and noting "these gradual changes take place on the scale of decades, permitting adaptation of organisms even including genetic selection."

Even this mitigating factor is not the end of the good news, for Hendriks et al. also write, "most experiments assessed organisms in isolation, rather than [within] whole communities," and the responses of other entities and processes within the community may buffer the negative impacts of CO_2-induced acidification. As an example, they note "sea-grass photosynthetic rates may increase by 50% with increased CO_2, which may deplete the CO_2 pool, maintaining an elevated pH that may protect associated calcifying organisms from the impacts of ocean acidification."

Describing another phenomenon that benefits corals, the researchers write, "seasonal changes in pCO_2 are in the range of 236–517 ppm in the waters of the northern East China Sea (Shim et al., 2007)," and "metabolically-active coastal ecosystems experience broad diel changes in pH, such as the diel changes of >0.5 pH units reported for sea grass ecosystems (Invers et al., 1997)," which they say represent "a broader range than that expected to result from ocean acidification expected during the 21st century." They note these fluctuations also "offer opportunities for adaptation to the organisms involved."

Hendriks et al. additionally state the models on which the ocean "acidification" threat is based "focus on bulk water chemistry and fall short of addressing conditions actually experienced by [marine] organisms," which are "separated from the bulk water phase by a diffusive boundary layer" and "photosynthetic activity"—such as that of the zooxanthellae hosted by corals—"depletes pCO_2 and raises pH (Kuhl et al., 1995) so that the pH actually experienced by organisms may differ greatly from that in the bulk water phase (Sand-Jensen et al., 1985)."

Hendriks et al. also note "calcification is an active process where biota can regulate intracellular calcium concentrations," so "marine organisms, like calcifying coccolithophores (Brownlee and Taylor, 2004), actively expel Ca^{2+} through the ATPase pump to maintain low intracellular calcium concentrations (Corstjens et al., 2001; Yates and Robbins, 1999)." They note, "as one Ca^{2+} is pumped out of the cell in exchange for $2H^+$ pumped into the cell, the resulting pH and Ca^{2+} concentrations increase the $CaCO_3$ saturation state near extracellular membranes and appear to enhance calcification (Pomar and Hallock, 2008)"—so much so, in fact, that "there is evidence that calcification could even increase in acidified seawater, contradicting the traditional belief that calcification is a critical process impacted by ocean acidification (Findlay et al., 2009)."

Hendriks et al. note the world's marine biota are "more resistant to ocean acidification than suggested by pessimistic predictions identifying ocean acidification as a major threat to marine biodiversity," and thus this phenomenon "may not be the widespread problem conjured into the 21st century" by the world's climate alarmists, echoing a similar conclusion reached at the turn of the last millennium (Idso *et al.*, 2000). Hendriks *et al.* conclude, "biological processes can provide homeostasis against changes in pH in bulk waters of the range predicted during the 21st century."

References

Appelhans, Y.S., Thomsen, J., Pansch, C., Melzner, F., and Wahl, M. 2012. Sour times: seawater acidification effects on growth, feeding behavior and acid-base status of *Asterias rubens* and *Carcinus maenas*. *Marine Ecology Progress Series* **459**: 85–97.

Arnold, K.E., Findlay, H.S., Spicer, J.I., Daniels, C.L., and Boothroyd, D. 2009. Effects of CO₂-related acidification on aspects of the larval development of the European lobster, *Homarus gammarus* (L.). *Biogeosciences* **6**: 1747–1754.

Borowitzka, M.A. and Larkum, A.W.D. 1976. Calcification in the green alga *Halimeda*. *Journal of Experimental Botany* **27**: 879–893.

Brownlee, C. and Taylor, A. 2004. Calcification in coccolithophores: a cellular perspective. In: Thierstein, H.R. and Young, J.R. (Eds.) *Coccolithophores.* Springer, Berlin, Germany, pp. 31–49.

Caldeira, K. and Wickett, M.E. 2003. Anthropogenic carbon and ocean pH. *Nature* **425**: 365.

Checkley, D.M., Dickson, A.G., Takahashi, M., Radish, J.A., Eisenkolb, N., and Asch, R. 2009. Elevated CO₂ enhances otolith growth in young fish. *Science* **324**: 1683.

Corstjens, P.L.A.M., Araki, Y., and Gonzalez, E.L. 2001. A coccolithophorid calcifying vesicle with a vacuolar-type ATPase proton pump: cloning and immunolocalization of the V0 subunit *c*. *Journal of Phycology* **37**: 71–78.

Denny, M.W. and Gaylord, B. 2010. Marine ecomechanics. *Annual Review of Marine Science* **2**: 89–114.

Denny, M. and Helmuth, B. 2009. Grand challenges. Confronting the physiological bottleneck: a challenge from ecomechanics. *Integrated Comparative Biology* **49**: 197–201.

Fabry, V.J., Seibel, B.A., Feely, R.A., and Orr, J.C. 2008. Impacts of ocean acidification on marine fauna and ecosystem processes. *ICES Journal of Marine Science* **65**: 414–432.

Findlay, H.S., Wood, H.L., Kendall, M.A., Spicer, J.I., Twitchett, R.J., and Widdicombe, S. 2011. Comparing the impact of high CO₂ on calcium carbonate structures in different marine organisms. *Marine Biology Research* **7**: 565–575.

Findlay, H.S., Wood, H.L., Kendall, M.A., Spicer, J.I., Twitchett, R.J., and Widdicombe, S. 2009. Calcification, a physiological process to be considered in the context of the whole organism. *Biogeosciences Discussions* **6**: 2267–2284.

Hendriks, I.E., Duarte, C.M., and Alvarez, M. 2010. Vulnerability of marine biodiversity to ocean acidification: A meta-analysis. *Estuarine, Coastal and Shelf Science* **86**: 157–164.

Hurd, C.L., Cornwall, C.E., Currie, K., Hepburn, C.D., McGraw, C.M., Hunter, K.A., and Boyd, P.W. 2011. Metabolically induced pH fluctuations by some coastal calcifiers exceed projected 22nd century ocean acidification: a mechanism for differential susceptibility? *Global Change Biology* **17**: 3254–3262.

Hurd, C.L., Hepburn, C.D., Currie, K.I., Raven, J.A., and Hunter, K.A. 2009. Testing the effects of ocean acidification on algal metabolism: considerations for experimental designs. *Journal of Phycology* **45**: 1236–1251.

Idso, S.B., Idso, C.D., and Idso, K.E. 2000. CO₂, global warming and coral reefs: Prospects for the future. *Technology* **7S**: 71–94.

Invers, O., Romero, J., and Perez, M. 1997. Effects of pH on seagrass photosynthesis: a laboratory and field assessment. *Aquatic Botany* **59**: 185–194.

IPCC. 2007. *Climate Change 2007: Synthesis Report.*

Kuhl, M., Cohen, Y., Dalsgaard, T., and Jorgensen, B.B. 1995. Microenvironment and photosynthesis of zooxanthellae in scleractinian corals studied with microsensors for O₂, pH and light. *Marine Ecology Progress Series* **117**: 159–172.

Kurihara, H., Ishimatsu, A., and Shirayama, Y. 2007. Effects of elevated seawater CO₂ concentration of the meiofauna. *Journal of Marine Science and Technology* **15**: 17–22.

Maier, C., Hegeman, J., Weinbauer, M.G., and Gattuso, J.-P. 2009. Calcification of the cold-water coral *Lophelia pertusa* under ambient and reduced pH. *Biogeosciences* **6**: 1671–1680.

McDonald, M.R., McClintock, J.B., Amsler, C.D., Rittschof, D., Angus, R.A., Orihuela, B., and Lutostanski K. 2009. Effects of ocean acidification over the life history of the barnacle *Amphibalanus amphitrite*. *Marine Ecology Progress Series* **385**: 179–187.

Pomar, L. and Hallock, P. 2008. Carbonate factories: a conundrum in sedimentary geology. *Earth-Science Reviews* **87**: 134–169.

Ries, J.B., Cohen, A.L., and McCorkle, D.C. 2009. Marine calcifiers exhibit mixed responses to CO₂-induced ocean acidification. *Geology* **37**: 1131–1134.

Sand-Jensen, K., Revsbech, N.P., and Barker Jorgensen, B.B. 1985. Microprofiles of oxygen in epiphyte communities on submerged macrophytes. *Marine Biology* **89**: 55–62.

Schubert, A., Maier, C., Riebesell, U., and Gattuso, J.-P. 2010. The impact of ocean acidification on calcification rates of Mediterranean cold-water corals. Poster presentation EPOCA Annual Meeting, Bremerhaven, Germany, p. 109.

Shim, J.H., Kim, D., Kang, Y.C., Lee, J.H., Jang, S.T., and Kim, C.H. 2007. Seasonal variations in pCO_2 and its controlling factors in surface seawater of the northern East China Sea. *Continental Shelf Research* **27**: 2623–2636.

Vogel, S. 1996. *Life in Moving Fluids: the Physical Biology of Flow*. Princeton University Press, Princeton, New Jersey, USA.

Widdicombe, S., Dupont, S., and Thorndyke, M. 2008. *Laboratory Experiments and Benthic Mesocosm Studies. Guide for Best Practices in Ocean Acidification Research and Data Reporting*. EPOCA, France.

Yates, K.K. and Robbins, L.L. 1999. Radioisotope tracer studies of inorganic carbon and Ca in microbially derived $CaCO_3$. *Geochimica et Cosmochimica Acta* **63**: 129–136.

6.4 Freshwater "Acidification"

The vast majority of studies of the effects of lower pH levels examine the topic as it pertains to marine life. However, a growing body of research investigates its potential effects on aquatic species inhabiting the world's freshwater lakes, rivers, and streams. That research suggests there may be great benefits in store for such aquatic life as the air's CO_2 concentration continues to rise.

6.4.1 Algae

The studies reviewed in this section examine what scientists have learned about potential impacts of falling freshwater pH levels on algae. The key findings, which challenge the alarming and negative projections of IPCC, are presented in the bullet points below, followed by an expanded discussion of those findings. (Citations for passages in quotation marks in the bullet points are included in the main body of the section.)

- A "doubled atmospheric CO_2 concentration would affect the growth of *C. pyrenoidosa* when it grows under bright solar radiation, and such an effect would increase by a great extent when the cell density becomes high."

- The effects of lower freshwater pH levels on algal production could be such that a "doubling of atmospheric CO_2 may result in an increase of the productivity of more than 50%."

- "Contrary to the dominating hypotheses in the literature," lower freshwater pH levels may lead to "positive, bottom-up effects on secondary production in some stream food webs."

- Lower freshwater pH levels may prevent bloom development and ambient toxicity of certain harmful algae.

Xia and Gao (2003) cultured cells of the freshwater alga *Chlorella pyrenoidosa* in Bristol's solution within controlled environment chambers maintained at low and high light levels (50 and 200 $\mu mol/m^2/s$) during 12-hour light periods followed by 12-hour dark periods for a total of 13 days, while the solutions in which the cells grew were continuously aerated with air of either 350 or 700 ppm CO_2. When they harvested the cells (in the exponential growth phase) at the conclusion of this period, they found the biomass (cell density) of the twice-ambient CO_2 treatment was 10.9% and 8.3% greater than that of the ambient-air treatment in the low- and high-light regimes, respectively, although only the high-light result was statistically significant. The two scientists conclude a "doubled atmospheric CO_2 concentration would affect the growth of *C. pyrenoidosa* when it grows under bright solar radiation, and such an effect would increase by a great extent when the cell density becomes high." Their data also suggest the same may happen, perhaps only to a lesser extent, when the alga grows under less-bright conditions.

Andersen and Andersen (2006) placed six 1.5-m-diameter flexible plastic cylinders in the littoral zone of Lake Hampen in central Jutland, Denmark. Three of the cylinders were maintained at the ambient CO_2 concentration of the air and three were enriched to 10 times ambient, and the researchers measured the CO_2-induced growth response of a mixture of several species of filamentous freshwater algae dominated by *Zygnema* species but also containing some *Mougeotia* and *Spirogyra*. After one full growing season (May to November), they determined the biomass of the microalgal mixture in the CO_2-enriched cylinders was increased by 220% in early July, by 90% in mid-August, and by 3,750% in mid-November.

Schippers *et al.* (2004a) note "it is usually thought that unlike terrestrial plants, phytoplankton will not show a significant response to an increase of atmospheric CO_2," but "most analyses have not examined the full dynamic interaction between phytoplankton production and assimilation, carbon-chemistry and the air-water flux of CO_2," and "the effect of photosynthesis on pH and the dissociation of carbon (C) species have been neglected in most studies."

Schippers *et al.* developed "an integrated model of phytoplankton growth, air-water exchange and C chemistry to analyze the potential increase of phytoplankton productivity due to an atmospheric CO_2 elevation." As a test of their model, they let the freshwater alga *Chlamydomonas reinhardtii* grow in 300 ml bottles filled with 150 ml of a nutrient-rich medium at enclosed atmospheric CO_2 concentrations of 350 and 700 ppm maintained at two air-water exchange rates characterized by CO_2 exchange coefficients of 2.1 and 5.1 m day^{-1}, as Shippers *et al.* (2004b) describe it, periodically measuring the biovolume of the solutions by means of an electronic particle counter.

The results of this effort, they write, "confirm the theoretical prediction that if algal effects on C chemistry are strong, increased phytoplankton productivity because of atmospheric CO_2 elevation should become proportional to the increased atmospheric CO_2," which suggests algal productivity "would double at the predicted increase of atmospheric CO_2 to 700 ppm." Although "strong algal effects (resulting in high pH levels) at which this occurs are rare under natural conditions," they predict effects on algal production in freshwater systems could be such that a "doubling of atmospheric CO_2 may result in an increase of the productivity of more than 50%."

Collins *et al.* (2006) propagated 10 replicate lines from each of two clones of *Chlamydomonas reinhardtii* within a phytotron by batch-culturing them in flasks through which air of 430 ppm CO_2 was continuously bubbled or air of gradually increasing CO_2 concentration was bubbled over the course of development of 600 generations of the microalga, when a concentration of 1,050 ppm was reached and maintained throughout the development of 400 more algal generations. They grew each of these sets of plants (low-CO_2-adapted and high-CO_2-adapted) for a short period of time at both 430 and 1,050 ppm CO_2 and determined their steady-state CO_2 uptake rates.

For the algae whose atmospheric CO_2 concentration had been continuously maintained at 430 ppm,

Collins *et al.* report abruptly increasing it to a value of 1,050 ppm led to a 143% increase in steady-state CO_2 uptake rate. For the algae that had experienced the gradual CO_2 increase from 430 to 1,050 ppm, there was a 550% increase in CO_2 uptake rate when the rate in the 1,050-ppm air was compared to the rate that prevailed when the air's CO_2 concentration was abruptly lowered to 430 ppm. For the algae experiencing the most realistic scenario—gradually going from a state of continuous 430-ppm CO_2 exposure to one of 1,050 ppm exposure over a period of 600 generations and then maintaining the higher CO_2 level for a further 400 generations, the increase in steady-state CO_2 uptake rate due to the long-term 620-ppm increase in atmospheric CO_2 concentration was a more modest 50%, which roughly translates to a 25% increase in growth for the more typical 300 ppm increase in atmospheric CO_2 concentration employed in numerous CO_2 enrichment studies of terrestrial plants.

If the results obtained by Collins *et al.* for the freshwater *Chlamydomonas reinhardtii* are typical of what to expect of marine microalgae—which Field *et al.* suggest may provide nearly half of the primary production of the planet—the totality of Earth's plant life may provide a significant brake upon the rate at which the air's CO_2 content may increase in the future, as well as the ultimate level to which it may rise. Collins *et al.* provide a rough indication of just how powerful this phenomenon may be when they note, "mathematical simulations have estimated that pre-industrial levels of CO_2 would have been as high as 460 ppm" without the operation of the well-known "biological pump" (Sarmiento and Toggweiler, 1984) by which dying phytoplankton sink carbon into deep ocean sediments, "whereas pre-industrial atmospheric CO_2 levels were [actually] around 280 ppm (Etheridge *et al.*, 1996)," or 180 ppm less.

Logothetis *et al.* (2004) note "the function and structure of the photosynthetic apparatus of many algal species resembles that of higher plants (Plumley and Smidt, 1984; Brown, 1988; Plumley *et al.*, 1993)," and "unicellular green algae demonstrate responses to increased CO_2 similar to those of higher plants in terms of biomass increases (Muller *et al.*, 1993)." Noting "little is known about the changes to their photosynthetic apparatus during exposure to high CO_2," they grew batches of the unicellular green alga *Scenedesmus obliquus* (wild type strain D3) autotrophically in liquid culture medium for several days in a temperature-controlled water bath of 30°C at low (55 µmol m^{-2} s^{-1}) and high (235 µmol m^{-2} s^{-1}) light intensity while continuously aerating the water with air of either 300 or 100,000 ppm CO_2. Exposure to the latter high CO_2 concentration produces a "reorganization of the photosynthetic apparatus" and "leads to enhanced photosynthetic rates, which ... leads to an immense increase of biomass." After five days under low light conditions, the CO_2-induced increase in biomass was approximately 300%, and under high light conditions it was approximately 600%.

Hargrave et al. (2009) "used free air CO_2 enrichment to compare effects of eCO_2 (i.e., double ambient ~ 720 ppm) relative to ambient CO_2 (aCO_2 ~ 360 ppm) on several ecosystem properties and functions in large, outdoor, experimental mesocosms that mimicked shallow sand-bottom prairie streams." They found the primary productivity of benthic algae inhabiting the streams "was about 1.6, 1.9, 2.5, and 1.3 times greater in the eCO_2 treatment on days 30, 45, 60, and 75, respectively." The carbon/phosphorus (C/P) ratio of the algae was on average 2 and 1.5 times greater in the eCO_2 treatment than in the aCO_2 treatment on days 45 and 90, respectively, implying a reduced availability of phosphorus, which would make the algae less nutritious and, therefore, less beneficial for its consumers.

However, the researchers observed eCO_2 "had positive effects on benthic invertebrates, significantly increasing chironomid density, biomass, and average size." Hargrave et al. state "chironomid density was about 3, 5, and 2.5 times greater in the eCO_2 treatment than in the aCO_2 treatment on days 30, 60, and 90, respectively," "biomass was about 4, 3, and 3 times greater in the eCO_2 treatment than in the aCO_2 treatment on days 30, 60, and 90, respectively," and "individual mass was about two times greater on days 30 and 60." Thus, "contrary to the dominating hypotheses in the literature," Hargrave et al. conclude "eCO_2 might have positive, bottom-up effects on secondary production in some stream food webs." They state their experimental findings and "the large literature from terrestrial and marine ecosystems suggests that future [i.e., higher] atmospheric CO_2 concentrations are likely to have broad reaching effects on autotrophs and consumers across terrestrial and aquatic biomes."

Joint et al. (2011) write "marine and freshwater assemblages have always experienced variable pH conditions," noting "phytoplankton blooms can rapidly reduce pCO_2, with a concomitant increase in pH," which subsequently declines as the blooms die out, demonstrating "pH is naturally variable and that marine organisms—particularly microbes—must already be capable of adapting to rapid and some-times large changes in pH." They note "oceanic pH can change by up to 0.06 pH unit during the year even in the oligotrophic Central Pacific, which does not experience the dramatic phytoplankton blooms of temperate oceans."

In the case of freshwater ecosystems, Joint et al. report, "Maberly (1996) showed that diel variations in a lake can be as much as 2–3 pH units," and "Talling (2006) showed that in some English lakes, pH could change by >2.5 pH units over a depth of only 14 m." They note, "phytoplankton, bacteria, archaea and metazoans are all present in lakes, and appear to be able to accommodate large daily and seasonal changes in pH."

Noting the "the impacts of elevated atmospheric CO_2 on freshwater habitats are still poorly understood," Wu et al. (2012) isolated specimens of the freshwater N_2-fixing cyanobacterium Cylindrospermopsis raciborskii from a pond near Dianchi Lake in Kunming (China). They cultured them semi-continuously for 18 days at low and high inorganic phosphorus (Pi) levels (0.022 μM and 22 μM, respectively) in contact with air of either 380 or 1,000 ppm CO_2, while measuring several important physiological functions of the cyanobacterium.

In the case of light-saturated net photosynthesis, the 620-ppm increase in the air's CO_2 content resulted in 37% and 74% increases in the low and high Pi treatments, respectively. The CO_2 increase resulted in 26% and 23% increases in biomass in the low and high Pi treatments, respectively. And the CO_2 increase resulted in 36% and 14% increases in nitrogen fixation in the low and high Pi treatments, respectively. Wu et al. say the cyanobacterial growth increase they observed "confirms previous studies with other algae (Burkhardt and Riebesell, 1997; Burkhardt et al., 1999; Clark and Flynn, 2000; Kim et al., 2006; Posselt et al., 2009; Kranz et al., 2010)," as well as the finding of Chinnasamy et al. (2009) that "the nitrogenase activity of Anabaena fertilissima increased with increasing levels of CO_2."

Prosser et al. (2012) write, "harmful algal blooms of Prymnesium parvum are global phenomena occur-ring in marine, estuarine and inland ecosystems," citing Moestrup (1994), Edvardsen and Paasche (1998), and Lundholm and Moestrup (2006). They note P. parvum, commonly known as "golden algae" or "Texas tide," is "a mixotrophic flagellated hapto-phyte known to produce toxins that may severely impact aquatic organisms," citing Brooks et al. (2010). Prosser et al. evaluated "whether pH influences P. parvum bloom development and ambient toxicity" by manipulating pH levels (7, 7.5,

8.5) of *in situ* experimental enclosures during 21-day pre-bloom development experiments in Lake Granbury, Texas (USA).

The 10 U.S. researchers report neutral pH levels preempted *P. parvum* bloom development, as "population densities never reached bloom proportions and no ambient toxicity to fish or cladocerans resulted." They found "higher pH (8.5) allowed bloom formation to occur" and "resulted in ambient toxicity," whereas at the other end of the pH spectrum, "reducing pH to 7 and 7.5 did not adversely affect phytoplankton or zooplankton biomass."

The results of the studies reviewed above are encouraging, suggesting the growth and productivity of freshwater algae may be enhanced as the air's CO_2 concentration rises and the pH levels of freshwater lakes, rivers, and streams decline, while also making it more difficult for blooms of some harmful algae to occur.

References

Andersen, T. and Andersen, F.O. 2006. Effects of CO_2 concentration on growth of filamentous algae and *Littorella uniflora* in a Danish softwater lake. *Aquatic Botany* **84**: 267–271.

Brooks, B.W., James, S.V., Valenti, J.T.W., Urena-Boeck, F., Serrano, C., Berninger, J.P., Schwierzke, L., Mydlarz, L.D., Grover, J.P., and Roelke, D.L. 2010. Comparative toxicity of Prymnesium parvum in inland waters. *Journal of the American Water Resources Association* **46**: 45–62.

Brown, J.S. 1988. Photosynthetic pigment organization in diatoms (Bacillariophyceae). *Journal of Phycology* **24**: 96–102.

Burkhardt, S. and Riebesell, U. 1997. CO_2 availability affects elemental composition (C:N:P) of the marine diatom *Skeletonema costatum*. *Marine Ecology Progress Series* **155**: 67–76.

Burkhardt, S., Riebesell, U., and Zondervan, I. 1999. Effects of growth rate, CO_2 concentration, and cell size on the stable carbon isotope fractions in marine phytoplankton. *Geochimica et Cosmochimica Acta* **63**: 3729–3741.

Chinnasamy, S., Ramakrishnan, B., Bhatnagar, A., Goyal, S.K., and Das, K.C. 2009. Carbon and nitrogen fixation by *Anabaena fertilissima* under elevated CO_2 and temperature. *Journal of Freshwater Ecology* **24**: 587–596.

Clark, D.R. and Flynn, K.J. 2000. The relationship between the dissolved inorganic carbon concentration and growth rate in marine phytoplankton. *Proceedings of the Royal Society B: Biological Sciences* **267**: 953–959.

Collins, S., Sultemeyer, D., and Bell, G. 2006. Changes in C uptake in populations of *Chlamydomonas reinhardtii* selected at high CO_2. P*lant, Cell and Environment* **29**: 1812–1819.

Edvardsen, B. and Paasche, E. 1998. Bloom dynamics and physiology of Prymnesium and Chrysochromulina. *NATO ASI Series* **41**: 193–208.

Etheridge, D.M., Steele, L.P., Langerfelds, R.L., Francey, R.J., Barnola, J.-M., and Morgan, V.I. 1996. Natural and anthropogenic changes in atmospheric CO_2 over the last 1000 years from air in Antarctic ice and firn CO_2. *Journal of Geophysical Research* **101**: 4115–4128.

Hargrave, C.W., Gary, K.P., and Rosado, S.K. 2009. Potential effects of elevated atmospheric carbon dioxide on benthic autotrophs and consumers in stream ecosystems: a test using experimental stream mesocosms. *Global Change Biology* **15**: 2779–2790.

Joint, I., Doney, S.C., and Karl, D.M. 2011. Will ocean acidification affect marine microbes? *The ISME Journal* **5**: 1–7.

Kim, J.-M., Lee, K., Shin, K., Kang, J.-H., Lee, H.-W., Kim, M., Jang, P.-G., and Jang, M.C. 2006. The effect of seawater CO_2 concentration on growth of a natural phytoplankton assemblage in a controlled mesocosm experiment. *Limnology and Oceanography* **51**: 1629–1636.

Kranz, S.A., Levitan, O., Richter, K.-U., Prasil, O., Berman-Frank, I., and Rost, B. 2010. Combined effects of CO_2 and light on the N_2-fixing cyanobacterium *Trichodesmium* IMS101: physiological responses. *Plant Physiology* **154**: 334–345.

Logothetis, K., Dakanali, S., Ioannidis, N., and Kotzabasis, K. 2004. The impact of high CO_2 concentrations on the structure and function of the photosynthetic apparatus and the role of polyamines. *Journal of Plant Physiology* **161**: 715–724.

Lundholm, N. and Moestrup, O. 2006. The biogeography of harmful algae. In: Graneli, E. and Turner, J.T. (Eds.) *Ecology of Harmful Algae*. Springer, Heidelberg, Germany, pp. 23–35.

Maberly, S.C. 1996. Diel, episodic and seasonal changes in pH and concentrations of inorganic carbon in a productive lake. *Freshwater Biology* **35**: 579–598.

Moestrup, O. 1994. Economic aspects: 'blooms', nuisance species, and toxins. *Systematics Association* **51**: 265–285.

Muller, C., Reuter, W., and Wehrmeyer, W. 1993. Adaptation of the photosynthetic apparatus of *Anacystis nidulans* to irradiance and CO_2-concentration. *Botanica Acta* **106**: 480–487.

Plumley, F.G., Marinson, T.A., Herrin, D.L. Ideuchi, M., and Schmidt, G.W. 1993. Structural relationships of the photosystem I and photosystem II chlorophyll a/b and a/c light-harvesting apoproteins of plants and algae. *Photochemistry and Photobiology* **57**: 143–151.

Plumley, F.G. and Smidt, G.W. 1984. Immunochemical characterization of families of light-harvesting pigment-protein complexes in several groups of algae. *Journal of Phycology* **20**: 10.

Posselt, A.J., Burford, M.A., and Shaw, G. 2009. Pulses of phosphate promote dominance of the toxic cyanophyte *Cylindrospermopsis raciborskii* in a subtropical water reservoir. *Journal of Phycology* **45**: 540–546.

Prosser, K.N., Valenti Jr., T.W., Hayden, N.J., Neisch, M.T., Hewitt, N.C., Umphres, G.D., Gable, G.M., Grover, J.P., Roelke, D.L., and Brooks, B.W. 2012. Low pH preempts bloom development of a toxic haptophyte. *Harmful Algae* **20**: 156–164.

Sarmiento, J.L. and Toggweiler, J.R. 1984. A new model for the oceans in determining atmospheric $p\mathrm{CO_2}$. *Nature* **308**: 621–624.

Schippers, P., Lurling, M., and Scheffer, M. 2004a. Increase of atmospheric CO_2 promotes phytoplankton productivity. *Ecology Letters* **7**: 446–451.

Schippers, P., Vermaat, J.E., de Klein, J., and Mooij, W.M. 2004b. The effect of atmospheric carbon dioxide elevation on plant growth in freshwater ecosystems. *Ecosystems* **7**: 63–74.

Talling, J.F. 2006. Interrelated seasonal shifts in acid-base and oxidation-reduction systems that determine chemical stratification in three dissimilar English lake basins. *Hydrobiologia* **568**: 275–286.

Wu, Z., Zeng, B., Li, R., and Song, L. 2012. Combined effects of carbon and phosphorus levels on the invasive cyanobacterium, *Cylindrospermopsis raciborskii*. *Phycologia* **51**: 144–150.

Xia, J. and Gao, K. 2003. Effects of doubled atmospheric CO_2 concentration on the photosynthesis and growth of *Chlorella pyrenoidosa* cultured at varied levels of light. *Fisheries Science* **69**: 767–771.

6.4.2 Macrophytes

The studies reviewed in this section examine what scientists have learned about potential impacts of lower freshwater pH levels on macrophytes aquatic plants. The key findings are presented in the bullet points below, followed by an expanded discussion of those findings. (Citations for passages in quotation marks in the bullet points are included in the main body of the section.)

- The ongoing rise in the air's CO_2 content will likely induce significant positive impacts on most freshwater macrophytes, including submersed, floating, and emergent species.

- The CO_2-induced growth enhancement of Corkscrew vallisneria (*Vallisneria tortifolia*) has been observed to increase linearly out to CO_2 concentrations 10 times the ambient value.

- Total biomass accumulation of *Vallisneria spinulosa* plants grown at an elevated CO_2 concentration of 1,000 ppm was "2.3 times that of plants grown in ambient CO_2, with biomass of leaves, roots, and rhizomes increasing by 106%, 183%, and 67%, respectively."

- A tenfold increase in aquatic CO_2 concentration enhanced the biomass production of *Littorella uniflora* by 78% across an entire growing season.

- A 300 ppm increase in CO_2 produced a 3.7-fold increase in total dry matter production in the water lily *Nymphaea marliac*.

- In a CO_2 enrichment study of the common water fern *Azolla pinnata*, "the debilitating effects of high temperatures were [found to be] reduced: in one case to a much less severe negative growth rate, in another case to merely a short period of zero growth rate, and in a third case to no discernible ill effects whatsoever—in spite of the fact that the ambient treatment plants in this instance all died."

- Elevated CO_2 and temperature—both singly and in combination—positively impacted root growth of water horsetail (*Equisetum fluviatile*).

Idso (1997) grew specimens of corkscrew vallisneria (*Vallisneria tortifolia*) for several multiweek periods in several 10- and 29-gallon glass tanks (containing 10-cm bottom-layers of common aquarium gravel) filled with tap water maintained within 0.5°C of either 18.2°C or 24.5°C. He maintained the semi-sealed air spaces above these "poor man's biospheres," as he named them, at a number of CO_2 concentrations. Upon harvesting the plants at the end of the study, he found the CO_2-induced growth enhancement was linear, and this linear relationship extended to the highest atmospheric CO_2 concentration studied: 2,100 ppm. In addition, he found the CO_2-induced growth increase of the plants in the higher of the two water temperature treatments (a 128% increase in going from an atmospheric CO_2 concentration of 365 ppm to one of 2,100 ppm) was 3.5 times greater than that of the plants in the lower water temperature treatment. Idso reports Titus *et al.* (1990), who studied the closely related *Vallisneria americana*, "observed that the biomass of their experimental plants also rose linearly with the CO_2 content of the air above the water within which they grew, and that [it] did so from the value of the [then] current global mean (365 ppm) to a concentration fully ten times larger."

Yan *et al.* (2006) collected turions of *Vallisneria spinulosa* from Liangzi Lake, Hubei Province (China) and planted them in tanks containing 15-cm-deep layers of fertile lake sediments, topped with 40 cm of lake water, placed in two glasshouses—one maintained at the ambient atmospheric CO_2 concentration of 390 ppm and the other at an elevated concentration of 1,000 ppm. They allowed the plants to grow for 120 days, harvested them, and determined the dry weights of their various organs. They found the "total biomass accumulation of plants grown in the elevated CO_2 was 2.3 times that of plants grown in ambient CO_2, with biomass of leaves, roots, and rhizomes increasing by 106%, 183%, and 67%, respectively." They report, "turion biomass increased 4.5-fold," because "the mean turion numbers per ramet and mean biomass per turion in elevated CO_2 were 1.7–4.3 and 1.9–3.4 times those in ambient CO_2."

Andersen *et al.* (2006) studied small, slow-growing evergreen perennials called isoetids that live submersed along the shores of numerous freshwater lakes. They obtained specimens of *Littorella uniflora* from sediment cores removed from Lake Hampen, Denmark, which they grew in 75-liter tanks with 10-cm overburdens of filtered lake water for 53 days. They measured various plant, water, and sediment properties throughout the experiment's duration, and then the researchers destructively harvested the plants and measured their biomass. Throughout this period, half of the tanks had ambient air bubbled through their waters, while the other half were similarly exposed to a mixture of ambient air and pure CO_2 that produced a tenfold increase in the air's CO_2 concentration. This ultra-CO_2-enrichment led to a 30% increase in plant biomass and "higher O_2 release to the sediment which is important for the cycling and retention of nutrients in sediments of oligotrophic softwater lakes." When the ultra-CO_2-enrichment was maintained for an entire growing season (May–November), Andersen and Andersen (2006a) report the tenfold increase in aquatic CO_2 concentration

enhanced the biomass production of *Littorella uniflora* by 78%.

Andersen and Andersen (2006b) propagated *Littorella uniflora* under sterile conditions in the absence of symbiotic arbuscular mycorrhizal fungi (AMF), after which they re-infected half of the plants with AMF and allowed both groups to grow for 60 days in water of either high (150 µM) or low (ambient, about 15 µM) CO_2 concentration in conditions where concentrations of NO_3- and PO^3_4- were low enough to limit plant growth. Under this experimental setup, the authors report, "both in treatments with and without AMF, high CO_2 concentration resulted in a significantly higher total biomass of *L. uniflora*, and the same was observed for both shoots and roots," although "the biomass of roots increased more than the biomass of shoots." They report, "in treatments without AMF, increasing the CO_2 concentration 10 times resulted in a change from a slightly negative growth to a twofold increase in biomass over the 60-day period," and "in treatments with AMF, the increase in CO_2 concentration resulted in a fourfold increase in biomass."

The researchers' work also demonstrated "*L. uniflora's* symbiosis with mycorrhiza improved the retention of N and P in the plants at very low nutrient concentrations in the water." Consequently, as they observed "hyphal infection increased fivefold under the raised CO_2 concentration," it is evident elevated aquatic CO_2 concentrations may also help isoetids by enhancing the magnitude and stability of their AMF symbiosis, which helps them retain vital nutrients.

Idso *et al.* (1990) studied an "in-between" type of plant—water lily (*Nymphaea marliac*)—which has submersed roots and rhizomes anchored in water-body sediments but also has floating leaves on the surface of the water and emergent flowers that protrude above the water surface. The water lilies were grown for two consecutive years in sunken metal stock tanks located out-of-doors at Phoenix, Arizona (USA) and enclosed within clear-plastic-wall open-top chambers through which air of either 350 or 650 ppm CO_2 was continuously circulated. In addition to the leaves of the plants being larger in the CO_2-enriched treatment, there were 75% more of them than in the ambient-air tanks at the conclusion of the initial five-month-long growing season, the scientists report. Each of the plants in the high-CO_2 tanks also produced twice as many flowers as the plants growing in ambient air, and the flowers that blossomed in the CO_2-enriched air were more substantial than those that bloomed in the air of ambient CO_2 concentration—they had more petals, the petals were longer, and they had a greater percent dry matter content, so the flowers weighed on average about 50% more than those in the ambient-air treatment. In addition, the stems that supported the flowers were slightly longer in the CO_2-enriched tanks, and the percent dry matter contents of both the flower and leaf stems were greater, so the total dry matter in the flower and leaf stems in the CO_2-enriched tanks exceeded that of the flower and leaf stems in the ambient-air tanks by approximately 60%.

There were also noticeable differences just above the surface of the soil that covered the bottoms of the tanks. Plants in the CO_2-enriched tanks had more and bigger basal rosette leaves, which were attached to longer stems of greater percent dry matter content, which led to the total biomass of these portions of the plants being 2.9 times greater than the total biomass of the corresponding portions of the plants in the ambient-air tanks. In addition, plants in the CO_2-enriched tanks had more than twice as many unopened basal rosette leaves.

The greatest differences of all, however, were within the soil that covered the bottoms of the stock tanks. When half of the plants were harvested at the conclusion of the first growing season, the number of new rhizomes produced over that period was 2.4 times greater in the CO_2-enriched tanks than in the ambient-air tanks, and the number of major roots produced there was 3.2 times greater. The percent dry matter contents of the new roots and rhizomes were also greater in the CO_2-enriched tanks. Overall, the total dry matter production within the submerged soils of the water lily ecosystems was 4.3 times greater in the CO_2-enriched tanks than in the ambient-air tanks, and the total dry matter production of all plant parts—those in the submerged soil, those in the free water, and those in the air above—was 3.7 times greater in the high-CO_2 enclosures.

Over the second growing season, the growth enhancement in the high-CO_2 tanks was somewhat less, but the plants in those tanks were so far ahead of the plants in the ambient-air tanks that in their first five months of growth they produced what it took the plants in the ambient-air tanks fully 21 months to produce.

Idso (1997) focused on an exclusively floating freshwater macrophyte, growing many batches of the common water fern (*Azolla pinnata*) over a wide range of atmospheric CO_2 concentrations at two water temperatures (18.2°C and 24.5°C) for periods of several weeks. A 900 ppm increase in the CO_2 concentration of the air above the tanks led to a 19% increase in the biomass production of the plants floating in the cooler water, but a 66% biomass increase in the plants floating in the warmer water.

In another study of *Azolla pinnata*, Idso *et al.* (1989) conducted three separate two- to three-month experiments in which they grew batches of the floating fern out-of-doors in adequately fertilized water contained in sunken metal stock tanks located within clear-plastic-wall open-top chambers continuously maintained at atmospheric CO_2 concentrations of either 340 or 640 ppm. At weekly intervals, the researchers briefly removed the plants from the water and weighed them, and they measured their photosynthetic rates at hourly intervals from dawn to dusk on selected cloudless days. They found the photosynthetic and growth rates of the plants growing in ambient air "first decreased, then stagnated, and finally became negative when mean air temperature rose above 30°C." In the high CO_2 treatment, they found "the debilitating effects of high temperatures were reduced: in one case to a much less severe negative growth rate, in another case to merely a short period of zero growth rate, and in a third case to no discernible ill effects whatsoever—in spite of the fact that the ambient treatment plants in this instance all died."

Ojala *et al.* (2002) studied an emergent freshwater macrophyte, growing water horsetail (*Equisetum fluviatile*) plants at ambient and double-ambient atmospheric CO_2 concentrations and ambient and ambient + 3°C air temperatures for three years, although the plants were subjected to the double-ambient CO_2 condition only for approximately five months of each year. The increase in air temperature boosted maximum shoot biomass by 60%, but the elevated CO_2 had no effect on this aspect of plant growth. Elevated CO_2 and temperature—both singly and in combination—positively impacted root growth, which was enhanced by 10, 15, and 25% by elevated air temperature, CO_2, and the two factors together, respectively.

The experimental findings discussed here indicate the ongoing rise in the air's CO_2 content likely will have significant positive impacts on most freshwater macrophytes, including submersed, floating, and emergent species.

References

Andersen, F.O. and Andersen, T. 2006b. Effects of arbuscular mycorrhizae on biomass and nutrients in the aquatic plant *Littorella uniflora*. *Freshwater Biology* **51**: 1623–1633.

Andersen, T. and Andersen, F.O. 2006a. Effects of CO_2 concentration on growth of filamentous algae and *Littorella uniflora* in a Danish softwater lake. *Aquatic Botany* **84**: 267–271.

Andersen, T., Andersen, F.O., and Pedersen, O. 2006. Increased CO_2 in the water around *Littorella uniflora* raises the sediment O_2 concentration. *Aquatic Botany* **84**: 294–300.

Idso, S.B. 1997. The Poor Man's Biosphere, including simple techniques for conducting CO_2 enrichment and depletion experiments on aquatic and terrestrial plants. *Environmental and Experimental Botany* **38**: 15–38.

Idso, S.B., Allen, S.G., Anderson, M.G., and Kimball, B.A. 1989. Atmospheric CO_2 enrichment enhances survival of Azolla at high temperatures. *Environmental and Experimental Botany* **29**: 337–341.

Idso, S.B., Allen, S.G., and Kimball, B.A. 1990. Growth response of water lily to atmospheric CO_2 enrichment. *Aquatic Botany* **37**: 87–92.

Ojala, A., Kankaala, P., and Tulonen, T. 2002. Growth response of *Equisetum fluviatile* to elevated CO_2 and temperature. *Environmental and Experimental Botany* **47**: 157–171.

Titus, J.E., Feldman, R.S., and Grise, D. 1990. Submersed macrophyte growth at low pH. I. CO_2 enrichment effects with fertile sediment. *Oecologia* **84**: 307–313.

Yan, X., Yu, D., and Li, Y.-K. 2006. The effects of elevated CO_2 on clonal growth and nutrient content of submerged plant *Vallisneria spinulosa*. *Chemosphere* **62**: 595–601.

6.5 Simultaneous Ocean Warming and "Acidification"

6.5.1 Effects on Marine Plants

The studies reviewed in this section examine what scientists have learned about potential impacts of rising ocean temperatures and lower ocean pH levels on various types of marine phytoplankton and macroalgae. The key findings, which challenge the alarming and negative projections of IPCC, are presented in the bullet points below, followed by an expanded discussion of those findings. (Citations for passages in quotation marks in the bullet points are included in the main body of the section.)

- Strains of one phytoplankton species, and even of a single population, can yield responses opposite to changes in temperature and CO_2, which can lead to contrasting predictions about the future.

- Laboratory experiments suggest increases in the air's temperature and CO_2 content may improve the productivity of two dominating filamentous cyanobacteria species of the Baltic Sea.

- Future ocean warming and acidification will significantly increase the biological extraction of nitrogen and carbon dioxide from the atmosphere by diazotrophic cyanobacteria.

- Atmospheric CO_2 enrichment and sea-surface warming likely will have a large positive influence on the growth of *Emiliania huxleyi*, based on findings of laboratory studies.

- Consistent with findings of laboratory experiments, over the past 220 years of warming and lower ocean pH levels , there has been a 40% increase in average *E. huxleyi* coccolith mass in the subpolar North Atlantic Ocean, based on analyses of real-world sediment-core data.

- Sediment cores taken from the Santa Barbara Basin on the North American Pacific margin indicate an approximate 33% increase in mean coccolith weight over the 87-year period 1917–2004.

- Modern *Coccolithus* populations in the Southern Ocean are, on average, more heavily calcified than their fossil counterparts from the Last Glacial Maximum (21.6–19.9 ka), the Holocene (4.2–3.1 ka), and the Transition between the two periods (16.2–15.6 ka).

- A literature review of experiments conducted on more than 100 marine macroalgae (macro-autotrophs) species finds "photosynthetic and growth rates of marine macro-autotrophs are likely to increase under elevated CO_2 similar to terrestrial C$_3$ species."

Fiorini *et al.* (2011) note coccolithophores "are considered to be the most productive calcifying organisms on the planet," and "they play a crucial role in the marine carbon cycle through calcification and photosynthetic carbon production (Rost and Riebesell, 2004)." They also note coccolithophores "contribute significantly to the flux of organic matter from the sea surface to deep waters and sediments

(Klaas and Archer, 2002)" and are "responsible for about half of the global surface ocean calcification."

Fiorini *et al.* (2011) examined the effects of the pCO_2 and temperature levels projected for the end of this century on photosynthesis, growth, and calcification during both life stages (haploid and diploid) of strain AC418 of the coccolithophore *Syracosphaera pulchra*, via a series of culture studies conducted in the laboratory, where they focused on both particulate inorganic carbon (PIC) and particulate organic carbon (POC). The three researchers report "neither the rate of calcification (production of particulate inorganic carbon) nor the PIC:POC ratio were significantly affected by elevated pCO_2, temperature or their interaction." They further state, "our results confirm that the expected 3°C increase in the present seawater temperature will not strongly affect the physiology of this eurythermal species" and "the effect of an elevated pCO_2 in seawater will not be significant on calcification or on the PIC:POC ratio in either life stage."

Feng *et al.* (2008) grew *Emiliania huxleyi*, which they isolated from the Sargasso Sea, by semi-continuous culture methods at two light intensities (low 50 and high 400 µmol photons/m²/sec), two temperatures (low 20 and high 24°C), and two CO_2 concentrations (low 375 and high 750 ppm). They found in the low-light environment, the chlorophyll *a*-normalized photosynthetic rates of the cocco-lithophores in all four temperature/CO_2 treatments attained maximum values at an irradiance of approximately 200 µmol photons/m²/sec. The maximum photosynthetic rate was lowest in the low-temperature, low-CO_2 (ambient) treatment, but was significantly increased by elevated temperature alone (by 55%) and by elevated CO_2 alone (by 95%). In the high-temperature, high-CO_2 (greenhouse) treatment the maximum photosynthetic rate was increased by 150% relative to the ambient treatment.

In the high-light environment, the chlorophyll *a*-normalized photosynthetic rates did not max out below the maximum irradiance tested (900 µmol photons/m²/sec) for any but the ambient treatment. Consequently, the equations fit to the data of the other treatments were extrapolated to their respective photosynthetic maxima, which produced corresponding maximum photosynthetic rate increases of 58%, 67%, and 92% for the elevated temperature alone, elevated CO_2 alone, and greenhouse treatments, respectively.

In the high-light greenhouse treatment characteristic of the expected future condition of Earth, the maximum photosynthetic rate was 178% greater than

in the low-light ambient treatment characteristic of the present. The seven researchers say their results indicate "future trends of CO_2 enrichment, sea-surface warming and exposure to higher mean irradiances from intensified [surface water] stratification will have a large influence on the growth of *Emiliania huxleyi*."

Another important group of phytoplankton are diatoms, which Sobrino *et al.* (2008) say "are responsible for almost 40% of the ocean primary productivity (Nelson *et al.*, 1995)." According to Kremp *et al.* (2012), "most of the laboratory studies investigating the effects of climate stressors on phytoplankton have been performed on single strains," and "the significant effects often found in such experiments are contrasted by the general lack of clear responses in natural populations," citing Engel *et al.* (2008). They hypothesize the "contradictory responses to changed climate conditions sometimes observed within the same species might be partly attributable to strain variability between or within populations," citing Langer *et al.* (2009) and noting these observations emphasize "the need to consider variability in studies aiming to understand the effects of climate change on phytoplankton species."

Kremp *et al.* studied "the effects of increased temperature and CO_2 availability, as predicted consequences of global change, on 16 genetically different isolates of the diatom *Skeletonema marinoi* from the Adriatic Sea and the Skagerrak (North Sea), and on eight strains of the PST (paralytic shellfish toxin)-producing dinoflagellate *Alexandrium ostenfeldii* from the Baltic Sea." They assessed maximum growth rates of acclimated isolates grown in batch cultures for five to 10 generations in a factorial design at 20 and 24°C, and present-day and next-century atmospheric CO_2 concentrations (385 and 750 ppm), respectively. The seven scientists found strains of one species, and even of a single population, "can be impacted in very different ways by climate stressors," noting "a particularly wide response range was found in the population of *S. marinoi* from the NW Adriatic sea, where temperature and CO_2 caused positive, negative or no effect at all."

Kremp *et al.* conclude, "depending on the strain of choice," experiments using single isolates of the population they studied "could have given opposite response patterns," which likely would have led to "contrasting predictions" about the future. Therefore, they write, "responses observed in single strain experiments may not be representative" of the species or population in question, and predictions for specific species behavior under future climatic conditions must "be treated with caution."

Noting "cyanobacteria such as *Synechococcus* and *Prochlorococcus* have a major impact on the global carbon cycle and contribute up to 50% of fixed carbon in marine systems (Partensky *et al.*, 1999)," Fu *et al.* (2007) studied "how CO_2 and temperature individually and together affect the physiology of these two species under identical growth conditions." They grew stock cultures of the two picocyanobacteria in one-liter bottles of autoclaved and filtered seawater maintained at temperatures of either 20 or 24°C in equilibrium with air of either 380 or 750 ppm CO_2. The five researchers discovered the growth rate and maximum photosynthetic rate in *Synechococcus* increased about 2.3-fold and 4-fold, respectively, in the high-temperature and high-CO_2 treatment relative to ambient conditions, but they remained unchanged in *Prochlorococcus*.

Fu *et al.* say their observations "could be taken to mean that in the future, rising temperature and CO_2 would stimulate growth or photosynthesis of [the] *Synechococcus* isolate but would have much less effect on [the] Procholrococcus strain," and such a result could "potentially influence competition between particular *Synechococcus* and *Prochlorococcus* ecotypes." However, they add, "we need to be very cautious about inferring ecosystem-scale shifts in broad taxonomic groups like picocyanobacteria from studies using only two isolates." They report stimulation of algal growth rates by elevated CO_2 also has been observed by Burkhardt and Riebesell (1997), Burkhardt *et al.* (1999), Yang and Gao (2003), Beardall and Raven (2004), and Kim *et al.* (2006).

Hutchins *et al.* (2007) note *Trichodesmium* species and other diazotrophic cyanobacteria support a large fraction of the total biological productivity of Earth's tropical and subtropical seas, and they exert a significant influence on the planet's carbon cycle by supplying much of the nitrogen that enables marine phytoplankton to maintain a level of productivity that removes vast amounts of CO_2 from the atmosphere. They hypothesized that if an increase in the air's CO_2 content or its temperature led to an increase in oceanic N_2 fixation, it also could lead to the biological extraction of more CO_2 from the atmosphere and a tempering of the CO_2 greenhouse effect via this negative feedback process.

To explore this possibility, the eight researchers grew cultures of Pacific and Atlantic Ocean isolates of *Trichodesmium* ecotypes across a range of atmospheric CO_2 concentrations characteristic of Earth's past (150 ppm), its current state (380 ppm), and possible future conditions (750, 1,250, and 1,500 ppm) at two temperatures (25 and 29°C) and at sufficient and limiting phosphorus concentrations (20 and 0.2 μmol L^{-1} of phosphate, respectively), in situations where the carbonate buffer system parameters in their artificial seawater culture media were "virtually identical to those found in natural seawater across the relevant range of CO_2 values."

Hutchins *et al.* found, at atmospheric CO_2 concentrations projected for the year 2100 (750 ppm), "N_2 fixation rates of Pacific and Atlantic isolates increased 35–100%, and CO_2 fixation rates increased 15–128% relative to present day CO_2 conditions (380 ppm)." In what they call one of their "most striking results," they found "increased CO_2 enhanced N_2 and CO_2 fixation and growth rates even under severely phosphorus-limited steady-state growth conditions." They also report "neither isolate could grow at 150 ppm CO_2," but "N_2 and CO_2 fixation rates, growth rates, and nitrogen:phosophorus ratios all increased significantly between 380 and 1500 ppm," and, "in contrast, these parameters were affected only minimally or not at all by a 4°C temperature change."

Hutchins *et al.* note current global estimates of N_2 fixation by *Trichodesmium* are about 60 x 10^9 kg N yr^{-1}, and if their experimental results can be extrapolated to the world's oceans, by 2100 this amount could increase to 81–120 x 10^9 kg N yr^{-1}. "If these estimates are coupled with modeling predictions of a 27% warming-induced expansion of suitable habitat (Boyd and Doney, 2002), calculations suggest that global N_2 fixation by *Trichodesmium* alone could range from 103–152 x 10^9 kg N yr^{-1} by the end of this century," which is to be compared to recent estimates for total pelagic N_2 fixation of 100–200 x 10^9 kg N yr^{-1} (Galloway *et al.*, 2004). They also note free-living unicellular cyano-bacteria in the ocean are believed to fix at least as much nitrogen as *Trichodesmium* (Montoya *et al.*, 2004), and endosymbiotic cyanobacteria also con-tribute substantially to N_2 fixation. Hence they conclude, "if N_2 fixation rates in these groups show commensurate increases with rising CO_2, the cumulative effect on the global nitrogen cycle could be considerably larger (e.g., a doubling)." In addition, they state their results indicate "like N_2 fixation, CO_2 fixation by *Trichodesmium* should also increase dramatically in the future because of CO_2 enrichment."

Hutchins *et al.* conclude, "many of our current concepts describing the interactions between oceanic nitrogen fixation, atmospheric CO_2, nutrient biogeo-chemistry, and global climate may need re-evaluation to take into account these previously unrecognized feedback mechanisms between atmospheric composition and ocean biology."

Karlberg and Wulff (2013) investigated the ramifications of potential future increases in the air's CO_2 content on the productivity of two dominating filamentous cyanobacteria species of the Baltic Sea (*Nodularia spumigena* and a mix of *Aphanizomenon* sp.) during the summer bloom of the Baltic Proper. The pair of researchers set out to experimentally determine the response of these two species to changes in that region's environment predicted to occur in response to IPCC's business-as-usual A1FI scenario described by Meehl *et al.* (2007): a temperature increase of 4°C, an atmospheric pCO_2 increase from 380 to 960 ppm, and a reduction in salinity from 7 to 4. Working in the laboratory, Karlberg and Wulff measured numerous responses of the two species of cyanobacteria, growing both separately and together, to different combinations of these environmental changes.

The two researchers report "increased temperature, from 12 to 16°C, had a positive effect on the biovolume and photosynthetic activity of both species," and "compared when growing separately, the biovolume of each species was lower when grown together." They also note "decreased salinity, from 7 to 4, and elevated levels of pCO_2, from 380 to 960 ppm, had no effect on the biovolume, but on [the photosynthetic activity] (*Fv/Fm*) of *N. spumigena* with higher *Fv/Fm* in salinity 7." Karlberg and Wulff say their results suggest "the projected A1FI scenario might be beneficial for the two species dominating the extensive summer blooms in the Baltic Proper." They caution their results "further stress the importance of studying interactions between species." They conclude, "long-term studies together with multifactorial and mesocosm/field experiments are needed to elucidate the future impact of climate change effects on Baltic filamentous cyanobacteria."

Grelaud *et al.* (2009) investigated "the morphometry (size, weight) of selected species of the order Isochrysidales (i.e., *E. huxleyi*, *G. muellerae* and *G. oceanica*) to understand how coccolithophores' carbonate mass is influenced by recent oceanographic global changes." They analyzed sediment cores taken from "the deep center of the Santa Barbara Basin (SBB) on the North American Pacific margin in the interval from AD 1917 to 2004." They found "morphometric parameters measured on *E. Huxleyi*, *G. muellerae* and *G. oceanica* indicate increasing coccolithophore shell carbonate mass from ~1917 until 2004 concomitant with rising pCO_2 and

sea surface temperature in the region of the SBB." Specifically, they note "a >33% increase in mean coccolith weight was determined for the order Isochrysidales over 87 years from ~1917 until 2004."

The three researchers note "the last century has witnessed an increasing net influx of atmospheric carbon dioxide into the world's oceans, a rising of pCO_2 of surface waters, and under-saturation with respect to aragonite, especially along the North American Pacific margin," which was the site of their study. They note those concerned about lower ocean pH levels predicted such conditions will "result in reduced coccolithophore carbonate mass and a concomitant decrease in size and weight of coccoliths." They discovered just the opposite appears to have occurred in the real world, even in places where the predicted calcification reductions were expected to be greatest.

Iglesias-Rodriguez *et al.* (2008) grew several batch incubations of the coccolithophore species *Emiliania huxleyi* in the laboratory, bubbling air of a number of different atmospheric CO_2 concentrations through the culture medium and determining the amounts of particulate inorganic carbon (PIC) and particulate organic carbon (POC) produced by the coccolithophores within the CO_2 treatments. In addition, they determined the change in average coccolithophore mass of *Emiliania huxleyi* over the past 220 years in the real world of nature, based on data they obtained from a sediment core extracted from the subpolar North Atlantic Ocean, over which period of time temperatures increased and the air's CO_2 concentration rose by approximately 90 ppm. The 13 researchers from the United Kingdom, France, and United States observed an approximate doubling of both PIC and POC between the culture media in equilibrium with air of today's CO_2 concentration and air of 750 ppm CO_2. They report the field evidence obtained from the deep-ocean sediment core they studied "is consistent with these laboratory conclusions, indicating that over the past 220 years there has been a 40% increase in average coccolith mass."

Cubillos *et al.* (2012) set out to adapt "an existing method to estimate coccolith calcite weight using birefringence (Beaufort, 2005)," which they decided was needed "to suit the large coccoliths of *Coccolithus pelagicus*," focusing "only on the central area, which is the thickest and most robust part of the coccolith." They applied this technique "to fossil and sediment trap material from the South Tasman Rise area of the Southern Ocean," based on three sediment samples each from the Last Glacial Maximum (21.6–19.9 ka), the Holocene (4.2–3.1 ka), and the

Transition between the two periods (16.2–15.6 ka), as well as modern-day trap samples. "Most strikingly," the five researchers report, "it appears that modern *Coccolithus* populations in the Southern Ocean are, on average, more heavily calcified than their fossil counterparts," a positive and encouraging finding. Cubillos *et al.* say their work reveals "substantial non-linearity and independency of variations (plasticity) in coccolith size, shape and volumetric weight between the investigated time intervals." They say they hope to study these phenomena "in more detail" in order to "unravel what environmental conditions are related to intra-specific phenotypic variability in ancient and modern coccolithophores."

Koch *et al.* (2013) write, "although seagrasses and marine macroalgae (macro-autotrophs) play critical ecological roles in reef, lagoon, coastal and open-water ecosystems, their response to ocean acidification (OA) and climate change is not well understood." They reviewed the scientific literature on these subjects, examining "marine macro-autotroph biochemistry and physiology relevant to their response to elevated dissolved inorganic carbon (DIC), carbon dioxide (CO_2), and lower carbonate (CO_3^{2-}) and pH," and also exploring "the effects of increasing temperature under climate change and the interactions of elevated temperature and CO_2."

The four researchers determined their "literature review of >100 species revealed marine macro-autotroph photosynthesis is overwhelmingly C_3 (>=85%) with most species capable of utilizing HCO_3^-," and "most are not saturated at current ocean DIC." They conclude, "photosynthetic and growth rates of marine macro-autotrophs are likely to increase under elevated CO_2 similar to terrestrial C_3 species." In addition, as "the photosynthesis of the majority of the species examined was not saturated at the current levels of DIC in the ocean and responded to an increase in CO_2," they conclude seagrasses and many marine macroalgae have the potential to respond positively, in terms of photosynthesis and growth, under elevated ocean CO_2 and OA.

References

Beardall, J. and Raven, J.A. 2004. Potential effects of global change on microalgal photosynthesis, growth and ecology. *Phycologia* **43**: 26–40.

Beaufort, L. 2005. Weight estimates of coccoliths using the optical properties (birefringence) of calcite. *Micropaleontology* **51**: 289–297.

Boyd, P.W. and Doney, S.C. 2002. Modelling regional responses by marine pelagic ecosystems to global climate change. *Geophysical Research Letters* **29**: 10.1029/2001GL014130.

Burkhardt, S. and Riebesell, U. 1997. CO_2 availability affects elemental composition (C:N:P) of the marine diatom *Skeletonema costatum*. *Marine Ecology Progress Series* **155**: 67–76.

Burkhardt, S., Riebesell, U., and Zondervan, I. 1999. Effects of growth rate, CO_2 concentration, and cell size on the stable carbon isotope fractions in marine phytoplankton. *Geochimica et Cosmochimica Acta* **63**: 3729–3741.

Cubillos, J.C., Henderiks, J., Beaufort, L., Howard, W.R., and Hallegraeff, G.M. 2012. Reconstructing calcification in ancient coccolithophores: Individual coccolith weight and morphology of *Coccolithus pelagicus* (sensu lato). *Marine Micropaleontology* **92–93**: 29–39.

Engel, A., Schulz, K., Riebesell, U., Bellerby, R., Delille, B., and Schartau, M. 2008. Effects of CO_2 on particle size distribution and phytoplankton abundance during a mesocosm bloom experiment (PeECE II). *Biogeosciences* **5**: 509–521.

Feng, Y., Warner, M.E., Zhang, Y., Sun, J., Fu, F.-X., Rose, J.M., and Hutchins, A. 2008. Interactive effects of increased pCO_2, temperature and irradiance on the marine coccolithophore *Emiliania huxleyi* (Prymnesiophyceae). *European Journal of Phycology* **43**: 87–98.

Fiorini, S., Middelburg, J.J., and Gattuso, J.-P. 2011. Effects of elevated CO_2 partial pressure and temperature on the coccolithophore *Syracosphaera pulchra*. *Aquatic Microbial Ecology* **64**: 221–232.

Fu, F.-X., Warner, M.E., Zhang, Y., Feng, Y., and Hutchins, D.A. 2007. Effects of increased temperature and CO_2 on photosynthesis, growth, and elemental ratios in marine *Synechococcus* and *Prochlorococcus* (cyanobacteria). *Journal of Phycology* **43**: 485–496.

Galloway, J.N., Dentener, F.J., Capone, D.G., Boyer, E.W., Howarth, R.W., Seitzinger, S.P., Asner, G.P., Cleveland, C.C., Green, P.A., Holland, E.A., Karl, D.M., Michaels, A.F., Porter, J.H., Townsend, A.R., and Vöosmarty, C.J. 2004. Nitrogen cycles: past, present, and future. *Biogeochemistry* **70**: 153–226.

Grelaud, M., Schimmelmann, A., and Beaufort, L. 2009. Coccolithophore response to climate and surface hydrography in Santa Barbara Basin, California, AD 1917–2004. *Biogeosciences* **6**: 2025–2039.

Hutchins, D.A., Fu, F.-X., Zhang, Y., Warner, M.E., Feng, Y., Portune, K., Bernhardt, P.W., and Mulholland, M.R. 2007. CO_2 control of *Trichodesmium* N_2 fixation, photosynthesis, growth rates, and elemental ratios: Implications for past, present, and future ocean biogeochemistry. *Limnology and Oceanography* **52**: 1293‾1304.

Karlberg, M. and Wulff, A. 2013. Impact of temperature and species interaction on filamentous cyanobacteria may be more important than salinity and increased *p*CO$_2$ levels. *Marine Biology* **160**: 2063–2072.

Kim, J.-M., Lee, K., Shin, K., Kang, J.-H., Lee, H.-W., Kim, M., Jang, P.-G., and Jang, M.C. 2006. The effect of seawater CO$_2$ concentration on growth of a natural phytoplankton assemblage in a controlled mesocosm experiment. *Limnology and Oceanography* **51**: 1629–1636.

Klaas, C. and Archer, D.E. 2002. Association of sinking organic matter with various types of mineral ballast in the deep sea: implications for the rain ratio. *Global Biogeochemical Cycles* **16**: 10.1029/2001GB001765.

Koch, M, Bowes, G., Ross, C., and Zhang, X.-H. 2013. Climate change and ocean acidification effects on seagrasses and marine macroalgae. *Global Change Biology* **19**: 103–132.

Kremp, A., Godhe, A., Egardt, J., Dupont, S., Suikkanen, S., Casabianca, S., and Penna, A. 2012. Intraspecific variability in the response of bloom-forming marine microalgae to changed climate conditions. *Ecology and Evolution* **2**: 1195–1207.

Langer, G., Nehrke, G., Probert, I., Ly, J., and Ziveri, P. 2009. Strain-specific responses of *Emiliana huxleyi* to changing seawater carbonate chemistry. *Biogeosciences* **6**: 2637–2646.

Meehl, G.A., Stocker, T.F., Collins, W.D., Friedlingstein, P., Gaye, A.T., Gregory, J.M., Kitoh, A., Knutti, R., Murphy, J.M., Noda, A., Raper, S.C.B., Watterson, I.G., Weaver, A.J., and Zhao, Z.-C. 2007. In: Solomon, S., Qin, D., Manning, M., Chen, Z., Marquis, M., Averyt, K.B., Tignor, M., and Miller, H.L. (Eds.) *Climate Change 2007: The Physical Science Basis*. Contribution of Working Group I to the Fourth Assessment Report of the Intergovernmental Panel on Climate Change. Cambridge University Press, Cambridge, United Kingdom, pp. 747–846.

Montoya, J.P., Holl, C.M., Zehr, J.P., Hansen, A., Villareal, T.A., and Capone, D.G. 2004. High rates of N$_2$ fixation by unicellular diazotrophs in the oligotrophic Pacific Ocean. *Nature* **430**: 1027‾1032.

Nelson, D.M., Treguer, P., Brzezinski, M.A., Leynaert, A., and Queguiner, B. 1995. Production and dissolution of biogenic silica in the ocean: Revised global estimates, comparison with regional data and relationship to biogenic sedimentation. *Global Biogeochemical Cycles* **9**: 359–372.

Rost, B. and Riebesell, U. 2004. Coccolithophores and the biological pump: responses to environmental changes. In: Thierstein, H.R. and Young, J.R. (Eds.) *Coccolithophores: From Molecular Processes to Global Impact*. Springer, New York, New York, USA, p. 99–125.

Sobrino, C., Ward, M.L., and Neale, P.J. 2008. Acclimation to elevated carbon dioxide and ultraviolet radiation in the diatom *Thalassiosira pseudonana*: Effects on growth, photosynthesis, and spectral sensitivity of photoinhibition. *Limnology and Oceanography* **53**: 494–505.

Yang, Y. and Gao, K. 2003. Effects of CO$_2$ concentrations on the freshwater microalgae, *Chlamydomonas reinhardtii*, *Chlorella pyrenoidosa* and *Scenedesmus obliquus* (Chlorophyta). *Journal of Applied Phycology* **15**: 379–389.

6.5.2 Effects on Marine Animals

6.5.2.1 Corals

6.5.2.1.1 Review Papers

Few studies have investigated the interactive effects of lower ocean pH levels and rising temperature. This section examines what scientists have learned from such studies, focusing on the impacts of these variables on coral reefs as reported in review papers on the topic. The key findings, all of which challenge the alarming and negative projections of IPCC, are presented in the bullet points below, followed by an expanded discussion of those findings. (Citations for passages in quotation marks in the bullet points are included in the main body of the section.)

- "Neither climate nor sea-level nor chemical changes in the oceans can elucidate the waxing and waning of reefs" throughout their history on Earth. The "boom and bust pattern" observed through geologic time is "impossible to explain by linear responses to physicochemical changes."

- Shallow water tropical reef organisms existed throughout the entire 540 million years of the Phanerozoic, which included times when sea surface temperatures were more than 7°C higher than those of today and the air's CO$_2$ concentration was as much as 6,000 ppm higher.

- Although the Paleocene-Eocene Thermal Maximum, some 55.8 million years ago, was "characterized by rapid sea surface temperature rise and a similar order of magnitude of CO$_2$ increase as present," there is evidence "reef assemblages in at least one oceanic setting were unaffected." Other reefs also have shown "greater resilience to past rapid warming and acidification than previously thought."

- Emerging evidence indicates there is variability in the coral calcification response to lower seawater pH levels, geographical variation in bleaching susceptibility and recovery, and potential adaptation to rapid warming and declining pH, supporting "an alternative scenario in which reef degradation occurs with greater temporal and spatial heterogeneity than current projections suggest."

Kiessling (2009), from the Museum fur Naturkunde of the Leibniz Institute for Research on Evolution and Biodiversity at the Humboldt University in Berlin, reviewed the state of knowledge of the long-term effects of changes in ocean temperature and the atmosphere's CO_2 concentration on the vigor of the planet's coral reefs as of 2009. With respect to global warming, Kiessling reports, "on geologic timescales, there is little evidence for climate change affecting reefs in a linear fashion," and "changes in mean global temperature as reconstructed from stable oxygen isotopes and the distribution of non-reef climate-sensitive sediments do not correspond to changes in reef abundance or latitudinal distribution," citing some of his own analyses of the subject (Kiessling, 2001a, 2002). He also states, "reports linking reef expansions and declines to climate change fail to explain why other changes in temperature did not lead to a similar response in reefs and why the reported (fairly modest) temperature changes would have such a dramatic effect."

Regarding lower ocean pH levels, the German researcher reports, "just like temperature," it is currently receiving much attention as "a control of reef development," but "the boom and bust pattern of reefs and hyper-calcifiers is difficult to explain with inferred long-term changes in the saturation state of ocean water, at least if the major trigger is atmospheric pCO_2," because "previous analyses failed to find any significant cross-correlation between changes in pCO_2 and changes in reef attributes," citing Kiessling (2001b, 2002).

In light of these and many other observations, Kiessling concludes "neither climate nor sea-level nor chemical changes in the oceans can elucidate the waxing and waning of reefs" throughout their history on Earth, and their "boom and bust pattern" is "impossible to explain by linear responses to physico-chemical changes." Furthermore, Kiessling writes,

"ecologically complex reef systems have been around for hundreds of millions if not billions of years," and "geologic models of CO_2 concentrations in the atmosphere suggest that these were much greater during most of Earth's history than today." This further suggests something other than CO_2-induced global warming and lower ocean pH levels must have been responsible for their prior "boom and bust" pattern of behavior.

In a major review article published in *Science*, Pandolfi *et al.* (2011) summarize "the most recent evidence for past, present and predicted future responses of coral reefs to environmental change, with emphasis on rapid increases in temperature and lower ocean pH levels and their effects on reef-building corals." They note, "many physiological responses in present-day coral reefs to climate change are interpreted as consistent with the imminent disappearance of modern reefs globally because of annual mass bleaching events, carbonate dissolution and insufficient time for substantial evolutionary responses." All of these interpretations, they demonstrate, may be incorrect.

The four researchers report shallow water tropical reef organisms existed throughout the entire 540 million years of the Phanerozoic, which included times when sea surface temperatures (SSTs) were more than 7°C higher than those of today and the air's CO_2 concentration was as much as 6,000 ppm higher. As to what they call "the most recent reef crisis," they report "the Paleocene-Eocene Thermal Maximum (PETM; 55.8 million years ago), was characterized by rapid SST rise and a similar order of magnitude of CO_2 increase as present," yet there is evidence "reef assemblages in at least one oceanic setting were unaffected (Robinson, 2011)" and other reefs also have shown "greater resilience to past rapid warming and acidification than previously thought."

More recently, during the Holocene, Pandolfi *et al.* state, "evidence from high-resolution proxy records suggests that tropical SSTs had the potential to repeatedly warm over centennial to millennial time scales (Rosenthal *et al.*, 2003; Schmidt *et al.*, 2004)." In one location, they report, SSTs rose "at rates comparable to those projected for the coming century (Lea *et al.*, 2003)," yet "none of these post-Last Glacial Maximum warming episodes appear to have interrupted reef growth."

As for current coral responses to SST increases, the four scientists note "numerous characteristics of coral hosts have the potential to confer differences in bleaching susceptibility," and "these characteristics vary substantially within and among coral species

(Baird *et al.*, 2009a; Csaszar *et al.*, 2010)." They note "some coral species also harbor multiple strains of zooxanthellae, which confer differential susceptibility of their hosts to bleaching (Rowan, 2004)." They note there is also "substantial variation in reef recovery in the aftermath of bleaching events (Baker *et al.*, 2008)."

The story is much the same regarding coral responses to lower ocean pH levels. Pandolfi *et al.* note, for example, studies have shown calcification has "increased under moderately elevated partial pressure of CO_2 (Rodolfo-Metalpa *et al.*, 2010; Jury *et al.*, 2010; Reynaud *et al.*, 2003), as has also been observed for some coralline algae, crustacea and echinoderms (Ries *et al.*, 2009)." They also note sensitivity of calcification to lower ocean pH levels "appears to be reduced when (i) studies are conducted over weeks or months (Ries *et al.*, 2009; Rodolfo-Metalpa *et al.*, 2010; Marubini *et al.*, 2001; Reynaud *et al.*, 2003) as opposed to less than one day (Langdon and Atkinson, 2005; Ohde and Hossain, 2004) or (ii) corals are reared under nutritionally replete conditions by feeding or elevating inorganic nutrient concentrations (Langdon and Atkinson, 2005; Ries *et al.*, 2009)."

The four researchers write, "because bleaching-susceptible species often have faster rates of recovery from disturbances, their relative abundances will not necessarily decline" in the future. They continue, "such species could potentially increase in abundance, depending on how demographic characteristics and competitive ability are correlated with thermal toler-ance and on the response of other benthic taxa, such as algae." They further note "the shorter generation times typical of more-susceptible species (Baird *et al.*, 2009b) may also confer faster rates of evolution of bleaching thresholds, which would further facilitate maintenance of, or increases to, the relative abundance of thermally sensitive but faster-evolving species (Baskett *et al.*, 2009)."

Pandolfi *et al.* state emerging evidence for variability in the coral calcification response to lower ocean pH levels, geographical variation in bleaching susceptibility and recovery, responses to past climate change, and potential rates of adaptation to rapid warming "supports an alternative scenario in which reef degradation occurs with greater temporal and spatial heterogeneity than current projections suggest." Further noting "non-climate-related threats already confronting coral reefs are likely to reduce the capacity of coral reefs to cope with climate change," they conclude "the best and most achievable thing we can do for coral reefs currently to deal with climate change is to seek to manage them well" by reducing more direct anthropogenic impacts such as fishing, pollution, and habitat destruction, which fragment populations or decrease population sizes and reduce the potential of coral reefs to adapt to warmer, lower pH conditions.

References

Baird, A.H., Bhagooli, R., Ralph, P.J., and Takahashi, S. 2009a. Coral bleaching: the role of the host. *Trends in Ecology and Evolution* **24**: 16–20.

Baird, A.H., Guest, J.R., and Willis, B.L. 2009b. Systematic and biogeographical patterns in the reproductive biology of scleractinian corals. *Annual Review of Ecology, Evolution and Systematics* **40**: 551–571.

Baker, A.C., Glynn, P.W., and Riegl, B. 2008. Climate change and coral reef bleaching: An ecological assessment of long-term impacts, recovery trends and future outlook. *Estuarine, Coastal and Shelf Science* **80**: 435–471.

Baskett, M.L, Gaines, S.D., and Nisbet, R.M. 2009. Symbiont diversity may help coral reefs survive moderate climate change. *Ecological Applications* **19**: 3–17.

Csaszar, N.B.M., Ralph, P.J., Frankham, R., Berkelmans, R., and van Oppen, M.J.H. 2010. Estimating the potential for adaptation of corals to climate warming. *PLoS ONE* **5**: e9751.

Jury, C.P., Whitehead, R.F., and Szmant, A.M. 2010. Effects of variations in carbonate chemistry on the calcification rates of *Madracis auretenra* (= *Madracis mirabilis sensu* Wells, 1973): bicarbonate concentrations best predict calcification rates. *Global Change Biology*: 10.1111/j.1365–2486.2009.02057.x.

Kiessling, W. 2001a. Paleoclimatic significance of Phanerozoic reefs. *Geology* **29**: 751–754.

Kiessling, W. 2001b. Phanerozoic reef trends based on the Paleoreefs database. In: Stanley, G.D. (Ed.) *The History and Sedimentology of Ancient Reef Systems*. Plenum Press, New York, New York, USA, pp. 41–88.

Kiessling, W. 2002. Secular variations in the Phanerozoic reef ecosystem. In: Kiessling, W., Flugel, E., and Golonka, J. (Eds.) *Phanerozoid Reef Patterns, Volume 22*. Society of Economic and Paleontological Mineralogy, Tulsa, Oklahoma, USA, pp. 625–690.

Kiessling, W. 2009. Geologic and biologic controls on the evolution of reefs. *Annual Review of Ecological and Evolutionary Systems* **40**: 173–192.

Kiessling, W., Flugel, E., and Golonka, J. (Eds.) 2002. *Phanerozoid Reef Patterns, Volume 22*. Society of Economic and Paleontological Mineralogy, Tulsa, Oklahoma, USA, 775 pp.

Langdon, C. and Atkinson, M.J. 2005. Effect of elevated pCO$_2$ on photosynthesis and calcification of corals and interactions with seasonal change in temperature/irradiance and nutrient enrichment. *Journal of Geophysical Research* **110**: 10.1029/2004JC002576.

Lea, D.W., Dorothy K. Pak, D.K., Peterson, L.C., and Hughen, K.A. 2003. Synchroneity of tropical and high-latitude Atlantic temperatures over the last glacial termination . *Science* **301**: 1361–1364.

Marubini, F., Barnett, H., Langdon, C., and Atkinson, M.J. 2001. Dependence of calcification on light and carbonate ion concentration for the hermatypic coral *Porites compressa*. *Marine Ecology Progress Series* **220**: 153–162.

Ohde, S. and Hossain, M.M. 2004. Effect of CaCO$_3$ (aragonite) saturation state of seawater on calcification of *Porites* coral. *Geochemical Journal* **38**: 613–621.

Pandolfi, J.M., Connolly, S.R., Marshall, D.J., and Cohen, A.L. 2011. Projecting coral reef futures under global warming and ocean acidification. *Science* **333**: 418–422.

Reynaud, S., Leclercq, N., Romaine-Lioud, S., Ferrier-Pages, C., Jaubert, J., and Gattuso, J.-P. 2003. Interacting effects of CO$_2$ partial pressure and temperature on photosynthesis and calcification in a scleractinian coral. *Global Change Biology* **9**: 1660–1668.

Ries, J.B., Cohen, A.L., and McCorkle, D.C. 2009. Marine calcifiers exhibit mixed responses to CO$_2$-induced ocean acidification. *Geology* **37**: 1131–1134.

Robinson, S.A. 2011. Shallow-water carbonate record of the Paleocene-Eocene Thermal Maximum from a Pacific Ocean guyot. *Geology* **39**: 51–54.

Rodolfo-Metalpa, R., Martin, S., Ferrier-Pages, C., and Gattuso, J.-P. 2010. Response of the temperate coral *Cladocora caespitosa* to mid- and long-term exposure to pCO$_2$ and temperature levels projected for the year 2100 AD. *Biogeosciences* **7**: 289–300.

Rosenthal, Y., Oppo, D., and Linsley, B.K. 2003. The amplitude and phasing of climate change during the last deglaciation in the Sulu Sea, western equatorial Pacific. *Geophysical Research Letters* **30**: 10.1029/2002GL016612.

Rowan, R. 2004. Coral bleaching: Thermal adaptation in reef coral symbionts. *Nature* **430**: 10.1038/430742a.

Schmidt, M.W., Spero, H.J., and Lea, D.W. 2004. Links between salinity variation in the Caribbean and North Atlantic thermohaline circulation. *Nature* **428**: 160–162.

6.5.2.1.2 A Model-based Study

This section reviews one model-based study that focuses on the impact of lower ocean pH levels in combination with higher temperatures on coral reefs.

Couce *et al.* (2013) note "there is concern that the growing frequency and severity of mass bleaching episodes may lead to species composition shifts and functional collapse in coral reefs in the near future." They also note global warming "has the potential to improve currently marginal environmental conditions and extend the range of tropical coral reefs into higher latitudes," as is "demonstrated in the fossil record in response to warmer geological periods (e.g., Lighty *et al.*, 1978; Veron, 1992; Precht and Aronson, 2004; Greenstein and Pandolfi, 2008; Woodroffe *et al.*, 2010; Kiessling *et al.*, 2012)." Less is known about the interacting effects of global warming and lower ocean pH levels, although these phenomena are projected to occur concurrently.

Couce *et al.* employed "a suite of statistical models based on the environmental factors thought to be limiting to the present equilibrium distribution of shallow-water coral reefs, perturbing them with Earth System Model projected future sea surface temperatures and aragonite saturation changes (the simulations used in Turley *et al.*, 2010)," while considering "a range of potential future CO$_2$ emissions scenarios" but focusing on "the consequences of the 'A2' scenario (characterized by regionally oriented economic development and high population growth, expecting ca. 850 ppm CO$_2$ by 2100)."

The three UK researchers write of their model-based results, "contrary to expectations, the combined impact of ocean surface temperature rise and acidification leads to little, if any, degradation in future habitat suitability across much of the Atlantic and areas currently considered 'marginal' for tropical corals, such as the eastern Equatorial Pacific." They note, "these results are consistent with fossil evidence of range expansions during past warm periods." Such findings, Couce *et al.* conclude, "present important implications for future coral reef management, as they suggest that more emphasis should be placed on conservation efforts on marginal reefs as they are not necessarily a 'lost cause'."

References

Couce, E., Ridgwell, A., and Hendy, E.J. 2013. Future habitat suitability for coral reef ecosystems under global warming and ocean acidification. *Global Change Biology* **19**: 3592–3606.

Greenstein, B.J. and Pandolfi, J.M. 2008. Escaping the heat: range shifts of reef coral taxa in costal Western Australia. *Global Change Biology* **14**: 513–528.

Kiessling, W., Simpson, C., Beck, B., Mewis, H., and Pandolfi, J.M. 2012. Equatorial decline of reef corals during the last Pleistocene interglacial. *Proceedings of the National Academy of Sciences USA* **109**: 21,378–21,383.

Lighty, R.G., Macintyre, I.G., and Stuckenrath, R. 1978. Submerged early Holocene barrier reef south-east Florida shelf. *Nature* **276**: 59–60.

Precht, W.F. and Aronson, R.B. 2004. Climate flickers and range shifts of reef corals. *Frontiers in Ecology and the Environment* **2**: 307–314.

Turley, C., Eby, M., Ridgwell, A.J., Schmidt, D.N., Findlay, H.S., Brownlee, C., Riebesel, U., Gattuso, J.-P., Fabry, V.J., and Feely, R.A. 2010. The societal challenge of ocean acidification. *Marine Pollution Bulletin* **60**: 787–792.

Veron, J. 1992. Environmental control of Holocene changes to the world's most northern hermatypic coral outcrop. *Pacific Science* **46**: 402–425.

Woodroffe, C.D., Brooke, B.P., Linklater, M., Kennedy, D.M., Jones, B.G., Buchanan, C., Mleczko, R., Hua, Q., and Zhao, J. 2010. Response of coral reefs to climate change: expansion and demise of the southernmost pacific coral reef. *Geophysical Research Letters* **37**: 10.1029/2010GL044067.

6.5.2.1.3 Laboratory Studies

Several laboratory studies have focused on the combined impacts of rising temperatures and falling ocean pH levels on coral reefs.. The key findings, all of which challenge the alarming and negative projections of IPCC, are presented in the bullet points below, followed by an expanded discussion of those findings. (Citations for passages in quotation marks in the bullet points are included in the main body of the section.)

- The "enhanced kinetics of calcification owing to higher temperatures has the potential to counter the effects of ocean acidification."

- The conventional belief that calcification rates will be affected by lower ocean pH levels may be unfounded for temperate zone corals.

- The study of a Mediterranean zooxanthellate coral, *Cladocora caespitosa*, revealed "an increase in CO$_2$, alone or in combination with elevated temperature, had no significant effect on photosynthesis, photosynthetic efficiency and calcification."

- Lower seawater pH due to atmospheric CO$_2$ enrichment and increased temperature (but short of reaching the bleaching level) "will both enhance active biotic calcification" of *Agaricia agaricites* corals.

- "The immediate effects of rising seawater temperature and ocean acidification may be tolerable for some species," possibly because the increased availability of CO$_{2(aq)}$ under ocean acidification conditions may enhance algal productivity, especially in *Symbiodinium* phylotypes with less efficient carbon-concentrating mechanisms that rely to a greater extent on the passive, diffusive uptake of CO$_{2(aq)}$ and its fertilization effect.

In a paper published in *Nature Climate Change*, McCulloch *et al.* (2012) describe how biogenic calcification occurs within an extracellular calcifying fluid located in the semi-isolated space between a coral's skeleton and its calicoblastic ectoderm, where during active calcification the pH of the calcifying fluid (pH$_{cf}$) is often increased relative to ambient seawater pH. At a typical seawater pH of ~8.1, for example, the pH of aragonitic corals shows a species-dependent range of 8.4 to 8.7, representing a systematic increase in pH$_{cf}$ relative to ambient sea water (ΔpH) of ~0.3–0.6 units. They report *in situ* measurements of pH within the calcifying medium of live coral polyps using microelectrodes (Al-Horani *et al.*, 2003; Ries, 2011a) and pH-sensitive dyes (Venn *et al.*, 2011) have registered enhanced pH$_{cf}$ values between 0.6 and 1.2—and sometimes up to 2—pH units above seawater during the day, when both net production and calcification are highest.

Using a model of pH regulation combined with abiotic calcification, McCulloch *et al.* show "the enhanced kinetics of calcification owing to higher temperatures has the potential to counter the effects of ocean acidification," and "the extra energy required to up-regulate pH is minor, only <1% of that generated by photosynthesis," which highlights the importance of maintaining the zooxanthellae-coral symbiosis for sustaining calcification. They further note their model predicts "a ~15% increase in calcification rates from the Last Glacial Maximum to the late Holocene," an increase they describe as being "consistent with the expansion of tropical habitats that occurred during this time despite P_{CO2} increasing."

Projecting into the future with their experimentally verified model, the four researchers assess the response of coral reefs "to both global warming, with mean tropical sea surface temperatures ~ 2°C higher, and with P_{CO2} increasing from present-day levels to ~1,000 ppm by the year 2100." For this scenario, they report their model predicts "either unchanged or only minimal effects on calcification rates." Thus, from a strictly chemical and kinetic perspective, their model indicates "ocean acidification combined with rising ocean temperatures should have only minimal effects on coral calcification," which they describe as "a direct outcome" of corals' ability to up-regulate pH at the site of calcification.

Rodolfo-Metalpa *et al.* (2010) collected three live colonies of the Mediterranean zooxanthellate coral *Cladocora caespitosa* in the Bay of Villefranche (Ligurian Sea, France) at about 25 meters depth in July 2006, plus three other colonies in February 2007. They divided the colonies into fragments and removed single polyps they attached to PVC plates and randomly assigned to aquariums continuously supplied with unfiltered seawater maintained at ambient or elevated water temperature (T or T + 3°C) in equilibrium with air of ambient or elevated CO_2 concentration (400 or 700 ppm). They subjected the polyps to "(1) mid-term perturbations (1 month) in summer and winter conditions of irradiance and temperature, and (2) a long-term perturbation (1 year), mimicking the seasonal changes in temperature and irradiance."

They found "an increase in CO_2, in the range predicted for 2100, does not reduce [the coral's] calcification rate," and "an increase in CO_2, alone or in combination with elevated temperature, had no significant effect on photosynthesis, photosynthetic efficiency and calcification." They report a 3°C rise in temperature in winter resulted in a 72% increase in gross photosynthesis and a significant increase in daytime calcification rate.

Rodolfo-Metalpa *et al.* conclude "the conventional belief that calcification rates will be affected by ocean acidification may not be widespread in temperate corals." They note Ries *et al.* (2009) have reported the calcification rate of the temperate coral *Oculina arbuscula* is also unaffected by an increase in atmospheric CO_2 concentration of up to 840 ppm, and a large decrease in calcification was found only at a CO_2 concentration in excess of 2,200 ppm. In addition, they write, "some marine invertebrates may be able to calcify in the face of ocean acidification or, contrary to what is generally

expected, may increase their calcification rates as reported on the ophiourid brittlestar *Amphiura filiformis* (Wood *et al.*, 2008), the seastar *Pisaster ochraceus* (Gooding *et al.*, 2009) exposed to lower pH (7.8–7.3), the Caribbean coral *Madracis mirabilis* at pH 7.6 (Jury *et al.*, 2010), and shown for coralline red algae, calcareous green algae, temperate urchins, limpets, crabs, lobsters and shrimp (Ries *et al.*, 2009)." They note there are many cases where "rates of photosynthesis are either not affected (e.g. Langdon *et al.*, 2003; Reynaud *et al.*, 2003; Schneider and Erez, 2006; Marubini *et al.*, 2008) or slightly increased (e.g. Langdon and Atkinson, 2005) at the level of CO_2 expected in 2100."

In a study designed to explore what controls calcification in corals, Sandeman (2012) suspended— by means of a torsion microbalance (as per Kesling and Crafts, 1962)—small pieces of coral he carefully removed from the edges of thin plates of *Agaricia agaricites* corals and lowered into gently stirred temperature-controlled seawater, after which he used the microbalance to measure coral net calcification rates over a range of seawater temperature and pH. He reported calcification rates of live *A. agaricites* coral increased by 15–17.7% per °C as seawater temperature rose from 27 to 29.5°C, and in his experiments in which the pH of the seawater was reduced from an average of 8.2 to 7.6, he observed calcification in living corals increased significantly. Similar experiments conducted with small portions of dead coral skeleton revealed "when the average pH was reduced from 8.2 to 7.5, calcification rate decreased." He determined the difference between calcification rates in going from seawater of pH 8.2 to seawater of pH 7.8 ranged from +30% for coral with no dead areas to −21.5% for coral with 30% dead exposed surface area.

The Trent University researcher from Peterborough, Ontario (Canada) says his findings suggest lower seawater pH due to atmospheric CO_2 enrichment and increased temperature (but short of reaching the bleaching level) "will both enhance active biotic calcification." He states the wide range of results between his and other scientists' studies of calcification rate and carbon dioxide "may be explainable in terms of the ratio of 'live' to 'dead' areas of coral," as is also suggested by the work of Rodolfo-Metalpa *et al.* (2011) and Ries (2011b), all of which leads him to conclude coral species that typically have smaller areas of exposed dead surface "may have a better chance of survival as pH levels drop."

Schoepf *et al.* (2013) note "since scleractinian corals are calcifying organisms that already live close to their upper thermal tolerance limits, both ocean warming and acidification severely threaten their survival and role as reef ecosystem engineers." They observe "no studies to date have measured energy reserve pools (i.e., lipid, protein, and carbohydrate) together with calcification under ocean acidification conditions under different temperature scenarios." Schoepf *et al.* studied the single and interactive effects of pCO_2 (382, 607, and 741 ppm) and temperature (26.5 and 29.0°C) on coral calcification, energy reserves (i.e., lipid, protein, and carbohydrate), chlorophyll *a,* and endosymbiont concentrations in four species of Pacific coral having different growth morphologies (*Acropora millepora, Pocillopora damicornis, Montipora monasteriata,* and *Turbinaria reniformis*).

The 13 researchers found coral energy reserves were largely *not* metabolized "in order to sustain calcification under elevated pCO_2 and temperature," as "maintenance of energy reserves has been shown to be associated with higher resistance to coral bleaching and to promote recovery from bleaching (Rodrigues and Grottoli, 2007; Anthony *et al.,* 2009)." They report lipid concentrations increased under lower ocean pH levels conditions in both *A. millepora* and *P. damicornis* and "were fully maintained in *M. monasteriata* and *T. reniformis.*" Protein, carbohydrate, and tissue biomass also were "overall maintained under ocean acidification conditions in all species." Thus "only one of the four corals species studied [*Acropora millepora*] decreased calcification in response to average ocean acidification levels expected by the second half of this century (741 ppm), even when combined with elevated temperature (+2.5°C)."

Schoepf *et al.* conclude "some corals could be more resistant to combined ocean acidification and warming expected by the end of this century than previously thought," so "the immediate effects of rising seawater temperature and ocean acidification may be tolerable for some species," possibly because the increased availability of $CO_{2(aq)}$ under lower ocean pH levels conditions may enhance algal productivity, especially in *Symbiodinium* phylotypes with less efficient carbon-concentrating mechanisms that rely to a greater extent on the passive, diffusive uptake of $CO_{2(aq)}$ and its fertilization effect, citing Herfort *et al.* (2008) and Brading *et al.* (2011).

References

Al-Horani, F.A., Al-Moghrabi, S.M., and de Beer, D. 2003. The mechanism of calcification and its relation to photosynthesis and respiration in the scleractinian coral *Galaxea fascicularis. Marine Biology* **142**: 419–426.

Anthony, K.R.N., Hoogenboom, M.O., Maynard, J.F., Grottoli, A.G., and Middlebrook, R. 2009. Energetics approach to predicting mortality risk from environmental stress: a case study of coral bleaching. *Functional Ecology* **23**: 539–550.

Brading, P., Warner, M.E., Davey, P., Smith, D.J., Achterberg, E.P., and Suggett D.J. 2011. Differential effects of ocean acidification on growth and photosynthesis among phylotypes of *Symbiodinium* (Dinophyceae). *Limnology and Oceanography* **56**: 927–938.

Gooding, R.A., Harley, C.D.G., and Tang, E. 2009. Elevated water temperature and carbon dioxide concentration increase the growth of a keystone echinoderm. *Proceedings of the National Academy of Sciences USA* **106**: 9316–9321.

Herfort, L., Thake, B., and Taubner, I. 2008. Bicarbonate stimulation of calcification and photosynthesis in two hermatypic corals. *Journal of Phycology* **44**: 91–98.

Jury, C.P., Whitehead, R.F., and Szmant, A.M. 2010. Effects of variations in carbonate chemistry on the calcification rates of *Madracis auretenra* (= *Madracis mirabilis sensu* Wells, 1973): bicarbonate concentrations best predict calcification rates. *Global Change Biology*: 10.1111/j.1365–2486.2009.02057.x.

Kesling, R.V. and Crafts, F.C. 1962. Ontogenetic increase in archimedian weight of the ostracod *Clamidotheca unispinosa* (Baird). *American Midland Naturalist* **68**: 149–153.

Langdon, C. and Atkinson, M.J. 2005. Effect of elevated pCO_2 on photosynthesis and calcification of corals and interactions with seasonal change in temperature, irradiance and nutrient enrichment. *Journal of Geophysical Research* **110**: 1–54.

Langdon, C., Broecker, W.S., Hammond, D.E., Glenn, E., Fitzsimmons, K., Nelson, S.G., Peng, T.-S., Hajdas, I., and Bonani, G. 2003. Effect of elevated CO_2 on the community metabolism of an experimental coral reef. *Global Biogeochemical Cycles* **17**: 10.1029/2002GB001941.

Marubini, F., Ferrier-Pages, C., Furla, P., and Allemand, D. 2008. Coral calcification responds to seawater acidification: a working hypothesis towards a physiological mechanism. *Coral Reefs* **27**: 491–499.

McCulloch, M., Falter, J., Trotter, J., and Montagna, P. Coral resilience to ocean acidification and global warming through pH up-regulation. *Nature Climate Change* **2**: 623–627.

Reynaud, S., Leclercq, N., Romaine-Lioud, S., Ferrier-Pages, C., Jaubert, J., and Gattuso, J.-P. 2003. Interacting effects of CO_2 partial pressure and temperature on photosynthesis and calcification in a scleractinian coral. *Global Change Biology* **9**: 1660–1668.

Ries, J.B. 2011a. A physicochemical framework for interpreting the biological calcification response to CO_2-induced ocean acidification. *Geochimica et Cosmochimica Acta* **75**: 4053–4064.

Ries, J. 2011b. Acid ocean cover up. *Nature Climate Change* **1**: 294–295.

Ries, J., Cohen, A., and McCorkle, D. 2008. Marine biocalcifiers exhibit mixed responses to CO_2-induced ocean acidification. In: *11th International Coral Reef Symposium*, Fort Lauderdale, Florida USA, 7–11 July, p. 229.

Rodolfo-Metalpa, R., Houlbreque, F., Tambutte, E., Boisson, F., Baggini, C., Patti, F.P., Jeffree, R., Fine, M., Foggo, A., Gattuso, J.P., and Hall-Spencer, J.M. 2011. Coral and mollusk resistance to ocean acidification adversely affected by warming. *Nature Climate Change* **1**: 308–312.

Rodolfo-Metalpa, R., Martin, S., Ferrier-Pages, C., and Gattuso, J.-P. 2010. Response of the temperate coral *Cladocora caespitosa* to mid- and long-term exposure to pCO_2 and temperature levels projected for the year 2100 AD. *Biogeosciences* **7**: 289–300.

Rodrigues, I.J. and Grottoli, A.G. 2007. Energy reserves and metabolism as indicators of coral recovery from bleaching. *Limnology and Oceanography* **52**: 1874–1882.

Sandeman, I.M. 2012. Preliminary results with a torsion microbalance indicate that carbon dioxide and exposed carbonic anhydrase in the organic matrix are the basis of calcification on the skeleton surface of living corals. *Revista de Biologia Tropical* **60** (Supplement 1): 109–126.

Schneider, K. and Erez, J. 2006. The effect of carbonate chemistry on calcification and photosynthesis in the hermatypic coral *Acropora eurystoma*. *Limnology and Oceanography* **51**: 1284–1293.

Schoepf, V., Grottoli, A.G., Warner, M.E., Cai, W-J., Melman, T.F., Hoadley, K.D., Pettay, D.T., Hu, X., Li, Q., Xu, H., Wang, Y., Matsui, Y., and Baumann, J.H. 2013. Coral energy reserves and calcification in a high-CO_2 world at two temperatures. *PLOS ONE* **8**: e75049.

Venn, A., Tambutte, E., Holcomb, M., Allemand, D., and Tambutte, S. 2011. Live tissue imaging shows reef corals elevate pH under their calcifying tissue relative to seawater. *PLoS ONE* **6**: e20013.

Wood, H.L., Spicer, J.I., and Widdicombe, S. 2008. Ocean acidification may increase calcification rates, but at a cost. *Proceedings of the Royal Society B* **275**: 1767–1773.

6.5.2.1.4 Field Studies

Several field studies have focused on the combined effects of lower ocean pH levels and higher temperatures. The key findings of these studies are presented in the bullet points below, followed by an expanded discussion of those findings. (Citations for passages in quotation marks in the bullet points are included in the main body of the section.)

- Over the period 1937–1996, *Montastraea faveolata* colonies located in the upper Florida Keys maintained rates of extension and calcification in spite of the combination of local environmental and climatic changes.

- A nearly three-century-long history of coral calcification in the South China Sea reveals an 11% increase between 1716 and 2005.

- Between 1900 and 2010, increases in *Porites* coral calcification on reefs in the southeast Indian Ocean ranged from small, non-significant positive trends, to increases as high as 23% per decade. In these regions, "the rate of change in the thermal environment of coral reefs is currently the primary driver of change in coral calcification rates," and "the large-scale phenomenon of ocean acidification is not currently limiting calcification on coral reefs uniformly at a global scale."

- Flexibility in community composition observed along latitudinal environmental gradients across the Great Barrier Reef "indicates that climate change is likely to result in a re-assortment of coral reef taxa rather than wholesale loss of entire reef ecosystems."

According to Cantin *et al.* (2009), "zooxanthellae (symbiotic dinoflagellates of the genus *Symbiodinium*) are critical to the survival of reef-building corals, providing a major source of energy from photosynthesis for cell maintenance, growth and reproduction of their coral hosts," and these services include the energetically expensive process of calcification (Idso *et al.*, 2000). Cantin *et al.* studied the amount of photosynthetic "rent" paid by two clades of *Symbiodinium* (C1 and D) to their coral hosts (juvenile *Acropora millepora*) for the privilege of living within the latter's calcareous "houses." This was done by measuring the "financial transfer" to nine-month-old corals developed "from crosses involving the same parent corals." This "planned parenthood" minimized any host genetic differences that otherwise might have influenced the physiology of the host-symbiont "lease agreement."

They found "*Symbiodinium* C1 exhibited a 121% greater capacity for translocation of photosynthate to *A. millepora* juveniles along with 87% greater relative electron transport through photosystem II under identical environmental conditions." In addition, the five researchers note "*A. tenuis* and *A. millepora* juveniles in a previous study exhibited 2 to 3 times faster growth rates when associated with *Symbiodinium* C1 compared to those associated with *Symbiodinium* D (Little *et al.*, 2004) at the same field site where juveniles were reared in the present study."

Cantin *et al.* conclude "the differences in carbon-based energy transfer between symbiont types may provide a competitive advantage to corals associating with *Symbiodinium* C1, particularly during their early life histories, when greater energy investment into rapid tissue and skeletal growth can prevent overgrowth of juveniles by competitors and mortality from grazers." They write, "as the community structure of coral reefs shift in response to global climate change and water quality impacts, opportunistic corals harboring symbionts that enable maximum rates of growth may similarly gain a competitive advantage." Consequently, in the economy of nature ample provision evidently has been made for corals to weather all sorts of environmental challenges that may come their way, including those IPCC contends will be driven by rising atmospheric CO_2 concentrations.

In studying coral calcification rates on Australia's Great Barrier Reef, De'ath *et al.* (2009) report there was a 14% drop in *Porites* calcification rate from 1990 to 2005 (although a graphical view of their data indicates the decline began around 1970) and this decline "is unprecedented in at least the past 400 years," which is indeed what their data show. Such statements, however, do not reveal the full story.

If, for example, their calcification history is followed back in time a mere 33 more years, from 1605 to 1572—when the air's CO_2 concentration was more than 100 ppm less than it is today and, therefore, was supposedly so much healthier for corals (according to the ocean "acidification" hypothesis)—it shows the coral calcification rate at that earlier time was approximately 21% lower than it was at its twentieth century peak.

Another way of looking at De'ath *et al.*'s data is to realize that from 1572 to 1970, *Porites* calcification rates on the Great Barrier Reef increased by about 27% as the atmospheric CO_2 concentration and air temperature rose concurrently. After 1970, calcification rates declined, but by a much smaller 14%, even as air temperature and CO_2 concentrations continued to increase, further obscuring the issue. De'ath *et al.* note, "the causes for the [1990 to 2005] Great Barrier Reef-wide decline in coral calcification of massive *Porites* remain unknown."

Three years later, the work of another research team provided a possible answer. Uthicke *et al.* (2012) state, "tropical coral reefs are currently under threat by a variety of regional and global stressors," with examples of the former being "land runoff and overfishing (e.g., Pandolfi *et al.*, 2003; Fabricius, 2005)," and examples of the latter "sea temperature increase and ocean acidification (Hoegh-Guldberg *et al.*, 2007; Fabricius *et al.*, 2011)." To determine which set of stressors is the most significant threat, Uthicke *et al.* analyzed sediment cores collected from inshore fringing coral reefs in the Whitsunday area of the Great Barrier Reef (GBR) of Australia. They collected these cores from three locations: inner near-shore reefs with low coral cover and high macroalgal abundance, intermediate reefs, and reefs at outer islands with low algal and high coral cover. They chose these three locations because inner near-shore reefs are typically the first to produce evidence of regional human impacts; reefs at outer islands are the last to experience the negative effects of human influence, as well as the most likely to exhibit evidence of global stressors; and intermediate reefs often show evidence of both.

The three researchers report benthic foraminiferal assemblages found in the cores of outer-island reefs unaffected by increased land runoff have been "naturally highly persistent over long (>2000 years) timescales." In both of the other zones, assemblages were also persistent, but only until 150 years ago, and assemblages less than 55 years old from inner near-shore and intermediate reefs were significantly different from older assemblages.

Uthicke *et al.* conclude they found support for the likelihood "increased land runoff since the start of land clearing and agriculture in the catchment of the Whitsunday Region of the GBR has left a signature in the foraminiferal assemblages of inner and intermediate areas of the study area," when previously the assemblages of these areas had been "persistent for at least several thousand years." In addition, and based on the fact "no changes were observed on outer reefs located away from land runoff," they propose "changes observed on inner and intermediate reefs were mainly driven by enhanced agricultural runoff after European settlement." And finally, they affirm "the hypothesis that global forcing, such as sea temperature increase or ocean acidification, altered the foraminiferal community found little support."

Browne (2012) writes "local stressors erode reef resilience, and therefore increase their vulnerability to global stressors that include ocean warming, [which is] predicted to increase the severity and intensity of coral bleaching events (Hoegh-Guldberg, 1999), ocean acidification, [which is] predicted to reduce calcification rates and reef growth (Kleypas et al., 1999), and increased storm and cyclone activity, [which is] predicted to reduce coral framework complexity and stability (Puotinen, 2004)." In a study designed to assess the overall impact of these several reef stressors, Browne describes how "coral growth rates (linear extension, density, calcification rates) of three fast-growing corals (Acropora, Montipora, Turbinaria) were studied in situ on Middle Reef, an inshore reef located on the central Great Barrier Reef (GBR)," in order to "assess the influence of changing environmental conditions on coral condition and reef growth."

Browne found "despite local anthropogenic pressures and global climate change, Middle Reef has a robust and resilient coral community," and "Acropora linear extension rates were comparable with rates observed at similar depths and sea surface temperatures on mid to offshore reefs on the GBR, and in the Caribbean." In addition, "Montipora and Turbinaria are abundant on inshore turbid reefs due to their adaptive capacities and are therefore an important source of carbonate for reef growth and development." Browne writes, "Montipora linear extension was greater than current estimates available, and Turbinaria, although characterized by slow linear extension, had a dense skeleton and hence may be more resilient to physical damage as ocean pH falls." Although both species "may be more susceptible during the warmer months due to multiple stressors, they were able to rapidly recover during the cooler months," Browne writes. "In summary," Browne concludes, "corals on Middle Reef are robust and resilient to their marginal environmental conditions."

Helmle et al. (2011) collected coral cores in May 1997 and June 1998 from seven Montastraea faveolata colonies located in the upper Florida Keys (USA), where they "were drilled at the location of maximum vertical growth of the colony." The scientists constructed chronologies from the annual density bands found in the cores and determined all of them had a 60-year common period from 1937 to 1996. For these cores the scientists obtained and analyzed annual extension, density, and calcification rates, to see how they varied over this period of intensifying warming and acidification of the global ocean.

The five U.S. scientists report their data show "no evidence of significant age effects" over the 1937–1996 period for extension, density, or calcification. Helmle et al. say their findings demonstrate "the measured corals have historically been able to maintain rates of extension and calcification over the 60-year period from 1937 to 1996 under the combination of local environmental and climatic changes." They also note calcification rates were positively related to sea surface temperature, "similar to results for Porites corals from Tahiti (Bessat and Buigues, 2001) and the Great Barrier Reef (Lough and Barnes, 1997)," but they say the Florida results explained only about 7% of the annual calcification variability as opposed to ~30% at the Pacific locations.

As for why the Florida Keys corals have fared so well, Helmle et al. suggest the answer could be "massive reef-building corals are not as susceptible to declines in Ω_{arag} [aragonite saturation state] as demonstrated by laboratory experiments; local processes, such as high seasonal variation in Ω_{arag} in the Florida Keys, may be temporarily enabling these corals to maintain their historical rates of calcification; the role of Ω_{arag} in controlling calcification is masked amidst considerable natural inter-annual variability; or the actual in situ reef-site carbonate chemistry is decoupled from the oceanic values, which could occur as a result of shifts in benthic community metabolism, mineral buffering and/or coastal biogeochemical processes."

Shi et al. (2012) state "rising atmospheric CO_2 and global warming are regarded as fatal threats to coral reefs," noting "IPCC has reported that by the end of this century, coral reefs will be the first ecological system that will become extinct," citing Wilkinson (2004). They write, "others contend that rising seawater temperature is conducive to enhanced coral calcification, and increased calcification will be higher than the decline caused by rising CO_2," so "coral calcification will increase by about 35% beyond pre-industrial levels by 2100, and no extinction of coral reefs will occur in the future," citing McNeil et al. (2004).

In late May of 2004 and 2007 Shi et al. extracted core samples of coral skeletons from several massive live and dead Porites lutea colonies comprising part of the Meiji Reef in the southern South China Sea, after which they analyzed their skeletal calcification rates by means of X-ray photography, which enabled them to construct a nearly three-century-long history of coral calcification rate for the period 1716–2005. The results of the six scientists' efforts are depicted in Figure 6.5.2.1.3.1.

As best as can be determined from the Chinese scientists' graph, over the period of time depicted—when IPCC claims the world warmed at a rate unprecedented over the past millennium or two, and when the atmosphere's CO_2 concentration rose to values not seen for millions of years—the two "fatal threats to coral reefs," even acting together, did not prevent coral calcification rates on Meiji Reef from rising by about 11% over the past three centuries.

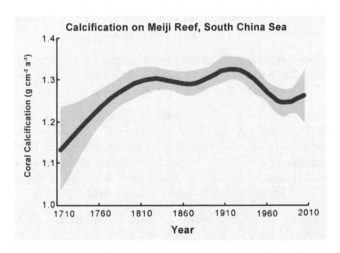

Figure 6.5.2.1.3.1. The long-term history of coral calcification rate on Meiji Reef. Adapted from Shi *et al.* (2012).

Cooper *et al.* (2012) studied coral reefs spanning an 11° latitudinal range in the southeast Indian Ocean, collecting 27 long cores from massive *Porites* coral colonies at six locations covering a north-south distance of about 1,000 km off the coast of Western Australia. From these cores they developed 1900–2010 histories of "annual extension (linear distance between adjacent density minima, cm/year), skeletal density (g/cm^3), and calcification rate (the product of skeletal density and annual extension, g/cm^2/year)," based on gamma densitometry data.

Cooper *et al.* report calcification rates at the Houtman Abrolhos Islands, where a relatively large sea surface temperature (SST) increase had occurred (0.10°C/decade), rose by 23.5%, and at Coral Bay and Tantabiddi, SST increases of 0.8 and 0.6°C/decade were associated with 8.7 and 4.9% increases in decadal calcification rates, respectively. They found smaller and non-significant positive trends in

calcification rates at Clerke and Imperieuse Reefs, where the increase in SST was only 0.2°C/decade.

The three Australian researchers say their latter non-significant findings are consistent with those of Helmle *et al.* (2011), who they say "found a similar non-correlation for the massive coral *Montastraea faveolata* in the Florida Keys between 1937 and 1996, when there was no significant SST warming." Regarding the large increases in calcification rates they documented at the rapidly warming Houtman Abrolhos Islands, they write, "Lough and Barnes (2000) documented a similar positive correlation, suggesting that calcification rates may, at least initially, increase with global warming." They conclude "the rate of change in the thermal environment of coral reefs is currently the primary driver of change in coral calcification rates," driving them ever-higher as temperatures continue to rise, and "the large-scale phenomenon of ocean acidification is not currently limiting calcification on coral reefs uniformly at a global scale."

Hughes *et al.* (2012) note, "contemporary research on how climate change affects coral reefs has matured beyond the simplistic 'canary in the coal mine' concept to a more nuanced recognition that climate-related pressures such as bleaching (due to the loss of symbiotic zooxanthellae) and ocean acidification do not affect all species equally." And "in this context," they note, "a critical issue for the future status of reefs will be their ability to maintain functional capacity in the face of the changes in species composition that are already underway due to multiple anthropogenic impacts."

Hughes *et al.* applied a "rigorous quantitative approach to examine large-scale spatial variation in the species composition and abundance of corals on mid-shelf reefs along the length of Australia's Great Barrier Reef, a biogeographic region where species richness is high and relatively homogeneous." They used "a hierarchical, nested sampling design to quantify scale-dependent patterns of coral abundances [for] five regions of the Great Barrier Reef [they] sampled from north to south, each 250–500 km apart." They thus identified and measured a total of 35,428 coral colonies on 33 reefs, categorizing each colony they encountered (including the majority of species that are too rare to analyze individually) into "ecologically relevant groups depending on their physiology, morphology and life history."

The seven scientists report the diverse pool of species they examined along the latitudinal gradient of the Great Barrier Reef "can assemble in markedly different configurations across a wide range of contemporary environments." Regarding temperature, for example, they indicate "the geographic ranges of 93% of the 416 coral species found on the Great Barrier Reef extend northwards toward the equator (e.g., to Papua New Guinea, the Solomon Islands, and/or the Indonesian archipelago)," whereas "46% are also found in colder conditions further to the south." As for lower ocean pH levels, they write, "globally, ocean surface pH has decreased by 0.1 unit since 1750 due to the uptake of atmospheric CO_2, with a smaller 0.06 decline recorded for the tropics," citing Kleypas *et al.* (2006). In contrast, they report contemporary variation in pH among various reef habitats on the Great Barrier Reef, as well as differences among short-term replicate measurements, span a range of 0.39 unit, from 8.37 to 7.98, citing Gagliano *et al.* (2010). And they note this short-term and habitat-scale variability literally swamps that of latitudinal trends.

Hughes *et al.* say their real-world observations "all point to a surprisingly resilient response by some elements of coral assemblages to spatial and temporal shifts in climatic conditions." They conclude, "the flexibility in community composition that we document along latitudinal environmental gradients indicates that climate change is likely to result in a re-assortment of coral reef taxa rather than wholesale loss of entire reef ecosystems." This clearly deflates the catastrophic prognostications put forth by IPCC with regard to the future of the planet's corals.

References

Bessat, F. and Buigues, D. 2001. Two centuries of variation in coral growth in a massive *Porites* colony from Moorea (French Polynesia): a response of ocean-atmosphere variability from south central Pacific. *Palaeogeography, Palaeoclimatology, Palaeoecology* **175**: 381–392.

Browne, N.K. 2012. Spatial and temporal variations in coral growth on an inshore turbid reef subjected to multiple disturbances. *Marine Environmental Research* **77**: 71–83.

Cantin, N.E., van Oppen, M.J.H., Willis, B.L., Mieog, J.C., and Negri, A.P. 2009. Juvenile corals can acquire more carbon from high-performance algal symbionts. *Coral Reefs* **28**: 405–414.

Cooper, T.F., O'Leary, R.A., and Lough, J.M. 2012. Growth of Western Australian corals in the Anthropocene. *Science* **335**: 593–596.

De'ath, G., Lough, J.M., and Fabricius, K.E. 2009. Declining coral calcification on the Great Barrier Reef. *Science* **323**: 116–119.

Fabricius, K.E. 2005. Effects of terrestrial runoff on the ecology of corals and coral reefs: review and synthesis. *Marine Pollution Bulletin* **50**: 125–146.

Fabricius, K.E., Langdon, C., Uthicke, S., Humphrey, C., Noonan, S., De'ath, G., Okazaki, R., Muehllehner, N., Glas, M.S., and Lough, J.M. 2011. Losers and winners in coral reefs acclimatized to elevated carbon dioxide concentrations. *Nature Climate Change* **1**: 165–169.

Gagliano, M., McCormick, M., Moore, J., and Depczynski, M. 2010. The basics of acidification: baseline variability of pH on Australian coral reefs. *Marine Biology* **157**: 1849–1856.

Helmle, K.P., Dodge, R.E., Swart, P.K., Gledhill, D.K., and Eakin, C.M. 2011. Growth rates of Florida corals from 1937 to 1996 and their response to climate change. *Nature Communications* **2**: 10.1038/ncomms1222.

Hoegh-Guldberg, O. 1999. Climate change, coral bleaching and the future of the world's coral reefs. *Marine and Freshwater Research* **50**: 839–866.

Hoegh-Guldberg, O., Mumby, P.J., Hooten, A.J., Steneck, R.S., Greenfield, P., Gomez, E., Harvell, C.D., Sale, P.F., Edwards, A.J., Caldeira, K., Knowlton, N, Eakin, C.M., Iglesias-Prieto, R., Muthiga, N., Bradbury, R.H., Dubi, A., and Hatziolos, M.E. 2007. Coral reefs under rapid climate change and ocean acidification. *Science* **318**: 1737–1742.

Hughes, T.P., Baird, A.H., Dinsdale, E.A., Moltschaniwskyj, N.A., Pratchett, M.S., Tanner, J.E., and Willis, B.L. 2012. Assembly rules of reef corals are flexible along a steep climatic gradient. *Current Biology* **22**: 736–741.

Idso, S.B., Idso, C.D., and Idso, K.E. 2000. CO_2, global warming and coral reefs: Prospects for the future. *Technology* **7S**: 71–94.

Kleypas, J.A., Buddemeier, R.W., Archer, D., Gattuso, J.P., Langdon, C., and Opdyke, B.N. 1999. Geochemical consequences of increased atmospheric carbon dioxide on coral reefs. *Science* **284**: 118–120.

Kleypas, J., Feeley, R.A., Fabry, V.J., Langdon, C., Sabine, C.L., and Robbins, L.L. 2006. *Impacts of Ocean Acidification on Coral Reefs and Other Marine Calcifiers: A Guide for Future Research*. Report of a workshop held April 18–20, 2005, St. Petersburg, Florida, USA, sponsored by NSF, NOAA and the U.S. Geological Survey.

Little, A.F., van Oppen, M.J.H., and Willis, B.L. 2004. Flexibility in algal endosymbioses shapes growth in reef corals. *Science* **304**: 1492–1494.

Lough, J.M. and Barnes, D.J. 1997. Several centuries of variation in skeletal extension, density and calcification in massive *Porites* colonies from the Great Barrier Reef: A proxy for seawater temperature and a background of variability against which to identify unnatural change. *Journal of Experimental and Marine Biology and Ecology* **211**: 29–67.

Lough, J.M. and Barnes, D.J. 2000. Environmental controls on growth of the massive coral *Porites*. *Journal of Experimental Marine Biology and Ecology* **245**: 225–243.

McNeil, B.I., Matear, R.J., and Barnes, D.J. 2004. Coral reef calcification and climate change: The effect of ocean warming. *Geophysical Research Letters* **31**: 10.1029/2004GL021541.

Pandolfi, J.M., Bradbury, R.H., Sala, E., Hughes, T.P., Bjorndal, K.A., Cooke, R.G., McArdle, D., McClenachan, L., Newman, M.J.H., Paredes, G., Warner, R.R., and Jackson, J.B.C. 2003. Global trajectories of the long-term decline of coral reef ecosystems. *Science* **301**: 955–958.

Puotinen, M.L. 2004. Tropical Cyclone Impacts on Coral Reef Communities: Modeling the Disturbance Regime in the Great Barrier Reef Region, 1969–2003. Ph.D. Thesis. James Cook University, Townsville, Queensland, Australia.

Shi, Q., Yu, K.F., Chen, T.R., Zhang, H.L., Zhao, M.X., and Yan, H.Q. 2012. Two centuries-long records of skeletal calcification in massive *Porites* colonies from Meiji Reef in the southern South China Sea and its responses to atmospheric CO_2 and seawater temperature. *Science China Earth Sciences* **55**: 10.1007/s11430–011–4320–0.

Uthicke, S., Patel, F., and Ditchburn, R. 2012. Elevated land runoff after European settlement perturbs persistent foraminiferal assemblages on the Great Barrier Reef. *Ecology* **93**: 111–121.

Wilkinson, C. 2004. *Status of Coral Reefs of the World: 2004*. Australian Institute of Marine Science Press, Townsville, Australia.

6.5.2.2 Echinoderms

This section examines what scientists have learned from studies focusing on the impacts of higher temperatures and lower seawater pH levels on echinoderms. The key findings are presented in the bullet points below, followed by an expanded discussion of those findings. (Citations for passages in quotation marks in the bullet points are included in the main body of the section.)

- The relative growth of juvenile sea stars increased linearly with temperature from 5°C to 21°C, while also responding positively to atmospheric CO_2 enrichment.

- Serpent starfish were able to successfully cope with the physiological changes brought about by a modest temperature increase and/or pH decline.

- The intertidal seastar *Parvulastra exigua* was shown to be resilient to elevated temperature and reduced pH, and "may possess scope for adaptation (evolutionary change) and/or acclimation via phenotypic plasticity" to withstand future changes in temperature and pH.

- The negative effects of a 0.35 to 0.55 CO_2-induced decline in seawater pH on the growth and calcification of the sea urchin *Tripneustes gratilla* can be largely overcome by an accompanying 3°C increase in water temperature.

- No significant effect of ocean warming and lower seawater pH levels on the percentage of egg fertilization in four intertidal and shallow subtidal echinoids was found, possibly reflecting adaptation to the large temperature and pH fluctuations that characterize their shallow water coastal habitats.

- In a combined pH decline/temperature increase study on the sea urchin *Psammechinus miliaris*, it was determined "current ocean pH levels are suboptimal for *P. miliaris* sperm-swimming speed and that reproductive success for certain marine species may benefit from a reduced pH ocean."

- Fertilization and embryonic development of the ecologically important sea urchin *Sterechinus neumayeri* to the blastula stage was "robust to levels of temperature and pH change predicted over coming decades."

- The ecologically important sea urchin *Centrostephanus rodgersii* displays a genetic variation in tolerance affirming its ability to successfully adapt to ocean warming and falling ocean pH levels..

Gooding *et al.* (2009) measured growth and feeding rates of juvenile sea stars (*Pisaster ochraceus*) maintained in 246-liter aquaria filled with recirculating natural seawater maintained at temperatures ranging from 5 to 21°C and constantly bubbled with ambient air of 380 ppm CO_2 or CO_2-enriched air of 780 ppm CO_2. They found "the relative growth (change in wet mass/initial wet mass) of juvenile *P. ochraceus* increased linearly with temperature from

5°C to 21°C," and it also responded positively to atmospheric CO_2 enrichment. The authors state "relative to control treatments, high CO_2 alone increased relative growth by ~67% over 10 weeks, while a 3°C increase in temperature alone increased relative growth by 110%." They also state increased CO_2 "had a positive but non-significant effect on sea star feeding rates, suggesting CO_2 may be acting directly at the physiological level to increase growth rates." Their data show the percentage of calcified mass in the sea stars dropped from approximately 12% to 11% in response to atmospheric CO_2 enrichment at 12°C, but it did not decline further in response to a subsequent 3°C warming at either ambient or elevated CO_2. The three Canadian researchers say their findings demonstrate "increased CO_2 will not have direct negative effects on all marine invertebrates, suggesting that predictions of biotic responses to climate should consider how different types of organisms will respond to changing climatic variables." They state, "responses to anthropogenic climate change, including ocean acidification, will not always be negative."

Wood et al. (2010) studied the serpent starfish (Ophiura ophiura), collecting 96 individuals with a disc diameter between 10 and 15 mm from Cawsand Bay, Plymouth Sound (50°09.77' N, 4°11.50' W). They exposed the brittlestars to three pH treatments (pH of 8.0, 7.7, or 7.3) and two temperature treatments (10.5°C or 15°C) for 40 days. They measured metabolism, calcification, mortality, motility, arm structure, and arm regeneration; the latter parameter was studied by removing either 10, 20, 30, or 40 mm of arm length on one of the animals' arms.

The researchers found survival was "100% at both temperatures and across all pH treatments"; metabolic rate increased as pH decreased in the low temperature treatment, but there was no significant difference across the different pH treatments in the high temperature regime; muscle appearance and density did not change over either the temperature or pH treatment ranges in established or regenerated arms; and a faster response time in movement (motility) was observed at low temperature and low pH. They also found brittlestars across "all treatments had the same net calcification throughout the experiment"; arm regeneration rate within the low temperature treatment was "unaffected by the length of arm lost and the rate was similar between all pH treatments"; and arm regeneration rate was significantly faster at higher temperatures than lower temperatures. Taken as a whole, the findings indicate the serpent starfish should be able to cope

successfully with the physiological changes brought about by any modest temperature increase and/or pH decline likely to occur in the future.

McElroy et al. (2012) measured the metabolic rates of adult specimens of the intertidal seastar Parvulastra exigua collected from Little Bay, Sydney (Australia) at conditions characteristic of high tide (ca. 18°C and pH 8.2), as well as at 3 and 6°C warmer conditions and at additional pH values of 7.8 and 7.6 "in all combinations." The measurements revealed "the metabolic response of P. exigua to increased temperature (+3°C and +6°C) at control pH [8.2] indicates that this species is resilient to periods of warming as probably often currently experienced by this species in the field." They also report they "did not observe a negative effect of acidification on rate of oxygen consumption at control temperature, a combination of stressors that this species currently experiences at night time low tide."

Although the metabolic response of P. exigua is resilient to current levels of extreme temperature and pH stress—which are equivalent to mean conditions predicted for the end of the twenty-first century—it is possible the extreme seawater temperatures and pH levels at that future time (if IPCC predictions prove true) will be greater than the extreme levels of today, which could prove to be a real challenge for the seastars. McElroy et al. point out, in the concluding paragraph of their report, "species such as P. exigua with a broad distribution from warm to cold temperate latitudes may possess scope for adaptation (evolutionary change) and/or acclimation via phenotypic plasticity (Visser, 2008), as suggested for sympatric echinoid and ophiuroid species (Byrne et al., 2011; Christensen et al., 2011)."

Brennand et al. (2010) reared embryos of the sea urchin Tripneustes gratilla in flow-through chambers filled with filtered seawater maintained at all combinations of three temperatures (24, 27, and 30°C) and three pH values (8.15, 7.8, and 7.6), where the 24°C/pH 8.15 combination represented normal control conditions. After five days of such exposure, they assessed the growth and development of the larvae.

Brennand et al. found "larvae reared at pH 7.6 and pH 7.8 had smaller post oral arms when compared with those reared at control pH." However, they report, "a +3°C warming diminished the negative effects of low pH/high CO_2," as was "seen in the similar post oral arm length of larvae treated at 27°C/pH 7.6 and 27°C/pH 7.8 and those reared in control temperature and pH." In addition, "as total length of calcite rods is largely comprised of the post oral arms, this measure [of calcification] followed a similar pattern."

The results of this study suggest the negative effects of a 0.35 to 0.55 CO_2-induced decline in seawater pH on the growth and calcification of the sea urchin *Tripneustes gratilla* can be largely overcome by a 3°C increase in water temperature. And since the projected maximum decline in seawater pH is somewhere in the range of 0.1 to 0.18 in the vicinity of AD 2100, there is little reason for concern about any negative impact of rising atmospheric CO_2 concentrations on this particular species of sea urchin, which is widely distributed throughout the Indo-Pacific region and well suited for production by aquaculture (Lawrence and Agatsuma, 2007; Juinio-Menez *et al.*, 1998; Dworjanyn *et al.* 2007).

Byrne *et al.* (2009) investigated the effects of lower ocean pH levels (pH values of 8.2–7.6, corresponding to atmospheric CO_2 concentrations of 230–690 ppm) and seawater temperature (20–26°C, where 20°C represents the recent thermal history of indigenous adults) on the fertilization of sea urchin (*Heliocidaris erythrogramma*) eggs and their subsequent development in what they call "the eastern Australia climate change hot spot," located near Sydney.

According to the authors, over the ranges of seawater pH and temperature they studied, there was "no effect of pH" and "no interaction between temperature and pH" on sea urchin egg fertilization. Seawater pH also had no effect on the longer-term development of fertilized sea urchin eggs; but the six scientists say warming led to "developmental failure at the upper warming (+4 to +6°C) level, regardless of pH." Even here, however, they appear quite hopeful, stating "it is not known whether gametes from *H. erythrogramma* adults acclimated to 24°C would have successful development in a +4°C treatment," noting their study "highlights the potentiality that adaptive phenotypic plasticity may help buffer the negative effects of warming, as suggested for corals." They write, "single stressor studies of thermotolerance in a diverse suite of tropical and temperate sea urchins show that fertilization and early development are robust to temperature well above ambient and the increases expected from climate change," citing Farmanfarmaian and Giese (1963), Chen and Chen (1992), and Roller and Stickle (1993).

Byrne *et al.* (2010a) examined the interactive effects of near-future (ca. AD 2070–2100) ocean warming (temperature increases of 2–6°C) and lower ocean pH levels (pH reductions of 0.2–0.6) on fertilization in four intertidal and shallow subtidal echinoids (*Heliocidaris erythrogramma*, *Heliocidaris Tuberculata*, *Tripneustes gratilla*, *Centrostephanus rodgersii*), an asteroid (*Patiriella regularis*), and an abalone (*Haliotis coccoradiata*), working with batches of eggs they collected from multiple females fertilized by sperm obtained from multiple males, all of which species were maintained in all combinations of three temperature and three pH treatments.

The eight researchers found "no significant effect of warming and acidification on the percentage of fertilization." Byrne *et al.* say their results indicate "fertilization in these species is robust to temperature and pH/PCO$_2$ fluctuation," and their findings "may reflect adaptation to the marked fluctuation in temperature and pH that characterizes their shallow water coastal habitats."

Byrne *et al.* (2010b) investigated the effects of projected near-future oceanic warming and acidification of the sea urchin *Heliocidaris erythrogramma* for conditions predicted for southeast Australia within the timeframe of 2070–2100: an increase in sea surface temperature of 2 to 4°C and a decline in pH of 0.2 to 0.4. Byrne *et al.* conducted multifactorial experiments that incorporated a titration of sperm density ($10-10^3$ sperm per ml) across a range of sperm-to-egg ratios (10:1–1500:1). They found "across all treatments there was a highly significant effect of sperm density, but no significant effect of temperature or interaction between factors." They state "low pH did not reduce the percentage of fertilization even at the lowest sperm densities used, and increased temperature did not enhance fertilization at any sperm density." They write, "a number of ecotoxicology and climate change studies, where pH was manipulated with CO_2 gas, show that sea urchin fertilization is robust to a broad pH range with impairment only at extreme levels well below projections for ocean acidification by 2100 (pH 7.1–7.4, 2,000–10,000 ppm CO_2)," citing Bay *et al.* (1993), Carr *et al.* (2006), and Kurihara and Shirayama (2004). Because neither seawater warming nor seawater acidification (caused by contact with CO_2-enriched air) had either a positive or a negative effect on sea urchin fertilization, the five scientists conclude "sea urchin fertilization is robust to climate change stressors."

According to Caldwell *et al.* (2011), "the reproductive processes and early life-stages of both calcifying and non-calcifying animals are believed to be particularly vulnerable to a reduced pH environment," but "there is as yet no clear and reliable predictor for the impacts of ocean acidification on marine animal reproduction." Caldwell *et al.* "investigated the combined effect of pH (8.06–7.67) and temperature (14–20°C) on percent sperm motility and swimming speed in the sea urchin *Psammechinus miliaris* using computer assisted sperm analysis (CASA)," working with specimens they collected from the Isle of Cumbrae (Scotland). "Surprisingly," the six scientists write, "sperm swimming performance benefited greatly from a reduced pH environment," as "both percent motility and swimming speeds were significantly enhanced at pHs below current levels." In light of the additional fact that sperm-activating peptides—which are believed to have evolved some 70 million years ago during a period of high atmospheric CO_2 concentration—are fully functional from pH 6.6 to 8.0 (Hirohashi and Vacquier, 2002), they state "the combined data on motility, swimming speed and SAP function at reduced pH indicates that sperm are sufficiently robust to allow functionality at pHs that would have been experienced in the paleo-ocean (*ca* pH 7.4–7.6) and which are within projections for near-future climate change scenarios." The UK researchers conclude "current ocean pH levels are suboptimal for *P. miliaris* sperm-swimming speed and … reproductive success for certain marine species may benefit from a reduced pH ocean."

Ericson *et al.* (2012) "examined the interactive effects of warming and acidification on fertilization and embryonic development of the ecologically important sea urchin *Sterechinus neumayeri* reared from fertilization in elevated temperature (+1.5°C and 3°C) and decreased pH (–0.3 and –0.5 pH units)." They found "fertilization using gametes from multiple males and females, to represent populations of spawners, was resilient to acidification at ambient temperature (0°C)," and development to the blastula stage was "robust to levels of temperature and pH change predicted over coming decades." The sea urchins the seven scientists studied thus appear well-equipped to deal with IPCC-predicted near-future increases in seawater temperature and acidification.

Ho *et al.* (2013) report, "the impact of increased temperature (2–4°C above ambient) and decreased pH (0.2–0.4 pH units below ambient) on fertilization in the Antarctic echinoid *Sterechinus neumayeri* across a range of sperm concentrations was investigated in cross-factorial experiments," where "gametes from multiple males and females in replicate experiments were used to reflect the multiple spawner scenario in nature." They examined this species because "polar marine organisms are among the most stenothermal in the world due to the stability of their environment over evolutionary time (Clarke, 1983)," which suggests they may be "sensitive to the slightest of

environmental perturbations, particularly [in] early life history stages (Barnes and Peck, 2008)."

The five researchers' work confirmed "the importance of considering both ocean warming and acidification," and they note "decreased pH did not affect fertilization." Warming, however, "enhanced fertilization … likely through stimulation of sperm motility and reduced water viscosity." In the concluding sentence of their paper's abstract, Ho *et al.* state their results indicate "fertilization in *S. neumayeri*, even at low sperm levels potentially found in nature, is resilient to near-future ocean warming and acidification."

Foo *et al.* (2012) write, "selection by stressful conditions will only result in adaptation if [1] variation in stress tolerance exists within a population, if [2] tolerance of stressors is heritable, and if [3] changes in tolerance traits are not constrained by negative genetic correlations with other fitness traits," citing references both old and recent: Darwin (1859) and Blows and Hoffmann (2005).

Foo *et al.* "quantified genetic variation in tolerance of early development of the ecologically important sea urchin *Centrostephanus rodgersii* to near-future (2100) ocean conditions projected for the southeast Australian global change hot spot," in which "multiple dam-sire crosses were used to quantify the interactive effects of warming (+2–4°C) and acidification (–0.3–0.5 pH units) across twenty-seven family lines" of the species. The four Australian researchers report, "significant genotype by environment interactions for both stressors [warming and acidification] at gastrulation indicated the presence of heritable variation in thermal tolerance and the ability of embryos to respond to changing environments." They say "positive genetic correlations for gastrulation indicated that genotypes that did well at lower pH also did well in higher temperatures." Thus, Foo *et al.* conclude "the presence of tolerant genotypes, and the lack of a trade-off between tolerance to pH and tolerance to warming contribute to the potential of *C. rodgersii* to adapt to concurrent ocean warming and acidification, adding to the resilience of this ecologically important species in a changing ocean."

References

Barnes, D.K.A. and Peck, L.S. 2008. Vulnerability of Antarctic shelf biodiversity to predicted regional warming. *Climate Research* **37**: 149–163.

Bay, S., Burgess, R., and Nacci, D. 1993. Status and applications of echinoid (Phylum Echinodermata) toxicity test methods. In: Landis, W.G., Hughes, J.S., and Lewis, M.A. (Eds.) *Environmental Toxicology and Risk Assessment.* American Society for Testing and Materials, Philadelphia, Pennsylvania, USA, pp. 281–302.

Blows, M.W. and Hoffmann, A.A. 2005. A reassessment of genetic limits to evolutionary change. *Ecology* **86**: 1371–1384.

Brennand, H.S., Soars, N., Dworjanyn, S.A., Davis, A.R., and Byrne, M. 2010. Impact of ocean warming and ocean acidification on larval development and calcification in the sea urchin *Tripneustes gratilla. PLoS ONE* **5**: 10.1371/journal.pone.0011372.

Byrne, M., Ho, M., Selvakumaraswamy, P., Nguyen, H.D., Dworjanyn, S.A., and Davis, A.R. 2009. Temperature, but not pH, compromises sea urchin fertilization and early development under near-future climate change scenarios. *Proceedings of the Royal Society B* **276**: 1883–1888.

Byrne, M., Selvakumaraswamy, P., Ho, M.A., Woolsey, E., and Nguyen, H.D. 2011. Sea urchin development in a global change hotspot, potential for southerly migration of thermotolerant propagules. *Deep-Sea Research II* **58**: 712–719.

Byrne, M., Soars, N.A., Ho, M.A., Wong, E., McElroy, D., Selvakumaraswamy, P., Dworjanyn, S.A., and Davis, A.R. 2010a. Fertilization in a suite of coastal marine invertebrates from SE Australia is robust to near-future ocean warming and acidification. *Marine Biology* **157**: 2061–2069.

Byrne, M., Soars, N.A., Selvakumaraswamy, P., Dworjanyn, S.A., and Davis, A.R. 2010b. Sea urchin fertilization in a warm, acidified and high pCO$_2$ ocean across a range of sperm densities. *Marine Environmental Research* **69**: 234–239.

Caldwell, G.S., Fitzer, S., Gillespie, C.S., Pickavance, G., Turnbull, E., and Bentley, M.G. 2011. Ocean acidification takes sperm back in time. *Invertebrate Reproduction and Development* **55**: 217–221.

Carr, R.S., Biedenbach, J.M., and Nipper, M. 2006. Influence of potentially confounding factors on sea urchin porewater toxicity tests. *Archives of Environmental Contamination and Toxicology* **51**: 573–579.

Chen, C.P. and Chen, B.Y. 1992. Effects of high temperature on larval development and metamorphosis of *Arachnoides placenta* (Echinodermata Echinoidea). *Marine Biology* **112**: 445–449.

Christensen, A.B., Nguyen, H.D., and Byrne, M. 2011. Thermotolerance and the effects of hypercapnia on the metabolic rate of the ophiuroid *Ophionereis schayeri*: inferences for survivorship in a changing ocean. *Journal of Experimental Marine Biology and Ecology* **403**: 31–38.

Clarke, A. 1983. Life in cold water, the physiological ecology of polar marine ectotherms. *Oceanography and Marine Biology: An Annual Review* **21**: 341–453.

Darwin, C. 1859. *On the Origin of Species.* John Murray, London, United Kingdom.

Dworjanyn, S.A., Pirozzi, I., and Liu, W. 2007. The effect of the addition of algae feeding stimulants to artificial diets for the sea urchin *Tripneustes gratilla. Aquaculture* **273**: 624–633.

Ericson, J.A., Ho, M.A., Miskelly, A., King, C.K., Virtue, P., Tilbrook, B., and Byrne, M. 2012. Combined effects of two ocean change stressors, warming and acidification, on fertilization and early development of the Antarctic echinoid *Sterechinus neumayeri. Polar Biology* **35**: 1027–1034.

Farmanfarmaian, A. and Giese, A.C. 1963. Thermal tolerance and acclimation in the western purple sea urchin, *Strongylocentrotus purpuratus. Physiol. Zool.* **36**: 237–343.

Foo, S.A., Dworjanyn, S.A., Poore, A.G.B., and Byrne, M. 2012. Adaptive capacity of the habitat modifying sea urchin *Centrostephanus rodgersii* to ocean warming and ocean acidification: Performance of early embryos. *PLoS ONE* **7**: e42497.

Gooding, R.A., Harley, C.D.G., and Tang, E. 2009. Elevated water temperature and carbon dioxide concentration increase the growth of a keystone echinoderm. *Proceedings of the National Academy of Sciences, USA*: 10.1073/pnas.0811143106.

Hirohashi, N. and Vacquier, V.D. 2002. Egg fucose polymer, sialoglycan, and speract all trigger the sea urchin sperm acrosome reaction. *Biochemical and Biophysical Research Communications* **296**: 833–839.

Ho, M.A., Price, C., King, C.K., Virtue, P., and Byrne, M. 2013. Effects of ocean warming and acidification on fertilization in the Antarctic echinoid *Sterechinus neumayeri* across a range of sperm concentrations. *Marine Environmental Research* **90**: 136–141.

Juinio-Menez, M.A., Macawaris, N., and Bangi, H. 1998. Community-based sea urchin (*Tripnuestes gratilla*) grow-out culture as a resource management tool. *Canadian Special Publication of Fisheries and Aquatic Science* **125**: 393–399.

Kurihara, H. and Shirayama, Y. 2004. Effects of increased atmospheric CO$_2$ on sea urchin early development. *Marine Ecology Progress Series* **274**: 161–169.

Lawrence, J.M. and Agatsuma, Y. 2007. Ecology of *Tripneustes*. In: Lawrence, J.M. (Ed.) *The Biology and Ecology of Edible Urchins.* Elsevier Science, Amsterdam, The Netherlands, pp. 499–520.

McElroy, D.J., Nguyen, H.D., and Byrne, M. 2012. Respiratory response of the intertidal seastar *Parvulastra exigua* to contemporary and near-future pulses of warming and hypercapnia. *Journal of Experimental Marine Biology and Ecology* **416–417**: 1–7.

Roller, R.A. and Stickle, W.B. 1993. Effects of temperature and salinity acclimations of adults on larval survival, physiology, and early development of *Lytechinus variegatus* (Echinodermata: Echinoidea). *Marine Biology* **116**: 583–591.

Visser, M.E. 2008. Keeping up with a warming world; assessing the rate of adaptation to climate change. *Proceedings of the Royal Society B* **275**: 649–659.

Wood, H.L., Spicer, J.I., Lowe, D.M., and Widdicombe, S. 2010. Interaction of ocean acidification and temperature; the high cost of survival in the brittlestar *Ophiura ophiura*. *Marine Biology* **157**: 2001–2013.

6.5.2.3 Other Marine Species

This section examines what scientists have learned in studies , focusing on the impacts of changing seawater temperature and pH levels on marine species not discussed in prior sections. The key findings are presented in the bullet points below, followed by an expanded discussion of those findings. (Citations for passages in quotation marks in the bullet points are included in the main body of the section.)

- A high tolerance to pH decline and rising temperature was observed during the larval growth stage of the Portuguese oyster.

- The often complex and severe spatial and temporal variability of environmental conditions in coastal ecosystems suggests organisms living there are preconditioned to be tolerant of lower ocean pH levels and warming.

- There is no evidence that predator-prey interactions among green crabs and periwinkles will change in the future under lower ocean pH levels and warming.

- Analyses of tube mineralogy, ultrastructure, and mechanical properties of the serpulid tubeworm *Hydroides elegans* reveal "predicted coastal warming may not hinder *H. elegans* ability to build normal tubes even in the face of projected near-future decreases in pH or salinity."

- Norway lobster (*Nephrops norvegicus*) "would benefit from global warming and be able to withstand the predicted decrease in ocean pH in the next century during their earliest life stages."

- Baltic cod (*Gadus morhua*), which live in sea waters naturally high in pCO_2 "may be adapted to conditions predicted in ocean acidification scenarios for centuries to come," as "no effect on hatching, survival, development, and otolith size was found at any stage in the development of Baltic cod" under projected future ocean pH levels and temperature scenarios.

- Polyps of the moon jellyfish have been shown to be tolerant of low pH and warmer temperatures, surviving and reproducing asexually. Yet analyses of "all available long-term datasets on changes in jellyfish abundance across multiple coastal stations" reveal there is no compelling evidence to support the view that the global abundance of jellyfish is increasing as a result of lower ocean pH levels and warming.

- Lower ocean pH levels and temperature increases were found to negatively impact the growth and survival of juvenile anemone fish. The negative effects were absent or reversed when the parents of the juveniles also experienced lower ocean pH levels and warming, revealing "conditions experienced by adults can have significant carry-over effects on the performance of their offspring … leading to improved capacity to cope with environmental stress."

- In a study of copepods, "higher production temperature induced a positive maternal effect resulting in faster hatching and indicating that the mothers can invest more in their eggs, and therefore produce better quality eggs."

Thiyagarajan and Ko (2012) conducted a number of laboratory studies designed to see how the larval growth stage of the Portuguese oyster responds to various "climate change stressors," investigating the effects of low pH (7.9, 7.6, 7.4) at ambient salinity (34 ppt) and low salinity (27 ppt), while "the combined effect of pH (8.1, 7.6), salinity (24 and 34 ppt) and temperature (24°C and 30°C) was examined using factorial experimental design." The two researchers write, "surprisingly, the early growth phase from hatching to 5-day-old veliger stage showed high tolerance to pH 7.9 and pH 7.6 at both 34 ppt and 27 ppt," and "larval shell area was significantly smaller at pH 7.4 only in low-salinity."

In the three-factor experiment (see Figure 6.5.2.3.1), they observed "shell area was affected by salinity and the interaction between salinity and temperature but not by other combinations." They also discovered "larvae produced the largest shell at the elevated temperature in low-salinity, regardless of pH."

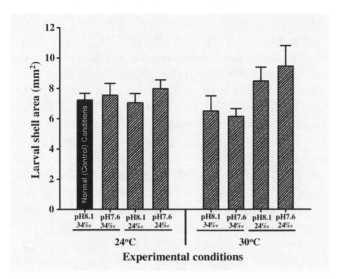

Figure 6.5.2.3.1. Mean shell area of the Portuguese oyster larvae exposed to a low-pH or elevated carbon dioxide treatment for five days at two levels of salinity (ambient and low-salinity) and temperature (ambient and elevated). Each bar represents the mean ± S.D. of four replicate cultures. Adapted from Thiyagarajan and Ko (2012).

Thiyagarajan and Ko conclude "the growth of the Portuguese oyster larvae appears to be robust to near-future pH level (>7.6) when combined with projected elevated temperature and low-salinity in the coastal aquaculture zones of [the] South China Sea."

Pansch *et al.* (2012) note to date "most studies have focused on ocean acidification (OA) effects in fully marine environments, while little attention has been devoted to more variable coastal ecosystems, such as the Western Baltic Sea." Since "natural spatial and temporal variability of environmental conditions such as salinity, temperature or CO_2 impose more complex stresses upon organisms inhabiting these habitats, species [living there] can be expected to be more tolerant to OA (or warming) than fully marine taxa."

Pansch *et al.* acquired data on the variability of temperature and pH within the inner Kiel Fjord of Schleswig-Holstein, Germany, and on "the responses of the barnacle *Amphibalanus improvisus* from this habitat to simulated warming and OA during its early development." They exposed *A. improvisus* nauplii

(the first larval stage of many crustaceans) and cyprids (the second larval stage of barnacles) to different temperatures (12, 20, and 27°C) and CO_2 (nominally 400, 1,250, and 3,250 ppm) treatments for eight and four weeks, respectively," while "survival, larval duration and settlement success were monitored."

The four researchers found a prolongation of the nauplius phase, which they acknowledge could "lead to a mismatch of the larvae with their phytoplankton prey." However, they note the predicted increase in seawater temperature would likely "accelerate nauplii development and, thus, may buffer OA effects." Such results, they write, have been observed "in sea urchin larvae and oysters, where higher temperatures mitigated negative effects of OA," citing Brennand *et al.* (2010) and Waldbusser *et al.* (2011). In their own study, however, they found just the opposite, saying "warming negatively impacted cyprid survival" but "OA counteracted these negative effects."

"It should also be stressed," they continue, "that only the most severe OA level applied herein (3,250 ppm CO_2) had occasional effects, whereas the OA conditions as predicted by the end of this century (1,250 ppm CO_2) in most cases did not affect *A. improvisus* larvae." In addition, and "interestingly," they report, "the major release of larvae and thus, development, settlement and first intense calcification in *A. improvisus* occurs during early summer when pH is lowest." They add, "*A. improvisus* is also found in stands of the brown macroalga *Fucus* spp. where 2,500 ppm CO_2 (pH 7.4) can be measured," and they note "another barnacle species, *Chthamalus stellatus*, was shown to survive and grow at extremely low mean pH of 6.6 in the vicinity of volcanic CO_2 vents in Ischia, Italy (Hall-Spencer *et al.*, 2008)."

Pansch *et al.* write, "given their present wide tolerance and the possibility to adapt to shifting environmental conditions over many generations, barnacles (*A. improvisus*) from the Western Baltic Sea might be able to overcome OA as predicted by the end of this century." And, "supporting this," they note Parker *et al.* (2011) have shown "selectively bred lines of the estuarine oyster *Saccostrea glomerata* to be more resilient to OA than wild populations."

Pansch *et al.* (2013) again collected juvenile barnacles (*Amphibalanus improvisus*) from Kiel Fjord in the western Baltic Sea and distributed them to different temperature and pH treatment combinations in a laboratory setting: seawater of two temperatures (20 and 24°C) and three pH levels (mean pCO_2 values of 700, 1,000, and 2,140 µatm). They fed the barnacles a mix of two marine diatoms every other day until day 24, after which they added specified amounts of brine shrimp until the end of the experiment, on day 62. The four German scientists observed "reduced growth rates as well as weakening of barnacle shells only under very high pCO_2 (>1930 µatm)." They state "even under these highly acidified conditions, and corroborating other recent investigations on barnacles (e.g., McDonald *et al.*, 2009; Findlay *et al.*, 2010a,b), these impacts were subtle and sub-lethal." And "furthermore," they write, "ocean warming as expected to occur in the future (IPCC, 2007) has the potential to mitigate the negative effects of ocean acidification (Brennand *et al.*, 2010; Waldbusser, 2011; present study)." The findings of Pansch *et al.*, as well as those of the other researchers they cite, indicate juvenile barnacles of the species they studied are already equipped to meet the challenges of a significantly warmed and acidified ocean should such challenges occur.

Landes and Zimmer (2012) state, "both ocean warming and acidification have been demonstrated to affect the growth, performance and reproductive success of calcifying invertebrates." However, they write, "relatively little is known regarding how such environmental change may affect interspecific interactions." They separately treated green crabs (*Carcinus maenas*, the predators) and periwinkles (*Littorina littorea*, their prey) under conditions that mimicked either ambient conditions (control) or warming and acidification (both separately and in combination), for five months, after which they assessed the predators, their prey, and the predator-prey interaction for CO_2- and warming-induced changes in response to the environmental perturbations imposed on them.

They found "acidification negatively affected the closer-muscle length of the crusher chela and correspondingly the claw-strength increment in *C. maenas*," and "the effects of warming and/or acidification on *L. littorea* were less consistent but indicated weaker shells in response to acidification." As might have been expected on the basis of these individual species responses to lower ocean pH levels and warming (weaker claw strength in the predator, but weaker shells in the prey), Landes and Zimmer say "on the community level," they "found no evidence that predator-prey interactions will change in the future."

Chan *et al.* (2013) write, "the majority of marine benthic invertebrates protect themselves from predators by producing calcareous tubes or shells that have remarkable mechanical strength," but "an elevation of CO_2 or a decrease in pH in the environment can reduce intracellular pH at the site of calcification and thus interfere with the animal's ability to accrete $CaCO_3$," which "may result in the animal producing severely damaged and mechanically weak tubes." They investigated how the interaction of environmental drivers affects the production of calcareous tubes by the serpulid tubeworm, *Hydroides elegans*, in a factorial manipulative experiment in which they analyzed the effects of pH (8.1 and 7.8), salinity (34 and 27%), and temperature (23 and 29°C) on the biomineral composition, ultrastructure, and mechanical properties of the tubeworm's tubes.

The five researchers report, "at an elevated temperature of 29°C, the tube calcite/aragonite ratio and Mg/Ca ratio were both increased, the Sr/Ca ratio was decreased, and the amorphous $CaCO_3$ content was reduced." And "notably," they emphasize, at elevated temperature with decreased pH and reduced salinity, "the constructed tubes had a more compact ultrastructure with enhanced hardness and elasticity compared to decreased pH at ambient temperature." Chan *et al.* conclude their "results from the analyses of tube mineralogy, ultrastructure and mechanical properties showed that predicted coastal warming may not hinder *H. elegans* ability to build normal tubes even in the face of projected near-future decreases in pH or salinity."

The Norway lobster (*Nephrops norvegicus*) is a decapod crustacean found on the continental shelf and slope throughout the northeastern Atlantic Ocean and the Mediterranean Sea. Styf *et al.* (2013) exposed berried Norway lobsters (females carrying fertilized eggs on the undersides of their abdomens) to four months of "the combination of six ecologically relevant temperatures (5–18°C) and reduced pH (by 0.4 units)," studying embryonic development of the species "by quantifying proxies for development rate and fitness including: % yolk consumption, mean heart rate, rate of oxygen consumption, and oxidative stress." The three Swedish scientists report "the rate of yolk consumption per day, as a measure of embryonic development rate, significantly increased with temperature," and lower pH "had no effect on development rate." They also found "pH had no effect on heart rate" and "there was no interaction between pH and temperature." Further, "there was no significant effect of temperature on oxidative stress when analyzed independent of embryonic age," but "there was a significantly higher level of oxidative stress in the control embryos compared with the embryos developed in low pH." They "observed no mortality nor abnormalities."

The three researchers conclude "this species

would benefit from global warming and be able to withstand the predicted decrease in ocean pH in the next century during their earliest life stages," a significant expression of optimism regarding a species considered the most important crustacean in all Europe (Nofima, 2012).

Winans and Purcell (2010) tested the ability of jellyfish to respond to changes in water temperature and pH during the early life stages. Polyps produced by medusae collected from the moon jellyfish (*Aurelia labiata*) in Dyes Inlet, Washington (USA) were arbitrarily assigned (18 each) to one of six treatments comprised of all combinations of two water temperatures (9 and 15°C) and three pH levels (7.2, 7.5 and 7.9), where they were allowed to develop under controlled conditions for 122 days. The researchers found "polyp survival was 100% after 122 days in seawater in all six temperature and pH combinations;" and because few polyps strobilated at 9°C and "temperature effects on budding were consistent with published results," they "did not analyze data from those three treatments further." At 15°C, there were also no significant effects of pH on the numbers of ephyrae or buds produced per polyp or on the numbers of statoliths per statocyst." However, they write, "statolith size was significantly smaller in ephyrae released from polyps reared at low pH."

Winans and Purcell conclude "*A. labiata* polyps are quite tolerant of low pH, surviving and reproducing asexually even at the lowest tested pH." Nevertheless, the authors note "the effects of small statoliths on ephyra fitness are unknown," which means the phenomenon could bode poorly for jellyfish. Winans and Purcell acknowledge many organisms "may be able to acclimate or adapt to slowly changing pH conditions." They report in Puget Sound "pH fluctuates from 7.2 to 9.6 in 2.4-meter deep water over the span of a couple of days," and "with such large pH fluctuations due to plant photosynthesis during the day and respiration at night, many organisms may be exposed to low pH conditions routinely."

That the findings of Winans and Purcell should not be considered as evidence of future jellyfish blooms is made clear by the study of Condon *et al.* (2013), who note there is "concern about the deterioration of the world's oceans," and that one line of evidence for this concern is "an increasing incidence of jellyfish blooms." They say this "perception," as they describe it, is "largely based on reports of increases in a few disparate regions (Condon *et al.*, 2012)" and on "an analysis of media reports and perceptions of scientific experts and

fishers (Brotz *et al.*, 2012)."

Condon *et al.* set out to analyze "all available long-term datasets on changes in jellyfish abundance across multiple coastal stations, using linear and logistic mixed models and effect-size analysis," in order "to test the null hypothesis that jellyfish population sizes and the occurrence of blooms have not significantly increased in the world's oceans."

The 22 researchers, from Argentina, Australia, Canada, Japan, Norway, Peru, Slovenia, Spain, the United Kingdom, and the United States, found "no robust evidence for a global increase in jellyfish." Although they acknowledge "there has been a small linear increase in jellyfish since the 1970s," they say "this trend was unsubstantiated by effect-size analysis that showed no difference in the proportion of increasing vs. decreasing jellyfish populations over all time periods examined." Instead, they report, "the strongest non-random trend indicated jellyfish populations undergo larger, worldwide oscillations with an approximate 20-year periodicity, including a rising phase during the 1990s that contributed to the perception of a global increase in jellyfish abundance." They conclude their research points normal "recurrent phases of rise and fall in jellyfish populations that society should be prepared to face."

Miller *et al.* (2012) note "a major limitation to predicting the effects of increasing [atmospheric] CO_2 concentrations on marine species and ecosystems is the lack of information on acclimation or adaptation to increased CO_2 over timescales relevant to climate change predictions," and "there is increasing evidence that the capacity for acclimation to environmental stress may depend on the history of previous life stages (Marshall and Morgan, 2011; Parker *et al.*, 2012)."

Miller *et al.* conditioned adult anemone fish, *Amphiprion melanopus*, to present-day (430 ppm), moderate (581 ppm), and high (1,032 ppm) CO_2 treatments—"consistent with projections for CO_2 concentrations in the atmosphere and ocean over the next 50–100 years." They allowed the fish to spawn naturally, after which juvenile fish from control parents were reared at either the control CO_2 or transferred to high CO_2 at each of three temperatures (28.5, 30.0, and 31.5°C), while "juveniles from parents in the moderate- and high-CO_2 treatments were reared in similar CO_2 conditions as their parents at each of the three temperatures."

They found "ocean conditions projected for the end of the century (approximately 1,000 ppm CO_2 and a temperature rise of 1.5–3.0°C) cause an increase in metabolic rate and decreases in length, weight, condition and survival of juvenile fish." But the five Australian researchers found "these effects are absent or reversed when parents also experience high CO_2 concentrations," indicating "conditions experienced by adults can have significant carry-over effects on the performance of their offspring (Bonduriansky and Day, 2009; Marshall and Morgan, 2011; Donelson *et al.*, 2012), often leading to improved capacity to cope with environmental stress (Bernardo, 1996; Donelson *et al.*, 2009)." Miller *et al.* conclude "parental effects prepare juveniles for similar conditions to those experienced in the parental generation," and, therefore, they suggest "non-genetic parental effects can dramatically alter the response of marine organisms to increasing CO_2 and demonstrate that some species have more capacity to acclimate to ocean acidification than previously thought."

Vehmaa *et al.* (2012) state "maternal effects are defined as cross-generation phenotypic plasticity, implying the capability of a mother to adjust the phenotype of her offspring [in] response to environmental cues that her offspring will encounter, in a manner that enhances offspring fitness (Parker and Begon, 1986; Lacey, 1998)," stating as an example, "Sydney rock oyster larvae are larger and develop faster in higher CO_2 conditions, if the adults also have been incubated in high CO_2 conditions (Parker *et al.*, 2012)."

Vehmaa *et al.* "tested the reproductive response of *Acartia* sp. calanoid copepods and the importance of maternal effects in determining the offspring quality in a changing environment according to a 2100 climate scenario of a pH decline by 0.4 unit and a temperature elevation of 3°C." They monitored the egg production of copepods incubated in four pH and temperature conditions for five consecutive days, and on days one, three, and five they divided the eggs and allowed them to hatch in conditions either the same as or different from those in which they were produced.

The three Finnish researchers report, "higher production temperature induced a positive maternal effect resulting in faster hatching and indicating that the mothers can invest more in their eggs, and therefore produce better quality eggs." They note the similar studies of Karell *et al.* (2008) and Jonasdottir *et al.* (2009) showed how "the egg quality in terms of maternal immunological or nutritional provisioning improved," and they suggest this phenomenon may explain "the declining effect of pH difference on egg hatching." Vehmaa *et al.* conclude maternal effects "are an important mechanism in the face of environmental change."

Frommel *et al.* (2013) provide evidence for the adaptive capacity of fish to overcome the potential threat of lower ocean pH levels as well. In spite of its predicted detrimental effects on calcifying organisms, studies of possible impacts of ocean acidification [OA] on fish "remain scarce," the research team found. And although "adults will most likely remain relatively unaffected by changes in seawater pH," they state the "early life-history stages are potentially more sensitive, due to the lack of gills with specialized ion-regulatory mechanisms." They studied the egg and early larval stages of Baltic cod (*Gadus morhua*), which they describe as "the commercially most important fish stock in the Baltic Sea." They examined the effects of lower ocean pH levels on a number of egg and larval properties of *G. morhua* "over the range of CO_2 concentrations predicted in future scenarios for the Baltic Sea (from current values of 380 µatm up to 3,200 µatm CO_2 water)," both "with and without the combination of increasing temperature."

They report "no effect on hatching, survival, development, and otolith size was found at any stage in the development of Baltic cod," where "in situ levels of pCO_2 are already at levels of 1,100 µatm with a pH of 7.2." Their data showed "the eggs and early larval stages of Baltic cod seem to be robust to even higher levels of OA (3,200 µatm), indicating an adaptational response to CO_2." Frommel *et al.* conclude, "since the Baltic Sea is naturally high in pCO_2, its fish stocks may be adapted to conditions predicted in ocean acidification scenarios for centuries to come."

References

Bernardo, J. 1996. Maternal effects in animal ecology. *American Zoologist* **36**: 83–105.

Bonduriansky, R. and Day, T. 2009. Nongenetic inheritance and its evolutionary implications. *Annual Review of Ecology, Evolution and Systematics* **40**: 103–125.

Brotz, L., Cheung, W.W.L., Kleisner, K., Pakhomov, E., and Pauly, D. 2012. Increasing jellyfish populations: Trends in large marine ecosystems. *Hydrobiologia* **690**: 3–20.

Brennand, H.S., Soars, N., Dworjanyn, S.A., Davis, A.R., and Byrne, M. 2010. Impact of ocean warming and ocean acidification on larval development and calcification in the sea urchin *Tripneustes gratilla*. *PLoS ONE* **5**: 10.1371/journal.pone.0011372.

Chan, V.B.S., Thiyagarajan, V., Lu, X.W., Zhang, T., and

Shih, K. 2013. Temperature dependent effects of elevated CO_2 on shell composition and mechanical properties of *Hydroides elegans*: Insights from a multiple stressor experiment. *PLOS ONE* **8**: e78945.

Condon, R.H., Duarte, C.M., Pitt, K.A., Robinson, K.L., Lucas, C.H., Sutherland, K.R., Mianzan, H.W., Bogeberg, M., Purcell, J.E., Decker, M.B., Uye, S.-i., Madin, L.P., Brodeur, R.D., Haddock, S.H.D., Malej, A., Parry, G.D., Eriksen, E., Quiñones, J., Acha, M., Harvey, M., Arthur, J.M., and Graham, W.M. 2013. Recurrent jellyfish blooms are a consequence of global oscillations. *Proceedings of the National Academy of Sciences* **110**: 1000–1005.

Condon, R.H., Graham, W.M., Duarte, C.M., Pitt, K.A., Lucas, C.H., Haddock, S.H.D., Sutherland, K.R., Robinson, K.L., Dawson, M.N., Decker, M.B., Mills, C.E., Purcell, J.E., Malej, A., Mianzan, H., Uye, S.-I., Gelcich, S., and Madin, L.P. 2012. Questioning the rise of gelatinous zooplankton in the world's oceans. *BioScience* **62**: 160–169.

Donelson, J.M., Munday, P.L., and McCormick, M.I. 2009. Parental effects on offspring life histories: when are they important? *Biology Letters* **5**: 262–265.

Donelson, J.M., Munday, P.L., and McCormick, M.I. 2012. Rapid transgenerational acclimation of a tropical reef fish to climate change. *Nature Climate Change* **2**: 30–32.

Findlay, H.S., Burrows, M.T., Kendall, M.A., Spicer, J.I., and Widdicombe, S. 2010a. Can ocean acidification affect population dynamics of the barnacle *Semibalanus balanoides* at its southern range edge? *Ecology* **91**: 2931–2940.

Findlay, H.S., Kendall, M.A., Spicer, J.I., and Widdicombe, S. 2010b. Relative influences of ocean acidification and temperature on intertidal barnacle post-larvae at the northern edge of their geographic distribution. *Estuarine, Coastal and Shelf Science* **86**: 675–682.

Frommel, A.Y., Schubert, A., Piatkowski, U., and Clemmesen C. 2013. Egg and early larval stages of Baltic cod, *Gadus morhua*, are robust to high levels of ocean acidification. *Marine Biology* **160**: 1825–1834.

Hall-Spencer, J.M., Rodolfo-Metalpa, R., Martin, S., Ransome, E., Fine, M., Turner, S.M., Rowley, S.J., Tedesco, D., and Buia, M. 2008. Volcanic carbon dioxide vents show ecosystem effects of ocean acidification. *Nature* **454**: 96–99.

IPCC. 2007. *Climate Change 2007: The Physical Science Basis*. Contribution of Working Group I to the Fourth Assessment Report of the Intergovernmental Panel on Climate Change. Cambridge University Press, Cambridge, United Kingdom.

Jonasdottir, S.H., Visser, A.W., and Jespersen, C. 2009. Assessing the role of food quality in the production and hatching of *Temora longicornis* eggs. *Marine Ecology Progress Series* **382**: 139–150.

Karell, P., Kontiainen, P., Pietiainen, H., Siitari, H., and Brommer, J.D. 2008. Maternal effects on offspring Igs and egg size in relation to natural and experimentally improved food supply. *Functional Ecology* **22**: 682–690.

Lacey, E.P. 1998. What is an adaptive environmentally induced parental effect? In: Mousseau, T. and Fox, C.W. (Eds.) *Maternal Effects as Adaptations*. Oxford University Press, Oxford, United Kingdom, pp. 54–66.

Landes, A. and Zimmer, M. 2012. Acidification and warming affect both a calcifying predator and prey, but not their interaction. *Marine Ecology Progress Series* **450**: 1–10.

Marshall, D.J. and Morgan, S.G. 2011. Ecological and evolutionary consequences of linked life-history stages in the sea. *Current Biology* **21**: R718-R725.

McDonald, M.R., McClintock, J.B., Amsler, C.D., Rittschof, D., Angus, R.A., Orihuela, B., and Lutostanski, K. 2009. Effect of ocean acidification over the life history of the barnacle *Amphibalanus amphitrite*. *Marine Ecology Progress Series* **385**: 179–187.

Miller, G.M., Watson, S.-A., Donelson, J.M., McCormick, M.I., and Munday, P.L. 2012. Parental environment mediates impacts of increased carbon dioxide on a coral reef fish. *Nature Climate Change* **2**: 858–861.

Nofima, the Norwegian Institute of Food. 2012. *Fishery and Aquaculture*. Tromso, Norway. Available at: http://www.nofima.no/.

Pansch, C., Nasrolahi, A., Appelhans, Y.S., and Wahl, M. 2012. Impacts of ocean warming and acidification on the larval development of the barnacle *Amphibalanus improvisus*. *Journal of Experimental Marine Biology and Ecology* **420–421**: 48–55.

Pansch, C., Nasrolahi, A., Appelhans, Y.S., and Wahl, M. 2013. Tolerance of juvenile barnacles (*Amphibalanus improvisus*) to warming and elevated pCO_2. *Marine Biology* **160**: 2023–2035.

Parker, G.A. and Begon, M. 1986. Optimal egg size and clutch size—effects of environment and maternal phenotype. *American Naturalist* **128**: 573–592.

Parker, L.M., Ross, P.M., and O'Connor, W.A. 2011. Populations of the Sydney rock oyster, Saccostrea glomerata, vary in response to ocean acidification. *Marine Biology* **158**: 689–697.

Parker, L.M., Ross, P.M., O'Connor, W.A., Borysko, L., Raftos, D.A., and Portner, H.-O. 2012. Adult exposure influences offspring response to ocean acidification in oysters. *Global Change Biology* **18**: 82–92.

Styf, H.J.K., Skold, H.N., and Eriksson, S.P. 2013. Embryonic response to long-term exposure of the marine crustacean *Nephrops norvegicus* to ocean acidification and elevated temperature. *Ecology and Evolution* **3**: 5055–5065.

Thiyagarajan, V. and Ko, G.W.K. 2012. Larval growth response of the Portuguese oyster (*Crassostrea angulata*) to multiple climate change stressors. *Aquaculture* **370–371**: 90–95.

Vehmaa, A., Brutemark, A., and Engstrom-Ost, J. 2012. Maternal effects may act as an adaptation mechanism for copepods facing pH and temperature changes. *PLOS ONE* **7**: e48538.

Waldbusser, G.G. 2011. The causes of acidification in Chesapeake Bay and consequences to oyster shell growth and dissolution. *Journal of Shellfish Research* **30**: 559–560.

Waldbusser, G.G., Voigt, E.P., Bergschneider, H., Green, M.A., and Newell, R.I.E. 2011. Biocalcification in the eastern oyster (*Crassostrea virginica*) in relation to long-term trends in Chesapeake Bay pH. *Estuaries and Coasts* **34**: 221–231.

Winans, A.K. and Purcell, J.E. 2010. Effects of pH on asexual reproduction and statolith formation of the scyphozoan, *Aurelia labiata*. *Hydrobiologia* **645**: 39–52.

7

Human Health

Key Findings

The following bulleted points summarize the main findings of this chapter:

- Warmer temperatures lead to a net decrease in temperature-related mortality, including deaths associated with cardiovascular disease, respiratory disease, and strokes. The evidence of this benefit comes from research conducted in every major country of the world.

- In the United States the average person who died because of cold temperature exposure lost in excess of 10 years of potential life, whereas the average person who died because of hot temperature exposure likely lost no more than a few days or weeks of life.

- Some 4,600 deaths are delayed each year as people in the U.S. move from cold northeastern states to warm southwestern states. Between 3 and 7% of the gains in longevity experienced by the U.S. population over the past three decades is due simply to people moving to warmer states.

- Cold-related deaths are far more numerous than heat-related deaths in the United States, Europe, and almost all countries outside the tropics. Coronary and cerebral thrombosis account for about half of all cold-related mortality.

- Global warming is reducing the incidence of cardiovascular diseases related to low temperatures and wintry weather by a much greater degree than it increases the incidence of cardiovascular diseases associated with high temperatures and summer heat waves.

- The adverse health impacts of cold temperatures, especially with respect to respiratory health, are more significant than those of high temperatures in many parts of the world, including Spain, Canada, Shanghai, and Taiwan. In the subtropical island of Taiwan, for example, researchers found low minimum temperatures were the strongest risk factor associated with outpatient visits for respiratory diseases.

- A vast body of scientific examination and research contradict the claim that malaria will expand across the globe and intensify as a result of CO_2-induced warming.

- Concerns over large increases in vector-borne diseases such as dengue as a result of rising temperatures are unfounded and unsupported by the scientific literature, as climatic indices are poor predictors for dengue disease.

- While climatic factors largely determine the geographical distribution of ticks, temperature and climate change are not among the significant factors determining the incidence of tick-borne diseases.

- The ongoing rise in the air's CO_2 content is not only raising the productivity of Earth's common food plants but also significantly increasing the quantity and potency of the many health-promoting substances found in their tissues, which are the ultimate sources of sustenance for essentially all animals and humans.

- Atmospheric CO_2 enrichment positively impacts the production of numerous health-promoting substances found in medicinal or "health food" plants, and this phenomenon may have contributed to the increase in human life span that has occurred over the past century or so.

- There appears to be little reason to expect any significant CO_2-induced increases in human-health-harming substances produced by plants as the atmosphere's CO_2 concentration continues to rise.

Introduction

Carbon dioxide (CO_2) does not seriously affect human health until the CO_2 content of the air reaches approximately 15,000 ppm (Luft *et al.*, 1974; Schaefer, 1982), more than 37 times greater than the current concentration of atmospheric CO_2. There is no reason to be concerned about any direct adverse human health consequences of the ongoing rise in the air's CO_2 content now or in the future, as even extreme model projections do not indicate anthro-

pogenic activities will raise the air's CO_2 concentration above 1,000 to 2,000 ppm.

Nevertheless, IPCC contends rising CO_2 concentrations are causing several *indirect* threats to human health, which they project will worsen as the air's CO_2 concentration rises in the future. According to a draft from the Working Group II contribution to IPCC's *Fifth Assessment Report,*

> The most important effect of climate change is that it will exacerbate current risks to health *[very high confidence]*. In recent decades, climate change has contributed to levels of ill-health (*likely*). If climate change continues as projected in scenarios in the next few decades, the major increases of ill-health compared to no climate change will occur through:
>
> > Greater incidence of injury, disease, and death due to more intense heat waves, storms, floods, and fires. [*very high confidence*]
> >
> > Increased risk of under-nutrition resulting from diminished food production in poor regions. [*high confidence*]
> >
> > Increased risks of food- and water-borne diseases and vector-borne infections. [*high confidence*]
>
> … positive effects will be out-weighed, world-wide, by the magnitude and severity of the negative effects of climate change. [*high confidence*] ((IPCC-II, 2013a, Chapter 11, Human Health, p. 3; italics in original, bold removed and formatting changed).

We should note before going on that IPCC's assignment of "confidence" levels to each of these claims is purely a rhetorical device and not based on any statistical tests. (Idso *et al.*, 2013) Placing these expressions of opinion in italics and brackets doesn't make any of these dubious or untrue statements any more credible or true.

In a draft Technical Summary of the same document, Working Group II claims, "The health of human populations is sensitive to shifts in weather patterns and other aspects of climate change [*very high confidence*] and "There is emerging evidence of non-linearities in response (such as greater-than-expected mortality due to heat waves) as climates become more extreme" (IPCC-II, 2013b, Technical Summary, p. 16; italics in original, bold removed).

As shown in the material presented in this chapter, however, IPCC's view of the impacts of rising temperatures and atmospheric CO_2 on human health is simply wrong. Numerous peer-reviewed studies demonstrate a warmer planet is beneficial to humanity, as warmer temperatures in all parts of the world lead to decreases in temperature-related mortality. The medical literature shows warmer temperatures and a smaller difference between daily high and low temperatures, as occurred during the twentieth and early twenty-first centuries, reduce mortality rates due to cardiovascular and respiratory disease and stroke occurrence.

Similarly, the research is quite clear that climate has exerted only a minimal influence on recent trends in vector-borne diseases such as malaria, dengue fever, and tick-borne diseases. Other factors, many of them related to economic and technological setbacks or progress and not to weather, are far more important factors determining the transmission and prevalence of such diseases.

Finally, IPCC entirely overlooks several positive effects of rising levels of atmospheric CO_2 on human health. Carbon dioxide fertilization, for example, has been shown to enhance certain health-promoting substances in plants, such as antioxidants, vitamin C, and fatty acids, and promote the growth of plants such as St. John's wort used for the treatment of a variety of illnesses. In this way, global warming portends great health benefits for humans. IPCC makes no mention of these benefits.

References

Idso, C.D., Carter, R.M., Singer, S.F., and Soon, W. 2013. Scientific critique of IPCC's 2013 "Summary for Policymakers," *Policy Brief.* Nongovernmental International Panel on Climate Change (NIPCC), October.

IPCC-II. 2013a. Chapter 11, Human Health, Working Group II, *IPCC Fifth Assessment Report,* dated March 28.

IPCC-II. 2013b. Technical Summary, Working Group II, *IPCC Fifth Assessment Report,* dated March 28.

Luft, U.C., Finkelstein, S., and Elliot, J.C. 1974. Respiratory gas exchange, acid-base balance, and electrolytes during and after maximal work breathing 15 mm Hg PICO2. In: Nahas, G. and Schaefer, K.E. (Eds.) *Carbon Dioxide and Metabolic Regulations.* Springer-Verlag, New York, NY, pp. 273–281.

Schaefer, K.E. 1982. Effects of increased ambient CO_2 levels on human and animal health. *Experientia* **38**: 1163–1168.

7.1 Hot vs. Cold Weather

- Warmer temperatures lead to a net decrease in temperature-related mortality, including deaths associated with cardiovascular disease, respiratory disease, and strokes. The evidence of this benefit comes from research conducted in every major country of the world.

According to IPCC, rising atmospheric carbon dioxide concentrations cause global warming, and this temperature increase will lead to greater human mortality. However, examination of pertinent real-world data reveals warmer temperatures lead to a decrease in temperature-related deaths, and this phenomenon represents one of the many indirect benefits of atmospheric CO_2 enrichment that IPCC has long downplayed and ignored.

As illustrated in the research described below, it is abundantly clear unseasonable cold temperatures cause far more health-related maladies and deaths than do unseasonable warm temperatures.

7.1.1 Asia

Behar (2000) studied sudden cardiac death (SCD) and acute myocardial infarction (AMI) in Israel, concentrating on the role temperature may play in the incidence of these health problems. Behar notes "most of the recent papers on this topic have concluded that a peak of SCD, AMI and other cardiovascular conditions is usually observed in low temperature weather during winter." He cites an Israeli study by Green *et al.* (1994), which reported between 1976 and 1985 "mortality from cardiovascular disease was higher by 50% in mid-winter than in mid-summer, both in men and women and in different age groups," even though summer temperatures in the Negev, where much of the work was conducted, often exceed 30°C and winter temperatures typically do not drop below 10°C. Behar concludes these results "are reassuring for populations living in hot countries."

Several researchers have examined the relationship between temperature and human health in Shanghai, China. Kan *et al.* (2003), for example, investigated the association between temperature and daily mortality from 1 June 2000 to 31 December 2001, finding a V-like relationship between total mortality and temperature that had a minimum mortality risk at 26.7°C. Above this optimum temperature, they observe, "total mortality increased by 0.73% for each degree Celsius increase; while for temperatures below the optimum value, total mortality decreased by 1.21% for each degree Celsius increase." The net effect of a warming in Shanghai, China, therefore, would likely be reduced mortality on the order of 0.5% per degree Celsius increase in temperature, or perhaps more, since the warming of the past few decades has been primarily manifested in increases in daily minimum temperatures, with much smaller increases at the high end of the temperature spectrum. Hence, the recovery of Earth from the global chill of the Little Ice Age has had a positive effect on the health of the people of Shanghai that should continue into the foreseeable future if the planet continues to warm.

Tan *et al.* (2007) used a multivariate analysis "to investigate the relationships between mortality and heat wave intensity, duration, and timing within the summer season, along with levels of air pollution," for the exceptional heat waves of 1998 and 2003. "For heat waves in both summers," the researchers write, "mortality was strongly associated with the duration of the heat wave." Whereas the heat wave of 2003 was of much greater duration than the heat wave of 1998 (19 days in 2003 vs. 11 days in 1998), the mortality experienced in 2003 was much less than that experienced in 1998 (6.3 deaths/heat day in 2003 vs. 13.3 deaths/heat day in 1998). Tan *et al.* write, "since the meteorological conditions and pollution levels for the two heat waves were alike, we conclude that improvements in living conditions in Shanghai, such as increased use of air conditioning [1.35/ household in 2003 vs. 0.69/household in 1998], larger living areas [13.8 m²/person in 2003 vs. 9.7 m²/person in 1998], and increased urban green space, along with higher levels of heat awareness and the implementation of a heat warning system, were responsible for the lower levels of human mortality in 2003 compared to 1998."

Kan *et al.* (2007) examined the association between Diurnal Temperature Range (DTR, defined as daily maximum temperature minus daily minimum temperature) and human mortality, using daily weather and mortality data from Shanghai over the period 1 January 2001 to 31 December 2004 via a semi-parametric generalized additive model after controlling for covariates including time trend, day of week, temperature, humidity, and outdoor air pollution levels. For cold days (below 23°C), "a 1°C increase of the 3-day moving average of DTR corresponded to 1.41%, 1.76% and 1.47% increases in total non-accidental, cardiovascular and respiratory mortality," respectively, whereas for warm days

(above 23°C), "an increase of 1°C DTR corresponded to 1.13%, 1.91% and 0.54% increases in total non-accidental, cardiovascular and respiratory mortality."

Kan *et al.* say their data suggest "even a slight increase in DTR is associated with a substantial increase in mortality." In addition, they note over the past century global warming has been characterized by "the daily minimum temperature increasing at a faster rate ... than the daily maximum, resulting in a decrease in the DTR for many parts of the world." Their results suggest that in addition to the reduction in human mortality typically provided by the increase in daily mean temperature, the accompanying decrease in DTR also should have been tending to reduce human mortality.

Ma *et al.* (2011) analyzed weather data from the Shanghai Meteorological Bureau to investigate the impact of heat waves and cold spells on hospital admissions in Shanghai, China. They defined a heat wave as a period of at least seven consecutive days with daily maximum temperature above 35.0°C and daily average temperatures above the 97th percentile during the study period. They defined a cold spell as a period of at least seven consecutive days with daily maximum temperature and daily average temperatures below the 3rd percentile during the study period. For one heat wave (24 July to 2 August, 2007) and one cold spell (28 January to 3 February, 2008), they obtained daily hospital admission data for these periods from the Shanghai Health Insurance Bureau.

The four researchers report the number of excess (above normal) hospital admissions during the eight-day heat wave was 352—driven by a 2% increase in all-cause admissions, an 8% increase in admissions due to cardiovascular problems, and a 6% increase in admissions related to respiratory problems. During the 10-day cold spell there were 3,725 excess admissions, driven by 38%, 33%, and 32% increases in admissions due to all-cause, cardiovascular, and respiratory problems, respectively. Ma *et al.* conclude "the cold spell seemed to have a larger impact on hospital admission than the heat wave in Shanghai."

Cheng and Kan (2012) employed a generalized additive model with penalized splines to analyze mortality, air pollution, temperature, and covariate data over the period 1 January 2001 through 31 December 2004 in Shanghai, focusing on particulate matter of diameter 10 μm or less (commonly referred to as PM_{10}) and ozone (O_3). Cheng and Kan report they "did not find a significant interaction between air pollution and higher temperature [>85th percentile days]," but "the interaction between PM_{10} and extreme low temperature [<15th percentile days] was statistically significant for both total and cause-specific mortality." Compared to normal temperature days (15th-85th percentile), they found a 10-μg/m³ increase in PM_{10} on extreme low temperature days led to all-cause mortality rising from 0.17% to 0.40%. They add, "the interaction pattern of O_3 with low temperature was similar," noting their finding of "a stronger association between air pollution and daily mortality on extremely cold days confirms those of three earlier seasonal analyses in Hong Kong, Shanghai and Athens," citing Touloumi et al. (1996), Wong et al. (1999, 2001), and Zhang et al. (2006).

Wang et al. (2013) write, "a large change in temperature within one day may cause a sudden change in the heart rate and circulation of elderly people, which all may act to increase the risk of cardiopulmonary and other diseases, even leading to fatal consequences." They further note, "it has been shown that a rise of the minimum temperature has occurred at a rate three times that of the maximum temperature during the twentieth century over most parts of the world, which has led to a decrease of the diurnal temperature range (Karl et al., 1984, 1991)."

Wang et al. evaluated the short-term effect of diurnal temperature range (DTR) on emergency room (ER) admissions among elderly adults in Beijing. As they describe it, "after controlling the long-time and seasonal trend, weather, air pollution and other confounding factors, a semi-parametric generalized additive model (GAM) was used to analyze the exposure-effect relationship between DTR and ER admissions among elderly adults with different lag structures from 2009 to 2011 in Beijing," where they "stratified groups by age and gender."

The nine researchers report "significant associations were found between DTR and four major causes of daily ER admissions among elderly adults in Beijing." They state "a 1°C increase in the 8-day moving average of DTR (lag 07) corresponded to an increase of 2.08% in respiratory ER admissions and 2.14% in digestive ER admissions," and "a 1°C increase in the 3-day and 6-day moving average of DTR (lag 02 and lag 05) corresponded to a 0.76% increase in cardiovascular ER admissions, and a 1.81% increase in genitourinary ER admissions, respectively." They add, "people aged 75 years and older were associated more strongly with DTR than the 65–74 age group."

Guo et al. (2012) note knowledge of the health effects of extreme temperatures on mortality comes mainly from developed countries, particularly from regions with temperate climates, and they say "few studies have been conducted in developing countries, particularly in tropical regions." They used a Poisson regression model combined with a distributed lag non-linear model to examine the nonlinear and delayed effects of temperature on cause-specific and age-specific mortality, employing data from 1999 to 2008 for Chiang Mai, Thailand (18°47'N, 98°59'E), with a population of 1.6 million people. Controlling for season, humidity, ozone, and particulate matter (PM_{10}) pollution, the three researchers found "both hot and cold temperatures resulted in immediate increase in all mortality types and age groups," but "the hot effects on all mortality types and age groups were short-term, while the cold effects lasted longer." The cold effects were greater, with more people dying from them than from the effects of heat.

Lindeboom et al. (2012) write, "while the association of weather and mortality has been well documented for moderate climate zones, little is known about sub-tropical zones, particularly Bangladesh." They aimed "to assess the short-term relationship of temperature and rainfall on daily mortality after controlling for seasonality and time-trends." Working with daily mortality and weather data for the period 1983–2009 pertaining to Matlab, Bangladesh, where a rigorous health and demographic surveillance system (HDSS) has been operational since 1966, Lindeboom et al. applied time series Poisson regression with cubic spline functions that allowed for lagged effects of weather on mortality, controlling for time trends and seasonal patterns.

The four researchers report "mortality in the Matlab surveillance area shows overall weak associations with rainfall, and stronger negative association with temperature." They determined there was "a 1.4% increase in mortality with every 1°C decrease in mean temperature at temperatures below 29.2°C," but only "a 0.2% increase in mortality with every 1°C increase in mean temperature." In addition, they note the "elderly, aged 60 years and above, seem to be most affected at lower temperatures, with a 5.4% increase in mortality with every 1°C decrease in temperature below 23°C." Lindeboom et al. further report the Bangladesh Meteorological Department data on minimum and maximum temperatures observed in 1950–2010 "showed an increasing trend," but they note the increase was faster for minimum temperature, as opposed to maximum temperature.

Wu et al. (2013) note "numerous studies have reported the association between ambient temperature and mortality," but "few multi-city studies have been conducted in subtropical regions in developing countries." They first assessed the health effects of temperature on mortality in four subtropical cities of China (Changsha, Kunming, Guangzhou, and Zhuhai) by means of a "double threshold-natural cubic spline" distributed lag non-linear model at different temporal lags. They used the combined results to conduct a meta-analysis to estimate the overall cold and hot effects on mortality at different lag days. The 11 researchers report a U-shaped relationship between temperature and mortality was found in the four cities, indicating "mortality is usually lowest around a certain temperature and higher at lower or higher temperatures," as they say also was found by Alberdi *et al.* (1998), Huynen *et al.* (2001), Curriero *et al.* (2002), O'Neill *et al.* (2003), Armstrong (2006), Laaidi *et al.* (2006), and Kan *et al.* (2007). In addition, "the hot effect peaked at the current day, and then diminished with lag days; whereas "the cumulative cold effect increased gradually with lag days, with the highest effect at lag 0–27."

Although "both low and high temperatures were associated with increased mortality in the four subtropical Chinese cities," Wu *et al.* state the "cold effect was more durable and pronounced than the hot effect."

Yang *et al.* (2013) examined the effects of Diurnal Temperature Range (DTR) on human mortality rates, as well as whether the effects were different for different individual characteristics, such as gender, age, and education level. This was accomplished using daily meteorological data for the period 1 January 2003 through 31 December 2010 obtained from the China Meteorological Data Sharing System, which included daily mean temperature plus minimum and maximum temperatures collected from a single station located in the heart of the urban area of Guangzhou City (the largest metropolis in Southern China), along with individual data for all 189,379 registered deaths that occurred over the same time period, which they obtained from the Guangzhou Center for Disease Control and Prevention.

They found "a linear DTR-mortality relationship, with evidence of increasing mortality with DTR increase," where "the effect of DTR occurred immediately and lasted for four days," such that over that time period, a 1°C increase in DTR was associated with a 0.47% increase in non-accidental mortality. They also found "the elderly, females and residents with less education have been identified as more vulnerable to rapid temperature change within a single day." In addition, they report there was a joint adverse effect with temperature "when mean temperature was below 22°C, indicating that high DTR enhanced cold-related mortality."

In light of their findings, the eight researchers speculate the expected "decrease in DTR in future climate scenarios might lead to two benefits: one from decreasing the adverse effects of DTR [which is reduced due to greater warming at night than during the day], and the other from decreasing the interaction effect with temperature [which is expected to rise with greenhouse warming]."

References

Alberdi, J.C., Diaz, J., Montero, J.C., and Miron, I. 1998. Daily mortality in Madrid community 1986–1992: relationship with meteorological variables. *European Journal of Epidemiology* **14**: 571–578.

Armstrong, B. 2006. Models for the relationship between ambient temperature and daily mortality. *Epidemiology* **17**: 624–631.

Behar, S. 2000. Out-of-hospital death in Israel—Should we blame the weather? *Israel Medical Association Journal* **2**: 56–57.

Cheng, Y. and Kan, H. 2012. Effect of the interaction between outdoor air pollution and extreme temperature on daily mortality in Shanghai, China. *Journal of Epidemiology* **22**: 28–36.

Curriero, F.L., Heiner, K.S., Samet, J.M., Zeger, S.L., Strug, L., and Patz, J.A. 2002. Temperature and mortality in 11 cities of the eastern United States. *American Journal of Epidemiology* **155**: 80–87.

Green, M.S., Harari, G., and Kristal-Boneh, E. 1994. Excess winter mortality from ischaemic heart disease and stroke during colder and warmer years in Israel. *European Journal of Public Health* **4**: 3–11.

Guo, Y., Punnasiri, K., and Tong, S. 2012. Effects of temperature on mortality in Chiang Mai city, Thailand: a time series study. *Environmental Health*: http://ehjournal.net/content/11/1/36.

Huynen, M.M., Martens, P., Schram, D., Weijenberg, M.P., and Kunst, A.E. 2001. The impact of heat waves and cold spells on mortality rates in the Dutch. *Environmental Health Perspectives* **109**: 463–470.

Kan, H., London, S.J., Chen, H., Song, G., Chen, G., Jiang, L., Zhao, N., Zhang, Y., and Chen, B. 2007. Diurnal temperature range and daily mortality in Shanghai, China. *Environmental Research* **103**: 424–431.

Kan, H-D., Jia, J., and Chen, B-H. 2003. Temperature and daily mortality in Shanghai: A time-series study. *Biomedical and Environmental Sciences* **16**: 133–139.

Karl, T.R., Jones, P.D., Knight, R.W., Kukla, G., Plummer,

N., Razuvayev, V., Gallo, K.P., Lindseay, J., Charlson, R.J., and Peterson, T.C. 1984. A new perspective on recent global warming: asymmetric trends of daily maximum and minimum temperature. *Bulletin of the American Meteorological Society* **74**: 1007–1023.

Karl, T.R., Kukla, G., Razuvayev, V.N., Changery, M.J., Quayle, R.G., Heim Jr., R.R., Easterling, D.R., and Fu, C.B. 1991. Global warming: evidence for asymmetric diurnal temperature change. *Geophysical Research Letters* **18**: 2253–2256.

Laaidi, M., Laaidi, K., and Besancenot, J.P. 2006. Temperature-related mortality in France, a comparison between regions with different climates from the perspective of global warming. *International Journal of Biometeorology* **51**: 145–153.

Lindeboom, W., Alam, N., Begum, D., and Streatfield, P.K. 2012. The association of meteorological factors and mortality in rural Bangladesh, 1983–2009. *Global Health Action* **5**: 61–73.

Ma, W., Xu, X., Peng, L., and Kan, H. 2011. Impact of extreme temperature on hospital admission in Shanghai, China. *Science of the Total Environment* **409**: 3634–3637.

O'Neill, M.S., Zanobetti, A., and Schwartz, J. 2003. Modifiers of the temperature and mortality association in seven US cities. *American Journal of Epidemiology* **157**: 1074–1082.

Tan, J., Zheng, Y., Song, G., Kalkstein, L.S., Kalkstein, A.J., and Tang, X. 2007. Heat wave impacts on mortality in Shanghai, 1998 and 2003. *International Journal of Biometeorology* **51**: 193–200.

Touloumi, G., Samoli, E., and Katsouyanni, K. 1996. Daily mortality and "winter type" air pollution in Athens, Greece—a time series analysis within the APHEA project. *Journal of Epidemiology and Community Health* **50**, Supplement 1: 47–51.

Wang, M-z., Zheng, S., He, S-l., Li, B., Teng, H-j., Wang, S-g., Yin, L., Shang, K-z., and Li, T-s. 2013. The association between diurnal temperature range and emergency room admissions for cardiovascular, respiratory, digestive and genitourinary disease among the elderly: A time series study. *Science of the Total Environment* **456–457**: 370–375.

Wong, C.M., Ma, S., Hedley, A.J., and Lam, T.H. 1999. Does ozone have any effect on daily hospital admissions for circulatory diseases? *Journal of Epidemiology and Community Health* **53**: 580–581.

Wong, C.M., Ma, S., Hedley, A.J., and Lam, T.H. 2001. Effect of air pollution on daily mortality in Hong Kong. *Environmental Health Perspectives* **109**: 335–340.

Wu, W., Xiao, Y., Li, G., Zeng, W., Lin, H., Rutherford,

S., Xu, Y., Luo, Y., Xu, X., Chu, C., and Ma, W. 2013. Temperature-mortality relationship in four subtropical Chinese cities: A time-series study using a distributed lag non-linear model. *Science of the Total Environment* **449**: 355–362.

Yang, J., Liu, H.-Z., Ou, C.-Q., Lin, G.-Z., Zhou, Q., Shen, G.-C., Chen, P.-Y., and Guo, Y. 2013. Global climate change: Impact of diurnal temperature range on mortality in Guangzhou, China. 2013. *Environmental Pollution* **175**: 131–136.

Zhang, Y., Huang, W., London, S.J., Song, G., Chen, G., Jiang, L., Zhao, N., Chen, B., and Kan, H. 2006. Ozone and daily mortality in Shanghai, China. *Environmental Health Perspectives* **114**: 1227–1232.

7.1.2 Europe

The early studies of Bull (1973) and Bull and Morton (1975a, b) in England and Wales demonstrate even normal changes in temperature are typically associated with inverse changes in death rates, especially in older people. That is, when temperatures rise, death rates fall, whereas when temperatures fall, death rates rise. In addition, at the lower end of the temperature range, Bull and Morton (1978) report, "there are more deaths the longer the 'run of days,'" while at the higher end of the temperature range the reverse is true"; i.e., "the longer the 'run' the fewer the deaths," suggesting people adapt more readily to extreme heat than to extreme cold. Such findings have been echoed in many studies across Europe.

Keatinge and Donaldson (2001) analyzed the effects of temperature, wind, rain, humidity, and sunshine during high pollution days in the greater London area over the period 1976–1995 to determine which weather and/or pollution factors have the biggest influence on human mortality. They observed simple plots of mortality rate versus daily air temperature revealed a linear increase as temperatures fell from 15°C to near 0°C. Mortality rates at temperatures above 15°C, however, were "grossly alinear," as they describe it, showing no trend. Days with high SO_2, CO, or PM_{10} (particulate matter of diameter less than 10μm) concentrations were colder than average, but a multiple regression analysis revealed none of these pollutants was associated with a significant increase in mortality among people 50 years of age or older. Only low temperatures were found to have a significant effect on immediate mortality (one day after a temperature perturbation) and long-term mortality (up to 24 days after a temperature perturbation), with the net increase in mortality over the 24 days following a one-day fall in temperature amounting to 2.77 daily deaths per million people per degree Celsius temperature drop. Keatinge and Donaldson conclude "the large, delayed increase in mortality after low temperature is specifically associated with cold and is not due to associated patterns of wind, rain, humidity, sunshine, SO_2, CO, or smoke."

How does cold kill? The two scientists say "cold causes mortality mainly from arterial thrombosis and respiratory disease, attributable in turn to cold-induced hemoconcentration and hypertension [in the first case] and respiratory infections [in the second case]." McGregor (2005) notes "anomalous cold stress can increase blood viscosity and blood pressure due to the activation of the sympathetic nervous system which accelerates the heart rate and increases vascular resistance (Collins *et al.*, 1985; Jehn *et al.*, 2002; Healy, 2003; Keatinge *et al.*, 1984; Mercer, 2003; Woodhouse *et al.*, 1993)," adding, "anomalously cold winters may also increase other risk factors for heart disease such as blood clotting or fibrinogen concentration, red blood cell count per volume and plasma cholesterol." Keatinge and Donaldson conclude although "increases in mortality due to cold weather are large in many temperate regions ... effective protection against personal cold exposure virtually prevents excess winter mortality," even in places as cold as Siberia.

In a study explicitly considering personal cold exposure, Gemmell (2001) analyzed the answers of 858 respondents to pertinent health and housing questions put to them in the second sweep of the "West of Scotland Twenty-07 Study" conducted in 1991. This effort indicated "over and above socioeconomic factors and house conditions, inadequate home heating is associated with poor health in those aged 55–60." Gemmell notes, for example, "respondents who reported feeling cold in winter 'most of the time' were over three times more likely to suffer from a limiting condition and almost five times as likely to report 'fair' or 'poor' self assessed health," leading him to conclude "living in a cold house will almost certainly exacerbate existing conditions and may lead to early mortality." Gemmell suggests "affordable efficient methods of home heating could help reduce the number of people living in homes that are detrimental to their health."

Carson *et al.* (2006) analyzed London mortality and meteorological data for four periods of the twentieth century they "selected to avoid times of war and influenza pandemics: 1900–1910, 1927–1937, 1954–1964, and 1986–1996." They found "an increase in risk at low temperatures in each period, but the strength of association gradually declined over the century ... from a 2.5% increase in mortality for each degree-C fall in temperature below 15°C in 1900–1910 to approximately a 1.2% increase in mortality per degree-C fall in temperature in 1986–1996." At the other end of the temperature spectrum, their analyses "also provided some indication of heat-related mortality in the earlier periods of analysis, but not in 1954–1964 or 1986–1996."

These results suggest cold is a more effective killer than heat. In addition, they suggest the deadly effects of both extreme cold and extreme heat have been muted with the passage of time, "despite the aging of the population and a progressive increase in the prevalence of cardiorespiratory disease, as Carson *et al.* add, "which would otherwise tend to increase susceptibility" to temperature-induced death.

Another implication of their study results, Carson *et al.* write, is "the decline in vulnerability to cold and heat is most readily explained by beneficial changes relating to increasing wealth." Some of the items they mention are improvements in health care, nutrition, and housing; increased car ownership; climate-controlled transportation and shopping facilities; and improved clothing fabrics, although they say, "we cannot quantify or even identify all of the modifying factors that have contributed to this reduced susceptibility." Finally, they say "it is reasonable to conclude that a similar modification of risk will occur among populations in other settings, particularly in low- and middle-income countries, as they grow richer."

According to Christidis *et al.* (2010), "the IPCC AR4 states with very high confidence that climate change contributes to the global burden of disease and to increased mortality," citing the contribution of Confalonieri *et al.* (2007) to that document. In an effort to evaluate this *very-high-confidence* contention of IPCC, Christidis *et al.* extracted the numbers of daily deaths from all causes from death registration data supplied by the UK Office of National Statistics for men and women 50 years of age or older in England and Wales for the period 1976–2005, which they divided by daily estimates of population "obtained by fitting a fifth order polynomial to mid-year population estimates, to give mortality as deaths per million people." They then compared the death results with surface air temperature data that showed a warming trend during the same three-decade period of 0.47°C per decade. In addition, they employed a technique called optimal detection, which they describe as "a formal statistical methodology" that can be used to estimate the role played by human adaptation in the temperature-related changes in mortality they observed.

As expected, during the hottest portion of the year, warming led to increases in death rates, whereas during the coldest portion of the year warming led to decreases in death rates. The three scientists report if no adaptation had taken place, there would have been 1.6 additional deaths per million people per year due to warming in the hottest part of the year over the period 1976–2005, but there would have been 47 fewer deaths per million people per year due to warming in the coldest part of the year, for a lives-saved to life-lost ratio of 29.4, representing a huge net benefit of the warming experienced in England and Wales over the three-decade period of warming. When adaptation was included in the analysis, as was the case in the data they analyzed, they found there were only 0.7 death per million people per year due to warming in the hottest part of the year, but a decrease of fully 85 deaths per million people per year due to warming in the coldest part of the year, for a phenomenal lives-saved to live-lost ratio of 121.4. Such observations indicate IPCC's "very-high-confidence" conclusion is woefully wrong. Warming is highly beneficial to human health, even without any overt adaptation to it. And when adaptations are made, warming is incredibly beneficial in terms of lengthening the human lifespan.

In France, Laaidi et al. (2006) conducted an observational population study in six regions between 1991 and 1995 to assess the relationship between temperature and mortality in areas of widely varying climatic conditions and lifestyles, including urban (Paris), oceanic (Finistere), semi-continental (Cote-d'Or), or mountain (the Hautes-Alpes) climates and two types of Mediterranean climate, one relatively mild and sheltered (the Alpes-Maritimes) and the other more extreme and windy (the Herault). Daily death and cause-of-death data were provided by the Epidemiological Centre on the Medical Causes of Death, part of the country's National Institute for Health and Medical Research.

Laaidi et al. report "mean daily counts of deaths showed an asymmetrical V-like or U-like pattern with higher mortality rates at the time of the lowest temperatures experienced in the area than at the time of the highest temperatures," noting "between these two peaks, there is a critical temperature threshold, referred to as the thermal optimum, where mortality rates are minimal." This relationship varied somewhat between the two sexes and among different age groups and causes of death. In all cases, however,

they found "more evidence was collected showing that cold weather was more deadly than hot weather." These findings, the researchers say, are "broadly consistent with those found in earlier studies conducted elsewhere in Europe (Kunst et al., 1993; Ballester et al., 1997; Eurowinter Group, 1997; Keatinge et al., 2000a,b; Beniston, 2002; Muggeo and Vigotti, 2002), the United States (Curriero et al., 2002) and South America (Gouveia et al., 2003)." They also say their findings "give grounds for confidence in the near future," stating even a 2°C warming over the next half century "would not increase annual mortality rates."

Diaz et al. (2005) examined the effect of extreme winter temperature on mortality in Madrid, Spain for people older than 65, using data from 1,815 winter days over the period 1986–1997, during which time 133,000 deaths occurred. They found daily T_{max} was more closely correlated with mortality than was daily T_{min}, because, as they describe it, "very low Tmin occur mostly during stagnation episodes, characterized by very cold nights and sunny days, with a typical temperature range of between 15°C and 20°C," while "most of the days with very low Tmax occur under cloudy conditions, with very limited temperature ranges of around 5°C," so "human exposure to low temperatures during these days is longer than that occurring during the stagnation days associated with a very low Tmin." In addition, they note, "Tmin is usually recorded around 7 a.m., when very little human activity occurs outdoors, while Tmax is usually recorded at around 4 p.m."

Diaz et al. determined that as Tmax dropped below 6°C, which they describe as an unusually cold day (UCD), "the impact on mortality also increased significantly." They also found the impact of UCDs increased as the winter progressed, with the first UCD of the season producing an average of 102 deaths/day at a lag of eight days and the sixth UCD producing an average of 123 deaths/day at a lag of eight days. This behavior suggests, in their words, "acclimatisation does not occur, with every cold spell enhancing the pathologies produced in previous spells." Consequently, whereas they report "the impact of heat waves is reduced as they occur during a certain season, suggesting an acclimatisation to heat," just the opposite occurs in the case of recurring cold, which becomes ever more deadly with each new occurrence.

Fernandez-Raga et al. (2010) obtained from Spain's National Meteorological Institute data from weather stations situated in eight of the provincial capitals in the Castile-Leon region—a plateau in the northwestern part of the country that includes nine provinces "with a low population density that can be considered as ageing." The data covered the period 1980–1998, and they obtained contemporary mortality data from the country's National Institute for Statistics for deaths associated with cardio-vascular, respiratory, and digestive system diseases.

Analyses of the monthly averaged data revealed a number of interesting results. First, for all three of the disease types studied, Fernandez-Raga *et al.* found "the death rate is about 15% higher on a winter's day than on a summer's day," which they describe as "a result often found in previous studies," citing Fleming *et al.* (2000), Verlato *et al.* (2002), Grech *et al.* (2002), Law *et al.* (2002), and Eccles (2002). Second, in a finding that helps explain the first, the three researchers discovered when monthly averaged human death rates were plotted against monthly averages of daily mean, maximum, and minimum air temperature, the results nearly always took the form of a U-shaped concave parabola. And for all three disease types, they found all three temperatures (daily mean, maximum, and minimum) at which minimum death rates occurred—which they refer to as ideal or comfort temperatures—were within about 1–7°C of the maximum values typically reached by those three types of temperature, and they were anywhere from 14–24°C away from their minimum values. Consequently, the ideal or comfort temperatures always were very close to (and sometimes nearly identical to) the maximum values reached by the mean, maximum, and minimum temperatures experienced in the region, and they were much more removed from the minimum values of those three temperature parameters, as illustrated in Figure 7.1.2.1, which relates death rates due to cardiovascular diseases to mean air temperature.

The data of Figure 7.1.2.1 clearly demonstrate the people of the Castile-Leon region of Spain are much more likely to die from a cardiovascular disease in the extreme cold of winter than in the extreme heat of summer. The same holds true with respect to dying from respiratory and digestive system diseases.

Referencing the *Fourth Assessment Report* of

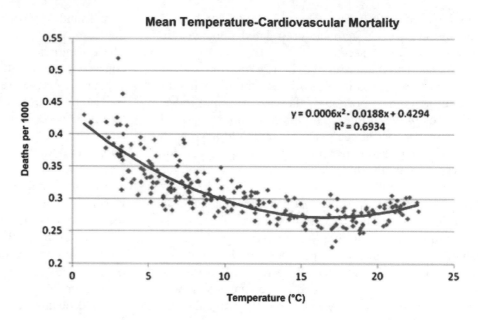

Figure 7.1.2.1. Monthly deaths in the Castile-Leon region of Spain attributable to cardiovascular disease. Adapted from Fernandez-Raga *et al.* (2010).

IPCC, Wichmann *et al.* (2011) write "temperature, a key climate change indicator, is expected to increase substantially in the Northern Hemisphere, with potentially grave implications for human health." Concerned about what that might mean for their homeland, the five Danish researchers investigated the association between the daily three-hour maximum apparent temperature (which reflects the physiological experience of combined exposure to humidity and temperature) and deaths due to cardiovascular disease (CVD), cerebrovascular disease (CBD), and respiratory disease (RD) in the nation's capital, Copenhagen, over the period 1999–2006.

During the warm half of the year (April–September), Wichmann *et al.* found a rise in temperature had an inverse or protective effect with respect to CVD mortality (a 1% decrease in death in response to a 1°C increase in apparent temperature). This finding is unusual but also has been observed in Dublin, Ireland, as reported by Baccini *et al.* (2008, 2011). Wichmann *et al.* found no association with RD and CBD mortality. At the other end of the thermal spectrum, during the cold half of the year, all three associations were inverse or protective. This finding, according to the researchers, is "consistent with other studies (Eurowinter Group, 1997; Nafstad *et al.*, 2001; Braga *et al.*, 2002; O'Neill *et al.*, 2003; Analitis *et al.*, 2008)."

Whereas many observers (including IPCC) continue to emphasize the primarily negative impact of summer heat waves on human death rates in low- and mid-latitude regions of Earth, essentially neglecting to report what happens there during winter cold spells, Wichmann *et al.*'s summer results tell a dramatically different story that is likely typical of higher latitudes. They also portray what tends to happen nearly everywhere in winter, noting during that cold part of the year "only protective effects [of warming] were observed."

Matzarakis *et al.* (2011) developed a relationship between heat stress and all-cause mortality in the densely populated city of Vienna (Austria), using a human biometeorological index known as the physiologically equivalent temperature or PET, which "describes the thermal situation by the air temperature of a reference environment, in which the core and the skin temperature is the same as in the complex outdoor environment." This reference environment is defined as "a room with a wind velocity < 0.1 m/sec, a vapor pressure of 12 hPa and a mean radiation temperature that equals the air temperature," as described in more detail by Mayer and Hoppe (1987).

Based on data from 1970–2007, and after adjusting the long-term mortality rate to account for temporal variations in the size of the population of Vienna, temporal changes in life expectancy, and the changing age structure of Vienna's population, the three researchers found a significant relationship between heat stress and mortality. Over this 38-year period, "some significant decreases of the sensitivity were found, especially in the medium heat stress levels," they report.

With respect to the cause of this decrease in heat stress sensitivity, Matzarakis *et al.* state in the final sentence of their abstract, these decreases in sensitivity "could indicate active processes of long-term adaptation to the increasing heat stress." In the discussion section of their paper, they write such sensitivity changes "were also found for other regions," citing Davis *et al.* (2003), Koppe (2005), Tan *et al.* (2007), and Donaldson and Keatinge (2008). In the conclusion of their paper, they refer to these changes as "positive developments."

Vocks *et al.* (2001) statistically evaluated the influence of various meteorological variables on the intensity of clinical symptoms (itching) caused by the skin disease atopic eczema in the high-mountain area of Davos, Switzerland for the period 1983–1989. Itching intensity was found to be inversely correlated with air temperature, air pressure, and water vapor pressure, such that an increase in any of these variables decreased the severity of itching. Examination of the three variables during periods of abrupt and/or prolonged change, on the order of several weeks to months, substantially improved the correlations. Such findings suggest future warming, whether local, regional, or global, will bring a measure of relief from itching to sufferers of atopic eczema.

In Germany, Laschewski and Jendritzky (2002) analyzed daily mortality rates in Baden-Wurttemberg (10.5 million inhabitants) over the 30-year period 1958–1997 to determine the sensitivity of the population of this moderate climatic zone to long- and short-term episodes of heat and cold. Their research indicates mortality shows "a marked seasonal pattern with a minimum in summer and a maximum in winter." With respect to short-term exposure to heat and cold, they found "cold spells lead to excess mortality to a relatively small degree, which lasts for weeks," and "the mortality increase during heat waves is more pronounced, but is followed by lower than average values in subsequent weeks." The authors say the latter observation suggests people who died from short-term exposure to heat possibly "would have died in the short term anyway."

With respect to this short-term mortality displacement in the case of heat-related deaths, it is worth noting Laschewski and Jendritzky's data demonstrate it is merely a displacement of deaths and not an overall increase. They found, for example, the mean duration of above-normal mortality for the 51 heat episodes that occurred from 1968 to 1997 was 10 days, with a mean increase in mortality of 3.9%, after which there was a mean decrease in mortality of 2.3% for 19 days. Hence, the net effect of the two perturbations was an overall decrease in mortality of 0.2% over the full 29-day period. This is additional evidence cold spells are more deadly than heat waves. Hence, global warming should be expected to confer significant benefits upon mankind in both the short- and long-term, for in both situations, cold kills but heat heals, especially in the long term, which is what global warming projections are all about.

Focusing on the Czech Republic, Kysely and Huth (2004) calculated deviations of the observed number of deaths from the expected number of deaths for each day of the year for the period 1992–2000. They found "the distribution of days with the highest excess mortality in a year is clearly bimodal, showing a main peak in late winter and a secondary one in summer." Regarding the smaller number of summer heat-wave-induced deaths, they also found "a large portion of the mortality increase is associated with the harvesting effect, which consists in short-term shifts in mortality and leads to a decline in the number of deaths after hot periods (e.g. Rooney *et al.*, 1998; Braga *et al.*, 2002; Laschewski and Jendritzky, 2002)." For the Czech Republic, they report, "the mortality displacement effect in the severe 1994 heat waves can be estimated to account for about 50% of the total number of victims." As they describe it, "people who would have died in the short term even in the absence of oppressive weather conditions made up about half of the total number of deaths." Hence, not only is the overall number of deaths typically smaller in the warmest part of the year than in the coldest time of the year in the Czech Republic, approximately half of the heat-related excess deaths associated with the severe 1994 heat waves likely would have occurred even without the unseasonable heat, as they were merely normal deaths simply hastened by unseasonably warm temperatures.

Kysely and Plavcova (2012) write, "there is much concern that climate change may be associated with large increases in heat-related mortality," but "growing evidence has been emerging that the relationships between temperature extremes and mortality impacts are nonstationary," and "most of these studies point to declining heat-related mortality in developed countries, including the US, Australia, the UK, the Netherlands and France (Davis *et al.*, 2002, 2003a, 2003b; Bi and Walker, 2001; Donaldson *et al.*, 2003; Garssen *et al.*, 2005; Carson *et al.*, 2006; Fouillet *et al.*, 2008; Sheridan *et al.*, 2009)." This is true, they note, despite "aging populations and prevailing rising trends in temperature extremes."

Most of the studies cited above were conducted in developed countries; the two Czech researchers note "much less is understood about temporal changes in the impacts of temperature extremes in developing (low- and middle-income) countries and in regions that have undergone (or are undergoing) a transition from the developing to the developed world," They note "post-communist Central and Eastern Europe is one such region, where pronounced changes have occurred over the past 20 years." They examined "temporal changes in mortality associated with spells of large positive temperature anomalies (hot spells) in extended summer season in the population of the Czech Republic (Central Europe) during 1986–2009."

Kysely and Plavcova found declining mortality trends in spite of rising temperature trends, just the opposite of what IPCC claims will occur in response to global warming. The Czech scientists add, "the finding on reduced vulnerability of the population remains unchanged if possible confounding effects of within-season acclimatization and mortality displacement are taken into account," and "neither does it depend on the changing age structure of the population, since similar (and slightly more pronounced) declines in the mortality impacts are found in the elderly (age group 70+ years) when examined separately."

Kysely and Plavcova write, "recent positive socioeconomic development following the collapse of communism in 1989 is the likely primary cause of the declining impacts of hot spells," and "other important factors have been enhanced media coverage and better public awareness of heat-related risks." They also note their key result "supports the idea that the adverse health effects of heat are largely preventable (e.g., Matthies and Menne, 2009)," ultimately concluding "climate change may have relatively little influence on heat-related deaths, particularly if the recent warming trend is viewed as an early manifestation of anthropogenic climate change." They continue, "it appears that changes in other factors that influence vulnerability of a population are dominant instead of temperature trends and that the level of adaptability to high ambient temperatures may be large."

Huynen *et al.* (2001) evaluated the impact of heat waves and cold spells on mortality rates of people of all ages throughout the Netherlands for the 19-year period 1 January 1979 through 31 December 1997. During heat waves they found a mean excess mortality of 39.8 deaths per day, whereas during cold spells they found a mean excess mortality of 46.6 deaths per day. These numbers indicate a typical cold-spell day kills at a rate 17% greater than a typical heat-wave day. They also report the heat waves of the period they studied ranged from six to 13 days in length, whereas the cold spells lasted from nine to 17 days, making the average cold spell approximately 37% longer than the average heat wave. Adjusting for this duration differential makes the number of deaths per cold spell in the Netherlands fully 60% greater than the number of deaths per heat wave. Also, excess mortality continued for the entire month after the cold spells, leading to even more deaths, whereas in the case of heat waves, there appeared to be mortality deficits in the following month, suggesting "some of the heat-induced increase in mortality can be attributed to those whose health was already compromised" or "who would have died in the short term anyway." That conclusion also was reached by Kunst *et al.* (1993), Alberdi *et al.* (1998), Eng and Mercer (1998), and others mentioned in this section. It is highly likely, therefore, that the 60% greater death toll calculated for Dutch cold spells compared to Dutch heat waves is a vast underestimate of the true differential killing power of these two temperature extremes.

In a letter to the editor of *Epidemiology*, the senior and second authors of the Huynen *et al.* paper discussed whether global climate change reduces thermal stress in the Netherlands (Martens and Huynen, 2001). Based on the predictions of nine GCMs for an atmospheric CO_2 concentration of 550 ppm in the year 2050—taken to imply a 50% increase in Dutch heat waves and a 67% drop in Dutch cold spells—they calculated a total mortality decrease of approximately 1,100 people per year for the country at that point in time.

In a multiregional study, Keatinge *et al.* (2000a) examined heat- and cold-related mortality in north Finland, south Finland, southwest Germany, the Netherlands, Greater London, north Italy, and Athens, Greece, in people aged 65–74. For each of these regions, they determined the 3°C temperature interval of lowest mortality and then evaluated mortality deviations from that base level as temperatures rose and fell by increments of 0.1°C. As they describe their findings, "all regions showed more annual cold related mortality than heat related mortality." Over the seven regions studied, annual cold-related deaths were nearly 10 times greater than annual heat-related deaths. Moreover, Keatinge *et al.* note the very successful adjustment of the populations in their study to widely different summer temperatures "gives grounds for confidence that they would adjust successfully, with little increase in heat related mortality, to the global warming of around 2°C predicted to occur in the next half century." They say their data suggest "any increases in mortality due to increased temperatures would be outweighed by much larger short term declines in cold related mortalities." For the entire population of Europe, therefore, even a 2°C increase in temperature, if it were to occur, would be a climate change for the better.

In a major assessment of cold-weather effects on mortality in Europe, Analitis *et al.* (2008) state, "in recent years, the effects of meteorologic factors on health have attracted renewed interest because of the observed and predicted climate change, which is expected to result in a general rise in temperature." This development, they write, has led to a "recent focus on heat-wave episodes," which may have fostered the perception cold-related mortality is not as important a public health concern as heat-related mortality.

Analitis *et al.* analyzed short-term effects of cold weather on mortality in 15 European cities: Athens,

Greece; Barcelona, Spain; Budapest, Hungary; Dublin, Ireland; Helsinki, Finland; Ljubljana, Slovenia; London, United Kingdom; Milan, Italy; Paris, France; Prague, Czech Republic; Rome, Italy; Stockholm, Sweden; Turin, Italy; Valencia, Spain; and Zurich, Switzerland. They assessed the effects of minimum apparent temperature on cause- and age-specific daily mortality over the cold half of the year (October–March), using data from 1990–2000 they analyzed via "Poisson regression and distributed lag models, controlling for potential confounders."

The international team of scientists—from Finland, Greece, Ireland, Italy, Slovenia, Spain, and Sweden—found "a 1°C decrease in temperature was associated with a 1.35% increase in the daily number of total natural deaths and a 1.72%, 3.30% and 1.25% increase in cardiovascular, respiratory, and cerebrovascular deaths, respectively." In addition, they report "the increase was greater for the older age groups," and the cold effect "persisted up to 23 days, with no evidence of mortality displacement." Analitis *et al.* conclude their results "add evidence that cold-related mortality is an important public health problem across Europe and should not be overlooked by public health authorities because of the recent focus on heat-wave episodes."

References

Alberdi, J.C., Diaz, J., Montero, J.C., and Miron, I. 1998. Daily mortality in Madrid community 1986–1992: relationship with meteorological variables. *European Journal of Epidemiology* **14**: 571–578.

Analitis, A., Katsouyanni, K., Biggeri, A., Baccini, M., Forsberg, B., Bisanti, L., Kirchmayer, U., Ballester, F., Cadum, E., Goodman, P.B., Hojs, A., Sunyer, J., Tiittanen, P., and Michelozzi, P. 2008. Effects of cold weather on mortality: Results from 15 European cities within the PHEWE project. *American Journal of Epidemiology* **168**: 1397–1408.

Baccini, M., Biggeri, A., Accetta, G., Kosatsky, T., Katsouyanni, K., Analitis, A., Anderson, H.R., Bisanti, L., D'Ippoliti, D., Danova, J., Forsberg, B., Medina, S., Paldy, A., Rabczenko, D., Schindler, C., and Michelozzi, P. 2008. Heat effects on mortality in 15 European cities. *Epidemiology* **19**: 711–719.

Baccini, M., Tom, K., and Biggeri, A. 2011. Impact of heat on mortality in 15 European cities: Attributable deaths under different weather scenarios. *Journal of Epidemiology and Community Health* **65**: 64–70.

Ballester, F., Corella, D., Perez-Hoyos, S., and Saez, M. 1997. Mortality as a function of temperature. A study in

Valencia, Spain, 1991–1993. *International Journal of Epidemiology* **26**: 551–561.

Beniston, M. 2002. Climatic change: possible impact on human health. *Swiss Medical Weekly* **132**: 332–337.

Bi, P. and Walker, S. 2001. Mortality trends for deaths related to excessive heat (E900) and excessive cold (E901), Australia, 1910–1997. *Environmental Health* **1**: 80–86.

Braga, A., Zanobetti, A., and Schwartz, J. 2002. The effect of weather on respiratory and cardiovascular deaths in 12 US cities. *Environmental Health Perspectives* **110**: 859–863.

Bull, G.M. 1973. Meteorological correlates with myocardial and cerebral infarction and respiratory disease. *British Journal of Preventive and Social Medicine* **27**: 108.

Bull, G.M. and Morton, J. 1975a. Seasonal and short-term relationships of temperature with deaths from myocardial and cerebral infarction. *Age and Ageing* **4**: 19–31.

Bull, G.M. and Morton, J. 1975b. Relationships of temperature with death rates from all causes and from certain respiratory and arteriosclerotic diseases in different age groups. *Age and Ageing* **4**: 232–246.

Bull, G.M. and Morton, J. 1978. Environment, temperature and death rates. *Age and Ageing* **7**: 210–224.

Carson, C., Hajat, S., Armstrong, B., and Wilkinson, P. 2006. Declining vulnerability to temperature-related mortality in London over the 20th century. *American Journal of Epidemiology* **164**: 77–84.

Christidis, N., Donaldson, G.C., and Stott, P.A. 2010. Causes for the recent changes in cold- and heat-related mortality in England and Wales. *Climatic Change* **102**: 539–553.

Collins, K.J., Easton, J.C., Belfield-Smith, H., Exton-Smith, A.N., and Pluck, R.A. 1985. Effects of age on body temperature and blood pressure in cold environments. *Clinical Science* **69**: 465–470.

Confalonieri, U., Menne, B., Akhtar, R., Ebi, K.L., Hauengue, M., Kovats, R.S., Revich, B., and Woodward, A. 2007. Human health. In: Parry, M.L. *et al.* (Eds.) *Climate Change 2007: Impacts, Adaptation and Vulnerability*. Cambridge University Press, Cambridge, United Kingdom.

Curriero, F.C., Heiner, K.S., Samet, J.M., Zeger, S.L., Strug, L., and Patz, J.A. 2002. Temperature and mortality in 11 cities of the Eastern United States. *American Journal of Epidemiology* **155**: 80–87.

Davis, R.E., Knappenberger, P.C., Novicoff, W.M., and Michaels, P.J. 2002. Decadal changes in heat-related human mortality in the Eastern US. *Climate Research* **22**: 175–184.

Davis, R.E., Knappenberger, P.C., Novicoff, W.M,. and Michaels, P.J. 2003a. Decadal changes in summer mortality in U.S. cities. *International Journal of Biometeorology* **47**: 166–175.

Davis, R.E., Knappenberger, P.C., Michaels, P.J., and Novicoff, W.M. 2003b. Changing heat-related mortality in the United States. *Environmental Health Perspectives* **111**: 1712–1718.

Diaz, J., Garcia, R., Lopez, C., Linares, C., Tobias, A., and Prieto, L. 2005. Mortality impact of extreme winter temperatures. *International Journal of Biometeorology* **49**: 179–183.

Donaldson, G.C. and Keatinge, W.R. 2008. Direct effects of rising temperatures on mortality in the UK. In: Kovats, R.S. (Ed.) *Health Effects of Climate Change in the UK 2008: An Update of the Department of Health Report 2001/2002*. Department of Health, United Kingdom, pp. 81–90.

Donaldson, G.C., Kovats, R.S., Keatinge, W.R., and McMichael, A.J. 2001. Heat- and cold-related mortality and morbidity and climate change. In: Maynard, R.L. (Ed.) *Health Effects of Climate Change in the UK*. Department of Health, London, UK, pp. 70–80.

Eccles, R. 2002. An explanation for the seasonality of acute upper respiratory tract viral infections. *Acta Oto-Laryngologica* **122**: 183–191.

Eng, H. and Mercer, J.B. 1998. Seasonal variations in mortality caused by cardiovascular diseases in Norway and Ireland. *Journal of Cardiovascular Risk* **5**: 89–95.

Eurowinter Group. 1997. Cold exposure and winter mortality from ischaemic heart disease, cerebrovascular disease, respiratory disease, and all causes in warm and cold regions of Europe. *The Lancet* **349**: 1341–1346.

Fernandez-Raga, M., Tomas, C., and Fraile, R. 2010. Human mortality seasonality in Castile-Leon, Spain, between 1980 and 1998: the influence of temperature, pressure and humidity. *International Journal of Biometeorology* **54**: 379–392.

Fleming, D.M., Cross, K.W., Sunderland, R., and Ross, A.M. 2000. Comparison of the seasonal patterns of asthma identified in general practitioner episodes, hospital admissions, and deaths. *Thorax* **55**: 662–665.

Fouillet, A., Rey, G., Wagner, V., Laaidi, K., Empereur-Bissonnet, P., Le Tertre, A., Frayssinet, P., Bessemoulin, P., Laurent, F., De Crouy-Chanel, P., Jougla, E., and Hemon, D. 2008. Has the impact of heat waves on mortality changed in France since the European heat wave of summer 2003? A study of the 2006 heat wave. *International Journal of Epidemiology* **37**: 309–317.

Garssen, J., Harmsen, C., and de Beer, J. 2005. The effect

of the summer 2003 heat wave on mortality in the Netherlands. *Euro Surveillance* **10**: 165–168.

Gemmell, I. 2001. Indoor heating, house conditions, and health. *Journal of Epidemiology and Community Health* **55**: 928–929.

Gouveia, N., Hajat, S., and Armstrong, B. 2003. Socioeconomic differentials in the temperature-mortality relationship in Sao Paulo, Brazil. *International Journal of Epidemiology* **32**: 390–397.

Grech, V., Balzan, M., Asciak, R.P., and Buhagiar, A. 2002. Seasonal variations in hospital admissions for asthma in Malta. *Journal of Asthma* **39**: 263–268.

Healy, J.D. 2003. Excess winter mortality in Europe: a cross country analysis identifying risk factors. *Journal of Epidemiology and Public Health* **57**: 784–789.

Huynen, M.M., Martens, P., Schram, D., Weijenberg, M.P., and Kunst, A.E. 2001. The impact of heat waves and cold spells on mortality rates in the Dutch. *Environmental Health Perspectives* **109**: 463–470.

Jehn, M., Appel, L.J., Sacks, F.M., and Miller III, E.R. 2002. The effect of ambient temperature and barometric pressure on ambulatory blood pressure variability. *American Journal of Hypertension* **15**: 941–945.

Keatinge, W.R., Coleshaw, S.R.K., Cotter, F., Mattock, M., Murphy, M., and Chelliah, R. 1984. Increases in platelet and red cell counts, blood viscosity, and arterial pressure during mild surface cooling: factors in mortality from coronary and cerebral thrombosis in winter. *British Medical Journal* **289**: 1404–1408.

Keatinge, W.R. and Donaldson, G.C. 2001. Mortality related to cold and air pollution in London after allowance for effects of associated weather patterns. *Environmental Research* **86**: 209–216.

Keatinge, W.R., Donaldson, G.C., Bucher, K., Jendritzky, G., Cordioli, E., Martinelli, M., Katsouyanni, K., Kunst, A.E., McDonald, C., Nayha, S., and Vuori, I. 2000b. Winter mortality in relation to climate. *International Journal of Circumpolar Health* **59**: 154–159.

Keatinge, W.R., Donaldson, G.C., Cordioli, E., Martinelli, M., Kunst, A.E., Mackenbach, J.P., Nayha, S., and Vuori, I. 2000a. Heat related mortality in warm and cold regions of Europe: Observational study. *British Medical Journal* **321**: 670–673.

Koppe, C. 2005. Gesundheitsrelevante Bewertung von thermischer Belastung unter Berucksichtigung der kurzfristigen Anpassung der Bevolkerung an die lokalen Witterungsverhaltnisse. Albert-Ludwigs-University of Freiburg, Germany.

Kunst, A.E., Looman, W.N.C., and Mackenbach, J.P. 1993. Outdoor temperature and mortality in the Netherlands: a

time-series analysis. *American Journal of Epidemiology* **137**: 331–341.

Kysely, J. and Huth, R. 2004. Heat-related mortality in the Czech Republic examined through synoptic and 'traditional' approaches. *Climate Research* **25**: 265–274.

Kysely, J. and Plavcova, E. 2012. Declining impacts of hot spells on mortality in the Czech Republic, 1986–2009: adaptation to climate change? *Climatic Change* **113**: 437–453.

Laaidi, M., Laaidi, K., and Besancenot, J.-P. 2006. Temperature-related mortality in France, a comparison between regions with different climates from the perspective of global warming. *International Journal of Biometeorology* **51**: 145–153.

Laschewski, G. and Jendritzky, G. 2002. Effects of the thermal environment on human health: an investigation of 30 years of daily mortality data from SW Germany. *Climate Research* **21**: 91–103.

Law, B.J., Carbonell-Estrany, X., and Simoes, E.A.F. 2002. An update on respiratory syncytial virus epidemiology: a developed country perspective. *Respiratory Medicine Supplement B* **96**: S1–S2.

Martens, P. and Huynen, M. 2001. Will global climate change reduce thermal stress in the Netherlands? *Epidemiology* **12**: 753–754.

Matthies, F. and Menne, B. 2009. Prevention and management of health hazards related to heatwaves. *International Journal of Circumpolar Health* **68**: 8–22.

Matzarakis, A., Muthers, S., and Koch, E. 2011. Human biometeorological evaluation of heat-related mortality in Vienna. *Theoretical and Applied Climatology* **105**: 1–10.

Mayer, H. and Hoppe, P. 1987. Thermal comfort of man in different urban environments. *Theoretical and Applied Climatology* **38**: 43–49.

McGregor, G.R. 2005. Winter North Atlantic Oscillation, temperature and ischaemic heart disease mortality in three English counties. *International Journal of Biometeorology* **49**: 197–204.

Mercer, J.B. 2003. Cold—an underrated risk factor for health. *Environmental Research* **92**: 8–13.

Muggeo, V.M.R. and Vigotti, M.A. 2002. Modelling trend in break-point estimation: an assessment of the heat tolerance and temperature effects in four Italian cities. In: Stasinopoulos, M. and Touloumi, G. (Eds.) *Proceedings of the 17th International Workshop on Statistical Modelling*, University of North London, Chania, Greece, pp. 493–500.

Nafstad, P., Skrondal, A., and Bjertness, E. 2001. Mortality and temperature in Oslo, Norway, 1990–1995. *European Journal of Epidemiology* **17**: 621–627.

O'Neill, M.S., Zanobetti, A., and Schwartz, J. 2003. Modifiers of the temperature and mortality association in seven US cities. *American Journal of Epidemiology* **157**: 1074–1082.

Rooney, C., McMichael, A.J., Kovats, R.S., and Coleman, M.P. 1998. Excess mortality in England and Wales, and in Greater London, during the 1995 heat wave. *Journal of Epidemiology and Community Health* **52**: 482–486.

Sheridan, S.C., Kalkstein, A.J., and Kalkstein, L.S. 2009. Trends in heat-related mortality in the United States, 1975–2004. *Natural Hazards* **50**: 145–160.

Tan, J., Zheng, Y., Tang, X., Guo, C., Li, L., Song, G., Zhen, X., Yuan, D., Kalkstein, A., and Chen, H. 2007. Heat wave impacts on mortality in Shanghai 1998 and 2003. *International Journal of Biometeorology* **51**: 193–200.

Verlato, G., Calabrese, R., and De Marco, R. 2002. Correlation between asthma and climate in the European Community Respiratory Health Survey. *Archives of Environmental Health* **57**: 48–52.

Vocks, E., Busch, R., Fröhlich, C., Borelli, S., Mayer, H., and Ring, J. 2001. Influence of weather and climate on subjective symptom intensity in atopic eczema. *International Journal of Biometeorology* **45**: 27–33.

Wichmann, J., Anderson, Z.J., Ketzel, M., Ellermann, T., and Loft, S. 2011. Apparent temperature and cause-specific mortality in Copenhagen, Denmark: A case-crossover analysis. *International Journal of Environmental Research and Public Health* **8**: 3712–3727.

Woodhouse, P.R., Khaw, K., and Plummer, M. 1993. Seasonal variation of blood pressure and its relationship to ambient temperature in an elderly population. *Journal of Hypertension* **11**: 1267–1274.

7.1.3 North America

Goklany and Straja (2000) examined trends in United States death rates over the period 1979–1997 due to excessive hot and cold weather. They report there were no trends in deaths due to either extreme heat or cold in the entire population or, "more remarkably," as they say, in the older, more-susceptible age groups, those aged 65 and over, 75 and over, and 85 and over. Deaths due to extreme cold in these older age groups exceeded those due to extreme heat by as much as 80% to 125%. With respect to the absence of trends in death rates attributable to either extreme heat or cold, Goklany and Straja say this "suggests that adaptation and technological change may be just as important determinants of such trends as more obvious meteorological and demographic factors."

Davis *et al.* (2002) studied changes in the impact of high temperatures on daily mortality rates over a period of four decades in six major metropolitan areas along a north-south transect in the eastern United States. They found few significant weather-mortality relationships for any decade or demographic group in the three southernmost cities examined, where warmer weather is commonplace. In the three northernmost cities, however, there were statistically significant decreases in population-adjusted mortality rates during hot and humid weather between 1964 and 1994. The authors write, "these statistically significant reductions in hot-weather mortality rates suggest that the populace in cities that were weather-sensitive in the 1960s and 1970s have become less impacted by extreme conditions over time because of improved medical care, increased access to air conditioning, and biophysical and infrastructural adaptations." They further note, "this analysis counters the paradigm of increased heat-related mortality rates in the eastern US predicted to result from future climate warming."

Davis *et al.* (2003) evaluated "annual excess mortality on days when apparent temperatures—an index that combines air temperature and humidity—exceeded a threshold value for 28 major metropolitan areas in the United States from 1964 through 1998." They found "for the 28-city average, there were 41.0 ± 4.8 excess heat-related deaths per year (per standard million) in the 1960s and 1970s, 17.3 ± 2.7 in the 1980s, and 10.5 ± 2.0 in the 1990s." Analyzing these results together with various types of ancillary data, they conclude, "this systematic desensitization of the metropolitan populace to high heat and humidity over time can be attributed to a suite of technologic, infrastructural, and biophysical adaptations, including increased availability of air conditioning." Consequently, because "all-causes mortality during heat stress events has declined despite increasingly stressful weather conditions in many urban and suburban areas ... heat-related mortality in the United States seems to be largely preventable at present." The technology and infrastructure advancements made possible by the economic progress of the past few decades have more than compensated for the increasing heat stress during this period of what IPCC describes as "unprecedented" global warming.

Davis *et al.* (2004) examined the seasonality of mortality due to all causes, using monthly data for 28 major U.S. cities from 1964 to 1998, then calculated the consequences of a future 1°C warming of the conglomerate of those cities. At all locations studied, they report "warmer months have significantly lower mortality rates than colder months." They calculate "a uniform 1°C warming results in a net mortality decline of 2.65 deaths (per standard million) per metropolitan statistical area." Since the annual death rate of about 9,500 deaths (per standard million) is so much larger, however, the "death benefits" of the warming are extremely small—a reduction in the annual number of deaths of less than 0.03%, which also pales in comparison to the nearly 20% reduction in annual mortality that has occurred as a consequence of technological advancements experienced between the 1960s–1970s and the 1990s.

The primary implication of Davis et al.'s findings, in their words, "is that the seasonal mortality pattern in US cities is largely independent of the climate and thus insensitive to climate fluctuations, including changes related to increasing greenhouse gases."

O'Neill et al. (2005) assessed the influence of air pollution and respiratory epidemics on empirical associations between apparent temperature, which "represents an individual's perceived air temperature," and daily mortality in Mexico's largest and third-largest cities: Mexico City and Monterrey, respectively. They report, "the effects of cold weather on all-age mortality were similar in Monterrey and Mexico City." When considering the entire temperature spectrum, they found "in Mexico City, the 7-day temperature mortality association has a hockey stick shape with essentially no effect of higher temperatures," whereas in Monterrey the function they fit to the data "shows a U-shape," with "a higher mortality risk at both ends of the distribution," although the effect is much weaker at the high-temperature end of the plot than at the low-temperature end, and the absolute value of the slope of the mortality vs. temperature relationship is smaller across the high-temperature range of the data.

Most interesting, perhaps, was the researchers' finding that "failure to control for respiratory epidemics and air pollution resulted in an overestimate of the impact of hot days by 50%," whereas "control for these factors had little impact on the estimates of effect of cold days." They note "most previous assessments of effects of heat waves on hot days have not controlled for air pollution or epidemics." In other words, the death-dealing effects of heat waves typically are not adjusted for concurrent effects of air pollution and respiratory epidemics, which often account for as much as half of the deaths attributed to hot temperatures; these two confounding factors do not appear to impact assessments of the effect of cold temperatures on deaths.

A prime example of the failure to account for concurrent air pollution effects on mortality occurred in the aftermath of the European heat wave of 2003. In analyzing the impact of air pollutants present during that episode in the United Kingdom, Stedman (2004) found 21–38% of the total excess deaths claimed to be due to high temperatures were actually the result of elevated concentrations of ozone and PM_{10} (particulate matter of diameter less than 10μm). Likewise, Fischer et al. (2004) determined 33–50% of the deaths attributed to the same heat wave in the Netherlands were caused by concurrent high ozone and PM_{10} concentrations. This factor is often unaccounted for in mortality-related studies of heat waves.

Deschenes and Moretti (2009) analyzed the relationship between weather and mortality, based on "data that include the universe of deaths in the United States over the period 1972–1988," in which they "match each death to weather conditions on the day of death and in the county of occurrence." This "high-frequency data and the fine geographical detail," they write, allow them "to estimate with precision the effect of cold and hot temperature shocks on mortality, as well as the dynamics of such effects." Most notably, the data allowed them to detect the existence or absence of a "harvesting effect," whereby the temperature-induced deaths are or are not subsequently followed by a drop in the normal death rate, which could compensate for the prior extreme temperature-induced deaths.

The two researchers say their results "point to widely different impacts of cold and hot temperatures on mortality." They discovered "hot temperature shocks are indeed associated with a large and immediate spike in mortality in the days of the heat wave," but "almost all of this excess mortality is explained by near-term displacement." As a result, "in the weeks that follow a heat wave, we find a marked decline in mortality hazard, which completely offsets the increase during the days of the heat wave," so "there is virtually no lasting impact of heat waves on mortality."

In the case of cold temperature days, they also found "an immediate spike in mortality in the days of the cold wave," but "there is no offsetting decline in the weeks that follow," so "the cumulative effect of one day of extreme cold temperature during a thirty-day window is an increase in daily mortality by as much as 10%." In addition, they write, "this impact of cold weather on mortality is significantly larger for females than for males," but "for both genders, the effect is mostly attributable to increased mortality due to cardiovascular and respiratory diseases."

Deschenes and Moretti state "the aggregate magnitude of the impact of extreme cold on mortality in the United States is large," noting it "roughly corresponds to 0.8% of average annual deaths in the United States during the sample period." They estimate "the average person who died because of cold temperature exposure lost in excess of ten years of potential life," whereas the average person who died because of hot temperature exposure likely lost no more than a few days or weeks of life.

Interestingly, Deschenes and Moretti report many people in the United States have taken advantage of these evident facts by moving "from cold northeastern states to warm southwestern states." Based on their findings, for example, they calculate "each year 4,600 deaths are delayed by the changing exposure to cold temperature due to mobility," and "3% to 7% of the gains in longevity experienced by the U.S. population over the past three decades are due to the secular movement toward warmer states in the West and the South, away from the colder states in the North."

References

Davis, R.E., Knappenberger, P.C., Michaels, P.J., and Novicoff, W.M. 2003. Changing heat-related mortality in the United States. *Environmental Health Perspectives* **111**: 1712–1718.

Davis, R.E., Knappenberger, P.C., Michaels, P.J., and Novicoff, W.M. 2004. Seasonality of climate-human mortality relationships in US cities and impacts of climate change. *Climate Research* **26**: 61–76.

Davis, R.E., Knappenberger, P.C., Novicoff, W.M., and Michaels, P.J. 2002. Decadal changes in heat-related human mortality in the eastern United States. *Climate Research* **22**: 175–184.

Deschenes, O. and Moretti, E. 2009. Extreme weather events, mortality, and migration. *The Review of Economics and Statistics* **91**: 659–681.

Fischer, P.H., Brunekreef, B., and Lebret, E. 2004. Air pollution related deaths during the 2003 heat wave in the Netherlands. *Atmospheric Environment* **38**: 1083–1085.

Goklany, I.M. and Straja, S.R. 2000. U.S. trends in crude death rates due to extreme heat and cold ascribed to weather, 1979–97. *Technology* **7S**: 165–173.

O'Neill, M.S., Hajat, S., Zanobetti, A., Ramierz-Aguilar, M., and Schwartz, J. 2005. Impact of control for air pollution and respiratory epidemics on the estimated associations of temperature and daily mortality. *International Journal of Biometeorology* **50**: 121–129.

Stedman, J.R. 2004. The predicted number of air pollution related deaths in the UK during the August 2003 heatwave. *Atmospheric Environment* **38**: 1087–1090.

7.1.4 Other Regions

In Brazil, Gouveia *et al.* (2003) extracted daily counts of deaths from all causes except violent deaths and neonatal deaths up to one month of age, from Sao Paulo's mortality information system for the period 1991–1994. They analyzed this data for the effects of temperature on the age groups of less than 15 years (children), 15–64 years (adults), and 65 years or older (elderly), determining "change points" at which heat and cold effects started.

Interestingly, the authors found the change points for both heat- and cold-induced deaths were identical: 20°C. For each 1°C increase above this value for a given and prior day's mean temperature, they observed a 2.6% increase in deaths from all causes in children, a 1.5% increase in deaths from all causes in adults, and a 2.5% increase in deaths from all causes in the elderly. For each 1°C decrease below the 20°C change point, the effect was greater, with increases in deaths from all causes in children, adults, and the elderly registering 4.0%, 2.6%, and 5.5%, respectively. These cooling-induced death rates were 54%, 73%, and 120% greater than those attributable to warming.

Bi *et al.* (2008) used correlation and auto-regressive integrated moving average regression analyses to derive relationships between various aspects of weather and mortality in the general population and elderly (65 years of age and older) of Brisbane, Australia, which they describe as having a subtropical climate, over the period 1986–1995. They found "death rates were around 50–80 per 100,000 in June, July, and August [winter], while they were around 30–50 per 100,000 in the rest of the year, including the summer," and "this finding applied both to the general population and to the elderly population, and to deaths from various causes."

In discussing their finding that "more deaths occurred in the winter than during other seasons of the year, although winter in Brisbane is very mild," the researchers note "it is understandable that more deaths would occur in winters in cold or temperate regions, but even in a subtropical region, as indicated in this study, a decrease in temperatures (in winters) may increase human mortality." The evidence continues to grow for extremes of cold leading to the deaths of many more people than extremes of heat, in both cold and warm climates.

Xu *et al.* (2013) preface their work by stating, "previous studies have found that high and cold temperatures increase the risk of childhood diarrhea," but much less is known about whether the within-day variation of temperature (i.e., the daily maximum minus minimum, or diurnal temperature range, DTR) has any effect on it. They write, "a Poisson generalized linear regression model combined with a distributed lag non-linear model was used to examine the relationship between diurnal temperature range and emergency department admissions for diarrhea among children under five years in Brisbane [Australia] from 1st January 2003 to 31st December 2009."

The six scientists found "a statistically significant relationship between diurnal temperature range and childhood diarrhea," such that "a 1°C increase in diurnal temperature range was associated with a 3% increase of Emergency Department Admissions for childhood diarrhea." They conclude, "as climate change continues, DTRs are likely to become more variable," and as a result, "the incidence of childhood diarrhea may increase." Other research suggests this is likely *not* to be the case: Karl *et al.* (1984, 1991) have shown during most of twentieth century global warming, daily minimum temperatures rose at a rate fully three times greater than daily maximum temperature over most of the world. DTRs actually declined over this period and must have led to significant decreases in emergency department admissions for diarrhea among children under five years of age, representing yet another positive health benefit of global warming.

Mrema *et al.* (2012) state "weather and climate changes are associated with a number of immediate and long-term impacts on human health that occur directly or indirectly, through mediating variables," but "few studies to date have established the empirical relationship between monthly weather and mortality in sub-Saharan Africa." Working with mortality data obtained from the Rufiji (Tanzania) Health and Demographic Surveillance System (RHDSS) for the period 1999 to 2010, Mrema *et al.* employed time-series Poisson regression models to estimate the association between monthly temperature—which ranges from 27.9 to 34.4°C in this tropical region—and mortality, adjusted for long-term trends, in three age groups (0–4, 5–59, 60+).

The four Tanzanian researchers report "mortality in all age groups peaked up at the mid of the year," which is "the time when the temperature is relatively lower compared to other periods of the year in Rufiji." If the monthly average temperature drops to a value of 24°C from the threshold, they state, "mortality will increase by 80.7%, 65.7% and 74% in age groups 0–4, 5–59 and over 60, respectively." Mrema *et al.* note "Rufiji's population is accustomed to a tropical climate and, like any other population, is exposed to cold temperatures relative to its average climate." Hence even in a warm, tropical region, relative cold kills far more people than relative heat.

Egondi *et al.* (2012) state, "many studies have established a link between weather (primarily temperature) and daily mortality in developed countries," but "little is known about this relationship in urban populations in sub-Saharan Africa." They employed mortality data from the Nairobi Urban Health and Demographic Surveillance System (NUHDSS) along with time-series models "to study the relationship between daily weather and mortality for a population of approximately 60,000 during the period 2003–2008."

"Overall," the six scientists report, "there are seasonal fluctuations in mortality, with the highest rates of death occurring during periods of relative cold." They also note "mortality risk over the year rises from the lowest mortality risk by about 40% in the 0–4 age group and by about 20% for all ages" in response to a drop in temperature. In addition, "the effects of low temperatures on mortality can last for days," and therefore, "although the world will get warmer in the future, the low temperature-related mortality is likely to remain an important concern." Such findings further demonstrate a change in the weather or shifting of the seasons to cooler conditions, rather than an equivalent increase in warmth, is typically the more deadly of the two types of temperature evolution, even in relatively warm places.

References

Bi, P., Parton, K.A., Wang, J., and Donald, K. 2008. Temperature and direct effects on population health in Brisbane, 1986–1995. *Journal of Environmental Health* **70** (8): 48–53.

Egondi, T., Kyobutungi, C., Kovats, S., Muindi, K., Ettarh, R., and Rocklov, J. 2012. Time-series analysis of weather and mortality patterns in Nairobi's informal settlements. *Global Health Action* **5**: 23–31.

Gouveia, N., Hajat, S., and Armstrong, B. 2003. Socioeconomic differentials in the temperature-mortality relationship in Sao Paulo, Brazil. *International Journal of Epidemiology* **32**: 390–397.

Karl, T.R., Jones, P.D., Knight, R.W., Kukla, G., Plummer, N., Razuvayev, V., Gallo, K.P., Lindseay, J., Charlson, R.J., and Peterson, T.C. 1984. A new perspective on recent global warming: asymmetric trends of daily maximum and minimum temperature. *Bulletin of the American Meteorological Society* **74**: 1007–1023.

Karl, T.R., Kukla, G., Razuvayev, V.N., Changery, M.J., Quayle, R.G., Heim Jr., R.R., Easterling, D.R., and Fu, C.B. 1991. Global warming: evidence for asymmetric diurnal temperature change. *Geophysical Research Letters* **18**: 2253–2256.

Mrema, S., Shamte, A., Selemani, M., and Masanja, H. 2012. The influence of weather on mortality in rural Tanzania: a time-series analysis 1999–2010. *Global Health Action* **5**: 33–43.

Xu, Z., Huang, C., Turner, L.R., Su, H., Qiao, Z., and Tong, S. 2013. Is diurnal temperature range a risk factor for childhood diarrhea? *PLoS One* **8**: e64713.

7.1.5 Multiple Regions

Studying North Carolina (USA); South Finland, comprising all of Finland except the northern provinces of Oulu and Lapland; and Southeast England, comprising Greater London, Essex, Kent, Sussex, Hampshire, Surrey, Berkshire, Oxfordshire, Buckinghamshire, and Bedfordshire, Donaldson *et al.* (2003) determined the mean daily May–August 3°C temperature band in which deaths of people aged 55 and above were at a minimum. They compared the numbers of heat- and cold-related deaths at temperatures above and below this optimum temperature interval for each region and determined how heat-related deaths in the three areas changed between 1971 and 1997 in response to the 1.0°C temperature rise experienced in North Carolina over this period, starting from an initial temperature of 23.5°C; the 2.1°C temperature rise experienced in Southeast England, starting from an initial temperature of 14.9°C; and the unchanging 13.5°C temperature of South Finland.

Donaldson *et al.* report the 3°C temperature band at which mortality was at its local minimum was lowest for the coldest region (South Finland), highest for the warmest region (North Carolina), and in between for the "in between" region (Southeast England), indicating the populations of these three regions are somewhat acclimated to their respective thermal climates. They also found cold-related mortality was greater than heat-related mortality in each region. With respect to changes in heat-related

mortality from 1971 to 1997, they determined for the coldest of the three regions (South Finland, where there was no change in temperature over the study period), heat-related deaths per million inhabitants in the 55-and-above age group declined from 382 to 99. In somewhat warmer Southeast England, where it warmed by 2.1°C over the study period, heat-related deaths per million of the at-risk age cohort declined, but only from 111 to 108. And in the warmest of the three regions (North Carolina, where mean daily May–August temperature rose by 1.0°C over the study period), corresponding heat-related deaths also fell from 228 to a mere 16 per million.

Such findings imply first that people can adapt to both warmer and cooler climates to some degree. Beyond that, local cooling tends to produce many more deaths than does local warming in all three of the areas studied. As for the dramatic decline in the number of heat-related deaths over a period of warming in the hottest area of the study (North Carolina), Donaldson *et al.* attribute this phenomenon to "the increase of air conditioning in the South Atlantic region of the U.S.A.," where they note "the percentage of households with some form of air conditioning in that region rose from 57% in 1978 to 72% in 1997." With respect to the declining heat-related deaths in the other two regions, they say, "the explanation is likely to lie in the fact that both regions shared with North Carolina an increase in prosperity, which could be expected to increase opportunities for avoiding heat stress."

In a review article touching on multiple aspects of temperature-related deaths, Keatinge and Donaldson (2004) report "cold-related deaths are far more numerous than heat-related deaths in the United States, Europe, and almost all countries outside the tropics," noting coronary and cerebral thrombosis account for about half of all cold-related mortality. In describing the mechanisms behind this cold temperature-death connection, they say cold stress causes an increase in arterial thrombosis "because the blood becomes more concentrated, and so more liable to clot during exposure to cold." The sequence of events, as they describe it, is as follows: "the body's first adjustment to cold stress is to shut down blood flow to the skin to conserve body heat," which "produces an excess of blood in central parts of the body," and to correct for this effect, "salt and water are moved out from the blood into tissue spaces," leaving behind "increased levels of red cells, white cells, platelets and fibrinogen" that lead to increased viscosity of the blood and a greater risk of clotting. In addition, cold stress "tends to suppress immune responses to infections," and respiratory infections typically "increase the plasma level of fibrinogen," which also "contributes to the rise in arterial thrombosis in winter."

Keatinge and Donaldson note "cold spells are closely associated with sharp increases in mortality rates," and "deaths continue for many days after a cold spell ends." On the other hand, "increased deaths during a few days of hot weather are followed by a lower than normal mortality rate," because "many of those dying in the heat are already seriously ill and even without heat stress would have died within the next 2 or 3 weeks."

Keatinge and Donaldson state, "since heat-related deaths are generally much fewer than cold-related deaths, the overall effect of global warming on health can be expected to be a beneficial one." As an example, and even including the heat-harvesting of naturally expected deaths, they report "the rise in temperature of 3.6°F expected over the next 50 years would increase heat-related deaths in Britain by about 2,000 but reduce cold-related deaths by about 20,000." Keatinge and Donaldson conclude, "the overall effect of global warming on health can be expected to be a beneficial one."

Hajat et al. (2005) analyzed the history of heat-wave-related deaths in three cities of contrasting wealth (defined as gross national income per capita)—Delhi (India), Sao Paulo (Brazil), and London (England)—based on daily numbers of nonviolent deaths derived from mortality registries for the four-year period January 1991 to December 1994, examining "time-series of daily mortality data in relation to daily ambient temperature using Poisson models and adjusting for season, relative humidity, rainfall, particulate air pollution, day of the week and public holidays," and using "unconstrained distributed lag models to identify the extent to which heat-related [death] excesses were followed by deficits." The latter phenomenon (mortality displacement) arises when people who die during heat waves would have died shortly thereafter even in the absence of the elevated warmth.

For each city, an increase in all-cause mortality was observed for same- and previous-day temperatures greater than 20°C, with excess deaths being greatest in Delhi and smallest in London. In Delhi, the excess of deaths persisted for three weeks, whereas in London it prevailed for only two days and was followed by deficits that led to the sum of the two effects being zero by day 11. In Sao Paulo, as might have been expected, the pattern of deaths was intermediate between these two extremes. Summed

over the course of 28 days, the risk of death associated with heat stress was 2.4% per degree greater than 20°C in Delhi, 0.8% in Sao Paulo, and negative 1.6% in London. These findings led Hajat et al. to conclude, "populations in low-income countries where life-threatening infections are still common may have the greatest vulnerability to the effects of heat," and "those most susceptible to heat are likely to remain susceptible if there is not due attention paid to infectious disease, diarrheal illness, and other major causes of early mortality in these poor populations."

Byremo et al. (2006) studied the effects of temperature on atopic eczema, "a chronic inflammatory skin disease characterized by itching, lesions and lichenification," especially at "the flexure sites of the major joints of the upper and lower extremities." The pain and itching associated with the disease, as they describe it, "may cause depressive symptoms, social isolation and reduced self-perception," lowering the quality of life in children and their caretakers. They report epidemiological studies suggest climate influences the disease's prevalence, noting "atopic eczema has been reported worldwide to be positively associated with latitude and negatively with temperature (Weiland et al., 2004)."

Byremo et al. transported 30 children, 4 to 13 years of age with severe atopic eczema, from their homes in Norway to the Canary Islands, where they stayed for four weeks before returning, and 26 similarly infected children of the same age group stayed at home in Norway the entire time. All were evaluated for various disease characteristics at the start of the study, at the conclusion of the group-of-30's four-week period of stay in the Canary Islands, and three months after the 30 children left the islands to return home to Norway. The specific disease parameters employed in the evaluation were the Scoring of Atopic Dermatitis, the Children's Dermatology Life Quality Index, skin colonization by Staphylococcus aureus, and pharmacological skin treatment.

Noting temperatures during the children's stay in the Canary Islands were much higher than those in Norway, Byremo et al. report the children's time in the warmer climate significantly reduced the severity of atopic eczema, and the youths improved in severity of eczema, quality of life, and bacterial skin culture, which was reflected in a reduction in the use of topical steroids, antihistamines, and topical antibiotics. These positive changes were observed at the conclusion of the four-week stay in the Canary Islands as well as back home in Norway three months later. The researchers state the four weeks spent in the

Canary Islands "led to a lasting improvement for the children," whereas "the control group did not show similar improvement."

Although greater exposure to sunlight and the effect of regularly bathing in seawater, such as the children did at the Canary Islands, likely played positive roles in reducing the severity of their atopic eczema, the results of this study are harmonious with the worldwide negative correlation that prevails between eczema and temperature, suggesting global warming may prove beneficial to people unfortunate enough to suffer from it.

According to Young and Kakinen (2010), "Arctic populations, especially indigenous people, could be considered as 'vulnerable,' because their health status generally shows disparities when compared to the national or more southern populations," and "it is not known if the harsh climate, and especially cold temperatures, could be a contributing or causative factor of the observed health inequalities." To shed some light on this subject, they determined "mean January and July temperatures ... for 27 Arctic regions based on weather station data for the period 1961–1990 and their association with a variety of health outcomes assessed by correlation and multiple linear regression analyses."

The two researchers report mean January temperature correlated negatively with several health outcomes, including infant mortality rate, age-standardized mortality rates (all causes, respiratory, cancer, injuries), perinatal mortality rate, and tuberculosis incidence rate, but it correlated positively with life expectancy. That is to say, as mean January temperature rose, life expectancy at birth rose as well, whereas the undesirable health metrics (such as mortality and disease incidence) declined. They report, "for every 10°C increase in mean January temperature, the life expectancy at birth among males increased by about six years," whereas "infant mortality rate decreased by about four deaths per thousand live births." Young and Kakinen conclude the cold climate of the Arctic is "significantly associated with higher mortality" and "should be recognized in public health planning," noting "within a generally cold environment, colder climate results in worse health."

References

Byremo, G., Rod, G., and Carlsen, K.H. 2006. Effect of climatic change in children with atopic eczema. *Allergy* **61**: 1403–1410.

Donaldson, G.C., Keatinge, W.R., and Nayha, S. 2003. Changes in summer temperature and heat-related mortality since 1971 in North Carolina, South Finland, and Southeast England. *Environmental Research* **91**: 1–7.

Hajat, S., Armstrong, B.G., Gouveia, N., and Wilkinson, P. 2005. Mortality displacement of heat-related deaths: A comparison of Delhi, Sao Paulo, and London. *Epidemiology* **16**: 613–620.

Keatinge, W.R. and Donaldson, G.C. 2004. The impact of global warming on health and mortality. *Southern Medical Journal* **97**: 1093–1099.

Weiland, S.K., Husing, A., Strachan, D.P., Rzehak, P., and Pearce, N. 2004. Climate and the prevalence of symptoms of asthma, allergic rhinitis, and atopic eczema in children. *Occupational and Environmental Medicine* **61**: 609–615.

Young, T.K. and Kakinen, T.M. 2010. The health of Arctic populations: Does cold matter? *American Journal of Human Biology* **22**: 129–133.

7.2 Cardiovascular Disease

- Global warming is reducing the incidence of cardiovascular diseases related to low temperatures and wintry weather by a much greater degree than it increases the incidence of cardiovascular diseases associated with high temperatures and summer heat waves.

According to IPCC, global warming will pose numerous challenges to human health, including premature death due to heat-induced cardiovascular problems. This section examines the results of studies that dealt with this important subject in the past decade or so.

Enquselassie *et al.* (1993) investigated the effects of extremes of temperature and rainfall, as well as intermediate levels, on the number of coronary events, both fatal and nonfatal, reported in the Hunter Region of New South Wales, Australia, located on the east coast of the country about 150 km north of Sydney, for the five-year period 1 July 1985 to 30 June 1990. "Daily temperature and rainfall," they write, "were taken as indicators of acute effects of weather and the month when an event occurred was used to indicate longer-term or seasonal effects."

Regarding seasonal effects, Enquselassie *et al.* report "fatal coronary events and non-fatal definite myocardial infarction were 20–40% more common in winter and spring than at other times of year." As to daily temperature effects, they found "rate ratios for deaths were significantly higher for low temperatures," noting "on cold days coronary deaths were up to 40% more likely to occur than at moderate temperatures." Effects of humidity and rainfall were negligible. The authors conclude their data "support the theory of increased risk of coronary mortality when temperatures are unusually low," and "avoiding temperature extremes could contribute to reduction in annual peaks in coronary events," which occur during the colder part of the year.

Thanks to Norwegian law, which requires all deaths be examined by a physician who diagnoses cause and reports it on the death certificate, Nafstad *et al.* (2001) were able to examine the effects of temperature on mortality due to all forms of cardiovascular disease for citizens of the country's capital over the period 1990 to 1995. Their analysis showed the average daily number of cardiovascular-related deaths was 15% higher in the winter months (October–March) than in the summer months (April–September), leading them to conclude "a milder climate would lead to a substantial reduction in average daily number of deaths."

Research in Israel conducted by Green *et al.* (1994) revealed that between 1976 and 1985, mortality from cardiovascular disease was higher by 50% in mid-winter than in mid-summer, both in men and in women, as well as in different age groups. Summer temperatures in the Negev, where much of the work was conducted, often exceeded 30°C, whereas winter temperatures typically did not drop below 10°C. These findings have been substantiated by several other Israeli studies, including those reviewed by Behar (2000), who wrote "most of the recent papers on this topic have concluded that a peak of sudden cardiac death, acute myocardial infarction and other cardiovascular conditions is usually observed in low temperature weather during winter."

Evidence of a seasonal variation in cardiac-related mortality also has been noted in the relatively mild climate of southern California in the United States. In a study of all 222,265 death certificates issued by Los Angeles County for deaths caused by coronary artery disease from 1985 through 1996, Kloner *et al.* (1999) found death rates in December and January were 33% higher than those observed in June through September. Likewise, based on a study of the Hunter region of New South Wales, Australia, which covered 1 July 1985 to 30 June 1990, Enquselassie *et al.* (1993) determined "fatal coronary events and non-fatal definite myocardial infarction were 20–40% more common in winter and spring than at other times of year." With respect to daily temperature effects, they found "rate ratios for deaths

were significantly higher for low temperatures," noting "on cold days coronary deaths were up to 40% more likely to occur than at moderate temperatures."

Hajat and Haines (2002) set out to determine whether the number of cardiovascular-related doctor visits by the elderly bore a similar relationship to cold temperatures. Based on data obtained between January 1992 and September 1995 for registered patients aged 65 and older from several practices in London, England, they found the number of general practitioner consultations was higher in the cool-season months (October–March) than in the warm-season months (April–September) for all cardio-vascular diseases.

In a study of both "hot" and "cold" cities in the United States—where Atlanta, Georgia; Birmingham, Alabama; and Houston, Texas comprised the "hot" group, and Canton, Ohio; Chicago, Illinois; Colorado Springs, Colorado; Detroit, Michigan; Minneapolis-St. Paul, Minnesota; New Haven, Connecticut; Pittsburgh, Pennsylvania; and Seattle and Spokane, Washington comprised the "cold" group—Braga *et al.* (2002) determined both the acute effects and lagged influence of temperature on cardiovascular-related deaths. They found in the hot cities neither hot nor cold temperatures had much impact on mortality related to cardiovascular disease (CVD). In the cold cities, on the other hand, both high and low temperatures were associated with increased CVD deaths. The effect of cold temperatures persisted for days, whereas the effect of high temperatures was restricted to the day of the death or the day before. For all CVD deaths, the hot-day effect was five times smaller than the cold-day effect. In addition, the hot-day effect included some "harvesting," where Braga *et al.* observed a deficit of deaths a few days later, which they did not observe for the cold-day effect.

Gouveia *et al.* (2003) determined the number of cardiovascular-related deaths in adults aged 15–64 years of age in Sao Paulo, Brazil over the period 1991–1994 increased by 2.6% for each 1°C decrease in temperature below 20°C, while they found no evidence for heat-induced deaths due to temperatures rising above 20°C. In the elderly (65 years of age and above), a 1°C warming above 20°C led to a 2% increase in deaths, but a 1°C cooling below 20°C led to a 6.3% increase in deaths, more than three times as many cardiovascular-related deaths due to cooling than to warming in the elderly.

For the period 1974–1999, McGregor *et al.* (2004) obtained data on ischaemic heart disease (IHD) and temperature for five English counties aligned on a north-south transect (Tyne and Wear,

West Yorkshire, Greater Manchester, West Midlands, and Hampshire) and analyzed them for relationships between the two parameters. They determined "the seasonal cycles of temperature and mortality are inversely related," and "the first harmonic accounts for at least 85% (significant at the 0.01 level) of the variance of temperature and mortality at both the climatological and yearly time scales." They also report "years with an exaggerated mortality peak are associated with years characterized by strong temperature seasonality," and "the timing of the annual mortality peak is positively associated with the timing of the lowest temperatures." McGregor *et al.* explain, "frequent exposure to cold causes a rise in IHD risk factors (Lloyd, 1991) through increasing blood pressure and viscosity, vasoconstriction, heart rate and angina (Morgan and Moran, 1997)."

Chang *et al.* (2004) analyzed data from the World Health Organization (WHO) Collaborative Study of Cardiovascular Disease and Steroid Hormone Contraception (WHO, 1995) to determine the effects of monthly mean temperature on rates of hospitalization for arterial stroke and acute myocardial infarction (AMI) among young women aged 15–49 from 17 countries in Africa, Asia, Europe, Latin America, and the Caribbean. These efforts revealed "among young women from 17 countries, the rate of hospitalized AMI, and to a lesser extent stroke, was higher with lower mean environmental air temperature." They report, "on average, a 5°C reduction in mean air temperature was associated with a 7 and 12% increase in the expected hospitalization rates of stroke and AMI, respectively." They also note "the findings of an inverse association between mean air temperature and hospitalization rate of AMI in this study are in agreement with several other studies," citing Douglas *et al.* (1990), Douglas *et al.* (1991), Mackenbach *et al.* (1992), Douglas *et al.* (1995), Seto *et al.* (1998), Danet *et al.* (1999), and Crawford *et al.* (2003). Finally, they note, "lagging the effects of temperature suggested that these effects were relatively acute, within a period of a month."

Bartzokas *et al.* (2004) "examined the relationship between hospital admissions for cardiovascular (cardiac in general including heart attacks) and/or respiratory diseases (asthma etc.) in a major hospital in Athens [Greece] and meteorological parameters for an 8-year period." Over the year, "there was a dependence of admissions on temperature" and low temperatures were "responsible for a higher number of admissions," they found. Specifically, "there was a decrease of cardiovascular or/and respiratory events from low to high values [of

temperature], except for the highest temperature class in which a slight increase was recorded."

Nakaji *et al.* (2004) evaluated seasonal trends in deaths in Japan due to various diseases, using nationwide vital statistics from 1970 to 1999 and recorded weather data, specifically, mean monthly temperature. The nine researchers note Japan has "bitterly cold winters," and their analysis indicates the numbers of deaths due to infectious and parasitic diseases including tuberculosis, respiratory diseases including pneumonia and influenza, diabetes, digestive diseases, and cerebrovascular and heart diseases rise to a maximum during that cold time of year. Of the latter two categories, they found peak mortality rates due to heart disease and stroke were one-and-a-half to two times greater in winter (January) than at the time of their yearly minimums (August and September). They conclude, in order "to reduce the overall mortality rate and to prolong life expectancy in Japan, measures must be taken to reduce those mortality rates associated with seasonal differences." They also note, "it has long been recognized that cold temperature acts as a trigger for coronary events," and "major infectious diseases are epidemic in winter."

Hence, to achieve the scientists' stated objectives, it is necessary to bring about a "reduction in exposure to cold environments," as they put it, which is precisely what global warming does, and what it does best by warming more in winter than in summer, as Nakaji *et al.* demonstrate to be the case in Japan, where winter warming over the past 30 years was twice as great as it was during the rest of the year.

In Sao Paulo, Brazil, where 12,007 deaths were observed from 1996 to 1998, Sharovsky *et al.* (2004) investigated "associations between weather (temperature, humidity and barometric pressure), air pollution (sulfur dioxide, carbon monoxide, and inhalable particulates), and the daily death counts attributed to myocardial infarction." Their efforts revealed "a significant association of daily temperature with deaths due to myocardial infarction ($p<0.001$), with the lowest mortality being observed at temperatures between 21.6 and 22.6°C." For all practical purposes, however, their data showed little variation in death rates from 18°C to just over 25°C, with the latter representing the typical upper limit of observed temperature in Sao Paulo, which is located on the Tropic of Capricorn at an altitude of 800 m. As mean daily temperature dropped below 18°C, however, death rates rose in essentially linear fashion to attain a value at 12°C (the typical lower limit of observed temperature in Sao Paulo) more than 35%

greater than the minimum baseline value registered between 21.6 and 22.6°C.

Sharovsky *et al.* say their findings "demonstrated a strong association between daily temperature and myocardial infarction in Sao Paulo, Brazil," which suggests "an acclimatization of the population to the local climate occurs and that myocardial infarction deaths peak in winter not only because of absolute low temperature but possibly secondary to a decrease relative to the average annual temperature." This indeed must be true, for deaths due to heart attacks are consistently greater in winter than in summer, as they write, "across many regions of the world (Marshall *et al.*, 1998; Douglas *et al.*, 1991; Seto *et al.*, 1998; Sheth *et al.*, 1999)."

Kovats *et al.* (2004) analyzed patterns of temperature-related hospital admissions and deaths in Greater London during the mid-1990s. For the three-year period 1994–1996, cardiovascular-related deaths were approximately 50% greater during the coldest part of the winter than during the peak warmth of summer, whereas respiratory-related deaths were nearly 150% greater in the depths of winter cold than at the height of summer warmth. Also, with respect to heat waves, the mortality impact of the notable heat wave of 29 July to 3 August 1995 was so tiny it could not be discerned among the random scatter of plots of three-year-average daily deaths from cardiovascular and respiratory problems versus day of year.

In a review article published in the *Southern Medical Journal*, Keatinge and Donaldson (2004) begin with a clear declaration of the relative dangers of heat and cold for human mortality, writing, "cold-related deaths are far more numerous than heat-related deaths in the United States, Europe, and almost all countries outside the tropics, and almost all of them are due to common illnesses that are increased by cold."

Keatinge and Donaldson report coronary and cerebral thrombosis account for about half of all cold-related deaths, and respiratory diseases account for approximately half of the rest. They say cold stress causes an increase in arterial thrombosis "because the blood becomes more concentrated, and so more liable to clot during exposure to cold." As they describe it, "the body's first adjustment to cold stress is to shut down blood flow to the skin to conserve body heat," which "produces an excess of blood in central parts of the body," and to correct for this effect, "salt and water are moved out from the blood into tissue spaces," leaving behind "increased levels of red cells, white cells, platelets and fibrinogen" that lead to increased viscosity of the blood and a greater risk of clotting.

As to respiratory-related deaths, the British scientists report the infections that cause them spread more readily in cold weather because people "crowd together in poorly ventilated spaces when it is cold." In addition, they say "breathing of cold air stimulates coughing and running of the nose, and this helps to spread respiratory viruses and bacteria." The "train of events leading to respiratory deaths," they continue, "often starts with a cold or some other minor infection of the upper airways," which "spreads to the bronchi and to the lungs," whereupon "secondary infection often follows and can lead to pneumonia." They also note cold stress "tends to suppress immune responses to infections," and respiratory infections typically "increase the plasma level of fibrinogen, and this contributes to the rise in arterial thrombosis in winter."

Keatinge and Donaldson also note "cold spells are closely associated with sharp increases in mortality rates," and "deaths continue for many days after a cold spell ends." On the other hand, they report, "increased deaths during a few days of hot weather are followed by a lower than normal mortality rate," because "many of those dying in the heat are already seriously ill and even without heat stress would have died within the next 2 or 3 weeks."

With respect to the implications of global warming for human mortality, Keatinge and Donaldson state "since heat-related deaths are generally much fewer than cold-related deaths"—and, it should be noted, consist primarily of deaths that typically would have occurred shortly even without excess heat—"the overall effect of global warming on health can be expected to be a beneficial one." They report, "the rise in temperature of 3.6°F expected over the next 50 years would increase heat-related deaths in Britain by about 2,000 but reduce cold-related deaths by about 20,000."

Keatinge and Donaldson concluded, "even in climates as warm as southern Europe or North Carolina [USA], cold weather causes more deaths than hot weather." They report "global warming will reduce this at first," but "the improvement is not likely to continue without action to promote defenses against cold." They report "people in regions with mild winters become careless about cold stress, protect themselves less effectively against cold, and generally have more winter deaths than people in colder regions," noting "climatic warming therefore calls for action to control cold stress as well as heat stress," and stating if appropriate precautions are taken, "rising temperatures could reduce overall mortality rates." Consequently, they conclude, "the overall effect of global warming on health can be expected to be a beneficial one."

McGregor (2005) noted "anomalous cold stress can increase blood viscosity and blood pressure due to the activation of the sympathetic nervous system which accelerates the heart rate and increases vascular resistance (Collins *et al.*, 1985; Jehn *et al.*, 2002; Healy, 2003; Keatinge *et al.*, 1984; Mercer, 2003; Woodhouse *et al.*, 1993)," while further noting "anomalously cold winters may also increase other risk factors for heart disease such as blood clotting or fibrinogen concentration, red blood cell count per volume and plasma cholesterol." He conducted an analysis to determine whether there was any association between the level of IHD mortality in three English counties (Hampshire, West Midlands, and West Yorkshire) and the winter-season North Atlantic Oscillation (NAO), which exerts a fundamental control on the nature of winter climate in Western Europe, focusing on the winters of 1974–1975 through 1998–1999.

McGregor found "generally below average monthly and all-winter IHD mortality is associated with strong positive values of the monthly or winter climate index which indicates the predominance of anomalously warm moist westerly flows of air over England associated with a positive phase of the NAO." At the other extreme, he found "winters with elevated mortality levels ... have been shown to be clearly associated with a negative NAO phase and anomalously low temperatures," adding "the occurrence of influenza ... helps elevate winter mortality above that of summer."

Carder *et al.* (2005) used generalized linear Poisson regression models to investigate the relationship between outside air temperature and deaths due to all non-accident causes in the three largest cities of Scotland (Glasgow, Edinburgh, and Aberdeen) between January 1981 and December 2001. They observed "an overall increase in mortality as temperature decreases," which "appears to be steeper at lower temperatures than at warmer temperatures," while "there is little evidence of an increase in mortality at the hot end of the temperature range." They also report "the observed relation between cold temperature and mortality was typically stronger among the elderly," and "cold temperature effects on mortality persist with lag periods of beyond two weeks." The seven scientists found, for temperatures below 11°C, a 1°C drop in the daytime mean temperature on any one day was associated with an increase in cardiovascular-caused mortality of

3.4% over the following month. At any season of the year a decline in air temperature in the major cities of Scotland leads to increases in deaths due to cardiovascular causes, whereas there is little or no such increase in mortality associated with heat waves.

Cagle and Hubbard (2005) examined the relationship between temperature and cardiac-related deaths in King County, Washington (USA) over the period 1980–2000 using Poisson regression analysis, based on information provided by the Washington State Department of Health on out-of-hospital deaths of all adults over the age of 54, plus historical meteorological data obtained from the National Climate Data Center for the Seattle-Tacoma International Airport. They determined there was an average of 2.86 cardiac-related deaths per day for all days when the maximum temperature fell within the broad range of 5–30°C. For days with maximum temperatures less than 5°C, the death rate rose by 15% to a mean value of 3.30, whereas on days with maximum temperatures greater than 30°C, death rates did not rise at all, actually dropping by 3% to a mean value of 2.78. In addition, "the observed association between temperature and death rate is not due to confounding by other meteorological variables," and "temperature continues to be statistically significantly associated with death rate even at a 5-day time lag."

Cagle and Hubbard describe a number of human haematological changes that occur upon exposure to cold, including a decrease in blood plasma volume (Bass and Henschel, 1956; Chen and Chien, 1977; Fregley, 1982; Collins *et al.*, 1985) that is accompanied by "a sympathetic nervous system reflex response to cold-induced stress (LeBlanc *et al.*, 1978; Collins *et al.*, 1985; LeBlanc, 1992)" and "an increase in packed cell volume due to increased numbers of red cells per unit volume (Keatinge *et al.*, 1984), increased platelet counts and platelet volume (Finkel and Cumming, 1965; Keatinge *et al.*, 1984), increased whole blood viscosity (Keatinge *et al.*, 1984), increased serum lipid levels (Keatinge *et al.*, 1984; Woodhouse *et al.*, 1993; Neild *et al.*, 1994), and increased plasma fibrinogen and factor VII clotting activity values (Keatinge *et al.*, 1984; Woodhouse *et al.*, 1994)." These haemodynamic and vasoconstrictive factors combine "to produce what Muller *et al.* (1994) refer to as 'acute risk factors' that may trigger a cardiac event." Vasoconstriction and concomitant increases in central blood volume and systolic blood pressure, for example, "put additional workload on the heart which may lead to increased arrhythmias (Amsterdam *et al.*, 1987), decreased thresholds for angina and abnormal myocardial contractions (De Lorenzo *et al.*, 1999), as well as increasing the risk of dislodging a vulnerable plaque which could lead to thrombosis (Muller *et al.*, 1994)," which "may occur through increased cardiac filling pressure and stroke volume which in turn increases cardiac oxygen requirements while lessening cardiac access to oxygen (Muza *et al.*, 1988; De Lorenzo *et al.*, 1999)." In addition, the Washington researchers report "greater blood viscosity also works to increase the load on the heart through greater resistance to flow (Frisancho, 1993) and increasing blood pressure (Keatinge *et al.*, 1984)."

Tam *et al.* (2009) employed daily mortality data for the years 1997 to 2002, obtained from the Hong Kong Census and Statistics Department, to examine the association between diurnal temperature range (DTR = daily maximum temperature minus daily minimum temperature) and cardiovascular disease among the elderly (people aged 65 and older). They report "a 1.7% increase in mortality for an increase of 1°C in DTR at lag days 0–3" and describe these results as being "similar to those reported in Shanghai." The four researchers state "a large fluctuation in the daily temperature—even in a tropical city like Hong Kong—has a significant impact on cardiovascular mortality among the elderly population." In addition, the DTR has declined significantly over many parts of the world as mean global temperature has risen over the past several decades (Easterling *et al.*, 1997), perhaps another reason why colder temperatures are a much greater risk to human life than are warmer temperatures.

Working in the nine urban districts of Shanghai, China, Cao *et al.* (2009) used time-series and case-crossover approaches to assess the relationship between DTR and coronary heart disease (CHD) deaths that occurred between 1 January 2001 and 31 December 2004, based on mortality data for elderly (66 years of age or older) people, obtained from the Shanghai Municipal Center of Disease Control and Prevention, and temperature data they obtained from a fixed-site station in the Xuhui District of Shanghai. They adjusted the data to account for the mortality impacts of long-term and seasonal trends in CHD mortality, day of week, temperature, relative humidity, and concomitant atmospheric concentrations of PM_{10}, SO_2, NO_2, and O_3, which they obtained from the Shanghai Environmental Monitoring Center. They found "a 1°C increase in DTR (lag = 2) corresponded to a 2.46% increase in CHD mortality on time-series analysis, a 3.21% increase on unidirectional case-crossover analysis, and a 2.13% increase on bidirectional case-crossover

analysis," and "the estimated effects of DTR on CHD mortality were similar in the warm and cool seasons." The seven scientists conclude their "data suggest that even a small increase in DTR is associated with a substantial increase in deaths due to CHD."

Employing a generalized additive statistical model that blends the properties of generalized linear models with additive models, Bayentin *et al.* (2010) analyzed the standardized daily hospitalization rates for ischemic heart disease (IHD) and their relationship with climatic conditions up to two weeks prior to the day of admission—controlling for time trends, day of the season, and gender—to determine the short-term effects of climate conditions on the incidence of IHD over the 1989–2006 time period for 18 health regions of Quebec. The authors report, "a decline in the effects of meteorological variables on IHD daily admission rates was observed over the period of 1989–2006." This observation, they write, "can partly be explained by the changes in surface air temperature," which they describe as warming "over the last few decades," as is further described by Bonsal *et al.* (2001) and Zhang *et al.* (2000) for the twentieth century portion of the study's duration. In addition, they note, "winters have been steadily warmer" while "summers have yet to become hotter for most regions," another beneficial characteristic of the warming experienced over most of the planet throughout the latter part of the twentieth century (Easterling *et al.*, 1997). The six scientists also report what they call their "counter-intuitive finding," that "cold temperatures resulted in a protective effect for women except for most Northern regions."

Toro *et al.* (2010) note "several studies have demonstrated that cardiovascular mortality has a seasonal distribution (Arntz *et al.*, 2000; Weerasinghe *et al.* 2002; Nakaji *et al.*, 2004; Kloner, 2006)" and "the relationship between cold weather and ischemic heart disease mortality is well established (Vuori, 1987; Gyllerup *et al.*, 1993; Gyllerup, 2000)." They state "cold temperature may be an important factor in bringing on the onset of life-threatening cardiac events, even in regions with relatively mild winters," citing Cagle and Hubbard (2005).

Working with data on 7,450 cardiovascular-related deaths that occurred in Budapest, Hungary between 1995 and 2004, where the deceased were "medico-legally autopsied," Toro *et al.* sought potential relationships between daily maximum, minimum, and mean temperature, air humidity, air pressure, wind speed, global radiation, and daily numbers of the heart-related deaths.

The six Hungarian scientists report and restate

their primary finding numerous times throughout their paper, writing, "both the maximum and the minimum daily temperatures tend to be lower when more death cases occur in a day," "on the days with four or more death cases, the daily maximum and minimum temperatures tend to be lower than on days without any cardiovascular death events," "the largest frequency of cardiovascular death cases was detected in cold and cooling weather conditions," "we found a significant negative relationship between temperature and cardiovascular mortality," "the analysis of 6-hour change of air pressure suggests that more acute or chronic vascular death cases occur during increasing air pressure conditions (implying cold weather fronts)," "we found a high frequency of cardiovascular death in cold weather," "a significant negative relationship was detected between daily maximum [and] minimum temperature[s] and the number of sudden cardiovascular death cases," and "a significant negative correlation was detected between daily mean temperature and cardiovascular mortality." In a summary statement regarding their work, Toro et al. write, "with these analyses, we confirmed the results of other studies (Donaldson et al., 1998; Gyllerup, 2000; Mercer, 2003) that mortality was in inverse relation to air temperature."

Bhaskaran et al. (2010) explored the short-term relationship between ambient temperature and risk of heart attacks (myocardial infarction) in England and Wales by analyzing daily time series data from 15 metropolitan areas. The data covered 84,010 hospital admissions from 2003–2006. They found a broadly linear relationship between temperature and heart attacks that was well characterized by log-linear models without a temperature threshold, such that each 1°C reduction in daily mean temperature was associated with a 2.0% cumulative increase in risk of myocardial infarction over the current and following 28 days. They also report heat had no detrimental effect, as an increased risk of myocardial infarction at higher temperatures was not detected. They found adults aged 75–84 and those with previous coronary heart disease seemed more vulnerable to the effects of cold than other age groups (P for interaction 0.001 or less in each case), whereas those taking aspirin were less vulnerable (P for interaction 0.007).

Kysely et al. (2011) write, "in the Czech Republic, mortality associated with heat waves (Kysely, 2004; Kysely and Kriz, 2008) and cold spells (Kysely et al., 2009) has been examined," but they note, "previous studies were based on different definitions and approaches which did not allow for a comparative analysis.

Working with a nationwide database of daily mortality records that cover the 21-year period 1986–2006—which, in their words, "encompasses seasons with the hottest summers on record (1992, 1994, 2003) as well as several very cold winters (1986/87, 1995/96, 2005/06)"—Kysely et al. compared the effects of hot and cold periods on cardiovascular mortality using analogous definitions for heat waves and cold spells based on quantiles of daily average temperature anomalies and did not incorporate any location-specific threshold, while excluding periods characterized by epidemics of influenza and acute respiratory infections that occur primarily in winter and are also responsible for many deaths. The four Czech scientists report "both hot and cold spells are associated with significant excess cardiovascular mortality," but "the effects of hot spells are more direct (unlagged) and typically concentrated in a few days of a hot spell, while cold spells are associated with indirect (lagged) mortality impacts persisting after a cold spell ends." Although they report "the mortality peak is less pronounced for cold spells," they determined "the cumulative magnitude of excess mortality is larger for cold than hot spells."

With respect to gender differences, the researchers found a "much larger excess mortality of females in hot spells and more lagged effects in females than males associated with cold spells." With respect to age, they report "effects of hot spells have a similar temporal pattern in all age groups but much larger magnitude in the elderly," whereas in the case of cold spells, "relative excess mortality is largest in the middle-aged population (25–59 years)."

Kysely et al. (2011) conclude, "in the context of climate change, substantial reductions in cold-related mortality are very likely in mid-latitudinal regions, particularly if the increasing adaptability of societies to weather is taken into account (cf. Christidis et al., 2010)," and "it is probable that reductions in cold-related mortality will be more important than possible increases in heat-related mortality."

Lim et al. (2012) state, "with the increasing concern directed at climate change, temperature-related environment variables have been studied as risk factors for cardiovascular and respiratory diseases, especially in European, Australian, and US cities," noting "in addition to heat or cold waves, diurnal temperature range (DTR) has been suggested as a predictor of mortality (Curriero et al., 2002) and was, in fact, found to be a risk factor for human health." Focusing on the four largest cities of Korea—the populations of which ranged from 2.5 to 9.8 million (Seoul, Incheon, Daegu, and Busan)—

Lim *et al.* obtained daily hospital admission information pertaining from the countrywide database of the Korea National Health Insurance Corporation, which covers 97% of Korea's population. They assessed the effects of increasing DTR on hospital admissions for the most common cardiovascular and respiratory diseases in those four cities for the period 2003–2006, employing two statistical approaches: "a Poisson generalized linear model (GLM) and a temperature-matched case-crossover (CC) design (Basu *et al.*, 2005)."

According to the three South Korean researchers, the data showed "the area-combined effects of DTR on cardiac failure and asthma were statistically significant," and the DTR effects on asthma admissions were greater for the elderly (75 years or older) than for the non-elderly group. "In particular," they write, "the effects on cardiac failure and asthma were significant with the percentage change of hospital admissions per 1°C increment of DTR at 3.0% and 1.1%, respectively."

Because the global warming of the past several decades has been associated with a decrease in DTR (global warming is predominantly caused by an increase in daily minimum temperature), it likely has helped to significantly reduce hospital admissions for cardiac failure and asthma in the larger cities of Korea and around the world. Lim *et al.* note DTR effects on nonaccidental, cardiovascular, and respiratory mortality or emergency admissions have been studied in a number of Asian countries, citing Cao *et al.* (2009), Chen *et al.* (2007), Kan *et al.* (2007), Liang *et al.* (2008), Liang *et al.* (2009), Lim *et al.* (2012), Shinkawa *et al.* (1990), Song *et al.* (2008), and Tam *et al.* (2009). Each of these studies, Lim *et al.* note, "reported a 1 to 2% increase in mortality risk per 1°C increase of DTR."

Wanitschek *et al.* (2013) note "previous studies reported an association of cold weather conditions with an excess incidence of acute coronary syndromes (ACS) according to hospital discharge reports (Eurowinter Group, 1997; Spencer *et al.*, 1998; Danet *et al.*, 1999; Kloner *et al.*, 1999; Dilaveris *et al.*, 2006)." However, they write, "whether these epidemiologic facts also translate into a significantly different rate of acute coronary angiographies between two consecutive winters characterized by a dramatic temperature increase is less clear."

Noting the 2005/2006 winter was very cold, whereas the 2006/2007 winter was extraordinarily warm, Wanitschek *et al.* studied the cases of patients who were suffering acute myocardial infarctions and had been referred to the University Clinic of Internal Medicine III (Cardiology) at Innsbruck Medical University, Tyrol, Austria, for coronary angiography (CA). They compared the patients' risk factors and in-hospital mortality rates between these two consecutive winters, the latter of which was 7.5°C warmer than the former. The two winters saw nearly identical CA cases (987 vs. 983). According to the six Austrian researchers, 12.9% of the CA cases in the colder winter were acute, while 10.4% of the cases in the warmer winter were acute. Diagnoses of STEMI (ST Elevation Myocardial Infarction) as an indication of acute CA were 74.in the colder winter 0 vs. 62.7% in the warmer. Wanitschek *et al.* conclude, "the average temperature increase of 7.5°C from the cold to the warm winter was associated with a decrease in acute coronary angiographies, in particular due to a lower incidence of STEMI referred for primary percutaneous intervention."

Vasconcelos *et al.* (2013) studied the health-related effects of a daily human-biometeorological index known as the Physiologically Equivalent Temperature or PET, which is based on the input parameters of air temperature, humidity, mean radiant temperature, and wind speed, as employed by Burkart *et al.* (2011), Grigorieva and Matzarakis (2011), and Cohen *et al.* (2012), focusing their attention on Lisbon and Oporto Counties in Portugal over the period 2003–2007. The five Portuguese researchers report there was "a linear relationship between daily mean PET, during winter, and the risk of myocardial infarction, after adjustment for confounding factors," thus confirming "the thermal environment, during winter, is inversely associated with acute myocardial infarction morbidity in Portugal." They observed "an increase of 2.2% of daily hospitalizations per degree fall of PET, during winter, for all ages." In Portugal and many other countries where low winter temperatures "are generally under-rated compared to high temperatures during summer periods," Vasconcelos *et al.* conclude cold weather is "an important environmental hazard" that is much more deadly than the heat of summer.

These several studies clearly demonstrate global warming is beneficial to humanity, reducing the incidence of cardiovascular diseases related to low temperatures and wintry weather by a much greater degree than it increases the incidence of cardiovascular diseases associated with high temperatures and summer heat waves.

References

Amsterdam, E.A., Laslett, L., and Holly, R. 1987. Exercise and sudden death. *Cardiology Clinics* **5**: 337–343.

Arntz, H.R., Willich, S.N., Schreiber, C., Bruggemann, T., Stren, R., and Schultheis, H.P. 2000. Diurnal, weekly and seasonal variation of sudden death. Population-based analysis of 24,061 consecutive cases. *European Heart Journal* **21**: 315–320.

Bartzokas, A., Kassomenos, P., Petrakis, M., and Celessides, C. 2004. The effect of meteorological and pollution parameters on the frequency of hospital admissions for cardiovascular and respiratory problems in Athens. *Indoor and Build Environment* **13**: 271–275.

Bass, D.E. and Henschel, A. 1956. Responses of body fluid compartments to heat and cold. *Physiology Review* **36**: 128–144.

Basu, R., Dominici, F., and Samet, J.M. 2005. Temperature and mortality among the elderly in the United States: a comparison of epidemiologic methods. *Epidemiology* **16**: 58–66.

Bayentin, L., El Adlouni, S., Ouarda, T.B.M.J., Gosselin, P., Doyon, B., and Chebana, F. 2010. Spatial variability of climate effects on ischemic heart disease hospitalization rates for the period 1989–2006 in Quebec, Canada. *International Journal of Health Geographics* **9**: 10.1186/1476-072X-9-5.

Behar, S. 2000. Out-of-hospital death in Israel—Should we blame the weather? *Israel Medical Association Journal* **2**: 56–57.

Bhaskaran, K., Hajat, S., Haines, A., Herrett, E. Wilkinson, P., and Smeeth, L. 2010. Short term effects of temperature on risk of myocardial infarction in England and Wales: time series regression analysis of the Myocardial Ischaemia National Audit Project (MINAP) registry. *British Medical Journal* **341**: c3823 doi: 10.1136/bmj.

Bonsal, B.R., Zhang, X., Vincent, L.A., and Hogg, W.D. 2001. Characteristics of daily and extreme temperatures over Canada. *Journal of Climate* **14**: 1959–1976.

Braga, A.L.F., Zanobetti, A., and Schwartz, J. 2002. The effect of weather on respiratory and cardiovascular deaths in 12 U.S. cities. *Environmental Health Perspectives* **110**: 859–863.

Burkart, K., Khan, M., Kramer, A., Breitner, S., Schneider, A., and Endlicher, W. 2011. Seasonal variations of all-cause and cause-specific mortality by age, gender, and socioeconomic condition in urban and rural areas of Bangladesh. *International Journal for Equity in Health* **10**: 10.1186/1475-9276-10-32.

Cagle, A. and Hubbard, R. 2005. Cold-related cardiac mortality in King County, Washington, USA 1980–2001. *Annals of Human Biology* **32**: 525–537.

Cao, J., Cheng, Y., Zhao, N., Song, W., Jiang, C., Chen, R., and Kan, H. 2009. Diurnal temperature range is a risk factor for coronary heart disease death. *Journal of Epidemiology* **19**: 328–332.

Carder, M., McNamee, R., Beverland, I., Elton, R., Cohen, G.R., Boyd, J., and Agius, R.M. 2005. The lagged effect of cold temperature and wind chill on cardiorespiratory mortality in Scotland. *Occupational and Environmental Medicine* **62**: 702–710.

Chang, C.L., Shipley, M., Marmot, M., and Poulter, N. 2004. Lower ambient temperature was associated with an increased risk of hospitalization for stroke and acute myocardial infarction in young women. *Journal of Clinical Epidemiology* **57**: 749–757.

Chen, G., Zhang, Y., Song, G., Jiang, L., Zhao, N., Chen, B., and Kan H. 2007. Is diurnal temperature range a risk factor for acute stroke death? *International Journal of Cardiology* **116**: 408–409.

Chen, R.Y.Z. and Chien, S. 1977. Plasma volume, red cell volume and thoracic duct lymph flow in hypothermia. *American Journal of Physiology* **233**: 605–612.

Christidis, N., Donaldson, G.C., and Stott, P.A. 2010. Causes for the recent changes in cold- and heat-related mortality in England and Wales. *Climatic Change* **102**: 539–553.

Cohen, P., Potchter, O., and Matzarakis, A. 2012. Daily and seasonal climatic conditions of green urban open spaces in the Mediterranean climate and their impact on human comfort. *Building and Environment* **51**: 285–295.

Collins, K.J., Easton, J.C., Belfield-Smith, H., Exton-Smith, A.N., and Pluck, R.A. 1985. Effects of age on body temperature and blood pressure in cold environments. *Clinical Science* **69**: 465–470.

Crawford, V.L.S., McCann, M., and Stout, R.W. 2003. Changes in seasonal deaths from myocardial infarction. *Quarterly Journal of Medicine* **96**: 45–52.

Curriero, F.C., Heiner, K.S., Samet, J.M., Zeger, S.L., Strug, L., and Patz, J.A. 2002. Temperature and mortality in 11 cities of the Eastern United States. *American Journal of Epidemiology* **155**: 80–87.

Danet, S., Richard, F., Montaye, M., Beauchant, S., Lemaire, B., Graux, C., Cottel, D., Marecaux, N., and Amouyel, P. 1999. Unhealthy effects of atmospheric temperature and pressure on the occurrence of myocardial infarction and coronary deaths—a 10-year survey—the Lille WHO-MONICA Project. *Circulation* **100**: E1–7.

De Lorenzo, F., Kadziola, Z., Mukherjee, M., Saba, N., and Kakkar, V.V. 1999. Haemodynamic responses and changes of haemostatic risk factors in cold-adapted humans. *Quarterly Journal of Medicine* **92**: 509–513.

Dilaveris, P., Synetos, A., Giannopoulos, G., Gialafos, E., Pantazis, A., and Stefanadis, C. 2006. Climate impacts on myocardial infarction deaths in the Athens territory: the CLIMATE study. *Heart* **92**: 1747–1751.

Donaldson, G.C., Tchernjavskii, V.E., Ermakov, S.P., Bucher, K., and Keatinge, W.R. 1998. Winter mortality and cold stress in Yekaterinburg, Russia: interview survey. *British Medical Journal* **316**: 514–518.

Douglas, A.S., Allan, T.M., and Rawles, J.M. 1991. Composition of seasonality of disease. *Scottish Medical Journal* **36**: 76–82.

Douglas, A.S., Al-Sayer, H., Rawles, M.M., and Allan, T.M. 1991. Seasonality of disease in Kuwait. *Lancet* **337**: 1393–1397.

Douglas, A.S., Dunnigan, M.G., Allan, T.M., and Rawles, J.M. 1995. Seasonal variation in coronary heart disease in Scotland. *Journal of Epidemiology and Community Health* **49**: 575–582.

Douglas, A.S., Russell, D., and Allan, T.M. 1990. Seasonal, regional and secular variations of cardiovascular and cerebrovascular mortality in New Zealand. *Australia and New Zealand Journal of Medicine* **20**: 669–676.

Easterling, D.R., Horton, B., Jones, P.D., Peterson, T.C., Karl, T.R., Parker, D.E., Salinger, M.J., Razuvayev, V., Plummer, N., Jamason, P., and Folland, C.K. 1997. Maximum and minimum temperature trends for the globe. *Science* **277**: 364–367.

Enquselassie, F., Dobson, A.J., Alexander, H.M., and Steele, P.L. 1993. Seasons, temperature and coronary disease. *International Journal of Epidemiology* **22**: 632–636.

Eurowinter Group. 1997. Cold exposure and winter mortality from ischaemic heart disease, cerebrovascular disease, respiratory disease, and all causes in warm and cold regions of Europe. *Lancet* **349**: 1341–1346.

Finkel, A. and Cumming, G.R. 1965. Effects of exercise in the cold on blood clotting and platelets. *Journal of Applied Physiology* **20**: 423–424.

Fregley, M.J. 1982. Water and electrolyte balance during exposure to cold. *Pharmacology and Therapeutics* **18**: 199–231.

Frisancho, A.R. 1993. *Human Adaptation and Accommodation.* University of Michigan Press, Ann Arbor, Michigan, USA.

Gouveia, N., Hajat, S., and Armstrong, B. 2003. Socioeconomic differentials in the temperature-mortality relationship in Sao Paulo, Brazil. *International Journal of Epidemiology* **32**: 390–397.

Green, M.S., Harari, G., and Kristal-Boneh, E. 1994. Excess winter mortality from ischaemic heart disease and stroke during colder and warmer years in Israel. *European Journal of Public Health* **4**: 3–11.

Grigorieva, E. and Matzarakis, A. 2011. Physiologically equivalent temperature as a factor for tourism in extreme climate regions in the Russian far east: preliminary results. *European Journal of Tourism, Hospitality and Recreation* **2**: 127–142.

Gyllerup, S. 2000. Cold climate and coronary mortality in Sweden. *International Journal of Circumpolar Health* **59**: 160–163.

Gyllerup, S., Lanke, J., Lindholm, L.H., and Schersten, B. 1993. Cold climate is an important factor in explaining regional differences in coronary mortality even if serum cholesterol and other established risk factors are taken into account. *Scottish Medical Journal* **38**: 169–172.

Hajat, S. and Haines, A. 2002. Associations of cold temperatures with GP consultations for respiratory and cardiovascular disease amongst the elderly in London. *International Journal of Epidemiology* **31**: 825–830.

Healy, J.D. 2003. Excess winter mortality in Europe: a cross country analysis identifying risk factors. *Journal of Epidemiology and Public Health* **57**: 784–789.

Jehn, M., Appel, L.J., Sacks, F.M., and Miller III, E.R. 2002. The effect of ambient temperature and barometric pressure on ambulatory blood pressure variability. *American Journal of Hypertension* **15**: 941–945.

Kan, H., London, S.J., Chen, H., Song, G., Chen, G., Jiang, L., Zhao, N., Zhang, Y., and Chen, B. 2007. Diurnal temperature range and daily mortality in Shanghai, China. *Environmental Research* **103**: 424–431.

Keatinge, W.R., Coleshaw, S.R.K., Cotter, F., Mattock, M., Murphy, M., and Chelliah, R. 1984. Increases in platelet and red cell counts, blood viscosity, and arterial pressure during mild surface cooling: factors in mortality from coronary and cerebral thrombosis in winter. *British Medical Journal* **289**: 1404–1408.

Keatinge, W.R. and Donaldson, G.C. 2004. The impact of global warming on health and mortality. *Southern Medical Journal* **97**: 1093–1099.

Kloner, R.A. 2006. Natural and unnatural triggers of myocardial infarction. *Progress in Cardiovascular Diseases* **48**: 285–300.

Kloner, R.A., Poole, W.K., and Perritt, R.L. 1999. When throughout the year is coronary death most likely to occur? A 12-year population-based analysis of more than 220,000 cases. *Circulation* **100**: 1630–1634.

Kovats, R.S., Hajat, S., and Wilkinson, P. 2004. Contrasting patterns of mortality and hospital admissions during hot weather and heat waves in Greater London, UK. *Occupational and Environmental Medicine* **61**: 893–898.

Kysely, J. 2004. Mortality and displaced mortality during heat waves in the Czech Republic. *International Journal of Biometeorology* **49**: 91–97.

Kysely, J. and Kriz, B. 2008. Decreased impacts of the 2003 heat waves on mortality in the Czech Republic: an improved response? *International Journal of Biometeorology* **52**: 733–745.

Kysely, J., Plavcova, E., Davidkovova, H., and Kyncl, J. 2011. Comparison of hot and cold spell effects on cardiovascular mortality in individual population groups in the Czech Republic. *Climate Research* **49**: 113–129.

Kysely, J., Pokorna, L., Kyncl, J., and Kriz, B. 2009. Excess cardiovascular mortality associated with cold spells in the Czech Republic. *BMC Public Health* **9**: 10.1186/1471-2458-9-19.

LeBlanc, J. 1992. Mechanisms of adaptation to cold. *Journal of Sports Medicine* **13**: S169–S172.

LeBlanc, J., Cote, J., Dulac, S., and Dulong, F.-Turcot. 1978. Effects of age, sex and physical fitness on responses to local cooling. *Journal of Applied Physiology* **44**: 813–817.

Liang, W.M., Liu, W.P., Chou, S.Y., and Kuo, H.W. 2008. Ambient temperature and emergency room admissions for acute coronary syndrome in Taiwan. *International Journal of Biometeorology* **52**: 223–229.

Liang, W.M., Liu, W.P., and Kuo, H.W. 2009. Diurnal temperature range and emergency room admissions for chronic obstructive pulmonary disease in Taiwan. *International Journal of Biometeorology* **53**: 17–23.

Lim, Y., Park, A., Hajat, S., and Kim, H. 2012. Modifiers of diurnal temperature range and mortality association in six Korean cities. *International Journal of Biometeorology* **56**: 33–42.

Lim, Y.-H., Hong, Y.-C., and Kim, H. 2012. Effects of diurnal temperature range on cardiovascular and respiratory hospital admissions in Korea. *Science of the Total Environment* **417–418**: 55–60.

Lloyd, E.L. 1991. The role of cold in ischaemic heart disease: a review. *Public Health* **105**: 205–215.

Mackenbach, J.P., Kunst, A.E., and Looman, C.W.N. 1992. Seasonal variation in mortality in the Netherlands. *Journal of Epidemiology and Community Health* **46**: 261–265.

Marshall, R.J., Scragg, R., and Bourke, P. 1988. An analysis of the seasonal variation of coronary heart disease and respiratory disease mortality in New Zealand. *International Journal of Epidemiology* **17**: 325–331.

McGregor, G.R. 2005. Winter North Atlantic Oscillation, temperature and ischaemic heart disease mortality in three English counties. *International Journal of Biometeorology* **49**: 197–204.

McGregor, G.R., Watkin, H.A., and Cox, M. 2004. Relationships between the seasonality of temperature and ischaemic heart disease mortality: implications for climate based health forecasting. *Climate Research* **25**: 253–263.

Mercer, J.B. 2003. Cold—an underrated risk factor for health. *Environmental Research* **92**: 8–13.

Morgan, M.D. and Moran, J.M. 1997. *Weather and People.* Prentice Hall, Englewood Cliffs, NJ, USA.

Muller, J.E. and Mangel, B. 1994. Circadian variation and triggers of cardiovascular disease. *Cardiology* **85** (Supplement 2): 3–10.

Muza, S.R., Young, A.J., Sawka, M.N., Bogart, J.E., and Pandolf, K.B. 1988. Respiratory and cardiovascular responses to cold stress following repeated cold water immersion. *Undersea Biomedical Research* **15**: 165–178.

Nafstad, P., Skrondal, A., and Bjertness, E. 2001. Mortality and temperature in Oslo, Norway, 1990–1995. *European Journal of Epidemiology* **17**: 621–627.

Nakaji, S., Parodi, S., Fontana, V., Umeda, T., Suzuki, K., Sakamoto, J., Fukuda, S., Wada, S., and Sugawara, K. 2004. Seasonal changes in mortality rates from main causes of death in Japan (1970–1999). *European Journal of Epidemiology* **19**: 905–913.

Neild, P.J., Syndercombe-Court, D., Keatinge, W.R., Donaldson, G.C., Mattock, M., and Caunce, M. 1994. Cold-induced increases in erythrocyte count, plasma cholesterol and plasma fibrinogen of elderly people without a comparable rise in protein C or factor X. *Clinical Science (London)* **86**: 43–48.

Seto, T.B., Mittleman, M.A., Davis, R.B., Taira, D.A., and Kawachi, I. 1998. Seasonal variation in coronary artery disease mortality in Hawaii: observational study. *British Medical Journal* **16**: 1946–1947.

Sharovsky, R., Cesar, L.A.M., and Ramires, J.A.F. 2004. Temperature, air pollution, and mortality from myocardial infarction in Sao Paulo, Brazil. *Brazilian Journal of Medical and Biological Research* **37**: 1651–1657.

Sheth, T., Nair, C., Muller, J., and Yusuf, S. 1999. Increased winter mortality from acute myocardial infarction and stroke: the effect of age. *Journal of the American College of Cardiology* **33**: 1916–1919.

Shinkawa, A., Ueda, K., Hasuo, Y., Kiyohara, Y., and Fujishima, M. 1990. Seasonal variation in stroke incidence in Hisayama, Japan. *Stroke* **21**: 1262–1267.

Song, G., Chen, G., Jiang, L., Zhang, Y., Zhao, N., Chen,

B., and Kan, H. 2008. Diurnal temperature range as a novel risk factor for COPD death. *Respirology* **13**: 1066–1069.

Spencer, F.A., Goldberg, R.J., Becker, R.C., and Gore, J.M. 1998. Seasonal distribution of acute myocardial infarction in the second National Registry of Myocardial Infarction. *Journal of the American College of Cardiology* **31**: 1226–1233.

Tam, W.W.S., Wong, T.W., Chair, S.Y., and Wong, A.H.S. 2009. Diurnal temperature range and daily cardiovascular mortalities among the elderly in Hong Kong. *Archives of Environmental and Occupational Health* **64**: 202–206.

Toro, K., Bartholy, J., Pongracz, R., Kis, Z., Keller, E., and Dunay, G. 2010. Evaluation of meteorological factors on sudden cardiovascular death. *Journal of Forensic and Legal Medicine* **17**: 236–242.

Vasconcelos, J., Freire, E., Almendra, R., Silva, G.L., and Santana, P. 2013. The impact of winter cold weather on acute myocardial infarctions in Portugal. *Environmental Pollution*: 10.1016/j.envpol.2013.01.037.

Vuori, I. 1987. The heart and the cold. *Annals of Clinical Research* **19**: 156–162.

Wanitschek, M., Ulmer, H., Sussenbacher, A., Dorler, J., Pachinger, O., and Alber, H.F. 2013. Warm winter is associated with low incidence of ST elevation myocardial infarctions and less frequent acute coronary angiographies in an alpine country. *Herz* **38**: 163–170.

Weerasinghe, D.P., MacIntyre, C.R., and Rubin, G.L. 2002. Seasonality of coronary artery deaths in New South Wales, Australia. *Heart* **88**: 30–34.

WHO. 1995. WHO Collaborative Study of Cardiovascular Disease and Steroid Hormone Contraception. A multinational case-control study of cardiovascular disease and steroid hormone contraceptives: description and validation of methods. *Journal of Clinical Epidemiology* **48**: 1513–1547.

Woodhouse, P.R., Khaw, K., and Plummer, M. 1993. Seasonal variation of blood pressure and its relationship to ambient temperature in an elderly population. *Journal of Hypertension* **11**: 1267–1274.

Zhang, X.B., Vincent, L.A., Hogg, W.D., and Niitsoo, A. 2000. Temperature and precipitation trends in Canada during the 20th century. *Atmosphere-Ocean* **38**: 395–429.

7.3 Respiratory Disease

- The adverse health impacts of cold temperatures, especially with respect to respiratory health, are more significant than those of high temperatures in many parts of the world, including Spain, Canada, Shanghai, and Taiwan. In the subtropical island of Taiwan, for example, researchers found low minimum temperatures were the strongest risk factor associated with outpatient visits for respiratory diseases.

According to IPCC, global warming will pose numerous challenges to human health, including the potential for an excess of deaths. This section examines the results of a number of studies conducted over the past decade or so that deal with this important subject as it applies to respiratory diseases. The studies show the excess death hypothesis from respiratory causes is 180 degrees out of phase with reality.

Hajat and Haines (2002) set out to determine whether the well-documented relationship between cold temperatures and respiratory mortality in the elderly extends to the number of visits by the elderly to general practitioners. They employed additive models to regress time-series of daily numbers of general practitioner consultations by the elderly against temperature. The consultation data they employed included visits to the doctor for asthma, lower respiratory diseases other than asthma, and upper respiratory diseases other than allergic rhinitis as obtained for registered patients aged 65 and older from several London practices between January 1992 and September 1995.

Hajat and Haines found the mean number of consultations was higher in cool-season months (October–March) than in warm-season months (April–September) for all respiratory diseases. At mean temperatures below 5°C, the relationship between respiratory disease consultations and temperature was linear, and stronger at a time lag of six to 15 days—a 1°C decrease in mean temperature below 5°C was associated with a 10.5% increase in all respiratory disease consultations.

Keatinge and Donaldson (2001) obtained similar results in their study of the effects of temperature on mortality in people over 50 years of age in the greater London area over the period 1976–1995. Simple plots of mortality rate versus daily air temperature revealed a linear increase in mortality as the air temperature fell from 15°C to near 0°C. Mortality rates at temperatures above 15°C, on the other hand, were, in their words, "grossly alinear," showing no trend. Low temperatures were shown to have a significant effect on both immediate (one day after the temperature perturbation) and long-term (up to 24 days after the temperature perturbation) mortality rates. Why are cold temperatures so deadly? Keatinge and

Donaldson say it is because "cold causes mortality mainly from arterial thrombosis and respiratory disease, attributable in turn to cold-induced hemoconcentration and hypertension and respiratory infections."

Nafstad *et al.* (2001) studied the association between temperature and daily mortality in citizens of Oslo, Norway over the period 1990 to 1995. Because Norwegian law requires all deaths be examined by a physician, who diagnoses the cause of death and reports it on the death certificate, the authors were able to categorize and examine the effects of temperature on mortality specifically associated with respiratory diseases. The results showed the mean daily number of respiratory-related deaths was considerably higher in winter (October–March) than in summer (April–September). Winter deaths associated with respiratory diseases were 47% more numerous than summer deaths. Nafstad *et al.* conclude, "a milder climate would lead to a substantial reduction in average daily number of deaths."

Braga *et al.* (2002) conducted a time-series analysis of both the acute and lagged influence of temperature and humidity on mortality rates in 12 U.S. cities, finding no clear evidence for a link between humidity and respiratory-related deaths. With respect to temperature, they found respiratory-related mortality increased in cities with more variable temperature. This phenomenon, they write, "suggests that increased temperature variability is the most relevant change in climate for the direct effects of weather on respiratory mortality." This finding bodes well for a potentially warmer world, for Robeson (2002) has clearly demonstrated, based on a 50-year study of daily temperatures at more than 1,000 U.S. weather stations, that temperature variability declines with warming, and at a very substantial rate, so this aspect of a warmer world also would lead to a reduction in respiratory-related deaths.

Gouveia *et al.* (2003) extracted daily counts of deaths from all causes, except violent deaths and neonatal deaths (up to one month of age), from Sao Paulo, Brazil's mortality information system for the period 1991–1994 and analyzed them for effects of temperature within three age groups: less than 15 years of age (children), 15–64 years old (adults), and more than 64 years old (elderly). This exercise revealed the change points (the temperatures above and below which temperature begins to impact mortality) for both heat- and cold-induced deaths were identical, at 20°C. For each 1°C increase above

this value for a given and prior day's mean temperature, Gouveia *et al.* observed a 2.6% increase in deaths from all causes in children, a 1.5% increase in deaths from all causes in adults, and a 2.5% increase in deaths from all causes in the elderly. For each 1°C decrease below the 20°C change point, the cold effect was greater, with increases in deaths from all causes in children, adults, and the elderly registering 4.0%, 2.6%, and 5.5%, respectively. These cooling-induced death rates are 54%, 73%, and 120% greater than those due to warming.

Findings with respect to respiratory-induced deaths were similar. Death rates due to a 1°C cooling were twice as great as death rates due to a 1°C warming in adults, and 2.8 times greater in the elderly.

Nakaji *et al.* (2004) evaluated seasonal trends in deaths due to various diseases in Japan, using nationwide vital statistics from 1970 to 1999 and concurrent mean monthly air temperature data. They found the numbers of deaths due to diabetes, digestive diseases, cerebrovascular and heart diseases, infectious and parasitic diseases including tuberculosis, and respiratory diseases including pneumonia and influenza all rise to a maximum during the coldest time of the year. Hence, the team of nine scientists concludes, "to reduce the overall mortality rate and to prolong life expectancy in Japan, measures must be taken to reduce those mortality rates associated with seasonal differences." Consequently, to achieve the scientists' stated objectives, it is necessary to bring about a "reduction in exposure to cold environments," as they put it.

Bartzokas *et al.* (2004) "examined the relationship between hospital admissions for cardiovascular (cardiac in general including heart attacks) and/or respiratory diseases (asthma etc.) in a major hospital in Athens [Greece] and meteorological parameters for an 8-year period." Over the whole year, they found, "there was a dependence of admissions on temperature," and low temperatures were "responsible for a higher number of admissions." Specifically, "there was a decrease of cardiovascular or/and respiratory events from low to high values [of temperature], except for the highest temperature class in which a slight increase was recorded."

Kovats *et al.* (2004) studied patterns of temperature-related hospital admissions and deaths in Greater London during the mid-1990s. For the three-year period 1994–1996, they found respiratory-related deaths were nearly 150% greater in the depth of winter cold than at the height of summer warmth. They also found the mortality impact of the heat wave of 29 July to 3 August 1995 (which boosted daily mortality by just over 10%) was so tiny it could not be discerned among the random scatter of plots of three-year-average daily deaths from cardiovascular and respiratory problems versus day of year. Similarly, in a study of temperature effects on mortality in three English counties (Hampshire, West Midlands, and West Yorkshire), McGregor (2005) found "the occurrence of influenza ... helps elevate winter mortality above that of summer."

Carder et al. (2005) used generalized linear Poisson regression models to investigate the relationship between outside air temperature and deaths due to all non-accident causes in the three largest cities of Scotland (Glasgow, Edinburgh, and Aberdeen) between January 1981 and December 2001. The authors observed "an overall increase in mortality as temperature decreases," which "appears to be steeper at lower temperatures than at warmer temperatures," and "there is little evidence of an increase in mortality at the hot end of the temperature range." They also state "the observed relation between cold temperature and mortality was typically stronger among the elderly," and "cold temperature effects on mortality persist with lag periods of beyond two weeks." Specifically, "for temperatures below 11°C, a 1°C drop in the daytime mean temperature on any one day was associated with an increase in respiratory mortality of 4.8% over the following month."

Noting "in temperate regions, respiratory disease adds greatly to the workload in general practice facilities and hospitals during the winter," partly because of increases in cases of "bronchiolitis in young children caused by infection with respiratory syncytial virus (RSV)," Donaldson (2006) studied the effect of annual mean daily air temperature on the length of the yearly RSV season. He used weekly data on laboratory reports of RSV isolation by the Health Protection Agency and National Health Service hospital laboratories in England and Wales for 1981–2004, along with meteorological data from four surface stations (Ringway, Squires Gate, Malvern, and Rothamsted) that "are representative of a roughly triangular area of the United Kingdom enclosed by Preston, London, and Bristol."

Reporting "climate change may be shortening the RSV season," Donaldson found "the seasons associated with laboratory isolation of respiratory syncytial virus (for 1981–2004) and RSV-related emergency department admissions (for 1990–2004) ended 3.1 and 2.5 weeks earlier, respectively, per 1°C increase in annual central England temperature (P = 0.002 and 0.043, respectively)." Consequently, since "no relationship was observed between the start of each season and temperature," he reports, "the RSV season has become shorter." He concludes, "these findings imply a health benefit of global warming in England and Wales associated with a reduction in the duration of the RSV season and its consequent impact on the health service."

According to Frei and Gassner (2008), from 1926 to 1991, hay fever prevalence in Switzerland rose from just under 1% of the country's population to just over 14%, but from 1991 to 2000 it simply fluctuated about a mean value on the order of 15%. In addition, the authors write, "several studies show that no further increase in asthma, hay fever and atopic sensitization in adolescents and adults has been observed during the 1990s and the beginning of the new century," citing Braun-Fahrlander et al. (2004) and Grize et al. (2006). To see what effect changes in pollen production might have had on this trend in respiratory ailments, Frei and Gassner analyzed daily average concentrations of birch and grass pollen monitored by the country's National Pollen Network at Basel for the period 1969–2007, at Locarno for 1989–2007, and at Zurich for 1982–2007.

The two researchers report "the pollen exposure has been decreasing in Basel since the beginning of the 1990s," and "in Locarno, most of the pollen species also show a decreasing trend," while in Zurich, "most of the pollen types have been increasing," although "some of the pollen counts of this station (grass, stinging nettle, mugwort and ragweed) have been decreasing in the period 1982–2007." In addition, they state the length of the pollen season has recently tended "to get shorter."

Frei and Gassner write, "parallel to the increasing hay fever rate, the pollen amounts of birch and grass were increasing from 1969 to 1990," but "subsequently, the pollen of these plant species decreased from 1991 to 2007." They say this finding "is more or less consistent with the changes of the hay fever rate that no longer increased during this period and even showed a tendency to decrease slightly." Nearly identical findings were presented a year later (Frei, 2009). Although some have claimed rising temperatures and CO_2 concentrations will lead to more pollen and more hay fever (Wayne et al., 2002), the analyses of Frei (2009) and Frei and Gassner (2008) suggest that is not true of Switzerland.

Jato et al. (2009) collected airborne samples of Poaceae pollen "using Hirst-type volumetric traps" in four cities in Galicia (Northwest Spain)—Lugo,

Santiago, Vigo, and Ourense—noting "the global climate change recorded over recent years may prompt changes in the atmospheric pollen season (APS). The subjected the data "to Spearman's correlation test and regression models, in order to detect possible correlations between different parameters and trends." They calculated the APS "using ten different methods, in order to assess the influence of each on survey results." The Poaceae family (composed chiefly of herbaceous grasses), Jato *et al.* write, "is the most diverse and prolific herbaceous plant family in urban areas," and "its pollen is considered a major aeroallergen, causing symptoms in over 80% of pollen allergy sufferers in Europe (D'Amato *et al.*, 2007)."

The four researchers report "all four cities displayed a trend towards lower annual total Poaceae pollen counts, lower peak values and a smaller number of days on which counts exceeded 30, 50 and 100 pollen grains/m^3." The percentage decline in annual pollen grain counts between 1993 and 2007 in Lugo was approximately 75%, and in Santiago the decline was 80%, as best as can be determined from the graphs of the researchers' data. In addition, they write, "the survey noted a trend towards delayed onset and shorter duration of the APS." Thus, even though there was a "significant trend towards increasing temperatures over the months prior to the onset of the pollen season," according the Spanish scientists, Poaceae pollen became far less of a negative respiratory health factor in the four Galician cities over the decade and a half of their study.

Miller *et al.* (2012) say "there is concern that climate change may affect hay fever and other allergic conditions by impacting pollen amount, pollen allergenicity, pollen season, and plant and pollen distribution," because "allergy and atopic disease rates are rising, and global warming has been implicated as a possible cause." They note, "concomitant with climate change over the time course of many of these studies are changes in air pollution levels, economic factors, and lifestyle," and they conducted a study to clarify the situation by separating these potentially confounding factors.

Miller *et al.* extracted annual prevalence data for frequent otitis media (defined as three or more ear infections per year), respiratory allergy, and non-respiratory seizures in children from the U.S. National Health Interview Survey for 1998 to 2006. They also obtained average annual temperatures for the same period from the U.S. Environmental Protection Agency. They performed "complex samples logistic regression analyses" to identify possible correlations between annual temperature and each of the three disease conditions, while controlling for age and sex.

The three researchers—from the David Geffen School of Medicine at the University of California at Los Angeles, Harvard Medical School, and Brigham and Women's Hospital in Boston—report the regression analysis found "annual temperature did not influence the prevalence of frequent otitis media," "annual temperature did not influence prevalence of respiratory allergy," and "annual temperature and sex did not influence seizure prevalence." Miller *et al.* conclude their findings "may demonstrate that average temperature is not likely to be the dominant cause of the increase in allergy burden or that larger changes in temperatures over a longer period are needed to observe this association." They conclude, "in the absence of more dramatic annual temperature changes, we do not expect prevalence of otitis media to change significantly as global warming may continue to affect our environment."

Xu *et al.* (2013) state "childhood asthma is a major global health issue, affecting more than 300 million people worldwide (Baena-Cagnani and Badellino, 2011)," and it "is regarded as a national health priority in several countries," citing Asher *et al.* (1995, 2006). They studied the relationship between diurnal temperature range (DTR) and the incidence of childhood asthma in Brisbane, Australia. For the study, "a Poisson generalized linear model combined with a distributed lag non-linear model was used to examine the relationship between DTR and emergency department admissions for childhood asthma in Brisbane from January 1st 2003 to December 31st 2009," and daily maximum and minimum temperatures in Brisbane for the same time period were retrieved from the Australian Bureau of Meteorology. Each day's DTR was calculated as the difference between its maximum and minimum temperatures.

The six scientists report "childhood asthma increased above a DTR of 10°C" and "was the greatest for lag 0–9 days, with a 31% increase in [hospital] emergency department admissions per 5°C increment of DTR," further noting, "male children and children aged 5–9 years appeared to be more vulnerable to the DTR effect than others." Since daily minimum temperatures have nearly always risen faster than have daily maximum temperatures in most locations around the globe whenever various regions have warmed, the study's results indicate the decrease in DTR under global warming should lead to a decline in the number of cases of childhood asthma.

Ge *et al.* (2013) also investigated respiratory

health and DTR. They write, "respiratory tract infection (RTI) is among the most common acute diseases worldwide, leading to considerable morbidity, complications, and days lost from work and school," citing Mourtzoukou and Falagas (2007). They report the DTR "has been identified as an independent risk factor for coronary heart disease (Cao *et al.*, 2009; Tam *et al.*, 2009), stroke (Shinkawa *et al.*, 1990; Kyobutungi *et al.*, 2005; Chen *et al.*, 2007), and chronic obstructive pulmonary disease (Song *et al.*, 2008)."

The researchers collected numbers of daily emergency-room visits for RTI at one of the largest medical establishments in Shanghai, China (Huashan Hospital) between 1 January 2008 and 30 June 2009, along with DTR data and data pertaining to possible confounding air pollutants (PM_{10}, SO_2, and NO_2). After making appropriate statistical analyses, the scientists determined increasing DTRs were closely associated with daily emergency-room visits for RTIs, such that "an increase of 1°C in the current-day and in the 2-day moving average DTR corresponded to a 0.94% and 2.08% increase in emergency-room visits for RTI, respectively."

Lin *et al.* (2013) state "high temperatures have garnered considerable attention in Europe and the U.S. because of their short-term adverse health impacts." However, they add, several studies have reported "the adverse health effects of cold temperatures may be more significant than those of high temperatures in Spain, Canada, Shanghai and Taiwan (Gomez-Acebo *et al.*, 2010; Lin *et al.*, 2011; Ma *et al.*, 2011; Martin *et al.*, 2012; Wang *et al.*, 2012)," and "mortality risk associated with low temperatures is likely underestimated when studies fail to address the prolonged effect of low temperature (Martin *et al.*, 2012; Mercer, 2003)." Working with data on daily area-specific deaths from all causes, circulatory diseases, and respiratory diseases, Lin *et al.* developed relationships between each of these cause-of-death categories and a number of cold-temperature related parameters for 2000–2008.

The five researchers discovered "mortality from [1] all causes and [2] circulatory diseases and [3] outpatient visits of respiratory diseases has a strong association with cold temperatures in the subtropical island, Taiwan." In addition, they found "minimum temperature estimated the strongest risk associated with outpatient visits of respiratory diseases."

The several studies described above clearly indicate a warmer world would be a much better world, especially with respect to the respiratory health of the world's citizens.

References

Asher, M., Keil, U., Anderson, H., Beasley, R., Crane, J., Martinez, F., Mitchell, E., Pearce, N., Sibbald, B., and Stewart, A. 1995. International study of asthma and allergies in childhood (ISAAC): rationale and methods. *European Respiration Journal* **8**: 483–491.

Asher, M.I., Montefort, S., Bjorksten, B., Lai, C.K.W., Strachan, D.P., Weiland, S.K., and Williams, H. 2006. Worldwide time trends in the prevalence of symptoms of asthma, allergic rhinoconjunctivitis, and eczema in childhood: ISAAC Phases One and Three repeat multi-country cross-sectional surveys. *Lancet* **368**: 733–743.

Baena-Cagnani, C. and Badellino, H. 2011. Diagnosis of allergy and asthma in childhood. *Current Allergy and Asthma Reports* **11**: 71–77.

Bartzokas, A., Kassomenos, P., Petrakis, M., and Celessides, C. 2004. The effect of meteorological and pollution parameters on the frequency of hospital admissions for cardiovascular and respiratory problems in Athens. *Indoor and Build Environment* **13**: 271–275.

Braga, A.L.F., Zanobetti, A., and Schwartz, J. 2002. The effect of weather on respiratory and cardiovascular deaths in 12 U.S. cities. *Environmental Health Perspectives* **110**: 859–863.

Braun-Fahrlander, C., Gassner, M., Grize, L., Takken-Sahli, K., Neu, U., Stricker, T., Varonier, H.S., Wuthrich, B., Sennhauser, F.H., and SCARPOL Team. 2004. No further increase in asthma, hay fever and atopic sensitization in adolescents living in Switzerland. *European Respiratory Journal* **23**: 407–413.

Cao, J., Chang, Y., Zhao, N., Song, W., Jiang, C., Chen., R., and Kan., H. 2009. Diurnal temperature range is a risk factor for coronary heart disease death. *Journal of Epidemiology* **19**: 328–332.

Carder, M., McNamee, R., Beverland, I., Elton, R., Cohen, G.R., Boyd, J., and Agius, R.M. 2005. The lagged effect of cold temperature and wind chill on cardiorespiratory mortality in Scotland. *Occupational and Environmental Medicine* **62**: 702–710.

Chen, G., Zhang, Y., Song, G., Jiang, L., Zhao, N., Chen, B., and Kan, H. 2007. Is diurnal temperature range a risk factor for acute stroke death? *International Journal of Cardiology* **116**: 408–409.

D'Amato, G., Cecchi, L., Bonini, S., Nunes, C., Annesi-Maesano, I., Behrendt, H., Liccardi, G., Popov, T., and van Cauwenberge, P. 2007. Allergenic pollen and pollen allergy in Europe. *Allergy* **62**: 976–990.

Donaldson, G.C. 2006. Climate change and the end of the respiratory syncytial virus season. *Clinical Infectious Diseases* **42**: 677–679.

Easterling, D.R., Horton, B., Jones, P.D., Peterson, T.C., Karl, T.R., Parker, D.E., Salinger, M.J., Razuvayev, V., Plummer, N., Jamason, P., and Folland, C.K. 1997. Maximum and minimum temperature trends for the globe. *Science* **277**: 364–367.

Frei, T. 2009. Trendwende bei der Pollinose und dem Pollenflug? *Allergologie* **32** (4): 123–127.

Frei, T. and Gassner, E. 2008. Trends in prevalence of allergic rhinitis and correlation with pollen counts in Switzerland. *International Journal of Biometeorology* **52**: 841–847.

Ge, W.Z., Xu, F., Zhao, Z.H., Zhao, J.Z., and Kan, H.D. 2013. Association between diurnal temperature range and respiratory tract infections. *Biomedical and Environmental Sciences* **26**: 222–225.

Gomez-Acebo, I., Dierssen-Sotos, T., and Llorca, J. 2010. Effect of cold temperatures on mortality in Cantabria (Northern Spain): a case-crossover study. *Public Health* **124**: 398–403.

Gouveia, N., Hajat, S., and Armstrong, B. 2003. Socioeconomic differentials in the temperature-mortality relationship in Sao Paulo, Brazil. *International Journal of Epidemiology* **32**: 390–397.

Grize, L., Gassner, M., Wuthrich, B., Bringolf-Isler, B., Takken-Sahli, K., Sennhauser, F.H., Stricker, T., Eigenmann, P.A., Braun-Fahrlander, C., and SCARPOL Team. 2006. Trends in prevalence of asthma, allergic rhinitis and atopic dermatitis in 5–7-year old Swiss children from 1992 to 2001. *Allergy* **61**: 556–562.

Hajat, S. and Haines, A. 2002. Associations of cold temperatures with GP consultations for respiratory and cardiovascular disease amongst the elderly in London. *International Journal of Epidemiology* **31**: 825–830.

Jato, V., Rodriguez-Rajo, F.J., Seijo, M.C., and Aira, M.J. 2009. Poaceae pollen in Galicia (N.W. Spain): characterization and recent trends in atmospheric pollen season. *International Journal of Biometeorology* **53**: 333–344.

Keatinge, W.R. and Donaldson, G.C. 2001. Mortality related to cold and air pollution in London after allowance for effects of associated weather patterns. *Environmental Research* **86**: 209–216.

Kovats, R.S., Hajat, S., and Wilkinson, P. 2004. Contrasting patterns of mortality and hospital admissions during hot weather and heat waves in Greater London, UK. *Occupational and Environmental Medicine* **61**: 893–898.

Kyobutungi, C., Grau, A., Stieglbauer, G., and Becher, H. 2005. Absolute temperature, temperature changes and stroke risk: a case-crossover study. *European Journal of Epidemiology* **20**: 693–698.

Lin, Y.-K., Ho, T.-J., and Wang, Y.-C. 2011. Mortality risk associated with temperature and prolonged temperature extremes in elderly populations in Taiwan. *Environmental Research* **111**: 1156–1163.

Lin, Y.-K., Wang, Y.-C., Lin, P.-L., Li, M.-H., and Ho, T.-J. 2013. Relationships between cold-temperature indices and all causes and cardiopulmonary morbidity and mortality in a subtropical island. *Science of the Total Environment* **461–462**: 627–635.

Ma, W., Xu, X., Peng, L., and Kan, H. 2011. Impact of extreme temperature on hospital admission in Shanghai, China. *Science of the Total Environment* **409**: 3634–3637.

Martin, S.L., Cakmak, S., Hebbern, C.A., Avramescu, M.L., and Tremblay, N. 2012. Climate change and future temperature-related mortality in 15 Canadian cities. *International Journal of Biometeorology* **56**: 605–619.

McGregor, G.R. 2005. Winter North Atlantic Oscillation, temperature and ischaemic heart disease mortality in three English counties. *International Journal of Biometeorology* **49**: 197–204.

Mercer, J.B. 2003. Cold—an underrated risk factor for health. *Environmental Research* **92**: 8–13.

Miller, M.E., Shapiro, N.L., and Bhattacharyya, N. 2012. Annual temperature and the prevalence of frequent ear infections in childhood. *American Journal of Otolaryngology—Head and Neck Medicine and Surgery* **33**: 51–55.

Mourtzoukou, E.G. and Falagas, M.E. 2007. Exposure to cold and respiratory tract infections. *International Journal of Tuberculosis and Lung Disease* **11**: 938–943.

Nafstad, P., Skrondal, A., and Bjertness, E. 2001. Mortality and temperature in Oslo, Norway. 1990–1995. *European Journal of Epidemiology* **17**: 621–627.

Nakaji, S., Parodi, S., Fontana, V., Umeda, T., Suzuki, K., Sakamoto, J., Fukuda, S., Wada, S., and Sugawara, K. 2004. Seasonal changes in mortality rates from main causes of death in Japan (1970–1999). *European Journal of Epidemiology* **19**: 905–913.

Robeson, S.M. 2002. Relationships between mean and standard deviation of air temperature: implications for global warming. *Climate Research* **22**: 205–213.

Shinkawa, A., Ueda, K., Hasuo, Y., Kiyohara, Y., and Fujishima, M. 1990. Seasonal variation in stroke incidence in Hisayama, Japan. *Stroke* **21**: 1262–1267.

Song, G., Chen, G., Jiang, L., Zhang, Y., Zhao, N., Chen, B., and Kan, H. 2008. Diurnal temperature range as a novel risk factor for COPD death. *Respirology* **13**: 1066–1069.

Tam, W.W., Wong, T.W., Chair, S.Y., and Wong, A.H.S. 2009. Diurnal temperature range and daily cardiovascular mortalities among the elderly in Hong Kong. *Archives of Environmental and Occupational Health* **64**: 202–206.

Wang, Y.C., Lin, Y.K., Chuang, C.Y., Li, M.H., Chou, C.H., Liao, C.H., and Sung, F.C. 2012. Associating emergency room visits with first and prolonged extreme temperature event in Taiwan: a population-based cohort study. *Science of the Total Environment* **416**: 97–104.

Wayne, P., Foster, S., Connolly, J., Bazzaz, F., and Epstein, P. 2002. Production of allergenic pollen by ragweed (*Ambrosia artemisiifolia* L.) is increased in CO_2-enriched atmospheres. *Annals of Allergy, Asthma, and Immunology* **88**: 279–282.

Xu, Z., Huang, C., Su, H., Turner, L.R., Qiao, Z., and Tong, S. 2013. Diurnal temperature range and childhood asthma: a time-series study. *Environmental Health* **12**: 10.1186/1476-069X-12-12.

7.4 Stroke Occurrence

According to IPCC, global warming will pose numerous challenges to human health, including the potential for an excess of deaths. This section examines the results of a number of studies conducted over the past decade or so that deal with this subject as it applies to strokes.

Feigin *et al.* (2000) conducted what they call "the first truly population-based study on the relationship between stroke occurrence and weather parameters in Russia," working within the city of Novosibirsk, Siberia, which has one of the highest stroke incidence rates in the world. Based on analyses of 2,208 patients with sex and age distributions similar to those of Russia as a whole, they found a statistically significant association between stroke occurrence and low ambient temperature over the period 1982–1993. In the case of ischemic stroke (IS), which accounted for 87% of all stroke types, they determined "the risk of IS occurrence on days with low ambient temperature [was] 32% higher than that on days with high ambient temperature." Given what they describe as "the highly significant association observed between low ambient temperature ($< -2.0°C$) and IS occurrence ($P = 0.02$), together with the proportion of days with such temperature in the region during a calendar year (41.3%)," they conclude the "very high stroke incidence in Novosibirsk, Russia may partially be explained by the highly prevalent cold factor there." They suggest the implementation of "preventive measures in [the] region, such as avoiding low temperature."

Hong *et al.* (2003) investigated the association between the onset of ischemic stroke and prior episodic decreases in temperature in 545 patients who suffered strokes in Incheon, Korea from January 1998 to December 2000. They report "decreased ambient temperature was associated with risk of acute ischemic stroke," with the strongest effect being seen on the day after exposure to cold weather, further noting "even a moderate decrease in temperature can increase the risk of ischemic stroke." They also found "risk estimates associated with decreased temperature were greater in winter than in the summer," which suggests "low temperatures as well as temperature changes are associated with the onset of ischemic stroke." Finally, they explain the reason for the 24- to 48-hour lag between exposure to cold and the onset of stroke "might be that it takes some time for the decreasing temperature to affect blood viscosity or coagulation," which is also suggested by the work of Keatinge *et al.* (1984), who found blood viscosity and the plasma fraction of platelets began to increase one hour after cold exposure and did not reach a peak until sometime beyond six hours later.

Nakaji *et al.* (2004) evaluated seasonal trends in deaths due to various diseases in Japan using nationwide vital statistics from 1970 to 1999 together with mean monthly temperature data. They note Japan has "bitterly cold winters," and their analysis indicates the number of deaths due to cerebrovascular disease rises to a maximum during that cold time of year. They found the peak mortality rate due to stroke was two times greater in winter (January) than at the time of its yearly minimum (August and September). The team of nine scientists say it is necessary to bring about a "reduction in exposure to cold environments," as they put it.

Chang *et al.* (2004) analyzed data from the World Health Organization (WHO) Collaborative Study of Cardiovascular Disease and Steroid Hormone Contraception (WHO, 1995) to determine the effects of monthly mean temperature on rates of hospitalization for arterial stroke and acute myocardial infarction among women aged 15–49 from 17 countries in Africa, Asia, Europe, Latin America, and the Caribbean. Among these women, a 5°C reduction in mean air temperature was associated with a 7% increase in the expected hospitalization rate due to stroke, and this effect was relatively acute, within a period of about a month, the scientists write.

Each spring, Asian dust storm (ADS) events originating in the deserts of Mongolia and China transport great quantities of fine particulate matter of 10µm diameter (PM_{10}) to populated cities of East Asia, including Taipei, Taiwan, where the tiny particles have the potential to affect people's lives in a very big way. In an attempt to assess one aspect of this phenomenon, Yang *et al.* (2005) identified 54 ADS events that affected Taipei from 1996 to 2001, and they evaluated the impacts of these events on hospital admissions for primary intracerebral hemorrhagic stroke (PIH), ischemic stroke (IS), as well as the conglomerate of strokes of all types. The scientists found associations between dust storms and total stroke admissions and PIH and IS admissions were prominent three days after ADS events, with the relative risk for total stroke admissions being 1.05, that for IS admissions being 1.04, and that for PIH admissions being 1.15, with the latter finding being deemed statistically significant. For this particular stroke category, they additionally determined risk of stroke rose by 2.67% for each 10 $\mu g/m^3$ increase in PM_{10} concentration above the normal mean value of 55.43 $\mu g/m^3$.

With respect to how the ongoing rise in the air's CO_2 content might impact this phenomenon, Chapter 1 of this volume discusses the well-documented increase in plant water use efficiency that results from increases in atmospheric CO_2 concentration. This benefit should allow more plants to grow in the arid source regions of the Asian dust clouds, which will help to stabilize the soil and decrease its susceptibility to wind erosion, thereby reducing the severity of ADS events. Second, the propensity for elevated CO_2 concentrations to increase moisture contents of soils beneath plant canopies as a consequence of CO_2-induced reductions in plant transpiration also should lead to greater ground cover and reduced wind erosion. Third, the ability of extra CO_2 in the atmosphere to enhance the growth of cryptobiotic soil crusts should stabilize the surface of the soil. And fourth, as noted by Zavaleta *et al.* (2003), global warming itself may increase soil moisture contents in water-limited regions by hastening plant senescence and thereby reducing the period of time over which transpiration-driven soil water losses occur.

If the air's CO_2 content continues to rise, even in the face of further warming, there should be a gradual reduction in the number of PM_{10}–induced strokes in the populace of Taipei, Taiwan, as well as in other places affected by Asian and other dust storms.

Gill *et al.* (2012) write, "in the past two decades, several studies reported that meteorologic changes are associated with monthly and seasonal spikes in the incidence of aneurysmal subarachnoid hemorrhage (aSAH)," and "analysis of data from large regional databases in both hemispheres has revealed increased seasonal risk for aSAH in the fall, winter and spring,"

citing Chyatte *et al.* (1994), Lejeune *et al.* (1994), Langmayr *et al.* (1995), Feigin *et al.* (2001), Abe *et al.* (2008), and Beseoglu *et al.* (2008). Gill *et al.* identified the medical records of 1,175 patients at the Johns Hopkins Hospital in Baltimore, Maryland (USA) who were admitted with a radiologically confirmed diagnosis of aSAH between 1 January 1991 and 1 March 2009. The researchers employed Poisson regression "to model the risk of a patient presenting with aSAH based on maximum ambient temperature (MAT), average relative humidity (ARH), and atmospheric pressure, clustering by season of the year to control for the previously reported relationship between season and aSAH presentation."

The six scientists report both "a one-day decrease in temperature and colder daily temperatures were associated with an increased risk of incident aSAH," and "these variables appeared to act synergistically" and were "particularly predominant in the fall, when the transition from warmer to colder temperatures occurred." Gill *et al.* add their study "is the first to report a direct relationship between a temperature decrease and an increased risk of aSAH," and "it also confirms the observations of several reports of an increased risk of aSAH in cold weather or winter," citing Lejeunne *et al.* (1994), Jakovljevic *et al.* (1996), and Nyquist *et al.* (2001).

References

Abe, T., Ohde, S., Ishimatsu, S., Ogata, H., Hasegawa, T., Nakamura, T., and Tokuda, Y. 2008. Effects of meteorological factors on the onset of subarachnoid hemorrhage: a time-series analysis. *Journal of Clinical Neuroscience* 15: 1005–1010.

Beseoglu, K., Hanggi, D., Stummer, W., and Steiger, H.J. 2008. Dependence of subarachnoid hemorrhage on climate conditions: a systematic meteorological analysis from the Dusseldorf metropolitan area. *Neurosurgery* 62: 1033–1038.

Chang, C.L., Shipley, M., Marmot, M., and Poulter, N. 2004. Lower ambient temperature was associated with an increased risk of hospitalization for stroke and acute myocardial infarction in young women. *Journal of Clinical Epidemiology* 57: 749–757.

Chyatte, D., Chen, T.L., Bronstein, K., and Brass, L.M. 1994. Seasonal fluctuation in the incidence of intracranial aneurysm rupture and its relationship to changing climatic conditions. *Journal of Neurosurgery* 81: 525–530.

Feigin, V.L., Anderson, C.S., Anderson, N.E., Broad, J.B., Pledger, M.J., and Bonita, R. 2001. Is there a temporal pattern to the occurrence of subarachnoid hemorrhage in the southern hemisphere? Pooled data from 3 large, population-based incidence studies in Australasia, 1981 to 1997. *Stroke* **32**: 613–619.

Feigin, V.L., Nikitin, Yu.P., Bots, M.L., Vinogradova, T.E., and Grobbee, D.E. 2000. A population-based study of the associations of stroke occurrence with weather parameters in Siberia, Russia (1982–92). *European Journal of Neurology* **7**: 171–178.

Gill, R.S., Hambridge, H.L., Schneider, E.B., Hanff, T., Tamargo, R.J., and Nyquist, P. 2012. Falling temperature and colder weather are associated with an increased risk of Aneurysmal Subarachnoid Hemorrhage. *World Neurosurgery* **79**: 136–142.

Hong, Y-C., Rha, J-H., Lee, J-T., Ha, E-H., Kwon, H-J., and Kim, H. 2003. Ischemic stroke associated with decrease in temperature. *Epidemiology* **14**: 473–478.

Jakovljevic, D., Salomaa, V., Sivenius, J., Tamminen, M., Sarti, C., Salmi, K., Kaarsalo, E., Narva, V., Immonen-Raiha, P., Torppa, J., and Tuomilehto, J. 1996. Seasonal variation in the occurrence of stroke in a Finnish adult population. The FINMONICA Stroke Register. Finnish Monitoring Trends and Determinants in Cardiovascular Disease. *Stroke* **27**: 1774–1779.

Keatinge, W.R., Coleshaw, S.R., Cotter, F., Mattock, M., Murphy, M., and Chelliah, R. 1984. Increases in platelet and red cell counts, blood viscosity, and arterial pressure during mild surface cooling: factors in mortality from coronary and cerebral thrombosis in winter. *British Medical Journal (Clinical Research Education)* **289**: 1405–1408.

Langmayr, J.J., Obwegeser, A., and Ortler, M. 1995. Seasonal rupture of aneurysms. *Journal of Neurosurgery* **83**: 182–183.

Lejeune, J.P., Vinchon, M., Amouyel, P., Escartin, T., Escartin, D., and Christiaens, J.L. 1994. Association of occurrence of aneurysmal bleeding with meteorology variations in north of France. *Stroke* **25**: 338–341.

Nakaji, S., Parodi, S., Fontana, V., Umeda, T., Suzuki, K., Sakamoto, J., Fukuda, S., Wada, S., and Sugawara, K. 2004. Seasonal changes in mortality rates from main causes of death in Japan (1970–1999). *European Journal of Epidemiology* **19**: 905–913.

Nyquist, P.A., Brown Jr., R.D., Wiebers, D.O., Crowson, C.S., and O'Fallon, W.M. 2001. Circadian and seasonal occurrence of subarachnoid and intracerebral hemorrhage. *Neurology* **56**: 190–193.

WHO. 1995. WHO Collaborative Study of Cardiovascular Disease and Steroid Hormone Contraception. A multinational case-control study of cardiovascular disease and steroid hormone contraceptives: description and validation of methods. *Journal of Clinical Epidemiology* **48**: 1513–1547.

Yang, C.-Y., Chen, Y.-S., Chiu, H.-F., and Goggins, W.B. 2005. Effects of Asian dust storm events on daily stroke admissions in Taipei, Taiwan. *Environmental Research* **99**: 79–84.

Zavaleta, E.S., Thomas, B.D., Chiariello, N.R., Asner, G.P., Shaw, M.R., and Field, C.B. 2003. Plants reverse warming effect on ecosystem water balance. *Proceedings of the National Academy of Science USA* **100**: 9892–9893.

7.5 Malaria

- A vast body of scientific examination and research contradict the claim that malaria will expand across the globe and intensify as a result of CO_2-induced warming.

According to IPCC, ""If climate change continues as projected in scenarios in the next few decades, the major increases of ill-health compared to no climate change will occur through …increased risks of food- and water-borne diseases and vector-borne infections. *[high confidence]*" (IPCC-II, 2013). Chapter 11, Human Health, Working Group II, *IPCC Fifth Assessment Report,* dated March 28, 2013, p. 3, italics in original, bold removed). This section investigates the reliability of IPCC's claim with respect to malaria.. According to the results of a vast body of scientific examination and research on this topic, there is little support for IPCC's claims. The next two sections will address the related claims regarding dengue fever and tick-borne diseases.

In a research report in *Science*, Rogers and Randolph (2000) note "predictions of global climate change have stimulated forecasts that vector-borne diseases will spread into regions that are at present too cool for their persistence." There are, however, several problems with this scenario.

According to Reiter (2000), claims that malaria resurgence is the product of CO_2-induced global warming ignore other important factors and disregard known facts. A historical analysis of malaria trends, for example, reveals this disease was an important cause of illness and death in England during a period of colder-than-present temperatures throughout the Little Ice Age. Its transmission began to decline only in the nineteenth century, during a warming phase, when, according to Reiter, "temperatures were already much higher than in the Little Ice Age." In short, malaria was prevalent in Europe during some of the coldest centuries of the past millennium, and it has only recently undergone widespread decline, when temperatures have been warming, Clearly, there are other factors at work that are more important than temperature. Such factors include the quality of public health services, irrigation and agricultural activities, land use practices, civil strife, natural disasters, ecological change, population change, use of insecticides, and the movement of people (Reiter, 2000; Reiter, 2001; Hay *et al.*, 2002).

Nevertheless, concerns have lingered about the possibility of widespread future increases in malaria due to global warming. These concerns are generally rooted in climate models that typically use only one, or at most two, climate variables in making their predictions of the future distribution of the disease over Earth, and they generally do not include any of the non-climatic factors listed in the preceding paragraph. When more variables are included, a less-worrisome future is projected. In one modeling study, for example, Rogers and Randolph (2000) employed five climate variables and obtained very different results. Briefly, they used the present-day distribution of malaria to determine the specific climatic constraints that best define that distribution, after which the multivariate relationship they derived from this exercise was applied to future climate scenarios derived from state-of-the-art climate models, in order to map potential future geographical distributions of the disease.

Their study revealed very little change: a 0.84% increase in potential malaria exposure under the "medium-high" scenario of global warming and a 0.92% decrease under the "high" scenario. Rogers and Randolph explicitly state their quantitative model "contradicts prevailing forecasts of global malaria expansion" and "highlights the use of multivariate rather than univariate constraints in such applications."

Hay *et al.* (2002) investigated long-term trends in meteorological data at four East African highland sites that experienced significant increases in malaria cases over the past couple of decades, reporting "temperature, rainfall, vapour pressure and the number of months suitable for *P. falciparum* transmission have not changed significantly during the past century or during the period of reported malaria resurgence." Thus these factors could not be responsible for the observed increases in malaria cases. Likewise, Shanks *et al.* (2000) examined trends in temperature, precipitation, and malaria rates in western Kenya over the period 1965–1997, finding no linkages among the variables.

Small *et al.* (2003) examined trends in a climate-driven model of malaria transmission between 1911 and 1995, using a spatially and temporally extensive gridded climate dataset to identify locations in Africa where the malaria transmission climate suitability index had changed significantly over this time interval. After determining areas of change, they more closely examined the underlying climate forcing of malaria transmission suitability for those localities. They found malaria transmission suitability did indeed increase because of climate change in specific locations of limited extent, but in Southern Mozambique, the only region for which climatic suitability consistently increased, the cause of the increase was increased precipitation, not temperature. Small *et al.* state, "climate warming, expressed as a systematic temperature increase over the 85-year period, does not appear to be responsible for an increase in malaria suitability over any region in Africa." They conclude "research on the links between climate change and the recent resurgence of malaria across Africa would be best served through refinements in maps and models of precipitation patterns and through closer examination of the role of nonclimatic influences," the great significance of which also has been demonstrated by Reiter *et al.* (2003) for dengue fever, another important mosquito-borne disease.

Zhou *et al.* (2004) employed a nonlinear mixed-regression model study that focused on the numbers of monthly malaria outpatients of the past 10–20 years in seven East African highland sites and their relationships to the numbers of malaria outpatients during the previous time period, seasonality, and climate variability. They state, "for all seven study sites, we found highly significant nonlinear, synergistic effects of the interaction between rainfall and temperature on malaria incidence, indicating that the use of either temperature or rainfall alone is not sensitive enough for the detection of anomalies that are associated with malaria epidemics." Githeko and Ndegwa (2001), Shanks *et al.* (2002), and Hay *et al.* (2002) reached the same conclusion. In addition, climate variability—not just temperature or not just warming—contributed less than 20% of the temporal variance in the number of malaria outpatients, and at only two out of the seven sites studied.

Zhou *et al.* conclude "malaria dynamics are largely driven by autoregression and/or seasonality in these sites," and "the observed large among-site variation in the sensitivity to climate fluctuations may be governed by complex interactions between climate and biological and social factors." The latter include "land use, topography, *P. falciparum* genotypes, malaria vector species composition, availability of vector control and healthcare programs, drug resistance, and other socioeconomic factors," including "failure to seek treatment or delayed treatment of malaria patients, and HIV infections in the human population," which they say have "become increasingly prevalent."

In a major review of the potential impacts of global warming on vector-borne diseases, Rogers and Randolph (2006) focus on recent upsurges of malaria in Africa, asking, "Has climate change already had an impact?" They demonstrate "evidence for increasing malaria in many parts of Africa is overwhelming, but the more likely causes for most of these changes to date include land-cover and land-use changes and, most importantly, drug resistance rather than any effect of climate," noting "the recrudescence of malaria in the tea estates near Kericho, Kenya, in East Africa, where temperature has not changed significantly, shows all the signs of a disease that has escaped drug control following the evolution of chloroquine resistance by the malarial parasite."

They explain, "malaria waxes and wanes to the beat of two rhythms: an annual one dominated by local, seasonal weather conditions and a *ca.* 3-yearly one dominated by herd immunity," noting "effective drugs suppress both cycles before they can be expressed," but "this produces a population which is mainly or entirely dependent on drug effectiveness, and which suffers the consequence of eventual drug failure, during which the rhythms reestablish themselves, as they appear to have done in Kericho."

Two more review papers on the subject followed two years later. In the first, Zell *et al.* (2008) write, "it is assumed that global warming is forced by the anthropogenic release of 'greenhouse gases,'" and a further "consistent assumption" has been a consequent "increased exposure of humans to tropical pathogens and their vectors." They also note "there is dissent about this hypothesis (Taubes, 1997; Reiter, 2001; Hay *et al.*, 2002; Reiter *et al.*, 2003; Randolph, 2004; Zell, 2004; Halstead, 2008)," and they explore it in more detail, examining the pertinent literature and describing "those mechanisms that have led to an increase of virus activity in recent years."

Based on their review, the three German researchers report "only very few examples point toward global warming as a cause of excess viral activity." Instead, they determined "coupled ocean/atmosphere circulations and continuous anthropogenic disturbances (increased populations of humans and domestic animals, socioeconomic instability, armed conflicts, displaced populations, unbalanced ecosystems, dispersal of resistant pathogens etc.) appear to be the major drivers of disease variability," and "global warming at best contributes."

In the second 2008 paper (Reiter, 2008), Paul Reiter—who works with the Insects and Infectious Disease Unit of the Institut Pasteur in Paris, France—writes, "man-made climate change has become a defining moral and political issue of our age," noting "speculations on its potential impact often focus on infectious diseases, and on malaria in particular," and "predictions are common that in the coming decades, tens—even hundreds—of millions more cases will occur in regions where the disease is already present, and that the vectors and the pathogens will move to higher latitudes and altitudes," infecting even more people.

In analyzing these claims, Reiter first discusses the mathematical models employed in this endeavor, after which he discusses common misconceptions and the nature of malaria in temperate regions. In the latter discussions he mentions such items as ecological change, new farm crops, new rearing practices, urbanization and mechanization, human living conditions, and medical care. Then, in a discussion of malaria in the tropics, he considers stable endemic malaria, unstable endemic malaria, birth rate, forest clearance, agriculture, movement of people, urbanization, insecticide resistance, resistance to drugs, degradation of the health infrastructure, and war and civil strife. He then treats three additional topics: Highland malaria in the tropics, Kenya Highlands, and New Guinea Highlands.

Reiter concludes, "simplistic reasoning on the future prevalence of malaria is ill-founded; malaria is not limited by climate in most temperate regions, nor in the tropics, and in nearly all cases, 'new' malaria at high altitudes is well below the maximum altitudinal limits for transmission." He further states, "future changes in climate may alter the prevalence and incidence of the disease, but obsessive emphasis on 'global warming' as a dominant parameter is indefensible; the principal determinants are linked to ecological and societal change, politics and economics." Reiter's conclusions have been borne out in additional studies of the subject.

Jackson *et al.* (2010) say "malaria is one of the most devastating vector-borne parasitic diseases in the tropical and subtropical regions of the world," noting it affects more than 100 countries. According to the World Health Organization, Africa carries the highest infection burden of any continent, with nearly

200 million cases reported in 2006, and the Centers for Disease Control and Prevention estimates between 700,000 and 2.7 million people each year die from the dreaded disease (Suh *et al.*, 2004). In addition, Jackson *et al.* report "the African region bears 90% of these estimated worldwide deaths," and "three-quarters of all malaria related deaths are among African children," citing Breman (2001). They opine, "malaria could be greatly affected by the influence of climate change," such as global warming.

The five U.S. researchers linked reported malaria cases and deaths from the years 1996 to 2006, obtained from the World Malaria Report (2008) for 10 countries in western Africa (Benin, Burkina Faso, Cote d'Ivoire, Gambia, Ghana, Liberia, Mali, Senegal, Sierra Leone, and Togo) with corresponding climate data from the U.S. National Oceanic and Atmospheric Administration's National Climatic Data Center. They searched for transitive relationships between the weather variables and malaria rates via spatial regression analysis and tests for correlation. Jackson *et al.* report their analyses showed "very little correlation exists between rates of malaria prevalence and climate indicators in western Africa." This result, as they describe it, "contradicts the prevailing theory that climate and malaria prevalence are closely linked and also negates the idea that climate change will increase malaria transmission in the region."

Stern *et al.* (2011) examined trends in temperature and malaria for the Highlands of East Africa, which span Rwanda, Burundi, and parts of Kenya, Tanzania, and Uganda, to resolve controversies over whether the area has warmed and malaria has become more prevalent. For temperature, the authors used three time series obtained from the Climatic Research Unit (CRU) for four locations. Temperature data for Kericho extend through 2009, but only through 2006 for the Highlands. For malaria, the researchers used a data set on malaria cases through May 2010 at a hospital in Kericho, Kenya, and data from more than 5,200 surveys on the prevalence of malaria though 2009 in the Highlands. They report temperature has increased significantly in the region, yet "malaria in Kericho and many other areas of East Africa has decreased during periods of unambiguous warming." Their paper does not attempt an explanation for the divergence in these trends.

In a model-based study, Nkurunziza and Pilz (2011) employed Bayesian generalized additive models (GAMs) to assess the impact of an increase in temperature on malaria transmission in Burundi. Overall, the two researchers write, "the results of the GAMs show that an increase in the maximum

temperature will cause an increase in minimum temperature," and "the increase in the latter will result in a decreasing maximum humidity, leading to a decrease in rainfall." These results, the writers continue, "suggest that an increased temperature will result in a shortening of the life span of mosquitoes (due to decreasing humidity) and decrease in the capacity of larva production and maturation (due to decreasing rainfall)." Thus, "the increase in temperature will not result in an increased malaria transmission in Burundi," which is "in good agreement with some previous works on the topic," citing as examples WHO, WMO, UNEP (2003), Lieshout *et al.* (2004), and Thomas (2004). In a final statement on the matter, Nkurunziza and Pilz note that in regions with endemic malaria transmission, such as Burundi, "the increase in temperature may lead to unsuitable climate conditions for mosquitoes survival and, hence, probably to a decreasing malaria transmission."

In another model-based study, Béguin *et al.* (2011) quantified the independent effects of climate and socioeconomic factors on the historical and projected future global distribution of malaria. The authors also provide estimates of the factors' separate and combined contributions to the populations at risk of malaria. Specifically, they estimated populations at risk of malaria (PAR) based on climatic variables, population growth, and GDP per capita (GDP$_{pc}$). GDP$_{pc}$ is an approximation for per-capita income ("income" for short) for 1990, 2010, and 2050, based on sensitivity analyses for the following three scenarios: (1) a worst-case scenario, in which income declines to 50% of its 2010 values by 2050; (2) a "growth reduction" scenario, in which income declines by 25% in 2030 and 50% in 2050, relative to the A1B scenario; and (3) a scenario in which income stays constant at 2010 values.

The PAR was derived from information on the presence or absence of *P. vivax* malaria in 1990 based on a logistic model for malaria presence that used three parameters: the mean temperature of the coldest month, the mean precipitation of the wettest month during the period 1961–1990, and the square root of income. Accordingly, the PAR does not directly reflect the health impacts of malaria. Secular technological change was ignored in this study. The results are presented in Table 7.5.1.

The authors observe, "under the A1B climate scenario, climate change has much weaker effects than GDP$_{pc}$ increase on the geographic distribution of malaria." This result is consistent with the few studies that have considered the impact of climate change and

Model type	Population at Risk 2030 [billions]	Population at Risk 2050 [billions]
Socioeconomic changes only (no climate change)	3.52	1.74
Socioeconomic and climatic changes (A1B scenario)	3.58 [3.55–3.60]	1.95 [1.93–1.96]
Socioeconomic changes and CC (slower growth scenario)	3.82 [3.39–3.84]	3.42 [3.28–3.45]
No growth scenario, only CC	4.61 [4.54–4.67]	5.20 [5.11–5.25]
Pessimistic growth scenario and CC	5.18 [5.07–5.30]	6.27 [6.19–6.32]

Table 7.5.1. Effects of Climate and Socioeconomic Factors on the Projected Future Global Distribution of Malaria. From Béguin *et al.* (2011).

socioeconomic factors on malaria. (See, e.g., Tol and Dowlatabadi, 2001; Bosello *et al.*, 2006). With respect to malaria, therefore, climate change is a relatively minor factor compared to economic development.

Kuhn *et al.* (2003) state, "there has been much recent speculation that global warming may allow the reestablishment of malaria transmission in previously endemic areas such as Europe and the United States." In particular, they note "the British Chief Medical Officer's recent report [*Getting Ahead of the Curve: A Strategy for Combating Infectious Diseases (Including Other Aspects of Health Protection)*, Department of Health (2002), London] asserted that 'by 2050 the climate of the UK may be such that indigenous malaria could become re-established.'" To investigate the robustness of this hypothesis, they analyzed the determinants of temporal trends in malaria deaths within England and Wales in 1840–1910.

With respect to temperature changes over the period of study, Kuhn *et al.* report "a 1°C increase or decrease was responsible for an increase in malaria deaths of 8.3% or a decrease of 6.5%, respectively," which explains "the malaria epidemics in the 'unusually hot summers' of 1848 and 1859." Nevertheless, the long-term near-linear temporal decline in malaria deaths over the period of study, the researchers write, "was probably driven by nonclimatic factors," among which they identify increasing livestock populations (which tend to divert mosquito biting from humans), decreasing acreages of marsh wetlands (where mosquitoes breed), as well as "improved housing, better access to health care and

medication, and improved nutrition, sanitation, and hygiene." They also note the number of secondary cases arising from each primary imported case "is currently minuscule," as demonstrated by the absence of any secondary malaria cases in the UK since 1953.

Although simplistic model simulations may suggest the increase in temperature predicted for Britain by 2050 is likely to cause an 8–14% increase in the potential for malaria transmission, Kuhn *et al.* say "the projected increase in proportional risk is clearly insufficient to lead to the reestablishment of endemicity." They note "the national health system ensures that imported malaria infections are detected and effectively treated and that gametocytes are cleared from the blood in less than a week." For Britain, therefore, they conclude "a 15% rise in risk might have been important in the 19th century, but such a rise is now highly unlikely to lead to the reestablishment of indigenous malaria," because "socioeconomic and agricultural changes" have greatly altered the cause-and-effect relationships of the past.

Hulden and Hulden (2009) analyzed malaria statistics collected in Finland from 1750 to 2008 via correlation analyses between malaria frequency per million people and all variables that have been used in similar studies throughout other parts of Europe, including temperature data, animal husbandry, consolidation of land by redistribution, and household size. They report "malaria was a common endemic disease in Finland in the 18th and 19th centuries and prevalent in the whole country" and "mortality during malaria epidemics usually varied between 0.85 and 3%." Thereafter, however, they found "malaria declined slowly in Finland without any deliberate counter-measures," such that "the last epidemic in Helsinki occurred in 1902" and "during the 1930s malaria was close to extinction." Over the entire period, "malaria frequency decreased from about 20,000–50,000 per 1,000,000 people to less than 1 per 1,000,000 people," they report.

When malaria was still common in the country, they did find "high peaks in malaria followed high temperatures in June–July," but overriding this within-year temperature response over the long term, "both highs and lows in malaria frequency [were] declining independently of temperature trends." The two Finnish researchers conclude, "indigenous malaria in Finland faded out evenly in the whole country during 200 years with limited or no counter measures or medication," making that situation "one of the very few opportunities where natural malaria dynamics can be studied in detail." Their study indicates "malaria in Finland basically was a sociological disease and that malaria trends were strongly linked to changes in the human household size and housing standard."

Childs *et al.* (2006) present a detailed analysis of malaria incidence in northern Thailand based on a quarter-century monthly time series (January 1977 through January 2002) of total malaria cases in the country's 13 northern provinces. Over this time period, when IPCC claims the world warmed at a rate and to a level unprecedented over the prior one to two millennia, Childs *et al.* report there was an approximately constant rate of decline in total malaria incidence (from a mean monthly incidence in 1977 of 41.5 cases per hundred thousand people to 6.72 cases per hundred thousand people in 2001). This decrease was due primarily to a reduction in cases positive for *Plasmodium falciparum* (mean monthly incidence in 1977 and 2001 of 28.6 and 3.22 cases per 100,000 people, respectively) and secondarily to a reduction in cases positive for *P. vivax* (mean monthly incidence in 1977 and 2001 of 12.8 and 3.5 cases per 100,000 people, respectively). Consequently, noting "there has been a steady reduction through time of total malaria incidence in northern Thailand, with an average decline of 6.45% per year," they say this result "reflects changing agronomic practices and patterns of immigration, as well as the success of interventions such as vector control programs, improved availability of treatment and changing drug policies."

Haque *et al.* (2010) analyzed monthly malaria case data for the malaria endemic district of Chittagong Hill Tracts in Bangladesh from January 1989 to December 2008, looking for potential relationships between malaria incidence and various climatic parameters (rainfall, temperature, humidity, sea surface temperature, and the El Niño-Southern Oscillation), as well as the normalized difference vegetation index (NDVI), a satellite-derived measure of surface vegetation greenness. The six scientists report, "after adjusting for potential mutual confounding between climatic factors there was no evidence for any association between the number of malaria cases and temperature, rainfall and humidity," and "there was no evidence of an association between malaria cases and sea surface temperatures in the Bay of Bengal and NINO3." Instead, they found "the best leading indicator of the number of malaria cases was NDVI at a lag of 0–3 months, and that NDVI was negatively associated with malaria cases," such that "each 0.1 increase in monthly NDVI was associated with a 30.4% decrease in malaria cases." Haque *et al.* write, "it seems counterintuitive that a low NDVI, an indicator of low vegetation greenness, is associated with increases in malaria cases," since the primary vectors of the disease in Bangladesh are associated with forests. In light of this surprising result, they state their study "draws attention again to the complex nature of the relationship between malaria and climate," which in the case of the highlands of Bangladesh appears to be nonexistent.

Paaijmans *et al.* (2012) state "the development rate of parasites and pathogens within vectors typically increases with temperature," and, therefore, "transmission intensity is generally assumed to be higher under warmer conditions." However, they note, "development is only one component of parasite/pathogen life history," adding, "there has been little research exploring the temperature sensitivity of other traits that contribute to transmission intensity."

Paaijmans *et al.* examined prior "standard assumptions" and explored the resulting implications "for our understanding of the effects of temperature on disease transmission" on the rodent malaria *Plasmodium yoelii* and the Asian malaria vector *Anopheles stephensi.* The three U.S. researchers found "vector competence (the maximum proportion of infectious mosquitoes, which implicitly includes parasite survival across the incubation period) tails off at higher temperatures, even though parasite development rate increases." Moreover, "the standard measure of the parasite incubation period (i.e., time until the first mosquitoes within a cohort become infectious following an infected blood-meal) is incomplete because parasite development follows a cumulative distribution, which itself varies with temperature." Finally, "including these effects in a simple model dramatically alters estimates of transmission intensity and reduces the optimum temperature for transmission." Paaijmans *et al.* conclude their results "challenge current understanding of the effects of temperature on malaria transmission dynamics," and they note their findings imply "control at higher temperatures might be more feasible than currently predicted." Therefore, in regard to "the possible effects of climate warming," they conclude "increases in temperature need not simply lead to increases in transmission."

Russell (2009), a professor in the Department of Medicine of the University of Sydney (Australia) and founding director of its Department of Medical Entomology, reports, "during the past 10 years, there has been increasing concern for health impacts of global warming in Australia, and continuing projections and predictions for increasing mosquito-borne disease as a result of climate change." He writes, these claims "are relatively simplistic, and do not take adequate account of the current or historic situations of the vectors and pathogens, and the complex ecologies that might be involved." Russell reviewed the consequences of these several inadequacies for malaria, dengue fever, the arboviral arthritides (Ross River and Barmah Forest viruses), and the arboviral encephalitides (Murray Valley encephalitis and Kunjin viruses) within the context of predictions of climate change modeled by Australia's Commonwealth Scientific and Industrial Research Organisation (CSIRO) and the Intergovernmental Panel on Climate Change (IPCC).

The abstract of Russell's paper begins with a question: "Will warming climate increase the risk or prevalence of mosquito-borne disease in Australia, as has been projected in a number of scientific publications and governmental reports?" His conclusion provides the answer: "there might be some increases in mosquito-borne disease in Australia with a warming climate, but with which mosquitoes and which pathogens, and where and when, cannot be easily discerned." He concludes, "of itself, climate change as currently projected, is not likely to provide great cause for public health concern with mosquito-borne disease in Australia."

Tuchman *et al.* (2003) took leaf litter from *Populus tremuloides* (Michaux) trees that had been grown out-of-doors in open-bottom root boxes located within open-top aboveground chambers maintained at atmospheric CO_2 concentrations of either 360 or 720 ppm for an entire growing season, incubated the leaf litter for 14 days in a nearby stream, and fed the incubated litter to four species of detritivorous mosquito larvae to assess its effect on their development rates and survivorship. They report larval mortality was 2.2 times higher for *Aedes albopictus* (Skuse) mosquitos that were fed leaf litter that had been produced in the high-CO_2 chambers than it was for those fed litter that had been produced in the ambient-air chambers. In addition, they found larval development rates of *Aedes triseriatus* (Say), *Aedes aegypti* (L.), and *Armigeres subalbatus* (Coquillett) were slowed by 78%, 25%, and 27%, respectively, when fed litter produced in the high-CO_2 as opposed to the ambient-CO_2 chambers, so mosquitoes of these species spent 20, 11, and 9 days longer in their respective larval stages when feeding on litter produced in the CO_2-enriched as compared to the ambient-CO_2 chambers. The researchers suggest "increases in lignin coupled with decreases in leaf nitrogen induced by elevated CO_2 and subsequent lower bacterial productivity [on the leaf litter in the water] were probably responsible for [the] decreases in survivorship and/or development rate of the four species of mosquitoes."

Concerning the significance of these findings, Tuchman *et al.* write, "the indirect impacts of an elevated CO_2 atmosphere on mosquito larval survivorship and development time could potentially be great," because longer larval development times could result in fewer cohorts of mosquitoes surviving to adulthood. With fewer mosquitoes, there should be lower levels of mosquito-borne diseases.

Zell (2004) states many people "assume a correlation between increasing disease incidence and global warming." However, he concludes after studying the issue in considerable depth, "the factors responsible for the emergence/reemergence of vector-borne diseases are complex and mutually influence each other." As an example of this complexity, he notes, "the incidence and spread of parasites and arboviruses are affected by insecticide and drug resistance, deforestation, irrigation systems and dams, changes in public health policy (decreased resources of surveillance, prevention and vector control), demographic changes (population growth, migration, urbanization), and societal changes (inadequate housing conditions, water deterioration, sewage, waste management)." Therefore, he continues, "it may be over-simplistic to attribute emergent/re-emergent diseases to climate change and sketch the menace of devastating epidemics in a warmer world." Zell states, "variations in public health practices and lifestyle can easily outweigh changes in disease biology," especially those that might be caused by global warming.

Nabi and Qader (2009) considered the climatic conditions that impact the spread of malaria—temperature, rainfall, and humidity—and the host of pertinent nonclimatic factors that play important roles in its epidemiology: the presence or absence of mosquito control programs, the availability or non-availability of malaria-fighting drugs, changing resistances to drugs, the quality of vector control, changes in land use, the availability of good health services, human population growth, human migrations, international travel, and standard of living. The two researchers report "global warming alone will not be of a great significance in the upsurge of malaria unless it is accompanied by a deterioration in other parameters like public health facilities, resistance to anti-malarial drugs, decreased mosquito control measures," etc. They say "no accurate prediction about malaria can truly be made," because "it is very difficult to estimate what the other factors will be like in the future." They do note, however, mosquito-borne diseases were a major public health problem in the United States from the 1600s to the mid-1900s, "with occasional epidemics." By the middle of the twentieth century, however, "malaria disappeared from the country along with the other mosquito borne diseases like Dengue and Yellow fever," and "this decline was attributed to overall improvements in living conditions and better public health measures." These factors have kept these diseases at bay throughout the latter half of the twentieth century as well, even though that period included what climate alarmists describe as "unprecedented global warming."

Nabi and Qader conclude "as public health workers, it would be more justifiable for us to exert our efforts on these other [non-climatic] parameters for the eradication and control of malaria."

Gething et al. (2010) observe, based on "model predictions" it is "reported widely in global climate policy debates that climate change is adding to the present-day burden of malaria and will increase both the future range and intensity of the disease," citing IPCC (2007) and the U.S. Environmental Protection Agency (2010). Noting "it has long been known that the range of malaria has contracted through a century of economic development and disease control (Hay et al., 2009)," when "global temperature increases have been unequivocal," Gething et al. explore this seeming incongruity by comparing "an evidence-based map of contemporary malaria endemicity (Hay et al., 2009)" with "the most reliable equivalent for the pre-intervention era, around 1900 (Lysenko et al.,

1968)," when malaria was "at its assumed historical peak," thereby providing a comparison of "the magnitude of observed changes in range and endemicity to those proposed to occur in response to climate change."

The six scientists—from the Spatial Ecology and Epidemiology Group, the Malaria Public Health and Epidemiology Group, and the Centre for Tropical Medicine of the UK's University of Oxford, plus the Departments of Biology and Geography and the Emerging Pathogens Institute of the United States' University of Florida—report "comparison of the historical and contemporary maps revealed that endemic/stable malaria is likely to have covered 58% of the world's land surface around 1900 but only 30% by 2007." They report, "even more marked has been the decrease in prevalence within this greatly reduced range, with endemicity falling by one or more classes in over two-thirds of the current range of stable transmission." They write, "widespread claims that rising mean temperatures have already led to increases in worldwide malaria morbidity and mortality are largely at odds with observed decreasing global trends in both its endemicity and geographic extent." Rather, "the combined natural and anthropogenic forces acting on the disease throughout the twentieth century have resulted in the great majority of locations undergoing a net reduction in transmission between one and three orders of magnitude larger than the maximum future increases proposed under temperature-based climate change scenarios."

Gething et al. conclude there has been "a decoupling of the geographical climate-malaria relationship over the twentieth century, indicating that non-climatic factors have profoundly confounded this relationship over time." They note "non-climatic factors, primarily direct disease control and the indirect effects of a century of urbanization and economic development, although spatially and temporally variable, have exerted a substantially greater influence on the geographic extent and intensity of malaria worldwide during the twentieth century than have climatic factors." As for the future, they conclude climate-induced effects "can be offset by moderate increases in coverage levels of currently available interventions."

The many findings described above make it clear a vast body of scientific examination and research contradict the claim that malaria will expand across the globe and intensify as a result of CO_2-induced warming.

References

Béguin, A., Hales, S., Rocklöv, J., Åström, C., Louis, V.R., and Sauerborn, R. 2011. The opposing effects of climate change and socio-economic development on the global distribution of malaria. *Global Environmental Change* **21**: 1209–1214.

Bosello, F., Roson, R., and Tol, R.S.J. 2006. Economy-wide estimates of the implications of climate change: human health. *Ecological Economics* **58**: 579–591.

Breman, J.G. 2001. The ears of the hippopotamus: manifestations, determinants, and estimates of the malaria burden. *American Journal of Tropical Medicine and Hygiene* **64**: 1–11.

Childs, D.Z., Cattadori, I.M., Suwonkerd, W., Prajakwong, S., and Boots, M. 2006. Spatiotemporal patterns of malaria incidence in northern Thailand. *Transactions of the Royal Society of Tropical Medicine and Hygiene* **100**: 623–631.

Gething, P.W., Smith, D.L., Patil, A.P., Tatem, A.J., Snow, R.W., and Hay, S.I. 2010. Climate change and the global malaria recession. *Nature* **465**: 342–345.

Githeko, A.K. and Ndegwa, W. 2001. Predicting malaria epidemics in the Kenyan highlands using climate data: A tool for decision makers. *Global Change and Human Health* **2**: 54–63.

Halstead, S.B. 2008. Dengue virus-mosquito interactions. *Annual Review of Entomology* **53**: 273–291.

Haque, U., Hashizume, M., Glass, G.E., Dewan, A.M., Overgaard, H.J., and Yamamoto, T. 2010. The role of climate variability in the spread of malaria in Bangladeshi highlands. *PLoS ONE* **5**: 10.1371/journal.pone.0014341.

Hay, S.I., Cox, J., Rogers, D.J., Randolph, S.E., Stern, D.I., Shanks, G.D., Myers, M.F., and Snow, R.W. 2002. Climate change and the resurgence of malaria in the East African highlands. *Nature* **415**: 905–909.

Hay, S.I., Guerra, C.A., Gething, P.W., Patil, A.P., Tatem, A.J., Noor, A.M., Kabaria, C.W., Manh, B.H., Elyazar, I.R.F., Brooker, S., Smith, D.L., Moyeed, R.A., and Snow, R.W. 2009. A world malaria map: *Plasmodium falciparum* endemicity in 2007. *PLoS Medicine* **6**: 10.1371/journal.pmed.1000048.

Hay, S.I., Rogers, D.J., Randolph, S.E., Stern, D.I., Cox, J., Shanks, G.D., and Snow, R.W. 2002. Hot topic or hot air? Climate change and malaria resurgence in East African highlands. *Trends in Parasitology* **18**: 530–534.

Hulden, L. and Hulden, L. 2009. The decline of malaria in Finland—the impact of the vector and social variables. *Malaria Journal* **8**: 10.1186/1475-2875-8-94.

Intergovernmental Panel on Climate Change. 2007. *Climate Change 2007: Impacts, Adaptation and Vulnerability*. Contribution of Working Group II to the Fourth Assessment Report of the Intergovernmental Panel on Climate Change. Parry, M.L., Canziani, O.F., Palutikof, J.P., van der Linden, P.J., and Hanson, C.E. (Eds.) Cambridge University Press.

Jackson, M.C., Johansen, L., Furlong, C., Colson, A., and Sellers, K.F. 2010. Modelling the effect of climate change on prevalence of malaria in western Africa. *Statistica Neerlandica* **64**: 388–400.

Kuhn, K.G., Campbell-Lendrum, D.H., Armstrong, B., and Davies, C.R. 2003. Malaria in Britain: Past, present, and future. *Proceedings of the National Academy of Science, USA* **100**: 9997–10001.

Lieshout, M.V., Kovats, R.S., Livermore, M.T.J., and Martens, P. 2004. Climate change and malaria: analysis of the SRES climate and socio-economic scenarios. *Global Environmental Change* **14**: 87–99.

Lysenko, A.J. and Semashko, I.N. 1968. Geography of malaria: a medico-geographic profile of an ancient disease. In: Lebedew, A.W. (Ed.) *Itogi Nauki: Medicinskaja Geografija*, Academy of Sciences, Moscow, Russia, pp. 25–146.

Nabi, S.A. and Qader, S.S. 2009. Is global warming likely to cause an increased incidence of malaria? *Libyan Journal of Medicine* **4**: 18–22.

Nkurunziza, H. and Pilz, J. 2011. Impact of increased temperature on malaria transmission in Burundi. *International Journal of Global Warming* **3**: 77–87.

Paaijmans, K.P., Blanford, S., Chan, B.H.K., and Thomas, M.B. 2012. Warmer temperatures reduce the vectorial capacity of malaria mosquitoes. *Biology Letters* **8**: 465–468.

Randolph, S.E. 2004. Evidence that climate change has caused 'emergence' of tick-borne diseases in Europe? *International Journal of Medical Microbiology* **293** (Supplement 37): 5–15.

Reiter, P. 2001. Climate change and mosquito-borne disease. *Environmental Health Perspectives* **109**: 141–161.

Reiter, P. 2000. From Shakespeare to Defoe: Malaria in England in the Little Ice Age. *Emerging Infectious Diseases* **6**: 1–11.

Reiter, P. 2008. Global warming and malaria: knowing the horse before hitching the cart. *Malaria Journal* **7** (Supplement 1): 10.1186/1475-2875-7-S1-S3.

Reiter, P., Lathrop, S., Bunning, M., Biggerstaff, B., Singer, D., Tiwari, T., Baber, L., Amador, M., Thirion, J., Hayes, J., Seca, C., Mendez, J., Ramirez, B., Robinson, J., Rawlings, J., Vorndam, V., Waterman, S., Gubier, D., Clark, G., and Hayes, E. 2003. Texas lifestyle limits transmission of Dengue virus. *Emerging Infectious Diseases* **9**: 86–89.

Rogers, D.J. and Randolph, S.E. 2000. The global spread of malaria in a future, warmer world. *Science* **289**: 1763–1766.

Rogers, D.J. and Randolph, S.E. 2006. Climate change and vector-borne diseases. *Advances in Parasitology* **62**: 345–381.

Russell, R.C. 2009. Mosquito-borne disease and climate change in Australia: time for a reality check. *Australian Journal of Entomology* **48**: 1–7.

Shanks, G.D., Biomndo, K., Hay, S.I., and Snow, R.W. 2000. Changing patterns of clinical malaria since 1965 among a tea estate population located in the Kenyan highlands. *Transactions of the Royal Society of Tropical Medicine and Hygiene* **94**: 253–255.

Shanks, G.D., Hay, S.I., Stern, D.I., Biomndo, K., and Snow, R.W. 2002. Meteorologic influences on *Plasmodium falciparum* malaria in the highland tea estates of Kericho, Western Kenya. *Emerging Infectious Diseases* **8**: 1404–1408.

Small, J., Goetz, S.J., and Hay, S.I. 2003. Climatic suitability for malaria transmission in Africa, 1911–1995. *Proceedings of the National Academy of Sciences USA* **100**: 15,341–15,345.

Stern, D.I., Gething, P.W., Kabaria, C.W., Temperley, T.H., Noor, A.M., Okiro, E.A., Shanks, G.D., Snow, R.W., and Hay, S.I. 2011. Temperature and Malaria Trends in Highland East Africa. *PLoS One* **6**: 10.1371/journal.pone.0024524.

Sun, K.N., Kain, K.C., and Keystone, J.S. 2004. Malaria. *Canadian Medical Association Journal* **170**: 1693–1702.

Taubes, G. 1997. Global warming: apocalypse not. *Science* **278**: 1004–1006.

Thomas, C. 2004. Malaria: a changed climate in Africa? *Nature* **427**: 690–691.

Tol, R.S.J. and Dowlatabadi, H. 2001. Vector-borne diseases, development & climate change. *Integrated Assessment* **2**: 173–181.

Tuchman, N.C., Wahtera, K.A., Wetzel, R.G., Russo, N.M., Kilbane, G.M., Sasso, L.M., and Teeri, J.A. 2003. Nutritional quality of leaf detritus altered by elevated atmospheric CO_2: effects on development of mosquito larvae. *Freshwater Biology* **48**: 1432–1439.

U.S. Environmental Protection Agency. 2010. Endangerment and Cause or Contribute Findings for Greenhouse Gases Under Section 202(a) of the Clean Air Act (Technical Support Document). U.S. Environmental Protection Agency.

WHO, WMO, UNEP. 2003. *Climate Change and Human Health—Risks and Responses: Summary*. Geneva, Switzerland.

Zell, R. 2004. Global climate change and the emergence/re-emergence of infectious diseases. *International Journal of Medical Microbiology* **293**, Suppl. 37: 16–26.

Zell, R., Krumbholz, A., and Wutzler, P. 2008. Impact of global warming on viral diseases: what is the evidence? *Current Opinion in Biotechnology* **19**: 652–660.

Zhou, G., Minakawa, N., Githeko, A.K., and Yan, G. 2004. Association between climate variability and malaria epidemics in the East African highlands. *Proceedings of the National Academy of Sciences, USA* **101**: 2375–2380.

7.6 Dengue Fever

- Concerns over large increases in vector-borne diseases such as dengue as a result of rising temperatures are unfounded and unsupported by the scientific literature, as climatic indices are poor predictors for dengue disease.

According to Ooi and Gubler (2009), "dengue/dengue hemorrhagic fever is the most important vector-borne viral disease globally," with more than half the world's population living in areas deemed to be at risk of infection. Also, they note, "many voices have raised concern that global warming is likely to increase the geographic distribution of the dengue mosquito vectors and the frequency and magnitude of dengue epidemics." Such concerns, as evidenced by the papers discussed below, are ill-founded.

In a major review of mosquito-borne diseases by one of the world's premier authorities on the subject, Reiter (2001) analyzed the history of malaria and dengue fever in an attempt to determine whether the incidence and range of influence of these diseases would indeed increase in response to CO_2-induced global warming. This review indicates the natural history of these vector-borne diseases is highly complex, and the interplay of climate, ecology, vector biology, and a number of other factors defies definition by the simplistic analyses utilized in models that generate predictions of future geographical changes in these diseases under various global warming scenarios.

That there has in fact been a resurgence of these diseases in parts of the world is true; but, as Reiter notes, it is "facile to attribute this resurgence to climate change." This he shows via a number of independent analyses that clearly demonstrate factors associated with politics, economics, and human activity are the principal determinants of the spread of these diseases. He describes these factors as being "much more significant" than climate in promoting disease expansion.

Two years later, Reiter took up the subject again, this time with 19 other scientists as coauthors (Reiter *et al.*, 2003). They began by noting "it has frequently been stated that dengue, malaria, and other mosquito-borne diseases will become common in the United States as a result of global warming (Watson *et al.*, 1996; Jetten and Focks, 1997; Patz *et al.*, 1998; Watson *et al.*, 1998)." The Intergovernmental Panel on Climate Change had played a key role in promoting this claim, but Reiter and his colleagues had acquired solid evidence to prove IPCC was simply wrong on this point.

In the summer of 1999, toward the end of a significant dengue outbreak in "los dos Laredos"—Laredo, Texas, USA (population 200,000) and Nuevo Laredo, Tamaulipas, Mexico (population 290,000)—the team of scientists conducted a seroepidemiologic survey to examine factors affecting dengue transmission in the two cities, located adjacent to each other on opposite sides of the Rio Grande and experience, according to the team, "massive cross-border traffic across three multi-lane bridges." They report "the incidence of recent cases, indicated by immunoglobulin M antibody serosurvey, was higher in Nuevo Laredo [16.0% vs. 1.3%], although the vector, *Aedes aegypti*, was more abundant in Laredo [91% vs. 37%]." Reiter *et al.* determined "environmental factors that affect contact with mosquitoes, such as air-conditioning and human behavior, appear to account for this paradox."

They found, for example, "the proportion of dengue infections attributable to lack of air-conditioning in Nuevo Laredo [where only 2% of the homes had central air-conditioning compared to 36% of the homes in Laredo] was 55%," which means 55% of the cases of dengue in Nuevo Laredo would not have occurred if all households there had had air-conditioning. Reiter *et al.* conclude, therefore, "if the current warming trend in world climates continues, air-conditioning may become even more prevalent in the United States, in which case, the probability of dengue transmission [there] will likely decrease." Likewise, if the economy of Mexico continues to grow, the use of air-conditioners likely will increase there as well, which likely would lead to even greater decreases in the occurrence of dengue fever in that country.

In a major review of the general subject of infectious diseases in a warming world, Roland Zell (2004) of the Institute for Virology and Antiviral Therapy at the Fredrich Schiller University in Jena, Germany, reviewed what was known about the putative link some scientists were postulating—and a host of climate alarmists were championing—between global warming and the spread of infectious diseases. Noting many people "assume a correlation between increasing disease incidence and global warming," he states that after studying the issue in considerable depth, he must conclude "the factors responsible for the emergence/reemergence of vector-borne diseases are complex and mutually influence each other." He notes "the incidence and spread of parasites and arboviruses are affected by insecticide and drug resistance, deforestation, irrigation systems and dams, changes in public health policy (decreased resources of surveillance, prevention and vector control), demographic changes (population growth, migration, urbanization), and societal changes (inadequate housing conditions, water deterioration, sewage, waste management)." Therefore, he continues, "it may be over-simplistic to attribute emergent/re-emergent diseases to climate change and sketch the menace of devastating epidemics in a warmer world." He reiterates "variations in public health practices and lifestyle can easily outweigh changes in disease biology."

Kyle and Harris (2008) note "dengue is a spectrum of disease caused by four serotypes of the most prevalent arthropod-borne virus affecting humans today," and "its incidence has increased dramatically in the past 50 years," to where "tens of millions of cases of dengue fever are estimated to occur annually, including up to 500,000 cases of the life-threatening dengue hemorrhagic fever/dengue shock syndrome." In an effort to better understand this increase, they conducted a thorough review of the pertinent scientific literature, exploring "the human, mosquito, and viral factors that contribute to the global spread and persistence of dengue, as well as the interaction between the three spheres, in the context of ecological and climate change."

With respect to the status of dengue fever within the context of global warming, they found "there has been a great deal of debate on the implications of global warming for human health," but "at the moment, there is no consensus." However, "in the case of dengue," they report, "it is important to note that even if global warming does not cause the mosquito vectors to expand their geographic range, there could still be a significant impact on transmission in endemic regions," because "a 2°C increase in temperature would simultaneously lengthen the lifespan of the mosquito and shorten the extrinsic incubation period of the dengue virus, resulting in more infected mosquitoes for a longer period of time." Nevertheless, they state there are "infrastructure and socioeconomic differences that exist today and already prevent the transmission of vector-borne diseases, including dengue, even in the continued presence of their vectors," citing Reiter (2001). It thus appears whatever advantages rising temperatures may confer upon the dengue virus vector, they can be more than overcome by proper implementation of modern vector control techniques.

In another review of the scientific literature, Wilder-Smith and Gubler (2008) note "the past two decades saw an unprecedented geographic expansion of dengue," reporting "each year an estimated 50 to 100 million dengue infections occur, with several hundred thousand cases of dengue hemorrhagic fever and about twenty thousand deaths." They too state, "global climate change is commonly blamed for the resurgence of dengue," but they add, "there are no good scientific data to support this conclusion." Wilder-Smith and Gubler reviewed what was known about the problem and pieced together a logical conclusion.

With respect to the occurrence of dengue infections, the two researchers report, "climate has rarely been the principal determinant of [their] prevalence or range," and "human activities and their impact on local ecology have generally been much more significant." They cite as contributing factors "urbanization, deforestation, new dams and irrigation systems, poor housing, sewage and waste management systems, and lack of reliable water systems that make it necessary to collect and store water," further noting "disruption of vector control programs, be it for reasons of political and social unrest or scientific reservations about the safety of DDT, has contributed to the resurgence of dengue around the world." In addition, they write "large populations in which viruses circulate may also allow more co-infection of mosquitoes and humans with more than one serotype of virus," which would appear to be borne out by the fact that "the number of dengue lineages has been increasing roughly in parallel with the size of the human population over the last two centuries." Most important, perhaps, is "the impact of international travel," of which they say "humans, whether troops, migrant workers, tourists, business travelers, refugees, or others, carry the virus into new geographic areas," and these movements "can lead to epidemic waves." The two researchers conclude, "population dynamics and viral evolution offer the most parsimonious explanation for the observed epidemic cycles of the disease, far more than climatic factors."

Russell (2009)—a professor in the Department of Medicine of the University of Sydney and founding director of its Department of Medical Entomology—reports, "during the past 10 years, there has been increasing concern for health impacts of global warming in Australia, and continuing projections and predictions for increasing mosquito-borne disease as a result of climate change." He notes these claims "are relatively simplistic, and do not take adequate account of the current or historic situations of the vectors and pathogens, and the complex ecologies that might be involved." He reviewed the consequences of these inadequacies for malaria, dengue fever, the arboviral arthritides (Ross River and Barmah Forest viruses) and the arboviral encephalitides (Murray Valley encephalitis and Kunjin viruses) within the context of predictions of climate changes modeled by Australia's Commonwealth Scientific and Industrial Research Organisation (CSIRO) and the Inter-governmental Panel on Climate Change (IPCC).

The abstract of Russell's paper begins with a question: "Will warming climate increase the risk or prevalence of mosquito-borne disease in Australia, as has been projected in a number of scientific publications and governmental reports?" His conclusion provides the answer: "there might be some increases in mosquito-borne disease in Australia with a warming climate, but with which mosquitoes and which pathogens, and where and when, cannot be easily discerned." He concludes, "of itself, climate change as currently projected, is not likely to provide great cause for public health concern with mosquito-borne disease in Australia."

Russell *et al.* (2009) report similar findings. The team of scientists note "dengue has emerged as a leading cause of morbidity in many parts of the tropics," and "Australia has had dengue outbreaks in northern Queensland." In addition, they report, "substantial increases in distribution and incidence of the disease in Australia are projected with climate change," or, more specifically, "with increasing temperatures." Russell *et al.* explored the soundness of these projections by reviewing the history of dengue in Australia.

This work showed the dengue vector (the *Aedes aegypti* mosquito) "was previously common in parts of Queensland, the Northern Territory, Western Australia and New South Wales," and it had, "in the past, covered most of the climatic range theoretically available to it," adding "the distribution of local dengue transmission has [historically] nearly matched the geographic limits of the vector." This being the case, they conclude the vector's current absence from much of Australia "is not because of a lack of a favorable climate." Thus, they reason "a temperature rise of a few degrees is not alone likely to be responsible for substantial increases in the southern distribution of *A. aegypti* or dengue, as has been recently proposed." Instead, they note, "dengue activity is increasing in many parts of the tropical and subtropical world as a result of rapid urbanization in developing countries and increased international travel, which distributes the viruses between countries." Instead of futile attempts to limit dengue transmission by controlling the world's climate, therefore, the medical researchers recommend "well resourced and functioning surveillance programs, and effective public health intervention capabilities, are essential to counter threats from dengue and other mosquito-borne diseases."

Johansson *et al.* (2009) write, "the mosquito-borne dengue viruses are a major public health problem throughout the tropical and subtropical regions of the world," and "changes in temperature and precipitation have well-defined roles in the transmission cycle and may thus play a role in changing incidence levels." Since "the El Niño Southern Oscillation (ENSO) is a multiyear climate driver of local temperature and precipitation world wide," and "previous studies have reported varying degrees of association between ENSO and dengue incidence," they looked for relationships between ENSO, local weather, and dengue incidence in Puerto Rico (1986–2006), Mexico (1985–2006), and Thailand (1983–2006) using wavelet analysis as a tool to identify time- and frequency-specific associations.

The three researchers report they "did not find evidence of a strong, consistent relationship in any of the study areas," and Rohani (2009), who wrote a Perspective piece on their study, states the three researchers found "no systematic association between multi-annual dengue outbreaks and El Niño Southern Oscillation." Thus, as stated in the "Editors' Summary" of Johansson *et al.*'s paper, their findings "provide little evidence for any relationship between ENSO, climate, and dengue incidence."

Shang *et al.* (2010) used logistic and Poisson regression models to analyze biweekly, laboratory-confirmed dengue cases in Taiwan at their onset dates of illness from 1998 to 2007, in order to "identify correlations between indigenous dengue and imported dengue cases (in the context of local meteorological factors) across different time lags." The researchers write, "the occurrence of indigenous dengue was significantly correlated with temporally-lagged cases

of imported dengue (2–14 weeks), higher temperatures (6–14 weeks), and lower relative humidity (6–20 weeks)," and "imported and indigenous dengue cases had a significant quantitative relationship in the onset of local epidemics." The six Taiwanese researchers conclude, "imported dengue cases are able to initiate indigenous epidemics when appropriate weather conditions are present," or as they state in another place, "imported dengue are able to serve as an initial facilitator, or spark, for domestic epidemics." They suggest "early detection and case management of imported cases through timely surveillance and rapid laboratory-diagnosis may avert large scale epidemics of dengue/dengue hemorrhagic fever," while noting "meteorology alone does not initiate an epidemic." Finally, they state, "an increase in viremic international travelers has caused global dengue hemorrhagic fever case numbers to surge in the past several decades."

Ooi and Gubler (2009a) examined "the history of dengue emergence" in order to determine "the major drivers for the spread of both the viruses and mosquito vectors to new geographic regions." The two researchers note "frequent and cyclical epidemics are reported throughout the tropical world, with regular importation of the virus via viremic travelers into both endemic and non-endemic countries." They state, "there is no good evidence to suggest that the current geographic expansion of the dengue virus and its vectors has been or will be due to global warming." Instead, they conclude, "the magnitude of movement of the human population and trade materials, uncontrolled and poorly planned expansion of urban centers and the lack of effective disease prevention in dengue-endemic regions have served to produce conditions ideal for dengue virus transmission and have been the principal drivers of epidemic dengue for the past three decades," citing Gubler (1998, 2004), Gubler *et al.* (2001), and Ooi and Gubler (2009b).

In another review paper, Dr. Paul Reiter of the Insects and Infectious Disease Unit of the Institut Pasteur in Paris writes, "it is widely stated that the incidence of vector-borne diseases will increase if global temperatures increase" (Reiter, 2010a); and while admitting temperature and rainfall do indeed "play a role" in the transmission of such diseases, he states, "many other factors are involved," citing a paper he wrote at the turn of the century (Reiter, 2001). In revisiting this subject, Reiter (2010a) reviewed the scientific literature, distilling the essence of the then-current state of knowledge pertaining to the potential for yellow fever and dengue transmission throughout modern-day Europe.

The review revealed "the introduction and rapidly expanding range of *Aedes albopictus* in Europe is an iconic example of the growing risk of the globalization of vectors and vector-borne diseases," and "the history of yellow fever and dengue in temperate regions confirms that transmission of both diseases could recur, particularly if *Aedes aegypti*, a more effective vector, were to be re-introduced." He states "conditions are already suitable for transmission."

In light of Reiter's findings, can we expect to face the problem of the two deadly diseases suddenly reappearing and racing across Europe, especially if the climate begins to warm again? Actually, it would not be incredibly surprising if that were to happen even if the climate were to cool, for Reiter concludes, "a more urgent emerging problem is the quantum leap in the mobility of vectors and pathogens that has taken place in the past four decades, a direct result of the revolution of transport technologies and global travel," as described in his recently published article (Reiter, 2010b).

Carbajo *et al.* (2012) report "dengue cases have increased during the last decades, particularly in non-endemic areas, and Argentina was no exception in the southern transmission fringe." Although temperature rise has been blamed for this geographical expansion of the disease, they write, "human population growth, increased travel and inefficient vector control may also be implicated." Thus, they evaluated the relative contributions of geographic, demographic, and climatic variables to the recent spread of the disease.

Carbajo *et al.* divided their study into two halves—a first decade that included the reemergence of the disease, and a second decade that included several epidemics—in which "annual dengue risk was modelled by a temperature-based mechanistic model as annual days of possible transmission," and "the spatial distribution of dengue occurrence was modelled as a function of the output of the mechanistic model, climatic, geographic and demographic variables for both decades."

They found dengue spatial occurrence "was positively associated with days of possible transmission, human population number, population fall and distance to water bodies." When considered separately, the researchers write, "the classification performance of demographic variables was higher than that of climatic and geographic variables." Thus, although useful in estimating annual transmission risk, Carbajo *et al.* conclude temperature "does not fully describe the distribution of dengue occurrence at the country scale," and "when taken separately, climatic variables performed worse than geographic or demographic variables," while acknowledging "a combination of the three types was best for this task."

These several observations indicate concerns over large increases in vector-borne diseases such as dengue as a result of rising temperatures are unfounded and unsupported by the scientific literature, as climatic indices are poor predictors for dengue disease.

References

Carbajo, A.E., Cardo, M.V., and Vezzani, D. 2012. Is temperature the main cause of dengue rise in non-endemic countries? The case of Argentina. *International Journal of Health Geographics* **11**: 10.1186/1476-072X-11-26.

Gubler, D.J. 1998. Dengue and dengue hemorrhagic fever. *Clinical Microbiology Reviews* **11**: 480–496.

Gubler, D.J. 2004. The changing epidemiology of yellow fever and dengue, 1900 to 2003: full circle? *Comparative Immunology, Microbiology and Infectious Diseases* **27**: 319–330.

Gubler, D.J., Reiter, P., Ebi, K.L., Yap, W., Nasci, R., and Patz, J.A. 2001. Climate variability and change in the United States: potential impacts on vector- and rodent-borne diseases. *Environmental and Health Perspectives* **109** (Suppl. 2): 223–233.

Jetten, T.H. and Focks, D.A. 1997. Potential changes in the distribution of dengue transmission under climate warming. *American Journal of Tropical Medicine and Hygiene* **57**: 285–297.

Johansson, M.A., Cummings, D.A.T., and Glass, G.E. 2009. Multiyear climate variability and dengue-El Niño Southern Oscillation, weather and dengue incidence in Puerto Rico, Mexico, and Thailand: A longitudinal data analysis. *PLoS Medicine* **6**: e1000168.

Kyle, J.L. and Harris, E. 2008. Global spread and persistence of dengue. *Annual Review of Microbiology* **62**: 71–92.

Ooi, E.E. and Gubler, D.J. 2009b. Dengue virus-mosquito interactions. In: Hanley, K.A. and Weaver, S.C. (Eds.) *Frontiers in Dengue Virus Research*. Caister Academic Press, UK, pp. 143–155.

Ooi, E.-E. and Gubler, D.J. 2009a. Global spread of epidemic dengue: the influence of environmental change. *Future Virology* **4**: 571–580.

Patz, J.A., Martens, W.J.M., Focks, D.A., and Jetten, T.H. 1998. Dengue fever epidemic potential as projected by general circulation models of global climate change. *Environmental Health Perspectives* **106**: 147–153.

Reiter, P. 2001. Climate change and mosquito-borne disease. *Environmental Health Perspectives* **109**: 141–161.

Reiter, P. 2010b. A mollusc on the leg of a beetle: Human activities and the global dispersal of vectors and vector-borne pathogens. In: Relman, D.A., Choffnes, E.R., and Mack, A. (Rapporteurs). *Infectious Disease Movement in a Borderless World.* The National Academies Press, Washington, DC, USA, p. 150–165.

Reiter, P. 2010a. Yellow fever and dengue: A threat to Europe? *Eurosurveillance* **15**: eurosurveillance.org/ViewArticle.aspx?Articleid=19509.

Reiter, P., Lathrop, S., Bunning, M., Biggerstaff, B., Singer, D., Tiwari, T., Baber, L., Amador, M., Thirion, J., Hayes, J., Seca, C., Mendez, J., Ramirez, B., Robinson, J., Rawlings, J., Vorndam, V., Waterman, S., Gubier, D., Clark, G., and Hayes, E. 2003. Texas lifestyle limits transmission of Dengue virus. *Emerging Infectious Diseases* **9**: 86–89.

Rohani, P. 2009. The link between dengue incidence and El Niño Southern Oscillation. *PLoS Medicine* **6**: e1000185.

Russell, R.C. 2009. Mosquito-borne disease and climate change in Australia: time for a reality check. *Australian Journal of Entomology* **48**: 1–7.

Russell, R.C., Currie, B.J., Lindsay, M.D., Mackenzie, J.S., Ritchie, S.A., and Whelan, P.I. 2009. Dengue and climate change in Australia: predictions for the future should incorporate knowledge from the past. *Medical Journal of Australia* **190**: 265–268.

Shang, C.-S., Fang, C.-T., Liu, C.-M., Wen, T.-H., Tsai, K.-H., and King, C.-C. 2010. The role of imported cases and favorable meteorological conditions in the onset of dengue epidemics. *PLoS* **4**: e775.

Watson, R.T., Zinyowera, M.C., and Moss, R.H. (Eds.) 1996. *Impacts, Adaptations and Mitigation of Climate Change: Scientific-Technical Analyses.* Contribution of Working Group II to the Second Assessment of the Intergovernmental Panel on Climate Change (IPCC). Cambridge University Press, Cambridge, UK.

Watson, R.T., Zinyowera, M.C., and Moss, R.H. (Eds.) 1998. *The Regional Impacts of Climate Change: An Assessment of Vulnerability.* Special Report of the Intergovernmental Panel on Climate Change (IPCC) Working Group II. Cambridge University Press, Cambridge, UK.

Wilder-Smith, A. and Gubler, D.J. 2008. Geographic expansion of Dengue: The impact of international travel. *Medical Clinics of North America* **92**: 1377–1390.

Zell, R. 2004. Global climate change and the emergence/re-emergence of infectious diseases. *International Journal of Medical Microbiology* **293**, Suppl. 37: 16–26.

7.7 Tick-Borne Diseases

- While climatic factors largely determine the geographical distribution of ticks, temperature and climate change are not among the significant factors determining the incidence of tick-borne diseases.

Randolph and Rogers (2000) state tick-borne encephalitis (TBE) "is the most significant vector-borne disease in Europe and Eurasia," having "a case morbidity rate of 10–30% and a case mortality rate of typically 1–2% but as high as 24% in the Far East." The disease is caused by a flavivirus (TBEV), which is maintained in natural rodent-tick cycles; humans may be infected with it if bitten by an infected tick or by drinking untreated milk from infected sheep or goats.

Early discussions on the relationship of TBE to global warming predicted the disease would expand its range and become more of a threat to humans in a warmer world. However, Randolph and Rogers note, "like many vector-borne pathogen cycles that depend on the interaction of so many biotic agents with each other and with their abiotic environment, enzootic cycles of TBEV have an inherent fragility," so "their continuing survival or expansion cannot be predicted from simple univariate correlations."

Confining their analysis to Europe, Randolph and Rogers first matched the present-day distribution of TBEV to the present-day distributions of five climatic variables: monthly mean, maximum, and minimum temperatures, plus rainfall and saturation vapor pressure, "to provide a multivariate description of present-day areas of disease risk." They applied this understanding to outputs of a general circulation model of the atmosphere that predicted how these five climatic variables may change in the future.

The results indicate the distribution of TBEV might expand both north and west of Stockholm, Sweden in a warming world. For most other parts of Europe, however, the two researchers say "fears for increased extent of risk from TBEV caused by global climate change appear to be unfounded." They report, "the precise conditions required for enzootic cycles of TBEV are predicted to be disrupted" in response to global warming, and the new climatic state "appears to be lethal for TBEV." This finding, they write, "gives the lie to the common perception that a warmer world will necessarily be a world under greater threat from vector-borne diseases." In the case of TBEV, they report the predicted change "appears to be to our advantage."

Noting "it is often suggested that one of the most important societal consequences of climate change may be an increase in the geographic distribution and transmission intensity of vector-borne disease," Estrada-Peña (2003) evaluated the effects of various abiotic factors on the habitat suitability of four tick species that are major vectors of livestock pathogens in South Africa. They report "year-to-year variations in the forecasted habitat suitability over the period 1983–2000 show a clear decrease in habitat availability, which is attributed primarily to increasing temperature in the region over this period." In addition, when climate variables were projected to the year 2015, Estrada-Peña found "the simulations show a trend toward the destruction of the habitats of the four tick species," just the opposite of what is often predicted about this disease.

Zell (2004) also has noted many people "assume a correlation between increasing disease incidence and global warming." He reviewed the scientific literature pertaining to the subject and determined "the factors responsible for the emergence/ reemergence of vector-borne diseases are complex and mutually influence each other." He cites as an example of this complexity, "the incidence and spread of parasites and arboviruses are affected by insecticide and drug resistance, deforestation, irrigation systems and dams, changes in public health policy (decreased resources of surveillance, prevention and vector control), demographic changes (population growth, migration, urbanization), and societal changes (inadequate housing conditions, water deterioration, sewage, waste management)."

Zell says "it may be over-simplistic to attribute emergent/re-emergent diseases to climate change and sketch the menace of devastating epidemics in a warmer world." Indeed, he concludes, "variations in public health practices and lifestyle can easily outweigh changes in disease biology."

Sarah Randolph (2010) of the University of Oxford's Department of Zoology in the United Kingdom examined the roles played by various factors that may influence the spread of tick-borne diseases. She begins by noting many vector-borne diseases "have shown marked increases in both distribution and incidence during the past few decades, just as human-induced climate change is thought to have exceeded random fluctuations." She adds, "this coincidence has led to the general perception that climate change has driven disease emergence." However, she notes, "climate change is the inevitable backdrop for all recent events," most of which no one would otherwise consider attributing to changes in the planet's temperature.

After describing some of the outbreaks of tick-borne disease in Europe over the past couple of decades, Randolph states "the inescapable conclusion is that the observed climate change alone cannot explain the full heterogeneity in the epidemiological change, either within the Baltic States or amongst Central and Eastern European countries," citing Sumilo et al. (2007). Instead, she writes, "a nexus of interrelated causal factors—abiotic, biotic and human—has been identified," and "each factor appears to operate synergistically, but with differential force in space and time, which would inevitably generate the observed epidemiological heterogeneity."

Many of these factors, she continues, "were the unintended consequences of the fall of Soviet rule and the subsequent socio-economic transition (Sumilo et al., 2008b)," among which she cites "agricultural reforms resulting in changed land cover and land use, and an increased reliance on subsistence farming; reduction in the use of pesticides, and also in the emission of atmospheric pollution as industries collapsed; increased unemployment and poverty, but also wealth and leisure time in other sectors of the population as market forces took hold."

Randolph concludes "there is increasing evidence from detailed analyses that rapid changes in the incidence of tick-borne diseases are driven as much, if not more, by human behavior that determines exposure to infected ticks than by tick population biology that determines the abundance of infected ticks," as per Sumilo et al. (2008a) and Randolph et al. (2008). She ends her analysis by stating, "while nobody would deny the sensitivity of ticks and tick-borne disease systems to climatic factors that largely determine their geographical distributions, the evidence is that climate change has not been the most significant factor driving the recent temporal patterns in the epidemiology of tick-borne diseases."

References

Estrada-Peña, A. 2003. Climate change decreases habitat suitability for some tick species (Acari: Ixodidae) in South Africa. *Onderstepoort Journal of Veterinary Research* **70**: 79–93.

Randolph, S.E. 2001. Tick-borne encephalitis in Europe. *The Lancet* **358**: 1731–1732.

Randolph, S.E. 2010. To what extent has climate change contributed to the recent epidemiology of tick-borne diseases? *Veterinary Parasitology* **167**: 92–94.

Randolph, S.E., Asokliene, L., Avsic-Zupanc, T., Bormane, A., Burri, C., Golovljova, I., Hubalek, Z., Knap, N., Kondrusik, M., Kupca, A., Pejcoch, M., Vasilenko, V., and Zygutiene, M. 2008. Variable spikes in TBE incidence in 2006 independent of variable tick abundance but related to weather. *Parasites and Vectors* 1: e44.

Randolph, S.E. and Rogers, D.J. 2000. Fragile transmission cycles of tick-borne encephalitis virus may be disrupted by predicted climate change. *Proceedings of the Royal Society of London Series B* **267**: 1741–1744.

Sumilo, D., Asokliene, L., Avsic-Zupanc, T., Bormane, A., Vasilenko, V., Lucenko, I., Golovljova, I., and Randolph, S.E. 2008a. Behavioral responses to perceived risk of tick-borne encephalitis: vaccination and avoidance in the Baltics and Slovenia. *Vaccine* **26**: 2580–2588.

Sumilo, D., Asokliene, L., Bormane, A., Vasilenko, V., Golovljova, I., and Randolph, S.E. 2007. Climate change cannot explain the upsurge of tick-borne encephalitis in the Baltics. *PLos ONE* **2**: e500.

Sumilo, D., Bormane, A., Asokliene, L., Vasilenko, V., Golovljova, I., Avsic-Zupanc, T., Hubalek, Z., and Randolph, S.E. 2008b. Socio-economic factors in the differential upsurge of tick-borne encephalitis in Central and Eastern Europe. *Reviews in Medical Virology* **18**: 81–95.

Zell, R. 2004. Global climate change and the emergence/re-emergence of infectious diseases. *International Journal of Medical Microbiology* **293**, Suppl. 37: 16–26.

7.8 Effects of CO_2

Among the lesser-known findings about CO_2 enrichment of the air is that several health-promoting substances are often enhanced in plants growing at higher CO_2 concentrations. As discussed in the subsections below, these enhancements portend great benefits for human health, and they represent an important reality the IPCC assessment reports ignore.

7.8.1 Antioxidants

Oxidation is a chemical process that occurs naturally in plants, animals, and humans. Although the process is vital for life, it also can produce free radicals, including reactive oxygen species (ROS), in a series of chain reactions that lead to cell damage and cell death. In humans, oxidative stress has been linked to cardiovascular disease, cancer, neurodegenerative disorders, and other chronic diseases. Nature's way of responding to the threats posed by such radicals is to neutralize and inhibit their reactions via complex systems of multiple types of antioxidants.

Plants, animals, and humans each harbor defense systems comprised of various types of antioxidants, including vitamin A, vitamin C, and vitamin E, and enzymes such as catalase, superoxide dismutase, and various peroxidases. Inadequate levels of antioxidants, or inhibition of antioxidant enzymes, can lead to oxidative stress.

The following subsections examine the impact of rising atmospheric CO_2 on antioxidant compounds and enzymes found in plants, illustrating major benefits it provides for both plants and humans. With respect to plants, higher levels of atmospheric CO_2 tend to reduce oxidative stress, resulting in a reduction in antioxidant enzyme activity because fewer such enzymes are needed to counter the stress. As a result, plants are able to direct more of their limited resources into the production of other plant tissues or processes essential to their continued growth and development. In some cases, such resources are invested into the production and enhancement of antioxidative compounds, and these compounds are known to provide health benefits to animals and humans.

7.8.1.1 Benefits to Plants

Environmental stresses induced by exposure to pollutants, drought, intense solar radiation, and high air or water temperatures generate highly reactive oxygenated compounds that damage plants. Ameliorating these stresses typically involves the production of antioxidant enzymes that scavenge and detoxify the highly reactive oxygenated compounds. When stresses are present, concentrations and/or activities of antioxidants in plants are generally observed to be high so as to counter the effects of the stress. A number of researchers have examined the impact of atmospheric CO_2 enrichment on this relationship, the results of which are discussed below.

In a study of two soybean genotypes, Pritchard *et al.* (2000) report three months' exposure to twice-ambient CO_2 concentrations reduced the activities of superoxide dismutase and catalase by an average of 23 and 39%, respectively. Likewise, Polle *et al.* (1997) show two years of atmospheric CO_2 enrichment reduced the activities of several key antioxidative enzymes, including catalase and superoxide dismutase, in beech seedlings. And Schwanz and Polle (1998) demonstrate this phenomenon can persist indefinitely, for they discovered similar reductions in these same enzymes in mature oak trees that had been growing near natural CO_2-emitting springs for 30 to 50 years.

The standard interpretation of these results is the observed reductions in the activities of antioxidative enzymes under CO_2-enriched conditions imply plants exposed to higher-than-current atmospheric CO_2 concentrations experience less oxidative stress and thus have a reduced need for antioxidant protection. This conclusion further suggests "CO_2-advantaged" plants will be able to funnel more of their limited resources into the production of other plant tissues or processes essential to their continued growth and development.

On the other hand, when oxidative stresses do occur under high CO_2 conditions, the enhanced rates of photosynthesis and carbohydrate production resulting from atmospheric CO_2 enrichment generally enable plants to better deal with such stresses by providing more of the raw materials needed for antioxidant enzyme synthesis. Thus, when CO_2-enriched sugar maple seedlings were subjected to an additional 200 ppb of ozone, Niewiadomska *et al.* (1999) report ascorbate peroxidase, which is the first line of enzymatic defense against ozone, significantly increased. Likewise, Schwanz and Polle (2001) note poplar clones grown at 700 ppm CO_2 exhibited a much greater increase in superoxide dismutase activity upon chilling induction than clones grown in ambient air. In addition, Lin and Wang (2002) found activities of superoxide dismutase and catalase were much higher in CO_2-enriched wheat than in ambiently grown wheat following the induction of water stress.

Baczek-Kwinta and Koscielniak (2003) grew two hybrid maize (*Zea mays* L.) genotypes—KOC 9431 (chill-resistant) and K103xK85 (chill-sensitive)—from seed in air of either ambient (350 ppm) or elevated (700 ppm) CO_2 concentration (AC or EC, respectively), after which the plants were exposed to air of 7°C for 11 days and then recovered in ambient air of 20°C for one day. Throughout this period, a number of physiological and biochemical parameters were measured on the plants' third fully expanded leaves. Among their many findings, the researchers note, "EC diminished the rate of superoxide radical formation in leaves in comparison to the AC control." In addition, "electrolyte leakage from the [leaf membrane] tissue, a parameter reflecting membrane injury, was significantly lower in samples of plants subjected to EC than AC." Finally, they discovered enrichment of the air with CO_2 successfully inhibited the decrease in the maximal quantum efficiency of photosystem 2, both after chilling and during the one-day recovery period.

Lumping these positive effects of elevated CO_2 together, the two scientists conclude, "the increase in atmospheric CO_2 concentration seems to be one of the protective factors for maize grown in cold temperate regions."

In a study focusing solely on temperature, Yu *et al.* (2004a) investigated how global warming might affect crop reactive oxygen species (ROS) scavenging activities and chelating capacities, the latter of which may inhibit radical-mediated oxidative chain reactions by stabilizing transition metals required to catalyze the formation of the first few radicals needed to initiate the radical reactions (Nawar, 1996). In one of the few studies to broach this subject, Wang and Zheng (2001) examined the effects of a group of day/night temperature combinations on the antioxidant activities of the juice of two strawberry varieties, finding, in the words of Yu *et al.*, "the highest day/night temperature resulted in fruits with the greatest phenolic content as well as antioxidant activities." Encouraged by this finding, Yu *et al.* (2004a) decided to explore the subject further in a study of winter wheat.

Yu *et al.* examined and compared flour extracts of three hard winter wheat varieties grown at five locations in Colorado for their radical scavenging properties, chelating capacities, and total phenolic contents. Although they found no statistically significant correlations, the scientists report "a correlation coefficient of 0.890 (P = 0.110) was detected for the chelating activity of Akron flour and the total hours of the growth location exceeding 32°C during the 6-week grain-filling period." Thus, although no firm conclusions could be drawn from the results of their study, in contrast to the study of Wang and Zheng (2001), Yu *et al.*'s findings are intriguing enough to lead them to state, "more research is needed to clarify how varieties and growing conditions alter the antioxidant properties of wheat, wheat flour and bran."

A different set of authors, Yu *et al.* (2004b), note "oxidative stress is potentially experienced by all aerobic life when exposed to UV-B radiation," and "elevated CO_2 can enhance the capacity of plants to resist stress-induced oxidative damage," citing Ren *et al.* (2001), who worked with terrestrial plants. Yu *et al.* set out to see whether this was also true of marine plants, focusing their attention on phytoplankton, which they describe as "the single most important ecosystem on our planet."

They grew the marine microalgae *Platymonas subcordiformis* (Wille) Hazen in the laboratory at ambient levels of atmospheric CO_2 concentration and

UV-B radiation flux density, and at elevated levels of 5,000 ppm CO_2 and UV-B radiation characteristic of that anticipated to result from a 25% stratospheric ozone depletion under clear sky conditions in summer. By itself, and by these means, the five researchers determined the elevated UV-B treatment significantly decreased microalgal dry weight, photosynthetic rate, chlorophyll *a* and carotenoid contents. The elevated CO_2 treatment by itself enhanced dry weight and photosynthetic rate, and chlorophyll *a* content and carotenoid content exhibited no major differences compared with those of ambient UV-B and ambient CO_2. They also report elevated UV-B by itself significantly increased the production of the toxic superoxide anion and hydrogen peroxide, as well as malonyldialdehyde, an end product of lipid peroxidation, whereas elevated CO_2 by itself did just the opposite. In addition, in the treatment consisting of both elevated UV-B and elevated CO_2, the concentrations of these three substances were lower than those observed in the elevated UV-B and ambient CO_2 treatment. Finally, they note elevated CO_2 decreased the levels of several antioxidative enzymes found in the microalgae, reflecting their reduced need for detoxification of reactive oxygen species in the elevated CO_2 treatment.

Yu *et al.* write their results suggest "CO_2 enrichment could reduce oxidative stress of reactive oxygen species to *P. subcordiformis*, and reduce the lipid peroxidation damage of UV-B to *P. subcordiformis*." They also state, "CO_2 enrichment showed a protective effect against the oxidative damage of UV-B-induced stress," and therefore, "elevated CO_2 can be [in] favor of enhancing the capacity of stress resistance." Put more simply, they conclude, "we have shown that algae grown under high CO_2 would better overcome the adverse impact of environmental stress factor[s] that act via generation of activated oxygen species."

Plants cultured *in vitro* are know to typically suffer from a number of physiological and biochemical impairments, such that upon transfer to *ex vitro* conditions they often experience severe oxidative stress. Carvalho *et al.* (2005) conducted an analysis of the extent to which this stress might be alleviated by a nominal doubling of the air's CO_2 content. They evaluated the damage done to the large subunit of rubisco in grapevine (*Vitis vinifera* L.) plantlets while exposed to *in vitro* conditions and the degree to which that damage was ameliorated by atmospheric CO_2 enrichment during subsequent exposure to *ex vitro* conditions.

The *in vitro* plantlet cultures were maintained in a growth chamber at a photon flux density (PFD) of 45 μmol m^{-2} s^{-1}, after which they were transferred to *ex vitro* conditions having a PFD of either 150 (low light) or 300 (high light) μmol m^{-2} s^{-1} and an air CO_2 concentration of either 350 (low CO_2) or 700 (high CO_2) ppm. A number of physiological and biochemical measurements were made on the plantlets at seven-day intervals over a period of 28 days.

Carvalho *et al.* found rubisco degradation products were present in the leaves of plantlets in both *in vitro* and *ex vitro* conditions. However, "under low CO_2 they were maintained for almost all of the 28 days of the acclimatization period, while becoming scarcely detected after 14 days under high CO_2 and after 7 days when high CO_2 was associated with high light." In addition, "patterns of soluble sugars in acclimatizing leaves under high light and high CO_2 also gave an indication of a faster acquisition of autotrophic characteristics." Carvalho *et al.*'s results thus demonstrate the beneficial impact of high CO_2 concentrations in reducing the oxidative stress induced by the transfer of *in vitro*-produced plantlets to *ex vitro* conditions, as "a net benefit from high CO_2 treatments was clearly visible, contributing to an increased stability of Rubisco." Also, "the disappearance of Rubisco large subunit degradation products in persistent leaves subjected to the *ex vitro* treatments may be considered an indicator of recovery from stress," they write.

Levine *et al.* (2008) grew well-watered and fertilized wheat plants (*Triticum aestivum*, cv Yocoro roho) from seed in custom-designed root modules—"consisting of a porous tube embedded in Turface (1–2 mm particle size) substrate containing 5 g Osmocote time release fertilizer per liter"—which were housed in Plexiglas chambers maintained at atmospheric CO_2 concentrations of either 400, 1,500, or 10,000 ppm for periods of 14, 21, and 28 days. The scientists measured a number of plant metabolic properties along with the leaf concentrations of several flavonoids that are capable of scavenging ROS. The 13 researchers report "elevated CO_2 promoted the accumulation of secondary metabolites (flavonoids) progressively to a greater extent as plants became mature." As best as can be determined from the bar graphs of their results, for example, the percentage increase in total wheat leaf flavonoid concentration in going from an atmospheric CO_2 concentration of 400 to 1,500 ppm was 22%, 38%, and 27% at 14, 21, and 28 days after planting, respectively, whereas in going from a CO_2

concentration of 400 to 10,000 ppm, the percentage increase in total flavonoid concentration was 38%, 56% and 86%, respectively, at 14, 21 and 28 days after planting. They report "both elevated CO_2 levels resulted in an overall 25% increase in biomass over the control plants."

The U.S., Japanese, and German scientists write, "the increased accumulation of secondary metabolites in plants grown under elevated CO_2 may have implications regarding plant-herbivore interactions, decomposition rates for inedible biomass, and potential beneficial effects on plant tolerance to water stress (Idso, 1988) and cold stress (Solecka and Kacperska, 2003) due to their potentials for the scavenging of reactive oxygen species (ROS)."

Varga et al. (2012) write, "as well as damaging numerous physiological functions, abiotic stress [such as drought] also leads to higher concentrations of reactive oxygen species, which are present in nature in all plants, but which may damage cell components and disturb metabolic processes when present in larger quantities," citing Omran (1980), Larson (1988), and Dat et al. (2000). They say "many authors have demonstrated that the [atmosphere's] CO_2 concentration has a substantial influence on the stress sensitivity of plants via changes in antioxidant enzyme activity," citing Fernandez-Trujillo et al. (2007), Ali et al. (2008), and Varga and Bencze (2009), so increases in the atmosphere's CO_2 concentration may increase various plant antioxidant enzymes and thereby reduce the negative effects of various abiotic stresses.

Varga et al. grew two varieties of winter wheat within phytotrons maintained at either 380 or 750 ppm CO_2, where the potted plants were watered daily and supplied with nutrient solution twice a week until the start of drought treatments, when drought was induced in three phases—at first node appearance, heading, and grain filling—by completely withholding water for seven days, which dropped the volumetric soil water content in the pots from 20–25% to 3–5%. The four researchers—all of whom were associated with the Agricultural Research Institute of the Hungarian Academy of Sciences—report they observed "changes in enzyme activity" that "indicated that enhanced CO_2 concentration delayed the development of drought stress up to first node appearance, and stimulated antioxidant enzyme activity when drought occurred during ripening, thus reducing the unfavorable effects of [drought] stress." Varga et al. conclude the increases in the antioxidant enzymes they analyzed "may help to neutralize the reactive oxygen species induced by stress during

various parts of the vegetation period," which may help society's crops better cope with whatever extremes of moisture insufficiency might be lurking in the future.

Perez-Lopez et al. (2009) noted soil salinity "is one of the major environmental constraints limiting plant productivity and distribution," affecting, as it does, "19.5% of the world's irrigated area" as well as "non-irrigated croplands and rangelands." They grew two barley (Hordeum vulgare L.) cultivars, Alpha and Iranis, within controlled-environment growth chambers at either ambient (350 ppm) or elevated (700 ppm) atmospheric CO_2 concentrations in a 3:1 perlite:vermiculite mixture watered with Hoagland's solution every two days until the first leaf was completely expanded at 14 days, after which a salinity treatment was administered by adding 0, 80, 160, or 240 mM NaCl to the Hoagland's solution every two days for 14 more days. After a total of 28 days, the primary leaf of each barley plant was harvested and assessed for a number of biochemical properties.

In the various ambient-air salinity treatments, the deleterious effects of reactive oxygen species on barley leaves were made apparent through ion leakage and increases in thiobarbituric acid reactive substances (TBARS), which rose as salt concentrations rose, Perez-Lopez et al. report. "On the other hand," they continue, "when [the] salinity treatment was imposed under elevated CO_2 conditions, lower solute leakage and TBARS levels were observed, suggesting that the oxidative stress caused by salinity was lower."

Perez-Lopez et al. write, "it is concluded that elevated CO_2 protects barley cultivars from oxidative stress," noting "the relief of oxidative stress damage observed in our barley leaves grown under a CO_2 enriched atmosphere has also been observed in alfalfa (Sgherri et al., 1998), pine (Vu et al., 1999) and oak (Schwanz and Polle, 2001b)." Thus it would appear the ongoing rise in the air's CO_2 content may help a wide variety of Earth's plants better cope with the many serious problems caused by high soil salinity.

Farfan-Vignolo and Asard (2012) note "grassland communities constitute an important fraction of the green surface of the Earth, and are worldwide an important source of cattle-food (Carlier et al., 2009; Ciais et al., 2011)." The pair of Belgian researchers investigated several physiological and molecular (antioxidant) responses to water deficit in two major grassland species (Lolium perenne L. and Medicago lupulina L.) under current ambient (A) and future elevated (E) atmospheric CO_2 concentrations and air temperatures (T), where $ECO_2 = ACO_2 + 375$ ppm, and where ET = AT + 3°C.

"Not surprisingly," they write, "drought caused significant increases in oxidative damage, i.e., in protein oxidation and lipid peroxidation levels." But they found "in both species the impact of drought on protein oxidation was reduced in future climate conditions [ECO$_2$ and ET]." And speaking of the stress-reducing effect of ECO$_2$, they say "this 'CO$_2$-protection effect' is reported for a variety of abiotic stress conditions and species," citing Schwanz and Polle (1998), Sgherri *et al.* (2000), Geissler *et al.* (2009), Perez-Lopez *et al.* (2009), Vurro *et al.* (2009), and Salazar-Parra *et al.* (2012). The scientists conclude they "find support for this effect at the level of oxidative cell damage and protein oxidation in water-deficit responses of *L. perenne* and *M. lupulina.*"

These observations make it clear plants exposed to higher-than-current atmospheric CO$_2$ concentrations are better equipped to deal with oxidative stress than plants growing at lower CO$_2$ concentrations. IPCC currently ignores these benefits.

References

Ali, M.B., Dewir, Y.H., Hahn, E., and Peak, K. 2008. Effect of carbon dioxide on antioxidant enzymes and ginsenoside production in root suspension cultures of *Panax ginseng*. *Environmental and Experimental Botany* **63**: 297–304.

Baczek-Kwinta, R. and Koscielniak, J. 2003. Antioxidative effect of elevated CO$_2$ concentration in the air on maize hybrids subjected to severe chill. *Photosynthetica* **41**: 161–165.

Carlier, L., Rotar, I., Vlahova, M., and Vidican, R. 2009. Importance and functions of grasslands. *Notulae Botanicae Horti Agrobotanici Cluj-Napoca* **37**: 25–30.

Carvalho, L.C., Esquivel, M.G., Martins, I., Ricardo, C.P., and Amancio, S. 2005. Monitoring the stability of Rubisco in micro-propagated grapevine (*Vitis vinifera* L.) by two-dimensional electrophoresis. *Journal of Plant Physiology* **162**: 365–374.

Ciais, P., Gervois, S., Vuichard, N., Piao, S.L., and Viovy, N. 2011. Effects of land use change and management on the European cropland carbon balance. *Global Change Biology* **17**: 320–338.

Dat, J., Vandenabeele, S., Vranova, A., Van Montagu, M., Inze, D., and Van Breusegem, F. 2000. Dual action of the active oxygen species during plant stress responses. *Cellular and Molecular Life Sciences* **57**: 779–995.

Farfan-Vignolo, E.R. and Asard, H. 2012. Effect of elevated CO$_2$ and temperature on the oxidative stress response to drought in *Lolium perenne* L. and *Medicago sativa* L. *Plant Physiology and Biochemistry* **59**: 55–62.

Fernandez-Trujillo, J.P., Nock, J.F., and Watkins, C.B. 2007. Antioxidant enzyme activities in strawberry fruit exposed to high carbon dioxide atmospheres during cold storage. *Food Chemistry* **104**: 1425–1429.

Geissler, N., Hussin, S., and Koyro, H.-W. 2009. Elevated atmospheric CO$_2$ concentration ameliorates effects of NaCl salinity on photosynthesis and leaf structure of *Aster tripolium* L. *Journal of Experimental Botany* **60**: 137–151.

Idso, S.B. 1988. Three phases of plant response to atmospheric CO$_2$ enrichment. *Plant Physiology* **87**: 5–7.

Larson, R.A. 1988. The antioxidants of higher plants. *Phytochemistry* **27**: 969–978.

Levine, L.H., Kasahara, H., Kopka, J., Erban, A., Fehrl, I., Kaplan, F., Zhao, W., Littell, R.C., Guy, C., Wheeler, R., Sager, J., Mills, A., and Levine, H.G. 2008. Physiologic and metabolic responses of wheat seedlings to elevated and super-elevated carbon dioxide. *Advances in Space Research* **42**: 1917–1928.

Lin, J.-S and Wang, G.-X. 2002. Doubled CO$_2$ could improve the drought tolerance better in sensitive cultivars than in tolerant cultivars in spring wheat. *Plant Science* **163**: 627–637.

Nawar, W.W. 1996. Lipids. In: Fennema, O.R. (Ed.) *Food Chemistry*. Marcel Dekker, New York, NY, USA, pp. 225–313.

Niewiadomska, E., Gaucher-Veilleux, C., Chevrier, N., Mauffette, Y., and Dizengremel, P. 1999. Elevated CO$_2$ does not provide protection against ozone considering the activity of several antioxidant enzymes in the leaves of sugar maple. *Journal of Plant Physiology* **155**: 70–77.

Omran, R.G. 1980. Peroxide levels and the activities of catalase, peroxidase and indoleacetic acid oxidase during and after chilling cucumber seedlings. *Plant Physiology* **65**: 407–408.

Perez-Lopez, U., Robredo, A., Lacuestra, M., Sgherri, C., Munoz-Rueda, A., Navari-Izzo, F., and Mena-Petite, A. 2009. The oxidative stress caused by salinity in two barley cultivars is mitigated by elevated CO$_2$. *Physiologia Plantarum* **135**: 29–42.

Polle, A., Eiblmeier, M., Sheppard, L., and Murray, M. 1997. Responses of antioxidative enzymes to elevated CO$_2$ in leaves of beech (*Fagus sylvatica* L.) seedlings grown under a range of nutrient regimes. *Plant, Cell and Environment* **20**: 1317–1321.

Pritchard, S.G., Ju, Z., van Santen, E., Qiu, J., Weaver, D.B., Prior, S.A., and Rogers, H.H. 2000. The influence of elevated CO$_2$ on the activities of antioxidative enzymes in two soybean genotypes. *Australian Journal of Plant Physiology* **27**: 1061–1068.

Ren, H.X., Chen, X., and Wu, D.X. 2001. Effects of elevated CO$_2$ on photosynthesis and antioxidative ability of broad bean plants grown under drought condition. *Acta Agronomica Sinica* **27**: 729–736.

Salazar-Parra, C., Aguirreolea, J., Sanchez-Diaz, M., Irigoyen, J.J., and Morales, F. 2012. Climate change (elevated CO$_2$, elevated temperature and moderate drought) triggers the antioxidant enzymes' response of grapevine cv. Tempranillo, avoiding oxidative damage. *Physiologia Plantarum* **144**: 99–110.

Schwanz, P. and Polle, A. 1998. Antioxidative systems, pigment and protein contents in leaves of adult mediterranean oak species (*Quercus pubescens* and *Q. ilex*) with lifetime exposure to elevated CO$_2$. *New Phytologist* **140**: 411–423.

Schwanz, P. and Polle, A. 2001a. Growth under elevated CO$_2$ ameliorates defenses against photo-oxidative stress in poplar (*Populus alba x tremula*). *Environmental and Experimental Botany* **45**: 43–53.

Schwanz, P. and Polle, A. 2001b. Differential stress responses of anti-oxidative systems to drought in pedunculate oak (*Quercus robur*) and maritime pine (*Pinus pinaster*) grown under high CO$_2$ concentrations. *Journal of Experimental Botany* **52**: 133–143.

Sgherri, C., Quartacci, M., Menconi, M., Raschi, A., and Navari-Izzo, F. 1998. Interactions between drought and elevated CO$_2$ on alfalfa plants. *Journal of Plant Physiology* **152**: 118–124.

Solecka, D. and Kacperska, A. 2003. Phenylpropanoid deficiency affects the course of plant acclimation to cold. *Physiologia Plantarum* **119**: 253–262.

Varga, B. and Bencze, S. 2009. Comparative study of drought stress resistance in two winter wheat varieties raised at ambient and elevated CO$_2$ concentration. *Cereal Research Communications* **37**: 209–212.

Varga, B., Janda, T., Laszlo, E., and Veisz, O. 2012. Influence of abiotic stresses on the antioxidant enzyme activity of cereals. *Acta Physiologiae Plantarum* **34**: 849–858.

Vu, J.C., Gesch, R., Allen, L.H., Boote, K., and Bowes, G. 1999. CO$_2$ enrichment delays a rapid, drought induced decrease in Rubisco small subunit transcript abundance. *Journal of Plant Physiology* **155**: 139–142.

Vurro, E., Bruni, R., Bianchi, A., and di Toppi, L.S. 2009. Elevated atmospheric CO$_2$ decreases oxidative stress and increases essential oil yield in leaves of *Thymus vulgaris* grown in a mini-FACE system. *Environmental and Experimental Botany* **65**: 99–106.

Wang, S.Y. and Zheng, W. 2001. Effect of plant growth temperature on antioxidant capacity in strawberry. *Journal of Agricultural and Food Chemistry* **49**: 4977–4982.

Yu, L., Haley, S., Perret, J., and Harris, M. 2004a. Comparison of wheat flours grown at different locations for their antioxidant properties. *Food Chemistry* **86**: 11–16.

Yu, J., Tang, X-X., Zhang, P-Y., Tian, J-Y., and Cai, H-J. 2004b. Effects of CO$_2$ enrichment on photosynthesis, lipid peroxidation and activities of antioxidative enzymes of *Platymonas subcordiformis* subjected to UV-B radiation stress. *Acta Botanica Sinica* **46**: 682–690.

7.8.1.2 Benefits to Humans

As discussed in the prior section, various environmental stresses generate highly reactive oxygenated compounds that damage plants. Ameliorating these stresses typically involves the production of antioxidant enzymes that scavenge and detoxify the highly reactive oxygenated compounds. When stresses are present, concentrations and/or activities of antioxidants in plants are generally observed to be high so as to counter the effects of the stress. However, plants exposed to higher-than-current atmospheric CO$_2$ concentrations experience less oxidative stress and thus have a reduced need for antioxidant protection, allowing them to funnel more of their limited resources into the production of other plant tissues or processes essential to their continued growth and development.

In some cases, such resources are invested into the production and enhancement of antioxidative compounds, and these compounds are known to provide health benefits to animals and humans that ingest these plants. The material in this section examines this CO$_2$-induced stimulation of antioxidant compounds, revealing another important benefit of atmospheric CO$_2$ enrichment that remains unreported by IPCC.

It is well-known that reactive oxygen species (ROS) generated during cellular metabolism or peroxidation of lipids and proteins play a causative role in the pathogenesis of cancer and coronary heart disease (CHD), as demonstrated by Slaga *et al.* (1987), Frenkel (1992), Marnett (2000), and Zhao *et al.* (2000). Wilcox *et al.* (2004), for example, note oxidative stress "has been related to cardiovascular disease, cancer, and other chronic diseases that account for a major portion of deaths today." Yu *et al.* (2004) note "antioxidant treatments may terminate ROS attacks and reduce the risks of CHD and cancer, as well as other ROS-related diseases such as Parkinson's disease (Neff, 1997; Chung et al., 1999; Wong et al., 1999; Espin et al., 2000; Merken and Beecher, 2000)," and "developing functional foods rich in natural antioxidants may improve human nutrition and reduce the risks of ROS-associated health problems."

Willcox et al. (2004) investigated the role of exogenous antioxidants in controlling oxidation and reviewed the evidence for their roles in preventing disease. The three nutrition experts state, "diet plays a vital role in the production of the antioxidant defense system by providing essential nutrient antioxidants such as vitamin E, C, and ß-carotene, other antioxidant plant phenols including flavonoids, and essential minerals that form important antioxidant enzymes." In addition, they note, "epidemiological data generally indicate a benefit of consuming diets that are higher in antioxidant nutrients, specifically diets high in fruits and vegetables."

While it may be much easier to obtain these antioxidants by simply popping a pill or two (or even three or four), and millions of people do so daily, that approach is probably not as effective as obtaining needed antioxidants via the food one eats.

Willcox et al. report, for example, that in many studies of antioxidant health benefits "it is not clear whether the benefit is derived from the specific nutrients under study or another food component having health benefits yet to be discovered," or perhaps "there is a particular combination of antioxidant nutrients that provide protection." Although some epidemiological studies "appear to demonstrate clear associations, direct tests of the relationships with clinical trials have not yielded similar results." They say "the most convincing evidence of antioxidant effect on cancer prevention involves feeding fruits and vegetables rather than individual antioxidants." But what role might atmospheric CO_2 play in the matter?

Wang et al. (2003) evaluated the effects of elevated CO_2 on the antioxidant activity and flavonoid content of strawberry fruit they grew out-of-doors in six clear-acrylic open-top chambers, two of which they maintained at the ambient atmospheric CO_2 concentration, two of which were maintained at ambient + 300 ppm CO_2, and two of which they maintained at ambient + 600 ppm CO_2 for a period of 28 months (from early spring of 1998 through June 2000). The fruits of their labor were harvested twice—"at the commercially ripe stage" in both 1999 and 2000—after which they had them analyzed for a number of antioxidant properties and flavonol

contents.

Wang et al. note "strawberries are good sources of natural antioxidants (Heinonen et al., 1998)." They further report, "in addition to the usual nutrients, such as vitamins and minerals, strawberries are also rich in anthocyanins, flavonoids, and phenolic acids," and "strawberries have shown a remarkably high scavenging activity toward chemically-generated radicals, thus making them effective in inhibiting oxidation of human low-density lipoproteins (Heinonen et al., 1998)." They note previous studies (Wang and Jiao, 2000; Wang and Lin, 2000) have shown "strawberries have high oxygen radical absorbance activity against peroxyl radicals, super-oxide radicals, hydrogen peroxide, hydroxyl radicals, and singlet oxygen."

They found strawberries had higher concentrations of ascorbic acid (AsA) and glutathione (GSH) when grown under enriched CO_2 conditions. In going from ambient to +300 ppm and +600 ppm CO_2, for example, AsA concentrations rose by 10 and 13%, respectively, and GSH concentrations increased by 3 and 171%, respectively. They also learned "an enriched CO_2 environment resulted in an increase in phenolic acid, flavonol, and anthocyanin contents of fruit." For nine flavonoids, for example, there was a mean concentration increase of 55 ± 23% in going from the ambient atmospheric CO_2 concentration to +300 ppm CO_2, and a mean concentration increase of 112 ± 35% in going from ambient to +600 ppm CO_2. In addition, the "high flavonol content was associated with high antioxidant activity."

Wang et al. note "anthocyanins have been reported to help reduce damage caused by free radical activity, such as low-density lipoprotein oxidation, platelet aggregation, and endothelium-dependent vasodilation of arteries (Heinonen et al., 1998; Rice-Evans and Miller, 1996)." In summarizing their findings, they write, "strawberry fruit contain flavonoids with potent antioxidant properties, and under CO_2 enrichment conditions, increased the[ir] AsA, GSH, phenolic acid, flavonol, and anthocyanin concentrations," further noting, "plants grown under CO_2 enrichment conditions also had higher oxygen radical absorbance activity against [many types of oxygen] radicals in the fruit."

Caldwell et al. (2005) note "the beneficial effects of isoflavone-rich foods have been the subject of numerous studies," specifically citing Messina (1999) and Birt et al. (2001), adding, "foods derived from soybeans are generally considered to provide both specific and general health benefits." They investigated how the isoflavone content of soybean seeds might be affected by the ongoing rise in the air's CO_2 content.

They grew well-watered and fertilized soybean plants from seed to maturity in pots within two controlled-environment chambers, one maintained at an atmospheric CO_2 concentration of 400 ppm and one at 700 ppm. The chambers were initially kept at a constant air temperature of 25°C. At the onset of seed fill, air temperature was reduced to 18°C until seed development was complete, in order to simulate average outdoor temperatures at this stage of plant development. In a second experiment, this protocol was repeated, except that the temperature during seed fill was maintained at 23°C, with and without drought (a third treatment). In a third experiment, seed-fill temperature was maintained at 28°C, with or without drought.

In the first experiment, where air temperature during seed fill was 18°C, the elevated CO_2 treatment increased the total isoflavone content of the soybean seeds by 8%. In the second experiment, where air temperature during seed fill was 23°C, the extra CO_2 increased total seed isoflavone content by 104%. In the third experiment, where air temperature during seed fill was 28°C, the CO_2-induced isoflavone increase was 101%. When drought stress was added as a third environmental variable, the extra CO_2 boosted total seed isoflavone content by 186% when seed-fill air temperature was 23°C, and at a seed-fill temperature of 28°C, it increased isoflavone content by 38%.

Under all the environmental circumstances studied by Caldwell et al., enriching the air with an extra 300 ppm of CO_2 increased the total isoflavone content of soybean seeds. The percent increases measured under the stress situations investigated were always greater than the percent increase measured under optimal growing conditions. Thus the direct effects of atmospheric CO_2 enrichment on the health-promoting properties of soybean seeds are likely universally beneficial and a boon to humans; Bernacchi et al. (2005) characterized the soybean as "the world's most important seed legume."

Ginseng (Panax ginseng), the roots of which are widely cultivated in China, South Korea, and Japan and have been used for medicinal purposes since Greek and Roman times, is known for its anti-inflammatory, diuretic, and sedative properties and is acknowledged to be an effective healing agent (Gillis, 1997; Ali et al., 2005). Normally, four to six years are required for ginseng roots to accumulate the amounts of the various phenolic compounds needed to produce their health-promoting effects. In an important step in the quest to develop an efficient culture system for the commercial production of ginseng root, Ali et al. (2005) investigated the effects of growing ginseng roots in suspension culture in bioreactors maintained in equilibrium with air enriched to CO_2 concentrations of 10,000 ppm, 25,000 ppm and 50,000 ppm for periods of up to 45 days.

Of most immediate concern in such an experiment would be the effects of the ultra-high CO_2 concentrations on root growth. Would they be toxic and lead to biomass reductions or even root death? The answer was a resounding no. After 45 days of growth at 10,000 ppm CO_2, for example, root dry weight was increased by fully 37% relative to the dry weight of roots produced in bioreactors in equilibrium with normal ambient air, and root dry mass was increased by 27% after 45 days at 25,000 ppm CO_2 and by a still smaller 9% after 45 days at 50,000 ppm CO_2. Although the optimum CO_2 concentration for ginseng root growth clearly resided at some value lower than 10,000 ppm in this study, the concentration at which root growth rate was reduced below that characteristic of ambient air was somewhere significantly above 50,000 ppm, for even at that high CO_2 concentration, root growth was still greater than in ambient air.

Almost everything else measured by Ali et al. was even more dramatically enhanced by the ultra-high CO_2 concentrations they employed in their experiment. After 45 days of treatment, total root phenolic concentrations were 58% higher at 10,000 ppm CO_2 than at ambient CO_2, 153% higher at 25,000 ppm CO_2, and 105% higher at 50,000 ppm CO_2, as best as can be determined from the bar graphs of their results. Total root flavonoid concentrations were enhanced by 228%, 383%, and 232%, respectively, at the same ultra-high CO_2 concentrations. Total protein contents rose by 14%, 22%, and 30%; non-protein thiol contents by 12%, 43%, and 62%; and cysteine contents by 27%, 65%, and 100% under the identical respective sets of conditions. In addition, there were equally large CO_2-induced increases in the activities of a large number of phenol biosynthetic enzymes.

Ali et al. note "the consumption of foodstuffs containing antioxidant phytonutrients such as flavonoids, polyphenolics, ascorbate, cysteine and non-protein thiol is advantageous for human health," citing Cervato et al. (2000) and Noctor and Foyer (1998). They conclude their technique for the culture of ginseng roots in CO_2-enriched bioreactors could be used for the large-scale production of an important health-promoting product that could be provided to the public in much greater quantities than is currently possible.

Stutte *et al.* (2008) studied *Scutellaria* plants, herbaceous perennials that possess numerous medicinal properties, noting they are "rich in physiologically active flavonoids that have a wide spectrum of pharmacological activity." They say leaf extracts of *Scutellaria barbata* have been found to be "limiting to the growth of cell lines associated with lung, liver, prostate, and brain tumors (Yin *et al.*, 2004)," and "extracts of *S. lateriflora* and the isolated flavonoids from the extracts have been shown to have antioxidant, anticancer, and antiviral properties (Awad *et al.*, 2003)." They investigated how the growth of these important plants, and their significant medicinal properties, might be affected by the ongoing rise in the air's CO_2 content.

Stutte *et al.* measured effects of elevated atmospheric CO_2 (1,200 and 3,000 ppm vs. a control value of 400 ppm) on plant biomass production and plant concentrations of six bioactive flavonoids—apigenin, baicalin, baicalein, chrysin, scutellarein, and wogonin—all of which, they write, "have been reported to have anticancer and antiviral properties," as described in the review papers of Joshee *et al.* (2002) and Cole *et al.* (2007). These experiments were conducted in a large step-in controlled-environment chamber that provided a consistent light quality, intensity, and photoperiod to six small plant growth chambers that had "high-fidelity control of relative humidity, temperature, and CO_2 concentration." Each chamber was designed to monitor nutrient solution uptake by six individual plants that they grew from seed for a period of 49 days.

With respect to plant productivity (fresh and dry weight production), the three U.S. researchers determined increasing the air's CO_2 concentration from 400 to 1,200 ppm resulted in a 36% increase in shoot fresh weight in *S. barbata* and a 54% increase in shoot dry matter, with no further increases between 1,200 and 3,000 ppm CO_2. In *S. lateriflora*, the corresponding increases in going from 400 to 1,200 ppm CO_2 were 62% and 44%, and in going to 3,000 ppm CO_2, the total increases were 122% and 70%, respectively.

For total flavonoid concentrations in the plants' vegetative tissues, Stutte *et al.* found, in *S. barbata* "the combined concentration of the six flavonoids measured increased by 48% at 1200 and 81% at 3000 ppm CO_2," and for *S. lateriflora* they report "the total flavonoid content increased by over 2.4 times at 1200 and 4.9 times at 3000 ppm CO_2." In consequence of the compounding effect of increases in both plant biomass and flavonoid concentration, the total flavonoid content in *S. barbata* rose by 72% in going from 400 to 1,200 ppm CO_2, and by 128% in going to 3,000 ppm CO_2. In *S. lateriflora* the corresponding increases were 320% and 1,270%. Stutte *et al.* conclude their results indicate "the yield and pharmaceutical quality of *Scutellaria* species can be enhanced with controlled environment production and CO_2 enrichment," and massively so, it appears. In addition, since they say more than 200 substances—of which more than 80% are flavonoids—have been found in a total of 65 *Scutellaria* species, it would also appear the "increased concentration of flavonoids through CO_2 enrichment," as they conclude, "has the potential to enhance the production and quality of medicinal plants."

References

Ali, M.B., Hahn, E.J., and Paek, K.-Y. 2005. CO_2-induced total phenolics in suspension cultures of *Panax ginseng* C.A. Mayer roots: role of antioxidants and enzymes. *Plant Physiology and Biochemistry* **43**: 449–457.

Awad, R., Arnason, J.T., Trudeau, V., Bergeron, C., Budziinski, J.W., Foster, B.C., and Merali, Z. 2003. Phytochemical and biological analysis of skullcap (*Scutellaria lateriflora* L.): A medicinal plant with anxiolytic properties. *Phytomedicine* **10**: 640–649.

Bernacchi, C.J., Morgan, P.B., Ort, D.R., and Long, S.P. 2005. The growth of soybean under free air [CO_2] enrichment (FACE) stimulates photosynthesis while decreasing *in vivo* Rubisco capacity. *Planta* **220**: 434–446.

Birt, D.F., Hendrich, W., and Wang, W. 2001. Dietary agents in cancer prevention: flavonoids and iso-flavonoids. *Pharmacology & Therapeutics* **90**: 157–177.

Caldwell, C.R., Britz, S.J., and Mirecki, R.M. 2005. Effect of temperature, elevated carbon dioxide, and drought during seed development on the isoflavone content of dwarf soybean [*Glycine max* (L.) Merrill] grown in controlled environments. *Journal of Agricultural and Food Chemistry* **53**: 1125–1129.

Cervato, G., Carabelli, M., Gervasio, S., Cittera, A., Cazzola, R., and Cestaro, B. 2000. Antioxidant properties of oregano (*Origanum vulgare*) leaf extracts. *Journal of Food Biochemistry* **24**: 453–465.

Chung, H.S., Chang, L.C., Lee, S.K., Shamon, L.A., Breemen, R.B.V., Mehta, R.G., Farnsworth, N.R., Pezzuto, J.M., and Kinghorn, A.D. 1999. Flavonoid constituents of chorizanthe diffusa with potential cancer chemopreventive activity. *Journal of Agricultural and Food Chemistry* **47**: 36–41.

Cole, I.B., Sacena, P.K., and Murch, S.J. 2007. Medicinal biotechnology in the genus *Scutellaria*. *In Vitro Cellular & Developmental Biology—Plant* **43**: 318–327.

Espin, J.C., Soler-Rivas, C., and Wichers, H.J. 2000. Characterization of the total free radical scavenger capacity of vegetable oils and oil fractions using 2,2-diphenyl-1-picryhydrazyl radical. *Journal of Agricultural and Food Chemistry* **48**: 648–656.

Frenkel, K. 1992. Carcinogen-mediated oxidant formation and oxidative DNA damage. *Pharmacology and Therapeutics* **53**: 127–166.

Gillis, C.N. 1997. *Panax ginseng* pharmacology: a nitric oxide link? *Biochemical Pharmacology* **54**: 1–8.

Heinonen, I.M., Meyer, A.S., and Frankel, E.N. 1998. Antioxidant activity of berry phenolics on human low-density lipoprotein and liposome oxidation. *Journal of Agricultural and Food Chemistry* **46**: 4107–4112.

Joshee, N., Patrick, T.S., Mentreddy, R.S., and Yadav, A.K. 2002. Skullcap: Potential medicinal crop. In: Janick, J. and Whipkey, A. (Eds.) *Trends in New Crops and New Uses*. ASHS Press, Alexandria, VA, USA, pp. 580–586.

Marnett, L.J. 2000. Oxyradicals and DNA damage. *Carcinogenesis* **21**: 361–370.

Merken, H.M. and Beecher, G.R. 2000. Measurement of food flavonoids by high-performance liquid chromatography: A review. *Journal of Agricultural and Food Chemistry* **48**: 577–599.

Messina, M.J. 1999. Legumes and soybeans: overview of their nutritional profiles and health effects. *American Journal of Clinical Nutrition* **70(S)**: 439s–450s.

Neff, J. 1997. Big companies take nutraceuticals to heart. *Food Processing* **58** (10): 37–42.

Noctor, G. and Foyer, C.H. 1998. Ascorbate and glutathione: keeping active oxygen under control. *Annual Review of Plant Physiology and Plant Molecular Biology* **49**: 249–279.

Rice-Evans, C.A. and Miller, N.J. 1996. Antioxidant activities of flavonoids as bioactive components of food. *Biochemical Society Transactions* **24**: 790–795.

Slaga, T.J., O'Connell, J., Rotstein, J., Patskan, G., Morris, R., Aldaz, M., and Conti, C. 1987. Critical genetic determinants and molecular events in multistage skin carcinogenesis. *Symposium on Fundamental Cancer Research* **39**: 31–34.

Stutte, G.W., Eraso, I., and Rimando, A.M. 2008. Carbon dioxide enrichment enhances growth and flavonoid content of two *Scutellaria* species. *Journal of the American Society for Horticultural Science* **133**: 631–638.

Wang, S.Y., Bunce, J.A., and Maas, J.L. 2003. Elevated carbon dioxide increases contents of antioxidant compounds in field-grown strawberries. *Journal of Agricultural and Food Chemistry* **51**: 4315–4320.

Wang, S.Y. and Jiao, H. 2000. Scavenging capacity of berry crops on superoxide radicals, hydrogen peroxide, hydroxyl radicals, and singlet oxygen. *Journal of Agricultural and Food Chemistry* **48**: 5677–5684.

Wang, S.Y. and Lin, H.S. 2000. Antioxidant activity in fruit and leaves of blackberry, raspberry, and strawberry is affected by cultivar and maturity. *Journal of Agricultural and Food Chemistry* **48**: 140–146.

Willcox, J.K., Ash, S.L., and Catignani, G.L. 2004. Antioxidants and prevention of chronic disease. *Critical Reviews in Food Science and Nutrition* **44**: 275–295.

Wong, S.S., Li, R.H.Y., and Stadlin, A. 1999. Oxidative stress induced by MPTP and MPP+: Selective vulnerability of cultured mouse astocytes. *Brain Research* **836**: 237–244.

Yin, X., Zhou, J., Jie, C., Xing, D., and Zhang, Y. 2004. Anticancer activity and mechanism of *Scutellaria barbata* extract on human lung cancer cell line A549. *Life Science* **75**: 2233–2244.

Zhao, J., Lahiri-Chatterjee, M., Sharma, Y., and Agarwal, R. 2000. Inhibitory effect of a flavonoid antioxidant silymarin on benzoyl peroxide-induced tumor promotion, oxidative stress and inflammatory responses in SENCAR mouse skin. *Carcinogenesis* **21**: 811–816.

7.8.2 Common Food Plants

• The ongoing rise in the air's CO_2 content is not only raising the productivity of Earth's common food plants but also significantly increasing the quantity and potency of the many health-promoting substances found in their tissues, which are the ultimate sources of sustenance for essentially all animals and humans.

Studies of the effects of atmospheric CO_2 enrichment on the quality of the plants that comprise our diets have typically lagged far behind studies designed to assess the effects of elevated CO_2 on the quantity of plant production. Some noteworthy exceptions were the early studies of Barbale (1970) and Madsen (1971, 1975), who discovered increasing the air's CO_2 content produced a modest increase in the vitamin C concentration of tomatoes, and Kimball and Mitchell (1981), who demonstrated enriching the air with CO_2 also stimulated the tomato plant's production of vitamin A. A few years later, Tajiri

(1985) found a mere one-hour-per-day doubling of the air's CO_2 concentration doubled the vitamin C contents of bean sprouts, and did so when applied over a period of only seven days.

Fast-forwarding a couple of decades, Idso *et al.* (2002) grew well-watered and fertilized sour orange trees out-of-doors at Phoenix, Arizona, in clear-plastic-wall open-top enclosures maintained at atmospheric CO_2 concentrations of either 400 or 700 ppm since November 1987, while evaluating the effects of the extra 300 ppm of CO_2 on the vitamin C concentrations of fully ripened fruit harvested over the eight-year period 1992–1999. In years when the production of fruit was approximately doubled by the extra CO_2, they found the fruit produced in the two CO_2 treatments were of approximately the same size, and the vitamin C concentration of the juice of the oranges grown in the CO_2-enriched air was enhanced by approximately 7% above that of the juice of the ambient-treatment oranges. In years when CO_2-enriched fruit numbers were more than doubled, however, the CO_2-enriched fruit were slightly smaller than the fruit produced in normal air, and the vitamin C concentration of the juice of the CO_2-enriched fruit rose even higher, to as much as 15% above that of the ambient-treatment fruit. In years when fruit numbers were less than doubled, the CO_2-enriched fruit were slightly larger than the ambient-treatment fruit, and the enhancement of the vitamin C concentration of the juice of the CO_2-enriched fruit was somewhat less than the base value of 7% typical of equal-size fruit.

With respect to the likely long-term equilibrium response of the trees, Idso *et al.* (2002) report that in five of the last six years of the study, "the 75% increase in atmospheric CO_2 concentration has increased: (1) the number of fruit produced by the trees by 74 ± 9%, (2) the fresh weight of the fruit by 4 ± 2%, and (3) the vitamin C concentration of the juice of the fruit by 5 ± 1%." The eight researchers conclude, "there is reason to believe that an atmospheric CO_2 enrichment of the magnitude expected over the current century may induce a large and sustained increase in the number of fruit produced by orange trees, a small increase in the size of the fruit, and a modest increase in the vitamin C concentration of the juice of the fruit, all of which effects bode well for this key agricultural product that plays a vital role in maintaining good health in human populations around the globe."

Further support for the significance of these observations was provided by Idso and Idso (2001), who note "these findings take on great significance when it is realized that scurvy—which is brought on by low intake of vitamin C—may be resurgent in industrial countries, especially among children (Ramar *et al.*, 1993; Gomez-Carrasco *et al.*, 1994), and that subclinical scurvy symptoms are increasing among adults (Dickinson *et al.*, 1994)." In addition, they report, "Hampl *et al.* (1999) have found that 12 to 20% of 12–18-year-old school children in the United States 'drastically under-consume' foods that supply vitamin C; while Johnston *et al.* (1998) have determined that 12 to 16% of U.S. college students have marginal plasma concentrations of vitamin C." Hence, "since vitamin C intake correlates strongly with the consumption of citrus juice (Dennison *et al.*, 1998), and since the only high-vitamin-C juice consumed in any quantity by children is orange juice (Hampl *et al.*, 1999), the modest role played by the ongoing rise in the air's CO_2 content in increasing the vitamin C concentration of orange juice could ultimately prove to be of considerable significance for public health in the United States and elsewhere."

Wang *et al.* (2003) grew strawberry plants in six clear-acrylic open-top chambers—two of which were maintained at the ambient atmospheric CO_2 concentration, two of which were maintained at ambient + 300 ppm CO_2, and two of which were maintained at ambient + 600 ppm CO_2—for a period of 28 months (from early spring of 1998 through June 2000), harvesting their fruit at the commercially ripe stage in both 1999 and 2000 and analyzing them for antioxidant properties and flavonol contents.

Wang *et al.* note strawberries are good sources of natural antioxidants and state, "in addition to the usual nutrients, such as vitamins and minerals, strawberries are also rich in anthocyanins, flavonoids, and phenolic acids," and "strawberries have shown a remarkably high scavenging activity toward chemically generated radicals, thus making them effective in inhibiting oxidation of human low-density lipoproteins (Heinonen *et al.*, 1998)." They note previous studies (Wang and Jiao, 2000; Wang and Lin, 2000) "have shown that strawberries have high oxygen radical absorbance activity against peroxyl radicals, superoxide radicals, hydrogen peroxide, hydroxyl radicals, and singlet oxygen."

The researchers determined, first, that strawberries had higher concentrations of ascorbic acid (AsA) and glutathione (GSH) "when grown under enriched CO_2 environments." In going from ambient to +300 ppm and +600 ppm CO_2, for example, AsA concentrations increased by 10 and 13%, respectively, and GSH concentrations increased by 3 and 171%, respectively. They also learned "an enriched CO_2 environment resulted in an increase in phenolic acid, flavonol, and anthocyanin contents of fruit." For nine flavonoids, for example, there was a mean concentration increase of 55 ± 23% in going from the ambient atmospheric CO_2 concentration to +300 ppm CO_2, and a mean concentration increase of 112 ± 35% in going from ambient to +600 ppm CO_2. In addition, the "high flavonol content was associated with high antioxidant activity." As for the significance of these findings, Wang *et al.* note "anthocyanins have been reported to help reduce damage caused by free radical activity, such as low-density lipoprotein oxidation, platelet aggregation, and endothelium-dependent vasodilation of arteries (Heinonen *et al.*, 1998; Rice-Evans and Miller, 1996)."

Wang *et al.* write, "strawberry fruit contain flavonoids with potent antioxidant properties, and under CO_2 enrichment conditions, increased their AsA, GSH, phenolic acid, flavonol, and anthocyanin concentrations," further noting "plants grown under CO_2 enrichment conditions also had higher oxygen radical absorbance activity against radicals in the fruit."

With respect to a major staple crop, soybeans, Caldwell *et al.* (2005) write "the beneficial effects of isoflavone-rich foods have been the subject of numerous studies (Birt *et al.*, 2001; Messina, 1999)," and "foods derived from soybeans are generally considered to provide both specific and general health benefits." Caldwell *et al.* examined how the isoflavone content of soybean seeds might be affected by the ongoing rise in the air's CO_2 content, growing well-watered and fertilized soybean plants from seed to maturity in pots within two controlled-environment chambers, one maintained at an atmospheric CO_2 concentration of 400 ppm and one at 700 ppm. The chambers were initially kept at a constant air temperature of 25°C; at the onset of seed fill, air temperature was reduced to 18°C until seed development was complete, to simulate average outdoor temperatures at this stage of plant development. In a second experiment, this protocol was repeated, except the temperature during seed fill was maintained at 23°C, with and without drought (a third treatment). In a third experiment, seed-fill temperature was maintained at 28°C, with or without drought.

In the first experiment, where air temperature during seed fill was 18°C, the elevated CO_2 treatment increased the total isoflavone content of the soybean seeds by 8%. In the second experiment, where air temperature during seed fill was 23°C, the extra CO_2 increased total seed isoflavone content by 104%. In the third experiment, where air temperature during seed fill was 28°C, the CO_2-induced isoflavone increase was 101%. When drought-stress was added as a third environmental variable, the extra CO_2 boosted total seed isoflavone content by 186% when seed-fill air temperature was 23°C, and at a seed-fill temperature of 28°C, it increased isoflavone content by 38%.

Under all environmental circumstances studied, therefore, enriching the air with an extra 300 ppm of CO_2 increased the total isoflavone content of soybean seeds. The percent increases measured under the stress situations were always greater than the percent increase measured under optimal growing conditions. Consequently, the direct effects of atmospheric CO_2 enrichment on the health-promoting properties of soybeans, which Bernacchi *et al.* (2005) characterize as "the world's most important seed legume," are likely universally beneficial.

Kim *et al.* (2005) note important flavonoids "are mainly found in the form of isoflavones in soybean seeds," including "phytoestrogens with various biological potentials such as antioxidative, pharmaceutical, oestrogenic and anticarcinogenic properties, with some acting as antiestrogens and being used as anticancer agents (Peterson and Barnes, 1991; Anderson *et al.*, 1995; Anthony *et al.*, 1996; Arjmandi *et al.*, 1996; Holt, 1997; Chung *et al.*, 2000)." They grew well-watered plants from seed to maturity in pots of sandy loam soil within the closed-environment plant growth facility of the National Horticultural Research Institute of Korea, where the plants were exposed to natural solar radiation and the natural daily course of ambient air temperature or elevated air temperature (= ambient + 5°C) with either normal soil nitrogen content or added nitrogen equivalent to an extra 40 kg N/ha, and they were maintained at either ambient CO_2 (360 ppm) or elevated CO_2 (650 ppm). At the end of the growing season, the plants were harvested and their total biomass determined. The concentrations of 12 isoflavones found in their seeds—three aglycons, three glucosides, three acetyl conjugates, and three malonyl conjugates—were quantitatively analyzed

Kim *et al.* found the CO_2-induced increase in total plant biomass at normal ambient temperatures was 96% in the case of normal soil nitrogen and 105% in the case of added nitrogen, and at the warmer temperatures it was 59% in the case of normal soil nitrogen and 68% in the case of added nitrogen. With respect to seed isoflavone concentrations, the CO_2-induced increases of all 12 isoflavones were fairly similar. As a group, at normal ambient temperatures the mean increase was 72% in the case of normal soil nitrogen and 59% in the case of added nitrogen, and at the warmer temperatures it was 72% in the case of normal soil nitrogen and 106% in the case of added nitrogen. Irrespective of soil nitrogen status and air temperature, therefore, increases in the air's CO_2 content produced large increases in soybean biomass, as well as soybean seed concentrations of 12 major isoflavones.

Schonhof et al. (2007) stated the glucosinolates contained in broccoli plants comprise a group of bioactive compounds responsible for many physiological effects, including enhancing the plant's flavor and helping to prevent cancer in people who consume them, citing Mikkelsen et al. (2002). In a set of three experiments conducted in a controlled greenhouse environment, Schonhof et al. grew well-watered and fertilized broccoli plants in large soil-filled containers at ambient (430–480 ppm) and elevated (685–820 ppm) atmospheric CO_2 concentrations to the stage where fully developed heads could be harvested for glucosinolate analyses. They report the roughly 65% increase in atmospheric CO_2 concentration increased the fresh weight of the broccoli heads by approximately 7% and increased the total glucosinolate concentration of the broccoli inflorescences by 14%, due primarily to identical 37% increases in two particular glucosinolates: glucoiberin and glucoraphanin. The four researchers conclude atmospheric CO_2 enrichment "can enhance the health-promoting quality of broccoli because of induced glucosinolate content changes."

Jin et al. (2009) grew well-watered and fertilized spinach from seed (five to each 3.5-liter pot filled with a loam soil) for approximately three weeks in controlled-environment chambers containing air of either 350 ppm or 800 ppm CO_2. They harvested the plants, weighed them, and measured the concentrations of several of the nutritive substances contained in their leaves. As best as can be determined from the graphs of their results, the extra 450 ppm of CO_2 increased the fresh weight of the spinach shoots by about 67% and their dry weight by approximately 57%. In addition, it boosted the soluble sugar concentrations of their leaves by approximately 29% and soluble protein concentrations by about 52%. The extra CO_2 also increased spinach leaf concentrations of ascorbate, glutathione, and total flavonoids by 21%, 16%, and 3%, respectively.

La et al. (2009) noted "epidemiological studies show there is a negative relationship between Brassicaceae vegetable intake and the risk of a number of cancers (Wattenberg, 1993; Kohlmeier and Su, 1997; Price et al., 1998)," adding, "it has been widely recognized that some of the cancer-chemoprotective activities in these vegetables are attributable to their contents of glucosinolates (Zhao et al., 1992; Wattenberg, 1993; Tawfiq et al., 1995; Fahey et al., 1997; Rosa et al., 1997; Holst and Williamson, 2004)." They set out to determine what effect the ongoing rise in the air's CO_2 content might have on the production of these important cancer-fighting agents in yet another common food plant.

The five scientists placed pairs of seedlings of Chinese kale in 1.8-L pots "fixed in a foam cavity with sponge" within growth chambers maintained at either 350 or 800 ppm CO_2, where the plant's roots were immersed in culture solutions treated with either 5.0 mmol nitrogen (N) per L (low N), 10 mmol N per L (medium N), or 20 mmol N per L (high N) and allowed to grow for 35 days. The plants then were separated into their primary morphological parts and weighed, and their bolting stems were ground into powder for glucosinolate analyses.

"Regardless of N concentration," the researchers write, the elevated CO_2 treatment "significantly increased plant height [15.64%], stem thickness [11.79%], dry weights of the total aerial parts [11.91%], bolting stems [15.03%], and roots [16.34%]." Also, the elevated CO_2 increased the total glucosinolate concentrations of the bolting stems in the low and medium N treatments by 15.59% and 18.01%, respectively, compared with those at ambient CO_2, although there was no such effect in the high N treatment. Consequently, in terms of the total amount of glucosinolate production within the bolting stems of Chinese kale, these results suggest increases of 33 to 36% may be obtained for plants growing in low to medium N conditions in response to a 450 ppm increase in the air's CO_2 concentration.

Gwynn-Jones et al. (2012) note "dwarf shrub berries are particularly valued by the human populations at Northern Latitudes as an autumn harvest, but are also consumed by a wide range of animals (Anderson, 1985)." They note the fruit of these shrubs contain high concentrations of flavonoids and anthocyanins (Heinonen et al., 1998; Faria et al., 2005; Heinonen, 2007), which can scavenge cancer-causing free-radicals (Martin-Aragon et al., 1998; Taruscio et al., 2004) and reduce the oxidative stress caused by these compounds in animals (Johnson and Felton, 2001). They state "there is already laboratory evidence suggesting that the consumption of Vaccinium myrtillus berry flavonoids by small mammals can increase the antioxidant capacity of their blood plasma which could promote their fitness," citing Talavera *et al.* (2006).

In an open-top chamber study conducted at the Abisko Scientific Research Station in Northern Sweden, Gwynn-Jones *et al.* assessed the impact of atmospheric CO_2 enrichment (600 vs. 360–386 ppm) on the berry quality of *Vaccinium myrtillus* and *Empetrum hermaphroditum* in the final year (2009) of a 17-year experiment. As best as can be determined from the 10 researchers' graphically presented results, it appears the mean concentration of quercetin glycosides in *V. myrtillus* was increased by approximately 46% by the approximate mean CO_2 concentration increase of 227 ppm. In *E. hermaphroditum*, syringetin glycoside concentrations were increased by about 36% by the extra CO_2, and five anthocyanins had their concentrations increased as follows: delphinidin-3-hexoside by about 51%, cyanidin-3-hexoside by about 49%, petunidin-3-hexoside by about 48%, malvidin-3-pentoside by about 46%, and malvidin-3-hexoside by about 59%. Gwynn-Jones *et al.* conclude, "consumers of *E. hermaphroditum* may gain higher antioxidant intake at elevated CO_2," and "some European bird species show preferential feeding towards berries with higher antioxidant contents (Catoni *et al.*, 2008), which could have important implications for the palatability and, therefore, seed dispersal of these species."

It is becoming increasingly evident the ongoing rise in the air's CO_2 content is not only raising the productivity of Earth's common food plants but also significantly increasing the quantity and potency of the many health-promoting substances found in their tissues, which are the ultimate sources of sustenance for essentially all animals and humans. As these foods make their way onto our dinner tables, they improve our health and help us better contend with the multitude of diseases and other maladies that regularly afflict us. It is possible, if not likely, that the lengthening of human lifespan that has occurred over the past half-century or more—as described by Horiuchi (2000) and Tuljapurkar *et al.* (2000)—may in some significant part be due to the concomitant CO_2-induced increases in the concentrations of the many health-promoting substances found in the various plant-derived foods we eat. Yet these real and many benefits continue to be ignored by IPCC.

References

Anderson, J.W., Johnstone, B.M., and Cook-Newell, M.E. 1995. Meta-analysis of the effects of soybean protein intake on serum lipids. *New England Journal of Medicine* **333**: 276–282.

Anthony, M.S., Clarkson, T.B., Hughes, C.L., Morgan, T.M., and Burke, G.L. 1996. Soybean isoflavones improve cardiovascular risk factors without affecting the reproductive system of peripubertal rhesus monkeys. *Journal of Nutrition* **126**: 43–50.

Arjmandi, B.H., Lee, A., Hollis, B.W., Amin, D., Stacewicz-Saounizakis, M., Guo, P., and Kukreja, S.C. 1996. Dietary soybean protein prevents bone loss in an ovariectomized rat model of osteoporosis. *Journal of Nutrition* **126**: 161–167.

Barbale, D. 1970. The influence of the carbon dioxide on the yield and quality of cucumber and tomato in the covered areas. *Augsne un Raza (Riga)* **16**: 66–73.

Bernacchi, C.J., Morgan, P.B., Ort, D.R., and Long, S.P. 2005. The growth of soybean under free air [CO_2] enrichment (FACE) stimulates photosynthesis while decreasing in vivo Rubisco capacity. *Planta* **220**: 434–446.

Birt, D.F., Hendrich, W., and Wang, W. 2001. Dietary agents in cancer prevention: flavonoids and isoflavonoids. *Pharmacology & Therapeutics* **90**: 157–177.

Caldwell, C.R., Britz, S.J., and Mirecki, R.M. 2005. Effect of temperature, elevated carbon dioxide, and drought during seed development on the isoflavone content of dwarf soybean [*Glycine max* (L.) Merrill] grown in controlled environments. *Journal of Agricultural and Food Chemistry* **53**: 1125–1129.

Chung, I.M., Kim, K.H., Ahn, J.K., Chi, H.Y., and Lee, J.O. 2000. Screening for antioxidative activity in soybean local cultivars in Korea. *Korean Journal of Crop Science* **45**: 328–334.

Dennison, B.A., Rockwell, H.L., and Baker, S.L. 1998. Fruit and vegetable intake in young children. *Journal of the American College of Nutrition* **17**: 371–378.

Dickinson, V.A., Block, G., and Russek-Cohen, E. 1994. Supplement use, other dietary and demographic variables, and serum vitamin C in NHANES II. *Journal of the American College of Nutrition* **13**: 22–32.

Fahey, J.W., Zhang, Y., and Talalay, P. 1997. Broccoli sprouts: an exceptionally rich source of inducers of enzymes that protect against chemical carcinogens. *Proceedings of the National Academy of Sciences, USA* **94**: 10,367–10,372.

Gomez-Carrasco, J.A., Cid, J.L.-H., de Frutos, C.B., Ripalda-Crespo, M.J., and de Frias, J.E.G. 1994. Scurvy in adolescence. *Journal of Pediatric Gastroenterology and Nutrition* **19**: 118–120.

Gwynn-Jones, D., Jones, A.G., Waterhouse, A., Winters, A., Comont, D., Scullion, J., Gardias, R., Graee, B.J., Lee, J.A., and Callaghan, T.V. 2012. Enhanced UV-B and elevated CO_2 impacts sub-Arctic shrub berry abundance, quality and seed germination. *Ambio* **41** (Supplement 3): 256–268.

Hampl, J.S., Taylor, C.A., and Johnston, C.S. 1999. Intakes of vitamin C, vegetables and fruits: which schoolchildren are at risk? *Journal of the American College of Nutrition* **18**: 582–590.

Heinonen, I.M., Meyer, A.S., and Frankel, E.N. 1998. Antioxidant activity of berry phenolics on human low-density lipoprotein and liposome oxidation. *Journal of Agricultural and Food Chemistry* **46**: 4107–4112.

Holst, B. and Williamson, G. 2004. A critical review of the bioavailability of glucosinolates and related compounds. *Natural Product Reports* **21**: 425–447.

Holt, S. 1997. Soya: the health food of the next millennium. *Korean Soybean Digest* **14**: 77–90.

Idso, S.B. and Idso, K.E. 2001. Effects of atmospheric CO_2 enrichment on plant constituents related to animal and human health. *Environmental and Experimental Botany* **45**: 179–199.

Idso, S.B., Kimball, B.A., Shaw, P.E., Widmer, W., Vanderslice, J.T., Higgs, D.J., Montanari, A., and Clark, W.D. 2002. The effect of elevated atmospheric CO_2 on the vitamin C concentration of (sour) orange juice. *Agriculture, Ecosystems and Environment* **90**: 1–7.

Jin, C.W., Du, S.T., Zhang, Y.S., Tang, C., and Lin, X.Y. 2009. Atmospheric nitric oxide stimulates plant growth and improves the quality of spinach (*Spinacia oleracea*). *Annals of Applied Biology* **155**: 113–120.

Johnston, C.S., Solomon, R.E., and Corte, C. 1998. Vitamin C status of a campus population: College students get a C minus. *Journal of American College Health* **46**: 209–213.

Kim, S.-H., Jung, W.-S., Ahn, J.-K., Kim, J.-A., and Chung, I.-M. 2005. Quantitative analysis of the isoflavone content and biological growth of soybean (*Glycine max* L.) at elevated temperature, CO_2 level and N application. *Journal of the Science of Food and Agriculture* **85**: 2557–2566.

Kimball, B.A. and Mitchell, S.T. 1981. Effects of CO_2 enrichment, ventilation, and nutrient concentration on the flavor and vitamin C content of tomato fruit. *HortScience* **16**: 665–666.

Kohlmeier L. and Su, L. 1997. Cruciferous vegetable consumption and colorectal cancer risk: meta-analysis of the epidemiological evidence. *FASEB Journal* **11**: 2141.

La, G.-X, Fang, P., Teng, Y.-B, Li, Y.-J, and Lin, X.-Y. 2009. Effect of CO_2 enrichment on the glucosinolate contents under different nitrogen levels in bolting stem of Chinese kale (*Brassica alboglabra* L.). *Journal of Zhejiang University Science B* **10**: 454–464.

Madsen, E. 1971. The influence of CO_2-concentration on the content of ascorbic acid in tomato leaves. *Ugeskr. Agron.* **116**: 592–594.

Madsen, E. 1975. Effect of CO_2 environment on growth, development, fruit production and fruit quality of tomato from a physiological viewpoint. In: Chouard, P. and de Bilderling, N. (Eds.) *Phytotronics in Agricultural and Horticultural Research*. Bordas, Paris, pp. 318–330.

Messina, M.J. 1999. Legumes and soybeans: overview of their nutritional profiles and health effects. *American Journal of Clinical Nutrition* **70**(S): 439s–450s.

Mikkelsen, M.D., Petersen, B., Olsen, C., and Halkier, B.A. 2002. Biosynthesis and metabolic engineering of glucosinolates. *Amino Acids* **22**: 279–295.

Peterson, G. and Barnes, S. 1991. Genistein inhibition of the growth of human breast cancer cell: independence from estrogen receptors and the multi-drug resistance gene. *Biochemistry and Biophysical Research Communications* **179**: 661–667.

Price, K.R., Casuscelli, F., Colquhoun, I.J., and Rhodes, M.J.C. 1998. Composition and content of flavonol glycosides in broccoli florets (*Brassica oleracea*) and their fate during cooking. *Journal of the Science of Food and Agriculture* **77**: 468–472.

Ramar, S., Sivaramakrishman, V., and Manoharan, K. 1993. Scurvy—a forgotten disease. *Archives of Physical Medicine and Rehabilitation* **74**: 92–95.

Rice-Evans, C.A. and Miller, N.J. 1996. Antioxidant activities of flavonoids as bioactive components of food. *Biochemical Society Transactions* **24**: 790–795.

Rosa, E., Heaney, R.K., Fenwick, G.R., and Portas, C.A.M. 1997. Glucosinolates in crop plants. *Horticultural Reviews* **19**: 99–215.

Schonhof, I., Klaring, H.-P., Krumbein, A., and Schreiner, M. 2007. Interaction between atmospheric CO_2 and glucosinolates in broccoli. *Journal of Chemical Ecology* **33**: 105–114.

Tajiri, T. 1985. Improvement of bean sprouts production by intermittent treatment with carbon dioxide. *Nippon Shokuhin Kogyo Gakkaishi* **32**(3): 159–169.

Tawfiq, N., Heaney, R.K., Pulumb, J.A., Fenwick, G.R., Musk, S.R., and Williamson, G. 1995. Dietary glucosinolates as blocking agents against carcinogenesis: glucosinolate breakdown products assessed by induction of quinine reductase activity in murine hepa1c1c7 cells. *Carcinogenesis* **16**: 1191–1194.

Wang, S.Y., Bunce, J.A., and Maas, J.L. 2003. Elevated carbon dioxide increases contents of antioxidant compounds in field-grown strawberries. *Journal of Agricultural and Food Chemistry* **51**: 4315–4320.

Wang, S.Y. and Jiao, H. 2000. Scavenging capacity of berry crops on superoxide radicals, hydrogen peroxide, hydroxyl radicals, and singlet oxygen. *Journal of Agricultural and Food Chemistry* **48**: 5677–5684.

Wang, S.Y. and Lin, H.S. 2000. Antioxidant activity in fruit and leaves of blackberry, raspberry, and strawberry is affected by cultivar and maturity. *Journal of Agricultural and Food Chemistry* **48**: 140–146.

Wattenberg, L.W. 1993. *Food and Cancer Prevention: Chemical and Biological Aspects.* Royal Society of Chemistry. London, UK.

Zhao, F., Evans, E.J., Bilsborrow, P.E., Schnug, E., and Syers, J.K. 1992. Correction for protein content in the determination of the glucosinolate content of rapeseed by the XRF method. *Journal of the Science of Food and Agriculture* **58**: 431–433.

7.8.3 Medicinal Plants

- Atmospheric CO_2 enrichment positively impacts the production of numerous health-promoting substances found in medicinal or "health food" plants, and this phenomenon may have contributed to the increase in human life span that has occurred over the past century or so.

Studies of the effects of atmospheric CO_2 enrichment on the amounts and concentrations of various health-promoting substances produced by medicinal or "health food" plants have lagged behind studies designed to assess the effects of elevated CO_2 on the quantity of plant production. Nevertheless, enough research has been conducted on this topic to reveal atmospheric CO_2 enrichment positively impacts these important substances.

Stuhlfauth *et al.* (1987), for example, found a near-tripling of the air's CO_2 content increased the dry weight production of the woolly foxglove plant (which produces the cardiac glycoside digoxin used in the treatment of cardiac insufficiency) by 63% under dry conditions and by 83% when well-watered, and the concentration of digoxin within the plant dry mass was enhanced by 11% under well-watered conditions and by 14% under conditions of water stress. Stuhlfauth and Fock (1990) obtained similar results in a field study, with a near-tripling of the air's CO_2 content leading to a 75% increase in plant dry weight production per unit land area and a 15% increase in digoxin per unit dry weight of plant material, resulting in an actual doubling of total digoxin yield per hectare of cultivated land.

Idso *et al.* (2000) grew spider lily plants out-of-doors at Phoenix, Arizona in clear-plastic-wall open-top enclosures that had their atmospheric CO_2 concentrations maintained at either 400 or 700 ppm for two consecutive two-year growth cycles. The 75% increase in the air's CO_2 concentration increased aboveground plant biomass by 48% and belowground (bulb) biomass by 56%. In addition, the extra CO_2 increased the concentrations of five bulb constituents possessing anticancer and antiviral properties. Mean percentage increases in these concentrations were, the researchers write, "6% for a two-constituent (1:1) mixture of 7-deoxynarciclasine and 7-deoxy-trans-dihydronarciclasine, 8% for pancratistatin, 8% for trans-dihydronarciclasine, and 28% for narciclasine, for a mean active-ingredient percentage concentration increase of 12%." Combined with the 56% increase in bulb biomass, these percentage concentration increases resulted in a mean active-ingredient increase of 75% for the 75% increase in the air's CO_2 concentration. The substances described above have been shown to be effective in fighting a number of devastating human maladies, including leukemia; ovary sarcoma; melanoma; and brain, colon, lung, and renal cancers, as well as Japanese encephalitis and yellow, dengue, Punta Tora, and Rift Valley fevers.

Zobayed and Saxena (2004) studied St. John's wort, a perennial herb native to Europe and West Asia that has been used for treatment of mild to moderate depression, inflammation, and wound healing (Brolis *et al.*, 1998; Stevinson and Ernst, 1999), and which has been reported to be a potential source for anticancer, antimicrobial, and antiviral medicines (Schempp *et al.*, 2002; Pasqua *et al.*, 2003). The two scientists grew shoots of the plant for 42 days under well-watered and fertilized conditions within a greenhouse, where the air's CO_2 concentration averaged 360 ppm, as well as in computer-controlled environment chambers maintained at a mean CO_2 concentration of 1,000 ppm, with all other environmental conditions being comparable between the two treatments.

On the final day of the study, Zobayed and Saxena determined the net photosynthetic rates of the plants in the CO_2-enriched chambers were 124% greater than those of the plants growing in ambient air, and their dry weights were 107% greater. The extra 640 ppm of CO_2 in the high-CO_2 treatment increased plant concentrations of hypericin and pseudohypericin (two of the major health-promoting substances in the plants) by just over 100%. Consequently, the 180% increase in the air's CO_2

content more than doubled the dry mass produced by the well-watered and fertilized St. John's wort plants, and it more than doubled the concentrations of hypericin and pseudohypericen found in their tissues. Thus the CO_2 increase more than quadrupled the total production of these two health-promoting substances.

Mosaleeyanon *et al.* (2005) also studied St. John's wort, growing well-watered and fertilized seedlings for 45 days in controlled-environment chambers at low, medium, and high light intensities (100, 300, and 600 μmol m^{-2} s^{-1}, respectively) at atmospheric CO_2 concentrations of 500, 1,000, and 1,500 ppm. On the 45th day of their experiment, the plants were harvested, and the hypericin, pseudohypericin, and hyperforin (another important health-promoting substance) they contained were extracted from their leaves and quantified.

Under all three light intensities employed in the study, the four researchers found the 1,000–ppm increase in atmospheric CO_2 concentration experienced in going from 500 to 1,500 ppm produced total plant biomass increases of approximately 32%. Over this same CO_2 range, hypericin concentrations rose by 78, 57, and 53%, respectively, under the low, medium, and high light intensities. Pseudohypericin concentrations rose by 70, 57, and 67%, and hyperforin concentrations rose by 102, 23, and 3%. Compared to plants growing out-of-doors in air of 380 ppm CO_2 and at light intensities on the order of 1,770 μmol m^{-2} s^{-1}, Mosaleeyanon *et al.* discovered total plant biomass was fully 30 times greater in the high-light, high-CO_2 controlled-environment treatment, and under the same conditions the concentrations of hypericin and pseudohypericin were 30 and 41 times greater. Thus the researchers demonstrated growing St. John's wort plants in CO_2-enriched air in controlled-environment chambers can enormously enhance both plant biomass and hypericin and pseudohypericin contents.

Ziska *et al.* (2005) grew well-watered and fertilized tobacco and jimson weed plants from seed in controlled-environment chambers maintained at atmospheric CO_2 concentrations of either 378 ppm (ambient) or 690 ppm (elevated) and mean air temperatures of either 22.1 or 27.1°C for 50 and 47 days after planting for tobacco and jimson weed, respectively. They sampled the plants at weekly intervals beginning at 28 days after planting for tobacco and 16 days for jimson weed, to determine the effects of these treatments on three plant alkaloids possessing important pharmacological properties: nicotine, in the case of tobacco, and atropine and scopolamine, in the case of jimson weed. At the time of final harvest they found the elevated CO_2 had increased the aboveground biomass production of tobacco by approximately 89% at 22.1°C and 53% at 27.1°C, and had increased that of jimson weed by approximately 23% and 14% at the same respective temperatures. The extra CO_2 also was found to have reduced the concentration of nicotine in tobacco and increased the concentration of scopolamine in jimson weed, but it had no significant effect on the concentration of atropine in jimson weed.

The two significant changes (reduced nicotine in tobacco and increased scopolamine in jimson weed) likely would be characterized as beneficial by most people; as the six scientists report, nicotine is acknowledged to have significant negative impacts on human health, and scopolamine is used as a sedative and as "an antispasmodic in certain disorders characterized by restlessness and agitation, (e.g., delirium tremens, psychosis, mania and Parkinsonism)." Nevertheless, Ziska *et al.* state "it can be argued that synthetic production of these secondary compounds alleviates any concern regarding environmental impacts on their production from botanical sources," but they note "developing countries (i.e., ~75% of the world population) continue to rely on ethno-botanical remedies as their primary medicine (e.g. use of alkaloids from jimson weed as treatment for asthma among native Americans and in India)." In addition, "for both developed and developing countries, there are a number of economically important pharmaceuticals derived solely from plants whose economic value is considerable (Raskin *et al.*, 2002)."

Another plant with an impressive history of medicinal use is ginseng. Well-known for its anti-inflammatory, diuretic, and sedative properties, and long acknowledged to be an effective healing agent (Gillis, 1997), ginseng is widely cultivated in China, South Korea, and Japan, where it has been used for medicinal purposes since Greek and Roman times. Normally, ginseng roots take four to six years to accumulate the amounts of the various phenolic compounds needed to produce their health-promoting effects.

Ali *et al.* (2005) investigated the consequences of growing ginseng plants in suspension culture in bioreactors maintained in equilibrium with air enriched to CO_2 concentrations of 10,000 ppm, 25,000 ppm, and 50,000 ppm for periods of up to 45 days. Of most immediate concern in such an experiment are the effects of the ultra-high CO_2 concentrations on root growth and whether they would be toxic and lead to biomass reductions or even root death. The answer, according to Ali *et al.*'s experiment was a resounding *no*. After 45 days of growth at 10,000 ppm CO_2, root dry weight was increased by about 37% relative to the dry weight of roots produced in bioreactors in equilibrium with ambient air, and it was increased by a lesser 27% after 45 days at 25,000 ppm CO_2 and by a still smaller 9% after 45 days at 50,000 ppm CO_2. Consequently, although the optimum CO_2 concentration for ginseng root growth likely resides somewhere below 10,000 ppm, the concentration at which root growth is reduced below that characteristic of ambient air resides somewhere above 50,000 ppm, for even at that extremely high CO_2 concentration, root growth was still greater than it was in ambient air.

Almost everything else measured by Ali *et al.* was even more dramatically enhanced by the ultra-high CO_2 concentrations. After 45 days of treatment, total root phenolic concentrations were 58% higher at 10,000 ppm CO_2 than at ambient CO_2, 153% higher at 25,000 ppm CO_2, and 105% higher at 50,000 ppm CO_2, as best as can be determined from the bar graphs of their results. Total root flavonoid concentrations were enhanced by 228%, 383%, and 232%, respectively; total protein contents rose by 14%, 22%, and 30%; non-protein thiol contents by 12%, 43%, and 62%; and cysteine contents by 27%, 65%, and 100%. There were equally large CO_2-induced increases in the activities of a large number of phenol biosynthetic enzymes.

Ali *et al.* state "the consumption of foodstuffs containing antioxidant phytonutrients such as flavonoids, polyphenolics, ascorbate, cysteine and non-protein thiol is advantageous for human health," citing Cervato *et al.* (2000) and Noctor and Foyer (1998). They conclude their technique for the culture of ginseng roots in CO_2-enriched bioreactors could be used for the large-scale production of an important health-promoting product that could be provided to the public in much greater quantities than is currently possible. It should be further noted that as the air's CO_2 content continues to climb, it likely will bring forth a substantial natural increase in the con-centrations of health-promoting substances in ginseng and other medicinal plants, leading to better human health the world over. It is likely this phenomenon already has played some role in the lengthening of human life span that has occurred since the dawn of the Industrial Revolution, as described by Horiuchi (2000) and Tuljapurkar *et al.* (2000), when the air's CO_2 concentration rose from roughly 280 ppm to its current value of close to 400 ppm.

Zou (2005) studied the brown seaweed *Hizikia fusiforme*, which serves as both a health-promoting food and a delicacy in China, Japan, and Korea. The researcher collected specimens from intertidal rocks along the coast of Nanao Island, Shantou (China) and maintained them in glass aquariums in filtered natural seawater enriched with 60 μM $NaNO_3$ and 6.0 μM NaH_2PO_4, where the plants were continuously aerated with either ambient air of 360 ppm CO_2 or CO_2-enriched air of 700 ppm CO_2. Zou measured the seaweed's relative growth and nitrogen assimilation rates as well as its nitrate reductase activity. Zou reports the slightly less than a doubling of the air's CO_2 concentration increased the seaweed's mean relative growth rate by about 50%, its mean rate of nitrate uptake during the study's 12-hour light periods by around 200%, and its nitrate reductase activity by approximately 20% over a wide range of substrate nitrate concentrations.

Zou notes "the extract of *H. fusiforme* has an immune-modulating activity on humans and this ability might be used for clinical application to treat several diseases such as tumors (Suetsuna, 1998; Shan *et al.*, 1999)." He also states the alga is "becoming one of the most important species for seaweed mariculture in China, owing to its high commercial value and increasing market demand." In addition, Zou reports "the intensive cultivation of *H. fusiforme* would remove nutrients more efficiently with the future elevation of CO_2 levels in seawater, which could be a possible solution to the problem of ongoing coastal eutrophication," which in turn suggests rising atmospheric CO_2 concentrations may additionally assist in the amelioration of this important environmental problem.

Hoshida *et al.* (2005) grew the marine alga unicellular *Nannochloropsis* sp.alga in batch culture under normal (370 ppm) and elevated (3,000 and 20,000 ppm) air CO_2 concentrations in an attempt to learn how elevated CO_2 impacted the alga's ability to produce eicosapentaenoic acid (EPA), a major polyunsaturated omega-3 fatty acid that may play an important role in human health related to the prevention of certain cardiovascular diseases (e.g. atherosclerosis, thrombogenesis) and the inhibition of tumor growth and inflammation, as described by Dyerberg *et al.* (1978), Hirai *et al.* (1989), Kinsella *et al.* (1990), and Sanders (1993).

The five researchers note "Nitsan *et al.* (1999) showed that supplementing the diet of hens with *Nannochloropsis* sp. led to an increased content of n-3 fatty acids in the egg yolk, indicating an additional role in enhancing the nutritional value of eggs," and they report "feeding *Nannochloropsis* sp. to rats caused a significant increase in the content of n-3 polyunsaturated fatty acids (Sukenik *et al.*, 1994)," suggesting the alga may play an "important role as the source for n-3 polyunsaturated fatty acids in human nutrition."

The Japanese scientists found "maximum EPA production was obtained when 20,000 ppm CO_2 was supplied 12 hours prior to the end of the exponential growth," and "total EPA production during 4-day cultivation was about twice that obtained with ambient air." They also report other researchers have obtained similar results, noting EPA is found mainly in thylakoid membranes (Sukenik *et al.*, 1989; Hodgson *et al.*, 1991), and prior experiments have shown "the amount of stroma thylakoid membrane increased in several plants under elevated CO_2 concentrations (Griffin *et al.*, 2001)." In addition, "in *Synechococcus lividus*, reduction and synthesis of thylakoid membrane occurred by CO_2 deprivation and elevation, respectively (Miller and Holt, 1977)," and "in *Chlorella vulgaris*, altering the ambient CO_2 concentration varied fatty acid composition (Tsuzuki *et al.*, 1990)." Finally, Hoshida *et al.* report, "the effect of CO_2 on fatty acid composition and/or fatty acid content had been reported in algae and higher plants (Tsuzuki *et al.*, 1990; Sergeenko *et al.*, 2000; He *et al.*, 1996; Radunz *et al.*, 2000)," and "increased EPA production caused by elevated CO_2 concentration was reported in *P. tricornutum* (Yongmanitchai and Ward, 1991)." Consequently, as the atmospheric CO_2 concentration continues to rise, concentrations of omega-3 fatty acids will be widely enhanced in both aquatic and terrestrial plants.

Ziska *et al.* (2008) note, "among medicinal plants, the therapeutic uses of opiate alkaloids from poppy (*Papaver* spp.) have long been recognized," and they considered it important "to evaluate the growth and production of opiates for a broad range of recent and projected atmospheric carbon dioxide concentrations," which they did for the wild poppy (*P. setigerum*). The authors grew well-watered and fertilized plants from seed within growth chambers maintained at atmospheric CO_2 concentrations of 300, 400, 500, and 600 ppm for a period of 90 to 100 days, quantifying plant growth and the production of the alkaloids morphine, codeine, papaverine, and noscapine, which were derived from latex obtained from capsules produced by the plants.

Relative to the plants grown at 300 ppm CO_2, those grown at 400, 500, and 600 ppm produced approximately 200, 275, and 390% more aboveground biomass, respectively, as best as can be determined from the researchers' bar graphs. In addition, "reproductively, increasing CO_2 from 300 to 600 ppm increased the number of capsules, capsule weight and latex production by 3.6, 3.0 and 3.7 times, respectively, on a per plant basis," so, ultimately, "all alkaloids increased significantly on a per plant basis." They conclude, "as atmospheric CO_2 continues to increase, significant effects on the production of secondary plant compounds of pharmacological interest (i.e. opiates) could be expected." These effects, they write, "are commonly accepted as having both negative (e.g. heroin) and positive (e.g. codeine) interactions with respect to public health."

Vurro *et al.* (2009) note thyme (a well-known culinary and medicinal herb) has "a considerable economic value in the nutraceutical and pharmaceutical industry (Vardar-Uenlue *et al.*, 2003; Konyalioglu *et al.*, 2006)," and "thyme essential oil possesses *per se* considerable antioxidant capacity (Economou *et al.*, 1991), and may therefore contribute towards the control of antioxidant status in the leaves." They grew well-watered one-year-old thyme plants for three additional months (10 June–10 September) in pots (filled with 40% sand, 25% clay, and 35% silt) out-of-doors within a mini-free-air CO_2-enrichment (FACE) system at Ravenna, Italy. The air's CO_2 concentration was maintained at approximately 500 ppm (during daylight hours only), and control plants were continuously exposed to air of approximately 370 ppm CO_2. They measured a number of plant characteristics at the end of each of the three months of the study.

The four researchers state "none of the plants grown under high levels of CO_2 for 90 days presented either significant differences in fresh weight and dry weight compared with controls, or macroscopic alteration of morphogenesis (number and length of nodes/internodes, branching, leaf area and chlorosis, etc.), at any of the sampling times." However, "in plants grown under elevated CO_2, a relative increase in oil yield of 32, 34 and 32% was, respectively, recorded in the first, second and third sampling-time (July, August and September)," and they observed a "general depression of the oxidative stress under elevated CO_2" that led to a "down-regulation of leaf reactive oxygen species-scavenging enzymes under elevated CO_2." In layman's terms, the Italian scientists say their results pointed to "a 'low cost' life strategy for growth under elevated CO_2, not requiring synthesis/activation of energy-intensive and expensive metabolic processes." This change in behavior should allow the plants to invest more energy in the production of essential plant oils that have, as Vurro *et al.* describe it, "considerable economic value in the nutraceutical and pharmaceutical industry."

Goncalves *et al.* (2009) write, "the impact of elevated carbon dioxide concentration on the quality of berries, must, and red wine (with special reference to volatile composition, phenolic content, and antioxidant activity) made from Touriga Franca, a native grape variety of *Vitis vinifera* L. for Port and Douro wine manufacturing grown in the Demarcated Region of Douro [northern Portugal], was investigated during 2005 and 2006." The six Portuguese researchers grew grapevines in open-top chambers maintained at either 365 or 550 ppm CO_2, finding, "in general, the increase of CO_2 did not affect berry characteristics" and "did not significantly change the total antioxidant capacity of the red wines." They write, "thirty-five volatile compounds belonging to seven chemical groups were identified," and, "generally, the same volatile compounds were present in all of the wines." Although some of these compounds were "slightly affected," they note "the red wine quality remained almost unaffected." Thus, Goncalves *et al.* say their study shows "the predicted rise in CO_2 might strongly stimulate grapevine photosynthesis and yield without causing negative impacts on the quality of grapes and red wine."

Bindi *et al.* (2001) conducted a two-year (1996, 1997) FACE study of 20-year-old grapevines (*Vitis vinifera* L., cv Sangiovese) near Rapolano, Siena (Italy). They enriched the air around the plants to 550 and 700 ppm (compared to ambient CO_2 levels in those two years that averaged 363 ppm, per Mauna Loa data), measuring numerous plant parameters in the process, including—after the fermentation process was completed—"the principal chemical compounds that determine the basic red wine quality." They report "elevated atmospheric CO_2 levels had a significant effect on biomass components (total and fruit dry weight) with increases that ranged from 40 to 45% in the 550 ppm treatment and from 45 to 50% in the 700 ppm treatment." In addition, "acid and sugar contents were also stimulated by rising CO_2 levels up to a maximum increase in the middle of the ripening season (8–14%)," but as the grapes reached the maturity stage, the CO_2 effect on these parameters gradually disappeared. In terms of various health-promoting substances contained in the wine itself, in response to the ~50% increase in atmospheric CO_2 concentration in going from ~363 to ~550 ppm CO_2, as can be calculated from the bar graphs of their results, the concentrations of total polyphenols, total flavonoids, total anthocyanins, and non-anthocyanin flavonoids in the wine rose by approximately 19%, 33%, 31%, and 38%, respectively. Bindi *et al.*

conclude, "the expected rise in CO_2 concentrations may strongly stimulate grapevine production without causing negative repercussions on quality of grapes and wine," and in fact their data suggest the ongoing rise in the air's CO_2 content might slightly enhance the health-protective properties of the wine.

Oliveira *et al.* (2010) write, "there is a growing interest in the use of inulin as a health food ingredient, as an alternative for low-calorie sweeteners, and as a dietary fiber and fat substitute (Ritsema and Smeekens, 2003)." In addition, they say "it is suggested" a daily intake of low amounts of inulin or its derivatives promotes the growth of beneficial bacteria in the intestinal tract, as well as anti-tumor effects, citing Roberfroid (2005). Hence, they studied *Vernonia herbacea*, a plant from the Brazilian Cerrado that accumulates inulin-type fructans in underground organs called rhizophores. The five Brazilian researchers grew well-watered and fertilized *V. herbacea* plants from rhizophore fragments for two months and then transferred them in groups of three to 3-L pots containing forest soil. The plants were maintained in open-top chambers in a glasshouse for 120 days at atmospheric CO_2 concentrations of either 380 or 760 ppm, and the scientists measured the plants' net photosynthetic rates, water use efficiencies, and fructan concentrations after 15, 30, 60, 90, and 120 days of treatment, as well as above- and below-ground biomass at the end of the experiment.

Oliveira *et al.* write, the "plants under elevated CO_2 presented increases in height (40%), photosynthesis (63%) and biomass of aerial (32%) and underground (47%) organs when compared with control plants." In addition, "water use efficiency was significantly higher in treated plants, presenting a 177% increase at day 60." They found fructan concentration remained unchanged, but because of the significant CO_2-induced increase in underground organ biomass, "a 24% increase in total fructan yield occurred."

Ghasemzadeh *et al.* (2010) write, "free radicals and single oxygen are recognized as major factors causing various chronic diseases such as cancer, diabetes, *etc.*," and as a result, they note, "the health maintenance function of antioxidant components in various foods has received much attention," citing Byers and Guerrero (1995) and Namiki (1990). They further observe, "phenolic acids and flavonoids are antioxidants with health benefits such as anti-inflammatory and anti-tumor effects (Heijnen *et al.*, 2001; Chun *et al.*, 2003; Harborne and Williams, 2000; Chen, 2004)," specifically noting "Sung-jin *et* al. (2008) showed that some flavonoid components in green tea are effective in inhibiting cancer or induce mechanisms that may kill cancer cells and inhibit tumor invasion."

The Malaysian researchers grew two varieties of Malaysian young ginger (*Zingiber officinale*)—Halia Bentong and Halia Bara—from rhizomes planted in a drip-irrigated 1:1 mixture of burnt rice husk and coco peat in polyethylene bags placed within controlled-environment chambers maintained at atmospheric CO_2 concentrations of either 400 or 800 ppm for a period of 16 weeks. They then harvested the plants and analyzed their leaves and rhizomes for a wide variety of phenolics and flavonoids, along with their free radical scavenging power, which is a measure of their ability to prevent dangerous reactive oxygen species from attacking various parts of the body and causing a large number of potentially life-threatening maladies. Malaysian young ginger is one of the medicinal/food plants used by Polynesians for more than 2,000 years in treating cancer, diabetes, high blood pressure, and many other illnesses

Ghasemzadeh *et al.* found, on average, "flavonoid compounds increased 44.9% in leaves and 86.3% in rhizomes of Halia Bentong and 50.1% in leaves and 79% in rhizomes of Halia Bara when exposed to elevated carbon dioxide conditions." Phenolic compounds increased even more: by 79.4% in leaves and 107.6% in rhizomes of Halia Bentong and 112.2% in leaves and 109.2% in rhizomes of Halia Bara. In addition, the increase in the CO_2 concentration from 400 to 800 ppm increased the free radical scavenging power by 30.0% in Halia Bentong and 21.4% in Halia Bara. Also, "the rhizomes exhibited more enhanced free radical scavenging power, with 44.9% in Halia Bentong and 46.2% in Halia Bara."

The three scientists say their results indicate "the yield and pharmaceutical quality of Malaysian young ginger varieties can be enhanced by controlled environment production and CO_2 enrichment."

Ghasemzadeh and Jaafar (2011) also focused on ginger (*Zingiber officinale* Roscoe), noting it is "an important horticultural crop in tropical Southeast Asia" and is the Asian continent's "most widely used herb." It "contains several interesting bioactive constituents and possesses health promoting properties (Rozanida *et al.*, 2005)." Ghasemzadeh and Jaafar lament "no information is available on the effect of CO_2 concentration on the polyphenolic content and scavenging capacity against active oxygen species of Malaysian young ginger varieties."

The two Malaysian scientists grew two varieties

of ginger (Halia Bentong and Halia Bara) from rhizomes placed in polyethylene bags filled with a 1:1 mixture of burnt rice husk and coco peat for a period of 16 weeks in controlled-environment chambers maintained at two atmospheric CO_2 concentrations (400 and 800 ppm). They measured a number of important plant properties during and after the growing period.

In response to the increase in the air's CO_2 content, Ghasemzadeh and Jaafar state, their research showed the rate of photosynthesis was increased by 65% in Halia Bentong and by 46% in Halia Bara, which led to total biomass increases of 48% in Halia Bentong and 76% in Halia Bara. Total flavonoids in the new rhizomes of Halia Bentong and Halia Bara rose by 82% and 118%, respectively, and total phenolics in the same two varieties rose by 154% and 183%, respectively.

The two researchers say their study revealed "ginger has good free radical scavenging ability and therefore can be used as a radical inhibitor or scavenger, acting possibly as a primary antioxidant." Also, increasing the CO_2 content of the atmosphere "can enhance the antioxidant activity of ginger extract, especially in its rhizomes," which can be of great value because it thereby "increases the concentrations of several therapeutic compounds."

Ibrahim and Jaafar (2011) report "the antioxidant properties in food have been a focus of interest in recent years due to the health maintenance functions of these components that can help reduce the risk of chronic diseases such as cancer, hypertension and diabetes." This phenomenon, they note, "is attributed to the high scavenging activity of antioxidants towards free radicals that are usually associated with these diseases (Namiki, 1990; Byers and Guerrero, 1995)." They used a randomized complete block design 3 by 3 experiment to study and distinguish the relationships among production of secondary metabolites, total phenolics, total flavonoids, gluthatione, oxidized gluthatione, soluble carbohydrate, and antioxidant activities of the Malaysian medicinal herb *Labisia pumila* Blume under three levels of CO_2 enrichment (400, 800, and 1,200 ppm) for 15 weeks.

The two Universiti Putra Malaysia researchers write, "secondary metabolites, glutathione, oxidized gluthathione and antioxidant activities in a descending manner came from the leaf enriched with 1200 ppm CO_2 > leaf 800 ppm CO_2 > leaf 400 ppm CO_2 > stem 1200 ppm CO_2 > stem 800 ppm CO_2 > stem 400 ppm CO_2 > root 1200 ppm CO_2 > root 800 ppm CO_2 > root 400 ppm CO_2," and "correlation analyses revealed strong significant positive coefficients of antioxidant activities with total phenolics, flavonoids, gluthatione and oxidized gluthatione," indicating "an increase in antioxidative activity of *L. pumila* under elevated CO_2 might be up-regulated by the increase in production of total phenolics, total flavonoids, glutathione, oxidized gluthatione and soluble sugar." Ibrahim and Jaafar conclude their study results imply "the medicinal potential of herbal plants such as *L. pumila* can be enhanced under elevated CO_2, which simultaneously improved the antioxidative activity that was indicated by the high oxygen radical absorbance activity against peroxyl radicals, superoxide radicals, hydrogen peroxide and hydroxyl radicals."

Also studying *Labisia pumila* Blume, Jaafar *et al.* (2012) wrote, "plant antioxidants have been a focus of attention in recent years due to the health preservation functions of these components that can help reduce the threat of chronic diseases such as cancer, diabetes and hypertension." These benefits, they note, are "attributed to the high scavenging activity of antioxidants towards free radicals that are usually associated with these diseases (Byers and Guerrero, 1995)." Among this group of plant compounds are phenolic acids and flavonoids, both of which exhibit, they state, "high anti-inflammatory and anti-carcinogenic activities (Heijnen *et al.*, 2001; Chun *et al.*, 2003)." In addition, phenolics and flavonoids can function as reducing agents, free radical scavengers, and quenchers of singlet oxygen formation (Chan *et al.*, 2008). Many of the components of polyphenols have been proven to have significant roles in curing cancer and other human ailments (Harborne and Williams, 2000).

Jaafar *et al.* conducted a split plot 3 x 3 experiment designed to examine the impact of 15 weeks of exposure to three concentrations of CO_2 (400, 800, and 1,200 ppm) on the phenolic and flavonoid compound profiles—as well as the antioxidant activities—of three varieties (*alata, pumila,* and *lanceolata*) of *Labisia pumila* Benth. or kacip fatimah, as it is commonly known throughout Southeast Asia. They describe the latter as "a sub-herbaceous plant with creeping stems from the family Myrsinaceae that is found widespread in Indochina and throughout the Malaysian forest"; it has historically been used to help maintain a healthy female reproductive system.

The three Malaysian researchers report that when exposed to elevated CO_2 (1200 ppm), "gallic acid increased tremendously, especially in var. *alata* and *pumila* (101–111%), whilst a large quercetin increase was noted in var. *lanceolata* (260%), followed closely by *alata* (201%)." They also found "caffeic acid was enhanced tremendously in var. *alata* (338–1100%) and *pumila* (298–433%)," and "rutin continued to increase by 262% after CO_2 enrichment." In addition, they note naringenin was enhanced by 1,100% in var. *pumila*. Finally, they report "the increase in production of plant secondary metabolites in *L. pumila* was followed by enhancement of the antioxidant activity under exposure of elevated CO_2."

Moghaddam *et al.* (2011) explain *Centella asiatica* or Gotu Kola is a small herbaceous annual plant that has been used as a medicinal herb or nutraceutical in Ayurvedic, African, and traditional Chinese medicine for more than 2,000 years, valued for its mildly antibacterial, antiviral, and anti-inflammatory properties. It also has been used as a rejuvenating diuretic herb that is purported to clear toxins, reduce inflammations and fevers, improve healing and immunity, improve memory, and provide a balancing effect on the nervous system.

The six scientists grew well-watered and fertilized *C. asiatica* plants for four to five weeks in individual polybags filled with a 1:1:1 mix of sand, coco dust, and compost within controlled environment chambers, where CO_2 concentrations of 400 and 800 ppm were maintained, the researchers write, "for two hours every day between 8:30 to 10:30 am." At the end of these four- to five-week periods the plants were harvested and their leaves assessed for total biomass and total flavonoid content. The latter substance is considered to be the source of the many health benefits attributed to the species.

Moghaddam *et al.* report the daily two-hour 400 ppm increase in the controlled environment chambers' atmospheric CO_2 concentration led to a 193% increase in *C. asiatica* leaf biomass, a 264% increase in plant water use efficiency, and a 171% increase in leaf total flavonoid content. The six scientists conclude, "collectively, the enhancement in yield and quality provides an economic motivation to produce a consistent pharmaceutical-grade product for commercial purposes," via what they describe as "controlled environment plant production." It also stands to reason the ongoing rise in the atmosphere's CO_2 concentration should be gradually increasing the medicinal potency of *C. asiatica* plants either growing wild or cultivated out-of-doors.

Ibrahim and Jaafar (2012) studied the oil palm *Elaeis guineensis* (Jacq.)—the highest-yielding vegetable oil producer in the world—which has gained wide recognition because of the health-promoting properties of some of its flavonoids and phenolics, which the two scientists describe as "natural antioxidants that may reduce oxidative damage to the human body," citing Mandel and Youdim (2004). For 15 weeks, the pair of researchers grew initially-five-month-old seedlings of three progenies of oil palm (deli AVROS, Deli Yangambi, and Deli URT) within growth chambers maintained at atmospheric CO_2 concentrations of either 400, 800, or 1,200 ppm, measuring a large number of important plant properties and processes.

Ibrahim and Jaafar discovered the production of total flavonoids and phenolics was highest under 1,200 and lowest at 400 ppm CO_2, and "the antioxidant activity, as determined by the ferric reducing/antioxidant potential (FRAP) activity increased with increasing CO_2 levels." In leaves, for example, they found the quantity of "total flavonoids was enhanced by 86% and 132%, respectively, in 800 and 1200 ppm compared to 400 ppm CO_2," and total phenolics "increased by 52% to 91% under elevated CO_2 compared to the ambient CO_2 condition." Ibrahim and Jaafar say their findings "suggest that enrichment with higher than ambient CO_2 level is able to enhance the production of gallic acid and rutin in oil palm seedlings." This finding is important because these bioactive components, as they describe them, "act as free radical scavengers, and hence can reduce the possibilities of major diseases such as cancers of leukemia, breast, bone and lung," citing Kaufman *et al.* (1999) and Wink (1999).

In light of the research discussed above, it is clear atmospheric CO_2 enrichment positively impacts the production of numerous health-promoting substances found in medicinal or "health food" plants, and this phenomenon may have contributed to the increase in human life span that has occurred over the past century or so (Horiuchi, 2000; Tuljapurkar and Boe, 2000). As the atmosphere's CO_2 content continues to rise, humanity may be helped even more in this regard in the years and decades to come.

References

Ali, M.B., Hahn, E.J., and Paek, K.-Y. 2005. CO_2-induced total phenolics in suspension cultures of *Panax ginseng* C.A. Mayer roots: role of antioxidants and enzymes. *Plant Physiology and Biochemistry* **43**: 449–457.

Bindi, M., Fibbi, L., and Miglietta, F. 2001. Free Air CO_2 Enrichment (FACE) of grapevine (*Vitis vinifera* L.): Growth and quality of grape and wine in response to elevated CO_2 concentrations. *European Journal of Agronomy* **14**: 145–155.

Brolis, M., Gabetta, B., Fuzzati, N., Pace, R., Panzeri, F., and Peterlongo, F. 1998. Identification by high-performance liquid chromatography-diode array detection-mass spectrometry and quantification by high-performance liquid chromatography-UV absorbance detection of active constituents of *Hypericum perforatum*. *Journal of Chromatography A* **825**: 9–16.

Byers, T. and Guerrero, N. 1995. Epidemiologic evidence for vitamin C and vitamin E in cancer prevention. *American Journal of Clinical Nutrition* **62**: 1385–1392.

Cervato, G., Carabelli, M., Gervasio, S., Cittera, A., Cazzola, R., and Cestaro, B. 2000. Antioxidant properties of oregano (*Origanum vulgare*) leaf extracts. *Journal of Food Biochemistry* **24**: 453–465.

Chan, E.W.C., Lim, Y.Y., Wong, L.F., Lianto, F.S., Wong, S.K., Lim, K.K., Joe, C.E., and Lim, T.Y. 2008. Antioxidant and tyrosinase inhibition properties of leaves and rhizomes of ginger species. *Food Chemistry* **109**: 477–483.

Chen, G. 2004. Effect of low fat and/or high fruit and vegetable diets on plasma level of 8-isoprostane-F2alpha in nutrition and breast health study. *Nutrition and Cancer* **50**: 155–160.

Chun, O.K., Kim, D.O., and Lee, C.Y. 2003. Superoxide radical scavenging activity of the major polyphenols in fresh plums. *Journal of Agriculture and Food Chemistry* **51**: 8067–8072.

Dyerberg, J., Bang, H.O., Stoffersen, E., Moncada, S., and Vane, J.R. 1978. Eicosapentaenoic acid and prevention of thrombosis and atherosclerosis. *Lancet* **2**: 117–119.

Economou, K.D., Oreopoulou, V., and Thomopoulos, C.D. 1991. Antioxidant activity of some plant extracts of the family Labiatae. *Journal of the American Oil Chemists' Society* **68**: 109–113.

Gillis, C.N. 1997. *Panax ginseng* pharmacology: a nitric oxide link? *Biochemical Pharmacology* **54**: 1–8.

Ghasemzadeh, A. and Jaafar, H.Z.E. 2011. Effect of CO_2 enrichment on synthesis of some primary and secondary metabolites in ginger (*Zingiber officinale* Roscoe). *International Journal of Molecular Sciences* **12**: 1101–1114.

Ghasemzadeh, A., Jaafar, H.Z.E., and Rahmat, A. 2010. Elevated carbon dioxide increases contents of flavonoids and phenolic compounds, and antioxidant activities in Malaysian young ginger (*Zingiber officinale* Roscoe.) varieties. *Molecules* **15**: 7907–7922.

Goncalves, B., Falco, V., Moutinho-Pereira, J., Bacelar, E., Peixoto, F., and Correia, C. 2009. Effects of elevated CO_2 on grapevine (*Vitis vinifera* L.): Volatile composition, phenolic content, and *in vitro* antioxidant activity of red wine. *Journal of Agricultural and Food Chemistry* **57**: 265–273.

Griffin, K.L., Anderson, O.R., Gastrich, M.D., Lewis, J.D., Lin, G., Schuster, W., Seemann, J.R., Tissue, D.T., Turnbull, M.H., and Whitehead, D. 2001. Plant growth in elevated CO_2 alters mitochondrial number and chloroplast fine structure. *Proceedings of the National Academy of Sciences, USA* **98**: 2473–2478.

Harborne, J.B. and Williams, C.A. 2000. Advances in flavonoid research science. *Phytochemistry* **55**: 481–504.

He, P., Radunz, A., Bader, K.P., and Schmid, G.H. 1996. Quantitative changes of the lipid and fatty acid composition of leaves of *Aleurites montana* as a consequence of growth under 700 ppm CO_2 in the atmosphere. *Zeitschrift fur Naturforscher* **51 C**: 833–840.

Heijnen, C.G., Haenen, G.R., Vanacker, F.A., Vijgh, W.J., and Bast, A. 2001. Flavonoids as peroxynitrite scavengers: the role of the hydroxyl groups. *Toxicology in Vitro* **15**: 3–6.

Hirai, A., Terano, T., Tamura, Y., and Yoshida, S. 1989. Eicosapentaenoic acid and adult diseases in Japan: Epidemiological and clinical aspects. *Journal of Internal Medicine, Supplement* **225**: 69–75.

Hodgson, P.A., Henderson, R.J., Sargent, J.R., and Leftley, J.W. 1991. Patterns of variation in the lipid class and fatty acid composition of *Nannochloropsis oculata* (Eustigmatophyceae) during batch culture. I. The growth cycle. *Journal of Applied Phycology* **3**: 169–181.

Horiuchi, S. 2000. Greater lifetime expectations. *Nature* **405**: 744–745.

Hoshida, H., Ohira, T., Minematsu, A., Akada, R., and Nishizawa, Y. 2005. Accumulation of eicosapentaenoic acid in *Nannochloropsis* sp. in response to elevated CO_2 concentrations. *Journal of Applied Phycology* **17**: 29–34.

Ibrahim, M.H. and Jaafar, H.Z.E. 2011. Increased carbon dioxide concentration improves the antioxidative properties of the Malaysian herb Kacip Fatimah (*Labisia pumila* Blume). *Molecules* **16**: 6068–6081.

Ibrahim, M.H. and Jaafar, H.Z.E. 2012. Impact of elevated carbon dioxide on primary, secondary metabolites and antioxidant responses of *Eleais guineensis* Jacq. (oil palm) seedlings. *Molecules* **17**: 5195–5211.

Idso, S.B., Kimball, B.A., Pettit III, G.R., Garner, L.C., Pettit, G.R., and Backhaus, R.A. 2000. Effects of atmospheric CO_2 enrichment on the growth and development of *Hymenocallis littoralis* (Amaryllidaceae) and the concentrations of several antineoplastic and antiviral constituents of its bulbs. *American Journal of Botany* **87**: 769–773.

Jaafar, H.Z.E., Ibrahim, M.H., and Karimi, E. 2012. Phenolics and flavonoids compounds, phenylanine ammonia lyase and antioxidant activity responses to

elevated CO_2 in *Labisia pumila* (Myrisinaceae). *Molecules* **17**: 6331–6347.

Kaufman, P.B., Cseke, L.J., Warber, S., Duke, J.A., and Brielmann, H.L. 1999. *Natural Products from Plants*. CRC Press, Boca Raton, Florida, USA.

Kinsella, J.E., Lokesh, B., and Stone, R.A. 1990. Dietary n-3 polyunsaturated fatty acids and amelioration of cardiovascular diseases: Possible mechanisms. *American Journal of Clinical Nutrition* **52**: 10–28.

Konyalioglu, S., Ozturk, B., and Meral, G.E. 2006. Comparison of chemical compositions and antioxidant activities of the essential oils of two *Ziziphora* taxa from Anatolia. *Pharmaceutical Biology* **44**: 121–126.

Mandel, S. and Youdim, M.B. 2004. Catechin polyphenols: Neurodegeneration and neuroprotection in neurodegenerative diseases. *Free Radical Biology and Medicine* **37**: 304–317.

Miller L.S. and Holt, S.C. 1977. Effect of carbon dioxide on pigment and membrane content in *Synechococcus lividus*. *Archives Microbiologie* **115**: 185–198.

Moghaddam, S.S., Jaafar, H.B., Aziz, M.A., Ibrahim, R., Rahmat, A.B., and Philip, E. 2011. Flavonoid and leaf gas exchange responses of *Centella asiatica* to acute gamma irradiation and carbon dioxide enrichment under controlled environment conditions. *Molecules* **16**: 8930–8944.

Mosaleeyanon, K., Zobayed, S.M.A., Afreen, F., and Kozai, T. 2005. Relationships between net photosynthetic rate and secondary metabolite contents in St. John's wort. *Plant Science* **169**: 523–531.

Namiki, M. 1990. Antioxidant/antimutagens in food. *Critical Reviews in Food Science and Nutrition* **29**: 273–300.

Nitsan, Z., Mokady, S., and Sukenik, A. 1999. Enrichment of poultry products with omega 3 fatty acids by dietary supplementation with the alga *Nannochloropsis* and mantur oil. *Journal of Agricultural and Food Chemistry* **47**: 5127–5132.

Noctor, G. and Foyer, C.H. 1998. Ascorbate and glutathione: keeping active oxygen under control. *Annual Review of Plant Physiology and Plant Molecular Biology* **49**: 249–279.

Oliveira, V.F., Zaidan, L.B.P., Braga, M.R., Aidar, M.P.M., and Carvalho, M.A.M. 2010. Elevated CO_2 atmosphere promotes plant growth and inulin production in the cerrado species *Vernonia herbacea*. *Functional Plant Biology* **37**: 223–231.

Pasqua, G., Avato, P., Monacelli, B., Santamaria, A.R., and Argentieri, M.P. 2003. Metabolites in cell suspension cultures, calli, and *in vitro* regenerated organs of *Hypericum perforatum* cv. Topas. *Plant Science* **165**: 977–982.

Radunz, A., Alfermann, K., and Schmid, G.H. 2000. State of the lipid and fatty acid composition in chloroplasts of *Nicotiana tabacum* under the influence of an increased CO_2 partial pressure of 700 p.p.m. *Biochemical Society Transactions* **28**: 885–887.

Raskin, I., Ribnicky, D.M., and Komarnytsky, S., *et al.* 2002. Plants and human health in the twenty-first century. *Trends in Biotechnology* **20**: 522–531.

Ritsema, T. and Smeekens, S. 2003. Fructans: beneficial for plants and humans. *Current Opinion in Plant Biology* **6**: 223–230.

Roberfroid, M.B. 2005. Introducing inulin-type fructans. *British Journal of Nutrition* **93**: S13–S25.

Rozanida, A.R., Nurul Izza, N., Mohd Helme, M.H., and Zanariah, H. 2005. *Xanwhite TM—A Cosmeceutical Product from Species in the Family Zingiberaceae.* Forest Research Institute, Selangor Malaysia, pp. 31–36.

Sanders, T.A.B. 1993. Marine oils: Metabolic effects and role in human nutrition. *Proceedings of the Nutrition Society* **52**: 457–472.

Schempp, C.M., Krikin, V., Simon-Haarhaus, G., Kersten, A., Kiss, J., Termeer, C.C., Gilb, B., Kaufmann, T., Borner, C., Sleeman, J.P., and Simon, J.C. 2002. Inhibition of tumour cell growth by hyperforin, a novel anticancer drug from St. John's wort that acts by induction of apoptosis. *Oncogene* **21**: 1242–1250.

Sergeenko, T.V., Muradyan, E.A., Pronina, N.A., Klyachko-Gurvich, G.L., Mishina, I.M., and Tsoglin, L.N. 2000. The effect of extremely high CO_2 concentration on the growth and biochemical composition of microalgae. *Russian Journal of Plant Physiology* **47**: 632–638.

Shan, B.E., Yoshida, Y., Kuroda, E., and Yamashita, U. 1999. Immunomodulating activity of seaweed extract on human lymphocytes *in vitro. International Journal of Immunopharmacology* **21**: 59–70.

Stevinson, C. and Ernst, E. 1999. *Hypericum* for depression: an update of the clinical evidence. *European Neuropsychopharmacology* **9**: 501–505.

Stuhlfauth, T. and Fock, H.P. 1990. Effect of whole season CO_2 enrichment on the cultivation of a medicinal plant, *Digitalis lanata. Journal of Agronomy and Crop Science* **164**: 168–173.

Stuhlfauth, T., Klug, K., and Fock, H.P. 1987. The production of secondary metabolites by *Digitalis lanata* during CO_2 enrichment and water stress. *Phytochemistry* **26**: 2735–2739.

Suetsuna, K. 1998. Separation and identification of angiotensin I-converting enzyme inhibitory peptides from peptic digest of *Hizikia fusiformis* protein. *Nippon Suisan Gakkaishi* **64**: 862–866.

Sukenik, A., Cameli, Y., and Berner, T. 1989. Regulation of fatty acid composition by irradiance level in the eustigmatophyte *Nannochloropsis* sp. *Journal of Phycology* **25**: 686–692.

Sukenik, A., Takahashi, H., and Mokady, S. 1994. Dietary lipids from marine unicellular algae enhance the amount of liver and blood omega-3 fatty acids in rats. *Annals of Nutrition and Metabolism* **38**: 85–96.

Sung-Jin, P., Hoon, M., Young-Youn, K., Jun-Young, P., Jun-Woo, P., Myung-Jin, K., and Soon-Min, H. 2008. Anticancer effects of genistein, green tea catechins, and cordycepin on oral squamous cell carcinoma. *Journal of Korean Oral and Maxillofacial Surgery* **34**: 1–10.

Tsuzuki, M., Ohnuma, E., Sato, N., Takaku, T., and Kawaguchi, A. 1990. Effects of CO_2 concentration during growth on fatty acid composition in microalgae. *Plant Physiology* **93**: 851–856.

Tuljapurkar, S., Li, N., and Boe, C. 2000. A universal pattern of mortality decline in the G7 countries. *Nature* **405**: 789–792.

Vardar-Uenlue, G., Candan, F., Soekmen, A., Daferera, D., Polissiou, M., Soekmen, M., Doenmez, E., and Tepe, B. 2003. Antimicrobial and antioxidant activity of the essential oil and methanol extracts of *Thymus pectinatus* Fisch. et Mey var. pectinatus (Lamiaceae). *Journal of Agricultural and Food Chemistry* **51**: 63–67.

Vurro, E, Bruni, R., Bianchi, A., and di Toppi, L.S. 2009. Elevated atmospheric CO_2 decreases oxidative stress and increases essential oil yield in leaves of *Thymus vulgaris* grown in a mini-FACE system. *Environmental and Experimental Botany* **65**: 99–106.

Wink, M. 1999. Introduction: Biochemistry, Role and Biotechnology of Secondary Products. CRS Press, Boca Raton, Florida, USA, pp. 1–16.

Yongmanitchai, W. and Ward, O.P. 1991. Growth of and omega-3 fatty acid production by *Phaeodactylum tricornutum* under different culture conditions. *Applied Environmental Microbiology* **57**: 419–425.

Ziska, L.H., Emche, S.D., Johnson, E.L., George, K., Reed, D.R., and Sicher, R.C. 2005. Alterations in the production and concentration of selected alkaloids as a function of rising atmospheric carbon dioxide and air temperature: implications for ethno-pharmacology. *Global Change Biology* **11**: 1798–1807.

Ziska, L.H., Panicker, S., and Wojno, H.L. 2008. Recent and projected increases in atmospheric carbon dioxide and the potential impacts on growth and alkaloid production in wild poppy (*Papaver setigerum* DC.). *Climatic Change* **91**: 395–403.

Zobayed, S. and Saxena, P.K. 2004. Production of St.

John's Wort plants under controlled environment for maximizing biomass and secondary metabolites. *In Vitro Cellular and Developmental Biology—Plant* **40**: 108–114.

Zou, D. 2005. Effects of elevated atmospheric CO_2 on growth, photosynthesis and nitrogen metabolism in the economic brown seaweed, *Hizikia fusiforme* (Sargassaceae, Phaeophyta). *Aquaculture* **250**: 726–735.

7.8.4 Health-Harming Substances

- There appears to be little reason to expect any significant CO_2-induced increases in human-health-harming substances produced by plants as the atmosphere's CO_2 concentration continues to rise.

Whereas IPCC makes no mention of the CO_2-induced enhancement of certain health-promoting substances in plants, as described in the subsections above, it is quick to point out the possibility of a CO_2-induced enhancement in certain health-*harming* substances. The research on that topic is the focus of this subsection.

Wayne *et al.* (2002) grew common ragweed plants from seed in controlled-environment glass-houses maintained at ambient (350 ppm) and enriched (700 ppm) atmospheric CO_2 concentrations for 84 days. They then sampled the pollen from the central plants of each stand, assessed the pollen's characteristics, and harvested all mature seeds and above-ground shoot material. They report, "stand-level pollen production was 61% higher in elevated versus ambient CO_2 environments" and "CO_2-induced growth stimulation of stand shoot biomass was similar to that of total pollen production." Although the researchers admit it would be "challenging to accurately predict the future threat to public health caused by CO_2-stimulated pollen production"— because "it is likely that plant pollen production will also be influenced by factors expected to change in concert with CO_2, including temperature, precipitation, and atmospheric pollutants"—they nevertheless suggest "the incidence of hay fever and related respiratory diseases may increase in the future."

Weber (2002) discussed the study of Wayne *et al.* in a guest editorial published in the same issue of the *Annals of Allergy, Asthma & Immunology*. He begins by noting "one can always wonder whether such manipulations [i.e., those employed in Wayne *et al.*'s study] have any relationship to present reality, or indeed, conditions that one can expect in the near future," and then proceeds methodically to his conclusion: "it would be premature to assume that increased pollen grain numbers necessarily lead to an increased aeroallergen exposure."

Weber notes, "allergenic activity of short ragweed will vary from year to year, even from the same source and supplier (Maasch *et al.*, 1987)," and he cites Lee *et al.* (1979) as having found "varying potency in plants at the same site from year to year, which [were] attributed to seasonal climatic differences, primarily of rainfall." The latter researchers found a four-fold range in the allergenic potency of ragweed pollen within a single county in Illinois (USA). Consequently, Weber concludes "a constant relationship between pollen mass and allergenic protein content is not a given," and it will remain speculative until scientists determine whether "the increased pollen grains seen with the increased ambient CO_2 levels maintain the same ratio of allergenic proteins."

A further demonstration of the tenuousness of the suggestion of Wayne *et al.*—that "the incidence of hay fever and related respiratory diseases may increase in the future" because of the near-universal growth-promoting effects of atmospheric CO_2 enrichment—is provided by Rogers *et al.* (2006). They collected and vernalized ragweed seeds by sowing them in containers kept in a refrigerator maintained at 4°C. They transferred one-third of the seeded containers at 15-day intervals to glasshouse modules maintained at atmospheric CO_2 concentrations of either 380 or 700 ppm, and the seeds were allowed to germinate (also at 15-day intervals, with the middle germination date approximating that of plants currently growing naturally in the vicinity of where the seeds were collected). They kept the seeds under well-watered and fertilized conditions until the seeds senesced. The researchers then harvested the seeds and conducted assessments of plant and allergenic pollen biomass.

As best as can be determined from the graphical representations of Rogers *et al.*'s data, the end-of-season CO_2-induced increase in aboveground plant biomass was about 16% for the date of emergence typical of the present, and the corresponding increase in pollen production was about 32%. For the 15-day earlier date of emergence, which was chosen to represent "anticipated advances of spring several decades into the future" based upon projected rates of future global warming, the end-of-season CO_2-induced change in aboveground plant biomass was only about +3%, and the end-of-season CO_2-induced change in pollen production was actually a negative 3%.

The most meaningful way of viewing the results, then, is to determine the change in pollen production that would occur in going from today's atmospheric CO_2 concentration and date-of-onset of spring (380 ppm, middle date of germination) to the elevated CO_2 concentration and earlier date-of-onset of biological spring (700 ppm, 15-day earlier date of germination); when this is done, the production of allergenic pollen is seen to rise by just 1–2%.

Caporn et al. (1999) studied bracken, a weed that poses a potential threat to human health in the United Kingdom and other regions, growing specimens for 19 months in controlled-environment chambers maintained at atmospheric CO_2 concentrations of 370 and 570 ppm and normal and high levels of fertilization. They found the elevated CO_2 consistently increased rates of net photosynthesis in bracken from 30 to 70%, depending on soil fertility and time of year. The elevated CO_2 did not increase total plant dry mass or the dry mass of any plant organs, including rhizomes, roots, and fronds. The only significant effect of the elevated CO_2 on bracken growth was observed in the normal nutrient regime, where elevated CO_2 reduced the area of bracken fronds.

Matros et al. (2006) grew tobacco plants in pots filled with quartz sand placed in controlled-climate chambers maintained at either 350 or 1,000 ppm CO_2 for eight weeks, irrigating them daily with a complete nutrient solution containing either 5 or 8 mM NH_4NO_3. Some of the plants in each treatment were mechanically infected with potato virus Y (PVY) when they were six weeks old. At the end of the study, the researchers report, the plants grown at elevated CO_2 and 5 mM NH_4NO_3 "showed a marked and significant decrease in content of nicotine in leaves as well as in roots," and at 8 mM NH_4NO_3 the same was found to be true of upper leaves but not of lower leaves and roots. In addition, with respect to the PVY part of the study, they found the plants grown at high CO_2 "showed a markedly decreased spread of virus."

Matros et al. report "tobacco plants grown under elevated CO_2 show a slight decrease of nicotine contents," and "elevated CO_2 resulted in reduced spread of PVY." Most people likely would consider both of these impacts beneficial; potato virus Y is economically important because it infects many crops and ornamental plants throughout the world, and nicotine is nearly universally acknowledged to have significant negative effects on human health (Topliss et al., 2002).

Mohan et al. (2006) investigated the effects of an extra 200 ppm of atmospheric CO_2 on the growth and development of Toxicodendron radicans, commonly known as poison ivy, as well as its effect on the plant's toxicity, over a period of six years at the Duke Forest FACE facility, where the noxious vine grew naturally in a loblolly pine plantation's understory. The researchers surrounded clumps of it with 4 cm plastic-mesh enclosures to protect them from damage by indigenous white-tailed deer. This long and detailed study revealed atmospheric CO_2 enrichment increased poison ivy photosynthesis by 77% and boosted its water use efficiency by 51%. At the end of the study's sixth year, the aboveground biomass of poison ivy plants in the CO_2-enriched plots was 62% greater than that of poison ivy plants in the ambient-treatment plots. In addition, the high-CO_2-grown plants produced "a more allergenic form of urushiol," the substance that produces the plant's allergic reaction in humans.

Not unsurprisingly, the seven scientists say their findings indicate under future levels of atmospheric CO_2, poison ivy "may grow larger and become more noxious than it is today." And so it may, but the story is not quite that simple, as the next study indicates.

Londre and Schnitzer (2006) studied woody vines or lianas, focusing on changes over a period of 45 years in 14 temperate deciduous forests of southern Wisconsin (USA). During that time (1959–1960 to 2004–2005), the air's CO_2 concentration rose by 65 ppm, the mean annual air temperature of the region rose by 0.94°C, and its mean winter air temperature rose by 2.40°C, but its mean annual precipitation did not change. The researchers found, contrary to their initial hypothesis, "liana abundance and diameter did not increase in the interiors of Wisconsin (USA) forests over the last 45 years." Toxicodendron radicans, or poison ivy—which they note "grew markedly better under experimentally elevated CO_2 conditions than did competing trees" in the study of Mohan et al. (2006)—decreased in abundance over this time period, and significantly.

The two researchers say their study suggests "lianas are limited in the interiors of deciduous forests of Wisconsin by factors other than increased levels of CO_2." It is likely, for example, the growth of interior-forest lianas was limited by the enhanced tree growth provided by the CO_2 increase, which resulted in the trees becoming more competitive with the vines because of CO_2-induced increases in tree leaf numbers, area, and thickness, all of which would lead to less light being transmitted to the lianas growing beneath the forest canopy. This phenomenon apparently negated the enhanced propensity for growth that was provided the vines by the increase in the atmosphere's CO_2 concentration—the potential growth was not realized because the declining light intensity prevented it.

Londre and Schnitzer provide support for this reasoning in their finding that "compared to the forest interior, lianas were >4 times more abundant within 15 m of the forest edge and >6 times more abundant within 5 m of the forest edge." The two researchers note this "strong gradient in liana abundance from forest edge to interior" "was probably due to light availability." In addition, they say their results "are similar to findings in tropical forests, where liana abundance is significantly higher along fragmented forest edges and within tree fall gaps."

In conclusion, there appears to be little reason to expect any significant CO_2-induced increases in human-health-harming substances produced by plants as the atmosphere's CO_2 concentration continues to rise.

References

Caporn, S.J.M., Brooks, A.L., Press, M.C., and Lee, J.A. 1999. Effects of long-term exposure to elevated CO_2 and increased nutrient supply on bracken (*Pteridium aquilinum*). *Functional Ecology* **13**: 107–115.

Lee, Y.S., Dickinson, D.B., Schlager, D., and Velu, J.G. 1979. Antigen E content of pollen from individual plants of short ragweed (*Ambrosia artemisiifolia*). *Journal of Allergy and Clinical Immunology* **63**: 336–339.

Londre, R.A. and Schnitzer, S.A. 2006. The distribution of lianas and their change in abundance in temperate forests over the past 45 years. *Ecology* **87**: 2973–2978.

Maasch, H.J., Hauck, P.R., and Oliver, J.D., *et al.* 1987. Allergenic activity of short ragweed pollen (*Ambrosia elatior*) from different years and/or suppliers: criteria for the selection of an in-house allergen reference preparation. *Annals of Allergy* **58**: 429–434.

Matros, A., Amme, S., Kettig, B., Buck-Sorlin, G.H., Sonnewald, U., and Mock, H.-P. 2006. Growth at elevated CO_2 concentrations leads to modified profiles of secondary metabolites in tobacco cv. SamsunNN and to increased resistance against infection with *potato virus Y*. *Plant, Cell and Environment* **29**: 126–137.

Mohan, J.E., Ziska, L.H., Schlesinger, W.H., Thomas, R.B., Sicher, R.C., George, K., and Clark, J.S. 2006. Biomass and toxicity responses of poison ivy (*Toxicodendron radicans*) to elevated atmospheric CO_2. *Proceedings of the National Academy of Sciences, USA* **103**: 9086–9089.

Rogers, C.A., Wayne, P.M., Macklin, E.A., Muilenberg, M.L., Wagner, C.J., Epstein, P.R., and Bazzaz, F.A. 2006. Interaction of the onset of spring and elevated atmospheric CO_2 on ragweed (*Ambrosia artemisiifolia* L.) pollen production. *Environmental Health Perspectives* **114**: 665–669.

Topliss, J.G., Clark, A.M., and Ernst, E., *et al.* 2002. Natural and synthetic substances related to human health. *Pure and Applied Chemistry* **74**: 1957–1985.

Wayne, P., Foster, S., Connolly, J., Bazzaz, F., and Epstein, P. 2002. Production of allergenic pollen by ragweed (*Ambrosia artemisiifolia* L.) is increased in CO_2-enriched atmospheres. *Annals of Allergy, Asthma, and Immunology* **88**: 279–282.

Weber, R.W. 2002. Mother Nature strikes back: global warming, homeostasis, and implications for allergy. *Annals of Allergy, Asthma & Immunology* **88**: 251–252.

Appendix 1

Acronyms

ABS	abscisic acid
AGB	aboveground biomass
aDGVM	adaptive dynamic global vegetation model
ADS	Asian dust storm
AFLP	amplified fragment length polymorphism
AGW	anthropogenic global warming
AM	arbuscular mycorrhizal
AMF	arbuscular mycorrhizal fungi
AMI	acute myocardial infarction
AMO	Atlantic Multidecadal Oscillation
APSIM	Agricultural Production Systems Simulator
AO/NAO	Arctic Oscillation/North Atlantic Oscillation
APS	atmospheric pollen season
ARPEGE	Action de Recherche Petite Echelle Grande Echelle (Research Project on Small and Large Scales)
AsA	ascorbic acid
AVHRR	Advanced Very High Resolution Radiometer
Ba	barium
BAI	basal area index
BioCON	Biodiversity, Carbon Dioxide, and Nitrogen Effects on Ecosystem Functioning
BIOME3	Biogeochemical Model
BP	before present
BSW	bog surface wetness
Bt	*Bacillus thuringiensis*
BTD	bluetongue disease
BTDV	bluetongue disease virus
BVOC	biogenic volatile organic compound
BYDV	barley yellow dwarf virus
C	carbon
C_3	C_3 carbon fixation pathway for photosynthesis
C_4	C_4 carbon fixation pathway for photosynthesis
Ca	CO_2 concentration in the air
CAM	crassulacean acid metabolism
CASA	Carnegie-Ames-Stanford Approach
CBD	cerebrovascular disease
CBSC	carbon-based secondary compounds
CCA	canonical correspondence analysis
CDC	Canadian Drought Code
CEC	carbon exchange capacity
CER	CO_2 exchange rate
CERES	Crop Environment Resources Synthesis
CEVSA	Carbon Exchanges in the Vegetation-Soil-Atmosphere System
CH_2CII	iodocarbon chloroiodomethane
CH_3C_1	methyl chloride
CH_4	methane
CH_2I_2	diiodomethane
CHD	coronary heart disease
CLEH	climate-linked epidemic hypothesis
CO_2	carbon dioxide
CPR	Continuous Plankton Recorder
CS_2	carbon disulfide
CSIRO	Commonwealth Scientific and Industrial Research Organization (Australia)

Cu	copper		**GPCP**	Global Precipitation Climatology Project
CVD	cardiovascular disease		**GPP**	gross primary production
CZCS	Coastal Zone Color Scanner		**gr**	gram(s)
DAE	days after emergence		**GSH**	glutathione
DAS	days after seeding		**GtC**	gigatons of carbon
DBH	diameter at breast height		**H_2O_2**	hydrogen peroxide
DGGE	denaturant gradient gel electrophoresis		**H_2S**	hydrogen sulfide
DHZR	dihydrozeatin ribosidem		**HC1**	Hidden Cave (Guadalupe Mountains)
DIC	dissolved organic carbon		**HR**	heterotrophic respiration
DM	dry matter		**HSG**	hematite stained grain
DMS	dimethyl sulfide		**IAA**	indole-3 acetic acid
DNA	deoxyribonucleic acid		**IC**	ischemic stroke
DOC	dissolved organic carbon		**IE**	infection efficiency
DTR	diurnal temperature range		**IMAR**	Inner Mongolia Autonomous Region
ECM	ectomycorrhizal		**iPA**	isopentenyl adenosine
EF-Tu	protein synthesis elongation factor		**IPCC**	Intergovernmental Panel on Climate Change
ENSO	El Niño-Southern Oscillation			
EPA	Environmental Protection Agency		**IPCC 2007-I**	Intergovernmental Panel on Climate Change – Group 1 Contribution
EU	European Union			
EVI	Enhanced Vegetation Index		**IPCC 2007-II**	Intergovernmental Panel on Climate Change – Group II Contribution
FA	fluctuating asymmetry			
FACE	free-air CO_2 enrichment		**IPCC 2007-III**	Intergovernmental Panel on Climate Change – Group III Contribution
FACTS	Forest Atmosphere Carbon Transfer and Storage			
			IPCC-FAR	Intergovernmental Panel on Climate Change – First Assessment Report
FATI	free-air temperature increase			
FAO	Food and Agriculture Organization		**IPCC-SAR**	Intergovernmental Panel on Climate Change – Second Assessment Report
Fe	iron			
FRAP	ferric reducing/antioxidant potential		**IPCC-TAR**	Intergovernmental Panel on Climate Change – Third Assessment Report
GA3	gibberellic acid			
GAM	generalized additive model		**IPCC-AR4**	Intergovernmental Panel on Climate Change – Fourth Assessment Report
GBR	Great Barrier Reef			
GCM	General Circulation Models		**IPCC-AR5**	Intergovernmental Panel on Climate Change – Fifth Assessment Report
GCTE	Global Change and Terrestrial Ecosystems			
			IUCN	International Union for Conservation of Nature
GDP	Gross Domestic Product			
GIMMS	Global Inventory Modeling and Mapping Studies		**IWUE (iWUE)**	intrinsic water use efficiency
			ka	thousand years
			kDa	kilodalton
GLO-PEM	Global Production Efficiency Model		**KPRNA**	Konza Prairie Research Natural Area
gNDVI	Normalized Difference Vegetation Index over the Growing Season		**kS**	specific conductivity
			LBM	larch budmoth
			LCLUC	land cover/land use change

LGM	Last Glacial Maximum		**PDO**	Pacific Decadal Oscillation
LIA	Little Ice Age		**PDSI**	Palmer Drought Severity Index
LIG	last interglacial		**PET**	physiologically equivalent temperature
LST	land surface temperature		**PETM**	Palaeocene-Eocene Thermal Maximum
m	meter		**PHACE**	prairie heating and CO_2 enrichment
Ma	million years		**PIH**	primary intracerebral hemorrhagic stroke
Ma BP	million years before present		**PM**	particulate matter
MAAT	mean annual air temperature		**PNL**	progressive nitrogen limitation
MODIS	moderate resolution imaging spectroradiometer		**PNUE**	photosynthetic nitrogen use efficiency
Mg	megagram		**POM**	particulate organic matter
MWP	Medieval Warm Period		**PopFACE**	poplar free-air CO_2 enrichment
MXD	maximum latewood density		**ppb**	parts per billion
N	nitrogen		**PPB**	purple phototrophic bacteria
N₂O	nitrous oxide		**ppm**	parts per million
NaCl	sodium chloride		**ppmv**	parts per million by volume
NAO	North Atlantic Oscillation		**PRECIS**	Providing Regional Climates for Impact Studies
NAS	National Academy of Sciences (USA)		**PSII**	photosystem II
NASA	National Aeronautics and Space Administration (USA)		**RD**	respiratory disease
NDVI	Normalized Difference Vegetation Index		**Rda**	area-based dark respiration
NEP	net ecosystem production		**Rdm**	mass-based dark respiration
NEE	net ecosystem exchange		**rDNA**	ribosomal deoxyribonucleic acid
NEEa	annual net ecosystem exchange		**RERCA**	recent rate of carbon accumulation
NH₄	ammonium		**ROS**	reactive oxygen species
NIPCC	Nongovernmental International Panel on Climate Change		**RSV**	respiratory syncytial virus
NOAA	National Oceanic and Atmospheric Administration (USA)		**RTI**	respiratory tract infection
NPP	net primary productivity		**RWP**	Roman Warm Period
NUE	nitrogen use efficiency		**SACC**	screen-aided CO_2 control
O₃	ozone		**SB**	Southern Beaufort Sea
OCS	carbonyl sulfide		**SCC**	Swiss canopy crane
OM	organic matter		**SCD**	sudden cardiac death
ORNL	Oak Ridge National Laboratory (USA)		**SCPDSI**	self-calibrating Palmer Drought Severity Index
OTC	open-top chamber		**SeaWiFS**	Sea-Viewing Wide Field-Of-View Sensor
P	phosphorous		**SEPP**	Science and Environmental Policy Project
PAR	photosynthetically active radiation		**SET**	surface elevation table
Pg	petagram		**SLR**	sea-level rise
PAL	Pathfinder AVHRR [Advanced Very High Resolution Radiometer] Land		**SO₂**	sulfur dioxide

SOC	soil organic carbon		**TRMM**	Tropical Rainfall Measuring Mission
SOM	soil organic matter		**TRW**	tree-ring width
SOS	start of spring		**TSD**	temperature-dependent sex determination
SPAR	soil-plant-atmosphere-research		**UCD**	unusually cold day
SPM	Summaries for Policymakers		**UN**	United Nations
SPS	sucrose-phosphate synthase		**UNEP**	United Nations Environment Program
SST	sea surface temperatures		**UNFCCC**	United Nations Framework Convention on Climate Change
TBARS	thiobarbituric acid reactive substance		**UNT**	unified neutral theory
TBE	tick-borne encephalitis		**UV**	ultraviolet
TBEV	tick-borne encephalitis virus		**VOC**	volatile organic compound
TDR	time domain reflectometry		**VPD**	vapor pressure deficit
TEM	terrestrial ecosystem model		**VSP**	vegetative storage protein
Tg	teragram		**WH**	Western Hudson Bay
Tmax	maximum temperature		**WHO**	World Health Organization
Tmin	minimum temperature		**WMO**	World Meteorological Organization
TMI	Tropical Rainfall Measuring Mission Microwave Imager		**WSC**	water-soluble carbohydrate
Topt	optimum temperature		**WT**	wild type
TP	Tibetan Plateau		**WUE**	water use efficiency
TRFO	tropical rainforest		**ZR**	zeatin riboside

Appendix 2

Authors, Contributors, and Reviewers

Lead Authors/Editors

Idso, Craig D.
Center for the Study of Carbon Dioxide and Global Change
USA

Idso, Sherwood B.
Center for the Study of Carbon Dioxide and Global Change
USA

Carter, Robert M.
Emeritus Fellow
Institute of Public Affairs
Australia

Singer, S. Fred
Science and Environmental Policy Project
USA

Contributors and Reviewers

Barnes, David J.
Australian Institute of Marine Science (retired)
Australia

Botkin, Daniel B.
University of Miami
University of California Santa Barbara USA

Cloyd, Raymond A.
Kansas State University
USA

Crockford, Susan
University of Victoria, B.C.
Canada

Cui, Weihong
Chinese Academy of Sciences
China

DeGroot, Kees
Shell International (retired)
The Netherlands

Dillon, Robert G.
Physician
USA

Dunn, John Dale
Physician
USA

Ellestad, Ole Henrik
Research Council of Norway (retired)
Norway

Goldberg, Fred
Swedish Polar Institute
Sweden

Goldman, Barry
Australian Museum Lizard Island Research Station
(retired)
Australia

Hoese, H. Dickson
Consulting Marine Biologist
USA

Jødal, Morten
Independent Scientist
Norway

Khandekar, Madhav
Environment Canada (retired)
Canada

Kutilek, Miroslav
Czech Technical University (emeritus)
Czech Republic

Leavitt, Steven W.
University of Arizona
Laboratory of Tree-Ring Research
USA

Maccabee, Howard
Doctors for Disaster Preparedness
USA

Marohasy, Jennifer
Central Queensland University
Australia

Ollier, Cliff
University of Western Australia
Australia

Petch, Jim
University of Manchester Trican
Manchester Metropolitan University
(retired)
United Kingdom

Reginato, Robert J.
Agricultural Research Service
U.S. Department of Agriculture
USA

Reiter, Paul
Laboratoire Insectes et Maladies Infectieuses
Institut Pasteur
France

Segalstad, Tom
Resource and Environmental Geology
University of Oslo
Norway

Sharp, Gary
Independent Consultant
Center for Climate/
Ocean Resources Study
USA

Starck, Walter
Independent Marine Biologist
Australia

Stockwell, David
Central Queensland University
Australia

Taylor, Mitchell
Lakehead University
Canada

Weber, Gerd
Independent Meteorologist
Germany

Wilson, Bastow
University of Otago
New Zealand

Wust, Raphael
James Cook University
Australia

Editors

Karnick , S.T.
The Heartland Institute
USA

Bast, Diane Carol
The Heartland Institute
USA

Several additional reviewers wish to remain anonymous.

Appendix 3

Table 1.1.1 — Plant Dry Weight (Biomass) Responses to Atmospheric CO_2 Enrichment

Table 1.1.1 reports the results of hundreds of peer-reviewed scientific studies indicating the biomass growth response of plants to a standardized 300 ppm increase in atmospheric CO_2 concentration. Plants are listed by common and/or scientific names, followed by the number of experimental studies conducted on each plant, the mean biomass response to a 300 ppm increase in the air's CO_2 content, and the standard error of that mean. Whenever the CO_2 increase for a given study was not exactly 300 ppm, a linear adjustment was computed. For example, if the CO_2 increase was 350 ppm and the growth response was a 60 percent enhancement, the adjusted 300 ppm CO_2 growth response was calculated as (300/350) x 60% = 51%.

The data in this table are printed by permission of the Center for the Study of Carbon Dioxide and Global Change and were taken from its Plant Growth database on 1 January 2014. The table summarizes CO_2 enrichment results from 3,586 separate experimental conditions conducted on 549 plant species. New data are added to the database at approximately weekly intervals and can be accessed free of charge at the center's Web site at http://www.co2science.org/data/plant_growth/dry/dry_subject.php. This online database also archives information pertaining to the experimental conditions under which each plant growth experiment was conducted, as well as the complete reference to the journal article from which the experimental results were obtained. The center's online database also lists percent increases in plant biomass for 600 and/or 900 ppm increases in the air's CO_2 concentration.

Plant Name	# of Studies	Mean CO_2 Growth Response	Standard Error
Abelmoschus esculentus [Okra]	1	8%	0%
Abies alba [Silver Fir]	5	33.20%	11.60%
Abies faxoniana [Minjiang Fir]	4	20.30%	2.90%
Abutilon theophrasti [Velvet Leaf]	14	32.10%	13.70%
Acacia karroo [Sweet Thorn]	3	53.70%	5.90%
Acacia aneura [Mulga Acacia]	1	0%	0%
Acacia auriculiformis [Acacia, Earleaf]	1	0%	0%
Acacia catechu [Black Cutch]	7	71.10%	10.70%
Acacia colei [Acacia]	1	89%	0%
Acacia coriacea [Wiry Wattle]	1	50%	0%
Acacia dealbata [Silver Wattle]	1	106%	0%
Acacia implexa	1	77%	0%
Acacia irrorata	1	64%	0%

Plant Name	# of Studies	Mean CO_2 Growth Response	Standard Error
Acacia magium [Brown Saiwood]	3	19%	6.90%
Acacia mearnsii [Black Wattle]	1	48%	0%
Acacia melanoxylon [Blackwood]	1	164%	0%
Acacia minuta [Coastal Scrub Wattle]	2	110%	22.60%
Acacia nilotica [Gum Arabic Tree]	11	241.50%	53.90%
Acacia saligna [Orange Wattle]	1	55%	0%
Acacia tetragonophylla [Acacia]	1	55%	0%
Acer barbatum [Southern Sugar Maple]	1	95%	0%
Acer pensylvanicum [Striped Maple]	4	28.80%	8.40%
Acer pseudoplatanus [Sycamore]	3	34.30%	12.80%
Acer rubrum [Red Maple]	13	44.20%	13.30%
Acer saccharum [Sugar Maple]	12	48.30%	13.10%
Achillea millefolium [Yarrow]	3	24.70%	12.60%

Plant Name	# of Studies	Mean CO₂ Growth Response	Standard Error
Aechmea cuculata x a. fasciata [Bromelaid Cv. Maya]	1	-6%	0%
Aechmea fasciata [Silver Vase Bromeliad]	5	26.20%	14.90%
Aechmea magdalenae [Understory Herb]	1	30%	0%
Agave deserti [Desert Agave]	4	34.80%	10.30%
Agave salmiana [Agave]	1	43%	0%
Agave vilmoriniana [Leaf Succulent]	2	14%	9.90%
Agropyron repens [C₃ Grass]	1	41%	0%
Agropyron smithii [Western Wheatgrass]	3	50.30%	42.20%
Agrostemma githago [Corncockle]	1	21%	0%
Agrostis canina [Velvet Bentgrass]	1	124%	0%
Agrostis capillaris [Colonial Bentgrass]	9	37.10%	11.70%
Ailanthus excelsa [Indian Tree Of Heaven]	1	49%	0%
Albizia procera [Tall Albiza]	8	125.60%	16.30%
Allium fistulosum [Scallion]	1	135%	0%
Alloteropsis semialata [Cockatoo Grass]	6	41.20%	3.70%
Alnus maximowiczii [Alder Tree]	4	0.80%	6.20%
Alnus glutinosa [Black Alder]	6	32.50%	6.10%
Alnus hirsuta [Manchurian Alder]	7	17.10%	5.70%
Alnus incana [Mountain Alder]	1	50%	0%
Alnus rubra [Red Alder]	6	34.50%	7.70%
Amaranthus hybridus [Slim Amaranth]	6	14%	5.60%
Amaranthus hypochondriacus [Grain Amaranth]	2	5.50%	3.90%
Amaranthus retroflexus [Redroot Amaranth]	17	6.40%	3.30%
Amaranthus tricolor [Amaranth]	1	20%	0%
Amaranthus viridis [Slender Amaranth]	4	-2.30%	3.20%
Ambrosia artemisiifolia [Annual Ragweed]	13	28.80%	7%
Ambrosia dumosa [White Burrobush]	2	164%	36.10%
Ambrosia trifida [Great Ragweed]	3	26%	8.20%
Amorpha canescens [Leadplant]	3	40.30%	63.30%
Amur Silvergrass [Miscanthus sacchariflorus]	1	-27%	0%
Ananas comosus [Pineapple]	2	5%	9.20%
Andropogon appendiculatus [Vlei Bluegrass]	6	50.50%	6.90%
Andropogon gerardii [Big Bluestem]	12	20.30%	7.20%
Andropogon virginicus [Broomsedge]	2	0%	0%
Anemone cylindrica [Candle Anemone]	1	84%	0%
Anthoxanthum odoratum [Sweet Vernal Grass]	1	170%	0%
Anthyllis vulneraria [Common Kidney	6	45.30%	17.50%

Plant Name	# of Studies	Mean CO₂ Growth Response	Standard Error
Vetch]			
Arabidopsis thaliana [Thale Cress]	17	162.30%	51.20%
Arachis glabrata [Florigraze Peanut]	2	20.50%	1.10%
Arachis hypogaea [Peanut]	38	60.30%	16.10%
Armeria maritima [Thrift Seapink]	1	-45%	0%
Arrhenatherum elatius [Tall Oatgrass]	7	18.60%	9.60%
Artemisia absinthium [Absinth Sagewort]	2	161.50%	44.20%
Artemisia tridentata [Big Sagebrush]	4	24.30%	6.10%
Asclepias syriaca [Common Milkweed]	3	31%	15.50%
Asclepias tuberosa [Butterfly Milkweed]	1	108%	0%
Aster pilosus [White Oldfield Aster]	2	62.50%	26.50%
Austrodanthonia caespitosa [Wallaby Grass]	2	78%	4.20%
Avena barbata [Slender Oat]	6	22.80%	5.80%
Avena fatua [Wild Oat]	8	32.90%	8.40%
Avena sativa [Red Oat]	15	40.60%	15.40%
Avicennia germinans [Black Mangrove]	2	22.50%	5.30%
Azolla caroliniana [Water Fern]	3	28%	9.10%
Azolla filiculoides [Water Fern]	4	20.80%	3.80%
Azolla pinnata [Water Fern]	4	54.30%	27%
Bauhinia variegata [Mountain Ebony]	7	78.90%	9.10%
Bellis perennis [Lawn Daisy]	3	95.70%	0.30%
Beta vulgaris [Common Beet]	33	65.70%	19.30%
Betula ermanii [Birch, Ermans]	2	6%	0.70%
Betula maximowicziana [Birch, Monarch]	2	15%	1.40%
Betula alleghaniensis [Yellow Birch]	15	34.30%	10.20%
Betula nana [Bog Birch]	1	0%	0%
Betula pendula [European White Birch]	32	32.30%	4.80%
Betula platyphylla [Japanese White Birch]	6	15.80%	3.40%
Betula populifolia [Gray Birch]	4	19.80%	8.30%
Betula pubescens [Downy Birch]	4	25.50%	6.50%
Bouteloua curtipendula [Sideoats Grama]	2	7%	22.60%
Bouteloua eriopoda [Black Grama]	1	21%	0%
Bouteloua gracilis [Blue Grama]	8	2.10%	9.80%
Brachypodium pinnatum [Heath Falsebrome]	1	0%	0%
Brassica alboglabra [Chinese Broccoli]	2	9%	0.70%
Brassica campestris	6	55.80%	8.50%
Brassica carinata [Abyssinian Mustard]	2	28%	1.40%

Appendix 3 – Plant Dry Weight (Biomass) Responses

Plant Name	# of Studies	Mean CO₂ Growth Response	Standard Error
Brassica juncea [India Mustard]	2	28.50%	1.80%
Brassica kaber [Field Mustard]	1	29%	0%
Brassica napus [Oilseed Rape]	38	43.80%	5.20%
Brassica nigra [Black Mustard]	2	40.50%	10.30%
Brassica oleracea [Broccoli]	5	28.80%	8.50%
Brassica rapa [Mustard]	1	21%	0%
Bromus erectus [Erect Brome]	7	34.60%	6.80%
Bromus hordeaceus [Soft Brome]	2	43%	9.90%
Bromus inermis [Smooth Brome]	1	-13%	0%
Bromus madritensis [Compact Brome]	2	7%	14.10%
Bromus mollis [Soft Brome]	2	53.50%	2.50%
Bromus rubens [Foxtail Brome]	2	25%	7.80%
Bromus sterilis [Poverty Brome]	1	0%	0%
Bromus tectorum [Cheatgrass]	1	36%	0%
Buchloe dactyloides [Buffalo Grass]	1	-5%	0%
Bulbophyllum longissimum [Orchid, Tropical]	4	15.50%	13.70%
Cajanus cajan [Pigeon Pea]	4	75%	20.50%
Calamagrostis angustifolia [Reed Grass]	24	14.80%	2.10%
Calamagrostis purpurea [Scandinavian Small Reed]	2	18%	7.80%
Calamagrostis epigeios [Chee Reedgrass]	2	98.50%	0.40%
Calcidiscus leptoporus [Marine Coccolithophore]	2	18.50%	3.20%
Calluna vulgaris [Heather]	9	17.10%	5.40%
Capsicum chinense [Yellow Lantern Chili]	1	49%	0%
Caragana intermedia [Deciduous Shrub of Semi-arid Northern China]	6	54.50%	4.50%
Cardamine hirsuta [Hairy Bittercress]	2	-0.50%	3.90%
Carex arenaria [Sand Sedge]	1	26%	0%
Carex bigelowii [Bigelow's Sedge]	1	0%	0%
Carex flacca [Heath Sedge]	5	73.80%	18.20%
Carex rostrata [Beaked Sedge]	1	44%	0%
Cariniana legalis [Jequitiba Tree]	2	20%	2.80%
Carpinus betulus [European Hornbeam]	3	35.30%	26.40%
Cassia fasciculata [Sleepingplant]	2	17.50%	27.20%
Cassia nictitans [Partridge Pea]	1	22%	0%
Cassia obtusifolia [Coffeeweed]	2	31.50%	7.40%
Castanea sativa [Sweet Chesnut]	4	12.80%	2.20%
Casuarina equisetifolia [Beach Sheoak]	1	54%	0%
Catopsis juncifolia [Bromeliad, Tropical]	4	13.30%	5.20%

Plant Name	# of Studies	Mean CO₂ Growth Response	Standard Error
Cenchrus ciliaris [Buffel Grass]	1	242%	0%
Centaurea solstitialis [Yellow Star Thistle]	1	500%	0%
Centella asiatica [Centella]	1	145%	0%
Cerastium fontanum [Chickweed]	1	51%	0%
Ceratonia siliqua [Carob]	10	38.10%	9.70%
Ceratophytum tetragonolobum	2	60%	42.40%
Chaetoceros muelleri [Marine Diatom]	2	18%	6.40%
Chamaecrista nictitans [Partridge Pea]	1	0%	0%
Chamelaucium uncinatum (Schauer) x Chamelaucium uncinatum (MS) [Lady Stephanie]	3	20.70%	3.40%
Chamerion angustifolium	1	228%	0%
Chamerops humilis [Mediterranean Fan Palm]	1	67%	0%
Chenopodium album [Lambsquarters]	20	46%	7.70%
Chenopodium bonus-henricus [Good King Henry]	1	21%	0%
Chlorella pyrenoidosa [Common Freshwater Microalga]	2	8%	0.70%
Chloris gayana [Rhodes Grass]	1	39%	0%
Cicer arietinum [Chickpea]	16	42.80%	3.80%
Cirsium arvense [Canadian Thistle]	3	83.30%	33.50%
Citrus [Ambersweet Orange Tree]	3	30.70%	1.20%
Citrus aurantium [Sour Orange Tree]	5	69.40%	9.10%
Citrus reticulata [Mandarin Orange Tree]	2	29.50%	3.90%
Citrus sinensis [Sweet Orange Tree]	2	38.50%	4.60%
Citrus sinensis x poncirus trifoliata [Carrizo Citrange]	2	40.50%	1.80%
Clarkia rubicunda [Ruby Chalice Fairyfan]	1	35%	0%
Coffea arabusta [Coffee]	2	175.50%	76.70%
Commelina benghalensis [Tropical Spiderwort]	1	61%	0%
Conium maculatum [Poison Hemlock]	1	21%	0%
Cornus florida [Eastern Flowering Dogwood]	2	121.50%	37.10%
Correa schlechtendalii	3	9.70%	0.30%
Crotalaria juncea [Sunn Hemp]	2	45%	9.90%
Croton urucurana [Dragons Blood Tree]	2	23.50%	4.60%
Cucumis melo [Cantaloupe]	3	4.70%	0.70%
Cucumis sativus [Garden Cucumber]	12	44.80%	6%
Cuphea viscosissima [Clammy Cuphea]	1	17%	0%
Cycas revoluta [Sago Palm]	1	172%	0%
Cynosurus cristatus [Crested Dogstailgrass]	1	30%	0%
Cyperus esculentus [Yellow Nutsedge]	1	16%	0%

Plant Name	# of Studies	Mean CO$_2$ Growth Response	Standard Error
Cyperus rotundus [Purple Nutsedge]	1	38%	0%
Dactylis glomerata [Orchardgrass]	15	18.30%	4.30%
Dalbergia latifolia [Indian Rosewood]	7	55.60%	7.80%
Danthonia richardsonii Cashmore [Wallaby Grass]	9	25%	8.60%
Datura stramonium [Jimsonweed]	3	36.70%	15.80%
Daucus carota [Carrot]	5	77.80%	32.30%
Deschampsia flexuosa [Wavy Hairgrass]	1	19%	0%
Desmazeria rigida [Ferngrass]	1	26%	0%
Digitalis purpurea [Purple Foxglove]	2	17.50%	2.50%
Digitaria natalensis [Natal Crabgrass]	6	13%	3.20%
Digitaria sanguinalis [Hairy Crabgrass]	2	39%	12.70%
Echinacea purpurea [Eastern Purple Coneflower]	4	191.50%	75.50%
Echinochloa crus-galli [Barnyard Grass]	19	49.80%	16.90%
Echium plantagineum [Salvation Jane]	4	15.80%	6.20%
Eichhornia crassipes [Common Water Hyacinth]	10	43.80%	12.20%
Elaeis guineensis [African Oil Palm]	1	89%	0%
Eleusine indica [Indian Goosegrass]	6	34%	17.40%
Elymus athericus	4	46.30%	20%
Elymus elymoides [Botlebrush Squirreltail]	1	24%	0%
Emiliania huxleyi [Marine Coccolithophores]	3	45%	34.70%
Epilobium hirsutum [Codlins and Cream]	1	9%	0%
Eragrostis curvula [Weeping Lovegrass]	7	48.10%	10.10%
Eragrostis orcuttiana [Annual Weed, C4]	1	462%	0%
Eragrostis racemosa [Narrowheart Lovegrass]	6	11.70%	1.80%
Erica tetralix [Crossleaf Heath]	4	23.80%	10.50%
Eriophorum vaginatum [Tussock Cottongrass]	5	105%	71.60%
Eucalyptus degluptax x e. camaldulensis [Eucalypt Hybrid]	2	45.50%	20.90%
Eucalyptus pauciflora [Snow Gum Tree]	10	67.10%	9.50%
Eucalyptus saligna [Sydney Blue Gum]	4	139.50%	46.80%
Eucalyptus cladocalyx [Sugargum]	2	87.50%	9.50%
Eucalyptus miniata [Darwin Woollybutt]	9	-2%	5.40%
Eucalyptus tetrodonta	9	132.80%	19.90%
Eupatorium adenophorum [Sticky Snakeroot]	5	27.40%	4.50%
Eupatorium japonicum [Pei Lan]	1	24%	0%
Eupatorium stoechadosmum [Orchid Herb]	3	15.30%	5.20%
Euphorbia lathyris [Myrtle Spurge]	2	36.50%	4.60%

Plant Name	# of Studies	Mean CO$_2$ Growth Response	Standard Error
Fagopyrum esculentum [Common Buckwheat]	3	17.30%	9.90%
Fagus crenata [Japanese Beech]	1	31%	0%
Fagus grandifolia [American Beech]	1	88%	0%
Fagus sylvatica [European Beech]	23	23.60%	6%
Ferocactus acanthodes [California Barrelcactus]	1	30%	0%
Festuca rubra [Red Fescue]	4	29.50%	12%
Festuca arundinacea [Tall Fescue]	11	25.40%	7.20%
Festuca elatior [Tall Meadow Fescue]	1	40%	0%
Festuca ovina [Sheep Fescue]	6	47.70%	16.60%
Festuca pratensis [Meadow Fescue]	11	20.30%	10%
Flaveria trinervia [Clustered Yellowtops]	1	46%	0%
Fragaria x ananassa [Hybrid Strawberry]	4	42.80%	13.10%
Fraxinus americana [White Ash]	4	33.80%	7.30%
Fraxinus excelsior [European Ash]	10	13.40%	3.60%
Fraxinus pennsylvanica [Green Ash]	1	32%	0%
Galactia elliottii [Elliott's Milkpea]	1	110%	0%
Gentianella germanica [Dwarf Gentian]	1	54%	0%
Ginkgo biloba [Maidenhair Tree]	1	78%	0%
Glycine max [Soybean]	190	45.50%	2.70%
Gmelina arborea [White Teak]	2	150.50%	6%
Gnaphalium affine [Cudweed]	1	21%	0%
Gonolobus cteniophorus	2	3.50%	12.40%
Gossypium hirsutum [Cotton]	41	58.40%	7.80%
Gracilaria lemaneiformis [Red Algae]	4	33.50%	13.90%
Grassland community in antwerp, belgium [Six Perennial Species]	1	48%	0%
Grassland, wyoming, usa [Four C$_3$ Grasses In A Mixed-grass Prairie]	1	45%	0%
Grassland, Species-poor on a peaty gley soil	1	50%	0%
Grassland, Species-rich on a brown Earth soil over limestone	1	56%	0%
Guzmania Hilda [Guzmania]	1	63%	0%
Gypsophila paniculata [Babysbreath Gypsophila]	1	23%	0%
Hedera helix [English Ivy]	3	66%	10.60%
Helianthemum nummularium [Sun Rose]	1	0%	0%
Helianthus annus [Sunflower]	13	36.50%	6.80%
Hemizonia congesta [Hayfield Tarweed]	2	48.50%	10.30%
Heterosigma akashiwo [A Marine Raphidophyte]	2	15%	2.10%
Heterotheca subaxillaris [Camphorweed]	1	20%	0%
Hizikia fusiforme [Hiziki (Brown	1	45%	0%

Plant Name	# of Studies	Mean CO$_2$ Growth Response	Standard Error
Seaweed)]			
Holcus lanatus [Common Velvetgrass]	11	38.50%	10.40%
Hordeum vulagare [Barley]	35	34.60%	3.40%
Hydrilla verticillata [Water Thyme]	7	21.90%	3.30%
Hymenocallis littoralis [Spider Lily]	2	52%	2.80%
Hyparrhenia rufa [Jaragua]	2	33.50%	1.80%
Hypericum perforatum [St. John's Wort]	1	72%	0%
Hypnea spinella [Red Seaweed]	1	66%	0%
Hyptis suaveolens [Wild Spikenard]	1	1720%	0%
Ilex aquifolium [English Holly]	1	15%	0%
Ipomoea cairica [Mile A Minute Vine]	1	61%	0%
Ipomoea pes-caprae [Beach Morning Glory]	1	29%	0%
Ipomoea batatas [Sweet Potato]	6	33.70%	9.30%
Ipomoea hederacea [Ivyleaf Morningglory]	2	-21%	8.50%
Ipomoea lacunosa [Whitestar]	2	15%	14.80%
Juncus effuses [Soft Rush]	1	-5%	0%
Kielmeyera coriacea [Tropical Savanna Tree]	3	88.70%	55.50%
Koeleria macrantha [Prairie Junegrass]	1	2%	0%
Krameria erecta [Littleleaf Ratany]	2	102.50%	1.10%
Kummerowia striata [Japanese Clover]	1	26%	0%
Lactuca sativa [Garden Lettuce]	2	18.50%	6%
Lantana camara [Lantana]	3	131.70%	40.30%
Larix decidua [European Larch]	1	142%	0%
Larix kaempferi [Japanese Larch]	4	26.80%	10.30%
Larix laricina [Tamarack]	1	56%	0%
Larrea tridentata [Creosote Bush]	8	104.90%	22.90%
Lasthenia californica [California Goldfields]	2	27%	26.90%
Layia platyglossa [Coastal Tidytips]	1	12%	0%
Ledum palustre [Wild Rosemary]	1	0%	0%
Lemna gibba [Swollen Duckweed]	2	47%	11.30%
Lepidium latifolium [Pepperweed]	2	40%	7.10%
Lespedeza capitata [Roundhead Lespedeza]	3	333.70%	136.10%
Lespedeza cuneata [Chinese Lespedeza]	1	0%	0%
Leymus chinensis [Chinese Lyme-grass]	2	19.50%	8.80%
Linum usitatissimum [Common Flax]	2	68.50%	18.70%
Linum usitatissimum [Common Flax] in mixed stands with Linum usitatissimum	2	63.50%	15.90%
Liquidambar styraciflua [Sweetgum]	20	132.40%	23.50%
Liriodendron tulipifera [Yellow Poplar]	3	34%	4.70%
Lolium multiflorum [Italian Ryegrass]	12	20%	3.80%
Lolium perenne [Perennial Ryegrass]	85	35.20%	4.60%
Lolium temulentum [Darnel Ryegrass]	3	44.70%	29.20%
Lomentaria articulata [Seaweed]	1	269%	0%
Lonicera japonica [Japanese Honeysuckle]	4	312.80%	73.70%
Lonicera sempervirens [Coral Honeysuckle]	1	30%	0%
Lotus corniculatus [Birdfoot Deer Vetch]	8	49.30%	12.90%
Lotus pedunculatus [Big Trefoil]	6	56%	26.50%
Lupinus angustifolius [Narrowleaf Lupine]	3	38%	7%
Lupinus luteus [European Yellow Lupine]	1	21%	0%
Lupinus perennis [Sundial Lupine]	11	56.40%	6.60%
Lycopersicon esculentum [Garden Tomato]	53	31%	3.50%
Lycopersicon lycopersicum [Tomato]	2	29.50%	5.30%
Macroptilium atropurpureum[Purple Bushbean]	1	43%	0%
Mangifera indica [Mango]	1	36%	0%
Manihot esculenta [Cassava]	4	13.80%	40.70%
Maranthes corymbosa	3	69%	14.30%
Medicago glomerata	1	17%	0%
Medicago lupulina [Black Medick]	6	45%	9.40%
Medicago minima [Burr Medick]	1	-6%	0%
Medicago sativa [Alfalfa]	85	37.40%	3.70%
Medicago truncatula [Barrelclover]	10	54.40%	6.30%
Melinis minutiflora [Molassesgrass]	2	32%	8.50%
Melinis repens [Red Natal Grass]	6	25.80%	7%
Mentha x piperita [Peppermint]	1	29%	0%
Microstegium vimineum [Nepalese Browntop]	3	-53.30%	15.60%
Mikania micrantha [Bittervine]	1	92%	0%
Miscanthus sacchariflorus [Amur Silvergrass]	1	-27%	0%
Molinia caerulea [Purple Moorgrass]	9	36.60%	9.40%
Nemophila menziesii [Menzies' Baby Blue Eyes]	1	0%	0%
Nicotiana tabacum [Cultivated Tobacco]	14	38.40%	7.40%
Nitzschia palea [Freshwater Diatom]	2	10%	4.90%
Nymphaea marliac [Water Lily]	2	162%	76.40%
Olea europaea [Olive Tree]	6	35.20%	14.10%
Onobrychis viciaefolia [Sainfoin]	1	21%	0%
Opuntia ficus-indica [Prickly Pear]	9	38.20%	13.30%

Plant Name	# of Studies	Mean CO$_2$ Growth Response	Standard Error	Plant Name	# of Studies	Mean CO$_2$ Growth Response	Standard Error
Orobanche minor [Hellroot]	1	0%	0%	Picea glauca [White Spruce]	7	106.10%	52.40%
Orontium aquaticum [Goldenclub]	12	19.80%	3%	Picea koraiensis [Spruce]	7	37.90%	8.70%
Oryza sativa [Rice]	219	36.10%	2%	Picea mariana [Black Spruce]	17	37.70%	10.60%
Oryzopsis hymenoides [Perennial Bunchgrass]	1	0%	0%	Picea sitchensis [Sitka Spruce]	7	20.70%	5%
Paederia scandens [Chinese Fever Vine]	1	14%	0%	Pinus banksiana [Jack Pine]	3	18.30%	8.80%
Panicum antidotale [Blue Panicgrass]	4	15.50%	6.30%	Pinus densiflora [Japanese Red Pine]	9	22.40%	7.60%
Panicum coloratum [Blue Panicgrass]	2	1%	15.60%	Pinus eldarica [Eldarica Pine]	1	153%	0%
Panicum dichotomiflorum (Fall Panicgrass)	1	24%	0%	Pinus koraiensis [Korean Pine]	2	27%	15.60%
Panicum laxum [Lax Panicgrass]	4	30%	11%	Pinus merkusii [Merkus Pine]	2	200%	43.10%
Panicum maximum [Guineagrass]	1	-2%	0%	Pinus nigra [Black Pine]	1	22%	0%
Panicum miliaceum [Broomcorn Millet]	1	-13%	0%	Pinus palustris [Longleaf Pine]	8	19%	7.40%
Panicum virgatum [Switchgrass]	1	-1%	0%	Pinus ponderosa [Ponderosa Pine]	47	63.30%	11.60%
Papaver setigerum [Dwarf Breadseed Poppy]	1	390%	0%	Pinus radiata [Monterey Pine]	1	36%	0%
Pascopyrum smithii [Western Wheatgrass]	5	63%	16.40%	Pinus strobus [Eastern White Pine]	3	31.70%	9%
Paspalum conjugatum [Hilograss]	1	18%	0%	Pinus sylvestris [Scots Pine]	63	35%	4.30%
Paspalum dilatatum [Dallas Grass]	2	71%	7.80%	Pinus taeda [Loblolly Pine]	67	60.90%	7.70%
Paspalum notatum [Bahiagrass]	3	10%	1.90%	Pinus uncinata [Mountain Pine]	1	0%	0%
Paspalum plicatulum [Brownseed Paspalum]	1	9%	0%	Pisum sativum [Garden Pea]	29	29.20%	3.10%
Pasture in Switzerland (Orchard Grass and Red Clover)	12	29.10%	5.70%	Plantago erecta [Dwarf Plantain]	2	4.50%	11.70%
Peanut, Rhizoma	1	57%	0%	Plantago lanceolata [Narrowleaf Plantain]	11	46.20%	15.20%
Pelargonium x hortorum [Pelargonium]	3	3.30%	12.80%	Plantago major [Common Plantain]	3	31.70%	4.60%
Petalostemum villosum [Silky Prairie-Clover]	3	-9.30%	23.40%	Plantago maritima [Sea Plantain]	3	101.70%	27.90%
Petunia hybrida [Petunia]	6	55%	9.80%	Plantago media [Hoary Plantain]	2	26.50%	5.30%
Phaeocystis [Phytoplankton]	1	0%	0%	Plantago virginica [Virginia Plantain]	1	45%	0%
Phalaris aquatica [Harding Grass]	13	24.60%	8.50%	Poa alpina [Alpine Bluegrass]	2	79.50%	4.60%
Phalaris arundinacea [Canary Grass]	8	34.30%	12.10%	Poa annua [Annual Bluegrass]	10	20.20%	9.10%
Pharus latifolius [Broad Stalkgrass]	1	144%	0%	Poa pratensis [Kentucky Bluegrass]	9	113.90%	29.80%
Phaseolus acutifolius [Tepary Bean]	2	70%	9.90%	Poa trivialis [Rough Bluegrass]	1	3%	0%
Phaseolus vulgaris [Garden Bean]	17	64.30%	20.30%	Polygonum cuspidatum [Japanese Knotweed]	3	48%	14.80%
Phleum pratense [Timothy]	20	14.90%	3.40%	Polygonum hydropiper [Marshpepper Knotweed]	2	40.50%	15.90%
Phragmites communis [Wetland Reed]	1	-8%	0%	Polygonum lapathifolium [Curlytop Knotweed]	5	19.40%	4.20%
Phragmites japonica [Wetland Reed]	1	-11%	0%	Polygonum pensylvanicum [Pennsylvania Smartweed]	3	55.70%	1.80%
Phyllanthus emblica [Emblic]	8	165%	16%	Polygonum persicaria [Spotted Ladysthumb]	2	38%	9.20%
Physalis peruviana [Peruvian Groundcherry]	1	23%	0%	Populus cathayana [Qing Yang]	4	39.80%	9.50%
Phytolacca americana [American Pokeweed]	8	-2.40%	13.80%	Populus tremula x alba [Poplar, Hybrid]	2	17%	0.70%
[Phytoplankton]	1	7%	0%	Populus alba [White Poplar]	14	43.90%	4.70%
Picea abies [Norway Spruce]	15	33.50%	4.90%	Populus deltoides [Eastern Cottonwood]	7	53.70%	13.60%

Appendix 3 – Plant Dry Weight (Biomass) Responses

Plant Name	# of Studies	Mean CO₂ Growth Response	Standard Error
Populus deltoides x Populus deltoides [Robusta Poplar Clone]	6	63.30%	13.70%
Populus euramericana [Robusta Poplar]	18	110.30%	37.60%
Populus grandidentata [Bigtooth Aspen]	1	29%	0%
Populus nigra [Black Poplar]	15	53.90%	12.20%
Populus tremula x Populus tremula [Hybrid Aspen]	6	40.30%	18%
Populus tremuloides [Quaking Aspen]	35	58.10%	9.30%
Populus trichocarpa [Black Cottonwood]	5	124%	93.20%
Populus trichocarpa x Populus trichocarpa [Hybrid Poplar]	7	76.70%	23.40%
Prorocentrum minimum [A Marine Dinoflagellate]	2	20%	3.50%
Prosopis flexuosa [Deciduous Tree]	1	42%	0%
Prosopis glandulosa [Honey Mesquite]	13	37.70%	5.20%
Prunella vulgaris [Selfheal]	2	78%	17.70%
Prunus avium [Sweet Cherry]	8	59.80%	7.80%
Prunus laurocerasus [English Laurel]	1	56%	0%
Prunus persica [Peach Tree]	4	27.80%	0.80%
Prunus serotina [Black Cherry]	2	42%	1.40%
Pseudotsuga menziesii [Douglas-Fir]	6	9.70%	3.90%
Pteridium revolutum [Hairy Bracken]	3	49%	7.40%
Pteridium aquilinum [Bracken]	4	45.30%	20.50%
Pteris vittata [Ladder brake]	3	38.30%	6.90%
Puccinellia maritima [Seaside Alkaligrass]	4	61%	31%
Pueraria lobata (Leguminous Weed)	1	98%	0%
Pyrrosia piloselloides [Tropical Fern]	1	78%	0%
Pyrus pyrifolia [Asian Pear]	2	23.50%	5.30%
Quercus alba L. [White Oak]	6	146.70%	30.10%
Quercus cerrioides [Oak]	1	35%	0%
Quercus chapmanii Sargenti [Chapman's Oak]	3	278.70%	90.80%
Quercus geminata [Sand Live Oak]	6	8.70%	4.50%
Quercus ilex L. [Holly Oak]	4	38%	4.80%
Quercus margaretta [Sand Post Oak]	2	20.50%	14.50%
Quercus mongolica [Mongolian Oak]	6	54.30%	19.50%
Quercus myrtifolia Wild. [Myrtle Oak]	9	136.90%	56.30%
Quercus petraea (Mattuschka) Liebl. [Durmast Oak]	6	53.20%	18.70%
Quercus robur L. [Pedunculate Oak]	8	30.60%	12.80%
Quercus rubra L. [Northern Red Oak]	7	55.30%	25.20%
Quercus suber L. [Cork Oak]	4	46.80%	13.70%
Raphanus sativus [Wild Radish]	22	71.20%	12.20%
Raphanus sativus x raphanistrum [Wild Radish]	1	33%	0%
Rhinanthus alectorolophus [European Yellowrattle]	2	75%	68.60%
Rhinanthus minor [Yellow Rattle]	1	50%	0%
Rhizophora mangle [American Mangrove]	3	39.30%	6.10%
Ricinus communis [Castor Bean]	7	53.60%	16.30%
Robinia pseudoacacia [Black Locust]	4	346%	242.10%
Rosa hybrida [Rose]	4	26.50%	7.90%
Rubus [Blackberry]	1	675%	0%
Rubus idaeus [Red Raspberry]	4	111.80%	32.80%
Rudbeckia hirta [Black-eyed Susan]	1	0%	0%
Rumex acetosella [Common Sheep Sorrel]	2	24%	2.10%
Rumex obtusifolius [Bitter Dock]	6	18.70%	12.50%
Saccharina latissima [Sugar Kelp]	74	35.10%	5.30%
Saccharum officinarum [Sugarcane]	11	34%	6.50%
Salix jiangsuensis [Willow]	2	38.50%	8.80%
Salix myrsinifolia [Dark Leaved Willow]	8	70.80%	13.70%
Salvia officinalis [Sage]	2	21%	11.30%
Salvia pitcheri [Pitcher Sage]	2	25.50%	2.50%
Sanguisorba minor [Small Burnet]	6	81.20%	15.20%
Schima superba[Subtropical Tree]	2	27.50%	11%
Schizachyrium scoparium [Little Bluestem]	9	18.20%	9%
Schoenoplectus americanus [Chairmaker's Bulrush]	1	27%	0%
Scindapsus aureus [Pothos]	1	39%	0%
Scirpus lacustris [Softstem Bulrush]	1	-2%	0%
Scirpus olneyi [Salt Marsh Sedge]	10	17.40%	7.70%
Sedum alfredii [Perennial Herb]	6	23.30%	2.40%
Senecio jacobea [Ragwort]	1	21%	0%
Senecio vulgaris [Common Groundsel]	2	66%	25.50%
Sesbania vesicaria [Bagpod]	1	60%	0%
Setaria glauca [Yellow Bristle Grass]	1	16%	0%
Seteria faberi [Japanese Bristlegrass]	5	18.80%	6.70%
Seteria viridis [Green Bristlegrass]	4	16%	0.80%
Shorea leprosula	2	38.50%	11%
Silene cretica in mixed stands with Silene cretica [Common Flax]	2	98.50%	17.30%
Silene latifolia [White Campion]	6	43.50%	9%
Silene noctiflora [Night-flowering Catchfly]	1	44%	0%
Sinapis alba [White Mustard]	4	21.30%	4.10%

Plant Name	# of Studies	Mean CO₂ Growth Response	Standard Error	Plant Name	# of Studies	Mean CO₂ Growth Response	Standard Error
Solanum viarum [Tropical Soda Apple]	1	39%	0%	Thinouia tomocarpa Standley	2	94%	28.30%
Solanum curtilobum [Shortlobe Solanum]	2	63%	5.70%	Thymus vulgaris [Thyme]	1	0%	0%
Solanum dulcamara [Climbing Nightshade]	10	46.50%	9.30%	Toxicodendron radicans [Poison Ivy]	7	75.70%	13.70%
Solanum lycopersicum [Tomato]	2	152.50%	23%	Trachypogon plumosus [C₄ South American Grass]	2	-28.50%	3.20%
Solanum melongena [Eggplant]	1	41%	0%	Tridens flavus [Purpletop Tridens]	1	0%	0%
Solanum muricatum [Pepino]	4	69.80%	20.50%	Trifolium alexandrium [Berseem]	1	41%	0%
Solanum tuberosum [White Potato]	36	29.50%	3.30%	Trifolium incarnatum [Crimson Clover]	2	21.50%	0.40%
Solidago canadensis [Canadian Goldenrod]	2	1750%	1237.40%	Trifolium pratense [Purple Clover]	6	16.30%	3.70%
Solidago rigida [Stiff Goldenrod]	1	27%	0%	Trifolium repens [White Clover]	49	64.90%	15.70%
Sorghastrum nutans [Yellow Indian Grass]	3	9.70%	14.40%	Trifolium subterraneum [Subterranean Clover]	1	756%	0%
Sorghum bicolor [Sorghum]	28	19.90%	3.50%	Trigonella foenum-graecum [Fenugreek]	2	91%	33.20%
Sorghum halepense [Johnsongrass]	3	-13%	14.30%	Triticum dicoccoides [Wheat]	1	378%	0%
Sorghum sudanense [Sudan Grass]	1	14%	0%	Triticum monococcum [Einkorn Wheat]	1	180%	0%
Spartina densiflora [Dense Flowered Cordgrass]	3	24.30%	12.40%	Triticum aestivum [Common Wheat]	260	33.40%	1.80%
Spartina alterniflora [Smooth Cordgrass]	2	0%	0%	Triticum turgidum [Rivet Wheat]	8	26.30%	1.80%
Spartina anglica [Common Cordgrass]	3	19%	25.10%	Tropaeolum majus [Nasturtium]	3	42.30%	10.80%
Spergula arvensis [Corn Spurrey]	2	-20%	7.80%	Tsuga canadensis [Eastern Hemlock]	3	34%	4.50%
Sphagnum cuspidatum [Toothed Sphagnum]	1	42%	0%	Typha augustifolia [Narrowleaf Cattail]	3	41.30%	8.50%
Sphagnum magellanicum [Magellan's Sphagnum]	1	26%	0%	Typha x glauca [White Cattail]	1	16%	0%
Sphagnum papillosum [Papillose Sphagnum]	2	57.50%	0.40%	Typha latifolia [Cattail]	2	12.50%	10.30%
Sphagnum recurvum [Recurved Sphagnum]	4	12.30%	7%	Ulmus alata [Winged Elm]	1	30%	0%
Spinacia oleracea [Spinach]	3	24.30%	5.70%	Urtica dioica [Stinging Nettle]	1	26%	0%
Sporobolus indicus [Smut Grass]	1	-5%	0%	Vaccinium myrtillus [Whortleberry]	6	60.70%	10%
Sporobolus pyramidalis [Whorled Dropseed]	6	33.50%	21.70%	Vallisneria tortifolia [Corkscrew Vallisneria]	2	14%	5.70%
Stipa thurberiana [Thurber Needlegrass]	1	11%	0%	Vernonia herbacea [Fructan Accumulating Plant]	2	31%	4.20%
Striga hermonthica [Purple Witchweed]	1	-65%	0%	Veronica didyma [Gray Field Speedwell]	1	26%	0%
Stylosanthes hamata [Pencil Flower]	1	18%	0%	Vicia cracca [Bird Vetch]	1	47%	0%
Stylosanthes scabra [Pencilflower]	2	72%	10.60%	Vicia faba [Faba Bean]	4	46.30%	13.50%
Symphiocarpos orbiculatus [Buck Brush]	2	98.50%	42.10%	Vicia lathyroides [Spring Vetch]	1	114%	0%
Syracosphaera pulchra [Marine Coccolithophore]	2	9%	2.80%	Vigna angularis [Adsuki Bean]	4	60%	5.20%
Taxodium distichum [Bald Cypress]	5	28%	5.40%	Vigna mungo [Blackgram]	2	87%	19.80%
Taxus baccata [English Yew]	5	28%	5.40%	Vigna radiata [Mungbean]	2	31.50%	16.60%
Tectona grandis [Teak, Common]	8	44.60%	7.20%	Vigna unguiculata [Blackeyed Pea]	4	77%	10.80%
Terminalia arjuna [Terminalia]	8	190.60%	35.10%	Viola x wittrockiana [Pansy]	1	30%	0%
Terminalia chebula [Myrobalan]	8	442.50%	52.50%	Vitis vinifera [Grapevine, Common]	5	68.20%	16.60%
Themeda triandra [Kangaroo Grass]	9	54.90%	15.80%	Vulpia microstachys [Small Fescue]	2	-4.50%	8.10%
				Wedelia chinensis [Herb, Perennial]	2	47.50%	0.40%

Plant Name	# of Studies	Mean CO_2 Growth Response	Standard Error
Wedelia trilobata [Creeping Daisy]	2	59.50%	0.40%
Weeds, Unspecified	2	0%	0%
Xanthium strumarium var. Xanthium strumarium [Canada Cockleburr]	7	30.60%	6.40%
Yucca brevifolia [Joshua Tree]	1	65%	0%
Yucca schidigera [Mojave Yucca]	1	86%	0%
Yucca whipplei [Chaparral Yucca]	1	13%	0%
Zea mays [Corn]	24	24.10%	5%
Zingiber officinale [Ginger]	2	46.50%	7.40%
Zizania latifolia [Manchurian Wildrice]	1	-5%	0%
Zostera marina [Eelgrass, Common]	1	24%	0%

Appendix 4

Table 1.1.2 — Plant Photosynthesis (Net CO_2 Exchange Rate) Responses to Atmospheric CO_2 Enrichment

Table 1.1.2. reports the results of peer-reviewed scientific studies measuring the photosynthetic growth response of plants to a 300 ppm increase in atmospheric CO_2 concentration. Plants are listed by common and/or scientific names, followed by the number of experimental studies conducted on each plant, the mean photosynthetic response to a 300 ppm increase in the air's CO_2 content, and the standard error of that mean. Whenever the CO_2 increase for a given study was not exactly 300 ppm, a linear adjustment was computed. For example, if the CO_2 increase was 350 ppm and the growth response was a 60 percent enhancement, the adjusted 300 ppm CO_2 growth response was calculated as (300/350) x 60% = 51%.

The data in this table appear by permission of the Center for the Study of Carbon Dioxide and Global Change and were taken from its Plant Growth database on 1 January 2014. In all, the table summarizes CO_2 enrichment results from 2,094 separate experimental conditions conducted on 472 plant species. New data are added to the database at approximately weekly intervals and can be accessed free of charge at the center's website at http://www.co2science.org/data/plant_growth/dry/dry_subject.php. This online database also archives information pertaining to the experimental conditions under which each plant growth experiment was conducted, as well as the complete reference to the journal article from which the experimental results were obtained. The center's online database also lists percent increases in plant photosynthetic rate for 600 and/or 900 ppm increases in the air's CO_2 concentration.

Plant Name	Number of Studies	Mean CO₂ Growth Response	Standard Error
Abelmoschus esculentus [Okra]	1	27%	0%
Abies alba [Silver Fir]	2	37.50%	15.20%
Abutilon theophrasti [Velvet Leaf]	6	46.70%	10.30%
Acacia catechu [Black Cutch]	1	24%	0%
Acacia nigrescens [Knob Thorn]	1	16%	0%
Acacia melanoxylon [Blackwood]	1	19%	0%
Acacia minuta [Coastal Scrub Wattle]	1	21%	0%
Acacia nilotica [Gum Arabic Tree]	4	71.50%	31.20%
Acer mono [Shantung Maple]	4	40.80%	15.10%
Acer rubrum [Red Maple]	17	94.80%	22.60%
Acer saccharinum [Silver Maple]	8	18.50%	7.80%
Acer saccharum [Sugar Maple]	3	64%	9%
Achillea millefolium [Yarrow]	5	27%	15.70%
Ackama rosaefolia [Small Bushy Tree]	1	-20%	0%

Plant Name	Number of Studies	Mean CO₂ Growth Response	Standard Error
Acmena acuminatissima [Tree]	2	40.50%	1.10%
Actinidia deliciosa [Kiwifruit]	1	113%	0%
Adenocaulon bicolor [American Trailplant]	2	38.50%	2.50%
Aechmea [CAM Bromeliad]	1	58%	0%
Agathis microstachya [Semi-Evergreen Rainforest Tree]	1	50%	0%
Agathis robusta [Queensland Kauri]	1	56%	0%
Agave deserti [Desert Agave]	2	34.50%	3.20%
Agave salmiana [Pulque Agave]	2	39.50%	6.70%
Agave vilmoriniana [Leaf Succulent]	2	37.50%	26.50%
Agropyron repens [Couch Grass]	3	42%	18.50%
Agropyron smithii [Western Wheatgrass]	2	-4.50%	6%
Agrostis canina [Velvet Bentgrass]	1	38%	0%
Agrostis capillaris [Colonial Bentgrass]	3	46.30%	20.20%

Plant Name	Number of Studies	Mean CO₂ Growth Response	Standard Error	Plant Name	Number of Studies	Mean CO₂ Growth Response	Standard Error
Albizia procera [Tall Albizia]	2	121%	19.10%	Azolla pinnata [Water Fern]	2	35%	24.70%
Alnus maximowiczii [Alder Tree]	4	32.80%	5.90%	Bauhinia variegata [Mountain Ebony]	1	16%	0%
Alnus firma [Alder]	4	83.50%	6.40%	Begonia x hiemalis [Begonia]	2	70%	21.20%
Alnus glutinosa [Black Alder]	3	51%	11.80%	Beilschmiedia pendula [Slugwood]	4	21.30%	7.70%
Alnus hirsuta [Manchurian Alder]	11	23.10%	11.80%	Beta vulgaris [Common Beet]	11	62.20%	9.30%
Alnus rubra [Red Alder]	8	73.90%	10.60%	Betula ermanii [Birch, Ermans]	2	53%	2.10%
Alocasia macrorrhiza [Giant Taro]	2	79%	18.40%	Betula albosinensis [Chinese Red Birch]	1	65%	0%
Alternanthera crucis [West Indian Joyweed]	1	91%	0%	Betula alleghaniensis [Yellow Birch]	6	35%	5.90%
Amaranthus viridis [Slender Amaranth]	2	-7%	6.40%	Betula davurica [Dahurian Birch]	1	52%	0%
Amaranthus hybridus [Slim Amaranth]	2	2.50%	1.80%	Betula maximowicziana [Monarch Birch]	8	31%	10.30%
Amaranthus hypochondriacus [Grain Amaranth]	1	9%	0%	Betula nanal [Bog Birch]	1	0%	0%
Amaranthus retroflexus [Redroot Amaranth]	5	10.20%	4.20%	Betula nigra [River Birch]	1	40%	0%
Ambrosia artemisiifolia [Annual Ragweed]	3	37.70%	5.20%	Betula papyrifera [Paper Birch]	57	60.80%	10.90%
Ambrosia cordifolia [Tuscon Burr Ragweed]	3	45.70%	3.80%	Betula pendula [European White Birch]	7	28.60%	7.80%
Ambrosia dumosa [White Burrobush]	4	85%	28%	Betula platyphylla [Broadleaf White Birch]	9	24.40%	7.10%
Amorpha canescens [Leadplant]	1	24%	0%	Betula pubescens Ehrh. [Downy Birch]	4	113.50%	67.20%
Anacardium excelsum	1	19%	0%	Bothriochloa caucasica [Caucasian Bluestem]	2	15.50%	11%
Anagallis arvensis [Scarlet Pimpernel]	1	45%	0%	Bouteloua curtipendula [Sideoats Grama]	2	18.50%	2.50%
Ananas comosus [Pineapple]	3	168.30%	55.80%	Bouteloua gracilis [Blue Grama]	4	49.80%	23%
Andropogon gerardii [Big Bluestem]	14	23.10%	5.70%	Brachychiton populneum [Whiteflower Kurrajong]	1	75%	0%
Andropogon glomeratus [Bushy Bluestem]	2	-1%	3.50%	Brachyglottis repanda [Rangiora]	1	120%	0%
Anemone cylindrica [Candle Anemone]	3	57.30%	18.50%	Brachypodium pinnatum [Heath Falsebrome]	1	59%	0%
Anemone raddeana [Anemone]	2	65%	24.70%	Brassica campestris [Rape Seed Mustard]	2	90.50%	37.10%
Anthoxanthum odoratum [Sweet Vernal Grass]	1	109%	0%	Brassica carinata [Abyssinian Mustard]	2	34.50%	10.30%
Anthyllis vulneraria [Common Kidney Vetch]	4	27.80%	10.30%	Brassica juncea [India Mustard]	2	50.50%	24.40%
Antirrhoea trichantha	1	33%	0%	Brassica napus [Canola]	12	63.50%	20.10%
Apple	2	105.50%	18.70%	Brassica nigra [Black Mustard]	2	39%	11.30%
Arabidopsis thaliana [Mouse Ear Cress]	9	56.20%	17%	Bromus erectus [Erect Brome]	6	30.20%	9.50%
Arachis hypogaea [Peanut]	7	44.30%	8.60%	Bromus inermis [Smooth Brome]	4	36%	9.40%
Arbutus unedo [Strawberry Tree]	4	91.30%	32.10%	Bromus madritensis [Compact Brome]	1	12%	0%
Armeria maritima [Thrift Seapink]	1	46%	0%	Bromus sterilis [Poverty Brome]	1	45%	0%
Arrhenatherum elatius [Tall Oatgrass]	1	39%	0%	Bromus tectorum [Cheatgrass]	1	56%	0%
Artemisia tridentata [Big Sagebrush]	2	31%	12.70%	Bryum pseudotriquetrum [Common Green Bryum Moss]	2	47.50%	10.30%
Asparagus officinalis [Garden Asparagus]	1	25%	0%	Bryum subrotundifolium	2	28.50%	8.10%
Avena barbata [Slender Oat]	2	52%	5.70%	Buchloe dactyloides [Buchloe dactyloides]	1	27%	0%
Avena fatua [Wild Oat]	2	53%	11.30%	Cajanus cajan [Pigeonpea]	2	137.50%	26.50%
Avena sativa [Red Oat]	2	32.50%	3.90%	Calamagrostis epigeios [Chee Reedgrass]	1	27%	0%

Appendix 4 – Plant Photosynthesis (Net CO_2 Exchange Rate) Responses

Plant Name	Number of Studies	Mean CO_2 Growth Response	Standard Error
Calluna vulgaris [Heather]	20	114.50%	48.50%
Calophyllum longifolium [Tropical Tree]	1	-15%	0%
Caloplaxa trachyphylla [Lichen]	1	38%	0%
Capsicum annuum [Bell Pepper]	3	41%	15.50%
Carex bigelowii [Bigelow's Sedge]	1	0%	0%
Carex curvula dominated alpine grassland	2	66.50%	15.20%
Carex flacca [Heath Sedge]	1	55%	0%
Carex paleacea [Chaffy Sedge]	1	34%	0%
Cariniana legalis [Jequitiba Tree]	2	39.50%	11%
Carpinus betulus [European Hornbeam]	4	14.80%	6.40%
Carya glabra [Pignut Hickory]	3	57.30%	22.80%
Carya ovata [Shagbark Hickory]	1	35%	0%
Castanea sativa [Sweet Chesnut]	2	66.50%	37.80%
Castanopsis hystrix [Chinkapin]	2	57%	3.50%
Cecropia longipes	1	17%	0%
Cenchrus ciliaris	1	31%	0%
Centella asiatica [Centella]	1	33%	0%
Ceratonia siliqua [Carob]	6	40.50%	7.50%
Cercis canadensis [Eastern Redbud]	3	127.30%	48%
Chamaenerion angustifolium [Narrowleaved Fireweed]	1	96%	0%
Chenopodium album [Lambsquarters]	6	43.30%	8.90%
Cirsium arvense [Canadian Thistle]	4	56.50%	8%
Cistus salviifolius [Cistus]	1	53%	0%
Citrus aurantium [Sour Orange]	12	111.60%	15.30%
Citrus madurensis [Calamondin]	2	195%	74.20%
Citrus paradisi Macfad. budded to Citrus paradisi Blanco (Cleopatra mandarin) rootstock [Marsh Grapefruit]	2	60%	4.90%
Citrus paradisi Macfad. budded to Citrus paradisi (L.) Raf. rootstock [Marsh Grapefruit]	2	70%	14.10%
Citrus reticulata [Mandarin Orange]	2	45.50%	8.80%
Citrus sinensis (L.) Osbeck budded to Citrus sinensis Blanco (Cleopatra manderin) rootstock [Washington Naval Orange]	2	52.50%	10.30%
Citrus sinensis (L.) Osbeck budded to Citrus sinensis (L.) Raf. rootstock [Washington Naval Orange]	2	43.50%	8.10%
Citrus sinensis (L.) Osbeck x Citrus sinensis Blanco (Cleoplatra manderin) [Valencia Orange]	2	42.50%	15.90%
Citrus sinensis (L.) Osbeck x Citrus sinensis (L.) Raf. [Valencia Orange]	2	54.50%	5.30%
Citrus sinensis [Sweet Orange]	2	57%	4.90%
Citrus sinensis x poncirus trifoliata [Carrizo Citrange]	2	76.50%	9.50%

Plant Name	Number of Studies	Mean CO_2 Growth Response	Standard Error
Cladonia rangiferina (L.) Wigg. [Fruticose Lichen]	1	31%	0%
Claoxylon sandwicense [Po'ola]	3	100%	12.50%
Coffea arabusta [Coffee]	2	271%	65.10%
Collema furfuraceum [Jelly Lichen]	1	42%	0%
Cordia alliodora [Spanish Elm]	1	41%	0%
Corynocarpus laevigatus [Karaka Nut]	1	79%	0%
Crocosphaera watsonii [Diazotrophic Cyanobacterium]	2	71%	38.20%
Croton urucurana [Dragons Blood Tree]	2	47%	17.70%
Cucumis melo [Cantaloupe]	4	56.80%	0.70%
Cucumis sativus [Garden Cucumber]	5	112.20%	68.60%
Cucurbita pepo [Zucchini]	2	34%	6.40%
Cyperus esculentus [Yellow Nutsedge]	1	-26%	0%
Cyperus rotundus [Purple Nutsedge]	1	6%	0%
Dactylis glomerata [Orchardgrass]	12	39.30%	7.20%
Dalbergia latifolia [Indian Rosewood]	1	9%	0%
Daucus carota [Carrot]	8	105.30%	38%
Dendrosenecio brassica [Afro-alpine Giant Rosette Plant]	1	65%	0%
Dendrosenecio keniodendron [Afro-alpine Giant Rosette Plant]	1	52%	0%
Digitalis purpurea [Purple Foxglove]	1	78%	0%
Digitaria sanguinalis [Hairy Crabgrass]	3	75.30%	32.70%
Dodonaea viscosa [Florida Hopbush]	1	42%	0%
Echinochloa crus-galli [Barnyard Grass]	8	24.40%	4.40%
Elaeis gulneensis [African Oil Palm]	1	105%	0%
Elatostema repens [Tropical Rain Forest Herb]	1	68%	0%
Eleusine indica [Indian Goosegrass]	1	72%	0%
Elymus elymoides [Bottlebrush Squirreltail]	1	21%	0%
Elymus repens [Couch Grass]	1	176%	0%
Emiliania huxleyi [Marine Coccolithophorid]	5	47.80%	13.10%
Encelia frutescens [Button Brittlebush]	1	30%	0%
Entandrophragma angolense [West African Mahogany]	3	63.30%	7.20%
Epilobium hirsutum [Codlins and Cream]	1	62%	0%
Eragrostis orcuttiana [Annual Weed, C4]	1	-44%	0%
Eriogonum inflatum [Native American Pipeweed]	2	42.50%	15.90%
Eucalyptus deglupta x e. camaldulensis [Rainbow Eucalyptus X Red River Gum Hybrid]	2	44%	20.50%
Eucalyptus saligna [Sydney Blue Gum]	8	42.30%	9.80%
Eucalyptus sideroxylon [Red Ironbark]	6	68.80%	9%
Eucalyptus urophylla [Rose Gum Tree]	2	67.50%	15.20%

Plant Name	Number of Studies	Mean CO$_2$ Growth Response	Standard Error	Plant Name	Number of Studies	Mean CO$_2$ Growth Response	Standard Error
Eucalyptus and Eucalyptus [Forest Canopy in Lysimeter]	1	53%	0%	Helianthus petiolaris [Prairie Sunflower]	2	20%	0%
Eucalyptus cladocalyx [Sugargum]	2	47.50%	27.20%	Heterotheca subaxillaris [Camphorweed]	1	17%	0%
Eucalyptus microtheca [Coolibah Tree]	1	57%	0%	Hevea brasiliensis [Rubber Tree]	8	85.90%	3.90%
Eucalyptus polyanthemus [Silver Dollar Gum]	1	75%	0%	Holcus lanatus [Common Velvetgrass]	1	85%	0%
Eucalyptus tetrodonta	3	26.30%	8.40%	Hordeum marinum [Sea Barley]	3	40.30%	7%
Eupatorium adenophorum [Sticky Snakeroot]	5	35%	3.80%	Hordeum vulagare [Barley]	25	56.80%	8.30%
Eupatorium japonicum [Pei Lan]	4	21.50%	6.80%	Hylocomium splendens [Splendid Feather Moss]	1	100%	0%
Eupatorium stoechadosmum [Orchid Herb]	3	19.70%	8.80%	Hymenaea courbaril [Stinkingtoe]	1	70%	0%
Evernia mesomorpha [Ring Lichen]	1	60%	0%	Hyparrhenia rufa [Jaragua]	1	70%	0%
Fagus crenata [Japanese Beech]	6	29.50%	5.70%	Hypnea spinella [Red Seaweed]	1	32%	0%
Fagus grandifolia [American Beech]	1	96%	0%	Hyptis suaveolens [Wild Spikenard]	1	88%	0%
Fagus sylvatica [European Beech]	14	58.70%	8.90%	Ipomoea cairica [Mile A Minute Vine]	1	56%	0%
Fargesia rufa [Bamboo, Dwarf]	2	39.50%	6%	Ipomoea carnea [Gloria De La Manana]	1	62%	0%
Fargesia denudata [Bamboo]	1	40%	0%	Ipomoea pes-caprae [Beach Morning Glory]	1	35%	0%
Feijoa sellowiana [Pineapple Guava]	1	55%	0%	Ipomoea batatas [Sweet Potato]	5	39.40%	10.80%
Ferocactus acanthodes [California Barrelcactus]	1	30%	0%	Jatropha curcas [Purging Nut]	3	49.30%	6.20%
Festuca arundinacea [Tall Fescue]	2	46.50%	2.50%	Jatropha gossypiifolia [Bellyache Bush]	1	73%	0%
Festuca pratensis [Meadow Fescue]	2	34.50%	1.80%	Juglans nigra [Black Walnut]	1	24%	0%
Festuca rupicola [Fescue]	2	112.50%	54.10%	Kalankoe blossfeldiana	1	47%	0%
Ficus insipida	1	47%	0%	Koeleria cristata [June Grass]	4	242.50%	189.90%
Ficus obtusifolia [Amate]	1	76%	0%	Krameria erecta[Littleleaf Ratany]	4	115.80%	28.60%
Filipendula vulgaris [Dropwort]	3	273.70%	81.70%	Lactuca serriola [Prickly Lettuce]	1	60%	0%
Flaveria floridana [Florida Yellowtops]	1	25%	0%	Lantana camara [Lantana]	1	245%	0%
Flaveria pringlei [Yellowtops]	1	33%	0%	Larix decidua [European Larch]	3	62.70%	4.80%
Flaveria trinervia [Clustered Yellowtops]	3	9%	3.70%	Larix kaempferi [Japanese Larch]	4	38.80%	16.80%
Fontinalis antipyretica [Antifever Fontinalis Moss]	2	235%	166.20%	Larix laricina [Tamarack]	1	47%	0%
Fragaria x ananassa [Hybrid Strawberry]	14	72.60%	12.50%	Larrea tridentata [Creosote Bush]	10	103.60%	24.40%
Fraxinus lanceolata [Green Ash]	1	60%	0%	Lasthenia californica [California Goldfields]	1	47%	0%
Fraxinus pennsylvanica [Green Ash]	5	62.40%	12.90%	Lecanora muralis [An Epilithic Lichen]	1	42%	0%
Freshwater Benthic Algae	1	68%	0%	Ledum palustre [Wild Rosemary]	1	0%	0%
Geum reptans [Avens]	1	84%	0%	Lemna gibba [Swollen Duckweed]	2	55.50%	3.90%
Geum rivale [Water Avens]	1	31%	0%	Lespedeza capitata [Roundhead Lespedeza]	1	14%	0%
Ginkgo biloba [Maidenhair Tree]	6	54%	15.80%	Leucadendron coniferum [Dune Conebush]	2	38%	14.10%
Glycine max [Soybean]	98	50.40%	7.40%	Leucadendron laureolum [Golden Conebush]	2	28.50%	5.30%
Gmelina arborea [White Teak]	1	114%	0%	Leucadendron meridianum [Limestone Conebush]	2	18%	10.60%
Gossypium hirsutum [Cotton]	20	44.20%	5.20%	Leucadendron xanthoconus [Sickle-leaf Conebush]	2	59%	9.90%
Gracilaria lemaneiformis [Red Alga]	2	20%	10.60%	Leymus chinensis [Chinese Lyme-grass]	2	133.50%	32.20%
Helianthus annuus [Sunflower]	19	51.80%	6.50%				

Appendix 4 – Plant Photosynthesis (Net CO_2 Exchange Rate) Responses

Plant Name	Number of Studies	Mean CO_2 Growth Response	Standard Error	Plant Name	Number of Studies	Mean CO_2 Growth Response	Standard Error
Liquidambar styraciflua [Sweetgum]	18	105.10%	21.80%	Paederia scandens [Chinese Fever Vine]	1	3%	0%
Liriodendron tulipifera [Yellow Poplar]	13	64.40%	12.40%	Panicum antidotale [Blue Panicgrass]	2	-2.50%	4.60%
Lobelia telekii [Afro-alpine Giant Rosette Plant]	1	52%	0%	Panicum dichotomiflorum [Fall Panicgrass]	1	18%	0%
Lolium mutiflorum [Italian Ryegrass]	3	18.30%	2.80%	Panicum laxum [Lax Panicgrass]	2	8.50%	5.30%
Lolium perenne [Perennial Ryegrass]	32	39.80%	3.70%	Panicum maximum [Guineagrass]	2	16%	3.50%
Lolium temulentum [Darnel Ryegrass]	2	23.50%	1.80%	Panicum miliaceum [Broomcorn Millet]	2	12%	2.10%
Lotus corniculatus [Birdfoot Deer Vetch]	1	38%	0%	Panicum virgatum [Switchgrass]	1	64%	0%
Luehea seemannii	2	20%	2.10%	Parmelia caperata [Foliose Lichen]	1	16%	0%
Lupinus arizonicus [Arizona Lupine]	3	15.70%	6.50%	Parmelia kurokawae [Foliose Lichen]	1	30%	0%
Lupinus perennis [Sundial Lupine]	4	57.30%	27%	Parmelia praesignis [Flavopunctelia Lichen]	1	60%	0%
Lycopersicon esculentum [Garden Tomato]	14	24.30%	4.90%	Parmelia reticulata [Netted Rimelia Lichen]	1	63%	0%
Lyonia mariana [Piedmont Staggerbush]	1	27%	0%	Pascopyrum smithii [Western Wheatgrass]	6	61.20%	14.90%
Malvastrum rotundifolium [Desert Fivespot]	3	33%	5.70%	Paspalum dilatatum [Dallas Grass]	4	80.80%	18.40%
Manihot esculenta [Cassava]	2	7%	34.60%	Paspalum notatum [Bahiagrass]	1	24%	0%
Medicago lupulina [Black Medic]	1	46%	0%	Peanut, Rhizoma	1	40%	0%
Medicago glomerata	1	16%	0%	Pelargonium x hortorum [Pelargonium]	3	19.30%	8.80%
Medicago minima [Burr Medick]	1	0%	0%	Peltigera canina [Felt Lichen]	1	24%	0%
Medicago sativa [Alfalfa]	19	24.60%	3.80%	Peltigera membranacea [Membraneous Felt Lichen]	1	83%	0%
Melinis minutiflora [Molassesgrass]	2	7.50%	12.40%	Peltigera polydactyla [Foliose Lichen]	1	83%	0%
Metasequoia glyptostroboides [Dawn Redwood]	3	86.30%	42.80%	Peltigera rufescens [Felt Lichen]	1	83%	0%
Mikania micrantha [Bittervine]	1	70%	0%	Petalostemum villosum [Silky Prairie Clover]	1	32%	0%
Nauclea diderrichii [Pioneer Tropical Tree]	3	69.70%	2.20%	Phalaenopsis [Orchid]	2	191%	2.10%
Nicotiana sylvestris [South American Tobacco]	1	55%	0%	Phalaris arundinacea [Canary Grass]	32	29.60%	2%
Nicotiana tabacum [Cultivated Tobacco]	9	68%	14.90%	Phalaris aquatica [Harding Grass]	2	39.50%	17.30%
Nostoc commune	1	5%	0%	Phaseolus vulgaris [Garden Bean]	24	55.80%	10.30%
Nothofagus cunninghamii [Myrtle Beech]	3	24.70%	13.20%	Phillyrea angustifolia [False Olive]	2	75%	10.60%
Nothofagus fusca [Red Beech]	3	40%	1.70%	Phleum pratense [Timothy]	3	30.30%	3.20%
Nymphaea marliac [Water Lily]	3	39.70%	12.40%	Phyllanthus emblica [Emblic]	2	71%	21.90%
Oenothera primiveris [Desert Eveningprimrose]	1	23%	0%	Phytolacca americana [American Pokeweed]	1	56%	0%
Olea europaea [Olive]	10	50.20%	12.60%	Picea glauca [White spruce]	1	197%	0%
Olearia ilicifolia [Holly-Leaved Daisybush]	1	79%	0%	Picea abies [Norway Spruce]	14	52.60%	6.60%
Opuntia ficus-indica [Prickly Pear]	7	26.70%	4.30%	Picea koraiensis [Spruce]	1	73%	0%
Ormosia pinnata [Tree]	2	45%	2.80%	Picea mariana [Black Spruce]	5	33.60%	9.20%
Orontium aquaticum [Goldenclub]	7	72.10%	9.30%	Picea sitchensis [Sitka Spruce]	2	23%	4.20%
Oryza sativa [Rice]	79	46.80%	4.80%	Pinus tabulaeformis [Chinese Red Pine]	2	60.50%	4.60%
Oryzopsis hymenoides [Perennial Bunchgrass]	1	47%	0%	Pinus banksiana [Pine, Jack]	4	34.80%	6.20%
Pachysandra terminalis [Japanese Spurge]	1	70%	0%	Pinus densiflora [Pine, Japonese Red]	5	26.40%	8%

Plant Name	Number of Studies	Mean CO₂ Growth Response	Standard Error	Plant Name	Number of Studies	Mean CO₂ Growth Response	Standard Error
Pinus eldarica [Pine, Eldarica]	2	133%	0%	Prochlorococcus [Marine Picocyanobacterium]	2	5.50%	2.50%
Pinus koraiensis [Pine, Korean]	3	58.30%	9.70%	Prunus armeniaca [Apricot]	4	62.80%	4.20%
Pinus merkusii [Pine, Merkus]	2	44.50%	3.20%	Prunus avium [Sweet Cherry]	1	38%	0%
Pinus patula [Mexican Yellow Pine]	1	47%	0%	Prunus persica [Peach]	4	37.50%	8.70%
Pinus ponderosa [Ponderosa Pine]	10	45.90%	8.80%	Prunus serotina [Black Cherry]	3	63.70%	5.70%
Pinus radiata [Monterey Pine]	13	40.20%	3.80%	Pseudobombax septenatum [Tropical Tree]	1	68%	0%
Pinus sylvestris [Scots Pine]	22	70.10%	25.20%	Pseudopanax arboreus [Puahou]	1	69%	0%
Pinus taeda [Loblolly Pine]	48	87.60%	9.80%	Pseudotsuga menziesii [Douglas-Fir]	17	32%	5.30%
Pinus uncinata [Mountain Pine]	2	44%	7.10%	Psychotria limonensis [Forest Shrub]	1	65%	0%
Piper auritum [Vera Cruz Pepper]	2	67.50%	5.30%	Pteridium aquilinum [Bracken]	8	93.80%	7.30%
Piper hispidum [Jamaican Pepper]	2	77.50%	15.90%	Puccinellia maritima [Seaside Alkaligrass]	5	84%	17.80%
Pisum sativum [Garden Pea]	4	37.80%	5%	Pyrrosia piloselloides [Tropical Fern]	1	19%	0%
Plantago asiatica [Plantago Asiatica]	2	38%	4.90%	Pyrus pyrifolia [Asian Pear]	4	64.50%	8.50%
Plantago erecta [Dwarf Plantain]	1	43%	0%	Quercus alba [White Oak]	3	142%	38.30%
Plantago lanceolata [Narrowleaf Plantain]	7	67.60%	21.30%	Quercus chapmanii [Chapman's Oak]	4	53%	4.10%
Plantago maritima [Sea Plantain]	1	-30%	0%	Quercus crispula [Mongolian Oak]	2	19%	3.50%
Platanus occidentalis [American Sycamore]	1	60%	0%	Quercus geminata [Sand Live Oak]	6	15.70%	5.90%
Poa annua [Annual Bluegrass]	6	62%	14%	Quercus ilex [Holly Oak]	11	91.40%	30.10%
Poa cookii [Bluegrass]	1	55%	0%	Quercus mongolica [Mongolian Oak]	24	74.80%	13.50%
Poa pratensis [Kentucky Bluegrass]	4	153.30%	54.10%	Quercus myrtifolia [Myrtle Oak]	9	60.60%	7.70%
Poa trivialis [Rough Bluegrass]	1	41%	0%	Quercus petraea [Durmast Oak]	2	23.50%	0.40%
Polygonum cuspidatum [Japanese Knotweed]	3	32.70%	3.50%	Quercus pubescens [Downy Oak]	5	136.80%	58.50%
Polygonum sachalinense [Giant Knotweed]	5	46.60%	8.30%	Quercus robur [Pedunculate Oak]	9	35.80%	6.20%
Polygoum persicaria [Spotted Ladysthumb]	2	-2.50%	1.80%	Quercus rubra [Northern Red Oak]	16	63%	10.40%
Populus tremula x alba [Hybrid Poplar]	1	23%	0%	Quercus suber [Cork Oak]	3	28.70%	16.90%
Populus tremula x populus tremuloides [Hybrid Aspen]	1	113%	0%	Ramalina menziesii [Menzies' Cartilage Lichen]	1	20%	0%
Populus alba [White Poplar]	6	79.80%	16.40%	Ranunculus acris [Tall Buttercup]	1	36%	0%
Populus cathayanna [Poplar]	9	24.60%	4.40%	Ranunculus [Buttercup]	1	47%	0%
Populus deltoides [Eastern Cottonwood]	9	32.60%	6.60%	Ranunculus glacialis [Glacier Buttercup]	3	44%	8.90%
Populus euramericana [Robusta Poplar]	25	77.20%	14.70%	Raphanus raphanistrum [Wild Radish]	2	32%	7.10%
Populus fremontii [Fremont's Cottonwood]	3	30.70%	15.90%	Raphanus sativus [Wild Radish]	8	30.40%	7%
Populus grandidentata [Bigtooth Aspen]	3	181.70%	60.70%	Raphanus sativus x raphanistrum [Wild Radish]	1	109%	0%
Populus nigra [Black Poplar]	6	73.20%	18.30%	Rhaphiolepsis indica [Indian Hawthorn]	1	79%	0%
Populus tremula x Populus tremula [Hybrid Aspen]	3	28.70%	3.30%	Rhizophora mangle [American Mangrove]	2	11.50%	0.40%
Populus tremuloides [Quaking Aspen]	54	80.30%	10.70%	Rhytidiadelphus triquetrus [Rough Goose Neck Moss]	1	66%	0%
Populus trichocarpa x populus deltoides [Hybrid Poplar]	2	37.50%	8.80%	Ricinus communis [Castor Bean]	2	34%	0%
Potentilla crantzii [Alpine Cinquefoil]	1	25%	0%	Rosa hybrida [Rose]	1	35%	0%

Appendix 4 – Plant Photosynthesis (Net CO$_2$ Exchange Rate) Responses

Plant Name	Number of Studies	Mean CO$_2$ Growth Response	Standard Error	Plant Name	Number of Studies	Mean CO$_2$ Growth Response	Standard Error
Rudbekia hirta [Blackeyed Susan]	1	5%	0%	Stipa thurberiana [Thurber needlegrass]	1	56%	0%
Rumex acetosa [Common Sorrel]	1	53%	0%	Stylosanthes hamata [Pencil Flower]	1	44%	0%
Saccharum officinarum [Sugarcane]	9	455.10%	417.80%	Swietenia macrophylla [Honduras Mahogany]	1	26%	0%
Salix jiangsuensis [Willow]	2	30%	12.70%	Symphiocarpos orbiculatus [Buch Brush]	2	105%	43.80%
Salvia nemorosa [Woodland Sage]	2	277.50%	136.10%	Synechococcus [Unicellular Marine Picocyanobacterium]	1	48%	0%
Salvia pitcheri [Pitcher Sage]	2	26.50%	1.80%	Talinum triangulare	1	357%	0%
Salvia pratensis [Introduced Sage]	1	47%	0%	Taxodium distichum [Cyprus, Bald]	7	95.10%	26.90%
Sanguisorba minor [Small Burnet]	5	31.60%	4%	Tectona grandis [Teak]	2	24%	9.20%
Schima superba [Sub-tropical Tree]	2	26%	6.40%	Terminalia arjuna [Terminalia]	2	194.50%	3.90%
Schizachyrium scoparium [Little Bluestem]	4	59.30%	17.70%	Terminalia chebula [Myrobalan]	2	147.50%	37.10%
Schoenoplectus americanus [Chairmaker's Bulrush]	1	27%	0%	Tetragastris panamensis [Tropical Tree]	1	14%	0%
Scirpus maritimus [Seaside Bulrush]	1	55%	0%	Themeda triandra [C$_4$ grass]	2	19%	3.50%
Scirpus olneyi [Salt Marsh Sedge]	8	57.80%	10.80%	Theobroma cacao [Cacao]	1	32%	0%
Scirpus robustus [Sedge]	2	60%	10.60%	Toxicodendron radicans [Poison Ivy]	1	116%	0%
Scrophularia desertorum [Desert Figwort]	3	50%	21%	Trachypogon plumosus [A C$_4$ South American Grass]	2	38.50%	2.50%
Sequoia sempervirens [Coastal Redwood]	3	77.70%	31.40%	Trifolium repens [White Clover]	22	49.40%	7.40%
Setaria faberi [Japanese Bristlegrass]	4	15%	7.10%	Trifolium subterraneum [Subterranean Clover]	1	19%	0%
Setaria viridis [Green Bristlegrass]	1	13%	0%	Triticum durum [Wheat, Durum]	2	59%	25.50%
Shorea leprosula]	2	57%	1.40%	Triticum aestivum [Common Wheat]	109	67.10%	8.60%
Silene noctiflora [Night-flowering Catchfly]	1	42%	0%	Tussock Tundra	2	237.50%	19.40%
Solanum curtilobum [Shortlobe Solanum]	1	46%	0%	Typha augustifolia [Narrowleaf Cattail]	1	57%	0%
Solanum dulcamara [Climbing Nightshade]	6	28.80%	3.10%	Typha latifolia [Common Cattail]	1	1%	0%
Solanum muricatum [Pepino]	2	74%	7.10%	Typha x glauca [White Cattail]	1	0%	0%
Solanum tuberosum [White Potato]	15	33.20%	5.50%	Urtica dioica L. [Stinging Nettle]	1	126%	0%
Solidago rigida [Stiff Goldenrod]	3	15%	5.40%	Vaccinium myrtillus [Whortleberry]	2	47%	9.20%
Sorghastrum nutans [Indian Grass]	3	371%	293.50%	Vernonia herbacea [Fructan Accumulating Plant]	1	50%	0%
Sorghum bicolor [Sorghum]	19	21.30%	2.80%	Viburnum marisii [Flowering Shrub]	1	63%	0%
Sorghum halapense [Johnsongrass]	1	12%	0%	Vicia faba [Faba Bean]	7	52.30%	10.50%
Spartina densiflora [Dense Flowerd Cordgrass]	6	17.50%	4.40%	Vigna radiata [Mungbean]	2	178%	18.40%
Spartina maritima [Small Cordgrass]	3	68%	4.20%	Vigna unguiculata [Blackeyed Pea]	5	65.60%	14.90%
Spartina patens [Saltmeadow Cordgrass]	6	12.30%	4.30%	Virola surinamensis [Tropical Tree]	1	31%	0%
Spartina alterniflora [Smooth Cordgrass]	1	19%	0%	Vitis vinifera [Grapevine, Common]	3	73.70%	21%
Spartina anglica [Common Cordgrass]	1	33%	0%	Vitis californica [California Wild Grape]	1	57%	0%
Spergularia maritima [Media Sandspurry]	1	81%	0%	Vulpia microstachys [Small Fescue]	1	125%	0%
Sphagnum fuscum [Sphagnum]	3	89.30%	6.60%	Wedelia chinensis [Herb, Perennial]	2	45.50%	6.70%
Spinacia oleracea [Spinach]	5	46.80%	11.40%	Wedelia trilobata [Creeping Daisy]	2	74%	1.40%
Stenocereus queretaroensis [Tree Cactus]	1	30%	0%	Xanthium strumarium L. [Rough Cocklebur]	4	30.80%	12.90%
				Zea mays L. [Corn]	23	26.10%	10.60%

Plant Name	Number of Studies	Mean CO_2 Growth Response	Standard Error
Zingiber officinale [Ginger]	2	41.50%	5.30%
Zostera noltii [Dwarf Eelgrass]	1	33%	0%